Stanley Gibbons
SIMPLIFIED
CATALOGUE

Stamps of the World 1992/93

An illustrated and priced three-volume guide to the postage stamps of the whole world, excluding changes of paper, perforation, shade and watermark

VOLUME 3

COMMONWEALTH COUNTRIES

STANLEY GIBBONS PUBLICATIONS LTD
London and Ringwood

By Appointment to
Her Majesty the Queen
Stanley Gibbons Limited
London
Philatelists

58th Edition

Published in Great Britain by
Stanley Gibbons Publications Ltd
Editorial, Sales Offices and Distribution Centre
5, Parkside, Christchurch Road,
Ringwood, Hampshire BH24 3SH
Telephone 0425 472363

ISBN: 085259-334-1

Published as Stanley Gibbons Simplified Stamp Catalogue from 1934 to 1970, renamed Stamps of the World in 1971, and produced in two (1982–88) or three (from 1989) volumes as Stanley Gibbons Simplified Catalogue of Stamps of the World.
This volume published November 1992

S.G. Item No. 2883 (92/93)

Origination by BPCC Whitefriars Ltd, Tunbridge Wells, Kent
Printed in Great Britain by Bemrose Security Printing, London & Derby

Stanley Gibbons
SIMPLIFIED CATALOGUE

Stamps of the World

This popular catalogue is a straightforward three-volume listing of the stamps that have been issued everywhere in the world since the very first–Great Britain's famous Penny Black in 1840.

This edition continues the three-volume format. Volume 1 (Foreign countries A–J) appeared in September, Volume 2 (Foreign countries K–Z) in October, and Volume 3 covering Commonwealth countries completes the trio.

Readers are reminded that the Catalogue Supplements, published in each issue of **Gibbons Stamp Monthly,** can be used to update the listings in **Stamps of the World** as well as our twenty-two part standard catalogue. To make the supplement even more useful the Type numbers given to the illustrations are now the same in the Stamps of the World as in the standard catalogues. The first Catalogue Supplement to this Volume appears in October 1992.

Gibbons Stamp Monthly can be obtained through newsagents or on postal subscription from Stanley Gibbons Magazines Ltd., 5, Parkside, Christchurch Road, Ringwood, Hants BH24 3SH.

The catalogue has many important features:

- As an indication of current values virtually every stamp is priced. Thousands of alterations have been made since the last edition.
- By being set out on a simplified basis that excludes changes of paper, perforation, shade or watermark it is particularly easy to use. (For its exact scope see "Information for users" pages following.)
- The thousands of illustrations and helpful descriptions of stamp designs make it of maximum appeal to collectors with thematic interests.
- Its catalogue numbers are the world-recognised Stanley Gibbons numbers throughout.
- Helpful introductory notes for the collector are included, backed by much historical, geographical and currency information.
- A very detailed index gives instant location of countries in this volume, and a cross-reference to those included in the other volumes.

Over 7,240 stamps and 2,040 new illustrations have been added to this 1992/93 edition. The 1992/93 three-volume edition contains over 297,900 stamps and 71,300 illustrations.

The listings in this edition are based on the standard catalogues: Part 1 (British Commonwealth) (1992/93 edition), Part 2 (Austria & Hungary) (4th edition), Part 3 (Balkans) (3rd edition), Part 4 (Benelux) (3rd edition), Part 5 (Czechoslovakia & Poland) (4th edition), Part 6 (France) (3rd edition), Part 7 (Germany) (4th edition), Part 8 (Italy & Switzerland) (3rd edition), Part 9 (Portugal & Spain) (3rd edition), Part 10 (Russia) (4th edition), Part 11 (Scandinavia) (3rd edition), Part 12 (Africa since Independence A-E) (2nd edition), Part 13 (Africa since Independence F-M) (1st edition), Part 14 (Africa since Independence N-Z) (1st edition), Part 15 (Central America) (2nd edition), Part 16 (Central Asia) (3rd edition), Part 17 (China) (4th edition), Part 18 (Japan & Korea) (3rd edition), Part 19 (Middle East) (4th edition), Part 20 (South America) (3rd edition), Part 21 (South-East Asia) (2nd edition) and Part 22 (United States) (3rd edition).

Stanley Gibbons Stamp Catalogue
Complete List of Parts

1 British Commonwealth
(Annual in two volumes)

Foreign Countries

2 Austria & Hungary (4th edition, 1988)
Austria · Bosnia & Herzegovina · U.N. (Vienna) · Hungary

3 Balkans (3rd edition, 1987)
Albania · Bulgaria · Greece & Islands · Rumania · Yugoslavia

4 Benelux (3rd edition, 1988)
Belgium & Colonies · Netherlands & Colonies · Luxembourg

5 Czechoslovakia & Poland (4th edition, 1991)
Czechoslovakia · Bohemia & Moravia · Slovakia · Poland

6 France (3rd edition, 1987)
France · Colonies · Andorra · Monaco

7 Germany (4th edition, 1992)
Germany · States · Colonies · Post Offices

8 Italy & Switzerland (3rd edition 1987)
Italy & Colonies · Fiume · San Marino · Vatican City · Trieste · Liechtenstein · Switzerland · U.N. (Geneva)

9 Portugal & Spain (3rd edition, 1991)
Andorra · Portugal & Colonies · Spain & Colonies

10 Russia (4th edition, 1991)
Russia · Baltic States · Mongolia · Tuva

11 Scandinavia (3rd edition, 1988)
Aland Islands · Denmark · Faroe Islands · Finland · Greenland · Iceland · Norway · Sweden

12 Africa since Independence A-E (2nd edition, 1983)
Algeria · Angola · Benin · Bophuthatswana · Burundi · Cameroun · Cape Verde · Central African Republic · Chad · Comoro Islands · Congo · Djibouti · Equatorial Guinea · Ethiopia

13 Africa since Independence F-M (1st edition, 1981)
Gabon · Guinea · Guinea-Bissau · Ivory Coast · Liberia · Libya · Malagasy Republic · Mali · Mauritania · Morocco · Mozambique

14 Africa since Independence N-Z (1st edition, 1981)
Niger Republic · Rwanda · St. Thomas & Prince · Senegal · Somalia · Sudan · Togo · Transkei · Tunisia · Upper Volta · Venda · Zaire

15 Central America (2nd edition, 1984)
Costa Rica · Cuba · Dominican Republic · El Salvador · Guatemala · Haiti · Honduras · Mexico · Nicaragua · Panama

16 Central Asia (3rd edition, 1992)
Afghanistan · Iran · Turkey

17 China (4th edition, 1989)
China · Taiwan · Tibet · Foreign P.O.s

18 Japan & Korea (3rd edition, 1992)
Japan · Ryukyus · Korean Empire · South Korea · North Korea

19 Middle East (4th edition, 1990)
Bahrain · Egypt · Iraq · Israel · Jordan · Kuwait · Lebanon · Oman · Qatar · Saudi Arabia · Syria · U.A.E. · Yemen A.R. · Yemen P.D.R.

20 South America (3rd edition, 1989)
Argentina · Bolivia · Brazil · Chile · Colombia · Ecuador · Paraguay · Peru · Surinam · Uruguay · Venezuela

21 South-East Asia (2nd edition, 1985)
Bhutan · Burma · Indonesia · Kampuchea · Laos · Nepal · Philippines · Thailand · Vietnam

22 United States (3rd edition, 1990)
U.S. & Possessions · Canal Zone · Marshall Islands · Micronesia · Palau · U.N. (New York, Geneva, Vienna)

Thematic Catalogues

Stanley Gibbons Catalogues for use with **Stamps of the World.**
Collect Aircraft on Stamps (forthcoming)
Collect Birds on Stamps (3rd edition, 1992)
Collect Butterflies and Other Insects on Stamps (1st edition, 1991)
Collect Chess on Stamps (1st edition, 1992)
Collect Fungi on Stamps (1st edition, 1991).
Collect Mammals on Stamps (1st edition, 1986).
Collect Railways on Stamps (2nd edition, 1990)
Collect Ships on Stamps (2nd edition forthcoming)

Information for users

Aim

The aim of this catalogue is to provide a straightforward illustrated and priced guide to the postage stamps of the whole world to help you to enjoy the greatest hobby of the present day.

Arrangement

The catalogue lists countries in alphabetical order and there is a complete index at the end of each volume. For ease of reference country names are also printed at the head of each page.

Within each country, postage stamps are listed first. They are followed by separate sections for such other categories as postage due stamps, parcel post stamps, express stamps, official stamps, etc.

All catalogue lists are set out according to dates of issue of the stamps, starting from the earliest and working through to the most recent. New issues received too late for inclusion in the main lists will be found as "Addenda" at the end of each volume.

Scope of the Catalogue

The *Simplified Catalogue of Stamps of the World* contains listings of postage stamps only. Apart from the ordinary definitive, commemorative and air-mail stamps of each country – which appear first in each list – there are sections for the following where appropriate:

- postage due stamps
- parcel post stamps
- official stamps
- express and special delivery stamps
- charity and compulsory tax stamps
- newspaper and journal stamps
- printed matter stamps
- registration stamps
- acknowledgement of receipt stamps
- late fee and too late stamps
- military post stamps
- recorded message stamps
- personal delivery stamps

We receive numerous enquiries from collectors about other items which do not fall within the categories set out above and which consequently do not appear in the catalogue lists. It may be helpful, therefore, to summarise the other kinds of stamp that exist but which we deliberately exclude from this postage stamp catalogue.

We do *not* list the following:

Fiscal or revenue stamps: stamps used solely in collecting taxes or fees for non-postal purposes. Examples would be stamps which pay a tax on a receipt, represent the stamp duty on a contract or frank a customs document. Common inscriptions found include: Documentary, Proprietary, Inter. Revenue, Contract Note.

Local stamps: postage stamps whose validity and use are limited in area, say to a single town or city, though in some cases they provided, with official sanction, services in parts of countries not covered by the respective government.

Local carriage labels and Private local issues: many labels exist ostensibly to cover the cost of ferrying mail from one of Great Britain's offshore islands to the nearest mainland post office. They are not recognised as valid for national or international mail. Examples: Calf of Man, Davaar, Herm, Lundy, Pabay, Stroma. Items from some other places have only the status of tourist souvenir labels.

Telegraph stamps: stamps intended solely for the prepayment of telegraphic communication.

Bogus or "phantom" stamps: labels from mythical places or non-existent administrations. Examples in the classical period were Sedang, Counani, Clipperton Island and in modern times Thomond and Monte Bello Islands. Numerous labels have also appeared since the War from dissident groups as propaganda for their claims and without authority from the home governments. Common examples are labels for "Free Albania", "Free Rumania" and "Free Croatia" and numerous issues for Nagaland, Indonesia and the South Moluccas ("Republik Maluku Selatan").

Railway letter fee stamps: special stamps issued by railway companies for the conveyance of letters by rail. Example: Talyllyn Railway. Similar services are now offered by some bus companies and the labels they issue likewise do not qualify for inclusion in the catalogue.

Perfins ("perforated initials"): numerous postage stamps may be found with initial letters or designs punctured through them by tiny holes. These are applied by private and public concerns as a precaution against theft and do not qualify for separate mention.

Information for users

Labels: innumerable items exist resembling stamps but – as they do not prepay postage – they are classified as labels. The commonest categories are:

- propaganda and publicity labels: designed to further a cause or campaign;
- exhibition labels: particularly souvenirs from philatelic events;
- testing labels: stamp-size labels used in testing stamp-vending machines;
- Post Office training school stamps: British stamps overprinted with two thick vertical bars or SCHOOL SPECIMEN are produced by the Post Office for training purposes;
- seals and stickers: numerous charities produce stamp-like labels, particularly at Christmas and Easter, as a means of raising funds and these have no postal validity.

Cut-outs: items of postal stationery, such as envelopes, cards and wrappers, often have stamps impressed or imprinted on them. They may usually be cut out and affixed to envelopes, etc., for postal use if desired, but such items are not listed in this catalogue.

Collectors wanting further information about exact definitions are referred to *Philatelic Terms Illustrated,* published by Stanley Gibbons and containing many illustrations in colour (third edition price £7.50 plus £2.75 postage and packing).

There is also a priced listing of the postal fiscals of Great Britain in our Part 1 *(British Commonwealth)* Catalogue and in Volume 1 of the *Great Britain Specialised* Catalogue (5th and later editions).

Although, as stated, none of the above qualify for inclusion in this postage stamp catalogue, this does not imply that they are of no interest to certain collectors. Indeed, in the 1950s, a group was formed in Great Britain called the "Cinderella Stamp Club", whose object is the study of all those stamps which Stanley Gibbons do *not* list in their catalogues.

Catalogue Numbers

Stanley Gibbons catalogue numbers are recognised universally and any individual stamp can be identified by quoting the catalogue number (the one at the left of the column) prefixed by the name of the country and the letters "S.G.". Do not confuse the catalogue number with the type numbers which refer to illustrations.

Prices

Prices in the left-hand column are for unused stamps and those in the right-hand column for used. Prices are given in pence and pounds:

100 pence (p) = 1 pound (£1).

Prices are shown as follows:

10 means 10p (10 pence);
1.75 means £1.75 (1 pound and 75 pence);
For £100 and above, prices are in whole pounds.

Our prices are for stamps in fine average condition, and in issues where condition varies we may ask more for the superb and less for the sub-standard.

The minimum price quoted is 10p which represents a handling charge rather than a basis for valuing common stamps.

The prices quoted are generally for the cheapest variety of stamps but it is worth noting that differences of watermark, perforation, or other details, outside the scope of this catalogue, may often increase the value of the stamp.

Where prices are not given in either column it is either because the stamps are not known to exist in that particular condition, or, more usually, because there is no reliable information as to value.

All prices are subject to change without prior notice and we give no guarantee to supply all stamps priced. Prices quoted for albums, publications, etc. advertised in this catalogue are also subject to change without prior notice.

Unused Stamps

In the case of stamps from *Great Britain* and the *Commonwealth,* prices for unused stamps of Queen Victoria to King George V are for lightly hinged examples. Unused prices for King Edward VIII and Queen Elizabeth II issues are for unmounted mint. The prices of unused *Foreign* stamps are for lightly hinged examples for those issued before 1946, thereafter for examples unmounted mint.

Used Stamps

Prices for used stamps refer to postally used examples, though for certain issues it is for cancelled-to-order.

Information for users

Guarantee

All stamps supplied by us are guaranteed originals in the following terms:

If not as described, and returned by the purchaser, we undertake to refund the price paid to us in the original transaction. If any stamp is certified as genuine by the Expert Committee of the Royal Philatelic Society, London, or by B.P.A. Expertising Ltd., the purchaser shall not be entitled to make any claim against us for any error, omission or mistake in such certificate.

Consumers' statutory rights are not affected by the above guarantee.

Currency

At the beginning of each country brief details give the currencies in which the values of the stamps are expressed. The dates, where given, are those of the earliest stamp issues in the particular currency. Where the currency is obvious, e.g. where the colony has the same currency as the mother country, no details are given.

Illustrations

Illustrations of stamps of Commonwealth countries (in Volume 3) and of any surcharges and overprints which are shown and not described are actual size; stamps of all foreign countries are reduced to ¾ linear, unless otherwise stated.

"Key-Types"

A number of standard designs occur so frequently in the stamps of the French, German, Portuguese and Spanish colonies that it would be a waste of space to repeat them. Instead these are all illustrated on page xii together with the descriptive names and letters by which they are referred to in the lists.

Type Numbers

These are the bold figures found below each illustration. References to "Type **6**", for example, in the lists of a country should therefore be understood to refer to the illustration below which the number **"6"** appears. These type numbers are also given in the second column of figures alongside each list of stamps, thus indicating clearly the design of each stamp. In the case of Key-Types – see above – letters take the place of the type numbers.

Where an issue comprises stamps of similar design, represented in this catalogue by one illustration, the corresponding type numbers should be taken as indicating this general design.

Where there are blanks in the type number column it means that the type of the corresponding stamps is that shown by the last number above in the type column of the same issue.

A dash (–) in the type column means that no illustration of the stamp is shown.

Where type numbers refer to stamps of another country, e.g. where stamps of one country are overprinted for use in another, this is always made clear in the text.

Stamp Designs

Brief descriptions of the subjects of the stamp designs are given either below or beside the illustrations, at the foot of the list of the issue concerned, or in the actual lists. Where a particular subject, e.g. the portrait of a well-known monarch, recurs frequently the description is not repeated, nor are obvious designs described.

Generally, the unillustrated designs are in the same shape and size as the one illustrated, except where otherwise indicated.

Surcharges and Overprints

Surcharges and overprints are usually described in the headings to the issues concerned. Where the actual wording of a surcharge or overprint is given it is shown in bold type.

Some stamps are described as being "Surcharged in words", e.g. **TWO CENTS,** and others "Surcharged in figures and words", e.g. **20 CENTS,** although of course many surcharges are in foreign languages and combinations of words and figures are numerous. There are often bars, etc., obliterating old values or inscriptions but in general these are only mentioned where it is necessary to avoid confusion.

No attention is paid in this catalogue to colours of overprints and surcharges so that stamps with the same overprints in different colours are not listed separately.

Numbers in brackets after the descriptions of overprinted or surcharged stamps are the catalogue numbers of the unoverprinted stamps.

Note – the words "inscribed" or "inscription" always refer to wording incorporated in the design of a stamp and not surcharges or overprints.

Coloured Papers

Where stamps are printed on coloured paper the description is given as e.g. "4 c. black on blue" – a stamp printed in black on blue paper. No attention is paid in this catalogue to differences in the texture of paper, e.g. laid, wove.

Information for users

Watermarks

Stamps having different watermarks, but otherwise the same, are not listed separately. No reference is therefore made to watermarks in this volume.

Stamp Colours

Colour names are only required for the identification of stamps, therefore they have been made as simple as possible. Thus "scarlet", "vermilion", "carmine" are all usually called red. Qualifying colour names have been introduced only where necessary for the sake of clearness.

Where stamps are printed in two or more colours the central portion of the design is in the first colour given, unless otherwise stated.

Perforations

All stamps are perforated unless otherwise stated. No distinction is made between the various gauges of perforation but early stamp issues which exist both imperforate and perforated are usually listed separately.

Where a heading states "Imperf. or perf." or "Perf. or rouletted" this does not necessarily mean that all values of the issue are found in both conditions.

Dates of Issue

The date given at the head of each issue is that of the appearance of the earliest stamp in the series. As stamps of the same design or issue are usually grouped together a list of King George VI stamps, for example, headed "1938" may include stamps issued from 1938 to the end of the reign.

Miniature Sheets

These are outside the scope of this catalogue but are listed in all other Stanley Gibbons catalogues.

"Appendix" Countries

We regret that, since 1968, it has been necessary to establish an Appendix (at the end of each country as appropriate) to which numerous stamps have had to be consigned. Several countries imagine that by issuing huge quantities of unnecessary stamps they will have a ready source of income from stamp collectors – and particularly from the less-experienced ones. Stanley Gibbons refuse to encourage this exploitation of the hobby and we do not stock the stamps concerned.

Two kinds of stamp are therefore given the briefest of mentions in the Appendix, purely for the sake of record. Administrations issuing stamps greatly in excess of true postal needs have the offending issues placed there. Likewise it contains stamps which have not fulfilled all the normal conditions for full catalogue listing.

These conditions are that the stamps must be issued by a legitimate postal authority, recognised by the government concerned, and are adhesives, valid for proper postal use in the class of service for which they are inscribed. Stamps, with the exception of such categories as postage dues and officials, must be available to the general public at face value with no artificial restrictions being imposed on their distribution.

The publishers of this catalogue have observed, with concern, the proliferation of 'artificial' stamp-issuing territories. On several occasions this has resulted in separately inscribed issues for various component parts of otherwise united states or territories.

Stanley Gibbons Publications Ltd have decided that where such circumstances occur, they will not, in the future, list these items in the SG catalogue without first satisfying themselves that the stamps represent a genuine political, historical or postal division within the country concerned. Any such issues which do not fulfil this stipulation will be recorded in the Catalogue Appendix only.

Stamps in the Appendix are kept under review in the light of any newly acquired information about them. If we are satisfied that a stamp qualifies for proper listing in the body of the catálogue it is moved there.

"Undesirable Issues"

The rules governing many competitive exhibitions – including the Melville Competition – are set by the Fédération Internationale de Philatelie and stipulate a downgrading of marks for stamps classed as "undesirable issues".

This catalogue can be taken as a guide to status. All stamps in the main listings and Addenda are acceptable. Stamps in the Appendix should not be entered for competition as these are the "undesirable issues".

Particular care is advised with Aden Protectorate States, Ajman, Bhutan, Chad, Fujeira, Khor Fakkan, Manama, Ras al Khaima, Sharjah, Umm al Qiwain and Yemen. Totally bogus stamps exist (as explained in Appendix notes) and these are to be avoided also for competition. As distinct from "undesirable stamps" certain categories are not covered in this catalogue purely by reason of its scope (see page v). Consult the particular competition rules to see if such are admissible even though not listed by us.

Information for users

Where to Look for More Detailed Listings

The present work deliberately omits details of paper, perforation, shade and watermark. But as you become more absorbed in stamp collecting and wish to get greater enjoyment from the hobby you may well want to study these matters.

All the information you require about any particular postage stamp will be found in the main Stanley Gibbons Catalogues.

Commonwealth countries in Volume 3 are covered by the Part 1 (British Commonwealth) Catalogue published annually in two volumes.

For foreign countries you can easily find which catalogue to consult by looking at the country headings in the present book.

To the right of each country name are code letters specifying which volume of our main catalogues contains that country's listing.

The code letters are as follows:

Pt. 2 Part 2

Pt. 3 Part 3 etc.

(See page iv for complete list of Parts.)

So, for example, if you want to know more about Chinese stamps than is contained in the *Simplified Catalogue of Stamps of the World* the reference to

CHINA Pt. 17

guides you to the Gibbons Part 17 *(China)* Catalogue listing for the details you require.

New editions of Parts 2 to 22 appear at irregular intervals.

Correspondence

Whilst we welcome information and suggestions we must ask correspondents to include the cost of postage for the return of any stamps submitted plus registration where appropriate. Letters should be addressed to "The Catalogue Editor".

Where information is solicited purely for the benefit of the enquirer we regret we cannot undertake to reply unless stamps or reply coupons are sent to cover the postage.

Identification of Stamps

We regret we do not give opinions as to the genuineness of stamps, nor do we identify stamps or number them by our Catalogue.

Users of this catalogue are referred to our companion booklet entitled *Stamp Collecting — How to Identify Stamps.* It explains how to look up stamps in this catalogue, contains a full checklist of stamp inscriptions and gives help in dealing with unfamiliar scripts. It is available from Stanley Gibbons at £1.95, postage extra.

Stanley Gibbons would like to complement your collection

At Stanley Gibbons we offer a range of services which are designed to complement your collection.

Our modern stamp shop, the largest in Europe, together with our rare stamp department has one of the most comprehensive stocks of Great Britain in the world, so whether you are a beginner or an experienced philatelist you are certain to find something to suit your special requirements.

Alternatively through our Mail Order services you can control the growth of your collection from the comfort of your own home. Our Postal Sales Department regularly sends out mailings of Special Offers. We can also help with your wants list—so why not ask us for those elusive items?

And don't forget Stanley Gibbons Auctions which holds, on average, 8–10 sales each year. Come along in person or send in a written bid for the items you require. For details of current subscription rate for Auction catalogues write to Stanley Gibbons Auctions Limited, 399 Strand, London WC2R 0LX.

Why not take advantage of the many services we have to offer? Visit our premises in the Strand or, for more information, write to the appropriate address on page x.

Stanley Gibbons Holdings Plc Addresses

Stanley Gibbons Limited,
Stanley Gibbons Auctions Limited
399 Strand, London WC2R 0LX

Auction Room and Specialist Stamp Departments. Open Monday–Friday 9.30 a.m. to 5 p.m.

Shop. Open Monday 9.30 a.m. to 5.30 p.m., Tuesday–Friday 8.30 a.m. to 5 p.m. and Saturday 10 a.m. to 4.00 p.m.

Telephone 071 836 8444 Fax 071 836 7342 for all departments.

Stanley Gibbons Publications Limited
5 Parkside, Christchurch Road,
Ringwood, Hants BH24 3SH.
Telephone 0425 472363 (24 hour answerphone service) Fax 0425 470247.

Publication Shop (at above address). Open Monday–Friday 9.30 a.m. to 3.30 p.m.

Publications Mail Order. FREEPHONE 0800 611622. Monday–Friday 8.30 a.m. to 5 p.m.

Stanley Gibbons Australia Pty. Ltd
P.O. Box 863J, Melbourne 3001,
Australia.
Telephone (01 0613) 670 3332 and Telex AA 37223.

Stanley Gibbons Publications Limited Overseas Representation

Stanley Gibbons Publications Ltd. are represented overseas by the following sole distributors (*) and main agents (**) and licensees (***).

Australia*
Lighthouse Philatelic (Aust.) Pty. Ltd., P.O. Box 763, New South Wales, 2012 Australia

Belgium and Luxembourg**
Philac, Rue du Midi 48, Bruxelles, Belgium 1000

Canada*
Lighthouse Publications (Canada) Ltd., 255 Duke Street, Montreal, Quebec, Canada H3C 2M2

Denmark**
Nordfrim, DK 5450, Otterup, Denmark.

France*
Davo France S.A.R.L., 25 Rue Monge, 75005 Paris, France.

Germany and Austria**
Ka-Be Briefmarkenalben-Verlag, Daimlerstrasse 15, Volkhardt GMBH, Goppingen, Germany.

Leuchtturm Albenverlag, Paul Koch KG Am Spakenberg 45, Postfach 1340, D-2054 Geesthacht, Germany.

Hong Kong**
Po-on Stamp Service, G.P.O. Box 2498, Hong Kong.

Israel**
Capital Stamps, P.O. Box 3769, Jerusalem 91036, Israel.

Italy*
Secrian Srl, Via Pantelleria 2, I-20156, Milan, Italy.

Japan**
Japan Philatelic Co. Ltd., P.O. Box 2, Suginami-Minami, Tokyo, Japan.

Netherlands*
Davo Publications, P.O. Box 411, 7400 AK Deventer, Netherlands.

New Zealand*
Philatelic Distributors Ltd., P.O. Box 863, New Plymouth, New Zealand.

Norway**
Wennergren-Cappelen AS, Nedre Vollgate 4, P.O. Box 738, Sentrum N-0105, Oslo 1, Norway.

Singapore***
Stanley Gibbons (Singapore) Pte Ltd, Raffles City P.O. Box 1689, Singapore 9117, Republic of Singapore. Telephone (010 65) 336 1998.

South Africa
Stanley Gibbons (Pty) Ltd., P.O. Box 930, Parklands, RSA 2121.***

Republic Coin and Stamp Accessories (Pty) Ltd., P.O. Box 260325, Excom 2023, Johannesburg, RSA.**

Sweden*
Chr Winther Soerensen AB, Box 43, S-310 Knaered, Sweden.

Switzerland**
Phila Service, Burgstrasse 160, Postfach CH 4125, Riehen 1, Switzerland

USA*
Lighthouse Publications Inc., P.O. Box 705, 274 Washington Avenue, Hackensack, New Jersey 07602–0705, U.S.A.

West Indies/Caribbean**
Hugh Dunphy, P.O. Box 413, Kingston 10, Jamaica, West Indies.

Abbreviations

Anniv.	denotes	Anniversary
Assn.	,,	Association
Bis.	,,	Bistre
Bl.	,,	Blue
Bldg.	,,	Building
Blk.	,,	Black
Br.	,,	British *or* Bridge
Brn.	,,	Brown
B.W.I.	,,	British West Indies
C.A.R.I.F.T.A.	,,	Caribbean Free Trade Area
Cent.	,,	Centenary
Chest.	,,	Chestnut
Choc.	,,	Chocolate
Clar.	,,	Claret
Coll.	,,	College
Commem.	,,	Commemoration
Conf.	,,	Conference
Diag.	,,	Diagonally
E.C.A.F.E.	,,	Economic Commission for Asia and Far East
Emer.	,,	Emerald
E.P.T. Conference	,,	European Postal and Telecommunications Conference
Exn.	,,	Exhibition
F.A.O.	,,	Food and Agriculture Organization
Fig.	,,	Figure
G.A.T.T.	,,	General Agreement on Tariffs and Trade
G.B.	,,	Great Britain
Gen.	,,	General
Govt.	,,	Government
Grn.	,,	Green
Horiz.	,,	Horizontal
H.Q.	,,	Headquarters
Imperf.	,,	Imperforate
Inaug.	,,	Inauguration
Ind.	,,	Indigo
Inscr.	,,	Inscribed or inscription
Int.	,,	International
I.A.T.A.	,,	International Air Transport Association
I.C.A.O.	,,	International Civil Aviation Organization
I.C.Y.	,,	International Co-operation Year
I.G.Y.	,,	International Geophysical Year
I.L.O.	,,	International Labour Office (or later, Organization)
I.M.C.O.	,,	Inter-Governmental Maritime Consultative Organization
I.T.U.	,,	International Telecommunication Union
Is.	,,	Islands
Lav.	,,	Lavender
Mar.	,,	Maroon
mm.	,,	Millimetres
Mult.	,,	Multicoloured
Mve.	denotes	Mauve
Nat.	,,	National
N.A.T.O.	,,	North Atlantic Treaty Organization
O.D.E.C.A.	,,	Organization of Central American States
Ol.	,,	Olive
Optd.	,,	Overprinted
Orge. *or* oran.	,,	Orange
P.A.T.A.	,,	Pacific Area Travel Association
Perf.	,,	Perforated
Post.	,,	Postage
Pres.	,,	President
P.U.	,,	Postal Union
Pur.	,,	Purple
R.	,,	River
R.S.A.	,,	Republic of South Africa
Roul.	,,	Rouletted
Sep.	,,	Sepia
S.E.A.T.O.	,,	South East Asia Treaty Organization
Surch.	,,	Surcharged
T.	,,	Type
T.U.C.	,,	Trades Union Congress
Turq.	,,	Turquoise
Ultram.	,,	Ultramarine
U.N.E.S.C.O.	,,	United Nations Educational, Scientific & Cultural Organization
U.N.I.C.E.F.	,,	United Nations Children's Fund
U.N.O.	,,	United Nations Organization
U.N.R.W.A.	,,	United Nations Relief and Works Agency for Palestine Refugees in the Near East
U.N.T.E.A.	,,	United Nations Temporary Executive Authority
U.N.R.R.A.	,,	United Nations Relief and Rehabilitation Administration
U.P.U.	,,	Universal Postal Union
Verm.	,,	Vermilion
Vert.	,,	Vertical
Vio.	,,	Violet
W.F.T.U.	,,	World Federation of Trade Unions
W.H.O.	,,	World Health Organization
Yell.	,,	Yellow

Arabic Numerals

As in the case of European figures, the details of the Arabic numerals vary in different stamp designs, but they should be readily recognised with the aid of this illustration:

٠	١	٢	٣	٤
0	1	2	3	4
٥	٦	٧	٨	٩
5	6	7	8	9

Key-Types

(see note on page vii)

French Group

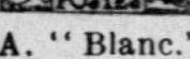

A. " Blanc."

B. " Mouchon."

C. " Merson."

D. " Tablet."

E.

F.

G.

H.

" International Colonial Exhibition."

I. " Faidherbe."

J. " Palms."

K. " Balay."

L. " Natives."

M. " Figure."

German Group

N. " Yacht."

O. " Yacht."

Spanish Group

X. " Alfonso XII."

Y. " Baby."

Z. "Curly Head"

Portuguese Group

P. " Crown."

Q. " Embossed."

R. " Figures."

S. " Carlos."

T. " Manoel."

U. " Ceres."

V. " Newspaper."

W. " Due."

STANLEY GIBBONS SIMPLIFIED CATALOGUE OF STAMPS OF THE WORLD—VOLUME 3 COMMONWEALTH COUNTRIES

ABU DHABI

The largest of the Trucial States in the Persian Gulf. Treaty relations with Great Britain expired on 31 December 1966, when the Abu Dhabi Post Office took over the postal services.

1964. 100 naye paise = 1 rupee.
1966. 1,000 fils = 1 dinar.

1. Shaikh Shakhbut bin Sultan.

3. Ruler's Palace.

1964.

1. 1. 5 n.p. green 80 60
2. – 15 n.p. brown .. .. 1·25 55
3. – 20 n.p. blue .. .. 1·40 55
4. – 30 n.p. orange .. .. 1·40 90
5. – 40 n.p. violet .. .. 2·75 20
6. – 50 n.p. bistre .. .. 2·50 55
7. – 75 n.p. black .. .. 2·75 1·00
8. 3. 1 r. green .. .. 3·75 90
9. 2 r. black .. .. 5·50 2·50
10. – 5 r. red .. .. 13·00 7·00
11. – 10 r. blue .. .. 18·00 13·00

DESIGNS—As Type **1**: 40 n.p. to 75 n.p. Mountain gazelle. As Type **3**: 5 r., 10 r. Oil and camels.

5. Saker Falcon.

1965. Falconry.

12. **5.** 20 n.p. brown and blue 5·50 80
13. – 40 n.p. brown and blue 7·00 2·00
14. – 2 r. sepia and turquoise 13·00 8·50

DESIGNS: 40 n.p., 2 r. Other types of Saker Falcon on gloved hand.

1966. Nos. 1/11 surch. in new currency ("Fils" only on Nos. 5/7) and ruler's portrait obliterated with bars.

15. 1. 5 f. on 5 n.p. green .. 4·50 4·00
16. 15 f. on 15 n.p. brown .. 4·50 2·00
17. 20 f. on 20 n.p. blue .. 4·50 3·25
18. 30 f. on 30 n.p. orange .. 6·00 6·00
19. – 40 f. on 40 n.p. violet .. 9·00 75
20. – 50 f. on 50 n.p. bistre .. 13·00 12·00
21. – 75 f. on 75 n.p. black .. 13·00 12·00
22. 3. 100 f. on 1 r. green .. 13·00 3·25
23. 200 f. on 2 r. black .. 18·00 12·00
24. – 500 f. on 5 r. red .. 30·00 35·00
25. – 1 d. on 10 r. blue .. 40·00 65·00

Independent Postal Administration issues are listed in volume 1.

ADEN

Peninsula on S. coast of Arabia. Formerly part of the Indian Empire. A Crown Colony from 1 April 1937 to 18 January 1963, when Aden joined the South Arabian Federation, whose stamps it then used. Attained independence on 30 November 1967, when the area was called Southern Yemen. It is now known as Yemen People's Democratic Republic. Aden stamps were also used in the Aden Protectorate.

1937. 16 annas = 1 rupee.
1951. 100 cents = 1 shilling.

1. Dhow.

1937.

1. 1. ½ a. green .. .. .. 2·75 1·25
2. 9 p. green .. .. .. 2·75 1·40
3. 1 a. brown .. .. .. 2·75 50
4. 2 a. red .. .. .. 2·75 2·00
5. 2½ a. blue .. .. .. 2·75 80
6. 3 a. red .. .. .. 9·00 6·00
7. 3½ a. blue .. .. .. 3·75 2·00
8. 8 a. purple .. .. .. 18·00 5·50
9. 1 r. brown .. .. .. 21·00 7·00
10. 2 r. yellow .. .. .. 45·00 16·00
11. 5 r. purple .. .. .. 80·00 60·00
12. 10 r. olive £150 £140

2. King George VI and Queen Elizabeth.

1937. Coronation.

13. **2.** 1 a. brown 65 60
14. 2½ a. blue .. .. 90 1·00
15. 3½ a. blue .. .. 1·25 1·75

3. Aidrus Mosque, Crater.

1939.

16. **3.** ½ a. green 50 50
17. – ¾ a. brown 50 90
18. – 1 a. blue 20 25
19. – 1½ a. red 45 60
20. **3.** 2 a. brown 20 25
21. – 2½ a. blue 30 30
22. – 3 a. brown and red .. 50 25
23. – 8 a. orange 35 40
23a. – 14 a. brown and blue .. 1·75 90
24. – 1 r. green .. .. 1·50 1·25
25. – 2 r. blue and mauve .. 4·00 1·75
26. – 5 r. brown and olive .. 10·00 6·00
27. – 10 r. brown and violet .. 18·00 10·00

DESIGNS: ¾ a., 5 r. Adenese Camel Corps. 1 a., 2 r. Harbour. 1½ a., 1 r. Adenese dhow. 2½ a., 8 a. Mukalla. 3 a., 14 a., 10 r. "Capture of Aden, 1839" (Capt. Rundle).

9. Houses of Parliament, London.

1946. Victory.

28. **9.** 1½ a. red 15 35
29. 2½ a. blue 15 20

10. King George VI and Queen Elizabeth. **11.**

1949. Royal Silver Wedding.

30. **10.** 1½ a. red 40 50
31. **11.** 10 r. purple .. .. 22·00 25·00

1949. 75th Anniv of U.P.U. As T **20/23** of Antigua surch with new values.

32. 2½ a. on 20 c. blue .. 50 90
33. 3 a. on 30 c. red .. 1·25 90
34. 8 a. on 50 c. orange .. 1·60 1·00
35. 1 r. on 1 s. blue .. 1·90 2·25

1951. Stamps of 1939 surch. in cents or shillings.

36. 5 c. on 1 a. blue 15 40
37. 10 c. on 2 a. brown 15 45
38. 15 c. on 2½ a. blue 20 85
39. 20 c. on 3 a. brown & red .. 25 40
40. 30 c. on 8 a. orange .. 25 50
41. 50 c. on 8 a. orange .. 25 35
42. 70 c. on 14 a. brown & blue 55 80
43. 1 s. on 1 r. green .. 35 30
44. 2 s. on 2 r. blue and mauve 3·75 2·50
45. 5 s. on 5 r. brown & olive .. 13·00 3·25
46. 10 s. on 10 r. brown & violet 17·00 8·00

13. Queen Elizabeth II. **14.** Minaret.

15. Camel Transport.

1953. Coronation.

47. **13.** 15 c. black and green .. 30 95

1953.

48 **14** 5 c. green 15 10
49a 5 c. turquoise 10 20
50 **15** 10 c. orange 30 10
51 10 c. red 10 20
52 – 15 c. turquoise 60 35
79 – 15 c. grey .. .. 30 1·25
54 – 25 c. red 30 20
81 – 35 c. blue .. .. 1·00 1·00
58 – 50 c. blue 15 10
60 – 70 c. grey 15 10
61a – 70 c. black 35 10
62 – 1 s. brown and violet .. 30 10
63 – 1 s. black and violet .. 45 10
64 – 1 s. 25 blue and black .. 2·00 40
65 – 2 s. brown and red .. 1·25 40
66 – 2 s. black and red .. 2·75 50
67 – 5 s. brown and blue .. 1·25 40
68 – 5 s. black and blue .. 2·00 40
69 – 10 s. brown and green .. 1·75 8·00
70 – 10 s. black and bronze .. 4·25 1·25
71 – 20 s. brown and lilac .. 6·50 10·00
72 – 20 s. black and lilac .. 29·00 13·00

DESIGNS—HORIZ. 15 c. Crater. 25 c. Mosque. 1 s. Dhow building. 20 s. (38 × 27 mm.). Aden in 1572. VERT. 35 c. Dhow. 50 c. Map. 70 c. Salt works. 1 s. 25, Colony's badge. 2 s. Aden Protectorate Levy. 5 s. Crater Pass. 10 s. Tribesmen.

1954. Royal Visit. As No. 62 but inscr. "ROYAL VISIT 1954".

73. 1 s. sepia and violet .. 30 30

1959. Revised Constitution. Optd. **REVISED CONSTITUTION 1959** (in Arabic on No. 74).

74. 15 c. green (No. 53) .. 15 70
75. 1 s. 25 blue and blk. (No. 64) 30 70

28. Protein Foods.

1963. Freedom from Hunger.

76. **28.** 1 s. 25 c. green .. .. 1·25 1·40

For later issues see **SOUTH ARABIAN FEDERATION.**

ADEN PROTECTORATE STATES

The states of the Eastern Aden Protectorate commonly known as the Hadhramaut.

The National Liberation Front took control on 1 October 1967, and full independence was granted by Great Britain on 30 November 1967. Now part of Yemen People's Democratic Republic.

1937. 16 annas = 1 rupee.
1951. 100 cents = 1 shilling.
1966. 1,000 fils = 1 dinar.

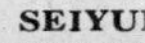

SEIYUN

1. Sultan of Seiyun.

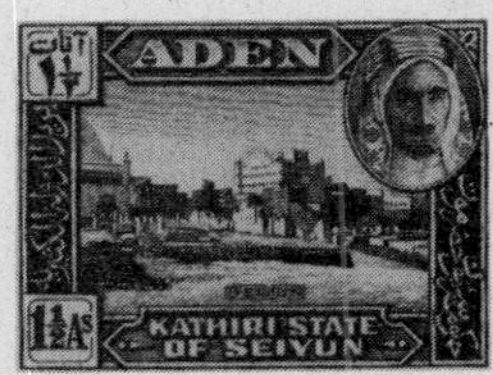

2. Seiyun.

1942.

1. 1. ½ a. green 15 35
2. ¾ a. brown 15 35
3. 1 a. blue 15 35
4. 2. 1½ a. red 15 40
5. – 2 a. sepia 15 50
6. – 2½ a. blue 20 75
7. – 3 a. sepia and red .. 35 50
8. – 8 a. red 20 50
9. – 1 r. green 40 50
10. – 2 r. blue and purple .. 5·00 7·50
11. – 5 r. brown and green .. 12·00 11·00

DESIGNS—VERT. 2 a. Tarim. 2½ a. Mosque at Seiyun. 1 r. South Gate, Tarim. 5 r. Mosque Entrance, Tarim. HORIZ. 3 a. Fortress at Tarim. 8 a. Mosque at Seiyun. 2 r. A Kathiri House.

1946. Victory. Optd. **VICTORY ISSUE 8th JUNE 1946.**

12. **2.** 1½ a. red 10 20
13. – 2½ a. blue (No. 6) .. 10 10

1949. Silver Wedding. As T **10/11** of Aden.

14. 1½ a. red 30 50
15. 5 r. green .. .. 9·50 8·00

1949. 75th Anniv of U.P.U. As T **20/23** of Antigua surch with new values.

16. 2½ a. on 20 c. blue .. 25 40
17. 3 a. on 30 c. red .. 40 55
18. 8 a. on 50 c. orange .. 40 60
19. 1 r. on 1 s. blue .. 60 90

1951. 1942 stamps surch. in cents or shillings.

20. **1.** 5 c. on 1 a. blue 15 20
21. – 10 c. on 2 a. sepia .. 15 20
22. – 15 c. on 2½ a. blue .. 15 20
23. – 20 c. on 3 a. sepia and red 15 20
24. – 50 c. on 8 a. red 15 20
25. – 1s. on 1 r. green 20 25
26. – 2s. on 2 r. blue and purple 2·00 7·50
27. – 5s. on 5 r. brown and green 8·00 20·00

1953. Coronation. As T **13** of Aden.

28. 15 c. black and green .. 30 95

DESIGNS—VERT. 35 c. Mosque at Selyun. 70 c. Qarn Adh Dhabi. 2 s. South Gate, Tarim. 10 s. Mosque entrance, Tarim HORIZ. 50 c. Fortress at Tarim 1 s. Mosque at Seiyun. 1 s. 25, Seiyun. 1 s. 50, Gheil Omer. 5 s. Kathiri house.

14. Sultan Hussein.

1954. As 1942 issue and new designs, but with portrait of Sultan Hussein as in T **14.**

29. **14.** 5 c. brown 10 10
30. 10 c. blue 15 10
31. **2.** 15 c. green 15 10
32. – 25 c. red 15 10
33. – 35 c. blue 15 10
34. – 50 c. brown and red .. 15 10
39. – 70 c. black 70 65
35. – 1 s. orange 15 10
40. – 1 s. 25 green .. .. 70 3·50
41. – 1 s. 50 violet .. .. 80 3·50
36. – 2 s. green .. .. 3·25 1·25
37. – 5 s. blue and violet .. 3·50 3·00
38. – 10 s. brown and violet .. 4·50 6·50

1966. Nos. 29 etc. surch. **SOUTH ARABIA** in English and Arabic, with value and bar.

42 **14** 5 f. on 5 c. 15 10
43 – 5 f. on 10 c. 15 10
44 **2** 10 f. on 15 c. 15 10
45 – 15 f. on 25 c. 15 10
46 – 20 f. on 35 c. 20 10
47 – 25 f. on 50 c. 15 15
61 – 35 f. on 70 c. 50 20
49 – 50 f on 1 s. 20 15
50 – 65 f. on 1 s. 25 .. .. 20 15
51 – 75 f. on 1 s. 50 .. .. 20 30
65 – 100 f. on 2 s. .. .. 2·00 85
53 – 250 f. on 5 s. .. .. 1·40 3·25
54 – 500 f. on 10 s. .. .. 1·75 3·75

Each value has two similar surcharges.

1966. Nos. 57, 59, 61/7 variously optd. as given below, together with Olympic "rings".

68. 10 f. on 15 c. (**LOS ANGELES 1932**) 15 10
69. 20 f. on 35 c (**BERLIN 1936**) .. 20 15
70. 35 f. on 70 c. **INTERNATIONAL COOPERATION**, etc) .. 20 15
71. 50 f. on 1 s. (**LONDON 1948**) 25 20
72. 65 f. on 1 s. 25 (**HELSINKI 1952**) .. 35 40
73. 75 f. on 1 s. 50 (**MELBOURNE 1956**) .. 40 45
74. 100 f. on 2 s. (**ROME 1960**) 50 55
75. 250 f. on 5 s. (**TOKYO 1964**) 1·00 1·25
76. 500 f. on 10 s. (**MEXICO CITY 1968**) .. .. 1·40 2·50

1966. World Cup Football Championships. Nos. 57, 59, 61/2, 65/7 optd. **CHAMPIONS ENGLAND** (10 f., 50 f. and 250 f.) or **FOOTBALL 1966** (others). Both with football symbol.

77. 10 f. on 15 c. 40 30
78. 20 f. on 35 c. 55 40
79. 35 f. on 70 c. 65 40
80. 50 f. on 1 s. 75 40
81. 100 f. on 2 s. .. .. 3·25 1·75
82. 250 f. on 5 s. .. .. 7·00 4·50
83. 500 f. on 10 s. .. .. 9·00 7·00

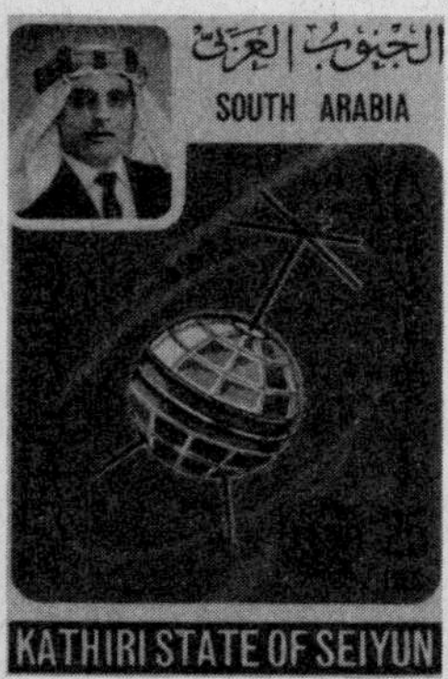

29. "Telstar".

1966. Cent. of I.T.U. (1965).

84. **29.** 5 f. green, black & vio. 85 25
85. – 10 f. purple, black & green 1·00 30
86. – 15 f. blue, black & orange 1·40 40
87. **29.** 25 f. green, black and red 2·00 50
88. – 35 f. purple, black & yell. 2·50 70
89. – 50 f. blue, black & brown 3·00 1·10
90. **29.** 65 f. green, black & yellow 3·75 1·25

DESIGNS: 10 f., 35 f. "Relay". 15 f., 50 f. "Ranger".

32. Churchill at Easel.

1966. Sir Winston Churchill's Paintings. Multicoloured.

91. 5 f. Type **32** .. .. 1·00 15
92. 10 f. "Antibes" .. .. 1·25 15
93. 15 f. "Flowers" .. .. 1·25 20
94. 20 f. "Tapestries" .. .. 1·40 35
95. 25 f. "Village, Lake Lugano" 1·60 35
96. 35 f. "Church, Lake Como" 1·75 40
97. 50 f. "Flowers at Chartwell" 2·25 65
98. 65 f. Type **32** .. .. 2·75 90

The 15, 35 and 50 f. are vert.

1967. "World Peace". Nos. 57, 59, 61/7 optd. **WORLD PEACE** and names as given below.

99. 10 f. on 15 c. (**PANDIT NEHRU**) 20 20
100. 20 f. on 35 c. (**WINSTON CHURCHILL**) .. .. 3·50 1·25
101. 35 f. on 70 c (**DAG HAMMARSKJOLD**) .. 50 50
102. 50 f. on 1 s. (**JOHN F. KENNEDY**) 60 60
103. 65 f. on 1 s. 25 (**LUDWIG ERHARD**) 70 70
104. 75 f. on 1 s. 50 (**LYNDON JOHNSON**) 80 80
105. 100 f. on 2 s. (**ELEANOR ROOSEVELT**) .. .. 1·00 1·00
106. 250 f. on 5 s. (**WINSTON CHURCHILL**) .. .. 9·00 6·50
107. 500 f. on 10 s. (**JOHN F. KENNEDY**) .. .. 4·75 6·50

40. "Master Crewe as Henry VIII" (Sir Joshua Reynolds).

1967. Paintings.

108. **40.** 5 f. multicoloured .. 25 25
109. – 10 f. multicoloured .. 30 30
110. – 15 f. multicoloured .. 35 35
111. – 20 f. multicoloured .. 40 40
112. – 25 f. multicoloured .. 45 45
113. – 35 f. multicoloured .. 65 65
114. – 50 f. multicoloured .. 75 75
115. – 65 f. multicoloured .. 1·00 1·00
116. – 75 f. multicoloured .. 1·25 1·25

PAINTINGS: 10 f. "The Dancer" (Degas). 15 f. "The Fifer" (Manet). 20 f. "Stag at Sharkey's" (boxing-match, G. Burrows). 25 f. "Don Manuel Osorio" (Goya). 35 f. "St. Martin Distributing His Cloak" (A. van Dyck). 50 f. "The Blue Boy" (Gainsborough). 65 f "The White Horse" (Gauguin). (45 × 60 mm.): 75 f. "Mona Lisa" (Da Vinci).

1967. American Astronauts. Nos. 57, 59, 61/2 and 65/6 optd. as below, all with space capsule.

117. 10 f. on 15 c. (**ALAN SHEPARD, JR.**) .. 45 60
118. 20 f. on 35 c. (**VIRGIL GRISSOM**) .. 60 70
119. 35 f. on 70 c. (**JOHN GLENN JR.**) .. 85 1·00
120. 50 f. on 1 s. (**SCOTT CARPENTER**) .. 85 1·00
121. 100 f. on 2 s. **WALTER SCHIRRA JR.**) .. 2·00 2·75
122. 250 f. on 5 s. (**GORDON COOPER JR.**) .. 3·25 4·00

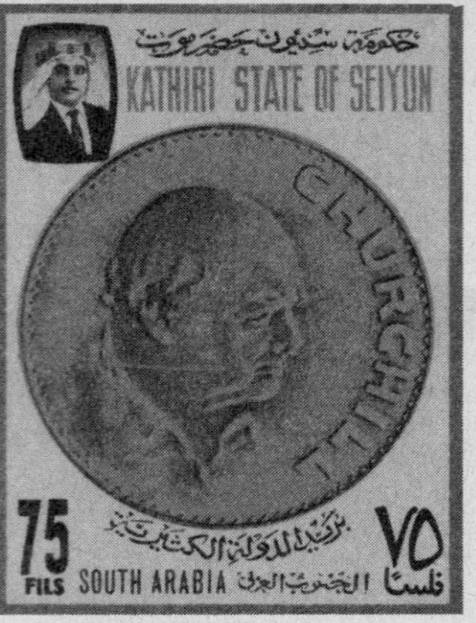

50. Churchill Crown.

1967. Churchill Commem.

123. **50.** 75 f. multicoloured .. 8·50 6·50

HADHRAMAUT

On the resignation of the Shaikh, the National Liberation Front took control on 17 September 1967, and full independence was granted by Great Britain on 30 November 1967. Now part of Southern Yemen.

(a) Issues inscribed "SHIHR and MUKALLA"

1. Sultan of Shihr and Mukalla.

2. Mukalla Harbour.

1942.

1. **1.** ½ a. green 15 25
2. ¾ a. brown 20 25
3. 1 a. blue 30 25
4. **2.** 1½ a. red 35 20
5. – 2 a. sepia.. .. .. 30 25
6. – 2½ a. blue 30 20
7. – 3 a. sepia and red .. 35 25
8. – 8 a. red 30 40
9. – 1 r. green 30 50
10. – 2 r blue and purple .. 7·00 6·00
11. – 5 r. brown and green .. 9·00 6·50

DESIGNS—VERT. 2 a. Gateway of Shihr. 3 a. Outpost of Mukalla. 1 r. Du'an. HORIZ. 2½ a. Shibam. 8 a. 'Einat. 2 r. Mosque in Hureidha. 5 r. Meshed.

1946. Victory. Optd. **VICTORY ISSUE 8th JUNE 1946.**

12. **2.** 1½ a. red 10 15
13. – 2½ a. blue 10 10

1949. Silver Wedding. As T **10/11** of Aden.

14. 1½ a. red 30 50
15. 5 r. green .. .. .. 9·50 8·50

1949. U.P.U. As T**20/23** of Antigua surch.

16. 2½ a. on 20 c. blue 20 20
17. 3 a. on 30 c. red 55 50
18. 8 a. on 50 c. orange .. 55 60
19. 1 r. on 1 s. blue 60 50

1951. Stamps of 1942 surch. in cents or shillings.

20. 5 c. on 1 a. blue 15 15
21. 10 c. on 2 a. sepia 15 15
22. 15 c. on 2½ a. blue 15 15
23. 20 c. on 3 a. sepia and red 15 20
24. 50 c. on 8 a. red 15 40
25. 1 s. on 1 r. green 30 25
26. 2 s. on 2 r. blue and purple 3·50 5·00
27. 5 s. on 5 r. brown and green 6·00 8·00

1953. Coronation. As T **13** of Aden.

28. 15 c. black and blue .. 30 55

(b) Issues inscribed "HADHRAMAUT".

11. Metal Work. **22.**

1955. Occupations. Portrait as in **T 11.** Nos. 36/40 horiz. designs.

29. **11.** 5 c. blue 10 10
30. – 10 c. black (Mat-making) 15 10
31. – 15 c. green (Weaving) .. 15 10
32. – 25 c. red (Pottery) .. 15 10
33. – 35 c. blue (Building) .. 15 10
34. – 50 c. orange (Date cultivation) 15 10
35. – 90 c. brown (Agriculture) 15 15
36. – 1 s. black & lilac (Fisheries) 20 10
37. – 1 s. 25 c. black and orange (Lime-burning) 30 45
38. – 2 s. black and blue (Dhow building) .. .. 2·00 60
39. – 5 s. black and green (Agriculture) .. .. 3·25 1·25
40. – 10 s. black & red (as No. 37) 3·50 2·00

1963. Occupations. As Nos. 29/40 but with inset portrait of Sultan Awadh bin Saleh el Qu'aiti, as in **T 22.**

41. **22.** 5 c. blue 10 10
42. – 10 c. black 10 10
43. – 15 c. green 10 10
44. – 25 c. red 10 10
45. – 35 c. blue 10 10
46. – 50 c. orange 10 10
47. – 70 c. brown (As No. 35) 15 20
48. – 1 s. black and lilac .. 20 10
49. – 1 s. 25 black and orange 35 65
50. – 2 s. black and blue .. 1·75 1·75
51. – 5 s. black and green .. 6·50 7·00
52. – 10 s. black and red .. 6·50 9·00

1966. Nos. 41/52 surch. **SOUTH ARABIA** in English and Arabic, with value and bar.

53. **5.** 5 f. on 5 c. 10 30
54. – 5 f. on 10 c. 10 30
55. – 10 f. on 15 c. 10 20
56. – 15 f. on 25 c. 10 30
57. – 20 f. on 35 c. 10 40
58. – 25 f. on 50 c. 10 30
59. – 35 f. on 70 c. 10 30
60. – 50 f. on 1 s. 10 15
61. – 65 f. on 1 s. 25 .. .. 25 25
62. – 100 f. on 2 s. 45 75
63. – 250 f. on 5 s. .. .. 1·00 1·50
64. – 500 f. on 10 s. .. .. 12·00 3·00

1966. Churchill Commem. Nos. 54/6 optd. **1874-1965 WINSTON CHURCHILL.**

65. 5 f. on 10 c. .. .. 3·50 4·75
66. 10 f. on 15 c. .. .. 4·00 5·00
67. 15 f. on 25 c. .. .. 6·00 7·50

1966. Pres. Kennedy Commem. Nos. 57/9 optd. **1917-63 JOHN F. KENNEDY.**

68. 20 f. on 35 c. .. .. 1·25 3·00
69. 25 f. on 50 c. .. .. 1·60 3·75
70. 35 f. on 70 c. .. .. 2·25 4·25

25. World Cup Emblem. (Actual size 55 × 55 mm.)

1966. World Cup Football Championships.

71. **25.** 5 f. purple and orange 1·40 25
72. – 10 f. violet and green .. 1·75 25
73. – 15 f. purple and orange 1·90 30
74. – 20 f. violet and green .. 2·25 40
75. **25.** 25 f. green and red .. 2·50 55
76. – 35 f. blue and yellow .. 3·00 80
77. – 50 f. green and red .. 3·50 1·10
78. **25.** 65 f. blue and yellow .. 4·00 1·40

DESIGNS: 10 f., 35 f. Wembley Stadium. 15 f., 50 f. Footballers. 20 f. Jules Rimet Cup and football.

29. Mexican Hat and Blanket. (Actual size 63 × 63 mm.)

1966. Pre-Olympic Games, Mexico (1968).

79. **29.** 75 f. sepia and green .. 1·25 1·25

30. Telecommunications Satellite.

1966. Int. Co-operation Year.

80	**30.**	5 f. mauve, purple & green	1·75	35
81.	–	10 f. multicoloured ..	2·00	35
82.	–	15 f. purple, blue and red	2·25	40
83.	**30.**	20 f. blue, purple and red	2·50	45
84.	–	25 f. multicoloured ..	2·75	50
85.	**30.**	35 f. purple, red and blue	3·75	80
86.	–	50 f. purple, green and red	5·00	1·25
87.	**30.**	65 f. brown, violet and red	5·50	1·75

DESIGNS: 10 f. Olympic runner (inscr. " ROME 1960 "). 15 f. Fishes. 25 f. Olympic runner (inscr. " TOKIO 1964 "). 50 f. Tobacco plant.

MAHRA SULTANATE OF QISHN AND SOCOTRA

The National Liberation Front took control on 1 October 1967, and full independence was granted by Great Britain on 30 November 1967. Now part of Southern Yemen.

1. Mahra Flag.

1967.

1.	**1.**	5 f. multicoloured ..	95	10
2.		10 f. multicoloured ..	95	15
3.		15 f. multicoloured ..	95	15
4.		20 f. multicoloured ..	95	20
5.		25 f. multicoloured ..	95	25
6.		35 f. multicoloured ..	95	25
7.		50 f. multicoloured ..	95	25
8.		65 f. multicoloured ..	95	25
9.		100 f. multicoloured ..	1·00	25
10.		250 f. multicoloured ..	1·25	35
11.		500 f. multicoloured ..	1·50	50

For later issues see **SOUTHERN YEMEN, YEMEN-PEOPLE'S DEMOCRATIC REPUBLIC** in volume 2.

APPENDIX

The following stamps have either been issued in excess of postal needs, or have not been made available to the public in reasonable quantities at face value.

SEIYUN

1967.

Hunting. 20 f.

Olympic Games, Grenoble. Postage 10, 25, 35, 50, 75 f.; Air 100, 200 f.

Scout Jamboree, Idaho. Air 150 f.

Paintings—Renoir. Postage 10, 35, 50, 65, 75 f.; Air 100, 200, 250 f.

Paintings—Toulouse-Lautrec. Postage 10, 35, 50, 65, 75 f.; Air 100, 200, 250 f.

Stated to have been occupied by the N.L.F. on 1st October, 1967.

HADHRAMAUT

1967.

Stampex, London. Postage 5, 10, 15, 20, 25 f.; Air 50, 65 f.

Amphilex International Stamp Exhibition, Amsterdam. Air 75 f.

Olympic Games, Mexico (1968). 75 f.

Paintings. Postage 5, 10, 15, 20, 25 f.; Air 50, 65 f.

Scout Jamboree, Idaho. Air 35 f.

Space Research. Postage 10, 25, 35, 50, 75 f.; Air 100, 250 f.

Stated to have been occupied by the N.L.F. on 17th September, 1967.

MAHRA

1967.

Scout Jamboree, Idaho. 15, 75, 100, 150 f.

President Kennedy, Commemoration Postage 10, 15, 25, 50, 75, 100, 150 f.; Air 250, 500 f.

Olympic Games, Mexico (1968). Postage 10, 25, 50 f.; Air 250, 500 f.

Stated to have been occupied by the N.L.F. on 1 October 1967.

Although the British Government did not officially relinquish control over Eastern Aden Protectorate (which comprises the above states) until 30 November 1967, to the National Liberation Front (later the Southern Yemen Republic), that Government claimed that the N.L.F. were in control of them on the dates given above and repudiated the contract under which the former rulers authorised some further new issues which were placed on the market. However, despite this claim there is some uncertainty as to whether any of these later issues were delivered and actually used for postal purposes.

AITUTAKI

Island in the S. Pacific.

1903. 12 pence = 1 shilling.
20 shillings = 1 pound.
1967. 100 cents = 1 dollar.

A. NEW ZEALAND DEPENDENCY.

The British Govt., who had exercised a protectorate over the Cook Islands group since the 1880's handed the islands, including Aitutaki to New Zealand administration in 1901. Cook Is. stamps were used from 1932 to 1972.

Stamps of New Zealand overprinted **AITUTAKI** and value in native language.

1903. Pictorial stamps.

1	**23.**	½d. green	3·25	6·50
2	**40.**	1d. red	4·50	5·50
4	**26.**	2½d. blue	8·00	11·00
5	**28.**	3d. brown	7·00	15·00
6	**31.**	6d. red	20·00	25·00
7	**34.**	1s. red	55·00	85·00

1911. King Edward VII stamps.

9	**51**	½d. green	75	2·50
10	**53**	1d. red	3·00	8·00
11	**51**	6d. red	35·00	70·00
12		1s. red	55·00	£120

1916. King George V stamps.

13.	**62.**	6d. red	7·50	22·00
14a.		1s. red	28·00	75·00

1917. King George V stamps optd. **AITUTAKI** only.

19	**62**	½d. green	1·00	4·00
20	**53**	1d. red	2·50	8·00
21	**62**	1½d. grey	3·50	20·00
22		1½d. brown	80	6·50
15		2½d. blue	1·40	10·00
16		3d. brown	1·25	12·00
17		6d. red	4·50	12·00
18		1s. red	12·00	22·00

1920. As 1920 pictorial stamps of Cook Is.

30	½d. black and green ..	2·00	7·50
25	1d. black and red ..	3·00	6·00
26	1½d. black and brown ..	6·00	11·00
32	2½d. black and blue ..	7·50	38·00
27	3d. black and blue ..	1·75	12·00
28	6d. brown and grey ..	5·00	14·00
29	1s. black and purple ..	8·50	16·00

B. PART OF COOK ISLANDS.

On 9 August 1972. Aitutaki became a Port of Entry into the Cook Islands. Whilst remaining part of the Cook Islands, Aitutaki has a separate postal service.

1972. Nos. 227/8, 230, 233/4, 238, 240/1, 243 and 244 of Cook Islands optd. **Aitutaki.**

33.	**79.**	½ c. multicoloured ..	30	80
34.	–	1 c. multicoloured ..	70	1·40
35.	–	2½ c. multicoloured ..	3·50	8·00
36.	–	4 c. multicoloured ..	70	85
37.	–	5 c. multicoloured ..	4·50	8·50
38.	–	10 c. multicoloured ..	4·50	6·50
39.	–	20 c. multicoloured ..	70	1·00
40.	–	25 c. multicoloured ..	70	1·00
41.	–	50 c. multicoloured ..	3·75	3·25
42.	–	$ 1 multicoloured ..	6·50	6·50

1972. Christmas. Nos. 406/8 of Cook Islands optd. **Aitutaki.**

43.	**130.**	1 c. multicoloured ..	10	10
44.	–	5 c. multicoloured ..	10	15
45.	–	10 c. multicoloured ..	10	25

1972. Royal Silver Wedding. As Nos. 413 and 415 of Cook Islands, but inscr. " **COOK ISLANDS Aitutaki** ".

46.	**131.**	5 c. black and silver ..	4·75	2·75
47.	–	15 c. black and silver ..	2·75	1·50

1972. No. 245 of Cook Islands optd. **AITUTAKI.**

48.	$2 multicoloured ..	60	1·00

1972. Nos. 227/8, 230, 233, 234, 238, 240, 241, 243 and 244 of Cook Islands optd. **AITUTAKI** within ornamental oval.

49.	**79.**	½ c. multicoloured ..	15	10
50.	–	1 c. multicoloured ..	15	10
51.	–	2½ c. multicoloured ..	20	10
52.	–	4 c. multicoloured ..	25	15
53.	–	5 c. multicoloured ..	25	15
54.	–	10 c. multicoloured ..	35	25
55.	–	20 c. multicoloured ..	70	50
56.	–	25 c. multicoloured ..	70	55
57.	–	50 c. multicoloured ..	1·25	90
58.	–	$1 multicoloured ..	1·75	1·75

13. " Christ Mocked " (Grunewald).

1973. Easter. Multicoloured.

59.	1 c. Type **13**	15	10
60.	1 c. " St. Veronica " (Van der Weyden)	15	10
61.	1 c. " The Crucified Christ with Virgin Mary, Saints and Angels " (Raphael)	15	10
62.	1 c. " Resurrection " (Piero della Francesca)	15	10
63.	5 c. " The Last Supper " (Master of Amiens) ..	20	15
64.	5 c. " Condemnation " (Holbein)	20	15
65.	5 c. " Christ on the Cross " (Rubens)	20	15
66.	5 c. " Resurrection " (El Greco)	20	15
67.	10 c. " Disrobing of Christ " (El Greco)	20	15
68.	10 c. " St. Veronica " (Van Oostsanen)	20	15
69.	10 c. " Christ on the Cross " (Rubens)	20	15
70.	10 c. " Resurrection " (Bouts)	20	15

1973. Silver Wedding Coinage. Nos. 417/23 of Cook Is. optd. **AITUTAKI.**

71.	**132.**	1 c. black, red & gold ..	10	10
72.	–	2 c. black, blue & gold	10	10
73.	–	5 c. black, green & silver	10	10
74.	–	10 c. black, blue & silver	15	10
75.	–	20 c. black, green & silver	20	15
76.	–	50 c. black, red & silver	40	30
77.	–	$1 black, blue & silver	65	45

1973. 10th Anniv. of Treaty Banning Nuclear Testing. Nos. 236, 238, 240 and 243 of Cook Is. optd. **AITUTAKI** within ornamental oval and **TENTH ANNIVERSARY CESSATION OF NUCLEAR TESTING TREATY.**

78.	8 c. multicoloured	15	15
79.	10 c. multicoloured	15	15
80.	20 c. multicoloured	30	20
81.	50 c. multicoloured	70	50

16. Red Hibiscus and Princess Anne.

1973. Royal Wedding. Multicoloured.

82.	25 c. Type **16**	25	10
83.	30 c. Capt. Mark Phillips and Blue Hibiscus ..	25	10

17. " Virgin and Child " (Montagna).

1973. Christmas. "Virgin and Child" paintings by artist listed below. Mult.

85.	1 c. Type **17**	10	10
86.	1 c. Crivelli	10	10
87.	1 c. Van Dyck	10	10
88.	1 c. Perugino	10	10
89.	5 c. Veronese (child on shoulder)	15	10
90.	5 c. Veronese (child on lap)	15	10
91.	5 c. Cima	15	10
92.	5 c. Memling	15	10
93.	10 c. Memling	20	10
94.	10 c. Del Colle	20	10
95.	10 c. Raphael	20	10
96.	10 c. Lotto	20	10

18. " Murex ramosus ".

1974. Sea-shells. Multicoloured.

97.	½ c. Type 18	35	40
98.	1 c. " Nautilus macromphallus " ..	35	40
99.	2 c. " Harpa major " ..	35	40
100.	3 c. " Phalium strigatum "	40	40
101.	4 c. " Cypraea talpa " ..	40	40
102.	5 c. " Mitra stictica " ..	40	40
103.	8 c. " Charonia tritonis " ..	45	40
104.	10 c. " Murex triremis " ..	45	40
105.	20 c. " Oliva sericea " ..	60	40
106.	25 c. " Tritonalia rubeta "	70	40
107.	60 c. " Strombus latissimus "	2·50	70
108.	$1 " Biplex perca " ..	1·75	1·10
109	$2 Queen Elizabeth II and " Terebra maculata " ..	6·00	7·00
110.	$5 Queen Elizabeth II and " Cypraea hesitat " ..	22·00	9·50

The $2 and $5 are larger, 53 × 25 mm.

19. Bligh and H.M.S. "Bounty".

1974. William Bligh's Discovery of Aitutaki. Multicoloured

114.	1 c. Type **19**	20	10
115.	1 c. H.M.S. "Bounty" ..	20	10
116.	5 c. Bligh, and H.M.S. "Bounty" at Aitutaki ..	40	15
117.	5 c. Aitutaki chart of 1856	40	15
118.	8 c. Capt. Cook and H.M.S. "Resolution"	65	20
119.	8 c. Map of Aitutaki and inset location map	65	20

See also Nos. 123/8.

20. Aitutaki Stamps of 1903, and Map.

1974. Centenary of Universal Postal Union. Multicoloured.

120.	25 c. Type **20**	65	40
121.	50 c. Surcharged 1903, and 1920, and map ..	85	60

1974. Air. As Nos. 114/119 in larger size (46 × 26 mm.), additionally inscr. "AIR MAIL".

123.	10 c. Type **19**	50	15
124.	10 c. H.M.S. "Bounty" ..	50	15
125.	25 c. Bligh, and H.M.S. "Bounty" at Aitutaki ..	65	25
126.	25 c. Aitutaki chart of 1856	65	25
127.	30 c. Capt. Cook and H.M.S. "Resolution" ..	65	25
128.	30 c. Map of Aitutaki and inset location map ..	65	25

21. "Virgin and Child" (Hugo van der Goes).

1974. Christmas. "Virgin and Child" paintings by artists named. Mult.

129.	1 c. Type **21**	10	10
130.	5 c. G. Bellini	10	10
131.	8 c. G. David	10	10
132.	10 c. A. da Messina ..	10	10
133.	25 c. J. Van Cleve ..	20	20
134.	30 c. Master of the Life of St. Catherine ..	20	20

22. Churchill as Schoolboy.

1974. Birth Centenary of Sir Winston Churchill. Multicoloured.

136. 10 c. Type **22** 30 25
137. 25 c. Churchill as young man 60 50
138. 30 c. Churchill with troops 75 60
139. 50 c. Churchill painting .. 1·10 80
140. $1 Churchill giving "V"-sign .. .. .. 2·00 1·50

1974. Children's Christmas Fund. Nos. 129/34 surch.

142. **21.** 1 c.+1 c. multicoloured 10 10
143. – 5 c.+1 c. multicoloured 10 10
144. – 8 c.+1 c. multicoloured 10 10
145. – 10 c.+1 c. multicoloured 10 10
146. – 25 c.+1 c. multicoloured 20 20
147. – 30 c.+1 c. multicoloured 20 20

24. Soviet and U.S. Flags.

1975. "Apollo-Soyuz" Space Project. Multicoloured.

148. 25 c. Type **24** 30 20
149. 50 c. Daedalus with space capsule 40 30

25. "Madonna and Child with Saints Francis and John" (Lorenzetti).

1975. Christmas. Multicoloured.

151. 6 c. } Type **25** 10 10
152. 6 c. } 10 10
153. 6 c. } 10 10
154. 7 c. } "Adoration of 10 10
155. 7 c. } the Kings" 10 10
156. 7 c. } (Van der Weyden) .. 10 10
157. 15 c. } "Madonna and 15 15
158. 15 c. } Child enthroned with Saints Onufrius and John the Baptist" .. 15 15
159. 15 c. } (Montagna) .. 15 15
160. 20 c. } "Adoration of .. 20 15
161. 20 c. } the Shepherds" .. 20 15
162. 20 c. } (Reni) .. 20 15

Type **25** shows the left-hand stamp of the 6 c. design.

1975. Children's Christmas Fund. Nos. 151/62 surch.

164. **25.** 6 c.+1 c. multicoloured 15 10
165. – 6 c.+1 c. multicoloured 15 10
166. – 6 c.+1 c. multicoloured 15 10
167. – 7 c.+1 c. multicoloured 15 10
168. – 7 c.+1 c. multicoloured 15 10
169. – 7 c.+1 c. multicoloured 15 10
170. – 15 c.+1 c. multicoloured 20 15
171. – 15 c.+1 c. multicoloured 20 15
172. – 15 c.+1 c. multicoloured 20 15
173. – 20 c.+1 c. multicoloured 25 20
174. – 20 c.+1 c. multicoloured 25 20
175. – 20 c.+1 c. multicoloured 25 20

26. "The Descent" (detail, 15th cent. Flemish School).

1976. Easter. Multicoloured.

176. 15 c. Type **26** 15 10
177. 30 c. "The Descent" (detail) 20 15
178. 35 c. "The Descent" (detail) 25 20

27. "The Declaration of Independence" (detail).

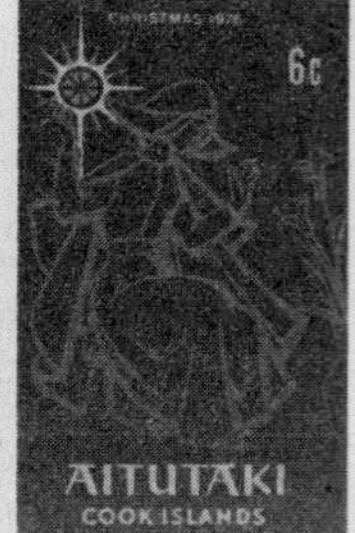

30. "The Visitation".

28. Cycling.

1976. Bicent. of American Revolution. Multicoloured.

180. 30 c. } 60 30
181. 30 c. } Type **27** 60 30
182. 30 c. } 60 30
183. 35 c. } "Surrender of Lord 70 40
184. 35 c. } Cornwallis at York- 70 40
185. 35 c. } town" (John Trumbull) 70 40
186. 50 c. } "The Resignation of 80 45
187. 50 c. } General Washington" 80 45
188. 50 c. } (John Trumbull) .. 80 45

Type **27** shows the left-hand stamp of the 30 c. design.

1976. Olympic Games, Montreal. Mult.

190. 15 c. Type **28** 20 15
191. 35 c. Sailing 40 20
192. 60 c. Hockey 55 25
193. 70 c. Sprinting 60 30

1976. Royal Visit to the U.S.A. Nos. 190/3 optd. **ROYAL VISIT JULY 1976.**

195. **28.** 15 c. multicoloured .. 25 15
196. – 35 c. multicoloured .. 40 25
197. – 60 c. multicoloured .. 60 40
198. – 70 c. multicoloured .. 70 45

1976. Christmas. Multicoloured.

200. 6 c. } Type **30** 10 10
201. 6 c. } 10 10
202. 7 c. } "Angel and 10 10
203. 7 c. } Shepherds" .. 10 10
204. 15 c. } "The Holy Family" 10 10
205. 15 c. } 10 10
206. 20 c. } "The Magi" .. 15 15
207. 20 c. } 15 15

Type **30** shows the left-hand stamp of the 6 c. design.

1976. Children's Christmas Fund. Nos. 200/07 surch.

209. **30.** 6 c.+1 c. multicoloured 10 10
210. – 6 c.+1 c. multicoloured 10 10
211. – 7 c.+1 c. multicoloured 10 10
212. – 7 c.+1 c. multicoloured 10 10
213. – 15 c.+1 c. multicoloured 15 15
214. – 15 c.+1 c. multicoloured 15 15
215. – 20 c.+1 c. multicoloured 15 15
216. – 20 c.+1 c. multicoloured 15 15

32. Alexander Graham Bell and First Telephone.

1977. Centenary of Telephone (1976).

218. **32.** 25 c. black, gold and red 20 15
219. – 70 c. black, gold & lilac 40 40

DESIGN: 70 c. Satellite and Earth station.

33. "Christ on the Cross" (detail).

1977. Easter. 400th Birth Anniv. of Rubens. Multicoloured.

221. 15 c. Type **33** 40 15
222. 20 c. "Lamentation for Christ" 50 20
223. 35 c. "Christ with Straw" 70 25

34. Capt. Bligh, George III and H.M.S. "Bounty".

1977. Silver Jubilee. Multicoloured.

225. 25 c. Type **34** 50 45
226. 35 c. Rev. Williams, George IV and Aitutaki Church 60 50
227. 50 c. Union Jack, Queen Victoria and island map 75 75
228. $1 Balcony scene 1953 1·25 1·25

35. The Shepherds.

1977. Christmas. Multicoloured.

230. 6 c. Type **35** 10 10
231. 6 c. Angel 10 10
232. 7 c. Mary, Jesus and Ox .. 10 10
233. 7 c. Joseph and donkey .. 10 10
234. 15 c. Three kings 10 10
235. 15 c. Virgin and Child .. 10 10
236. 20 c. Joseph 10 10
237. 20 c. Mary and Jesus on donkey 10 10

1977. Children's Christmas Fund. Nos. 230/7 surch. +1 c.

239. 6 c.+1 c. } Type **35** 10 10
240. 6 c.+1 c. } 10 10
241. 7 c.+1 c. } The Holy 10 10
242. 7 c.+1 c. } Family .. 10 10
243. 15 c.+1 c. } Virgin and Child with the Three 15 10
244. 15 c.+1 c. } Kings 15 10
245. 20 c.+1 c. } "The Flight 15 10
246. 20 c.+1 c. } into Egypt" 15 10

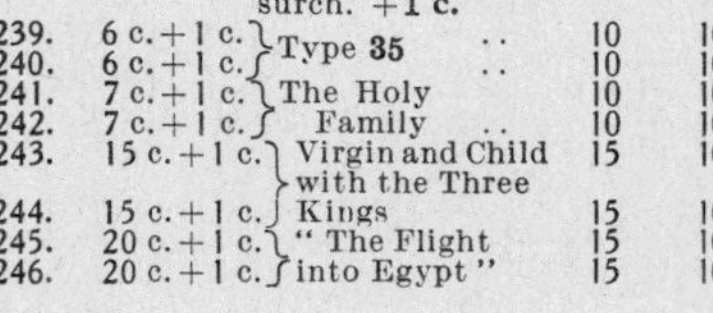

37. Hawaiian Goddess.

1978. Bicent. of Discovery of Hawaii. Mult.

248. 35 c. Type **37** 45 25
249. 50 c. Figurehead of H.M.S. "Resolution" (horiz.) 75 40
250. $1 Hawaiian temple figure 1·00 70

38. "Christ on the way to Calvary" (Martini).

1978. Easter. Paintings from the Louvre, Paris. Multicoloured.

252. 15 c. Type **38** 10 10
253. 20 c. "Pieta of Avignon" (E. Quanton) 15 10
254. 35 c. "The Pilgrims at Emmaus" (Rembrandt) 20 15

39. The Yale of Beaufort.

40. "Adoration of the Infant Jesus".

1978. 25th Anniv. of Coronation. Mult.

257. $1 Type **39** 55 65
258. $1 Queen Elizabeth II .. 55 65
259. $1 Aitutaki ancestral statue 55 65

1978. Christmas. 450th Death Anniv. of Durer. Multicoloured.

261. 15 c. Type **40** 35 15
262. 17 c. "The Madonna with Child" 40 15
263. 30 c. "The Madonna with the Iris" 55 20
264. 35 c. "The Madonna of the Siskin" 60 25

41. "Captain Cook" (Nathaniel Dance).

1979. Death Bicent. of Captain Cook. Mult.

266. 50 c. Type **41** .. .. 1·00 80
267. 75 c. H.M.S. "Resolution" and "Adventure" at Matavai Bay, Tahiti (W. Hodges) .. .. .. 1·75 95

42. Girl with Flowers.

1979. International Year of the Child. Mult.

269. 30 c. Type **42** 15 15
270. 35 c. Boy playing guitar .. 20 20
271. 65 c. Children in canoe .. 30 30

43. "Man writing a Letter" (painting by Gabriel Metsu).

1979. Death Centenary of Sir Rowland Hill. Multicoloured.

273. 50 c. Type **43** 80 80
274. 50 c. Sir Rowland Hill with Penny Black, 1903 ½d and 1911 1d stamps .. 80 80
275. 50 c. "Girl in Blue reading a Letter" (Jan Vermeer) 80 80
276. 65 c. "Woman writing a Letter" (Gerard Terborch) 85 85
277. 65 c. Sir Rowland Hill, with Penny Black, 1903 3d and 1920 ½d stamps .. 85 85
278. 65 c. "Lady reading a Letter" (Jan Vermeer) .. 85 85

44. " The Burial of Christ (left detail) (Quentin Metsys).

1980. Easter. Multicoloured.

280. 20 c. Type **44** 25 15
281. 30 c. " The Burial of Christ " (centre detail) 35 25
282. 35 c. " The Burial of Christ " (right detail) 40 30

45. Einstein as a Young Man.

1980. 25th Death Anniv. of Albert Einstein (physicist). Multicoloured.

284. 12 c. Type **45** 40 40
285. 12 c. Atom and "E = mc²" equation 40 40
286. 15 c. Einstein in middle-age 45 45
287. 15 c. Cross over nuclear explosion (Test Ban Treaty, 1963) 45 45
288. 20 c. Einstein as an old man 50 50
289. 20 c. Hand preventing atomic explosion .. 50 50

46. Ancestor Figure, Aitutaki.

1980. Third South Pacific Festival of Arts. Multicoloured.

291. 6 c. Type **46** 10 10
292. 6 c. Staff god image Rarotonga 10 10
293. 6 c. Trade adze, Mangaia 10 10
294. 6 c. Carved image of Tangaroa, Rarotonga .. 10 10
295. 12 c. Wooden image Aitutaki 10 10
296. 12 c. Hand club, Rarotonga 10 10
297 12 c. Carved mace " god ", Mangaia 10 10
298. 12 c. Fisherman's god, Rarotonga 10 10
299. 15 c. Ti'i image, Aitutaki 15 15
300. 15 c. Fisherman's god, Rarotonga (different) 15 15
301. 15 c. Carved mace " god ", Cook Islands 15 15
302. 15 c. Carved image of Tangaroa, Rarotonga (different) 15 15
303. 20c. Chief's headdress, Aitutaki 15 15
304. 20 c. Carved mace " god " Cook Islands, (different) 15 15
305. 20 c. Staff god image, Rarotonga (different) 15 15
306. 20 c. Carved image of Tangaroa, Rarotonga (different) 15 15

47. " The Virgin and Child " (13th century).

1980. Christmas. Sculptures of " The Virgin and Child ". Multicoloured.

308. 15 c. Type **47** 15 15
309. 20 c. 14th century .. 15 15
310. 25 c. 15th century .. 15 15
311. 35 c. 15th century (different) 20 20

48. " Mourning Virgin ".

1981. Easter. Details of Sculpture " Burial of Christ " by Pedro Roldan.

313. **48.** 30 c. gold and green .. 25 25
314. – 40 c. gold and lilac .. 30 30
315. – 50 c. gold and blue .. 30 30

DESIGNS: 40 c. " Christ ". 50 c. " Saint John ".

49. Gouldian Finch.

1981. Birds (1st series). Multicoloured.

317 1 c. Type **49** 35 30
318 1 c. Common starling .. 35 30
319 2 c. Golden whistler .. 40 30
320 2 c. Scarlet robin .. 40 30
321 3 c. Rufous fantail .. 40 30
322 3 c. Peregrine falcon .. 40 30
323 4 c. Java sparrow .. 50 30
324 4 c. Barn owl 50 30
325 5 c. Tahitian lory .. 50 30
326 5 c. White-breasted wood swallow 50 30
327 6 c. Purple swamphen .. 50 30
328 6 c. Rock dove 50 30
329 10 c. Chestnut-breasted mannikin 70 30
330 10 c. Zebra dove 70 30
331 12 c. Eastern reef heron .. 70 40
332 12 c. Common mynah .. 70 40
333 15 c. Whimbrel (horiz) .. 80 40
334 15 c. Black-browed albatross (horiz) .. 80 40
335 20 c. American golden plover (horiz) .. 1·00 55
336 20 c. White tern (horiz) .. 1·00 55
337 25 c. Spotbill duck (horiz) 1·25 70
338 25 c. Brown booby (horiz) 1·25 70
339 30 c. Great frigate bird (horiz) .. .. 1·50 80
340 30 c. Pintail (horiz) .. 1·50 80
341 35 c. Long-billed reed warbler .. .. 1·75 90
342 35 c. Pomarine skua .. 1·75 90
343 40 c. Banded rail .. 2·00 1·00
344 40 c. Spotted triller .. 2·00 1·00

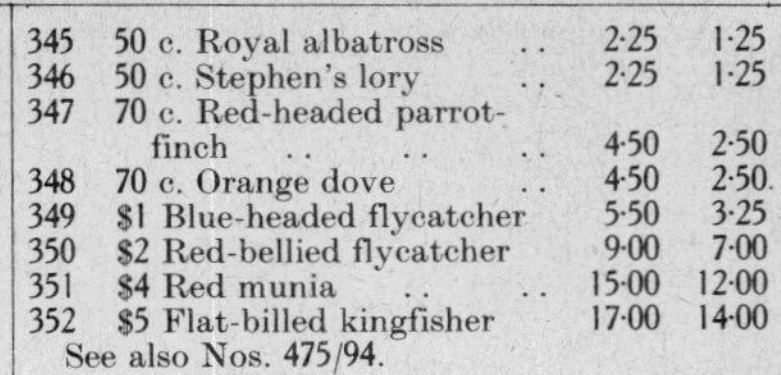

345 50 c. Royal albatross .. 2·25 1·25
346 50 c. Stephen's lory .. 2·25 1·25
347 70 c. Red-headed parrot-finch .. .. 4·50 2·50
348 70 c. Orange dove .. 4·50 2·50
349 $1 Blue-headed flycatcher 5·50 3·25
350 $2 Red-bellied flycatcher 9·00 7·00
351 $4 Red munia .. .. 15·00 12·00
352 $5 Flat-billed kingfisher 17·00 14·00

See also Nos. 475/94.

50. Prince Charles.

1981. Royal Wedding. Multicoloured.

391. 60 c. Type **50** 50 60
392. 80 c. Lady Diana Spencer 60 75
393. $1.40 Prince Charles and Lady Diana (87 × 70 mm.) 1·00 1·10

1981. International Year for Disabled Persons. Nos. 391/3 surch. **+ 5c.**

394. 60 c. + 5 c. Type **50** .. 1·25 1·25
395. 80 c. + 5 c. Lady Diana Spencer .. .. 1·75 1·75
396. $1.40 + 5 c. Prince Charles and Lady Diana .. 3·25 3·25

52. Footballers.

1981. World Cup Football Championship, Spain (1982). Football Scenes. Mult.

397. 12 c. Ball to left of stamp 35 35
398. 12 c. Ball to right .. 35 35
399. 15 c. Ball to right .. 40 40
400. 15 c. Ball to left .. 40 40
401. 20 c. Ball to left .. 50 50
402. 20 c. Ball to right .. 50 50
403. 25 c. Type **52** .. 55 55
404. 25 c. " ESPANA 82 " inscription 55 55

53. " The Holy Family ".

1981. Christmas. Etchings by Rembrandt.

406. **53.** 15 c. brown and gold .. 40 40
407. – 30 c. brown and gold .. 60 60
408. – 40 c. brown and gold .. 75 75
409. – 50 c. brown and gold .. 85 85

DESIGNS—VERT. 30 c. " Virgin with Child ". HORIZ. 40 c. " Adoration of the Shepherds ". 50 c. " The Holy Family ".

54. Princess of Wales.

1982. 21st Birthday of Princess of Wales. Multicoloured.

411 70 c. Type **54** 70 70
412 $1 Prince and Princess of Wales 85 85
413 $2 Princess Diana (different) .. .. 1·60 1·75

1982. Birth of Prince William of Wales. (1st issue). Nos. 391/3 optd.

415. 60 c. Type **50** .. .. 2·00 1·50
416. 60 c. Type **50** .. 2·00 1·50
417. 80 c. Lady Diana Spencer 2·50 1·75
418. 80 c. Lady Diana Spencer 2·50 1·75
419. $1.40 Prince Charles and Lady Diana .. .. 4·50 3·00
420. $1.40 Prince Charles and Lady Diana .. .. 4·50 3·00

OPTS. Nos. 415, 417 and 419, **21 JUNE 1982. PRINCE WILLIAM OF WALES.** Nos. 416, 418 and 420, **COMMEMORATING THE ROYAL BIRTH.**

1982. Birth of Prince William of Wales. (2nd issue). As Nos. 411/13 but inscr. " ROYAL BIRTH 21 JUNE 1982 PRINCE WILLIAM OF WALES ".

421. 70 c. Type **54** .. 70 70
422. $1 Prince and Princess of Wales 85 85
423. $2 Princess Diana (different) .. .. 1·60 1·60

56. " Virgin and Child " (12th-century sculpture).

1982. Christmas. Religious Sculptures. Multicoloured.

425. 18 c. Type **56** .. 50 50
426. 36 c. " Virgin and Child " (12th-century) 65 65
427. 48 c. " Virgin and Child " (13th-century) 75 75
428. 60 c. " Virgin and Child " (15th-century) 90 90

57. Aitutaki Bananas.

1983. Commonwealth Day. Multicoloured.

430. 48 c. Type **57** .. 90 50
431. 48 c. Ancient Ti'i image .. 90 50
432. 48 c. Tourist canoeing .. 90 50
433. 48 c. Captain William Bligh and chart 90 50

58. Scouts around Campfire.

1983. 75th Anniv. of Boy Scout Movement. Multicoloured.

434. 36 c. Type **58** .. .. 1·00 45
435. 48 c. Scout saluting .. 1·25 55
436. 60 c. Scouts hiking .. 1·50 75

1983. 15th World Scout Jamboree, Alberta, Canada. Nos. 434/6 optd **15th WORLD SCOUT JAMBOREE**.

438. 36 c. Type **58** .. .. 1·00 45
439. 48 c. Scout saluting .. 1·25 55
440. 60 c. Scouts hiking .. 1·50 75

60. Modern Sport Balloon.

1983. Bicentenary of Manned Flight.

442. 18 c. multicoloured .. 30 15
443. 36 c. multicoloured .. 50 30
444. 48 c. multicoloured .. 65 35
445. 60 c. multicoloured .. 80 45

DESIGNS: 36 c. to 60 c. showing different modern sports balloons.

1983. Various stamps surch. (a) Nos. 335/48 and 352.

447. 18 c. on 20 c. American Golden Plover .. 70 50
448. 18 c. on 20 c. White tern .. 70 50
449. 36 c. on 25 c. Spotbill duck 1·00 75
450. 36 c. on 25 c. Brown booby 1·00 75
451. 36 c. on 30 c. Great frigate bird .. .. .. 1·00 75
452. 36 c. on 30 c. Pintail .. 1·00 75
453. 36 c. on 35 c. Long-billed reed warbler .. .. 1·00 75
454. 36 c. on 35 c. Pomarine skua .. .. .. 1·00 75
455. 48 c. on 49 c. Banded rail 1·50 75
456. 48 c. on 40 c. Spotted triller 1·50 75
457. 48 c. on 50 c. Royal Albatross .. .. .. 1·50 75
458. 48 c. on 50 c. Stephen's lory .. .. .. 1·50 75
459. 72 c. on 70 c. Red-headed parrot finch .. .. 2·50 1·25
460. 72 c. on 70 c. Orange dove 2·50 1·25
461. $5.60 on $5 Flat-billed kingfisher (vert.) .. 13·00 7·50

(b) Nos. 392/3 and 412/3

462. 96 c. on 80 c. Lady Diana Spencer .. .. .. 4·75 2·50
463. 96 c. on $1 Prince and Princess of Wales .. 4·25 2·00
464. $1.20 on $1.40 Prince Charles and Lady Diana 4·75 2·50
465. $1.20 on $2 Princess Diana 4·25 2·00

63. International Mail.

1983. World Communications Year. Multicoloured.

466. 48 c. Type **63** 65 45
467. 60 c. Telecommunications 85 60
468. 96 c. Space satellite .. 1·25 90

64. " Madonna of the Chair ".

1983. Christmas. 500th Birth Anniv. of Raphael. Multicoloured.

470. 36 c. Type **64** 25 30
471. 48 c. " The Alba Madonna " 35 40
472. 60 c. "Conestabile Madonna" 50 55

65. Gouldian Finch.

1984. Birds (2nd series). Multicoloured.

475. 2 c. Type **65** 10 10
476. 3 c. Common Starling .. 10 10
477. 5 c. Scarlet Robin 10 10
478. 10 c. Golden Whistler .. 10 10
479. 12 c. Rufous Fantail .. 10 10
480. 18 c. Peregrine Falcon .. 10 10
481. 24 c. Barn Owl 15 20
482. 30 c. Java Sparrow .. 20 25
483. 36 c. White-breasted Wood Swallow 25 30
484. 48 c. Tahitian Lory 30 35
485. 50 c. Rock Dove 35 40
486. 60 c. Purple Swamphen .. 40 45
487. 72 c. Zebra Dove 50 55
488. 96 c. Chestnut-breasted Mannikin 65 70
489. $1.20 Common Mynah .. 80 85
490. $2.10 Eastern Reef Heron .. 1·40 1·50
491. $3 Blue-headed Flycatcher .. 2·00 2·10
492. $4.20 Red-bellied Flycatcher 2·75 3·00
493. $5.60 Red Munia .. 3·75 4·00
494. $9.60 Flat billed Kingfisher 6·25 6·50

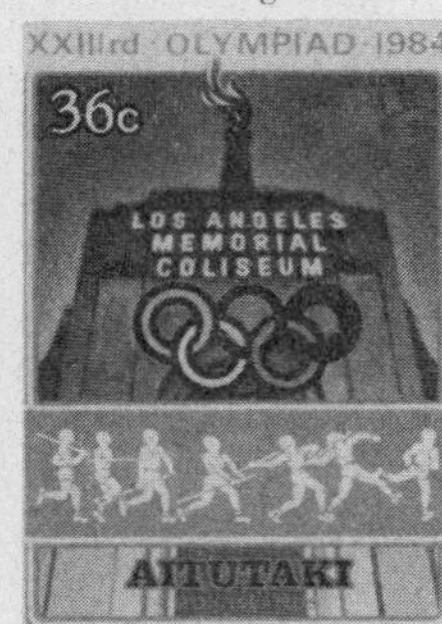

66. Javelin throwing.

1984. Olympic Games, Los Angeles. Multicoloured.

495. 36 c. Type **66** 30 35
496. 48 c. Shot-putting 40 45
497. 60 c. Hurdling 45 55
498. $2 Basketball .. .. 1·10 1·50

DESIGNS: Show Memorial Coliseum and various events.

1984. Olympic Gold Medal Winners. Nos. 495/8 optd.

500. 36 c. Type **66** (optd. **"Javelin Throw Tessa Sanderson Great Britain"**) 30 35
501. 48 c. Shot-putting (optd. **"Shot Put Claudia Losch Germany"**) 40 45
502. 60 c. Hurdling (optd. **"Heptathlon Glynis Nunn Australia"**) 45 55
503. $2 Basketball (optd. **"Team Basketball United States"**) .. .. .. 1·10 1·50

67. Capt. William Bligh and Chart.

1984. "Ausipex" International Stamp Exhibition, Melbourne, Multicoloured.

504. 60 c. Type **67** .. .. 1·25 1·25
505. 96 c. H.M.S. "Bounty" and map .. .. .. 1·50 1·50
506. $1.40 Aitutaki stamps of 1974, 1979 and 1981 with map .. .. .. 2·25 2·25

1984. Birth of Prince Henry (1st issue). No. 391 optd. **"15-9-84 Birth Prince Henry"** and surch. also.

508. $3 on 60 c. Type **50** .. 4·00 3·00

69. The Annunciation.

1984. Christmas. Details from Altarpiece, St. Paul's Church, Palencia, Spain. Multicoloured.

509. 36 c. Type **69** 30 35
510. 48 c. The Nativity .. 40 45
511. 60 c. The Epiphany .. 45 50
512. 96 c. The Flight into Egypt 75 80

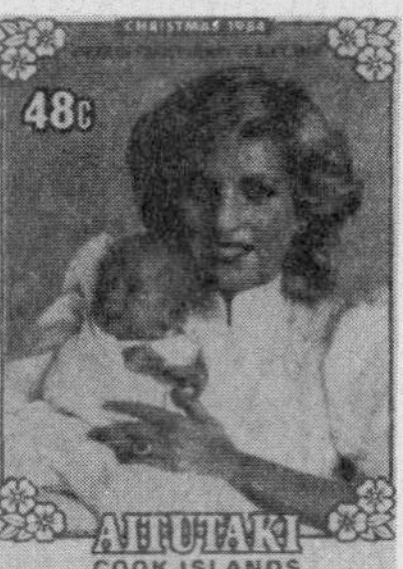

70. Princess Diana with Prince Henry.

1984. Birth of Prince Henry (2nd issue). Multicoloured.

514. 48 c. Type **70** 55 45
515. 60 c. Prince William with Prince Henry 60 50
516. $2.10 Prince and Princess of Wales with children .. 1·75 1·60

71. Grey Kingbird.

1985. Birth Bicentenary of John J. Audubon (ornithologist). Designs showing original paintings. Multicoloured.

518. 55 c. Type **71** 60 60
519. 65 c. Bohemian waxwing .. 65 65
520. 75 c. Summer tanager .. 75 75
521. 95 c. Common cardinal .. 90 90
522. $1.15 White-winged crossbill .. .. .. 1·10 1·10

72. The Queen Mother, aged Seven.

1985. Life and Times of Queen Elizabeth the Queen Mother. Multicoloured.

523. 55 c. Type **72** 45 50
524. 65 c. Engagement photograph, 1922 .. .. 50 55
525. 75 c. With young Princess Elizabeth 60 65
526. $1.30 With baby Prince Charles .. .. .. 1·00 1·10

73. "The Calmady Children" (T. Lawrence)

1985. International Youth Year. Mult.

528. 75 c. Type **73** 75 55
529. 90 c. "Madame Charpentier's Children" (Renoir) .. 85 65
530. $1.40 "Young Girls at Piano" (Renoir) .. 1·50 1·00

74. "Adoration of the Magi" (Giotto) and "Giotto" Spacecraft.

1985. Christmas. Appearance of Halley's Comet (1st issue). Multicoloured.

532. 95 c. Type **74** 75 80
533. 95 c. As Type **74** but showing "Planet A" spacecraft 75 80
534. $1.15 Type **74** 90 95
535. $1.15 As No. 533 .. .. 90 95

75. Halley's Comet, A.D. 684 (from "Nuremberg Chronicle").

1986. Appearance of Halley's Comet (2nd issue). Multicoloured.

537. 90 c. Type **75** 65 70
538. $1.25 Halley's Comet, 1066 (from Bayeux Tapestry) 85 90
539. $1.75 Halley's Comet, 1456 (from "Lucerne Chronicles") .. .. 1·25 1·40

76. Queen Elizabeth II on Coronation Day (from photo by Cecil Beaton).

1986. 60th Birthday of Queen Elizabeth II.

542. **76.** 95 c. multicoloured .. 85 85

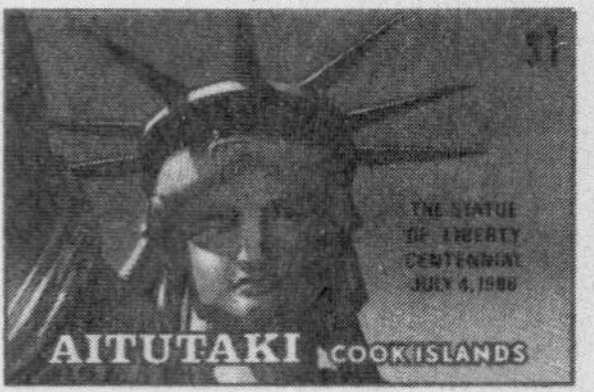

77. Head of Statue of Liberty.

1986. Centenary of Statue of Liberty. Multicoloured

544. $1 Type **77** 70 75
545. $2.75 Statue of Liberty at sunset .. .. .. 1·90 2·00

78. Prince Andrew and Miss Sarah Ferguson

1986. Royal Wedding.

547. **78.** $2 multicoloured .. 2·00 2·00

MORE DETAILED LISTS

are given in the Stanley Gibbons Catalogues referred to in the country headings.
For lists of current volumes see Introduction.

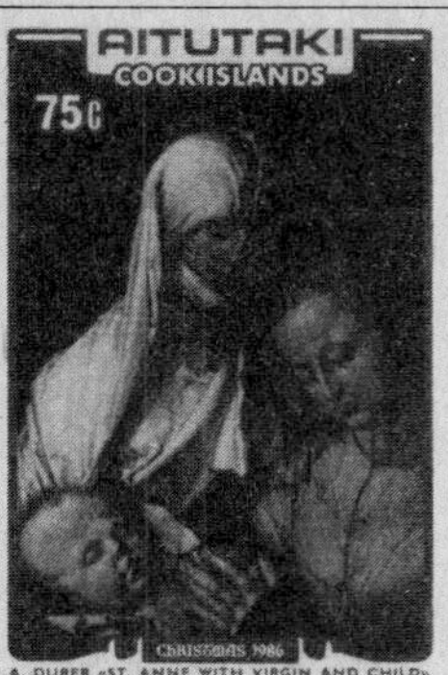

79. "St. Anne with Virgin and Child".

1986. Christmas. Paintings by Dürer. Mult.

551. 75 c. Type **79** .. .. 1·00 1·00
552. $1.35 "Virgin and Child" .. 1·50 1·50
553. $1.95 "The Adoration of the Magi" .. .. 2·00 2·00
554. $2.75 "Madonna of the Rosary" .. .. .. 2·50 2·50

1986. Visit of Pope John Paul II to South Pacific. Nos. 551/4 optd. **NOVEMBER 21–24 1986 FIRST VISIT TO SOUTH PACIFIC** and surch also.

556. 75 c.+10 c. Type **79** .. 1·50 1·50
557. $1.35+10 c. "Virgin and Child" .. .. .. 2·00 2·00
558. $1.95+10 c. "The Adoration of the Magi" .. 2·50 2·50
559. $2.75+10 c. "Madonna of the Rosary" .. .. 3·25 3·25

1987. Hurricane Relief Fund. Nos. 544/5, 547, 551/4 and 556/9 surch. **HURRICANE RELIEF +50 c.**

561. 75 c.+50 c. Type **79** .. 1·75 1·75
562. 75 c.+10 c.+50 c. Type **79** 2·00 2·00
563. $1.+50 c. Type **77** .. 2·25 2·25
564. $1.35+50 c. "Virgin and Child" (Durer) .. .. 2·40 2·40
565. $1.35+10 c.+50 c. "Virgin and Child" (Durer) .. 2·50 2·50
566. $1.95+50 c. "The Adoration of the Magi" (Durer) 3·00 3·00
567. $1.95+10 c.+50 c. "The Adoration of the Magi" (Durer) .. .. 3·00 3·00
568. $2+59 c. Type **78** .. .. 3·00 3·00
569. $2.75+50 c. Statue of Liberty at sunset .. 3·50 3·50
570. $2.75+50 c. "Madonna of the Rosary" (Durer) .. 3·50 3·50
571. $2.75+10 c.+50 c. "Madonna of the Rosary" (Durer) .. 3·50 3·50

1987. Royal Ruby Wedding. Nos. 391/3 surch. **2.50 Royal Wedding 40th Anniv.**

572. $2.50 on 60 c. Type **50** .. 2·50 2·50
573. $2.50 on 80 c. Lady Diana Spencer .. .. .. 2·50 2·50
574. $2.50 on $1.40 Prince Charles and Lady Diana (87×70 mm.) .. .. 2·50 2·50

83. Angels.

1987. Christmas. Details of angels from "Virgin with Garland" by Rubens.

575. **83.** 70 c. multicoloured .. 85 85
576. – 85 c. multicoloured .. 1·00 1·00
577. – $1.50 multicoloured .. 1·75 1·75
578. – $1.85 multicoloured .. 2·00 2·00

84 Chariot racing and Athletics

1988. Olympic Games, Seoul. Ancient and modern Olympic sports. Multicoloured.

581 70 c. Type **84** 60 70
582 85 c. Greek runners and football 70 80
583 95 c. Greek wrestling and handball 75 85
584 $1.40 Greek hoplites and tennis .. .. .. 1·25 1·40

1988. Olympic Medal Winners, Los Angeles. Nos. 581/4 optd.

586 70 c. Type 84 (optd **"FLORENCE GRIFFTH JOYNER UNITED STATES 100 M AND 200 M"**) .. 55 60
587 85 c. Greek runners and football (optd **"GELINDO BORDIN ITALY MARATHON"**) .. 65 70
588 95 c. Greek wrestling and handball (optd **"HITOSHI SAITO JAPAN JUDO"**) .. 70 75
589 $1.40 Greek hoplites and tennis (optd **"STEFFI GRAF WEST GERMANY WOMEN'S TENNIS"**) 1·10 1·25

85 "Adoration of the Shepherds" (detail)

1988. Christmas. Paintings by Rembrandt. Multicoloured.

590 55 c. Type **85** 70 70
591 70 c. "The Holy Family" 80 80
592 85 c. "Presentation in the Temple" 90 90
593 95 c. "The Holy Family" (different) .. .. 1·00 1·00
594 $1.15 "Presentation in the Temple" (different) .. 1·25 1·25

86 H.M.S. "Bounty" leaving Spithead and Capt. Bligh

1989. Bicentenary of Discovery of Aitutaki by Capt. Bligh. Multicoloured.

596 55 c. Type **86** 80 80
597 65 c. Breadfruit plants .. 90 90
598 75 c. Old chart showing Aitutaki and Capt. Bligh 1·10 1·10
599 95 c. Native outrigger and H.M.S. "Bounty" off Aitutaki .. .. 1·50 1·50
600 $1.65 Fletcher Christian confronting Bligh .. 2·00 2·00

87 "Apollo 11" Astronaut on Moon

1989. 20th Anniv of First Manned Landing on Moon. Multicoloured.

602 75 c. Type **87** 55 60
603 $1.15 Conducting experiment on Moon .. 85 90
604 $1.80 Astronaut on Moon carrying equipment .. 1·40 1·50

88 Virgin Mary

1989. Christmas. Details from "Virgin in the Glory" by Titian. Multicoloured.

606 70 c. Type **88** 70 70
607 85 c. Christ Child 85 85
608 95 c. Angel 95 95
609 $1.25 Cherubs .. .. 1·40 1·40

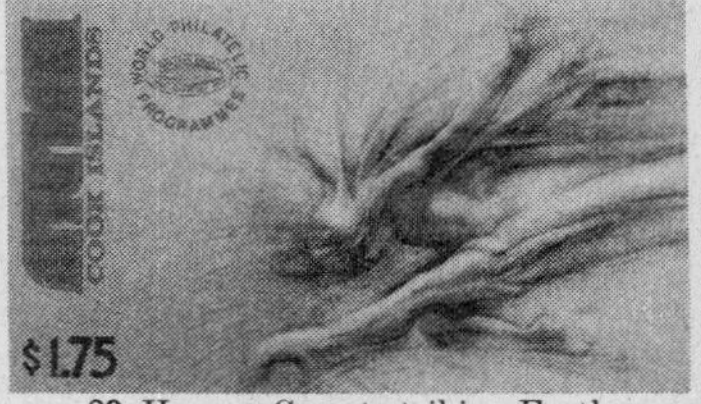

89 Human Comet striking Earth

1990. Protection of the Environment. Mult.

611 $1.75 Type **89** .. .. 1·40 1·50
612 $1.75 Comet's tail .. 1·40 1·50

Nos. 611/12 were printed together, se-tenant, forming a composite design.

91 "Madonna of the Basket" (Correggio)

1990. Christmas. Religious Paintings. Mult.

615 70 c. Type **91** 55 55
616 85 c. "Virgin and Child" (Morando) 70 70
617 95 c. "Adoration of the Child" (Tiepolo) .. 80 80
618 $1.75 "Mystic Marriage of St. Catherine" (Memling) 1·40 1·40

1990. "Birdpex '90" Stamp Exhibition, Christchurch, New Zealand. Nos. 349/50 optd **Birdpex'90** and bird's head.

620 $1 Blue-headed flycatcher 1·00 1·00
621 $2 Red-bellied flycatcher 1·50 1·50

1991. 65th Birthday of Queen Elizabeth II No. 352 optd **COMMEMORATING 65th BIRTHDAY OF H.M. QUEEN ELIZABETH II.**

622 $5 Flat-billed kingfisher 3·25 3·50

93 "The Holy Family" (A. Mengs)

1991. Christmas. Religious Paintings. Mult.

623 80 c. Type **93** 55 60
624 90 c. "Virgin and the Child" (Lippi) 60 65
625 $1.05 "Virgin and Child" (A. Durer) 70 75
626 $1.75 "Adoration of the Shepherds" (G. De La Tour) .. .. .. 1·10 1·25

OFFICIAL STAMPS

1978. Nos. 98/105, 107/10 and 227/8 optd. **O.H.M.S.** or surch also.

O 1. 1 c. multicoloured .. 55 10
O 2. 2 c. multicoloured .. 65 10
O 3. 3 c. multicoloured .. 65 10
O 4. 4 c. multicoloured .. 65 10
O 5. 5 c. multicoloured .. 65 10
O 6. 8 c. multicoloured .. 75 10
O 7. 10 c. multicoloured .. 85 15
O 8. 15 c. on 60 c. mult. .. 1·50 20
O 9. 18 c. on 60 c. mult. .. 1·50 20
O 10. 20 c. multicoloured .. 1·50 20
O 11. 50 c. multicoloured .. 2·50 55
O 12. 60 c. multicoloured .. 3·25 70
O 13. $1 multicoloured (No. 108) 4·00 1·00
O 14. $2 multicoloured .. 6·50 1·50
O 15. $4 on $1 multicoloured (No. 228) .. .. 9·00 2·50
O 16. $5 multicoloured .. 9·50 3·50

1985. Nos. 351/2, 430/3, 475, 477/94 optd **O.H.M.S.** or surch also.

O17 2 c. Type **65** 10 10
O18 5 c. Scarlet robin .. 10 10
O19 10 c. Golden whistler .. 10 10
O20 12 c. Rufous fantail .. 10 10
O21 18 c. Peregrine falcon .. 10 10
O22 20 c. on 24 c. Barn owl 10 15
O23 30 c. Java sparrow .. 20 25
O24 40 c. on 36 c. White-breasted wood swallow 25 30
O25 50 c. Rock dove .. 35 40
O26 55 c. on 48 c. Tahitian lory 35 40
O27 60 c. Purple swamphen 40 45
O28 65 c. on 72 c. Zebra dove 45 50
O38 75 c. on 48 c. Type **57** .. 50 55
O39 75 c. on 48 c. Ancient Ti'i image 50 55
O40 75 c. on 48 c. Tourist canoeing 50 55
O41 75 c. on 48 c. Captain William Bligh and chart 50 55
O29 80 c. on 96 c. Chestnut-breasted mannikin .. 55 60
O30 $1.20 Common mynah 80 85
O31 $2.10 Eastern reef heron 1·40 1·50
O32 $3 Blue-headed flycatcher .. .. 2·00 2·10
O33 $4.20 Red-bellied flycatcher .. .. 2·75 3·00
O34 $5.60 Red munia .. 3·75 4·00
O35 $9.60 Flat-billied kingfisher .. .. 6·25 6·50
O36 $14 on $4 Red munia (35×48 mm) .. 9·25 9·50
O37 $18 on $5 Flat-billed kingfisher .. .. .. 12·00 12·50

ALWAR

A state of Rajputana N. India. Now uses Indian stamps.

12 pies = 1 anna; 16 annas = 1 rupee.

1. Native Dagger.

1877. Roul or perf.

No.	Type	Description	Unused	Used
1a	1.	¼ a. blue	2·00	50
5		¼ a. green	2·00	1·50
2b		1 a. brown	1·40	60

ANGUILLA

St. Christopher, Nevis and Anguilla were granted Associated Statehood on 27 February 1967, but following a referendum Anguilla declared her independence and the St. Christopher authorities withdrew. On 7 July 1969, the Anguilla post office was officially recognised by the Government of St. Christopher, Nevis and Anguilla and normal postal communications via St. Christopher were resumed.

By the Anguilla Act of 27 July 1971, the island was restored to direct British control.

100 cents = 1 West Indian dollar.

1967. Nos. 129/44 of St. Kitts–Nevis optd. **Independent Anguilla** and bar.

No.	Type	Description	Unused	Used
1.	–	½ c. sepia and blue ..	20·00	18·00
2.	33.	1 c. multicoloured ..	22·00	6·50
3.	–	2 c. multicoloured ..	24·00	1·25
4.	–	3 c. multicoloured ..	24·00	4·50
5.	–	4 c. multicoloured ..	24·00	5·50
6.	–	5 c. multicoloured ..	90·00	18·00
7.	–	6 c. multicoloured ..	40·00	9·00
8.	–	10 c. multicoloured ..	24·00	6·50
9.	–	15 c. multicoloured ..	50·00	11·00
10.	–	20 c. multicoloured ..	85·00	12·00
11.	–	25 c. multicoloured ..	70·00	20·00
12.	–	50 c. multicoloured ..	—	£450
13.	–	60 c. multicoloured ..	—	£850
14.	–	$1 yellow and blue ..	—	£400
15.	–	$2. 50 multicoloured ..	—	£300
16.	–	$5 multicoloured ..	—	£300
		Set of 16	£8000	£2250

The above stamps were issued by the governing Council and have been accepted for international mail. Owing to the limited stocks available for overprinting, the sale of the stamps was personally controlled by the Postmaster and no orders from the trade were accepted.

2. Mahogany Tree, The Quarter.

1967.

No.	Type	Description	Unused	Used
17.	2.	1 c. green, brown and orge.	10	20
18.	-	2 c. turquoise and black ..	10	20
19.	-	3 c. black and green ..	10	10
20.	-	4 c. blue and black ..	10	10
21.	-	5 c. multicoloured ..	10	10
22.	-	6 c. red and black ..	10	10
23.	-	10 c. multicoloured ..	15	10
24.	-	15 c. multicoloured ..	30	20
25.	-	20 c. multicoloured ..	40	20
26.	-	25 c. multicoloured ..	50	20
27.	-	40 c. green, turq. and black	80	25
28.	-	60 c. multicoloured ..	1·50	1·25
29.	-	$1 multicoloured ..	1·75	2·00
30.	-	$2·50 multicoloured ..	2·00	2·00
31.	-	$5 multicoloured ..	3·50	3·75

DESIGNS: 2 c. Sombrero Lighthouse. 3 c. St. Mary's Church. 4 c. Valley Police Station. 5 c. Old Plantation House, Mt. Fortune. 6 c. Valley Post Office. 10 c. Methodist Church, West End 15 c. Wall-Blake Airport. 20 c. Aircraft over Sandy Ground. 25 c. Island Harbour. 40 c. Map of Anguilla. 60 c. Hermit Crab and Starfish. $1, Hibiscus. $2·50, Local scene. $5, Spiny Lobster.

On 9 January 1969, Anguilla reaffirmed her independence from St. Kitts and issued Nos. 17/31 optd. **INDEPENDENCE JANUARY, 1969.**

17. Yachts in Lagoon.

1968. Anguillan Ships. Multicoloured.

No.	Description	Unused	Used
32.	10 c. Type **17**	15	10
33.	15 c. Boat on Beach ..	20	10
34.	25 c. Schooner "Warspite"	30	15
35.	40 c. Schooner "Atlantic Star"	35	20

18. Purple-throated Carib.

1968. Anguillan Birds. Multicoloured.

No.	Description	Unused	Used
36.	10 c. Type **18**	75	15
37.	15 c. Bananaquit	95	20
38.	25 c. Black-necked stilt (horiz.)	1·25	20
39.	40 c. Royal tern (horiz.) ..	1·50	30

19. Guides' Badge and Anniversary Years.

1968. 35th Anniv. of Anguillan Girl Guides. Multicoloured.

No.	Description	Unused	Used
40.	10 c. Type **19**	10	10
41.	15 c. Badge and Silhouettes of Guides (vert.) ..	15	10
42.	25 c. Guides Badge and Headquarters, Valley ..	20	15
43.	40 c. Association and Proficiency Badges (vert.) ..	25	15

20. The Three Kings.

1968. Christmas.

No.	Type	Description	Unused	Used
44.	20.	1 c. black and red ..	10	10
45.	–	10 c. black and blue ..	10	10
46.	–	15 c. black and brown ..	15	10
47.	–	40 c. black and blue ..	15	10
48.	–	50 c. black and green ..	20	15

DESIGNS—VERT. 10 c. The Wise Men. 15 c. Holy Family and Manger. HORIZ. 40 c. The Shepherds. 50 c. Holy Family and Donkey.

21. Bagging Salt.

1969. Anguillan Salt Industry. Multicoloured.

No.	Description	Unused	Used
49.	10 c. Type **21**	10	10
50.	15 c. Packing salt	15	10
51.	40 c. Salt pond	20	10
52.	50 c. Loading salt	20	10

22. "The Crucifixion" (Studio of Massys).

1969. Easter Commem. Multicoloured.

No.	Description	Unused	Used
53.	25 c. Type **22**	15	10
54.	40 c. "The Last Supper" (Ascr. to Roberti) ..	20	15

23. Amaryllis.

1969. Flowers of the Caribbean Mult.

No.	Description	Unused	Used
55.	10 c. Type **23**	20	10
56.	15 c. Bougainvillea ..	25	10
57.	40 c. Hibiscus	45	20
58.	50 c. "Cattleya" Orchid ..	85	40

24. Turbans and Star Shells.

1969. Sea Shells. Multicoloured.

No.	Description	Unused	Used
59.	10 c. Type **24**	20	10
60.	15 c. Spiny oysters ..	20	10
61.	40 c. Scotch, Royal and Smooth Scotch bonnets	30	15
62.	50 c. Triton trumpet ..	40	20

1969. Christmas. Nos. 17, 25/8 optd. with different seasonal emblems.

No.	Description	Unused	Used
63.	1 c. multicoloured	10	10
64.	20 c. multicoloured ..	20	10
65.	25 c. multicoloured ..	20	10
66.	40 c. multicoloured ..	25	15
67.	60 c. multicoloured ..	40	20

30. Red Goatfish.

1969. Fishes. Multicoloured.

No.	Description	Unused	Used
68.	10 c. Type **30**	30	15
69.	15 c. Blue Striped Grunts ..	45	15
70.	40 c. Mutton Grouper ..	55	20
71.	50 c. Banded Butterfly Fish	65	20

31. "Morning Glory".

1970. Flowers. Multicoloured.

No.	Description	Unused	Used
72.	10 c. Type **31**	25	10
73.	15 c. Blue Petrea	40	10
74.	40 c. Hibiscus	60	15
75.	50 c. "Flame Tree" ..	70	20

32. "Deposition" (Rosso Fiorentino).

1970. Easter. Multicoloured.

No.	Description	Unused	Used
76.	10 c. "The Ascent to Calvary" (Tiepolo)	20	10
77.	20 c. "Crucifixion" (Masaccio)	30	10
78.	40 c. Type **32**	35	15
79.	60 c. "The Ascent to Calvary" (Murillo) ..	40	15

Nos. 76 and 79 are horiz.

33. Scout Badge and Map.

1970. 40th Anniv. of Scouting in Anguilla. Multicoloured.

No.	Description	Unused	Used
80.	10 c. Type **33**	15	10
81.	15 c. Scout camp, and cubs practising First Aid ..	20	10
82.	40 c. Monkey bridge ..	25	15
83.	50 c. Scout H.Q. building and Lord Baden-Powell	35	15

34. Boatbuilding.

1970. Multicoloured.

No.	Description	Unused	Used
84.	1 c. Type **34**	10	20
85.	2 c. Road Construction ..	10	20
86.	3 c Quay, Blowing Point ..	10	15
87.	4 c. Broadcaster, Radio Anguilla	10	30
88.	5 c. Cottage Hospital Extension	10	30
89.	6 c. Valley Secondary School	10	30
90.	10 c. Hotel Extension ..	15	30
91.	15 c. Sandy Ground ..	20	30
92.	20 c. Supermarket and Cinem	35	30
93.	25 c. Bananas and Mangoes	35	60
94.	40 c. Wall Blake Airport ..	45	70
95.	60 c. Sandy Ground Jetty ..	65	90
96.	$1 Administration Buildings	1·25	1·40
97.	$2·50 Livestock	1·50	3·00
98.	$5 Sandy Hill Bay	2·50	3·75

35. "The Adoration of the Shepherds" (Reni).

1970. Christmas. Multicoloured.

No.	Description	Unused	Used
99.	1 c. Type **35**	10	10
100.	20 c. "The Virgin and Child" (Gozzoli) ..	30	15
101.	25 c. "Mystic Nativity" (detail, Botticelli) ..	30	15
102.	40 c. "The Santa Margherita Madonna" (detail, Mazzola)	40	20
103.	50 c. "The Adoration of the Magi" (detail, Tiepolo)	40	20

36. "Ecce Homo" (detail, Correggio).

1971. Easter. Paintings. Multicoloured.

No.	Description	Unused	Used
104.	10 c. Type **36**	15	10
105.	15 c. "Christ appearing to St. Peter" (detail, Carracci)	25	10
106.	40 c. "Angels weeping over the Dead Christ" (detail, Guercino)	30	10
107.	50 c. "The Supper at Emmaus" (detail, Caravaggio) ..	30	15

The 40 c. and 50 c. designs are horiz.

37. "Hypolimnas misippus".

1971. Butterflies. Multicolourd.

No.	Description		
108	10 c. Type **37** ..	80	70
109	15 c. "Junonia evarete" ..	1·00	80
110	40 c. "Agraulis vanillae" ..	1·60	1·25
111	50 c. "Danaus plexippus" ..	1·90	1·50

38. "Magnanime" and "Amiable" in Battle.

1971. Sea-battles of the West Indies. Multicoloured.

No.	Description		
112.	10 c. Type **38**	70	70
113.	15 c. H.M.S. "Duke", "Glorieux" and H.M.S. "Agamemnon" ..	85	85
114.	25 c. H.M.S. "Formidable" and H.M.S. "Namur" against "Ville de Paris" ..	1·25	1·25
115.	40 c. H.M.S. "Canada" ..	1·40	1·40
116.	50 c. H.M.S. "St. Albans" and wreck of "Hector"	1·60	1·60

Nos. 112/116 were issued in horizontal **se-tenant** strips within the sheet to form a **composite** design.

39. "The Ansidei Madonna" (detail, Raphael).

1971. Christmas. Multicoloured.

No.	Description		
117.	20 c. Type **39**	20	20
118.	25 c. "Mystic Nativity" (detail, Botticelli)	20	20
119.	40 c. "Adoration of the Shepherds" (detail, ascr. to Murillo)	30	30
120.	50 c. "The Madonna of the Iris" (detail, ascr. to Durer)	35	35

40. Map of Anguilla and St. Martin by Thomas Jefferys, 1775.

1972. Caribbean Maps depicting Anguilla. Multicoloured.

No.	Description		
121.	10 c. Type **40**	20	10
122.	15 c. Samuel Fahlberg's Map, 1814	30	15
123.	40 c. Thomas Jefferys' Map, 1775 (horiz.) ..	40	25
124.	50 c. Capt. E. Barnett's Map, 1847 (horiz.)	50	25

41. "Jesus Buffeted".

1972. Easter. Multicoloured.

No.	Description		
125.	10 c. Type **41**	25	25
126.	15 c. "The Way of Sorrows"	30	30
127.	25 c. "The Crucifixion" ..	30	30
128.	40 c. "Descent from the Cross"	35	35
129.	50 c. "The Burial" ..	40	40

42. Loblolly Tree.

1972. Multicoloured.

No.	Description		
130.	1 c. Spear fishing	10	30
131.	2 c. Type **42**	10	30
132.	3 c. Sandy ground ..	10	30
133.	4 c. Ferry at Blowing Point	15	20
134	5 c. Agriculture	15	30
135.	6 c. St. Mary's Church ..	25	20
136.	10 c. St. Gerrard's Church	25	30
137.	15 c. Cottage hospital extension	25	30
138.	20 c. Public library ..	30	35
139.	25 c. Sunset at Blowing Point	40	50
140.	40 c. Boat building ..	1·50	1·50
141.	60 c. Hibiscus	4·00	3·00
142.	$1 Magnificent Frigate Bird	8·00	5·50
143.	$2·50 Frangipani ..	6·00	6·50
144.	$5 Brown Pelican ..	13·00	12·00
144a.	$10 Green-back turtle ..	18·00	18·00

1972. Royal Silver Wedding. As T. **52**, of Ascension, but with Schooner and Common dolphin in background.

No.	Description		
145.	25 c. green	1·00	1·50
146.	40 c. brown	1·10	1·75

44. Flight into Egypt.

1972. Christmas. Multicoloured.

No.	Description		
147.	1 c. Type **44**	10	10
148.	20 c. Star of Bethlehem	25	20
149.	25 c. Holy Family ..	25	20
150.	40 c. Arrival of the Magi	30	25
151.	50 c. Adoration of the Magi	30	25

MINIMUM PRICE

The minimum price quoted is 10p which represents a handling charge rather than a basis for valuing common stamps. For further notes about prices see introductory pages.

45. "The Betrayal of Christ".

1973. Easter. Multicoloured.

No.	Description		
152.	1 c. Type **45**	10	10
153.	10 c. "The Man of Sorrows"	10	10
154.	20 c. "Christ bearing the Cross"	15	15
155.	25 c. "The Crucifixion" ..	15	15
156.	40 c. "The Descent from the Cross"	15	15
157.	50 c. "The Resurrection"	20	20

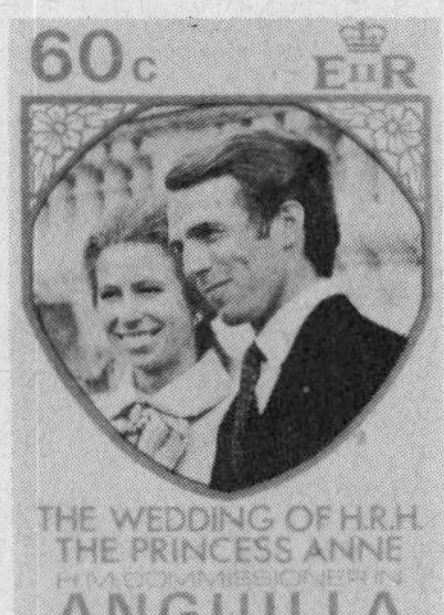

46. "Santa Maria".

1973. Columbus Discovers the West Indies. Multicoloured.

No.	Description		
159.	1 c. Type **46**.	10	10
160.	20 c. Early map	75	75
161.	40 c. Map of voyages ..	90	90
162.	70 c. Sighting land ..	1·50	1·50
163.	$1·20 Landing of Columbus	2·25	2·25

47. Princess Anne and Captain Mark Phillips.

1973. Royal Wedding. Multicoloured. Background colours given.

No.	Description		
165. **47.**	60 c. green	20	10
166.	$1·20 mauve	30	15

48. "The Adoration of the Shepherds" (Reni).

1973. Christmas. Multicoloured.

No.	Description		
167	1 c. Type **48**	10	10
168	10 c. "The Madonna and Child with Saints Jerome and Dominic" (Filippino Lippi)	10	10
169	20 c. "The Nativity" (Master of Brunswick) ..	15	15
170	25 c. "Madonna of the Meadow" (Bellini)	15	15
171	40 c. "Virgin and Child" (Cima)	20	20
172	50 c. "Adoration of the Kings" (Geertgen) ..	20	20

49. "The Crucifixion" (Raphael).

1974. Easter. Details of Raphael's "Crucifixion".

No.	Description		
174. **49.**	1 c. multicoloured ..	10	10
175. –	15 c. multicoloured ..	15	10
176. –	20 c. multicoloured ..	20	15
177. –	25 c. multicoloured ..	20	15
178. –	40 c. multicoloured ..	20	15
179. –	$1 multicoloured ..	25	25

50. Churchill Making "Victory" Sign.

1974. Birth Centenary of Sir Winston Churchill. Multicoloured.

No.	Description		
181.	1 c. Type **50**	10	10
182.	20 c. Churchill with Roosevelt	30	20
183.	25 c. Wartime broadcast ..	30	20
184.	40 c. Birthplace, Blenheim Palace	40	30
185.	60 c. Churchill's statue ..	50	35
186.	$1·20 Country residence, Chartwell	70	55

51. U.P.U. Emblem.

1974. Centenary of U.P.U.

No.	Description		
188. **51.**	1 c. black and blue ..	10	10
189.	20 c. black and orange ..	15	15
190.	25 c. black and yellow ..	15	15
191.	40 c. black and mauve ..	25	25
192.	60 c. black and green ..	40	40
193.	$1·20 black and blue ..	60	60

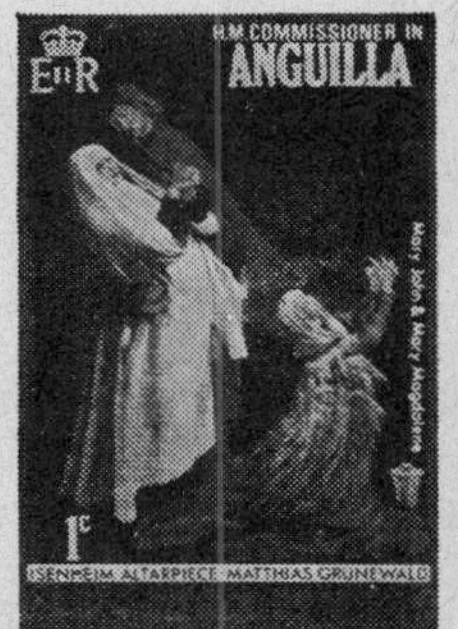

52. Anguillan pointing to Star.

1974. Christmas. Multicoloured.

No.	Description		
195.	1 c. Type **52**	10	10
196.	20 c. Child in Manger ..	15	15
197.	25 c. King's offering ..	15	15
198.	40 c. Star over map of Anguilla	15	15
199.	60 c. Family looking at Star	20	20
200.	$1·20 Angels of Peace ..	30	30

53. "Mary, John and Mary Magdalene" (Matthias Grunewald).

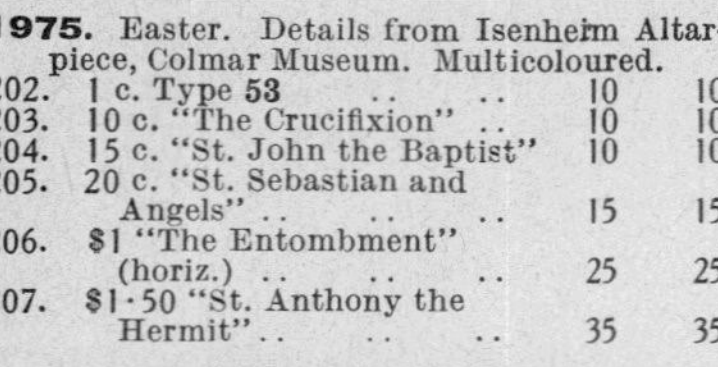

1975. Easter. Details from Isenheim Altar-piece, Colmar Museum. Multicoloured.

202. 1 c. Type **53** 10 10
203. 10 c. "The Crucifixion" .. 10 10
204. 15 c. "St. John the Baptist" 10 10
205. 20 c. "St. Sebastian and Angels" 15 15
206. $1 "The Entombment" (horiz.) 25 25
207. $1·50 "St. Anthony the Hermit" 35 35

54. Statue of Liberty.

1975. Bicent of American Revolution. Mult.

209. 1 c. Type **54** 10 10
210. 10 c. The Capitol 15 10
211. 15 c. " Congress voting for Independence " (Pine and Savage) 20 15
212. 20 c. Washington and map 20 15
213. $1 Boston Tea Party .. 50 40
214. $1·50 Bicentenary logo .. 70 60

55. " Madonna, Child and the Infant John the Baptist" (Raphael).

1975. Christmas. "Madonna and Child" paintings by artists named. Mult.

216. 1 c. Type **55** 10 10
217. 10 c. Cima 15 10
218. 15 c. Dolci 20 10
219. 20 c. Durer 20 15
220. $1 Bellini 35 25
221. $1·50 Botticelli 45 35

1976. New Constitution. Nos. 130 etc. optd. **NEW CONSTITUTION 1976,** or surch. also.

223. 1 c. Spear fishing 15 20
224. 2 c. on 1 c. Spear fishing .. 15 20
225. 2 c. Type **42** .. .. 1·75 90
226. 3 c. on 40 c. Boat building 15 30
227. 4 c. Ferry at Blowing Point 15 30
228. 5 c. on 40 c. Boat building 15 30
229. 6 c. St. Mary's Church .. 15 30
230. 10 c. on 20 c. Public Library 15 35
231. 10 c. St. Gerard's Church 2·50 1·00
232. 15 c. Cottage Hospital extension 25 50
233. 20 c. Public Library .. 25 40
234. 25 c. Sunset at Blowing Point 25 40
235. 40 c. Boat Building .. 45 40
236. 60 c. Hibiscus 70 70
237. $1 Magnificent Frigate Bird 2·75 2·00
238. $2·50 Frangipani .. .. 2·25 2·25
239. $5 Brown Pelican .. .. 5·00 6·00
240. $10 Green-back Turtle .. 4·00 6·00

57. Almond.

1976. Flowering Trees. Multicoloured.

241. 1 c. Type **57** 10 10
242. 10 c. Autograph 10 10
243. 15 c. Calabash 15 15
244. 20 c. Cordia 15 15
245. $1 Papaya 35 45
246. $1·50 Flamboyant 45 55

58. The Three Marys.

1976. Easter. Showing portions of the Altar Frontal Tapestry, Rheinau. Multicoloured.

248. 1 c. Type **58** 10 10
249. 10 c. The Crucifixion .. 10 10
250. 15 c. Two Soldiers .. 15 15
251. 20 c. The Annunciation .. 15 15
252. $1 The complete tapestry (horiz.) 65 65
253. $1·50 The Risen Christ .. 80 80

59. French Ships approaching Anguilla.

1976. Bicent. of Battle of Anguilla. Mult.

255. 1 c. Type **59** 10 10
256. 3 c. Sailing boat leaving Anguilla 50 35
257. 15 c. Capture of "Le Desius" 75 55
258. 25 c. "La Vaillante forced aground .. 1·10 80
259. $1 H.M.S. "Lapwing" .. 1·50 1·25
260. $1.50 "Le Desius" burning 2·00 1·75

60. " Christmas Carnival " (A. Richardson).

1976. Christmas. Children's Paintings. Multicoloured.

262. 1 c. Type **60** 10 10
263. 3 c. "Dreams of Christmas Gifts" (J. Connor) .. 10 10
264. 15 c. "Carolling" (P. Richardson) 15 15
265. 25 c. "Candle-light Procession" (A. Mussington) .. 20 20
266. $1 "Going to Church" (B. Franklin) 40 30
267. $1.50 "Coming Home for Christmas" (E. Gumbs) 50 40

61. Prince Charles and H.M.S. " Minerva ".

1977. Silver Jubilee. Multicoloured.

269 25 c. Type **61** 15 10
270 40 c. Prince Philip landing by launch at Road Bay, 1964 .. .. 20 15
271 $1.20 Coronation scene .. 35 25
272 $2.50 Coronation regalia and map of Anguilla .. 50 40

62. Yellow-crowned Night Heron.

1977. Multicoloured.

274. 1 c. Type **62** 15 20
275. 2 c. Great Barracuda .. 15 20
276. 3 c. Queen Conch .. 30 30
277. 4 c. Spanish Bayonet (flower) 20 15
278. 5 c. Trunkfish 30 10
279. 6 c. Cable and Wireless building 15 15
280. 10 c. American Kestrel .. 1·75 70
281. 15 c. Ground orchid .. 2·00 80
282. 20 c. Parrotfish .. .. 1·75 75
283. 22 c. Lobster fishing boat 35 45
284. 35 c. Boat race 40 45
285. 50 c. Sea bean 70 45
286. $1 Sandy Island 60 45
287. $2·50 Manchineel .. .. 1·00 1·00
288. $5 Ground Lizard .. 2·00 1·75
289. $10 Red-billed Tropic Bird 7·00 4·25

63. " The Crucifixion " (Massys).

1977. Easter. Paintings by Castagno ($1.50) or Ugolino (others). Multicoloured.

291. 1 c. Type **63** 10 10
292. 3 c. " The Betrayal " .. 10 10
293. 22 c. " The Way to Calvary " 20 20
294. 30 c. " The Deposition " .. 25 25
295. $1 " The Resurrection " .. 50 50
296. $1·50 " The Crucifixion" 65 65

1977. Royal Visit. Nos. 269/72 optd. **ROYAL VISIT TO WEST INDIES.**

298. 25 c. Type **61** 15 10
299. 40 c. Prince Philip landing at Road Bay, 1964 .. 20 20
300. $1.20 Coronation scene .. 30 30
301. $1.50 Coronation regalia and map of Anguilla .. 50 50

65. " Le Chapeau de Paille ".

1977. 400th Birth Anniv. of Rubens. Mult.

303. 25 c. Type **65** 15 15
304. 40 c. " Helen Fourment and her Two Children " 20 25
305. $1·20 " Rubens and his Wife " 60 65
306. $2·50 " Marchesa Brigida Spinola-Doria " .. 75 95

1977. Christmas. Nos. 262/7 optd. **1977** or surch. also.

308. 1 c. Type **60** 10 10
309. 5 c. on 3. c " Dreams of Christmas Gifts " .. 10 10
310. 12 c. on 15 c. " Carolling " 15 15
311. 18 c. on 25 c. " Candlelight Procession " 20 20
312. $1 " Going to Church on Christmas Eve " .. 45 45
313. $2·50 on $1·50 " Coming Home for Christmas " .. 90 90

1978. Easter. Nos. 303/6 optd. **EASTER 1978.**

315. 25 c. Type **65** 20 20
316. 40 c. " Helen Fourment with her Two Children " 25 25
317. $1·20 " Rubens and his Wife " 50 50
318. $2·50 " Marchesa Brigida Spinola-Doria " .. 85 85

68. Coronation Coach at Admiralty Arch.

1978. 25th Anniv. of Coronation. Mult.

320. 22 c. Buckingham Palace 10 10
321. 50 c. Type **68** 15 15
322. $1·50 Balcony Scene .. 25 20
323. $2·50 Royal coat of arms 40 30

1978. Anniversaries. Nos. 283/4 and 287 optd. **VALLEY SECONDARY SCHOOL 1953-1978** and Nos. 285/6 and 288 optd. **ROAD METHODIST CHURCH 1878-1978,** or surch. also.

325. 22 c. Lobster fishing boat 20 15
326. 35 c. Boat race 30 20
327. 50 c. Sea bean 40 30
328. $1 Sandy Island 50 40
329. $1·20 on $5 Ground Lizard 60 45
330. $1·50 on $2.50 Manchineel 75 55

71. Mother and Child.

1978. Christmas. Children's Paintings. Multicoloured.

331. 5 c. Type **71** 10 10
332. 12 c. Christmas masquerade 10 10
333. 18 c. Christmas dinner .. 10 10
334. 22 c. Serenading 10 10
335. $1 Child in manger .. 45 20
336. $2·50 Family going to Church 90 40

1979. International Year of the Child. As Nos. 331/6, but additionally inscr. **"1979 INTERNATIONAL YEAR OF THE CHILD"** and emblem. Borders in different colours

338. 5 c. Type **71** 10 10
339. 12 c. Christmas masquerade 10 10
340. 18 c. Christmas dinner .. 15 15
341. 22 c. Serenading 15 15
342. $1 Child in manger .. 60 60
343. $2.50 Family going to Church 90 90

1979. Nos. 274/7 and 279/80 surch.

345. 12 c. on 2 c. Great Barracuda 50 40
346. 14 c. on 4 c. Spanish Bayonet 40 40
347. 18 c. on 3 c. Queen Conch 70 45
348. 25 c. on 6 c. Cable and Wireless Building .. 50 40
349. 38 c. on 10 c. American Kestrel .. .. 1·00 60
350. 40 c. on 1 c. Type **62** .. 1·00 60

73. Valley Methodist Church.

1979. Easter. Church Interiors. Mult.

351. 5 c. Type **73** 10 10
352. 12 c. St. Mary's Anglican Church, The Valley .. 10 10
353. 18 c. St. Gerard's Roman Catholic Church, The Valley 15 15
354. 22 c. Road Methodist Church 15 15
355. $1·50 St. Augustine's Anglican Church, East End 60 60
356. $2·50 West End Methodist Church 75 75

HAVE YOU READ THE NOTES AT THE BEGINNING OF THIS CATALOGUE?

These often provide answers to the enquiries we receive.

74. Cape of Good Hope 1d. "Woodblock" of 1881.

1979. Death Centenary of Sir Rowland Hill. Multicoloured.

No.	Description	Unused	Used
358.	1 c. Type **74**	10	10
359.	1 c. U.S.A. "inverted Jenny" of 1918	10	10
360.	22 c. Penny Black ("V.R." Official)	15	15
361.	35 c. Germany 2 m. "Graf Zeppelin" of 1928 ..	20	20
362.	$1.50 U.S.A. $5 "Columbus" of 1893 ..	60	60
363.	$2.50 Great Britain £5 orange of 1882	95	95

75. Wright "Flyer I" (1st powered Flight, 1903).

1979. History of Powered Flight. Mult.

No.	Description	Unused	Used
365.	5 c. Type **75**	10	10
366.	12 c. Louis Bleriot at Dover after Channel crossing, 1909	15	10
367.	18 c. Vickers "Vimy" (1st non-stop crossing of Atlantic, 1919) ..	20	15
368.	22 c. "Spirit of St. Louis" (1st solo Atlantic flight by Charles Lindbergh, 1927)	20	20
369.	$1·50 LZ 127 "Graf Zeppelin", 1928 ..	70	60
370.	$2·50 "Concorde", 1979	1·50	90

76. Sombrero Island.

1979. Outer Islands. Multicoloured.

No.	Description	Unused	Used
372.	5 c. Type **76**	10	10
373.	12 c. Anguillita Island ..	15	15
374.	18 c. Sandy Island ..	20	20
375.	25 c. Prickly Pear Cays ..	25	25
376.	$1 Dog Island ..	50	50
377.	$2·50 Scrub Island ..	90	90

77. Red Poinsettia.

1979. Christmas. Multicoloured.

No.	Description	Unused	Used
379.	22 c. Type **77**	40	30
380.	35 c. Kalanchoe	50	40
381.	$1·50 Cream Poinsettia ..	90	80
382.	$2·50 White Poinsettia ..	1·25	1·25

78. Exhibition Scene.

1979. "London 1980" International Stamp Exhibition (1st issue). Mult.

No.	Description	Unused	Used
384.	35 c. Type **78**	15	20
385.	50 c. Earls Court Exhibition Centre ..	20	25
386.	$1·50 Penny Black and Two-penny Blue stamps	55	60
387.	$2·50 Exhibition Logo ..	90	95

See also Nos. 407/9.

79. Games Site.

1980. Winter Olympic Games, Lake Placid, U.S.A. Multicoloured.

No.	Description	Unused	Used
389.	5 c. Type **79**	10	10
390.	18 c. Ice hockey	10	10
391.	35 c. Ice skating	15	20
392.	50 c. Bobsleighing ..	20	25
393.	$1 Skiing	40	45
394.	$2·50 Luge-tobogganing	90	95

80. Salt ready for "Reaping".

1980. Salt Industry. Multicoloured.

No.	Description	Unused	Used
396.	5 c. Type **80**	10	10
397.	12 c. Tallying salt ..	15	15
398.	18 c. Unloading salt flats	20	15
399.	22 c. Salt storage heap ..	20	15
400.	$1 Salt for bagging and grinding	50	40
401.	$2·50 Loading salt for export	70	70

1980. Anniversaries. Nos. 280, 282 and 287/8 optd. **50th Anniversary Scouting 1980** (10 c., $2·50.) **75th Anniversary Rotary 1980** (others).

No.	Description	Unused	Used
403.	10 c. American Kestrel.	30	10
404.	20 c. Parrotfish ..	35	15
405.	$2·50 Manchineel ..	1·25	1·00
406.	$5 Ground Lizard ..	2·00	1·90

83. Palace of Westminster and Great Britain 1970 9d. "Philympia" Commem.

1980. "London 1980" International Stamps Exhibition (2nd issue). Multicoloured.

No.	Description	Unused	Used
407.	50 c. Type **83**	35	30
408.	$1·50 City Hall, Toronto and "Capex 1978" stamp of Canada	60	55
409.	$2·50 Statue of Liberty and 1976 "Interphil" stamp of U.S.A. ..	80	85

84. Queen Elizabeth the Queen Mother.

1980. 80th Birthday of The Queen Mother.

No.	Description	Unused	Used
411. **84.**	35 c. multicoloured ..	25	20
412.	50 c. multicoloured ..	35	25
413.	$1·50 multicoloured ..	75	65
414.	$3 multicoloured ..	2·75	1·40

85. Brown Pelicans.

1980. Christmas. Birds. Multicoloured.

No.	Description	Unused	Used
416.	5 c. Type **85**	30	10
417.	22 c. Great blue heron ..	75	20
418.	$1.50 Barn swallow ..	1·75	60
419.	$3 Ruby-throated hummingbird	2·25	1·40

1980. Separation from St. Kitts. Nos. 274, 277, 280/9, 334 and 418/19 optd. **SEPARATION 1980**, or surch. also.

No.	Description	Unused	Used
421.	1 c. Type **62**	10	20
422.	2 c. on 4 c. Spanish bayonet	10	20
423.	5 c. on 15 c. Ground orchid	15	25
424.	5 c. on $1.50 Barn swallow	15	25
425.	5 c. on $3 Ruby-throated hummingbird	15	25
426.	10 c. American kestrel ..	20	30
427.	12 c. on $1 Sandy Island ..	20	30
428.	14 c. on $2.50 Manchineel	20	30
429.	15 c. Ground orchid ..	25	30
430.	18 c. on $5 Ground lizard	25	30
431.	20 c. Parrotfish ..	25	30
432.	22 c. Lobster fishing boat	25	30
433.	25 c. on 15 c. Ground orchid	30	35
434.	35 c. Boat race	30	35
435.	38 c. on 22 c. Seranading ..	30	35
436.	40 c. on 1 c. Type **62** ..	30	35
437.	50 c. Sea bean	35	40
438.	$1 Sandy Island	50	70
439.	$2.50 Manchineel	1·00	1·40
440.	$5 Ground lizard	2·25	2·75
441.	$10 Red-billed tropic bird	5·00	5·50
442.	$10 on 6 c. Cable and Wireless Building ..	5·00	5·50

87. First Petition for Separation, 1825.

1980. Separation from St. Kitts. Multicoloured.

No.	Description	Unused	Used
443.	18 c. Type **87**	10	10
444.	22 c. Referendum ballot paper, 1967	10	10
445.	35 c. Airport blockade, 1967	15	15
446.	50 c. Anguillan flag ..	20	20
447.	$1 Separation celebration, 1980	35	35

88. "Nelson's Dockyard" (R. Granger Barrett).

1981. 175th Death Anniv. of Lord Nelson. Multicoloured.

No.	Description	Unused	Used
449.	22 c. Type **88**	45	15
450.	35 c. "Ships in which Nelson Served" (Nicholas Pocock) ..	55	25
451.	50 c. "H.M.S. Victory" (Monamy Swaine) ..	70	30
452.	$3 "Battle of Trafalgar" (Clarkson Stanfield) ..	1·75	1·50

89. Minnie Mouse being chased by Bees.

1981. Easter. Walt Disney Cartoon Characters. Multicoloured.

No.	Description	Unused	Used
454	1 c. Type **89**	10	10
455	2 c. Pluto laughing at Mickey Mouse	10	10
456	3 c. Minnie Mouse tying ribbon round Pluto's neck	10	10
457	5 c. Minnie Mouse confronted by love-struck bird who fancies her bonnet	10	10
458	7 c. Dewey and Huey admiring themselves in mirror	10	10
459	9 c. Horace Horsecollar and Clarabelle Cow out for a stroll	10	10
460	10 c. Daisy Duck with hat full of Easter eggs ..	10	10
461	$2 Goofy unwrapping Easter hat	1·90	1·90
462	$3 Donald Duck in his Easter finery	2·25	1·60

90. Prince Charles, Lady Diana Spencer and St. Paul's Cathedral.

1981. Royal Wedding. Multicoloured.

No.	Description	Unused	Used
464.	50 c. Type **90**	35	25
465.	$2·50 Althorp	65	75
466.	$3 Windsor Castle ..	70	90

91. Children playing in Tree.

1981. 35th Anniv. of U.N.I.C.E.F. Mult.

No.	Description	Unused	Used
470.	5 c. Type **91**	10	10
471.	10 c. Children playing by pool	10	10
472.	15 c. Children playing musical instruments ..	10	10
473.	$3 Children playing with pets	1·40	1·40

1981. Christmas. Designs as T **89** showing scenes from Walt Disney's cartoon film "The Night Before Christmas".

No.	Description	Unused	Used
475.	1 c. multicoloured ..	10	10
476.	2 c. multicoloured ..	10	10
477.	3 c. multicoloured ..	10	10
478.	5 c. multicoloured ..	10	10
479.	7 c. multicoloured ..	10	10
480.	10 c. multicoloured ..	10	10
481.	12 c. multicoloured ..	10	10
482.	$2 multicoloured ..	1·90	1·25
483.	$3 multicoloured ..	1·90	1·60

92. Red Grouper.

1982. Multicoloured.

No.	Description	Unused	Used
485.	1 c. Type **92**	15	10
486.	5 c. Ferry service, Blowing Point	15	10
487.	10 c. Racing Boats ..	15	10
488.	15 c. Majorettes ..	15	10
489.	20 c. Launching boat, Sandy Hill	25	10
490.	25 c. Corals	55	20

No.	Description	Unused	Used
491.	30 c. Little Bay cliffs ..	25	15
492.	35 c. Fountain Cave interior	1·00	40
493.	40 c. Sunset over Sandy Island	30	20
494.	45 c. Landing at Sombrero	50	40
495.	60 c. Seine fishing	1·75	70
496.	75 c. Boat race at sunset, Sandy Ground	70	55
497.	$1 Bagging lobster at Island Harbour ..	1·75	1·00
498.	$5 Brown Pelicans ..	9·50	5·00
499.	$7.50 Hibiscus ..	8·00	5·00
500.	$10 Queen Triggerfish ..	10·00	8·50

1982. No. 494 surch. **50 c.**

No.	Description	Unused	Used
501.	50 c. on 45 c. Landing at Sombrero	35	35

94. Anthurium and "Heliconius charithonia"

1982. Easter. Flowers and Butterflies. Multicoloured.

No.	Description	Unused	Used
502	10 c. Type **94**	15	10
503	35 c. Bird of Paradise and "Junonia evarete" ..	25	20
504	75 c. Allamanda and "Danaus plexippus" ..	45	40
505	$3 Orchid Tree and "Biblis hyperia"	1·60	1·60

95. Lady Diana Spencer in 1961.

1982. 21st Birthday of Princess of Wales. Multicoloured.

No.	Description	Unused	Used
507.	10 c. Type **95**	10	10
508.	30 c. Lady Diana Spencer in 1968	20	20
509.	40 c. Lady Diana in 1970	25	25
510.	60 c. Lady Diana in 1974	35	35
511.	$2 Lady Diana in 1981 ..	1·10	1·10
512.	$3 Lady Diana in 1981 (different) ..	1·40	1·40

96. Pitching Tent.

1982. 75th Anniv. of Boy Scout Movement. Multicoloured.

No.	Description	Unused	Used
515.	10 c. Type **96**	35	15
516.	35 c. Scout band	70	40
517.	75 c. Yachting	95	75
518.	$3 On parade	2·50	2·50

1982. World Cup Football Championship, Spain. Horiz. designs as T **89** showing scenes from Walt Disney's cartoon film "Bedknobs and Broomsticks".

No.	Description	Unused	Used
520.	1 c. multicoloured ..	10	10
521.	3 c. multicoloured ..	10	10
522.	4 c. multicoloured ..	10	10
523.	5 c. multicoloured ..	10	10
524.	7 c. multicoloured ..	10	10
525.	9 c. multicoloured ..	10	10
526.	10 c. multicoloured ..	10	10
527.	$2.50 multicoloured ..	1·25	1·25
528.	$3 multicoloured ..	1·50	1·50

1982. Commonwealth Games, Brisbane. Nos. 487, 495/6 and 498 optd. **COMMONWEALTH GAMES 1982.**

No.	Description	Unused	Used
530.	10 c. Racing boats ..	10	10
531.	60 c. Seine fishing ..	35	35
532.	75 c. Boat race at sunset, Sandy Ground	45	45
533.	$5 Brown Pelicans ..	2·75	2·75

1982. Birth Centenary of A. A. Milne (author). Designs as T **89**.

No.	Description	Unused	Used
534.	1 c. multicoloured ..	10	10
535.	2 c. multicoloured ..	10	10
536.	3 c. multicoloured ..	10	10
537.	5 c. multicoloured ..	10	10
538.	7 c. multicoloured ..	15	10
539.	10 c. multicoloured ..	20	10
540.	12 c. multicoloured ..	20	10
541.	20 c. multicoloured ..	25	15
542.	$5 multicoloured ..	3·25	2·75

DESIGNS—HORIZ. 1 c. to $5 Scenes from various "Winnie the Pooh" stories.

98. Culture.

1983. Commonwealth Day. Multicoloured.

No.	Description	Unused	Used
544.	10 c. Type **98**	10	10
545.	35 c. Anguilla and British flags	30	30
546.	75 c. Economic co-operation	60	60
547.	$2·50, Salt industry (salt pond)	3·00	1·75

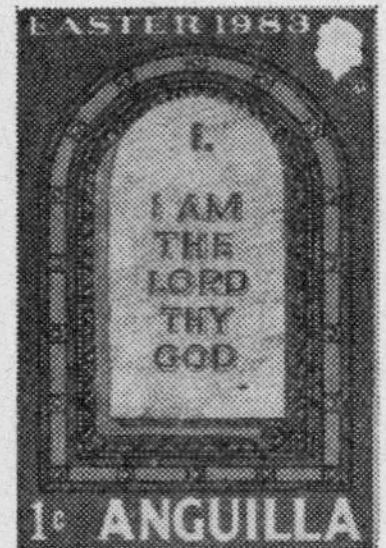

99. "I am the Lord Thy God".

1983. Easter. The Ten Commandments. Multicoloured.

No.	Description	Unused	Used
549	1 c. Type **99**	10	10
550	2 c. "Thou shalt not make any graven image" ..	10	10
551	3 c. "Thou shalt not take My Name in vain" ..	10	10
552	10 c. "Remember the Sabbath Day"	15	10
553	35 c. "Honour thy father and mother"	30	20
554	60 c. "Thou shalt not kill"	50	35
555	75 c. "Thou shalt not commit adultery" ..	60	40
556	$2 "Thou shalt not steal"	1·50	1·00
557	$2.50 "Thou shalt not bear false witness"	1·75	1·25
558	$5 "Thou shalt not covet"	2·75	2·50

100. Leatherback Turtle.

1983. Turtles. Multicoloured.

No.	Description	Unused	Used
560.	10 c. Type **100**	35	20
561.	35 c. Hawksbill Turtle ..	60	35
562.	75 c. Green Turtle.. ..	1·00	55
563.	$1 Loggerhead Turtle ..	1·25	85

101. Montgolfier Hot Air Balloon, 1783.

1983. Bicentenary of Manned Flight. Mult.

No.	Description	Unused	Used
565.	**10 c. Type 101**	20	10
566.	**60 c. Blanchard and Jefferies crossing English Channel by balloon, 1785** ..	55	35
567.	**$1 Henri Giffard's steam driven airship, 1852** ..	70	50
568.	**$2·50, Otto Lillienthal and glider, 1890-96** ..	1·60	1·25

102. Boy's Brigade Band and Flag.

1983. Centenary of Boys' Brigade. Mult.

No.	Description	Unused	Used
570.	**10 c. Type 102**	15	15
571.	**$5 Brigade members marching**	2·75	2·75

1983. 150th Anniv. of Abolition of Slavery. Nos. 487, 493 and 497/8 optd. **150TH ANNIVERSARY ABOLITION OF SLAVERY ACT.**

No.	Description	Unused	Used
573.	**10 c. Racing boats**	10	10
574.	**40 c. Sunset over Sandy Island**	20	25
575.	**$1 Bagging lobster at Island Harbour**	45	50
576.	**$5 Brown Pelicans** ..	2·50	2·75

104. Jiminy on Clock ("Cricket on the Hearth").

1983. Christmas. Walt Disney Cartoon Characters. Multicoloured.

No.	Description	Unused	Used
577.	**1 c. Type 104**	10	10
578.	**2 c. Jiminy with fiddle ("Cricket on the Hearth")**	10	10
579.	**3 c. Jiminy among toys ("Cricket on the Hearth")**	10	10
580.	**4 c. Mickey as Bob Crachit ("A Christmas Carol")**	10	10
581.	**5 c. Donald Duck as Scrooge ("A Christmas Carol")**	10	10
582.	**6 c. Mini and Goofy in "The Chimes"**	10	10
583.	**10 c. Goofy sees an imp appearing from bells ("The Chimes")** ..	10	10
584.	**$2 Donald Duck as Mr. Pickwick ("The Pickwick Papers")**	2·00	1·25
585.	**$3 Disney characters as Pickwickians ("The Pickwick Papers")**	2·25	1·60

105. 100 Metres Race.

1984. Olympic Games, Los Angeles. Multicoloured.

A. Inscr. "1984 Los Angeles".
B. Inscr. "1984 Olympics Los Angeles" and Olympic emblem.

No.	Description	A Unused	A Used	B Unused	B Used
587.	1 c. Type **105** ..	10	10	10	10
588.	2 c. Long jumping ..	10	10	10	10
589.	3 c. Shot-putting ..	10	10	10	10
590.	4 c. High jumping ..	10	10	10	10
591.	5 c. 400 Metres race	10	10	10	10
592.	6 c. Hurdling	10	10	10	10
593.	10 c. Discus-throwing	10	10	10	10
594.	$1 Pole-vaulting ..	1·00	80	1·00	80
595.	$4 Javelin-throwing	3·00	2·50	3·00	2·50

106. "Justice".

1984. Easter. Multicoloured.

No.	Description	Unused	Used
597.	10 c. Type **106**	15	10
598.	25 c. "Poetry" ..	20	20
599.	35 c. "Philosophy" ..	30	30
600.	40 c. "Theology" ..	30	30
601.	$1 "Abraham and Paul" ..	75	70
602.	$2 "Moses and Matthew"	1·40	1·40
603.	$3 "John and David" ..	2·00	1·90
604.	$4 "Peter and Adam" ..	2·25	2·25

Nos. 597/604 show details from "La Stanza della Segnatura" by Raphael.

1984. Nos. 485, 491, 498/500 surch.

No.	Description	Unused	Used
606.	25 c. on $7.50 Hibiscus ..	20	20
607.	35 c. on 30 c. Little Bay cliffs	25	25
608.	60 c. on 1 c. Red grouper	45	45
609.	$2.50 on $5 Brown pelicans	1·40	1·50
610.	$2.50 on $10 Queen triggerfish	1·40	1·50

108. 1913 1d. Kangaroo Stamp.

1984. "Ausipex 84" International Stamp Exhibition. Multicoloured.

No.	Description	Unused	Used
611.	10 c. Type **108** ..	15	15
612.	75 c. 1914 6d. Laughing Kookaburra	70	60
613.	$1 1932 2d. Sydney Harbour Bridge	95	80
614.	$2.50 1938 10s. King George VI	2·00	1·75

109. Thomas Fowell Buxton.

1984. 150th Anniv. of Abolition of Slavery. Multicoloured.

No.	Description	Unused	Used
616.	10 c. Type **109**	10	10
617.	25 c. Abraham Lincoln ..	25	25
618.	35 c. Henri Christophe ..	35	35
619.	60 c. Thomas Clarkson ..	50	50
620.	75 c. William Wilberforce	60	60
621.	$1 Olaudah Equiano ..	70	70
622.	$2.50 General Charles Gordon	1·60	1·60
623.	$5 Granville Sharp ..	3·00	3·00

1984. Universal Postal Union Congress, Hamburg. Nos. 486/7 and 498 optd. **U.P.U. CONGRESS HAMBURG 1984** or surch. also (No. 626).

No.	Description	Unused	Used
625.	5 c. Ferry service, Blowing Point	10	10
626.	20 c. on 10 c. Racing boats	15	15
627.	$5 Brown pelicans ..	3·50	3·50

1984. Birth of Prince Henry. Nos. 507/12 optd. **BIRTH PRINCE HENRY 15.9.84.**

No.	Description	Unused	Used
628.	10 c. Type **95**	10	10
629.	30 c. Lady Diana Spencer in 1968	20	25
630.	40 c. Lady Diana in 1970 ..	25	30
631.	60 c. Lady Diana in 1974 ..	40	45
632.	$2 Lady Diana in 1981 ..	1·25	1·40
633.	$3 Lady Diana in 1981 (different)	1·50	2·25

112. Christmas in Sweden.

1984. Christmas. Walt Disney Cartoon Characters. National Scenes. Multicoloured.

636. 1 c. Type **112** 10 10
637. 2 c. Italy 10 10
638. 3 c. Holland 10 10
639. 4 c. Mexico 10 10
640. 5 c. Spain 10 10
641. 10 c. Disneyland, U.S.A. .. 10 10
642. $1 Japan .. .. .. 1·50 65
643. $2 Anguilla .. .. 2·00 1·10
644. $4 Germany .. .. 3·25 2·25

113. Icarus in Flight

1984. 40th Anniv. of International Civil Aviation Authority. Multicoloured

646 60 c. Type **113** 35 45
647. 75 c. "Solar Princess" (abstract) 45 60
648. $2.50, I.C.A.O. emblem (vert.) .. .. .. 1·50 1·75

114. Barn Swallow

1985. Birth Bicentenary of John J. Audubon (ornithologist). Multicoloured.

650. 10 c. Type **114** 15 10
651. 60 c. American Wood stork 45 40
652. 75 c. Roseate tern 50 45
653. $5 Osprey .. .. .. 2·75 3·00

115. The Queen Mother visiting King's College Hospital, London.

1985. Life and Times of Queen Elizabeth the Queen Mother. Multicoloured.

655. 10 c. Type **115** 10 10
656. $2 The Queen Mother inspecting Royal Marine Volunteer Cadets, Deal 1·10 1·25
657. $3 The Queen Mother outside Clarence House 1·60 1·75

116. White-tailed Tropic Bird.

1985. Birds. Multicoloured.

659. 5 c. Brown pelican .. 30 30
660. 10 c. Mourning dove .. 30 30
661. 15 c. Magnificent frigate bird (inscr. "Man-o-War") 30 30
662. 20 c. Antillean crested hummingbird 30 30
663. 25 c. Type **116** 30 30
664. 30 c. Caribbean elaenia .. 30 30
665. 35 c. Black-whiskered vireo 1·75 1·40
665a. 35 c. Lesser Antillean bullfinch 30 35
666. 40 c. Yellow-crowned night heron 40 50
667. 45 c. Pearly-eyed thrasher 30 40
668. 50 c. Laughing gull .. 30 40
669. 65 c. Brown booby .. 35 50
670. 80 c. Grey kingbird .. 55 60
671. $1 Audubon's shearwater 75 75
672. $1.35 Roseate tern .. 75 1·00
673. $2.50 Bananaquit .. .. 2·00 2·00
674. $5 Belted kingfisher .. 2·50 3·00
675. $10 Green heron .. .. 4·50 6·00

1985. 75th Anniv. of Girl Guide Movement. Nos. 486, 491, 496 and 498 optd. **GIRL GUIDES 75TH ANNIVERSARY 1910–1985.**

676. 5 c. Ferry service, Blowing Point 15 10
677. 30 c. Little Bay cliffs .. 35 25
678. 75 c. Boat race at sunset, Sandy Ground .. 70 50
679. $5 Brown Pelicans .. 3·75 3·50

118. Goofy as Huckleberry Finn Fishing.

1985. 150th Birth Anniv. of Mark Twain (author). Walt Disney cartoon characters in scenes from "Huckleberry Finn". Mult.

680. 10 c. Type **118** 15 15
681. 60 c. Pete as Pap surprising Huck 60 60
682. $1 "Multiplication tables" 85 85
683. $3 The Duke reciting Shakespeare .. .. 2·25 2·25

119. Hansel and Gretel (Mickey and Minnie Mouse) awakening in Forest.

1985. Birth Bicentenaries of Grimm Brothers (folklorists). Designs showing Walt Disney cartoon characters in scenes from "Hansel and Gretel". Multicoloured.

685. 5 c. Type **119** 10 10
686. 50 c. Hansel and Gretel find the gingerbread house 25 30
687. 90 c. Hansel and Gretel meeting the Witch .. 45 50
688. $4 Hansel and Gretel captured by the Witch 2·00 2·10

120. Statue of Liberty and "Danmark" (Denmark).

1985. Centenary of the Statue of Liberty (1986). The Statue of Liberty and Cadet ships.

690. 10 c. Type **120** 40 40
691. 20 c. "Eagle" (U.S.A.) .. 55 55
692. 60 c. "Amerigo Vespucci" (Italy) .. .. .. 1·00 1·00
693. 75 c. "Sir Winston Churchill" (Great Britain) .. .. .. 1·25 1·25
694. $2 "Nippon Maru" (Japan) 2·00 2·00
695. $2.50 "Gorch Fock" (West Germany) .. .. 2·25 2·25

1985. 80th Anniv. of Rotary (10, 35 c.) and International Youth Year (others). Nos. 487, 491 and 497 optd. or surch. also.

697. 10 c. Racing boats (optd. **80TH ANNIVERSARY ROTARY 1985** and emblem) 10 10
698. 35 c. on 30 c. Little Bay cliffs (surch. **80TH ANNIVERSARY ROTARY 1985** and emblem) 25 25
699. $1 Bagging lobster at Island Harbour (optd. **INTERNATIONAL YOUTH YEAR** and emblem) 70 70
700. $5 on 30 c. Little Bay cliffs (surch. **INTERNATIONAL YOUTH YEAR** and emblem) .. .. .. 3·50 3·50

123. Johannes Hevelius (astronomer) and Mayan Temple Observatory.

1986. Appearance of Halley's Comet Mult.

701. 5 c. Type **123** 20 20
702. 10 c. "Viking Lander" space vehicle on Mars, 1976 .. .. .. 20 20
703. 60 c. Comet in 1664 (from Theatri Cosmicum, 1668) 70 70
704. $4 Comet over Mississippi riverboat, 1835 (150th birth anniv. of Mark Twain) .. .. .. 3·00 3·00

124. "The Crucifixion".

1986. Easter.

706. **124.** 10 c. multicoloured .. 15 15
707. – 25 c. multicoloured .. 25 25
708. – 45 c. multicoloured .. 45 45
709. – $4 multicoloured .. 2·75 2·75

Designs: 25 c. to $4. Different stained glass windows from Chartres Cathedral.

125. Princess Elizabeth inspecting Guards, 1946.

1986. 60th Birthday of Queen Elizabeth II.

711. **125.** 20 c. black and yellow 15 15
712. – $2 multicoloured .. 1·25 1·25
713. – $3 multicoloured .. 1·75 1·75

Designs: $2 Queen at Garter ceremony. $3 At Trooping the Colour.

1986. "Ameripex" International Stamp Exhibition. Chicago. Nos. 659, 667, 671, 673 and 675 optd. **AMERIPEX 1986.**

715. 5 c. Brown pelican .. 10 10
716. 45 c. Pearly-eyed thrasher 35 35
717. $1 Audubon's shearwater 65 65
718. $2.50 Bananaquit .. .. 1·50 1·50
719. $10 Green heron .. .. 5·50 5·50

127. Prince Andrew and Miss Sarah Ferguson.

1986. Royal Wedding. Multicoloured.

720. 10 c. Type **127** 10 10
721. 35 c. Prince Andrew .. 20 25
722. $2 Miss Sarah Ferguson .. 1·00 1·10
723. $3 Prince Andrew and Miss Sarah Ferguson (different) .. .. 1·50 1·60

1986. International Peace Year. Nos. 616/23 optd. **INTERNATIONAL YEAR OF PEACE.**

725. 10 c. Type **109** 10 10
726. 25 c. Abraham Lincoln .. 20 20
727. 35 c. Henri Christophe .. 30 30
728. 60 c. Thomas Clarkson .. 45 45
729. 75 c. William Wilberforce 50 50
730. $1 Olaudah Equiano .. 65 65
731. $2.50 General Gordon .. 1·50 1·50
732. $5 Granville Sharp .. 2·75 2·75

129. Trading Sloop.

1986. Christmas. Ships. Multicoloured.

734. 10 c. Type **129** 30 30
735. 45 c. "Lady Rodney" (cargo liner) 75 75
736. 80 c. "West Derby" (sailing ship) 90 90
737. $3 "Warspite" (local sloop) 2·75 2·75

130. Christopher Columbus with Astrolabe.

1986. 500th Anniv. (1992) of Discovery of America by Columbus. Multicoloured.

739. 5 c. Type **130** 10 10
740. 10 c. Columbus on board ship 15 15
741. 35 c. "Santa Maria" .. 60 60
742. 80 c. King Ferdinand and Queen Isabella of Spain (horiz.) 80 80
743. $4 Caribbean Indians smoking tobacco (horiz.) 2·75 2·75

131. "Danaus plexippus".

1987. Easter. Butterflies. Multicoloured.

No.	Description	Unused	Used
745	10 c. Type **131**	20	20
746	80 c. "Anartia jatrophae"	70	70
747	$1 "Heliconius charithonia"	90	90
748	$2 "Junonia evarete" ..	1·50	1·50

132. Old Goose Iron and Modern Electric Iron (illustration reduced actual size 59 × 28 mm.).

1987. 20th Anniv. of Separation from St. Kitts-Nevis. Multicoloured.

No.	Description	Unused	Used
750.	10 c. Type **132**	10	10
751.	35 c. Old East End School and Albena Lake-Hodge Comprehensive College	15	20
752.	45 c. Past and present markets	20	25
753.	80 c. Previous sailing ferry and new motor ferry, Blowing Point	35	40
754.	$1 Original mobile office and new telephone exchange	45	50
755.	$2 Open-air meeting, Burrowes Park and House of Assembly in session	90	95

1987. "Capex '87" International Stamp Exhibition, Toronto. Nos. 665a, 667, 670 and 675 optd. **CAPEX '87.**

No.	Description	Unused	Used
757.	35 c. Lesser Antillean bullfinch	20	20
758.	45 c. Pearly-eyed thrasher	25	25
759.	80 c. Grey kingbird ..	40	40
760.	$10 Green heron	5·00	5·00

1987. 20th Anniv. of Independence. Nos. 659, 661/4 and 665a/75 optd. **20 YEARS OF PROGRESS 1967–1987,** No. 762 surch. also.

No.	Description	Unused	Used
761.	5 c. Brown pelican ..	15	20
762.	10 c. on 15 c. Magnificent frigate bird	15	20
763.	15 c. Magnificent frigate bird	15	20
764.	20 c. Antillean crested hummingbird ..	20	25
765.	25 c. Type **116**	20	25
766.	30 c. Caribbean elaenia ..	30	35
767.	35 c. Lesser Antillean bullfinch	35	40
768.	40 c. Yellow-crowned night heron	35	40
769.	45 c. Pearly-eyed thrasher	40	50
770.	50 c. Laughing gull ..	40	50
771.	65 c. Brown booby ..	45	55
772.	80 c. Grey kingbird ..	55	65
773.	$1 Audubon's shearwater	65	75
774.	$1.35 Roseate tern ..	80	90
775.	$2.50 Bananaquit	1·50	1·75
776.	$5 Belted kingfisher ..	2·75	3·25
777.	$10 Green heron	5·50	7·00

135. Wicket Keeper and Game in Progress.

1987. Cricket World Cup. Multicoloured.

No.	Description	Unused	Used
778.	10 c. Type **135**	25	20
779.	35 c. Batsman and local Anguilla team	45	40
780.	45 c. Batsman and game in progress	55	50
781.	$2.50 Bowler and game in progress	1·75	1·90

136. West Indian Top Shell.

1987. Christmas. Sea Shells and Crabs. Multicoloured.

No.	Description	Unused	Used
783.	10 c. Type **136**	10	10
784.	35 c. Ghost crab	25	25
785.	50 c. Spiny Caribbean vase	40	40
786.	$2 Great Land crab ..	1·25	1·25

1987. Royal Ruby Wedding. Nos. 665a, 671/2 and 675 optd. **40TH WEDDING ANNIVERSARY H.M. QUEEN ELIZABETH II H.R.H. THE DUKE OF EDINBURGH.**

No.	Description	Unused	Used
788.	35 c. Lesser Antillean bullfinch	15	20
789.	$1 Audubon's shearwater	45	50
790.	$1.35 Roseate tern ..	60	65
791.	$10 Green heron	4·50	4·75

138 "Crinum erubescens"

1988. Easter. Lilies. Multicoloured.

No.	Description	Unused	Used
792	30 c. Type **138**	15	15
793	45 c. Spider lily	25	25
794	$1 "Crinum macowanii" ..	50	50
795	$2.50 Day lily	1·25	1·25

139 Relay Racing

1988. Olympic Games, Seoul. Multicoloured.

No.	Description	Unused	Used
797	35 c. Type **139**	30	30
798	45 c. Windsurfing ..	40	40
799	50 c. Tennis	50	50
800	80 c. Basketball ..	70	70

140 Common Sea Fan

1988. Christmas. Marine Life. Multicoloured.

No.	Description	Unused	Used
802	35 c. Type **140**	15	20
803	80 c. Coral crab	40	45
804	$1 Grooved brain coral ..	45	50
805	$1.60 Queen triggerfish ..	65	70

1988. Visit of Princess Alexandra. Nos. 665a, 670/1 and 673 optd **H.R.H. PRINCESS ALEXANDRA'S VISIT NOVEMBER 1988.**

No.	Description	Unused	Used
807	35 c. Lesser Antillean bullfinch	25	25
808	80 c. Grey kingbird ..	55	55
809	$1 Audubon's shearwater	65	65
810	$2.50 Bananaquit ..	1·40	1·40

142 Wood Slave

1989. Lizards. Multicoloured.

No.	Description	Unused	Used
811	45 c. Type **142**	20	25
812	80 c. Slippery back ..	40	45
813	$2.50 "Iguana delicatissima"	1·25	1·40

143 "Christ Crowned with Thorns" (detail) (Bosch)

1989. Easter. Religious Paintings. Mult.

No.	Description	Unused	Used
815	35 c. Type **143**	15	20
816	80 c. "Christ bearing the Cross" (detail) (Gerard David)	40	45
817	$1 "The Deposition" (detail) (Gerard David)	45	50
818	$1.60 "Pieta" (detail) (Rogier van der Weyden)	75	80

144 University Arms

1989. 40th Anniv of University of the West Indies.

No.	Description	Unused	Used
820	**144** $5 multicoloured ..	2·40	2·50

1989. 20th Anniv of First Manned Landing on Moon. Nos. 670/2 and 674 optd **20th ANNIVERSARY MOON LANDING.**

No.	Description	Unused	Used
821	80 c. Grey kingbird ..	40	45
822	$1 Audubon's shearwater	45	50
823	$1.35 Roseate tern ..	65	70
824	$5 Belted kingfisher ..	2·40	2·50

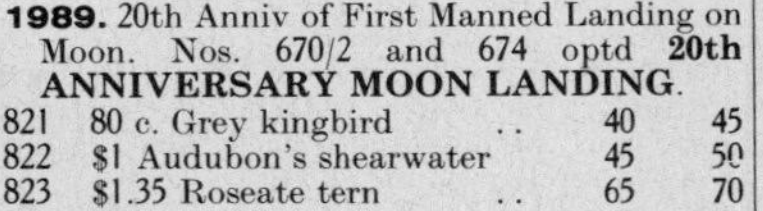

146 Lone Star (house), 1930

1989. Christmas. Historic Houses. Mult.

No.	Description	Unused	Used
825	5 c. Type **146**	10	10
826	35 c. Whitehouse, 1906 ..	15	20
827	45 c. Hodges House ..	20	25
828	80 c. Warden's Place ..	40	45

147 Blear Eye

1990. Fishes. Multicoloured.

No.	Description	Unused	Used
830	5 c. Type **147**	10	10
831	10 c. Redman	10	10
832	15 c. Speckletail	10	10
833	25 c. Grunt	10	15
834	30 c. Amber jack	10	15
835	35 c. Red hind	15	20
836	40 c. Goatfish	15	20
837	45 c. Old wife	20	25
838	50 c. Butter fish	20	25
839	65 c. Shell fish	25	30
840	80 c. Yellowtail snapper ..	35	40
841	$1 Katy	40	45
842	$1.35 Mutton grouper ..	55	60
843	$2.50 Doctor fish	1·00	1·10
844	$5 Angelfish	2·10	2·25
845	$10 Barracuda ..	4·25	4·50

148 The Last Supper

1990. Easter. Multicoloured.

No.	Description	Unused	Used
846	35 c. Type **148**	15	20
847	45 c. The Trial	20	25
848	$1.35 The Crucifixion ..	55	60
849	$2.50 The Empty Tomb ..	1·00	1·10

149 G.B. 1840 Penny Black

1990. "Stamp World London 90" International Stamp Exhibition. Multicoloured

No.	Description	Unused	Used
851	25 c. Type **149**	10	10
852	50 c. G.B. 1840 Twopenny Blue	20	25
853	$1.50 Cape of Good Hope 1861 1d. "woodblock" (horiz)	60	65
854	$2.50 G.B. 1882 £5 (horiz)	1·00	1·10

1990. Anniversaries and Events. Nos. 841/4 optd.

No.	Description	Unused	Used
856	$1 Katy (optd **EXPO '90**)	40	45
857	$1.35 Mutton Grouper (optd **1990 INTERNATIONAL LITERACY YEAR**) ..	55	60
858	$2.50 Doctor fish (optd **WORLD CUP FOOTBALL CHAMPIONSHIPS 1990**)	1·00	1·10
859	$5 Angelfish (optd **90TH BIRTHDAY H.M. THE QUEEN MOTHER**)	2·00	2·10

HAVE YOU READ THE NOTES AT THE BEGINNING OF THIS CATALOGUE?

These often provide answers to the enquiries we receive.

151 Mermaid Flag

1990. Island Flags. Multicoloured.

860 50 c. Type **151** 20 25
861 80 c. New Anguilla official flag 30 35
862 $1 Three Dolphins flag .. 40 45
863 $5 Governor's official flag 2·00 2·10

152 Laughing Gulls

1990. Christmas. Sea Birds. Multicoloured.

864 10 c. Type **152** 15 15
865 35 c. Brown booby .. 25 25
866 $1.50 Bridled tern .. 85 85
867 $3.50 Brown pelican .. 1·75 1·75

1991. Easter. Nos. 846/9 optd **1991**.

869 35 c. Type **148** 15 20
870 45 c. The Trial 20 25
871 $1.35 The Crucifixion .. 55 60
872 $2.50 The Empty Tomb .. 1·00 1·10

154 Angel

1991. Christmas.

874 **154** 5 c. violet, brown & blk 10 10
875 – 35 c. multicoloured .. 15 20
876 – 80 c. multicoloured .. 30 35
877 – $1 multicoloured .. 40 45

DESIGNS—VERT. 35 c. Father Christmas. HORIZ. 80 c. Church and house; $1 Palm trees at night.

155 Angels with Palm Branches outside St. Gerard's Church

1992. Easter. Multicoloured.

879 35 c. Type **155** 15 20
880 45 c. Angels singing outside Methodist Church .. 20 25
881 80 c. Village (horiz) .. 30 35
882 $1 Congregation going to St. Mary's Church .. 40 45
883 $5 Dinghy regatta (horiz) 2·00 2·10

ANTIGUA

One of the Leeward Is., Br. W. Indies. Used general issues for Leeward Is., concurrently with Antiguan stamps until 1 July 1956. Ministerial Government introduced on 1 January 1960. Achieved Associated Statehood on 3 March 1967 and Independence within the Commonwealth on 1 November 1981.

Nos. 718/22 and 733 onwards are inscribed "Antigua & Barbuda".

1862. 12 pence = 1 shilling.
20 shillings = 1 pound.
1951. 100 cents = 1 West Indian dollar.

1.

3.

1862.

5. **1.** 1d. mauve .. .. £110 40·00
25. 1d. red .. .. 80 2·25
29. 6d. green .. .. 55·00 £120

1879.

21. **3.** ½d. green .. .. 1·40 10·00
22. 2½d. brown .. .. £130 45·00
27. 2½d. blue .. .. 5·00 11·00
23. 4d. blue .. .. £275 15·00
28. 4d. brown .. .. 1·25 2·00
30. 1s. mauve £160 £120

4.

5.

8.

1903.

31 **4** ½d. black and green .. 2·00 3·50
41 ½d. green .. .. 1·00 2·50
32 1d. black and red .. 3·75 40
43 1d. red .. .. 2·50 1·40
45 2d. purple and brown .. 3·25 18·00
34 2½d. black and blue .. 8·00 10·00
46 2½d. blue .. .. 6·00 13·00
47 3d. green and brown .. 6·00 15·00
48 6d. purple and black .. 7·50 26·00
37 1s. blue and purple .. 23·00 42·00
50 2s. green and violet .. 42·00 65·00
39 2s. 6d. black and purple .. 16·00 42·00
40 **5** 5s. green and violet .. 60·00 70·00

1913. Head of King George V.

51. **5.** 5s. green and violet .. 60·00 85·00

1916. Optd. **WAR STAMP.**

52. **4.** ½d. green 40 65
54. 1½d. orange 35 65

1921.

62 ½d. green 35 20
63 1d. red 75 20
64 1d. violet .. .. 1·25 1·50
67 1½d. orange .. .. 1·50 7·00
68 1½d. red .. .. 1·25 1·75
69 1½d. brown .. .. 1·50 60
70 2d. grey .. .. 1·00 75
72 2½d. blue .. .. 3·00 5·50
73 2½d. yellow .. .. 1·25 15·00
74 3d. purple on yellow .. 4·00 8·50
56 4d. black & red on yellow 1·25 5·00
75 6d. purple .. .. 2·75 5·00
57 1s. black on green .. 3·75 6·00
58 2s. purple & blue on blue 7·50 17·00
78 2s. 6d. black & red on blue 15·00 20·00
79 3s. green and violet .. 18·00 45·00
80 4s. black and red .. 42·00 48·00
60 5s. green & red on yellow 8·00 25·00
61 £1 purple and black on red £170 £225

9. Old Dockyard, English Harbour.

12. Sir Thomas Warner and "Concepcion".

1932. Tercent. Designs with medallion portrait of King George V.

81. **9.** ½d. green .. .. .. 1·50 3·75
82. 1d. red .. .. .. 2·00 2·00
83. 1½d. brown .. .. .. 3·00 3·75
84. – 2d. grey .. .. .. 3·75 14·00
85. – 2½d. blue .. .. .. 3·75 7·50
86. – 3d. orange .. .. .. 3·75 12·00
87. – 6d. violet .. .. .. 11·00 12·00
88. – 1s. olive .. .. .. 14·00 24·00
89. – 2s. 6d. purple .. .. 40·00 48·00
90. **12.** 5s black and brown .. 80·00 £110

DESIGNS—HORIZ. 2d. to 3d. Government House, St. John's. 6d. to 2s. 6d. Nelson's "Victory".

13. Windsor Castle.

1935. Silver Jubilee.

91. **13.** 1d. blue and red .. 1·50 1·00
92. 1½d. blue and grey .. 1·75 45
93. 2½d. brown and blue .. 3·75 1·00
94. 1s. grey and purple .. 7·50 11·00

1937. Coronation. As T **2** of Aden.

95. 1d red 50 35
96. 1½d. brown 60 30
97. 2½d. blue .. .. .. 1·75 75

15. English Harbour.

16. Nelson's Dockyard.

1938.

98 **15** ½d. green 15 40
99 **16** 1d. red 50 40
110a 1½d. brown .. .. 1·25 75
101 **15** 2d. grey 30 30
102 **16** 2½d. blue 30 45
103 – 3d. orange 30 30
104 – 6d. violet 60 30
105 – 1s. black and brown .. 1·25 45
106a – 2s. 6d. purple .. 16·00 4·50
107 – 5s. olive .. .. 11·00 7·00
108 **16** 10s. mauve .. 16·00 23·00
109 – £1 green .. 22·00 28·00

DESIGNS: HORIZ. 3d., 2s. 6d., £1, Fort James, VERT. 6d., 1s. 5s., St. John's Harbour.

1946. Victory. As T **9** of Aden.

110. 1½d. brown 15 10
111. 3d. orange 15 20

1949. Silver Wedding. As T **10/11** of Aden.

112. 2½d. blue 20 30
113. 5s. green .. .. 7·50 4·25

20. Hermes, Globe and Forms of Transport.

21. Hemispheres, Aeroplane and Steamer.

22. Hermes and Globe.

23. U.P.U. Monument.

1949. 75th Anniv of U.P.U.

114 **20** 2½d. blue 40 50
115 **21** 3d. orange 80 75
116 **22** 6d. purple 80 75
117 **23** 1s. brown 80 75

24. Arms of University.

25. Princess Alice.

1951. Inaug of B.W.I. University College.

118 **24** 3 c. black and brown .. 35 20
119 **25** 12 c. black and violet .. 45 40

1953. Coronation. As T **13** of Aden.

120. 2 c. black and green .. 10 30

27. Martello Tower.

DESIGNS — HORIZ. ½ c., 6 c., 60 c., $4.80, Fort James. VERT. 12 c. 24 c., $1.20, St. John's Harbour.

1953. Designs as 1938 issues but with portrait of Queen Elizabeth II as in T **27**.

120a – ½ c. brown 20 20
121 **14** 1 c. grey 15 10
122 **16** 2 c. green 15 10
123 – 3 c. black and yellow .. 20 10
153 **14** 4 c. red 30 10
154 **16** 5 c. black and lilac .. 20 10
155 – 6 c. yellow 40 30
156 **27** 8 c. blue 30 15
157 – 12 c. violet 30 15
158 – 24 c. black and brown .. 70 70
130 **27** 48 c. purple and blue .. 3·25 1·25
131 – 60 c. purple .. .. 4·00 80
132a – $1.20 olive .. .. 2·00 70
133 **16** $2.40 purple .. .. 7·50 12·00
134 – $4.80 slate .. .. 8·50 16·00

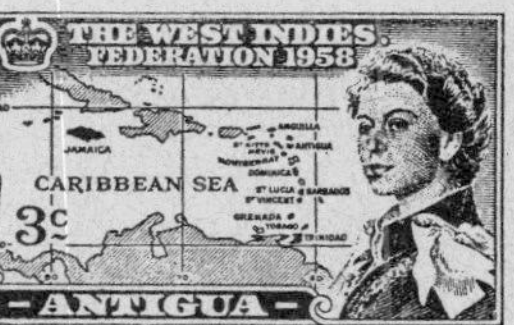

28. Federation Map.

1958. Inauguration of British Caribbean Federation.

135 **28** 3 c. green 60 25
136 6 c. blue 80 70
137 12 c. red 90 40

1960. New Constitution. Optd. **COMMEMORATION ANTIGUA CONSTITUTION.**

138. **16.** 3 c. black and yellow .. 15 15
139. – 12 c. violet (No. 128) .. 15 15

30. Nelson's Dockyard and Admiral Nelson.

1961. Restoration of Nelson's Dockyard.

140 **30** 20 c. purple and brown 50 40
141 30 c. green and blue .. 60 40

31. Stamp of 1862 and R.M.S.P. "Solent" at English Harbour.

1962. Stamp Cent.

142 **31** 3 c. purple and green .. 30 10
143 10 c. blue and green .. 40 10
144 12 c. sepia and green .. 45 10
145 50 c. brown and green .. 1·10 55

1963. Freedom from Hunger. As T **28** of Aden.

146. 12 c. green 15 15

33. Red Cross Emblem.

1963. Centenary of Red Cross.

147 **33** 3 c. red and black .. 20 30
148 12 c. red and blue .. 50 70

34. Shakespeare and Memorial Theatre, Stratford-upon-Avon.

1964. 400th Birth Anniv. of Shakespeare.

164 **34** 12 c. brown 15 10

1965. No. 157 surch **15c.**

165 15 c. on 12 c. violet .. 10 10

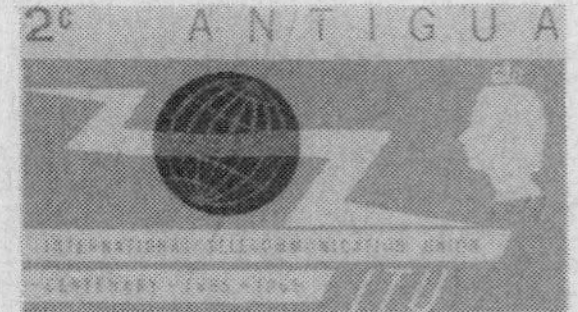

36. I.T.U. Emblem.

1965. Centenary of I.T.U.

166 **36** 2 c. blue and red .. 20 15
167 50 c. yellow and blue .. 1·25 80

37. I.C.Y. Emblem.

1965. Int. Co-operation Year.

168 **37** 4 c. purple & turquoise 15 10
169 15 c. green and lavender 25 20

38. Sir Winston Churchill, and St. Paul's Cathedral in Wartime.

1966. Churchill Commem. Designs in black, red and gold with background in colours given.

170 **38** ½ c. blue 10 10
171 4 c. green 30 10
172 25 c. brown 65 30
173 35 c. violet 75 40

39. Queen Elizabeth II and Duke of Edinburgh.

1966. Royal Visit.

174 **39** 6 c. black and blue .. 1·75 1·10
175 15 c. black and mauve .. 2·00 1·40

40. Footballer's Legs, Ball and Jules Rimet Cup.

1966. World Cup Football Championships.

176 **40** 6 c. multicoloured .. 15 15
177 35 c. multicoloured .. 50 25

41. W.H.O. Building.

1966. Inaug. of W.H.O. Headquarters, Geneva.

178 **41** 2 c. black, green & blue 15 15
179 15 c. black, pur. & brn. 70 25

42. Nelson's Dockyard.

1966.

234 **42** ½ c. green and turquoise 10 20
235 – 1 c. purple and red .. 10 15
236 – 2 c. slate and orange .. 10 10
183 – 3 c. red and black .. 10 10
238 – 4 c. violet and brown .. 15 15
185 – 5 c. blue and olive .. 10 10
186 – 6 c. salmon and purple .. 15 10
187 – 10 c. green and red .. 15 10
188 – 15 c. brown and blue .. 30 10
189 – 25 c. slate and sepia .. 35 20
244 – 35 c. red and brown .. 60 1·00
245 – 50 c. green and black .. 70 2·00
192 – 75 c. blue & ultramarine 1·50 2·50
246 – $1 red and olive .. 1·25 3·50
194 – $2.50 black and red .. 3·00 4·75
195 – $5 green and violet .. 5·00 6·50

DESIGNS: 1 c. Old Post Office, St. John's. 2 c. Health Centre. 3 c. Teacher's Training College. 4 c. Martello Tower, Barbuda. 5 c. Ruins of Officers' Quarters, Shirley Heights. 6 c. Government House, Barbuda. 10 c. Princess Margaret School. 15 c. Air Terminal Building. 25 c. General Post Office. 35 c. Clarence House. 50 c. Government House, St. John's. 75 c. Administration Building. $1, Courthouse, St. John's. $2.50, Magistrates' Court. $5 St. John's Cathedral.

54. "Education".

55. "Science".

56. "Culture".

1966. 20th Anniv. of U.N.E.S.C.O.

196. **54.** 4 c. violet, yell. & orge. 15 10
197. **55.** 25 c. yellow, violet & ol. 35 10
198. **56.** $1 black, purple & orge. 1·75 1·75

57. State Flag and Maps.

1967. Statehood. Multicoloured.

199. 4 c. Type **57** 10 10
200. 15 c. State Flag 10 10
201. 25 c. Premier's Office and State Flag 10 10
202. 35 c. As 15 c. 15 15

60. Gilbert Memorial Church.

1967. Attainment of Autonomy by the Methodist Church.

203. **60.** 4 c. black and red 10 10
204. – 25 c. black and green .. 15 15
205. – 35 c. black and blue .. 15 15

DESIGNS: 25 c. Nathaniel Gilbert's House. 35 c. Caribbean and Central American Map.

63. Coat of Arms.

1967. 300th Anniv. of Treaty of Breda and Grant of New Arms.

206. **63.** 15 c. multicoloured .. 15 10
207. 35 c. multicoloured .. 15 10

64. Settlers' Ship.

1967. 300th Anniv. of Barbuda Settlement.

208. **64.** 4 c. blue 10 10
209. – 6 c. purple 10 10
210. **64.** 25 c. green 15 10
211. – 35 c. black 15 15

DESIGN: 6 c., 35 c. Blaeu's Map of 1665.

66. Tracking Station.

1968. N.A.S.A. Apollo Project. Inauguration of Dow Hill Tracking Station.

212. **66.** 4 c. blue, yellow & black 10 10
213. – 15 c. blue, yell. & black 20 10
214. – 25 c. blue, yell. & black 20 10
215. – 50 c. blue, yell. & black 30 20

DESIGNS: 15 c. Antenna and Spacecraft taking off. 25 c. Spacecraft approaching Moon. 50 c. Re-entry of Space Capsule.

70. Limbo-dancing.

1968. Tourism. Multicoloured.

216. ½ c. Type **70** 10 10
217. 15 c. Water-skier & Bathers 15 10
218. 25 c. Yachts and beach .. 20 10
219. 35 c. Underwater swimming 20 10
220. 50 c. Type **70** 30 35

74. Old Harbour in 1768.

1968. Opening of St. John's Deep Water Harbour.

221. **74.** 2 c. blue and red .. 10 10
222. – 15 c. green and sepia .. 20 10
223. – 25 c. yellow and blue .. 25 10
224. – 35 c. Salmon and emer. 30 10
225. **74.** $1 black 70 45

DESIGNS: 15 c. Old Harbour in 1829. 25 c. Freighter and Chart of New Harbour. 35 c. New Harbour.

78. Parliament Buildings.

1969. Tercent. of Parliament. Multicoloured.

226. 4 c. Type **78** 10 10
227. 15 c. Antigua Mace and Bearer 15 10
228. 25 c. House of Representatives' Room .. 15 10
229. 50 c. Coat of arms and Seal of Antigua .. 25 35

82. Freight Transport.

1969. 1st Anniv. of Caribbean Free Trade Area.

230. **82.** 4 c. black and purple .. 10 10
231. 15 c. black and blue .. 15 10
232. – 25 c. brn., black & ochre 15 15
233. – 35 c. choc., blk. and brn. 15 15

DESIGN—VERT. 25 c., 35 c. Crate of cargo.

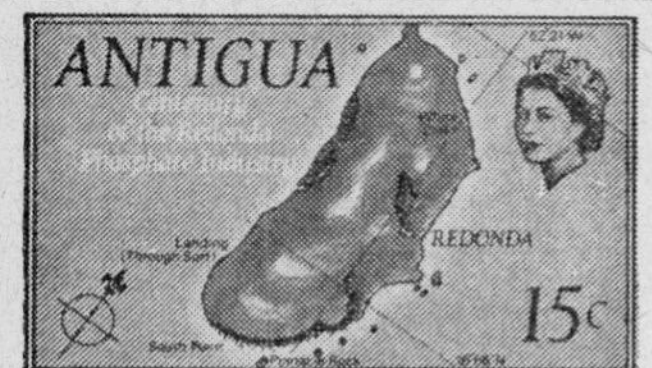

84. Island of Redonda (Chart).

1969. Centenary of Redonda Phosphate Industry. Multicoloured.

249.	15 c. Type **84**	20	10
250.	25 c. View of Redonda from the sea	20	10
251.	50 c. Type **84**	45	45

86. "The Adoration of the Magi" (Marcillat).

1969. Christmas. Stained Glass Windows. Multicoloured.

252.	6 c. Type **86**	10	10
253.	10 c. "The Nativity" (unknown German artist, 15th cent.)	10	10
254.	35 c. Type **86**	15	10
255.	50 c. As 10 c.	35	30

1970. Surch. **20c.** and bars.

256.	20 c. on 25 c. (No. 189)	10	10

89. Coat of Arms.

1970. Coil Stamps.

257. **89.**	5 c. blue	10	10
258.	10 c. green	10	15
259.	25 c. red	20	25

90. Sikorski "S-38".

1970. 40th Anniv. of Antiguan Air Services. Multicoloured.

260.	5 c. Type **90**	20	10
261.	20 c. Dornier "DO-X"	35	10
262.	35 c. Hawker Siddeley "HS-748"	45	10
263.	50 c. Douglas "C-124C" (Globemaster II)	60	60
264.	75 c. Vickers "VC-10"	80	1·00

91. Dickens and Scene from "Nicholas Nickleby".

1970. Death Cent. of Charles Dickens.

265. **91.**	5 c. bistre, sepia & blk.	10	10
266. –	20 c. turquoise, sepia and black	10	10
267. –	35 c. blue, sepia & black	15	10
268. –	$1 red, sepia and black	45	50

DESIGNS: All stamps show Dickens and scene from: 20 c. "Pickwick Papers". 35 c. "Oliver Twist". $1, "David Copperfield".

92. Carib Indian and War Canoe.

1970. Multicoloured.

269	½ c. Type **92**	10	30
270	1 c. Columbus and "Nina"	25	25
271	2 c. Sir Thomas Warner's emblem and "Concepcion"	40	25
325	3 c. Viscount Hood and H.M.S. "Barfleur"	35	30
326	4 c. Sir George Rodney and H.M.S. "Formidable"	35	30
274	5 c. Nelson and H.M.S. "Boreas"	50	30
275	6 c. William IV and H.M.S. "Pegasus"	50	40
329	10 c. "Blackbeard" and pirate ketch	55	30
277	15 c. Collingwood and H.M.S. "Pelican"	2·00	1·00
278	20 c. Nelson and H.M.S. "Victory"	1·25	60
279	25 c. R.M.S.P. "Solent"	1·25	60
280	35 c. George V (when Prince George) and H.M.S. "Canada"	1·60	70
281	50 c. H.M.S. "Renown" (battle cruiser)	3·50	2·00
331	75 c. "Federal Maple" (freighter)	5·50	3·00
332	$1 "Sol Quest" (yacht) and class emblem	4·50	1·75
333	$2.50 H.M.S. "London" (destroyer)	4·50	6·50
285	$5 "Pathfinder" (tug)	7·00	7·50

93. "The Small Passion" (detail) (Durer).

1970. Christmas.

286. **93.**	3 c. black and blue	10	10
287. –	10 c. purple and pink	10	10
288. **93.**	35 c. black and red	20	10
289. –	50 c. black and lilac	30	30

DESIGN: 10 c., 50 c. "Adoration of the Magi" (detail) (Durer).

94. 4th King's Own Regt., 1759.

1970. Military Uniforms (1st series). Multicoloured.

290.	½ c. Type **94**	10	10
291.	10 c. 4th West India Regt., 1804.	50	10
292.	20 c. 60th Regt., The Royal American, 1809	90	25
293.	35 c. 93rd Regt., Sutherland Highlanders, 1826-34	1·25	30
294.	75 c. 3rd West India Regt., 1851	2·25	2·25

See also Nos. 303/7, 313/17, 353/7 and 380/4.

MORE DETAILED LISTS
are given in the Stanley Gibbons Catalogues referred to in the country headings. For lists of current volumes see Introduction.

95. Market Woman casting Vote.

1971. 20th Anniv. of Adult Suffrage.

296. **95.**	5 c. brown	10	10
297. –	20 c. olive	10	10
298. –	35 c. purple	10	10
299. –	50 c. blue	15	30

DESIGNS: People voting: 20 c. Executive. 35 c. Housewife. 50 c. Artisan.

96. "The Last Supper".

1971. Easter. Works by Durer.

300. **96.**	5 c. black, grey & red	10	10
301. –	35 c. black, grey & violet	10	10
302. –	75 c. black, grey & gold	20	30

DESIGNS: 35 c. "The Crucifixion". 75 c. "The Resurrection".

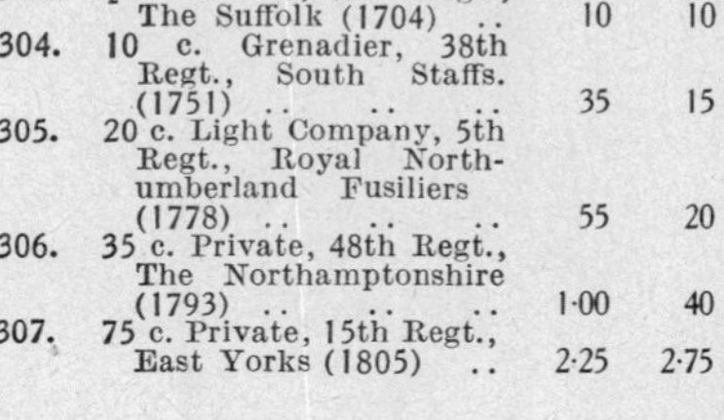

1971. Military Uniforms (2nd series). As T **94.** Multicoloured.

303.	½ c. Private, 12th Regt., The Suffolk (1704)	10	10
304.	10 c. Grenadier, 38th Regt., South Staffs. (1751)	35	15
305.	20 c. Light Company, 5th Regt., Royal Northumberland Fusiliers (1778)	55	20
306.	35 c. Private, 48th Regt., The Northamptonshire (1793)	1·00	40
307.	75 c. Private, 15th Regt., East Yorks (1805)	2·25	2·75

97. "Madonna and Child" (detail, Veronese).

1971. Christmas. Multicoloured.

309.	3 c. Type **97**	10	10
310.	5 c. "Adoration of the Shepherds" (detail, Veronese)	10	10
311.	35 c. Type **97**	20	10
312.	50 c. As 5 c.	30	30

1972. Military Uniforms (3rd series). As T **94.** Multicoloured.

313.	½ c. Battalion Company Officer, 25th Foot, 1815	10	10
314.	10 c. Sergeant, 14th Foot, 1837	35	10
315.	20 c. Private, 67th Foot, 1853	60	15
316.	35 c. Officer, Royal Artillery, 1854	1·00	20
317.	75 c. Private, 29th Foot, 1870	1·60	1·75

98. Cowrie Helmet.

1972. Shells. Multicoloured.

319.	3 c. Type **98**	15	10
320.	5 c. Measeled Cowrie	15	10
321.	35 c. West Indian Fighting Conch	55	10
322.	50 c. Hawk Wing Conch	1·10	95

99. St. John's Cathedral, Side View.

1972. Christmas and 125th Anniv. of St. John's Cathedral. Multicoloured.

335.	35 c. Type **99**	20	10
336.	50 c. Cathedral interior	25	20
337.	75 c. St. John's Cathedral	30	50

1972. Royal Silver Wedding. As T **52,** of Ascension, but with floral background.

339.	20 c. blue	15	15
340.	35 c. blue	15	15

101. Batsman and Map.

1972. 50th Anniv. of Rising Sun Cricket Club. Multicoloured.

341.	5 c. Type **101**	45	25
342.	35 c. Batsman and wicket keeper	1·40	1·25
343.	$1 Club badge	2·75	3·50

102. Yacht and Map.

1972. Inaug. of Antigua and Barbuda Tourist Office in New York. Multicoloured.

345.	35 c. Type **102**	15	10
346.	50 c. Yachts	20	15
347.	75 c. St. John's G.P.O.	25	30
348.	$1 Statue of Liberty	30	35

103. "Episcopal Coat of Arms".

1973. Easter. Multicoloured.

350. **103.**	5 c. Type **103**	10	10
351. –	35 c. "The Crucifixion"	10	10
352. –	75 c. "Arms of 1st Bishop of Antigua"	20	30

Nos. 350/2 show different stained-glass windows from St. John's Cathedral.

1973. Military Uniforms (4th series). As T **94**. Multicoloured.

353. ½ c. Private, Zachariah Tiffin's Regt., of Foot, 1701 .. .. .. 10 10
354. 10 c. Private, 63rd Regt., of Foot, 1759 .. .. 20 10
355. 20 c. Light Company Officer, 35th Regt., of Foot, 1828 30 15
356. 35 c. Private, 2nd West India Regt., 1853 55 15
357. 75 c. Sergeant, 49th Regt., 1858 .. .. .. 1·25 1·00

104. Butterfly Costumes

1973. Carnival. Multicoloured.

359. 5 c. Type **104** 10 10
360. 20 c. Carnival street scene 15 10
361. 35 c. Carnival troupe .. 20 10
362. 75 c. Carnival Queen .. 30 30

105. " Virgin of the Milk Porridge " (Gerard David).

1973. Christmas. Multicoloured.

364. 3 c. Type **105** 10 10
365. 5 c. " Adoration of the Magi " (Stomer) .. 10 10
366. 20 c. " The Granducal Madonna " (Raphael).. 20 10
367. 35 c. " Nativity with God the Father and Holy Ghost " (Battista) .. 30 10
368. $1 " Madonna and Child " (Murillo).. .. .. 60 60

106. Princess Anne and Captain Mark Phillips.

1973. Royal Wedding.

370. **106.** 35 c. multicoloured .. 15 10
371. – $2 multicoloured .. 35 25

The $2 is as Type **106** but has a different border.

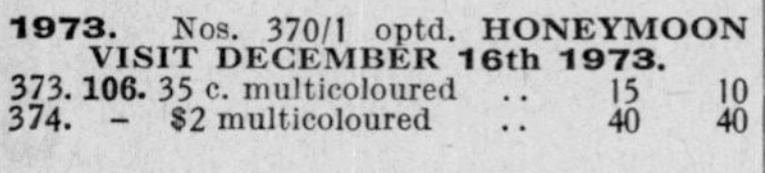

1973. Nos. 370/1 optd. **HONEYMOON VISIT DECEMBER 16th 1973.**

373. **106.** 35 c. multicoloured .. 15 10
374. – $2 multicoloured .. 40 40

108. Coat of Arms of Antigua and University.

1974. 25th Anniv. of University of West Indies. Multicoloured.

376. 5 c. Type **108** 10 10
377. 20 c. Extra-mural art .. 10 10
378. 35 c. Antigua campus .. 10 10
379. 75 c. Antigua chancellor 20 25

1974. Military Uniforms (5th series). As T **94**. Multicoloured.

380. ½ c Officer, 59th Foot, 1797 10 10
381. 10 c. Gunner, Royal Artillery, 1800 .. 30 10
382. 20 c. Private, 1st West India Regt., 1830 .. 40 10
383. 35 c. Officer, 92nd Foot, 1843 .. .. 55 10
384. 75 c. Private, 23rd Foot, 1846 .. .. 90 60

109. English Postman Mailcoach and Helicopter.

1974. Centenary of U.P.U. Multicoloured.

386. ½ c. Type **109** 10 10
387. 1 c. Bellman, mail steamer "Orinoco" and satellite 10 10
388. 2 c. Train guard, post-bus and hydrofoil 10 10
389. 5 c. Swiss messenger, Wells Fargo coach and "Concorde" 10 10
390. 20 c. Postillion, Japanese postmen and carrier pigeon 30 10
391. 35 c. Antiguan postman, flying-boat and tracking station 45 15
392. $1 Medieval courier, American express train and Boeing "747" .. 1·50 1·10

On the ½ c. English is spelt "Enlish" and on the 2 c. Postal is spelt "Fostal".

110. Traditional Player.

1974. Antiguan Steel Bands.

394. **110.** 5 c. dull red, red & black 10 10
395. – 20 c. brn. light brn. & blk. 10 10
396. – 35 c. light grn. grn. & blk. 10 10
397. – 75 c. blue, dull bl. & blk. 20 20

DESIGNS—HORIZ. 20 c. Traditional band. 35 c. Modern band. VERT. 75 c. Modern player.

111. Footballers.

1974. World Cup Football Championships.

399. **111.** 5 c. multicoloured .. 10 10
400. – 35 c. multicoloured .. 10 10
401. – 75 c. multicoloured .. 25 30
402. – $1 multicoloured .. 30 40

Nos. 400/2 show various footballing designs similar to Type **111**.

1974. Earthquake Relief Fund. Nos. 400/2 and 397 optd. or surch. **EARTHQUAKE RELIEF.**

404. 35 c. multicoloured .. 20 10
405. 75 c. multicoloured .. 30 25
406. $1 multicoloured 40 30
407. $5 on 75 c. dull blue, blue and black .. .. 1·50 2·00

113. Churchill as Schoolboy and School College Building, Harrow.

1974. Birth Centenary of Sir Winston Churchill. Multicoloured.

408. 5 c. Type **113**. .. 10 10
409. 35 c. Churchill and St. Paul's Cathedral .. 20 10
410. 75 c. Coat of arms and catafalque 30 35
411. $1 Churchill, " reward " notice and South African escape route .. 50 60

114. "Madonna of the Trees" (Bellini).

1974. Christmas. " Madonna and Child " paintings by named artists. Multicoloured.

413. ½ c. Type **114** 10 10
414. 1 c. Raphael 10 10
415. 2 c. Van der Weyden .. 10 10
416. 3 c. Giorgione 10 10
417. 5 c. Manaegna 10 10
418. 20 c. Vivarini 15 10
419. 35 c. Montagna 25 10
420. 75 c. Lorenzo Costa .. 45 60

1975. Nos. 390/2 and 282 surch.

422. 50 c. on 20 c. multicoloured 1·50 2·00
423. $2.50 on 35 c. mult. .. 3·50 6·00
424. $5 on $1 multicoloured .. 5·00 8·00
425. $10 on 75 c. mult. .. 5·50 8·50

116. Carib War Canoe, English Harbour, 1300.

1975. Nelson's Dockyard. Multicoloured.

427. 5 c. Type **116** 15 10
428. 15 c. Ship of the line, English Harbour, 1770 .. 50 10
429. 35 c. HMS " Boreas " at anchor, and Lord Nelson, 1787 .. .. 80 15
430. 50 c. Yachts during " Sailing Week ", 1974 .. .. 85 40
431. $1 Yacht Anchorage, Old Dockyard, 1970.. .. 1·25 1·10

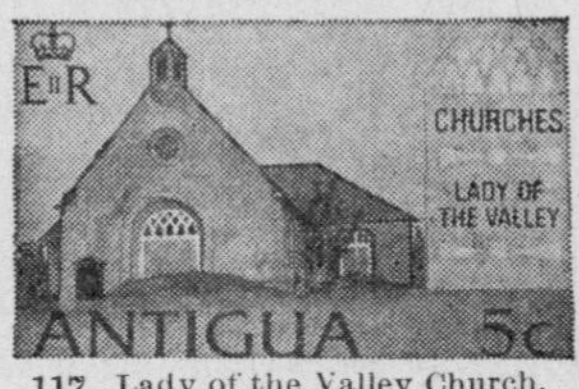

117. Lady of the Valley Church.

1975. Antiguan Churches. Multicoloured.

433. 5 c. Type **117**. 10 10
434. 20 c. Gilbert Memorial .. 10 10
435. 35 c. Grace Hill Moravian 15 10
436. 50 c. St. Phillips .. 20 20
437. $1 Ebenezer Methodist .. 35 50

118. Map of 1721 and Sextant of 1640.

1975. Maps of Antigua. Multicoloured.

439. 5 c. Type **118** 15 10
440. 20 c. Map of 1775 and galleon 35 10
441. 35 c. Maps of 1775 and 1955 45 15
442. $1 1973 maps of Antigua and English Harbour .. 1·10 1·25

119. Scout Bugler.

1975. World Scout Jamboree, Norway. Multicoloured.

444. 15 c. Type **119** 25 15
445. 20 c. Scouts in camp .. 30 15
446. 35 c. "Lord Baden-Powell" (D. Jagger) 50 20
447. $2 Scout dancers from Dahomey .. .. 1·50 1·75

120. " Eurema elathea ".

1975. Butterflies. Multicoloured.

449 ½ c. Type **120** 10 10
450 1 c. "Danaus plexippus" .. 10 10
451 2 c. "Phoebis philea" .. 10 10
452 5 c. "Hypolimnas misippus" 15 10
453 20 c. "Eurema proterpia" 60 60
454 35 c. "Battus polydamas" 90 90
455 $2 "Cynthia cardui" .. 4·00 7·00

No. 452 is incorrectly captioned "Marpesia petreus thetys".

121. " Madonna and Child " (Correggio).

1975. Christmas. " Madonna and Child " paintings by artists named. Mult.

457. ½ c. Type **121** 10 10
458. 1 c. El Greco 10 10
459. 2 c. Durer 10 10
460. 3 c. Antonello 10 10
461. 5 c. Bellini 10 10
462. 10 c. Durer (different) .. 10 10
463. 35 c. Bellini (different) .. 30 10
464. $2 Durer (different again) 85 70

122. Vivian Richards.

1975. World Cricket Cup Winners. Mult.

466. 5 c. Type **122** 80 20
467. 35 c. Andy Roberts .. 1·75 60
468. $2 West Indies Team (horiz.) 4·50 6·00

123. Antillean Crested Hummingbird.

1976. Multicoloured.

469. ½ c. Type **123** 20 30
470. 1 c. Imperial Amazon .. 30 30
471. 2 c. Zenaida Dove .. 30 30
472. 3 c. Loggerhead Kingbird 30 30
473. 4 c. Red-necked Pigeon .. 30 30
474. 5 c. Rufous-throated Solitaire 40 10
475. 6 c. Orchid tree 30 30
476. 10 c. Bougainvillea .. 30 10
477. 15 c. Geiger tree 35 10
478. 20 c. Flamboyant 35 20
479. 25 c. Hibiscus 40 15
480. 35 c. Flame of the Wood 40 20
481. 50 c. Cannon at Fort James 55 40
482. 75 c. Premier's Office .. 60 65
483. $1 Potworks Dam .. 75 80
484. $2.50 Diamond irrigation scheme .. .. 2·00 2·00
485. $5 Government House .. 3·50 3·50
486. $10 Coolidge International Airport .. .. 4·50 6·00

Nos. 484/6 are larger, 44 × 28 mm.

124. Privates, Clark's Illinois. Regt.

1976. Bicent. of American Revolution. Mult.

487.	½ c. Type **124**	10	10
488.	1 c. Rifleman, Pennsylvania Militia	10	10
489.	2 c. Powder horn	10	10
490.	5 c. Water bottle	10	10
491.	35 c. American flags ..	35	10
492.	$1 Privateer " Montgomery "	1·00	55
493.	$5 Sloop " Ranger " ..	3·50	3·50

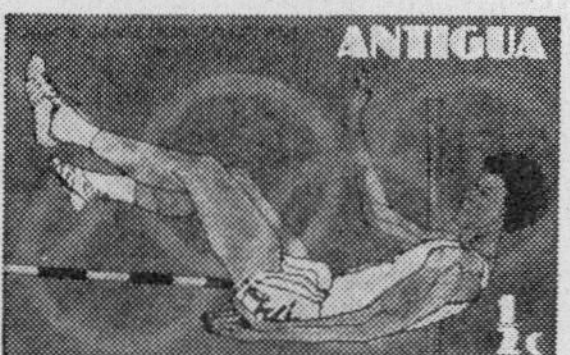

125. High Jump.

1976. Olympic Games, Montreal.

495.	**125.**	½ c. brn., yell. & blk.	10	10
496.	–	1 c. violet, bl. & blk.	10	10
497.	–	2 c. green and black	10	10
498.	–	15 c. blue and black ..	10	10
499.	–	30 c. brn., yell. & blk.	15	15
500.	–	$1 orange, red & black	40	40
501.	–	$2 red and black	70	80

DESIGNS: 1 c. Boxing. 2 c. Pole vault. 15 c. Swimming. 30 c. Running. $1, Cycling. $2 Shot put.

126. Water Skiing.

1976. Water Sports. Multicoloured.

503.	½ c. Type **126**	10	10
504.	1 c. Sailing	10	10
505.	2 c. Snorkeling	10	10
506.	20 c. Deep sea fishing ..	15	10
507.	50 c. Scuba diving ..	35	35
508.	$2 Swimming	1·00	1·25

127. French Angelfish.

1976. Fish. Multicoloured.

510.	15 c. Type **127**	25	15
511.	30 c. Yellowfin Grouper ..	40	30
512.	50 c. Yellowtail Snappers	55	50
513.	90 c. Shy Hamlet ..	80	80

128. The Annunciation.

1976. Christmas. Multicoloured.

514.	8 c. Type **128** ..	10	10
515.	10 c. The Holy Family ..	10	10
516.	15 c. The Magi ..	10	10
517.	50 c. The Shepherds ..	20	25
518.	$1 Epiphany scene ..	30	50

129. Mercury and U.P.U. Emblem.

1976. Special Events, 1976. Multicoloured.

519.	½ c. Type **129**	10	10
520.	1 c. Alfred Nobel	10	10
521.	10 c. Space satellite ..	20	10
522.	50 c. Viv Richards and Andy Roberts	1·75	1·00
523.	$1 Bell and telephones ..	1·75	1·60
524.	$2 Yacht " Freelance " ..	2·50	2·75

130. Royal Family.

1977. Silver Jubilee. Multicoloured. (a) Perf.

526.	10 c. Type **130**	10	10
527.	30 c. Royal Visit, 1966 ..	10	10
528.	50 c. The Queen enthroned	15	15
529.	90 c. The Queen after Coronation	25	20
530.	$2.50 Queen and Prince Charles	45	35

(b) Roul. × imperf. Self-adhesive.

532.	50 c. As 90 c. ..	35	60
533.	$5 The Queen and Prince Philip	2·50	3·50

Nos. 532/3 come from booklets.

131. Making Camp.

1977. Caribbean Scout Jamboree, Jamaica. Multicoloured.

534.	½ c. Type **131**	10	10
535.	1 c. Hiking	10	10
536.	2 c. Rock-climbing ..	10	10
537.	10 c. Cutting logs ..	10	10
538.	30 c. Map and sign reading	20	10
539.	50 c. First aid	35	20
540.	$2 Rafting	1·50	1·50

132. Carnival Costume.

1977. 21st Anniversary of Carnival. Mult.

542.	10 c. Type **132**	10	10
543.	30 c. Carnival Queen	20	10
544.	50 c. Butterfly costume ..	25	15
545.	90 c. Queen of the band ..	35	25
546.	$1 Calypso King and Queen	35	30

1977. Royal Visit. Nos. 526/30 optd. **ROYAL VISIT 28th OCTOBER 1977.**

548.	10 c. Type **130**	10	10
549.	30 c. Royal Visit, 1966 ..	10	10
550.	50 c. The Queen enthroned	15	10
551.	90 c. The Queen after Coronation	25	20
552.	$2·50 Queen and Prince Charles	45	35

134. " Virgin and Child Enthroned " (Tura).

1977. Christmas. Paintings by artists listed. Multicoloured.

554.	½ c. Type **134**	10	10
555.	1 c. Crivelli	10	10
556.	2 c. Lotto	10	10
557.	8 c. Pontormo	10	10
558.	10 c. Tura (different) ..	10	10
559.	25 c. Lotto (different) ..	20	10
560.	$2 Crivelli (different) ..	75	60

135. Pineapple.

1977. 10th Anniv. of Statehood. Mult.

562.	10 c. Type **135**	10	10
563.	15 c. State flag	10	10
564.	50 c. Police band	50	20
565.	90 c. Premier V.C. Bird ..	35	30
566.	$2 State Coat of Arms ..	60	60

136. " Glider III ", 1902.

1978. 75th Anniv. of Powered Flight. Mult.

568.	½ c. Type **136**	10	10
569.	1 c. " Flyer I ", 1903 ..	10	10
570.	2 c. Launch system and engine	10	10
571.	10 c. Orville Wright (vert.)	10	10
572.	50 c. " Flyer III ", 1905 ..	35	15
573.	90 c. Wilbur Wright (vert.)	50	30
574.	$2 Wright " Model B ", 1910	80	80

137. Sunfish Regatta.

1978. Sailing Week. Multicoloured.

576.	10 c. Type **137**	15	10
577.	50 c. Fishing and work boat race	35	20
578.	90 c. Curtain Bluff race ..	60	35
579.	$2 Power boat rally ..	1·25	1·25

138. Queen Elizabeth and Prince Philip.

1978. 25th Anniv. of Coronation. Mult. (a) Perf.

581.	10 c. Type **138**	10	10
582.	30 c. Crowning	10	10
583.	50 c. Coronation procession	15	10
584.	90 c. Queen seated in St. Edward's Chair ..	20	15
585.	$2·50 Queen wearing Imperial State Crown ..	40	40

(b) Roul. × imperf. Self-adhesive. Horiz designs as Type **138**

587.	25 c. Glass Coach ..	15	30
588.	50 c. Irish State Coach ..	25	50
589.	$5 Coronation Coach ..	2·50	3·00

Nos. 587/9 come from booklets.

140. Player running with Ball.

1978. World Cup Football Championships, Argentina. Multicoloured.

590.	10 c. Type **140**	10	10
591.	15 c. Players in front of goal	10	10
592.	$3 Referee and player ..	2·00	1·75

141. Petrea.

1978. Flowers. Multicoloured.

594.	25 c. Type **141**	25	10
595.	50 c. Sunflower	35	20
596.	90 c. Frangipani	60	30
597.	$2 Passion Flower ..	1·25	1·10

142. " St. Ildefonso receiving the Chasuble from the Virgin ".

1978. Christmas. Paintings by Rubens. Multicoloured.

599.	8 c. Type **142**	10	10
600.	25 c. " The Flight of St. Barbara "	20	10
601.	$2 " Madonna and child, with St. Joseph, John the Baptist and Donor.	95	55

The painting shown on No. 601 is incorrectly attributed to Rubens on the stamp. The artist was Sebastiano del Piombo.

143. 1d. Stamp of 1863.

1979. Death Centenary of Sir Rowland Hill. Multicoloured.

603.	25 c. Type **143**	10	10
604.	50 c. 1840 Penny Black ..	25	15
605.	$1 Mail coach and woman posting letter, c. 1840 ..	45	30
606.	$2 Modern transport ..	1·00	75

144. "The Deposition from the Cross" (painting).

1979. Easter. Works by Durer.

608. **144.** 10 c. multicoloured .. 10 10
609. – 50 c. multicoloured .. 35 20
610. – $4 black, mauve & yell. 1·50 90

DESIGNS: 50 c., "Christ on the Cross – The Passion" (wood engraving). $4, "Man of Sorrows with Hands Raised" (wood engraving).

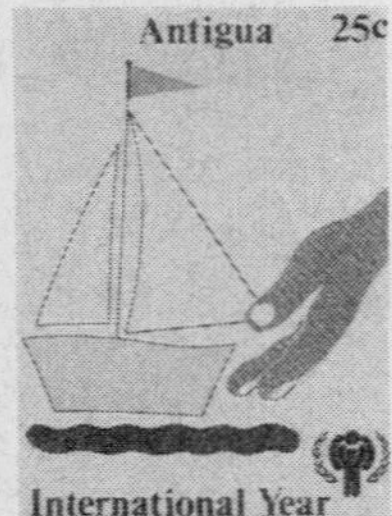

145. Toy Yacht and Child's Hand.

1979. International Year of the Child. Multicoloured.

612. 25 c. Type **145** 10 10
613. 50 c. Rocket 25 15
614. 90 c. Car 40 25
615. $2 Toy train .. .. 1·00 90

Nos. 612/15 also show the hands of children of different races.

146. Yellowjack.

1979. Fish. Multicoloured.

617. 30 c. Type **146** 30 15
618. 50 c. Bluefin Tuna .. 40 25
619. 90 c. Sailfish 60 40
620. $3 Wahoo.. .. .. 2·00 1·75

147. Cook's Birthplace, Marton.

1979. Death Bicentenary of Captain Cook. Multicoloured.

622. 25 c. Type **147** 45 30
623. 50 c. H.M.S. "Endeavour 65 65
624. 90 c. Marine chronometer 80 80
625. $3 Landing at Botany Bay 2·00 3·00

148. The Holy Family.

1979. Christmas. Multicoloured.

627. 8 c. Type **148** 10 10
628. 25 c. Virgin and Child on ass 15 10
629. 50 c. Shepherd and star .. 30 30
630. $4 Wise Men with gifts .. 1·40 1·75

149. Javelin Throwing.

1980. Olympic Games, Moscow. Mult.

632. 10 c. Type **149** 10 10
633. 25 c. Running 15 10
634. $1 Pole vault 40 40
635. $2 Hurdles 65 75

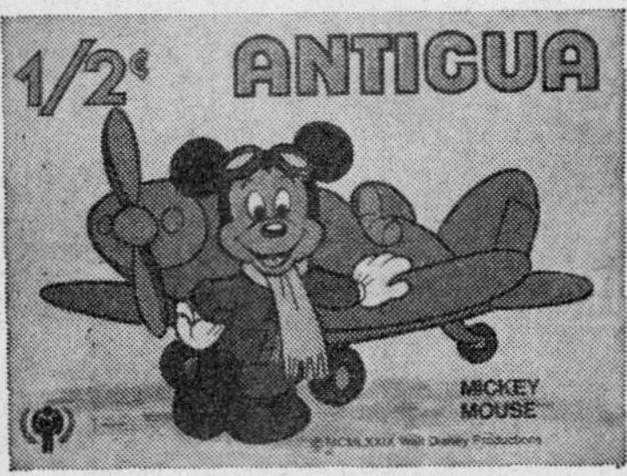

150. Mickey Mouse and Aeroplane.

1980. International Year of the Child. Walt Disney Cartoon Characters. Multicoloured.

637. ½ c. Type **150** 10 10
638. 1 c. Donald Duck driving car (vert.) 10 10
639. 2 c. Goofy driving taxi .. 10 10
640. 3 c. Mickey and Minnie Mouse on motorcycle .. 10 10
641. 4 c. Huey, Dewey and Louie on a bicycle for three 10 10
642. 5 c. Grandma Duck and truck of roosters .. 10 10
643. 10 c. Mickey Mouse in jeep (vert.) 10 10
644. $1 Chip and Dale in Yacht 1·50 1·00
645. $4 Donald Duck riding toy train (vert.) .. .. 3·25 3·00

1980. "London 1980" International Stamp Exhibition. Nos. 603/6 optd. **LONDON 1980.**

647. 25 c. 1d. stamp of 1863 .. 20 15
648. 50 c. Penny Black .. 30 20
649. $1 Stage-coach and woman posting letter, c. 1840 .. 55 40
650. $2 Modern mail transporting .. .. .. 1·50 1·25

152. "David" (statue, Donatello).

1980. Famous Works of Art. Multicoloured.

651. 10 c. Type **152** 10 10
652. 30 c. "The Birth of Venus" (painting, Botticelli) (horiz.) 25 15
653. 50 c. "Reclining Couple" (sarcophagus), Cerveteri (horiz.) 35 35
654. 90 c. "The Garden of Earthly Delights" (painting by Bosch) (horiz.) .. 55 55
655. $1 "Portinari Altarpiece" (painting, van der Goes) (horiz.) 65 65
656. $4 "Eleanora of Toledo and her son, Giovanni de'Medici (painting, Bronzino) .. .. 2·00 2·50

153. Anniversary Emblem and Headquarters, U.S.A.

1980. 75th Anniv. of Rotary International. Multicoloured.

658. 30 c. Type **153** 30 20
659. 50 c. Rotary anniversary emblem and Antigua Rotary Club banner .. 35 30
660. 90 c. Map of Antigua and Rotary emblem .. 50 50
661. $3 Paul P. Harris (founder) and Rotary emblem .. 1·75 2·00

154. Queen Elizabeth the Queen Mother.

1980. 80th Birthday of The Queen Mother.

663. **154.** 10 c. multicoloured .. 20 10
664. $2·50 multicoloured 2·25 2·50

155. Ringed Kingfisher.

1980. Birds. Multicoloured.

666. 10 c. Type **155** 35 15
667. 30 c. Plain Pigeon 55 30
668. $1 Green-throated Carib.. 1·50 1·10
669. $2 Black-necked Stilt .. 1·75 2·00

1980. Christmas. Walt Disney's "Sleeping Beauty". As Type **150.** Mult.

671. ½ c. The Bad Fairy with her raven 10 10
672. 1 c. The good fairies .. 10 10
673. 2 c. Aurora 10 10
674. 4 c. Aurora pricks her finger 10 10
675. 8 c. The prince 10 10
676. 10 c. The prince fights the dragon 10 10
677. 25 c. The prince awakens Aurora with a kiss .. 15 15
678. $2 The prince and Aurora's betrothal .. .. 1·60 1·75
679. $2·50 The prince and princess .. .. 2·25 2·00

156. Diesel Locomotive No. 15.

1981. Sugar Cane Railway Locomotives. Multicoloured.

681. 25 c. Type **156** 15 15
682. 50 c. Narrow-gauge steam locomotive 30 30
683. 90 c. Diesel locomotives Nos. 1 and 10 .. .. 55 55
684. $3 Steam locomotive hauling sugar cane .. .. 2·00 2·00

1981. Independence. Nos 475/6 and 478/86 optd. "**INDEPENDENCE 1981**".

686. 6 c. Orchid Tree 10 10
687. 10 c. Bougainvillea .. 10 10
688. 20 c. Flamboyant 10 10
689. 25 c. Hibiscus 15 15
690. 35 c. Flame of the Wood.. 20 20
691. 50 c. Cannon at Fort James 35 35
692. 75 c. Premier's Office .. 40 40
693. $1 Potworks Dam .. 55 55
694. $2·50 Irrigation scheme, Diamond Estate .. 1·25 1·25
695. $5 Government House .. 2·50 2·50
696. $10 Coolidge International Airport .. .. .. 4·50 5·00

158. "Pipes of Pan".

1981. Birth Centenary of Picasso. Mult.

697. 10 c. Type **158** 10 10
698. 50 c. "Seated Harlequin" 30 30
699. 90 c. "Paulo as Harlequin" 55 55
700. $4 "Mother and Child" 2·50 2·50

159. Prince Charles and Lady Diana Spencer.

1981. Royal Wedding (1st issue). Mult.

702. 25 c. Type **159** 15 10
703. 50 c. Glamis Castle .. 25 20
704. $4 Prince Charles skiing .. 1·25 1·40

160. Prince of Wales at Investiture, 1969.

1981. Royal Wedding (2nd issue). Mult. Roul. × imperf. self-adhesive.

706. 25 c. Type **160** 20 20
707. 25 c. Prince Charles as baby, 1948 .. .. 20 20
708. $1 Prince Charles at R.A.F. College, Cranwell, 1971 40 40
709. $1 Prince Charles attending Hill House School, 1956 .. .. 40 40
710. $2 Prince Charles and Lady Diana Spencer .. 75 75
711. $2 Prince Charles at Trinity College, 1967 .. 75 75
712. $5 Prince Charles and Lady Diana (different) .. 1·50 1·50

161. Irene Joshua (founder).

1981. 50th Anniv. of Antigua Girl Guide Movement. Multicoloured.

713. 10 c. Type **161** 10 10
714. 50 c. Campfire sing-song 35 35
715. 90 c. Sailing 65 65
716. $2.50 Animal tending .. 1·75 1·75

162. Antigua and Barbuda Coat of Arms.

1981. Independence. Multicoloured.

718.	10 c. Type **162**	10	10
719.	50 c. Pineapple, with Antigua and Barbuda flag and map	25	15
720.	90 c. Prime Minister Vere Bird	50	30
721.	$2.50 St. John's Cathedral (38 × 25 mm.)	1·00	1·40

163. " Holy Night " (Jacques Stella).

1981. Christmas. Paintings. Multicoloured.

723.	8 c. Type **163**	15	10
724.	30 c. " Mary with Child " (Julius Schnorr von Carolfeld)	30	15
725.	$1 " Virgin and Child " (Alonso Cano)	80	70
726.	$3 " Virgin and Child " (Lorenzo di Credi)	2·25	3·00

164. Swimming.

1981. International Year of Disabled People. Sports for the Disabled. Mult.

728.	10 c. Type **164**	10	10
729.	50 c. Discus-throwing	30	30
730.	90 c. Archery	55	55
731.	$2 Baseball	1·40	1·40

165. Scene from Football Match.

1982. World Cup Football Championship, Spain.

733.	**165.**	10 c. multicoloured	15	10
734.	–	50 c. multicoloured	40	35
735.	–	90 c. multicoloured	65	60
736.	–	$4 multicoloured	3·00	3·00

DESIGNS: 50 c. to $4, Scenes from various matches.

166. European " A-300 (Airbus) ".

1982. Coolidge International Airport. Multicoloured.

738.	10 c. Type **166**	10	10
739.	50 c. Hawker-Siddeley " 748 "	30	30
740.	90 c. De Havilland " DCH6 " (Twin Otter) "	60	60
741.	$2.50 Britten-Norman " Islander "	1·50	1·50

167. Cordia.

1982. Death Centenary of Charles Darwin. Fauna and Flora. Multicoloured.

743.	10 c. Type **167**	15	10
744.	50 c. Small Indian mongoose (horiz.)	45	40
745.	90 c. Corallita	75	75
746.	$2 Mexican bulldog bat (horiz.)	2·00	2·75

168. Queen's House, Greenwich.

1982. 21st Birthday of Princess of Wales. Multicoloured.

748.	90 c. Type **168**	45	45
749.	$1 Prince and Princess of Wales	50	50
750.	$4 Princess Diana	2·00	2·00

170. Boy Scouts decorating Streets for Independence Parade.

1982. 75th Anniv. of Boy Scout Movement. Multicoloured.

752.	10 c. Type **170**	15	10
753.	50 c. Boy Scout giving helping hand during street parade	40	40
754.	90 c. Boy Scouts attending H.R.H. Princess Margaret at Independence Ceremony	75	75
755.	$2.50 Cub Scout giving directions to tourists	1·75	2·25

1982. Birth of Prince William of Wales. Nos. 748/50 optd. **ROYAL BABY 21.6.82.**

757.	90 c. Type **168**	45	45
758.	$1 Prince and Princess of Wales	50	50
759.	$4 Princess Diana	2·00	2·00

172. Roosevelt in 1940.

1982. Birth Centenary of Franklin D. Roosevelt. (Nos. 761, 763 and 765/6) and George Washington. 250th Birth Anniv. (others). Multicoloured.

761.	10 c. Type **172**	15	10
762.	25 c. Washington as blacksmith	30	15
763.	45 c. Churchill, Roosevelt and Stalin at Yalta Conference	70	25
764.	60 c. Washington crossing the Delaware (vert.)	70	25
765.	$1 "Roosevelt Special" train (vert.)	1·25	55
766.	$3 Portrait of Roosevelt (vert.)	1·90	1·75

173. " Annunciation ".

1982. Christmas. Religious Paintings by Raphael. Multicoloured.

769.	10 c. Type **173**	10	10
770.	30 c. " Adoration of the Magi "	15	15
771.	$1 " Presentation at the Temple "	50	50
772.	$4 "Coronation of the Virgin"	2·10	2·25

174. Tritons and Dolphins.

1983. 500th Birth Anniv. of Raphael. Details from "Galatea" Fresco. Multicoloured.

774.	45 c. Type **174**	20	25
775.	50 c. Sea Nymph carried off by Triton	25	30
776.	60 c. Winged angel steering Dolphins (horiz.)	30	35
777.	$4 Cupids shooting arrows (horiz.)	1·90	2·00

175. Pineapple Produce.

1983. Commonwealth Day. Multicoloured.

779.	25 c. Type **175**	15	15
780.	45 c. Carnival	20	25
781.	60 c. Tourism	30	35
782.	$3 Airport	1·25	1·50

176. T.V. Satellite Coverage of Royal Wedding.

1983. World Communications Year. Mult.

783.	15 c. Type **176**	40	15
784.	50 c. Police communications	1·75	1·00
785.	60 c. House-to-train telephone call	1·75	1·00
786.	$3 Satellite earth station with planets Jupiter and Saturn	3·75	4·25

177. Bottlenose Dolphin.

1983. Whales. Multicoloured.

788.	15 c. Type **177**	65	20
789.	50 c. Fin whale	1·25	70
790.	60 c. Bowhead whale	1·50	80
791.	$3 Spectacled porpoise	3·25	3·75

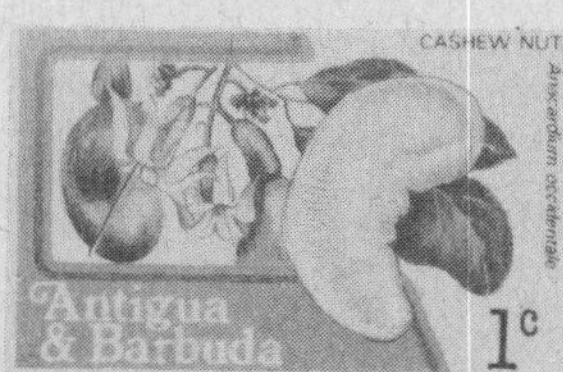

178. Cashew Nut.

1983. Fruits and Flowers. Multicoloured.

793.	1 c. Type **178**	10	10
794.	2 c. Passion Fruit	10	10
795.	3 c. Mango	10	10
796.	5 c. Grapefruit	10	10
797.	10 c. Pawpaw	15	10
798.	15 c. Breadfruit	20	10
799.	20 c. Coconut	25	10
800.	25 c. Oleander	30	10
801.	30 c. Banana	40	10
802.	40 c. Pineapple	40	20
803.	45 c. Cordia	50	30
804.	50 c. Cassia	60	30
805.	60 c. Poui	70	40
806.	$1 Frangipani	1·00	55
807.	$2 Flamboyant	1·75	1·25
808.	$2·50, Lemon	2·00	1·50
809.	$5 Lignum Vitae	4·00	4·00
810.	$10 National flag and coat of arms	6·50	8·50

179. Dornier " Do X " Flying Boat.

1983. Bicentenary of Manned Flight. Mult.

811.	30 c. Type **179**	65	25
812.	50 c. Supermarine " S.6B ", seaplane	75	50
813.	60 c. Curtiss " 9C " biplane and airship U.S.S. "Akron"	90	70
814.	$4 " Pro Juventute " balloon	3·25	4·00

180. " Sibyls and Angels " (detail) (Raphael).

1983. Christmas. 500th Birth Anniv. of Raphael.

816.	**180.**	10 c. multicoloured	25	20
817.	–	30 c. multicoloured	55	35
818.	–	$1 multicoloured	1·25	1·00
819.	–	$4 multicoloured	3·50	4·25

DESIGNS—HORIZ. 10 c. to $4, Different details from " Sibyls and Angels ".

181. John Wesley (founder). **182.** Discus.

1983. Bicentenary of Methodist Church (1984). Multicoloured.

821.	15 c. Type **181**	20	15
822.	50 c. Nathaniel Gilbert (founder in Antigua)	60	40
823.	60 c. St. John Methodist Church steeple	65	55
824.	$3 Ebenezer Methodist Church, St. John's	2·50	3·50

1984. Olympic Games, Los Angeles. Mult.

825.	25 c. Type **182**	15	15
826.	50 c. Gymnastics	30	30
827.	90 c. Hurdling	55	55
828.	$3 Cycling	2·00	2·25

183. "Booker Vanguard" (freighter).

1984. Ships. Multicoloured.

830.	45 c. Type **183**	1·00	55
831.	50 c. S.S. "Canberra" (liner)	1·25	70
832.	60 c. Sailing boats	1·50	85
833.	$4 "Fairwind" (liner)	4·50	5·50

184. Chenille.

1984. Universal Postal Union Congress, Hamburg. Multicoloured.

835. 15 c. Type **184** 30 15
836. 50 c. Shell Flower 80 55
837. 60 c. Anthurium 90 70
838. $3 Angels Trumpet .. 3·75 4·25

1984. Various stamps surch.

(a) Nos. 702/4

840 $2 on 25 c. Type **159** .. 5·00 5·00
841 $2 on 50 c. Glamis Castle 5·00 5·00
842 $2 on $4 Prince Charles skiing .. .. .. 5·00 5·00

(b) Nos. 748/50

844 $2 on 90 c. Type **168** .. 4·00 3·00
845 $2 on $1 Prince and Princess of Wales .. 4·00 3·00
846 $2 on $4 Princess Diana .. 4·00 3·00

(c) Nos. 757/9

848 $2 on 90 c. Type **168** .. 4·00 3·00
849 $2 on $1 Prince and Princess of Wales .. 4·00 3·00
850 $2 on $4 Princess Diana .. 4·00 3·00

(d) Nos. 779/82

852 $2 on 25 c. Type **175** .. 1·25 1·25
853 $2 on 45 c. Carnival .. 1·25 1·25
854 $2 on 60 c. Tourism .. 1·25 1·25
855 $2 on $3 Airport .. 1·25 1·25

187. Abraham Lincoln.

1984. Presidents of the United States of America. Multicoloured.

856. 10 c. Type **187** 10 10
857. 20 c. Harry S. Truman .. 15 15
858. 30 c. Dwight D. Eisenhower 25 25
859. 40 c. Ronald W. Reagan .. 30 30
860. 90 c. Gettysburg Address, 1863 .. .. .. 70 65
861. $1.10 Formation of N.A.T.O. 1949 .. .. 80 75
862. $1.50 Eisenhower during the war .. .. .. 1·10 1·10
863. $2 Reagan and Caribbean Basin Initiative .. .. 1·40 1·40

188. View of Moravian Mission.

1984. 150th Anniv. of Abolition of Slavery. Multicoloured.

864. 40 c. Type **188** 80 50
865. 50 c. Antigua Courthouse, 1823 .. .. .. 90 65
866. 60 c. Planting sugar-cane, Monks Hill 95 75
867. $3 Boiling house, Delaps' estate .. .. .. 3·50 4·25

189. Rufous-sided Towhee.

1984. Songbirds. Multicoloured.

869. 40 c. Type **189** .. .. 1·00 55
870. 50 c. Parula warbler .. 1·10 70
871. 60 c. House wren .. .. 1·25 80
872. $2 Ruby-crowned kinglet 2·50 2·75
873. $3 Common flicker .. 3·50 4·00

190. Grass-skiing.

1984. "Ausipex" International Stamp Exhibition, Melbourne, Australian Sports. Multicoloured.

875. $1 Type **190** .. .. 1·50 1·25
876. $5 Australian Football .. 4·50 4·75

191. "The Virgin and Infant with Angels and Cherubs".

1984. 450th Death Anniv. of Correggio (painter). Multicoloured.

878 25 c. Type **191** 30 20
879 60 c. "The Four Saints" .. 70 50
880 90 c. "St. Catherine" .. 75 75
881 $3 "The Campori Madonna" .. .. .. 3·00 3·00

192. "The Blue Dancers".

1984. 150th Birth Anniv. of Edgar Degas (painter). Multicoloured.

883. 15 c. Type **192** 30 15
884. 50 c. "The Pink Dancers" 70 50
885. 70 c. "Two Dancers" .. 95 75
886. $4 "Dancers at the Bar" .. 3·75 4·25

193. Sir Winston Churchill.

1984. Famous People. Multicoloured.

888. 60 c. Type **193** .. .. 1·75 1·50
889. 60 c. Mahatma Gandhi .. 1·75 1·50
890. 60 c. John F. Kennedy .. 1·75 1·50
891. 60 c. Mao Tse-tung .. 1·75 1·50
892. $1 Churchill with General De Gaulle, Paris, 1944 (horiz.) .. .. .. 2·25 2·00
893. $1 Gandhi leaving London by train, 1931 (horiz.) .. 2·25 2·00
894. $1 Kennedy with Chancellor Adenauer and Mayor Brandt, Berlin, 1963 (horiz.) .. .. 2·25 2·00
895. $1 Mao Tse-tung with Lin Piao, Peking, 1969 (horiz.) .. .. .. 2·25 2·00

194. Donald Duck fishing.

1984. Christmas. Walt Disney Cartoon Characters. Multicoloured.

897. 1 c. Type **194** 10 10
898. 2 c. Donald Duck lying on beach 10 10
899. 3 c. Donald Duck and nephews with fishing rods and fishes 10 10
900. 4 c. Donald Duck and nephews in boat .. 10 10
901. 5 c. Wearing diving masks 10 10
902. 10 c. In deckchairs reading books 10 10
903. $1 With toy shark's fin .. 1·75 1·10
904. $2 In sailing boat .. .. 2·50 1·90
905. $5 Attempting to propel boat .. .. .. 4·25 4·00

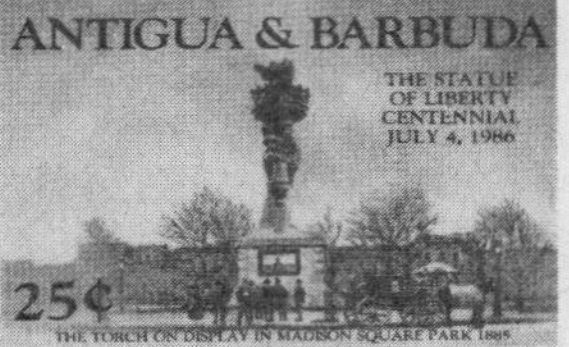

195. Torch from Statue in Madison Square Park, 1885.

1985. Centenary (1986) of Statue of Liberty. Multicoloured.

907. 25 c. Type **195** 20 20
908. 30 c. Statue of Liberty and scaffolding (Restoration and Renewal") (vert.) .. 20 20
909. 50 c. Frederic Bartholdi (sculptor) supervising construction, 1876 .. 30 30
910. 90 c. Close-up of Statue .. 55 55
911. $1 Statue and sailing ship ("Operation Sail", 1976) (vert.) 60 60
912. $3 Dedication ceremony, 1886 .. .. .. 1·75 1·75

196. Arawak Pot Sherd and Indians making Clay Utensils.

1985. Native American Artefacts. Mult.

914. 15 c. Type **196** 15 10
915. 50 c. Arawak body design and Arawak Indians tattooing 30 30
916. 60 c. Head of the god "Yocahu" and Indians harvesting manioc .. 40 40
917. $3 Carib war club and Carib Indians going into battle .. .. .. 1·75 2·25

197. Triumph 2hp "Jap", 1903.

1985. Centenary of the Motorcycle. Mult.

919. 10 c. Type **197** 55 15
920. 30 c. "Indian Arrow", 1949 80 30
921. 60 c. BMW "R100RS" 1976 .. .. .. 1·25 70
922. $4 Harley-Davidson "Model II", 1916 .. 4·25 4·50

198. Slavonian Grebe.

1985. Birth Bicentenary of John J. Audubon (ornithologist) (1st issue). Multicoloured. Designs showing original paintings.

924. 90 c. Type **198** .. .. 1·25 75
925. $1 British storm petrel .. 1·40 85
926. $1.50 Great blue heron .. 1·75 1·50
927. $3 Double-crested cormorant .. .. 3·00 3·25

See also Nos. 990/3.

199. "Anaea cyanea".

1985. Butterflies. Multicoloured.

929 25 c. Type **199** 85 30
930 60 c. "Leodonta dysoni" 1·50 70
931 90 c. "Junea doraete" .. 2·00 85
932 $4 "Prepona pylene" .. 5·50 4·50

200. Cessna "172".

1985. 40th Anniv. of International Civil Aviation Organisation. Multicoloured.

934. 30 c. Type **200** .. 1·00 30
935. 90 c. Fokker "DVII" .. 2·00 90
936. $1.50 Spad "VII" .. .. 2·75 1·50
937. $3 Boeing "747" .. .. 4·25 4·25

201. Maimonides.

1985. 850th Birth Anniv. of Maimonides (physician, philosopher and scholar).

939. **201.** $2 green .. .. 2·25 2·25

202. Young Farmers with Produce.

1985. International Youth Year. Mult.

941. 25 c. Type **202** 15 20
942. 50 c. Hotel management trainees 25 30
943. 60 c. Girls with goat and boys with football ("Environment") .. 35 40
944. $3 Windsurfing ("Leisure") 1·60 1·75

MORE DETAILED LISTS
are given in the Stanley Gibbons Catalogues referred to in the country headings.
For lists of current volumes see Introduction.

203. The Queen Mother attending Church.

1985. Life and Times of Queen Elizabeth the Queen Mother. Multicoloured.

946. $1 Type **203** 55 60
947. $1.50 Watching children playing in London garden 80 85
948. $2.50 The Queen Mother in 1979 .. .. .. 1·25 1·40

Stamps as Nos. 946/8 but with face values of 90 c., $1 and $3 exists from additional sheetlets with changed background colours.

204. Magnificent Frigate Bird.

1985. Marine Life. Multicoloured.

950. 15 c. Type **204** 65 20
951. 45 c. Brain coral .. .. 1·10 60
952. 60 c. Cushion star .. .. 1·50 80
953. $3 Spotted moray eel .. 4·50 5·00

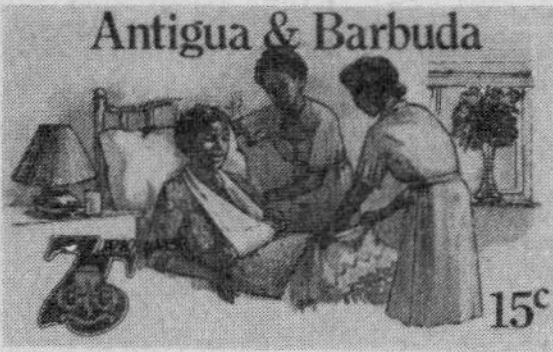

205. Girl Guides Nursing.

1985. 75th Anniv. of Girl Guide Movement. Multicoloured.

955. 15 c. Type **205** 50 15
956. 45 c. Open-air Girl Guide meeting .. .. .. 1·00 45
957. 60 c. Lord and Lady Baden-Powell .. .. 1·25 65
958. $3 Girl Guides gathering flowers .. .. .. 3·25 3·00

206. Bass Trombone.

1985. 300th Birth Anniv. of Johann Sebastian Bach (composer). Multicoloured.

960. 25 c. Type **206** .. .. 1·10 40
961. 50 c. English horn .. .. 1·50 75
962. $1 Violino piccolo .. .. 2·50 1·40
963. $3 Bass rackett .. .. 4·75 5·50

207. Flags of Great Britain and Antigua.

1985. Royal Visit. Multicoloured.

965. 60 c. Type **207** .. .. 1·00 45
966. $1 Queen Elizabeth II (vert.) .. .. .. 1·75 1·00
967. $4 Royal Yacht "Britannia" .. .. 4·25 3·75

1985. 150th Birth Anniv. of Mark Twain (author). As T **118** of Anguilla showing Walt Disney cartoon characters in scenes from "Roughing It". Multicoloured.

969. 25 c. Donald Duck and Mickey Mouse meeting Indians 25 20
970. 50 c. Mickey Mouse, Donald Duck and Goofy canoeing 40 35
971. $1.10 Goofy as Pony Express Rider 80 70
972. $1.50 Donald Duck and Goofy hunting buffalo .. 1·10 95
973. $2 Mickey Mouse and silver mine .. .. 1·60 1·40

1985. Birth Bicentenaries of Grimm Brothers (folklorists). As T **119** of Anguilla showing Walt Disney cartoon characters in scenes from "Spindle, Shuttle and Needle". Multicoloured.

975. 30 c. The Prince (Mickey Mouse) searches for a bride) 60 35
976. 60 c. The Prince finds the Orphan Girl (Minnie Mouse) 85 60
977. 70 c. The Spindle finds the Prince .. .. .. 1·00 70
978. $1 The Needle tidies the Girl's House .. .. 1·50 1·25
979. $3 The Prince proposes .. 3·25 3·75

208. Benjamin Franklin and U.N. (New York) 1953 U.P.U. 5 c. Stamp.

1985. 40th Anniv. of United Nations Organization. Multicoloured.

981. 40 c. Type **208** 75 55
982. $1 George Washington Carver (agricultural chemist) and 1982 Nature Conservation 28 c. stamp .. .. 1·75 1·50
983. $3 Charles Lindbergh (aviator) and 1978 I.C.A.O. 25 c. stamp .. 3·75 4·25

Nos. 975/7 each include a United Nations (New York) stamp design.

209. "Madonna and Child" (De Landi).

1985. Christmas. Religious Paintings. Mult.

985. 10 c. Type **209** 25 15
986. 25 c. "Madonna and Child" (Berlinghiero) 50 25
987. 60 c. "The Nativity" (Fra Angelico) 80 50
988. $4 "Presentation in the Temple" (Giovanni di Paolo) .. .. .. 3·75 4·25

1986. Birth Bicentenary of John J. Audubon (ornithologist) (2nd issue). Designs as T **198** showing original paintings. Multicoloured.

990. 60 c. Mallard .. .. 1·25 75
991. 90 c. North American black duck .. .. 1·50 1·00
992. $1.50 Pintail .. .. 2·00 2·50
993. $3 American wigeon .. .. 3·75 4·25

210. Football, Boots and Trophy.

1986. World Cup Football Championship, Mexico. Multicoloured.

995. 30 c. Type **210** 60 30
996. 60 c. Goalkeeper (vert.) .. 85 60
997. $1 Referee blowing whistle (vert.) .. .. .. 1·50 1·10
998. $4 Ball in net .. .. 4·00 4·50

1986. Appearance of Halley's Comet (1st issue). As T **123** of Anguilla. Multicoloured.

1000. 5 c. Edmond Halley and Old Greenwich Observatory 10 10
1001. 10 c. "Me 163B Komet" (fighter aircraft), 1944 15 10
1002. 60 c. Montezuma (Aztec Emperor) and Comet in 1517 (from "Historias de las Indias de Neuva Espana") 60 45
1003. $4 Pocahontas saving Capt. John Smith and Comet in 1607 .. .. 2·75 3·00

See also Nos. 1047/50.

1986. 60th Birthday of Queen Elizabeth II. As T **125** of Anguilla.

1005. 60 c. black and yellow .. 35 35
1006. $1 multicoloured .. 55 55
1007. $4 multicoloured .. 2·10 2·10

Designs: 60 c. Wedding photograph, 1947; $1 Queen at Trooping the Colour. $4 In Scotland.

211. Tug.

1986. Local Boats. Multicoloured.

1009. 30 c. Type **211** 25 20
1010. 60 c. Game fishing boat .. 45 35
1011. $1 Yacht 75 60
1012. $4 Lugger with auxiliary sail .. .. .. 2·50 3·00

212. "Hiawatha Express".

1986. "Ameripex '86" International Stamp Exhibition, Chicago. Famous American Trains. Multicoloured.

1014. 25 c. Type **212** 70 30
1015. 50 c. "Grand Canyon Express" .. .. 1·00 65
1016. $1 "Powhattan Arrow Express" .. .. 1·60 1·25
1017. $3 "Empire State Express" .. .. 3·75 4·00

213. Prince Andrew and Miss Sarah Ferguson.

1986. Royal Wedding. Multicoloured.

1019. 45 c. Type **213** 45 35
1020. 60 c. Prince Andrew .. 50 45
1021. $4 Prince Andrew with Prince Philip .. .. 2·50 3·00

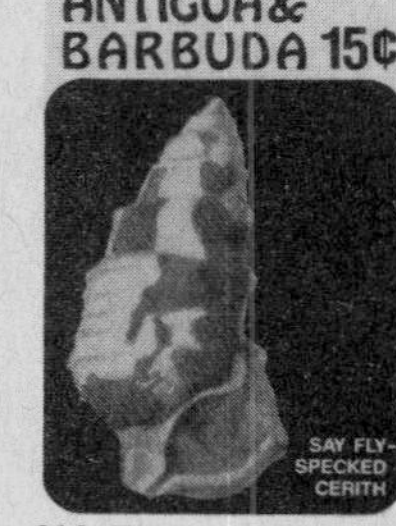

214. Fly-specked Cerith.

1986. Sea Shells. Multicoloured.

1023. 15 c. Type **214** 55 20
1024. 45 c. Smooth Scotch Bonnet .. .. 1·25 70
1025. 60 c. West Indian Crown Conch .. .. .. 1·50 90
1026. $3 Murex Ciboney .. 5·00 5·50

215. Water Lily.

1986. Flowers. Multicoloured.

1028. 10 c. Type **215** 15 15
1029. 15 c. Queen of the Night 20 15
1030. 50 c. Cup of Gold .. 55 40
1031. 60 c. Beach Morning Glory 70 45
1032. 70 c. Golden Trumpet .. 80 55
1033. $1 Air Plant .. .. 1·10 75
1034. $3 Purple Wreath .. 2·50 2·50
1035. $4 Zephyr Lily .. .. 3·00 3·25

1986. World Cup Football Championship Winners, Mexico. Nos. 995/8 optd. **WINNERS Argentina 3 W. Germany 2.**

1037 30 c. Type **210** 30 30
1038 60 c. Goalkeeper (vert) .. 50 50
1039 $1 Referee blowing whistle (vert) 75 75
1040 $4 Ball in net .. .. 2·75 3·25

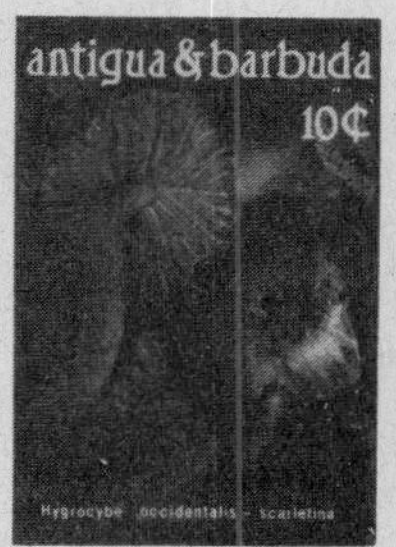

217. "Hygrocybe occidentalis var. scarletina".

1986. Mushrooms. Multicoloured.

1042. 10 c. Type **217** 35 15
1043. 50 c. "Trogia buccinalis" 1·10 55
1044. $1 "Collybia subpruinosa" .. .. 1·75 1·10
1045. $4 "Leucocoprinus brebissonii" .. .. 4·50 4·75

(**218**).

1986. Appearance of Halley's Comet (2nd issue). Nos. 1000/3 optd. with T **218**.

1047. 5 c. Edmond Halley and Old Greenwich Observatory 10 10
1048. 10 c. "Me 163B Komet" (fighter aircraft), 1944 10 10
1049. 60 c. Montezuma (Aztec emperor) and comet in 1517 (from "Historias de las Indias de Neuva Espana") 55 55
1050. $4 Pocahontas saving Capt. John Smith and comet in 1607 .. .. 3·00 3·00

219. Auburn "Speedster" (1933).

1986. Centenary of First Benz Motor Car. Multicoloured.

1052. 10 c. Type **219** 10 10
1053. 15 c. Mercury "Sable" (1986) 15 10
1054. 50 c. Cadillac (1959) .. 45 30
1055. 60 c. Studebaker (1950) .. 55 45
1056. 70 c. Lagonda "V-12" (1939) 70 55
1057. $1 Adler "Standard" (1930) 90 75
1058. $3 DKW (1956) .. .. 2·25 2·50
1059. $4 Mercedes "500K" (1936) .. .. .. 2·75 3·00

220. Young Mickey Mouse playing Santa Claus.

1986. Christmas. Designs showing Walt Disney cartoon characters as babies. Mult.

1061. 25 c. Type **220** 35 35
1062. 30 c. Mickey and Minnie Mouse building snowman 40 40
1063. 40 c. Aunt Matilda and Goofy baking 45 45
1064. 60 c. Goofy and Pluto .. 65 65
1065. 70 c. Pluto, Donald and Daisy Duck carol singing 75 75
1066. $1.50 Donald Duck, Mickey Mouse and Pluto stringing popcorn .. .. .. 1·25 1·25
1067. $3 Grandma Duck and Minnie Mouse .. .. 2·50 2·50
1068. $4 Donald Duck and Pete .. .. .. 2·75 2·75

221. Arms of Antigua. **222.** "Canada I" (1981).

1986.

1070. **221.** 10 c. blue 20 20
1071. – 25 c. red 30 35

DESIGN: 25 c. Flag of Antigua.

1987. America's Cup Yachting Championship. Multicoloured.

1072. 30 c. Type **222** 20 20
1073. 60 c. "Gretel II" (1970) .. 35 35
1074. $1 "Sceptre" (1958) .. 65 65
1075. $3 "Vigilant" (1893) .. 1·75 1·75

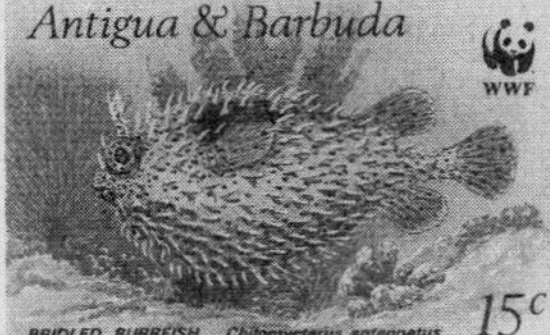

223. Bridled Burrfish.

1987. Marine Life. Multicoloured.

1077. 15 c. Type **223** 35 20
1078. 30 c. Common noddy .. 60 35
1079. 40 c. Nassau grouper .. 65 45
1080. 50 c. Laughing gull .. 1·00 70
1081. 60 c. French angelfish .. 1·00 70
1082. $1 Porkfish .. .. 1·25 1·10
1083. $2 Royal tern .. .. 2·50 2·50
1084. $3 Sooty tern .. .. 3·25 3·25

Nos. 1078, 1080 and 1083/4 are without the World Wildlife Fund logo shown on Type **223**.

224. Handball.

1987. Olympic Games, Seoul (1988) (1st issue). Multicoloured.

1086. 10 c. Type **224** 10 10
1087. 60 c. Fencing 25 30
1088. $1 Gymnastics 45 50
1089. $3 Football .. .. 1·40 1·75

See also Nos. 1222/5.

225. "The Profile".

1987. Birth Centenary of Marc Chagall (artist). Multicoloured.

1091. 10 c. Type **225** 10 10
1092. 30 c. "Portrait of the Artist's Sister" .. 15 15
1093. 40 c. "Bride with Fan" .. 20 25
1094. 60 c. "David in Profile" .. 25 30
1095. 90 c. "Fiancee with Bouquet" 40 45
1096. $1 "Self Portrait with Brushes" 45 50
1097. $3 "The Walk" .. .. 1·40 1·75
1098. $4 "Three Candles" .. 1·75 2·00

226. "Spirit of Australia" (fastest powerboat), 1978.

1987. Milestones of Transportation. Mult.

1100. 10 c. Type **226** 20 15
1101. 15 c. Siemen's electric locomotive, 1879 .. 30 20
1102. 30 c. U.S.S. "Triton" (first submerged circumnavigation), 1960 .. .. .. 35 25
1103. 50 c. Trevithick's steam carriage (first passenger-carrying vehicle), 1801 .. .. 50 40
1104. 60 c. U.S.S. "New Jersey" (battleship), 1942 .. .. .. 60 45
1105. 70 c. Draisine bicycle 1818 .. .. .. 60 50
1106. 90 c. S.S. "United States" (holder of Blue Riband), 1952 .. .. 80 65
1107. $1.50 Cierva "C.4" (first autogiro), 1923 .. 1·00 1·00
1108. $2 Curtiss "NC.4" (first transatlantic flight), 1919 .. .. .. 1·25 1·25
1109. $3 "Queen Elizabeth 2" (liner), 1969 .. .. 2·00 2·00

227. Lee Iacocca at Unveiling of Restored Statue.

1987. Centenary of Statue of Liberty (1986) (2nd issue). Multicoloured.

1110. 15 c. Type **227** 15 15
1111. 30 c. Statue at sunset (side view) 20 20
1112. 45 c. Aerial view of head 30 30
1113. 50 c. Lee Iacocca and torch 35 35
1114. 60 c. Workman inside head of Statue (horiz.) 35 35
1115. 90 c. Restoration work (horiz.) 50 50
1116. $1 Head of Statue .. 55 55
1117. $2 Statue at sunset (front view) .. .. .. 1·00 1·25
1118. $3 Inspecting restoration work (horiz.) .. .. 1·60 1·75
1119. $5 Statue at night .. 2·50 3·00

228. Grace Kelly.

1987. Entertainers. Multicoloured.

1120. 15 c. Type **228** 30 20
1121. 30 c. Marilyn Monroe .. 40 35
1122. 45 c. Orson Welles .. 45 40
1123. 50 c. Judy Garland .. 50 45
1124. 60 c. John Lennon .. 75 65
1125. $1 Rock Hudson .. 85 75
1126. $2 John Wayne .. .. 1·40 1·40
1127. $3 Elvis Presley .. .. 2·25 2·25

229. Scouts around Camp Fire and Red Kangaroo.

1987. 16th World Scout Jamboree, Australia. Multicoloured.

1128. 10 c. Type **229** 25 10
1129. 60 c. Scouts canoeing and blue-winged kookaburra 70 40
1130. $1 Scouts on assault course and ring-tailed rock wallaby .. .. 1·00 80
1131. $3 Field kitchen and koala .. .. .. 2·00 2·25

230. Whistling Frog.

1987. "Capex '87" International Stamp Exhibition, Toronto. Reptiles and Amphibians. Multicoloured.

1133. 30 c. Type **230** 15 15
1134. 60 c. Croaking lizard .. 25 30
1135. $1 Antiguan anole .. 45 50
1136. $3 Red-footed tortoise .. 1·40 1·75

1987. 10th Death Anniv. of Elvis Presley (entertainer). No. 1127 optd. **10th ANNIVERSARY 16th AUGUST 1987.**

1138. $3 Elvis Presley .. .. 2·00 2·25

232. House of Burgesses, Virginia ("Freedom of Speech")

1987. Bicentenary of U.S. Constitution. Multicoloured.

1139. 15 c. Type **232** 10 10
1140. 45 c. State Seal, Connecticut 20 25
1141. 60 c. State Seal, Delaware 25 30
1142. $4 Governor Morris (Pennsylvania delegate) (vert.) .. 1·75 1·90

233. "Madonna and Child" (Bernardo Daddi). **234.** Wedding Photograph, 1947.

1987. Christmas. Religious Paintings. Mult.

1144. 45 c. Type **233** 20 25
1145. 60 c. St. Joseph (detail, "The Nativity" (Sano di Pietro)) 25 30
1146. $1 Virgin Mary (detail, "The Nativity" (Sano di Pietro)) 45 50
1147. $4 "Music-making Angel" (Melozzo da Forli) .. .. .. 1·75 2·25

1988. Royal Ruby Wedding.

1149. **234.** 25 c. brn., blk. & bl. 15 15
1150. – 60 c. multicoloured .. 30 30
1151. – $2 brn., blk. & grn. 90 95
1152. – $3 multicoloured .. 1·40 1·50

DESIGNS: 60 c. Queen Elizabeth II. $2 Princess Elizabeth and Prince Philip with Prince Charles at his Christening, 1948. $3 Queen Elizabeth (from photo by Tim Graham), 1980.

235 Great Blue Heron

1988. Birds of Antigua. Multicoloured.

1154 10 c. Type **235** 20 15
1155 15 c. Ringed kingfisher (horiz) 20 15
1156 50 c. Bananaquit (horiz) 40 30
1157 60 c. Purple gallinule (horiz) 40 30
1158 70 c. Blue-hooded euphonia (horiz) .. 50 35
1159 $1 Brown-throated conure ("Caribbean Parakeet") 70 55
1160 $3 Troupial (horiz) .. 2·00 2·25
1161 $4 Purple-throated carib (horiz) .. .. 2·25 2·75

236 First Aid at Daycare Centre, Antigua

1988. Salvation Army's Community Service. Multicoloured.

No.	Description	Unused	Used
1163	25 c. Type **236**	35	35
1164	30 c. Giving penicillin injection, Indonesia	35	35
1165	40 c. Children at daycare centre, Bolivia	45	45
1166	45 c. Rehabilitation of the handicapped, India	45	45
1167	50 c. Training blind man, Kenya	55	55
1168	60 c. Weighing baby, Ghana	55	55
1169	$1 Training typist, Zambia	90	90
1170	$2 Emergency food kitchen, Sri Lanka	1·60	1·60

237 Columbus's Second Fleet, 1493

1988. 500th Anniv (1992) of Discovery of America by Columbus (1st issue). Mult.

No.	Description	Unused	Used
1172	10 c. Type **237**	15	10
1173	30 c. Painos Indian village and fleet	20	15
1174	45 c."Santa Mariagalante" (flagship) and Painos village	25	25
1175	60 c. Painos Indians offering Columbus fruit and vegetables	30	30
1176	90 c. Painos Indian and Columbus with parrot	45	45
1177	$1 Columbus landing on island	50	50
1178	$3 Spanish soldier and fleet	1·40	1·50
1179	$4 Fleet under sail	1·75	2·00

See also Nos. 1267/70, 1360/7 and 1503/10.

238 "Bust of Christ"

1988. Easter. 500th Birth Anniv of Titian (artist). Multicoloured.

No.	Description	Unused	Used
1181	30 c. Type **238**	15	15
1182	40 c. "Scourging of Christ"	20	25
1183	45 c. "Madonna in Glory with Saints"	20	25
1184	50 c. "The Averoldi Polyptych" (detail)	25	30
1185	$1 "Christ Crowned with Thorns"	45	50
1186	$2 "Christ Mocked"	90	95
1187	$3 "Christ and Simon of Cyrene"	1·40	1·50
1188	$4 "Crucifixion with Virgin and Saints"	1·75	2·00

239 Two Yachts rounding Buoy

1988. Sailing Week. Multicoloured.

No.	Description	Unused	Used
1190	30 c. Type **239**	25	15
1191	60 c. Three yachts	40	30
1192	$1 British yacht under way	60	50
1193	$3 Three yachts (different)	1·50	2·00

240 Mickey Mouse and Diver with Porpoise

1988. Disney EPCOT Centre, Orlando, Florida. Designs showing cartoon characters and exhibits. Multicoloured.

No.	Description	Unused	Used
1195	1 c. Type **240**	10	10
1196	2 c. Goofy and Mickey Mouse with futuristic car (vert)	10	10
1197	3 c. Mickey Mouse and Goofy as Atlas (vert)	10	10
1198	4 c. Mickey Mouse and "Edaphosaurus" (prehistoric reptile)	10	10
1199	5 c. Mickey Mouse at Journey into Imagination exhibit	10	10
1200	10 c. Mickey Mouse collecting vegetables (vert)	10	10
1201	25 c. Type **240**	15	15
1202	30 c. As 2 c.	15	15
1203	40 c. As 3 c.	20	25
1204	60 c. As 4 c.	25	30
1205	70 c. As 5 c.	30	35
1206	$1.50 As 10 c.	70	75
1207	$3 Goofy and Mickey Mouse with robot (vert)	1·40	1·50
1208	$4 Mickey Mouse and Clarabelle at Horizons exhibit	1·75	1·90

1988. Stamp Exhibitions. Nos. 1083/4 optd.

No.	Description	Unused	Used
1210	$2 Royal tern (optd **Praga '88**, Prague)	90	95
1211	$3 Sooty tern (optd **INDEPENDENCE 40**, Israel)	1·40	1·50

242 Jacaranda

1988. Flowering Trees. Multicoloured.

No.	Description	Unused	Used
1213	10 c. Type **242**	20	15
1214	30 c. Cordia	25	20
1215	50 c. Orchid tree	40	40
1216	90 c. Flamboyant	50	50
1217	$1 African tulip tree	55	55
1218	$2 Potato tree	1·10	1·10
1219	$3 Crepe myrtle	1·40	1·60
1220	$4 Pitch apple	1·75	2·25

243 Gymnastics

1988. Olympic Games, Seoul (2nd issue). Mult.

No.	Description	Unused	Used
1222	40 c. Type **243**	20	25
1223	60 c. Weightlifting	25	30
1224	$1 Water polo (horiz)	45	50
1225	$3 Boxing (horiz)	1·40	1·50

244 "Danaus plexippus"

1988. Caribbean Butterflies. Multicoloured.

No.	Description	Unused	Used
1227	1 c. Type **244**	10	10
1228	2 c. "Greta diaphanus"	10	10
1229	3 c. "Calisto archebates"	10	10
1230	5 c. "Hamadryas feronia"	10	10
1231	10 c. "Mestra dorcas"	10	10
1232	15 c. "Hypolimnas misippus"	10	10
1233	20 c. "Dione juno"	10	10
1234	25 c. "Heliconius charithonia"	10	15
1235	30 c. "Eurema pyro"	10	15
1236	40 c. "Papilio androgeus"	15	20
1237	45 c. "Anteos maerula"	20	25
1238	50 c. "Aphrissa orbis"	20	25
1239	60 c. "Astraptes xagua"	25	30
1240	$1 "Heliopetes arsalte"	40	45
1241	$2 "Polites baracoa"	85	90
1242	$2.50 "Phocides pigmalion"	1·00	1·10
1243	$5 "Prepona amphitoe"	2·10	2·25
1244	$10 "Oarisma nanus"	4·25	4·50
1244a	$20 "Parides lycimenes"	8·50	8·75

245 President Kennedy and Family

1988. 25th Death Anniv of John F. Kennedy (American statesman). Multicoloured.

No.	Description	Unused	Used
1245	1 c. Type **245**	10	10
1246	2 c. Kennedy commanding "PT109"	10	10
1247	3 c. Funeral cortege	10	10
1248	4 c. In motorcade, Mexico City	10	10
1249	30 c. As 1 c.	15	15
1250	60 c. As 4 c.	25	30
1251	$1 As 3 c.	45	50
1252	$4 As 2 c.	1·60	1·75

246 Minnie Mouse carol singing

1988. Christmas. "Mickey's Christmas Chorale". Designs showing Walt Disney cartoon characters. Multicoloured

No.	Description	Unused	Used
1254	10 c. Type **246**	10	10
1255	25 c. Pluto	15	15
1256	30 c. Mickey Mouse playing ukelele	15	15
1257	70 c. Donald Duck and nephew	35	35
1258	$1 Mordie and Ferdie carol singing	45	50
1259	$1 Goofy carol singing	45	50
1260	$1 Chip n'Dale sliding off roof	45	50
1261	$1 Two of Donald Duck's nephews at window	45	50
1262	$1 As 10 c.	45	50
1263	$1 As 25 c.	45	50
1264	$1 As 30 c.	45	50
1265	$1 As 70 c.	45	50

Nos. 1258/65 were printed together, se-tenant, forming a composite design.

247 Arawak Warriors

1989. 500th Anniv of Discovery of America by Columbus (1992) (2nd issue). Pre-Columbian Arawak Society. Multicoloured.

No.	Description	Unused	Used
1267	$1.50 Type **247**	65	70
1268	$1.50 Whip dancers	65	70
1269	$1.50 Whip dancers and chief with pineapple	65	70
1270	$1.50 Family and camp fire	65	70

Nos. 1267/70 were printed together, se-tenant, forming a composite design.

248 De Havilland "Comet 4" Airliner

1989. 50th Anniv of First Jet Flight. Mult.

No.	Description	Unused	Used
1272	10 c. Type **248**	10	10
1273	30 c. Messerschmitt "Me 262" fighter	10	15
1274	40 c. Boeing "707" airliner	15	20
1275	60 c. Canadair "F-86 Sabre" fighter	25	30
1276	$1 Lockheed "F-104 Starfighter" fighters	40	45
1277	$2 McDonnell Douglas "DC-10" airliner	85	90
1278	$3 Boeing "747" airliner	1·25	1·40
1279	$4 McDonnell "F-4 Phantom" fighter	1·75	1·90

249 "Festivale"

1989. Caribbean Cruise Ships. Multicoloured.

No.	Description	Unused	Used
1281	25 c. Type **249**	10	15
1282	45 c. "Southward"	20	25
1283	50 c. "Sagafjord"	20	25
1284	60 c. "Daphne"	25	30
1285	75 c. "Cunard Countess"	30	35
1286	90 c. "Song of America"	40	45
1287	$3 "Island Princess"	1·25	1·40
1288	$4 "Galileo"	1·75	1·90

250 "Fish swimming by Duck half-submerged in Stream"

1989. Japanese Art. Paintings by Hiroshige. Multicoloured.

No.	Description	Unused	Used
1290	25 c. Type **250**	10	15
1291	45 c. "Crane and Wave"	20	25
1292	50 c. "Sparrows and Morning Glories"	20	25
1293	60 c. "Crested Blackbird and Flowering Cherry"	25	30
1294	$1 "Great Knot sitting among Water Grass"	40	45
1295	$2 "Goose on a Bank of Water"	85	90
1296	$3 "Black Paradise Flycatcher and Blossoms"	1·25	1·40
1297	$4 "Sleepy Owl perched on a Pine Branch"	1·75	1·90

251 Mickey and Minnie Mouse in Helicopter over River Seine

1989. "Philexfrance 89" International Stamp Exhibition, Paris. Walt Disney cartoon characters in Paris. Multicoloured.

1299 1 c. Type **251** 10 10
1300 2 c. Goofy and Mickey Mouse passing Arc de Triomphe 10 10
1301 3 c. Mickey Mouse painting picture of Notre Dame 10 10
1302 4 c. Mickey and Minnie Mouse with Pluto leaving Metro station 10 10
1303 5 c. Minnie Mouse as model in fashion show 10 10
1304 10 c. Daisy Duck, Minnie Mouse and Clarabelle as Folies Bergere dancers 10 10
1305 $5 Mickey and Minnie Mouse shopping in street market .. .. 2·10 2·25
1306 $6 Mickey and Minnie Mouse, Jose Carioca and Donald Duck at pavement cafe .. 2·50 2·75

252 Goalkeeper

1989. World Cup Football Championship, Italy (1990). Multicoloured.

1308 15 c. Type **252** 10 10
1309 25 c. Goalkeeper moving towards ball 10 15
1310 $1 Goalkeeper reaching for ball 40 45
1311 $4 Goalkeeper saving goal 1·75 1·90

253 "Mycena pura"

1989. Fungi. Multicoloured.

1313 10 c. Type **253** 10 10
1314 25 c. "Psathyrella tuberculata" 10 15
1315 50 c. "Psilocybe cubensis" 20 25
1316 60 c. "Leptonia caeruleocapitata" .. 25 30
1317 75 c. "Xeromphalina tenuipes" 30 35
1318 $1 "Chlorophyllum molybolites" 40 45
1319 $3 "Marasmius haematocephalus" .. 1·25 1·40
1320 $4 "Cantharellus cinnabarinos" .. 1·75 1·90

254 Desmarest's Hutia

1989. Local Fauna. Multicoloured.

1322 25 c. Type **254** 10 15
1323 45 c. Caribbean monk seal 20 25
1324 80 c. Mustache bat (vert) 25 30
1325 $4 American manatee (vert) .. .. .. 1·75 1·90

255 Goofy and Old Printing Press

1989. "American Philately". Walt Disney cartoon characters with stamps and the logo of the American Philatelic Society. Mult.

1327 1 c. Type **255** 10 10
1328 2 c. Donald Duck cancelling first day cover for Mickey Mouse .. 10 10
1329 3 c. Donald Duck's nephews reading recruiting poster for Pony Express riders .. 10 10
1330 4 c. Morty and Ferdie as early radio broadcasters 10 10
1331 5 c. Donald Duck and water buffalo watching television 10 10
1332 10 c. Donald Duck with stamp album 10 10
1333 $4 Daisy Duck with computer system .. 1·75 1·90
1334 $6 Donald's nephews with stereo radio, trumpet and guitar .. .. 2·50 2·75

256 Mickey Mouse and Donald Duck with Locomotive "John Bull", 1831

1989. "World Stamp Expo '89" International Stamp Exhibition, Washington. Walt Disney cartoon characters and locomotives. Mult.

1336 25 c. Type **256** 10 15
1337 45 c. Mickey Mouse and friends with "Atlantic", 1832 .. .. .. 20 25
1338 50 c. Mickey Mouse and Goofy with "William Crooks", 1861 .. .. 20 25
1339 60 c. Mickey Mouse and Goofy with "Minnetonka", 1869 .. .. 25 30
1340 $1 Chip n'Dale with "Thatcher Perkins", 1863 .. .. .. 40 45
1341 $2 Mickey and Minnie Mouse with "Pioneer", 1848 .. .. .. 85 90
1342 $3 Mickey Mouse and Donald Duck with cog railway locomotive "Peppersass", 1869 .. 1·25 1·40
1343 $4 Mickey Mouse with Huey, Dewey and Louie aboard N.Y. World's Fair "Gimbels Flyer", 1939 .. .. 1·75 1·90

258 Launch of "Apollo 11"

1989. 20th Anniv of First Manned Landing on Moon. Multicoloured.

1346 10 c. Type **258** 10 10
1347 45 c. Aldrin on Moon .. 20 25
1348 $1 Module "Eagle" over Moon (horiz) 40 45
1349 $4 Recovery of "Apollo 11" crew after splashdown (horiz) .. .. 1·75 1·90

259 "The Small Cowper Madonna" (Raphael)

260 Star-eyed Hermit Crab

1989. Christmas. Paintings by Raphael and Giotto. Multicoloured.

1351 10 c. Type **259** 10 10
1352 25 c. "Madonna of the Goldfinch" (Raphael) 10 15
1353 30 c. "The Alba Madonna" (Raphael) .. 10 15
1354 50 c. Saint (detail, "Bologna Altarpiece") (Giotto) 20 25
1355 60 c. Angel (detail, "Bologna Altarpiece") (Giotto) 25 30
1356 70 c. Angel slaying serpent (detail, "Bologna Altarpiece") (Giotto) 30 35
1357 $4 Evangelist (detail, "Bologna Altarpiece") (Giotto) .. .. 1·75 1·90
1358 $5 "Madonna of Foligno" (detail) (Raphael) .. 2·10 1·25

1990. 500th Anniv (1992) of Discovery of America by Columbus (3rd issue). New World Natural History—Marine Life. Mult.

1360 10 c. Type **260** 10 10
1361 20 c. Spiny lobster .. 10 10
1362 25 c. Magnificent banded fanworm 10 15
1363 45 c. Cannonball jellyfish 20 25
1364 60 c. Red-spiny sea star 25 30
1365 $2 Peppermint shrimp .. 85 90
1366 $3 Coral crab .. .. 1·25 1·40
1367 $4 Branching fire coral .. 1·75 1·90

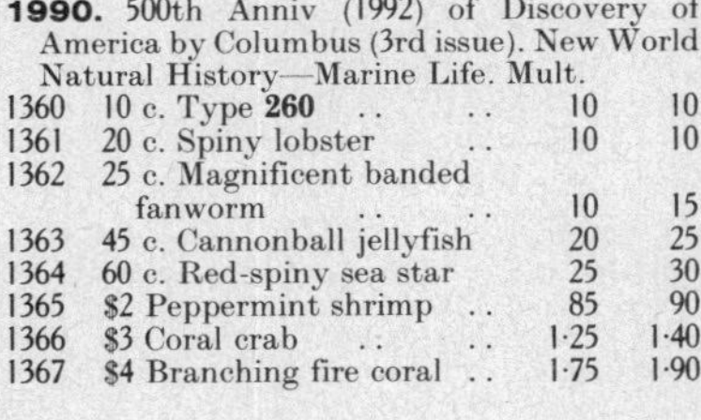

261 "Vanilla mexicana"

1990. "Expo '90" International Garden and Greenery Exhibition, Osaka. Orchids. Mult.

1369 15 c. Type **261** 10 10
1370 45 c. "Epidendrum ibaguense" 20 25
1371 50 c. "Epidendrum secundum" 20 25
1372 60 c. "Maxillaria conferta" 25 30
1373 $1 "Oncidium altissimum" 40 45
1374 $2 "Spiranthes lanceolata" 85 90
1375 $3 "Tonopsis utricularioides" .. .. 1·25 1·40
1376 $5 "Epidendrum nocturnum" .. .. 2·10 2·25

262 Queen Victoria and Queen Elizabeth II

1990. 150th Anniv of the Penny Black.

1378 **262** 45 c. green 20 25
1379 – 60 c. mauve 25 30
1380 – $5 blue .. .. 2·10 2·25

DESIGNS: 60 c., $5 As Type **262**, but with different backgrounds.

263 "Britannia" (mail steamer), 1840

1990. "Stamp World London 90" International Stamp Exhibition.

1382 **263** 50 c. green and red .. 20 25
1383 – 75 c. brown and red 30 35
1384 – $4 blue and red .. 1·75 1·90

DESIGNS: 75 c. Railway sorting carriage, 1892; $4 Imperial Airways flying boat "Centaurus", 1938.

264 Flamefish

1990. Reef Fishes. Multicoloured.

1386 10 c. Type **264** 10 10
1387 15 c. Coney 10 10
1388 50 c. Squirrelfish .. 20 25
1389 60 c. Sergeant major .. 25 30
1390 $1 Yellowtail snapper .. 40 45
1391 $2 Rock beauty 85 90
1392 $3 Spanish hogfish .. 1·25 1·40
1393 $4 Striped parrotfish .. 1·75 1·90

265 "Voyager 2" passing Saturn

1990. Achievements in Space. Multicoloured.

1395 45 c. Type **265** 20 25
1396 45 c. "Pioneer 11" photographing Saturn 20 25
1397 45 c. Astronaut in transporter 20 25
1398 45 c. Space shuttle "Columbia" 20 25
1399 45 c. "Apollo 10" command module on parachutes 20 25
1400 45 c. "Skylab" space station 20 25
1401 45 c. Astronaut Edward White in space .. 20 25
1402 45 c. "Apollo" spacecraft on joint mission .. 20 25
1403 45 c. "Soyuz" spacecraft on joint mission .. 20 25

1404 45 c. "Mariner 1" passing Venus 20 25
1405 45 c. "Gemini 4" capsule 20 25
1406 45 c. "Sputnik 1" .. 20 25
1407 45 c. Hubble space telescope 20 25
1408 45 c. "X-15" rocket plane 20 25
1409 45 c. "Bell X-1" aircraft 20 25
1410 45 c. "Apollo 17" astronaut and lunar rock formation .. 20 25
1411 45 c. Lunar Rover .. 20 25
1412 45 c. "Apollo 14" lunar module 20 25
1413 45 c. Astronaut Buzz Aldrin on Moon .. 20 25
1414 45 c. Soviet "Lunokhod" lunar vehicle 20 25

266 Queen Mother in Evening Dress

1990. 90th Birthday of Queen Elizabeth the Queen Mother.

1415 **266** 15 c. multicoloured .. 10 10
1416 – 35 c. multicoloured .. 15 20
1417 – 75 c. multicoloured .. 30 35
1418 – $3 multicoloured .. 1·25 1·40

DESIGNS: Nos. 1416/18, Recent photographs of the Queen Mother.

267 Mickey Mouse as Animator

1990. Mickey Mouse in Hollywood. Walt Disney cartoon characters. Multicoloured.

1420 25 c. Type **267** 10 15
1421 45 c. Minnie Mouse learning lines while being dressed .. 20 25
1422 50 c. Mickey Mouse with clapper board .. 20 25
1423 60 c. Daisy Duck making-up Mickey Mouse .. 25 30
1424 $1 Clarabelle Cow as Cleopatra 40 45
1425 $2 Mickey Mouse directing Goofy and Donald Duck 85 90
1426 $3 Mickey Mouse directing Goofy as birdman .. 1·25 1·40
1427 $4 Donald Duck and Mickey Mouse editing film .. .. .. 1·75 1·90

268 Men's 20 Kilometres Walk

1990. Olympic Games, Barcelona (1992). Mult.

1429 50 c. Type **268** 20 25
1430 75 c. Triple jump .. 30 35
1431 $1 Men's 10,000 metres .. 40 45
1432 $5 Javelin .. .. 2·10 2·25

269 Huey and Dewey asleep ("Christmas Stories")

1990 International Literacy Year. Walt Disney cartoon characters illustrating works by Charles Dickens. Multicoloured.

1434 15 c. Type **269** 10 10
1435 45 c. Donald Duck as Poor Jo looking at grave ("Bleak House") 20 25
1436 50 c. Dewey as Oliver asking for more ("Oliver Twist") .. 20 25
1437 60 c. Daisy Duck as The Marchioness ("Old Curiosity Shop") .. 25 30
1438 $1 Little Nell giving nosegay to her grand-father ("Little Nell") .. 40 45
1439 $2 Scrooge McDuck as Mr. Pickwick ("Pickwick Papers") .. 85 90
1440 $3 Minnie Mouse as Florence and Mickey Mouse as Paul ("Dombey and Son") 1·25 1·40
1441 $5 Minnie Mouse as Jenny Wren ("Our Mutual Friend") .. .. 2·10 2·25

1990. World Cup Football Championship Winners, Italy. Nos. 1308/11 optd **Winners West Germany 1 Argentina 0**.

1443 15 c. Type **252** 10 10
1444 25 c. Goalkeeper moving towards ball 10 10
1445 $1 Goalkeeper reaching for ball 40 45
1446 $4 Goalkeeper saving goal 1·75 1·90

271 Pearly-eyed Thrasher

1990. Birds. Multicoloured.

1448 10 c. Type **271** 10 10
1449 25 c. Purple-throated carib 10 15
1450 50 c. Common yellow-throat 20 25
1451 60 c. American kestrel .. 25 30
1452 $1 Yellow-bellied sapsucker 40 45
1453 $2 Purple gallinule .. 85 90
1454 $3 Yellow-crowned night heron .. .. 1·25 1·40
1455 $4 Blue-hooded euphonia 1·75 1·90

272 "Madonna and Child with Saints" (detail, Sebastiano del Piombo)

1990. Christmas. Paintings by Renaissance Masters. Multicoloured.

1457 25 c. Type **272** 10 15
1458 30 c. "Virgin and Child with Angels" (detail, Grunewald) (vert) .. 10 15
1459 40 c. "The Holy Family and a Shepherd" (detail, Titian) .. 15 20
1460 60 c. "Virgin and Child" (detail, Lippi) (vert) .. 25 30
1461 $1 "Jesus, St. John and Two Angels" (Rubens) 40 45
1462 $2 "Adoration of the Shepherds" (detail, Vincenzo Catena) .. 85 90
1463 $4 "Adoration of the Magi" (detail, Giorgione) .. .. 1·75 1·90
1464 $5 "Virgin and Child adored by Warrior" (detail, Vincenzo Catena) .. .. 2·10 2·25

273 "Rape of the Daughters of Leucippus" (detail)

1991. 350th Death Anniv of Rubens. Mult.

1466 25 c. Type **273** 10 15
1467 45 c. "Bacchanal" (detail) 20 25
1468 50 c. "Rape of the Sabine Women" (detail) .. 20 25
1469 60 c. "Battle of the Amazons" (detail) .. 25 30
1470 $1 "Rape of the Sabine Women" (different detail) 40 45
1471 $2 "Bacchanal" (different detail) 85 90
1472 $3 "Rape of the Sabine Women" (different detail) .. .. 1·25 1·40
1473 $4 "Bacchanal" (different detail) .. .. 1·75 1·90

274 U.S. Troops cross into Germany, 1944

1991. 50th Anniv of Second World War. Mult.

1475 10 c. Type **274** 10 10
1476 15 c. Axis surrender in North Africa, 1943 .. 10 10
1477 25 c. U.S. tanks invade Kwalajalein, 1944 .. 10 15
1478 45 c. Roosevelt and Churchill meet at Casablanca, 1943 .. 20 25
1479 50 c. Marshal Badoglio, Prime Minister of Italian anti-fascist government, 1943 .. 20 25
1480 $1 Lord Mountbatten, Supreme Allied Commander South-east Asia, 1943 .. .. 40 45
1481 $2 Greek victory at Koritza, 1940 .. .. 85 90
1482 $4 Anglo-Soviet mutual assistance pact, 1941 .. 1·75 1·90
1483 $5 Operation Torch landings, 1942 .. .. 2·10 2·25

275 Locomotive "Prince Regent", Middleton Colliery, 1812

1991. Cog Railways. Multicoloured.

1485 25 c. Type **275** 10 10
1486 30 c. Snowdon Mountain Railway 10 10
1487 40 c. First railcar at Hell Gate, Manitou & Pike's Peak Railway, U.S.A. 15 20
1488 60 c. Pnka rack railway, Amberawa, Java .. 25 30
1489 $1 Green Mountain Railway, Maine, 1883 .. 40 45
1490 $2 Cog locomotive "Pike's Peak", 1891 .. .. 85 90
1491 $4 Vitznau–Rigi Railway, Switzerland, and Mt Rigi hotel local post stamp .. .. .. 1·70 1·90
1492 $5 Leopoldina Railway, Brazil .. .. .. 2·10 2·25

276 "Heliconius charithonia"

1991. Butterflies. Multicoloured.

1494 10 c. Type **276** 10 10
1495 35 c. "Marpesia petreus" 15 20
1496 50 c. "Anartia amathea" 20 25
1497 75 c. "Siproeta stelenes" 30 35
1498 $1 "Battus polydamas" 40 45
1499 $2 "Historis odius" .. 85 90
1500 $4 "Hypolimnas misippus" .. .. .. 1·75 1·90
1501 $5 "Hamadryas feronia" 2·10 2·25

277 Hanno the Phoenician, 450 B.C.

1991. 500th Anniv (1992) of Discovery of America by Columbus (4th issue). History of Exploration.

1503 10 c. Type **277** 10 10
1504 15 c. Pytheas the Greek, 325 B.C. 10 10
1505 45 c. Erik the Red discovering Greenland, 985 A.D. 20 25
1506 60 c. Leif Eriksson reaching Vinland, 1000 A.D. 25 30
1507 $1 Scylax the Greek in the Indian ocean, 518 A.D. 40 45
1508 $2 Marco Polo sailing to the Orient, 1259 A.D. .. 85 90
1509 $4 Ship of Queen Hatshepsut of Egypt, 1493 B.C. .. .. .. 1·75 1·90
1510 $5 St. Brendan's coracle, 500 A.D. .. .. 2·10 2·25

278 "Camille Roulin" (Van Gogh)

1991. Death Cent of (1990) Vincent van Gogh (artist). Multicoloured.

1512 5 c. Type **278** 10 10
1513 10 c. "Armand Roulin" .. 10 10
1514 15 c. "Young Peasant Woman with Straw Hat sitting in the Wheat" 10 10
1515 25 c. "Adeline Ravoux" .. 10 15
1516 30 c. "The Schoolboy" .. 10 10
1517 40 c. "Doctor Gachet" .. 15 20
1518 50 c. "Portrait of a Man" 20 25
1519 75 c. "Two Children" .. 30 35
1520 $2 "The Postman Joseph Roulin" 85 90
1521 $3 "The Seated Zouave" 1·25 1·40
1522 $4 "L'Arlesienne" .. 1·75 1·90
1523 $5 "Self-Portrait, November/December 1888" .. .. .. 2·10 2·25

279 Mickey Mouse as Champion Sumo Wrestler

1991. "Philanippon '91" International Stamp Exhibition, Tokyo. Walt Disney cartoon characters participating in martial arts. Multicoloured.

No.	Description		
1525	10 c. Type **279**	10	10
1526	15 c. Goofy using the tonfa (horiz)	10	10
1527	45 c. Donald Duck as a Ninja (horiz)	20	25
1528	60 c. Mickey armed for Kung fu	25	30
1529	$1 Goofy with Kendo sword	40	45
1530	$2 Mickey and Donald demonstrating Aikido (horiz)	85	90
1531	$4 Mickey and Donald in Judo bout (horiz)	1·75	1·90
1532	$5 Mickey performing Yabusame (mounted archery)	2·10	2·25

280 Queen Elizabeth and Prince Philip in 1976

1991. 65th Birthday of Queen Elizabeth II. Multicoloured.

No.	Description		
1534	15 c. Type **280**	10	10
1535	20 c. The Queen and Prince Philip in Portugal, 1985	10	10
1536	$2 Queen Elizabeth II	85	90
1537	$4 The Queen and Prince Philip at Ascot, 1986	1·75	1·90

1991. 10th Wedding Anniv of Prince and Princess of Wales. As T **280**. Mult.

No.	Description		
1539	10 c. Prince and Princess of Wales at party, 1986	10	10
1540	40 c. Separate portraits of Prince, Princess and sons	15	20
1541	$1 Prince Henry and Prince William	40	45
1542	$5 Princess Diana in Australia and Prince Charles in Hungary	2·10	2·25

281 Daisy Duck teeing-off

1991. Golf. Walt Disney cartoon characters. Multicoloured.

No.	Description		
1544	10 c. Type **281**	10	10
1545	15 c. Goofy playing ball from under trees	10	10
1546	45 c. Mickey Mouse playing deflected shot	20	25
1547	60 c. Mickey hacking divot out of fairway	25	30
1548	$1 Donald Duck playing ball out of pond	40	45
1549	$2 Minnie Mouse hitting ball over pond	85	90
1550	$4 Donald in a bunker	1·75	1·90
1551	$5 Goofy trying snooker shot into hole	2·10	2·25

282 Moose receiving Gold Medal

1991. 50th Anniv of Archie Comics, and Olympic Games, Barcelona (1992). Mult.

No.	Description		
1553	10 c. Type **282**	10	10
1554	25 c. Archie playing polo on a motorcycle (horiz)	10	15
1555	40 c. Archie and Betty at fencing class	15	20
1556	60 c. Archie joining girls' volleyball team	25	30
1557	$1 Archie with tennis ball in his mouth	40	45
1558	$2 Archie running marathon	85	90
1559	$4 Archie judging women's gymnastics (horiz)	1·75	1·90
1560	$5 Archie watching the cheer-leaders	2·10	2·25

283 Presidents De Gaulle and Kennedy, 1961

1991. Birth Centenary of Charles de Gaulle (French statesman). Multicoloured.

No.	Description		
1562	10 c. Type **283**	10	10
1563	15 c. General De Gaulle with Pres. Roosevelt, 1945 (vert)	10	15
1564	45 c. Pres. De Gaulle with Chancellor Adenauer, 1962 (vert)	20	25
1565	60 c. De Gaulle at Arc de Triomphe, Liberation of Paris, 1944 (vert)	25	30
1566	$1 General De Gaulle crossing the Rhine, 1945	40	45
1567	$2 General De Gaulle in Algiers, 1944	85	90
1568	$4 Presidents De Gaulle and Eisenhower, 1960	1·75	1·90
1569	$5 De Gaulle returning from Germany, 1968 (vert)	2·10	2·25

284 Parliament Building and Map

1991. 10th Anniv of Independence.

No.	Description		
1571 **284**	10 c. multicoloured	10	10

285 Lilienthal's Signature and Glider Flugzeug Nr. 5

1991. Centenary of Otto Lilienthal's Gliding Experiments.

No.	Description		
1573 **285**	$2 multicoloured	85	90

286 Driver in Modern Locomotive

1991. Centenary of Trans-Siberian Railway.

No.	Description		
1574 **286**	$2.50 multicoloured	1·00	1·10

287 Germans celebrating Reunification

1991. Bicentenary of Brandenburg Gate, Germany. Multicoloured.

No.	Description		
1575	25 c. Type **287**	10	15
1576	$2 Chariot driver and Gate at night	85	90
1577	$3 Statues from podium	1·25	1·40

288 "Don Giovanni" and Mozart

1991. Death Bicentenary of Mozart. Mult.

No.	Description		
1579	$1.50 Type **288**	60	65
1580	$4 St. Peter's Cathedral, Salzburg	1·75	1·90

289 Cubs erecting Tent

1991. 17th World Scout Jamboree, Korea. Multicoloured.

No.	Description		
1581	75 c. Type **289**	30	35
1582	$2 Lord Baden-Powell and members of 3rd Antigua Methodist cub pack (vert)	85	90
1583	$3.50 Cubs and camp fire	1·40	1·50

290 Nimitz Class Carrier and Ticonderoga Class Cruiser

1991. 50th Anniv of Japanese Attack on Pearl Harbor. Multicoloured.

No.	Description		
1585	$1 Type **290**	40	45
1586	$1 Tourist launch	40	45
1587	$1 U.S.S. "Arizona" memorial	40	45
1588	$1 Wreaths on water and aircraft	40	45
1589	$1 White tern	40	45
1590	$1 Japanese Zeros over Pearl City	40	45
1591	$1 Zeros attacking	40	45
1592	$1 Battleship "Row" in flames	40	45
1593	$1 U.S.S. "Nevada" underway	40	45
1594	$1 Zeros returning to carriers	40	45

291 "The Annunciation" (Fra Angelico)

1991. Christmas. Religious Paintings by Fra Angelico. Multicoloured.

No.	Description		
1595	10 c. Type **291**	10	10
1596	30 c. "Nativity"	10	10
1597	40 c. "Adoration of the Magi"	15	20
1598	60 c. "Presentation in the Temple"	25	30
1599	$1 "Circumcision"	40	45
1600	$3 "Flight into Egypt"	1·25	1·40
1601	$4 "Massacre of the Innocents"	1·75	1·40
1602	$5 "Christ teaching in the Temple"	2·10	2·25

292 Queen Elizabeth II and Bird Sanctuary

1992. 40th Anniv of Queen Elizabeth II's Accession. Multicoloured.

No.	Description		
1604	10 c. Type **292**	10	10
1605	30 c. Nelson's Dockyard	10	10
1606	$1 Ruins on Shirley Heights	40	45
1607	$5 Beach and palm trees	2·10	2·25

ASCENSION

An island in S. Atlantic. A dependency of St. Helena.

1922. 12 pence = 1 shilling.
20 shilling = 1 pound.
1971. 100 pence = 1 pound.

1922. Stamps of St. Helena, optd. ASCENSION.

No.	Description		
1.	½d. black and green	2·75	7·00
2.	1d. green	3·25	8·00
3.	1½d. red	12·00	30·00
4.	2d. black and slate	10·00	10·00
5.	3d. blue	10·00	14·00
6.	8d. black and purple	24·00	28·00
9.	1s. black on green	24·00	29·00
7.	2s. black and blue on blue	£100	£110
8.	3s. black and violet	£150	£170

2. Badge of St. Helena.

1924.

No.	Description		
10.	½d. black	2·00	5·50
11.	1d. black and green	3·25	4·50
12.	1½d. red	4·75	14·00
13.	2d. black and grey	5·00	3·50
14.	3d. blue	3·75	8·00
15.	4d. black on yellow	35·00	60·00
15d.	5d. purple and green	10·00	18·00
16.	6d. black and purple	42·00	65·00
17.	8d. black and violet	10·00	25·00
18.	1s. black and brown	16·00	30·00
19.	2s. black & blue on blue	55·00	75·00
20.	3s. black on blue	80·00	85·00

3. Georgetown.

4. Ascension Island.

DESIGNS—HORIZ. 1½d. The Pier. 3d. Long Beach. 5d. Three Sisters. 1s. Sooty Tern. 5s. Green mountain.

1934. Medallion portrait of King George V. (except 1s.).

No.	Description		
21. 3.	½d. black and violet	70	80
22. 4.	1d. black and green	1·60	1·25
23. –	1½d. black and red	1·50	2·00
24. 4.	2d. black and orange	1·75	2·00
25. –	3d. black and blue	1·75	1·50
26. –	5d. black and blue	2·00	3·00
27. 4.	8d. black and brown	4·00	4·75
28. –	1s. black and red	12·00	6·00
29. 4.	2s. 6d. black and purple	28·00	32·00
30. –	5s. black and brown	45·00	55·00

1935. Silver Jubilee. As T **13** of Antigua.

No.	Description		
31.	1½d. blue and red	3·50	3·75
32.	2d. blue and grey	8·50	13·00
33.	5d. green and blue	12·00	13·00
34.	1s. grey and purple	18·00	25·00

1937. Coronation. As T **2** of Aden.

No.	Description		
35.	1d. green	50	50
36.	2d. orange	1·25	40
37.	3d. blue	1·50	50

10. The Pier.

1938.

No.	Description		
38b A.	½d. black and violet	40	65
39 B.	1d. black and green	48·00	8·00
39b	1d. black and orange	45	40
39d C.	1d. black and green	30	30
40b 10.	1½d. black and red	70	80
40d	1½d. black and pink	45	80
41a B.	2d. black and orange	80	40
41c	2d. black and red	35	30
42 D	3d. black and blue	£100	26·00
42b	3d. black and grey	60	50
42d B	4d. black and blue	3·00	1·75
43 C	6d. black and blue	4·75	50
44a A	1s. black and brown	3·00	1·25
45 10	2s. 6d. black and red	26·00	7·00
46a D	5s. black and brown	30·00	22·00
47a C	10s. black and purple	60·00	48·00

DESIGNS: A, Georgetown. B, Green Mountain C, Three Sisters. D, Long Beach.

1946. Victory. As T **9** of Aden.

No.	Description		
48.	2d. orange	40	30
49.	4d. blue	40	30

1948. Silver Wedding. As T **10/11** of Aden.

No.	Description		
50.	3d. black	50	30
51.	10s. mauve	42·00	35·00

1949. U.P.U. As T **20/23** of Antigua.

No.	Description		
52.	3d. red	1·40	1·00
53.	4d. blue	5·50	1·10
54.	6d. olive	6·00	2·00
55.	1s. black	6·00	1·50

1953. Coronation. As Type **13** of Aden.

No.	Description		
56.	3d. black and grey	1·25	1·50

15. Water Catchment.

1956.

No.	Description		
57. 15.	½d. black and brown	10	25
58. –	1d. black and mauve	55	35
59. –	1½d. black and orange	30	35
60. –	2d. black and red	70	40
61. –	2½d. black and brown	60	55
62. –	3d. black and blue	2·00	1·00
63. –	4d. black and turquoise	1·25	1·00
64. –	6d. black and blue	1·25	90
65. –	7d. black and olive	1·00	1·00
66. –	1s. black and red	1·00	90
67. –	2s. 6d. black and purple	24·00	6·50
68. –	5s. black and green	30·00	15·00
69. –	10s. black and purple	48·00	32·00

DESIGNS: 1d. Map of Ascension. 1½d. Georgetown. 2d. Map showing Atlantic cables. 2½d. Mountain Road. 3d. White-tailed Tropic Bird. 4d. Long-finned Tunny. 6d. Rollers on seashore. 7d. Turtles. 1s. Land Crab. 2s. 6d. Sooty Tern. 5s. Perfect Crater. 10s. View of Ascension.

28. Brown Booby.

1963. Birds. Multicoloured.

No.	Description		
70.	1d. Type **28**	20	15
71.	1½d. White-capped Noddy	35	15
72.	2d. White Tern	35	15
73.	3d. Red-billed Tropic Bird	45	15
74.	4½d. Common Noddy	45	20
75.	6d. Sooty Tern	45	20
76.	7d. Ascension Frigate-Bird	45	20
77.	10d. Blue-faced Booby	45	20
78.	1s. White-tailed Tropic Bird	50	20
79.	1s. 6d. Red-billed Tropic Bird	3·25	1·50
80.	2s. 6d. Madeiran Storm Petrel	4·25	3·00
81.	5s. Red-footed Booby (brown phase)	6·00	3·50
82.	10s. Ascension Frigate-Birds	12·00	4·50
83.	£1 Red-footed Booby (white phase)	22·00	7·00

1963. Freedom from Hunger. As T **28** of Aden.

No.	Description		
84.	1s. 6d. red	3·00	40

1963. Cent of Red Cross. As T **33** of Antigua.

No.	Description		
85.	3d. red and black	2·50	60
86.	1s. 6d. red and blue	5·50	2·00

1965. Cent of I.T.U. As T **36** of Antigua.

No.	Description		
87.	3d. mauve and violet	1·25	25
88.	6d. turquoise and brown	1·50	30

1965. I.C.Y. As T **37** of Antigua.

No.	Description		
89.	1d. purple and turquoise	50	20
90.	6d. green and lavender	1·50	50

1966. Churchill Commemoration. As T **38** of Antigua.

No.	Description		
91.	1d. blue	50	25
92.	3d. green	2·75	70
93.	6d. brown	3·50	75
94.	1s. 6d. violet	4·50	1·25

1966. World Cup Football Championship. As T **40** of Antigua.

No.	Description		
95.	3d. multicoloured	1·25	30
96.	6d. multicoloured	1·50	40

1966. Inauguration of W.H.O. Headquarters, Geneva. As T **41** of Antigua.

No.	Description		
97.	3d. black, green and blue	1·75	40
98.	1s. 6d. black, purple & ochre	4·25	1·10

42. Satellite Station.

1966. Opening of Apollo Communication Satellite Earth Station.

No.	Description		
99. 42.	4d. black and violet	15	15
100.	8d. black and green	20	15
101.	1s. 3d. black and brown	25	15
102.	2s. 6d. black and blue	35	20

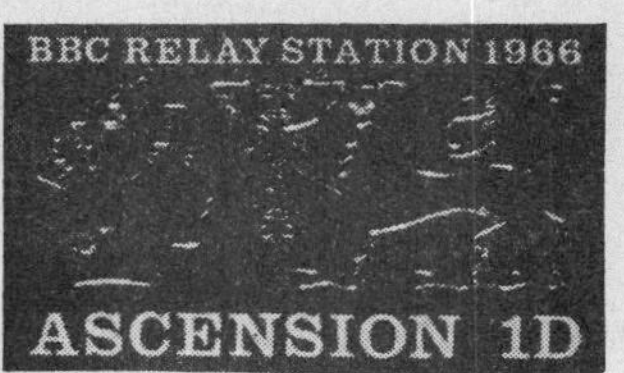

43. B.B.C. Emblem.

1966. Opening of B.B.C. Relay Station.

No.	Description		
103. 43.	1d. gold and blue	10	10
104. –	3d. gold and green	15	15
105. –	6d. gold and violet	20	20
106. –	1s. 6d. gold and red	20	35

1967. 20th Anniv. of U.N.E.S.C.O. As T **54/56** of Antigua.

No.	Description		
107.	3d. multicoloured	2·25	80
108.	6d. yellow, violet and olive	3·50	1·00
109.	1s. 6d. black, pur. & orge.	5·50	1·40

44. Human Rights Emblem and Chain Links.

1968. Human Rights Year

No.	Description		
110. 44.	6d. orge., red and blk.	20	10
111.	1s. 6d. blue, red & blk.	30	15
112.	2s. 6d. grn., red & blk.	35	20

45. Ascension Black-Fish.

1968. Fishes (1st series).

No.	Description		
113. 45.	4d. black and blue	60	20
114. –	8d. multicoloured	75	35
115. –	1s. 9d. multicoloured	1·00	40
116. –	2s. 3d. multicoloured	1·25	45

DESIGNS: 8d. Leather-jacket. 1s. 9d. Tunny. 2s. 3d. Mako Shark.

See also Nos. 117/120 and 126/9.

1969. Fishes (2nd series). As T **45**. Mult.

No.	Description		
117.	4d. Sailfish	90	55
118.	6d. Old Wife	1·25	70
119.	1s. 6d. Yellowtail	2·00	1·25
120.	2s. 11d. Jack	3·75	2·25

46. H.M.S. "Rattlesnake".

1969. Royal Naval Crests (1st series).

No.	Description		
121. 46.	4d. multicoloured	50	15
122. –	9d. multicoloured	70	15
123. –	1s. 9d. blue and gold	1·25	25
124. –	2s. 3d. multicoloured	1·50	30

DESIGNS: 9d. H.M.S. "Weston". 1s. 9d. H.M.S. "Undaunted", 2s. 3d. H.M.S. "Eagle".

See also Nos. 130/3, 149/52, 154/7 and 166/9.

1970. Fishes (3rd series). As T **45**. **Mult.**

No.	Description		
126.	4d. Wahoo	3·50	1·50
127.	9d. Coal-fish	3·50	1·50
128.	1s. 9d. Dolphin	4·75	2·25
129.	2s. 3d. Soldier fish	4·75	2·25

1970. Royal Naval Crests (2nd series). As T **46**. Multicoloured.

No.	Description		
130.	4d. H.M.S. "Penelope"	1·25	35
131.	9d. H.M.S. "Carlisle"	1·50	60
132.	1s. 6d. H.M.S. "Amphion"	2·00	85
133.	2s. 6d. H.M.S. "Magpie"	2·50	1·25

50. Early Chinese Rocket.

1971. Decimal Currency. Evolution of Space Travel. Multicoloured.

No.	Description		
135.	½p. Type **50**	15	15
136.	1p. Medieval Arab astronomers	20	15
137.	1½p. Tycho Brahe's observatory, quadrant and supernova	30	30
138.	2p. Galileo, Moon and telescope	40	30
139.	2½p. Isaac Newton, instruments and apple	80	60
140.	3½p. Harrison's chronometer and ship	85	55
141.	4½p. Space rocket taking off	1·00	50
142.	5p. World's largest telescope, Palomar	1·00	60
143.	7½p. World's largest radio telescope, Jodrell Bank	4·00	1·75
144.	10p. "Mariner VII" and Mars	3·50	1·60
145.	12½p. "Sputnik II" and Space dog, Laika	6·00	2·00
146.	25p. Walking in Space	7·50	2·25
147.	50p. "Apollo XI" crew on Moon	4·75	2·50
148.	£1 Future Space Research station	5·50	4·50

Nos. 137/40, 142/5 and 147/8 are horiz.

1971. Royal Naval Crests (3rd series). As T **46**. Multicoloured.

No.	Description		
149.	2p. H.M.S. "Phoenix"	1·00	30
150.	4p. H.M.S. "Milford"	1·50	55
151.	9p. H.M.S. "Pelican"	1·75	80
152.	15p. H.M.S. "Oberon"	2·00	1·00

1972. Royal Naval Crests (4th series). As T **46**. Multicoloured.

No.	Description		
154.	1½p. H.M.S. "Lowestoft"	65	50
155.	3p. H.M.S. "Auckland"	85	75
156.	6p. H.M.S. "Nigeria"	1·10	1·25
157.	17½p. H.M.S. "Bermuda"	2·25	2·50

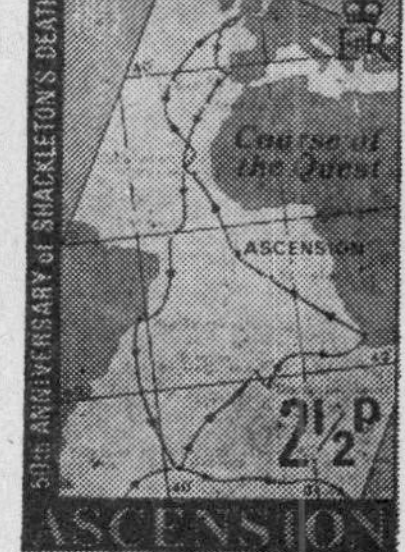

51. Course of the "Quest".

1972. 50th Anniv. of Shackleton's Death. Multicoloured.

No.	Description		
159.	2½p. Type **51**	1·00	60
160.	4p. Shackleton and "Quest" (horiz.)	1·10	70
161.	7½p. Shackleton's cabin and "Quest" (horiz.)	1·25	75
162.	11p. Shackleton's statue and memorial	1·40	1·00

INDEX

Countries can be quickly located by referring to the index at the end of this volume.

52. Land Crab and Mako Shark.

1972. Royal Silver Wedding. Multicoloured

164. **52.** 2p. violet 15 10
165. 16p. red 35 30

1973. Royal Naval Crests (5th series) As T **46**. Multicoloured

166. 2p. H.M.S. " Birmingham " 2·50 1·00
167. 4p. H.M.S. " Cardiff " .. 3·00 1·00
168. 9p. H.M.S. " Penzance " 4·00 1·25
169. 13p. H.M.S. " Rochester " 4·50 1·50

53. Green Turtle.
(Illustration reduced. Actual size 53 × 27 mm.).

1973. Turtles. Multicoloured.

171. 4p. Type **53** .. .. 3·25 1·00
172. 9p. Loggerhead turtle .. 3·50 1·50
173. 12p. Hawksbill turtle .. 3·75 1·50

54. Sergeant, R.M. Light Infantry, 1900.

1973. 50th Anniv. of Departure of Royal Marines from Ascension. Multicoloured.

174. 2p. Type **54** .. .. 2·50 1·25
175. 6p. R.M. Private, 1816 .. 3·50 1·75
176. 12p. R.M. Light Infantry Officer, 1880 .. .. 4·00 2·25
177. 20p. R.M. Artillery Colour Sergeant, 1910 .. .. 4·50 2·50

1973. Royal Wedding. As T **47** of Anguilla. Multicoloured. Background colours given.

178. 2p. brown 15 10
179. 18p. green 25 15

55. Letter and H.Q., Berne.

1974. Cent. of Universal Postal Union. Mult.

180. 2p. Type **55** 25 30
181. 9p. Hermes and U.P.U. monument 40 45

56. Churchill as a Boy, and Birthplace, Blenheim Palace.

1974. Birth Centenary of Sir Winston Churchill. Multicoloured.

182. 5p. Type **56** 40 40
183. 25p. Churchill as statesman, and U.N. Building .. 1·00 1·00

57. "Skylab 3" and Photograph of Ascension.

1975. Space Satellites. Multicoloured.

185. 2p. Type **57** 30 30
186. 18p. " Skylab 4 " Command module and photograph 40 40

58. U.S.A.F. " Starlifter ".

1975. Wideawake Airfield. Multicoloured.

187. 2p. Type **58** .. .. 1·25 65
188. 5p. R.A.F. " Hercules " .. 1·75 85
189. 9p. Vickers " VC-10 " .. 2·00 1·40
190. 24p. U.S.A.F. " Galaxy " 3·00 2·75

1975. " Apollo-Soyuz " Space Link. Nos. 141 and 145/6 optd. **APOLLO-SOYUZ LINK 1975.**

192. $4\frac{1}{2}$p. multicoloured .. 15 15
193. $12\frac{1}{2}$p. multicoloured .. 25 20
194. 25p. multicoloured .. 45 35

60. Arrival of Royal Navy, 1815.

1975. 160th Anniv. Occupation. Mult.

195. 2p. Type **60** 35 25
196. 5p. Water supply, Dampiers Drip 50 40
197. 9p. First landing, 1815 .. 60 60
198. 15p. The garden on Green Mountain 75 85

61. Yellow Canaries.

1976. Multicoloured

199. 1p Type **61** 30 35
200. 2p. White Tern (vert.) .. 35 35
201. 3p. Common Waxbill .. 35 40
202. 4p. White-capped Noddy (vert.) 35 40
203. 5p. Common Noddy .. 50 50
204. 6p. Common Mynah .. 50 50
205. 7p. Madeiran Storm Petrel (vert.) 55 55
206. 8p. Sooty Tern 60 60
207. 9p. Blue-faced Booby (vert.) 60 65
208. 10 p. Red-footed Booby .. 60 70
209. 15 p. Bare-throated Francolin (vert.) .. .. 1·25 1·50
210. 18p. Brown Booby (vert.) 1·25 1·50
211. 25p. Red-billed Bo'sun Bird 1·40 1·50
212. 50p. Yellow-billed Tropic Bird .. .. .. 2·25 2·50
213. £1 Ascension Frigate-Bird (vert.) .. .. 2·75 3·25
214. £2 Boatswain Bird Island Sanctuary .. .. 5·50 6·50

No. 214 is larger, 50 + 38 mm.

63. G.B. Penny Red with Ascension Postmark.

1976. Festival of Stamps, London.

215. **63.** 5p. red, black & brown 20 15
216. – 9p. green, black & brn. 30 20
217. – 25p. multicoloured .. 50 45

DESIGNS—VERT. 9p. $\frac{1}{2}$d. stamp of 1922. HORIZ. 25p. "Southampton Castle" (liner).

64. U.S. Base, Ascension.

1976. Bicent. of American Revolution. Mult.

219. 8p. Type **64** 90 40
220. 9p. NASA Station at Devils Ashpit 90 45
221. 25p. " Viking " landing on Mars .. .. .. 1·50 80

65. Visit of Prince Philip, 1957.

1977. Silver Jubilee. Multicoloured.

222. 8p. Type **65** 15 15
223. 12p. Coronation Coach leaving Buckingham Palace (horiz.) 25 20
224. 25p. Coronation Coach (horiz.) 45 40

66. Tunnel carrying Water Pipe.

1977. Water Supplies. Multicoloured.

225. 3p. Type **66** 20 15
226. 5p. Breakneck Valley wells 30 20
227. 12p. Break tank (horiz.) .. 55 35
228. 25p. Water catchment (horiz.) 90 65

67. Mars Bay Location, 1877.

1977. Centenary of Visit of Professor Gill (astronomer). Multicoloured.

229. 3p. Type **67** 25 20
230. 8p. Instrument sites, Mars Bay 35 25
231. 12p. Sir David and Lady Gill 55 40
232. 25p. Maps of Ascension .. 90 70

68. Lion of England.

1978. 25th Anniv. of Coronation.

233. **68.** 25p. yell., brn. & silver 60 65
234. – 25p. multicoloured .. 60 65
235. – 25p. yell., brn. & silver 60 65

DESIGNS: No. 234, Queen Elizabeth II. No. 235, Green Turtle.

70. Flank of Sisters, Sisters' Red Hill and East Crater.

1978. Ascension Island Volcanic Rock Formations. Multicoloured.

236. 3p. Type **70** 20 20
237. 5p. Holland's Crater (Hollow Tooth) .. 30 30
238. 12p. Street Crater, Lower Valley Crater and Bear's Back 40 40
239. 15p. Butt Crater, Weather post and Green Mountain 45 45
240. 25p. Flank of Sisters, Thistle Hill and Two Boats Village 50 50

Nos. 236/40 were issued as a se-tenant strip within the sheet, forming a composite design.

71. " The Resolution " (H. Roberts).

1979. Bicentenary of Captain Cook's Voyages, 1768–79. Multicoloured.

242. 3p. Type **71** 45 25
243. 8p. Cook's chronometer .. 65 40
244. 12p. Green Turtle .. 75 50
245. 25p. Flaxman/Wedgwood medallion of Cook .. 1·00 70

72. St. Mary's Church, Georgetown.

1979. Ascension Day. Multicoloured.

246. 8p. Type **72** 30 20
247. 12p. Map of Ascension .. 40 30
248. 50p. " The Ascension " (painting by Rembrandt) 1·00 90

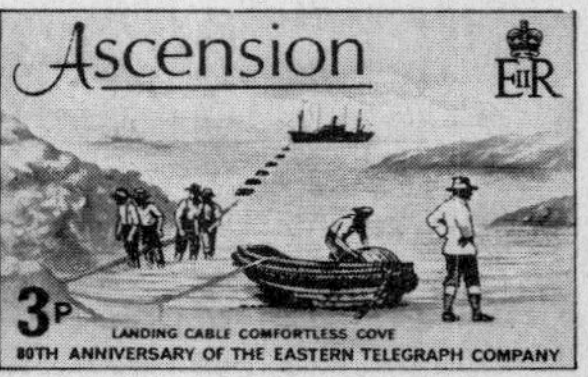

73. Landing Cable, Comfortless Cove.

1979. 80th Anniv. Eastern Telegraph Company's Arrival on Ascension.

No.	Type	Description	Unused	Used
249.	73.	3p. black and red	15	10
250.	–	8p. black and green ..	25	20
251.	–	12p. black and yellow ..	30	25
252.	–	15p. black and violet ..	35	35
253.	–	25p. black and brown ..	50	50

DESIGNS—HORIZ. 8p. C.S. "Anglia", 15p. C.S. "Seine", 25p. Cable and wireless earth station. VERT. 12p. Map of Atlantic cable network.

74. 6d. 1938 Stamp.

1979. Death Centenary of Sir Rowland Hill.

No.	Type	Description	Unused	Used
254.	74.	3p. black and blue ..	10	10
255.	–	8p. black, green and pale green	20	20
256.	–	12p. black, blue and pale blue	25	25
257.	–	50p. black and red ..	90	90

DESIGNS—HORIZ. 8p. 1956 5s. definitive. VERT. 12p. 1924 3s. stamp. 50p. Sir Rowland Hill.

75. " Anogramma ascensionis ".

1980. Ferns and Grasses. Multicoloured.

No.	Description	Unused	Used
258.	3 p. Type 75	10	10
259.	6p. "Xiphopteris ascensionense"	20	15
260.	8p. "Sporobolus caespitosus"	20	15
261.	12p. "Sporobolus durus" (vert.)	30	25
262.	18p. "Dryopteris ascensionis" (vert.) ..	40	35
263.	24p. "Marattia purpurascens" (vert.) ..	50	50

76. 17th Century, Bottle Post.

1980. "London 1980" International Stamp Exhibition. Multicoloured.

No.	Description	Unused	Used
264.	8p. Type 76	25	20
265.	12p. Chance calling ship, 19th century	35	25
266.	15p. "Garthcastle II" (regular mail service from 1863)	40	30
267.	50p. "St Helena" (mail services, 1980)	1·00	90

77. H.M. Queen Elizabeth the Queen Mother.

1980. 80th Birthday of the Queen Mother.

No.	Type	Description	Unused	Used
269.	77.	15p. multicoloured ..	40	40

78. Lubbock's Yellowtail.

1980. Fishes. Multicoloured.

No.	Description	Unused	Used
270.	3p. Type 78	20	15
271.	10p. Resplendent Angelfish	35	25
272.	25p. Hedgehog Butterflyfish	60	50
273.	40p. Marmalade Razorfish	80	65

79. H.M.S. " Tortoise ".

1980. 150th Anniv. of Royal Geographical Society. Multicoloured.

No.	Description	Unused	Used
274.	10p. Type 79	45	40
275.	15p. "Wideawake Fair" ..	55	45
276.	60p. Mid-Atlantic Ridge (38 × 48 mm.)	1·10	1·25

80. Green Mountain Farm, 1881.

1981. Green Mountain Farm. Multicoloured.

No.	Description	Unused	Used
277.	12p. Type 80	45	35
278.	15p. Two Boats, 1881 ..	50	40
279.	20p. Green Mountain and Two Boats, 1981 ..	60	50
280.	30p. Green Mountain Farm, 1981	80	70

81. Cable and Wireless Earth Station.

1981. " Space Shuttle " Mission and Opening of 2nd Earth Station.

No.	Type	Description	Unused	Used
281.	81.	15p. black, blue and pale blue	30	35

82. Poinsettia.

83. Solanum.

1981. Flowers. Multicoloured.

No.	Description	Unused	Used
282.	1p. Type 82	40	30
283.	2p. Clustered Wax Flower	50	35
284.	3p. Kolanchoe (vert.) ..	50	35
285.	4p. Yellow Pops	55	35
286.	5p. Camels Foot Creeper ..	55	35
287.	8p. White Oleander	55	40
288.	10p. Ascension Lily (vert.)	45	50
289.	12p. Coral Plant (vert.) ..	70	45
290.	15p. Yellow Allamanda ..	50	50
291.	20p. Ascension Euphorbia	60	80
292.	30p. Flame of the Forest (vert.)	90	80
293.	40p. Bougainvillea " King Leopold "	1·25	1·25
294.	50p. Type 83	1·25	1·75
295	£1 Ladies Petticoat ..	2·00	3·00
296.	£2 Red Hibiscus	3·75	4·75

Nos. 294/6 are as Type 83.

84. Map by Maxwell, 1793.

1981. Early Maps of Ascension.

No.	Type	Description	Unused	Used
297.	84.	10p. blk., gold and blue	40	35
298.	–	12p. blk., gold and grn.	45	35
299.	–	15p. blk., gold and stone	50	40
300.	–	40p. blk., gold and yell.	85	85

DESIGNS: 12p. Maxwell, 1793 (different). 15p. Ekeberg and Chapman, 1811. 40p. Campbell, 1819.

85. Wedding Bouquet from Ascension.

1981. Royal Wedding. Multicoloured.

No.	Description	Unused	Used
302.	10p. Type 85	25	25
303.	15p. Prince Charles in Fleet Air Arm flying kit ..	30	30
304.	50p. Prince Charles and Lady Diana Spencer ..	85	85

87. " Interest ".

1981. 25th Anniv. of Duke of Edinburgh Award Scheme. Multicoloured.

No.	Description	Unused	Used
305.	5p Type 87	15	15
306.	10p. "Physical acitivities"	20	20
307.	15p. "Service"	25	25
308.	40p. Duke of Edinburgh ..	70	70

88. Scout crossing Rope Bridge.

1982. 75th Anniv. of Boy Scout Movement.

No.	Type	Description	Unused	Used
309.	88.	10 p. black, blue and light blue	45	35
310.	–	15 p. black, brown and yellow	55	50
311.	–	25 p. black, mauve and light mauve	75	60
312.	–	40 p. black, red and orange	1·10	85

DESIGNS: 15 p. 1st Ascension Scout Group flag. 25 p. Scouts learning to use radio. 40 p. Lord Baden-Powell.

89. Charles Darwin.

1982. 150th Anniv. of Charles Darwin's Voyage. Multicoloured.

No.	Description	Unused	Used
314.	10 p. Type 89	50	40
315.	12 p. Darwin's pistols ..	55	50
316.	15 p. Rock Crab	60	55
317.	40 p. H.M.S. " Beagle " ..	1·10	95

90. Fairey " Swordfish ".

1982. 40th Anniv. of Wideawake Airfield. Multicoloured.

No.	Description	Unused	Used
318.	5 p. Type 90	50	35
319.	10 p. North American " B-25C (Mitchell) " ..	70	40
320.	15 p. Boeing " EC-135N (Aria) "	90	55
321.	50 p. Lockheed " Hercules "	1·50	1·10

91. Ascension Coat of Arms.

1982. 21st Birthday of Princess of Wales. Multicoloured.

No.	Description	Unused	Used
322.	12 p. Type 91	35	30
323.	15 p. Lady Diana Spencer in Music Room, Buckingham Palace	40	35
324.	25 p. Bride and Earl Spencer leaving Clarence House	65	55
325.	50 p. Formal portrait ..	1·10	1·00

1982. Commonwealth Games, Brisbane. Nos. 290/1 optd. **1st PARTICIPATION COMMONWEALTH GAMES 1982.**

No.	Description	Unused	Used
326.	15p. Yellow Allamanda ..	30	40
327.	20p. Ascension Euphorbia	40	45

94. Bush House, London.

1982. 50th Anniv. of B.B.C. External Broadcasting. Multicoloured.

No.	Description	Unused	Used
328.	5p. Type 94	25	25
329.	10p. Atlantic relay station	35	35
330.	25p. Lord Reith, first Director-General ..	75	75
331.	40p. King George V making his first Christmas broadcast, 1932	1·00	1·00

95. "Marasmius echinosphaerus".

1983. Fungi. Multicoloured.

No.	Description	Unused	Used
332	7p. Type 95	35	25
333	12p. "Chlorophyllum molybdites"	45	35
334	15p. "Leucocoprinus cepaestripes"	50	40
335	20p. "Lycoperdon marginatum"	65	50
336	50p. "Marasmiellus distantifolius"	1·10	1·00

HAVE YOU READ THE NOTES AT THE BEGINNING OF THIS CATALOGUE?

These often provide answers to the enquiries we receive.

96. Aerial View of Georgetown.

1983. Island Views (1st series). Multicoloured.

337.	12p. Type **96**	25	30
338.	15p. Green Mountain farm	30	35
339.	20p. Boatswain Bird Island	40	45
340.	60p. Telemetry Hill by night	1·25	1·40

See also Nos. 367/70.

97. "Wessex 5" Helicopter of No. 845 Naval Air Squadron.

1983. Bicentenary of Manned Flight. British Military Aircraft. Multicoloured.

341.	12p. Type **97**	60	35
342.	15p. "Vulcan B2" of No. 44 Squadron	70	40
343.	20p. "Nimrod MR2P" of No. 120 Squadron	85	50
344.	60p. "Victor K2" of No. 55 Squadron	1·75	1·60

98. Iguanid.

1983. Introduced Species. Multicoloured.

345.	12p. Type **98**	30	30
346.	15p. Common rabbit . .	35	35
347.	20p. Cat	45	45
348.	60p. Donkey	1·40	1·40

99. "Tellina antonii Philippi".

1983. Sea Shells. Multicoloured.

349.	7p. Type **99**	20	20
350.	12p. "Nodipecten nodosus"	30	30
351.	15p. "Cypraea lurida oceanic Sch"	35	35
352.	20p. "Nerita ascensionis Gmelin"	45	45
353.	50p. "Micromelo undatus (Bruguiere)"	1·10	1·10

100. 1922 1½d. Stamp.

1984. 150th Anniv. of St. Helena as a British Colony. Multicoloured.

354.	12p. Type **100**	35	35
355.	15p. 1922 2d. stamp . .	40	40
356.	20p. 1922 8d. stamp . .	45	45
357.	60p. 1922 1s. stamp . .	1·25	1·40

102. Naval Semaphore.

1984. 250th Anniv. of "Lloyd's List" (newspaper). Multicoloured.

359.	12p. Type **102**	30	30
360.	15p. "Southampton Castle" (liner)	35	35
361.	20p. Pier Head	45	45
362.	70p. "The Dane" (mail ship)	1·50	1·50

103. Penny Coin and Yellowfin Tuna.

1984. New Coinage. Multicoloured.

363.	12p. Type **103**	50	35
364.	15p. Twopenny coin and donkey	60	40
365.	20p. Fifty pence coin and Green Turtle	75	50
366.	70p. Pound coin and Sooty Tern	2·00	1·75

1984. Island Views (2nd series). As T **96**. Multicoloured.

367.	12p. The Devil's Riding-school	30	30
368.	15p. St. Mary's Church . .	35	35
369.	20p. Two Boats Village . .	45	45
370.	70p. Ascension from the sea	1·50	1·50

104. Bermuda Cypress.

1985. Trees. Multicoloured.

371.	7p. Type **104**	45	20
372.	12p. Norfolk Island Pine . .	55	30
373.	15p. Screwpine	65	35
374.	20p. Eucalyptus	80	45
375.	65p. Spore Tree	2·00	1·40

105. The Queen Mother with Prince Andrew at Silver Jubilee Service.

1985. Life and Times of Queen Elizabeth the Queen Mother. Multicoloured.

376.	12p. With the Duke of York at Balmoral, 1924	30	30
377.	15p. Type **105**	35	35
378.	20p. The Queen Mother at Ascot	45	45
379.	70p. With Prince Henry at his christening (from photo by Lord Snowdon)	1·50	1·50

106. 32 Pdr. Smooth Bore Muzzle-loader, *c.* 1820, and Royal Marine Artillery Hat Plate, *c.* 1816.

1985. Guns on Ascension Island. Mult.

381.	12p. Type **106**	50	35
382.	15p. 7 inch rifled muzzle-loader c. 1866 and Royal Cypher on barrel	60	40
383.	20p. 7 pdr rifled muzzle-loader, c. 1877, and Royal Artillery Badge . .	70	50
384.	70p. 5.5 inch gun, 1941, and crest from H.M.S. "Hood"	2·00	1·75

107. Guide Flag.

1985. 75th Anniv. of Girl Guide Movement and International Youth Year. Multicoloured.

385.	12p. Type **107**	55	45
386.	15p. Practising first aid . .	65	40
387.	20p. Camping	75	50
388.	70p. Lady Baden-Powell . .	2·25	2·00

108. "Clerodendrum fragrans".

1985. Wild Flowers. Multicoloured.

389.	12p. Type **108**	45	35
390.	15p. Shell ginger	55	40
391.	20p. Cape daisy	65	50
392.	70p. Ginger lily	2·00	1·75

109. Newton's Reflector Telescope.

1986. Appearance of Halley's Comet. Mult.

393.	12p. Type **109**	60	40
394.	15p. Edmond Halley and Old Greenwich Observatory	70	45
395.	20p. Short's Gregorian telescope and comet, 1759 . .	80	55
396.	70p. Ascension satellite tracking station and ICE spacecraft	2·25	1·75

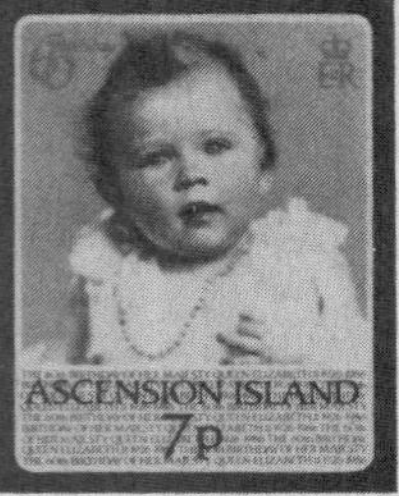

110. Princess Elizabeth in 1926.

1986. 60th Birthday of Queen Elizabeth II. Multicoloured.

397.	7p. Type **110**	15	20
398.	15p. Queen making Christmas broadcast, 1952 . .	30	35
399.	20p. At Garter ceremony, Windsor Castle, 1983 . .	40	45
400.	35p. In Auckland, New Zealand, 1981	70	75
401.	£1 At Crown Agents' Head Office, London, 1983 . .	2·00	2·10

111. 1975 Space Satellites 2p. Stamp.

1986. "Ameripex '86" International Stamp Exhibition, Chicago. Designs showing previous Ascension stamps. Multicoloured.

402.	12p. Type **111**	25	30
403.	15p. 1980 "London 1980" International Stamp Exhibition 50p	30	35
404.	20p. 1976 Bicentenary of American Revolution 8p.	40	45
405.	70p. 1982 40th Anniv. of Wideawake Airfield 10p.	1·40	1·50

112. Prince Andrew and Miss Sarah Ferguson.

1986. Royal Wedding. Multicoloured.

407.	15p. Type **112**	35	35
408.	35p. Prince Andrew aboard H.M.S. "Brazen"	75	75

113. H.M.S. "Ganymede" (c. 1811).

1986. Ships of the Royal Navy. Mult.

409.	1p. Type **113**	15	15
410.	2p. H.M.S. "Kangaroo" (c. 1811)	15	15
411.	4p. H.M.S. "Trinculo" (c. 1811)	20	20
412.	5p. H.M.S. "Daring" (c. 1811)	20	20
413.	9p. H.M.S. "Thais" (c. 1811)	30	30
414.	10p. H.M.S. "Pheasant" (1819)	30	30
415.	15p. H.M.S. "Myrmidon" (1819)	40	40
416.	18p. H.M.S. "Atholl" (1825)	40	40
417.	20p. H.M.S. "Medina" (1830)	45	45
418.	25p. H.M.S. "Saracen" (1840)	60	60
419.	30p. H.M.S. "Hydra" (c. 1845)	70	70
420.	50p. H.M.S. "Sealark" (1849)	1·25	1·25
421.	70p. H.M.S. "Rattlesnake" (1868) . .	1·75	1·75
422.	£1 H.M.S. "Penelope" (1889)	2·40	2·40
423.	£2 H.M.S. "Monarch" (1897)	4·50	4·50

114. Cape Gooseberry.

1987. Edible Bush Fruits. Multicoloured.

No.	Description	Unused	Used
424.	12p. Type **114**	55	55
425.	15p. Prickly pear	60	60
426.	20p. Guava	70	70
427.	70p. Loquat	1·75	1·75

115. Ignition of Rocket Motors.

1987. 25th Anniv. of First American Manned Earth Orbit. Multicoloured.

No.	Description	Unused	Used
428.	15p. Type **115**	45	45
429.	18p. Lift-off	50	50
430.	25p. Re-entry	65	65
431.	£1 Splashdown	2·25	2·25

116. Captains in Full Dress raising Red Ensign.

1987. 19th-century Uniforms (1st series). Royal Navy, 1815–20. Multicoloured.

No.	Description	Unused	Used
433.	25p. Type **116**	60	60
434.	25p. Surgeon and seamen	60	60
435.	25p. Seaman with water-carrying donkey	60	60
436.	25p. Midshipman and gun	60	60
437.	25p. Commander in undress uniform surveying	60	60

See also Nos. 478/82.

117. "Cynthia cardui".

1987 Insects (1st series). Multicoloured.

No.	Description	Unused	Used
438	15p. Type **117**	55	55
439	18p. "Danaus chrysippus"	60	60
440	25p. "Hypolimnas misippus"	75	75
441	£1 "Lampides boeticus"	2·25	2·25

See also Nos. 452/5 and 483/6.

118. Male Ascension Frigate Birds.

1987. Sea Birds (1st series). Multicoloured.

No.	Description	Unused	Used
442.	25p. Type **118**	80	80
443.	25p. Juvenile Ascension frigate bird, brown booby and white boobies	80	80
444.	25p. Male Ascension frigate bird and white boobies	80	80
445.	25p. Female Ascension frigate bird	80	80
446.	25p. Adult male feeding juvenile Ascension frigate bird	80	80

Nos. 442/6 were printed together, se-tenant, forming a composite design.

See also Nos 469/73.

1987. Royal Ruby Wedding. Nos. 397/401 optd. **40TH WEDDING ANNIVERSARY.**

No.	Description	Unused	Used
447.	7p Type **110**	15	20
448.	15p Queen making Christmas broadcast, 1952	30	35
449.	20p. At Garter ceremony, Windsor Castle, 1983	40	45
450.	35p. In Auckland, New Zealand, 1981	70	75
451.	£1 At Crown Agents' Head Office, London, 1983	2·00	2·10

1988. Insects (2nd series). As T **117**. Mult.

No.	Description	Unused	Used
452	15p. "Gryllus bimaculatus" (field cricket)	50	50
453	18p. "Ruspolia differeus" (bush cricket)	55	55
454	25p. "Chilomenus lunata" (ladybird)	70	70
455	£1 "Diachrysia orichalcea" (moth)	2·25	2·25

120. Bate's Memorial, St. Mary's Church.

1988. 150th Death Anniv. of Captain William Bate (garrison commander, 1828–38). Mult.

No.	Description	Unused	Used
456.	9p. Type **120**	35	35
457.	15p. Commodore's Cottage	45	45
458.	18p. North East Cottage	50	50
459.	25p. Map of Ascension	70	70
460.	70p. Captain Bate and marines	1·75	1·75

121 H.M.S. "Resolution" (ship of the line), 1667

1988. Bicentenary of Australian Settlement. Ships of the Royal Navy. Multicoloured.

No.	Description	Unused	Used
461	9p. Type **121**	45	35
462	18p. H.M.S. "Resolution" (Captain Cook), 1772	65	55
463	25p. H.M.S. "Resolution" (battleship), 1892	85	75
464	65p. H.M.S. "Resolution" (battleship), 1916	1·50	1·50

1988. "Sydpex '88" National Stamp Exhibition, Sydney. Nos. 461/4 optd **SYDPEX 88 30.7.88 -7.8.88.**

No.	Description	Unused	Used
465	9p. Type **121**	25	25
466	18p. H.M.S. "Resolution" (Captain Cook), 1772	40	40
467	25p. H.M.S. "Resolution" (battleship), 1892	55	55
468	65p. H.M.S. "Resolution" (battleship), 1916	1·40	1·40

1988. Sea Birds (2nd series). Sooty Tern. As T **118**. Multicoloured.

No.	Description	Unused	Used
469	25p. Pair displaying	90	90
470	25p. Turning egg	90	90
471	25p. Incubating egg	90	90
472	25p. Feeding chick	90	90
473	25p. Immature sooty tern	90	90

Nos. 469/73 were printed together, se-tenant, forming a composite design of a nesting colony.

123 Lloyd's Coffee House, London, 1688

1988. 300th Anniv of Lloyd's of London. Mult.

No.	Description	Unused	Used
474	8p. Type **123**	25	25
475	18p. "Alert" (cable ship) (horiz)	50	50
476	25p. Satellite recovery in space (horiz)	70	70
477	65p. "Good Hope Castle" on fire off Ascension, 1973	1·50	1·50

1988. 19th-century Uniforms (2nd series). Royal Marines 1821-34. As T **116**. Mult.

No.	Description	Unused	Used
478	25p. Marines landing on Ascension, 1821	90	90
479	25p. Officer and Marine at semaphore station, 1829	90	90
480	25p. Sergeant and Marine at Octagonal Tank, 1831	90	90
481	25p. Officers at water pipe tunnel, 1833	90	90
482	25p. Officer supervising construction of barracks, 1834	90	90

1989. Insects (3rd series). As T **117**. Mult.

No.	Description	Unused	Used
483	15p. Trichoptilus wahlbergi" (moth)	40	35
484	18p. "Lucilia sericata" (fly)	45	40
485	25p. "Alceis ornatus" (weevil)	60	55
486	£1 "Polistes fuscatus" (wasp)	2·40	2·10

124 Two Land Crabs

1989. Ascension Land Crabs. Multicoloured.

No.	Description	Unused	Used
487	15p. Type **124**	40	40
488	18p. Crab with claws raised	45	45
489	25p. Crab on rock	60	60
490	£1 Crab in surf	2·25	2·25

126 "Apollo 7" Tracking Station, Ascension

1989. 20th Anniv of First Manned Landing on Moon. Multicoloured.

No.	Description	Unused	Used
493	15p. Type **126**	30	35
494	18p. Launch of "Apollo 7" (30×30 mm)	35	40
495	25p. "Apollo 7" emblem (30×30 mm)	50	55
496	70p. "Apollo 7" jettisoning expended Saturn rocket	1·40	1·50

127 "Queen Elizabeth 2" and Aircraft Carrier in New York Harbour

1989. "Philexfrance 89" International Stamp Exhibition, Paris, and "World Stamp Expo '89", Washington. Designs Showing Statue of Liberty and Centenary celebrations. Multicoloured.

No.	Description	Unused	Used
498	15p. Type **127**	30	35
499	15p. Cleaning statue	30	35
500	15p. Statue of Liberty	30	35
501	15p. Crown of statue	30	35
502	15p. Warships and New York skyline	30	35
503	15p. French warship and skyscrapers	30	35

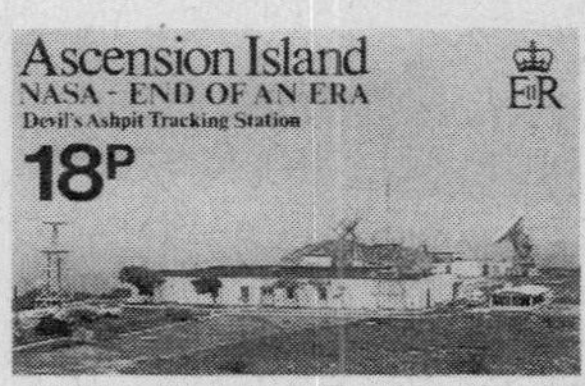

128 Devil's Ashpit Tracking Station

1989. Closure of Devil's Ashpit Tracking Station, Ascension. Multicoloured.

No.	Description	Unused	Used
504	18p. Type **128**	45	50
505	25p. Launch of shuttle "Atlantis"	50	55

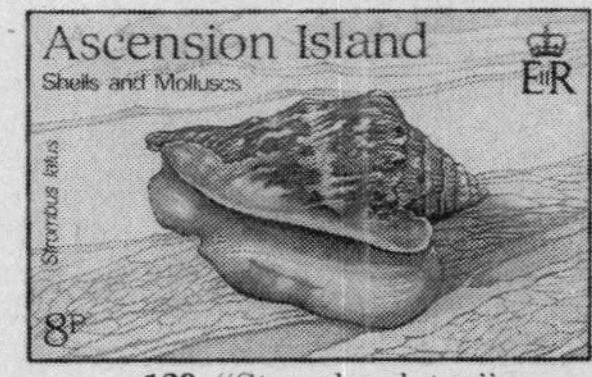

129 "Strombus latus"

1989. Sea Shells. Multicoloured.

No.	Description	Unused	Used
506	8p. Type **129**	25	20
507	18p. "Tonna galea"	45	40
508	25p. "Harpa doris"	60	55
509	£1 "Charonia variegata"	2·25	2·25

130 Donkeys

131 Seaman's Pistol, Hat and Cutlass

1989. Multicoloured.

No.	Description	Unused	Used
510	18p. Type **130**	35	40
511	25p. Green turtle	50	55

1990. Royal Navy Equipment, 1815–20. Mult.

No.	Description	Unused	Used
512	25p. Type **131**	60	60
513	25p. Midshipman's belt plate, button, sword and hat	60	60
514	25p. Surgeon's hat, sword and instrument chest	60	60
515	25p. Captain's hat, telescope and sword	60	60
516	25p. Admiral's epaulette, megaphone, hat and pocket	60	60

See also Nos. 541/5.

132 Pair of Ascension Frigate Birds with Young

1990. Ascension Frigate Bird. Multicoloured.

517	9p. Type **132**	30	30
518	10p. Fledgeling	35	35
519	11p. Adult male in flight	35	35
520	15p. Female and immature birds in flight	40	40

133 Penny Black and Twopence Blue

1990. "Stamp World London 90" International Stamp Exhibition. Multicoloured.

521	9p. Type **133**	30	30
522	18p. Ascension postmarks used on G.B. stamps	50	50
523	25p. Unloading mail at Wideawake Airfield	75	75
524	£1 Mail van and Main Post Office	2·25	2·25

134 "Queen Elizabeth, 1940" (Sir Gerald Kelly)

1990. 90th Birthday of Queen Elizabeth the Queen Mother.

525	**134**	25p. multicoloured	75	75
526	–	£1 black and lilac	2·25	2·25

DESIGN—(29 × 37 mm) £1 King George VI and Queen Elizabeth with Bren-gun carrier.

136 "Madonna and Child" (sculpture, Dino Felici)

1990. Christmas. Works of Art. Multicoloured.

527	8p. Type **136**	30	30
528	18p. "Madonna and Child" (anon)	60	60
529	25p. "Madonna and Child with St. John" (Johann Gebhard)	85	85
530	65p. "Madonna and Child" (Giacomo Gritti)	2·00	2·00

137 "Garth Castle" (mail ship), 1910

1990. Maiden Voyage of "St. Helena II". Multicoloured.

531	9p. Type **137**	35	35
532	18p. "St. Helena I" during Falkland Islands campaign, 1982	55	55
533	25p. Launch of "St. Helena II"	75	75
534	70p. Duke of York launching "St. Helena II"	2·00	2·00

1991. 175th Anniv of Occupation. Nos. 418, 420 and 422 optd **BRITISH FOR 175 YEARS**.

536	25p. H.M.S. "Saracen" (1840)	75	75
537	50p. H.M.S. "Sealark" (1849)	1·50	1·50
538	£1 H.M.S. "Penelope" (1889)	2·50	2·50

139 Queen Elizabeth II at Trooping the Colour

1991. 65th Birthday of Queen Elizabeth II and 70th Birthday of Prince Philip. Mult.

539	25p. Type **139**	75	80
540	25p. Prince Philip in naval uniform	75	70

1991. Royal Marines Equipment, 1821–44. As T **131**. Multicoloured.

541	25p. Officer's shako, epaulettes, belt plate and button	70	75
542	25p. Officer's cap, sword, epaulettes and belt plate	70	75
543	25p. Drum major's shako and staff	70	75
544	25p. Sergeant's shako, chevrons, belt plate and canteen	70	75
545	25p. Drummer's shako and side-drum	70	75

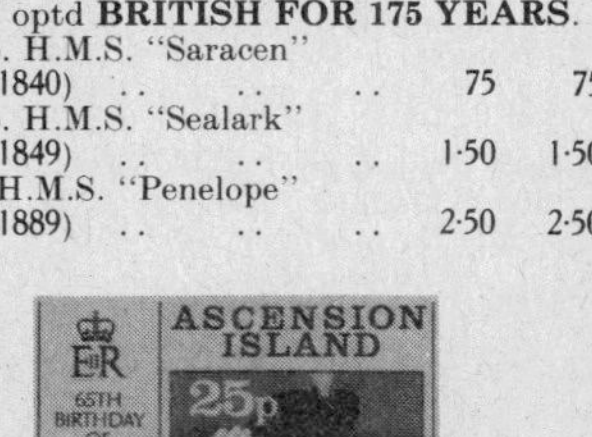

140 B.B.C. World Service Relay Station

1991. 25th Anniv of B.B.C. Atlantic Relay Station. Multicoloured.

546	15p. Type **140**	30	35
547	18p. Transmitters at English Bay	35	40
548	25p. Satellite receiving station (vert)	50	55
549	70p. Antenna support tower (vert)	1·40	1·50

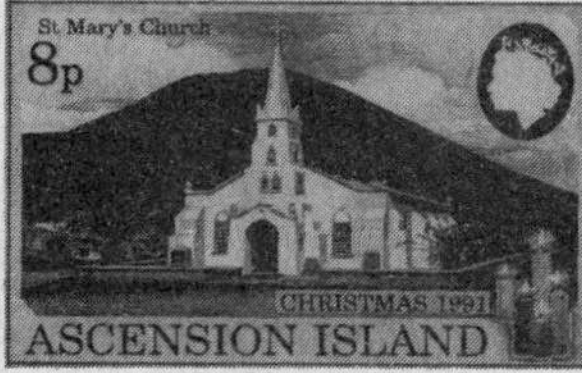

141 St. Mary's Church

1991. Christmas. Ascension Churches. Mult.

550	8p. Type **141**	15	20
551	18p. Interior of St. Mary's Church	35	40
552	25p. Our Lady of Ascension Grotto	50	55
553	65p. Interior of Our Lady of Ascension Grotto	1·25	1·40

142 Blackfish

1991. Fishes. Multicoloured.

554	1p. Type **142**	10	10
555	2p. Five finger	10	10
556	4p. Resplendent angelfish	10	10
557	5p. Silver fish	10	15
558	9p. Gurnard	20	25
559	10p. Blue dad	20	25
560	15p. Cunning fish	30	35
561	18p. Grouper	35	40
562	20p. Moray eel	40	45
563	25p. Hardback soldierfish	50	55
564	30p. Blue marlin	60	65
565	50p. Wahoo	1·00	1·10
566	70p. Yellowfin tuna	1·40	1·50
567	£1 Blue shark	2·00	2·10
568	£2.50 Bottlenose dolphin	5·00	5·25

143 Holland's Crater

1992. 40th Anniv of Queen Elizabeth II's Accession. Multicoloured.

569	9p. Type **143**	20	25
570	15p. Green Mountain	30	35
571	18p. Boatswain Bird Island	35	40
572	25p. Three portraits of Queen Elizabeth	50	55
573	70p. Queen Elizabeth II	1·40	1·50

The portraits shown on the 25p. are repeated from the three lower values of the set.

144 Compass Rose and "Eye of the Wind" (cadet ship)

1992. 500th Anniv of Discovery of America by Columbus and Re-enactment Voyages. Multicoloured.

574	9p. Type **144**	20	25
575	18p. Map of re-enactment voyages and "Soren Larsen" (cadet ship)	35	40
576	25p. "Santa Maria", "Pinta" and "Nina"	50	55
577	70p. Columbus and "Santa Maria"	1·40	1·50

POSTAGE DUE STAMPS

D **1**. Outline Map of Ascension.

1986.

D1.	D **1**	1p. dp. brown & brn.	10	10
D2.		2p. brown and orange	10	10
D3.		5p. brown and orange	10	10
D4.		7p. black and violet	15	20
D5.		10p. black and blue	20	25
D6.		25p. black and green	50	55

AUSTRALIA

An island continent to the S.E. of Asia. A Commonwealth consisting of the states of New S. Wales, Queensland, S. Australia, Tasmania, Victoria and W. Australia.

1913. 12 pence = 1 shilling.
20 shillings = 1 pound.
1966. 100 cents = 1 dollar.

1. Eastern Grey Kangaroo.

1913.

1	**1**	½d. green	5·00	1·50
2eb		1d. red	6·50	50
3		2d. grey	24·00	2·75
36		2½d. blue	22·00	7·00
37		3d. green	27·00	3·00
6		4d. orange	48·00	22·00
8		5d. brown	40·00	28·00
38		6d. blue	48·00	6·00
73		6d. brown	20·00	1·00
133		9d. violet	20·00	75
40a		1s. green	35·00	2·50
41		2s. brown	£150	9·00
134		2s. red	5·00	45
135		5s. grey and yellow	£100	9·50
136		10s. grey and red	£250	£100
44		£1 brown and blue	£1300	£700
137		£1 grey	£425	£150
138		£2 black and red	£1600	£300

3.

4. Laughing Kookaburra.

1913.

29a	**3**	½d green	3·25	60
94		½d. orange	1·50	75
30		1d. red	7·00	20
57		1d. violet	4·50	60
125		1d. green	1·50	10
59		1½d. brown	4·75	30
61		1½d. green	2·00	25
97		1½d. red	1·50	30
62a		2d. orange	15·00	35
127		2d. red	1·75	10
99		2d. brown	7·00	7·00
128		3d. blue	16·00	55
32		4d. orange	38·00	2·25
64		4d. violet	9·00	10·00
65		4d. blue	48·00	5·50
129		4d. green	16·00	80
92		4½d. violet	15·00	3·00
130		5d. brown	14·00	15
131		1s. 4d. blue	70·00	3·25

1913.

19.	**4.**	6d. red	70·00	38·00

8. Parliament House, Canberra.

1927. Opening of Parliament House.

105.	**8.**	1½d. red	60	50

1928. National Stamp Exhibition, Melbourne.

106.	**4.**	3d. blue	4·25	4·25

9. "DH66" Biplane and Pastoral Scene.

1929. Air.

115.	**9.**	3d. green	10·00	3·25

10. Black Swan.

1929. Centenary Western Australia.

116. **10.** 1½d. red .. .. 1·00 1·25

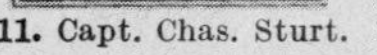

11. Capt. Chas. Sturt. **17.** Superb Lyrebird.

13. The "Southern Cross" above Hemispheres.

1930. Centenary of Sturt's Exploration of River Murray.

117. **11.** 1½d. red .. .. .. 1·00 45
118. 3d. blue .. .. .. 3·75 5·00

1930. Surch. in words.

119. **5a.** 2d. on 1½d. red .. .. 1·00 40
120. 5d. on 4½d. violet .. 7·00 7·50

1931. Kingsford Smith's Flights.

121. **13.** 2d. red (postage) .. 75 45
122. 3d. blue .. .. .. 5·00 4·00
123. 6d. purple (air) .. .. 10·00 10·00

1931. Air. As T **13** but inscr. "AIR MAIL SERVICE".

139. – 6d. brown .. .. 16·00 12·00

1931. Air. No. 139 optd. **O.S.**

139a. – 6d. brown .. .. 35·00 42·00

1932.

140. **17.** 1s. green .. .. 50·00 1·00

18. Sydney Harbour Bridge.

1932.

144 **18.** 2d. red .. .. .. 2·75 85
142 3d. blue .. .. .. 4·00 7·00
143 5s. green £375 £180

19. Laughing Kookaburra.

1932.

146. **19.** 6d. red .. .. .. 25·00 45

20. Melbourne and R. Yarra.

1934. Centenary of Victoria.

147. **20.** 2d. red .. .. .. 2·50 1·25
148. 3d. blue .. .. .. 6·00 5·50
149. 1s. black .. .. .. 48·00 12·00

21. Merino Ram.

1934. Death Centenary of Capt. John MacArthur.

150. **21.** 2d. red .. .. .. 3·25 1·25
151. 3d. blue .. .. .. 9·00 8·00
152. 9d. purple .. .. .. 35·00 32·00

22. Hermes.

1934.

153b 22 1s. 6d. purple .. .. 8·00 45

23. Cenotaph, Whitehall. **24.** King George V on "Anzac".

1935. 20th Anniv. of Gallipoli Landing.

154. **23.** 2d. red 80 30
155. 1s. black .. .. 48·00 38·00

1935. Silver Jubilee.

156. **24.** 2d. red .. .. .. 1·00 30
157. 3d. blue .. .. .. 6·00 6·00
158. 2s. violet .. .. 45·00 38·00

25. Amphitrite and Telephone Cable.

1936. Opening of Submarine Telephone Cable to Tasmania.

159. **25.** 2d. red 60 35
160 3d. blue .. .. .. 2·50 3·25

26. Site of Adelaide, 1836. Old Gum Tree Glenelg; King William St., Adelaide.

1936. Centenary of South Australia.

161. **26.** 2d. red .. .. .. 1·00 30
162. 3d. blue .. .. .. 5·50 4·50
163. 1s. green .. .. 10·00 8·00

27. Wallaroo. **28.** Queen Elizabeth.

29. King George VI. **30.**

31. King George VI. **33.** Merino Ram.

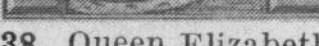

38. Queen Elizabeth.

DESIGNS—As Type **28.** 4d. Koala. 6d. Kookaburra, 1s. Lyre Bird. As Type **33**: 9d. Platypus. As Type **38**: 10s. K. George VI.

40. King George VI and Queen Elizabeth.

1937.

228 **27.** ½d. orange 20 10
165 **28.** 1d. green 30 10
180 – 1d. green .. .. 1·50 10
181 – 1d. purple .. .. 1·25 10
182 **29.** 1½d. purple .. .. 4·50 7·50
183 1½d. green .. .. 1·00 30
167 **30.** 2d. red 30 10
184 – 2d. red .. .. .. 2·50 10
185 **30.** 2d. purple 50 50
186 **31.** 3d. blue .. .. .. 42·00 2·25
187 3d. brown 30 10
188 – 4d. green .. .. 1·50 10
188a **33.** 5d. purple .. .. 45 1·50
189a – 6d. brown .. .. 1·75 10
190 – 9d. brown 80 10
191 – 1s. green .. .. 1·00 10
175a **31.** 1s 4d. mauve .. .. 1·50 1·50
176a **38.** 5s. red .. .. .. 7·00 1·50
177 – 10s. purple .. .. 35·00 11·00
178 **40.** £1 slate .. .. 60·00 28·00

Nos. 180 and 184 are as Types **28 and 30** but with completely shaded background.

41. Governor Phillip at Sydney Cove. (J. Allcot).

1937. 150th Anniv. of New South Wales.

193. **41.** 2d. red .. .. 2·00 15
194. 3d. blue .. .. 10·00 2·25
195. 9d. purple .. .. 22·00 8·00

42. A.I.F. and Nurse.

1940. Australian Imperial Forces.

196. **42.** 1d. green .. .. 1·50 70
197. 2d. red .. .. .. 1·50 15
198. 3d. blue .. .. .. 9·00 6·50
199. 6d. purple .. .. 20·00 10·00

1941. Surch. with figures and bars.

200. **30.** 2½d. on 2d. red .. 1·25 20
201. **31.** 3½d. on 3d. blue . 1·50 1·50
202. **33.** 5½d. on 5d. purple .. 7·50 3·25

46a. Queen Elizabeth. **47.** King George VI.

48. King George VI. **49.**

50. Emu. **52.** Duke and Duchess of Gloucester.

1942.

203. **46a.** 1d. purple 20 10
204. 1½d. green 20 10
204a. **47.** 2d. purple 40 25
205. **48.** 2½d. red 20 10
206. **49.** 3½d. blue 25 10
207. **50.** 5½d. grey 65 10

1945. Royal Visit.

209. **52.** 2½d. red 10 10
210. 3½d. blue 15 25
211. 5½d. grey 20 30

53. Star and Wreath.

1946. Victory. Inscr. "PEACE 1945".

213. **53.** 2½d. red 10 10
214. – 3½d. blue 25 75
215. – 5½d. green 30 50

DESIGNS—HORIZ. 3½d. Flag and dove. VERT. 5½d. Angel.

56. Sir Thomas Mitchell and Queensland.

1946. Centenary of Mitchell's Central Queensland Exploration.

216. **56.** 2½d. red 10 10
217. 3½d. blue 20 50
218. 1s. green 25 20

57. Lt. John Shortland, R.N. **58.** Steel Foundry.

1947. 150th Anniv. of City of Newcastle.

219. **57.** 2½d. lake 10 10
220. **58.** 3½d. blue 20 40
221. – 5½d. green 20 30

DESIGN—As Type **58:** HORIZ. 5½d. Coal carrier Cranes.

60. Queen Elizabeth II when Princess.

1947. Wedding of Princess Elizabeth.

222 **60** 1d. purple 15 10

61. Hereford Bull. **61a.** Hermes and Globe.

62. Aboriginal Art. **62a.** Commonwealth Coat of Arms.

1948.

223. **61.** 1s. 3d. brown .. .. 1·75 85
223a. **61a.** 1s. 6d. brown .. .. 1·75 10
224. **62.** 2s. brown .. .. 2·00 10
224a. **62a.** 5s. red .. .. .. 7·00 20
224b. 10s. purple .. .. 30·00 45
224c. £1 blue .. .. 48·00 2·75
224d. £2 green .. .. £100 14·00

63. William J. Farrer. **64.** Ferdinand von Mueller.

1948. W. J. Farrer (wheat research).

225. **63.** 2½d. red 10 10

1948. Sir Ferdinand von Mueller (botanist).

226. **64.** 2½d. red 10 10

65. Boy Scout.

65. "Henry Lawson". (Sir Lionel Lindsey).

1948. Pan-Pacific Scout Jamboree, Wonga Park.

227. 65. 2½d. lake 10 10

For 3½d. value dated "1952–53", see No. 254.

1949. Birth Anniv. of Henry Lawson (poet).

231. 66. 2½d. purple 15 10

67. Mounted Postman and Aeroplane.

1949. 75th Anniversary of U.P.U.

232. 67. 3½d. blue 20 25

68. Lord Forrest of Bunbury.

1949. Lord Forrest (explorer and politician).

233. 68. 2½d. red 15 10

69. King George VI.

70. Queen Elizabeth.

POSTAGE 7½d AUSTRALIA

81. King George VI. 80.

71. Aborigine.

82. King George VI.

1950.

236	70	1½d. green	15	10
237		2d. green	15	10
234	69	2½d. red	10	10
235a		2½d. brown	15	15
235		3d. red	15	10
235b		3d. green	15	10
248	81	3½d. purple	10	10
249		4½d. red	15	60
250		6½d. brown	15	55
251		6½d. green	10	15
247	80	7½d. blue	15	45
238	71	8½d. brown	15	40
252	82	1s. 0½d. blue	35	30
253	71	2s. 6d. brown (21 × 25½ mm)	2·50	35

AUSTRALIA ONE HUNDRED YEARS

72. 73.

Reproduction of First Stamps of N.S.W. and Victoria.

1950. Centenary of Australian States Stamps.

239. 72. 2½d. purple 10 10
240. 73. 2½d. purple 10 10

75. Sir Henry Parkes.

DESIGNS—As Type **70**: No. 242, Sir Edmund Barton. As Type **77**: No. 243. Opening first Federal Parliament.

77. Federal Parliament House, Canberra.

1951. 50th Anniv. of Commonwealth. Inscr. as in T **75** and **77**.

241. 75. 3d. lake 30 10
242. – 3d. lake 30 10
243. – 5½d. blue .. .. .. 20 1·50
244. 77. 1s. 6d. brown 35 50

78. E. H. Hargraves.

3d AUSTRALIA 3d 100 YEARS RESPONSIBLE GOVERNMENT IN VICTORIA 1951

79. C. J. Latrobe.

1951. Cent. of Discovery of Gold in Australia.

245. 78. 3d. purple 30 10

1951. Centenary of Responsible Government in Victoria.

246. 79. 3d. purple 30 10

1952. Pan-Pacific Scout Jamboree, Greystanes. As T **65** but dated "1952–53".

254. 65. 3½d. lake 10 10

83. Butter.

86. Queen Elizabeth II.

1953. Food Production. Inscr. "PRODUCE FOOD!".

255. 83. 3d. green 30 10
256. – 3d. green (Wheat) .. 30 10
257. – 3d. green (Beef) .. 30 10
258. 83. 3½d. red 30 10
259. – 3½d. red (Wheat) .. 30 10
260. – 3½d. red (Beef) .. 30 10

1953.

261. 86. 1d. purple 15 10
261a. 2½d. blue 20 10
262. 3d. green 20 10
263. 3½d. red 20 10
263a. 6½d. orange .. .. 1·50 10

87. Queen Elizabeth II.

1953. Coronation.

264. 87. 3½d. red 35 10
265. 7½d. violet .. .. 1·50 55
266. 2s. turquoise .. .. 5·50 30

88. Young Farmers and Calf.

1953. 25th Anniv. of Australian Young Farmers' Clubs.

267. 88. 3½d. brown and green .. 10 10

89. Lt.-Gov. D. Collins.

90. Lt.-Gov. W. Paterson.

91. Sullivan Cove, Hobart, 1804.

1953. 150th Anniversary of Settlement in Tasmania.

268. 89. 3½d. purple 30 10
269. 90. 3½d. purple 30 10
270. 91. 2s. green .. .. 2·00 2·50

92. Stamp of 1853.

1953. 1st Cent. of Tasmania Postage Stamps.

271. 92. 3d. red 10 10

93. Queen Elizabeth II and Duke of Edinburgh.

94. Queen Elizabeth II.

95. "Telegraphic Communications".

1954. Royal Visit.

272. 93. 3½d. red 20 10
273. 94. 7½d. purple 35 60
274. 93. 2s. green 85 40

1954. Centenary of Telegraph.

275. 95. 3½d. brown 10 10

96. Red Cross and Globe.

1954. 40th Anniv. Australian Red Cross Society.

276. 96. 3½d. blue and red .. 10 10

97. Black Swan.

1954. Cent. of Western Australian Stamp.

277. 97. 3½d. black 10 10

98. Locomotives of 1854 and 1954.

1954. Centenary of Australian Railways.

278. 98. 3½d. purple 20 10

99. Territory Badge.

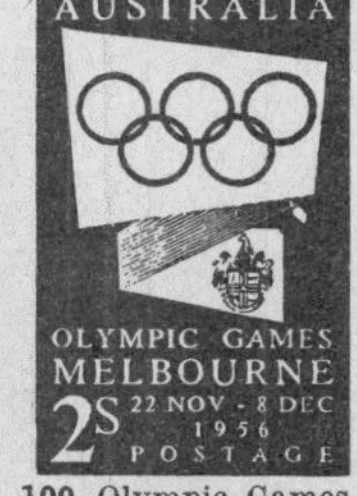

100. Olympic Games Symbol.

1954. Australian Antarctic Research.

279. 99. 3½d. black 15 10

1954. Olympic Games Propaganda.

280. 100. 2s. blue 70 40
280a. 2s. green .. .. 2·00 85

ROTARY INTERNATIONAL 1905–1955 "INTERNATIONAL UNDERSTANDING" 3½d AUSTRALIA

101. Rotary Symbol, Globe and Flags.

U.S.A. MEMORIAL 3½d AUSTRALIA

103. American Memorial, Canberra.

1955. 50th Anniv. of Rotary International.

281. 101. 3½d. red 10 10

1955. Australian-American Friendship.

283. 103. 3½d. blue 10 10

113. Queen Elizabeth II. 102.

1955.

294. 113. 4d. lake 30 10
294a. 7½d. violet .. .. 1·25 1·25
295. 10d. blue .. .. 1·50 30
282. 102. 1s. 0½d. blue .. 3·00 40
282a. 1s. 7d. brown .. .. 3·50 15

104. Cobb & Co. Coach (from dry-print by Sir Lionel Lindsey).

1955. Mail-coach Pioneers Commem.

284. 104. 3½d. sepia 25 10
285. 2s. brown .. .. 75 1·40

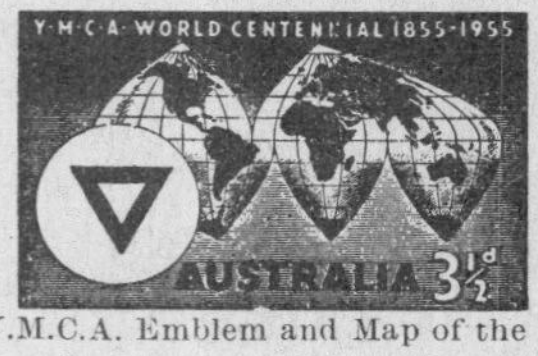

105. Y.M.C.A. Emblem and Map of the World.

1955. World Cent. of Y.M.C.A.

286. 105. 3½d. green and red .. 10 10

106. Florence Nightingale, and Young Nurse.

3½d FIRST STAMP OF SOUTH AUSTRALIA 3½d 1855 1955 AUSTRALIA

107. Queen Victoria.

1955. Nursing Profession Commemoration.

287. 106. 3½d. lilac 10 10

1955. Centenary of South Australian Postage Stamp.

288. 107. 3½d. green 10 10

108. Badges of N.S.W., Victoria and Tasmania.

1956. Centenary of Responsible Govt. in N.S.W., Victoria and Tasmania.

289. 108. 3½d. lake 10 10

109. Arms of Melbourne. **110.** Olympic Torch and Symbol.

111. Collins Street, Melbourne.

1956. Olympic Games, Melbourne.

290. **109.** 4d. red 25 10
291. **110.** $7\frac{1}{2}$d. blue 40 70
292. **111.** 1s. multicoloured . . 40 20
293. – 2s. multicoloured . . 50 70

DESIGN: As Type **111**: 2s. Melbourne across R. Yarra.

115. S. Australia Coat of Arms.

1957. Centenary of Responsible Government in South Australia.

296 **115** 4d. brown 10 10

116. Map of Australia and Caduceus.

1957. Royal Flying Doctor Service of Australia.

297 **116** 7d. blue 15 10

117. "The Spirit of Christmas" (Child) (after Sir Joshua Reynolds).

1957. Christmas.

298 **117** $3\frac{1}{2}$d. red 10 10
299 4d. purple 10 10

118. Super-Constellation Airliner.

1958. Inaug. of Australian "Round-the-World" Air Service.

301. **118.** 2s. blue 60 85

119. Hall of Memory, Sailor and Airmen.

1958.

302. **119.** $5\frac{1}{2}$d. lake 55 30
303. – $5\frac{1}{2}$d. lake 55 30

No. 303 shows a soldier and servicewoman instead of the sailor and airman.

120. Sir Charles Kingsford Smith and the "Southern Cross". **122.** The Nativity.

121. Silver Mine, Broken Hill.

1958. 30th Anniv. of 1st Air Crossing of the Tasman Sea.

304. **120.** 8d. blue 60 85

1958. 75th Anniv. of Founding of Broken Hill.

305. **121.** 4d. brown 15 10

1958. Christmas Issue.

306. **122.** $3\frac{1}{2}$d. red 15 10
307. 4d. violet 15 10

124. Queen Elizabeth II.

126. Queen Elizabeth II. **127.**

128. Queen Elizabeth II. **129.**

1959.

308. – 1d. purple 10 10
309. **124.** 2d. brown 30 15
311. **126.** 3d. turquoise . . 15 10
312. **127.** $3\frac{1}{2}$d. green . . 15 15
313. **128.** 4d. red . . . . 1·50 10
314. **129.** 5d. blue 70 10

No. 308 shows a head and shoulders portrait as in Type **128** and is vert.

131. Numbat. **137.** Christmas Bells.

142. Aboriginal Stockman.

1959.

316. **131.** 6d. brown . . . . 2·00 10
317. – 8d. red 75 10
318. – 9d. sepia . . . . 2·75 35
319. – 11d. blue . . . . 1·00 15
320. – 1s. green . . . . 4·50 30
321. – 1s. 2d. purple . . 1·00 15
322. **137.** 1s. 6d. red on yellow 2·50 80
323. – 2s. blue . . . . 1·25 10
324. – 2s. 3d. green on yellow . . . . 1·75 10
324a. – 2s. 3d. green . . 8·00 1·50
325. – 2s. 5d. brown on yellow . . . . 7·00 45
326. – 3s red . . . . 1·75 10
327. **142.** 5s. brown . . . . 25·00 75

DESIGNS—As Type **131**—VERT. 8d. Tiger Cat. 9d. Eastern grey kangaroo. 11d. Common rabbit bandicoot. 1s. Platypus. HORIZ. 1s. 2d. Thylacine. As Type **137**. 2s. Flannel Flower 2s. 3d. Wattle. 2s. 5d. Banksia (plant). 3s. Waratah.

143. Postmaster Isaac Nichols boarding the Brig "Experiment".

1959 150th Anniv. of Australian P.O.

331. **143.** 4d. slate 15 10

144. Parliament House, Brisbane and Arms of Queensland. **145.** "The Approach of the Magi".

1959. Cent. of Queensland Self-Government.

332. **144.** 4d. lilac and green . . 10 10

1959. Christmas.

333. **145.** 5d. violet 10 10

146. Girl Guide and Lord Baden-Powell.

1960. Golden Jubilee of Girl Guide Movement.

334. **146.** 5d. blue 30 15

147. "The Overlanders" (after Sir Daryl Lindsay).

1960. Centenary of Northern Territory Exploration.

335. **147.** 5d. mauve 15 15

148. "Archer" and Melbourne Cup.  **149** Queen Victoria.

1960. 100th Melbourne Cup Race Commem.

336. **148.** 5d. sepia 15 10

1960. Centenary of Queensland Stamps.

337. **149.** 5d. green 25 10

150. Open Bible and Candle.

1960. Christmas Issue.

338. **150.** 5d. lake 10 10

151. Colombo Plan Bureau Emblem. **152.** Melba (after bust by Sir Bertram Mackennal).

1961. Colombo Plan.

339. **151.** 1s. brown 10 10

1961. Birth Centenary of Dame Nellie Melba (singer).

340. **152.** 5d. blue 30 15

153. Open Prayer Book and Text.

1961. Christmas issue.

341. **153.** 5d. brown 10 10

154. J. M. Stuart. **155.** Flynn's Grave and Nursing Sister.

1962. Centenary of Stuart's South to North Crossing of Australia.

342. **154.** 5d. red 15 10

1962. 50th Anniv. of Australian Inland Mission.

343. **155.** 5d. multicoloured . . 30 15

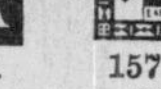

156. "Woman". **157.** "Madonna and Child".

1962. "Associated Country Women of the World" Conference, Melbourne.

344. **156.** 5d. green 10 10

1962. Christmas.

345. **157.** 5d. violet 15 10

158. Perth and Kangaroo Paw (plant).

1962. British Empire and Commonwealth Games, Perth. Multicoloured.

346. 5d. Type **158** 40 10
347. 2s. 3d. Arms of Perth and running track . . . . 3·00 2·50

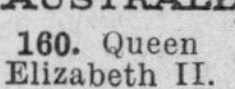

160. Queen Elizabeth II. **163.** Centenary Emblem.

162. Arms of Canberra and W. B. Griffin (architect).

1963. Royal Visit.
348. **160.** 5d. green 35 10
349. – 2s. 3d. lake .. .. 2·00 3·25
DESIGN: 2s. 3d. Queen Elizabeth II and Duke of Edinburgh.

1963. 50th Anniversary of Canberra.
350. **162.** 5d. green 15 10

1963. Centenary of Red Cross
351. **163.** 5d. red, grey and blue 25 10

164. Blaxland, Lawson and Wentworth on Mt. York.

1963. 150th Anniv. of First Crossing of Blue Mountains.
352. **164.** 5d. blue 15 10

165. "Export".

1963. Export Campaign.
353. **165.** 5d. red 10 10

1963. As T **160** but smaller (17½×21½ mm.) "5D" at top right replacing "ROYAL VISIT 1963" and oak leaves omitted.
354. 5d. green.. .. .. 55 10
354b. 5d. red 45 10

167. Tasman and "Heemskerk".

1963. Navigators.
355. **167.** 4s. blue .. .. 4·50 40
356. – 5s. brown .. .. 6·00 60
357. – 7s. 6d. olive .. .. 17·00 16·00
358. – 10s. purple .. .. 42·00 4·25
359. – £1 violet .. .. 48·00 12·00
360. – £2 sepia .. .. 85·00 70·00
DESIGNS—HORIZ. (As Type **167**): 7s. 6d. Captain Cook. 10s. Flinders and "Investigator" VERT. (20¼×25½ mm.): 5s. Dampier and "Roebuck". £1, Bass and whale boat. £2, Admiral King and "Mermaid".

173. "Peace on Earth . . .". **176.** Black-backed Magpie.

174. "Commonwealth Cable".

1963. Christmas.
361. **173.** 5d. blue 10 10

1963. Opening of COMPAC (Trans-Pacific Telephone Cable).
362. **174.** 2s. 3d. multicoloured 3·25 4·00

1964.
363. – 6d. multicoloured .. 50 25
364. **176.** 9d. black, grey & green 1·50 3·25
365. – 1s. 6d. multicoloured.. 1·00 1·25
366. – 2s. yellow, black & pink 2·50 50
367. – 2s. 5d. multicoloured.. 7·00 3·00
368. – 2s. 6d. multicoloured.. 4·25 2·75
369. – 3s. multicoloured .. 4·00 1·50
BIRDS—HORIZ. 6d. Yellow-tailed Thornbill. 2s. 6d. Scarlet Robin. VERT. 1s. 6d. Galah (cockatoo). 2s. Golden Whistler (Thickhead). 2s. 5d. Blue Wren. 3s. Straw-necked Ibis.

182. "Bleriot" Aircraft (type flown by M. Guillaux, 1914).

1964. 50th Anniv. of 1st Australian Airmail Flight.
370. **182.** 5d. green 40 10
371. 2s. 3d. red .. .. 2·50 2·00

183. Child looking at Nativity Scene. **184.** "Simpson and his Donkey".

1964. Christmas.
372. **183.** 5d. red, blue, buff & blk. 10 10

1965. 50th Anniv. of Gallipoli Landing.
373. **184.** 5d. brown 50 10
374. 8d. blue .. .. 80 2·00
375 2s. 3d. purple .. .. 1·40 2·00

185. "Tele-communications". **186.** Sir Winston Churchill.

1965. Centenary of I.T.U.
376. **185.** 5d. black, brown & blue 30 10

1965. Churchill Commem.
377. **186.** 5d. black, grey & blue 15 10

187. General Monash. **189.** I.C.Y. Emblem.

188. Hargrave and "Seaplane" (1902).

1965. Birth Centenary of General Sir John Monash (engineer and soldier).
378. **187.** 5d. multicoloured 15 10

1965. 50th Death Anniv. of Lawrence Hargrave (aviation pioneer).
379. **188.** 5d. multicoloured 15 10

1965. Int. Co-operation Year.
380. **189.** 2s. 3d. green and blue 1·75 2·00

190. "Nativity Scene".

1965. Christmas.
381. **190.** 5d. multicoloured .. 15 10

191. Queen Elizabeth II. **192.** Blue-faced Honeyeater.

1966. Decimal currency. As earlier issues but with values in cents and dollars as in T **191/2**. Also some new designs.
382. **191.** 1 c. brown 25 10
383. 2 c. green 90 10
384. 3 c. green 90 10
404. 3 c. blk., pink & grn. 20 40
385. 4 c. red 20 10
405. 4 c. blk., brn. & red 45 20
405a. 5 c. blk., brn. & bl. 60 10
386. 5 c. mult. (as 363) 25 10
386c. **191.** 5 c. blue .. .. 2·50 10
387. **192.** 6 c. multicoloured .. 70 40
387a. 6 c. orange 45 10
388. – 7 c. multicoloured .. 1·50 10
388a. **191.** 7 c. purple .. .. 1·50 15
389. – 8 c. multicoloured .. 1·50 25
390. – 9 c. multicoloured .. 1·50 15
391. – 10 c. multicoloured.. 1·50 10
392. – 13 c. multicoloured.. 3·25 25
393. – 15 c. mult. (as 365) .. 2·50 50
394. – 20 c. yell. blk. & pink (as 366) .. 7·50 15
395. – 24 c. multicoloured.. 90 55
396. – 25 c. mult. (as 368) .. 5·00 20
397. – 30 c. mult. (as 369) .. 24·00 45
398. **167.** 40 c. blue .. .. 12·00 10
399. – 50 c. brown (as 356) 15·00 10
400. – 75 c. olive (as 357) .. 1·00 1·50
401. – $1 purple (as 358) .. 3·75 15
402. – $2 violet (as 359) .. 10·00 30
403. – $4 brown (as 360) .. 9·50 5·00
DESIGNS—VERT. 7 c. Humbug fish. 8 c. Coral fish. 9 c. Hermit crab. 10 c. Anemone fish. 13 c. Red-necked Avocet. HORIZ. 24 c. Azure Kingfisher.

200. "Saving Life".

1966. 75th Anniv. Royal Life Saving Society.
406. **200.** 4 c. black, bright blue and blue .. 15 10

201. "Adoration of the Shepherds".

1966. Christmas.
407. **201.** 4 c. black and olive .. 10 10

202. "Eendracht". **203.** Open Bible.

1966. 350th Anniv. of Dirk Hartog's Landing in Australia.
408. **202.** 4 c. multicoloured .. 10 10

1967. 150th Anniv. of British and Foreign Bible Society in Australia.
409. **203.** 4 c. multicoloured .. 10 10

204. Ancient Keys and Modern Lock.

1967. 150th Anniv. of Australian Banking.
410. **204.** 4 c. black, blue & green 10 10

205. Lions Badge and 50 Stars.

1967. 50th Anniversary of Lions Int.
411. **205.** 4 c. black, gold & blue 10 10

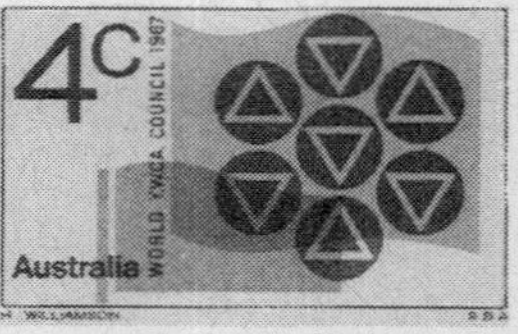

206. Y.W.C.A. Emblem.

1967. World Y.W.C.A. Council Meeting, Monash University, Victoria.
412. **206.** 4 c. multicoloured .. 10 10

207. Anatomical Figures.

1967. 5th World Gynaecology and Obstetrics Congress, Sydney.
413. **207.** 4 c. black, blue & violet 10 10

1967. No. 385 surch.
414. **191.** 5 c. on 4 c. red .. 70 10

209. Christmas Bells and Gothic Arches.

1967. Christmas. Multicoloured.
415. 5 c. Type **209** .. 20 10
416. 25 c. Religious symbols (vert.) .. .. .. 1·25 1·75

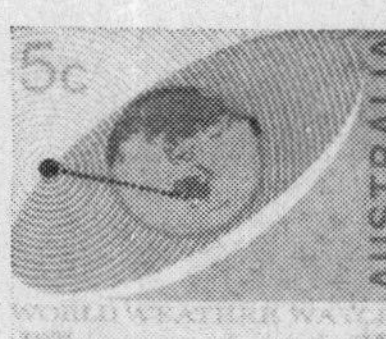

211. Satellite in Orbit.

1968. World Weather Watch. Multicoloured.
417. 5 c. Type **211** 30 10
418. 20 c. World Weather Map 1·75 3·75

213. Radar Antenna. **214.** Kangaroo Paw (Western Australia).

1968. World Telecommunications Intelsat II.
419. **213.** 25 c. blue, black & grn. 3·00 5·50

1968. State Floral Emblems. Multicoloured.
420. 6 c. Type **214** 45 55
421. 13 c. Pink Heath (Victoria) 55 30
422. 15 c. Tasmanian Blue Gum (Tasmania) .. .. 2·00 20
423. 20 c. Sturt's Desert Pea (South Australia) .. 9·00 30
424. 25 c. Cooktown Orchid (Queensland) .. .. 4·50 50
425. 30 c. Waratah (New South Wales) .. .. .. 1·00 10

220. Soil Sample Analysis.

1968. Int. Soil Science Congress and World Medical Assn. Assembly. Multicoloured.
426. 5 c. Type **220** 10 10
427. 5 c. Rubber-gloved hands syringe and head of Hippocrates. 10 10

222. Athlete carrying Torch, and Sunstone Symbol. **224.** Houses and Dollar Signs.

1968. Olympic Games, Mexico City. Mult.
428. 5 c. Type **222** 30 10
429. 25 c. Sunstone Symbol and Mexican Flag .. 45 1·50

1968. Building and Savings Societies Congress.
430. **224.** 5 c. multicoloured .. 10 30

225. Church Window and View of Bethlehem. **226.** Edgeworth David (geologist).

1968. Christmas.
431. **225.** 5 c. multicoloured .. 10 10

1968. Famous Australians. (1st series).
432. **226.** 5 c. green on myrtle .. 75 15
433. – 5 c. black on blue .. 75 15
434. – 5 c. brown on buff .. 75 15
435. – 5 c. violet on lilac .. 75 15
DESIGNS: No. 433, A. B. Paterson (poet). No. 434, Albert Namatjira (artist). No. 435, Caroline Chrisholm (social worker).
Nos. 432/5 were only issued in booklets and exist with one or two sides imperf.
See also Nos. 446/9. 479/82. 505/8, 537/40, 590/5, 602/7 and 637/40.

230. Macquarie Lighthouse.

1968. 150th Anniv. of Macquarie Lighthouse.
436. **230.** 5 c. black on yellow .. 10 20

231. Pioneers and Modern Building, Darwin.

1969. Centenary of Northern Territory Settlement.
437. **231.** 5 c. brn. olive & ochre 10 10

232. Melbourne Harbour.

1969. 6th Biennial Conference of International Association of Ports and Harbours.
438. **232.** 5 c. multicoloured .. 15 10

233. Concentric Circles (Symbolising Management, Labour and Government).

1969. 50th Anniv. of I.L.O.
439. **233.** 5 c. multicoloured .. 15 10

234. Sugar Cane. **238.** "The Nativity" (stained glass window).

1969. Primary Industries. Multicoloured.
440. 7 c. Type **234** .. .. 1·25 2·50
441. 15 c. Timber .. .. 4·00 6·00
442. 20 c. Wheat .. .. 1·25 80
443. 25 c. Wool .. .. 2·50 2·25

1969. Christmas. Multicoloured.
444. 5 c. Type **238** 20 10
445. 25 c. "Tree of Life", Christ in crib and Christmas Star (abstract).. .. 1·00 1·50

240. Edmund Barton. **244.** Capt. Ross Smith's Vickers "Vimy", 1919.

1969. Famous Australians (2nd series). Prime Ministers.
446. **240.** 5 c. black on green .. 90 20
447. – 5 c. black on green .. 90 20
448. – 5 c. black on green .. 90 20
449. – 5 c. black on green .. 90 20
DESIGNS: No 447, Alfred Deakin. No. 448, J. C. Watson. No. 449, G. H. Reid.
Nos. 446/9 were only issued in booklets and only exist with one or two adjacent sides imperf.

1969. 50th Anniv. of 1st England–Australia Flight.
450. **244.** 5 c. multicoloured .. 15 10
451. – 5 c. red, black & green 15 10
452. – 5 c. multicoloured .. 15 10
DESIGNS: No. 451, Lt. H. Fysh and Lt. P. McGinness 1919 Survey with Ford car. No. 452, Capt. Wrigley and Sgt. Murphy in "BE 2E" take off to meet the Smiths.

247. Symbolic Track and Diesel Locomotive.

1970. Sydney-Perth Standard Gauge Railway Link.
453. **247.** 5 c. multicoloured .. 15 10

248. Australian Pavilion, Osaka.

1970. World Fair, Osaka. Expo. 70.
454. **248.** 5 c. multicoloured .. 15 10
455. – 20 c. red and black .. 35 65
DESIGN: 20 c. "Southern Cross" and "from the Country of the south with warm feelings" (message).

251. Australian Flag.

1970. Royal Visit.
456. – 5 c. black and ochre .. 25 15
457. **251.** 30 c. multicoloured .. 75 2·00
DESIGN: 5 c. Queen Elizabeth II and Duke of Edinburgh.

252. Lucerne Plant, Bull and Sun.

1970. 11th Int. Grasslands Congress.
458. **252.** 5 c. multicoloured .. 10 25

253. Captain Cook and H.M.S. "Endeavour". **259.** Sturt's Desert Rose.

1970. Bicentenary Captain Cook's Discovery of Australia's East Coast. Multicoloured.
459. 5 c. Type **253** 35 10
460. 5 c. Sextant and H.M.S. "Endeavour" 35 10
461. 5 c. Landing at Botany Bay 35 10
462. 5 c. Charting and exploring 35 10
463. 5 c. Claiming possession .. 35 10
464. 30 c. Captain Cook, H.M.S. "Endeavour", Sextant, Aborigines and Kangaroo (63 × 30 mm.) 1·50 2·75
Nos. 459/63 were issued together se-tenant in horiz. strips of five, forming a composite design.

1970. Coil Stamps. Multicoloured.
465a 2 c. Type **259** 35 20
466 4 c. Type **259** .. .. 70 1·25
467 5 c. Golden Wattle .. 20 10
468 6 c. Type **259** .. .. 1·25 1·00
468b 7 c. Sturt's Desert Pea .. 40 30
468d 10 c. As 7 c. 30 25

264. Snowy Mountains Scheme.

1970. National Development (1st series). Multicoloured.
469. 7 c. Type **264** 30 65
470. 8 c. Ord River scheme .. 15 15
471. 9 c. Bauxite to aluminium 15 15
472. 10 c. Oil and natural gas .. 40 10
See also Nos. 541/4.

265. Rising Flames.

1970. 16th Commonwealth Parliamentary Association Conference, Canberra.
473. **265.** 6 c. multicoloured .. 10 10

266. Milk Analysis and Dairy Herd.

1970. 18th Int. Dairy Congress, Sydney.
474. **266.** 6 c. multicoloured .. 10 10

267. "The Nativity". **268.** U.N. "Plant" and Dove of Peace.

1970. Christmas.
475. **267.** 6 c. multicoloured .. 10 10

1970. 25th Anniv. of United Nations.
476. **268.** 6 c. multicoloured .. 15 10

269. Boeing "707" and Avro "504".

1970. 50th Anniv. of QANTAS Airline.
477. **269.** 6 c. multicoloured .. 35 10
478. – 30 c. multicoloured .. 90 1·50
DESIGN: 30 c. Avro "504" and Boeing "707".

1970. Famous Australians (3rd series). As T **226.**
479. 6 c. blue on pink .. .. 1·50 20
480. 6 c. black on flesh .. 1·50 20
481. 6 c. purple on pink .. 1·50 20
482. 6 c. lake on pink .. .. 1·50 20
DESIGNS: No. 479, The Duigan brothers (pioneer aviators). No. 480, Lachlan Macquarie (Governor of N.S.W.). No. 481, Adam Lindsay Gordon (poet). No. 482, E. J. Eyre (explorer).
These stamps were only issued in booklets and have one or two sides imperf.

271. "Theatre".

1971. "Australia-Asia". Multicoloured.
483. 7 c. Type **271** 35 60
484. 15 c. "Music" .. .. 60 1·00
485. 20 c. "Sea Craft" 55 90

272. The Southern Cross.

1971. Cent. of Australian Natives' Assoc.
486. **272.** 6 c. black, red and blue 10 10

273. Market "Graph".

1971. Cent. of Sydney Stock Exchange.
487. 273. 6 c. multicoloured .. 10 10

274. Rotary Emblem.

1971. 50th Anniv. of Rotary International in Australia.
488. 274. 6 c. mutlicoloured .. 15 10

275. "Mirage" Jets and "D.H.9a" Biplane. 276. Draught-horse, Cat and Dog.

1971. 50th Anniversary of R.A.A.F.
489. 275. 6 c. multicoloured .. 15 10

1971. Animals. Multicoloured.
490. 6 c. Type **276** 20 10
491. 12 c. Vet and lamb ("Animal Science") .. 45 45
492. 18 c. Red Kangaroo ("Fauna Conservation") 60 75
493. 24 c. Guide-dog ("Animals Aid to Man") .. .. 1·50 2·25
The 6 c. commemorates the Centenary of the Australian R.S.P.C.A.

277. Bark Painting.

1971. Aboriginal Art. Multicoloured.
494. 20 c. Type **277** .. 20 20
495. 25 c. Body decoration .. 20 40
496. 30 c. Cave painting (vert.) 30 20
497. 35 c. Grave posts (vert.) 30 15

278. The Three Kings and the Star.

1971. Christmas. Colours of star and colour of "AUSTRALIA" given.
498. 278. 7 c. blue, mve. & brn. 1·00 15
499. 7 c. mve., brn. & white 1·00 15
500. 7 c. mve., white & blk. 7·00 80
501. 7 c. blk., green & blk. 1·00 15
502. 7 c. lilac, green & mve. 1·00 15
503. 7 c. blk., brn. & white 1·00 15
504. 7 c. blue, mve. & green 30·00 2·25

1972. Famous Australians. (4th series). As Type **240**. Prime Ministers.
505. 7 c. blue 70 20
506. 7 c. blue 70 20
507. 7 c. red 70 20
508. 7 c. red 70 20
DESIGNS: No. 505, Andrew Fisher. No. 506, W. M. Hughes. No. 507, Joseph Cook. No. 508, S. M. Bruce.
Nos. 505/8 were only issued in booklets and only exist with one or two adjacent sides imperf.

280. Cameo Brooch.

1972. 50th Anniv. of Country Women's Assn.
509. 280. 7 c. multicoloured .. 20 10

281. Fruit.

1972. Primary Industries. Multicoloured.
510. 20 c. Type **281** .. .. 3·50 4·50
511. 25 c. Rice .. .. .. 3·50 5·50
512. 30 c. Fish .. .. .. 3·50 3·50
513. 35 c. Beef .. .. .. 8·00 2·00

282. Worker in Wheelchair. 284. Athletics.

283. Telegraph Line.

1972. Rehabilitation of the Disabled.
514. 282. 12 c. brown and green 10 10
515. – 18 c. green and orange 50 35
516. – 24 c. blue and brown .. 15 10
DESIGNS—HORIZ. 18 c. Patient and teacher. VERT. 24 c. Boy playing with ball.

1972. Cent. of Overland Telegraph Line.
517. 283. 7 c. multicoloured .. 15 15

1972. Olympic Games, Munich. Mult.
518. 7 c. Type **284** 25 20
519. 7 c. Rowing 25 20
520. 7 c. Swimming 25 20
521. 35 c. Equestrian .. .. 2·25 4·50

285. Numerals and Computer Circuit.

1972. 10th Int. Congress of Accountants, Sydney.
522. 285. 7 c. multicoloured .. 15 15

286. Australian-built Harvester.

1972. Pioneer Life. Multicoloured.
523. 5 c. Pioneer Family (vert.) 15 10
524. 10 c. Water-pump (vert.) .. 40 10
525. 15 c. Type **286** 15 10
526. 40 c. House 30 50
527. 50 c. Stage Coach 80 20
528. 60 c. Morse key (vert.) .. 50 85
529. 80 c. "Gem" (paddle-steamer) 60 85

287. Jesus with Children.

1972. Christmas. Multicoloured.
530. 7 c. Type **287** 30 10
531. 35 c. Dove and spectrum motif (vert.) .. .. 7·00 8·50

288. "Length".

1973. Metric Conversion. Multicoloured.
532. 7 c. Type **288** 40 40
533. 7 c. "Volume" 40 40
534. 7 c. "Mass" 40 40
535. 7 c. "Temperature" (horiz.) 40 40

289. Caduceus and Laurel Wreath.

1973. 25th Anniv. of World Health Organization.
536. 289. 7 c. multicoloured .. 30 15

1973. Famous Australians (5th series). As Type **226**.
537. 7 c. brown and black .. 50 25
538. 7 c. lilac and black .. 50 25
539. 7 c. brown and black .. 50 25
540. 7 c. lilac and black .. 50 25
PORTRAITS: No. 537, William Wentworth (statesman and explorer). No. 538, Isaac Isaacs (1st Australian-born Governor-General). No. 539, Mary Gilmore (writer). No. 540, Marcus Clarke (author).

291. Shipping. 292. Banded Coral Shrimp.

1973. National Development (2nd series). Multicoloured.
541. 20 c. Type **291** .. .. 4·50 4·25
542. 25 c. Iron ore and steel .. 4·50 4·50
543. 30 c. Beef roads .. .. 4·75 4·50
544. 35 c. Mapping .. .. 4·00 4·50

1973. Marine Life and Gemstones. Mult.
545. 1 c. Type **292** 10 10
546. 2 c. Fiddler crab 10 10
547. 3 c. Coral crab 10 10
548. 4 c. Mauve stinger 30 55
549. 6 c. Chrysoprase (vert.) .. 30 10
550. 7 c. Agate (vert.) 30 10
551. 8 c. Opal (vert.) 30 10
552. 9 c. Rhodonite (vert.) .. 60 15
552a. 10 c. Star sapphire (vert.) 30 10

293. Children at Play.

1973. 50th Anniv. of Legacy (Welfare Organization).
553. 293. 7 c. brown, red & green 30 10

294. John Baptising Jesus.

1973. Christmas. Multicoloured.
554. 7 c. Type **294** 35 10
555. 30 c. The Good Shepherd 1·40 1·50

295. Sydney Opera House.

1973. Architecture.
556. 295. 7 c. blue and pale blue 30 15
557. – 10 c. ochre and brown 80 70
558. – 40 c. grey, brown & blk. 1·00 1·50
559. – 50 c. multicoloured .. 1·25 2·50
DESIGNS—HORIZ. 10 c. Buchanan's Hotel, Townsville. 40 c. Como House, Melbourne. VERT. 50 c. St. James' Church, Sydney.

296. Wireless Receiver and Speaker.

1973. 50th Anniv. of Regular Radio Broadcasting.
560. 296. 7 c. blue, red and black 15 10

297. Common Wombat. 298. "Sergeant of Light Horse" (G. Lambert).

1974. Animals. Multicoloured.
561. 20 c. Type **297** 35 10
562. 25 c. Short-nosed echidna 75 60
563. 30 c. Brush-tailed possum 40 15
564. 75 c. Pygmy glider .. 1·00 85

1974. Australian Paintings. Multicoloured.
565. $1 Type **298** .. .. 1·00 10
566. $2 "Red Gums of the Far North" (H. Heysen) .. 1·50 25
566a. $4 "Shearing the Rams" (Tom Roberts) .. 3·00 2·25
567. $5 "McMahon's Point" (Sir Arthur Streeton) .. 5·50 2·25
567a. $10 "Coming South" (Tom Roberts) .. 8·50 3·50
The $2 and $4 are horiz. designs.

299. Supreme Court Judge.

1974. 150th Anniv. of Australia's Third Charter of Justice.
568. 299. 7 c. multicoloured .. 20 10

300. Rugby Football.

1974. Non-Olympic Sports. Multicoloured.
569. 7 c. Type **300** 55 35
570. 7 c. Bowls 55 35
571. 7 c. Australian football (vert.) 55 35
572. 7 c. Cricket (vert.) 55 35
573. 7 c. Golf (vert.) 55 35
574. 7 c. Surfing (vert.) 55 35
575. 7 c. Tennis (vert.) 55 35

301. " Transport of Mails ".

1974. Centenary of U.P.U. Multicoloured.

576. 7 c. Type **301** 40 20
577. 30 c. Three-part version of Type **301** (vert.) .. 1·25 1·90

302. Letter " A " and W. C. Wentworth (co-founder). **304.** "The Adoration of the Magi ".

1974. 150th Anniv. of First Independent Newspaper. "The Australian".

578. **302.** 7 c. black and brown 30 30

1974. No. 551 surch.

579. 9 c. on 8 c. multicoloured 15 15

1974. Christmas. Woodcuts by Durer.

580. **304.** 10 c. black on cream .. 25 10
581. – 35 c. black on cream .. 80 1·00

DESIGN: 35 c. " The Flight into Egypt ".

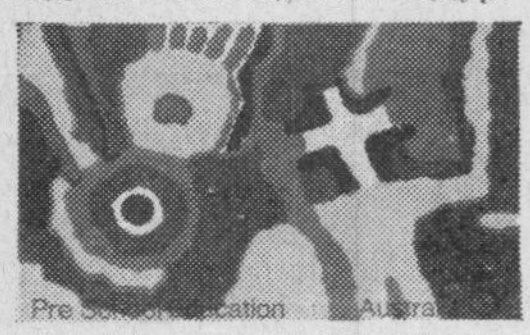
305. " Pre-School Education ".

1974. Education in Australia. Multicoloured.

582. 5 c. Type **305** 50 40
583. 11 c. " Correspondence Schools " 50 25
584. 15 c. " Science Education " 80 40
585. 60 c. " Advanced Education " (vert.) .. .. .. 2·00 2·75

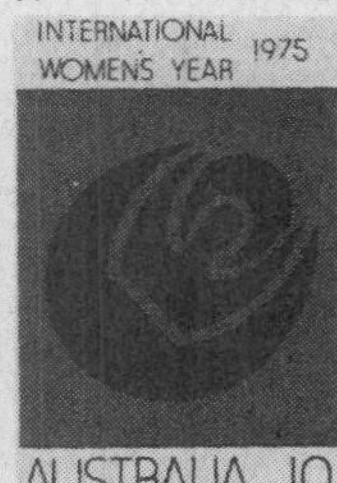

306. "Road Safety". **307.** Australian Women's Year Emblem.

1975. Environmental Dangers. Multicoloured.

586. 10 c. Type **306** 40 40
587. 10 c. " Pollution " (horiz.) 40 40
588. 10 c. " Bush Fires " (horiz.) 40 40

1975. International Women's Year.

589. **307.** 10 c. bl., grn. & vio... 20 15

308. J. H. Scullin.

1975. Famous Australians (6th series). Prime Ministers. Multicoloured.

590. 10 c. Type **308** 25 30
591. 10 c. J. A. Lyons 25 30
592. 10 c. Earle Page 25 30
593. 10 c. Arthur Fadden .. 25 30
594. 10 c. John Curtin 25 30
595. 10 c. J. B. Chifley .. 25 30

309. Atomic Absorption Spectrophotometry.

1975. Scientific Development. Multicoloured.

596. 11 c. Type **309** 60 40
597. 24 c. Radio astronomy .. 1·40 1·90
598. 33 c. Immunology .. 1·75 2·50
599. 48 c. Oceanography .. 2·50 2·75

310. Logo of Australian Postal Commission.

1975. Inauguration of Australian Postal and Telecommunications Commissions.

600. **310.** 10 c. blk., red & grey 25 10
601. – 10 c. blk., orge. & grey 25 10

DESIGN: No. 601a, Logo of Australian Telecommunications Commission.

311. Edith Cowan. **312.** " Helichrysum thomsonii ".

1975. Famous Australians (7th series). Australian Women. Multicoloured.

602. 10 c. Type **311** 45 55
603. 10 c. Louisa Lawson .. 45 55
604. 10 c. "Henry Richardson" (pen-name of Ethel Richardson) 45 55
605. 10 c. Catherine Spence 45 55
606. 10 c. Constance Stone .. 45 55
607. 10 c. Truganini 45 55

1975. Wild Flowers. Mult.

608. 18 c. Type **312** 25 10
609. 45 c. " Callistemon teretifolius " (horiz.) 50 10

313. "Tambaran" House and Sydney Opera House. **314.** Epiphany Scene.

1975. Independence of Papua New Guinea. Multicoloured.

610. 18 c. Type **313** 35 10
611. 25 c. "Freedom" (bird in flight) (horiz.) .. .. 90 1·25

1975. Christmas.

612. **314.** 15 c. multicoloured .. 25 10
613. – 45 c. vio., bl. & silver 1·00 2·40

DESIGN—HORIZ. 45 c. " Shining Star ".

315. Australian Coat of Arms.

1976. 75th Anniversary of Nationhood.

614. **315.** 18 c. multicoloured .. 35 20

316. Telephone-user, circa 1878.

1976. Centenary of Telephone.

615. **316.** 18 c. multicoloured .. 20 15

317. John Oxley.

1976. 19th Century Explorers. Mult.

616. 18 c. Type **317** 40 40
617. 18 c. Hume and Hovell .. 40 40
618. 18 c. John Forrest .. 40 40
619. 18 c. Ernest Giles .. 40 40
620. 18 c. William Gosse .. 40 40
621. 18 c. Peter Warburton .. 40 40

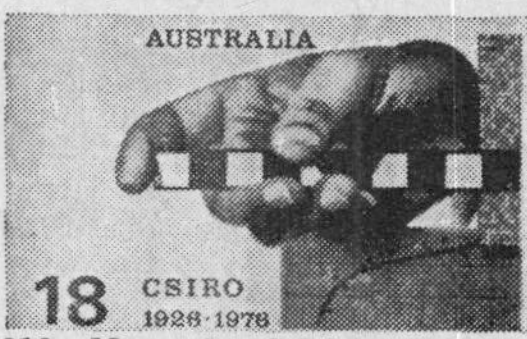

318. Measuring Stick, Graph and Computer Tape.

1976. 50th Anniv. of Commonwealth Scientific and Industrial Research Organization.

622. **318.** 18 c. multicoloured .. 20 15

319. Football.

1976. Olympic Games, Montreal. Mult.

623. 18 c. Type **319** 30 20
624. 18 c. Gymnastics (vert.) .. 30 20
625. 25 c. Diving (vert.) .. 50 50
626. 40 c. Cycling 70 70

320. Richmond Bridge, Tasmania.

1976. Australian Scenes. Multicoloured.

627. 5 c. Type **320** 15 10
628. 25 c. Broken Bay, N.S.W. 40 20
629. 35 c. Wittenoom Gorge, W.A. 35 20
630. 50 c. Mt. Buffalo, Victoria (vert.) 70 30
631. 70 c. Barrier Reef .. 1·00 1·25
632. 85 c. Ayers Rock, N.T... 1·00 1·75

321. Blamire Young (designer of first Australian stamp).

1976. National Stamp Week.

633. **321.** 18 c. multicoloured .. 15 15

322. " Virgin and Child " (detail, Simone Contarini).

1976. Christmas.

635. **322.** 15 c. mauve and blue 25 10
636. – 45 c. multicoloured .. 70 80

DESIGN: Toy koala bear and decorations.

323. John Gould.

1976. Famous Australians. (8th series). Scientists. Multicoloured.

637. 18 c. Type **323** 50 45
638. 18 c. Thomas Laby .. 50 45
639. 18 c. Sir Baldwin Spencer 50 45
640. 18 c. Griffith Taylor .. 50 45

324. "Music". **325.** Queen Elizabeth II.

1977. Performing Arts. Multicoloured.

641. 20 c. Type **324** 25 25
642. 30 c. Drama 40 35
643. 40 c. Dance 55 40
644. 60 c. Opera .. .. 1·00 1·75

1977. Silver Jubilee. Multicoloured.

645. 18 c. Type **325** 20 10
646. 45 c. The Queen and Duke of Edinburgh 50 80

326. Fielder and Wicket Keeper.

1977. Centenary of Australia–England Test Cricket.

647. 18 c. Type **326** 35 40
648. 18 c. Umpire and batsman 35 40
649. 18 c. Fielders 35 40
650. 18 c. Batsman and umpire 35 40
651. 18 c. Bowler and fielder.. 35 40
652. 45 c. Batsman facing bowler 75 1·00

327. Parliament House.

1977. 50th Anniv. of Opening of Parliament House, Canberra

653. **327.** 18 c. multicoloured .. 15 10

328. Trade Union Workers.

1977. 50th Anniv. of Australian Council of Trade Unions.

654. **328.** 18 c. multicoloured .. 15 10

329. Surfing Santa.

1977. Christmas. Multicoloured.

655. 15 c. Type **329** 25 10
656. 45 c. Madonna and Child.. 1·00 90

330. National Flag.

1978. Australia Day.

657. **330.**	18 c. multicoloured ..	20	15

331. Harry Hawker and Sopwith " Camel ".

1978. Early Australian Aviators. Mult.

658.	18 c. Type **331**	35	45
659.	18 c. Bert Hinkler and Avro " Avian " ..	35	45
660.	18 c. Sir Charles Kingsford Smith and " Southern Cross "	35	45
661.	18 c. Charles Ulm and " Southern Cross " ..	35	45

332. Beechcraft " Baron " landing at Station Airstrip.

1978. 50th Anniv. of Royal Flying Doctor Service.

663. **332.**	18 c. multicoloured ..	20	15

333. Illawarra Flame Tree. **334.** Sturt's Desert Rose and Map.

1978. Trees. Multicoloured.

664.	18 c. Type **333**	35	15
665.	25 c. Ghost Gum	65	1·50
666.	40 c. Grass Tree	1·00	2·00
667.	45 c. Cootamundra Wattle	1·00	1·25

1978. Establishment of Government for the Northern Territory.

668. **334.**	18 c. multicoloured ..	20	15

335. Hooded Plover.

1978. Australian Birds (1st series). Mult.

669.	1 c. Spotted-sided Finch	10	15
670.	2 c. Crimson Finch ..	10	15
671.	5 c. Type **335**	15	10
672.	15 c. Forest Kingfisher (vert.)	20	15
673.	20 c. Australian Dabchick	50	10
674.	20 c. Eastern Yellow Robin	20	10
675.	22 c. White-tailed Kingfisher 22 × 29 mm. ..	30	10
676.	25 c. Masked Plover	70	35
677.	30 c. Oystercatcher ..	80	25
678.	40 c. Variegated Wren (vert.	30	45
679.	50 c. Flame Robin (vert.)	40	50
680.	55 c. Comb-crested Jacana	85	60

See also Nos. 734/40.

336. 1928 3d. National Stamp Exhibition Commemorative.

1978. 50th Anniv. of National Stamp Week and National Stamp Exhibition.

694. **336.**	20 c. multicoloured ..	15	15

337. " The Madonna and the Child " (after van Eyck).

1978. Christmas. Multicoloured.

696.	15 c. Type **337**	30	10
697.	25 c. " The Virgin and Child " (Marmion) ..	45	55
698.	55 c. " The Holy Family " (del Vaga)	70	90

338. " Tulloch ".

1978. Horse-Racing. Multicoloured.

699.	20 c. Type **338**	35	10
700.	35 c. " Bernborough " (vert.)	60	70
701.	50 c. " Phar Lap " (vert.)	85	1·00
702.	55 c. " Peter Pan " ..	90	1·00

339. Raising the Flag, Sydney Cove, 26th January, 1788.

1979. Australia Day.

703. **339.**	20 c. multicoloured ..	15	15

340. P.S. " Canberra ".

1979. Ferries and Murray River Steamers. Multicoloured.

704.	20 c. Type **340**	35	10
705.	35 c. M.V. " Lady Denman "	60	85
706.	50 c. P.S. " Murray River Queen "	80	1·25
707.	55 c. H.V. " Curl Curl " ..	90	1·25

341. Port Campbell, Victoria.

1979. National Parks. Multicoloured.

708.	20 c. Type **341**	25	25
709.	20 c. Uluru, Northern Territory	25	25
710.	20 c. Royal, New South Wales	25	25
711.	20 c. Flinders Ranges, South Australia ..	25	25
712.	20 c. Nambung, Western Australia ..	25	25
713.	20 c. Girraween, Queensland (vert.) ..	25	25
714.	20 c. Mount Field, Tasmania (vert.)	25	25

342. " Double Fairlie " Type Locomotive, Western Australia.

1979. Steam Railways. Multicoloured.

715.	20 c. Type **342**	30	10
716.	35 c. Locomotive "Puffing Billy", Victoria	55	70
717.	50 c. Locomotive, Pichi Richi Line, South Australia	80	1·10
718.	55 c. Locomotive, Zig Zag Railway, New South Wales	90	1·25

343. Symbolic Swan.

1979. 150th Anniv. of Western Australia.

719. **343.**	20 c. multicoloured ..	15	15

344. Children playing on Slide.

1979. International Year of the Child.

720. **344.**	20 c. multicoloured ..	15	10

345. Letters and Parcels.

1979. Christmas. Multicoloured.

721.	15 c. " Christ's Nativity " (Eastern European icon)	15	10
722.	25 c. Type **345** ..	25	50
723.	55 c. " Madonna and Child " (Buglioni)	40	75

346. Fly-Fishing.

1979. Fishing.

724. **346.**	20 c. multicoloured ..	20	10
725. –	35 c. blue and violet	35	70
726. –	50 c. multicoloured ..	40	90
727. –	55 c. multicoloured ..	45	85

DESIGNS: 35 c. Spinning. 50 c. Deep sea game fishing. 55 c. Surf fishing.

347. Matthew Flinders.

1980. Australia Day.

728. **347.**	20 c. multicoloured ..	20	10

348. Dingo.

1980. Dogs. Multicoloured.

729.	20 c. Type **348**	40	10
730.	25 c. Border Collie ..	40	40
731.	35 c. Australian Terrier ..	60	70
732.	50 c. Australian Cattle Dog	1·40	1·75
733.	55 c. Australian Kelpie ..	1·10	1·40

1980. Birds (2nd series). As T **335**. Mult.

734.	10 c. Golden shouldered parrot (vert.)	30	10
734b.	18 c. Spotted catbird (vert.)	60	95
735.	28 c. Australian bee eater (vert.)	50	30
736.	35 c. Regent bower bird (vert.)	35	10
737.	45 c. Masked wood swallow	40	10
738.	60 c. Australian king parrot (vert.)	50	15
739.	80 c. Rainbow pitta ..	85	65
740.	$1 Black-backed magpie (vert.)	85	10

349. Queen Elizabeth II. **350.** " Once a jolly Swagman camp'd by a Billabong ".

1980. Birthday of Queen Elizabeth II.

741. **349.**	22 c. multicoloured ..	25	20

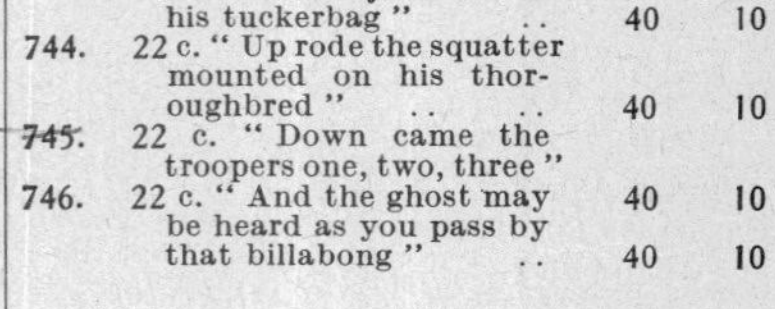

1980. Folklore. " Waltzing Matilda ". Mult.

742.	22 c. Type **350**	40	10
743.	22 c. " And he sang as he shoved that jumbuck in his tuckerbag " ..	40	10
744.	22 c. " Up rode the squatter mounted on his thoroughbred "	40	10
745.	22 c. " Down came the troopers one, two, three "		
746.	22 c. " And the ghost may be heard as you pass by that billabong " ..	40	10
		40	10

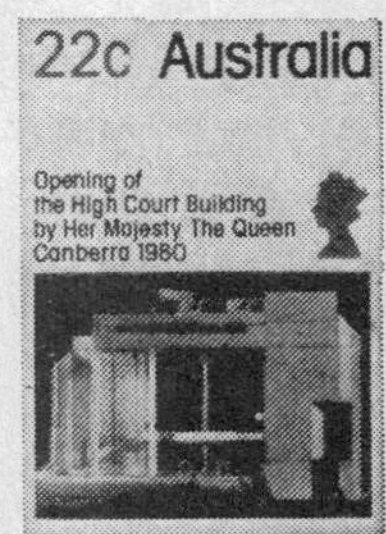

351. High Court Building, Canberra.

1980. Opening of High Court Building.

747. **351.**	22 c. multicoloured ..	20	20

352. Salvation Army.

1980. Community Welfare. Multicoloured.

748.	22 c. Type **352**	40	40
749.	22 c. St. Vincent de Paul Society (vert.) ..	40	40
750.	22 c. Meals on Wheels (vert.)	40	40
751.	22 c. " Life. Be in it " ..	40	40

353. Postbox, c. 1900. **354.** " Holy Family " (painting, Prospero Fontana).

1980. National Stamp Week. Multicoloured.
752. 22 c. Type **353** 30 10
753. 22 c. Postman, facing left 30 10
754. 22 c. Mail van 30 10
755. 22 c. Postman, facing right 30 10
756. 22 c. Postman and postbox 30 10

1980. Christmas. Multicoloured.
758. 15 c. "The Virgin Enthroned" (Justin O'Brien) (detail) 15 10
759. 28 c. Type **354** 25 40
760. 60 c. "Madonna and Child" (Sculpture by School of M. Zuern) .. .. 50 1·10

355. " Wackett ", 1941.

1980. Australian Aircraft. Multicoloured.
761. 22 c. Type **355** 35 10
762. 40 c. " Winjeel ", 1955 .. 60 85
763. 45 c. " Boomerang ", 1944 70 95
764. 60 c. " Nomad ", 1975 .. 90 1·25

356. Flag in shape of Australia.

1981. Australia Day.
765. **356.** 22 c. multicoloured .. 20 20

357. Caricature of Darby Munro (jockey) **358.** 1931 Kingsford Smith's Flights 6d. Commemorative.

1981. Sporting Personalities. Caricatures. Mult.
766. 22 c. Type **357** 30 10
767. 35 c. Victor Trumper (cricket) 65 70
768. 55 c. Sir Norman Brookes (tennis) 85 90
769. 60 c. Walter Lindrum (billiards) .. .. 90 1·00

1981. 50th Anniv. of Official Australia–U.K. Airmail Service.
770. **358.** 22 c. lilac, red and blue 20 10
771. – 60 c. lilac, red and blue 50 90
DESIGN—HORIZ. 60 c. As T **358**, but format changed.

359. Apex Emblem and Map of Australia.

1981. 50th Anniv. of Apex (young men's service club).
772. **359.** 22 c. multicoloured .. 20 20

360. Queen's Personal Standard for Australia.

1981. Birthday of Queen Elizabeth II.
773. **360.** 22 c. multicoloured .. 20 20

361. " Licence Inspected ".

1981. Gold Rush Era. Sketches by S. T. Gill. Multicoloured.
774. 22 c. Type **361** 20 25
775. 22 c. " Puddling " 20 25
776. 22 c. " Quality of washing stuff " 20 25
777. 22 c. " On route to deposit gold " 20 25

362. "On the Wallaby Track" (Fred McCubbin).

1981. Paintings. Multicoloured.
778. $2 Type **362** .. .. 1·75 30
779. $5 "A Holiday at Mentone 1888" (Charles Conder) .. 4·75 1·50

363. Thylacine.

363a. Blue Mountain Tree Frog.

363b. "Papilio ulysses" (butterfly).

1981. Wildlife. Multicoloured.
781 1 c. Lace monitor .. 10 20
782 3 c. Corroboree frog .. 10 10
783 4 c. "Euschemon rafflesia" (butterfly) (vert) 70 35
784 5 c. Queensland hairy-nosed wombat (vert) .. 10 10
785 10 c. "Ornithoptera priamus" (butterfly) (vert) 70 10
786 15 c. Eastern snake-necked tortoise .. 20 30
787 20 c. "Graphium macleayanus" (butterfly) (vert) 1·00 35
788 24 c. Type **363** 35 10
789 25 c. Common rabbit-bandicoot (vert) 35 10
790 27 c. Type **363a** .. 35 20
791 27 c. Type **363b** .. 1·25 30
792 30 c. Bridle nail-tailed wallaby (vert) 40 15
792a 30 c. "Pseudalmenus chlorinda" (butterfly) (vert) .. .. 1·25 20

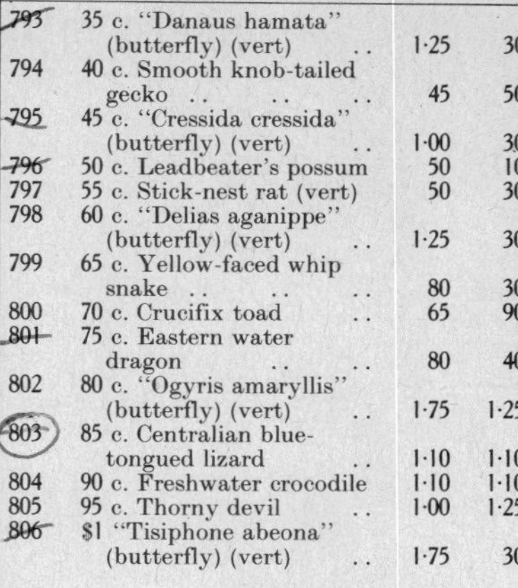

793 35 c. "Danaus hamata" (butterfly) (vert) .. 1·25 30
794 40 c. Smooth knob-tailed gecko 45 50
795 45 c. "Cressida cressida" (butterfly) (vert) 1·00 30
796 50 c. Leadbeater's possum 50 10
797 55 c. Stick-nest rat (vert) 50 30
798 60 c. "Delias aganippe" (butterfly) (vert) .. 1·25 30
799 65 c. Yellow-faced whip snake 80 30
800 70 c. Crucifix toad .. 65 90
801 75 c. Eastern water dragon 80 40
802 80 c. "Ogyris amaryllis" (butterfly) (vert) .. 1·75 1·25
803 85 c. Centralian blue-tongued lizard 1·10 1·10
804 90 c. Freshwater crocodile 1·10 1·10
805 95 c. Thorny devil .. 1·00 1·25
806 $1 "Tisiphone abeona" (butterfly) (vert) .. 1·75 30

364. Prince Charles and Lady Diana Spencer.

1981. Royal Wedding.
821. **364.** 24 c. multicoloured .. 25 10
822. 60 c. multicoloured .. 75 1·00

365. " Cortinarius cinnabarinus ".

1981. Australian Fungi. Multicoloured.
823. 24 c. Type **365** 35 10
824. 35 c. " Coprinus comatus " 50 50
825. 55 c. " Armillaria luteobubalina " .. 70 70
826. 60 c. " Cortinarius austrovenetus " 80 80

366. Disabled People playing Basketball.

1981. International Year for Disabled Persons.
827. **366.** 24 c. multicoloured .. 20 20

367. " Christmas Bush for His Adorning ".

1981. Christmas. Scenes and Verses from Carols by W. James and J. Wheeler. Mult.
828. 18 c. Type **367** 25 10
829. 30 c. " The Silver Stars are in the Sky " 35 25
830. 60 c. " Noeltime " 60 70

368. Globe depicting Australia. **369.** Ocean Racing Yacht.

1981. Commonwealth Heads of Government Meeting, Melbourne.
831. **368.** 24 c. black, blue & gold 20 10
832. 60 c. blk., blue & silver 50 75

1981. Yachts. Multicoloured.
833 24 c. Type **369** 35 10
834 35 c. "Sharpie" 50 50
835 55 c. "12 Metre" 75 85
836 60 c. "Sabot" .. .. 1·00 1·00

370. Aborigine, Governor Phillip (founder of N.S.W. 1788) and Post World War II Migrant.

1982. Australia Day. " Three Great Waves of Migration ".
837. **370.** 24 c. multicoloured .. 35 25

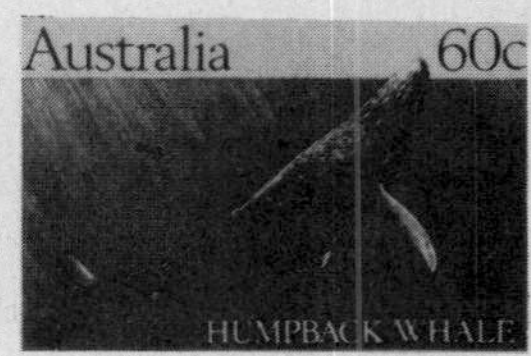

371. Humpback Whale.

1982. Whales. Multicoloured.
838. 24 c. Sperm whale 40 10
839. 35 c. Black right whale (vert.) 60 60
840. 55 c. Blue whale (vert.) .. 1·10 1·10
841. 60 c. Type **371** .. .. 1·25 1·25

372. Queen Elizabeth II. **373.** " Marjorie Atherton ".

1982. Birthday of Queen Elizabeth II.
842. **372.** 27 c. multicoloured .. 35 15

1982. Roses. Multicoloured.
843. 27 c. Type **373** 40 15
844. 40 c. " Imp " 55 65
845. 65 c. " Minnie Watson " .. 95 1·25
846. 75 c. " Satellite " .. 1·10 1·40

374. Radio Announcer and 1930-style Microphone.

1982. 50th Anniv. of ABC (Australian Broadcasting Commission.) Multicoloured.
847. 27 c. Type **374** 30 40
848. 27 c. ABC logo 30 40

375. Forbes Post Office.

1982. Historic Australian Post Offices. Multicoloured.

849. 27 c. Type **375** 40 35
850. 27 c. Flemington Post Office 40 35
851. 27 c. Rockhampton Post Office 40 35
852. 27 c. Kingston S.E. Post Office (horiz.) 40 35
853. 27 c. York Post Office (horiz.) 40 35
854. 27 c. Launceston Post Office 40 35
855. 27 c. Old Post and Telegraph Station, Alice Springs (horiz.) .. 40 35

376. Early Australian Christmas Card.

1982. Christmas. Multicoloured.

856. 21 c. Bushman's Hotel with Cobb's coach arriving (horiz.) 30 10
857. 35 c. Type **376** 50 60
858. 75 c. Little girl offering Christmas pudding to swagman .. .. 75 1·40

377. Boxing.

1982. Commonwealth Games, Brisbane.

859. **377.** 27 c. stone, yellow and red 25 20
860. – 27 c. yellow, stone and green 25 20
861. – 27 c. stone, yellow and brown 25 20
862. – 75 c. multicoloured .. 75 90

DESIGNS: No. 860, Archery. No. 861, Weight-lifting. No. 862, Pole-vaulting.

378. Sydney Harbour Bridge 5s. Stamp of 1932

1982. National Stamp Week.

864. **378.** 27 c. multicoloured .. 35 30

379. "Yirawala" Bark Painting.

1982. Opening of Australian National Gallery.

865. **279.** 27 c. multicoloured .. 30 25

380. Mimi Spirits Dancing.

1982. Aboriginal Culture. Music and Dance.

866. **380.** 27 c. multicoloured .. 25 10
867. – 40 c. multicoloured .. 40 50
868. – 65 c. multicoloured .. 70 80
869. – 75 c. multicoloured .. 80 1·10

DESIGNS: 40 c. to 75 c. Aboriginal Bark Paintings of Mimi Spirits.

381. "Eucalyptus calophylla" 'Rosea'.

1982. Eucalyptus Flowers. Multicoloured.

870. 1 c. Type **381** 10 20
871. 2 c. "Eucalyptus casia" .. 10 20
872. 3 c. "Eucalyptus ficifolia" 35 55
873. 10 c. "Eucalyptus globulus" 35 55
874. 27 c. "Eucalyptus forrestiana" 35 40

382. Shand Mason Steam Fire Engine, 1891.

1983. Historic Fire Engines. Multicoloured.

875. 27 c. Type **382** 35 10
876. 40 c. Hotchkiss fire engine, 1914 .. .. .. 50 60
877. 65 c. Ahrens-Fox PS2 fire engine, 1929 .. .. 90 1·25
878. 75 c. Merryweather manual fire appliance, 1851 .. 1·00 1·40

383. H.M.S. "Sirius".

1983. Australia Day. Multicoloured.

879. 27 c. Type **383** 40 50
880. 27 c. H.M.S. "Supply" .. 40 50

384. Stylised Kangaroo and Kiwi.

385. Equality and Dignity.

1983. Closer Economic Relationship Agreement with New Zealand.

881. **384.** 27 c. multicoloured .. 30 30

1983. Commonwealth Day. Multicoloured.

882. 27 c. Type **385** 25 25
883. 27 c. Liberty and Freedom 25 25
884. 27 c. Social Justice and Co-operation 25 25
885. 75 c. Peace and Harmony 70 1·10

386. R.Y. "Britannia" passing Sydney Opera House.

1983. Birthday of Queen Elizabeth II.

886. **386.** 27 c. multicoloured .. 45 30

387. "Postal and Telecommunications Services".

1983. World Communications Year.

887. **387.** 27 c. multicoloured .. 30 30

388. Badge of the Order of St. John.

1983. Centenary of St. John Ambulance in Australia.

888. **388.** 27 c. black and blue .. 35 30

389. Jaycee Members and Badge.

1983. 50th Anniversary of Australian Jaycees.

889. **389.** 27 c. multicoloured .. 30 30

390. "The Bloke".

392. Sir Paul Edmund de Strzelecki.

391. Nativity Scene.

1983. Folklore. "The Sentimental Bloke" (humorous poem by C. J. Dennis). Mult.

890. 27 c. Type **390** 45 45
891. 27 c. " Doreen–The Intro " 45 45
892. 27 c. " The Stror 'at Coot " 45 45
893. 27 c. " Hitched " 45 45
894. 27 c. " The Mooch o' Life " 45 45

1983. Christmas. Children's Paintings. Multicoloured.

895. 24 c. Type **391** 20 10
896. 35 c. Kookaburra 35 45
897. 85 c. Father Christmas in sleigh over beach .. 90 1·10

1983. Explorers of Australia. Multicoloured.

898. 30 c. Type **392** 35 40
899. 30 c. Ludwig Leichhardt .. 35 40
900. 30 c. William John Wills and Robert O'Hara Burke .. 35 40
901. 30 c. Alexander Forrest .. 35 40

393. Cook Family Cottage, Melbourne.

1984. Australia Day.

902. **393.** 30 c. black and stone 30 35

394. Charles Ulm, " Faith in Australia " and Trans-Tasman Cover.

1984. 50th Anniv. of First Official Airmail Flights, New Zealand–Australia and Australia–Papua New Guinea. Mult.

903. 45 c. Type **394** 65 90
904. 45 c. As Type **394** but showing flown cover to Papua New Guinea .. 65 90

395. Thomson " Steamer ", 1898.

1984. Veteran and Vintage Cars. Mult.

905. 30 c. Type **395** 45 55
906. 30 c. Tarrant, 1906 .. 45 55
907. 30 c. Gordon & Co. " Australian Six ", 1919 .. 45 55
908. 30 c. Summit, 1923 .. 45 55
909. 30 c. Chic, 1924 .. .. 45 55

396. Queen Elizabeth II.

1984. Birthday of Queen Elizabeth II.

910. **396.** 30 c. multicoloured .. 30 35

397. "Cutty Sark".

1984. Clipper Ships. Multicoloured.

911. 30 c. Type **397** 40 25
912. 45 c. "Orient" (horiz.) .. 70 70
913. 75 c. "Sobraon" (horiz.) .. 1·25 1·25
914. 85 c. "Thermopylae" .. 1·25 1·25

398. Freestyle.

1984. Skiing. Multicoloured.

915. 30 c. Type **398** 40 45
916. 30 c. Downhill racer .. 40 45
917. 30 c. Slalom (horiz.) .. 40 45
918. 30 c. Nordic (horiz.) .. 40 45

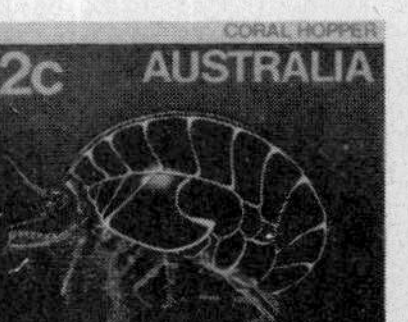

399. Coral Hopper.

1984. Marine Life. Multicoloured.

No.	Description	Unused	Used
919.	2 c. Type **399**	10	15
920.	3 c. Jimble	10	15
921.	5 c. Tasselled angler fish	10	10
922.	10 c. Stonefish	20	10
923.	20 c. Red handfish	45	25
924.	25 c. Orange-tipped cowrie	45	25
925.	30 c. Choat's wrasse	45	30
926.	33 c. Leafy sea-dragon	35	10
927.	40 c. Red velvet fish	65	40
928.	45 c. Textile cone	80	35
929.	50 c. Blue-lined surgeon fish	80	40
930.	55 c. Bennett's nudibranch	80	50
931.	60 c. Lionfish	90	60
932.	65 c. Stingaree	90	65
933.	70 c. Blue-ringed octopus	90	65
934.	80 c. Pineapple fish	1·25	70
935.	85 c. Regal angel fish	90	50
936.	90 c. Crab-eyed goby	1·00	75
937.	$1 Crown of thorns starfish	1·50	80

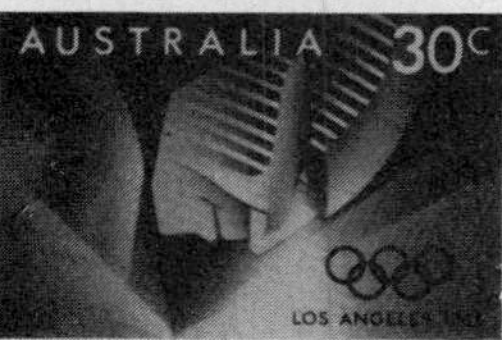

400. Before the Event.

1984. Olympic Games. Los Angeles. Multicoloured.

No.	Description	Unused	Used
941.	30 c. Type **400**	35	35
942.	30 c. During the Event	35	35
943.	30 c. After the Event (vert.)	35	35

401. Australian 1913 1 d. Kangaroo Stamp.

402. "Angel" (stained-glass window St. Francis' Church. Melbourne).

1984. "Ausipex 84" International Stamp Exhibition, Melbourne.

No.	Description	Unused	Used
944. **401.**	30 c. multicoloured	35	30

1984. Christmas. Stained-glass Windows. Multicoloured.

No.	Description	Unused	Used
946.	24 c. "Angel and Child" (Holy Trinity Church, Sydney)	40	20
947.	30 c. "Veiled Virgin and Child" (St. Mary's Catholic Church, Geelong)	55	20
948.	40 c. Type **402**	70	60
949.	50 c. "Three Kings" (St. Mary's Cathedral, Sydney)	90	80
950.	85 c. "Madonna and Child" (St. Bartholomew's Church, Norwood)	1·25	1·25

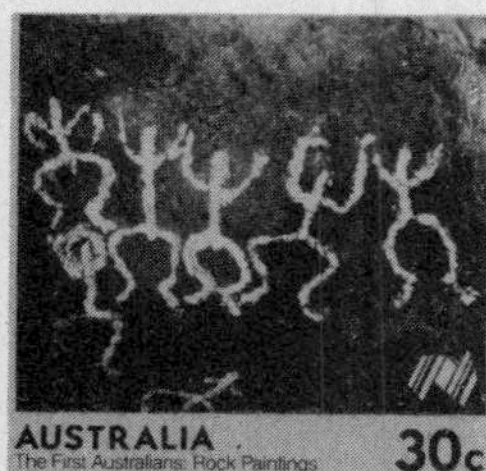

403. "Stick Figures". (Cobar Region).

1984. Bicentenary (1988) of Australian Settlement. (1st issue). The First Australians. Multicoloured.

No.	Description	Unused	Used
951.	30 c. Type **403**	45	45
952.	30 c. "Bunjil" (large figure), Grampians	45	45
953.	30 c. "Quikans" (tall figures), Cape York	45	45
954.	30 c. "Wandjina Spirit and Baby Snakes" (Gibb River)	45	45
955.	30 c. "Rock Python" (Gibb River)	45	45
956.	30 c. "Silver Barramundi" (fish) (Kakadu National Park)	45	45
957.	30 c. Bicentenary emblem	45	45
958.	85 c. "Rock Possum" (Kakadu National Park)	1·10	1·25

See also Nos. 972/5, 993/6, 1002/7, 1019/22, 1059/63, 1064/6, 1077/81, 1090/2, 1110, 1137/41, 1145/8 and 1149.

404. Yellow-tufted Honeyeater.

1984. 150th Anniv. of Victoria.

No.	Description	Unused	Used
959.	30 c. Type **404**	35	55
960.	30 c. Leadbeater's Possum	35	55

405. "Musgrave Ranges" (Sidney Nolan).

1985. Australia Day. Birth Bicentenary of Dorothea Mackellar (author of poem "My Country"). Multicoloured.

No.	Description	Unused	Used
961.	30 c. Type **405**	45	55
962.	30 c. "The Walls of China" (Russell Drysdale)	45	55

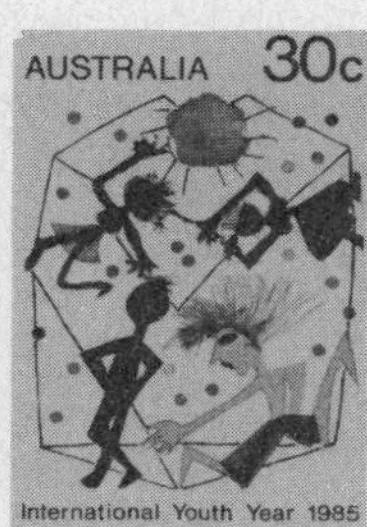

406. Young People of Different Races and Sun.

1985. International Youth Year.

No.	Description	Unused	Used
963. **406.**	30 c. multicoloured	35	30

407. Royal Victorian Volunteer Artillery.

1985. 19th-Century Australian Military Uniforms. Multicoloured.

No.	Description	Unused	Used
964.	33 c. Type **407**	60	60
965.	33 c. Western Australian Pinjarrah Cavalry	60	60
966.	33 c. New South Wales Lancers	60	60
967.	33 c. New South Wales Contingent to the Sudan	60	60
968.	33 c. Victorian Mounted Rifles	60	60

408. District Nurse of early 1900s.

1985. Centenary of District Nursing Services.

No.	Description	Unused	Used
969. **408.**	33 c. multicoloured	40	35

409. Sulphur-crested Cockatoos.

1985. Multicoloured, background colour given.

No.	Description	Unused	Used
970. **409.**	1 c. flesh	1·25	1·75
971.	33 c. turquoise	45	55

410. Abel Tasman and Journal Entry.

1985. Bicentenary (1988) of Australian Settlement (2nd issue). Navigators. Mult.

No.	Description	Unused	Used
972.	33 c. Type **410**	45	35
973.	33 c. Dirk Hartog's "Eendracht" (detail, Aert Anthonisz)	45	35
974.	33 c. "William Dampier" (detail, T. Murray)	45	35
975.	90 c. Globe and hand with extract from Dampier's journal	1·10	1·50

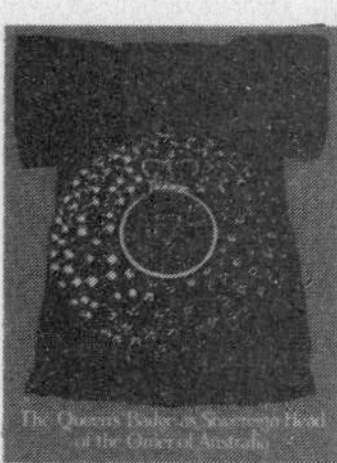

411. Sovereign's Badge of Order of Australia.

412. Tree, and Soil running through Hourglass ("Soil")

1985. Queen Elizabeth II's Birthday.

No.	Description	Unused	Used
977. **411.**	33 c. multicoloured	35	30

1985. Conservation. Multicoloured.

No.	Description	Unused	Used
978.	33 c. Type **412**	45	20
979.	50 c. Washing on line and smog ("air")	70	85
980.	80 c. Tap and flower ("water")	1·10	1·40
981.	90 c. Chain encircling flames ("energy")	1·25	1·75

413. "Elves and Fairies" (Annie Rentoul and Ida Rentoul Outhwaite).

1985. Classic Australian Children's Books. Multicoloured.

No.	Description	Unused	Used
982.	33 c. Type **413**	50	60
983.	33 c. "The Magic Pudding" (Norman Lindsay)	50	60
984.	33 c. "Ginger Meggs" (James Charles Bancks)	50	60
985.	33 c. "Blinky Bill" (Dorothy Wall)	50	60
986.	33 c. "Snugglepot and Cuddlepie" (May Gibbs)	50	60

414. Dish Aerials.

1985. Electronic Mail Service.

No.	Description	Unused	Used
987. **414.**	33 c. multicoloured	35	30

415. Angel in Sailing Ship.

1985. Christmas. Multicoloured.

No.	Description	Unused	Used
988.	27 c. Angel with holly wings	30	15
989.	33 c. Angel with bells	35	15
990.	45 c. Type **415**	50	50
991.	55 c. Angel with star	65	70
992.	90 c. Angel with Christmas tree bauble	1·00	1·25

416. Astrolabe ("Batavia", 1629).

1985. Bicentenary (1988) of Australian Settlement (3rd issue). Relics from Early Shipwrecks. Multicoloured.

No.	Description	Unused	Used
993.	33 c. Type **416**	40	15
994.	50 c. German beardman jug ("Vergulde Draeck", 1656)	70	70
995.	90 c. Wooden bobbins ("Batavia", 1629) and encrusted scissors ("Zeewijk", 1727)	1·40	1·50
996.	$1 Silver and brass buckle ("Zeewijk", 1727)	1·60	1·50

417. Aboriginal Wandjina Spirit, Map of Australia and Egg.

418. AUSSAT Satellite, Moon and Earth's Surface.

1986. Australia Day.

No.	Description	Unused	Used
997. **417.**	33 c. multicoloured	40	30

1986. AUSSAT National Communications Satellite System. Multicoloured.

No.	Description	Unused	Used
998.	33 c. Type **418**	50	15
999.	80 c. AUSSAT satellite in orbit	1·50	1·60

419. H.M.S. "Buffalo".

1986. 150th Anniv. of South Australia. Multicoloured.

1000 33 c. Type **419** 60 70
1001 33 c. "City Sign" sculpture (Otto Hajek), Adelaide 60 70

Nos. 1000/1 were printed together se-tenant, the background of each horizontal pair showing an extract from the colony's Letters Patent of 1836.

420. "Banksia serrata".

1986. Bicentenary of Australian Settlement (1988) (4th issue). Cook's Voyage to New Holland. Multicoloured.

1002. 33 c. Type **420** 60 35
1003. 33 c. "Hibiscus meraukensis" 60 35
1004. 50 c. "Dillenia alata" .. 90 80
1005. 80 c. "Correa reflexa" .. 1·60 1·50
1006. 90 c. "Joseph Banks" (botanist) (Reynolds) and Banks with Dr. Solander .. .. 2·00 1·75
1007. 90 c. "Sydney Parkinson" (self-portrait) and Parkinson drawing .. .. 2·00 1·75

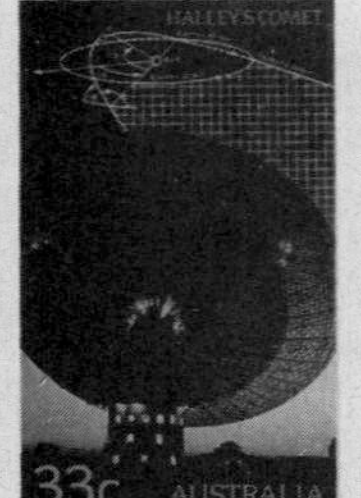

421. Radio Telescope, Parkes, and Diagram of Comet's Orbit.

422. Queen Elizabeth II.

1986. Appearance of Halley's Comet.

1008. **421.** 33 c. multicoloured .. 50 35

1986. 60th Birthday of Queen Elizabeth.

1009. **422.** 33 c. multicoloured .. 45 35

423. Brumbies (wild horses).

1986. Australian Horses. Multicoloured.

1010. 33 c. Type **423** 60 15
1011. 80 c. Mustering .. .. 1·50 1·50
1012. 90 c. Show-jumping .. 1·75 1·75
1013. $1 Child on pony .. 2·00 2·00

424. "The Old Shearer stands".

1986. Folklore. Scenes and Verses from the Folksong "Click go the Shears". Mult.

1014. 33 c. Type **424** 65 70
1015. 33 c. "The ringer looks around" 65 70
1016. 33 c. "The boss of the board" 65 70
1017. 33 c. "The tar-boy is there" 65 70
1018. 33 c. "Shearing is all over" 65 70

Nos. 1014/18 were printed together, se-tenant, forming a composite design.

425. "King George III" (A. Ramsay) and Convicts.

1986. Bicentenary of Australian Settlement (1988) (5th issue). Convict Settlement in New South Wales. Multicoloured.

1019. 33 c. Type **425** 70 40
1020. 33 c. "Lord Sydney" (Gilbert Stuart) and convicts 70 40
1021. 33 c. "Captain Arthur Phillip" (F. Wheatley) and ship 70 40
1022. $1 "Captain John Hunter" (W. B. Bennett) and aborigines .. .. 2·75 2·75

426. Red Kangaroo.

427. Royal Bluebell.

1986. Australian Wildlife (1st series). Multicoloured

1023. 36 c. Type **426** 55 55
1024. 36 c. Emu 55 55
1025. 36 c. Koala 55 55
1026. 36 c. Laughing kookaburra 55 55
1027. 36 c. Platypus 55 55

See also Nos. 1072/6.

1986. Alpine Wildflowers. Multicoloured.

1028. 3 c. Type **427** 25 25
1029. 5 c. Alpine Marsh Marigold .. .. 80 1·00
1030. 25 c. Mount Buffalo Sunray .. .. 80 1·00
1031. 36 c. Silver Snow Daisy .. 50 30

428. Pink Enamel Orchid.

1986. Native Orchids. Multicoloured.

1032. 36 c. Type **428** 70 20
1033. 55 c. "Dendrobium nindii" .. .. 1·25 1·00
1034. 90 c. Duck Orchid .. 1·90 2·00
1035. $1 Queen of Sheba Orchid .. .. .. 2·00 2·00

429. "Australia II" crossing Finishing Line.

1986. Australian Victory in America's Cup, 1983. Multicoloured.

1036. 36 c. Type **429** 65 55
1037. 36 c. Boxing kangaroo flag of winning syndicate 65 55
1038. 36 c. America's Cup trophy 65 55

430. Dove with Olive Branch and Sun.

1986. International Peace Year.

1039. **430.** 36 c. multicoloured .. 65 35

431. Mary and Joseph.

1986. Christmas. Scenes from children's nativity play. Multicoloured.

1040a 30 c. Type **431** 30 30
1041 36 c. Three Wise Men leaving gifts 50 45
1042 60 c. Angels (horiz.) .. 90 1·50

432. Australian Flag on Printed Circuit Board.

1987. Australia Day. Multicoloured.

1044. 36 c. Type **432** 35 35
1045. 36 c. "Australian Made" Campaign logos 35 35

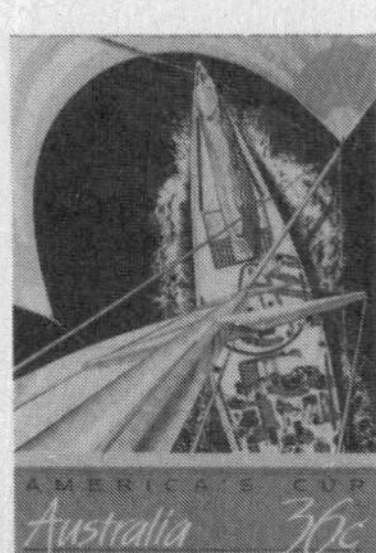

433. Aerial View of Yacht.

1987. America's Cup Yachting Championship. Multicoloured.

1046. 36 c. Type **433** 40 20
1047. 55 c. Two yachts tacking 80 90
1048. 90 c. Two yachts turning 1·25 1·40
1049. $1 Two yachts under full sail .. .. .. 1·40 1·50

434. Grapes and Melons.

1987. Australian Fruit. Multicoloured.

1050. 36 c. Type **434** 40 20
1051. 65 c. Tropical and sub-tropical fruits .. .. 85 1·00
1052. 90 c. Citrus fruit, apples and pears .. .. 1·25 1·40
1053. $1 Stone and berry fruits 1·40 1·60

435. Livestock.

1987. Agricultural Shows. Multicoloured.

1054. 36 c. Type **435** 60 20
1055. 65 c. Produce .. .. 1·25 1·40
1056. 90 c. Sideshows .. .. 1·75 2·00
1057. $1 Competitions .. .. 1·90 2·00

436. Queen Elizabeth in Australia, 1986.

1987. Queen Elizabeth II's Birthday.

1058. **436.** 36 c. multicoloured .. 50 40

437. Convicts on Quay.

1987. Bicentenary of Australian Settlement (1988) (6th issue). Departure of the First Fleet. Multicoloured.

1059. 36 c. Type **437** 65 70
1060. 36 c. Royal Marines officer and wife 65 70
1061. 36 c. Sailors loading supplies 65 70
1062. 36 c. Officers being ferried to ships .. 65 70
1063. 36 c. Fleet in English Channel 65 70

See also Nos. 1064/6, 1077/81 and 1090/2.

1987. Bicentenary of Australian Settlement (1988) (7th issue). First Fleet at Tenerife. As T **437**. Multicoloured.

1064. 36 c. Ferrying supplies, Santa Cruz 50 65
1065. 36 c. Canary Islands fishermen and departing fleet 50 65
1066. $1 Fleet arriving at Tenerife .. .. 1·25 1·40

Nos. 1064/5 were printed together, se-tenant, forming a composite design.

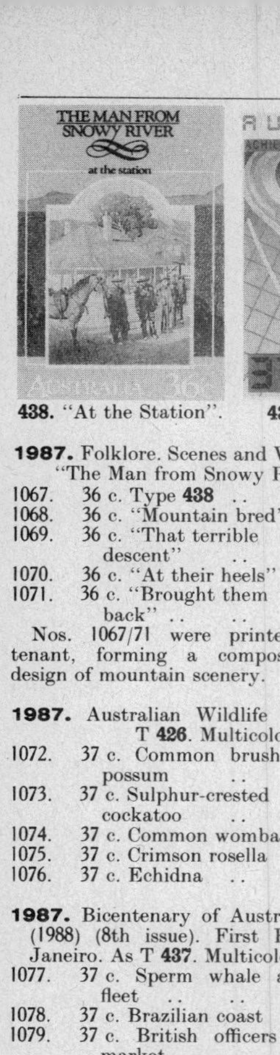

438. "At the Station". 439. Bionic Ear.

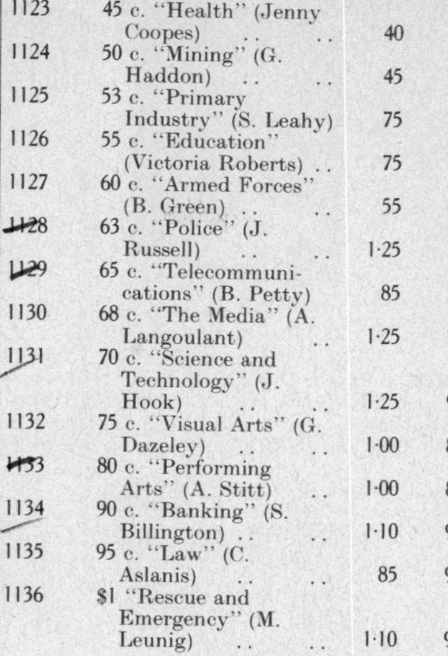

1987. Folklore. Scenes and Verses from Poem "The Man from Snowy River". Mult.
1067. 36 c. Type **438** 65 70
1068. 36 c. "Mountain bred" .. 65 70
1069. 36 c. "That terrible descent" 65 70
1070. 36 c. "At their heels" .. 65 70
1071. 36 c. "Brought them back" 65 70
Nos. 1067/71 were printed together, se-tenant, forming a composite background design of mountain scenery.

1987. Australian Wildlife (2nd series). As T **426**. Multicoloured.
1072. 37 c. Common brushtail possum 50 50
1073. 37 c. Sulphur-crested cockatoo 50 50
1074. 37 c. Common wombat .. 50 50
1075. 37 c. Crimson rosella .. 50 50
1076. 37 c. Echidna 50 50

1987. Bicentenary of Australian Settlement (1988) (8th issue). First Fleet at Rio de Janeiro. As T **437**. Multicoloured.
1077. 37 c. Sperm whale and fleet 60 70
1078. 37 c. Brazilian coast .. 60 70
1079. 37 c. British officers in market 60 70
1080. 37 c. Religious procession 60 70
1081. 37 c. Fleet leaving Rio .. 60 70
Nos. 1077/81 were printed together, se-tenant, forming a composite design.

1987. Australian Achievements in Technology, Multicoloured.
1082. 37 c. Type **439** 40 35
1083. 53 c. Microchips 65 60
1084. 63 c. Robotics 75 70
1085. 68 c. Ceramics 80 75

440. Catching Crayfish.

1987. "Aussie Kids". Multicoloured.
1086. 37 c. Type **440** 35 35
1087. 55 c. Playing cat's cradle 65 65
1088. 90 c. Young football supporters 95 95
1089. $1 Children with kangaroo .. .. 1·10 1·10

1987. Bicentenary of Australian Settlement (1988) (9th issue). First Fleet at Cape of Good Hope. As T **437**. Multicoloured.
1090. 37 c. Marine checking list of livestock 50 50
1091. 37 c. Loading livestock .. 50 50
1092. $1 First Fleet at Cape Town .. .. .. 1·25 1·25
Nos. 1090/1 were printed together, se-tenant, forming a composite design.

ABORIGINAL CRAFTS Australia 3c
Spearthrower (detail), Western Australia

441. Detail of Spearthrower, Western Australia.

1987. Aboriginal Crafts. Multicoloured.
1093. 3 c. Type **441** .. .. 80 1·00
1094. 15 c. Shield pattern, New South Wales .. .. 1·00 1·40
1095. 37 c. Basket weave, Queensland .. .. 80 1·00
1096. 37 c. Bowl design Central Australia .. 80 1·00
1097. 37 c. Belt pattern Northern Territory .. 80 1·00

442. Grandmother and Granddaughters with Candles.

1987. Christmas. Designs showing carol singing by candlelight. Multicoloured.
1098. 30 c. Type **442** 40 40
1099. 30 c. Father and daughters 40 40
1100. 30 c. Four children .. 40 40
1101. 30 c. Family 40 40
1102. 30 c. Six teenagers .. 40 40
1103. 37 c. Choir (horiz.) .. 45 45
1104. 63 c. Father and two children (horiz.) .. 75 75

1988. Bicentenary of Australian Settlement (10th issue). Arrival of First Fleet. As T **437**. Multicoloured.
1105. 37 c. Aborigines watching arrival of Fleet, Botany Bay .. 60 60
1106. 37 c. Aborigine family and anchored ships .. 60 60
1107. 37 c. Fleet arriving at Sydney Cove 60 60
1108. 37 c. Ship's boat .. 60 60
1109. 37 c. Raising the flag, Sydney Cove, 26 January 1788 .. 60 60
Nos. 1105/9 were printed together, se-tenant, forming a composite design.

443. Koala with Stockman's Hat and Eagle dressed as Uncle Sam.

1988. Bicentenary of Australian Settlement (11th issue). Joint issue with U.S.A.
1110. **443.** 37 c. multicoloured .. 60 35

444 "Religion" (A. Horner)

1988. "Living Together". Designs showing cartoons. Multicoloured (except 30 c.).
1111 1 c. Type **444** .. 10 10
1112 2 c. "Industry" (P. Nicholson) 10 10
1113 3 c. "Local Government" (A. Collette) 10 10
1114 4 c. "Trade Unions" (Liz Honey) .. 10 10
1115 5 c. "Parliament" (Bronwyn Halls) .. 15 10
1116 10 c. "Transport" (Meg Williams) 15 10
1117 15 c. "Sport" (G. Cook) 15 20
1118 20 c. "Commerce" (M. Atcherson) 35 20
1119 25 c. "Housing" (C. Smith) 25 30
1120 30 c. "Welfare" (R. Tandberg) (black and lilac) 30 35
1121 37 c. "Postal Services" (P. Viska) 35 40
1121b 39 c. "Tourism" (J. Spooner) 55 50
1122 40 c. "Recreation" (R. Harvey) 35 40
1123 45 c. "Health" (Jenny Coopes) 40 45
1124 50 c. "Mining" (G. Haddon) 45 50
1125 53 c. "Primary Industry" (S. Leahy) 75 70
1126 55 c. "Education" (Victoria Roberts) .. 75 55
1127 60 c. "Armed Forces" (B. Green) 55 60
1128 63 c. "Police" (J. Russell) .. .. 1·25 75
1129 65 c. "Telecommunications" (B. Petty) 85 75
1130 68 c. "The Media" (A. Langoulant) .. 1·25 75
1131 70 c. "Science and Technology" (J. Hook) .. 1·25 90
1132 75 c. "Visual Arts" (G. Dazeley) .. .. 1·00 80
1133 80 c. "Performing Arts" (A. Stitt) .. 1·00 80
1134 90 c. "Banking" (S. Billington) .. .. 1·10 90
1135 95 c. "Law" (C. Aslanis) 85 90
1136 $1 "Rescue and Emergency" (M. Leunig) .. .. 1·10 90

445 "Government House, Sydney, 1790" (George Raper)

1988. Bicentenary of Australian Settlement (12th issue). "The Early Years, 1788-1809". Multicoloured.
1137 37 c. Type **445** 50 50
1138 37 c. "Government Farm, Parramatta, 1791" ("The Port Jackson Painter") .. 50 50
1139 37 c. "Parramatta Road, 1796" (attr Thomas Watling) 50 50
1140 37 c. "View of Sydney Cove, c. 1800" (detail) (Edward Dayes) .. 50 50
1141 37 c. "Sydney Hospital, 1803", (detail) (George William Evans) .. 50 50
Nos. 1137/41 were printed together, se-tenant, forming a composite background design from the painting, "View of Sydney from the East Side of the Cove, c. 1808" by John Eyre.

446 Queen Elizabeth II (from photo by Tim Graham)

1988. Queen Elizabeth II's Birthday.
1142 **446** 37 c. multicoloured .. 45 40

447 Expo '88 Logo

1988. "Expo '88" World Fair, Brisbane.
1143 **447** 37 c. multicoloured .. 35 40

448 New Parliament House

1988. Opening of New Parliament House, Canberra.
1144 **448** 37 c. multicoloured .. 35 40

449 Early Settler and Sailing Clipper

1988. Bicentenary of Australian Settlement (13th issue). Multicoloured.
1145 37 c. Type **449** 65 70
1146 37 c. Queen Elizabeth II with British and Australian Parliament Buildings 65 70
1147 $1 W. G. Grace (cricketer) and tennis racquet .. 1·75 1·90
1148 $1 Shakespeare, John Lennon (entertainer) and Sydney Opera House .. .. .. 1·75 1·90
Stamps in similar designs were also issued by Great Britain.

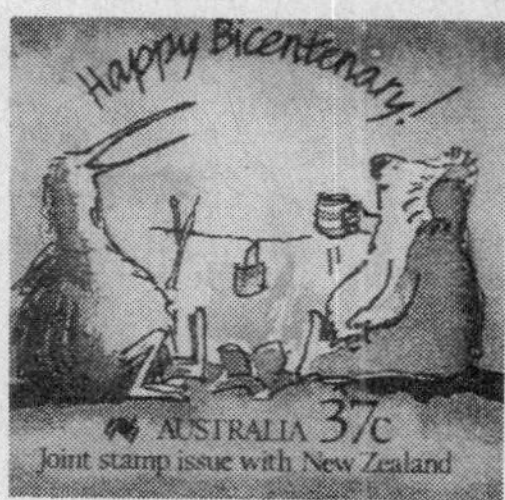

450 Kiwi and Koala at Campfire

1988. Bicentenary of Australian Settlement (14th issue).
1149 **450** 37 c. multicoloured .. 65 40
A stamp in a similar design was also issued by New Zealand.

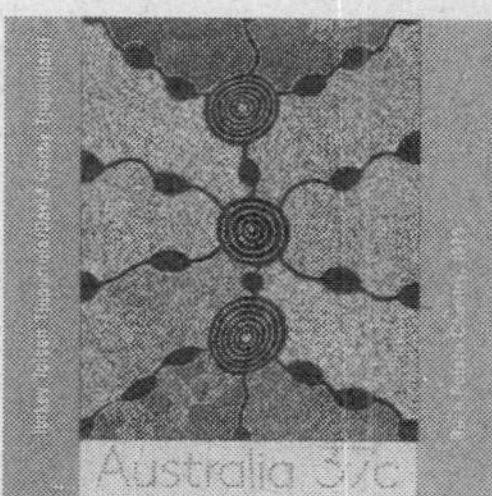

451 "Bush Potato Country" (Turkey Tolsen Tjupurrula and David Corby Tjapaltjarri)

1988. Art of the Desert. Aboriginal Paintings from Central Australia. Multicoloured.
1150 37 c. Type **451** 35 40
1151 55 c. "Courtship Rejected" (Limpi Puntungka Tjapangati) 55 60
1152 90 c. "Medicine Story" (artist unknown) .. 90 1·10
1153 $1 "Ancestor Dreaming" (Tim Leura Tjapaltjarri) .. .. 95 1·25

452 Basketball

1988. Olympic Games, Seoul. Multicoloured.

1154	37 c. Type **452**	35	40
1155	65 c. Athlete crossing finish line . .	60	65
1156	$1 Gymnast with hoop . .	95	1·00

453 Rod and Mace

1988. 34th Commonwealth Parliamentary Conference, Canberra.

1157	**453**	37 c. multicoloured . .	50	60

454 Necklace by Peter Tully

1988. Australian Crafts. Multicoloured.

1158	2 c. Type **454**	50	75
1159	5 c. Vase by Colin Levy	50	75
1160	39 c. Teapot by Frank Bauer . .	40	35

455 Pinnacles Desert

1988. Panorama of Australia. Mult.

1161	39 c. Type **455**	35	40
1162	55 c. Flooded landscape, Arnhem Land . .	50	55
1163	65 c. Twelve Apostles, Victoria . .	60	65
1164	70 c. Mountain Ash Wood	65	70

456 "The Nativity" (Danielle Hush)

1988. Christmas. Multicoloured.

1165	32 c. Type **456**	30	35
1166	39 c. "Koala as Father Christmas" (Kylie Courtney)	35	40
1167	63 c. "Christmas Cockatoo" (Benjamin Stevenson)	60	65

457 Sir Henry Parkes

1989. Australia Day. Centenary of Federation Speech by Sir Henry Parkes (N.S.W. Prime Minister).

1168	**457**	39 c. multicoloured . .	35	40

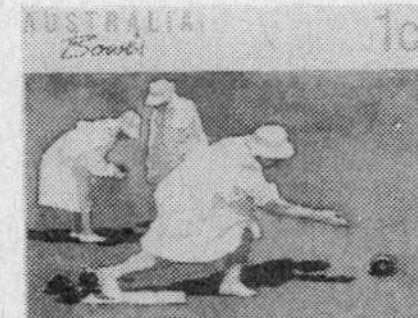

458 Bowls

1989. Sports. Multicoloured

1169	1 c. Type **458**	10	10
1170	2 c. Tenpin-bowling . .	10	10
1171	3 c. Australian football . .	10	10
1172	5 c. Kayaking and canoeing	10	10
1174	10 c. Sailboarding . .	10	15
1176	20 c. Tennis	20	25
1179	39 c. Fishing	55	55
1180	41 c. Cycling	40	35
1181	43 c. Skateboarding . .	40	45
1184	55 c. Kite-flying	50	55
1186	65 c. Rock-climbing . .	60	65
1187	70 c. Cricket	65	70
1188	75 c. Netball	70	75
1189	80 c. Squash	75	80
1190	85 c. Diving	80	85
1191	90 c. Soccer	85	90
1192	$1 Fun-run	90	1·00
1193	$1.10 Golf	1·00	1·10
1194	$1.20 Hang-gliding . .	1·10	1·25

See also Nos. 1259/60.

459 Merino

1989. Sheep in Australia. Multicoloured.

1195	39 c. Type **459**	35	40
1196	39 c. Poll Dorset . .	35	40
1197	85 c. Polwarth . .	80	85
1198	$1 Corriedale	95	1·00

460 Adelaide Botanic Garden

1989. Botanic Gardens. Multicoloured.

1199	$2 Noroo, New South Wales	1·90	2·00
1200	$5 Mawarra, Victoria . .	4·50	4·75
1201	$10 Type **460** . .	9·25	9·50
1201a	$20 "A View of the Artist's House and Garden in Mills Plains, Van Diemen's Land" (John Glover) . .	18·00	19·00

461 "Queen Elizabeth II" (sculpture, John Dowie)

1989. Queen Elizabeth II's Birthday.

1202	**461**	39 c. multicoloured . .	35	40

462 Arrival of Immigrant Ship, 1830's

1989. Colonial Development (1st issue). Pastoral Era 1810–1850. Multicoloured.

1203	39 c. Type **462**	40	40
1204	39 c. Pioneer cottage and wool dray	40	40
1205	39 c. Squatter's home-stead	40	40
1206	39 c. Shepherd with flock (from Joseph Lycett's "Views of Australia")	40	40
1207	39 c. Explorer in desert (after watercolour by Edward Frome) . .	40	40

See also Nos. 1254/8 and 1264/8.

463 Gladys Moncrieff and Roy Rene

1989. Australian Stage and Screen Personalities. Multicoloured.

1208	39 c. Type **463**	35	40
1209	85 c. Charles Chauvel and Chips Rafferty . .	80	85
1210	$1 Nellie Stewart and J. C. Williamson . .	95	1·00
1211	$1.10 Lottie Lyell and Raymond Longford . .	1·00	1·10

464 "Impression" (Tom Roberts)

1989. Australian Impressionist Paintings. Multicoloured.

1212	41 c. Type **464**	40	45
1213	41 c. "Impression for Golden Summer" (Sir Arthur Streeton) . .	40	45
1214	41 c. "All on a Summer's Day" (Charles Conder) (vert)	40	45
1215	41 c. "Petit Dejeuner" (Frederick McCubbin)	40	45

465 Freeways

1989. The Urban Environment.

1216	**465**	41 c. black, pur & grn	60	65
1217	–	41 c. blk, pur & mve	60	65
1218	–	41 c. black, pur & bl	60	65

DESIGNS: No. 1217, City buildings, Melbourne; No. 1218, Commuter train at platform.

466 Hikers outside Youth Hostel

1989. 50th Anniv of Australian Youth Hostels.

1219	**466**	41 c. multicoloured . .	45	45

467 Horse Tram, Adelaide, 1878

1989. Historic Trams. Multicoloured.

1220	41 c. Type **467** . .	50	50
1221	41 c. Steam tram, Sydney, 1884	50	50
1222	41 c. Cable tram, Melbourne, 1886 . .	50	50
1223	41 c. Double-deck electric tram, Hobart, 1893 . .	50	50
1224	41 c. Combination electric tram, Brisbane, 1901 . .	50	50

468 "Annunciation" (15th-century Book of Hours)

1989. Christmas. Illuminated Manuscripts. Multicoloured.

1225	36 c. Type **468**	35	40
1226	41 c. "Annunciation to the Shepherds" (Wharncliffe Book of Hours, c. 1475) . .	45	45
1227	80 c. "Adoration of the Magi" (15th-century Parisian Book of Hours)	95	95

469 Radio Waves and Globe

1989. 50th Anniv of Radio Australia.

1228	**469**	41 c. multicoloured . .	45	45

470 Golden Wattle

471 Australian Wildflowers

1990. Australia Day.

1229	**470**	41 c. multicoloured . .	45	45

1990. Greetings Stamp.

1230	**471**	41 c. multicoloured . .	45	45
1231		43 c. multicoloured . .	35	40

472 Dr. Constance Stone (first Australian woman doctor), Modern Doctor and Nurses

1990. Cent of Women in Medical Practice.
1232 **472** 41 c. multicoloured .. 45 45

473 Greater Glider

1990. Animals of the High Country. Mult.
1233 41 c. Type **473** 55 45
1234 65 c. Tiger cat ("Spotted-tailed Quoll") 80 75
1235 70 c. Mountain pygmy-possum 85 80
1236 80 c. Brush-tailed rock-wallaby 95 90

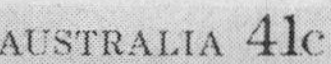
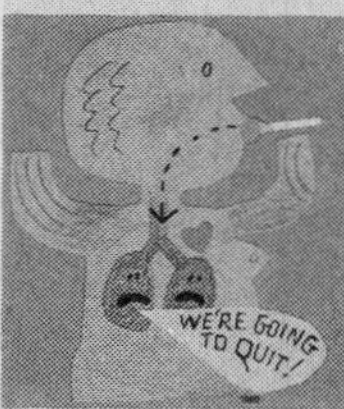

474 "Stop Smoking"

1990. Community Health. Multicoloured.
1237 41 c. Type **474** 55 45
1238 41 c. "Drinking and driving don't mix" .. 55 45
1239 41 c. "No junk food, please" 55 45
1240 41 c. "Guess who's just had a checkup?" .. 55 45

475 Soldiers from Two World Wars

476 Queen at Australian Ballet Gala Performance, London, 1988

1990. "The Anzac Tradition". Multicoloured.
1241 41 c. Type **475** 45 40
1242 41 c. Fighter pilots and munitions worker .. 45 40
1243 65 c. Veterans and Anzac Day parade 75 75
1244 $1 Casualty evacuation, Vietnam, and disabled veteran .. .. 1·10 1·10
1245 $1.10 Letters from home and returning troop-ships .. .. 1·25 1·25

1990. Queen Elizabeth II's Birthday.
1246 **476** 41 c. multicoloured .. 40 40

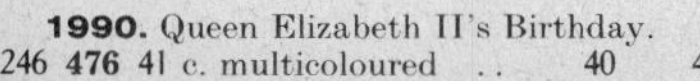

477 New South Wales 1861 5s. Stamp

1990. 150th Anniv of the Penny Black. Designs showing stamps. Multicoloured.
1247 41 c. Type **477** 45 60
1248 41 c. South Australia 1855 unissued 1s. 45 60
1249 41 c. Tasmania 1853 4d. .. 45 60
1250 41 c. Victoria 1867 5s. .. 45 60
1251 41 c. Queensland 1897 unissued 6d. 45 60
1252 41 c. Western Australia 1855 4d. with inverted frame 45 60

478 Gold Miners on way to Diggings

1990. Colonial Development (2nd issue). Gold Fever. Multicoloured.
1254 41 c. Type **478** 45 45
1255 41 c. Mining camp 45 45
1256 41 c. Panning and washing for gold 45 45
1257 41 c. Gold Commissioner's tent 45 45
1258 41 c. Moving gold under escort 45 45

1990. As Nos. 1180/1, but self-adhesive.
1259 41 c. Cycling 50 60
1260 43 c. Skateboarding .. 40 45

479 Glaciology Research

1990. Australian–Soviet Scientific Co-operation in Antarctica. Multicoloured.
1261 41 c. Type **479** 45 40
1262 $1.10 Krill (marine biology research) .. 1·25 1·25

Stamps in similar designs were also issued by Russia.

480 Auctioning Building Plots

1990. Colonial Development (3rd series). Boomtime. Multicoloured.
1264 41 c. Type **480** 40 40
1265 41 c. Colonial mansion .. 40 40
1266 41 c. Stock exchange .. 40 40
1267 41 c. Fashionable society .. 40 40
1268 41 c. Factories 40 40

481 "Salmon Gums" (Robert Juniper)

482 "Adelaide Town Hall" (Edmund Gouldsmith)

1990. "Heidelberg and Heritage" Art Exhibition. Multicoloured.
1269 28 c. Type **481** 20 25
1270 43 c. "The Blue Dress" (Brian Dunlop) .. 35 40

1990. 150th Anniv of Local Government.
1271 **482** 43 c. multicoloured .. 35 40

483 Laughing Kookaburras and Gifts

1990. Christmas. Multicoloured.
1272 38 c. Type **483** 40 40
1273 43 c. Baby Jesus with koalas and wallaby (vert) 40 40
1274 80 c. Possum on Christmas tree .. 80 1·00

484 National Flag

1991. Australia Day. 90th Anniv of Australian Flag.
1275 **484** 43 c. blue, red & grey 40 40
1276 – 90 c. multicoloured .. 95 1·10
1277 – $1 multicoloured .. 1·10 1·25
1278 – $1.20 red, blue & grey 1·40 1·50

DESIGNS: 90 c. Royal Australian Navy ensign; $1 Royal Australian Air Force standard; $1.20, Australian merchant marine ensign.

485 Black-necked Stork

1991. Waterbirds. Multicoloured.
1279 43 c. Type **485** 50 40
1280 43 c. Black swan (horiz) .. 50 40
1281 85 c. Cape Barren goose 1·00 1·25
1282 $1 Chestnut teal (horiz) .. 1·25 1·40

486 Recruitment Poster (Women's Services)

1991. Anzac Day. 50th Anniversaries.
1283 **486** 43 c. multicoloured .. 50 40
1284 – 43 c. black, grn & brn 50 40
1285 – $1.20 multicoloured .. 1·40 1·60

DESIGNS: 43 c. (No. 1284) Patrol (Defence of Tobruk); $1.20, "V-P Day Canberra" (Harold Abbot) (Australian War Memorial).

487 Queen Elizabeth at Royal Albert Hall, London

489 "Bondi" (Max Dupain)

488 "Tectocris diophthalmus" (bug)

1991. Queen Elizabeth II's Birthday.
1286 **487** 43 c. multicoloured .. 60 45

1991. Insects. Multicoloured.
1287 43 c. Type **488** 50 45
1288 43 c. "Cizara ardeniae" (hawk moth) 50 45
1289 80 c. "Petasida ephippigera" (grasshopper) 90 1·00
1290 $1 "Castiarina producta" (beetle) .. .. 1·10 1·25

1991. 150 Years of Photography in Australia.
1291 **489** 43 c. black, brn & blue 50 50
1292 – 43 c. black, grn & brn 50 50
1293 – 70 c. black, grn & brn 80 80
1294 – $1.20 black, brn & grn 1·25 1·25

DESIGNS: No. 1292, "Gears for the Mining Industry, Vickers Ruwolt, Melbourne" (Wolfgang Sievers); 1293, "The Wheel of Youth" (Harold Cazneaux); 1294, "Teacup Ballet" (Olive Cotton).

490 Singing Group

1991. Australian Radio Broadcasting. Designs showing listeners and scenes from radio programmes. Multicoloured.
1295 43 c. Type **490** 50 45
1296 43 c. "Blue Hills" serial 50 45
1297 85 c. "The Quiz Kids" .. 95 1·00
1298 $1 "Argonauts' Club" children's programme .. 1·00 1·00

491 Puppy

492 George Vancouver (1791) and Edward Eyre (1841)

1991. Domestic Pets. Multicoloured.
1299 43 c. Type **491** 40 45
1300 43 c. Kitten 40 45
1301 70 c. Pony 65 70
1302 $1 Cockatoo 90 95

1991. Exploration of Western Australia.

1303 **492** $1.05 multicoloured .. 95 1·00

493 "Seven Little Australians" (Ethel Turner)

1991. Australian Writers of the 1890s. Mult.

1305 43 c. Type **493** 40 45
1306 75 c. "On Our Selection" (Steele Rudd) 70 75
1307 $1 "Clancy of the Overflow" (poem, A. B. Paterson) (vert) .. 90 95
1308 $1.20 "The Drover's Wife" (short story, Henry Lawson) (vert) 1·10 1·25

494 Shepherd

1991. Christmas. Multicoloured.

1309 38 c. Type **494** 35 40
1310 43 c. Infant Jesus 40 45
1311 90 c. Wise Man 85 90

495 Parma Wallaby

1992. Threatened Species. Multicoloured.

1312 45 c. Type **495** 40 45
1313 45 c. Ghost bat 40 45
1314 45 c. Long-tailed dunnart 40 45
1315 45 c. Little pygmy-possum 40 45
1316 45 c. Dusky hopping-mouse 40 45
1317 45 c. Squirrel glider .. 40 45

496 Basket of Wild Flowers

1992. Greetings Stamp.

1318 **496** 45 c. multicoloured .. 40 45

497 Noosa River, Queensland

1992. Wetlands and Waterways. Mult.

1319 20 c. Type **497** 20 25
1320 45 c. Lake Eildon, Victoria 40 45

1992. As Nos. 1312/17, but self-adhesive.

1321 45 c. Type **495** 40 45
1322 45 c. Squirrel glider .. 40 45
1323 45 c. Dusky hopping-mouse 40 45
1324 45 c. Little pygmy-possum 40 45
1325 45 c. Long-tailed dunnart 40 45
1326 45 c. Ghost bat 40 45

498 "Young Endeavour" (brigantine)

1992. Australia Day. Sailing Ships. Mult.

1333 45 c. Type **498** 40 45
1334 45 c. "Britannia" (yacht) (vert) 40 45
1335 $1.05 "Akarana" (cutter) (vert) .. .. 95 1·00
1336 $1.20 "John Louis" (pearling lugger) .. 1·10 1·25

499 Bombing of Darwin

1992. 50th Anniv of Second World War Battles. Multicoloured.

1338 45 c. Type **499** 40 45
1339 75 c. Anti-aircraft gun and fighters, Milne Bay 70 75
1340 75 c. Infantry on Kokoda Trail 70 75
1341 $1.05 H.M.A.S. "Australia" (cruiser) and American carrier, Coral Sea .. 95 1·00
1342 $1.20 Australians advancing, El Alamein 1·10 1·25

500 "Helix Nebula"

1992. International Space Year. Mult.

1343 45 c. Type **500** 40 45
1344 $1.05 "The Pleiades" .. 95 1·00
1345 $1.20 "Spiral Galaxy, NGC 2997" .. .. 1·10 1·25

501 Hunter Valley, New South Wales

1992. Vineyard Regions. Multicoloured.

1347 45 c. Type **501** 40 45
1348 45 c. North East Victoria 40 45
1349 45 c. Barossa Valley, South Australia .. 40 45
1350 45 c. Coonawarra, South Australia .. 40 45
1351 45 c. Margaret River, Western Australia .. 40 45

503 3½d. Stamp of 1953

1992. Queen Elizabeth II's Birthday.

1352 **503** 45 c. multicoloured .. 40 45

OFFICIAL STAMPS

1931. Overprinted **O.S.**

(a) Kangaroo issue.

O 133. **1.** 6d. brown .. .. 40·00 30·00

(b) King George V issue.

O 128 **5a.** ½d. orange .. .. 9·50 1·50
O 129 1d. green .. .. 4·00 45
O 130 2d. red .. .. 6·00 55
O 131 3d. blue .. .. 7·50 5·00
O 126 4d. olive .. .. 40·00 3·75
O 132 5d. brown .. .. 65·00 38·00

(c) Various issues.

O 123. **13.** 2d. red .. .. 55·00 16·00
O 134. **18.** 2d. red .. .. 8·00 2·00
O 124. **13.** 3d. blue .. .. £200 38·00
O 135. **18.** 3d. blue .. .. 20·00 5·50
O 136. **17.** 1s. green .. .. 80·00 35·00

POSTAGE DUE STAMPS

D 1.

D 3.

1902. White space below value at foot.

D 1. D **1.** ½d. green .. .. 2·75 3·00
D 2. 1d. green .. .. 8·00 4·00
D 3. 2d. green .. .. 24·00 3·50
D 4. 3d. green .. .. 38·00 17·00
D 5. 4d. green .. .. 38·00 10·00
D 6. 6d. green .. .. 55·00 9·00
D 7. 8d. green .. .. 95·00 70·00
D 8. 5s. green .. .. £180 70·00

1902. White space filled in.

D 22 D **3.** ½d. green .. .. 4·25 3·00
D 23 1d. green .. .. 4·25 1·25
D 47 2d. green .. .. 20·00 3·25
D 25 3d. green .. .. 32·00 4·25
D 26 4d. green .. .. 32·00 3·50
D 17 5d. green .. .. 32·00 9·00
D 28 6d. green .. .. 48·00 8·50
D 29 8d. green .. .. 85·00 25·00
D 18 10d. green .. .. 60·00 12·00
D 19 1s. green .. .. 55·00 10·00
D 20 2s. green .. .. 95·00 16·00
D 33 5s. green .. .. £140 18·00
D 43 10s. green £2000 £1000
D 44 20s. green £3750 £2000

1908. As Type D **3,** but stroke after figure of value, thus " 5/– ".

D 58. D **3.** 1s. green .. .. 75·00 8·00
D 60. 2s. green £900 £1000
D 59. 5s. green .. .. £225 48·00
D 61. 10s. green £2000 £1700
D 62. 20s. green £5000 £4250

D **7.**

D **10.**

1909.

D 132 D **7.** ½d. red and green .. 1·00 1·75
D 120 1d. red and green .. 60 60
D 93 1½d. red and green .. 1·50 9·00
D 121 2d. red and green .. 3·75 80
D 134 3d. red and green .. 1·75 2·50
D 109 4d. red and green .. 3·75 2·00
D 124 5d. red and green .. 6·00 2·50
D 137 6d. red and green .. 2·75 2·75
D 126 7d. red and green .. 4·00 8·50
D 127 8d. red and green .. 10·00 25·00
D 139 10d. red and green .. 5·50 3·25
D 128 1s. red and green .. 16·00 1·25
D 70 2s. red and green .. 70·00 16·00
D 71 5s. red and green .. 75·00 16·00
D 72 10s. red and green .. £225 £140
D 73 £1 red and green .. £425 £225

1953.

D 140 D **10.** 1s. red and green .. 3·00 3·50
D 130 2s. red and green .. 18·00 12·00
D 131a 5s. red and green .. 12·00 70

AUSTRALIAN ANTARCTIC TERRITORY

By an Order in Council of 7 February 1933, the territory S. of latitude 60°S. between 160th and 145th meridians of East longitude (excepting Adelie Land) was placed under Australian administration.

1966. 100 cents = 1 dollar.

1. 1954 Expedition at Vestfold Hills and Map.

1957.

1 2s. blue .. .. .. 1·75 70

2. Members of Shackleton Expedition at S. Magnetic Pole 1909.

DESIGNS—As Type **3**—VERT. 1s. Dog-team and iceberg. 2s. 3d. Map of Antarctica and Emperor Penguins.

3. Weazel and Team.

1959.

2. 5d on 4d. black and sepia .. 60 15
3. 8d on 7d. black and blue .. 4·50 2·00
– 1s. myrtle .. .. .. 4·50 1·75
– 2s. 3d. green .. .. 10·00 4·00

6.

7. Sir Douglas Mawson (Expedition leader).

1961.

6. 5d. blue .. .. .. 1·50 15

1961. 50th Anniv. of 1911–14 Australian Antarctic Expedition.

7. **7.** 5d. myrtle 35 15

8. Aurora and Camera Dome.

1966. Multicoloured.

8 1 c. Type **8** 70 30
9 2 c. Emperor penguins .. 2·25 70
10 4 c. Ship and iceberg .. 70 70
11 5 c. Banding southern elephant-seals .. .. 2·75 1·75
12 7 c. Measuring snow strata 80 60
13 10 c. Wind gauges .. 1·00 60
14 15 c. Weather balloon .. 4·00 2·00
15 20 c. Helicopter (horiz) .. 4·25 2·25
16 25 c. Radio operator (horiz) 5·00 3·75
17 50 c. Ice-compression tests (horiz) .. .. .. 17·00 9·00
18 $1 Parahelion ("mock sun") (horiz) .. .. 42·00 15·00

11. Sastrugi (Snow Ridges).

1971. 10th Anniv. of Antarctic Treaty.

19. **11.** 6 c. blue and black .. 1·25 1·00
20. – 30 c. multicoloured .. 6·50 6·50

DESIGN: 30 c. Pancake ice.

12. Capt. Cook, Sextant and Compass.

1972. Bicentenary of Cook's Circumnavigation of Antarctica. Mult.

21. 7 c. Type **12** .. .. 2·50 75
22. 35 c. Chart and H.M.S. "Resolution" .. .. 8·50 6·00

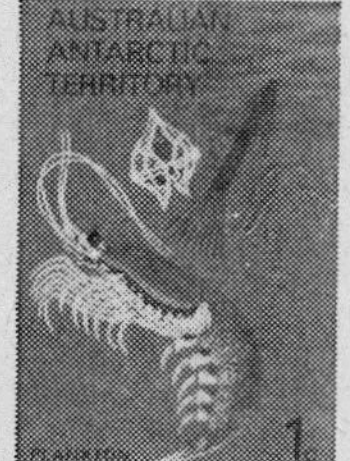

13. Plankton.

1973. Multicoloured.

23. 1 c. Type **13** 20 15
24. 5 c. Mawson's "Gipsy Moth", 1931 .. .. 30 30
25. 7 c. Adelie Penguin .. 2·25 60
26. 8 c. Rymill's "Fox Moth", 1934-7 .. .. 40 30
27. 9 c. Leopard seal (horiz.) .. 40 30
28. 10 c. Killer whale (horiz.) .. 5·50 1·25
29. 20 c. Wandering Albatross (horiz.) .. 90 60
30. 25 c. Wilkins' Lockheed "Vega", 1928 (horiz.) .. 50 60
31. 30 c. Ellsworth's Northrop "Gamma", 1935 .. 50 60
32. 35 c. Christensen's Avro "Avian", 1934 (horiz.) .. 50 60
33. 50 c. Byrd's "Tri-Motor", 1929 .. .. 60 60
34. $1 Sperm whale .. .. 1·00 1·40

14. Admiral Byrd (expedition leader), Aircraft and Map of South Pole.

1979. 50th Anniv. of First Flight over South Pole. Multicoloured.

35. 20 c. Type **14** .. 50 40
36. 55 c. Admiral Byrd, aircraft and Antarctic terrain 1·25 1·60

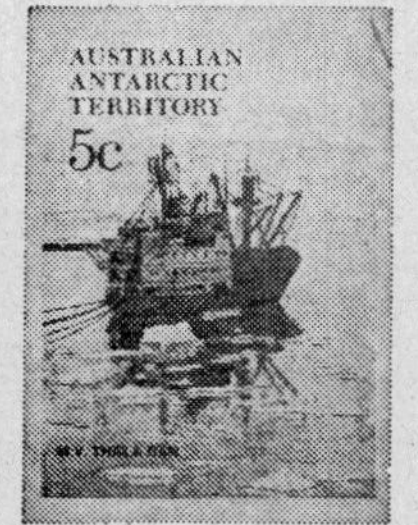

15. M.V. "Thala Dan".

1979. Ships. Multicoloured.

37. 1 c. S.Y. "Aurora" (horiz.) 10 10
38. 2 c. R.Y. "Penola" .. 20 10
39. 5 c. Type **15** .. 20 30
40. 10 c. H.M.S. "Challenger" (horiz.) .. 35 10
41. 15 c. S.S. "Morning" (bow view) (horiz.) .. 1·60 2·50
42. 15 c. S.Y. "Nimrod" (stern view) (horiz.) .. 75 30
43. 20 c. R.R.S. "Discovery II" (horiz.) .. 40 70
44. 22 c. R.Y.S. "Terra Nova" 70 90
45. 25 c. S.S. "Endurance" .. 60 85
46. 30 c. S.S. "Fram" (horiz.) 60 85
47. 35 c. M.S. "Nella Dan" (horiz.) 80 85
48. 40 c. M.S. "Kista Dan" 90 45
49. 45 c. "L'Astrolabe" (horiz.) 70 50
50. 50 c. S.S. "Norvegia" (horiz.) 70 55
51. 55 c. S.Y. "Discovery" .. 85 1·60
52. $1 H.M.S. "Resolution" 1·75 2·25

No. 41 is incorrectly inscribed "S.Y. Nimrod".

16. Sir Douglas Mawson in Antarctic Terrain.

1982. Birth Centenary of Sir Douglas Mawson (Antarctic explorer). Multicoloured.

53. 27 c. Type **16** 50 30
54. 75 c. Sir Douglas Mawson and map of Australian Antarctic Territory .. 1·50 2·25

17. Light-mantled Sooty Albatross.

1983. Regional Wildlife. Multicoloured.

55. 27 c. Type **17** 80 80
56. 27 c. King cormorant .. 80 80
57. 27 c. Southern elephant seal 80 80
58. 27 c. Royal penguin .. 80 80
59. 27 c. Dove prion 80 80

18. Antarctic Scientist.

1983. 12th Antarctic Treaty Consultative Meeting. Canberra.

60. **18.** 27 c. milticoloured .. 75 50

19. Prismatic Compass and Lloyd-Creak Dip Circle.

1984. 75th Anniv. of Magnetic Pole Expedition. Multicoloured.

61. 30 c. Type **19** 85 40
62. 85 c. Aneroid barometer and theodolite .. .. 1·90 1·25

20. Dog Team pulling Sledge.

1984. Antarctic Scenes. Multicoloured.

63. 2 c. Summer afternoon Mawson station 10 10
64. 5 c. Type **20** 10 10
65. 10 c. Late summer evening, MacRobertson Land .. 10 15
66. 15 c. Prince Charles Mountains 15 20
67. 20 c. Summer morning Wilkesland 20 25
68. 25 c. Sea-ice and iceberg .. 25 30
69. 30 c. Mount Coates 30 35
70. 33 c. "Iceberg Alley", Mawson 30 35
71. 36 c. Early winter evening, Casey Station .. 35 40
72. 45 c. Brash ice (vert.) .. 40 45
73. 60 c. Midwinter shadows, Casey Station 55 60
74. 75 c. Coastline 70 75
75. 85 c. Landing strip 80 85
76. 90 c. Pancake ice (vert.) .. 85 90
77. $1 Emperor penguins .. 90 95

21. Prince Charles Mountains near Mawson Station.

1986. 25th Anniv. of Antarctic Treaty.

78. **21.** 36 c. multicoloured .. 1·25 35

22 Hourglass Dolphins and "Nella Dan"

1988. Environment, Conservation and Technology. Multicoloured.

79 37 c. Type **22** 65 60
80 37 c. Emperor penguins and Davis Station 65 60
81 37 c. Crabeater seal and helicopter 65 60
82 37 c. Adelie penguins and tracked vehicle .. 65 60
83 37 c. Grey-headed albatross and photographer .. 65 60

23 "Antarctica"

1989. Antarctic Landscape Paintings by Sir Sidney Nolan. Multicoloured.

84 39 c. Type **23** 60 50
85 39 c. "Iceberg Alley" .. 60 50
86 60 c. "Glacial Flow" .. 85 75
87 80 c. "Frozen Sea" .. 1·10 1·00

24 "Aurora Australis"

1991. 30th Anniv of Antarctic Treaty (43 c.) and maiden voyage of "Aurora Australis" (research ship) ($1.20). Multicoloured.

88 43 c. Type **24** 50 50
89 $1.20 "Aurora Australis" off Heard Island .. .. 1·10 1·25

BAHAMAS

A group of islands in the Br. W. Indies, S.E. of Florida. Self-Government introduced on 7 January 1964. The islands became an independent member of the British Commonwealth on 10 July 1973.

1859. 12 pence = 1 shilling.
20 shillings = 1 pound
1966. 100 cents = 1 dollar.

1.

BAHAMAS FOUR PENCE

2.

1859. Imperf.

2 1 1d. rose .. .. .. 38·00 £1500

3.

5.

1860. Perf.

40 1 1d. red .. .. .. 35·00 12·00
27 2 4d. red .. .. .. £225 60·00
30 6d. violet .. .. .. £160 60·00
39a 3 1s. green .. .. .. 6·50 7·00

1883. Surch. **FOURPENCE.**

45. **2.** 4d. on 6d. violet £550 £400

1884.

48. **5.** 1d. red .. .. .. 3·75 1·50
52. 2½d. blue .. .. .. 8·50 1·50
53. 4d. yellow .. .. .. 8·50 3·75
54. 6d. mauve .. .. .. 4·00 22·00
56. 5s. green .. .. .. 60·00 65·00
57. £1 red £300 £225

6. Queen's Staircase, Nassau.

1901.

111 6 1d. black and red .. 70 1·00
76 3d. purple on buff .. 3·25 4·50
77 3d. black and brown .. 55 2·25
59 5d. black and orange .. 8·00 35·00
78 5d. black and mauve .. 2·25 5·50
113 2s. black and blue .. 15·00 28·00
61 3s. black and green .. 20·00 40·00

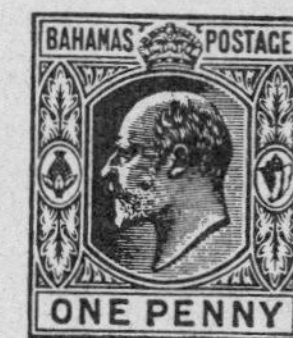

7.

8.

1902.

71 7 ½d. green .. .. .. 3·25 1·25
62 1d. red .. .. .. 1·50 90
63 2½d. blue .. .. .. 6·50 1·25
64 4d. yellow .. .. .. 11·00 30·00
66 6d. brown .. .. .. 13·00 32·00
67 1s. black and red .. .. 12·00 28·00
69 5s. purple and blue .. 48·00 60·00
70 £1 green and black .. £250 £300

1912.

115 8 ½d. green 20 40
116 1d. red 60 15
117 1½d. brown .. .. 85 1·00
118 2d. grey .. .. .. 85 2·75
119 2½d. blue .. .. .. 70 2·75
120 3d. purple on yellow .. 4·50 15·00
121 4d. yellow .. .. 70 5·00
122 6d. brown .. .. 60 1·25
123 1s. black and red .. 2·50 5·50
124 5s. purple and blue .. 27·00 42·00
125 £1 green and black .. £150 £250

1917. Optd. **1.1.17** and Red Cross.

90 6 1d. black and red .. 30 85

1918. Optd **WAR TAX** in one line.

96 8 ½d. green .. .. .. 30 1·40
97 1d. red 30 35
93 6 1d. black and red .. 1·60 2·50
98 3d. purple on yellow .. 40 1·50
100 3d. black and brown .. 30 4·00
99 8 1s. black and red .. 2·50 2·75

1919. Optd. WAR CHARITY 3.6.18.
101 6 1d. black and red .. 30 2·25

1919. Optd. WAR TAX in two lines.
102 8 ½d. green .. .. .. 20 1·25
103 1d. red .. .. .. 20 1·50
105 6 3d. black and brown .. 30 5·00
104 8 1s. black and red .. 4·75 18·00

16.

1920. Peace Celebration.
106 16 ½d. green .. .. 55 3·50
107 1d. red .. .. 2·50 70
108 2d. grey .. .. 2·50 6·50
109 3d. brown .. .. 2·50 8·50
110 1s. green .. .. 10·00 27·00

17. Seal of the Colony.

1930. Tercentenary of the Colony.
126 17 1d. black and red .. 1·50 2·50
127 3d. black and brown .. 3·00 11·00
128 5d. black and violet .. 3·00 11·00
129 2s. black and blue .. 18·00 35·00
130 3s. black and green .. 32·00 55·00

1931. As T 17, but without dates at top.
131 2s. black and blue .. 1·50 50
132 3s. black and green .. 1·50 85

1935. Silver Jubilee. As T 13 of Antigua.
141. 1½d. blue and red .. 70 90
142. 2½d. brown and blue .. 2·25 3·00
143. 6d. blue and olive .. 5·00 6·50
144. 1s. grey and purple .. 6·00 8·00

19. Greater Flamingo (in flight).

1935.
145. 19. 8d. blue and red .. 4·50 2·75

1937. Coronation. As T 2 of Aden.
146. ½d. green 15 15
147. 1½d. brown 30 40
148. 2½d. blue 50 60

20. King George VI.

DESIGNS—As Type 15. HORIZ. 6d. Fort Charlotte. 8d. Flamingoes.

21. Sea Garden, Nassau.

1938.
149 20. ½d. green 15 60
149c ½d. purple .. .. 40 2·50
150 1d. red .. .. 8·50 4·75
150a 1d. grey 20 30
151 1½d. brown 40 55
152 2d. grey .. .. 13·00 9·00
152b 2d. red 30 55
152c 2d. green 30 80
153 2½d. blue .. .. 3·00 2·00
153a 20 2½d. violet 30 55
154 3d. violet .. .. 10·00 5·00
154a 3d. blue 30 90
154b 3d. red .. .. 50 2·75
158 21 4d. blue and orange .. 80 30
159 – 6d. green and blue .. 60 25
160 – 8d. blue and red .. 2·25 90
154c 20 10d. orange .. .. 1·50 20
155 1s. black and red .. 1·75 25
156b 5s. purple and blue .. 20·00 5·00
157a £1 green and black .. 48·00 32·00

1940. Surch.
161. 20. 3d. on 2½d. blue .. 40 40

1942. 450th Anniv. of Landing of Columbus. Optd. 1492 LANDFALL OF COLUMBUS 1942.
162. 20. ½d. green 20 60
163. 1d. grey 20 60
164. 1½d. brown 30 50
165. 2d. red 30 65
166. 2½d. blue 30 65
167. 3d. blue 30 65
168. 21. 4d. blue and orange .. 40 90
169. – 6d. grn. & blue (No. 159) 40 1·75
170. – 8d. blue & red (No. 160) 65 70
171. 20. 1s. black and red .. 75 80
172. 17. 2s. black and blue .. 6·50 8·00
173a. 3s. black and green .. 3·50 6·00
174. 20. 5s. purple and blue .. 10·00 8·00
175a. £1 green and black .. 22·00 18·00

1946. Victory. As T 9 of Aden.
176. 1½d. brown 10 10
177. 3d. blue 10 10

26. Infant Welfare Clinic.

1948. Tercentenary of Settlement of Island of Eleuthera. Inscr. as in T 26.
178. 26. ½d. orange 20 50
179. – 1d. olive 20 35
180. – 1½d. yellow 25 70
181. – 2d. red 30 40
182. – 2½d. brown 35 60
183. – 3d. blue 40 75
184. – 4d. black 40 70
185. – 6d. green .. .. 1·00 70
186. – 8d. violet 35 70
187. – 10d. red 35 15
188. – 1s. brown 60 30
189. – 2s. purple .. .. 4·00 7·50
190. – 3s. blue .. .. 6·00 7·50
191. – 5s. mauve .. .. 3·75 4·00
192. – 10s. grey .. .. 6·00 8·00
193. – £1 red .. .. 9·00 9·50

DESIGNS: 1d. Agriculture. 1½d., Sisal. 2d. Straw work. 2½d., Dairy. 3d. Fishing fleet. 4d. Island settlement. 6d. Tuna fishing. 8d. Paradise Beach. 10d. Modern hotels. 1s. Yacht racing. 2s. Water sports — skiing. 3s. Shipbuilding. 5s. Transportation. 10s. Salt production. £1, Parliament Buildings.

1948. Silver Wedding. As T 10/11 of Aden.
194. 1½d. brown 15 25
195. £1 grey .. .. 28·00 26·00

1949. 75th Anniv of U.P.U. As T 20/23 of Antigua.
196. 2½d. violet 35 40
197. 3d. blue .. .. 80 1·00
198. 6d. blue .. .. 90 1·00
199. 1s. red 90 75

1953. Coronation. As T 13 of Aden.
200. 6d. black and blue .. 15 35

42. Infant Welfare Clinic.

1954. Designs as Nos. 178/93 but with portrait of Queen Elizabeth II and without commemorative inscr. as in T 42.
201. 42. ½d. black and red .. 10 40
202. – 1d. olive and brown .. 10 10
203. – 1½d. blue and black .. 15 40
204. – 2d. brown and green .. 15 15
205. – 3d. black and red .. 30 30
206. – 4d. turquoise and purple 30 25
207. – 5d. brown and blue .. 1·40 2·25
208. – 6d. blue and black .. 30 10
209. – 8d. black and lilac .. 30 25
210. – 10d. black and blue .. 30 10
211. – 1s. blue and brown .. 40 10
212. – 2s. orange and black .. 1·75 70
213. – 2s. 6d. black and blue .. 3·25 1·50
214. – 5s. green and orange .. 12·00 75
215. – 10s. black and slate .. 6·50 1·75
216. – £1 black and violet .. 12·00 5·00

DESIGNS: 1½d., Island settlement. 4d. Water sports—Skiing. 5d. Dairy. 6d. Transportation. 2s. Sisal. 2s. 6d. Shipbuilding. 5s. Tuna fishing. Other values the same as for the corresponding values in Nos. 178/93.

43. Queen Elizabeth II.

1959. Centenary of Bahamas Stamp.
217. 43. 1d. black and red .. 20 10
218. 2d. black and green .. 25 40
219. 6d. black and blue .. 25 45
220. 10d. black and brown .. 25 45

44. Christ Church Cathedral.

1962. Centenary of Nassau.
221. 44. 8d. green 25 20
222. – 10d. violet 25 15
DESIGN 10d. Nassau Public Library.

1963. Freedom from Hunger. As T 28 of Aden.
223. 8d. sepia 40 35

1963. Bahamas Talks. Nos. 209/10 optd. BAHAMAS TALKS 1962.
224. 8d. black and lilac .. 40 45
225. 10d. black and blue .. 50 55

1963. Cent of Red Cross. As T 33 of Antigua.
226. 1d red and black .. 25 30
227. 10d. red and blue .. 1·25 2·00

1964. New Constitution. Nos. 201/16 optd. NEW CONSTITUTION 1964.
228. 42. ½d. black and red .. 10 30
229. – 1d. olive and brown .. 10 15
230. – 1½d. blue and black .. 40 30
231. – 2d. brown and green .. 10 20
232. – 3d. black and red .. 40 30
233. – 4d. turquoise and purple 40 45
234. – 5d. brown and blue .. 30 65
235. – 6d. blue and black .. 30 30
236. – 8d. black and lilac .. 40 30
237. – 10d. black and blue .. 30 15
238 – 1s. blue and brown .. 35 15
239. – 2s. brown and black .. 1·50 1·75
240. – 2s. 6d. black and blue .. 2·00 2·50
241. – 5s. green and orange .. 4·25 3·25
242. – 10s. black and slate .. 4·00 5·50
243. – £1 black and violet .. 7·50 13·00

1964. 400th Birth Anniv of Shakespeare. As T 34 of Antigua.
244 6d. turquoise 10 10

1964. Olympic Games, Tokyo. No. 211 surch. with Olympic "rings" symbol and value.
245. 8d. on 1s. blue and brown 10 10

49. Colony's Badge.

1965.
247. 49. ½d. multicoloured .. 15 60
248. – 1d. slate, blue & orange 25 20
249. – 1½d. red, green & brown 15 70
250. – 2d. slate, green & blue .. 15 10
251. – 3d. red, blue and purple 80 20
252. – 4d. green, blue & brown 55 1·00
253. – 6d. green, blue and red 30 10
254. – 8d. purple, blue & bronze 50 30
255. – 10d. brown, grn. & violet 25 10
256a. – 1s. multicoloured .. 30 10
257. – 2s. brown, blue & green 1·00 1·00
258. – 2s. 6d. olive, blue & red 2·00 2·00
259. – 5s. brown, blue & green 2·25 1·00
260. – 10s. red, blue and brown 8·00 2·25
261. – £1 brown, blue and red 9·00 5·00

DESIGNS: 1d. Out Island Regatta. 1½d. Hospital. 2d. High School. 3d. Greater Flamingo. 4d. R.M.S. "Queen Elizabeth". 6d. "Development". 8d. Yachting. 10d. Public Square. 1s. Sea Garden. 2s. Old Cannon at Fort Charlotte. 2s. 6d. Sikorsky "S-38" Seaplane (1929) and Boeing "707" Airliner. 5s. Williamson Film Project (1914) and Undersea Post Office (1939). 10s. Conch Shell. £1, Columbus' Flagship.

1965. Cent of I.T.U. As T 36 of Antigua.
262. 1d. green and orange .. 15 10
263. 2s. purple and olive .. 65 35

1965. No. 254 surch.
264. – 9d. on 8d. purple, blue and bronze 15 10

1965. I.C.Y. As T 37 of Antigua.
265. ½d. purple and turquoise 10 20
266. 1s. green and lavender .. 30 40

1966. Churchill Commem. As T 38 of Antigua.
267. ½d. blue 10 25
268. 2d. green 30 30
269. 10d. brown 65 85
270. 1s. violet .. .. 75 1·40

1966. Royal Visit. As T 39 of Antigua, but inscr. "to the Caribbean" omitted.
271. 6d. black and blue .. 90 50
272. 1s. black and mauve .. 1·60 1·25

1966. Decimal currency. Nos. 247/61 surch.
273. 49. 1 c. on ½d. multicoloured 10 10
274. – 2 c. on 1d. slate, blue and orange .. 10 10
275. – 3 c. on 2d. slate, green and blue .. 10 10
276. – 4 c. on 3d. red, bl. & pur. 20 10
277. – 5 c. on 4d. green, blue and brown .. 15 30
278. – 8 c. on 6d. grn., bl. & red 15 20
279. – 10 c. on 8d. purple, blue and bronze .. 25 40
280. – 11 c. on 1½d. red, green and brown .. 15 20
281. – 12 c. on 10d. brown, grn. and violet .. 15 10
282. – 15 c. on 1s. multicoloured 25 10
283. – 22 c. on 2s. brown, blue and green .. 60 80
284. – 50 c. on 2s. 6d. olive, blue and red .. 90 1·10
285. – $1 on 5s. brown, blue and green .. 1·25 1·50
286. – $2 on 10s. red, bl. & brn. 3·50 3·50
287. – $3 on £1 brn., bl. & red 5·00 4·00

1966. World Cup Football Championships. As T 40 of Antigua.
288. 8 c. multicoloured .. 15 15
289. 15 c. multicoloured .. 25 25

1966. Inauguration of W.H.O. Headquarters, Geneva. As T 41 of Antigua.
290. 11 c. black, green and blue 25 20
291. 15 c. black, purple & ochre 30 25

1966. 20th Anniv. of U.N.E.S.C.O. As T 54/6 of Antigua.
292. 3 c. multicoloured .. 15 10
293. 15 c. yellow, violet & olive 35 30
294. $1 black, purple & orange 1·50 2·25

1967. As Nos. 247/51, 253/9 and 261 but values in decimal currency, and new designs for 5 c. and $2.
295. 49. 1 c. multicoloured .. 10 60
296. – 2 c. slate, blue & green 15 10
297. – 3 c. slate, green & violet 10 10
298. – 4 c. red, lt. blue & blue 2·50 20
299. – 5 c. black, blue & purple 60 40
300. – 8 c. green, blue & brown 25 10
301. – 10 c. pur., blue & red .. 30 40
302. – 11 c. red, green and blue 25 40
303. – 12 c. brown, grn. & olive 25 10
304. – 15 c. multicoloured .. 55 10
305. – 22 c. brown, blue & red 70 65
306. – 50 c. olive, blue & grn. 2·00 75
307. – $1 maroon, blue & pur. 2·00 60
308. – $2 multicoloured .. 7·00 2·00
309. – $3 brown, blue & pur. 3·75 2·00
NEW DESIGNS: 5 c. "Oceanic". $2, Conch Shell (different).

69. Bahamas Crest.

1967. Diamond Jubilee of World Scouting. Multicoloured.
310. 3 c. Type 69 .. .. 20 15
311. 15 c. Scout badge 25 15

71. Globe and Emblem.

1968. Human Rights Year. Multicoloured.
312. 3 c. Type 71 .. .. 10 10
313. 12 c. Scales of Justice and Emblem 20 10
314. $1 Bahamas Crest & Emblem 60 80

HAVE YOU READ THE NOTES AT THE BEGINNING OF THIS CATALOGUE?
These often provide answers to the enquiries we receive.

74. Golf.

1968. Tourism. Multicoloured.

315.	5 c. Type **74**	55	30
316.	11 c. Yachting	80	30
317.	15 c. Horse-racing ..	80	35
318.	50 c. Water-skiing ..	1·75	2·50

78. Racing Yacht and Olympic Monument.

1968. Olympic Games, Mexico City.

319. **78.**	5 c. brn., yell. and grn.	25	15
320. –	11 c. multicoloured ..	35	25
321. –	50 c. multicoloured ..	80	1·40
322. **78.**	$1 grey, blue and violet	1·75	3·00

DESIGNS: 11 c. Long jumping and Olympic Monument. 50 c. Running and Olympic Monument.

81. Legislative Building.

1968. 14th Commonwealth Parliamentary Conf. Multicoloured.

323.	3 c. Type **81**	10	10
324.	10 c. Bahamas Mace and Westminster Clock Tower	15	15
325.	12 c. Local Straw Market	15	20
326.	15 c. Horse drawn Surrey	20	25

Nos. 324/5 are vert.

85. Obverse and reverse of $100 Gold Coin.

1968. Gold Coins Commemorating the first General Election under the New Constitution.

327. **85.**	3 c. red on gold ..	20	25
328. –	12 c. green on gold ..	35	50
329. –	15 c. purple on gold ..	40	60
330. –	$1 black on gold ..	1·75	2·50

OBVERSE AND REVERSE OF: 12 c. $50 Gold Coin. 15 c. $20 Gold Coin. $1, $10 Gold Coin.

89. First Flight Postcard of 1919.

1969. 50th Anniv. of Bahamas Airmail Services.

331. **89.**	12 c. multicoloured ..	50	40
332. –	15 c. multicoloured ..	60	85

DESIGN: 15 c. Sikorsky "S-38" Seaplane of 1929.

91. Game-Fishing Boats.

1969. Tourism. One Millionth Visitor to Bahamas. Multicoloured.

333.	3 c. Type **91**	35	10
334.	11 c. Paradise Beach ..	50	15
335.	"Sunfish" sailing boats ..	50	15
336.	15 c. Rawson Square and parade	60	25

92. "The Adoration of the Shepherds" (Louis le Nain).

1969. Christmas. Multicoloured.

338.	3 c. Type **92** ..	10	10
339.	11 c. "The Adoration of the Shepherds" (Poussin) ..	15	15
340.	12 c. "The Adoration of the Kings" (Gerard David)	15	15
341.	15 c. "The Adoration of the Kings" (Vincenzo Foppa)	20	25

93. Badge of Girl Guides.

1970. Diamond Jubilee of Girl Guides' Association. Multicoloured.

342.	3 c. Type **93**	20	10
343.	12 c. Badge of Brownies	35	20
344.	15 c. Badge of Rangers	40	35

94. New U.P.U. Headquarters and Emblem.

1970. New U.P.U. Headquarters Building.

345. **94.**	3 c. multicoloured ..	10	10
346.	15 c. multicoloured ..	20	30

95. Coach and Globe.

1970. "Goodwill Caravan". Multicoloured.

347.	3 c. Type **95**	30	10
348.	11 c. Train and globe ..	80	20
349.	12 c. "Canberra" (liner), yacht & globe	80	25
350.	15 c. Airliner and globe ..	80	55

96. Nurse, Patients and Greater Flamingo.

1970. Cent. of British Red Cross. Mult.

352.	3 c. Type **96**	25	10
353.	15 c. Hospital and dolphin	30	40

97. "The Nativity" (detail, Pittoni).

1970. Christmas. Multicoloured.

354.	3 c. Type **97**	10	10
355.	11 c. "The Holy Family" (detail, Anton Raphael Mengs)	15	15
356.	12 c. "The Adoration of the Shepherds" (detail, Giorgione)	15	15
357.	15 c. "The Adoration of the Shepherds" (detail, School of Seville) ..	25	30

98. International Airport.

1971. Multicoloured.

359	1 c. Type **98**	10	30
360	2 c. Breadfruit	15	35
361	3 c. Straw Market ..	15	30
362	4 c. Hawksbill turtle ..	1·25	3·25
363	5 c. Grouper	35	40
364	6 c. As 4 c.	35	80
365	7 c. Hibiscus	1·50	1·50
464	8 c. Yellow Elder.. ..	1·50	30
367	10 c. Bahamian sponge boat	40	30
368	11 c. Greater Flamingoes	1·25	70
369	12 c. As 7 c.	2·00	3·00
370	15 c. Bonefish	40	55
466	16 c. As 7 c.	70	35
371	18 c. Royal Poinciana ..	55	65
467	21 c. As 2 c.	1·00	80
372	22 c. As 18 c.	2·75	6·50
468	25 c. As 4 c.	75	40
469	40 c. As 10 c.	1·25	75
470	50 c. Post Office, Nassau	1·75	1·75
471	$1 Pineapple (vert.) ..	2·25	2·50
472	$2 Crawfish (vert.) ..	3·75	5·50
525	$3 Junkanoo (vert.) ..	4·50	7·00

99. Snowflake.

1971. Christmas.

377. **99.**	3 c. pur., orge. and gold	10	10
378. –	11 c. blue and gold ..	20	15
379. –	15 c. multicoloured ..	20	20
380. –	18 c. blue, ultram. & gold	25	25

DESIGNS: 11 c. "Peace on Earth" (doves). 15 c. Arms of Bahamas and holly. 18 c. Starlit lagoon.

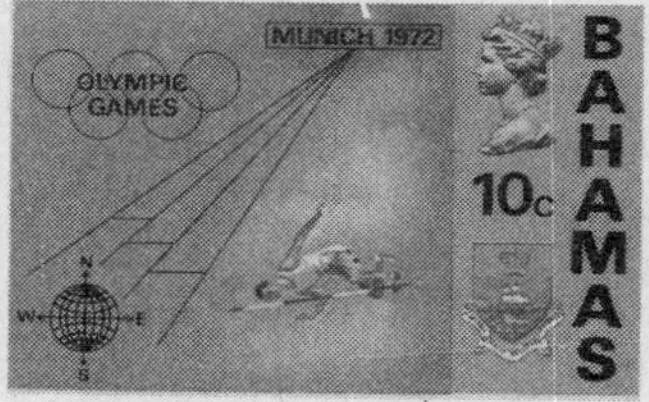

100. High jumping.

1972. Olympic Games, Munich. Multicoloured.

382.	10 c. Type **100**	20	25
383.	11 c. Cycling	25	30
384.	15 c. Running	30	45
385.	18 c. Sailing	50	70

101. Shepherd.

1972. Christmas. Multicoloured.

387.	3 c. Type **101**	10	10
388.	6 c. Bells	10	10
389.	15 c. Holly and Cross ..	15	20
390.	20 c. Poinsettia ..	25	45

1972. Royal Silver Wedding. As T **52**, of Ascension, but with Mace and Galleon in background.

393.	11 c. pink	15	15
394.	18 c. violet	15	20

104. Weather Satellite.

1973. Cent. of I.M.O./W.M.O. Mult.

410.	15 c. Type **104**	30	25
411.	18 c. Weather radar ..	40	35

105. C. A. Bain (national hero).

1973. Independence. Multicoloured.

412.	3 c. Type **105**	10	10
413.	11 c. Coat of arms ..	15	10
414.	15 c. Bahamas flag ..	20	15
415.	$1 Governor-General, M. B. Butler	90	1·00

106. "The Virgin in Prayer" (Sassoferrato).

1973. Christmas. Multicoloured.

417.	3 c. Type **106** ..	10	10
418.	11 c. "Virgin and Child with St. John" (Filippino Lippi) ..	15	15
419.	15 c. "A Choir of Angels" (Simon Marmion) ..	15	15
420.	18 c. "The Two Trinities" (Murillo)..	25	25

107. "Agriculture and Sciences".

1974. 25th Anniv. of University of West Indies. Multicoloured.

422.	15 c. Type **107** ..	20	25
423.	18 c. "Arts, Engineering and General Studies" ..	25	30

108. U.P.U. Monument, Berne.

1974. Centenary of U.P.U.

424. **108.**	3 c. multicoloured ..	10	10
425. –	13 c. multicoloured (vert.)	20	25
426. –	14 c. multicoloured ..	20	30
427. –	18 c. multicoloured (vert.)	25	35

DESIGNS: As Type **108** but showing different arrangements of the U.P.U. Monument.

109. Roseate Spoonbills.

1974. 15th Anniv. of Bahamas National Trust. Multicoloured.

No.	Description	Unused	Used
429.	13 c. Type **109**	85	65
430.	14 c. White-crowned Pigeon	85	65
431.	21 c. White-tailed Tropic Birds	1·25	1·00
432.	36 c. Cuban Amazon ..	1·60	1·60

110. "The Holy Family" (Jacques de Stella).

1974. Christmas. Multicoloured.

No.	Description	Unused	Used
434.	8 c. Type **110**	10	10
435.	10 c. "Madonna and Child" (16th Century Brescian School)	15	15
436.	12 c. "Virgin and Child with St. John the Baptist and St. Catherine" (Previtali)	15	15
437.	21 c. "Virgin and Child with Angels" (Previtali) ..	25	30

111. "Anteos maerula".

1975. Butterflies. Multicoloured.

No.	Description	Unused	Used
439	3 c. Type **111**	25	15
440	14 c. "Eurema nicippe" ..	80	50
441	18 c. "Papilio andraemon"	95	65
442	21 c. "Euptoieta hegesia"	1·10	85

112. Sheep Husbandry.

1975. Economic Diversification. Mult.

No.	Description	Unused	Used
444.	3 c. Type **112** ..	10	10
445.	14 c. Electric-reel fishing (vert.)	20	15
446.	18 c. Farming	25	20
447.	21 c. Oil Refinery (vert.)	45	35

113. Rowena Rand (evangelist).

1975. International Women's Year.

No.	Description	Unused	Used
449. 113.	14 c. brn., light bl. & bl.	20	25
450. –	18 c. yell., grn. & brn..	25	30

DESIGN: 18 c. I.W.Y. symbol and Harvest symbol.

114. "Adoration of the Shepherds" (Perugino).

1975. Christmas. Multicoloured.

No.	Description	Unused	Used
451.	3 c. Type **114**	10	10
452.	8 c. "Adoration of the Magi" (Ghirlandaio) ..	20	10
453.	18 c. As 8 c.	35	40
454.	21 c. Type **114**	45	60

115. Telephones, 1876 and 1976.

1976. Centenary of Telephone. Multicoloured.

No.	Description	Unused	Used
456.	3 c. Type **115**	10	10
457.	16 c. Radio-telephone link, Deleporte	25	30
458.	21 c. Alexander Graham Bell	35	45
459.	25 c. Satellite	40	55

116. Map of North America.

1976. Bicent. of American Revolution. Multicoloured.

No.	Description	Unused	Used
475.	16 c. Type **116**	30	30
476.	$1 John Murray, Earl of Dunmore	1·50	1·75

117. Cycling.

1976. Olympic Games, Montreal.

No.	Description	Unused	Used
478. 117.	8 c. mauve, blue and light blue ..	15	10
479. –	16 c. orange, brown and light blue	20	15
480. –	25 c. blue, mauve and light blue ..	25	25
481. –	40 c. brown, orange and light blue	30	55

DESIGNS: 16 c. Jumping. 25 c. Sailing. 40 c. Boxing.

118. "Virgin and Child" (detail, Lippi).

1976. Christmas. Multicoloured.

No.	Description	Unused	Used
483.	3 c. Type **118**	10	10
484.	21 c. "Adoration of the Shepherds" (School of Seville)	15	15
485.	25 c. "Adoration of the Kings" (detail, Foppa)	15	20
486.	40 c. "Virgin and Child" (detail, Vivarini) ..	25	40

119. Queen beneath Cloth of Gold Canopy.

1977. Silver Jubilee. Multicoloured.

No.	Description	Unused	Used
488.	8 c. Type **119**	10	10
489.	16 c. The Crowning ..	15	15
490.	21 c. Taking the Oath ..	15	15
491.	40 c. Queen with sceptre and orb	25	30

120. Featherduster.

1977. Marine Life. Multicoloured.

No.	Description	Unused	Used
493.	3 c. Type **120**	15	15
494.	8 c. Pork Fish and cave ..	30	20
495.	16 c. Elkhorn Coral	55	40
496.	21 c. Soft Coral and sponge	65	55

121. Scouts around Campfire and Home-made Shower.

1977. 6th Caribbean Scout Jamboree. Mult.

No.	Description	Unused	Used
498.	16 c. Type **121**	50	20
499.	21 c. Boating scenes ..	60	25

1977. Royal Visit. Nos. 488/91 optd. **Royal Visit October 1977.**

No.	Description	Unused	Used
500.	8 c. Type **119**	15	10
501.	16 c. The Crowning ..	20	15
502.	21 c. Taking the Oath ..	25	25
503.	40 c. Queen with Sceptre and Orb	30	40

123. Virgin and Child.

1977. Christmas. Multicoloured.

No.	Description	Unused	Used
505.	3 c. Type **123**	10	10
506.	16 c. The Magi	20	25
507.	21 c. Nativity Scene ..	25	40
508.	25 c. The Magi and star ..	30	45

124. Public Library, Nassau (Colonial).

1978. Architectural Heritage.

No.	Description	Unused	Used
510. 124.	3 c. black and green ..	10	10
511. –	8 c. black and blue ..	15	10
512. –	16 c. black and mauve	20	20
513. –	18 c. black and pink ..	25	30

DESIGNS: 8 c. St. Matthew's Church. 16 c. Government House. 18 c. The Hermitage, Cat Island.

125. Sceptre, St. Edward's Crown and Orb.

1978. 25th Anniv. of Coronation. Mult.

No.	Description	Unused	Used
515.	16 c. Type **125**	15	10
516.	$1 Queen in Coronation regalia	50	65

126. Coat of Arms within Wreath and Three Ships.

1978. Christmas.

No.	Description	Unused	Used
532. 126.	5 c. gold, lake and red	15	10
533. –	21 c. gold, deep blue and blue	30	25

DESIGN: 21 c. Three angels with trumpets.

127. Child reaching for Adult.

1979. International Year of the Child. Multicoloured.

No.	Description	Unused	Used
535.	5 c. Type **127**	15	10
536.	16 c. Boys playing leap-frog	30	35
537.	21 c. Girls skipping ..	40	50
538.	25 c. Bricks with I.Y.C. emblem	40	60

128. Sir Rowland Hill and Penny Black.

1979. Death Centenary of Sir Rowland Hill. Multicoloured.

No.	Description	Unused	Used
540.	10 c. Type **128**	25	10
541.	21 c. Printing press, 1840 and 6d. stamp of 1862 ..	35	30
542.	25 c. Great Britain 1856 6d. with "A 05" (Nassau) cancellation, and 1840 2d. Blue	40	45
543.	40 c. Early mailboat and 1d. stamp of 1859 ..	50	55

129. Commemorative Plaque and Map of Bahamas.

1979. 250th Anniv. of Parliament. Mult.

545. 16 c. Type 129 .. .. 20 10
546. 21 c. Parliament buildings 25 15
547. 25 c. Legislative Chamber 25 15
548. $1 Senate Chamber .. 70 80

130. Goombay Carnival Headdress.

1979. Christmas.

550. 130. 5 c. multicoloured .. 10 10
551. – 10 c. multicoloured .. 10 10
552. – 16 c. multicoloured .. 15 10
553. – 21 c. multicoloured .. 20 20
554. – 25 c. multicoloured .. 20 20
555. – 40 c. multicoloured .. 30 35

DESIGNS: 10 c. to 40 c. Various Carnival costumes.

131. Landfall of Columbus, 1492.

1980. Multicoloured.

557 1 c. Type 131 20 40
558 3 c. Blackbeard the pirate 20 35
559 5 c. Eleutheran Adventurers (Articles and Orders, 1647) 30 20
560 10 c. Ceremonial mace .. 20 30
561 12 c. The Loyalists, 1783–1788 .. .. .. 20 40
562 15 c. Slave trading, Vendue House .. .. .. 2·25 40
563 16 c. Wrecking in the 1800's 30 40
564 18 c. Blockade running (American Civil War).. 40 60
565 21 c. Bootlegging, 1919–1929 .. .. .. 40 60
566 25 c. Pineapple cultivation 40 60
567 40 c. Sponge clipping .. 70 85
568 50 c. Tourist development 75 75
569 $1 Modern agriculture .. 1·40 2·25
570 $2 Modern air and sea transport .. .. 3·00 3·00
571 $3 Banking (Central Bank) 3·50 4·00
572 $5 Independence, 10 July 1973 .. .. .. 5·50 6·00

132. Virgin and Child.

1980. Christmas Straw-work. Multicoloured.

573. 5 c. Three Kings 10 10
574. 21 c. Type 132 .. .. 25 10
575. 25 c. Angel 25 15
576. $1 Christmas Tree .. 75 70

133. Disabled Person with Walking Stick.

1981. International Year of Disabled People. Multicoloured.

578. 5 c. Type 133 .. .. 10 10
579. $1 Disabled person in wheel-chair .. .. .. 1·25 1·25

134. Grand Bahama Tracking Site.

1981. Space Exploration. Multicoloured.

581. 10 c. Type 134 .. .. 15 15
582. 20 c. Satellite view of Bahamas (vert.) .. 35 40
583. 25 c. Satellite view of Eleuthera 40 50
584. 50 c. Satellite view of Andros and New Province (vert.) 65 80

135. Prince Charles and Lady Diana Spencer.

1981. Royal Wedding. Multicoloured.

586. 30 c. Type 135 .. .. 75 25
587. $2 Prince Charles and Prime Minister Pindling .. 3·75 1·75

136. Bahama Pintail.

1981. Wildlife (1st series). Birds. Mult.

589. 5 c. Type 136 .. .. 50 15
590. 20 c. Reddish Egret .. 80 40
591. 25 c. Brown Booby .. 90 45
592. $1 Black-billed Whistling Duck .. .. .. 2·00 3·25

See also Nos. 626/9, 653/6 and 690/3.

1981. Commonwealth Finance Ministers' Meeting. Nos. 559/60, 566 and 568 optd. **COMMONWEALTH FINANCE MINISTER'S MEETING 21-23 SEPTEMBER 1981.**

594. 5 c. Eleutheran Adventurers (Articles and Orders, 1647) 10 15
595. 10 c. Ceremonial Mace .. 15 20
596. 25 c. Pineapple cultivation 40 60
597. 50 c. Tourist development 75 1·25

138. Poultry.

1981. World Food Day. Multicoloured.

598. 5 c. Type 138. .. .. 10 10
599. 20 c. Sheep 30 35
600. 30 c. Lobsters 40 50
601. 50 c. Pigs .. .. .. 75 1·75

139. Father Christmas.

1981. Christmas. Multicoloured.

603. 5 c. Type 139 .. .. 25 25
604. 5 c. Mother and child .. 25 25
605. 5 c. St. Nicholas, Holland 25 25
606. 25 c. Lussibruden, Sweden 50 50
607. 25 c. Mother and child (different) 50 50
608. 25 c. King Wenceslas, Czechoslovakia.. .. 50 50
609. 30 c. Mother with child on knee 50 50
610. 30 c. Mother carrying child 50 50
611. $1 Christkindl Angel, Germany .. .. 1·00 1·00

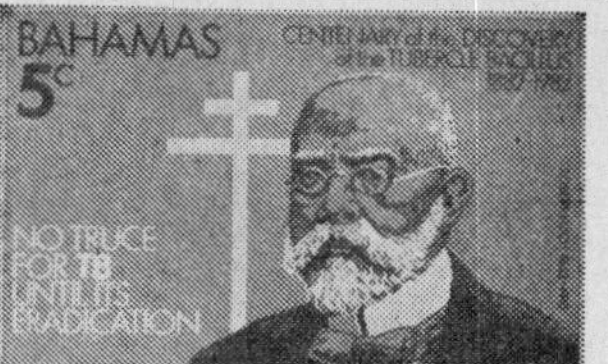

140. Robert Koch.

1982. Centenary of Discovery of Tubercle Bacillus by Robert Koch.

612. 140. 5 c. blk., brn. & lilac .. 30 10
613. – 16 c. blk., brn. & orge... 65 40
614. – 21 c. multicoloured .. 75 45
615. – $1 multicoloured .. 2·50 3·50

DESIGNS: 16 c. Stylised infected person. 21 c. Early and modern microscopes. $1 Mantoux test.

141. Greater Flamingo (male).

1982. Greater Flamingoes. Multicoloured.

617. 25 c. Type 141 .. .. 65 75
618. 25 c. Female 65 75
619. 25 c. Female with nestling 65 75
620. 25 c. Juvenile 65 75
621. 25 c. Immature bird .. 65 75

142. Lady Diana Spencer at Ascot, June 1981.

1982. 21st Birthday of Princess of Wales. Multicoloured

622. 16 c. Bahamas coat of arms 20 10
623. 25 c. Type 142 .. .. 35 15
624. 40 c. Bride and Earl Spencer arriving at St. Paul's 50 20
625. $1 Formal portrait .. 1·00 1·25

1982. Wildlife (2nd series). Mammals. As Type 136. Multicoloured.

626. 10 c. Buffy flower bat .. 25 15
627. 16 c. Bahaman hutia .. 40 25
628. 21 c. Common racoon .. 55 55
629. $1 Common dolphin .. 1·75 1·75

143. House of Assembly Plaque.

1982. 28th Commonwealth Parliamentary Association Conference. Multicoloured.

631. 5 c. Type 143. .. .. 15 10
632. 25 c. Association coat of arms 45 35
633. 40 c. Coat of arms .. 70 60
634. 50 c. House of Assembly.. 85 75

INDEX
Countries can be quickly located by referring to the index at the end of this volume.

144. Wesley Methodist Church, Baillou Hill Road.

1982. Christmas. Churches. Multicoloured.

635. 5 c. Type 144 .. .. 10 10
636. 12 c. Centreville Seventh Day Adventist Church 20 20
637. 15 c. The Church of God of Prophecy, East Street.. 25 25
638. 21 c. Bethel Baptist Church, Meeting Street 30 30
639. 25 c. St. Francis Xavier Catholic Church, Highbury Park 35 50
640. $1 Holy Cross Anglican Church, Highbury Park 1·50 2·50

145. Prime Minister Lyndon O. Pindling.

1983. Commonwealth Day. Multicoloured.

641. 5 c. Type 145 .. .. 10 10
642. 25 c. Bahamian and Commonwealth flags .. 40 40
643. 35 c. Map showing position of Bahamas 50 50
644. $1 Ocean liner .. .. 1·40 1·40

1983. Nos. 562/5 surch.

645. 20 c. on 15 c. Slave, Trading Vendue House 50 35
646. 31 c. on 21 c. Bootlegging, 1919-29 .. .. .. 60 55
647. 35 c. on 16 c. Wrecking in the 1800's 70 60
648. 80 c. on 18 c. Blockade running (American Civil War) 1·50 1·40

147. Customs Officers and Liner.

1983. 30th Anniv. of Customs Co-operation Council. Multicoloured.

649. 31 c. Type 147 .. .. 1·25 45
650. $1 Customs officers and airliner .. .. .. 2·50 2·00

148. Raising the National Flag. 149. " Loyalist Dreams ".

1983. 10th Anniv. of Independence.

651. 148. $1 multicoloured .. 1·25 1·40

1983. Wildlife (3rd series). Butterflies. As T 136.

653. 5 c. multicoloured .. 40 10
654. 25 c. multicoloured .. 85 40
655. 31 c. black, yellow & red.. 95 45
656. 50 c. multicoloured .. 1·25 70

DESIGNS: 5 c. "Atalopedes carteri". 25 c. "Ascia monuste". 31 c. "Phoebis agarithe". 50 c. "Dryas julia".

1983. Bicentenary of Arrival of American Loyalists in the Bahamas. Multicoloured.

658. 5 c. Type 149 .. .. 10 10
659. 31 c. New Plymouth, Abaco (horiz.) 45 50
660. 35 c. New Plymouth Hotel (horiz.) 50 70
661. 50 c. " Island Hope " .. 65 90

150. Consolidated " Catalina ".

1983. Air. Bicentenary of Manned Flight. Multicoloured.

663. 10 c. Type **150** 15 15
664. 25 c. Avro " Tudor IV " .. 35 30
665. 31 c. Avro " Lancastrian " 40 45
666. 35 c. Consolidated " Commodore " 45 50

For these stamps without the Manned Flight logo, see Nos. 699/702.

151. " Christmas Bells " (Monica Pinder). **152.** 1861 4d. Stamp.

1983. Christmas. Children's Paintings. Multicoloured.

667. 5 c. Type **151** .. 10 10
668. 20 c. " Flamingo " (Cory Bullard) 25 30
669. 25 c. " Yellow Hibiscus with Christmas Candle " (Monique Bailey) .. 35 40
670. 31 c. " Santa goes a-sailing " (Sabrina Seiler) (horiz.) 40 45
671. 35 c. " Silhouette scene with Palm Trees " (James Blake) 45 50
672. 50 c. " Silhouette scene with Pelicans " (Erik Russell) (horiz.) 65 70

1984. 125th Anniv. of First Bahamas Postage Stamp. Multicoloured.

673. 5 c. Type **152** 15 10
674. $1 1859 1d. stamp .. 1·60 1·50

153. R.M.S. "Trent".

1984. 250th Anniv. of "Lloyd's List" (newspaper). Multicoloured.

675. 5 c. Type **153** 10 10
676. 31 c. R.M.S. "Orinoco" .. 55 60
677. 35 c. Nassau harbour .. 60 65
678. 50 c. M.V. "Oropesa" (container ship) 90 95

154. Running.

1984. Olympic Games, Los Angeles.

679. **154.** 5 c. green, black and gold 10 10
680. – 25 c. blue, black and gold 45 50
681. – 31 c. red, black and gold 55 60
682. – $1 brown, black and gold 1·75 2·00

DESIGNS: 25 c. Shot-putting. 31 c. Boxing. $1 Basketball.

HAVE YOU READ THE NOTES AT THE BEGINNING OF THIS CATALOGUE?
These often provide answers to the enquiries we receive.

155. Bahamas and Caribbean Community Flags.

1984. 5th Conference of Caribbean Community Heads of Government.

684. **155.** 50 c. multicoloured .. 90 95

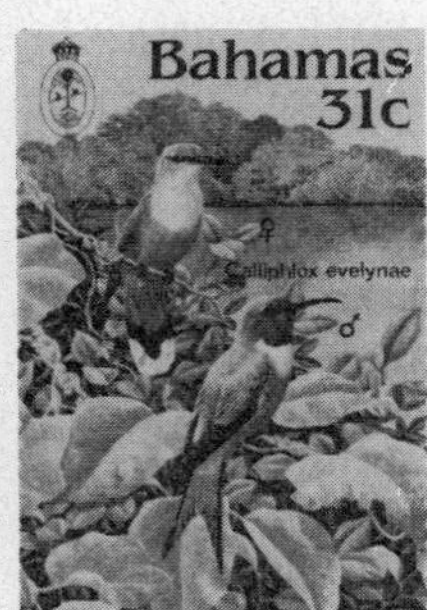

156. Bahama Woodstar.

1984. 25th Anniv. of National Trust. Mult.

685 31 c. Type **156** .. .. 90 1·00
686 31 c. Belted kingfishers, greater flamingos and "Eleutherodactylus planirostris" (frog) 90 1·00
687 31 c. Black-necked stilts, greater flamingos and "Phoebis sennae" (butterfly) .. .. 90 1·00
688 31 c. "Urbanus proteus" (butterfly) and "Chelonia mydas" (turtle) .. .. 90 1·00
689 31 c. Osprey and greater flamingos .. .. 90 1·00

Nos. 685/9 were printed together in horizontal strips of 5 forming a composite design.

1984. Wildlife (4th series). Reptiles and Amphibians. As T **136**.

690. 5 c. Allens' Cay Iguana .. 25 10
691. 25 c. Curly-tailed Lizard .. 75 50
692. 35 c. Greenhouse Frog .. 90 65
693. 50 c. Atlantic Green Turtle .. 1·40 95

157. "The Holy Virgin with Jesus and Johannes" (19th-century porcelain plaque after Titian)

1984. Christmas. Religious Paintings. Multicoloured.

695. 5 c. Type **157** 10 10
696. 31 c. "Madonna with Child in Tropical Landscape" (aquarelle, Anais Colin) 55 60
697. 35 c. The Holy Virgin with the "Child" (miniature on ivory, Elena Caula) 60 65

1985. Air. As Nos. 663/6, but without Manned Flight Logo.

699 10 c. Type **150** .. 20 20
700 25 c. Avro "Tudor IV" .. 40 40
701 31 c. Avro "Lancastrian" 45 45
702 35 c. Consolidated "Commodore" 45 45

158. Brownie Emblem and Conch.

1985. International Youth Year. 75th Anniv. of Girl Guide Movement. Multicoloured.

703. 5 c. Type **158.** 15 10
704. 25 c. Tents and coconut palm 60 50
705. 31 c. Guide salute and greater flamingos .. 80 60
706. 35 c. Ranger emblem and marlin 85 65

159. Killdeer.

1985. Birth Bicentenary of John J. Audubon (ornithologist). Multicoloured.

708. 5 c. Type **159** 40 10
709. 31 c. Mourning Dove (vert.) 85 55
710. 35 c. "Mourning Dove" (John J. Audubon) (vert.) 95 60
711. $1 "Killdeer" (John J. Audubon) .. .. 1·75 1·60

160. The Queen Mother at Christening of Peter Phillips, 1977.

1985. Life and Times of Queen Elizabeth the Queen Mother. Multicoloured.

712. 5 c. Visiting Auckland, New Zealand, 1927 .. 10 10
713. 25 c. Type **160** 40 40
714. 35 c. The Queen Mother attending church .. 55 55
715. 50 c. With Prince Henry at his christening (from photo by Lord Snowdon) 75 75

161. Ears of Wheat and Emblems.

1985. 40th Anniv. of U.N.O. and F.A.O.

717. **161.** 25 c. multicoloured .. 40 40

162. Queen Elizabeth II.

1985. Commonwealth Heads of Government Meeting, Nassau. Multicoloured.

718. 31 c. Type **162** .. .. 1·25 1·10
719. 35 c. Bahamas Prime Minister's flag and Commonwealth emblem 1·50 1·40

163. "Grandma's Christmas Bouquet" (Alton Roland Lowe)

1985. Christmas. Paintings by Alton Roland Lowe. Multicoloured.

736. 5 c. Type **163** 20 10
737. 25 c. "Junkanoo Romeo and Juliet" (vert.) .. 75 65
738. 31 c. "Bunce Gal" (vert.) 95 90
739. 35 c. "Home for Christmas" .. .. 1·25 1·10

1986. 60th Birthday of Queen Elizabeth II. As T **110** of Ascension. Multicoloured.

741. 10 c. Princess Elizabeth, aged one, 1927 .. .. 15 20
742. 25 c. The Coronation, 1953 35 40
743. 35 c. Queen making speech at Commonwealth Banquet, Bahamas, 1985 50 55
744. 40 c. In Djakova, Yugoslavia, 1972 .. 55 60
745. $1 At Crown Agents Head Office, London, 1983 .. 1·40 1·50

164. 1980 1 c. and 18 c. Definitive Stamps.

1986. "Ameripex '86" International Stamp Exhibition, Chicago.

746. **164.** 5 c. multicoloured .. 10 10
747. – 25 c. multicoloured .. 35 40
748. – 31 c. multicoloured .. 40 45
749. – 50 c. multicoloured .. 70 75
750. – $1 blk., grn. & bl. .. 1·40 2·00

DESIGNS:—HORIZ. (showing Bahamas stamps)—25 c. 1969 50th Anniversary of Bahamas Airmail Service pair. 31 c. 1976 Bicentenary of American Revolution 16 c., 50 c. 1981 Space Exploration miniature sheet. VERT—$1 Statue of Liberty. No. 750 also commemorates the Centenary of the Statue of Liberty.

1986. Royal Wedding. As T **112** of Ascension. Multicoloured.

756. 10 c. Prince Andrew and Miss Sarah Ferguson .. 20 20
757. $1 Prince Andrew .. .. 1·60 1·60

165. Rock Beauty (juvenile).

1986. Fishes. Multicoloured.

791 5 c. Type **165** 15 15
759 10 c. Stoplight Parrotfish 20 15
793 15 c. Jackknife Fish .. 25 30
761 20 c. Flamefish 55 50
762 25 c. Swissguard Basslet .. 70 50
763 30 c. Spotfin Butterflyfish 45 45
764 35 c. Queen Triggerfish .. 50 50
765 40 c. Four-eyed Butterflyfish 55 55
766 45 c. Fairy Basslet .. 60 60
767 50 c. Queen Angelfish .. 70 70
797 60 c. Blue Chromis .. 1·00 1·00
769 $1 Spanish Hogfish .. 1·40 1·40
799 $2 Harlequin Bass .. 2·50 3·25
771 $3 Blackbar Soldier Fish .. 3·25 3·75
772 $5 Pygmy Angelfish .. 4·75 5·50
773 $10 Red Hind .. .. 11·00 13·00

166. Christ Church Cathedral, Nassau, 1861.

1986. 125th Annivs. of City of Nassau, Diocese and Cathedral. Multicoloured.

774. 10 c. Type **166** 15 20
775. 40 c. Christ Church Cathedral, 1986 .. .. 55 60

167. Man and Boy looking at Crib.

1986. Christmas. International Peace Year. Multicoloured.

777. 10 c. Type **167** 15 20
778. 40 c. Mary and Joseph journeying to Bethlehem 55 60
779. 45 c. Children praying and Star of Bethlehem .. 65 80
780. 50 c. Children exchanging gifts 70 85

168. Great Isaac Lighthouse.

1987. Lighthouses. Multicoloured.

782. 10 c. Type **168** 55 20
783. 40 c. Bird Rock lighthouse 1·75 1·00
784. 45 c. Castle Island lighthouse .. .. 1·75 1·10
785. $1 "Hole in the Wall" lighthouse .. .. 2·75 3·50

169. Anne Bonney.

1987. Pirates and Privateers of the Caribbean. Multicoloured.

786. 10 c. Type **169** 45 20
787. 40 c. Edward Teach ("Blackbeard") .. .. 1·40 75
788. 45 c. Captain Edward England .. .. .. 1·50 85
789. 50 c. Captain Woodes Rogers .. .. .. 1·60 95

170. Bahamasair Boeing "737".

1987. Air. Aircraft. Multicoloured.

800 15 c. Type **170** 15 20
801 40 c. Eastern airlines Boeing "757" 45 50
802 45 c. Pan Am Airbus "A300" 50 55
803 50 c. British Airways Boeing "747" 60 65

171. Cruise Liner and Catamaran.

1987. Tourist Transport. Multicoloured.

804. 40 c. Type **171** 55 55
805. 40 c. Liners and speedboat 55 55
806. 40 c. Game fishing boat and cruising yacht .. 55 55
807. 40 c. Game fishing boat and racing yachts .. 55 55
808. 40 c. Fishing boat and schooner 55 55
809. 40 c. Bahamasair airliner 55 55
810. 40 c. Bahamasair and Pan Am Boeing airliners .. 55 55
811. 40 c. Light aircraft and radio beacon 55 55
812. 40 c. Aircraft and Nassau control tower 55 55
813. 40 c. Helicopter and parked aircraft 55 55

Nos. 804/8 and 809/13 were each printed together, se-tenant, forming a composite design.

172. "Cattleyopsis lindenii".

1987. Christmas. Orchids. Multicoloured.

814. 10 c. Type **172** 30 10
815. 40 c. "Encyclia lucayana" 90 60
816. 45 c. "Encyclia hodgeana" 95 70
817. 50 c. "Encyclia lleidae" .. 1·25 80

173. King Ferdinand and Queen Isabella of Spain.

1988. 500th Anniv. (1992) of Discovery of America by Columbus (1st issue). Mult.

819. 10 c. Type **173** 30 15
820. 40 c. Columbus before Talavera Committee .. 85 55
821. 45 c. Lucayan village .. 90 60
822. 50 c. Lucayan potters .. 95 65

See also Nos. 844/7, 870/3, 908/11 and 933/6.

174 Whistling Ducks in Flight

1988. Black-billed Whistling Duck. Mult.

824 5 c. Type **174** 30 15
825 10 c. Whistling duck in reeds 40 15
826 20 c. Pair with brood .. 65 40
827 45 c. Pair wading .. 1·00 1·00

175 Grantstown Cabin, c. 1820

1988. 150th Anniv of Abolition of Slavery. Multicoloured.

828 10 c. Type **175** 15 15
829 40 c. Basket-making, Grantstown 50 55

176 Olympic Flame, High Jumping, Hammer throwing, Basketball and Gymnastics

1988. Olympic Games, Seoul. Designs taken from painting by James Martin. Mult.

830 10 c. Type **176** 15 15
831 40 c. Athletics, archery, swimming, long jumping, weightlifting and boxing .. 50 55
832 45 c. Javelin throwing, gymnastics, hurdling and shot put .. 55 60
833 $1 Athletics, hurdling, gymnastics and cycling 1·25 1·40

1988. 300th Anniv of Lloyd's of London. As T **123** of Ascension. Multicoloured.

835 10 c. Lloyd's List of 1740 20 15
836 40 c. Freeport Harbour (horiz) 60 55
837 45 c. Space shuttle over Bahamas (horiz) .. 65 60
838 $1 "Yarmouth Castle" on fire .. .. 1·40 1·40

177 "Oh Little Town of Bethlehem"

1988. Christmas. Carols. Multicoloured.

839 10 c. Type **177** 15 15
840 40 c. "Little Donkey" .. 50 55
841 45 c. "Silent Night" .. 55 60
842 50 c. "Hark the Herald Angels Sing" 60 65

1989. 500th Anniv (1992) of Discovery of America by Columbus (2nd issue). As T **173**. Multicoloured.

844 10 c. Columbus drawing chart 20 15
845 40 c. Types of caravel .. 70 70
846 45 c. Early navigational instruments 75 75
847 50 c. Arawak artefacts .. 80 85

178 Cuban Emerald

1989. Hummingbirds. Multicoloured.

849 10 c. Type **178** 30 15
850 40 c. Ruby-throated hummingbird .. 80 90
851 45 c. Bahama woodstar .. 85 95
852 50 c. Rufous hummingbird 95 1·10

179 Teaching Water Safety

1989. 125th Anniv of International Red Cross. Multicoloured.

853 10 c. Type **179** .. 30 20
854 $1 Henri Dunant (founder) and Battle of Solferino 2·00 2·10

1989. 20th Anniv of First Manned Landing on Moon. As T **126** of Ascension. Multicoloured.

855 10 c. "Apollo 8" Communications Station, Grand Bahama 15 20
856 40 c. Crew of "Apollo 8" (30 × 30 mm) 50 55
857 45 c. "Apollo 8" emblem (30 × 30 mm) 55 60
858 $1 The Earth seen from "Apollo 8" .. .. 1·25 1·40

180 Church of the Nativity, Bethlehem

1989. Christmas. Churches of the Holy Land. Multicoloured.

860 10 c. Type **180** 15 20
861 40 c. Basilica of the Annunciation, Nazareth 50 55
862 45 c. Tabgha Church, Galilee 55 60
863 $1 Church of the Holy Sepulchre, Jerusalem .. 1·25 1·40

181 1974 U.P.U. Centenary 13 c. Stamp and Globe

1989. "World Stamp Expo '89" International Stamp Exhibition, Washington. Multicoloured.

865 10 c. Type **181** 25 20
866 40 c. 1970 New U.P.U. Headquarters Building 3 c. and building .. 70 60
867 45 c. 1986 "Ameripex '86" $1 and Capitol, Washington 75 75
868 $1 1949 75th anniversary of U.P.U. 2½d. and Bahamasair airliner .. 1·90 2·25

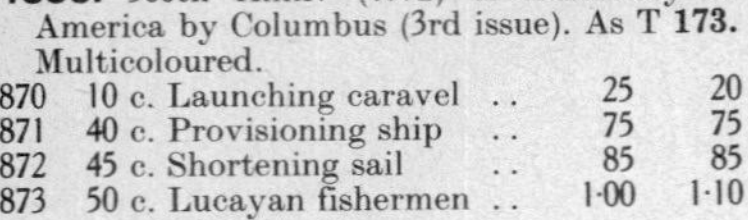

1990. 500th Anniv (1992) of Discovery of America by Columbus (3rd issue). As T **173**. Multicoloured.

No.	Description	Unused	Used
870	10 c. Launching caravel ..	25	20
871	40 c. Provisioning ship ..	75	75
872	45 c. Shortening sail ..	85	85
873	50 c. Lucayan fishermen ..	1·00	1·10

182 Bahamas Flag, O.A.S. Headquarters and Centenary Logo

1990. Centenary of Organization of American States.

No.	Type	Description	Unused	Used
875	182	40 c. multicoloured ..	65	65

184 Teacher with Boy

1990. International Literacy Year. Mult.

No.	Description	Unused	Used
877	10 c. Type **184**	20	15
878	40 c. Three boys in class ..	60	70
879	50 c. Teacher and children with books ..	75	85

1990. 90th Birthday of Queen Elizabeth the Queen Mother. As T **134** of Ascension.

No.	Description	Unused	Used
880	40 c. multicoloured ..	50	50
881	$1.50 black and ochre ..	2·00	2·00

DESIGNS—21 × 36 mm. 40 c. "Queen Elizabeth 1938" (Sir Gerald Kelly). 29 × 37 mm. $1.50, Queen Elizabeth at garden party, France, 1938.

185 Cuban Amazon preening

1990. Cuban Amazon (Bahamian Parrot). Multicoloured.

No.	Description	Unused	Used
882	10 c. Type **185**	25	20
883	40 c. Pair in flight ..	70	65
884	45 c. Cuban amazon's head	80	75
885	50 c. Perched on branch ..	1·00	1·00

186 The Annunciation

1990. Christmas. Multicoloured.

No.	Description	Unused	Used
887	10 c. Type **186**	20	15
888	40 c. The Nativity	55	55
889	45 c. Angel appearing to Shepherds	65	65
890	$1 The three Kings ..	1·60	1·75

187 Green Heron

1991. Birds. Multicoloured.

No.	Description	Unused	Used
892	5 c. Type **187**	10	10
893	10 c. Turkey vulture ..	10	15
894	15 c. Osprey	15	20
895	20 c. Clapper rail	25	30
896	25 c. Royal tern	30	35
897	30 c. Key West quail dove	35	40
898	40 c. Smooth-billed ani ..	45	50
899	45 c. Burrowing owl ..	50	55
900	50 c. Hairy woodpecker ..	60	65
901	55 c. Mangrove cuckoo ..	65	70
902	60 c. Bahama mockingbird	70	75
903	70 c. Red-winged blackbird	80	85
904	$1 Thick-billed vireo ..	1·10	1·25
905	$2 Bahama yellowthroat	2·25	2·40
906	$5 Stripe-headed tanager	5·75	6·00
907	$10 Greater Antillean bullfinch	11·50	12·00

1991. 500th Anniv (1992) of Discovery of America by Columbus (4th issue). As T **173**. Multicoloured.

No.	Description	Unused	Used
908	15 c. Columbus navigating by stars	25	25
909	40 c. Fleet in mid-Atlantic	65	65
910	55 c. Lucayan family worshipping at night ..	85	85
911	60 c. Map of First Voyage	95	95

1991. 65th Birthday of Queen Elizabeth II and 70th Birthday of Prince Philip. As T **139** of Ascension. Multicoloured.

No.	Description	Unused	Used
913	15 c. Prince Philip ..	50	50
914	$1 Queen Elizabeth II ..	1·25	1·25

188 Radar Plot of Hurricane Hugo

1991. International Decade for Natural Disaster Reduction. Multicoloured.

No.	Description	Unused	Used
915	15 c. Type **188**	15	20
916	40 c. Diagram of hurricane	45	50
917	55 c. Flooding caused by Hurricane David, 1979	65	70
918	60 c. U.S. Dept of Commerce weather reconnaissance Lockheed WP-3D Orion	70	75

189 The Annunciation

1991. Christmas. Multicoloured.

No.	Description	Unused	Used
919	15 c. Type **189**	15	20
920	55 c. Mary and Joseph travelling to Bethlehem	65	70
921	60 c. Angel appearing to the shepherds	70	75
922	$1 Adoration of the kings	1·10	1·25

190 First Progressive Liberal Party Cabinet

1992. 25th Anniv of Majority Rule. Mult.

No.	Description	Unused	Used
924	15 c. Type **190**	15	20
925	40 c. Signing of Independence Constitution ..	45	50
926	55 c. Prince of Wales handing over Constitutional Instrument (vert)	65	70
927	60 c. First Bahamian Governor-General, Sir Milo Butler (vert) ..	70	75

1992. 40th Anniv of Queen Elizabeth II's Accession. As T **143** of Ascension. Mult.

No.	Description	Unused	Used
928	15 c. Queen Elizabeth with bouquet	15	20
929	40 c. Queen Elizabeth with flags	45	50
930	55 c. Queen Elizabeth at display	65	70
931	60 c. Three portraits of Queen Elizabeth ..	70	75
932	$1 Queen Elizabeth II ..	1·10	1·25

1992. 500th Anniv of Discovery of America by Columbus (5th issue). As T **173**. Mult.

No.	Description	Unused	Used
933	15 c. Lucayans sighting fleet	15	20
934	40 c. "Santa Maria" and dolphins	45	50
935	55 c. Lucayan canoes approaching ships ..	65	70
936	60 c. Columbus giving thanks for landfall ..	70	75

191 Templeton, Galbraith and Hansberger Ltd Building

1992. 20th Anniv of Templeton Prize for Religion.

No.	Type	Description	Unused	Used
938	191	55 c. multicoloured ..	65	70

192 Pole Vaulting

1992. Olympic Games, Barcelona. Mult.

No.	Description	Unused	Used
939	15 c. Type **192**	15	20
940	40 c. Javelin	45	50
941	55 c. Hurdling	65	70
942	60 c. Basketball	70	75

SPECIAL DELIVERY STAMPS

1916. Optd. **SPECIAL DELIVERY** (letters with serifs).

No.	Type	Description	Unused	Used
S 1.	6.	5d. black and orange ..	5·00	22·00

1917. Optd. **SPECIAL DELIVERY** (letters without serifs).

No.	Type	Description	Unused	Used
S 2.	6.	5d. black and orange ..	45	4·00
S 3.		5d. black and mauve ..	30	1·25

BAHAWALPUR

A former state of Pakistan, now merged in West Pakistan.

12 pies = 1 anna, 16 annas = 1 rupee.

(1.)

1947. Nos. 265/8, 269a/77 and 259/62 of India optd. with Type **1**.

No.	Type	Description	Unused
1.	100a.	3 p. slate	6·00
2.		½ a. purple	6·00
3.		9 p. green	6·00
4.		1 a. red	6·00
5.	101.	1½ a. violet	5·50
6.		2 a. red	5·50
7.		3 a. violet	5·50
8.		3½ a. blue	5·50
9.	102.	4 a. brown	7·00
10.		6 a. green	7·00
11.		8 a. violet	7·00
12.		12 a. lake	7·00
13.	–	14 a. purple	40·00
14.	93.	1 r. grey and brown ..	18·00
15.		2 r. purple and brown ..	£400
16.		5 r. green and blue ..	£425
17.		10 r. purple and red ..	£450

2. Amir Muhammad Bahwal Khan I Abbasi.

1948. Bicentenary Commem.

No.	Type	Description	Unused	Used
18.	2.	½ a. black and red ..	30	1·25

4. H.H. the Amir of Bahawalpur.

5. The Tombs of the Amirs.

1948.

No.	Type	Description	Unused	Used
19.	4.	3 p. black and blue ..	20	7·00
20.		½ a. black and red ..	20	7·00
21.		9 p. black and green ..	20	7·00
22.		1 a. black and red ..	20	7·00
23.		1½ a. black and violet ..	20	7·00
24.	5.	2 a. green and red ..	20	8·00
25.	–	4 a. orange and brown ..	30	9·00
26.	–	6 a. violet and blue ..	30	10·00
27.	–	8 a. red and violet ..	30	10·00
28.	–	12 a. green and red ..	35	11·00
29.	–	1 r. violet and brown ..	3·50	16·00
35.	–	1 r. green and orange ..	25	9·00
30.	–	2 r. green and red ..	7·50	20·00
36.	–	2 r. black and red ..	30	12·00
31.	–	5 r. black and violet ..	11·00	30·00
37.	–	5 r. brown and blue ..	30	20·00
32.	–	10 r. red and black ..	18·00	45·00
38.	–	10 r. brown and green ..	35	25·00

DESIGNS—HORIZ. 2 a. As Type **5**. 6 a. Fort Derawar from the Lake. 8 a. Nur-Mahal Palace. 12 a. Sadiq-Garh Palace. Larger (46 × 32 mm.): 10 r. Three generations of Rulers. VERT. As Type 5: 4 a. Mosque in Sadiq-Gerh. 1 r., 2 r., 5 r. H.H. the Amir of Bahawalpuf.

12. H.H. the Amir of Bahawalpur and Mahomed Ali Jinnah.

1948. 1st Anniv. of Union with Pakistan.

No.	Type	Description	Unused	Used
33.	12.	1½a. red and green ..	10	1·00

13. Soldiers of 1848 and 1948.

1948. Centenary of Multan Campaign.
34. **13.** 1½ a. black and red .. 20 4·75

14. Irrigation.

1949. Silver Jubilee of Accession of H.H. the Amir of Bahawalpur.
39. **14.** 3 p. black and blue .. 10 4·75
40. – ½ a. black and orange .. 10 4·75
41. – 9 p. black and green .. 10 4·75
42. – 1 a. black and red .. 10 4·75
DESIGNS: ½ a. Wheat. 9 p. Cotton. 1 a. Sahiwal bull.

17. U.P.U. Monument, Berne.

1949. 75th Anniv. of U.P.U.
43. **17.** 9 p. black and green .. 20 2·00
44. – 1 a. black and mauve .. 20 2·00
45. – 1½ a. black and orange .. 20 2·00
46. – 2½ a. black and blue .. 20 2·00

OFFICIAL STAMPS

O 4. Eastern White Pelicans.

1945. As Type O 4 with Arabic opt.
O 1. – ½ a. black and green .. 1·25 4·00
O 2. – 1 a. black and red .. 1·75 3·00
O 7. – 1 a. black and brown .. 22·00 40·00
O 3. – 2 a. black and violet .. 2·75 4·50
O 4. O **4.** 4 a. black and olive .. 6·50 12·00
O 5. – 8 a. black and brown .. 5·50 7·00
O 6. – 1 r. black and orange .. 5·50 7·00
DESIGNS: ½ a. Panjnad Weir. 1 a. (No. O 2), Camel and calf. 1 a. (No. O 3), Baggage camels. 2 a. Blackbuck Antelopes. 8 a. Juma Masjid Palace, Fort Derawar. 1 r. Temple at Pattan Muanaria.

(O 8.)

1945. Types as Nos. O 1, etc., in new colours and without Arabic opt. (a) Surch. as Type O 8.
O 11. ½ a. on 8 a. black and purple (as No. O 5) .. 4·25 2·00
O 12. 1½ a. on 1 r. black and orange (as No. O 6) .. 14·00 3·00
O 13. 1½ a. on 2 r. black and blue (as No. O 1) .. 60·00 3·25
(b) Optd. **SERVICE** and Arabic inscription.
O 14. ½ a. black and red (as No. O 1) .. .. 1·00 5·50
O 15. 1 a. black and red (as No. O 2) .. .. 1·50 6·50
O 16. 2 a. black and orange (as No O 3) .. .. 2·75 17·00

1945. As Type 4 but inscr. "SERVICE" at left.
O 17. 3 p. black and blue .. 60 3·25
O 18. 1½ a. black and violet .. 4·50 4·75

O 11. Allied Banners.

1946. Victory.
O 19. O **11.** 1½ a. green and grey 1·75 1·75

1948. Stamps of 1948 with Arabic opt. as in Type O 4.
O 20. **4.** 3 p. black and blue .. 15 5·50
O 21. – 1 a. black and red .. 15 4·50
O 22. **5.** 2 a. green and red .. 15 6·00
O 23. – 4 a. orange and brown .. 15 8·00
O 24. – 1 r. green and orange .. 15 9·00
O 25. – 2 r. black and red .. 15 11·00
O 26. – 5 r. chocolate and blue .. 20 19·00
O 27. – 10 r. brown and green .. 30 24·00

1949. 75th Anniv. of U.P.U. Optd. as in Type O 4.
O 28. **17.** 9 p. black and green .. 15 4·50
O 29. – 1 a. black and mauve .. 15 4·50
O 30. – 1½ a. black and orange .. 15 4·50
O 31. – 2½ a. black and blue .. 15 4·50

BAHRAIN

An archipelago in the Persian Gulf on the Arabian coast. An independent shaikhdom with Indian and, later, British postal administration. The latter was closed on 1 January 1966, when the Bahrain Post Office took over.

1933. 12 pies = 1 anna; 16 annas = 1 rupee.
1957. 100 naye paise = 1 rupee.

Stamps of India overprinted **BAHRAIN**.

1933. King George V.
1 **55.** 3 p. grey .. .. 1·50 45
2 **56.** ½ a. green .. .. 5·00 3·25
15 **79.** ½ a. green .. .. 2·75 55
3 **80.** 9 p. green .. .. 3·25 80
4 **57.** 1 a. brown .. .. 5·00 2·50
16 **81.** 1 a. brown .. .. 4·50 40
5 **82.** 1 a. 3 p. mauve .. .. 2·75 45
6 **70.** 2 a. orange .. .. 7·00 4·50
17 **59.** 2 a. orange .. .. 16·00 7·50
7 **62.** 3 a. blue .. .. 19·00 30·00
18 3 a. red .. .. 4·75 30
8 **83.** 3 a. 6 p. blue .. .. 2·75 30
9 **71.** 4 a. green .. .. 18·00 30·00
19 **63.** 4 a. olive .. .. 3·00 30
10 **65.** 8 a. mauve .. .. 3·00 25
11 **66.** 12 a. red .. .. 4·25 60
12 **67.** 1 r. brown and green .. 14·00 7·50
13 2 r. red and orange .. 27·00 35·00
14 5 r. blue and violet .. 85·00 £110

1938. King George VI.
20. **91.** 3 p. slate .. .. .. 3·00 85
21. ½ a. brown 50 10
22. 9 p. green .. .. 1·00 30
23. 1 a. red 70 10
24. **92.** 2 a. red .. .. 3·00 40
26. – 3 a. green (No. 253) .. 32·00 3·00
27. – 3½ a. blue (No. 254) .. 2·50 1·75
28. – 4 a. brown (No. 255) .. £100 45·00
30. – 8 a. violet (No. 257) .. £120 35·00
31. – 12 a. red (No. 258) .. 90·00 48·00
32. **93.** 1 r. slate and brown .. 2·50 1·25
33. 2 r. purple and brown .. 15·00 1·75
34. 5 r. green and blue .. 30·00 13·00
35. 10 r. purple and red .. 65·00 17·00
36. 15 r. brown and green .. 42·00 38·00
37 25 r. slate and purple .. 95·00 65·00

1942. King George VI.
38. **100a** 3 p. slate 30 20
39. ½ a. mauve .. .. 1·25 45
40. 9 p. green .. .. 3·25 3·50
41. 1 a. red .. .. 1·50 20
42. **101.** 1 a. 3 p. bistre .. .. 3·00 5·00
43. 1½ a. violet .. .. 3·25 1·00
44. 2 a. red .. .. 1·00 65
45. 3 a. violet .. .. 4·75 2·50
46. 3½ a. blue .. .. 2·50 5·50
47. **102.** 4 a. brown .. .. 1·25 50
48. 6 a. green .. .. 6·50 5·50
49. 8 a. violet .. .. 1·00 75
50. 12 a. purple .. .. 2·00 1·50

Stamps of Great Britain surcharged **BAHRAIN** and new value in Indian currency.

1948. King George VI.
51. **128.** ½ a. on ½d. pale green .. 30 20
71. ½ a. on ½d. orange .. 20 20
52. 1 a. on 1d. pale red .. 30 30
72. 1 a. on 1d. blue .. 30 10
53. 1½ a. on 1½d. pale brown 30 40
73. 1½ a. on 1½d. green .. 30 4·75
54. 2 a. on 2d. pale orange 30 20
74. 2 a. on 2d. brown .. 30 25
55. 2½ a. on 2½d. light blue 50 80
75. 2½ a. on 2½d. red .. 30 4·75
56. 3 a. on 3d. pale violet .. 30 10
76. **129.** 4 a. on 4d. blue .. 30 80
57. 6 a. on 6d. purple .. 30 10
58. 1 r. on 1s. brown .. 90 10
59. 2 r. on 2s. 6d. green .. 3·00 3·75
60. 5 r. on 5s. red .. 4·00 4·50
60a. – 10 r. on 10s. bright blue (No. 478a) .. .. 55·00 40·00

1948. Silver Wedding.
61. **137.** 2½ a. on 2½d. blue .. 30 30
62. **138.** 15 r. on £1 blue .. 35·00 40·00

1948. Olympic Games.
63. **139.** 2½ a. on 2½d. blue .. 30 55
64. **140.** 3 a. on 3d. violet .. 35 75
65. – 6 a. on 6d. purple .. 75 1·25
66. – 1 r. on 1s. brown .. 1·00 2·00

1949. U.P.U.
67. **143.** 2½ a. on 2½d. blue .. 35 90
68. **144.** 3 a. on 3d. violet .. 65 1·50
69. – 6 a. on 6d. purple .. 65 1·75
70. – 1 r. on 1s. brown .. 1·10 1·50

1951. Pictorial stamps (Nos. 509/11).
77. **147.** 2 r. on 2s. 6d. green .. 11·00 3·50
78. – 5 r. on 5s. red .. 12·00 3·50
79. – 10 r. on 10s. blue .. 22·00 6·00

1952. Queen Elizabeth II.
80 **154** ½ a. on ½d. orange .. 10 10
81 1 a. on 1d. blue .. 10 10
82 1½ a. on 1½d. green .. 10 10
83 2 a. on 2d. brown .. 10 10
84 **155** 2½ a. on 2½d. red .. 20 20
85 3 a. on 3d. lilac .. 30 10
86 4 a. on 4d. blue .. 5·00 20
99 **157** 6 a. on 6d. purple .. 50 40
88 **160** 12 a. on 1s. 3d. green .. 3·00 20
89 1 r. on 1s. 6d. blue .. 3·00 10

1953. Coronation.
90. **161.** 2½ a. on 2½d. red .. 1·25 75
91. – 4 a. on 4d. blue .. 2·25 1·50
92. **163.** 12 a. on 1s. 3d. green .. 2·50 1·50
93. – 1 r. on 1s. 6d. blue .. 6·00 50

1955. Pictorial stamps (Nos. 595a/598a).
94 **166** 2 r. on 2s. 6d. brown .. 5·50 1·25
95 – 5 r. on 5s. red .. 11·00 2·75
96 – 10 r. on 10s. blue .. 20·00 2·75

1957. Queen Elizabeth II.
102. **157.** 1 n.p. on 5d. brown .. 10 10
103. **154.** 3 n.p. on ½d. orange .. 30 30
104. 6 n.p. on 1d. blue .. 30 30
105. 9 n.p. on 1½d. green .. 30 20
106. 12 n.p. on 2d. pale brn 30 20
107. **155.** 15 n.p. on 2½d. red .. 25 15
108. 20 n.p. on 3d. lilac .. 20 10
109. 25 n.p. on 4d. blue .. 75 75
110. **157.** 40 n.p. on 6d. purple .. 40 10
111. 50 n.p. on 9d. olive .. 3·50 3·50
112. 75 n.p. on 1s. 3d. green 2·25 50

1957. World Scout Jubilee Jamboree.
113. **170.** 15 n.p. on 2½d. red .. 25 35
114. **171.** 25 n.p. on 4d. blue .. 30 35
115. – 75 n.p. on 1s. 3d. green 40 45

16. Shaikh Sulman bin Hamed al-Khalifa.

1960.
117. [illegible] n.p. blue 10 10
118. [illegible]5 n.p. orange 10 10
119. [illegible]0 n.p. violet 10 10
120. [illegible]0 n.p. bistre 10 10
121. [illegible]0 n.p. grey 15 10
122. [illegible] n.p. green 15 10
123. [illegible]5 n.p. brown 25 15
124. 1 r. black .. .. 1·00 20
125. – 2 r. red .. .. .. 2·75 50
126. – 5 r. blue .. .. .. 4·50 1·50
127. – 10 r. green .. .. 11·00 2·00
The rupee values are larger (27 × 32½ mm.)

18. Shaikh Isa bin Sulman al-Khalifa.

19. Air Terminal Muharraq.

1964.
128. **18.** 5 n.p. blue 10 10
129. – 15 n.p. orange 10 10
130. – 20 n.p. violet 10 10
131. – 30 n.p. bistre 10 10
132. – 40 n.p. slate 15 10
133. – 50 n.p. green 15 10
134. – 75 n.p. brown 25 10
135. **19.** 1 r. black .. .. 1·25 20
136. 2 r. red .. .. 6·00 35
137. – 5 r. blue .. .. 8·00 4·75
138. – 10 r. myrtle .. .. 10·00 4·75
DESIGNS—As Type **19**: 5 r., 10 r. Deep water harbour.

For later issues see Volume 1.

INDEX

Countries can be quickly located by referring to the index at the end of this volume.

BAMRA

A state in India. Now uses Indian stamps.

12 pies = 1 anna; 16 annas = 1 rupee.

1.

8.

1888.
1. **1.** ¼ a. black on yellow .. £140
2. ½ a. black on red .. 70·00
3. 1 a. black on blue .. 42·00
4. 2 a. black on green .. 65·00 £140
5. 4 a. black on yellow .. 48·00
6. 8 a. black on red .. 38·00

1890. Imperf.
27 **8.** ¼ a. black on red 60 65
11 ½ a. black on green .. 1·00 1·25
13 1 a. black on yellow .. 1·60 1·25
16 2 a. black on red .. .. 1·60 1·60
19 4 a. black on red .. .. 3·50 2·50
22 8 a. black on red .. .. 7·00 8·00
25 1 r. black on red .. .. 15·00 18·00

BANGLADESH

Formerly the Eastern wing of Pakistan. Following a landslide victory at the Pakistan General Election in December 1970, for the local party favouring autonomy, the constitution was suspended and military rule imposed from West Pakistan. Unrest continued, culminating in guerrilla warfare and the intervention of India on the side of the East Bengalis. The new state became effective after the surrender of the Pakistan army in December 1971.

1971. 100 paisa = 1 rupee.
1972. 100 paisa = 1 taka.

1. Map of Bangladesh.

3. " Martyrdom ".

1971.
1. **1.** 10 p. indigo, orange & blue 10 10
2. – 20 p. multicoloured .. 10 10
3. – 50 p. multicoloured .. 10 10
4. – 1 r. multicoloured .. 10 10
5. – 2 r. turquoise, blue and red 25 35
6 – 3 r. light-green, grn. & blue 30 45
7. – 5 r. multicoloured .. 50 75
8. – 10 r. gold, red and blue .. 1·00 1·75
DESIGNS: 20 p. " Dacca University Massacre ". 50 p. " 75 Million People ". 1 r. Flag of Independence. 2 r. Ballot box. 3 r. Broken chain. 5 r. Shaikh Majibur Rahman. 10 r. " Support Bangla Desh " and map.

1971. Liberation. Nos. 1 and 7/8 optd. **BANGLADESH LIBERATED.**
9. 10 p. indigo, orge. and blue 10 10
10. 5 r. multicoloured .. 1·50 1·50
11. 10 r. gold, red and blue .. 2·00 2·25

The remaining values of the original issue were also overprinted and placed on sale in Great Britain but were not issued in Bangladesh.

On the 1 February 1972 the Agency placed on sale a further issue in the flag, map and Sheikh Mujib designs in new colours and new currency (100 paisa = 1 taka). This issue proved to be unacceptable to the Bangladesh authorities who declared them to be invalid for postal purposes, no supplies being sold within Bangladesh. The values comprise 1, 2, 3, 5, 7, 10, 15, 20, 25, 40, 50, 75 p., 1, 2 and 5 t.

1972. In Memory of the Martyrs.
12. **3.** 20p. green and red .. 30 30

4. Flames of Independence.

1972. 1st Anniv. of Independence.

13. 4. 20p. lake and red .. 15 10
14. 60p. blue and red .. 20 20
15. 75p. violet and red .. 25 30

5. Doves of Peace.

1972. Victory Day.

16. 5. 20 p. multicoloured .. 15 10
17. 60 p. multicoloured .. 20 20
18. 75 p. multicoloured .. 20 20

6. "Homage to Martyrs". 7. Embroidered Quilt.

8. Court of Justice.

1973. In Memory of the Martyrs.

19. 6. 20 p. multicoloured .. 15 10
20. 60 p. multicoloured .. 30 30
21. 1 t. 35 multicoloured .. 65 70

1973.

22. 7. 2 p. black 10 20
23. – 3 p. green 10 20
24. – 5 p. brown 10 10
25. – 10 p. black 10 10
26. – 20 p. green 40 10
27. – 25 p. mauve .. .. 1·25 10
28. – 50 p. purple 75 10
29. – 60 p. grey 60 15
30. – 75 p. orange 65 15
31. – 90 p. brown 75 20
32. 8. 1 t. violet .. .. .. 2·75 10
33. – 2 t. green .. .. .. 3·50 40
34. – 5 t. blue .. .. .. 3·75 1·00
35. – 10 t. pink .. .. .. 4·25 2·50

DESIGNS—VERT. As Type **7**. 3 p. Jute field. 5 p. Jack fruit. 10 p. Bullocks ploughing. 20 p. Rakta jaba (flower). 25 p. Tiger. 60 p. Bamboo grove. 75 p. Plucking tea. 90 p. Handicrafts. As Type **8**. 2 t. Date tree. HORIZ. (28×22 mm.). 50 p. Hilsa (fish). As Type **8**. 5 t Fishing boat. 10 t. Sixty-dome mosque, Bagerhat.

See also Nos. 49/51a. and 64 etc.

9. Flame Emblem.

1973. 25th Anniv. of Declaration of Human Rights.

36. 9. 10 p. multicoloured .. 10 10
37. 1 t. 25 multicoloured .. 20 20

10. Family, Map and Graph.

1974. First Population Census.

38. 10. 20 p. multicoloured .. 10 10
39. 25 p. multicoloured .. 10 10
40. 75 p. multicoloured .. 20 20

11. Copernicus and Heliocentric System.

1974. 500th Birth Anniv. of Copernicus.

41. 11. 25 p. orge., viol. & blk. 10 10
42. 75 p. orge., grn. & blk... 25 40

12. U.N. H.Q. and Bangladesh Flag.

1974. Bangladesh's Admission to the U.N.

43. 12. 25 p. multicoloured .. 10 10
44. 1 t. multicoloured .. 25 30

13. U.P.U. Emblem.

1974. Centenary of Universal Postal Union. Multicoloured.

45. 25 p. Type **13** 10 10
46. 1 t. 25 Mail runner .. 20 15
47. 1 t. 75 Type **13** .. 25 25
48. 5 t. As 1 t. 25 .. .. 80 1·40

14. Courts of Justice.

1974. As Nos. 32/5 with revised inscriptions.

49. 14. 1 t. violet .. .. 1·50 10
50. – 2 t. olive .. .. 1·75 70
51. – 5 t. blue .. .. 2·25 70
51a. – 10 t. pink .. .. 6·00 3·25

MORE DETAILED LISTS
are given in the Stanley Gibbons Catalogues referred to in the country headings.
For lists of current volumes see Introduction.

15. Tiger. 16. Symbolic Family.

1974. Wildlife Preservation. Multicoloured.

52. 25 p. Type **15** 70 10
53. 50 p. Tiger cub .. .. 1·25 60
54. 2 t. Tiger in stream .. 2·75 3·25

1974. World Population Year. "Family Planning for All". Multicoloured.

55. 25p. Type **16** 15 10
56. 70 p. Village family .. 25 40
57. 1 t. 25 Heads of family (horiz.) 40 85

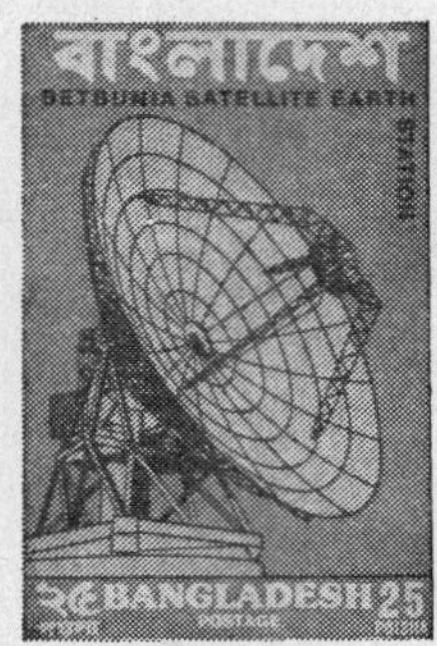

17. Radar Antenna.

1975. Inauguration of Betbunia Satellite Earth Station.

58. 17. 25 p. black, silver and red 10 10
59. 1 t. black, silver and blue 20 40

18. Woman's Head.

1975. International Women's Year.

60. 18. 50 p. multicoloured .. 10 10
61. 2 t. multicoloured .. 25 55

1976. As Nos 24/31 and 49/51a but redrawn in smaller size.

64. – 5 p. green 20 10
65. – 10 p. black 20 10
66. – 20 p. green 60 10
67. – 25 p. mauve .. .. 1·00 10
68. – 50 p. purple .. .. 1·50 10
69. – 60 p. grey 40 15
70. – 75 p. green .. .. 1·25 35
71. – 90 p. brown 40 15
72. 14. 1 t. violet .. .. 2·00 10
73. – 2 t. green .. .. 2·50 10
74. – 5 t. blue .. .. 2·75 80
75. – 10 t. red .. .. 3·50 1·25

Nos. 64/71 are 23×18 mm (50p) or 18×23 mm. (others) and Nos 72/75 are 20×32 mm (2 t.) or 32×20 mm. (others).

19. Telephones of 1876 and 1976.

1976. Centenary of Telephone.

76. 19. 2 t. 25 multicoloured .. 25 20
77. – 5 t. red, green and black 55 65

DESIGN: 5 t. Alexander Graham Bell.

20. Eye and Nutriments.

1976. Prevention of Blindness.

78. 20. 30 p. multicoloured .. 15 10
79. 2 t. 25 multicoloured .. 50 65

21. Liberty Bell.

1976. Bicent. of American Revolution. Mult.

80. 30 p. Type **21** 10 10
81. 2 t. 25 Statue of Liberty .. 30 25
82. 5 t. "Mayflower" .. 80 50
83. 10 t. Mount Rushmore .. 80 80

22. Industry, Science, Agriculture and Education.

1976. 25th Anniv. of Colombo Plan.

85. 22. 30 p. multicoloured .. 15 10
86. 2 t. 25 multicoloured .. 35 35

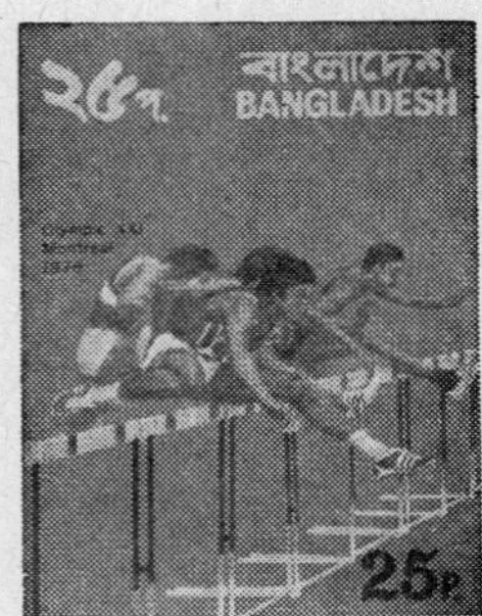

23. Hurdling.

1976. Olympic Games, Montreal. Mult.

87. 25 p. Type **23** 10 10
88. 30 p. Running (horiz.) .. 10 10
89. 1 t. Pole vaulting 10 10
90. 2 t. 25 Swimming (horiz.) .. 30 30
91 3 t. 50 Gymnastics 55 55
92. 5 t. Football 80 80

24. The Blessing.

1977. Silver Jubilee. Multicoloured.

93. 30 p. Type **24** 10 10
94. 2 t. 25 Queen Elizabeth II 35 35
95. 10 t. Queen Elizabeth and Prince Philip .. .. 1·00 1·00

25. Qazi Nazrul Islam (poet).

1977. Qazi Nazrul Islam. Commemoration.

97.	25.	40 p. green and black ..	10	10
98.	–	2 t. 25 brn., red & light brn.	30	30

DESIGN—HORIZ. 2 t. 25, Head and shoulders portrait.

26. Bird with Letter.

1977. 15th Anniv. of Asian–Oceanic Postal Union.

99.	26.	30 p. red, blue and grey	10	10
100.		2 t. 25 red, blue & grey	20	25

27. Sloth Bear.

1977. Animals. Multicoloured.

101.	40 p. Type **27**	20	10
102.	1 t. Spotted deer	30	10
103.	2 t. 25 Leopard (horiz.) ..	75	20
104.	3 t. 50 Gaur (horiz.) ..	80	35
105.	4 t. Indian elephant (horiz.)	1·50	50
106.	5 t. Tiger (horiz.)	1·75	75

The Bengali numerals on the 40p. resemble "80", and that on the 4 t. resembles "8".

28. Camp Fire and Tent.

1978. First National Scout Jamboree.

107.	28.	40 p. red, blue & pale blue	25	10
108.	–	3 t. 50 lilac, grn. & blue	85	30
109.	–	5 t. grn., blue & red ..	1·00	45

DESIGNS—HORIZ. 3 t. 50, Scout stretcher-team. VERT. 5 t. Scout salute.

29. "Michelia champaca".

1978. Flowers. Multicoloured.

110.	40 p. Type **29**	30	10
111.	1 t. "Cassia fistula" ..	45	10
112.	2 t. 25 "Dedonix regia"	70	25
113.	3 t. 50 "Nymphaea nouchali"	90	50
114.	4 t. "Butea monosperma"	1·00	70
115.	5 t. "Anthocephalus indicus"	1·10	75

30. St. Edward's Crown and Sceptres.

1978. 25th Anniv. of Coronation. Mult.

116.	40 p. Type **30**	10	10
117.	3 t. 50 Balcony scene ..	25	35
118.	5 t. Queen Elizabeth and Prince Philip	40	55
119.	10 t. Coronation portrait by Cecil Beaton ..	80	1·00

31. Sir Alan Cobham's "DH 50".

1978. 75th Anniv. of Powered Flight.

121.	31.	40 p. multicoloured ..	10	10
122.	–	2 t. 25 brown and blue ..	40	35
123.	–	3 t. 50 brown and yellow	55	55
124.	–	5 t. multicoloured ..	2·75	2·00

DESIGNS: 2 t. 25, Captain Hans Bertram's seaplane "Atlantis". 3 t. 50, Wright brothers' "Flyer I". 5 t. "Concorde".

32. Fenchuganj Fertiliser Factory.

33. Tawaf-E-Ka'aba, Mecca.

1978.

125.	–	5 p. brown	10	10
126.	32.	10 p. blue	10	10
127.	–	15 p. orange	10	10
128.	–	20 p. red	10	10
129.	–	25 p. blue	15	10
130.	–	30 p. green	40	10
131.	–	40 p. purple	20	10
132.	–	50 p. black	1·00	35
134.	–	80 p. brown	15	10
136.	–	1 t. violet	1·00	10
137.	–	2 t. blue	40	50

DESIGNS–HORIZ. 5 p. Lalbag Fort. 25 p. Jute on a boat. 40 p., 50 p. Baitul Mukarram Mosque. 1 t. Dotara (musical instrument). 2 t. Karnaphuli Dam. VERT. 15 p. pineapple. 20 p. Bangladesh gas. 30 p. Banana Tree. 80 p. Mohastan Garh.

1978. Pilgrimage to Mecca. Multicoloured

140.		40 p. Type **33**	15	10
141.		3 t. Pilgrims in Wuquf, Arafat (horiz.)	40	30

34. Jasim Uddin.

1979. 3rd Death Anniv. of Jasim Uddin (poet).

142.	34.	40 p. multicoloured ..	20	20

35. Moulana Abdul Hamid Khan Bhashani.

1979. 3rd Death Anniv. of Moulana Abdul Hamid Khan Bhashani (national leader).

143.	35.	40 p. multicoloured ..	30	20

36. Sir Rowland Hill.

1979. Death Centenary of Sir Rowland Hill.

144.	36.	40 p. blue, red and pale blue	10	10
145.	–	3 t. 50 multicoloured ..	35	30
146.	–	10 t. multicoloured ..	80	1·00

DESIGNS: 3 t. 50, Sir Rowland Hill and first Bangladesh stamp. 10 t. Sir Rowland Hill and Bangladesh U.P.U. stamp.

37. Children with Hoops.

1979. International Year of the Child. Mult.

148.	40 p. Type **37**	10	10
149.	3 t. 50 Boy with kite ..	35	35
150.	5 t. Children jumping ..	50	50

38. Rotary International Emblem.

1980. 75th Anniv. of Rotary International.

152.	38.	40 p. black, red & yellow	15	10
153.	–	5 t. gold and blue ..	50	45

DESIGN: 5 t. Rotary emblem (different).

39. Canal Digging.

1980. Mass Participation in Canal Digging.

154.	39.	40 p. multicoloured ..	30	30

40. A. K. Fazlul Huq.

1980. 18th Death Anniv. of A. K. Fazlul Huq (national leader).

155.	40.	40 p. multicoloured ..	20	20

41. Early Forms of Mail Transport.

1980. "London 1980" International Stamp Exhibition. Multicoloured.

156.	1 t. Type **41**	10	10
157.	10 t. Modern forms of mail transport	90	85

42. Dome of the Rock.

1980. Palestinian Warfare.

159.	42.	50 p. lilac	40	20

43. Outdoor Class.

1980. Education.

160.	43.	50 p. multicoloured ..	30	20

44. Beach Scene.

1980. World Tourism Conference, Manila. Multicoloured.

161.	50 p. Type **44**	30	30
162.	5 t. Beach scene (different)	60	70

45. Mecca.

1980. Moslem Year 1400 A.H. Commem.

164.	45.	50 p. multicoloured ..	20	20

HAVE YOU READ THE NOTES AT THE BEGINNING OF THIS CATALOGUE?

These often provide answers to the enquiries we receive.

46. Begum Roquiah.

1980. Birth Centenary of Begum Roquiah (campaigner for women's rights).
165. **46.** 50 p. multicoloured .. 10 10
166. 2 t. multicoloured .. 20 20

47. Spotted Deer and Scout Emblem.

1981. 5th Asia-Pacific and 2nd Bangladesh Scout Jamboree.
167. **47.** 50 p. multicoloured .. 15 10
168. 5 t. multicoloured .. 60 70

1981. Second Population Census. Nos. 38/40 optd. **2ND CENSUS 1981.**
169. **10.** 20 p. multicoloured .. 10 10
170. 25 p. multicoloured .. 10 10
171. 75 p. multicoloured .. 20 20

49. Queen Elizabeth the Queen Mother.

1981. 80th Birthday of The Queen Mother.
172. **49.** 1 t. multicoloured .. 15 15
173. 15 t. multicoloured .. 3·00 2·50

50. Revolutionary with Flag and Submachine-gun.

1981. 10th Anniv. Independence. Mult.
175. 50p. Type **50** 15 10
176. 2 t. Figures on map symbolising Bangladesh life-style 25 30

51. Bangladesh Village and Farm Scenes.

1981. U.N. Conference on Least Developed Countries, Paris.
177. **51.** 50 p. multicoloured .. 35 15

52. Kemal Ataturk in Civilian Dress.

1981. Birth Centenary of Kemal Ataturk (Turkish statesman).
178. 50 p. Type **52** 20 15
179. 1 t. Kemal Ataturk in uniform 30 25

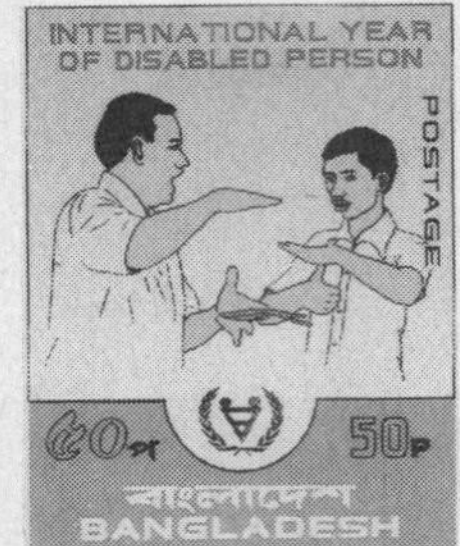

53. Deaf People using Sign Language.

1981. International Year for Disabled Persons. Multicoloured.
180. 50 p. Type **53** 20 15
181. 2 t. Disabled person writing (horiz.) 60 50

54. Farm Scene and Wheat Ear.

1981. World Food Day.
182. **54.** 50 p. multicoloured .. 40 30

55. River Scene.

1982. 10th Anniv. Human Environment Conference.
183. **55.** 50 p. multicoloured .. 40 30

56. Dr. M. Hussain.

1982. 1st Death Anniv of Dr. Motahar Hussain (educationist).
184 **56** 50 p. multicoloured .. 40 30

57. Knotted Rope surrounding Bengali " 75 ".

1982. 75th Anniv. of Boy Scout Movement and 125th Birth Anniv. of Lord Baden-Powell. Multicoloured.
185. 50 p. Type **57** 50 25
186. 2 t. Lord Baden-Powell. (vert.) .. .. .. 1·50 1·50

সম্মিলিত
সশস্ত্র বাহিনী দিবস
২১ নভেম্বর,৮২
58.

1982. Armed Forces' Day. No. 175 optd with T **58**.
187. 50 p. Type **50** 70 50

59. Captain Mohiuddin Jahangir.

1983. Heroes and Martyrs of the Liberation. Multicoloured, background colour of commemorative plaque given.
188. 50 p. Type **59** (orange) .. 20 20
189. 50 p. Sepoy Hamidur Rahman (green) .. 20 20
190. 50 p. Sepoy Mohammed Mustafa Kamal (red) .. 20 20
191. 50 p. Muhammed Ruhul Amin (yellow) .. 20 20
192. 50 p. Flt. Lt. M. Matiur Rahman (brown) .. 20 20
193. 50 p. Lance-Naik Munshi Abdur Rob (brown) .. 20 20
194. 50 p. Lance-Naik Nur Mouhammad (green) .. 20 20

60. Metric Scales.

1983. Introduction of Metric Weights and Measures. Multicoloured.
195. 50 p. Type **60** 20 20
196. 2 t. Weights, jug and tape measure (horiz.) .. 70 90

61. Dr. Robert Koch.

1983. Centenary (1982) of Robert Koch's Discovery of Tubercle Bacillus. Mult.
197. 50 p. Type **61** 35 25
198. 1 t. Microscope, slide and X-ray .. .. .. 90 1·00

62. Open Stage Theatre.

1983. Commonwealth Day. Multicoloured.
199. 1 t. Type **62** 10 15
200. 3 t. Boat race 20 30
201. 10 t. Snake dance 65 90
202. 15 t. Picking tea .. .. 1·00 1·50

63. Dr. Muhammed Shahidulla.

1983. Dr. Muhammed Shahidulla (Bengali scholar). Commemoration.
203. **63.** 50 p. multicoloured .. 45 30

64. Magpie Robin.

1983. Birds of Bangladesh. Multicoloured.
204. 50 p. Type **64** 85 30
205. 2 t. White-breasted Kingfisher (vert.) .. .. 1·75 1·40
206. 3 t. 75 Lesser Golden-backed Woodpecker (vert.) .. .. 2·00 1·75
207. 5 t. White-winged Wood Duck .. .. 2·50 2·50

65. "Macrobrachium rosenbergii".

1984. Fishes. Multicoloured.
209. 50 p. Type **65** 50 30
210. 2 t. "Stromateus cinereus" 1·25 85
211. 3 t. 75 "Labeo rohita" .. 1·75 1·25
212. 5 t. "Anaba testudineus" 2·25 2·00

1983. Visit of Queen Elizabeth II, No. 95 optd. **Nov '83 Visit of Queen.**
214. 10 t. Queen Elizabeth and Prince Philip .. .. 2·00 2·25

67. Conference Hall, Dhaka.

1983. 14th Islamic Foreign Ministers' Conference. Dhaka. Multicoloured.
215. 50 p. Type **67** 25 25
216. 5 t. Old Fort, Dhaka .. 75 1·00

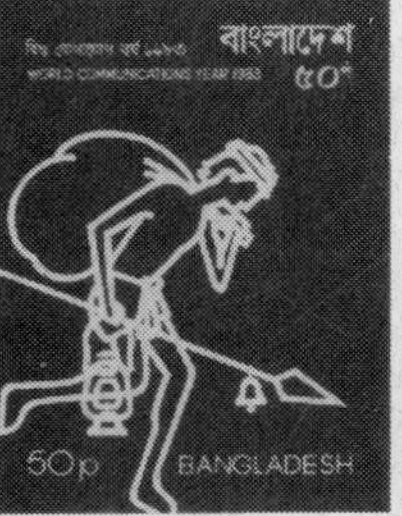

68. Early Mail Runner. 69. Carrying Mail by Boat.

1983. World Communications Year. Mult.
217. 50 p. Type **68.** 20 10
218. 5 t. Sailing ship, steam train and jet airliner .. 1·25 60
219. 10 t. Mail runner and dish aerial (horiz.) .. .. 1·90 1·40

1983. Postal Communications.

220. **69.** 5 p. blue 10 10
221. – 10 p. purple 10 10
222. – 15 p. blue 10 10
223. – 20 p. black 10 10
224. – 25 p. grey 10 10
225. – 30 p. brown 10 10
226. – 50 p. brown 10 10
227. – 1 t. blue 10 10
228. – 2 t. green 10 10
228a. – 3 t. brown 50 20
229. – 5 t. purple .. .. 1·25 75

DESIGNS—HORIZ. (22 × 17 mm.) 10 p. Counter, Dhaka G.P.O. 15 p. I.W.T.A. Terminal, Dhaka. 20 p. Inside railway travelling post office. 30 p. Emptying pillar box. 50 p. Mobile post office van (30 × 19 mm.) 1 t. Kamalapur Railway Station, Dhaka. 2 t. Zia International Airport. 3 t. Sorting mail by machine. 5 t. Khulna G.P.O. VERT. (17 × 22 mm.) 25 p. Delivering a letter.

প্রথম বাংলাদেশ জাতীয় ডাকটিকিট প্রদর্শনী-১৯৮৪

(**70**).

1984. 1st National Stamp Exhibition (1st issue). Nos 161/2 optd with T **70** (5 t.) or "First Bangladesh National Philatelic Exhibition—1984" (50 p.).

230 **44.** 50 p. multicoloured .. 30 40
231. – 5 t. multicoloured .. 50 70

71. Girl with Stamp Album.
(Illustration reduced. Actual size 67 × 34 mm).

1984. 1st National Stamp Exhibition (2nd issue). Multicoloured.

232. 50 p. Type **71** 30 35
233. 7 t. 30 Boy with stamp album 70 75

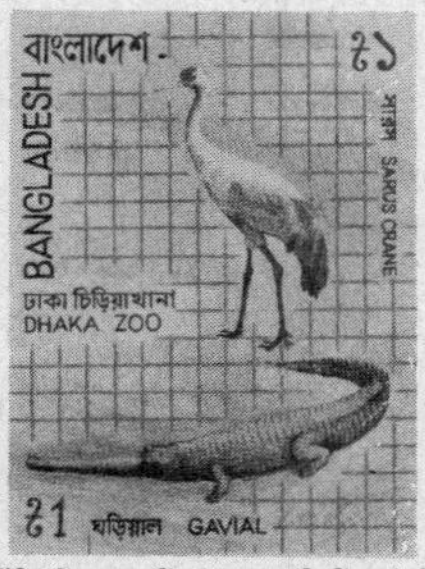

72. Sarus Crane and Gavial.

1984. Dhaka Zoo. Multicoloured.

235. 1 t. Type **72** 75 50
236. 2 t. Common peafowl and tiger .. .. .. 1·25 1·50

73. Eagle attacking Hen with Chicks.

1984. Centenary of Postal Life Insurance. Multicoloured.

237. 1 t. Type **73** 25 20
238. 5 t. Bangladesh family and postman's hand with insurance cheque .. 75 80

74. Abbasuddin Ahmad (singer).

খুলনাপেক্স—৮৪

(**75**).

1984. Abbasuddin (Ahmad (singer) Commemoration.

239. **74.** 3 t. multicoloured .. 40 30

1984. "Khulnapex-84" Stamp Exhibition. No. 86 optd. with T **75**.

240 **22** 2 t. 25 multicoloured .. 40 30

76. Cycling.

1984. Olympic Games, Los Angeles. Mult.

241. 1 t. Type **76** 20 15
242. 5 t. Hockey 90 80
243. 10 t. Volleyball .. .. 1·40 1·50

77. Farmer with Rice and Sickle.

1985. 9th Annual Meeting of Islamic Development Bank, Dhaka. Multicoloured.

244. 1 t. Type **77** 20 15
245. 5 t. Citizens of four races 60 70

78. Mother and Baby.

1985. Child Survival Campaign. Mult.

246. 1 t. Type **78** 20 10
247. 10 t. Young child and growth graph .. .. 1·10 90

উপজেলা নির্বাচন ১৯৮৫

(**79**).

1985. Local Elections. Nos 110/15 optd. with T **79**.

248 40 p. Type **29** 10 15
249 1 t. "Cassia fistula" .. 10 20
250 2 t.25 "Delonix regia" .. 15 35
251 3 t.50 "Nymphaea nouchali" 20 45
252 4 t. "Butea monosperma" 20 45
253 5 t. "Anthocephalus indicus" 30 55

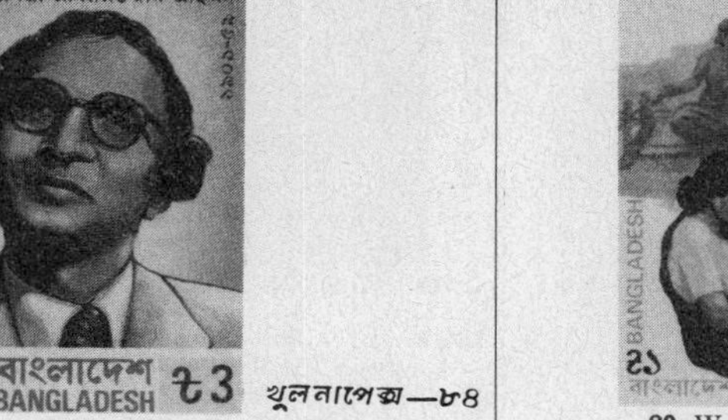

80. Women working at Traditional Crafts.

1985. United Nations Decade for Women. Multicoloured.

254. 1 t. Type **80** 15 10
255. 10 t. Women with microscope, computer terminal and in classroom 80 85

81. U.N. Building, New York, Peace Doves and Flags.

1985. 40th Anniv. of United Nations Organization and 11th Anniv. of Bangladesh Membership. Multicoloured.

256. 1 t. Type **81** 10 10
257. 10 t. Map of world and Bangladesh flag .. 80 90

82. Head of Youth, Flowers and Symbols of Commerce and Agriculture.

1985. International Youth Year. Mult.

258. 1 t. Type **82** 10 10
259. 5 t. Head of youth, flowers and symbols of industry 40 60

83. Emblem and Seven Doves.

1985. 1st Summit Meeting of South Asian Association for Regional Co-operation, Dhaka. Multicoloured.

260. 1 t. Type **83** 10 10
261. 5 t. Flags of member nations and lotus blossom 40 60

MINIMUM PRICE

The minimum price quoted is 10p which represents a handling charge rather than a basis for valuing common stamps. For further notes about prices see introductory pages.

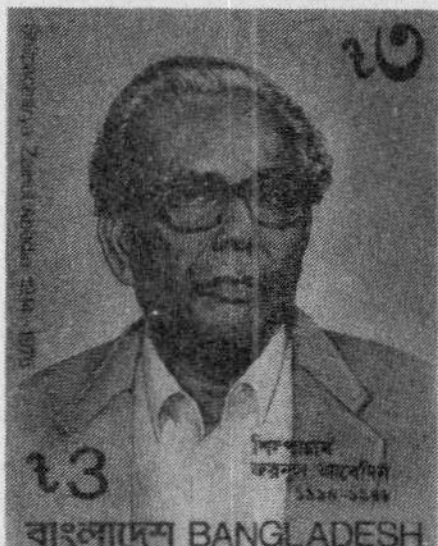

84. Zainul Abedin.

1985. 10th Death Anniv. of Zainul Abedin (artist).

262. **84.** 3 t. multicoloured .. 40 30

তৃতীয় বাংলাদেশ
জাতীয় জাম্বুরী
১৯৮৫-৮৬

(**85**).

1985. Third National Scout Jamboree. No. 109 optd. with T **85**.

263. 5 t. green, blue and red .. 75 60

86. "Fishing Net" (Safiuddin Ahmed).

1986. Bangladesh Paintings. Multicoloured.

264 1 t. Type **86** 15 10
265. 5 t. "Happy Return" (Quamrul Hassan) .. 40 50
266. 10 t. "Levelling the Ploughed Field" (Zainul Abedin) 70 80

87. Two Players competing for Ball.

1986. World Cup Football Championship, Mexico. Multicoloured.

267. 1 t. Type **87** 20 10
268. 10 t. Goalkeeper and ball in net .. .. .. 1·10 80

88. General M. A. G. Osmani.

1986. General M. A. G. Osmani (army commander-in-chief) Commemoration.

270. **88.** 3 t. multicoloured. .. 40 30

1986. South Asian Association for Regional Co-operation Seminar. No. 183 optd. **SAARC SEMINAR '86.**

271. **55.** 50 p. multicoloured .. 40 35

90. Butterflies and Nuclear Explosion.

1986. International Peace Year. Mult.
272. 1 t. Type **90** 30 15
273. 10 t. Flowers and ruined buildings .. .. 1·40 1·10

1987. Conference for Development. Nos. 152/3 optd **CONFERENCE FOR DEVELOPMENT '87**, No. 275 surch also.
275. **38.** 1 t. on 40 p. black, red and yellow 10 15
276. – 5 t. gold and blue .. 30 60

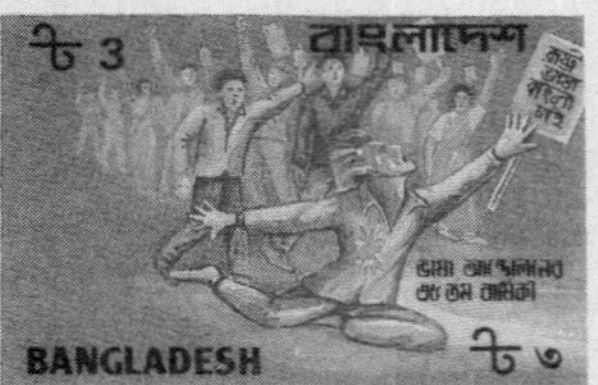

92. Demonstrators with Placards.

1987. 35th Anniv. of Bangla Language Movement. Multicoloured.
277. 3 t. Type **92** 40 50
278. 3 t. Martyrs' Memorial .. 40 50
Nos. 277/8 were printed together, se-tenant, forming a composite design.

93. Nurse giving Injection. **94.** Pattern and Bengali Script.

1987. World Health Day.
279. **93.** 1 t. black and blue .. 50 40
See also No. 295.

1987. Bengali New Year. Multicoloured.
280. 1 t. Type **94** 10 10
281. 10 t. Bengali woman .. 40 60

95. Jute Shika.

1987. Export Products. Multicoloured.
282. 1 t. Type **95** 10 10
283. 5 t. Jute carpet (horiz.) .. 20 30
284. 10 t. Cane table lamp .. 40 60

96. Ustad Ayet Ali Khan and Surbahar.

1987. 20th Death Anniv. of Ustad Ayet Ali Khan (musician and composer).
285. **96.** 5 t. multicoloured .. 40 40

97. Palanquin.

1987. Transport. Multicoloured.
286. 2 t. Type **97** 15 15
287. 3 t. Bicycle rickshaw .. 20 20
288. 5 t. River steamer .. 30 35
289. 7 t. Express diesel train .. 40 50
290. 10 t. Bullock cart 45 75

98. H. S. Suhrawardy.

1987. Hossain Shahid Suhrawardy (politician) Commem.
291. **98.** 3 t. multicoloured .. 20 30

99. Villagers fleeing from Typhoon.

1987. International Year of Shelter for the Homeless. Multicoloured.
292. 5 t. Type **99** 20 30
293. 5 t. Villagers and modern houses 20 30

100. President Ershad addressing Parliament.

1987. 1st Anniv. of Return to Democracy.
294. **100.** 10 t. multicoloured .. 40 60

1988. World Health Day. As T **93**.
295 25 p. brown 20 15
Design: 25 p. Oral rehydration.

101. Woman planting Palm Saplings.

1988. I.F.A.D. Seminar on Agricultural Loans for Rural Women. Multicoloured.
296. 3 t. Type **101** 15 20
297. 5 t. Village woman milking cow 20 40

102 Basketball

1988. Olympic Games, Seoul. Multicoloured.
298 5 t. Type **102** 20 25
299 5 t. Weightlifting .. 20 25
300 5 t. Tennis 20 25
301 5 t. Rifle-shooting .. 20 25
302 5 t. Boxing 20 25

103 Interior of Shait Gumbaz Mosque, Bagerhat

1988. Historical Buildings. Multicoloured.
303 1 t. Type **103** 10 10
304 4 t. Paharpur Monastery 10 10
305 5 t. Kantanagar Temple, Dinajpur 10 10
306 10 t. Lalbag Fort, Dhaka 15 15

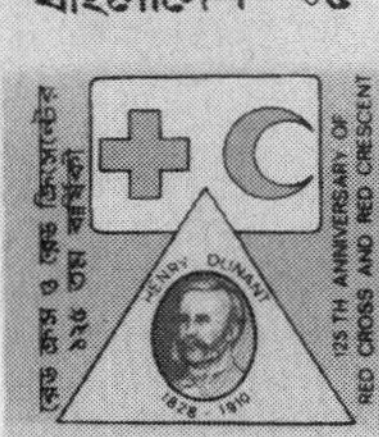

104 Henri Dunant (founder), Red Cross and Crescent

1988. 125th Anniv of International Red Cross and Red Crescent. Multicoloured.
307 5 t. Type **104** 20 25
308 10 t. Red Cross workers with patient .. 40 45

105 Dr. Qudrat-i-Khuda in Laboratory

1988. Dr. Qudrat-i-Khuda (scientist) Commemoration.
309 **105** 5 t. multicoloured .. 20 25

106 Wicket-keeper

1988. Asia Cup Cricket. Multicoloured.
310 1 t. Type **106** 40 50
311 5 t. Batsman 60 75
312 10 t. Bowler 75 90

107 Labourers, Factory and Technician

1988. 32nd Meeting of Colombo Plan Consultative Committee, Dhaka.
313 **107** 3 t. multicoloured .. 10 10
314 10 t. multicoloured .. 40 45

108 Dhaka G.P.O. Building (Illus reduced, actual size 55 × 31 mm)

1988. 25th Anniv of Dhaka G.P.O. Building. Multicoloured.
315 1 t. Type **108** 10 10
316 5 t. Post Office counter .. 20 25

৫ম জাতীয় রোভার মুট
১৯৮৮-৮৯
(109)

1988. 5th National Rover Scout Moot. No. 168 optd with T **109**.
317 **47** 5 t. multicoloured .. 30 30

110 Bangladesh Airport

1989. Bangladesh Landmarks.
318 **110** 3 t. black and blue 10 10
319 – 5 t. black and brown 15 20
320 – 10 t. red .. 30 35
321 – 20 t. multicoloured .. 60 65
DESIGNS—VERT. (22 × 33 mm) 5 t. Curzon Hall. (19½ × 31½ mm) 10 t. Fertiliser Factory, Chittagong. HORIZ. (33 × 23 mm) 20 t. Postal Academy, Rajshahi.

চতুর্থ দ্বিবার্ষিক এশীয়
চারুকলা প্রদর্শনী
বাংলাদেশ ১৯৮৯
(111)

1989. 4th Biennial Asian Art Exhibition. No. 266 optd with T **111**.
322 10 t. "Levelling the Ploughed Field" (Zainul Abedin) 40 45

112 Irrigation Methods and Student with Telescope

1989. 12th National Science and Technology Week.

323 **112** 10 t. multicoloured .. 40 45

113 Academy Logo

1989. 75th Anniv of Police Academy, Sardah.

324 **113** 10 t. multicoloured .. 40 45

114 Rejoicing Crowds, Paris, 1789

1989. Bicent of French Revolution. Mult.

325 17 t. Type **114** 70 75

326 17 t. Storming the Bastille, 1789 .. .. .. 70 75

115 Sowing and Harvesting

1989. 10th Anniv of Asia–Pacific Integrated Rural Development Centre. Multicoloured.

329 5 t. Type **115** 45 45

330 10 t. Rural activities .. 50 50

Nos. 329/30 were printed together, se-tenant, forming a composite design.

116 Helper and Child playing with Baby

1989. 40th Anniv of S.O.S International Children's Village. Multicoloured.

331 1 t. Type **116** 15 10

332 10 t. Foster mother with children 55 55

117 U.N. Soldier on Watch

1989. 1st Anniv of Bangladesh Participation in U.N. Peace-keeping Force. Multicoloured.

333 4 t. Type **117** 25 20

334 10 t. Two soldiers checking positions 60 65

118 Festival Emblem

1989. 2nd Asian Poetry Festival, Dhaka.

335 **118** 2 t. red, dp red & green 15 10

336 – 10 t. multicoloured .. 60 65

DESIGN: 10 t. Festival emblem and hall.

119 State Security Printing Press

1989. Inauguration of State Security Printing Press, Gazipur.

337 **119** 10 t. multicoloured .. 65 65

120 Water Lilies and T.V. Emblem

1989. 25th Anniv of Bangladesh Television. Multicoloured.

338 5 t. Type **120** 30 30

339 10 t. Central emblem and water lilies 65 80

121 Gharial in Shallow Water

1990. Endangered Wildlife. Gharial. Mult.

340 50 p. Type **121** 20 20

341 2 t. Gharial feeding .. 30 30

342 4 t. Gharials basking on sand bank 45 45

343 10 t. Two gharials resting 90 90

122 Symbolic Family

1990. Population Day.

344 **122** 6 t. multicoloured .. 35 35

123 Justice S.M. Murshed

1990. 10th Death Anniv of Justice Syed Mahbub Murshed.

345 **123** 5 t. multicoloured .. 35 35

124 Boy learning Alphabet

1990. International Literacy Year. Mult.

346 6 t. Type **124** 35 40

347 10 t. Boy teaching girl to write 75 60

125 Penny Black with "Stamp World London 90" Exhibition Emblem

1990. 150th Anniv of the Penny Black. Mult.

348 7 t. Type **125** 50 45

349 10 t. Penny Black, 1983 World Communications Year stamp and Bengali mail runner 75 65

126 Goalkeeper and Ball

1990. World Cup Football Championship, Italy. Multicoloured.

350 8 t. Type **126** 60 60

351 10 t. Footballer with ball 80 80

127 Mango

1990. Fruit. Multicoloured.

353 1 t. Type **127** 10 10

354 2 t. Guava 10 10

355 3 t. Water melon 15 15

356 4 t. Papaya 20 25

357 5 t. Bread fruit 30 35

358 10 t. Carambola 60 70

128 Man gathering Wheat

1990. U.N. Conference on Least Developed Countries, Paris.

359 **128** 10 t. multicoloured .. 60 60

129 Map of Asia with Stream of Letters

1990. 20th Anniv of Asia–Pacific Postal Training Centre. Multicoloured.

360 2 t. Type **129** 20 20

361 6 t. Map of Pacific with stream of letters .. 30 30

Nos. 360/1 were printed together, se-tenant, forming a composite map design.

130 Canoe Rowing

1990. Asian Games, Beijing. Multicoloured.

362 2 t. Type **130** 15 10

363 4 t. Kabaddi 25 25

364 8 t. Wrestling 45 45

365 10 t. Badminton 70 70

131 Lalan Shah

1990. 1st Death Anniv of Lalan Shah (poet).

366 **131** 6 t. multicoloured .. 40 35

132 U.N. Logo and "40"

1990. 40th Anniv of United Nations Development Programme.

367 132 6 t. multicoloured .. 40 35

133 Immunization

1990.

368 133 2 t. brown 10 10
369 – 6 t. blue and yellow .. 20 25

DESIGN—HORIZ (30×19 mm). 6 t. Salimullah Hall.

135 "Danaus chrysippus"

1990. Butterflies. Multicoloured.

376 6 t. Type 135 .. .. 35 35
377 6 t. "Precis almana" .. 35 35
378 10 t. "Ixias pyrene" .. 50 55
379 10 t. "Danaus plexippus" 50 55

136 Drugs attacking Bangladesh

1991. U.N. Anti-Drugs Decade. Mult.

380 2 t. Type 136 .. .. 20 15
381 4 t. "Drug" snake around globe 25 25

137 Silhouetted People on Map

1991. 3rd National Census.

382 137 4 t. multicoloured .. 10 15

138 "Invincible Bangla" (statue)

1991. 20th Anniv of Independence. Mult.

383 4 t. Type 138 .. .. 10 15
384 4 t. "Freedom Fighter" (statue) 10 15
385 4 t. Mujibnagar Memorial 10 15
386 4 t. Eternal flame .. 10 15
387 4 t. National Martyrs' Memorial 10 15

Nos. 383/7 were issued together, se-tenant, forming a omposite design.

139 Pres. Rahman Seated

1991. 10th Death Anniv of President Ziaur Rahman. Multicoloured.

388 50 p. Type 139 .. .. 10 10
389 2 t. Pres. Rahman's head in circular decoration .. 10 10

140 Red Giant Flying Squirrel

1991. Endangered Species. Multicoloured.

391 2 t. Type 140 .. .. 10 10
392 4 t. Black-faced monkey (vert) 10 15
393 6 t. Great Indian hornbill (vert) 20 25
394 10 t. Armoured pangolin .. 30 35

141 Kaikobad

1991. 40th Death Anniv of Kaikobad (poet).

395 141 6 t. multicoloured .. 20 25

142 Rabindranath Tagore and Temple

1991. 50th Death Anniv of Rabindranath Tagore (poet).

396 142 4 t. multicoloured .. 10 10

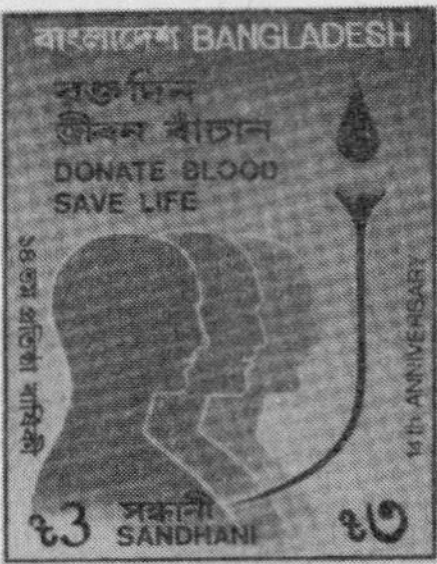

143 Voluntary Blood Donation Programme

1991. 14th Anniv of "Sandhani" (medical students' association).

397 143 3 t. black and red .. 10 10
398 – 5 t. multicoloured .. 15 20

DESIGN: 5 t. Blind man and eye

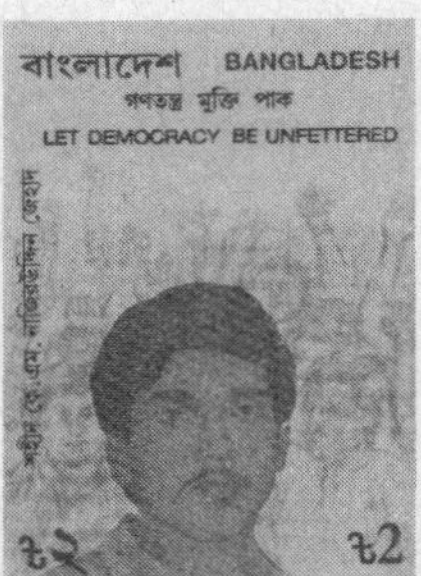

144 Shahid Naziruddin and Crowd

1991. 1st Death Anniv of Shahid Naziruddin Jahad (democrat).

399 144 2 t. black, green & brn 10 10

145 Shaheed Noor Hossain with Slogan on Chest

1991. 4th Death Anniv of Shaheed Noor Hossain (democrat).

400 145 2 t. multicoloured .. 10 10

146 Bronze Stupa

1991. Archaeological Relics from Mainamati. Multicoloured.

401 4 t. Type 146 .. .. 10 15
402 4 t. Earthenware and bronze pitchers .. 10 15
403 4 t. Remains of Salban Vihara Monastery .. 10 15
404 4 t. Gold coins .. 10 15
405 4 t. Terracotta plaque .. 10 15

147 Demonstrators

1991. 1st Anniv of Mass Uprising.

406 147 4 t. multicoloured .. 10 15

148 Munier Chowdhury

1991. 20th Anniv of Independence. Martyred Intellectuals. Each brown and black.

407 2 t. Type 148 .. .. 10 10
408 2 t. Ghyasuddin Ahmad .. 10 10
409 2 t. Rashidul Hasan .. 10 10
410 2 t. Muhammad Anwar Pasha 10 10
411 2 t. Dr. Muhammad Mortaza 10 10
412 2 t. Shahid Saber .. 10 10
413 2 t. Fazlur Rahman Khan 10 10
414 2 t. Ranada Prasad Saha 10 10
415 2 t. Adhyaksha Joges Chandra Ghose .. 10 10
416 2 t. Santosh Chandra Bhattacharyya .. 10 10
417 2 t. Dr. Gobinda Chandra Deb 10 10
418 2 t. A. Muniruzzaman .. 10 10
419 2 t. Mufazzal Haider Chaudhury 10 10
420 2 t. Dr. Abdul Alim Choudhury 10 10
421 2 t. Sirajuddin Hossain .. 10 10
422 2 t. Shahidulla kaiser .. 10 10
423 2 t. Altaf Mahmud .. 10 10
424 2 t. Dr. Jyotirmay Guha Thakurta 10 10
425 2 t. Dr. Muhammad Abul Khair 10 10
426 2 t. Dr. Serajul Haque Khan 10 10
427 2 t. Dr. Mohammad Fazle Rabbi 10 10
428 2 t. Mir Abdul Quyyum .. 10 10
429 2 t. Golam Mostafa .. 10 10
430 2 t. Dhirendranath Dutta 10 10
431 2 t. S. Mannan .. 10 10
432 2 t. Nizamuddin Ahmad .. 10 10
433 2 t. Abul Bashar Chowdhury 10 10
434 2 t. Selina Parveen .. 10 10
435 2 t. Dr. Abul Kalam Azad 10 10
436 2 t. Saidul Hassan .. 10 10

149 "Penaeus monodon"

1991. Shrimps. Multicoloured.

437 6 t. Type 149 .. .. 20 25
438 6 t. "Metapenaeus monoceros" 20 25

150 Death of Raihan Jaglu

1992. 5th Death Anniv of Shaheed Mirze Abu Raihan Jaglu.

439 150 2 t. multicoloured .. 10 10

OFFICIAL STAMPS

1973. Nos. 22, etc. optd. **SERVICE.**

O 1. 7. 2 p. black 10 20
O 2. – 3 p. green 10 20
O 3. – 5 p. brown 15 10
O 4. – 10 p. black 15 10
O 5. – 20 p. green 60 10
O 6. – 25 p. mauve .. .. 1·50 10
O 7. – 60 p. grey .. .. 1·75 40
O 8. – 75 p. orange 65 15
O 9. 8. 1 t. violet .. .. 6·00 3·00
O 10. – 5 t. blue .. .. 3·75 4·00

1974. Nos. 49/51 optd. **SERVICE.**

O 11. 14. 1 t. violet .. .. 2·00 25
O 12. – 2 t. olive .. .. 3·00 90
O 13. – 5 t. blue .. .. 4·50 3·00

1976. Nos. 64/70 and 72/4 optd. **SERVICE.**

O 14.	–	5 p. green	20	15
O 15.	–	10 p. black	40	15
O 16.	–	20 p. green	60	15
O 17.	–	25 p. mauve	1·50	15
O 18.	–	50 p. purple	1·50	15
O 19.	–	60 p. grey	20	20
O 20.	–	75 p. olive	20	25
O 21.	**14.**	1 t. blue	1·50	20
O 22.	–	2 t. green	35	40
O 23.	–	5 t. blue	20	30

1981. Nos. 125/9 and 131/7 optd **SERVICE.**

O24	–	5 p. brown	20	15
O25	**32**	10 p. blue	20	15
O26	–	15 p. orange	20	20
O27	–	20 p. red	30	20
O28	–	25 p. blue	80	50
O29	–	30 p. green	40	30
O30	–	40 p. purple	50	15
O31	–	50 p. black	30	10
O32	–	80 p. brown	60	15
O33	–	1 t. violet	30	15
O34	–	2 t. blue	35	60

1983. Nos 220/8 optd. **Service.**

O 35	**69**	5 p. blue	10	10
O 36	–	10 p. purple	10	10
O 37	–	15 p. blue	10	10
O 38	–	20 p. black	10	10
O 39	–	25 p. grey	10	10
O 40	–	30 p. brown	10	10
O 41	–	50 p. brwn	10	10
O 42	–	1 t. blue	10	10
O 43	–	2 t. green	10	10

BARBADOS

An island in the Br. W. Indies, E. of the Windward Is., attained self-government on 16th October, 1961 and achieved independence within the Commonwealth on 30 November 1966.

1950. 100 cents = 1 Barbados dollar.

1. Britannia. 2.

1852. Imperf.

8	1	(½d.) green	85·00	£200
10		(1d.) blue	19·00	50·00
4a		(2d.) slate	£250	£1100
5		(4d.) red	45·00	£300
11a	2	6d. red	£700	£250
12a		1s. black	£140	70·00

1860. Perf.

21	**1.**	(½d.) green	7·00	7·50
24		(1d.) blue	19·00	3·00
25		(4d.) red	60·00	22·00
32	**2.**	6d. red	55·00	11·00
33		6d. orange	70·00	20·00
35		1s. black	28·00	6·00

1873. Perf.

72.	**2.**	½d. green	5·50	50
73.		1d. blue	24·00	30
63.		3d. brown	£325	£110
75.		3d. mauve	75·00	3·50
76.		4d. red	70·00	7·00
79.		6d. yellow	90·00	1·00
81.		1s. purple	£100	2·75

3. 4.

1873.

64.	**3.**	5s. red	£950	£300

1878. Half of No. 64 surch. **1 D.**

86.	**3.**	1d. on half 5s. red	£3250	£600

1882.

90.	**4.**	½d. green	3·75	80
92.		1d. red	2·75	25
93		2½d. blue	42·00	70
96		3d. purple	3·25	8·50
97		4d. grey	£160	2·00
99		4d. brown	2·75	60
100		6d. brown	50·00	26·00
102		1s. brown	17·00	21·00
103		5s. bistre	£140	£170

1892. Surch. **HALF-PENNY.**

104.	**4.**	½d. on 4d. brown	30	1·00

6. Seal of Colony. 7.

1892.

105	**6**	¼d. grey and red	70	10
163		¼d. brown	50	30
106		½d. green	40	10
107		1d. red	1·50	10
108		2d. black and orange	6·00	65
166		2d. grey	3·75	8·50
109		2½d. blue	4·75	15
110		5d. olive	4·75	4·50
111		6d. mauve and red	5·00	2·00
168		6d. purple	4·00	14·00
112		8d. orange and blue	2·50	15·00
113		10d. green and red	4·50	6·50
169		1s. black on green	7·50	14·00
114		2s. 6d. black and orange	32·00	35·00
144		2s. 6d. violet and green	23·00	48·00

1897. Diamond Jubilee.

116.	**7.**	¼d. grey and red	55	15
117.		½d. green	1·50	15
118.		1d. red	2·25	10
119.		2½d. blue	4·00	25
120.		5d. brown	8·50	10·00
121.		6d. mauve and red	13·00	13·00
122.		8d. orange and blue	4·75	14·00
123.		10d. green and red	28·00	30·00
124.		2s. 6d. black and orange	30·00	40·00

8. Nelson Monument.

1906. Death Centenary of Nelson.

145	**8**	¼d. black and grey	2·00	30
146		½d. black and green	4·00	15
147		1d. black and red	3·25	15
148		2d. black and yellow	1·75	3·50
149		2½d. black and blue	3·75	1·00
150		6d. black and mauve	15·00	18·00
151		1s. black and red	16·00	30·00

9. "Olive Blossom", 1650. 11.

1906. Tercent. of Annexation of Barbados.

152.	**9.**	1d. black, blue and green	9·00	25

1907. Surch. **Kingston/Relief/Fund 1d.**

153.	**6.**	1d. on 2d. blk. & orge.	1·25	4·25

1912.

170.	**11.**	¼d. brown	30	15
171.		½d. green	85	10
172.		1d. red	1·25	10
173.		2d. grey	2·00	7·50
174.		2½d. blue	1·25	30
175.		3d. purple on yellow	1·25	5·00
176.		4d. red & black on yellow	1·25	8·50
177.		6d. purple	4·50	6·50

Larger type, with portrait at top centre.

178.		1s. black on green	4·25	7·00
179.		2s. blue and pur. on blue	26·00	38·00
180.		3s. violet and green	48·00	48·00

14.

1916.

181	**14.**	¼d. brown	45	15
182		½d. green	1·10	15
183a		1d. red	2·00	15
184		2d. grey	3·50	8·00
185		2½d. blue	80	50
186		3d. purple on yellow	1·50	2·50
187		4d. red on yellow	70	7·00
199		4d. black and red	60	2·75
188		6d. purple	2·00	3·25
189		1s. black on green	6·50	5·00
190		2s. purple on blue	14·00	7·50
191		3s. violet	28·00	65·00
200		3s. green and violet	16·00	35·00

1917. Optd. **WAR TAX.**

197.	**11.**	1d. red	15	15

16.

1920. Victory. Inscr. "VICTORY 1919".

201.	**16.**	¼d. black and brown	20	50
202.		½d. black and green	60	15
203.		1d. black and red	70	10
204.		2d. black and grey	1·75	6·00
205.		2½d. indigo and blue	2·75	6·50
206.		3d. black and purple	1·60	2·75
207.		4d. black and green	1·75	3·50
208.		6d. black and orange	2·50	5·50
209.	–	1s. black and green	6·00	13·00
210.	–	2s. black and brown	11·00	15·00
211.	–	3s. black and orange	13·00	19·00

The 1s. to 3s. show Victory full-face.

18. 19.

1921.

217.	**18.**	¼d. brown	15	10
219.		½d. green	70	15
220.		1d. red	70	10
221.		2d. grey	1·60	20
222.		2½d. blue	1·50	3·75
213.		3d. purple on yellow	1·25	4·25
214.		4d. red on yellow	1·75	5·00
225.		6d. purple	2·25	4·50
215.		1s. black on green	4·50	11·00
227.		2s. purple on blue	10·00	18·00
228.		3s. violet	13·00	35·00

1925. Inscr. "POSTAGE & REVENUE".

229	**19.**	¼d. brown	10	10
230		½d. green	10	10
231		1d. red	25	10
231ba		1½d. orange	90	55
232		2d. grey	40	1·75
233		2½d. blue	50	50
234		3d. purple on yellow	50	35
235		4d. red on yellow	50	75
236		6d. purple	50	50
237		1s. black on green	1·50	3·25
238		2s. purple on blue	6·00	6·50
238a		2s. 6d. red on blue	15·00	20·00
239		3s. violet	9·00	13·00

20. King Charles I and King George V.

1927. Tercent. of Settlement of Barbados.

240.	**20.**	1d. red	60	30

1935. Silver Jubilee. As T **13** of **Antigua.**

241.		1d. blue and red	25	20
242.		1½d. blue and grey	1·75	2·25
243.		2½d. brown and blue	2·00	85
244.		1s. grey and purple	9·50	13·00

1937. Coronation. As T **2** of Aden.

245.		1d. red	30	15
246.		1½d. brown	40	30
247.		2½d. blue	70	45

21. Badge of the Colony.

1938. "POSTAGE & REVENUE" omitted.

248.	**21.**	½d. green	2·25	15
248b.		½d. yellow	10	15
249a.		1d red	11·00	10
249c.		1d. green	10	10
250.		1½d. orange	10	10
250b.		2d. mauve	35	80
250c.		2d. red	10	10
251.		2½d. blue	50	30
252b.		3d. brown	15	20
252c.		3d. blue	10	40
253.		4d. black	15	10
254.		6d. violet	20	10
254a.		8d. mauve	45	90
255a.		1s. olive	20	10
256.		2s. 6d. purple	2·50	85
256a.		5s. blue	2·50	3·00

22. Kings Charles I, George VI. Assembly Chamber and Mace.

1939. Tercentenary of General Assembly.

257.	**22.**	½d. green	1·25	25
258.		1d. red	1·25	25
259.		1½d. orange	1·25	60
260.		2½d. blue	1·25	1·25
261.		3d. brown	1·40	2·00

1946. Victory. As T **9** of Aden.

262.		1½d. orange	10	10
263.		3d. brown	10	10

1947. Surch. **ONE PENNY.**

264.	**17.**	1d. on 2d. red	15	40

1948. Silver Wedding. As T **10/11** of Aden.

265. 1½d. orange 25 10
266. 5s. blue .. .. 9·00 4·50

1949. U.P.U. As T **20/23** of Antigua.

267. 1½d. orange 30 25
268. 3d. blue 40 35
269. 4d. grey 70 50
270. 1s. olive 80 60

24. Dover Fort.

35. Seal of Barbados.

1950.

271. **24.** 1 c. blue 15 90
272. – 2 c. green 15 45
273. – 3 c. brown and green .. 15 60
274. – 4 c. red 15 20
275. – 6 c. blue 15 60
276. – 8 c. blue and purple .. 55 50
277. – 12 c. blue and olive .. 90 30
278. – 24 c. red and black .. 70 30
279. – 48 c. violet .. .. 6·00 3·50
280. – 60 c. green and lake .. 6·00 4·00
281. – $1.20 c. red and olive .. 6·50 2·50
282. **35.** $2.40 c. black .. .. 12·00 7·00

Designs—As Type **24**: horiz. 2 c. Sugar cane breeding. 3 c. Public buildings. 6 c. Casting net. 8 c. "Frances W. Smith" (schooner). 12 c. Flying fish. 24 c. Old Main Guard Garrison. 60 c. Careenage. vert. 4 c. Statue of Nelson. 48 c. St. Michael's Cathedral. $1.20 c. Map and wireless mast.

1951. Inauguration of B.W.I. University College. As T **24/25** of Antigua.

283 3 c. brown and blue .. 15 15
284 12 c. blue and olive .. 30 40

36. King George VI and Stamp of 1852.

1952. Centenary of Barbados Stamp.

285. **36.** 3 c. green and slate .. 15 20
286. 4 c. blue and red .. 15 20
287. 12 c. slate and green 15 20
288. 24 c. brown and sepia 15 20

37. Harbour Police.

1953. As 1950 issue but with portrait or cypher (No. 319) of Queen Elizabeth II as in T **37**.

289 **24.** 1 c. blue 10 30
290 – 2 c. orange & turquoise 15 20
291 – 3 c. black and green .. 15 20
292 – 4 c. black and orange .. 20 15
293 **37.** 5 c. blue and red .. 20 20
294 – 6 c. brown 15 20
295 – 8 c. black and blue .. 70 20
296 – 12 c. blue and olive .. 60 50
297 – 24 c. red and black .. 45 10
298 – 48 c. violet .. .. 2·00 80
299 – 60 c. green and purple 6·00 1·50
300 – $1.20 red and olive .. 14·00 1·50
301 **35.** $2.40 black .. .. 7·50 1·25

1953. Coronation. As T **13** of Aden.

302. 4 c. black and orange.. 10 10

1958. British Caribbean Federation. As T **28** of Antigua.

303. 3 c. green 20 15
304. 6 c. blue 30 60
305. 12 c. red 35 15

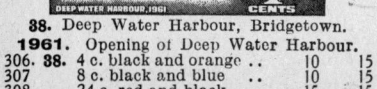

38. Deep Water Harbour, Bridgetown.

1961. Opening of Deep Water Harbour.

306. **38.** 4 c. black and orange .. 10 15
307 8 c. black and blue .. 10 15
308. 24 c. red and black .. 15 15

39. Scout Badge and Map of Barbados.

1962. Golden Jubilee of Barbados Boy Scout Association.

309. **39.** 4 c. black and orange 20 10
310. 12 c. blue & brown .. 40 15
311. $1.20 red & green .. 1·10 1·50

1965. Cent of I.T.U. As T **36** of Antigua.

320. 2 c. lilac and red .. 25 15
321. 48 c. yellow and drab. .. 1·00 1·00

40. Deep Sea Coral.

1965.

322 **40.** 1 c. black, pink and blue 10 15
323 – 2 c. brown, yell. & mauve 10 15
324 – 3 c. brown and orange.. 45 35
344 – 3 c. brown and orange 30 70
325 – 4 c. blue and green .. 15 10
326 – 5 c. sepia, red and lilac 20 10
327 – 6 c. multicoloured .. 45 10
328 – 8 c. multicoloured .. 25 10
329 – 12 c. multicoloured .. 35 10
330 – 15 c. black, yellow & red 60 55
331 – 25 c. blue and ochre .. 95 60
332 – 35 c. red and green .. 1·25 15
333 – 50 c. blue and green .. 1·50 70
354 – $1 multicoloured .. 3·25 80
335 – $2.50 multicoloured .. 2·50 1·25
355a – $5 multicoloured .. 8·50 7·00

Designs: 2 c. Lobster (wrongly inscr. "Panulirus" for "Palinurus"). 3 c. (No. 324) Sea Horse (wrongly inscr. "Hippocanpus"). 3 c. (No. 344) (correctly inscr. "Hippocampus"). 4 c. Sea Urchin. 5 c. Staghorn Coral. 6 c. Butterfly Fish. 8 c. File Shell. 12 c. Balloon Fish. 15 c. Angel Fish. 25 c. Brain Coral. 35 c. Brittle Star. 50 c. Flying Fish. $1, Queen Conch Shell. $2·50, Fiddler Crab. vert. $5, Dolphin.

1966. Churchill Commem. As T **38** of Antigua.

336. 1 c. blue 10 10
337. 4 c. green 30 10
338. 25 c. brown 70 40
339. 35 c. violet 80 60

1966. Royal Visit. As T **39** of Antigua.

340. 3 c. black and blue .. 40 25
341. 35 c. black and mauve .. 1·60 80

54. Arms of Barbados.

1966. Independence. Multicoloured.

356. 4 c. Type **54** 10 10
357. 25 c. Hilton Hotel (horiz.) 10 10
358. 35 c. G. Sobers (Test cricketer) 40 15
359. 50 c. Pine Hill Dairy (horiz) 40 15

1967. 20th Anniv. of U.N.E.S.C.O. As T **54/56** of Antigua.

360. 4 c. multicoloured .. 30 10
361. 12 c. yellow, violet & olive 70 45
362. 25 c. black, purple & orange 1·00 85

58. Policeman and Anchor.

1967. Cent. of Harbour Police. Multicoloured.

363. 4 c. Type **58** 10 10
364. 25 c. Policeman with telescope 20 10
365. 35 c. "BPI" (police launch) (horiz.) 20 10
366. 50 c. Policeman outside H.Q. 25 15

The 25 c. and 50 c. are horiz.

62. Governor-General Sir Winston Scott, G.C.M.G. **67.** Radar Antenna.

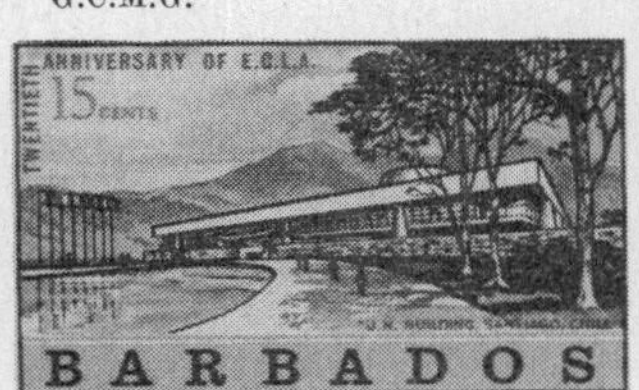

66. U.N. Building, Santiago, Chile.

1967. 1st Anniv. of Independence. Mult.

367. 4 c. Type **62** 10 10
368. 25 c. Independence Arch .. 15 10
369. 35 c. Treasury Building .. 15 10
370. 50 c. Parliament Building 15 20

Nos. 368/70 are horiz.

1968. 20th Anniv. of Economic Commission for Latin America.

371. **66.** 15 c. multicoloured .. 10 10

1968. World Meteorological Day. Mult.

372. 3 c. Type **67** 10 10
373. 25 c. Meteorological Institute (horiz.) 20 10
374. 50 c. Harp Gun and Coat of Arms 25 15

70. Lady Baden-Powell and Guide at Camp Fire.

1968. Golden Jubilee of Girl Guiding in Barbados.

375. **70.** 3 c. blue, blk. & gold 15 10
376. – 25 c. blue, blk. & gold 35 15
377. – 35 c. yell., blk. & gold 45 15

Designs: 25 c. Lady Baden-Powell and Pax Hill. 35 c. Lady Baden-Powell and Guides' Badge.

73. Hands breaking Chain, and Human Rights Emblem.

1968. Human Rights Year.

378. **73.** 4 c. violet, brown & grn. 10 10
379. – 25 c. blk., blue & yellow 10 10
380. – 35 c. multicoloured .. 10 10

Designs: 25 c. Human Rights Emblem and family enchained. 35 c. Shadows of refugees beyond opening fence.

76. Racehorses in the Paddock.

1969. Horse-Racing. Multicoloured.

381. 4 c. Type **76** 15 10
382. 25 c. Starting-Gate .. 25 10
383. 35 c. On the flat 25 10
384. 50 c. The Winning-post .. 30 20

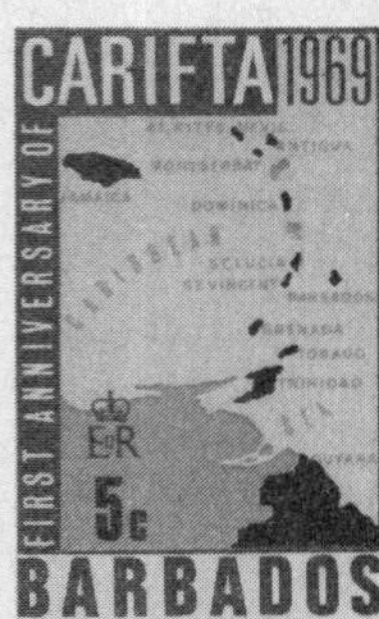

80. Map showing "CARIFTA" Countries.

1969. 1st Anniv. of "CARIFTA". Mult.

386. 5 c. Type **80** 10 10
387. 12 c. "Strength in Unity" 10 10
388. 25 c. Type **80** (horiz.) .. 10 10
389. 50 c. As 12 c. 15 20

82. I.L.O. Emblem and "1919-1969".

1969. 50th Anniversary of I.L.O.

390. **82.** 4 c. black, green & blue 10 10
391. 25 c. blk, mauve & red 10 10

1969. No. 363 surch **ONE CENT**.

392. **58.** 1 c. on 4 c. mult. .. 10 10

84. National Scout Badge.

1969. Independence of Barbados Boy Scouts Assn., and 50th Anniv. of Barbados Sea Scouts. Multicoloured.

393. 5 c. Type **84** 10 10
394. 25 c. Sea Scouts rowing .. 35 10
395. 35 c. Scouts around camp-fire 45 10
396. 50 c. Scouts and National Scout H.Q. 60 40

1970. No. 346 surch **4**.

398. 4 c. on 5 c. sepia, red & lilac 10 10

89. Lion at Gun Hill.

1970. Multicoloured.

399. 1 c. Type **89** 10 20
400. 2 c. Trafalgar Fountain .. 20 30
401. 3 c. Montefiore Drinking Fountain 10 30
402. 4 c. St. James' Monument 10 10
403. 5 c. St. Ann's Fort .. 10 10
404. 6 c. Old Sugar Mill, Morgan Lewis .. .. .. 35 1·25
405. 8 c. The Cenotaph .. 10 10
406. 10 c. South Point Lighthouse 65 15
407. 12 c. Barbados Museum .. 30 10
408. 15 c. Sharon Moravian Church 30 15
409. 25 c. George Washington House 25 15

410. 35 c. Nicholas Abbey .. 30 65
411. 50 c. Bowmanston Pumping Station .. 40 75
412. $1 Queen Elizabeth Hospital 70 2·25
413. $2.50 Sugar Factory .. 2·00 4·00
467. $5 Seawell Int. Airport .. 4·00 5·50
The 12 c. to $5 are horiz.

105. Primary Schoolgirl.

1970. 25th Anniv. of U.N. Multicoloured.
415. 4 c. Type **105** .. 10 10
416. 5 c. Secondary Schoolboy 10 10
417. 25 c. Technical Student .. 35 10
418. 50 c. University Building 55 45

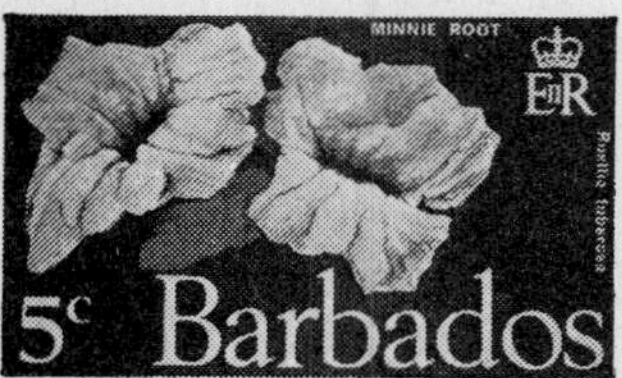

106. Minnie Root.

1970. Flowers of Barbados. Multicoloured.
419. 1 c. Barbados Easter Lily 10 20
420. 5 c. Type **106** .. 30 10
421. 10 c. Eyelash Orchid .. 70 10
422. 25 c. Pride of Barbados .. 85 55
423. 35 c. Christmas Hope 90 70
The 1 c. and 25 c. are vert.

107. " Via Dolorosa " Window, St. Margaret's Church, St. John.

1971. Easter. Multicoloured.
425. 4 c. Type **107** 10 10
426. 10 c. "The Resurrection" (Benjamin West) .. 10 10
427. 35 c. Type **107** 15 10
428. 50 c. As 10 c. 30 60

108. Sail-fish Craft.

1971. Tourism. Multicoloured.
429. 1 c. Type **108** 10 10
430. 5 c. Tennis 15 10
431. 12 c. Horse-riding .. 20 10
432. 25 c. Water-skiing .. 30 20
433. 50 c. Scuba-diving .. 50 65

109. S. J. Prescod (politician).

1971. Death Cent. of Samuel Jackman Prescod.
434. **109.** 3 c. multicoloured .. 10 10
435. 35 c. multicoloured .. 15 10

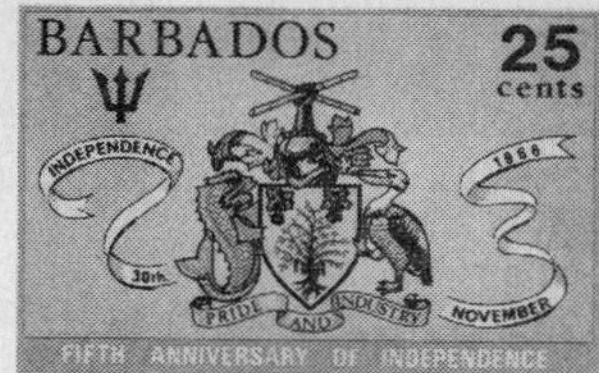

110. Arms of Barbados.

1971. 5th Anniv. of Independence. Mult.
436. 4 c. Type **110** 10 10
437. 15 c. National flag and map 20 10
438. 25 c. Type **110** 30 10
439. 50 c. As 15 c. 60 55

111. Transmitting " Then and Now ".

1972. Cent. of Cable Link. Multicoloured.
440. 4 c. Type **111** 10 10
441. 10 c. Cable Ship " Stanley Angwin " .. 15 10
442. 35 c. Barbados Earth Station and " Intelsat 4 ".. 35 15
443. 50 c. Mt. Misery and Tropospheric Scatter Station.. 50 80

112. Map and Badge.

1972. Diamond Jubilee of Scouts. Mult.
444. 5 c. Type **112** 10 10
445. 15 c. Pioneers of Scouting 15 10
446. 25 c. Scouts 30 15
447. 50 c. Flags.. .. .. 50 75
Nos. 445/7 are horiz.

113. Mobile Library.

1972. Int. Book Year. Multicoloured.
448. 4 c. Type **113** 10 10
449. 15 c. Visual-aids van .. 10 10
450. 25 c. Public Library .. 20 10
451. $1 Codrington College .. 1·25 1·50

114. Potter's Wheel.

1973. Pottery in Barbados. Mult.
468. 5 c. Type **114** 10 10
469. 15 c. Kilns 20 10
470. 25 c. Finished products .. 25 10
471. $1 Market scene .. .. 90 1·10

115. First Flight, 1911.

1973. Aviation.
472. **115.** 5 c. multicoloured .. 15 10
473. – 15 c. multicoloured .. 60 10
474. – 25 c. blue, blk. & cobalt 85 20
475. – 50 c. multicoloured .. 1·50 1·50
DESIGNS: 15 c. First flight to Barbados, 1928. 25 c. Passenger aircraft, 1939. 50 c. "VC-10" airliner, 1973.

116. University Chancellor.

1973. 25th Anniv. of University of West Indies. Multicoloured.
476. 5 c. Type **116** 10 10
477. 25 c. Sherlock Hall .. 20 15
478. 35 c. Cave Hill Campus .. 25 25

1974. No. 462 surch.
479. 4 c. on 25 c. multicoloured 10 10

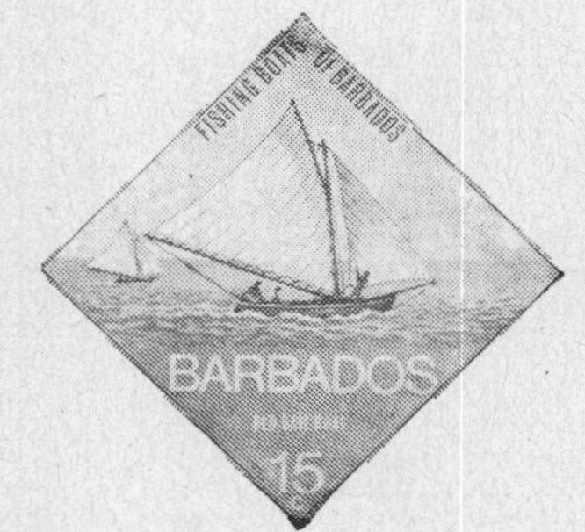

118. Old Sail Boat.

1974. Fishing Boats of Barbados. Mult.
480. 15 c. Type **118** 20 15
481. 35 c. Rowing-boat .. 45 25
482. 50 c. Motor fishing-boat .. 60 60
483. $1 "Calamar" (fishing boat) .. .. .. 1·00 1·10

119. " Cattleya Gaskelliana Alba ".

1974. Orchids. Multicoloured.
510 1 c. Type **119** 15 45
511 2 c. " Renanthera storiei " 15 45
512 3 c. " Dendrobium " " Rose Marie " 15 45
546 4 c. " Epidendrum ibaguense " 45 1·50
514 5 c. " Schomburgkia humboldtii " 35 10
490 8 c. " Oncidium ampliatum " 65 45
515 10 c. " Arachnis maggie oei " 35 10
492 12 c. " Dendrobium aggregatum " 45 40
517 15 c. "Paphiopedilum puddle" 70 15
493a 20 c. " Spathoglottis " " The Gold " .. .. 4·75 3·75
518 25 c. " Epidendrum ciliare " (Eyelash) 70 10
495 35 c. "Bletia patula" 1·75 90
519 45 c. " Phalaenopsis schilleriana " " Sunset Glow " 60 15
496 50 c. As 45 c. .. .. 2·75 1·75
497 $1 "Ascocenda" "Red Gem" 3·50 3·25
498 $2.50 "Brassolaeliocattleya" " Nugget " .. .. 3·50 3·25
499 $5 " Caularthron bicornatum " .. .. 3·50 6·00
500 $10 " Vanda " " Josephine Black " .. .. .. 4·00 11·00
The 1 c., 20 c., 25 c., $2.50 and $5 are horiz. the rest are vert.

120. 4d. Stamp of 1882, and U.P.U. Emblem.

1974. Centenary of Universal Postal Union.
501. **120.** 8 c. mauve, orge. & grn. 10 10
502. – 35 c. red, orge. & brown 20 10
503. – 50 c. ultram., bl. & silver 25 30
504. – $1 blue, brown & black 55 80
DESIGNS: 35 c. Letters encircling the globe. 50 c. U.P.U. emblem and arms of Barbados. $1, Map of Barbados, sailing-ship and aeroplane.

121. Royal Yacht " Britannia ".

1975. Royal Visit. Multicoloured.
506. 8 c. Type **121** 20 15
507. 25 c. Type **121** 50 25
508. 35 c. Sunset and palms .. 60 30
509. $1 As 35 c. .. .. 1·75 2·00

122. St. Michael's Cathedral.

1975. 150th Anniv. of Anglican Diocese. Mult.
526. 5 c. Type **122** 10 10
527. 15 c. Bishop Coleridge .. 15 10
528. 50 c. All Saints' Church .. 45 50
529. $1 " Archangel Michael and Satan " (Stained-glass window, St. Michael's Cathedral, Bridgetown) 70 80

123. Pony Float.

1975. Crop-over Festival. Multicoloured.
531. 8 c. Type **123** 10 10
532. 25 c. Man on stilts .. 10 10
533. 35 c. Maypole dancing .. 15 10
534. 50 c. Cuban dancers .. 30 45

124. Barbados Coat of Arms. 125. 17th-Century Sailing Ship.

1975. Coil Definitives.
536. **124.** 5 c. blue 15 50
537. 25 c. violet 25 75

1975. 350th Anniv. of First Settlement. Mult.
538. 4 c. Type **125** 25 10
539. 10 c. Bearded fig tree and fruit 30 15
540. 25 c. Ogilvy's 17-century map 50 30
541. $1 Captain John Powell .. 2·00 3·00

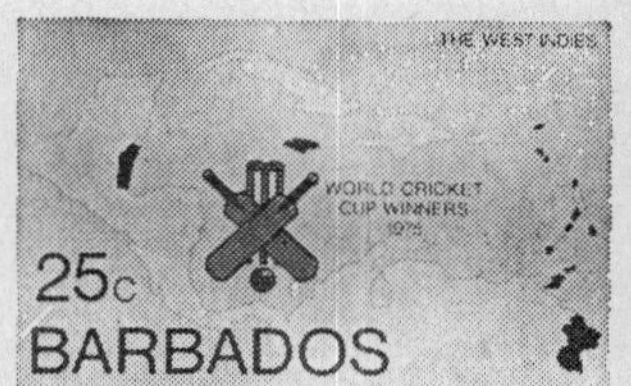

126. Map of the Caribbean.

1976. West Indian Victory in World Cricket Cup.
559. **126.** 25 c. multicoloured .. 1·00 1·00
560. – 45 c. black and purple.. 1·25 1·75
DESIGN—VERT 45 c. The Prudential Cup.

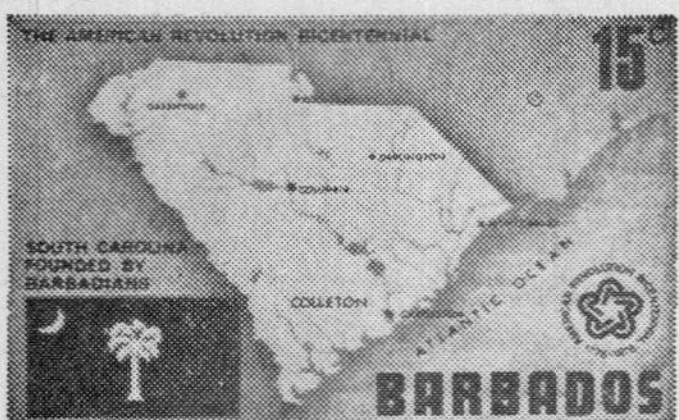

127. Flag and Map of South Carolina.

1976. Bicent. of American Revolution. Mult.
561. 15 c. Type **127** 25 15
562. 25 c. George Washington and map of Bridgetown 30 15
563. 50 c. Independence Declaration 40 60
564. $1 Prince Hall .. .. 60 1·50

128. Early Postman.

1976. 125th Anniv. of Post Office Act. Mult.
565. 8 c. Type **128** 10 10
566. 35 c. Modern postman .. 25 10
567. 50 c. Early letter 30 25
568. $1 Delivery van 50 75

129. Coast Guard Vessels.

1976. 10th Anniv. of Independence. Mult.
569. 5 c. Type **129** 15 10
570. 15 c. Reverse of currency note 15 10
571. 25 c. Barbados national anthem 20 20
572. $1 Independence Day parade .. .. .. 55 1·25

130. Arrival of Coronation Coach at Westminster Abbey.

1977. Silver Jubilee. Multicoloured.
574. 15 c. Queen knighting Garfield Sobers 1975 .. 60 25
575. 50 c. Type **130** 75 40
576. $1 Queen entering Abbey 1·10 70

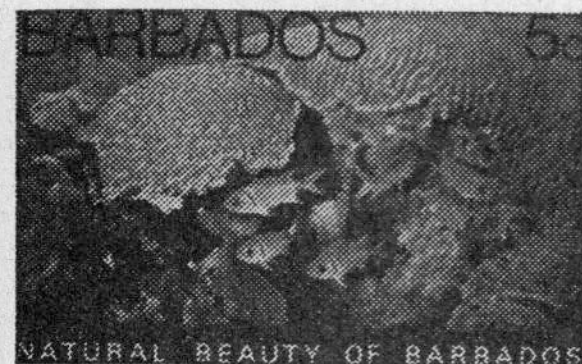

131. Underwater Park.

1977. Natural Beauty of Barbados. Mult.
577. 5 c. Type **131** 15 10
578. 35 c. Royal Palms (vert.) 30 10
579. 50 c. Underwater caves .. 40 35
580. $1 Stalagmite in Harrison's Cave (vert.) .. 70 1·00

132. Maces of the House of Commons.

1977. 13th Regional Conference of Commonwealth Parliamentary Association.
582. **132.** 10 c. orge., yell. & brn. 10 10
583. – 25 c. green, orange and dark green 10 10
584. – 50 c. multicoloured .. 20 20
585. – $1 blue, orange and deep blue 55 75

DESIGNS—VERT. 25 c. Speaker's Chair. 50 c. Senate Chamber. HORIZ. $1, Sam Lord's Castle.

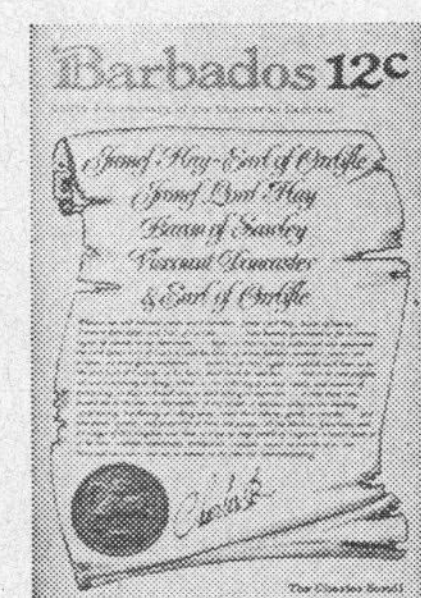

133. The Charter Scroll.

1977. 350th Anniv. of Granting of Charter to Earl of Carlisle. Multicoloured.
586. 12 c. Type **133** 15 10
587. 25 c. The earl receiving charter 15 10
588. 45 c. The earl and Charles I (horiz.) 30 35
589. $1 Ligon's map, 1657 (horiz.) .. .. .. 50 1·00

1977. Royal Visit. As Nos. 574/6 but inscr. "SILVER JUBILEE ROYAL VISIT".
590. 15 c. Garfield Sobers being knighted, 1975 .. .. 40 40
591. 50 c. Type **130** 60 50
592. $1 Queen entering Abbey 90 75

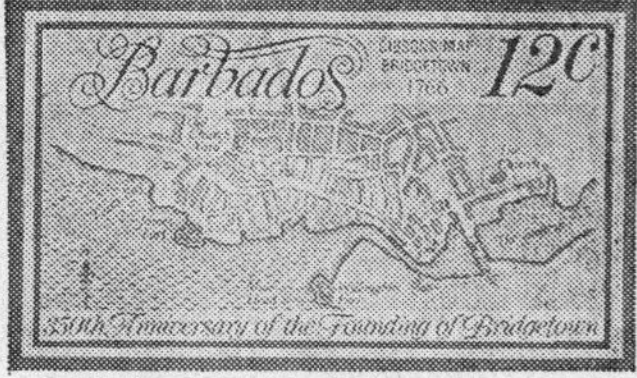

134. Gibson's Map of Bridgetown, 1766.

1978. 350th Anniv. of Founding of Bridgetown.
593. **134.** 12 c. multicoloured .. 15 10
594. – 25 c. black, green & gold 20 10
595. – 45 c. multicoloured .. 25 15
596. – $1 multicoloured .. 40 60

DESIGNS: 25 c. "A Prospect of Bridgetown in Barbados" (engraving by S. Copens, 1695). 45 c. "Trafalgar Square, Bridgetown" (drawing by J. M. Carter, 1835). $1, The Bridges, 1978.

135. Pelican.

1978. 25th Anniv. of Coronation.
597. – 50 c. olive, black & blue 25 50
598. – 50 c. multicoloured .. 25 50
599. **135.** 50 c. olive, black & blue 25 50

DESIGNS: No. 597, Griffin of Edward III. No. 598, Queen Elizabeth II.

136. Barbados Bridge League Logo.

1978. 7th Regional Bridge Tournament, Barbados. Multicoloured.
600. 5 c. Type **136** 10 10
601. 10 c. Emblem of World Bridge Federation .. 15 10
602. 45 c. Central American and Caribbean Bridge Federation emblem 25 10
603. $1 Playing cards on map of Caribbean 40 60

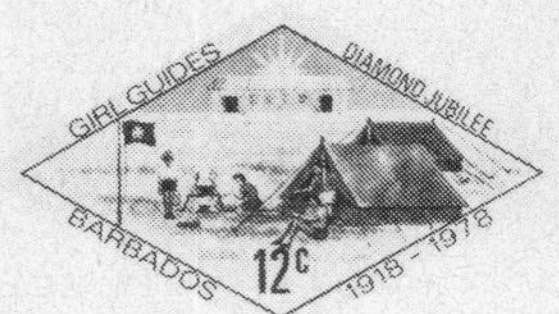

137. Camp Scene.

(Illustration reduced. Actual size 60 × 35 mm).

1978. Diamond Jubilee of Guiding. Mult.
605. 12 c. Type **137** 20 15
606. 28 c. Community work .. 30 15
607. 50 c. Badge and "60" (vert.) 40 20
608. $1 Guide badge (vert.) .. 60 60

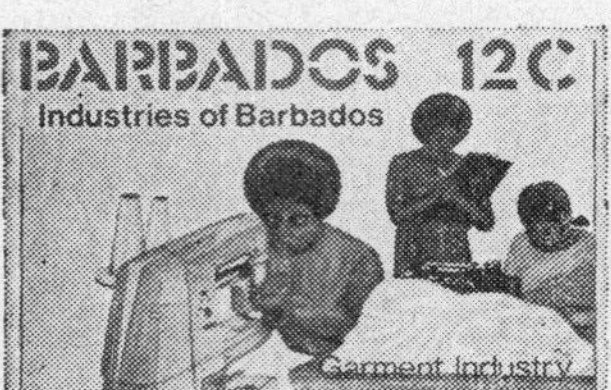

138. Garment Industry.

1978. Industries of Barbados. Multicoloured.
609. 12 c. Type **138** 10 10
610. 28 c. Cooper (vert.) .. 15 20
611. 45 c. Blacksmith (vert.) .. 20 40
612. 50 c. Wrought iron working 25 40

139. Early Mail Steamer.

1979. Ships. Multicoloured.
613. 12 c. Type **139** 30 10
614. 25 c. "Queen Elizabeth 2" in Deep Water Harbour 45 15
615. 50 c. "Ra II" nearing Barbados 65 65
616. $1 Early mail steamer (different) .. .. .. 90 1·50

140. 1953 1 c. Definitive Stamp.

1979. Death Centenary of Sir Rowland Hill. Multicoloured.
617. 12 c. Type **140** 15 15
618. 28 c. 1975 350th Anniv. of first settlement 25 c. commemorative (vert.) 20 25
619. 45 c. Penny Black with Maltese Cross postmark (vert.) 30 35

1979. St. Vincent Relief Fund. No. 495 surch. **ST. VINCENT RELIEF FUND 28 c. + 4 c.**
621. 28 c. + 4 c. on 35 c. "Bletia patula" 30 30

142. Grassland Yellow Finch.

1979. Birds. Multicoloured.
622 1 c. Type **142** 10 40
623 2 c. Grey Kingbird .. 10 40
624 5 c. Lesser Antillean Bullfinch 10 30
625 8 c. Magnificent Frigate Bird (Cobbler) 10 30
626 10 c. Cattle Egret .. 10 30
627 12 c. Green Heron .. 15 35
627a 15 c. Carib Grackle .. 3·50 1·50
628 20 c. Antillean Crested Hummingbird .. 20 35
629 25 c. Scaly-breasted Ground Dove 20 40
630 28 c. As 15 c. 50 60
631 35 c. Green-throated Carib 30 60
631b 40 c. Red necked Pigeon 3·50 1·50
632 45 c. Zenaida Dove .. 35 60
633 50 c. As 40 c. 55 80
633a 55 c. American Golden Plover .. .. 3·25 1·00
633b 60 c. Bananaquit .. .. 3·75 2·00
634 70 c. As 60 c. 55 90
635 $1 Caribbean Elaenia .. 1·00 1·25
636 $2·50 American Redstart 2·00 3·50
637 $5 Belted Kingfisher .. 3·25 6·00
638 $10 Moorhen .. .. 6·50 12·00

143. Unloading H.A.R.P. Gun on Railway Wagon at Foul Bay.

1979. Space Projects Commemorations. Mult.
639. 10 c. Type **143** 10 10
640. 12 c. H.A.R.P. gun on railway wagon under tow (vert.) 20 15
641. 20 c. Firing launcher (vert.) 15 15
642. 28 c. Bath Earth Station and "Intelsat" 25 25
643. 45 c. "Intelsat" over Caribbean 35 35
644. 50 c. "Intelsat" over Atlantic (vert.) 35 45

144. Family.

1979. International Year of the Child. **Mult.**
646. 12 c. Type **144** 10 10
647. 28 c. Ring of children and map of Barbados .. 15 15
648. 45 c. Child with teacher 20 20
649. 50 c. Children playing .. 20 20
650. $1 Children and kite .. 35 45

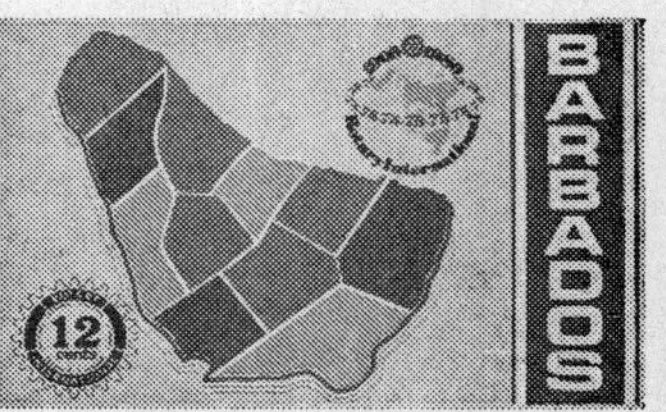

145. Map of Barbados.

1980. 75th Anniv. of Rotary International. Multicoloured.
651. 12 c. Type **145** 10 10
652. 28 c. Map of Caribbean .. 15 15
653. 50 c. Globe (anniversary emblem) 20 25
654. $1 Paul P. Harris (founder) 35 60

146. Private, Artillery Company, Barbados Volunteer Force, circa 1909.

1980. Barbados Regiment. Multicoloured.

655. 12 c. Type **146** 20 10
656. 35 c. Drum Major, Zouave uniform 35 15
657. 50 c. Sovereign's and Regimental Colours 40 30
658. $1 Barbados Regiment Corps of Women .. 65 70

148. Underwater Scenery.

1980. Underwater Scenery.

660. **148.** 12 c. multicoloured .. 15 10
661. – 28 c. multicoloured .. 25 15
662. – 50 c. multicoloured .. 40 25
663. – $1 multicoloured .. 65 70

Nos. 661/3 show various underwater scenes.

149. Bathsheba Railway Station.

1981. Early Transport. Multicoloured.

665. 12 c. Type **149** 10 10
666. 28 c. Cab stand in The Green 20 15
667. 45 c. Animal-drawn tram 30 25
668. 70 c. Horse-drawn bus .. 45 50
669. $1 Railway Station, Fairchild Street 60 85

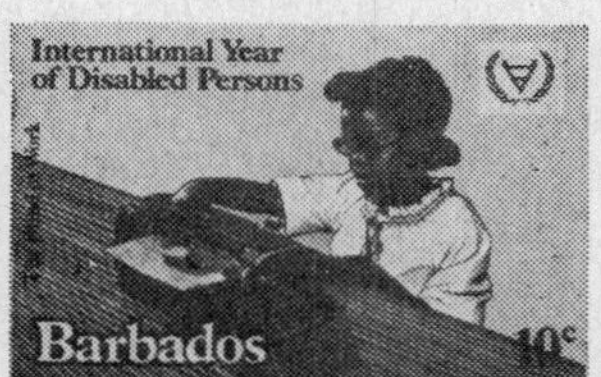

150. The Blind at Work.

1981. International Year for Disabled Persons. Multicoloured.

670. 10 c. Type **150** 15 10
671. 25 c. Sign language (vert.) 30 20
672. 45 c. "Be alert to the white cane" (vert.) 55 35
673. $2·50 Children at play .. 2·00 2·75

151. Prince Charles dressed for Polo.

1981. Royal Wedding. Multicoloured.

674. 28 c. Wedding bouquet from Barbados 20 10
675. 50 c. Type **151** 25 15
676. $2·50 Prince Charles and Lady Diana Spencer .. 80 1·25

152. Landship Manoeuvre.

1981. Carifesta (Caribbean Festival of Arts), Barbados. Multicoloured.

677. 15 c. Type **152** 15 15
678. 20 c. Yoruba dancers .. 15 15
679. 40 c. Tuk band 25 25
680. 55 c. Sculpture by Frank Collymore 35 35
681. $1 Harbour scene .. 60 75

1981. Nos. 630, 632 and 634 surch.

682. 15 c. on 28 c. Carib Grackle 15 15
683. 40 c. on 45 c. Zenaida Dove 20 35
684. 60 c. on 70 c. Bananaquit .. 30 45

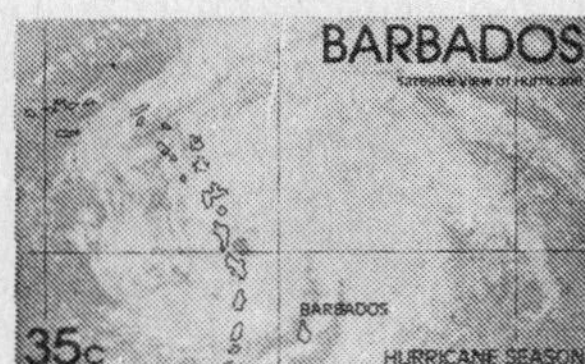

154. Satellite view of Hurricane.

1981. Hurricane Season.

685. **154.** 35 c. black and blue .. 30 20
686. – 50 c. multicoloured .. 40 35
687. – 60 c. multicoloured .. 50 50
688. – $1 multicoloured .. 75 90

DESIGNS: 50 c. Hurricane "Gladys" from "Apollo 7". 60 c. Police Department on hurricane watch. $1, Hurricane hunter (McDonnell "F2H–2P (Banshee)" jet aircraft).

155. Twin Falls.

1981. Harrison's Cave. Multicoloured.

689. 10 c. Type **155** 10 10
690. 20 c. Stream in Rotunda Room 20 15
691. 55 c. Formations in Rotunda Room 40 50
692. $2.50 Cascade Pool .. 1·25 2·25

156. Black Belly Ram.

1982. Black Belly Sheep. Multicoloured.

693. 40 c. Type **156** 30 30
694. 50 c. Black belly ewe .. 30 35
695. 60 c. Ewe with lambs .. 40 60
696. $1 Ram and ewe, with map of Barbados .. .. 65 1·50

157. Barbados Coat of Arms and Flag.

1982. President Reagan's Visit. Mult.

697. 20 c. Type **157** 65 75
698. 20 c. U.S.A. coat of arms and flag 65 75
699. 55 c. Type **157** .. .. 1·00 1·25
700. 55 c. As No. 698 .. .. 1·00 1·25

158. Lighter.

1982. Early Marine Transport. Mult.

701. 20 c. Type **158** 20 15
702. 35 c. Rowing boat .. 35 25
703. 55 c. Speightstown schooner 50 40
704. $2.50 Inter-colonial schooner .. .. 2·00 2·25

159. Bride and Earl Spencer Proceding up the Aisle.

1982. 21st Birthday of Princess of Wales. Multicoloured.

705. 20 c. Barbados coat of arms 20 15
706. 60 c. Princess at Llanelwedd, October, 1981 .. 55 50
707. $1.20 Type **159** .. .. 90 1·10
708. $2.50 Formal portrait .. 1·50 1·90

160. "To Help other People".

1982. 75th Anniv. of Boy Scout Movement. Multicoloured.

709. 15 c. Type **160** 50 10
710. 40 c. "I Promise to do my Best" (horiz.) 80 25
711. 55 c. "To do my Duty to God, the Queen and my Country" (horiz.) .. 1·00 40
712. $1 National and Troop flags .. .. .. 1·50 1·25

161. Arms of George Washington.

1982. 250th Birth Anniv. of George Washington. Multicoloured.

714. 10 c. Type **161** 10 10
715. 55 c. Washington House, Barbados 45 45
716. 60 c. Washington with troops 50 50
717. $2. 50 Washington taking Oath .. .. .. 1·60 1·60

162. "Agraulis vanillae".

1983. Butterflies. Multicoloured.

718 20 c. Type **162** 55 15
719 40 c. "Danaus plexippus" 75 40
720 55 c. "Hypolimnas misippus" 90 45
721 $2·50 "Hemiargus hanno" 2·25 2·00

163. Map of Barbados and Satellite View.

1983. Commonwealth Day. Multicoloured.

722. 15 c. Type **163** 25 10
723. 40 c. Tourist beach .. 40 20
724. 60 c. Sugar cane harvesting 60 40
725. $1 Cricket match .. .. 1·50 1·10

164. U.S. Navy Dirigible.

1983. Bicentenary of Manned Flight.

726. 20 c. Type **164** 45 10
727. 40 c. Douglas "DC3" .. 60 30
728. 55 c. Vickers "Viscount" 75 60
729. $1 Lockheed "Tristar" .. 1·25 1·75

165. Nash "600", 1941.

1983. Classic Cars. Multicoloured.

730. 25 c. Type **165** 30 20
731. 45 c. Dodge, 1938 .. .. 40 30
732. 75 c. Ford "Model AA", 1930 .. .. .. 60 70
733. $2·50 Dodge "Four", 1918 .. .. .. 1·75 2·25

166. Game in Progress.

167. Angel playing Lute (detail "The Virgin and Child") (Masaccio).

1983. Table Tennis World Cup Competition. Multicoloured.

734. 20 c. Type **166** 25 20
735. 65 c. Map of Barbados .. 50 55
736. $1 World Table Tennis Cup 75 1·00

1983. Christmas. 50th Anniv. of Barbados Museum.

737. **167.** 10 c. multicoloured .. 25 10
738. – 25 c. multicoloured .. 45 20
739. – 45 c. multicoloured .. 65 35
740. – 75 c. black and gold 1·00 1·00
741. – $2·50 multicoloured .. 3·00 3·50

DESIGNS—HORIZ. 45 c. "The Barbados Museum" (Richard Day). 75 c. "St. Ann's Garrison" (W. S. Hedges). $2.50 Needham's Point, Carlisle Bay. VERT. 25 c., $2 Different details from "The Virgin and Child" (Masaccio).

168. Track and Field Events.

1984. Olympic Games, Los Angeles.
745. **168.** 50 c. green, black and brown 50 45
746. – 65 c. orange, black and brown 70 60
747. – 75 c. blue, black and deep blue 80 70
748. – $1 brown, black and yellow .. .. 1·00 90
DESIGNS: 65 c. Shooting. 75 c. Sailing. $1 Cycling.

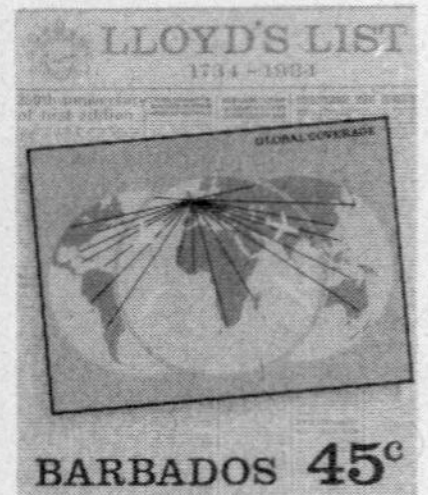

169. Global Coverage.

1984. 250th Anniv. of "Lloyd's List" (newspaper). Multicoloured.
750. 45 c. Type **169** 65 40
751. 50 c. Bridgetown harbour .. 70 50
752. 75 c. "Philosopher", 1857 .. 95 70
753. $1 "Sea Princess", 1984 .. 1·10 95

171. Local Junior Match.

1984. 60th Anniv. of World Chess Federation. Multicoloured.
755. 25 c. Type **171** 80 25
756. 45 c. Staunton and 19th-century Knight .. .. 1·10 45
757. 65 c. Staunton and 18th-century Queen .. .. 1·40 70
758. $2 Staunton and 17th-century Castle .. .. 2·75 3·00

172. Poinsettia.

1984. Christmas. Flowers. Multicoloured.
759. 50 c. Type **172** .. .. 1·25 60
760. 65 c. Snow-on-the-Mountain .. .. 1·50 80
761. 75 c. Christmas Candle .. 1·75 1·50
762. $1 Christmas Hope .. 2·00 2·25

173. Pink-tipped Anemone.

1985. Marine Life. Multicoloured.
794 1 c. Bristle Worm 20 30
795 2 c. Spotted Trunkfish .. 20 30
765 5 c. Coney 30 15
797 10 c. Type **173** 30 15
798 20 c. Christmas Tree Worm 30 30
799 25 c. Hermit Crab 40 40
800 35 c. Animal Flower .. 60 35
801 40 c. Vase Sponge 50 50
802 45 c. Spotted Moray .. 60 50
803 50 c. Ghost Crab 60 60
804 65 c. Flamingo Tongue Snail 65 70
805 75 c. Sergeant Major .. 70 75
806 $1 Caribbean Warty Anemone 85 85
807 $2.50 Green Turtle .. 2·00 1·75
808 $5 Rock Beauty (fish) .. 4·50 3·25
809 $10 Elkhorn Coral .. .. 9·00 8·00

174. The Queen Mother at Docks.

1985. Life and Times of Queen Elizabeth the Queen Mother. Multicoloured.
779. 25 c. In the White Drawing Room, Buckingham Palace, 1930s 15 20
780. 65 c. With Lady Diana Spencer at Trooping the Colour, 1981 .. .. 45 50
781. 75 c. Type **174** 55 60
782. $1 With Prince Henry at his christening (from photo by Lord Snowdon) 70 75

175. Peregrine Falcon.

1985. Birth Bicentenary of John J. Audubon (ornithologist). Designs showing original paintings. Multicoloured.
784. 45 c. Type **175** .. .. 1·10 45
785. 65 c. Prairie Warbler (vert.) .. .. .. 1·25 75
786. 75 c. Great Blue Heron (vert.) .. .. .. 1·50 1·00
787. $1 Yellow Warbler (vert.) 1·75 1·75

176. Intelsat Satellite orbiting Earth.

1985. 20th Anniv. of Intelsat Satellite System.
788. **176.** 75 c. multicoloured .. 75 60

177. Traffic Policeman.

1985. 150th Anniv. of Royal Barbados Police. Multicoloured.
789. 25 c. Type **177** 75 20
790. 50 c. Police Band on bandstand .. .. .. 1·25 55
791. 65 c. Dog handler .. .. 1·50 80
792. $1 Mounted policeman in ceremonial uniform .. 1·75 1·75

1986. 60th Birthday of Queen Elizabeth II. As T **110** of Ascension. Multicoloured.
810. 25 c. Princess Elizabeth aged two, 1928 .. .. 15 20
811. 50 c. At University College of West Indies, Jamaica, 1953 .. .. .. 35 40
812. 65 c. With Duke of Edinburgh, Barbados, 1985 .. .. .. 45 50
813. 75 c. At banquet in Sao Paulo, Brazil, 1968 .. 55 60
814. $2 At Crown Agents Head Office, London, 1983 .. 1·40 1·50

178. Trans-Canada "North Star DC-472" Airliner.

1986. "Expo '86" World Fair, Vancouver. Multicoloured.
815. 50 c. Type **178** 35 40
816. $2.50 "Lady Nelson" (liner) .. .. 1·75 1·90

1986. "Ameripex '86" International Stamp Exhibition, Chicago. As T **164** of Bahamas, showing Barbados stamps. Multicoloured.
817. 45 c. 1976 Bicentenary of American Revolution 25 c. 60 35
818. 50 c. 1976 Bicentenary of American Revolution 25 c. 65 40
819. 65 c. 1981 Hurricane Season $1 .. .. 75 50
820. $1 1982 Visit of President Reagan 55 c. × 2 .. 95 75

1986. Royal Wedding. As T **112** of Ascension. Multicoloured.
822. 45 c. Prince Andrew and Miss Sarah Ferguson .. 60 35
823. $1 Prince Andrew in Midshipman's uniform .. 1·00 75

179. Transporting Electricity Poles, 1923.

1986. 75th Anniv. of Electricity in Barbados. Multicoloured.
824. 10 c. Type **179** 15 10
825. 25 c. Heathman Ladder, 1935 (vert.) 25 20
826. 65 c. Transport fleet, 1941 60 50
827. $2 Bucket truck, 1986 (vert.) .. .. .. 1·60 1·75

180. "Alpinia purpurata" and Church Window.

1986. Christmas. Multicoloured.
828. 25 c. Type **180** 20 20
829. 50 c. "Anthurium andraeanum" 45 45
830. 75 c. "Heliconia rostrata" 75 70
831. $2 "Heliconia × psittacorum .. .. 1·50 2·25

181. Shot Putting.

1987. 10th Anniv. of Special Olympics. Multicoloured.
832. 15 c. Type **181** 25 15
833. 45 c. Wheelchair racing .. 45 30
834. 65 c. Long jumping .. 60 50
835. $2 Logo and slogan .. 1·75 2·00

182. Barn Swallow.

1987. "Capex '87" International Stamp Exhibition, Toronto. Birds. Multicoloured.
836. 25 c. Type **182** 75 30
837. 50 c. Yellow warbler .. 1·00 70
838. 65 c. Audubon's shearwater .. .. .. 1·25 1·00
839. 75 c. Black-whiskered vireo 1·40 1·25
840. $1 Scarlet tanager .. 1·60 2·00

183. Sea Scout saluting.

1987. 75th Anniv. of Scouting in Barbados. Multicoloured.
841. 10 c. Type **183** 20 10
842. 25 c. Scout jamboree .. 30 20
843. 65 c. Scout badges .. 65 45
844. $2 Scout band .. .. 1·60 1·75

184. Bridgetown Synagogue.

1987. Restoration of Bridgetown Synagogue. Multicoloured.
845. 50 c. Type **184** 90 75
846. 65 c. Interior of Synagogue 1·10 85
847. 75 c. Ten Commandments (vert.) .. .. .. 1·40 1·25
848. $1 Marble laver (vert.) .. 1·75 2·00

185. Arms and Colonial Seal.

1987. 21st Anniv. of Independence. Mult.
849. 29 c. Type **185** 20 20
850. 45 c. Flags of Barbados and Great Britain .. 30 30
851. 65 c. Silver dollar and one penny coins 55 45
852. $2 Colours of Barbados Regiment .. .. 1·40 1·40

186. Herman C. Griffith.

1988. West Indian Cricket. Each showing portrait, cricket equipment and early belt buckle. Multicoloured.

854	15 c. E. A. Manny Martindale	50	20
855	45 c. George Challenor ..	90	45
856	50 c. Type **186**	1·00	70
857	75 c. Harold Austin ..	1·40	90
858	$2 Frank Worrell ..	2·50	2·75

187 "Kentropyx borckianus"

1988. Lizards of Barbados. Multicoloured.

859	10 c. Type **187**	30	10
860	50 c. "Hemidactylus mabouia"	80	35
861	65 c. "Anolis extremus" ..	90	55
862	$2 "Gymnophthalmus underwoodii"	2·25	2·00

188 Cycling

1988. Olympic Games, Seoul. Multicoloured.

863	25 c. Type **188**	15	20
864	45 c. Athletics	25	30
865	75 c. Relay swimming ..	45	50
866	$2 Yachting	1·25	1·40

1988. 300th Anniv of Lloyd's of London. As T **123** of Ascension.

868	40 c. multicoloured ..	45	30
869	50 c. multicoloured ..	55	35
870	65 c. multicoloured ..	70	45
871	$2 blue and red	1·75	2·00

DESIGNS: VERT—40 c. Royal Exchange, 1774; $2 Sinking of "Titanic", 1912. HORIZ—50 c. Early sugar mill; 65 c. "Author" (container ship).

189 Harry Bayley and Observatory

1988. 25th Anniv of Harry Bayley Observatory. Multicoloured.

872	25 c. Type **189**	40	20
873	65 c. Observatory with North Star and Southern Cross constellations ..	75	45
874	75 c. Andromeda galaxy ..	85	50
875	$2 Orion constellation ..	2·00	2·25

190 LIAT BAe "748"

1989. 50th Anniv of Commercial Aviation in Barbados. Multicoloured.

876	25 c. Type **190**	40	20
877	65 c. Panam Douglas "DC-8"	70	50
878	75 c. British Airways "Concorde" at Grantley Adams Airport ..	85	60
879	$2 Caribbean Air Cargo Boeing "707-351c" ..	2·00	2·25

191 Assembly Chamber

1989. 350th Anniv of Parliament.

880	**191**	25 c. multicoloured ..	30	20
881	–	50 c. multicoloured ..	45	35
882	–	75 c. blue and black ..	70	50
883	–	$2.50 multicoloured ..	1·75	2·00

DESIGNS: 50 c. The Speaker; 75 c. Parliament Buildings, c. 1882; $2.50, Queen Elizabeth II and Prince Philip in Parliament.

192 Brown Hare

1989. Wildlife Preservation. Multicoloured.

884	10 c. Type **192**	20	10
885	50 c. Red-footed tortoise (horiz)	50	35
886	65 c. Savanna ("Green") monkey	60	45
887	$2 "Bufo marinus" (toad) (horiz)	1·75	1·60

193 Bread 'n Cheese

1989. Wild Plants. Multicoloured.

921	2 c. Type **193**	10	10
922	5 c. Scarlet cordia ..	10	10
923	10 c. Columnar cactus ..	10	10
924	20 c. Spiderlily	10	15
925	25 c. Rock balsam ..	15	20
895	30 c. Hollyhock	15	20
927	45 c. Yellow shak-shak ..	25	30
928	50 c. Whitewood	30	35
898	55 c. Bluebell	30	35
930	65 c. Prickly sage ..	40	45
900	70 c. Seaside samphire ..	40	45
901	80 c. Flat-hand dildo ..	45	50
902	$1.10 Lent tree	65	70
934	$2.50 Rodwood	1·40	1·50
935	$5 Cowitch	3·00	3·25
936	$10 Maypole	5·75	6·00

194 Water Skiing

1989. "World Stamp Expo '89" International Stamp Exn, Washington. Watersports. Mult.

906	25 c. Type **194**	35	25
907	50 c. Yachting	60	55
908	65 c. Scuba diving ..	80	75
909	$2.50 Surfing	2·75	3·00

195 Barbados 1852 1d. Stamp

1990. 150th Anniv of the Penny Black and "Stamp World London 90" International Stamp Exhibition.

910	**195**	25 c. green, blk & yell	30	20
911	–	50 c. multicoloured ..	45	35
912	–	65 c. multicoloured ..	55	50
913	–	$2.50 multicoloured	2·25	2·50

DESIGNS: 50 c. 1d. 1882 Queen Victoria stamp; 65 c. 1899 2d. stamp; $2.50 1912 3d. stamp.

196 Bugler and Jockeys

1990. Horse Racing. Multicoloured.

915	25 c. Type **196**	35	25
916	45 c. Horse and jockey in parade ring	50	45
917	75 c. At the finish ..	75	65
918	$2 Leading in the winner (vert)	2·00	2·25

1990. 90th Birthday of Queen Elizabeth the Queen Mother. As T **134** of Ascension.

919	75 c. multicoloured ..	60	45
920	$2.50 black and green ..	1·90	2·10

DESIGNS—21 × 36 mm. 75 c. Lady Elizabeth Bowes-Lyon, April 1923 (from painting by John Lander). 29 × 37 mm. $2.50, Lady Elizabeth Bowes-Lyon on her engagement, January 1923.

197 "Orthemis ferruginea" (dragonfly)

1990. Insects. Multicoloured.

937	50 c. Type **197**	35	30
938	65 c. "Ligyrus tumulosus" (beetle)	50	45
939	75 c. "Neoconocephalus sp." (grasshopper) ..	60	50
940	$2 "Bostra maxwelli" (stick-insect) ..	1·10	1·25

1990. Visit of the Princess Royal. Nos. 925, 901 and 903 optd **VISIT OF HRH THE PRINCESS ROYAL OCTOBER 1990**.

941	25 c. Rock balsam ..	20	15
942	80 c. Flat-hand dildo ..	60	60
943	$2.50 Rodwood	1·90	2·00

199 Star

1990. Christmas. Multicoloured.

944	20 c. Type **199**	20	15
945	50 c. Figures from crib ..	40	35
946	$1 Stained glass window ..	70	65
947	$2 Angel (statue)	1·25	1·50

200 Adult Male Yellow Warbler

1991. Endangered Species. Yellow Warbler. Multicoloured.

948	10 c. Type **200**	20	15
949	20 c. Pair feeding chicks in nest	25	20
950	45 c. Female feeding chicks in nest	45	35
951	$1 Male with fledgeling ..	95	95

201 Sorting Daily Catch

1991. Fishing in Barbados. Multicoloured.

952	5 c. Type **201**	10	10
953	50 c. Line fishing (horiz) ..	40	40
954	75 c. Fish cleaning (horiz) ..	60	60
955	$2.50 Game fishing ..	1·75	2·00

202 Masonic Building, Bridgetown

1991. 250th Anniv of Freemasonry in Barbados (1990).

956	**202**	25 c. multicoloured ..	15	20
957	–	65 c. multicoloured ..	40	45
958	–	75 c. black, yell & brn	45	50
959	–	$2.50 multicoloured ..	1·40	1·50

DESIGNS: 65 c. Compass and square (masonic symbols); 75 c. Royal Arch jewel; $2.50, Ceremonial apron, columns and badge.

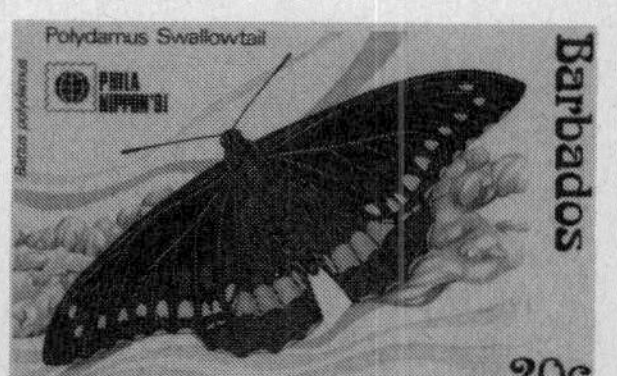

203 "Battus polydamus"

1991. "Philanippon '91" International Stamp Exhibition, Tokyo. Butterflies. Mult.

960 20 c. Type **203** 10 15
961 50 c. "Urbanus proteus" (vert) 30 35
962 65 c. "Phoebis sennae" .. 40 45
963 $2.50 "Junonia evarete" (vert) .. .. .. 1·40 1·50

204 School Class

1991. 25th Anniv of Independence. Mult.

965 10 c. Type **204** 10 10
966 25 c. Barbados Workers' Union Labour college .. 15 20
967 65 c. Building a house 40 45
968 75 c. Sugar cane harvesting 45 50
969 $1 Health clinic 60 65

205 Jesus carrying Cross

1992. Easter. Multicoloured.

971 35 c. Type **205** 20 25
972 70 c. Crucifixion 40 45
973 90 c. Descent from the Cross 50 55
974 $3 Risen Christ .. .. 1·75 1·90

POSTAGE DUE STAMPS

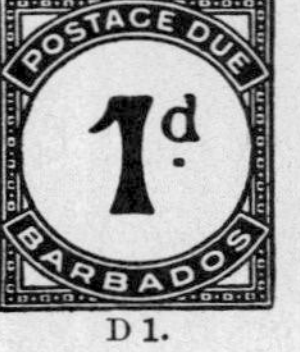

D 1.

D 2.

1934.

D 1. **D 1.** ½d. green .. .. 50 2·00
D 2. 1d. black 70 70
D 3. 3d. red .. .. 15·00 16·00

1950. Values in cents.

D 7 D 1 1 c. green .. .. 30 2·50
D 5a 2 c. black .. .. 40 2·00
D 9 6 c. red .. .. 50 3·00

1976.

D 14a. **D 2.** 1 c. mauve & pink 10 10
D 15a. – 2 c. blue & lt. blue 10 10
D 16a. – 5 c. brown & yell. 10 10
D 17a. – 10 c. blue & lilac .. 10 10
D 18a. – 25 c. deep green & green 15 20
D 19. – $1 red & deep red 60 65

DESIGNS: Nos. D15/19 show different floral backgrounds.

BARBUDA

One of the Leeward Is., Br. W. Indies. Dependency of Antigua. Used stamps of Antigua and Leeward Is. concurrently. The issues from 1968 are also valid for use in Antigua. From 1971 to 1973 the stamps of Antigua were again used.

1922. 12 pence = 1 shilling.
20 shillings = 1 pound.
1951. 100 cents = 1 West Indian dollar.

1922. Stamps of Leeward Islands optd. **BARBUDA.**

1. **11.** ½d. green .. .. .. 1·00 7·50
2. 1d. red .. .. .. 1·00 7·00
3. 2d. grey .. .. .. 1·00 7·00
4. 2½d. blue .. .. .. 1·00 7·50
9. 3d. purple on yellow .. 1·00 8·00
5. 6d. purple .. .. 1·50 14·00
10. 1s. black on green .. 1·50 8·00
6. 2s. purple and blue on blue 8·50 38·00
7. 3s. green and violet .. 27·00 70·00
8. 4s. black and red .. .. 35·00 70·00
11. 5s. green & red on yellow 65·00 £120

2. Map of Barbuda.

1968.

12. **2.** ½ c. brown, black and pink 10 10
13. – 1 c. orange, black and flesh 15 10
14. – 2 c. brown, red and rose .. 15 10
15. – 3 c. brown, yellow & lemon 15 10
16. – 4 c. black, green and light green 15 10
17. – 5 c. turquoise and black .. 15 10
18. – 6 c. black, purple and lilac 20 10
19. – 10 c. black, blue & cobalt 20 10
20. – 15 c. black, green & turq. 20 30

3. Great Amberjack.

1968. Fishes. Multicoloured.

20a. 20 c. Great Barracuda .. 1·50 2·00
21. 25 c. Type **3** 40 25
22. 35 c. French Angelfish .. 40 25
23. 50 c. Porkfish 40 45
24. 73 c. Striped Parrotfish .. 70 80
25. $1 Longspine Squirrelfish 85 2·00
26. $2·50 Catalufa .. .. 1·50 5·00
27. $5 Blue Chromis .. .. 3·75 7·50

10. Sprinting and Aztec Sun-stone.

1968. Olympic Games, Mexico. Multicoloured.

28. 25 c. Type **10** 20 25
29. – 35 c. High-jumping and Aztec statue 25 25
30. – 75 c. Yachting and Aztec lion mask 40 45

14. "The Ascension" (Orcagna).

1969. Easter Commem.

32. **14.** 25 c. black and blue .. 15 45
33. – 35 c. black and red .. 15 50
34. – 75 c. black and lilac .. 15 55

15. Scout Enrolment Ceremony.

1969. 3rd Caribbean Scout Jamboree. Mult.

35. 25 c. Type **15** 30 55
36. 35 c. Scouts around camp fire 45 65
37. 75 c. Sea Scouts rowing boat 55 85

18. "Sistine Madonna" (Raphael).

1969. Christmas.

38. **18.** ½ c. multicoloured .. 10 10
39. 25 c. multicoloured .. 10 15
40. 35 c. multicoloured .. 10 20
41. 35 c. multicoloured .. 20 35

19. William I (1066-87).

1970. English Monarchs. Multicoloured.

42. 35 c. Type **19** 30 15
43. 35 c. William II (1087-1100) 15 15
44. 35 c. Henry I (1100-35) .. 15 15
45. 35 c. Stephen (1135-54) .. 15 15
46. 35 c. Henry II. (1154-89) .. 15 15
47. 35 c. Richard I (1189-99) .. 15 15
48. 35 c. John (1199-1216) .. 15 15
49. 35 c. Henry III (1216-72) .. 15 15
50. 35 c. Edward I (1272-1307) 15 15
51. 35 c. Edward II (1307-27) .. 15 15
52. 35 c. Edward III (1327-77) 15 15
53. 35 c. Richard II (1377-99) .. 15 15
54. 35 c. Henry IV (1399-1413) 15 15
55. 35 c. Henry V (1413-22) .. 15 15
56. 35 c. Henry VI (1422-61) .. 15 15
57. 35 c. Edward IV (1462-83) .. 15 15
58. 35 c. Edward V (April-June
56. 1483) 15 15
59. 35 c. Richard III (1483-85) 15 15
60. 35 c. Henry VII (1485-1509) 15 15
61. 35 c. Henry VIII (1509-47) 15 15
62. 35 c. Edward VI (1547-53) .. 15 15
63. 35 c. Lady Jane Grey (1553) 15 15
64. 35 c. Mary I (1553-8) .. 15 15
65. 35 c. Elizabeth I (1558-1603) 15 15
56. 35 c. James I (1603-25) .. 15 15
67. 35 c. Charles I (1625-49) .. 15 15
68. 35 c. Charles II (1649-1685) 15 15
69. 35 c. James II (1685-1688) .. 15 15
70. 35 c. William III (1689-1702) 15 15
71. 35 c. Mary II (1689-1694) .. 15 15
72. 35 c. Anne (1702-1714) .. 15 15
73. 35 c. George I (1714-1727) .. 15 15
74. 35 c. George II (1727-1760) 15 15
75. 35 c. George III (1760-1820) 15 15
76. 35 c. George IV (1820-1830) 15 15
77. 35 c. William IV (1830-1837) 15 15
78. 35 c. Victoria (1837-1901) .. 15 15

See also Nos. 710/15.

1970. No. 12 surch.

79. **2.** 20 c. on ½ c. brn., blk. & pink 10 20

21. "The Way to Calvary" (Ugolino).

1970. Easter. Paintings. Multicoloured.

80. 25 c. Type **21** 15 30
81. 35 c. "The Deposition from the Cross" (Ugolino) .. 15 30
82. 75 c. Crucifix (The Master of S. Francesco) 15 35

22. Oliver is introduced to Fagin ("Oliver Twist").

1970. Death Centenary of Charles Dickens. Multicoloured.

83. 20 c. Type **22** 10 15
84. 75 c. Dickens and scene from "The Old Curiosity Shop" 20 40

23. "Madonna of the Meadows" (G. Bellini).

1970. Christmas. Multicoloured.

85. 20 c. Type **23** 10 25
86. 50 c. "Madonna, Child and Angels" (from Wilton diptych) 15 30
87. 75 c. "The Nativity" (della Francesca) 15 35

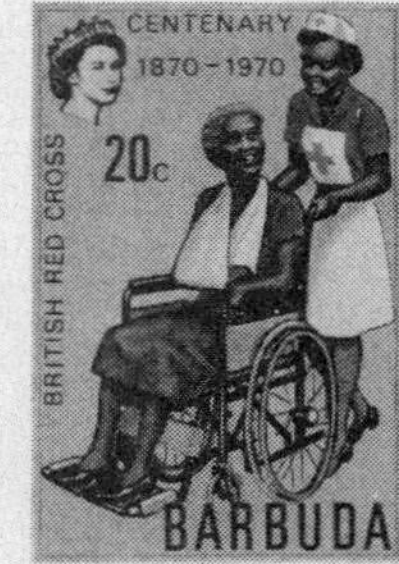

24. Nurse with Patient in Wheelchair.

1970. Cent. of British Red Cross. Mult.

88. 20 c. Type **24** 15 30
89. 35 c. Nurse giving Patient Magazines (horiz.) .. 20 40
90. 75 c. Nurse and Mother weighing Baby (horiz.) .. 25 70

25. "Angel with Vases".

1971. Easter. "Mond" Crucifixion by Raphael. Multicoloured.

91. 35 c. Type **25** 15 65
92. 50 c. "Christ crucified" .. 15 75
93. 75 c. "Angel with vase" .. 15 80

26. Martello Tower.

1971. Tourism. Multicoloured.

94. 20 c. Type **26** 10 25
95. 25 c. Sailing boats 10 30
96. 50 c. Hotel bungalows .. 15 35
97. 75 c. Government House and Mystery Stone 20 40

27. "The Granducal Madonna" (Raphael).

1971. Christmas. Multicoloured.

98. ½ c. Type **27** 10 10
99. 35 c. "The Asidei Madonna" (Raphael) 10 20
100. 50 c. "The Madonna and Child" (Botticelli) .. 15 25
101. 75 c. "The Madonna of the Trees" (Bellini) .. 15 30

Four stamps to commemorate the 500th Birth Anniv. of Durer were prepared in late 1971, but their issue was not authorised by the Antigua Government.

1973. Royal Wedding. Nos. 370/1 of Antigua optd. **BARBUDA** twice.

102. **106.** 35 c. multicoloured .. 10·00 4·25
103. $2 multicoloured .. 5·00 2·25

1973. Ships. Nos. 269/85 of Antigua optd. **BARBUDA.**

116. **92.** ½ c. multicoloured .. 15 20
104. – 1 c. multicoloured .. 15 20
105. – 2 c. multicoloured .. 25 25
117. – 3 c. multicoloured .. 25 25
106. – 4 c. multicoloured .. 30 30
107. – 5 c. multicoloured .. 40 40
108. – 6 c. multicoloured .. 40 40
109. – 10 c. multicoloured .. 45 45
118. – 15 c. multicoloured .. 35 50
110. – 20 c. multicoloured .. 55 60
111. – 25 c. multicoloured .. 55 60
112. – 35 c. multicoloured .. 55 70
113. – 50 c. multicoloured .. 55 70
114. – 75 c. multicoloured .. 55 70
119. – $1 multicoloured .. 55 70
115. – $2·50 multicoloured .. 1·50 1·50
121. – $5 multicoloured .. 1·75 2·50

1973. Military Uniforms. Nos. 353, 355 and 357 of Antigua optd. **BARBUDA.**

122. ½ c. multicoloured 10 10
123. 20 c. multicoloured .. 10 10
124. 75 c. multicoloured .. 30 15

1973. Carnival. Nos. 360/2 of Antigua optd. **BARBUDA.**

126. 20 c. multicoloured .. 10 10
127. 35 c. multicoloured .. 10 10
128. 75 c. multicoloured .. 20 25

1973. Christmas. Nos. 364/68 of Antigua optd. **BARBUDA.**

130. **105.** 3 c. multicoloured .. 10 10
131. – 5 c. multicoloured .. 10 10
132. – 20 c. multicoloured .. 10 10
133. – 35 c. multicoloured .. 15 15
134. – $1 multicoloured .. 30 30

1973. Honeymoon Visit. Nos. 373/4 of Antigua additionally optd. **BARBUDA.**

136. 35 c. multicoloured .. 40 20
137. $2 multicoloured .. 1·25 60

1974. University of West Indies. Nos. 376/9 of Antigua optd. **BARBUDA.**

139. 5 c. multicoloured .. 10 10
140. 20 c. multicoloured .. 10 10
141. 35 c. multicoloured .. 15 15
142. 75 c. multicoloured .. 15 15

1974. Military Uniforms. Nos. 380/4 of Antigua optd. **BARBUDA.**

143. ½ c. multicoloured .. 10 10
144. 10 c. multicoloured .. 10 10
145. 20 c. multicoloured .. 20 10
146. 35 c. multicoloured .. 25 10
147. 75 c. multicoloured .. 45 25

1974. Centenary of U.P.U. (1st issue). Nos. 386/92 of Antigua optd. with either a or b.

(a). **BARBUDA 13 JULY 1922.**

148. ½ c. multicoloured .. 10 10
150. 1 c. multicoloured .. 10 10
152. 2 c. multicoloured .. 15 15
154. 5 c. multicoloured .. 15 15
156. 20 c. multicoloured .. 40 70
158. 35 c. multicoloured .. 80 1·50
160. $1 multicoloured .. 2·25 4·00

(b). **BARBUDA 15 SEPT. 1874 G.P.U.** ("General Postal Union").

149. ½ c. multicoloured .. 10 10
151. 1 c. multicoloured .. 10 10
153. 2 c. multicoloured .. 15 15
155. 5 c. multicoloured .. 15 15
157. 20 c. multicoloured .. 40 70
159. 35 c. multicoloured .. 80 1·50
161. $1 multicoloured .. 2·25 4·00

1974. Antiguan Steel Bands. Nos. 394/97 of Antigua optd. **BARBUDA.**

163. 5 c. dull red, red & blk. .. 10 10
164. 20 c. brn., light brn. & blk. 10 10
165. 35 c. light grn., grn. & blk. 10 10
166. 75 c. dull blue, blue & blk. 20 20

39. Footballers.

1974. World Cup Football Championships (1st issue).

168. **39.** 35 c. multicoloured .. 10 10
169. – $1·20 multicoloured .. 25 35
170. – $2·50 multicoloured .. 35 50

DESIGNS: $1·20, $2·50, Footballers in action similar to Type **39**.

1974. World Cup Football Championships (2nd issue). Nos. 399/402 of Antigua optd. **BARBUDA.**

172. **111.** 5 c. multicoloured .. 10 10
173. – 35 c. multicoloured .. 10 10
174. – 75 c. multicoloured .. 15 15
175. – $1 multicoloured .. 20 25

41. Ship Letter of 1833.

1974. Centenary of Universal Postal Union. (2nd issue). Multicoloured.

177. 35 c. Type **41** .. 15 15
178. $1·20 Stamps and postmark of 1922 .. .. 50 75
179. $2·50 Mailplane over map of Barbuda .. .. 75 1·25

42. Greater Amberjack.

1974. Multicoloured.

181. ½ c. Oleander, Rose Bay .. 10 30
182. 1 c. Blue Petrea 10 30
183. 2 c. Poinsettia 10 30
184. 3 c. Cassia tree 10 30
185. 4 c. Type **42** 10 30
186. 5 c. Holy Trinity School .. 15 15
187. 6 c. Snorkeling 15 20
188. 10 c. Pilgrim Holiness Church 15 20
189. 15 c. New Cottage Hospital 15 20
190. 20 c. Post Office and Treasury 15 20
191. 25 c. Island jetty and boats 30 30
192. 35 c. Martello Tower .. 30 30
193. 50 c. Warden's House .. 30 30
194. 75 c. Inter-island aircraft 75 1·00
195. $1 Tortoise 70 80
196. $2·50 Spiny lobster .. 1·50 2·00
197. $5 Magnificent Frigate Bird 9·00 5·50
197b. $10 Hibiscus .. .. 9·00 9·50

The 50 c. to $1 are 39 × 25 mm., $2.50 and $5 45 × 29 mm., $10 34 × 48 mm.

The ½ to 3 c., 25 c. and $10 are vert.

1974. Birth Cent. of Sir Winston Churchill. (1st issue). Nos. 408/11 of Antigua optd. **BARBUDA.**

198. **113.** 5 c. multicoloured .. 10 10
199. – 35 c. multicoloured .. 20 15
200. – 75 c. multicoloured .. 35 45
201. – $1 multicoloured .. 55 70

43. Churchill making Broadcast.

1974. Birth Centenary of Sir Winston Churchill. (2nd issue). Multicoloured.

203. 5 c. Type **43** 10 10
204. 35 c. Churchill and Chartwell 10 10
205. 75 c. Churchill painting .. 20 20
206. $1 Churchill making "V"-sign 25 30

1974. Christmas. Nos. 413/20 of Antigua optd. **BARBUDA.**

208. **114.** ½ c. multicoloured .. 10 10
209. – 1 c. multicoloured .. 10 10
210. – 2 c. multicoloured .. 10 10
211. – 3 c. multicoloured .. 10 10
212. – 5 c. multicoloured .. 10 10
213. – 20 c. multicoloured .. 10 10
214. – 35 c. multicoloured .. 15 15
215. – 75 c. multicoloured .. 30 30

1975. Nelson's Dockyard. Nos. 427/31 of Antigua optd. **BARBUDA.**

217. **116.** 5 c. multicoloured .. 15 15
218. – 15 c. multicoloured .. 25 25
219. – 35 c. multicoloured .. 35 35
220. – 50 c. multicoloured .. 50 50
221. – $1 multicoloured .. 80 80

45. Ships of the Line.

1975. Sea Battles. Battle of the Saints, 1782. Multicoloured.

223. 35 c. Type **45** .. .. 2·00 85
224. 50 c. H.M.S. "Ramillies" .. 2·00 1·00
225. 75 c. Ships firing broadsides 2·25 1·25
226. 95 c. Sailors fleeing burning ship .. .. 2·50 1·50

1975. "Apollo-Soyuz" Space Project. No. 197 optd. **U.S.A.-U.S.S.R. SPACE CO-OPERATION 1975** with **APOLLO** (No. 227) and **SOYUZ** (No. 228).

227. $5 multicoloured .. .. 6·50 9·00
228. $5 multicoloured .. .. 6·50 9·00

47. Officer, 65th Foot, 1763.

1975. Military Uniforms. Multicoloured.

229. 35 c. Type **47** 75 75
230. 50 c. Grenadier, 27th Foot 1701-10 .. .. 90 90
231. 75 c. Officer, 21st Foot, 1793-6 .. .. .. 1·00 1·00
232. 95 c. Officer, Royal Regt. of Artillery, 1800 .. .. 1·25 1·25

1975. 25th Anniv. of United Nations. Nos. 203/6 optd. **30th ANNIVERSARY UNITED NATIONS 1945–1975.**

233. **43.** 5 c. multicoloured .. 10 10
234. – 35 c. multicoloured .. 10 15
235. – 75 c. multicoloured .. 15 20
236. – $1 multicoloured .. 20 30

1975. Christmas. Nos. 457/64 of Antigua optd. **BARBUDA.**

237. **121.** ½ c. multicoloured .. 10 10
238. – 1 c. multicoloured .. 10 10
239. – 2 c. multicoloured .. 10 10
240. – 3 c. multicoloured .. 10 10
241. – 5 c. multicoloured .. 10 10
242. – 10 c. multicoloured .. 10 10
243. – 35 c. multicoloured .. 15 20
244. – $2 multicoloured .. 60 1·00

1975. World Cup Cricket Winners Nos. 466/8 of Antigua optd. **BARBUDA.**

246. **122.** 5 c. multicoloured .. 75 85
247. – 35 c. multicoloured .. 1·50 1·75
248. – $2 multicoloured .. 3·25 4·00

51. Surrender of Cornwallis at Yorktown (Trumbull).

1976. Bicent. of American Revolution. Mult.

249. 15 c. } Type **51** 15 15
250. 15 c. } 15 15
251. 15 c. } 15 15
252. 35 c. } The .. 30 30
253. 35 c. } Battle of .. 30 30
254. 35 c. } Princetown .. 30 30
255. $1 } Surrender of .. 60 50
256. $1 } General Burgoyne .. 60 50
257. $1 } at Saratoga .. 60 50
258. $2 } Jefferson presenting .. 90 80
259. $2 } Declaration of .. 90 80
260. $2 } Independence .. 90 80

Type **51** shows the left-hand stamp of the 15 c. design.

52. Bananaquits.

1976. Birds. Multicoloured.

262 35 c. Type **52** .. .. 2·50 70
263 50 c. Blue-hooded euphonia 2·75 80
264 75 c. Royal tern .. .. 3·00 90
265 90 c. Killdeer .. .. 3·25 1·25
266 $1.25 Common cowbird .. 4·50 1·50
267 $2 Purple gallinule .. 6·00 2·25

1976. Royal Visit to the U.S.A. Nos. 249/60 additionally inscr. "H.M. QUEEN ELIZABETH ROYAL VISIT 6th JULY. H.R.H. DUKE OF EDINBURGH".

268. 15 c. multicoloured .. 15 15
269. 15 c. multicoloured .. 15 15
270. 15 c. multicoloured .. 15 15
271. 35 c. multicoloured .. 30 30
272. 35 c. multicoloured .. 30 30
273. 35 c. multicoloured .. 30 30
274. $1 multicoloured .. 60 60
275. $1 multicoloured .. 60 60
276. $1 multicoloured .. 60 60
277. $2 multicoloured .. 90 90
278. $2 multicoloured .. 90 90
279. $2 multicoloured .. 90 90

1976. Christmas. Nos. 514/8 of Antigua optd. **BARBUDA.**

281. **128.** 8 c. multicoloured .. 10 10
282. – 10 c. multicoloured .. 10 10
283. – 15 c. multicoloured .. 10 10
284. – 50 c. multicoloured .. 15 15
285. – $1 multicoloured .. 25 30

1976. Olympic Games, Montreal. Nos. 495/501 of Antigua optd. **BARBUDA.**

286. **125.** ½ c. brn., yell. and blk. 10 10
287. – 1 c. violet and black .. 10 10
288. – 2 c. green and black .. 10 10
289. – 15 c. blue and black .. 10 10
290. – 30 c. brn., yell. and blk. 10 10
291. – $1 orge., red and black 20 20
292. – $2 rd and black .. 35 35

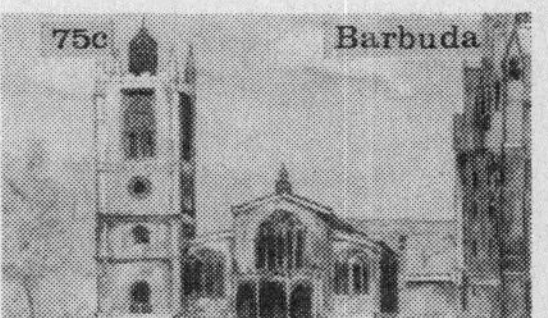

55. P.O. Tower, Telephones and Alexander Graham Bell.

1977. Centenary of First Telephone Transmission. Multicoloured.

294. 75 c. Type **55** 30 35
295. $1.25 T.V. Transmission by Satellite 45 55
296. $2 Globe showing satellite transmission scheme .. 65 75

56. St. Margaret's Church, Westminster.

1977. Silver Jubilee (1st issue). Multicoloured.

298. 75 c. Type **56** 15 15
299. 75 c. Street decorations .. 15 15
300. 75 c. Westminster Abbey 15 15
301. $1.25 Part of Coronation procession 25 25
302. $1.25 Coronation Coach .. 25 25
303. $1.25 Postillions 25 25

1977. Nos. 469/86 of Antigua optd. **BARBUDA.**
305. ½ c. Antillean crested hummingbird 20 20
306. 1 c. Imperial amazon 30 20
307. 2 c. Zenaida dove 30 20
308. 3 c. Loggerhead kingbird 30 20
309. 4 c. Red-necked pigeon 30 20
310. 5 c. Rufous-throated solitaire 30 20
311. 6 c. Orchid tree 25 20
312. 10 c. Bougainvillea 25 20
313. 15 c. Geiger tree 25 25
314. 20 c. Flamboyant 30 25
315. 25 c. Hibiscus 30 25
316. 35 c. Flame of the Wood 35 30
317. 50 c. Cannon at Fort James 40 40
318. 75 c. Premier's Office 40 40
319. $1 Potworks Dam 50 60
320. $2.50 Irrigation scheme 1·25 1·60
321. $5 Government House 2·75 3·25
322. $10 Coolidge Airport 5·50 7·50

1977. Silver Jubilee (2nd issue). Nos. 526/30 of Antigua optd. **BARBUDA.** (a) Perf.
323. 10 c. Royal Family 20 25
324. 30 c. Royal visit, 1966 40 45
325. 50 c. The Queen enthroned 60 70
326. 90 c. The Queen after Coronation 1·10 1·40
327. $2.50 The Queen and Prince Charles 3·00 3·75
(b) Roul. × imperf. Self-adhesive.
329. 50 c. Queen after Coronation 1·00 1·50
330. $5 The Queen and Prince Philip 14·00 16·00
Nos. 329/30 come from booklets.

1977. Caribbean Scout Jamboree, Jamaica. Nos. 534/40 of Antigua optd. **BARBUDA.**
331. ½ c. Type **131** 10 10
332. 1 c. Hiking 10 10
333. 2 c. Rock-climbing 10 10
334. 10 c. Cutting logs 10 10
335. 30 c. Map and sign reading 40 40
336. 50 c. First aid 55 55
337. $2 Rafting 2·00 2·00

1977. 21st Anniv. of Carnival. Nos. 542/46 of Antigua optd. **BARBUDA.**
339. 10 c. Type **312** 10 10
340. 30 c. Carnival Queen 10 10
341. 50 c. Butterfly costume 15 20
342. 90 c. Queen of the Band 20 30
343. $1 Calypso King and Queen 25 40

61. Royal Yacht "Britannia".

1977. Royal Visit (1st issue). Multicoloured.
345. 50 c. Type **61** 25 20
346. $1·50 Jubilee emblem 40 35
347. $2·50 Union Jack and flag of Antigua 60 50

1977. Royal Visit (2nd issue). Nos. 548/52 of Antigua optd. **BARBUDA.**
349. 10 c. Royal Family 15 10
350. 30 c. Queen Elizabeth and Prince Philip in car 30 15
351. 50 c. Queen enthroned 40 20
352. 90 c. Queen after Coronation 70 30
353. $2·50 The Queen and Prince Charles 1·75 80

1977. Christmas. Nos. 554/60 of Antigua optd. **BARBUDA.**
355. ½ c. Type **134** 10 10
356. 1 c. Crivelli 10 10
357. 2 c. Lotto 10 10
358. 8 c. Pontormo 10 10
359. 10 c. Tura (different) 10 10
360. 25 c. Lotto (different) 15 10
361. $2 Crivelli (different) 45 45

64. Zeppelin "LZ 1".

1977. Special Events, 1977. Multicoloured.
363. 75 c. Type **64** 50 35
364. 75 c. German Battleship and Naval Airship "L 31" 50 35
365. 75 c. "Graf Zeppelin" in hangar 50 35
366. 75 c. Military Airship gondola 50 35
367. 95 c. Sputnik 1 70 35
368. 95 c. Vostok rocket 70 35
369. 95 c. Voskhod rocket 70 35
370. 95 c. Space walk 70 35
371. $1·25 Fuelling for flight 1·40 45
372. $1·25 Leaving New York 1·40 45
373. $1·25 "Spirit of St. Louis" 1·40 45
374. $1·25 Welcome in England 1·40 45
375. $2 Lion of England 2·00 70
376. $2 Unicorn of Scotland 2·00 70
377. $2 Yale of Beaufort 2·00 70
378. $2 Falcon of Plantagenets 2·00 70
379. $5 } 3·00 2·00
380. $5 } "Daniel in the Lions 3·00 2·00
381. $5 } Den" (Rubens) 3·00 2·00
382. $5 } 3·00 2·00
EVENTS: 75 c. 75th Anniv. of Navigable Airships. 95 c. 20th Anniv. of U.S.S.R. Space Programme. $1·25, 50th Anniv. of Lindbergh's Transatlantic Flight. $2, Silver Jubilee of Queen Elizabeth II. $5, 400th Birth Anniv. of Rubens.
Nos. 379/82 form a composite design.

1978. 10th Anniv. of Statehood. Nos. 562/6 of Antigua optd. **BARBUDA.**
384. 10 c. Type **135** 10 10
385. 15 c. State flag 10 10
386. 50 c. Police band 20 15
387. 90 c. Premier V. C. Bird 20 20
388. $2 State Coat of Arms 40 40

66. "Pieta" (sculpture) (detail).

1978. Easter. Paintings and Sculptures by Michelangelo. Multicoloured.
390. 75 c. Type **66** 15 15
391. 95 c. "The Holy Family" 20 20
392. $1·25 "Libyan sibyl" (from the Sistine Chapel) 25 25
393. $2 "The Flood" (from the Sistine Chapel) 35 35

1978. 75th Anniv. of Powered Flight. Nos. 568/74 of Antigua optd. **BARBUDA.**
395. ½ c. "Glider III", 1902 10 10
396. 1 c. "Flyer I", 1903 10 10
397. 2 c. Launch system and engine 10 10
398. 10 c. Orville Wright (vert.) 10 10
399. 50 c. "Flyer III", 1905 25 15
400. 90 c. Wilbur Wright (vert.) 35 15
401. $2 Wright "Model B", 1910 60 45

1978. Sailing Week. Nos. 576/79 of Antigua optd. **BARBUDA.**
403. 10 c. Sunfish regatta 15 10
404. 50 c. Fishing and work boat race 35 25
405. 90 c. Curtain Bluff race 40 35
406. $2 Power boat rally 75 75

68. St. Edward's Crown.

1978. 25th Anniv. of Coronation. (1st issue). Multicoloured.
408. 75 c. Type **68** 15 15
409. 75 c. Imperial State Crown 15 15
410. $1.50 Queen Mary's Crown 25 25
411. $1.50 Queen Mother's Crown 25 25
412. $2.50 Queen Consort's Crown 45 45
413. $2.50 Queen Victoria's Crown 45 45

1978. 25th Anniv. of Coronation. (2nd issue). Nos. 581/5 of Antigua optd. **BARBUDA.**
415. 10 c. Queen Elizabeth and Prince Philip 10 10
416. 30 c. The Crowning 10 10
417. 50 c. Coronation procession 15 15
418. 90 c. Queen seated in St. Edward's Chair 20 20
419. $2.50 Queen wearing Imperial State Crown 50 60

1978. 25th Anniv. of Coronation. (3rd issue). As Nos. 587/9 of Antigua additionally inscr. "BARBUDA".
421. 25 c. Glass Coach 1·25 1·75
422. 50 c. Irish State Coach 1·25 1·75
423. $5 Coronation Coach 3·50 4·00

1978. World Cup Football Championship, Argentina. Nos. 590/2 of Antigua optd. **BARBUDA.**
424. 10 c. Player running with ball 10 10
425. 15 c. Players in front of goal 10 10
426. $3 Referee and player 1·00 1·25

1978. Flowers. As Nos. 594/7 of Antigua optd. **BARBUDA.**
428. 25 c. Petrea 25 30
429. 50 c. Sunflower 50 60
430. 90 c. Frangipani 70 80
431. $2 Passion Flower 1·25 1·60

1978. Christmas. As Nos. 599/601 of Antigua optd. **BARBUDA.**
433. 8 c. "St. Idefonso receiving the Chasuble from the Virgin" 10 10
434. 25 c. "The Flight of St. Barbara" 15 15
435. $2 "Madonna and child, with St. Joseph, John the Baptist and Donor" 60 1·25

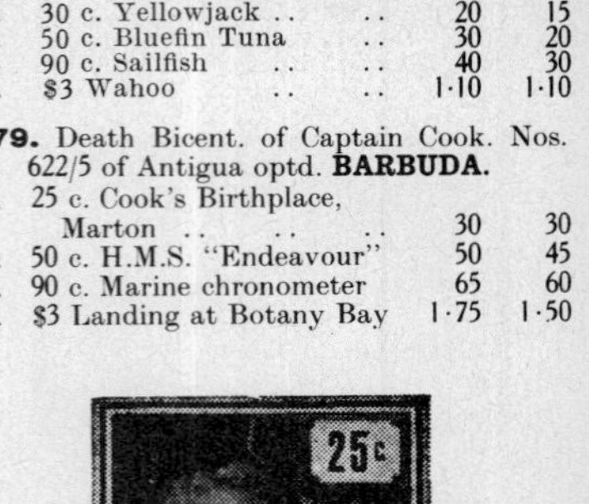

70. Blackbar Soldierfish.

1978. Flora and Fauna. Multicoloured.
437 25 c. Type **70** 1·25 1·25
438 50 c. "Cynthia cardui" (butterfly) 2·00 2·00
439 75 c. Dwarf poinciana 2·50 2·50
440 95 c. "Heliconius charithonia" (butterfly) 3·25 3·25
441 $1.25 Bougainvillea 3·25 3·25

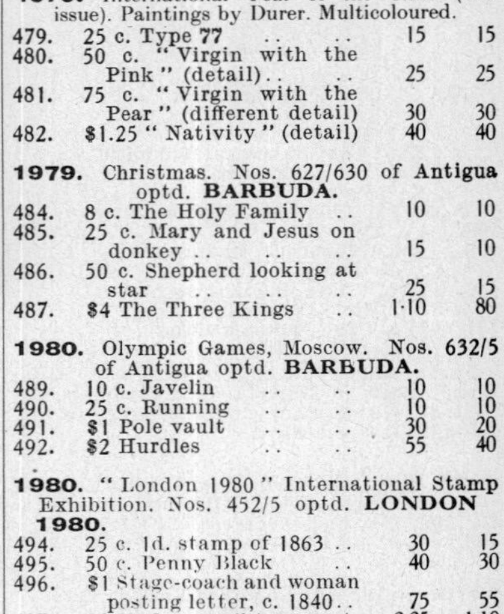

71. Footballers and World Cup. 72. Sir Rowland Hill.

1978. Anniversaries and Events.
442. 75 c. Type **71** 65 65
443. 95 c. Wright Brothers and "Flyer I" (horiz.) 75 75
444. $1.25 "Double Eagle II" and map of Atlantic (horiz.) 90 90
445. $2 Prince Philip paying homage to the Queen 2·75 2·75
EVENTS: 75 c. Argentina—Winners of World Cup Football Championship. 95 c. 75th anniv. of powered flight. $1.25, First Atlantic Crossing by balloon. $2, 25th anniv. of Coronation.

1979. Death Centenary of Sir Rowland Hill. (1st issue). Multicoloured.
447. 75 c. Type **72** 45 50
448. 95 c. Mail coach, 1840 (horiz.) 55 60
449. $1.25, London's first pillar box, 1855 (horiz.) 60 70
450. $2 Mail leaving St. Martin's Le Grand Post Office, London 90 95

1979. Death Centenary of Sir Rowland Hill. (2nd issue). Nos. 603/6 of Antigua optd. **BARBUDA.**
452. 25 c. 1d. Stamp of 1863 15 15
453. 50 c. Penny Black 20 20
454. $1 Stage-coach and woman posting letter, c. 1840 35 30
455. $2 Modern mail transport 80 60

1979. Easter. Works of Durer. Nos. 608/10 of Antigua optd. **BARBUDA.**
457. 10 c. multicoloured 10 10
458. 50 c. multicoloured 20 20
459. $4 black, mauve & yellow 90 1·10

74. Passengers alighting from British Airways Boeing "747".

1979. 30th Anniv. of International Civil Aviation Organization. Multicoloured.
461. 75 c. Type **74** 45 80
462. 95 c. Air traffic control 50 90
463. $1.25 Ground crew-man directing Boeing "707" on runway 60 1·10

1979. International Year of the Child (1st issue). Nos. 612/15 of Antigua optd. **BARBUDA.**
464. 25 c. Yacht 20 15
465. 50 c. Rocket 35 25
466. 90 c. Car 50 35
467. $2 Toy train 1·25 60

1979. Fishes. Nos. 617/20 of Antigua optd. **BARBUDA.**
469. 30 c. Yellowjack 20 15
470. 50 c. Bluefin Tuna 30 20
471. 90 c. Sailfish 40 30
472. $3 Wahoo 1·10 1·10

1979. Death Bicent. of Captain Cook. Nos. 622/5 of Antigua optd. **BARBUDA.**
474. 25 c. Cook's Birthplace, Marton 30 30
475. 50 c. H.M.S. "Endeavour" 50 45
476. 90 c. Marine chronometer 65 60
477. $3 Landing at Botany Bay 1·75 1·50

77. "Virgin with the Pear"

1979. International Year of the Child (2nd issue). Paintings by Durer. Multicoloured.
479. 25 c. Type **77** 15 15
480. 50 c. "Virgin with the Pink" (detail) 25 25
481. 75 c. "Virgin with the Pear" (different detail) 30 30
482. $1.25 "Nativity" (detail) 40 40

1979. Christmas. Nos. 627/630 of Antigua optd. **BARBUDA.**
484. 8 c. The Holy Family 10 10
485. 25 c. Mary and Jesus on donkey 15 10
486. 50 c. Shepherd looking at star 25 15
487. $4 The Three Kings 1·10 80

1980. Olympic Games, Moscow. Nos. 632/5 of Antigua optd. **BARBUDA.**
489. 10 c. Javelin 10 10
490. 25 c. Running 10 10
491. $1 Pole vault 30 20
492. $2 Hurdles 55 40

1980. "London 1980" International Stamp Exhibition. Nos. 452/5 optd. **LONDON 1980.**
494. 25 c. 1d. stamp of 1863 30 15
495. 50 c. Penny Black 40 30
496. $1 Stage-coach and woman posting letter, c. 1840 75 55
497. $2 Modern mail transport 2·25 1·10

80. "Apollo II" Crew Badge.

1980. 10th Anniv. of "Apollo II" Moon Landing. Multicoloured.
498. 75 c. Type **80** 25 25
499. 95 c. Plaque left on Moon 30 30
500. $1.25 Rejoining the mother-ship 40 40
501. $2 "Lunar Module" 65 65

81. American Widgeon.

1980. Birds. Multicoloured.
503. 1 c. Type **81** 30 15
504. 2 c. Snowy plover 35 15
505. 4 c. Rose-breasted grosbeak 40 20
506. 6 c. Mangrove cuckoo 40 20
507. 10 c. Adelaide's warbler 40 20
508. 15 c. Scaly-breasted thrasher 45 25
509. 20 c. Yellow-crowned night heron 45 25
510. 25 c. Bridled quail dove 45 25
511. 35 c. Carib grackle 55 30
512. 50 c. Northern pintail 65 35
513. 75 c. Black-whispered vireo 80 45

514. $1 Blue-winged teal .. 1·00 70
515. $1.50 Green-throated carib (vert.) .. .. .. 1·25 80
516. $2 Red-necked pigeon (vert.) .. .. .. 2·00 1·25
517. $2.50 Wied's crested fly-catcher (vert.) .. .. 2·50 1·50
518. $5 Yellow-bellied sap-sucker (vert.) .. .. 3·25 2·50
519. $7.50 Caribbean elaenia (vert.) .. .. .. 4·25 4·00
520. $10 Great egret (vert.) .. 5·00 5·00

1980. Famous Works of Art. Nos. 651/7 of Antigua optd. **BARBUDA.**
521. 10 c. " David " (statue, Donatello) 10 10
522. 30 c. " The Birth of Venus " (painting, Sandro Botticelli) 15 15
523. 50 c. " Reclining Couple " (sarcophagus), Cerveteri 20 20
524. 90 c. " The Garden of Earthly Delights " (painting, Hieronymus Bosch) .. 25 25
525. $1 " Portinari Altarpiece " (painting, Hugo van der Goes) 25 25
526. $4 " Eleanora of Toledo and her Son Giovanni de'Medici (painting, Agnolo Bronzino) 80 80

1980. 75th Anniv. of Rotary International. Nos. 651/4 of Antigua optd. **BARBUDA.**
528. 30 c. Rotary Headquarters 15 15
529. 50 c. Antigua Rotary banner 20 20
530. 90 c. Map of Antigua .. 25 25
531. $3 Paul P. Harris (founder) 65 65

1980. 80th Birthday of The Queen Mother. Nos. 663/4 of Antigua optd. **BARBUDA.**
533. 10 c. multicoloured .. 30 15
534. $2.50 multicoloured .. 3·00 1·50

1980. Birds. Nos. 666/9 of Antigua optd. **BARBUDA.**
536. 10 c. Ringed Kingfisher .. 65 40
537. 30 c. Plain Pigeon .. 1·00 55
538. $1 Green-throated Carib 1·75 1·40
539. $2 Black necked Stilt .. 2·50 2·75

1981. Sugar Cane Railway Locomotives. Nos. 681/4 of Antigua optd. **BARBUDA**
541. 25 c. Diesel locomotive No. 15 .. .. .. 80 25
542. 50 c. Narrow-gauge steam locomotive .. .. 1·00 35
543. 90 c. Diesel locomotive Nos. 1 and 10 .. .. 1·25 45
544. $3 Steam locomotive hauling sugar cane .. .. 2·50 1·40

84. Florence Nightingale.

1981. Famous Women.
546. 84. 50 c. multicoloured .. 30 30
547. – 90 c. multicoloured .. 55 55
548. – $1 multicoloured .. 60 60
549. – $4 black, brown & lilac 1·75 1·75
DESIGNS: 90 c. Marie Curie. $1 Amy Johnson. $4 Eleanor Roosevelt.

85. Goofy in Motor-boat.

1981. Walt Disney Cartoon Characters. Multicoloured.
550. 10 c. Type **85** 25 10
551. 20 c. Donald Duck reversing car into sea 30 15
552. 25 c. Mickey Mouse asking tug-boat to take on more than it can handle .. 40 20
553. 30 c. Porpoise turning tables on Goofy 50 25
554. 35 c. Goofy in sailing boat 50 25
555. 40 c. Mickey Mouse and boat being lifted out of water by fish 60 30
556. 75 c. Donald Duck fishing for flying-fish with butterfly net 75 45
557. $1 Minnie Mouse in brightly decorated sailing boat .. 85 55
558. $2 Chip and Dale on floating ship-in-bottle .. 1·60 1·10

1981. Birth Centenary of Picasso. Nos. 697/700 of Antigua optd. with **BARBUDA.**
560. 10 c. " Pipes of Pan " .. 10 10
561. 50 c. " Seated Harlequin " 25 25
562. 90 c. " Paulo as Harlequin " 45 45
563. $4 " Mother and Child " 1·60 1·60

87. Buckingham Palace. 88.
(Illust. reduced. Actual size 65 mm × 26 mm).

1981. Royal Wedding. (1st issue). Buildings. Each printed in black on either pink, green or lilac backgrounds.
565. $1 } Type 87/8 .. .. 70 70
566. $1 } .. 70 70
567. $1.50 } Caernarvon Castle 85 85
568. $1.50 } .. 85 85
569. $4 } Highgrove House .. 1·75 1·75
570. $4 } .. 1·75 1·75
Same prices for any background colour. The two versions of each value form composite designs.

1981. Royal Wedding (2nd issue). Nos. 702/5 of Antigua optd. **BARBUDA.**
572. 25 c. Prince Charles and Lady Diana Spencer .. 25 25
573. 50 c. Glamis Castle .. 35 35
574. $4 Prince Charles skiing .. 1·40 1·40

89. " Integration and Travel ".

1981. International Year of Disabled Persons.
576. 89. 50 c. multicoloured .. 65 25
577. – 90 c. black, orange and green 85 40
578. – $1 black, blue and green 95 45
579. – $4 black yell. and brown 2·50 1·75
DESIGNS: 90 c. Braille and sign language. $1 " Helping hands ". $4 " Mobility aids for disabled ".

1981. Royal Wedding (3rd issue). Booklet stamps. Nos. 706/12 of Antigua optd. **BARBUDA.**
580. 25 c. Prince of Wales at Investiture, 1969 .. 25 25
581. 25 c. Prince Charles as baby, 1948 .. .. 25 25
582. $1 Prince Charles at R.A.F. College, Cranwell, 1971 45 45
583. $1 Prince Charles attending Hill House School, 1956 .. .. 45 45
584. $2 Prince Charles and Lady Diana Spencer .. 80 80
585. $2 Prince Charles at Trinity College, 1967 .. 80 80
586. $5 Prince Charles and Lady Diana .. .. 2·25 3·00

1981. Independence. No. 686/96 of Antigua additionally optd. **BARBUDA.**
587. 6 c. Orchid Tree 50 15
588. 10 c. Bougainvillea .. 55 15
589. 20 c. Flamboyant .. 70 20
590. 25 c. Hibiscus 80 25
591. 35 c. Flame of the Wood .. 90 30
592. 50 c. Cannon at Fort James 1·10 45
593. 75 c. Premier's Office .. 1·25 60
594. $1 Potworks Dam .. 1·50 65
595. $2.50 Irrigation scheme, Diamond Estate .. 3·50 2·00
596. $5 Government House and Gardens .. .. 4·25 2·75
597. $10 Coolidge International Airport .. .. 6·00 4·75

1981. 50th Anniv. of Antigua Girl Guide Movement. Nos. 713/16 of Antigua optd. **BARBUDA.**
598. 10 c. Irene Joshua (founder) 45 10
599. 50 c. Campfire sing-song .. 1·00 30
600. 90 c. Sailing .. .. 1·40 45
601. $2.50 Animal tending .. 2·75 1·40

1981. International Year of Disabled People. Sport for the Disabled. Nos. 728/31 of Antigua optd. **BARBUDA.**
603. 10 c. Swimming 30 15
604. 50 c. Discus throwing .. 65 35
605. 90 c. Archery 85 60
606. $2 Baseball .. .. 1·75 1·60

1981. Christmas. Paintings. No. 726/6 of Antigua optd. **BARBUDA.**
608. 8 c. " Holy Night " (Jacques Stella) .. 10 10
609. 30 c. " Mary with Child " (Julius Schnorr von Carolfeld) 20 20
610. $1 " Virgin and Child " (Alonso Cano) 40 40
611. $3 " Virgin and Child " (Lorenzo di Credi) .. 1·10 1·10

93. Princess of Wales.

1982. Birth of Prince William of Wales (1st issue).
613. 93. $1 multicoloured .. 50 50
614. $2.50 multicoloured .. 1·10 1·10
615. $5 multicoloured .. 2·25 2·25

1982. South Atlantic Fund. Booklet stamps. Nos 580/6 surch. **S. Atlantic Fund + 50 c.**
617. 25 c.+50 c. Prince of Wales at Investiture, 1969 .. 20 20
618. 25 c.+50 c. Prince Charles as baby, 1948 .. .. 20 20
619. $1+50 c. Prince Charles at R.A.F. College, Cranwell, 1971 .. .. 45 45
620. $1+50 c. Prince Charles attending Hill House School, 1956 .. .. 45 45
621. $2+50 c. Prince Charles and Lady Diana Spencer 75 75
622. $2+50 c. Prince Charles at Trinity College, 1967 75 75
623. $5+50 c. Prince Charles and Lady Diana .. 2·00 2·00

1982. 21st Birthday of Princess of Wales. (1st issue). As Nos. 613/16 but inscr. "Twenty First Birthday Greetings to H.R.H. The Princess of Wales."
624. $1 multicoloured .. 45 45
625. $2.50 multicoloured .. 1·25 1·25
626. $5 multicoloured .. 2·40 2·40

1982. 21st Birthday of Princess of Wales (2nd issue). Nos. 748/51 of Antigua optd. **BARBUDA MAIL.**
628. 90 c. Queen's House, Greenwich 45 45
629. $1 Prince and Princess of Wales 50 50
630. $4 Princess of Wales .. 1·50 1·50

1982. Birth of Price William of Wales (2nd issue). Nos. 757/9 of Antigua optd. **ROYAL BABY 21.6.82.**
632. 90 c. Queen's House, Grenwich 45 45
633. $1 Prince and Princess of Wales 50 50
634. $4 Princess of Wales .. 2·00 2·00

1982. Birth Centenary of Franklin D. Roosevelt and 250th Birth Anniv. of George Washington. Nos. 761/6 of Antigua optd. **BARBUDA MAIL.**
636. 10 c. Roosevelt in 1940 .. 15 10
637. 25 c. Washington as blacksmith 20 15
638. 45 c. Churchill, Roosevelt and Stalin at Yalta Conference 35 25
639. 60 c. Washington crossing Delaware 45 35
640. $1 " Roosevelt Special " train 65 55
641. $3 Portrait of Roosevelt .. 1·75 1·75

1982. Christmas. Religious Paintings by Raphael. Nos. 769/72 of Antigua optd. **BARBUDA MAIL.**
644. 10 c. " Annunciation " .. 10 10
645. 30 c. " Adoration of the Magi " 15 15
646. $1 " Presentation at the Temple " 40 40
647. $4 " Coronation of the Virgin " .. .. 1·75 1·75

1983. 500th Birth Anniv. of Raphael. Details from "Galatea" Fresco. Nos. 774/7 of Antigua optd. **BARBUDA MAIL.**
649. 45 c. Tritons and Dolphins 20 20
650. 50 c. Sea Nymph carried off by Triton 25 25
651. 60 c. Winged angel steering Dolphins (horiz.) .. 30 30
652. $4 Cupids shooting arrows 1·60 1·60

1983. Commonwealth Day. Nos. 779/82 of Antigua optd. **BARBUDA MAIL.**
654. 25 c. Pineapple produce .. 40 50
655. 45 c. Carnival 60 70
656. 60 c. Tourism 85 95
657. $3 Airport .. .. 2·25 3·00

1983. World Communications Year. Nos. 783/6 of Antigua optd. **BARBUDA MAIL.**
658. 15 c. T.V. satellite coverage of Royal Wedding .. 40 20
659. 50 c. Police communications 1·25 55
660. 60 c. House-to-diesel train telephone call .. .. 1·25 65
661. $3 Satellite earth station with planets Jupiter and Saturn .. .. .. 2·75 1·75

97. Vincenzo Lunardi's Balloon Flight, London, 1785.

1983. Bicentenary of Manned Flight. Mult.
663. $1 Type **97** 50 50
664. $1.50, Montgolfier brothers' balloon flight, Paris, 1783 75 75
665. $2.50, Blanchard and Jeffries' Cross-Channel balloon flight, 1785 .. .. 1·25 1·25

1983. Whales. Nos. 788/92 of Antigua optd. **BARBUDA MAIL.**
667. 15 c. Bottlenose Dolphin .. 65 30
668. 50 c. Finback Whale .. 1·75 90
669. 60 c. Bowhead Whale .. 2·00 1·00
670. $3 Spectacled Porpoise .. 4·25 2·75

1983. Bicentenary of Manned Flight. (2nd issue). Nos. 811/15 of Antigua optd. **BARBUDA MAIL.**
672. 30 c. Dornier " Do X " flying boat 50 25
673. 50 c. Supermarine " S.6B " seaplane 60 35
674. 60 c. Curtiss " 9C " biplane and airship U.S.S. "Akron" 75 40
675. $4 Pro Juventute balloon 3·50 3·25

1983. Nos. 565/70 surch.
677. 45 c. on $1 Type **87** .. 55 55
678. 45 c. on $1 Type **88** .. 55 55
679. 50 c. on $1.50 Caernarvon Castle 60 60
680. 50 c. on $1.50 Caernarvon Castle 60 60
681. 60 c. on $4 Highgrove House (left) 70 70
682. 60 c. on $4 Highgrove House (right) 70 70

1983. Nos. 793/810 of Antigua optd. **BARBUDA MAIL.**
683. 1 c. Cashew Nut 10 10
684. 2 c. Passion Fruit 10 10
685. 3 c. Mango 10 10
686. 5 c. Grapefruit 10 10
687. 10 c. Pawpaw 10 10
688. 15 c. Breadfruit 15 10
689. 20 c. Coconut 20 15
690. 25 c. Oleander 20 15
691. 30 c. Banana 25 20
692. 40 c. Pineapple 30 25
693. 45 c. Cordia 35 30
694. 50 c. Cassia 40 30
695. 60 c. Poui 40 30
696. $1 Frangipani 60 50
697. $2 Flamboyant .. .. 1·25 1·25
698. $2.50 Lemon .. .. 1·75 1·75
699. $5 Lignum Vitae .. .. 2·75 2·75
700. $10 National Flag and coat of arms .. .. .. 5·00 5·50

1983. Christmas. 500th Birth Anniv. of Raphael. Nos. 816/20 of Antigua optd. **BARBUDA MAIL.**
701. 10 c. multicoloured .. 10 10
702. 30 c. multicoloured .. 15 20
703. $1 multicoloured 45 50
704. $4 multicoloured .. 1·50 1·75

1983. Bicentenary (1984) of Methodist Church. Nos. 821/4 of Antigua optd. **BARBUDA MAIL.**
706. 15 c. Type **181** 20 15
707. 50 c. Nathaniel Gilbert (founder in Antigua) .. 40 30
708. 60 c. St. John Methodist Church steeple 45 35
709. $3 Ebenezer Methodist Church, St. John's .. 1·75 1·75

INDEX

Countries can be quickly located by referring to the index at the end of this volume.

100. Edward VII.

1984. Members of British Royal Family. Multicoloured.

710.	$1 Type **100**	1·25	1·25
711.	$1 George V	1·25	1·25
712.	$1 George VI	1·25	1·25
713.	$1 Elizabeth II	1·25	1·25
714.	$1 Charles, Prince of Wales	1·25	1·25
715.	$1 Prince William of Wales	1·25	1·25

1984. Olympic Games, Los Angeles (1st issue). Nos. 825/8 of Antigua optd. **BARBUDA MAIL.**

716.	25 c. Discus	15	20
717.	50 c. Gymnastics	35	40
718.	90 c. Hurdling	50	60
719.	$3 Cycling	1·25	1·50

1984. Ships. Nos. 830/3 of Antigua optd. **BARBUDA MAIL.**

721.	45 c. "Booker Vanguard" (freighter)	1·25	45
723.	50 c. "Canberra" (liner)	1·25	50
723.	60 c. Sailing boats	1·50	60
724.	$4 "Fairwind" (liner)	3·75	2·75

1984. Universal Postal Union Congress, Hamburg. Nos. 835/8 of Antigua optd. **BARBUDA MAIL.**

726.	15 c. Chenille	30	15
727.	50 c. Shell Flower	65	50
728.	60 c. Anthurium	80	60
729.	$3 Angels Trumpet	2·00	2·00

101. Olympic Stadium, Athens, 1896.

1984. Olympic Games, Los Angeles (2nd issue). Multicoloured.

731.	$1.50 Type **101**	1·00	1·10
732.	$2.50 Olympic stadium, Los Angeles, 1984	1·50	1·75
733.	$5 Athlete carrying Olympic torch	2·50	2·75

1984. Presidents of the United States of America. Nos. 856/63 of Antigua optd. **BARBUDA MAIL.**

735.	10 c. Abraham Lincoln	10	10
736.	20 c. Harry Truman	15	15
737.	30 c. Dwight Eisenhower	20	25
738.	40 c. Ronald Reagan	25	30
739.	90 c. Gettysburg Address, 1863	50	55
740.	$1.10 Formation of N.A.T.O., 1949	60	65
741.	$1.50 Eisenhower during Second World War	80	85
742.	$2 Reagan and Caribbean Basin Initiative	1·00	1·25

1984. Abolition of Slavery. Nos. 864/7 of Antigua optd. **BARBUDA MAIL.**

743.	40 c. View of Moravian Mission	30	30
744.	50 c. Antigua Courthouse, 1823	40	40
745.	60 c. Planting sugar-cane, Monks Hill	45	45
746.	$3 Boiling house, Delaps' Estate	1·90	1·90

1984. Songbirds. Nos. 869/73 of Antigua optd. **BARBUDA MAIL.**

748.	40 c. Rufous-sided towhee	45	45
749.	50 c. Parula warbler	50	50
750.	60 c. House wren	55	55
751.	$2 Ruby-crowned kinglet	1·50	1·50
752.	$3 Common flicker	2·25	2·25

1984. 450th Death Anniv. of Correggio (painter). Nos. 878/81 of Antigua optd. **BARBUDA MAIL.**

754.	25 c. "The Virgin and Infant with Angels and Cherubs"	15	20
755.	60 c. "The Four Saints"	40	45
756.	90 c. "St. Catherine"	60	65
757.	$3 "The Campori Madonna"	1·75	2·25

1984. 'Ausipex" International Stamp Exhibition, Melbourne. Australian Sports Nos. 875/6 of Antigua optd. **BARBUDA MAIL.**

759.	$1 Grass-skiing	70	75
760.	$5 Ausralian Football	3·00	3·75

1984. 150th Birth Anniv. of Edgar Degas (painter). Nos. 883/6 of Antigua optd. **BARBUDA MAIL.**

762.	15 c. "The Blue Dancers"	10	10
763.	50 c. "The Pink Dancers"	30	40
764.	70 c. "Two Dancers"	45	55
765.	$4 "Dancers at the Bar"	2·40	3·25

1985. Famous People. Nos. 888/96 of Antigua optd. **BARBUDA MAIL.**

767.	60 c. Winston Churchill	1·25	80
768.	60 c. Mahatma Gandhi	1·25	80
769.	60 c. John F. Kennedy	1·25	80
770.	60 c. Mao Tse-tung	1·25	80
771.	$1 Churchill with General De Gaulle, Paris, 1944 (horiz.)	1·75	1·00
772.	$1 Gandhi leaving London by train, 1931 (horiz.)	1·75	1·00
773.	$1 Kennedy with Chancellor Adenauer and Mayor Brandt, Berlin, 1963 (horiz.)	1·75	1·00
774.	$1 Mao Tse-tung with Lin Piao, Peking, 1969 (horiz.)	1·75	1·00

103. Lady Elizabeth Bowes-Lyon, 1907. and Camellias.

1985. The Life and Times of Queen Elizabeth the Queen Mother. Multicoloured.

776.	15 c. Type **103**	10	10
777.	45 c. Duchess of York, 1926, and "Elizabeth of Glamis" roses	25	30
778.	50 c. The Queen Mother after the Coronation, 1937	25	30
779.	60 c. In Garter robes, 1971, and Dog Roses	35	40
780.	90 c. Attending Royal Variety show, 1967, and red Hibiscus	50	55
781.	$2 The Queen Mother in 1982, and blue Plumbago	1·10	1·25
782.	$3 Receiving 82nd birthday gifts from children, and Morning Glory	1·60	1·75

104. Roseate Tern.

1985. Birth Bicentenary of John J. Audubon (ornithologist) (1st issue). Designs showing original paintings. Multicoloured.

783.	45 c. Type **104**	35	30
784.	50 c. Mangrove Cuckoo	35	30
785.	60 c. Yellow-crowned Night Heron	45	40
786.	$5 Brown Pelican	3·00	3·25

See also Nos. 794/7 and 914/17.

1985. Centenary (1986) of Statue of Liberty. Nos. 907/13 of Antigua optd. **BARBUDA MAIL.**

787.	25 c. Torch from statue in Madison Square Park, 1885	15	20
788.	30 c. Statue of Liberty and scaffolding ("Restoration and Renewal") (vert.)	15	20
789.	50 c. Frederic Bartholdi (sculptor) supervising construction, 1876	25	30
790.	90 c. Close-up of Statue	50	55
791.	$1 Statue and sailing ship ("Operation Sail", 1976) (vert.)	55	60
792.	$3 Dedication ceremony, 1886 (vert.)	1·60	1·75

1985. Birth Bicentenary of John J. Audubon (ornithologist) (2nd issue). Nos 924/8 of Antigua optd. **BARBUDA MAIL.**

794.	90 c. Slavonian grebe	1·50	1·25
795.	$1 British storm petrel	1·75	1·40
796.	$1.50 Great blue heron	2·25	1·75
797.	$3 Double-crested cormorant	3·25	2·75

1985. Butterflies. Nos. 929/33 of Antigua optd. **BARBUDA MAIL.**

799	25 c. "Anaea cyanea"	1·25	80
800	60 c. "Leodonta dysoni"	2·00	1·25
801	90 c. "Junea doraete"	2·25	1·50
802	$4 "Prepona pylene"	5·00	4·25

1985. Centenary of Motorcycle. Nos 919/23 of Antigua optd. **BARBUDA MAIL.**

804.	10 c. Triumph 2hp "Jap", 1903	30	10
805.	30 c. Indian "Arrow", 1949	50	20
806.	60 c. BMW "R100RS", 1976	75	40
807.	$4 Harley-Davidson "Model II", 1916	3·00	2·75

1985. 85th Birthday of Queen Elizabeth the Queen Mother. Nos. 776/82 optd. **4th Aug 1900–1985.**

809.	15 c. Type **103**	30	10
810.	45 c. Duchess of York, 1926, and "Elizabeth of Glamis" roses	60	30
811.	50 c. The Queen Mother after the Coronation, 1937	60	30
812.	60 c. In Garter robes, 1971, and Dog Roses	70	40
813.	90 c. Attending Royal Variety show, 1967, and red Hibiscus	85	55
814.	$2 The Queen Mother in 1982, and blue Plumbago	1·60	1·25
815.	$3 Receiving 82nd birthday gifts from children, and Morning Glory	2·25	1·75

1985. Native American Artefacts. Nos. 914/18 of Antigua optd. **BARBUDA MAIL.**

816.	15 c. Arawak pot sherd and Indians making clay utensils	15	10
817.	50 c. Arawak body design and Arawak Indians tattooing	30	30
818.	60 c. Head of the god "Yocahu" and Indians harvesting manioc	40	40
819.	$3 Carib war club and Carib Indians going into battle	1·60	1·75

1985. 40th Anniv. of International Civil Aviation Organization. Nos. 934/8 of Antigua optd. **BARBUDA MAIL.**

821.	30 c. Cessna "172"	20	20
822.	90 c. Fokker "DVII"	55	55
823.	$1.50 Spad "VII"	85	85
824.	$3 Boeing "747"	1·75	1·75

1985. Life and Times of Queen Elizabeth the Queen Mother (2nd series). Nos. 946/8 of Antigua optd. **BARBUDA MAIL.**

826.	$1 The Queen Mother attending church	1·50	1·50
827.	$1.50 Watching children playing in London garden	1·75	1·75
828.	$2.50 The Queen Mother in 1979	2·25	2·25

1985. 850th Birth Anniv. of Maimonides (physician, philosopher and scholar). No. 939 of Antigua optd. **BARBUDA MAIL.**

830.	$2 green	1·75	1·75

1985. (25 Nov). Marine Life. Nos. 950/3 of Antigua optd. **BARBUDA MAIL.**

832.	15 c. Magnificent Frigate Bird	70	40
833.	45 c. Brain Coral	1·00	70
834.	60 c. Cushion Star	1·25	85
835.	$3 Spotted Moray Eel	3·75	3·25

1986. International Youth Year. Nos. 941/5 of Antigua optd. **BARBUDA MAIL.**

837.	25 c. Young farmers with produce	15	15
838.	50 c. Hotel management trainees	25	30
839.	60 c. Girls with goat and boys with football ("Environment")	30	35
840.	$3 Windsurfing ("Leisure")	1·50	1·60

1986. Royal Visit. Nos. 965/8 of Antigua optd. **BARBUDA MAIL.**

842.	60 c. Flags of Great Britain and Antigua	30	35
843.	$1 Queen Elizabeth II (vert.)	50	55
844.	$4 Royal Yacht "Britannia"	2·00	2·10

1986. 75th Anniv. of Girl Guide Movement. Nos. 955/8 of Antigua optd. **BARBUDA MAIL.**

846.	15 c. Girl Guides nursing	55	40
847.	45 c. Open-air Girl Guide meeting	1·25	1·25
848.	60 c. Lord and Lady Baden-Powell	1·50	1·50
849.	$3 Girl Guides gathering flowers	3·75	3·75

1986. 300th Birth Anniv. of Johann Sebastian Bach (composer). Nos 960/3 of Antigua optd. **BARBUDA MAIL.**

851.	25 c. multicoloured	75	60
852.	50 c. multicoloured	1·25	1·10
853.	$1 multicoloured	1·75	1·75
854.	$3 multicoloured	3·75	3·75

1986. Christmas. Religious Paintings. Nos. 985/8 of Antigua optd. **BARBUDA MAIL.**

856.	10 c. "Madonna and Child" (De Landi)	30	20
857.	25 c. "Madonna and Child" (Berlinghiero)	55	45
858.	60 c. "The Nativity" (Fra Angelico)	1·00	75
859.	$4 "Presentation in the Temple" (Giovanni di Paolo)	3·25	3·75

108. Queen Elizabeth II meeting Members of Legislature.

1986. 60th Birthday of Queen Elizabeth II (1st issue). Multicoloured.

861.	$1 Type **108**	1·50	1·50
862.	$2 Queen with Head-mistress of Liberta School	2·00	2·00
863.	$2.50 Queen greeted by Governor-General of Antigua	2·25	2·25

See also Nos. 872/4.

109. Halley's Comet over Barbuda Beach.

1986. Appearance of Halley's Comet (1st issue). Multicoloured.

865.	$1 Type **109**	1·75	1·75
866.	$2.50 Early telescope and dish aerial (vert.)	3·00	3·00
867.	$5 Comet and World map	4·75	4·75

See also Nos. 886/89.

1986. 40th Anniv. of United Nations Organization. Nos. 981/3 of Antigua optd. **BARBUDA MAIL.**

868.	40 c. Benjamin Franklin and U.N. (New York) 1953 U.P.U. 5 c. stamp	85	85
869.	$1 George Washington Carver (agricultural chemist) and 1982 Nature Conservation 28 c. stamp	1·50	1·50
870.	$3 Charles Lindbergh (aviator) and 1978 I.C.A.O. 25 c. stamp	2·75	2·75

1986. 60th Birthday of Queen Elizabeth II (2nd issue). Nos. 1005/7 of Antigua optd. **BARBUDA MAIL.**

872.	60 c. black and yellow	90	90
873.	$1 multicoloured	1·50	1·50
874.	$4 multicoloured	3·25	3·25

1986. World Cup Football Championship, Mexico. Nos. 995/8 of Antigua optd. **BARBUDA MAIL.**
876. 30 c. Football, boots and trophy 85 85
877. 60 c. Goalkeeper (vert.) .. .. 1·40 1·40
878. $1 Referee blowing whistle (vert.) .. .. .. 1·90 1·90
879. $4 Ball in net .. .. 4·25 4·25

1986. "Ameripex '86" International Stamp Exhibition, Chicago. Famous American Trains. Nos. 1014/17 of Antigua optd. **BARBUDA MAIL.**
881. 25 c. "Hiawatha Express" 90 90
882. 50 c. "Grand Canyon Express" .. .. 1·40 1·40
883. $1 "Powhattan Arrow Express" .. .. 2·25 2·25
884. $3 "Empire State Express" 4·50 4·50

1986. Appearance of Halley's Comet (2nd issue). Nos. 1000/3 of Antigua optd. **BARBUDA MAIL.**
886. 5 c. Edmond Halley and Old Greenwich Observatory 35 35
887. 10 c. "Me 163B Komet" (fighter aircraft), 1944 .. 35 35
888. 60 c. Montezuma (Aztec Emperor) and Comet in 1517 (from "Historias de las Indias de Neuva Espana") .. .. 1·25 1·25
889. $4 Pocahontas saving Capt. John Smith and Comet in 1607 .. .. 4·00 4·00

1986. Royal Wedding. Nos. 1019/21 of Antigua optd. **BARBUDA MAIL.**
891. 45 c. Prince Andrew and Miss Sarah Ferguson .. 45 45
892. 60 c. Prince Andrew .. 55 55
893. $4 Prince Andrew with Prince Philip .. .. 2·75 2·75

1986. Sea Shells. Nos. 1023/6 of Antigua optd. **BARBUDA MAIL.**
895. 15 c. Fly-specked Cerith .. 80 80
896. 45 c. Smooth Scotch Bonnet .. .. .. 1·50 1·50
897. 60 c. West Indian Crown Conch .. .. .. 2·00 2·00
898. $3 Murex Ciboney .. .. 5·00 5·00

1986. Flowers. Nos. 1028/35 of Antigua optd. **BARBUDA MAIL.**
900. 10 c. "Nymphaea ampla" (water lily) 20 20
901. 15 c. Queen of the Night .. 30 30
902. 50 c. Cup of Gold 50 50
903. 60 c. Beach Morning Glory 55 55
904. 70 c. Golden Trumpet .. 70 70
905. $1 Air Plant 85 85
906. $3 Purple Wreath .. .. 2·25 2·25
907. $4 Zephyr Lily .. .. 2·75 2·75

1986. Mushrooms. Nos. 1042/5 of Antigua optd. **BARBUDA MAIL.**
909 10 c. "Hygrocybe occidentalis var scarletina" .. 40 30
910 50 c. "Trogia buccinalis" 1·25 1·00
911 $1 "Collybia subpruinosa" 2·00 1·75
912 $4 "Leucocoprinus brebissonii" .. .. 5·00 4·00

1986. Birth Bicentenary of John J. Audubon (ornithologist) (3rd issue). Nos. 990/3 of Antigua optd. **BARBUDA MAIL.**
914. 60 c. Mallard 50 50
915. 90 c. North American black duck 70 70
916. $1.50 American pintail .. 1·25 1·25
917. $3 Wigeon .. .. 2·00 2·00

1987. Local Boats. Nos. 1009/12 of Antigua optd. **BARBUDA MAIL.**
918. 30 c. Tugboat 30 30
919. 60 c. Game fishing boat .. 45 45
920. $1 Yacht 75 75
921. $4 Lugger with auxiliary sail .. .. .. 2·50 2·50

1987. Centenary of First Benz Motor Car. Nos. 1052/9 of Antigua optd. **BARBUDA MAIL.**
923. 10 c. Auburn "Speedster" (1933) 15 15
924. 15 c. Mercury "Sable" (1986) 20 20
925. 50 c. Cadillac (1959) .. 45 45
926. 60 c. Studebaker (1950) .. 45 45
927. 70 c. Lagonda "V-12" (1939) 50 50
928. $1 Adler "Standard" (1930) 65 65
929. $3 DKW (1956) .. .. 1·75 1·75
930. $4 Mercedes "500K" (1936) 2·25 2·25

1987. World Cup Football Championship Winners, Mexico. Nos. 1037/40 of Antigua optd. **BARBUDA MAIL.**
932. 30 c. Football, boots and trophy 30 30
933. 60 c. Goalkeeper (vert.) .. 45 45
934. $1 Referee blowing whistle (vert.) 70 70
935. $4 Ball in net .. .. 2·00 2·00

1987. America's Cup Yachting Championship. Nos. 1072/5 of Antigua optd. **BARBUDA MAIL.**
936. 30 c. "Canada I" (1981) .. 20 20
937. 60 c. "Gretel II" (1970) .. 35 35
938. $1 "Sceptre" (1958) .. 60 60
939. $3 "Vigilant" (1893) .. 1·75 1·75

1987. Marine Life. Nos. 1077/84 of Antigua optd. **BARBUDA MAIL.**
941. 15 c. Bridled burrfish .. 20 20
942. 30 c. Common noddy .. 35 35
943. 40 c. Nassau grouper .. 35 35
944. 50 c. Laughing gull .. 55 55
945. 60 c. French angelfish .. 55 55
946. $1 Porkfish 65 65
947. $2 Royal tern .. .. 1·50 1·50
948. $3 Sooty tern .. .. 2·00 2·00

1987. Milestones of Transportation. Nos. 1100/9 of Antigua optd. **BARBUDA MAIL.**
950. 10 c. "Spirit of Australia" (fastest powerboat), 1978 25 25
951. 15 c. Siemen's electric locomotive, 1879 .. .. 45 45
952. 30 c. U.S.S. "Triton" (first submerged circumnavigation), 1960 .. .. 55 55
953. 50 c. Trevithick's steam carriage (first passenger-carrying vehicle), 1801 .. 70 70
954. 60 c. U.S.S. "New Jersey" (battleship), 1942 .. 75 75
955. 70 c. Draisine bicycle, 1818 80 80
956. 90 c. "United States" (holder of Blue Riband), 1952 .. .. .. 1·00 1·00
957. $1.50 Cierva "C.4" (first autogiro), 1923 .. .. 1·50 1·50
958. $2 Curtiss "NC.4" (first transatlantic flight), 1919 1·75 1·75
959. $3 "Queen Elizabeth 2" (liner), 1969 .. .. 2·50 2·50

110. Shore Crab.

1987. Marine Life. Multicoloured.
960. 5 c. Type **110** 30 30
961. 10 c. Sea cucumber .. 30 30
962. 15 c. Stop light parrotfish 40 40
963. 25 c. Banded coral shrimp 45 45
964. 35 c. Spotted drum .. 50 50
965. 60 c. Thorny starfish .. 75 75
966. 75 c. Atlantic trumpet triton 85 85
967. 90 c. Feather star and yellow beaker sponge .. 1·00 1·00
968. $1 Blue gorgonian (vert.) 1·10 1·10
969. $1.25 Slender filefish (vert.) 1·40 1·40
970. $5 Barred hamlet (vert.) .. 4·00 4·00
971. $7.50 Fairy basslet (vert.) 6·50 6·50
972. $10 Fire coral and butterfly fish (vert.) .. .. 8·00 8·00

1987. Olympic Games, Seoul (1988). Nos. 1086/9 of Antigua optd. **BARBUDA MAIL.**
973. 10 c. Handball 15 10
974. 60 c. Fencing 30 30
975. $1 Gymnastics 50 50
976. $3 Football .. .. 1·50 1·60

1987. Birth Centenary of Marc Chagall (artist). Nos. 1091/8 of Antigua optd. **BARBUDA MAIL.**
978. 10 c. "The Profile" .. 10 10
979. 30 c. "Portrait of the Artist's Sister" 15 15
980. 40 c. "Bride with Fan" .. 20 25
981. 60 c. "David in Profile" .. 25 30
982. 90 c. "Fiancee with Bouquet" 40 45
983. $1 "Self Portrait with Brushes" 45 50
984. $3 "The Walk" .. .. 1·40 1·50
985. $4 "Three Candles" .. 1·75 1·90

1987. Centenary (1986) of Statue of Liberty (2nd issue). Nos. 1110/19 of Antigua optd. **BARBUDA MAIL.**
987. 15 c. Lee Iacocca at unveiling of restored statue 10 10
988. 30 c. Statue at sunset (side view) 15 15
989. 45 c. Aerial view of head .. 20 25
990. 50 c. Lee Iacocca and torch 25 30
991. 60 c. Workmen inside head of statue (horiz.) .. 25 30
992. 90 c. Restoration work (horiz.) 40 45
993. $1 Head of statue 45 50
994. $2 Statue at sunset (front view) 90 95
995. $3 Inspecting restoration work (horiz.) .. .. 1·40 1·50
996. $5 Statue at night .. 2·25 2·40

1987. Entertainers. Nos. 1120/7 of Antigua optd. **BARBUDA MAIL.**
997. 15 c. Grace Kelly .. 30 30
998. 30 c. Marilyn Monroe .. 45 45
999. 45 c. Orson Welles .. 50 50
1000. 50 c. Judy Garland .. 65 65
1001. 60 c. John Lennon .. 85 85
1002. $1 Rock Hudson .. 90 90
1003. $2 John Wayne .. .. 1·60 1·60
1004. $3 Elvis Presley .. .. 2·25 2·25

1987. "Capex '87" International Stamp Exhibition, Toronto. Reptiles and Amphibians. Nos. 1133/6 of Antigua optd. **BABUDA MAIL.**
1005. 30 c. Whistling frog .. 20 20
1006. 60 c. Croaking lizard .. 35 35
1007. $1 Antiguan anole .. 55 55
1008. $3 Red-footed tortoise .. 1·60 1·60

1988. Christmas. Religious Paintings. Nos. 1144/7 of Antigua optd. **BARBUDA MAIL.**
1010. 45 c. "Madonna and Child" (Bernardo Daddi) 20 25
1011. 60 c. St. Joseph (detail, "The Nativity" (Sano di Pietro)) 25 30
1012. $1 Virgin Mary (detail, "The Nativity" (Sano di Pietro)) 45 50
1013. $4 "Music-making Angel" (Melozzo da Forli) .. .. 1·75 1·90

1988. Salvation Army's Community Service. Nos.1163/70 of Antigua optd **BARBUDA MAIL.**
1015 25 c. First aid at daycare centre, Antigua .. 35 35
1016 30 c. Giving penicillin injection, Indonesia .. 35 35
1017 40 c. Children at daycare centre, Bolivia .. 45 45
1018 45 c. Rehabilitation of the handicapped, India .. 45 45
1019 50 c. Training blind man, Kenya 55 55
1020 60 c. Weighing baby, Ghana 55 55
1021 $1 Training typist, Zambia 85 85
1022 $2 Emergency food kitchen, Sri Lanka 1·50 1·50

1988. Bicentenary of U.S. Constitution. Nos. 1139/42 of Antigua optd **BARBUDA MAIL.**
1024 15 c. House of Burgesses, Virginia ("Freedom of Speech") 10 10
1025 45 c. State Seal, Connecticut 20 25
1026 60 c. State Seal, Delaware 25 30
1027 $4 Gouverneur Morris (Pennsylvania delegate) (vert) .. .. 1·75 1·90

1988. Royal Ruby Wedding. Nos. 1149/52 of Antigua optd **BARBUDA MAIL.**
1029 25 c. brown, black & blue 20 20
1030 60 c. multicoloured .. 35 35
1031 $2 brown, black and green 1·00 1·00
1032 $3 multicoloured .. 1·40 1·50
2·75 2·75

1988. Birds of Antigua. Nos. 1154/61 of Antigua optd **BARBUDA MAIL.**
1034 10 c. Great blue heron .. 25 25
1035 15 c. Ringed kingfisher (horiz) 25 25
1036 50 c. Bananaquit (horiz) 55 55
1037 60 c. Purple gallinule (horiz) 55 55
1038 70 c. Blue-hooded euphonia (horiz) .. 60 60
1039 $1 Brown-throated conure ("Caribbean Parakeet") 80 80
1040 $3 Troupial (horiz) .. 1·75 1·75
1041 $4 Purple-throated carib (horiz) .. .. 2·00 2·00

1988. 500th Anniv (1992) of Discovery of America by Columbus (1st issue). Nos. 1172/9 of Antigua optd **BARBUDA MAIL.**
1043 10 c. Columbus's second fleet, 1493 .. .. 15 15
1044 30 c. Painos Indian village and fleet 20 20
1045 45 c. "Santa Mariagalante" (flagship) and Painos village 35 35
1046 60 c. Painos Indians offering Columbus fruit and vegetables .. 35 35
1047 90 c. Painos Indian and Columbus with parrot 60 60
1048 $1 Columbus landing on island 65 65
1049 $3 Spanish soldier and fleet .. .. 1·50 1·50
1050 $4 Fleet under sail .. 2·00 2·00
See also Nos. 1112/15, 1177/84 and 1285/91.

1988. 500th Birth Anniv of Titian. Nos. 1181/8 of Antigua optd **BARBUDA MAIL.**
1052 30 c. "Bust of Christ" .. 15 15
1053 40 c. "Scourging of Christ" 20 25
1054 45 c. "Madonna in Glory with Saints" 20 25
1055 50 c. "The Averoldi Polyptych" (detail) .. 25 30
1056 $1 "Christ Crowned with Thorns" 45 50
1057 $2 "Christ Mocked" .. 90 95
1058 $3 "Christ and Simon of Cyrene" .. .. 1·40 1·50
1059 $4 "Crucifixion with Virgin and Saints" .. 1·75 2·00

1988. 16th World Scout Jamboree, Australia. Nos. 1128/31 of Antigua optd **BARBUDA MAIL.**
1061 10 c. Scouts around camp fire and red kangaroo 15 15
1062 60 c. Scouts canoeing and blue-winged kookaburra 45 45
1063 $1 Scouts on assault course and ring-tailed rock wallaby .. 70 70
1064 $3 Field kitchen and koala .. .. .. 1·75 1·75

1988. Sailing Week. Nos. 1190/3 of Antigua optd **BARBUDA MAIL.**
1066 30 c. Two yachts rounding buoy 20 20
1067 60 c. Three yachts .. 45 45
1068 $1 British yacht under way 70 70
1069 $3 Three yachts (different) .. .. 1·60 1·60

1988. Flowering Trees. Nos. 1213/20 of Antigua optd **BARBUDA MAIL.**
1071 10 c. Jacaranda 10 10
1072 30 c. Cordia 15 15
1073 50 c. Orchid tree .. 20 25
1074 90 c. Flamboyant .. 40 45
1075 $1 African tulip tree .. 45 50
1076 $2 Potato tree 80 85
1077 $3 Crepe myrtle .. .. 1·25 1·40
1078 $4 Pitch apple .. .. 1·60 1·75

1988. Olympic Games, Seoul. Nos. 1222/5 of Antigua optd **BARBUDA MAIL.**
1080 40 c. Gymnastics .. 20 25
1081 60 c. Weightlifting .. 25 30
1082 $1 Water polo (horiz) .. 45 50
1083 $3 Boxing (horiz) .. 1·25 1·40

1988. Caribbean Butterflies. Nos. 1227/44 of Antigua optd **BARBUDA MAIL.**
1085 1 c. "Danaus plexippus" 10 10
1086 2 c. "Greta diaphanus" 10 10
1087 3 c. "Calisto archebates" 10 10
1088 5 c. "Hamadryas feronia" 10 10
1089 10 c. "Mestra dorcas" .. 10 10
1090 15 c. "Hypolimnas misippus" 10 10
1091 20 c. "Dione juno" .. 10 10
1092 25 c. "Heliconius charithonia" 10 15
1093 30 c. "Eurema pyro" .. 10 15
1094 40 c. "Papilio androgeus" 15 20
1095 45 c. "Anteos maerula" 20 25
1096 50 c. "Aphrissa orbis" .. 20 25
1097 60 c. "Astraptes xagua" 25 30
1098 $1 "Heliopetes arsalte" 40 45
1099 $2 "Polites baracoa" .. 85 90
1100 $2.50 "Phocides pigmalion" .. .. 1·00 1·10
1101 $5 "Prepona amphitoe" 2·10 2·25
1102 $10 "Oarisma nanus" .. 4·25 4·50
1102a $20 "Parides lycimenes" 8·50 8·75

1989. 25th Death Anniv of John F. Kennedy (American statesman). Nos. 1245/52 of Antigua optd **BARBUDA MAIL.**
1103 1 c. President Kennedy and family 10 10
1104 2 c. Kennedy commanding "PT109" 10 10
1105 3 c. Funeral cortege .. 10 10
1106 4 c. In motorcade, Mexico 10 10
1107 30 c. As 1 c. 15 20
1108 60 c. As 4 c. 30 35
1109 $1 As 3 c. 45 50
1110 $4 As 2 c. .. .. 1·90 2·00

1989. 500th Anniv (1992) of Discovery of America by Columbus (2nd issue). Pre-Columbian Arawak Society. Nos. 1267/70 of Antigua optd **BARBUDA MAIL.**

1112 $1.50 Arawak warriors 70 75
1113 $1.50 Whip dancers 70 75
1114 $1.50 Whip dancers and chief with pineapple 70 75
1115 $1.50 Family and camp fire 70 75

1989. 50th Anniv of First Jet Flight. Nos. 1272/9 of Antigua optd **BARBUDA MAIL.**

1117 10 c. De Havilland "Comet 4" airliner 10 10
1118 30 c. Messerschmitt "Me 262" fighter 15 20
1119 40 c. Boeing "707" airliner 20 25
1120 60 c. Canadair "F-86 Sabre" fighter 30 35
1121 $1 Lockheed "F-104 Starfighter" fighters 45 50
1122 $2 McDonnell Douglas "DC-10" airliner 95 1·00
1123 $3 Boeing "747" airliner 1·50 1·60
1124 $4 McDonnell "F-4 Phantom" fighter 1·90 2·00

1989. Caribbean Cruise Ships. Nos. 1281/8 of Antigua optd **BARBUDA MAIL.**

1126 25 c. "Festivale" 15 15
1127 45 c. "Southward" 25 25
1128 50 c. "Sagafjord" 30 30
1129 60 c. "Daphne" 35 35
1130 75 c. "Cunard Countess" 40 40
1131 90 c. "Song of America" 45 45
1132 $3 "Island Princess" 1·60 1·60
1133 $4 "Galileo" 2·00 2·00

1989. Japanese Art. Paintings by Hiroshige. Nos. 1290/7 of Antigua optd **BARBUDA MAIL.**

1135 25 c. "Fish swimming by Duck half-submerged in Stream" 10 15
1136 45 c. "Crane and Wave" 20 25
1137 50 c. "Sparrows and Morning Glories" 25 30
1138 60 c. "Crested Blackbird and Flowering Cherry" 30 35
1139 $1 "Great Knot sitting among Water Grass" 45 50
1140 $2 "Goose on a Bank of Water" 95 1·00
1141 $3 "Black Paradise Flycatcher and Blossoms" 1·50 1·60
1142 $4 "Sleepy Owl perched on a Pine Branch" 1·90 2·00

1989. World Cup Football Championship, Italy (1990). Nos. 1308/11 of Antigua optd **BARBUDA MAIL.**

1144 15 c. Goalkeeper 10 10
1145 25 c. Goalkeeper moving towards ball 10 15
1146 $1 Goalkeeper reaching for ball 45 50
1147 $4 Goalkeeper saving goal 1·90 2·00

1989. Christmas. Paintings by Raphael and Giotto. Nos. 1351/8 of Antigua optd **BARBUDA MAIL.**

1149 10 c. "The Small Cowper Madonna" (Raphael) 10 10
1150 25 c. "Madonna of the Goldfinch" (Raphael) 10 15
1151 30 c. "The Alba Madonna" (Raphael) 15 20
1152 50 c. Saint (detail, "Bologna Altarpiece") (Giotto) 25 30
1153 60 c. Angel (detail, "Bologna Altarpiece") (Giotto) 30 35
1154 70 c. Angel slaying serpent (detail, "Bologna Altarpiece") (Giotto) 35 40
1155 $4 Evangelist (detail, "Bologna Altarpiece") (Giotto) 1·90 2·00
1156 $5 "Madonna of Foligno" (Raphael) 2·40 2·50

1990. Fungi. Nos. 1313/20 of Antigua optd **BARBUDA MAIL.**

1158 10 c. Lilac fairy helmet 20 20
1159 25 c. Rough psathyrella (vert) 20 20
1160 50 c. Golden tops 40 40
1161 60 c. Blue cap (vert) 45 45
1162 75 c. Brown cap (vert) 50 50
1163 $1 Green gill (vert) 65 65
1164 $3 Red pinwheel 1·75 1·75
1165 $4 Red hanterelle 2·00 2·00

1990. Local Fauna. Nos. 1322/5 optd **BARBUDA MAIL.**

1167 25 c. Desmarest's hutia 25 25
1168 45 c. Caribbean monk seal 45 45
1169 60 c. Mustache bat (vert) 55 55
1170 $4 American manatee (vert) 2·25 2·25

1990. 20th Anniv of First Manned Landing on Moon. Nos. 1346/9 optd **BARBUDA MAIL.**

1172 10 c. Launch of "Apollo 11" 15 15
1173 45 c. Aldrin on Moon 35 35
1174 $1 Module "Eagle" over Moon (horiz) 60 60
1175 $4 Recovery of "Apollo 11" crew after splashdown (horiz) 2·40 2·40

1990. 500th Anniv (1992) of Discovery of America by Columbus (3rd issue). New World Natural History—Marine Life. Nos. 1360/7 of Antigua optd **BARBUDA MAIL.**

1177 10 c. Star-eyed hermit crab 15 15
1178 20 c. Spiny lobster 20 20
1179 25 c. Magnificent banded fanworm 20 20
1180 45 c. Cannonball jellyfish 35 35
1181 60 c. Red-spiny sea star 45 45
1182 $2 Peppermint shrimp 1·00 1·00
1183 $3 Coral crab 1·40 1·40
1184 $4 Branching fire coral 1·75 1·75

1990. "EXPO 90" International Garden and Greenery Exhibition, Osaka. Orchids. Nos.1369/76 of Antigua optd **BARBUDA MAIL.**

1186 15 c. "Vanilla mexicana" 25 25
1187 45 c. "Epidendrum ibaguense" 45 45
1188 50 c. "Epidendrum secundum" 45 45
1189 60 c. "Maxillaria conferta" 50 50
1190 $1 "Onicidium altissimum" 75 75
1191 $2 "Spiranthes lanceolata" 1·25 1·25
1192 $3 "Tonopsis utricularioides" 1·75 1·75
1193 $5 "Epidendrum nocturnum" 2·75 2·75

1990. Reef Fishes. Nos. 1386/93 of Antigua optd **BARBUDA MAIL.**

1195 10 c. Flamefish 15 15
1196 15 c. Coney 20 20
1197 50 c. Squirrelfish 45 45
1198 60 c. Sergeant major 50 50
1199 $1 Yellowtail snapper 70 70
1200 $2 Rock beauty 1·25 1·25
1201 $3 Spanish hogfish 1·60 1·60
1202 $4 Striped parrotfish 2·00 2·00

1990. 1st Anniv of Hurricane Hugo. Nos. 971/2 surch **1st Anniversary Hurricane Hugo 16th September, 1989–1990.**

1204 $5 on $7.50 Fairy basslet (vert) 2·25 2·25
1205 $7.50 on $10 Fire coral and butterfly fish (vert) 3·25 3·25

1990. 90th Birthday of Queen Elizabeth the Queen Mother. Nos. 1415/18 of Antigua optd **BARBUDA MAIL.**

1206 15 c. multicoloured 15 15
1207 35 c. multicoloured 20 20
1208 75 c. multicoloured 35 35
1209 $3 multicoloured 1·25 1·25

1990. Achievements in Space. Nos. 1395/1414 of Antigua optd **BARBUDA MAIL.**

1211 45 c. "Voyager 2" passing Saturn 25 25
1212 45 c. "Pioneer 11" photographing Saturn 25 25
1213 45 c. Astronaut in transporter 25 25
1214 45 c. Space shuttle "Columbia" 25 25
1215 45 c. "Apollo 10" command module on parachutes 25 25
1216 45 c. "Skylab" space station 25 25
1217 45 c. Astronaut Edward White in space 25 25
1218 45 c. "Apollo" spacecraft on joint mission 25 25
1219 45 c. "Soyuz" spacecraft on joint mission 25 25
1220 45 c. "Mariner 1" passing Venus 25 25
1221 45 c. "Gemini 4" capsule 25 25
1222 45 c. "Sputnik 1" 25 25
1223 45 c. Hubble space telescope 25 25
1224 45 c. "X-15" rocket plane 25 25
1225 45 c. "Bell X-1" aircraft 25 25
1226 45 c. "Apollo 17" astronaut and lunar rock formation 25 25
1227 45 c. Lunar rover 25 25
1228 45 c. "Apollo 14" lunar module 25 25
1229 45 c. Astronaut Buzz Aldrin on Moon 25 25
1230 45 c. Soviet "Lunokhod" lunar vehicle 25 25

1990. Christmas. Paintings by Renaissance Masters. Nos. 1457/64 of Antigua optd **BARBUDA MAIL.**

1231 25 c. "Madonna and Child with Saints (detail, Sebastiano del Piombo) 10 10
1232 30 c. "Virgin and Child with Angels" (detail, Grunewald) (vert) 10 15
1233 40 c. "The Holy Family and a Shepherd" (detail, Titian) 15 20
1234 60 c. "Virgin and Child" (detail, Lippi) (vert) 25 30
1235 $1 "Jesus, St. John and Two Angels" (Rubens) 40 45
1236 $2 "Adoration of the Shepherds" (detail, Vincenzo Catena) 80 85
1237 $4 "Adoration of the Magi" (detail, Giorgione) 1·60 1·75
1238 $5 "Virgin and Child adored by Warrior" (detail, Vincenzo Catena) 2·00 2·10

1991. 150th Anniv of the Penny Black. Nos. 1378/80 of Antigua optd **BARBUDA MAIL.**

1240 45 c. green 20 25
1241 60 c. mauve 25 30
1242 $5 blue 2·00 2·10

1991. "Stamp World London 90" International Stamp Exhibition. Nos. 1382/4 of Antigua optd **BARBUDA MAIL.**

1244 50 c. green and red 20 25
1245 75 c. brown and red 30 35
1246 $4 blue and red 1·60 1·75

119 Troupial

1991. Wild Birds. Multicoloured.

1248 60 c. Type **119** 25 30
1249 $2 Adelaide's warbler ("Christmas Bird") 85 90
1250 $4 Rose-breasted grosbeak 1·75 1·90
1251 $7 Stolid flycatcher 3·00 3·25

1991. Olympic Games, Barcelona (1992). Nos. 1429/32 of Antigua optd **BARBUDA MAIL.**

1252 50 c. Men's 20 kilometres walk 20 25
1253 75 c. Triple jump 30 35
1254 $1 Men's 10,000 metres 40 45
1255 $5 Javelin 2·10 2·25

1991. Birds. Nos. 1448/55 of Antigua optd **BARBUDA MAIL.**

1257 10 c. Pearly-eyed thrasher 10 10
1258 25 c. Purple-throated carib 10 15
1259 50 c. Common yellowthroat 20 25
1260 60 c. American kestrel 25 30
1261 $1 Yellow-bellied sapsucker 40 45
1262 $2 Purple gallinule 85 90
1263 $3 Yellow-crowned night heron 1·25 1·40
1264 $4 Blue-hooded euphonia 1·75 1·90

1991. 350th Death Anniv of Rubens. Nos. 1466/73 of Antigua optd **BARBUDA MAIL.**

1266 25 c. "Rape of the Daughters of Leucippus" (detail) 10 10
1267 45 c. "Bacchanal" (detail) 20 25
1268 50 c. "Rape of the Sabine Women" (detail) 20 25
1269 60 c. "Battle of the Amazons" (detail) 25 30
1270 $1 "Rape of the Sabine Women" (different detail) 40 45
1271 $2 "Bacchanal" (different detail) 85 90
1272 $3 "Rape of the Sabine Women" (different detail) 1·25 1·40
1273 $4 "Bacchanal" (different detail) 1·75 1·90

1991. 50th Anniv of Second World War. Nos. 1475/83 of Antigua optd **BARBUDA MAIL.**

1275 10 c. U.S. troops cross into Germany, 1944 10 10
1276 15 c. Axis surrender in North Africa, 1943 10 10
1277 25 c. U.S. tanks invade Kwalajalein, 1944 10 10
1278 45 c. Roosevelt and Churchill meet at Casablanca, 1943 20 25
1279 50 c. Marshall Badoglio, Prime Minister of Italian anti-facist government, 1943 20 25
1280 $1 Lord Mountbatten, Supreme Allied Commander South-east Asia, 1943 40 45
1281 $2 Greek victory at Koritza, 1940 80 85
1282 $4 Anglo-Soviet mutual assistance pact, 1941 1·75 1·90
1283 $5 Operation Torch landings, 1942 2·10 2·25

1991. 500th Anniv (1992) of Discovery of America by Columbus (4th issue). History of Exploration. Nos. 1503/10 of Antigua optd **BARBUDA MAIL.**

1285 10 c. multicoloured 10 10
1286 15 c. multicoloured 10 10
1287 45 c. multicoloured 20 25
1288 60 c. multicoloured 25 30
1289 $1 multicoloured 40 45
1290 $2 multicoloured 80 85
1291 $4 multicoloured 1·75 1·90
1292 $5 multicoloured 2·10 2·25

1991. Butterflies. Nos. 1494/1501 of Antigua optd **BARBUDA MAIL.**

1294 10 c. "Heliconius charitonia" 10 10
1295 35 c. "Marpesia petreus" 15 20
1296 50 c. "Anartia amathea" 20 25
1297 75 c. "Siproeta stelenes" 30 35
1298 $1 "Battus polydamas" 40 45
1299 $2 "Historis odius" 80 85
1300 $4 "Hypolimnas misippus" 1·75 1·90
1301 $5 "Hamadryas feronia" 2·10 2·25

1991. 65th Birthday of Queen Elizabeth II. Nos. 1534/7 of Antigua optd **BARBUDA MAIL.**

1303 15 c. Queen Elizabeth and Prince Philip in 1976 10 10
1304 20 c. The Queen and Prince Philip in Portugal, 1985 10 10
1305 $2 Queen Elizabeth II 80 85
1306 $4 The Queen and Prince Philip at Ascot, 1986 1·75 1·90

1991. 10th Wedding Anniv of Prince and Princess of Wales. Nos. 1539/42 of Antigua optd **BARBUDA MAIL.**

1308 10 c. Prince and Princess of Wales at party, 1986 10 10
1309 40 c. Separate portraits of Prince, Princess and sons 15 20
1310 $1 Prince Henry and Prince William 40 45
1311 $5 Princess Diana in Australia and Prince Charles in Hungary 2·10 2·25

1991. Christmas. Religious Paintings by Fra Angelico. Nos. 1595/1602 of Antigua optd **BARBUDA MAIL.**

1313 10 c. "The Annunciation" 10 10
1314 30 c. "Nativity" 15 20
1315 40 c. "Adoration of the Magi" 15 20
1316 60 c. "Presentation in the Temple" 25 30
1317 $1 "Circumcision" 40 45
1318 $3 "Flight into Egypt" 1·15 1·25
1319 $4 "Massacre of the Innocents" 1·75 1·90
1320 $5 "Christ teaching in the Temple" 2·10 2·25

1992. Death Cent (1990) of Vincent van Gogh (artist). Nos. 1512/24 of Antigua optd **BARBUDA MAIL.**

1321 5 c. "Camille Roulin" 10 10
1322 10 c. "Armand Roulin" 10 10
1323 15 c. "Young Peasent Woman with Straw Hat sitting in the Wheat" 10 10
1324 25 c. "Adeline Ravoux" 10 10
1325 30 c. "The Schoolboy" 10 15
1326 40 c. "Doctor Gachet" 15 20
1327 50 c. "Portrait of a Man" 20 25
1328 75 c. "Two Children" 30 35
1329 $2 "The Postman Joseph Roulin" 85 90
1330 $3 "The Seated Zouave" 1·25 1·40
1331 $4 "L'Arlesienne" 1·75 1·90
1332 $5 "Self-Portrait, November/December 1888" 2·10 2·25

BARWANI

A state of Central India. Now uses Indian stamps.

12 pies = 1 anna; 16 annas = 1 rupee

1. Rana Ranjitsingh. 2.

1921.

No.	Type	Description	Unused	Used
3	1	¼ a. green	11·00	40·00
28b		¼ a. blue	1·25	5·50
37		¼ a. black	2·50	13·00
18		½ a. pink	80	5·50
4		½ a. blue	16·00	60·00
14		½ a. green	1·25	9·00
10	2	1 a. red	1·40	10·00
39		1 a. brown	7·00	11·00
11		2 a. purple	1·75	10·00
41		2 a. red	19·00	55·00
31		4 a. orange	45·00	70·00
42a		4 a. green	9·00	18·00

DESIGN: 4 a. Another portrait of Rana Ranjitsingh.

4. Rana Devi Singh. 5.

1932.

No.	Type	Description	Unused	Used
32.	4.	¼ a. slate	80	7·50
33.		½ a. green	1·40	7·50
34.		1 a. brown	1·60	7·50
35.		2 a. purple	3·00	12·00
36.		4 a. olive	6·00	18·00

1938.

No.	Type	Description	Unused	Used
43.	5.	1 a. brown	15·00	30·00

BASUTOLAND

An African territory under Br. protection, N.E. of Cape Province. Self-Government introduced on 1 April 1965. Attained independence on 4 October 1966, when the country was renamed Lesotho.

1961. 100 cents = 1 rand.

1. King George V, Nile Crocodile and Mountains.

1933.

No.	Type	Description	Unused	Used
1.	1.	½d. green	60	75
2.		1d. red	60	35
3.		2d. purple	70	35
4.		3d. blue	70	60
5.		4d. grey	2·50	6·50
6.		6d. yellow	3·00	1·50
7.		1s. orange	3·75	4·50
8.		2s. 6d. brown	20·00	40·00
9.		5s. violet	42·00	60·00
10.		10s. olive	£100	£110

1935. Silver Jubilee. As T **13** of Antigua.

No.	Description	Unused	Used
11.	1d. blue and red	45	25
12.	2d. blue and grey	55	75
13.	3d. brown and blue	3·25	1·00
14.	6d. grey and purple	3·75	1·25

1937. Coronation. As T 2 of Aden.

No.	Description	Unused	Used
15.	1d. red	35	10
16.	2d. purple	40	55
17.	3d. blue	65	75

1938. As T 1, but portrait of King George VI.

No.	Description	Unused	Used
18.	½d. green	20	30
19.	1d. red	40	30
20.	1½d. blue	40	30
21.	2d. purple	30	25
22.	3d. blue	30	50
23.	4d. grey	1·25	2·00
24.	6d. yellow	40	50
25.	1s. orange	40	45
26.	2s. 6d. brown	7·00	5·00
27.	5s. violet	16·00	8·50
28.	10s. olive	16·00	15·00

1945. Victory. Stamps of South Africa optd. **Basutoland.** Alternate stamps inscr. in English or Afrikaans.

No.	Type	Description	Unused	Used
29.	55.	1d. brown and red	20	25
30.		2d. blue and violet	20	30
31.		3d. blue	20	50

Prices are for bi-lingual pairs.

5. King George VI and Queen Elizabeth.

1947. Royal Visit.

No.	Type	Description	Unused	Used
32.	–	1d. red	10	10
33.	5.	2d. green	10	10
34.	–	3d. blue	10	10
35.	–	1s. mauve	10	10

DESIGNS—VERT. 1d. King George VI. HORIZ. 3d. Queen Elizabeth II as Princess and Princess Margaret. 1s. The Royal Family.

1948. Silver Wedding. As T **10/11** of Aden.

No.	Description	Unused	Used
36.	1½d. blue	20	10
37.	10s. green	27·00	22·00

1949. U.P.U. As T **20/23** of Antigua.

No.	Description	Unused	Used
38.	1½d. blue	30	25
39.	3d. blue	1·10	50
40.	6d. orange	1·25	70
41.	1s. brown	1·25	80

1953. Coronation. As T **13** of Aden.

No.	Description	Unused	Used
42.	2d. black and purple	10	20

8. Qiloane.

9. Mohair (Shearing Goats).

DESIGNS — HORIZ. 1d. Orange River. 2d. Mosuto horseman. 3d. Basuto household. 4½d. Maletsunyane Falls. 6d. Herd-boy with lesiba. 1s. Pastoral scene. 1s. 3d. 'Plane over Lancers' Gap. 2s. 6d. Old Fort, Leribe. 5s. Mission cave house.

1954.

No.	Type	Description	Unused	Used
43.	8.	½d. black and sepia	10	10
44.	–	1d. black and green	10	10
45.	–	2d. blue and orange	60	10
46.	–	3d. sage and red	80	10
47.	–	4½d. indigo and blue	70	10
48.	–	6d. brown and green	1·25	10
49.	–	1s. bronze and purple	1·25	20
50.	–	1s. 3d. brown & turquoise	7·50	3·50
51.	–	2s. 6d. blue and red	5·50	5·50
52.	–	5s. black and red	4·75	8·50
53.	9.	10s. black and purple	16·00	20·00

1959. Surch. ½d. and bar.

No.	Description	Unused	Used
54.	½d. on 2d. blue and orange (No. 45)	10	10

20. "Chief Moshoeshoe I" (engraving by Delangle).

DESIGNS: 1s. Council House. 1s. 3d. Mosuto horseman.

1959. Inauguration National Council.

No.	Type	Description	Unused	Used
55.	20.	3d. black and olive	15	10
56.	–	1s. red and green	20	10
57.	–	1s. 3d. blue and orange	35	25

1961. Nos. 43/53 surch.

No.	Type	Description	Unused	Used
58	8.	½ c. on ½d. black and sepia	10	10
59	–	1 c. on 1d. black & green	10	10
60	–	2 c. on 2d. blue & orange	10	10
61	–	2½ c. on 3d. green and red	10	10
62	–	3½ c. on 4½d. indigo & blue	10	10
63	–	5 c. on 6d. brown & green	10	10
64	–	10 c. on 1s. green & purple	10	10
65a	–	12½c. on 1s. 3d. brown and turquoise	20	10
66	–	25 c. on 2s. 6d. blue & red	15	30
67a	–	50 c. on 5s. black and red	90	1·25
68b	9.	1 r. on 10s. black & purple	2·50	3·50

26 Basuto Household.

1961. As 1954 but value in new currency as in T **26**.

No.	Type	Description	Unused	Used
69	8	½ c. black and brown	10	15
70	–	1 c. black & green (as 1d.)	10	30
71	–	2 c. blue & orge (as 2d.)	40	70
86	26	2½ c. green and red	50	15
73	–	3½ c. indigo & bl (as 4½d.)	25	80
74	–	5 c. brown & grn (as 6d.)	30	35
75	–	10 c. green & pur (as 1s.)	20	20
90	–	12½ c. brown and green (as 1s. 3d.)	2·25	1·50
77	–	25 c. bl & red (as 2s. 6d.)	2·50	6·00
78	–	50 c. black & red (as 5s.)	4·50	7·00
79	9	1 r. black and purple	13·00	8·50

1963. Freedom from Hunger. As T **28** of Aden.

No.	Description	Unused	Used
80.	12½ c. violet	40	15

1963. Cent of Red Cross. As T **33** of Antigua.

No.	Description	Unused	Used
81.	2½ c. red and black	20	10
82.	12½ c. red and blue	60	50

27. Mosotho Woman and Child.

1965. New Constitution. Inscr. "SELF GOVERNMENT 1965". Multicoloured.

No.	Description	Unused	Used
94.	2½ c. Type **27**	10	10
95.	3½ c. Maseru Border Post	15	10
96.	5 c. Mountain Scene	15	10
97.	12½ c. Legislative Buildings	25	30

1965. Cent of I.T.U. As T **36** of Antigua.

No.	Description	Unused	Used
98	1 c. red and purple	15	10
99	20 c. blue and brown	35	30

1965. I.C.Y. As T **37** of Antigua.

No.	Description	Unused	Used
100	½ c. purple and turquoise	10	10
101	12½ c. green and lavender	45	35

1966. Churchill Commem. As T **38** of Antigua.

No.	Description	Unused	Used
102	1 c. blue	15	25
103	2½ c. green	40	10
104	10 c. brown	60	25
105	22½ c. violet	80	50

OFFICIAL STAMPS

1934. Nos. 1/3 and 6 optd **OFFICIAL.**

No.	Type	Description	Unused	Used
O 1	1	½d. green	£2000	£2000
O 2		1d. red	£1300	£1000
O 3		2d. purple	£750	£550
O 4		6d. yellow	£10000	£4500

POSTAGE DUE STAMPS

1933. As Type D **1** of Barbados.

No.	Description	Unused	Used
D 1b.	1d. red	30	50
D 2a.	2d. violet	30	1·00

D 2.

1956.

No.	Type	Description	Unused	Used
D 3.	D 2.	1d. red	15	1·50
D 4.		2d. violet	15	2·00

1961. Surch.

No.	Type	Description	Unused	Used
D 5.	D 2.	1 c. on 1d. red	10	25
D 6.		1 c. on 2d. violet	10	25
D 7.		5 c. on 2d. violet	15	25
D 8.	–	5 c. on 2d. vio.(No.D2a)	1·50	5·50

1964. As Type D **2**, but values in decimal currency.

No.	Description	Unused	Used
D 9.	1 c. red	1·25	4·75
D 10.	5 c. violet	1·25	4·75

For later issues see **LESOTHO.**

BATUM

Batum, a Russian port on the Black Sea, had been taken by Turkish troops during the First World War. Following the Armistice British Forces occupied the town on 1 December 1918. Batum was handed over to the National Republic of Georgia on 7 July 1920.

100 kopeks = 1 rouble.

1.

БАТУМ. ОБ.

Руб 10 Руб

(2.)

1919.

No.	Type	Description	Unused	Used
1.	1.	5 k. green	2·25	3·00
2.		10 k. blue	2·25	3·00
3.		50 k. yellow	60	80
4.		1 r. brown	85	1·10
5.		3 r. violet	4·00	4·50
6.		5 r. brown	5·00	5·50

1919. Arms types of Russia surch. as T **2.**

No.	Description	Unused	Used
7.	10 r. on 1 k. orange	15·00	17·00
8.	10 r. on 3 k. red	8·00	9·50
9.	10 r. on 5 k. purple	£140	£140
10.	10 r. on 10 on 7 k. blue	£140	£140

1919. T 1 optd. **BRITISH OCCUPATION.**

No.	Type	Description	Unused	Used
11	1.	5 k. green	4·00	4·50
12		10 k. blue	4·00	4·50
13		25 k. yellow	3·50	4·00
14		1 r. blue	2·25	2·75
15		2 r. pink	60	80
16		3 r. violet	60	80
17		5 r. brown	85	1·10
18		7 r. red	2·00	2·50

1919. Arms type of Russia surch. with Russian inscription, **BRITISH OCCUPATION** and new value.

No.	Description	Unused	Used
19	10 r. on 3 k. red	7·00	8·00
20a	15 r. on 1 k. orange	18·00	18·00
29	25 r. on 5 k. purple	16·00	17·00
30a	25 r. on 10 on 7 k. blue	25·00	25·00
31a	25 r. on 20 on 14 k. red and blue	25·00	25·00
32a	25 r. on 25 k. purple & grn	38·00	38·00
33	25 r. on 50 k. green & pur	25·00	25·00
21	50 r. on 1 k. orange	£110	£110
34	50 r. on 2 k. green	38·00	38·00
35	50 r. on 3 k. red	38·00	38·00
36	50 r. on 4 k. red	35·00	35·00
37	50 r. on 5 k. purple	26·00	26·00
27	50 r. on 10 k. blue	£600	£600
28	50 r. on 15 k. blue and brown	£160	£160

1920. Romanov type of Russia surch with Russian inscr, **BRITISH OCCUPATION** and new value.

No.	Description	Unused	Used
41	50 r. on 4 k. red	23·00	26·00

1920. Nos. 11, 13 and 3 surch with new value (50 r. with **BRITISH OCCUPATION** also).

No.	Type	Description	Unused	Used
42	1.	25 r. on 5 k. green	11·00	11·00
43		25 r. on 25 k. yellow	9·00	9·00
44a		50 r. on 50 k. yellow	6·00	6·00

1920. T 1 optd. **BRITISH OCCUPATION.**

No.	Type	Description	Unused	Used
45	1.	1 r. brown	30	1·10
46		2 r. blue	40	1·10
47		3 r. pink	40	1·10
48		5 r. black	40	1·10
49		7 r. yellow	40	1·10
50		10 r. green	40	1·10
51		15 r. violet	70	2·00
52		25 r. red	60	1·60
53		50 r. blue	85	2·50

BECHUANALAND

A colony and protectorate in Central S. Africa. British Bechuanaland (colony) was annexed to Cape of Good Hope in 1895. Internal Self-Government in the protectorate introduced on 1st March, 1965. Attained independence on 30th September, 1966, when the country was renamed Botswana.

1885. 12 pence = 1 shilling.
20 shillings = 1 pound.
1961. 100 cents = 1 rand.

A. BRITISH BECHUANALAND

BRITISH

British Bechuanaland (1.)

BECHUANALAND (2.)

1885. Stamps of Cape of Good Hope ("Hope" seated) optd. with T **1.**

No.	Type	Description	Unused	Used
4.	6.	½d. black	6·50	11·00
5.		1d. red	8·50	8·50
6.		2d. brown	28·00	12·00
2.		3d. red	30·00	32·00
3.		4d. blue	55·00	60·00
7.		6d. purple	60·00	28·00
8.		1s. green	£200	£130

1887. Stamps of Gt. Britain (Queen Victoria) optd. with T **2.**

No.	Description	Unused	Used
9.	½d. red	60	90

3.

4.

1887.
10. 3. 1d. lilac and black 12·00 1·25
11. 2d. lilac and black 40·00 80
12. 3d. lilac and black 3·25 4·75
13. 4d. lilac and black 38·00 2·75
14. 6d. lilac and black 42·00 3·25
15. 4. 1s. green and black 28·00 4·50
16. 2s. green and black 45·00 35·00
17. 2s. 6d. green and black 60·00 40·00
18. 5s. green and black 80·00 £100
19. 10s. green and black £170 £275
20. – £1 lilac and black £900 £800
21. – £5 lilac and black £2750 £1300
Nos. 20/1 are as Type 4 but larger, 23 × 39½ mm.

1888. Surch.
22. 3. "1d." on 1d. lilac & black 7·50 5·00
23. "2d." on 2d. lilac & black 14·00 2·50
25. "4d." on 4d. lilac & black £150 £160
26. "6d." on 6d. lilac & black 70·00 17·00
28. 4. "1s." on 1s. green & black £100 55·00

1888. Surch. **ONE HALF-PENNY** and bars.
29. 3. ½d. on 3d. lilac and black £100 £120

British
Bechuanaland.
(9.)

British
Bechuanaland
(10.)

1889. Stamp of Cape of Good Hope ("Hope" seated) optd. with T **9**.
30. 6. ½d. black 3·25 16·00

1891. Stamps of Cape of Good Hope ("Hope" seated) optd with T **10**, reading up or down.
38 6 1d. red 1·60 2·00
32 2d. brown 3·25 2·25

1891. Stamps of Gt. Britain (Queen Victoria) optd. **BRITISH BECHUANALAND.**
33. 57. 1d. lilac 4·50 60
34. 73. 2d. green and red 3·50 2·25
35. 76. 4d. green and brown 2·50 50
36. 79. 6d. purple on red 3·00 1·75
37. 82. 1s. green 13·00 16·00

B. BECHUANALAND PROTECTORATE.

1888. No. 9 to 19 optd. **Protectorate** or surch. also.
40. 71. ½d. red 2·75 18·00
41. 3. 1d. on 1d. lilac and black 5·50 11·00
42. 2d. on 2d. lilac and black 17·00 17·00
43. 3d. on 3d. lilac and black 80·00 £110
51. 4d. on 4d. lilac and black 55·00 32·00
45. 6d. on 6d. lilac and black 48·00 40·00
46. 4. 1s. green and black 55·00 48·00
47. 2s. green and black £425 £550
48. 2s. 6d. green and black £500 £650
49. 5s. green and black £1100 £1500
50. 10 s. green and black £3000 £4000

1889. Stamp of Cape of Good Hope ("Hope" seated) optd. **Bechuanaland Protectorate.**
52. 6. ½d. black 2·75 22·00

1889. No. 9 surch. **Protectorate Fourpence.**
53. 71. 4d. on ½d. red 13·00 2·75

1897. Stamp of Cape of Good Hope ("Hope" seated) optd. as T **2**.
56. 6. ½d. green 2·25 6·00

Stamps of Gt. Britain overprinted
BECHUANALAND PROTECTORATE.

1897. Queen Victoria.
59. 71. ½d. red 60 1·50
60. ½d. green 1·25 2·00
61. 57. 1d. lilac 3·00 45
62. 73. 2d. green and red 2·25 4·50
63. 75. 3d. purple on yellow 5·50 8·50
64. 76. 4d. green and brown 10·00 11·00
65. 79. 6d. purple on red 16·00 11·00

1904. King Edward VII.
66 83 ½d. turquoise 80 90
68 1d. red 4·25 25
69 2½d. blue 3·50 5·00
70 – 1 s. green & red (No. 314) 28·00 60·00

1912. King George V.
73 105. ½d. green 1·10 1·75
72 102. 1d. red 55 60
92 104. 1d. red 75 70
75 105. 1½d. brown 1·75 3·00
93 106. 2d. orange 1·50 1·00
78 104. 2½d. blue 2·50 14·00
79 106. 3d. violet 5·50 12·00
80 4d. grey 5·50 14·00
81 107. 6d. purple 6·50 14·00
82 108. 1s. brown 7·00 18·00
88 109. 2s. 6d. brown 90·00 £160
89 5s. red £120 £225

22. King George V, Baobab Tree and Cattle drinking.

1932.
99. 22. ½d. green 60 30
100. 1d. red 60 25
101. 2d. brown 70 30
102. 3d. blue 90 50
103. 4d. orange 1·00 3·25
104. 6d. purple 2·50 1·50
105. 1s. black and olive 5·00 7·00
106. 2s. black and orange 22·00 35·00
107. 2s. 6d. black and red 19·00 30·00
108. 3s. black and purple 32·00 40·00
109. 5s. black and blue 42·00 45·00
110. 10s. black and brown 90·00 £100

1935. Silver Jubilee. As T **13** of Antigua.
111. 1d. blue and red 30 75
112. 2d. blue and black 75 75
113. 3d. brown and blue 75 1·00
114. 6d. grey and purple 1·75 1·00

1937. Coronation. As T **2** of Aden.
115. 1d. red 35 40
116. 2d. brown 60 55
117. 3d. blue 60 70

1938. As T **22**, but portrait of King George VI
118b ½d. green 1·00 1·75
119 1d. red 15 35
120a 1½d. blue 30 55
121 2d. brown 15 30
122 3d. blue 20 80
123 4d. orange 30 1·40
124a 6d. purple 2·25 2·25
125 1s. black and olive 1·25 1·75
126 2s. 6d. black and red 10·00 7·50
127 5s. black and blue 23·00 7·50
128 10s. black and brown 11·00 14·00

1945. Victory. Stamps of South Africa optd. **Bechuanaland.** Alternate stamps inscr. in English or Afrikaans.
129. 55. 1d. brown and red 20 25
130. 2d. blue & vio. (No. 109) 20 35
131. 3d. blue (No. 110) 20 35
Prices for bi-lingual pairs.

1947. Royal Visit. As Nos. 32/5 of Basutoland.
132. 1d. red 10 10
133. 2d. green 10 10
134. 3d. blue 10 10
135. 1s. mauve 10 10

1948. Silver Wedding. As T **10/11** of Aden.
136. 1½d. blue 30 10
137. 10s. grey 22·00 25·00

1949. U.P.U. As T **20/23** of Antigua.
138. 1½d. blue 25 15
139. 3d. blue 55 50
140. 6d. mauve 60 80
141. 1s. olive 80 80

1953. Coronation. As T **13** of Aden.
142. 2d. black and brown 10 30

1955. As T **22** but portrait of Queen Elizabeth II, facing right.
143 ½d. green 30 15
144 1d. red 40 10
145 2d. brown 60 20
146 3d. blue 1·40 30
146b 4d. orange 4·50 5·00
147 4½d. blue 1·00 35
148 6d. purple 60 50
149 1s. black and olive 80 60
150 1s. 3d. black and lilac 7·00 7·50
151 2s. 6d. black and red 7·50 7·50
152 5s. black and blue 8·00 5·50
153 10s. black and brown 14·00 14·00

26. Queen Victoria. Queen Elizabeth II and Landscape.

1960. 75th Anniv. of Protectorate.
154. 26. 1d. sepia and black 15 15
155. 3d. mauve and black 20 10
156. 6d. blue and black 20 20

1961. Stamps of 1955 surch.
157. 1 c. on 1d. red 20 10
158. 2 c. on 2d. brown 10 10
159. 2½ c. on 2d. brown 15 10
160. 2½ c. on 3d. blue 1·75 1·50
161d. 3½ c. on 4d. orange 15 10
162a. 5 c. on 6d. purple 15 10
163. 10 c. on 1s. black and olive 15 10
164. 12½ c. on 1s. 3d. blk. & lilac 25 15
165. 25 c. on 2s. 6d. black & red 1·25 40
166. 50 c. on 5s. black and blue 1·75 65
167b. 1 r. on 10s. black & brown 3·25 2·00

28. African Golden Oriole.

1961.
168. 28. 1 c. multicoloured 45 30
169. – 2 c. orange, black & olive 45 60
170. – 2½ c. multicoloured 45 10
171. – 3½c. multicoloured 50 50
172. – 5 c. multicoloured 1·25 50
173. – 7½ c. multicoloured 60 60
174. – 10 c. multicoloured 75 50
175. – 12½ c. multicoloured 11·00 3·25
176. – 20 c. brown and drab 50 70
177. – 25 c. sepia and lemon 50 75
178. – 35 c. blue and orange 80 1·50
179. – 50 c. sepia and olive 1·00 2·25
180. – 1 r. black and brown 3·00 2·50
181. – 2 r. brown and turquoise 17·00 7·50
DESIGNS—VERT. 2 c. Hoopoe. 2½ c. Scarlet-chested Sunbird. 3½ c. Yellow-rumped Bishop. 5 c. Swallow-tailed Bee Eater. 7½ c. African Grey Hornbill. 10 c. Red-headed Weaver. 12½ c. Brown-hooded Kingfisher. 20 c. Woman musician. 35 c. Woman grinding maize. 1 r. Lion. 2 r. Police Camel Patrol. HORIZ. 25 c. Baobab tree. 50 c. Bechuana Ox.

1963. Freedom from Hunger. As T **28** of Aden.
182. 12½ c. green 25 15

1963. Cent of Red Cross. As T **33** of Antigua.
183. 2½ c. red and black 20 10
184. 12½ c. red and blue 40 35

1964. 400th Birth Anniv of Shakespeare. As T **34** of Antigua.
185. 12½ c. brown 15 15

C. BECHUANALAND

42. Map and Gaberones Dam.

1965. New Constitution.
186. 42. 2½ c. red and gold 10 10
187. 5 c. blue and gold 10 15
188. 12½ c. brown and gold 10 15
189. 25 c. green and gold 15 35

1965. Cent of I.T.U. As T **36** of Antigua.
190. 2½ c. red and yellow 20 10
191. 12½ c. mauve and brown 45 30

1965. I.C.Y. As T **37** of Antigua.
192. 1 c. purple and turquoise 10 10
193. 12½ c. green and lavender 60 55

1966. Churchill Commem. As T **38** of Antigua.
194. 1 c. blue 15 15
195. 2½ c. green 25 10
196. 12½ c. brown 65 20
197. 20 c. violet 70 25

43. Haslar Smoke Generator.

1966. Bechuanaland Royal Pioneer Corps.
198. 43. 2½ c. blue, red and green 15 10
199. – 5 c. brown and blue 15 10
200. – 15 c. blue, red and green 20 10
201. – 35 c. multicoloured 30 60
DESIGNS: 5 c. Bugler. 15 c. Gun-site. 35 c. Regimental Cap Badge.

POSTAGE DUE STAMPS

1926. Postage Due stamps of Gt. Britain optd. **BECHUANALAND PROTECTORATE.**
D 1. D 1. ½d. green 3·25 45·00
D 2. 1d. red 3·25 40·00
D 3. 2d. black 6·00 70·00

D 3.

1932.
D4 D 3 ½d. green 4·50 18·00
D5a 1d. red 30 5·00
D6b 2d. violet 60 8·00

1961. Surch.
D 7. D 3. 1 c. on 1d. red 25 50
D 8. 2 c. on 2d. violet 25 1·10
D 9. 5 c. on ½d. green 20 60

1961. As Type D 3 but values in decimal currency.
D 10. 1 c. red 15 50
D 11. 2 c. violet 15 70
D 12. 5 c. green 30 1·00

For later issues see **BOTSWANA.**

BELIZE

British Honduras was renamed Belize on the 1st June 1973 and the country became independent within the Commonwealth on 21 September 1981.

100 cents = 1 dollar.

1973. Nos. 256/66 and 277/8 of British Honduras optd. **BELIZE** and two stars.
347. – ½ c. Multicoloured. 10 10
348. 63. 1 c. black, brn. & yell. 10 10
349. – 2 c. black, green & yell. 10 10
350. – 3 c. black, brown & lilac 10 10
351. – 4 c. multicoloured 10 10
352. – 5 c. black and red 10 10
353. – 10 c. multicoloured 15 15
354. – 15 c. multicoloured 20 20
355. – 25 c. multicoloured 35 35
356. – 50 c. multicoloured 55 55
357. – $1 multicoloured 90 1·25
358. – $2 multicoloured 1·75 2·00
359. – $5 multicoloured 2·50 3·75

1973. Royal Wedding. As T **47** of Anguilla. Background colours given. Multicoloured.
360. 26 c. blue 15 10
361. 50 c. brown 15 20

82. Crana.

1974. As Nos. 256/66 and 276/78 of British Honduras. Multicoloured.
362. ½ c. Type **82** 10 10
363. 1 c. Jew Fish 10 10
364. 2 c. White-lipped peccary 10 10
365. 3 c. Grouper 10 10
366. 4 c. Collared anteater 10 10
367. 5 c. Bone Fish 10 10
368. 10 c. Paca 15 15
369. 15 c. Dolphin 20 20
370. 25 c. Kinkajou 35 35
371. 50 c. Mutton Snapper 60 70
372. $1 Tayra 1·00 1·50
373. $2 Great Barracuda 1·50 2·00
374. $5 Puma 5·50 3·50

83. Deer.

1974. Mayan Artefacts (1st series). Pottery Motifs. Multicoloured.
375. 3 c. Type **83** 10 10
376. 6 c. Jaguar deity 15 10
377. 16 c. Sea monster 20 10
378. 26 c. Cormorant 30 10
379. 50 c. Scarlet macaw 50 40
See also Nos 398/402.

84. "Parides arcas".

1974. Butterflies of Belize. Multicoloured.
380 ½ c. Type **84** 40 50
381 1 c. "Evenus regalis" 45 40
405 2 c. "Colobura dirce" 35 45
383 3 c. "Catonephele numilia" 40 45
384 4 c. "Battus belus" 45 50
385 5 c. "Callicore patelina" 85 45
386 10 c. "Diaethria astala" 70 35
410 15 c. "Nessaea aglaura" 75 45
388 16 c. "Prepona pseudo-joiceyi" 1·75 1·75
412 25 c. "Papilio thoas" 95 40
390 26 c. "Hamadryas arethusa" 2·50 4·25
413 35 c. Type **84** 4·50 3·75
391 50 c. "Panthiades bathildis" 1·50 50
392 $1 "Caligo uranus" 3·50 1·50
393 $2 "Heliconius sapho" 3·00 1·25
394 $5 "Eurytides philolaus" 3·75 4·00
395 $10 "Philaethria dido" 10·00 4·00

85. Churchill when Prime Minister, and Coronation Scene.

1974. Birth Centenary of Sir Winston Churchill. Multicoloured.

396. 50 c. Type **85** 20 20
397. $1 Churchill in stetson, and Williamsburg Liberty Bell 30 30

86. The Actun Balam Vase.

1975. Mayan Artefacts (2nd series). Multicoloured.

398. 3 c. Type **86** 10 10
399. 6 c. Seated figure 10 10
400. 16 c. Costumed priest . . 20 10
401. 26 c. Head with headdress 25 20
402. 50 c. Layman and priest . . 35 40

87. Musicians.

1975. Christmas. Multicoloured.

435. 6 c. Type **87** 10 10
436. 26 c. Children and " crib " 15 10
437. 50 c. Dancer and drummers (vert.) 25 20
438. $1 Family and map (vert.) 45 50

88. William Wrigley Jr. and Chicle Tapping.

1976. Bicent. of American Revolution. Mult.

439. 10 c. Type **88** 10 10
440. 35 c. Charles Lindbergh . . 25 40
441. $1 J. L. Stephens (archaeologist) . . . . . . 60 1·00

89. Cycling.

1976. Olympic Games, Montreal. Mult.

442. 35 c. Type **89** 15 10
443. 45 c. Running 20 15
444. $1 Shooting 35 50

1976. No. 390 surch.

445. 20 c. on 26 c. multicoloured 50 80

1976. West Indian Victory in World Cricket Cup. As Nos. 559/60 of Barbados.

446. 35 c. multicoloured . . 50 50
447. $1 black and purple . . 1·10 1·75

1976. No. 426 surch.

448. 5 c. on 15 c. multicoloured 70 1·60

92. Queen and Bishops.

1977. Silver Jubilee. Multicoloured.

449. 10 c. Royal Visit, 1975 . . 10 10
450. 35 c. Queen and Rose Window 30 20
451. $2 Type **92** . . . . 80 1·25

93. Red-capped Manakin.

1977. Birds (1st series). Multicoloured.

452. 8 c. Type **93** 75 20
453. 10 c. Hooded Oriole . . 90 25
454. 25 c. Blue-crowned Motmot 1·25 55
455. 35 c. Slaty-breasted Tinamou 1·50 75
456. 45 c. Ocellated Turkey . . 1·75 1·10
457. $1 White Hawk . . . . 3·00 3·25

See also Nos. 467/72, 486/91 and 561/6.

94. Laboratory Workers.

1977. 75th Anniv. of Pan-American Health Organization. Multicoloured.

459. 35 c. Type **94** 20 20
460. $1 Mobile medical unit . . 40 65

1978. Nos. 386 and 413 optd **BELIZE DEFENCE FORCE 1ST JANUARY 1978.**

462 10 c. "Diaethria astala" . . 30 15
463 35 c. Type **84** 70 40

96. White Lion of Mortimer.

1978. 25th Anniversary of Coronation.

464. **96.** 75 c. brn., red and silver 25 30
465. – 75 c. multicoloured . . 25 30
466. – 75 c. brn., red and silver 25 30

DESIGNS: No. 465, Queen Elizabeth II. No. 466, Jaguar (Maya god of Day and Night).

1978. Birds (2nd series). As T **93**. Mult.

467. 10 c. White-capped Parrot 35 30
468. 25 c. Crimson-collared Tanager 80 45
469. 35 c. Citreoline Trogon . . 1·00 55
470. 45 c. American Finfoot . . 1·25 1·40
471. 50 c. Muscovy Duck . . 1·40 1·60
472. $1 King Vulture . . . . 1·90 3·00

97. " Russelia sarmentosa ".

1978. Christmas. Wild Flowers and Ferns. Multicoloured.

474. 10 c. Type **97** 15 10
475. 15 c. " Lygodium polymorphum " 20 10
476. 35 c. " Heliconia aurantiaca " 30 15
477. 45 c. " Adiantum tetraphyllum " 35 30
478. 50 c. " Angelonia ciliaris " 35 40
479. $1 " Thelypteris obliterata " 60 80

98. Internal Airmail Service, 1937.

1979. Centenary of U.P.U. Membership. Multicoloured.

480. 5 c. Type **98** 10 10
481. 10 c. M.V. "Heron H", 1949. . . . . . . 15 10
482. 35 c. Dorey (canoe) mail, 1920 . . . . . . 20 20
483. 45 c. Steam Creek Railway mail, 1910 . . . . 55 55
484. 50 c. Mounted mail courier, 1882 . . . . . . 40 40
485. $2 R.M.S. "Eagle", 1856 . . 1·10 1·40

1979. No. 413 surch.

487. 15 c. on 35 c. Type **84** . . 30 1·00

1979. Birds (3rd series). As T **93**. Mult.

488. 10 c. Boat-billed Heron . . 40 10
489. 25 c. Grey-necked Wood Rail 65 20
490. 35 c. Lineated Woodpecker 75 30
491. 45 c. Blue-grey Tanager . . 80 40
492. 50 c. Laughing Falcon . . 80 70
493. $1 Long-tailed Hermit . . 1·25 1·40

101. Paslow Building, Belize G.P.O.

1979. 25th Anniv. of Coronation. Mult.

495. 25 c. Type **101** 20 10
496. 50 c. Houses of Parliament 35 10
497. 75 c. Coronation State Coach 55 10
498. $1 Queen on horseback (vert.) 70 10
499. $2 Prince of Wales (vert.) . . 1·40 15
500. $3 Queen and Duke of Edinburgh (vert.) . . 2·10 20
501. $4 Portrait of Queen (vert.) 2·75 25
502. $5 St. Edward's Crown . . 3·50 30

102. Safety Aeroplane (1909).

1979. Death Centenary of Sir Rowland Hill. 75th Anniv. of I.C.A.O. (International Civil Aviation Organization). Multicoloured.

504. 4 c. Type **102** 15 10
505. 25 c. Boeing "707-720" . . 30 10
506. 50 c. "Concorde" 60 10
507. 75 c. Handley Page "W8b" (1922) 55 10
508. $1 Avro "F" (1912) . . 70 10
509. $1.50 Cody (1910) . . . . 1·25 15
510. $2 Triplane II (1909) . . 1·50 25
511. $3 Santos Dumont's aeroplane (1906) . . . . 2·25 35
512. $4 First motorized flight, Wright brothers (1903) . . 2·75 50

103. Handball.

1979. Olympic Games, Moscow (1980). Multicoloured.

514. 25 c. Type **103** 20 10
515. 50 c. Weightlifting 35 10
516. 75 c. Athletics 55 10
517. $1 Football 70 10
518. $2 Yachting . . . . 1·40 15
519. $3 Swimming . . . . 1·75 20
520. $4 Boxing . . . . 2·00 25
521. $5 Cycling . . . . 2·50 30

104. Olympic Torch.

1979. Winter Olympic Games, Lake Placid (1980). Multicoloured.

523. 25 c. Type **104** 20 10
524. 50 c. Giant Slalom 35 10
525. 75 c. Figure-skating . . 55 10
526. $1 Slalom skiing 70 10
527. $2 Speed-skating . . . . 1·40 15
528. $3 Cross-country skiing . . 2·10 20
529. $4 Shooting . . . . 2·75 25
530. $5 Gold, Silver and Bronze medals . . . . . . 3·50 30

105. " Cypraea zebra ".

1980. Shells. Multicoloured.

532. 1 c. Type **105** 10 10
533. 2 c. " Macrocallista maculata " 10 10
534. 3 c. " Arca zebra " (vert.) 15 10
535. 4 c. "Chama macerophylla" (vert.) 20 10
536. 5 c. " Latirus cariniferus " 20 10
537. 10 c. " Conus spurius " (vert.) 30 10
538. 15 c. " Murex cabritii " (vert.) 40 10
539. 20 c. " Atrina rigida " . . 45 10
540. 25 c. " Chlamys imbricata " (vert.) 45 10
541. 35 c. " Conus granulatus " (vert.) 60 10
542. 45 c. " Tellina radiata " (vert.) 75 10
543. 50 c. " Leucozonia nassa leucozonalis " 85 10
544. 85 c. " Tripterotyphis triangularis " . . . . 1·25 10
545. $1 " Strombus gigas " (vert.) 1·50 10
546. $2 " Strombus gallus " (vert.) . . . . 2·75 30
547. $5 " Fasciolaria tulipa " . . 5·00 75
548. $10 " Arene cruentata " . . 8·00 1·25

106. Girl and Flower Arrangement.

1980. International Year of the Child. Multicoloured.

550.	25 c. Type **106**	20	10
551.	50 c. Boy holding football	30	10
552.	75 c. Boy with butterfly ..	45	10
553.	$1 Girl holding doll	60	10
554.	$1.50 Boy carrying basket of fruit	95	15
555.	$2 Boy holding shell ..	1·25	20
556.	$3 Girl holding posy ..	1·90	25
557.	$4 Boy and girl wrapped in blanket	2·50	30

1980. No. 412 surch.

560.	10 c. on 25 c. "Papilio thoas"	40	70

108. Jabiru.

1980. Birds (4th series). Multicoloured.

561.	10 c. Type **108**	2·75	2·00
562.	25 c. Barred antshrike ..	3·00	2·00
563.	35 c. Northern royal flycatcher	3·00	2·25
564.	45 c. White-necked puff-bird	3·25	2·50
565.	50 c. Ornate hawk-eagle ..	3·25	2·75
566.	$1 Golden-masked tanager	4·00	3·25

109. Speed Skating.

1980. Winter Olympic Games, Lake Placid. Medal Winners. Multicoloured.

568.	25 c. Type **109**	20	10
569.	50 c. Ice-hockey	30	10
570.	75 c. Figure-skating ..	45	10
571.	$1 Alpine-skiing	60	10
572.	$1.50 Giant slalom (women)	95	15
573.	$2 Speed-skating (women)	1·25	20
574.	$3 Cross-country skiing ..	1·90	25
575.	$5 Giant slalom ..	3·00	30

1980. "ESPAMER" International Stamp Exhibition. Madrid. Nos. 560/5 optd. **BELIZE ESPAMER '80 MADRID 3–12 OCT 1980** (Nos. 577/9) or surch. also.

577.	10 c. Type **107** ..	1·50	1·50
578.	25 c. Barred antshrike ..	1·75	1·75
579.	35 c. Northern royal fly-catcher	2·00	2·00
580.	40 c. on 45 c. White-necked puffbird	2·25	2·25
581.	40 c. on 50 c. Ornate hawk-eagle	2·25	2·25
582.	40 c. on $1 Golden-masked tanager	2·25	2·25

111. Witch in Sky.

1980. Fairy Tales. "Sleeping Beauty".

583.	25 c. multicoloured ..	25	10
584.	40 c. multicoloured ..	35	10
585.	50 c. multicoloured ..	45	10
586.	75 c. multicoloured ..	60	10
587.	$1 multicoloured	70	15
588.	$1.50 multicoloured ..	1·10	20
589.	$3 multicoloured	2·10	25
590.	$4 multicoloured	2·75	30

DESIGNS: Illustrations from the story.

112. H.M. Queen Elizabeth the Queen Mother

1980. 80th Birthday of H.M. Queen Elizabeth the Queen Mother.

592. **112.**	$1 multicoloured ..	85	30

113. The Annunciation.

1980. Christmas. Multicoloured.

594.	25 c. Type **113**	20	10
595.	50 c. Bethlehem	35	10
596.	75 c. The Holy Family ..	55	10
597.	$1 The Nativity	70	10
598.	$1.50 The Flight into Egypt	90	15
599.	$2 Shepherds following the Star	1·10	20
600.	$3 Virgin, Child & Angel	1·60	25
601.	$4 Adoration of the Kings	1·90	30

1981. "WIPA" International Stamp Exhibition, Vienna. Nos. 598 and 601 surch.

603.	$1 on $1.50 The Flight into Egypt	60	65
604.	$2 on $4 Adoration of the Kings	1·25	1·40

115. Paul Harris (founder).

1981. 75th Anniv. of Rotary International. Multicoloured.

606.	25 c. Type **115**	20	25
607.	50 c. Emblems of Rotary activities	35	35
608.	$1 75th Anniversary emblem	70	65
609.	$1.50 Educational scholarship programme ..	1·10	1·00
610.	$2 "Project Hippocrates"	1·40	1·40
611.	$3 Emblems	2·10	2·00
612.	$5 Emblem & handshake	3·50	3·25

Nos 609 and 612 are horiz.

116. Coat of Arms of Prince of Wales.

1981. Royal Wedding. Multicoloured. (a) Size 22 × 38 mm.

614.	50 c. Type **116**	35	40
615.	$1 Prince Charles in military uniform ..	70	75
616.	$1.50 Royal couple ..	1·10	1·25
	(b) Size 25 × 42 mm. with gold borders.		
617.	50 c. Type **116**	35	15
618.	$1 As No. 615	70	35
619.	$1·50 As No. 616	1·10	45

1981. No. 538 surch.

621.	10 c. on 15 c. "Murex cabritii"	1·00	1·40

118. Athletics.

1981. History of the Olympics. Mult.

622.	85 c. Type **118**	60	10
623.	$1 Cycling	70	10
624.	$1·50 Boxing	1·10	10
625.	$2 1984 Games—Los Angeles & Sarajevo ..	1·40	20
626.	$3 Baron Pierre de Coubertin	2·10	30
627.	$5 Olympic Flame ..	3·50	40

1981. Independence Commemoration (1st issue). Optd. **Independence 21 Sept., 1981.** (a) On Nos. 532/44 and 546/8.

629.	1 c. Type **105**	10	10
630.	2 c. "Macrocallista maculata"	10	10
631.	3 c. "Arca zebra" (vert.)	10	10
632.	4 c. "Chama macerophylla" (vert.)	10	10
633.	5 c. "Latirus cariniferus"	10	10
634.	10 c. "Conus spurius" (vert.)	10	10
635.	15 c. "Murex cabritii" (vert.)	15	10
636.	20 c. "Atrina rigida" ..	15	15
637.	25 c. "Chlamys imbricata" (vert.)	25	25
638.	35 c. "Conus granulatus"	30	30
639.	45 c. "Tellina radiata" (vert.)	40	35
640.	50 c. "Leucozonia nassa leucozonalis" ..	40	35
641.	85 c. "Tripterotyphis triangularis" ..	65	60
642.	$2 "Strombus gallus" (vert.)	1·50	1·40
643.	$5 "Fasciolaria tulipa" ..	3·50	3·25
644.	$10 "Arene cruentata" ..	6·50	6·50
	(b) On Nos. 606/12.		
646.	25 c. Type **115**	20	25
647.	50 c. Emblems of Rotary activities	35	35
648.	$1 75th Anniversary emblem	70	65
649.	$1·50 Educational scholarship programme ..	1·10	1·00
650.	$2 "Project Hippocrates"	1·40	1·40
651.	$3 Emblems	2·10	2·00
652.	$5 Emblems and handshake	3·50	3·25

See also Nos. 657/62.

1981. "ESPAMER" International Stamp Exhibition, Buenos Aires. No. 609 surch.

654.	$1 on $1.50 Educational scholarship programme ..	1·00	1·00

122. Black Orchid.

1981. Independence Commemoration (2nd issue). Multicoloured.

657.	10 c. Belize Coat of Arms (horiz.)	30	10
658.	35 c. Map of Belize ..	50	30
659.	50 c. Type **122**	1·00	35
660.	85 c. Baird's Tapir (horiz.)	1·10	60
661.	$1 Mahogany Tree ..	1·25	65
662.	$2 Keel-billed Toucan (horiz.)	2·50	1·40

123. Uruguayan Footballer.

1981. World Cup Football Championship, Spain (1st issue). Multicoloured.

664.	10 c. Type **123**	30	10
665.	25 c. Italian footballer ..	45	10
666.	50 c. German footballer ..	55	15
667.	$1 Brazilian footballer ..	90	35
668.	$1·50 Argentinian footballer	1·50	45
669.	$2 English footballer ..	2·00	1·40

See also Nos. 721/6.

124. British 19th-century Warship.

1981. Sailing Ships. Multicoloured.

671.	10 c. Type **124**	40	15
672.	25 c. "Madagascar" (1837)	75	25
673.	35 c. Brig "Whitby" (1838)	1·00	25
674.	55 c. "China" (1838) ..	1·25	35
675.	85 c. "Swiftsure" (1850) ..	1·75	50
676.	$2 "Windsor Castle" (1857)	3·00	70

1982. "ESSEN '82" International Stamp Exhibition. West Germany. Nos. 662 and 669 optd. **ESSEN 82** and surch. also.

678.	$1 on $2 Keel-billed toucan	1·25	75
679.	$1 on $2 English footballer	1·25	75

126. Princess Diana.

1982. 21st Birthday of Princess of Wales. (a) Size 22 × 38 mm.

680. **126.**	50 c. multicoloured ..	35	35
681.	$1 multicoloured ..	70	65
682.	$1.50 multicoloured ..	1·10	1·00

(b) Size 25 × 43 mm.

683. 50 c. multicoloured .. 35 10
684. $1 multicoloured .. 70 20
685. $1.50 multicoloured .. 1·10 30

DESIGNS: Portraits of Princess of Wales with different backgrounds.

127. Lighting Camp-fire.

1982. 125th Birth Anniv. of Lord Baden-Powell. Multicoloured.

687. 10 c. Type **127** 25 10
688. **25 c. Bird watching** .. 40 25
689. **35 c. Three scouts, one playing guitar** 50 30
690. **50 c. Hiking** 60 35
691. **85 c. Scouts with flag** .. 90 60
692. **$2 Saluting** .. .. 2·00 1·40

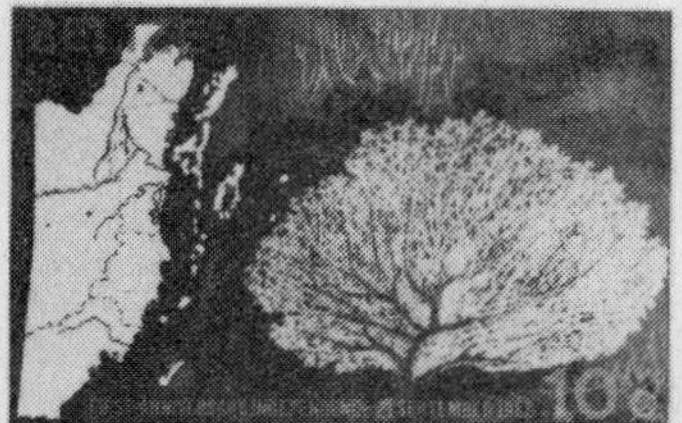

128. "Gorgonia ventalina".

1982. 1st Anniv. of Independence. Marine Life.

694. 10 c. Type **128** 35 10
695. 35 c. " Carpiuis corallinus " 75 10
696. 50 c. " Plexaura flexuasa " 1·00 10
697. 85 c. " Candylactis gigantea " 1·50 15
698. $1 " Stenopus hispidus " .. 1·75 30
699. $2 " Abudefduf saxatilus " 2·25 50

1982. " BELGICA 82 " International Stamp Exhibition, Brussels. Nos. 687/92 optd. **BELGICA 82 INT YEAR OF THE CHILD 1975. SIR ROWLAND HILL 1879 CENTENARY OF BIRTH.**

701. 10 c. Type **127** 50 30
702. 25 c. Bird watching .. 1·40 75
703. 35 c. Three scouts, one playing guitar .. .. 1·75 1·00
704. 50 c. Hiking .. .. 2·25 1·50
705. 85 c. Scouts with flag .. 3·75 2·50
706. $2 Saluting .. .. 9·00 6·50

1982. Birth of Prince William of Wales (1st issue). Nos. 680/5 optd. **BIRTH OF H.R.H. PRINCE WILLIAM ARTHUR PHILIP LOUIS 21ST JUNE 1982.**

(a) Size 22 × 38 mm.

707. 50 c. multicoloured .. 35 35
708. $1 multicoloured 70 65
709. $1.50 multicoloured .. 1·10 1·00

(b) Size 25 × 43 mm.

710. **50 c. multicoloured** .. 35 35
711. **$1 multicoloured** 70 65
712. **$1.50 multicoloured** .. 1·10 1·00

1982. Birth of Prince William of Wales (2nd issue). Nos. 614–19 optd. **BIRTH OF H.R.H. PRINCE WILLIAM ARTHUR PHILIP LOUIS 21ST JUNE 1982** in gold.

(a) Size 22 × 38 mm.

714 50 c. Type **116** .. .. 2·50 1·00
715 $1 Prince Charles in military uniform .. 5·00 2·00
716 $1.50 Royal couple .. 7·50 3·00

(b) Size 25 × 42 mm.

717. 50 c. Type **116** 35 35
718. $1 As No. 715 .. .. 70 70
719. $1.50 As No. 716 .. .. 1·10 1·10

131. Scotland v New Zealand.

1982. World Cup Football Championship, Spain (2nd issue). Multicoloured.

721. 20 c. + 10 c. Type **131** .. 40 35
722. **30 c. + 15 c. Scotland v New Zealand (different)** .. 50 35
723. **40 c. + 20 c. Kuwait v France** 60 35
724. **60 c. + 50 c. Italy v Brazil** 90 50
725. **$1 + 50 c. France v Northern Ireland** .. .. .. 1·50 65
726. **$1.50 + 75 c. Austria v Chile** 2·00 75

133. Belize Cathedral.

1983. Visit of Pope John Paul II.

729. **133.** 50 c. multicoloured .. 1·50 70

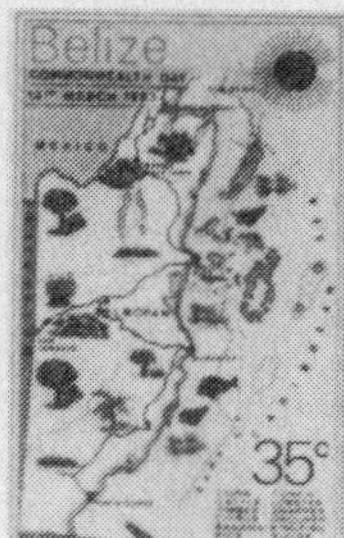

134. Map of Belize.

1983. Commonwealth Day. Multicoloured.

731. 35 c. Type **134** 25 30
732. **50 c. " Maya Stella " from Lamanai Indian church (horiz.)** 35 35
733. **85 c. Supreme Court Building (horiz.)** 60 60
734. **$2 University Centre, Belize (horiz.)** .. .. .. 1·40 1·40

1983. No. 658 surch.

735. 10 c. on 35 c. Map of Belize

136. Lana's "Flying boat" 1670.

1983. Bicentenary of Manned Flight. Mult.

736. 10 c. Type **136** 20 15
737. 25 c. Barthelemy Lourenco's flying machine, 1709 .. 40 30
738. 50 c. Guyton de Morveau's airship 50 40
739. 85 c. Early dirigible .. 80 70
740. $1 The " Clement Bayard " 95 85
741. $1.50 " R-34 " airship .. 1·40 1·25

1983. Nos. 662 and 699 surch.

743. $1.25 on $2 Keel-billed Toucan .. .. .. 3·50 4·00
744. $1.25 on $2 "Abudefduf saxatilus" .. .. 5·50 5·00

1983. No. 541 surch.

746. 10 c. on 35 c. "Conus granulatus" .. .. .. 20·00

141. Altun Ha.

1983. Maya Monuments. Multicoloured.

747. 10 c. Type **141** 10 10
748. 15 c. Xunantunich 10 10
749. 75 c. Cerros 55 60
750. $3 Lamanal .. .. .. 1·40 1·50

142. Belmopan Earth Station.

1983. World Communications Year. Mult.

752. 10 c. Type **142** 20 10
753. 15 c. "Telstar 2" 25 15
754. 75 c. U.P.U. logo 80 90
755. $2 M.V. "Heron H" Mail Service .. .. .. 2·00 2·50

143. Jaguar Cub.

1983. The Jaguar. Multicoloured.

756. 5 c. Type **143** 20 10
757. 10 c. Adult Jaguar 25 10
758. 85 c. Jaguar in river .. 1·50 1·10
759. $1 Jaguar on rock .. .. 1·75 1·50

144. Pope John Paul II.

1983. Christmas.

761. **144.** 10 c. multicoloured .. 25 10
762. 15 c. multicoloured 30 10
763. 75 c. multicoloured .. .. 1·00 75
764. $2 multicoloured .. .. 2·25 2·00

145. Foureye Butterflyfish.

1984. Marine Life from the Belize Coral Reef. Multicoloured.

766. 1 c. Type **145** 15 10
767. 2 c. Cushion Star 15 10
768. 3 c. Flower Coral 15 10
769. 4 c. Fairy Basslet 15 10
770. 5 c. Spanish Hogfish .. 15 10
771. 6 c. Star-Eyed Hermit Crab 20 10
772. 10 c. Sea Fans and Fire Sponge 25 10
773. 15 c. Blueheads 30 20
774. 25 c. Blue Striped Grunt .. 35 25
775. 50 c. Coral Crab 60 40
776. 60 c. Tube Sponge 75 45
777. 75 c. Brain Coral 85 55
778. $1 Yellow-tail Snapper .. 1·25 70
779. $2 Common Lettuce Slug 2·25 2·00
780. $5 Yellow Damselfish .. 4·00 4·00
781. $10 Rock Beauty .. .. 7·50 9·00

1984. Visit of the Archbishop of Canterbury. Nos. 772 and 775 optd. **VISIT OF THE LORD ARCHBISHOP OF CANTERBURY 8th–11th MARCH 1984.**

782. 10 c. Sea Fans and Fire Sponge 30 20
783. 50 c. Coral Crab 65 65

147. Shooting.

1984. Olympic Games, Los Angeles. Mult.

(a) Sheet Stamps.

784. 25 c. Type **147** 25 25
785. 75 c. Boxing 60 60
786. $1 Marathon 80 80
787. $2 Cycling .. .. 1·40 1·60

(b) Booklet stamps. Similar designs to T **147** but Royal cypher replaced by Queen's head.

789. 5 c. Marathon 15 30
790. 20 c. Sprinting 25 40
791. 25 c. Shot-putting 30 50
792. $2 Olympic torch .. .. 1·50 2·00

148. British Honduras 1866 1s. Stamp.

1984. "Ausipex" International Stamp Exhibition, Melbourne. Multicoloured.

793. 15 c. Type **148** 15 15
794. 30 c. Bath mail coach, 1784 25 25
795. 65 c. Sir Rowland Hill and Penny Black 55 55
796. 75 c. British Honduras railway locomotive, 1910 .. 65 65
797. $2 Royal Exhibition buildings, Melbourne .. 1·50 1·75

149. Prince Albert.

1984. 500th Anniv. (1985) of British Royal House of Tudor. Multicoloured.

799. 50 c. Type **149** 45 55
800. 50 c. Queen Victoria 45 55
801. 75 c. King George VI .. 70 90
802. 75 c. Queen Elizabeth the Queen Mother 70 90
803. $1 Princess of Wales .. 90 1·25
804. $1 Prince of Wales .. .. 90 1·25

150. White-fronted Amazon.

1984. Parrots. Multicoloured.

806. $1 Type **150** .. .. 1·50 1·25
807. $1 White-capped parrot (horiz.) .. .. .. 1·50 1·25
808. $1 Mealy amazon (horiz.) 1·50 1·25
809. $1 Red-lored amazon .. 1·50 1·25

Nos 806/9 were issued together, se-tenant forming a composite design.

151. Effigy Censer, 1450 (Santa Rita Site).

1984. Maya Artefacts. Multicoloured.

811. 25 c. Type **151** 25 25
812. 75 c. Vase, 675 (Actun Chapat) 60 60
813. $1 Tripod vase, 500 (Santa Rita site) 80 80
814. $2 Sun god Kinich Ahau, 600 (Altun Ha site) .. 1·75 1·75

152. Governor-General inspecting Girl Guides.

1985. International Youth Year and 75th Anniv. of Girl Guide Movement. Multicoloured.

815. 25 c. Type **152** 40 40
816. 50 c. Girl Guides camping 60 60
817. 90 c. Checking map on hike 95 95
818. $1.25 Students in laboratory .. .. .. 1·25 1·25
819. $2 Lady Baden-Powell (founder) .. .. 1·75 1·75

153. White-tailed Kite.

1985. Birth Bicentenary of John J. Audubon (ornithologist). Designs showing original paintings. Multicoloured.

820. 10 c. Type **153** 35 10
821. 15 c. Cuvier's Kinglet (horiz.) 45 15
822. 25 c. Painted Bunting .. 60 30
822a. 60 c. As 25 c. (1988) .. 80 60
823. 75 c. Belted Kingfisher .. 1·00 85
824. $1 Northern Cardinal .. 1·40 1·00
825. $3 Long-billed Curlew (horiz.) .. .. .. 2·75 3·00

154. The Queen Mother with Princess Elizabeth, 1928

1985. Life and Times of Queen Elizabeth the Queen Mother. Multicoloured.

827. 10 c. Type **154** 10 10
828. 15 c. The Queen Mother, 1980 .. .. .. 10 10
829. 75 c. Waving to the crowd, 1982 .. .. .. 55 60
830. $5 Four generations of Royal Family at Prince William's Christening .. 3·50 3·75

1985. Inauguration of New Government. Nos. 772/3 and 775 optd. **INAUGURATION OF NEW GOVERNMENT—21st DECEMBER 1984.**

832. 10 c. Sea Fans and Fire Sponge 20 10
833. 15 c. Blueheads 25 15
834. 50 c. Coral Crab 75 40

156. British Honduras 1935 Silver Jubilee 25 c. stamp and King George V with Queen Mary in Carriage. (Illustration reduced, actual size 68 × 32 mm.).

1985. 50th Anniv. of First Commonwealth Omnibus Issue. Designs showing British Honduras/Belize stamps. Multicoloured.

835. 50 c. Type **156** 35 40
836. 50 c. 1937 Coronation 3 c., and King George VI and Queen Elizabeth in Coronation robes .. 35 40
837. 50 c. 1946 Victory 3 c. and Victory celebrations .. 35 40
838. 50 c. 1948 Royal Silver Wedding 4 c. and King George VI and Queen Elizabeth at Westminster Abbey service 35 40
839. 50 c. 1953 Coronation 4 c. and Queen Elizabeth II in Coronation robes .. 35 40
840. 50 c. 1966 Churchill 25 c., Sir Winston Churchill and fighter aircraft .. 35 40
841. 50 c. 1972 Royal Silver Wedding 50 c. and 1948 Wedding photograph .. 35 40
842. 50 c. 1973 Royal Wedding 50 c. and Princess Anne and Capt. Mark Phillips at their Wedding .. 35 40
843. 50 c. 1977 Silver Jubilee $2 and Queen Elizabeth II during tour 35 40
844. 50 c. 1978 25th anniv. of Coronation 75 c. and Imperial Crown 35 40

157. Mounted Postboy and Early Letter to Belize.

1985. 350th Anniv. of British Post Office. Multicoloured.

846. 10 c. Type **157** 30 10
847. 15 c. Packet ship beating off privateer 45 15
848. 25 c. P.O. packet "Duke of Marlborough" 50 25
849. 75 c. P.O. packet "Diana" 1·00 60
850. $1 Falmouth P.O. packet ship .. .. .. 1·25 1·00
851. $3 S.S. "Conway" .. .. 3·00 3·00

1985. Commonwealth Heads of Govenment Meeting, Nassau, Bahamas. Nos. 827/30 optd **COMMONWEALTH SUMMIT CONFERENCE, BAHAMAS 16th-22nd OCTOBER 1985.**

852 10 c. Type **154** 10 10
853 15 c. The Queen Mother, 1980 .. .. .. 10 15
854 75 c. Waving to the crowd, 1982 .. .. .. 55 60
855 $5 Four generations of Royal Family at Prince William's Christening .. 3·50 3·75

1985. 80th Anniv of Rotary International. Nos. 815/9 optd **80th ANNIVERSARY OF ROTARY INTERNATIONAL.**

857 25 c. Type **152** 35 25
858 50 c. Girl Guides camping 50 40
859 90 c. Checking map on hike 80 70
860 $1.25 Students in laboratory .. .. 1·25 95
861 $2 Lady Baden-Powell (founder) .. .. 1·75 1·50

160. Royal Standard and Belize Flag.

1985. Royal Visit. Multicoloured.

862. 25 c. Type **160** 35 50
863. 75 c. Queen Elizabeth II .. 80 1·00
864. $4 Royal Yacht "Britannia" (81 × 39 mm.) .. .. 2·75 3·00

161. Mountie in Canoe (Canada).

1985. Christmas. 30th Anniv. of Disneyland, U.S.A. Designs showing dolls from "It's a Small World" exhibition. Multicoloured.

866. 1 c. Type **161** 10 10
867. 2 c. Indian chief and squaw (U.S.A.) 10 10
868. 3 c. Incas climbing Andes (South America) .. 10 10
869. 4 c. Africans beating drums (Africa) 10 10
870. 5 c. Snake-charmer and dancer (India and Far East) 10 10
871. 6 c. Boy and girl with donkey (Belize) 10 10
872. 50 c. Musician and dancer (Balkans) 50 50
873. $1.50, Boys with camel (Egypt and Saudi Arabia) .. .. .. 1·40 1·40
874. $3 Woman and girls playing with kite (Japan) .. .. .. 2·50 2·50

1985. World Cup Football Championship, Mexico (1986) (1st issue). Nos. 835/44 optd. **PRE "WORLD CUP FOOTBALL" MEXICO 1986.**

876. 50 c. Type **156** 40 40
877. 50 c. 1937 Coronation 3 c., and King George VI and Queen Elizabeth in Coronation robes .. 40 40
878. 50 c. Victory 3 c., and Victory celebrations .. 40 40
879. 50 c. 1948 Royal Silver Wedding 4 c., and King George VI and Queen Elizabeth at Westminister Abbey service 40 40
880. 50 c. 1953 Coronation 4 c., and Queen Elizabeth II in Coronation robes .. 40 40
881. 50 c. 1966 Churchill 25 c., Sir Winston Churchill and fighter aircraft .. 40 40
882. 50 c. 1972 Royal Silver Wedding 50 c., and 1948 wedding photograph .. 40 40
883. 50 c. 1973 Royal Wedding 50 c., and Princess Anne and Capt. Mark Phillips at their Wedding .. 40 40
884. 50 c. 1977 Silver Jubilee $2, and Queen Elizabeth II during tour 40 40
885. 50 c. 1978 25th anniv. of Coronation 75 c., and Imperial Crown 40 40

See also Nos. 936/9.

163. Indian Costume.

1986. Costumes of Belize. Multicoloured.

887. 5 c. Type **163** 40 15
888. 10 c. Maya 45 15
889. 15 c. Garifuna 50 20
890. 25 c. Creole 65 30
891. 50 c. Chinese .. .. 1·10 70
892. 75 c. Lebanese .. .. 1·50 1·10
893. $1 European c 1900 .. 1·75 1·50
894. $2 Latin .. .. 2·25 2·25

164. Pope Pius X.

1986. Easter. 20th-century Popes. Mult.

896. 50 c. Type **164** .. .. 1·00 1·00
897. 50 c. Benedict XV .. 1·00 1·00
898. 50 c. Pius XI .. .. 1·00 1·00
899. 50 c. Pius XII .. .. 1·00 1·00
900. 50 c. John XXIII .. .. 1·00 1·00
901. 50 c. Paul VI .. .. 1·00 1·00
902. 50 c. John Paul I .. .. 1·00 1·00
903. 50 c. John Paul II .. 1·00 1·00

165. Princess Elizabeth aged Three.

1986. 60th Birthday of Queen Elizabeth II. Multicoloured.

905. 25 c. Type **165** 15 20
906. 50 c. Queen wearing Imperial State Crown .. 35 40
907. 75 c. At Trooping the Colour 50 55
908. $3 Queen wearing diadem 2·10 2·25

166. Halley's Comet and Japanese "Planet A" Spacecraft.

1986. Appearance of Halley's Comet. Mult.

910. 10 c. Type **166** 20 20
911. 15 c. Halley's Comet, 1910 30 30
912. 50 c. Comet and European "Giotto" spacecraft .. 40 40
913. 75 c. Belize Weather Bureau 70 70
914. $1 Comet and U.S.A. space telescope 95 95
915. $2 Edmond Halley .. 1·50 1·50

167. George Washington.

1986. United States Presidents. Mult.

917. 10 c. Type **167** 35 35
918. 20 c. John Adams 40 40
916. 30 c. Thomas Jefferson .. 45 45
920. 50 c. James Madison .. 60 60
922. $1.50 James Monroe .. 1·25 1·25
922. $2 John Quincy Adams .. 1·50 1·50

168. Auguste Bartholdi (sculptor) and Statue's Head.

1986. Centenary of Statue of Liberty. Multicoloured.

924. 25 c. Type **168** 40 40
925. 50 c. Statue's head at U.S. Centennial Celebration, Philadelphia, 1876 .. 70 70
926. 75 c. Unveiling Ceremony, 1886 .. .. .. 80 80
927. $3 Statue of Liberty and flags of Belize and U.S.A. .. .. .. 2·25 2·25

169. British Honduras 1866 1 s. Stamp.

1986. "Ameripex" International Stamp Exhibition, Chicago. Multicoloured.

929. 10 c. Type **169** 40 40
930. 15 c. 1981 Royal Wedding $1.50 stamp 55 55
931. 50 c. U.S.A. 1918 24 c. air-mail inverted centre error 75 75
932. 75 c. U.S.S. "Constitution" (frigate) .. .. .. 1·00 1·00
933. $1 Liberty Bell .. .. 1·25 1·25
934. $2 White House .. .. 1·60 1·60

170. English and Brazilian Players.

1986. World Cup Football Championship, Mexico (2nd issue). Multicoloured.

936. 25 c. Type **170** 75 75
937. 50 c. Mexican player and Maya statues .. .. 1·10 1·10
938. 75 c. Two Belizean players 1·50 1·50
939. $3 Aztec stone calendar .. 2·50 2·50

171. Miss Sarah Ferguson.

1986. Royal Wedding. Multicoloured.

941. 25 c. Type **171** 25 25
942. 75 c. Prince Andrew .. 65 65
943. $3 Prince Andrew and Miss Sarah Ferguson (92 × 41 mm) .. .. 2·25 2·25

1986. World Cup Football Championship Winners, Mexico. Nos. 936/9 optd. **ARGENTINA–WINNERS 1986.**

945. 25 c. Type **170** 60 60
946. 50 c. Mexican player and Maya statues .. .. 1·00 1·00
947. 75 c. Two Belizean players 1·40 1·40
948. $3 Aztec stone calendar .. 2·50 2·50

1986. "Stockholmia '86" International Stamp Exhibition, Sweden. Nos. 929/34. optd. **STOCKHOLMIA 86** and emblem.

950. 10 c. Type **169** 40 40
951. 15 c. 1981 Royal Wedding $1.50 stamp 50 50
952. 50 c. U.S.A. 1918 24 c. airmail inverted centre error 70 70
953. 75 c. U.S.S. "Constitution" 90 90
954. $1 Liberty Bell .. .. 1·10 1·10
955. $2 White House .. .. 1·60 1·60

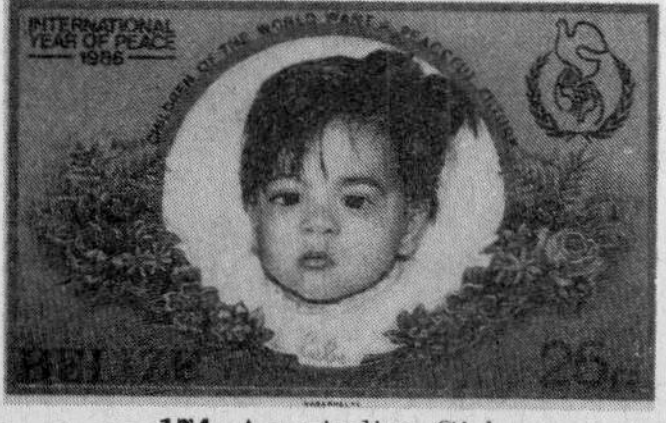

174. Amerindian Girl.

1986. International Peace Year. Mult.

957. 25 c. Type **174** 45 45
958. 50 c. European boy and girls 70 70
959. 75 c. Japanese girl .. 1·00 1·00
960. $3 Indian boy and European girl .. .. 2·25 2·25

175. "Amanita lilloi".

1986. Fungi and Toucans. Multicoloured.

962. 5 c. Type **175** 50 50
963. 10 c. Keel-billed toucan .. 60 60
964. 25 c. "Boletellus cubensis" 75 75
965. 25 c. Collared aracari .. 75 75
966. 75 c. "Psilocybe caerulescens" .. .. 1·25 1·25
967. $1 Emerald toucanet .. 1·25 1·25
968. $1.25 Crimson-rumped toucanet .. .. .. 1·25 1·25
969. $2 "Russula puiggarii" .. 1·50 1·50

176. Jose Carioca.

1986. Christmas. Designs showing Walt Disney cartoon characters in scenes from "Saludos Amigos". Multicoloured.

970. 2 c. Type **176** 10 10
971. 3 c. Jose Carioca, Panchito and Donald Duck .. 10 10
972. 4 c. Daisy Duck as Rio Carnival dancer .. 10 10
973. 5 c. Mickey and Minnie Mouse as musician and dancer 10 10
974. 6 c. Jose Carioca using umbrella as flute .. 10 10
975. 50 c. Donald Duck and Panchito 85 85
976. 65 c. Jose Carioca and Donald Duck playing hide and seek .. 1·10 1·10
977. $1.35 Donald Duck playing maracas .. .. .. 1·75 1·75
978. $2 Goofy as matador .. 2·50 2·50

177. Princess Elizabeth in Wedding Dress, 1947.

1987. Royal Ruby Wedding. Multicoloured.

980. 25 c. Type **177** 25 20
981. 75 c. Queen and Duke of Edinburgh, 1972 .. 55 50
982. $1 Queen on her 60th birthday 75 75
983. $4 in Garter robes .. .. 2·75 3·00

178. "America II", 1983.

1987. America's Cup Yachting Championship. Multicoloured.

985. 25 c. Type **178** 30 25
986. 75 c. "Stars and Stripes", 1987 .. .. .. 60 50
987. $1 "Australia II", 1983 .. 80 70
988. $4 "White Crusader" .. 3·00 3·25

179 "Mother and Child"

1987. Wood Carvings by George Gabb. Mult.

990 25 c. Type **179** 15 20
991 75 c. "Standing Form" .. 45 50
992 $1 "Love-doves" .. 60 65
993 $4 "Depiction of Music" 2·40 2·50

180 Black-handed Spider Monkey

1987. Primates. Multicoloured

995 25 c. Type **180** 25 20
996 75 c. Black howler monkey 55 50
997 $1 Spider monkeys with baby 75 70
998 $4 Two black howler monkeys .. .. 3·00 3·25

181 Guides on Parade

1987. 50th Anniv of Girl Guide Movement in Belize. Multicoloured.

1000 25 c. Type **181** 25 20
1001 75 c. Brownie camp .. 55 60
1002 $1 Guide camp 75 80
1003 $4 Olave, Lady Baden-Powell .. .. 2·75 3·00

182 Indian Refugee Camp

1987. International Year of Shelter for the Homeless. Multicoloured.

1005 25 c. Type **182** 25 20
1006 75 c. Filipino family and slum 55 50
1007 $1 Family in Middle East shanty town 75 70
1008 $4 Building modern house in Belize .. 2·75 3·00

183 "Laelia euspatha"

1987. Christmas. Orchids. Illustrations from Sanders's "Reichenbachia". Multicoloured.

1009 1 c. Type **183** 30 30
1010 2 c. "Cattleya citrina" .. 30 30
1011 3 c. "Masdevallia backhousiana" .. 30 30
1012 4 c. "Cypripedium tautzianum" 30 30
1013 5 c. "Trichopilia suavis alba" 30 30
1014 6 c. "Odontoglossum hebraicum" 30 30
1015 7 c. "Cattleya trianaei schroederiana" .. 30 30
1016 10 c. "Saccolabium giganteum" 45 45
1017 30 c. "Cattleya warscewiczii" 60 60
1018 50 c. "Chysis bractescens" 80 80
1019 70 c. "Cattleya rochellensis" 90 90
1020 $1 "Laelia elegans schilleriana" .. .. 1·00 1·00
1021 $1.50 "Laelia anceps percivaliana" .. .. 1·40 1·40
1022 $3 "Laelia gouldiana" .. 1·90 1·90

184 Christ condemned to Death

1988. Easter. The Stations of the Cross. Mult.

1024 40 c. Type **184** 30 30
1025 40 c. Christ carrying the Cross 30 30
1026 40 c. Falling for the first time 30 30
1027 40 c. Christ meets Mary .. 30 30
1028 40 c. Simon of Cyrene helping to carry the Cross 30 30
1029 40 c. Veronica wiping the face of Christ .. 30 30
1030 40 c. Christ falling a second time 30 30
1031 40 c. Consoling the women of Jerusalem 30 30
1032 40 c. Falling for the third time 30 30
1033 40 c. Christ being stripped 30 30
1034 40 c. Christ nailed to the Cross 30 30
1035 40 c. Dying on the Cross 30 30
1036 40 c. Christ taken down from the Cross .. 30 30
1037 40 c. Christ being laid in the sepulchre 30 30

185 Basketball

1988. Olympic Games, Seoul. Multicoloured.

1038	10 c. Type **185**	10	10
1039	25 c. Volleyball	15	20
1040	60 c. Table tennis ..	35	40
1041	75 c. Diving	45	50
1042	$1 Judo	60	65
1043	$2 Hockey	1·25	1·40

186 Public Health Nurse, c. 1912

1988. 125th Anniv of International Red Cross. Multicoloured.

1045	60 c. Type **186**	50	40
1046	75 c. Hospital ship and ambulance launch, 1937	65	55
1047	$1 Ambulance at hospital tent, 1956	80	70
1048	$2 Ambulance plane, 1940	1·40	1·60

187 Collared Anteater ("Ants Bear")

1989. Small Animals of Belize. Multicoloured.

1049	10 c. Paca ("Gibnut") ..	25	25
1050	25 c. Four-eyed opossum (vert)	35	35
1051	50 c. Type **187**	60	60
1052	60 c. As 10 c.	75	75
1053	75 c. Red brocket ..	85	85
1054	$2 Collared peccary ..	1·75	1·75

1989. 20th Anniv of First Manned Landing on Moon. As T **126** of Ascension. Multicoloured.

1055	25 c. Docking of "Apollo 9" modules ..	15	20
1056	50 c. "Apollo 9" command service module in Space (30 × 30 mm)	30	35
1057	75 c. "Apollo 9" emblem (30 × 30 mm)	45	50
1058	$1 "Apollo 9" lunar module in space ..	60	65

1989. No. 771 surch.

1060	5 c. on 6 c. Star-eyed hermit crab	3·00	70

190 Wesley Church

1989. Christmas. Belize Churches.

1062	**190**	10 c. blk, pink & brn	10	10
1063	–	25 c. blk, lilac & mve	15	20
1064	–	60 c. black, turq & bl	35	40
1065	–	75 c. blk, grn & lt grn	45	50
1066	–	$1 black, pale yellow and yellow ..	60	65

DESIGNS: 25 c. Baptist Church; 60 c. St. John's Anglican Cathedral; 75 c. St. Andrew's Presbyterian Church; $1 Holy Redeemer Roman Catholic Cathedral.

191 White-winged Tanager and "Catonephele numilia"

1990. Birds and Butterflies. Multicoloured.

1067	5 c. Type **191**	10	10
1068	10 c. Keel-billed toucan and "Nessaea aglaura"	10	10
1069	15 c. Magnificent frigate bird and "Eurytides philolaus"	10	10
1070	25 c. Jabiru and "Heliconius sapho"	15	20
1071	30 c. Great blue heron and "Colobura dirce" ..	15	20
1072	50 c. Northern oriole and "Hamadryas arethusia"	30	35
1073	60 c. Scarlet macaw and "Evenus regalis" ..	35	40
1074	75 c. Red-legged honey-creeper and "Callicore patelina"	45	50
1075	$1 Spectacled owl and "Caligo uranus" ..	60	65
1076	$2 Green jay and "Philaethria dido" ..	1·10	1·25
1077	$5 Turkey vulture and "Battus belus" ..	3·00	3·25
1078	$10 Osprey and "Papilio thoas"	5·75	6·00

1990. First Belize Dollar Coin. No. 1075 optd **FIRST DOLLAR COIN 1990.**

1079	$1 Spectacled owl and "Caligo uranus" ..	80	80

193 Green Turtle

1990. Turtles. Multicoloured.

1080	10 c. Type **193**	15	10
1081	25 c. Hawksbill turtle ..	20	20
1082	60 c. Saltwater loggerhead turtle	40	35
1083	75 c. Freshwater loggerhead turtle	55	55
1084	$1 Bocatora turtle ..	70	70
1085	$2 Hicatee turtle ..	1·25	1·40

194 Fairey Battle

1990. 50th Anniv of the Battle of Britain. Multicoloured.

1086	10 c. Type **194**	15	10
1087	25 c. Bristol Beaufort ..	20	20
1088	60 c. Bristol Blenheim IV	40	35
1089	75 c. Armstrong-Whitworth Whitley ..	55	55
1090	$1 Vickeers-Armstrong Wellington	70	70
1091	$2 Handley-Page Hampden	1·25	1·40

195 "Cattleya bowringiana"

1990. Christmas. Orchids. Multicoloured.

1092	25 c. Type **195**	25	20
1093	50 c. "Rhyncholaelia digbyana"	35	35
1094	60 c. "Sobralia macrantha"	45	40
1095	75 c. "Chysis bractescens"	60	55
1096	$1 "Vanilla planifolia" ..	70	70
1097	$2 "Epidendrum polyanthum"	1·25	1·40

196 Common Iguana

1991. Reptiles and Mammals. Multicoloured.

1098	25 c. Type **196**	25	25
1099	50 c. Morelet's crocodile	40	40
1100	60 c. American manatee	45	45
1101	75 c. Boa constrictor ..	55	55
1102	$1 Baird's tapir ..	70	70
1103	$2 Jaguar	1·25	1·25

1991. 65th Birthday of Queen Elizabeth II and 70th Birthday of Prince Philip. As T **139** of Ascension. Multicoloured.

1104	$1 Queen Elizabeth II wearing tiara	60	65
1105	$1 Prince Philip wearing panama	65	65

197 Weather Radar

1991. International Decade for Natural Disaster Reduction.

1106	**197**	60 c. multicoloured ..	45	45
1107	–	75 c. multicoloured ..	55	55
1108	–	$1 blue and black ..	70	70
1109	–	$2 multicoloured ..	1·25	1·25

DESIGNS: 75 c. Weather station; $1 Floods in Belize after Hurricane Hattie, 1961; $2 Satellite image of Hurricane Gilbert.

198 Thomas Ramos and Demonstration

1991. 10th Anniv of Independence. Famous Belizians. Multicoloured.

1110	25 c. Type **198**	15	20
1111	60 c. Sir Isaiah Morter and palm trees ..	35	40
1112	75 c. Antonio Soberanis and political meeting ..	45	50
1113	$1 Santiago Ricalde and cutting sugar-cane ..	60	65

199 "Anansi the Spider"

1991. Christmas. Folklore. Multicoloured.

1114	25 c. Type **199**	15	20
1115	50 c. "Jack-o-Lantern" ..	30	35
1116	60 c. "Tata Duende" (vert)	35	40
1117	75 c. "Xtabai"	45	50
1118	$1 "Warrie Massa" (vert)	60	65
1119	$2 "Old Heg"	1·10	1·25

200 "Gongora quinquenervis"

1992. Easter. Orchids. Multicoloured.

1120	25 c. Type **200**	15	20
1121	50 c. "Oncidium sphacelatum"	30	35
1122	60 c. "Encyclia bratescens"	35	40
1123	75 c. "Epidendrum ciliare"	45	50
1124	$1 "Psygmorchis pusilla"	60	65
1125	$2 "Galeandra batemanii"	1·10	1·25

POSTAGE DUE STAMPS

D 2.

1976.

D 6.	D **2.**	1 c. red and green ..	10	45
D 7.	–	2 c. purple and violet	10	45
D 8.	–	5 c. green and brown	15	55
D 9.	–	15 c. green and red..	20	80
D 10.	–	25 c. orange & green	30	90

DESIGNS: Nos. D 7/10 as Type D **2** but with different frames.

BERMUDA

A group of islands in the W. Atlantic, E. of N. Carolina. Usually regarded by collectors as part of the Br. W. Indies group, though this is not strictly correct.

1865. 12 pence = 1 shilling.
20 shillings = 1 pound.
1970. 100 cents = 1 dollar (U.S).

9. Queen Victoria.

13. Dry Dock.

1865. Portrait. Various frames.

No.	Type	Description	Unused	Used
19	9	½d. stone	1·50	3·50
21a		½d. green	1·90	70
24a		1d. red	3·50	20
25		2d. blue	35·00	3·25
26a		2d. purple	2·50	1·25
27a		2½d. blue	4·00	40
0		3d. yellow	£150	60·00
8		3d. grey	18·00	5·50
0		4d. red	12·00	1·50
4		4d. brown	24·00	35·00
7		6d. mauve	22·00	12·00
11		1s. green	11·00	£100
29a		1s. brown	13·00	11·00

1874. Surch. in words

No.	Type	Description	Unused	Used
15.	9.	1d. on 2d. blue	£700	£350
16.		1d. on 3d. yellow.. ..	£450	£350
17.		1d. on 1s. green	£500	£250
12.		3d. on 1d. red	£8000	
14.		3d. on 1s. green	£1200	£650

1901. Surch. **ONE FARTHING** and bar.

No.	Type	Description	Unused	Used
30.	9.	¼d. on 1s. grey	30	30

1902.

No.	Type	Description	Unused	Used
34a	13.	¼d. brown and violet ..	50	2·00
31		½d. black and green ..	6·00	1·25
41		½d. green..	3·75	2·50
32		1d. brown and red ..	7·00	10
42		1d. red	13·00	10
37		2d. grey and orange ..	7·50	10·00
38		2½d. brown and blue ..	8·50	12·00
43		2½d. blue..	12·00	5·75
33		3d. mauve and green ..	1·75	1·75
39		4d. blue and brown ..	3·00	11·00

14. Badge of the Colony.

15.

1910.

No.	Type	Description	Unused	Used
76b	14.	¼d. brown	70	1·25
77		½d. green..	50	15
79		1d. red	6·00	30
79b		1½d. brown	3·50	35
80		2d. grey	1·00	1·50
82a		2½d. blue..	1·75	35
81a		2½d. green	1·00	1·50
84		3d. purple on yellow ..	80	1·00
83		3d. blue	15·00	25·00
85		4d. red on yellow ..	1·00	1·25
86		6d. purple	80	80
51		1s. black on green ..	2·00	3·75
51b	15.	2s. purple & blue on blue	11·00	32·00
52		2s. 6d. black & red on bl.	18·00	50·00
52b		4s. black and red ..	60·00	75·00
53c		5s. green & red on yell.	35·00	55·00
92c		10s. green & red on green	£130	£170
93		12s. 6d. black & orange	£300	£350
55		£1 purple & black on red	£400	£600

1918 Optd. **WAR TAX.**

No.	Type	Description	Unused	Used
56.	14.	1d. red	35	40

18.
Tercent. of Representative Institutions.

(a) **1920.** 1st Issue.

No.	Type	Description	Unused	Used
59.	18.	¼d. brown..	60	6·50
60.		½d. green	1·25	7·00
65.		1d. red	1·00	30
61.		2d. grey	8·50	23·00
66.		2½d. blue	6·50	8·00
62.		3d. purple on yellow ..	8·00	20·00
63.		4d. black & red on yellow	8·50	18·00
67.		6d. purple	15·00	38·00
64.		1s. black on green ..	16·00	38·00

19.

(b) **1921.** 2nd Issue.

No.	Type	Description	Unused	Used
74.	19.	¼d. brown	35	2·75
75.		½d. green	2·75	6·00
76.		1d. red	2·00	35
68.		2d. grey	4·50	15·00
69.		2½d. blue	8·00	3·00
70.		3d. purple on yellow ..	4·00	12·00
71.		4d. red on yellow ..	14·00	17·00
72.		6d. purple	8·00	29·00
73.		1s. black on green ..	21·00	32·00

1935. Silver Jubilee. As T **13** of Antigua.

No.	Type	Description	Unused	Used
94.		1d. blue and red	45	55
95.		1½d. blue and grey ..	70	95
96.		2½d. brown and blue ..	1·40	90
97.		1s. grey and purple ..	9·00	14·00

20. Hamilton Harbour.

22. "Lucie" (yacht).

1936.

No.	Type	Description	Unused	Used
98.	20.	½d. green	10	10
99.	–	1d. black and red ..	15	15
100.	–	1½d. black and brown..	75	15
101.	22.	2d. black and blue ..	4·50	2·00
102.	–	2½d. blue	80	25
103.	–	3d. black and red ..	2·25	90
104.	–	6d. red and violet ..	60	10
105.	–	1s. green	3·25	4·75
106.	20.	1s. 6d. brown	30	10

DESIGNS—HORIZ. 1d., 1½d. South Shore, nr. Spanish Rock. 3d. Point House, Warwick Parish. VERT. 2½d., 1s. Grape Bay, Paget Parish. 6d. House at Par-la-Ville, Hamilton.
The 1d., 1½d., 2½d. and 1s. values include a portrait of King George V.

1937. Coronation. As T **2** of Aden.

No.	Type	Description	Unused	Used
107.		1d. red	50	50
108.		1½d. brown	60	45
109.		2½d. blue	1·10	1·50

26. Ships in Hamilton Harbour.

DESIGNS—VERT. 3d. St. David's Lighthouse. The 2½d. and 1s. are as 1935, but with King George VI portrait.

28. White-tailed Tropic Bird, Arms of Bermuda and Native Flower.

1938.

No.	Type	Description	Unused	Used
110	26	1d. black and red ..	40	20
111b		1½d. blue and brown..	1·25	35
112	22	2d. blue and black ..	38·00	5·00
112a	–	2d. blue and red ..	1·50	80
113	–	2½d. blue	11·00	90
113c	–	2½d. blue and sepia ..	1·50	80
114	–	3d. black and red ..	11·00	70
114a	–	3d. black and blue ..	1·50	40
114c	28	7½d. blk., blue & green	3·75	2·25
115	–	1s. green	1·75	50

As T **15**, but King George VI portrait.

No.	Type	Description	Unused	Used
116b		2s. purple & blue on blue	7·00	1·50
117d		2s. 6d. blk. & red on blue	13·00	9·00
118f		5s. green and red on yell.	13·00	11·00
119f		10s. green & red on grn.	22·00	32·00
120b		12s. 6d. grey and orange	70·00	40·00
121c		£1 purple & black on red	45·00	60·00

1940. Surch. **HALFPENNY XX.**

No.	Type	Description	Unused	Used
122.	26.	½d. on 1d. black and red	15	45

1946. Victory. As T **9** of Aden.

No.	Type	Description	Unused	Used
123.		1½d. brown	15	15
124.		3d. blue..	15	15

1948. Silver Wedding. As T **10** and **11** of Aden.

No.	Type	Description	Unused	Used
125.		1½d. brown	30	50
126.		£1 red	48·00	48·00

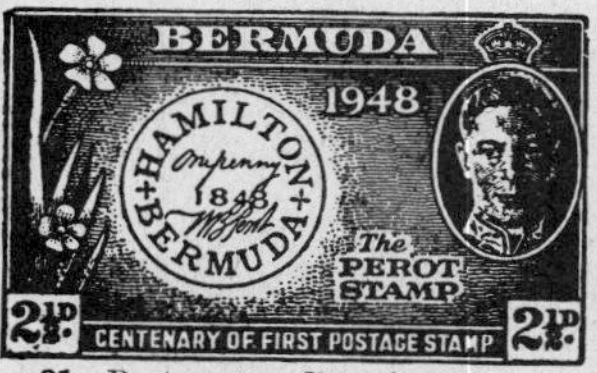

31. Postmaster Perot's Stamp.

1949. Cent. of Postmaster Perot's Stamp.

No.	Type	Description	Unused	Used
127.	31.	2½d. blue and brown ..	15	15
128.		3d. black and blue ..	15	15
129.		6d. violet and green ..	15	15

1949. U.P.U. As T **20/23** of Antigua.

No.	Type	Description	Unused	Used
130.		2½d. black	75	75
131.		3d. blue..	90	75
132.		6d. purple	1·00	75
133.		1s. green	1·00	75

1953. Coronation. As T **13** of Aden.

No.	Type	Description	Unused	Used
134.		1½d. black and blue ..	35	15

34. Easter Lily.

43. Hog Coin.

1953.

No.	Type	Description	Unused	Used
135a	–	½d. olive	10	25
136a	–	1d. black and red ..	15	10
137	34.	1½d. green	20	10
138	–	2d. blue and red ..	40	30
139	–	2½d. red	1·25	50
140	–	3d. purple	30	10
141	–	4d. black and blue ..	30	30
142	–	4½d. green	45	80
143	–	6d. black and turquoise	4·00	40
156	–	6d. black and mauve ..	30	15
143a	–	8d. black and red ..	1·75	20
143b	–	9d. violet	6·00	1·50
144	–	1s. orange	40	15
145	–	1s. 3d. blue	1·50	30
146	–	2s. brown	2·00	85
147	–	2s. 6d. red	1·75	45
148	43.	5s. red	10·00	85
149	–	10s. blue	9·00	4·50
150	–	£1 multicoloured ..	20·00	19·00

DESIGNS—HORIZ. ½d. Easter lilies, 1d., 4d. Postmaster Perot's stamp. 2d. "Victory II" (racing dinghy). 2½d. Sir George Somers and "Sea Venture". 3d., 1s. 3d. Map of Bermuda, 4½d., 9d. "Sea Venture" inter-island boat, coin and Perot stamp. 6d. (No. 143), 8d. White-tailed Tropic Bird. 6d. (No. 156), Perot's Post Office. 1s. Early Bermuda coins. 2s. Arms of St. George's 10s. Obverse and reverse of hog coin. £1 Arms of Bermuda. VERT. 2s. 6d. Warwick Fort. No. 156 commemorates the restoration and reopening of Perot's Post Office.

1953. Royal Visit. As No. 143a but inscr "ROYAL VISIT 1953".

No.	Type	Description	Unused	Used
151.		6d. black and turquoise	30	20

1953. Three Power Talks. Nos. 140 and 145 optd **Three Power Talks December, 1953.**

No.	Type	Description	Unused	Used
152.		3d. purple	10	10
153.		1s. 3d. blue	10	10

1956. 50th Anniv of United States–Bermuda Yacht Race. Nos. 143a and 145 optd **50th ANNIVERSARY US–BERMUDA OCEAN RACE 1956.**

No.	Type	Description	Unused	Used
154.		8d. black and red.. ..	20	25
155.		1s. 3d. blue	20	30

49. Arms of King James 1 and Queen Elizabeth II.

1959. 350th Anniv. of Settlement. Arms in red, yellow and blue. Frame colours given.

No.	Type	Description	Unused	Used
157.	49.	1½d. blue	20	10
158.		3d. grey..	25	30
159.		4d. purple	30	35
160.		8d. violet	30	15
161.		9d. olive	30	80
162.		1s 3d. brown	30	25

50. The Old Rectory, St. George's, c. 1730.

1962.

No.	Type	Description	Unused	Used
163.	50.	1d. purple, blk. & orge.	10	35
164.	–	2d. multicoloured ..	10	15
165.	–	3d. brown and blue ..	10	10
166.	–	4d. brown and mauve	20	35
167.	–	5d. blue and red ..	75	2·00
168.	–	6d. blue, grn. & bl. ..	20	20
169.	–	8d. blue, green & orge.	30	20
170.	–	9d. blue and brown ..	25	25
197.	–	10d. violet and ochre..	75	60
171.	–	1s. multicoloured ..	20	10
172.	–	1s. 3d. lake, grey & bistre	50	15
173.	–	1s 6d. violet and ochre	1·50	2·50
199.	–	1s 6d. blue and red ..	3·25	1·75
174.	–	2s. brown and orange	2·00	1·25
175.	–	2s 3d. sepia and green	2·00	5·50
176.	–	2s 6d. sep., grn. & yell.	55	35
177.	–	5s. purple and green ..	1·25	1·50
178.		10s. mve, grn. & buff..	4·00	5·00
179.	–	£1 blk., olive & orge...	14·00	13·00

DESIGNS: 2d. Church of St. Peter, St. George's. 3d. Government House, 1892. 4d. The Cathedral, Hamilton, 1894. 5d., 1s. 6d. (No. 199) H.M. Dockyard, 1811. 6d. Perot's Post Office, 1848. 8d. G.P.O., Hamilton, 1869. 9d. Library, Par-la-Ville. 10d., 1s. 6d. (No. 173) Bermuda cottage, c. 1705. 1s. Christ Church, Warwick, 1719. 1s. 3d. City Hall, Hamilton, 1960. 2s. Town of St. George. 2s. 3d. Bermuda house, c. 1710. 2s. 6d. Bermuda house, early 18th century. 5s. Colonial Secretariat, 1833. 10s. Old Post Office, Somerset, 1890. £1. The House of Assembly, 1815.

1963. Freedom from Hunger. As T **28** of Aden.

No.	Type	Description	Unused	Used
180.		1s. 3d. sepia	80	35

1963. Cent of Red Cross. As T **33** of Antigua.

No.	Type	Description	Unused	Used
181.		3d. red and black ..	75	25
182.		1s. 3d. red and blue ..	2·00	1·75

67. "Tsotsi in the Bundu". (Finn class yacht.).

1964. Olympic Games, Tokyo.

No.	Type	Description	Unused	Used
183.	67.	3d. red, violet and blue	10	10

1965. Cent of I.T.U. As T **36** of Antigua.

No.	Type	Description	Unused	Used
184.		3d. blue and green ..	75	25
185.		2s. yellow and blue ..	1·50	1·25

68. Scout Badge and St. Edward's Crown.

1965. 50th Anniv. of Bermuda Boy Scouts Association.
186. 68. 2s. multicoloured .. 50 50

1965. I.C.Y. As T **37** of Antigua.
187. 4d. purple and turquoise.. 50 20
188. 2s. 6d. green and lavender 1·50 80

1966. Churchill Commem. As T **38** of Antigua.
189. 3d. blue 50 20
190. 6d. green .. .. .. 1·00 45
191. 10d. brown .. .. 1·25 75
192. 1s. 3d. violet .. .. 1·50 1·75

1966. World Cup Football Championship. As T **40** of Antigua.
193. 10d. multicoloured .. 50 15
194. 2s. 6d. multicoloured .. 75 65

1966. 20th Anniv. of U.N.E.S.C.O. As T **54/56** of Antigua.
201. 4d. multicoloured .. 60 15
202. 1s. 3d. yellow, violet & olive 1·25 65
203. 2s. black, purple & orange 2·00 1·25

69. G.P.O. Building.

1967. Opening of New General Post Office.
204. 69. 3d. multicoloured .. 10 10
205. 1s. multicoloured .. 10 10
206. 1s. 6d. multicoloured .. 15 20
207. 2s. 6d. multicoloured .. 15 30

70. "Mercury" (cable ship) and Chain Links.

1967. Inauguration of Bermuda–Tortola Telephone Service. Multicoloured.
208. 3d. Type **70** .. 10 10
209. 1s. Map, telephone and microphone 10 10
210. 1s. 6d. Telecommunications media 20 20
211. 2s. 6d. "Mercury" (cable ship) and Marine Fauna 25 30

74. Human Rights Emblem and Doves.

1968. Human Rights Year.
212. 74. 3d. indigo, blue & green 10 10
213. 1s. brown, blue & lt. bl. 10 10
214. 1s. 6d. black, blue & red 10 10
215. 2s. 6d. grn., bl. & yellow 15 15

75. Mace and Queen's Profile.

1968. New Constitution.
216. 75. 3d. multicoloured .. 10 10
217. 1s. multicoloured .. 10 10
218. – 1s. 6d. yell., blk. & bl. 10 15
219. – 2s. 6d. lilac, black and yellow 15 20

DESIGN: 1s. 6d., 2s. 6d., Houses of Parliament, and House of Assembly, Bermuda.

MINIMUM PRICE

The minimum price quoted is 10p which represents a handling charge rather than a basis for valuing common stamps. For further notes about prices see introductory pages.

77. Football, Athletics and Yachting.

1968. Olympic Games, Mexico.
220. 77. 3d. multicoloured .. 10 10
221. 1s. multicoloured .. 10 10
222. 1s. 6d. multicoloured .. 15 15
223. 2s. 6d. multicoloured .. 20 30

78. Brownie and Guide.

1969. 50th Anniv. of Girl Guides. Mult.
224. 3d. Type **78** 10 10
225. 1s. Type **78** 20 10
226. 1s. 6d. Guides and Badge 25 25
227. 2s. 6d. As 1s. 6d. .. 35 50

80 Emerald-studded Gold Cross and Seaweed.

1969. Underwater Treasure. Multicoloured.
228. 4d. Type **80** 20 10
229. 1s. 3d. Emerald-studded gold cross and sea-bed .. 35 15
230. 2s. As Type **80** 45 55
231. 2s. 6d. As 1s. 3d. .. 45 80

1970. Decimal Currency. Nos. 163/79 surch.
232. 1 c. on 1d. pur., blk. & orge. 10 40
233. 2 c. on 2d. multicoloured .. 10 10
234. 3 c. on 3d. brown and blue 10 10
235. 4 c. on 4d. brown & mauve 10 10
236. 5 c. on 8d. blue, grn. & orge. 15 35
237. 6 c. on 6d. grey, grn. & blue 15 30
238. 9 c. on 9d. blue and brown 30 55
239. 10 c. on 10d. violet & ochre 30 45
240. 12 c. on 1s. multicoloured 30 15
241. 15 c. on 1s. 3d. lake, grey and bistre .. .. 1·50 1·00
242. 18 c. on 1s. 6d. blue & red 80 65
243. 24 c. on 2s. brown & orange 85 75
244. 30 c. and 2s. 6d. sepia, green and yellow .. .. 1·00 1·25
245. 36 c. on 2s. 3d. sepia & grn. 1·75 2·50
246. 60 c. on 5s. purple & green 2·25 2·75
247. $1.20 on 10s. mauve, green and buff .. .. .. 4·00 8·50
248. $2.40 on £1 black, olive and orange .. .. 7·00 14·00

83. Spathiphyllum.

1970. Flowers. Multicoloured.
249. 1 c. Type **83** 10 20
250. 2 c. Bottlebrush 20 25
251. 3 c. Oleander (vert.) .. 10 10
252. 4 c. Bermudiana.. .. 10 10
253. 5 c. Poinsettia 30 20
254. 6 c. Hibiscus 30 30
255. 9 c. Cereus 20 35
256. 10 c. Bougainvillea (vert.) 20 15
257. 12 c. Jacaranda 80 60
258. 15 c. Passion Flower .. 90 1·40
258a. 17 c. As 15 c. .. .. 2·25 2·00
259. 18 c. Coralita .. .. 1·75 2·25
259a. 20 c. As 18 c. .. .. 2·25 2·00
260. 24 c. Morning Glory .. 1·50 3·25
260a. 25 c. As 24 c. .. .. 2·25 2·50
261. 30 c. Tecoma .. .. 1·00 1·25
262. 36 c. Angel's Trumpet .. 1·25 2·25
262a. 40 c. as 36 c. .. .. 2·25 2·75
263. 60 c. Plumbago .. .. 1·75 2·75
263a. $1 As 60 c. .. .. 3·00 3·75
264. $1.20 Bird of Paradise Flower .. .. .. 2·75 3·50
264a. $2 As $1.20 .. .. 5·00 7·00
265. $2.40 Chalice Cup .. 5·50 9·00
265a. $3 As $2.40 .. .. 9·00 10·00

1970. 350th Anniv. of Bermuda Parliament. Multicoloured.
266. 4 c. Type **84** 10 10
267. 15 c. The Sessions House, Hamilton 25 15
268. 18 c. St. Peter's Church, St. George's 25 20
269. 24 c. Town Hall, Hamilton 35 45

85. Street Scene, St. George's.

1971. "Keep Bermuda Beautiful". Mult.
271. 4 c. Type **85** 20 10
272. 15 c. Horseshoe Bay .. 55 45
273. 18 c. Gibbs Hill Lighthouse 1·00 1·10
274. 24 c. Hamilton Harbour .. 1·25 1·75

86. Building of the "Deliverance".

1971. Voyage of the "Deliverance". Mult.
275. 4 c. Type **86** 50 20
276. 15 c. "Deliverance" and "Patience" at Jamestown (vert.) .. .. .. 1·50 1·75
277. 18 c. Wreck of the "Sea Venture" (vert.) .. 1·75 2·25
278. 24 c. "Deliverance" and "Patience" on high seas 1·90 2·50

87. Green overlooking Ocean View.

1971. Golfing in Bermuda. Multicoloured.
279. 4 c. Type **87** 30 10
280. 15 c. Golfers at Port Royal 60 60
281. 18 c. Castle Harbour .. 70 60
282. 24 c. Belmont 85 85

1971. Anglo-American Talks. Nos. 252, 258, 259 and 260 optd. **HEATH-NIXON DECEMBER 1971.**
283. 4 c. Bermudiana 10 10
284. 15 c. Passion Flower .. 10 20
285. 18 c. Coralita 15 55
286. 24 c. Morning Glory .. 20 70

89. Bonefish.

1972. World Fishing Records. Multicoloured.
287. 4 c. Type **89** 30 10
288. 15 c. Wahoo 35 30
289. 18 c. Yellowfin Tuna .. 40 45
290. 24 c. Greater Amberjack .. 45 70

1972. Royal Silver Wedding. As T **52** of Ascension, but with "Admiralty Oar" and Mace in background.
291. 4 c. violet.. .. .. 10 10
292. 15 c. red 15 30

91. Palmetto.

1973. Tree Planting Year. Multicoloured.
293. 4 c. Type **91** 30 10
294. 15 c. Olivewood Bark .. 90 75
295. 18 c. Bermuda Cedar .. 1·00 1·00
296. 24 c. Mahogany .. .. 1·10 1·40

1973. Royal Wedding. As T **47** of Anguilla. Background colour given. Mult.
297. 15 c. mauve 10 15
298. 18 c. blue 10 15

92. Bernard Park, Pembroke, 1973.

1973. Centenary of Lawn Tennis. Mult.
299. 4 c. Type **92** 30 10
300. 15 c. Clermont Court, 1873 60 50
301. 18 c. Leamington Spa Court, 1872 .. .. 70 1·00
302. 24 c. Staten Island Courts, 1874 .. .. .. 85 1·25

93. Weather Vane, City Hall.

1974. 50th Anniv. of Rotary in Bermuda. Multicoloured.
320. 5 c. Type **93** 15 10
321. 17 c. St. Peter's Church, St. George's 45 35
322. 20 c. Somerset Bridge .. 50 1·00
323. 25 c. Map of Bermuda, 1626 60 1·60

94. Jack of Clubs and "good bridge hand".

1975. World Bridge Championships, Bermuda. Multicoloured.
324. 5 c. Type **94** 25 10
325. 17 c. Queen of Diamonds and Bermuda Bowl .. 65 50
326. 20 c. King of Hearts and Bermuda Bowl .. .. 70 1·60
327. 25 c. Ace of Spades and Bermuda Bowl .. .. 80 1·75

95. Queen Elizabeth II and the Duke of Edinburgh.

1975. Royal Visit.
328. 95. 17 c. multicoloured .. 60 65
329. 20 c. multicoloured .. 65 1·60

96. "Cavalier" Flying-boat, 1937.

1975. 50th Anniv. of Air-mail Service. Mult.

330.	5 c. Type **96**	40	10
331.	17 c. Airship " Los Angeles ", 1925	1·25	75
332.	20 c. Lockheed " Constellation ", 1946	1·40	2·00
333.	25 c. Boeing " 747 ", 1970	1·50	2·75

97. Supporters of American Army raiding Royal Magazine.

1975. Bicentenary of Gunpowder Plot, St. George's. Multicoloured.

335.	5 c. Type **97**	20	10
336.	17 c. Setting off for raid	40	30
337.	20 c. Loading gunpowder aboard American ship	45	70
338.	25 c. Gunpowder on beach	50	80

98. Launching "Ready" (bathysphere).

1976. 50th Anniv. of Bermuda Biological Station. Multicoloured.

357.	5 c. Type **98**	35	10
358.	17 c. View from the sea (horiz.)	70	60
359.	20 c. H.M.S. " Challenger ", 1873 (horiz.)	75	2·00
360.	25 c. Beebe's Bathysphere descent, 1934	1·00	2·25

99. " Christian Radich ".

1976. Tall Ships Race, 1976. Multicoloured.

361.	5 c. Type **99**	50	20
362.	12 c. " Juan Sebastian de Elcano "	90	1·50
363.	17 c. U.S.C.G. " Eagle "	1·10	1·50
364.	20 c. " Winston S. Churchill "	1·25	2·25
365.	40 c. " Kruzenshtern "	1·75	2·75
366.	$1 " Cutty Sark " trophy	2·75	6·00

100. Silver Trophy and Club Flags.

1976. 75th Anniv. of St. George's v. Somerset Cricket Cup Match. Multicoloured.

367.	5 c. Type **100**	35	10
368.	17 c. Badge and Pavilion, St. George's Club	75	55
369.	20 c. Badge and Pavilion, Somerset Club	1·00	2·50
370.	25 c. Somerset playing field	1·50	3·50

101. Royal Visit, 1975.

1977. Silver Jubilee. Multicoloured.

371.	5 c. Type **101**	15	10
372.	20 c. St. Edward's Crown	25	20
373.	$1 The Queen in Chair of Estate	80	1·25

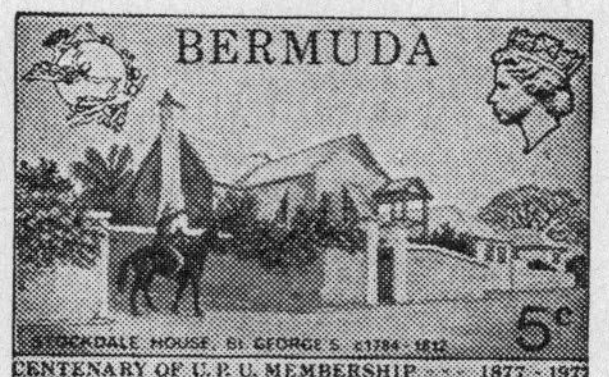

102. Stockdale House, St. George's, 1784–1812.

1977. Centenary of U.P.U. Membership. Multicoloured.

374.	5 c. Type **102**	15	10
375.	15 c. Perot Post Office and stamp	35	50
376.	17 c. St. George's P.O. c. 1860	35	50
377.	20 c. Old G.P.O., Hamilton, c. 1935	45	60
378.	40 c. New G.P.O., Hamilton, 1967	75	1·10

103. 17th-Century Ship approaching Castle Is.

1977. Piloting. Multicoloured.

379.	5 c. Type **103**	25	10
380.	15 c. Pilot leaving ship, 1795	45	50
381.	17 c. Pilots rowing out to paddle-steamer	60	50
382.	20 c. Pilot gigs and brig " Harvest Queen "	75	1·50
383.	40 c. Modern pilot cutter and R.M.S. " Queen Elizabeth 2 "	1·25	2·50

104. Great Seal of Queen Elizabeth I.

1978. 25th Anniv. of Coronation. Mult.

384.	8 c. Type **104**	10	10
385.	50 c. Great Seal of Queen Elizabeth II	30	30
386.	$1 Queen Elizabeth II	60	75

105. White-tailed Tropic Bird.

1978. Wildlife. Multicoloured.

387	3 c. Type **105**	60	40
388	4 c. White-eyed vireo	75	40
389	5 c. Eastern bluebird	75	35
390	7 c. Whistling frog	50	40
391	8 c. Common cardinal (Redbird)	85	35
392	10 c. Spiny lobster	20	10
393	12 c. Land crab	30	40
394	15 c. Lizard (Skink)	30	15
395	20 c. Foureye butterfly fish	30	30
396	25 c. Red hind	30	20
397	30 c. "Danaus plexippus" (butterfly)	1·75	1·50
398	40 c. Rock beauty	45	90
399	50 c. Banded butterfly fish	55	60
400	$1 Blue angelfish	95	1·75
401	$2 Humpback whale	2·00	2·75
402	$3 Green turtle	2·75	3·00
403	$5 Cahow	6·50	6·00

106. Map by Sir George Somers, 1609.

1979. Antique Maps. Multicoloured.

404.	8 c. Type **106**	15	10
405.	15 c. Map by John Seller, 1685	20	15
406.	20 c. Map by H. Moll, 1729–40 (vert.)	25	25
407.	25 c. Map by Desbruslins, 1740	30	30
408.	50 c. Map by Speed, 1626	45	70

107. Policeman and Policewoman.

1979. Centenary of Police. Multicoloured.

409.	8 c. Type **107**	20	10
410.	20 c. Policeman directing traffic (horiz.)	45	45
411.	25 c. Police launch (horiz.)	50	50
412.	50 c. Police car and motor-cycle	90	1·00

108. 1d. " Perot " Stamp of 1848 and 1840 Penny Black.

1980. Death Cent. of Sir Rowland Hill. Mult.

413.	8 c. Type **108**	10	10
414.	20 c. " Perot " and Sir Rowland Hill	15	25
415.	25 c. " Perot " and early letter	15	30
416.	50 c. " Perot " and " Paid 1 " cancellation	25	70

109. British Airways "Tristar 500" approaching Bermuda.

1980. " London 1980 " International Stamp Exhibition. Multicoloured.

417.	25 c. Type **109**	30	15
418.	50 c. " S.S. Orduna " at Grassy Bay, 1926	45	35
419.	$1 " Delta " at St. George's Harbour, 1856	85	1·00
420.	$2 " Lord Sidmouth " in Old Ship Channel, St. George's, 1818	1·40	1·75

110. Gina Swainson (" Miss World 1979–80 ").

1980. " Miss World 1979–80 " Commemoration. Multicoloured.

421.	8 c. Type **110**	15	10
422.	20 c. Miss Swainson after crowning ceremony	20	20
423.	50 c. Miss Swainson on Peacock Throne	35	35
424.	$1 Miss Swainson in Bermuda carriage	70	90

111. Queen Elizabeth the Queen Mother.

1980. 80th Birthday of The Queen Mother.

425.	**111.** 25 c. multicoloured	30	40

112. Bermuda from Satellite.

1980. Commonwealth Finance Ministers Meeting. Multicoloured.

426.	8 c. Type **112**	10	10
427.	20 c. " Camden "	20	30
428.	25 c. Princess Hotel, Hamilton	20	40
429.	50 c. Government House	35	1·00

113. Kitchen, 18th-century.

1981. Heritage Week. Multicoloured.

430.	8 c. Type **113**	15	10
431.	25 c. Gathering Easter lilies, 20th-century	40	50
432.	30 c. Fishing, 20th-century	50	65
433.	40 c. Stone cutting, 19th-century	55	75
434.	50 c. Onion shipping, 19th-century	65	90
435.	$1 Privateering, 17th-century	1·50	2·25

114. Wedding Bouquet from Bermuda.

115. " Service ", Hamilton.

1981. Royal Wedding. Multicoloured.

436.	30 c. Type **114**	30	30
437.	50 c. Prince Charles as Royal Navy Commander	50	55
438.	$1 Prince Charles and Lady Diana Spencer	90	1·25

1981. 25th Anniv. of Duke of Edinburgh Award Scheme. Multicoloured.

439. 10 c. Type **115** 15 10
440. 25 c. " Outward Bound ", Paget Island 25 20
441. 30 c. " Expedition ", St. David's Island 25 30
442. $1 Duke of Edinburgh .. 80 1·25

116 " Conus species ".

1982. Sea-Shells. Multicoloured.

443. 10 c. Type **116** 25 10
444. 25 c. " Bursa finlayi " .. 60 65
445. 30 c. " Sconsia striata " .. 65 80
446. $1 " Murex pterynotus lightbourni " .. .. 1·75 2·75

117. Regimental Colours and Colour Party.

1982. Bermuda Regiment. Multicoloured.

447. 10 c. Type **117** 35 10
448. 25 c. Queen's Birthday Parade 75 60
449. 30 c. Governor inspecting Guard of Honour .. 85 85
450. 40 c. Beating the Retreat 90 90
451. 50 c. Ceremonial gunners 1·00 1·25
452. $1 Guard of Honour, Royal visit, 1975 .. .. 1·75 2·75

118. Charles Fort.

1982. Historic Bermuda Forts. Multicoloured.

453. 10 c. Type **118** 20 20
454. 25 c. Pembroks Fort .. 50 75
455. 30 c. Southampton Fort (horiz.) .. .. 60 1·00
456. $1 Smiths Fort and Pagets Fort (horiz.) .. .. 1·75 3·50

119. Arms of Sir Edwin Sandys.

1983. Coats of Arms (1st series). Multicoloured.

457. 10 c. Type **119** .. 45 15
458. 25 c. Arms of the Bermuda Company .. .. 1·25 85
459. 50 c. Arms of William Herbert, Earl of Pembroke 2·00 2·25
460. $1 Arms of Sir George Somers .. .. .. 2·75 3·75

See also Nos. 482/5 and 499/502.

120. Early Fitted Dinghy.

1983. Fitted Dinghies. Multicoloured.

461. 12 c. Type **120** 20 15
462. 30 c. Modern Dinghy inshore 45 65
463. 40 c. Early Dinghy (different) 60 80
464. $1 Modern dinghy with red and white spinnaker .. 1·50 2·75

121. Curtiss " Jenny " Seaplane.

1983. Bicentenary of Manned Flight. Mult.

465. 12 c. Type **121** (First Flight over Bermuda') 30 15
466. 30 c. Pilot Radio, " Stinson " seaplane (First completed flight between U.S. and Bermuda) 65 70
467. 40 c. Short "Empire" flying boat "Cavalier". (First scheduled passenger flight) 80 1·00
468. $1 U.S.S. " Los Angeles " (airship) moored to U.S.S. " Patoka " .. .. 1·75 3·00

122. Joseph Stockdale.

1984. Bicentenary of Bermuda's First Newspaper and Postal Service. Mult.

469. 12 c. Type **122** 20 15
470. 30 c. " The Bermuda Gazette " 50 70
471. 40 c. Stockdale's postal service (horiz.) .. .. 70 1·00
472. $1 " Lady Hammond " (mail boat) (horiz.) .. 2·00 3·25

123. Sir Thomas Gates and Sir George Somers.

1984. 375th Anniv. of First Settlement in Bermuda. Multicoloured

473. 12 c. Type **123** 20 15
474. 30 c. Jamestown, Virginia .. 50 70
475. 40 c. Wreck of "Sea Venture" 90 1·00
476. $1 Fleet leaving Plymouth, Devon .. .. 2·00 3·25

124. Swimming.

1984. Olympic Games, Los Angeles. Multicoloured.

478. 12 c. Type **124** 25 15
479. 30 c. Track and field events (horiz.) 60 60
480. 40 c. Equestrian 80 85
481. $1 Sailing (horiz.) .. .. 2·25 2·75

1984. Coats of Arms (2nd series). As T **119**. Multicoloured.

482. 12 c. Arms of Henry Wriothesley, Earl of Southampton .. 40 15
483. 30 c. Arms of Sir Thomas Smith 85 85
484. 40 c. Arms of William Cavendish Earl of Devonshire .. .. .. 1·10 1·25
485. $1 Town arms of St. George .. .. .. 2·50 3·00

125. Buttery.

1985. Bermuda Architecture. Multicoloured.

486. 12 c. Type **125** 35 15
487. 30 c. Limestone rooftops (horiz.) 70 70
488. 40 c. Chimneys (horiz.) .. 85 85
489. $1.50 Entrance archway .. 2·75 3·25

126. Osprey.

1985. Birth Bicentenary of John J. Audubon (ornithologist). Designs showing original drawings. Multicoloured.

490. 12 c. Type **126** 80 25
491. 30 c. Yellow-crowned night heron .. .. .. 1·25 65
492. 40 c. Great egret (horiz.) .. 1·50 85
493. $1.50 Eastern bluebird .. 3·00 3·25

127. The Queen Mother with Grandchildren, 1980.

1985. Life and Times of Queen Elizabeth the Queen Mother. Multicoloured.

494. 12 c. Queen Consort, 1937 25 15
495. 30 c. Type **127** 50 50
496. 40 c. At Clarence House on 83rd birthday 60 60
497. $1.50 With Prince Henry at his christening (from photo by Lord Snowdon) 2·25 2·75

1985. Coats of Arms (3rd series). Designs as T **119**. Multicoloured.

499. 12 c. Hamilton 55 15
500. 30 c. Paget .. .. 1·10 80
501. 40 c. Warwick .. .. 1·25 1·25
502. $1.50 City of Hamilton .. 3·25 3·75

128. Halley's Comet and Bermuda Archipelago.

1985. Appearance of Halley's Comet. Multicoloured.

503. 15 c. Type **128** 75 25
504. 40 c. Halley's Comet, A.D. 684 (from Nuremberg Chronicles, 1493) .. 1·50 1·25
505. 50 c. "Halley's Comet, 1531" (from Peter Apian woodcut, 1532) .. .. 1·75 1·50
506. $1.50, "Halley's Comet, 1759" (Samuel Scott) .. 3·25 3·50

129. "Constellation" (1943).

1986. Ships Wrecked on Bermuda. Mult.

507 3 c. Type **129** 10 10
508 5 c. "Early Riser" (1876) .. 10 10
509 7 c. "Madiana" (1903) .. 10 10
510 10 c. "Curlew" (1856) .. 10 15
511 12 c. "Warwick" (1619) .. 15 20
512 15 c. H.M.S. "Vixen" (1890) 15 20
512c 18 c. As 7 c. 20 25
513 20 c. "San Pedro" (1594) .. 25 30
514 25 c. "Alert" (1877) .. 30 35
515 40 c. "North Carolina" (1880) 45 50
516 50 c. "Mark Antonie" (1777) 60 65
517 60 c. "Mary Celestia" (1864) 70 75
517c 70 c. "Caesar" (1818) .. 80 85
518 $1 "L'Herminie" (1839) .. 1·10 1·25
519 $1.50 As 70 c. .. .. 1·75 1·90
520 $2 "Lord Amherst" (1778) 2·25 2·40
521 $3 "Minerva" (1849) .. 3·50 3·75
522 $5 "Caraquet" (1923) .. 5·75 6·00
523 $8 H.M.S. "Pallas" (1783) 9·25 9·50

1986. 60th Birthday of Queen Elizabeth II. As T **110** of Ascension. Multicoloured.

524. 15 c. Princess Elizabeth aged three, 1929 .. 30 30
525. 40 c. With Earl of Rosebery at Oaks May Meeting, Epsom, 1954 .. 60 60
526. 50 c. With Duke of Edinburgh, Bermuda, 1975 .. .. .. 75 75
527. 60 c. At British Embassy, Paris, 1972 .. .. 90 90
528. $1.50 At Crown Agents Head Office, London, 1983 .. .. .. 2·25 2·50

1986. "Ameripex '86" International Stamp Exhibition, Chicago. As T **164** of Bahamas, showing Bermuda stamps. Multicoloured.

529. 15 c. 1984 375th Anniv. of Settlement miniature sheet 55 30
530. 40 c. 1973 Lawn Tennis Centenary 24 c. 85 70
531. 50 c. 1983 Bicentenary of Manned Flight 12 c. .. 1·00 1·00
532. $1 1976 Tall Ships Race 17 c. .. .. .. 2·00 2·50

1986. 25th Anniv. of World Wildlife Fund. No. 402 surch.

534. 90 c. on $3 Green turtle .. 2·00 1·75

17. Pope Paul VI, Africa, and Papal Arms.

1969. Visit of Pope Paul to Africa. Multi-coloured; background colours given.

No.	Description		
39. **17.**	4d. orange	40	1·75
40. –	6d. blue	55	3·50
41. –	9d. green	75	4·75
42. –	3s. mauve	2·25	10·00

Designs: Pope Paul VI, map of Africa and—6d. Arms of Vatican. 9d. St. Peter's Basilica. 3s. Statue of St. Peter.

BIJAWAR

A state of Central India. Now uses Indian stamps.

12 pies = 1 anna; 16 annas = 1 rupee.

1. Maharaja Sir Sarwant Singh Bahadur. **2.**

1935.

No.	Description		
6 1	3 p. brown	50	1·25
2	6 p. red	1·00	1·00
3	9 p. violet	1·00	1·50
4	1 a. blue	1·40	1·90
5	2 a. green	1·75	2·75

1937.

No.	Description		
11. **2.**	4 a. orange	3·00	35·00
12.	6 a. lemon	3·00	35·00
13.	8 a. green	3·50	42·00
14.	12 a. blue	4·50	48·00
15.	1 r. violet	18·00	75·00

BOTSWANA

Formerly Bechuanaland Protectorate, attained independence on 30 September 1966, and changed its name to Botswana.

1966. 100 cents = 1 rand.
1976. 100 thebe = 1 pula.

47. National Assembly Building.

1966. Independence. Multicoloured.

No.	Description		
202. **28.**	2½ c. Type, **47**	15	10
203.	5 c. Abattoir Lobatsi	15	10
204.	15 c. National Airways "Dakota"	30	10
205.	35 c. State House, Gaberones	30	20

1966. Nos. 168/81 of Bechuanaland optd. **REPUBLIC OF BOTSWANA.**

No.	Description		
206. **28.**	1 c. multicoloured	25	10
207. –	2 c. orange, black & olive	30	10
208. –	2½ c. multicoloured	30	10
209. –	3½ c. multicoloured	40	15
210. –	5 c. multicoloured	40	40
211. –	7½ c. multicoloured	40	50
212. –	10 c. multicoloured	60	20
213. –	12½ c. multicoloured	3·50	1·25
214. –	20 c. brown and drab	60	45
215. –	25 c. sepia and lemon	60	70
216. –	35 c. blue and orange	75	85
217. –	50 c. sepia and olive	50	70
218. –	1 r. black and brown	75	1·25
219. –	2 r. brown and turquoise	1·25	2·50

52. Golden Oriole.

1967. Multicoloured.

No.	Description		
220.	1 c. Type **52**	30	15
221.	2 c. Hoopoe	40	10
222.	3 c. Groundscraper Thrush	55	10
223.	4 c. Cordon-bleu	55	10
224.	5 c. Secretary Bird	55	10
225.	7 c. Yellow-billed Hornbill	60	70
226.	10 c. Burchell's Gonolek	60	15
227.	15 c. Malachite Kingfisher	5·00	75
228.	20 c. African Fish Eagle	4·50	70
229.	25 c. Go-away Bird	2·50	60
230.	35 c. Scimitar-bill	4·75	90
231.	50 c. Comb Duck	3·25	1·50
232.	1 r. Levaillant's Barbet	6·00	3·25
233.	2 r. Didric Cuckoo	9·50	11·00

66. Students and University.

1967. 1st Conferment of University Degrees.

No.	Description		
234. **66.**	3 c. sepia, blue & orange	10	10
235.	7 c. sepia, blue & turquoise	10	10
236.	15 c. sepia, blue and red	10	10
237.	35 c. sepia, blue & violet	20	10

67. Bushbuck.

1967. Chobe Game Reserve. Multicoloured.

No.	Description		
238.	3 c. Type **67**	10	10
239.	7 c. Sable Antelope	15	15
240.	35 c. Fishing on the Chobe River	70	55

70. Arms of Botswana and Human Rights Emblem.

1968. Human Rights Year.

No.	Description		
241. **70.**	3 c. multicoloured	10	10
242. –	15 c. multicoloured	20	10
243. –	25 c. multicoloured	20	20

The designs of Nos. 242/3 are similar, but are arranged differently.

73. Eland and Giraffe Rock Paintings, Tsodilo Hills.

1968. Opening of National Museum and Art Gallery. Multicoloured.

No.	Description		
244.	3 c. Type **73**	30	10
245.	7 c. Girl wearing ceremonial beads	35	15
246.	10 c. "Baobab Trees" (Thomas Baines)	35	25
247.	15 c. National Museum and art gallery (72 × 19 mm)	50	60

No. 245 is vert. and the size is 31 × 48 mm.

77. African Family, and Star over Village.

1968. Christmas.

No.	Description		
249. **77.**	1 c. multicoloured	10	10
250.	2 c. multicoloured	10	10
251.	5 c. multicoloured	10	10
252.	25 c. multicoloured	15	25

78. Scout, Lion and Badge in frame.

1969. 22nd World Scout Conf., Helsinki. Multicoloured.

No.	Description		
253.	3 c. Type **78**	30	10
254.	15 c. Scouts cooking over open fire	80	55
255.	25 c. Scouts around camp fire	85	75

The 15 c. is vert.

81. Woman, Child and Christmas Star.

1969. Christmas.

No.	Description		
256. **81.**	1 c. blue and brown	10	10
257.	2 c. olive and brown	10	10
258.	4 c. yellow and brown	10	10
259.	35 c. brown and violet	20	20

82. Diamond Treatment Plant, Orapa.

1970. Developing Botswana. Multicoloured.

No.	Description		
261.	3 c. Type **82**	40	15
262.	7 c. Copper-nickel mining	70	15
263.	10 c. Copper-nickel mine, Selebi-Pikwe (horiz.)	85	25
264.	35 c. Orapa Diamond mine and diamonds (horiz.)	2·00	85

83. Mr. Micawber ("David Copperfield").

1970. Death Centenary of Charles Dickens. Multicoloured.

No.	Description		
265.	3 c. Type **83**	20	10
266.	7 c. Scrooge ("A Christmas Carol")	25	10
267.	15 c. Fagin ("Oliver Twist")	45	30
268.	25 c. Bill Sykes ("Oliver Twist")	75	55

84. U.N. Building and Emblem. (Illustration reduced. Actual size 59 × 21 mm.)

1970. 25th Anniv. of United Nations.

No.	Description		
270. **84.**	15 c. blue, brown & silver	30	30

85. Crocodile.

1970. Christmas. Multicoloured.

No.	Description		
271.	1 c. Type **85**	10	10
272.	2 c. Giraffe	10	10
273.	7 c. Elephant	10	10
274.	25 c. Rhinoceros	30	45

86. Sorghum.

1971. Important Crops. Multicoloured.

No.	Description		
276.	3 c. Type **86**	10	10
277.	7 c. Millet	10	10
278.	10 c. Maize	15	10
279.	35 c. Groundnuts	45	40

87. Map and Head of Cow.

1971. Fifth Anniv. of Independence.

No.	Description		
280. **87.**	3 c. black, brown & grn.	10	10
281. –	4 c. black, lt. bl. & bl.	10	10
282. –	7 c. black & orange	20	10
283. –	10 c. multicoloured	25	15
284. –	20 c. multicoloured	80	1·10

Designs: 4 c. Map and cogs. 7 c. Map and common zebra. 10 c. Map and sorghum stalk crossed by tusk. 20 c. Arms and map of Botswana.

88. King bringing Gift of Gold.

1971. Christmas. Multicoloured.

No.	Description		
285.	2 c. Type **88**	10	10
286.	3 c. King bringing frankincense	10	10
287.	7 c. King bringing myrrh	10	10
288.	20 c. Three Kings behold the star	35	50

INDEX

Countries can be quickly located by referring to the index at the end of this volume.

89. Orion.

1972. "Night Sky".

290. **89.** 3c. blue, blk. and red .. 25 10

291. – 7c. blue, black and yell. 50 60

292. – 10c. grn., blk. and orge. 65 75

293. – 20c. blue, blk. and green 1·10 1·25

CONSTELLATIONS: 7c. The Scorpion. 10c. The Centaur. 20c. The Cross.

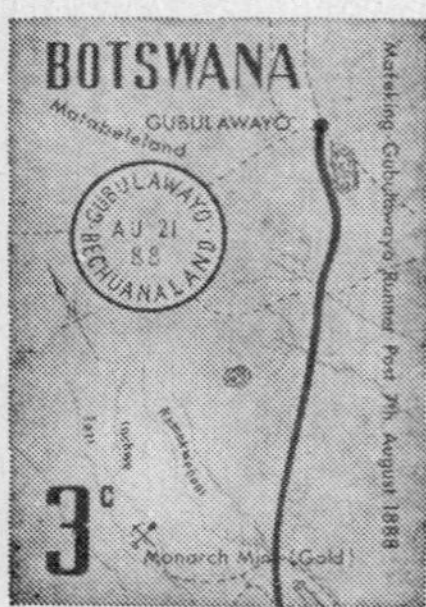

90. Postmark and Map.

1972. Mafeking-Gubulawayo Runner Post. Multicoloured.

294. 3 c. Type **90** 30 10

295. 4 c. Bechuanaland stamp and map 30 35

296. 7 c. Runners and map 45 50

297. 20 c. Mafeking postmark and map 1·10 1·25

For these designs with change inscription see Nos. 652/5.

91. Cross, Map and Bells.

1972. Christmas. Each with Cross and Map. Multicoloured.

299. 2 c. Type **91** 10 10

300. 3 c. Cross, map and candle 10 10

301. 7 c. Cross, map and Christmas tree 15 20

302. 20 c. Cross, map, star and holly 40 55

92. Thor.

1973. Centenary of I.M.O./W.M.O. Norse myths. Multicoloured.

304. 3 c. Type **92** 15 10

305. 4 c. Sun God's chariot (horiz.) 20 15

306. 7 c. Ymir, the frost giant.. 25 15

307. 20 c. Odin and Sleipnir (horiz.) 75 60

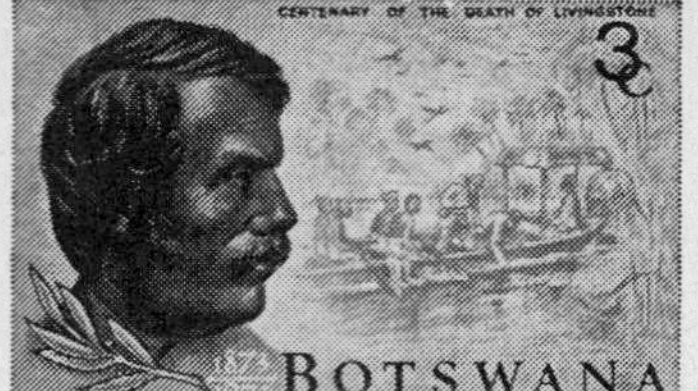

93. Livingstone and River Scene.

1973. Death Centenary of Dr. Livingstone. Multicoloured.

308. 3 c. Type **93** 10 10

309. 20 c. Livingstone meeting Stanley 50 60

94. Donkey and Foal at Village Trough.

1973. Christmas. Multicoloured.

310. 3 c. Type **94** 10 10

311. 4 c. Shepherd and flock (horiz.) 10 10

312. 7 c. Mother and child 10 10

313. 20 c. Kgotla meeting (horiz.) 40 60

95. Gaborone Campus.

1974. 10th Anniv. of University of Botswana, Lesotho and Swaziland. Multicoloured.

314. 3 c. Type **95** 10 10

315. 7 c. Kwaluseni Campus 10 10

316. 20 c. Roma Campus 15 20

317. 35 c. Map and flags of the three countries 20 35

96. Methods of Mail Transport. (Illustration reduced. Actual size 58 × 21 mm.).

1974. Centenary of U.P.U. Multicoloured.

318. 2 c. Type **96** 45 35

319. 3 c. Post Office, Palapye, circa 1889 45 35

320. 7 c. Bechuanaland Police Camel Post, circa 1900 70 70

321. 20 c. Mail-planes of 1920 and 1974 2·50 2·50

97. Amethyst.

1974. Botswana Minerals. Multicoloured.

322. 1 c. Type **97** 60 45

323. 2 c. Agate—"Botswana Pink" 60 45

324. 3 c. Quartz 65 45

325. 4 c. Copper nickel 70 50

326. 5 c. Moss agate 70 50

327. 7 c. Agate 80 50

328. 10 c. Stilbite 90 55

329. 15 c. Moshaneng Banded Marble 2·00 1·00

330. 20 c. Gem diamonds 3·25 1·25

331. 25 c. Chrysotile 3·50 90

332. 35 c. Jasper 4·25 1·75

333. 50 c. Moss quartz 4·50 3·25

334. 1 r. Citrine 7·50 7·50

335. 2 r. Chalcopyrite 17·00 15·00

98. "Stapelia variegata".

1974. Christmas. Multicoloured.

336. 2 c. Type **98** 20 15

337. 7 c. "Hibiscus lunarifolius" 50 20

338. 15 c. "Ceratotheca triloba" 1·10 75

339. 20 c. "Nerine laticoma" 1·25 85

99. President Sir Seretse Khama.

1975. 10th Anniv. of Self-Government.

341. **99.** 4 c. multicoloured 10 10

342. 10 c. multicoloured 15 10

343. 20 c. multicoloured 25 15

344. 35 c. multicoloured 45 35

100. Ostrich.

1975. Rock Paintings, Tsodilo Hills. Mult.

346. 4 c. Type **100** 25 10

347. 10 c. White rhinoceros 70 10

348. 25 c. Spotted hyena 1·75 45

349. 35 c. Scorpion 2·00 90

101. Map of British Bechuanaland, 1885.

1975. Anniversaries. Multicoloured.

351. 6 c. Type **101** 30 15

352. 10 c. Chief Khama, 1875 40 15

353. 25 c. Chiefs Sebele, Bathoen and Khama, 1895 (horiz.) 80 65

EVENTS: 6 c. 90th Anniv. of Protectorate. 10 c. Centenary of Khama's Accession. 25 c. 80th Anniv. of Chiefs' visit to London.

102. "Aloe marlothii".

1975. Christmas. Aloes. Multicoloured.

354. 3 c. Type **102** 20 10

355. 10 c. "Aloe lutescens" 55 35

356. 15 c. "Aloe zebrina" 90 1·00

357. 25 c. "Aloe littoralis" 1·25 1·60

103. Drum.

1976. Traditional Musical Instruments. Mult.

358. 4 c. Type **103** 15 10

359. 10 c. Hand Piano 25 10

360. 15 c. Segankuru (violin) 30 20

361. 25 c. Kudu Signal Horn 40 40

104. One Pula Note.

1976. First National Currency. Mult.

362. 4 c. Type **104** 15 10

363. 10 c. Two pula note 20 10

364. 15 c. Five pula note 35 20

365. 25 c. Ten pula note 45 45

1976. Nos. 322/35 surch. in new currency.

367. 1 t. on 1 c. multicoloured 60 45

368. 2 t. on 2 c. multicoloured 60 40

369. 3 t. on 3 c. multicoloured 60 40

370. 4 t. on 4 c. multicoloured 85 40

371. 5 t. on 5 c. multicoloured 85 30

372. 7 t. on 7 c. multicoloured 85 50

373. 10 t. on 10 c. multicoloured 85 50

374. 15 t. on 15 c. multicoloured 2·25 65

375. 20 t. on 20 c. multicoloured 4·50 65

376. 25 t. on 25 c. multicoloured 3·50 75

377. 35 t. on 35 c. multicoloured 3·50 1·00

378. 50 t. on 50 c. multicoloured 4·50 1·50

379. 1 p. on 1 r. multicoloured 6·00 3·50

380. 2 p. on 2 r. multicoloured 9·00 8·00

106. Botswanan Cattle.

1976. 10th Anniv. of Independence. Mult.

381. 4 t. Type **106** 15 10

382. 10 t. Deer, Okavango Delta (vert.) 30 10

383. 15 t. School and pupils 40 20

384. 25 t. Rural weaving (vert.) 55 30

385. 35 t. Miner (vert.) 90 50

107. "Colophosphermum mopane".

1976. Christmas Trees. Multicoloured.

386. 3 t. Type **107** 15 10

387. 4 t. "Baikiaea plurijuga" 15 10

388. 10 t. "Sterculia rogersii" 40 15

389. 25 t. "Acacia nilotica" 80 50

390. 40 t. "Kigelia africana" 1·25 90

108. Coronation Coach.

1977. Silver Jubilee. Multicoloured.

391. 4 t. The Queen and Sir Seretse Khama .. 10 10
392. 25 t. Type **108** 20 15
393. 40 t. The Recognition .. 35 45

109. African Clawless Otter.

1977. Diminishing Species. Multicoloured.

394. 3 t. Type **109** 35 30
395. 4 t. Serval 35 30
396. 10 t. Bat-eared fox .. 90 40
397. 25 t. Temminck's ground pangolin .. .. .. 2·00 1·25
398. 40 t. Brown hyena .. 3·00 2·50

110. Cwihaba Caves.

1977. Historical Monuments. Multicoloured.

399. 4 t. Type **110** 20 10
400. 5 t. Khama Memorial .. 20 10
401. 15 t. Green's Tree .. 45 40
402. 20 t. Mmajojo Ruins .. 45 45
403. 25 t. Ancient morabaraba board 45 50
404. 35 t. Matsieng's footprint 55 60

111. "Hypoxij nitida". **112.** Little Black Bustard.

1977. Christmas. Lilies. Multicoloured.

406. 3 t. Type **111** 15 10
407. 5 t. "Haemanthus magnificus" 15 10
408. 10 t. "Boophane disticha" 35 10
409. 25 t. "Vellozia retinervis" 75 35
410. 40 t. "Ammocharis coranica" .. .. .. 1·00 75

1978. Birds. Multicoloured.

411. 1 t. Type **112** 30 45
412. 2 t. Marabou stork .. 30 45
413. 3 t. Green wood hoopoe .. 30 45
414. 4 t. Carmine bee eater .. 30 40
415. 5 t. African jacana .. 30 40
416. 7 t. African paradise flycatcher 40 40
417. 10 t. Bennett's woodpecker 75 40
418. 15 t. Red bishop 60 70
419. 20 t. Crowned plover .. 60 80
420. 25 t. Giant kingfisher .. 60 85
421. 30 t. White-faced whistling duck 60 50
422. 35 t. Green heron 60 80
423. 45 t. Black-headed heron.. 65 90
424. 50 t. Spotted eagle owl .. 2·00 85
425. 1 p. Gabar goshawk .. 1·25 1·25
426. 2 p. Martial eagle .. .. 2·00 4·50
427. 5 p. Saddle-bill stork .. 9·50 9·50

113. Tawana making Kaross.

1978. Okavango Delta. Multicoloured.

428. 4 t. Type **113** 10 10
429. 5 t. Tribe localities .. 10 10
430. 15 t. Bushman collecting roots 30 30
431. 20 t. Herero woman milking 35 35
432. 25 t. Yei poling "mokoro" (canoe) 40 40
433. 35 t. Mbukushu fishing .. 55 55

114. "Caralluma lutea".

1978. Christmas. Flowers. Multicoloured.

435. 5 t. Type **114** 25 10
436. 10 t. "Hoodia lugardii" 35 15
437. 15 t. "Ipomoea transvaalensis" 65 40
438. 25 t. "Ansellia gigantea" 70 55

115. Sip Well.

1979. Water Development. Multicoloured.

439. 3 t. Type **115** 10 10
440. 5 t. Watering pit 15 10
441. 10 t. Hand dug well .. 15 10
442. 22 t. Windmill 30 30
443. 50 t. Modern drilling rig .. 55 55

116. Pottery.

1979. Handicrafts. Multicoloured.

444. 5 t. Type **116** 10 10
445. 10 t. Clay modelling .. 15 10
446. 25 t. Basketry 30 25
447. 40 t. Beadwork 50 50

117. British Bechuanaland 1885 1d. Stamp and Sir Rowland Hill.

1979. Death Centenary of Sir Rowland Hill. Multicoloured.

449. 5 t. Type **117** 15 10
450. 25 t. Bechuanaland Protectorate 1932 2d. stamp 45 40
451. 45 t. 1967 Hoopoe 2 c. definitive stamp .. 55 65

118. Children Playing.

1979. International Year of the Child. Multicoloured.

452. 5 t. Type **118** 10 10
453. 10 t. Child playing with doll (vert.) 20 20

119. "Ximenia caffra".

1979. Christmas. Flowers. Multicoloured.

454. 5 t. Type **119** 10 10
455. 10 t. "Sclerocarya caffra" 20 20
456. 15 t. "Hexalobus monopetalus" 35 35
457. 25 t. "Ficus soldanella" 45 45

120. Flap-necked Chameleon.

1980. Reptiles. Multicoloured.

458. 5 t. Type **120** 10 10
459. 10 t. Leopard Tortoise .. 15 15
460. 25 t. Puff Adder 60 40
461. 40 t. White-throated Monitor 80 60

121. Rock Breaking.

1980. Early Mining. Multicoloured.

462. 5 t. Type **121** 15 10
463. 10 t. Ore hoisting .. 20 15
464. 15 t. Ore transport .. 40 30
465. 20 t. Ore crushing .. 45 35
466. 25 t. Smelting 50 45
467. 35 t. Tool and products .. 65 60

122. "Chiwele and the Giant".

1980. Folktales. Multicoloured.

468. 5 t. Type **122** 10 10
469. 10 t. "Kgori is not deceived" (vert.) 15 10
470. 30 t. "Nyambi's wife and Crocodile" (vert.) .. 45 45
471. 45 t. "Clever Hare" (horiz.) 60 60

The 10 t. and 30 t. are 28×37 mm. and the 45 t. 44×27 mm.

123. Game watching, Makgadikgadi Pans. (Illustration reduced. Actual size 58×22 mm.).

1980. World Tourism Conference, Manila.

472. **123.** 5 t. multicoloured .. 35 20

124. "Acacia gerrardii". **126.** "Anax imperator" (dragonfly).

125. Heinrich von Stephan and Botswana 3d. and 3 c. U.P.U. Stamps.

1980. Christmas. Multicoloured.

473. 6 t. Type **124** 10 10
474. 10 t. "Acacia nilotica" .. 20 10
475. 25 t. "Acacia erubescens" 45 30
476. 40 t. "Dichrostachys cinerea" 70 70

1981. 150th Birth Anniv. of Heinrich von Stephan (founder of Universal Postal Union). Multicoloured.

477. 6 t. Type **125** 20 15
478. 20 t. 6d. and 7 c. U.P.U. stamps 55 55

1981. Insects. Multicoloured.

479 6 t. Type **126** 15 10
480 7 t. "Sphodromantis gastrica" (mantid) .. 15 15
481 10 t. "Zonocerus elegans" (grasshopper) 20 15
482 20 t. "Kheper nigroaeneus" (beetle) 35 35
483 30 t. "Papilio demodocus" (butterfly) 70 50
484 45 t. "Acanthocampa belina" (moth larva) .. 80 65

127. Camphill Community Rankoromane, Otse.

1981. International Year for Disabled Persons. Multicoloured.

486. 6 t. Type **127** .. 15 10
487. 20 t. Resource Centre for the Blind, Mochudi 40 35
488. 30 t. Tlamelong Rehabilitation Centre, Tlokweng 50 45

128. Woman reading Letter.

1981. Literacy Programme. Multicoloured.

489. 6 t. Type **128** 15 10
490. 7 t. Man filling in form .. 15 15
491. 20 t. Boy reading newspaper 40 35
492. 30 t. Child being taught to read 55 45

129. Sir Seretse Khama and Building.

1981. 1st Death Anniv. of Sir Seretse Khama (former President). Multicoloured.

493. 6 t. Type **129** 10 10
494. 10 t. Seretse Khama and building (different) .. 15 15
495. 30 t. Seretse Khama and Botswana flag 45 45
496. 45 t. Seretse Khama and building (different) .. 70 70

1981. Nos. 417 and 422 surch.

497. 25 t. on 35 t. Green heron 1·25 1·25
498. 30 t. on 10 t. Bennett's woodpecker .. .. 1·25 1·25

131. Traditional Ploughing.

1981. Cattle Industry. Multicoloured.

499.	6 t. Type **131**	10	10
500.	20 t. Agricultural show ..	35	35
501.	30 t. Botswana Meat Commission	45	45
502.	45 t. Vaccine Institute, Botswana	70	70

132. " Nymphaea caerulea ".

1981. Christmas. Flowers. Multicoloured.

503.	6 t. Type **132**	20	10
504.	10 t. " Nymphoides indica "	30	10
505.	25 t. " Nymphaea lotus "	70	50
506.	40 t. " Ottelia kunenensis "	1·00	90

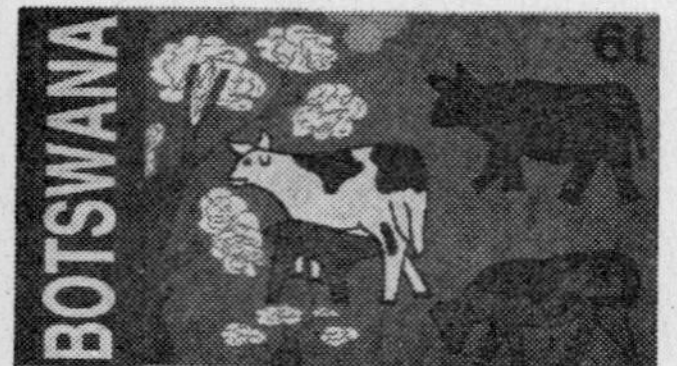

133. " Cattle Post Scene " (Boitumelo Golaakwena).

1982. Children's Art. Multicoloured.

507.	6 t. Type **133**	40	10
508.	10 t. " Kgotla Meeting " (Reginald Klinck) ..	50	15
509.	30 t. " Village Water Supply " (Keromemang Matswiri)	1·25	45
510.	45 t. " With the Crops " (Kennedy Balemoge) ..	1·75	70

134. Common Type.

1982. Traditional Houses. Multicoloured.

511.	6 t. Type **134**	40	10
512.	10 t. Kgatleng type ..	50	15
513.	30 t. North Eastern type	1·25	80
514.	45 t. Sarwa type	1·75	1·75

135. African Masked Weaver.

1982. Birds. Multicoloured.

515.	1 t. Type **135**	35	40
516.	2 t. Lesser double-collared sunbird	45	40
517.	3 t. Red-throated bee eater	45	40
518.	4 t. Ostrich	45	40
519.	5 t. Grey-headed gull ..	45	30
520.	6 t. African pygmy goose	45	20
521.	7 t. Cattle egret	45	15
522.	8 t. Lanner falcon ..	65	45
523.	10 t. Yellow-billed stork ..	50	15
524.	15 t. Red-billed pintail (horiz.)	60	15
525.	20 t. Barn owl (horiz.) ..	2·00	45
526.	25 t. Hammerkop (horiz.)	1·25	55
527.	30 t. South African stilt (horiz.)	1·50	55
528.	35 t. Blacksmith plover (horiz.)	1·50	70
529.	45 t. Senegal wattled plover (horiz.)	1·75	85
530.	50 t. Helmet guineafowl (horiz.)	2·00	1·40
531.	1 p. Cape vulture (horiz.)	3·75	3·50
532.	2 p. Augur buzzard (horiz.)	5·00	5·50

136. " Coprinus comatus ".

1982. Christmas. Fungi. Multicoloured.

533	7 t. Type **136**	65	10
534	15 t. "Lactarius deliciosus"	1·10	25
535	35 t. "Amanita pantherina"	2·00	65
536	50 t. "Boletus edulis" ..	2·75	1·25

137. President Quett Masire.

1983. Commonwealth Day. Multicoloured.

537.	7 t. Type **137**	10	10
538.	15 t. Native Dancers ..	15	20
539.	35 t. Melbourne conference centre	45	50
540.	45 t. Meeting of Heads of State, Melbourne ..	55	60

138. Wattled Crane.

1983. Endangered Species. Multicoloured.

541.	7 t. Type **138**	65	15
542.	15 t. "Aloe lutescens" ..	80	45
543.	35 t. Roan Antelope ..	1·25	1·25
544.	50 t. Ivory Palm	1·50	2·00

139. Wooden Spoons.

1983. Traditional Artifacts. Multicoloured.

545.	7 t. Type **139**	10	10
546.	15 t. Personal ornaments ..	15	20
547.	35 t. Ox-hide Milk Bag ..	45	50
548.	50 t. Decorated Knives ..	55	60

140. " Patntala flavescens ".

1983. Christmas. Dragonflies. Multicoloured.

550	6 t. Type **140**	20	10
551	15 t. "Anax imperator" ..	35	20
552	25 t. "Trithemis arteriosa"	50	40
553	45 t. "Chlorolestes elegans"	85	95

141. Sorting Diamonds.

1984. Mining Industry. Multicoloured.

554.	7 c. Type **141**	45	15
555.	15 c. Lime kiln	70	35
556.	35 c. Copper-nickel smelter plant (vert.)	1·25	65
557.	50 c. Stockpiled coal (vert.)	1·50	1·50

142. Riding Cattle.

1984. Traditional Transport. Multicoloured.

558.	7 t. Type **142**	10	10
559.	25 t. Sledge	25	35
560.	35 t. Wagon	35	45
561.	50 t. Two-wheeled donkey cart	50	75

143. Avro "504" Aircraft.

1984. 40th Anniv. of International Civil Aviation Organization. Multicoloured.

562.	7 t. Type **143**	35	10
563.	10 t. Westland "Wessex"	45	15
564.	15 t. Junkers "Ju 52/3M"	70	35
565.	25 t. De Havilland "Dragon Six"	80	50
566.	35 t. Douglas "DC3 Dakota"	90	70
567.	50 t. Fokker "F27 Friendship"	1·10	1·50

144. "Papilio demodocus".

1984. Christmas. Butterflies. Multicoloured.

568	7 t. Type **144**	60	15
569	25 t. "Byblia anvatara" ..	1·00	60
570	35 t. "Danaus chrysippus"	1·25	85
571	50 t. "Graphium taboranus"	1·60	2·00

No. 570 is incorrectly inscribed "Hypolimnas misippus".

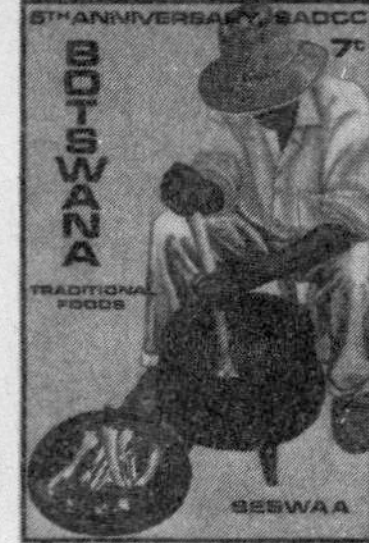

145. Seswaa (meat dish).

1985. 5th Anniv. of Southern African Development Co-ordination Conference. Traditional Foods. Multicoloured.

572.	7 t. Type **145**	10	10
573.	15 t. Bogobe (cereal porridge)	10	15
574.	25 t. Madila (soured coagulated cow's milk)	15	20
575.	50 t. Phane (caterpillars) ..	35	40

146. 1885 British Bechuanaland Overprint on Cape of Good Hope ½d.

1985. Centenary of First Bechuanaland Stamps.

577.	**146.**	7 t black, grey-black and red	35	10
578.	–	15 t. black, brown and yellow	45	10
579.	–	25 t. black and red ..	65	30
580.		35 t. black, blue and gold	75	40
581.	–	50 t. multicoloured ..	85	85

DESIGNS—VERT—15 t. 1897 Bechuanaland Protectorate overprint on G.B. 3d.; 25 t. Bechuanaland Protectorate 1932 1d. definitive. HORIZ.—35 t. Bechuanaland 1965 Internal Self-Government 5 c.; 50 t. Botswana 1966 Independence 2½ c.

147. Bechuanaland Border Police, 1885–95.

1985. Centenary of Botswana Police. Mult.

582.	7 t. Type **147**	70	15
583.	10 t. Bechuanaland Mounted Police, 1895–1902	90	25
584.	25 t. Bechuanaland Protectorate Police, 1903–66	1·50	80
585.	50 t. Botswana Police, from 1966	2·00	1·75

148. "Cucumis metuliferus".

1985. Christmas. Edible Wild Cucumbers. Multicoloured.

586.	7 t. Type **148**	25	10
587.	15 t. "Acanthosicyos naudinianus"	35	30
588.	25 t. "Coccinia sessifolia"	60	50
589.	50 t. "Momordica balsamina"	1·00	1·40

149. Mr. Shippard and Chief Gaseitsiwe of the Bangwaketse.

1985. Centenary of Declaration of Bechuanaland Protectorate. Multicoloured.

590. 7 t. Type **149** 15 10
591. 15 t. Sir Charles Warren and Chief Sechele of the Bakwena 25 20
592. 25 t. Rev. Mackenzie and Chief Khama of the Bamangwato 40 30
593. 50 t. Map showing Protectorate 70 70

150. Halley's Comet over Serowe.

1986. Appearance of Halley's Comet. Multicoloured.

595. 7 t. Type **150** 30 10
596. 15 t. Comet over Bobonong at sunset 50 15
597. 35 t. Comet over Gomare at dawn 70 40
598. 50 t. Comet over Thamaga and Letlhakeng 85 70

151. Milk Bag.

1986. Traditional Milk Containers. Mult.

599. 8 t. Type **151** 10 10
600. 15 t. Clay pot and calabashes 15 15
601. 35 t. Wooden milk bucket 35 35
602. 50 t. Milk churn 45 45

153. "Ludwigia stogonifera".

1986. Christmas. Flowers of Okavango. Multicoloured.

604. 8 t. Type **153** 50 10
605. 15 t. "Sopubia mannii" .. 90 40
606. 35 t. "Commelina diffusa" 1·50 85
607. 35 t. "Hibiscus diversifolius" .. .. 2·00 2·50

154. Divining.

1987. Traditional Medicine. Multicoloured.

608. 8 t. Type **154** 25 10
609. 15 t. Lightning prevention 45 25
610. 35 t. Rain making .. 75 45
611. 50 t. Blood letting .. 90 95

1987. Nos. 520, 523 and 530 surch.

612. 3 t. on 6 t. African pygmy goose 15 15
613. 5 t. on 10 t. Yellow-billed stork 15 15
614. 20 t. on 50 t. Helmet guineafowl (horiz.) .. 30 25

156. Oral Rehydration Therapy.

1987. U.N.I.C.E.F. Child Survival Campaign. Multicoloured.

615. 8 t. Type **156** 10 10
616. 15 t. Growth monitoring .. 15 15
617. 35 t. Immunization .. 35 50
618. 50 t. Breast feeding .. 45 80

157. Cape Fox.

1987. Animals of Botswana. Multicoloured.

619. 1 t. Type **157** 10 10
620. 2 t. Lechwe 10 10
621. 3 t. Zebra 10 10
622. 4 t. Duiker 10 10
623. 5 t. Banded mongoose .. 10 10
624. 6 t. Rusty-spotted genet .. 10 10
625. 8 t. Hedgehog 10 10
626. 10 t. Scrub hare 10 10
627. 12 t. Hippopotamus .. 10 10
628. 15 t. Suricate 10 15
629. 20 t. Caracal 10 15
630. 25 t. Steenbok 15 20
631. 30 t. Gemsbok 15 20
632. 35 t. Square-lipped rhinoceros 20 25
633. 40 t. Mountain reedbuck .. 20 25
634. 50 t. Rock Dassie 25 30
635. 1 p. Giraffe 55 60
636. 2 p. Tsessebe .. .. 1·10 1·25
637. 3 p. Side-striped jackal .. 1·60 1·75
638. 5 p. Hartebeest .. .. 2·75 3·00

158. "Cyperus articulatus".

1987. Christmas. Grasses and Sedges of Okavango. Multicoloured.

639. 8 t. Type **158** 10 10
640. 15 t. Broomgrass 15 15
641. 30 t. "Cyperus alopurcides" 35 30
642. 1 p. Bulrush sedge .. 85 80

159. Planting Seeds with Digging Stick.

1988. Early Cultivation. Multicoloured.

644. 8 t. Type **159** 10 10
645. 15 t. Using iron hoe .. 15 15
646. 35 t. Wooden ox-drawn plough 30 30
647. 50 t. Villagers using lesotlas 40 45

160 Red Lechwe at Water-hole

1988. Red Lechwe. Multicoloured.

648 10 t. Type **160** 20 10
649 15 t. Red lechwe and early morning sun 25 15
650 35 t. Female and calf .. 40 30
651 75 t. Herd on the move .. 80 60

161 Gubulawayo Postmark and Route Southwards to Tati

1988. Centenary of Mafeking–Gubalawayo Runner Post. Designs as Nos. 294/7, but redrawn smaller with changed inscription as in T **161**. Multicoloured.

652 10 t. Type **161** 20 10
653 15 t. Bechuanaland 1888 6d. on 6d. stamp and route from Tati southwards 30 20
654 30 t. Runners and twin routes south from Shoshong 50 40
655 60 t. Mafeking postmark and routes to Bechuanaland and Transvaal 75 65

162 Pope John Paul II and Outline Map of Botswana

1988. Visit of Pope John Paul II. Mult.

657 10 t. Type **162** 15 10
658 15 t. Pope John Paul II .. 20 15
659 30 t. Pope giving blessing and outline map .. 30 35
660 80 t. Pope John Paul II (different) 65 70

163 National Museum and Art Gallery, Gaborone

1988. 20th Anniv of National Museum and Art Gallery, Gaborone. Multicoloured.

661 8 t. Type **163** 10 10
662 15 t. Pottery 15 15
663 30 t. Blacksmith's buffalo bellows 25 25
664 60 t. Children and mobile museum van 45 50

164 "Grewia flava"

1988. Flowering Plants of South-eastern Botswana. Multicoloured.

665 8 t. Type **164** 10 10
666 15 t. "Cienfuegosia digitata" 15 15
667 40 t. "Solanum seaforthianum" .. 35 35
668 75 t. "Carissa bispinosa" .. 60 60

165 Basket Granary

1989. Traditional Grain Storage. Mult.

669 8 t. Type **165** 10 10
670 15 t. Large letlole granary 15 15
671 30 t. Pot granary .. 25 30
672 60 t. Two types of serala .. 40 50

166 Female Slaty Egret with Eggs

1989. Slaty Egret. Multicoloured.

673 8 t. Type **166** 20 10
674 15 t. Chicks in nest .. 30 10
675 30 t. Slaty egret in flight 40 30
676 60 t. Pair building nest .. 65 60

167 "My Work at Home" (Ephraim Seeletso)

1989. Children's Paintings. Multicoloured.

678 10 t. Type **167** 20 10
679 15 t. "My Favourite Game" (hopscotch) (Neelma Bhatia) (vert) 20 15
680 30 t. "My Favourite Toy" (clay animals) (Thabo Habana) 35 40
681 1 p. "My School Day" (Thabo Olesitse) .. 85 1·25

168 "Eulophia angolensis"

171 Telephone Engineer

169 Bechuanaland 1965 New Constitution 25 c. Stamp (25th anniv of Self Government)

1989. Christmas. Orchids. Multicoloured.
682 8 t. Type **168** 25 10
683 15 t. "Eulophia hereroensis" 40 15
684 30 t. "Eulophia speciosa" 60 40
685 60 t. "Eulophia petersii" 1·00 85

1990. Anniversaries.
686 **169** 8 t. multicoloured .. 20 10
687 – 15 t. multicoloured .. 20 15
688 – 30 t. multicoloured .. 30 35
689 – 60 t. black, blue & yell 55 60
DESIGNS: 15 t. Casting vote in ballot box (25th anniv of First Elections); 30 t. Outline map and flags of Southern African Development Coordination Conference countries (10th anniv); 60 t. Penny Black (150th anniv of first postage stamp).

1990. Nos. 619, 624 and 627 surch.
690 10 t. on 1 t. Type **157** .. 15 10
691 20 t. on 6 t. Rusty-spotted genet 20 20
692 50 t. on 12 t. Hippopotamus 45 50

1990. "Stamp World London 90" International Stamp Exhibition. Multicoloured.
693 8 t. Type **171** 10 10
694 15 t. Transmission pylon .. 10 10
695 30 t. Public telephone .. 20 25
696 2 p. Testing circuit board 1·50 1·60

172 Young Children

1990. Traditional Dress. Multicoloured.
697 8 t. Type **172** 10 10
698 15 t. Young woman .. 15 15
699 30 t. Adult man 25 25
700 2 p. Adult woman .. 1·25 1·40

173 "Acacia nigrescens"

1990. Christmas. Flowering Trees. Mult.
702 8 t. Type **173** 15 10
703 15 t. "Peltophorum africanum" 20 10
704 30 t. "Burkea africana" .. 25 30
705 2 p. "Pterocarpus angolensis" .. .. 1·40 1·50

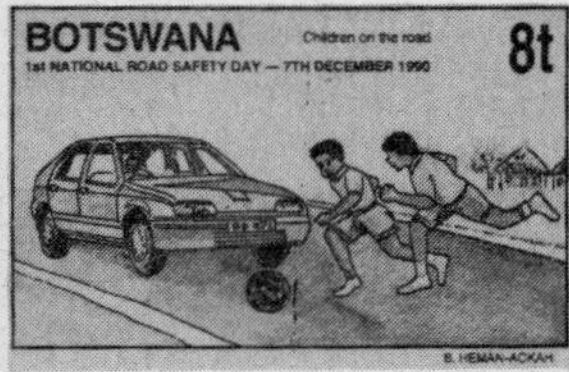

174 Children running in front of Car

1990. 1st National Road Safety Day. Mult.
706 8 t. Type **174** 15 10
707 15 t. Careless overtaking .. 25 15
708 30 t. Cattle on road .. 35 30

175 Cattle

1991. Rock Paintings. Multicoloured.
709 8 t. Type **175** 15 10
710 15 t. Cattle, drying frames and tree 20 15
711 30 t. Animal hides .. 30 30
712 2 p. Family herding cattle 1·40 1·50

176 Children

1991. National Census. Multicoloured.
713 8 t. Type **176** 10 10
714 15 t. Village 10 15
715 30 t. School 15 20
716 2 p. Hospital .. .. 1·10 1·25

177 Tourists viewing Elephants

1991. African Tourism Year. Okavango Delta. Multicoloured.
717 8 t. Type **177** 15 10
718 15 t. Crocodiles basking on river bank 20 15
719 35 t. Fish eagles and aircraft 30 30
720 2 p. Okavango wildlife (26 × 44 mm) .. .. 1·40 1·60

178 "Harpagophytum procumbens"

1991. Christmas. Seed Pods. Multicoloured.
721 8 t. Type **178** 10 10
722 15 t. "Tylosema esculentum" 10 10
723 30 t. "Abrus precatorius" 15 20
724 2 p. "Kigelia africana" .. 1·10 1·25

1992. Nos. 621, 624 and 627 surch.
725 8 t. on 12 t. Hippopotamus 10 10
726 10 t. on 12 t. Hippopotamus 10 10
727 25 t. on 6 t. Rusty-spotted genet 15 20
728 40 t. on 3 t. Zebra .. 20 25

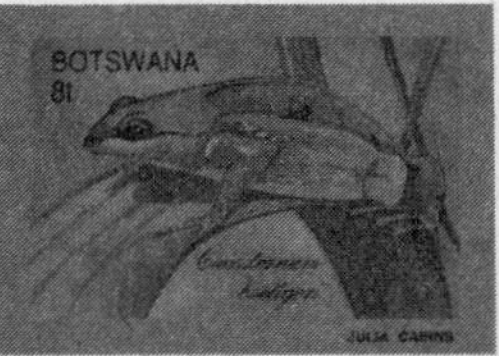

179 "Cacosternum boettgeri"

1992. Climbing Frogs. Multicoloured.
729 8 t. Type **179** 10 10
730 10 t. "Hyperolius marmoratus angolensis" (vert) 10 10
731 40 t. "Bufo fenoulheti" .. 20 25
732 1 p. "Hyperolius sp." (vert) 55 60

POSTAGE DUE STAMPS

1967. Nos. D 10/2 of Bechuanaland optd. **REPUBLIC OF BOTSWANA.**
D 13. D 1. 1 c. red .. .. 15 1·50
D 14. 2 c. violet .. .. 15 1·75
D 15. 5 c. green .. .. 20 1·75

D 5. African Elephant. D 6. Common Zebra.

1971.
D 16. D 5. 1 c. red .. .. 55 1·50
D 17. 2 c. violet .. .. 65 1·75
D 18. 6 c. brown .. .. 1·10 2·50
D 19. 14 c. green .. .. 1·75 3·00

1977.
D 25 D 6. 1 t. black and red .. 10 10
D 26 2 t. black and green .. 10 10
D 27 4 t. black and red .. 10 10
D 28 10 t. black and blue .. 10 10
D 29 16 t. black & brown .. 10 10

BRITISH ANTARCTIC TERRITORY

Constituted in 1962 comprising territories south of latitude 60° S., from the former Falkland Is. Dependencies.

1963. 12 pence = 1 shilling.
20 shillings = 1 pound.
1971. 100 (new) pence = 1 pound.

1. M.V. "Kista Dan".

1963.
1. 1. ½d. blue 45 85
2. – 1d. brown 70 50
3. – 1½d. red and purple .. 70 50
4. – 2d. purple 70 50
5. – 2½d. myrtle 80 50
6. – 3d. turquoise .. .. 1·75 50
7. – 4d. sepia .. .. .. 1·25 60
8. – 6d. olive and blue .. 2·00 85
9. – 9d. green .. .. .. 2·25 75
10. – 1s. turquoise .. .. 1·50 50
11. – 2s. violet and brown .. 14·00 5·00
12. – 2s. 6d. blue .. .. 14·00 5·50
13. – 5s. orange and red .. 20·00 8·50
14. – 10s. blue and green .. 45·00 22·00
15. – £1 black and blue .. 85·00 48·00
15a.– £1 red and black £150 £120
DESIGNS: 1d. Manhauling. 1½d. Muskeg (tractor). 2d. Skiing. 2½d. Beaver (aircraft). 3d. R.R.S. "John Biscoe". 4d. Camp scene. 6d. H.M.S. "Protector". 9d. Sledging. 1s. Otter (aircraft). 2s. Huskies. 2s. 6d. Helicopter. 5s. Snocat (tractor). 10s. R.R.S. "Shackleton". £1 (No. 15), Antarctic map. £1 (No. 15a.), H.M.S. "Endurance".

1966. Churchill Commemoration. As T **38** of Antigua.
16. – ½d. blue 80 70
17. 1d. green .. .. .. 3·00 1·00
18. 1s. brown .. .. .. 21·00 3·50
19. 2s. violet .. .. .. 24·00 4·50

17. Lemaire Channel and Icebergs.

1969. 25th Anniv. of Continuous Scientific Work.
20. 17. 3½d. black, blue & ultram. 3·50 1·75
21. – 6d. multicoloured .. 3·50 1·75
22. – 1s. black, blue and red .. 3·50 1·75
23. – 2s. black, orange and turq. 4·25 2·00
DESIGNS: 6d. Radio Sonde balloon. 1s. Muskeg pulling tent equipment. 2s. Surveyors with theodolite.

1971. Decimal Currency. Nos. 1/14 surch.
24. ½p. on ½d. blue .. .. 60 1·25
25. 1p. on 1d. brown .. .. 1·00 40
26. 1½p. on 1½d. red and purple 1·25 35
27. 2p. on 2d. purple .. .. 1·25 30
28. 2½p. on 2½d. green .. .. 1·75 40
29. 3p. on 3d. blue .. .. 2·50 55
30. 4p. on 4d. brown .. .. 2·25 55
31. 5p. on 6d. green and blue 4·25 2·25
32. 6p. on 9d. green .. .. 9·00 4·00
33. 7½p. on 1s. blue .. .. 9·00 4·25
34. 10p. on 2s. violet & brown 16·00 10·00
35. 15p. on 2s. 6d. blue .. 16·00 10·00
36. 25p. on 5s. orange & red .. 22·00 13·00
37. 50p. on 10s. blue & green 60·00 35·00

19. Setting up Camp.

1971. 10th Anniv. of Antarctic Treaty. Multicoloured.
38. 1½p. Type **19** .. .. 5·50 2·50
39. 4p. Snow Petrels .. .. 9·50 4·00
40. 5p. Weddell Seals .. .. 9·50 4·00
41. 10p. Adelie Penguins .. 14·00 6·00
Nos. 38/41 each include Antarctic Map and Queen Elizabeth in their design.

1972. Royal Silver Wedding. As Type **52** of Ascension, but with Kerguelen fur seals and Emperor penguins in background.

42. 5p. brown .. .. .. 3·75 1·50
43. 10p. green .. .. .. 3·75 1·50

21. James Cook and H.M.S. "Resolution".

1973. Multicoloured.

64a ½p. Type **21** 65 55
65 1p. Thaddeus Von Bellingshausen and "Vostok" 45 75
66 1½p. James Weddell and "Jane" 45 75
67 2p. John Biscoe & "Tula" 1·25 80
68 2½p. J.S.C. Dumont d'Urville and "L'Astrolabe" 1·00 80
49 3p. James Clark Ross and H.M.S. "Erebus" .. 95 1·50
70 4p. C. A. Larsen and "Jason" .. .. 45 1·50
51 5p. Adrien de Gerlache and "Belgica" .. .. 1·00 1·50
72 6p. Otto Nordenskjold and "Antarctic" .. .. 70 1·50
73 7½p. W. S. Bruce and "Scotia" .. .. 1·50 1·75
74 10p. Jean-Baptiste Charcot and "Pourquoi Pas?" .. 1·25 2·00
75 15p. Ernest Shackleton and "Endurance" .. .. 1·25 1·50
76 25p. Hubert Wilkins and "San Francisco" .. 1·25 1·50
77a 50p. Lincoln Ellsworth and "Polar Star" .. .. 1·25 1·75
78a £1 John Rymill and "Penola" .. .. 2·00 3·50

The 25p. and 50p. show aircraft; the rest show ships.

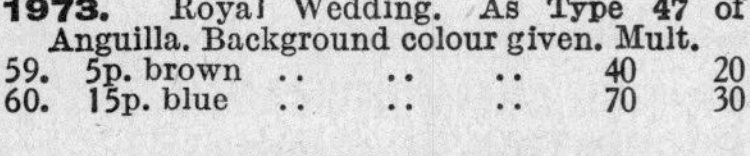

1973. Royal Wedding. As Type **47** of Anguilla. Background colour given. Mult.

59. 5p. brown 40 20
60. 15p. blue 70 30

22. Churchill and Churchill Peninsula, B.A.T.

1974. Birth Centenary of Sir Winston Churchill. Multicoloured.

61. 5p. Type **22** .. .. 1·75 1·50
62. 15p. Churchill and "Trepassey" .. .. 2·25 2·00

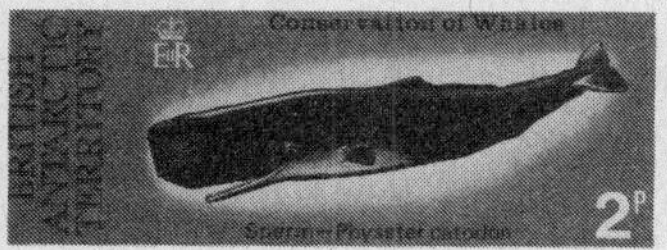

23. Sperm Whale. (Illustration reduced, actual size 58 × 21 mm).

1977. Conservation of Whales. Mult.

79. 2p. Type **23** .. .. 3·75 1·75
80. 8p. Fin Whale .. .. 4·75 2·25
81. 11p. Humpback Whale .. 5·50 2·25
82. 25p. Blue Whale .. .. 7·00 3·00

24. The Queen Before Taking the Oath.

1977. Silver Jubilee. Multicoloured.

83. 6p. Prince Philip's visit, 1956/7 .. .. 95 20
84. 11p. The Coronation Oath 1·25 30
85. 33p. Type **24** .. .. 1·50 45

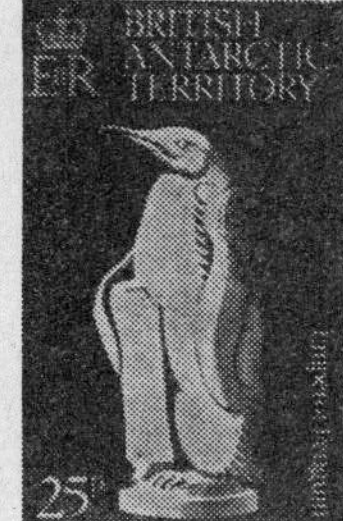

25. Emperor Penguin.

1978. 25th Anniv. of Coronation.

86. – 25p. green, deep green and silver .. .. 1·10 65
87. – 25p. multicoloured .. 1·10 65
88. **25.** 25p. green, deep green and silver .. .. 1·10 65

DESIGNS: No. 86, Black Bull of Clarence. No. 87, Queen Elizabeth II.

26. Macaroni Penguins.

1979. Penguins. Multicoloured.

89. 3p. Type **26** .. .. 7·00 4·75
90. 8p. Gentoo penguins .. 2·75 1·75
91. 11p. Adelie penguins .. 3·00 2·00
92. 25p. Emperor penguins .. 4·00 2·50

27. Sir John Barrow and "Tula".

1980. 150th Anniv. of Royal Geographical Society. Former Presidents. Multicoloured.

93. 3p. Type **27** 20 10
94. 7p. Sir Clement Markham and "Discovery" .. 25 25
95. 11p. Lord Curzon and launch "James Caird" .. 30 30
96. 15p. Sir William Goodenough 35 35
97. 22p. Sir James Wordie .. 50 55
98. 30p. Sir Raymond Priestley 60 65

28. Map of Antarctic.

1981. 20th Anniv. of Antarctic Treaty.

99. **28.** 10p. blk., blue & light blue 30 60
100. – 13p. blk., blue and grn. 35 70
101. – 25p. blk., blue & mauve 50 85
102. – 26p. blk., brn. and red 50 90

DESIGNS: 13p. Conservation research ("scientific co-operation"). 25p. Satellite image mapping ("technical co-operation"). 26p. Global geophysics ("scientific co-operation").

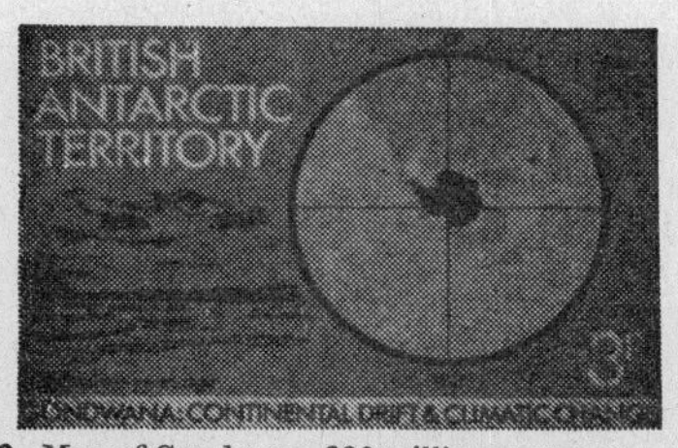

29. Map of Gondwana 280 million years ago and Contemporary Landscape Scene.

1982. Gondwana—Continental Drift and Climatic Change. Maps of Gondwana showing position of continents, and contemporary landscapes. Multicoloured.

103. 3p. Type **29** 20 35
104. 6p. 260 million years ago 25 45
105. 10p. 230 million years ago 30 55
106. 13p. 175 million years ago 35 60
107. 25p. 50 million years ago 55 70
108. 26p. Present day .. 55 70

30. British Antarctic Territory Coat of Arms.

1982. 21st Birthday of Princess of Wales. Multicoloured.

109. 5p. Type **30** 20 20
110. 17p. Princess of Wales (detail of painting by Bryan Organ) 45 50
111. 37p. Wedding ceremony 85 1·00
112. 50p. Formal portrait .. 95 1·40

31. Leopard Seal.
(Illustration reduced. Actual size 57 × 22mm.)

1983. 10th Anniv. of Antarctic Seal Conservation Convention. Multicoloured.

113. 5p. Type **31** 35 35
114. 10p. Weddell seals .. 40 40
115. 13p. Southern elephant seals 45 45
116. 17p. Kerguelen fur seals .. 55 55
117. 25p. Ross seals 65 65
118. 34p. Crabeater seals .. 85 85

32. De Havilland "Twin Otter".

1983. Bicentenary of Manned Flight. Mult.

119. 5 p. Type **32** 25 20
120. 13 p. De Havilland "Single Otter" 40 35
121. 17 p. Consolidated "Canso" 55 45
122. 50 p. Lockheed "Vega" .. 1·10 1·10

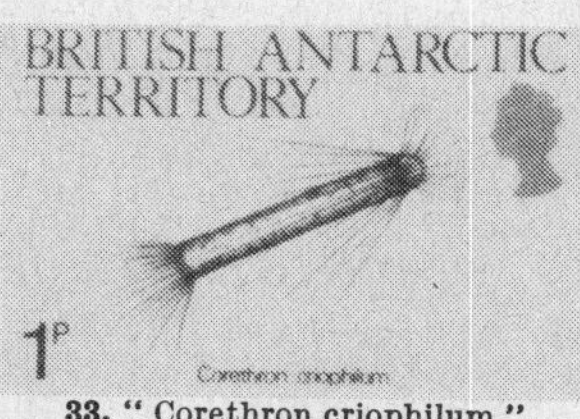

33. "Corethron criophilum".

1984. Marine Life. Multicoloured.

123. 1p. Type **33** 25 40
124. 2p. "Desmonema gaudichaudi" 30 40
125. 3p. "Tomopteris carpenteri" 30 45
126. 4p. "Pareuchaeta antarctica" 35 50
127. 5p. "Antarctomysis maxima" 35 50
128. 6p. "Antarcturus signiensis 40 60
129. 7p. "Serolis cornuta" .. 40 60
130. 8p. "Parathemisto gaudichaudii" 45 70
131. 9p. "Bovallia gigantea" .. 45 70
132. 10p. "Euphausia superba" 45 70
133. 15p. "Colossendeis australis" 60 80
134. 20p. "Todarodes sagittatus" 65 90
135. 25p. "Notothenia neglecta" 70 90
136. 50p. "Chaenocephalus aceratus" .. .. 1·25 1·60
137. £1 Crabeater seal .. .. 1·75 2·00
138. £3 Antarctic marine food chain .. .. .. 5·00 5·50

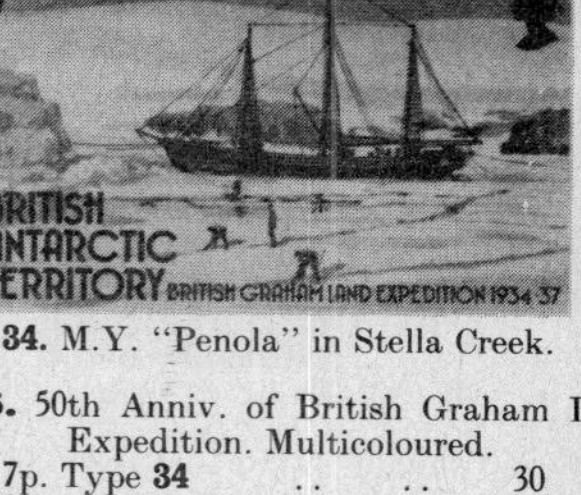

34. M.Y. "Penola" in Stella Creek.

1985. 50th Anniv. of British Graham Land Expedition. Multicoloured.

139. 7p. Type **34** 30 35
140. 22p. Northern Base, Winter Island 60 80
141. 27p. D. H. "Fox Moth" at Southern Base, Barry Island 70 90
142. 54p. Dog Team near Ablation Point, George VI Sound .. .. 1·25 1·75

35. Robert McCormick and McCormick's Skua.

1985. Early Naturalists. Multicoloured.

143. 7p. Type **35** .. .. 1·00 75
144. 22p. Sir Joseph Dalton Hooker and "Deschampsia antarctica" .. .. 1·40 1·10
145. 27p. Jean René C. Quoy and Hourglass Dolphin 1·60 1·40
146. 54p. James Weddell and Weddell Seal .. .. 2·50 2·00

36. Dr. Edmond Halley.

1986. Appearance of Halley's Comet. Mult.

147. 7p. Type **36** 75 45
148. 22p. Halley Station, Antarctica .. .. 1·25 80
149. 27p. "Halley's Comet, 1531" (from Peter Apian woodcut, 1532) .. .. 1·40 90
150. 54p. "Giotto" spacecraft .. 2·25 1·50

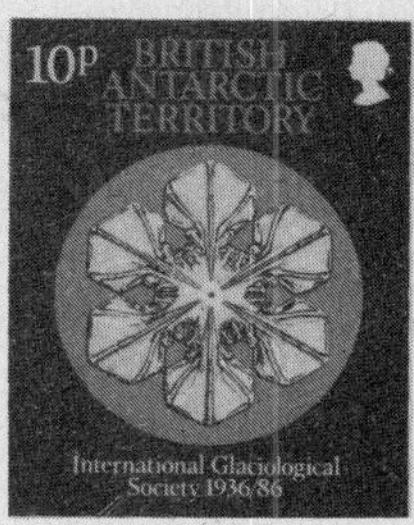

37. Snow Crystal.

1986. 50th Anniv. of International Glaciological Society. Snow crystals.

151. **37.** 10p. light blue and blue 50 50
152. – 24p. green & deep green 80 80
153. – 29p. mauve & dp. mve. 90 90
154. – 58p. blue and violet .. 1·25 1·75

MORE DETAILED LISTS
are given in the Stanley Gibbons Catalogues referred to in the country headings.
For lists of current volumes see Introduction.

38. Captain Scott, 1904.

1987. 75th Anniv. of Captain Scott's Arrival at South Pole. Multicoloured.

No.	Description	Unused	Used
155.	10p. Type **38**	45	45
156.	24p. Hut Point and "Discovery", Ross Island, 1902–4	80	80
157.	29p. Cape Evans Hut, 1911–13	95	1·00
158.	58p. Scott's expedition at South Pole, 1912 ..	1·60	1·75

39. I.G.Y. Logo.

1987. 30th Anniv. of International Geophysical Year.

No.	Type	Description	Unused	Used
159.	**39.**	10p. black and green ..	30	45
160.	–	24p. multicoloured ..	60	85
161.	–	29p. multicoloured ..	75	95
162.	–	58p. multicoloured ..	1·40	2·00

DESIGNS: 24p. Port Lockroy. 29p. Argentine Islands. 58p. Halley Bay.

40. Aurora over South Ice Plateau Station.

1988. 30th Anniv. of Commonwealth Trans-Antarctic Expedition. Multicoloured.

No.	Description	Unused	Used
163.	10p. Type **40**	30	30
164.	24p. "Otter" aircraft at Theron Mountains ..	60	60
165.	29p. Seismic ice-depth sounding	70	70
166.	58p. "Sno-cat" over crevasse	1·25	1·40

41 "Xanthoria elegans"

1989. Lichens. Multicoloured.

No.	Description	Unused	Used
167	10p. Type **41**	40	50
168	24p. "Usnea aurantiaco-atra" ..	80	1·00
169	29p. "Cladonia chloroph-aea"	85	1·10
170	58p. "Umbilicaria antarctica" ..	1·50	2·00

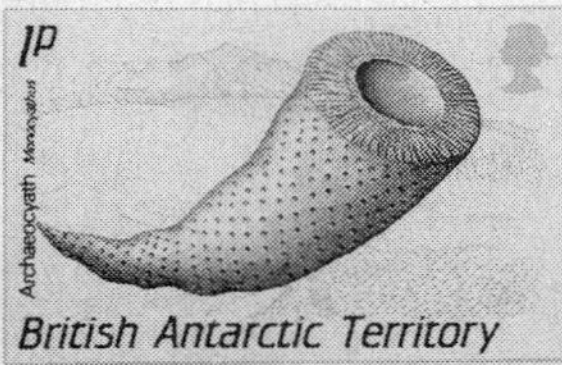

42 "Monocyathus" (archaeocyath)

1990. Fossils. Multicoloured.

No.	Description	Unused	Used
171	1p. Type **42**	10	10
172	2p. "Lingulella" (brachio-pod)	10	10
173	3p. "Triplagnoslus" (trilo-bite)	10	10
174	4p. "Lyriaspis" (trilobite)	10	10
175	5p. "Glossopteris" leaf (gymnosperm)	10	10
176	6p. "Gonatosorus" (fern)	10	10
177	7p. "Belemnopsis" (belem-nite)	15	20
178	8p. "Sanmartinoceras" (ammonite)	15	20
179	9p. "Pinna" (mussel) ..	20	25
180	10p. "Aucellina" (mussel)	20	25
181	20p. "Trigonia" (mussel) ..	40	45
182	25p. "Perissoptera" (conch shell)	50	55
183	50p. "Ainoceras" (ammo-nite)	1·00	1·10
184	£1 "Gunnarites" (ammo-nite)	2·00	2·10
185	£3 "Hoploparia" (crayfish)	6·00	6·25

1990. 90th Birthday of Queen Elizabeth the Queen Mother. As T **134** of Ascension.

No.	Description	Unused	Used
186	26p. multicoloured ..	1·25	1·25
187	£1 black and brown ..	3·25	3·25

DESIGNS—21 × 36 mm. 26p. Wedding of Prince Albert and Lady Elizabeth Bowes-Lyon, 1923. 29 × 37 mm. £1 The Royal Family, 1940.

43 Late Cretaceous Forest and Southern Beech Fossil

1991. Age of the Dinosaurs. Multicoloured.

No.	Description	Unused	Used
188	12p. Type **43**	40	40
189	26p. Hypsilophodont dinosaurs and skull ..	80	80
190	31p. Frilled Sharks and tooth	90	90
191	62p. Mosasaur, Plesiosaur, and Mosasaur vertebra	1·75	1·75

44 Launching Meteorological Balloon, Halley IV Station

1991. Discovery of Antarctic Ozone Hole. Multicoloured.

No.	Description	Unused	Used
192	12p. Type **44**	35	35
193	26p. Measuring ozone with Dobson spectrophoto-meter	75	75
194	31p. Satellite map showing ozone hole	80	80
195	62p. ER-2 aircraft and graph of chlorine monoxide and ozone levels	1·60	1·75

45 Researching Dry Valley

1991. 30th Anniv of Antarctic Treaty.

No.	Type	Description	Unused	Used
196	**45**	12p. multicoloured ..	35	35
197	–	26p. multicoloured ..	65	65
198	–	31p. black and green ..	75	75
199	–	62p. multicoloured	1·50	1·60

DESIGNS: 26p. Relief map of ice sheet; 31p. BIOMASS logo; 62p. Ross seal.

46 "H.M.S. "Erebus" and H.M.S. "Terror" in the Antarctic" (J. Carmichael)

1991. Maiden Voyage of "James Clark Ross" (research ship). Multicoloured.

No.	Description	Unused	Used
200	12p. Type **46**	25	30
201	26p. Launch of "James Clark Ross"	50	55
202	31p. "James Clark Ross" in Antarctica	60	65
203	62p. Scientific research ..	1·25	1·40

1991. Birth Bicent of Michael Faraday (scientist). Nos. 200/3 additionally inscr "200th Anniversary M. Faraday 1791–1867".

No.	Description	Unused	Used
204	12p. Type **46**	25	30
205	26p. Launch of "James Clark Ross"	50	55
206	31p. "James Clark Ross" in Antarctica	60	65
207	62p. Scientific research ..	1·25	1·40

BRITISH COLUMBIA AND VANCOUVER ISLAND

1860. 12 pence = 1 shilling.
20 shillings = 1 pound.
1865. 100 cents = 1 dollar.

Former British colonies, now a Western province of the Dominion of Canada, whose stamps are now used.

1.

1860. Imperf. or perf.

No.	Type	Description	Unused	Used
2.	**1.**	2½d. pink	£275	£180

VANCOUVER ISLAND

2.

1865. Imperf. or perf.. Various frames.

No.	Type	Description	Unused	Used
13.	**2.**	5 c. red	£200	£130
14.	–	10 c. blue	£200	£140

BRITISH COLUMBIA

4. Emblems of United Kingdom.

1865.

No.	Type	Description	Unused	Used
21.	**4.**	3d. blue	70·00	60·00

1868. Surch. in words or figures and words.

No.	Type	Description	Unused	Used
28	4	2 c. brown	70·00	70·00
29		5 c. red	85·00	85·00
24		10 c. red	£400	£400
31		25 c. yellow	£100	£100
26		50 c. mauve	£400	£350
27		$1 green	£600	£700

BRITISH COMMONWEALTH OCCUPATION OF JAPAN

Stamps used by British Commonwealth Occupation Forces, 1946–49.

12 pence = 1 shilling.
20 shillings = 1 pound.

1946. Stamps of Australia optd. **B.C.O.F JAPAN 1946.**

No.	Type	Description	Unused	Used
J 1.	**27.**	½d. orange	2·00	4·00
J 2.	**46.**	1d. purple	2·00	1·50
J 3.	**31.**	3d. brown	1·25	1·75
J 4.	–	6d. brown (No. 189a)..	11·00	8·00
J 5.	–	1s. green (No. 191) ..	11·00	9·00
J 6.	**1.**	2s. red	38·00	42·00
J 7.	**38.**	5s. red	£110	£130

BRITISH EAST AFRICA

Now incorporated in Kenya and Uganda.

16 annas = 100 cents = 1 rupee.

1890. Stamps of Gt. Britain (1881) surch. **BRITISH EAST AFRICA COMPANY** and value in annas.

No.	Type	Description	Unused	Used
1.	**57.**	½ a. on 1d. lilac ..	£325	£200
2.	**73.**	1 a. on 2d. green & red ..	£400	£275
3.	**78.**	4 a. on 5d. purple & blue	£450	£275

3. Arms of the Company. **11.**

1890. Nos. 16/19 are larger (24 × 25 mm.).

No.	Type	Description	Unused	Used
~~4b~~	3	½ a. brown	70	2·00
5		1 a. green	3·00	3·50
6		2 a. red	2·75	3·25
7b		2½ a. black on yellow ..	3·75	3·25
~~8a~~		3 a. black on red ..	1·25	2·00
9		4 a. brown	2·50	4·50
11a		4½ a. purple	2·50	12·00
29		5 a. black on blue ..	1·25	9·50
30		7½ a. black	1·25	9·50

12 3 8 a. blue .. .. 5·50 6·50
13 8 a. grey £250 £225
14 1 r. red .. .. 6·00 9·00
15 1 r. grey £225 £225
16 – 2 r. red .. .. .. 11·00 15·00
17 – 3 r. purple .. .. 8·00 18·00
18 – 4 r. blue .. .. 12·00 24·00
19 – 5 r. green .. .. 30·00 45·00

1891. With handstamped or pen surcharges. Initialled in black.
20. **3.** ½ a. on 2 a. red £2500 £750
31. ½ a. on 3 a. black on red .. £180 45·00
32. 1 a. on 3 a. black on red .. £2250 £1100
26. 1 a. on 4 a. brown £2500 £800

1894. Surch. in words and figures
27. **3.** 5 a. on 8 a. blue .. .. 50·00 70·00
28. 7½ a. on 1 r. red .. .. 50·00 70·00

1895. Optd. **BRITISH EAST AFRICA.**
33. **3.** ½ a. brown .. .. 55·00 20·00
34. 1 a. green .. .. 60·00 60·00
35. 2 a. red .. .. £110 85·00
36. 2½ a. black on yellow .. 90·00 48·00
37. 3 a. black on red .. .. 42·00 35·00
38. 4 a. brown .. .. 38·00 35·00
39. 4½ a. purple .. .. £100 80·00
40. 5 a. black on blue .. £120 90·00
41. 7½ a. black .. .. 75·00 75·00
42. 8 a. blue .. .. 75·00 65·00
43. 1 r. red .. .. 42·00 42·00
44. – 2 r. red £180 £180
45. – 3 r. purple £110 £100
46. – 4 r. blue £110 £100
47. – 5 r. green £250 £225

1895. Surch. with large **2½.**
48. **3.** 2½ a. on 4½ a. purple .. 75·00 60·00

1895. Stamps of India (Queen Victoria) optd. **British East Africa.**
49. **23.** ½ a. turquoise .. .. 3·00 3·00
50. – 1 a. purple .. .. 2·75 3·25
51. – 1½ a. brown .. .. 3·75 3·00
52. – 2 a. blue .. .. 3·25 2·50
53. – 2½ a. green .. .. 5·00 2·50
54. – 3 a. orange .. .. 7·50 8·00
55a. – 4 a. green (No. 96) .. 18·00 15·00
56. – 6 a. brown (No. 80) .. 22·00 27·00
57c. – 8 a. mauve .. .. 28·00 35·00
58. – 12 a. purple on red .. 19·00 26·00
59. – 1 r. grey (No. 101) .. 45·00 48·00
60. **37.** 1 r. green and red .. 26·00 40·00
61. **38.** 2 r. red and orange .. 48·00 75·00
62. 3 r. brown and green .. 60·00 85·00
63. 5 r. blue and violet .. 75·00 95·00

1895. No. 51 surch. with small **2½.**
64. "2½" on 1½ a. brown .. 38·00 32·00

1896.
65 11 ½ a. green 85 45
66a 1 a. red .. .. 1·50 30
67 2 a. brown .. .. 1·50 2·75
68 2½ a. blue .. .. 4·50 1·10
69 3 a. grey .. .. 2·50 4·75
70 4 a. green .. .. 5·50 2·50
71 4½ a. yellow .. .. 3·37 7·50
72 5 a. brown .. .. 7·50 4·00
73 7½ a. mauve .. .. 5·00 16·00
74 8 a. grey .. .. 2·50 4·50
75 1 r. blue .. .. 22·00 17·00
76 2 r. orange .. .. 50·00 24·00
77 3 r. violet .. .. 50·00 27·00
78 4 r. red .. .. 50·00 48·00
79 5 r. brown .. .. 50·00 40·00

1897. Stamps of Zanzibar. 1896, optd. **British East Africa.**
80. **3.** ½ a green and red .. .. 35·00 35·00
81. 1 a. blue and red .. .. 60·00 60·00
82. 2 a. brown and red .. 25·00 20·00
83. 4½ a. orange and red .. 32·00 25·00
84. 5 a. brown and red .. 35·00 28·00
85. 7½ a. mauve and red .. 38·00 35·00

1897. As last, surch. **2½.**
86. **3.** "2½" on 1 a. blue and red 70·00 50·00
89. "2½" on 3 a. grey and red 65·00 48·00

1897. As Type 11, but larger.
92a. 1 r. blue .. .. .. 24·00 17·00
93. 2 r. orange .. .. .. 48·00 48·00
94. 3 r. violet .. .. .. 48·00 65·00
95. 4 r. red £100 £140
96. 5 r. brown £110 £150
97. 10 r. brown £150 £225
98. 20 r. green £550 £1000
99. 50 r. mauve £1800 £2750

BRITISH FORCES IN EGYPT

SPECIAL SEALS AND STAMPS FOR THE USE OF BRITISH FORCES IN EGYPT

A. SEALS

A 1.

1932. (a) Inscr. "POSTAL SEAL".
A 1. **A 1.** 1 p. blue and red .. 40·00 2·50
(b) Inscr. "LETTER SEAL".
A 2. **A1.** 1 p. blue and red .. 14·00 55

A 2.

1932. Christmas Seals.
A 3. **A 2.** 3 m. black on blue .. 32·00 50·00
A 4. 3 m. lake .. .. 6·00 15·00
A 5. 3 m. blue .. .. 7·00 12·00
A 6. 3 m. red .. .. 1·25 10·00

A 3.

1934.
A 9. **A 3.** 1 p. red 90 85
A 8. 1 p. green .. .. 3·00 2·75

1935. Silver Jubilee. Optd. **JUBILEE COMMEMORATION 1935.**
A 10. **A 3.** 1 p. blue £200 £180

1935. Provisional Christmas Seal. Optd. **Xmas 1935 3 Milliemes.**
A 11. **A 3.** 3 m. on 1 p. red .. 15·00 50·00

B. POSTAGE STAMPS

A 6. King Fuad I.

A 7. King Farouk.

1936.
A 12. **A 6.** 3 m. green 75 60
A 13. 10 m. red .. .. 1·00 10

1939.
A 14. **A 7.** 3 m. green .. .. 60 2·00
A 15. 10 m. red 60 10

BRITISH GUIANA

Situated on the N.E. coast of S. America. A British colony granted full internal self-Government in August, 1951. Attained independence on 26th May, 1966, when the country was renamed Guyana.

100 cents = 1 dollar.

1.

1850. Imperf. Used
1. **1.** 2 c. black on red .. .. — £55000
2. 4 c. black on orange .. .. — £2750
4. 8 c. black on green .. .. — £2000
5. 12 c. black on blue .. .. — £1700

Prices are for used stamps cut round. Stamps cut square are worth much more.

2.

3. Seal of the Colony.

1852. Imperf.
9. **2.** 1 c. black on magenta .. £8500 £4250
10. 4 c. black on blue .. £10000 £4500

1853. Imperf.
12. **3.** 1 c. red £2000 £800
20. 4 c. blue £800 £300

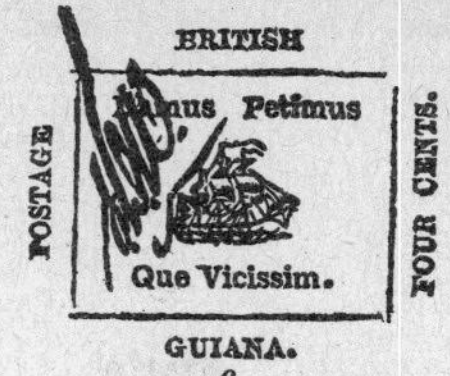

6.

1856. Imperf.
23. **6.** 1 c. black on magenta ..
24. 4 c. black on magenta .. — £5500
26. 4 c. black on blue .. — £32000

7.

9.

1860. Perf.
29 1 c. red £900 £170
40 1 c. brown .. .. £250 75·00
85 1 c. black .. .. .. 7·50 2·00
87 2 c. orange .. .. 13·00 1·25
89 4 c. blue .. .. .. 60·00 11·00
92 6 c. blue .. .. .. £100 24·00
95 8 c. red .. .. .. 95·00 12·00
98 12 c. lilac .. .. £110 12·00
99 12 c. grey .. .. £100 15·00
64 24 c. green .. .. £130 50·00
78 24 c. green .. .. £100 8·00
82 48 c. red .. .. .. £130 42·00

The prices quoted for Nos. 29/82 are for fine copies with four margins. Medium specimens can be supplied at much lower rates.

10.

16.

1862. Various borders. Roul.
116. **10** 1 c. black on red .. £1200 £225
119. 2 c. black on yellow .. £1200 £200
122. 4 c. black on blue .. £1300 £250

The above prices are for stamps signed in the centre by the Postmaster. Unsigned stamps are worth considerably less.

1876.
126 16 1 c. grey .. .. .. 2·75 1·40
171 2 c. orange .. .. 20·00 15
172 4 c. blue .. .. .. 75·00 5·00
173 6 c. brown .. .. 5·00 6·50
174 8 c. red .. .. .. 80·00 40
131 12 c. violet .. .. 50·00 1·25
132 24 c. green .. .. 60·00 3·00
133 48 c. brown .. .. £100 14·00
134 96 c. olive £425 £250

1878. Optd. with thick horiz. or horiz. and vert. bars. (a) On postage stamps.
137. **16.** 1 c. on 6 c. brown .. 38·00 65·00
141. **9.** 1 c. on 6 c. blue .. £130 80·00
(b) On official stamps of 1875 and 1877.
138. **7.** 1 c. black .. .. £120 70·00
139. **16.** 1 c. grey .. .. £110 50·00
140. 2 c. orange .. .. £130 65·00
144. 4 c. blue .. .. £130 70·00
145. 6 c. brown .. .. £150 75·00
146. **7.** 8 c. red £275 £110
148. **16.** 8 c. red .. .. £225 85·00

1881. Surch. with figure. Old value barred out in ink. (a) On postage stamps.
152. **9.** "1" on 48 c. red .. 32·00 5·00
149. **16.** "1" on 96 c. olive .. 3·50 5·00
150. "2" on 96 c. olive .. 4·00 8·50
(b) On stamps optd. **OFFICIAL.**
153 **7.** "1" on 12 c. lilac .. £100 60·00
154 **16.** "1" on 48 c. brown .. £120 80·00
155 "2" on 12 c. violet .. 60·00 20·00
157 "2" on 24 c. green .. 65·00 30·00

26.

30.

1882.
162 **26** 1 c. black on red .. 35·00 28·00
165 2 c. black on yellow .. 50·00 40·00

Each stamp is perforated with the word "SPECIMEN".

1888. T **16** without value in bottom tablet, surch. **INLAND REVENUE** and value.
175. **16.** 1 c. purple 60 20
176. 2 c. purple .. .. 1·25 30
177. 3 c. purple 60 20
178. 4 c. purple .. .. 2·50 30
179. 6 c. purple .. .. 2·50 1·75
180. 8 c. purple .. .. 1·50 25
181. 10 c. purple .. .. 6·00 2·50
182. 20 c. purple .. .. 17·00 10·00
183. 40 c. purple .. .. 20·00 17·00
184. 72 c. purple .. .. 32·00 32·00
185. $1 green £400 £325
186. $2 green £180 £160
187. $3 green .. .. .. £110 90·00
188. $4 green £325 £325
189. $5 green £225 £160

1889. No. 176 surch. with additional **2.**
192. **16.** "2" on 2 c. purple .. 60 15

1889.
193 **30.** 1 c. purple and grey .. 1·50 90
213 1 c. green 30 10
194 2 c. purple and orange .. 1·25 10
234 2 c. purple and red .. 3·25 25
241 2 c. purple & black on red 5·00 10
253 2 c. red .. .. .. 6·00 10
195 4 c. purple and blue .. 4·00 1·50
254 4 c. brown and purple .. 2·25 60
214 5 c. blue .. .. .. 2·50 10
243 5 c. pur. and blue on blue 6·50 3·50
198 6 c. purple and brown .. 6·00 3·75
236 6 c. black and blue .. 6·50 11·00
256 6 c. grey and black .. 13·00 7·00
199 8 c. purple and red .. 6·50 60
215 8 c. purple and black .. 2·50 2·75
200a 12 c. purple and mauve .. 8·50 2·00
257 12 c. orange and purple .. 4·00 4·00
246 24 c. purple and green .. 5·00 6·00
202 48 c. purple and red .. 13·00 9·00
247 48 c. grey and brown .. 18·00 25·00
248 60 c. green and red .. 24·00 55·00
203 72 c. purple and brown .. 23·00 29·00
205 96 c. purple and red .. 65·00 70·00
250 96 c. blk. & red on yell. 35·00 45·00

1890. Nos. 185/8 surch. **ONE CENT.**
207. **16.** 1 cent on $1 green .. 90 35
208. 1 cent on $2 green .. 50 60
209. 1 cent on $3 green .. 1·40 1·25
210. 1 cent on $4 green .. 2·00 4·50

32. Mount Roraima.

33. Kaieteur Falls.

37.

1898. Jubilee.
216. **32.** 1 c. black and red .. 2·75 25
217. **33.** 2 c. brown and blue .. 5·00 90
219. **32.** 5 c. green and brown .. 18·00 2·00
220. **33.** 10 c. black and red .. 15·00 20·00
221. **32.** 15 c. brown and blue .. 18·00 16·00

1899. Nos. 219/21 surch. **TWO CENTS.**
222. **32.** 2 c. on 5 c. grn. & brn. 1·60 1·10
223. **33.** 2 c. on 10 c. blk. & red 60 1·40
224. **32.** 2 c. on 15 c. brn. & blue 1·25 1·25

1905. T **30,** but inscr. "REVENUE", optd. **POSTAGE AND REVENUE.**
251. **30.** $2.40 green and violet £160 £250

1913.
272 **37.** 1 c. green .. .. 1·50 25
260 2 c. red 50 10
274 2 c. violet 50 10
275 4 c. brown and purple 1·50 10
262 5 c. blue 60 85
263 6 c. grey and black .. 75 85
276 6 c. blue .. .. .. 2·00 25
264 12 c. orange and violet 70 90
278 24 c. purple and green 1·50 4·50
279 48 c. grey and purple 8·00 3·50
280 60 c. green and red 6·50 30·00
281 72 c. purple and brown 7·00 30·00
282 96 c. black & red on yell. 13·00 32·00

1918. Optd. **WAR TAX** in two lines.
271. **37.** 2 c. red 15 15

INDEX

Countries can be quickly located by referring to the index at the end of this volume.

39. Ploughing a Rice Field.

40. Indian shooting Fish. 41. Kaieteur Falls.

42. Public Buildings, Georgetown.

1931. Centenary of County Union.

283. 39. 1 c. green 1·00 75
284. 40. 2 c. brown 1·00 10
285. 41. 4 c. red 1·75 35
286. 42. 6 c. blue 1·25 2·50
287. 41. $1 violet 18·00 35·00

43. Ploughing a Rice Field.

44. Gold Mining. 53. South America.

1934.

288. 43. 1 c. green 40 30
289. 40. 2 c. brown 1·00 15
290. 44. 3 c. red 15 10
291. 41. 4 c. violet 1·50 35
292. – 6 c. blue 2·50 1·75
293. – 12 c. orange 10 10
294. – 24 c. purple 1·75 2·50
295. – 48 c. black 6·50 6·50
296. 41. 50 c. green 9·00 13·00
297. – 60 c. brown 25·00 26·00
298. – 72 c. purple 1·25 70
299. – 96 c. black 20·00 28·00
300. – $1 violet 32·00 24·00

DESIGNS—HORIZ. 6 c. Shooting logs over falls. 12 c. Stabroek Market. 24 c. Sugar canes in punts. 48 c. Forest road. 60 c. Victoria Regia lilies. 72 c. Mt. Roraima. $1, Botanical Gardens. VERT. 96 c. Sir Walter Raleigh and his son.

The 2 c., 4 c. and 50 c. are without the dates shown in Types **40/44** and the 12 c., 48 c., 72 c. and 96 c. have no portrait.

1935. Silver Jubilee. As Type **13** of Antigua.

301. 2 c. blue and grey 15 10
302. 6 c. brown and blue 80 30
303. 12 c. green and blue 1·25 3·75
304. 24 c. grey and purple 3·50 4·75

1937. Coronation. As Type **2** of Aden.

305. 2 c. brown 15 10
306. 4 c. grey 50 15
307. 6 c. blue 75 75

1938. Designs as for same values of 1934 issue (except where indicated) but with portrait of King George VI (as in T **53**) where portrait of King George V previously appeared.

308a 43. 1 c. green 10 10
309 – 2 c. violet (As 4 c.) 30 10
310 53. 4 c. red and black 40 10
311 – 6 c. blue (As 2 c.) 25 10
312a – 24 c. green 1·00 10
313 – 36 c. violet (As 4 c.) 1·00 10
314 – 48 c. orange 50 30
315 – 60 c. brown (As 6 c.) 4·75 2·50
316 – 96 c. purple 2·00 2·00
317 – $1 violet 5·50 35
318 – $2 purple (As 72 c.) 4·00 8·00
319 – $3 brown 23·00 20·00

DESIGN—HORIZ. $3, Victoria Regia lilies.

1946. Victory. As Type **9** of Aden.

320. 3 c. red 10 10
321. 6 c. blue 10 10

1948. Silver Wedding. As Type **10** and **11** of Aden.

322. 3 c. red 10 20
323. $3 brown 9·00 13·00

1949. U.P.U. As Types **20/23** of Antigua.

324. 4 c. red 20 15
325. 6 c. blue 25 35
326. 12 c. orange 25 30
327. 24 c. green 25 45

1951. Inauguration of B.W.I. University College. As Types **24/25** of Antigua.

328. 3 c. black and red 15 10
329. 6 c. black and blue 25 10

1953. Coronation. As Type **13** of Aden.

330. 4 c. black and red 10 10

55. G.P.O., Georgetown.

1954.

331. 55. 1 c. black 10 10
332. – 2 c. myrtle 10 10
333. – 3 c. olive and brown 1·75 10
334. – 4 c. violet 10 10
335. – 5 c. red and black 20 10
336. – 6 c. green 10 10
337. – 8 c. blue 10 10
338a. – 12 c. black and brown 15 10
360. – 24 c. black and orange 1·50 10
340. – 36 c. red and black 55 30
341a. – 48 c. blue and brown 40 40
342. – 72 c. red and green 6·50 2·75
364. – $1 multicoloured 6·50 90
344. – $2 mauve 8·50 2·50
345. – $5 blue and black 11·00 10·00

DESIGNS—HORIZ. 2 c. Botanical Gardens. 3 c. Victoria Regia lilies. 5 c. Map of Caribbean. 6 c. Rice combine-harvester. 8 c. Sugar cane entering factory. 24 c. Bauxite mining. 36 c. Mt. Roraima. $1, Channel-billed Toucan. $2, Dredging gold. VERT. 4 c. Amerindian shooting fish. 12 c. Felling Greenheart, 48 c. Kaieteur Falls, 72 c. Arapaimia (fish). $5, Arms, British Guiana.

70.

1961. History and Culture Week.

346. 70. 5 c. sepia and red 10 10
347. 6 c. sepia and green 10 10
348. 30 c. sepia and orange 20 20

1963. Freedom from Hunger. As T **28** of Aden.

349. 20 c. violet 30 10

1963. Cent of Red Cross. As T **33** of Antigua.

350. 5 c. red and black 10 15
351. 20 c. red and blue 35 25

71. Weightlifting.

1964. Olympic Games, Tokyo.

367. 71. 5 c. orange 10 10
368. 8 c. blue 10 10
369. 25 c. mauve 20 20

1965. Cent of I.T.U. As T **36** of Antigua.

370. 5 c. green and olive 10 15
371. 25 c. blue and mauve 20 15

1965. I.C.Y. As T **37** of Antigua.

372. 5 c. purple and turquoise 10 10
373. 25 c. green and lavender 25 20

72. St. George's Cathedral, Georgetown.

1966. Churchill Commem.

374. 72. 5 c. black, red and gold 30 10
375. 25 c. black, blue & gold 1·10 40

1966. Royal Visit. As T **39** of Antigua.

376. 3 c. black and blue 50 15
377. 25 c. black and mauve 1·50 60

OFFICIAL STAMPS

1875. Optd. **OFFICIAL.**

O 1. 7. 1 c. black 26·00 11·00
O 2. 2 c. orange £100 14·00
O 3. 8 c. red £250 95·00
O 4. 12 c. lilac £950 £400
O 5. 9. 24 c. green £650 £180

1877. Optd. **OFFICIAL.**

O 6. 16. 1 c. grey £150 55·00
O 7. 2 c. orange 70·00 13·00
O 8. 4 c. blue 75·00 20·00
O 9. 6 c. brown £1700 £400
O 10. 8 c. red £1600 £325

POSTAGE DUE STAMPS

1940. As Type D 1 of Barbados, but inscr. " BRITISH GUIANA ".

D1a 1 c. green 75 3·25
D2a 2 c. black 75 2·75
D3 4 c. blue 30 4·25
D4 12 c. red 14·00 8·50

For later issues see GUYANA.

BRITISH HONDURAS

A Br. colony on the E. coast of Central America. Self-government was granted on 1 Jan. 1964. The country was renamed Belize from 1 June 1973.

1866. 12 pence = 1 shilling.
20 shillings = 1 pound.
1888. 100 cents = 1 dollar.

1.

2 CENTS (2.) 2 CENTS (4.)

1866.

17. 1. 1d. blue 38·00 13·00
18. 1d. red 18·00 11·00
13. 3d. brown 85·00 15·00
20. 4d. mauve 70·00 3·00
9. 6d red £160 27·00
21. 6d. yellow £250 £160
16. 1s. green £160 11·00
22. 1s. grey £250 £140

1888. Surch. as T **2.**

27. 1. 2 c. on 1d. red 7·00 15·00
25. 2 c. on 6d. red 70·00 65·00
26. 3 c. on 3d. brown 55·00 5·00
28. 10 c. on 4d. mauve 30·00 15·00
29. 20 c. on 6d. yellow 27·00 30·00
30. 50 c. on 1s. grey £325 £450

No. 30 surch. **TWO.**

35. 1. " TWO " on 50 c. on 1s. grey 35·00 65·00

1888. Surch. as T **4.**

36. 1. 1 c. on 1d. green 25 85
37. 2 c. on 1d. red 20 1·25
38. 3 c. on 3d. brown 75 1·25
39. 6 c. on 3d. blue 1·10 7·50
40. 10 c. on 4d. mauve 1·60 40
41. 20 c. on 6d. yellow 7·50 14·00
42. 50 c. on 1s. grey 17·00 48·00

1891. No. 40 surch. **6** and bar.

43. 1. " 6 " on 10 c. on 4d. mauve 40 1·50

Nos. 38 and 39 surch.

49. 1. " FIVE " on 3 c. on 3d. brown 40 1·40
50. " 15 " on 6 c. on 3d. blue 6·00 17·00

8.

NOTE: 10 c. (A) inscr. "POSTAGE POSTAGE"; (B) inscr. "POSTAGE & REVENUE".

1891.

51. 8. 1 c. green 80 30
52. 2 c. red 75 10
53. 2 c. brown 3·00 1·25
54. 5 c. blue 12·00 30
55. 5 c. black & blue on blue 5·50 85
56. 6 c. blue 3·00 55
57. 8 10 c. mauve and green (A) 8·50 7·50
58. 10 c. purple and green (B) 4·00 7·00
59a. 12 c. mauve and green 2·50 2·00
60. 24 c. yellow and blue 5·50 14·00
61. 25 c. brown and green 30·00 55·00
62. 50 c. green and red 17·00 35·00
63. $1 green and red 35·00 60·00
64. $2 green and blue 45·00 75·00
65. $5 green and black £190 £250

1899. Optd. **REVENUE.**

66. 8. 5 c. blue 3·75 2·00
67. 10 c. mauve and green 3·00 11·00
68. 25 c. brown and green 2·75 20·00
69. 1. 50 c. on 1s. grey £120 £225

14. 16.

1902.

84. 14. 1 c. green 90 1·50
85. 2 c. purple & black on red 1·50 20
96. 2 c. red 2·25 10
86. 5 c. black & blue on blue 1·75 20
97. 5 c. blue 1·75 10
87. 10 c. purple and green 4·00 9·50
83. 20 c. purple 3·00 14·00
89. 25 c. purple and orange 6·00 29·00
100. 25 c. black on green 2·75 35·00
90. 50 c. green and red 10·00 45·00
91. $1 green and red 28·00 55·00
92. $2 green and blue 60·00 £100
93. $5 green and black £180 £250

1913.

101. 16. 1 c. green 40 15
102a. 2 c. red 1·10 25
103. 3 c. orange 30 15
104. 5 c. blue 2·00 30
105. 10 c. purple and green 2·75 6·50
106. 25 c. black on green 1·25 9·00
107. 50c. purple & blue on blue 4·00 9·00
108. $1 black and red 6·50 19·00
109. $2 purple and green 48·00 55·00
110. $5 purple & black on red £170 £190

1915. Optd. with pattern of wavy lines.

111a. 16. 1 c. green 25 5·00
112. 2 c. red 60 50
113. 5 c. blue 25 2·50

1916. Optd. **WAR** in small letters.

114 16 1 c. green (No. 111a) 10 30
116 1 c. green (No. 101) 20 1·25
118 3 c. orange (No. 103) 20 1·60

1918. Optd. **WAR** in large letters 3 mm. high.

119. 16. 1 c. green 10 25
120. 3 c. orange 10 75

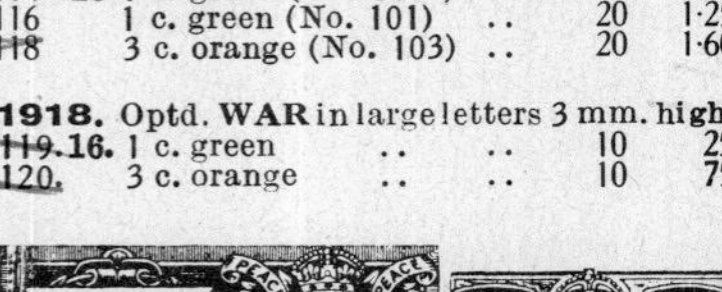

21. 22.

1921. Peace.

121. 21. 2 c. red 1·00 25

As last, but without word " PEACE "

123. 4 c. grey 2·00 25

1922.

126. 22 1 c. green 75 2·00
127. 2 c. brown 30 15
128. 2 c. red 45 10
129. 3 c. orange 4·00 2·50
130. 4 c. grey 90 20
131. 5 c. blue 90 55
132. 10 c. purple and olive 60 25
133. 25 c. black on green 80 4·00
134. 50 c. purple & blue on blue 2·50 9·00
136. $1 black and red 4·00 14·00
137. $2 green and purple 27·00 60·00
125. $5 purple and black on red £170 £190

1932. Optd. **BELIZE RELIEF FUND PLUS** and value.

138. 22. 1 c. + 1 c. green 70 4·50
139. 2 c. + 2 c. red 75 4·50
140. 3 c. + 3 c. orange 85 5·50
141. 4 c. + 4 c. grey 1·50 9·50
142. 5 c. + 5 c. blue 4·00 13·00

1935. Silver Jubilee. As T **13** of Antigua.

143. 3 c. blue and black 35 45
144. 4 c. green and blue 70 50
145. 5 c. brown and blue 1·25 60
146. 25 c. grey and purple 1·25 1·75

1937. Coronation. As T **2** of Aden.

147. 3 c. orange 30 25
148. 4 c. grey 60 25
149. 5 c. blue 70 40

24. Maya figures.

1938.

150. 24. 1 c. purple and green .. 10 35
151. – 2 c. black and red .. 10 30
152. – 3 c. purple and brown .. 10 10
153. – 4 c. black and green .. 10 10
154. – 5 c. purple and blue .. 10 10
155. – 10 c. green and brown .. 35 15
156. – 15 c. brown and blue .. 35 10
157. – 25 c. blue and green .. 90 45
158. – 50 c. black and purple .. 4·75 1·40
159. – $1 red and olive .. 13·00 3·50
160. – $2 blue and purple .. 14·00 12·00
161. – $5 red and brown .. 16·00 19·00

Designs—vert. 2 c. Chicle tapping. 3 c. Cohune palm. $1, Court House, Belize. $2, Mahogany felling. $5, Arms of Colony. horiz. 4 c. Local products. 5 c. Grapefruit. 10 c. Mahogany logs in river. 15 c. Sergeant's Cay. 25 c. Dorey. 50 c. Chicle industry.

1946. Victory. As T **9** of Aden.

162. 3 c. brown 10 5
163. 5 c. blue 10 10

1948. Silver Wedding. As T **10** and **11** of Aden.

164. 4 c. green 15 35
165. $5 brown .. .. .. 13·00 28·00

36. Island of St. George's Cay.

1949. 150th Anniv. of Battle of St. George's Cay.

166. 36. 1 c. blue and green .. 10 10
167. 3 c. blue and brown .. 10 15
168. 4 c. olive and violet .. 10 20
169. – 5 c. brown and blue .. 20 10
170. – 10 c. green and brown .. 20 10
171. – 15 c. green and blue .. 20 10

Designs: 5, 10 and 15 c. H.M.S. "Merlin".

1949. U.P.U. As T **20/23** of Antigua.

172. 4 c. green 20 15
173. 5 c. blue 35 15
174. 10 c. brown 45 35
175. 25 c. blue 50 40

1951. Inauguration of B.W.I. University College. As T **24/25** of Antigua.

176. 3 c. violet and brown .. 35 20
177. 10 c. green and brown .. 35 20

1953. Coronation. As T **13** of Aden.

178 4 c. black and green .. 15 30

39. Baird's Tapir

49. Mountain Orchid.

1953.

179 – 1 c. green and black .. 10 20
180a 39. 2 c. brown and black .. 30 10
181 – 3 c. lilac and mauve .. 10 10
182 – 4 c. brown and green .. 20 20
183 – 5 c. olive and red .. 10 10
184 – 10 c. slate and blue .. 10 10
185 – 15 c. green and violet .. 15 10
186 – 25 c. blue and brown .. 4·00 1·00
187 – 50 c. brown and purple 1·75 1·25
188 – $1 slate and brown .. 4·00 3·25
189 – $2 red and grey .. 6·00 4·00
190 49. $5 purple and slate .. 25·00 14·00

Designs—horiz. 1 c. Arms of British Honduras Legislative. 3 c. Mace and Council Chamber. 4 c. Pine industry. 5 c. Spiny lobster. 10 c. Stanley Field Airport. 15 c. Maya Frieze. 25 c. "Morpho peleides" (butterfly). $1, Nine-banded armadillo. $2, Hawkesworth Bridge. vert. 50 c. Maya Indian.

50. "Belize from Fort George, 1842." (C. J. Hullmandel).

1960. Post Office Centenary.

191. 50. 2 c. green 10 10
192. – 10 c. red 10 10
193. – 15 c. blue 10 15

Designs: 10 c. Public Seals, 1860 and 1960. 15 c. Tamarind tree, Newtown Barracks.

1961. New Constitution. Stamps of 1953 optd. **NEW CONSTITUTION 1960.**

194. 39. 2 c. brown and black .. 10 10
195. – 3 c. lilac and mauve .. 15 10
196. – 10 c. slate and blue .. 15 10
197. – 15 c. green and violet .. 20 10

1962. Hurricane Hattie Relief Fund. Stamps of 1953 optd. **HURRICANE HATTIE.**

198. 1 c. green and black .. 10 10
199. 10 c. slate and blue .. 10 10
200. 25 c. blue and brown .. 60 30
201. 50 c. brown and purple .. 25 35

55. Great Curassow.

1962. Birds in natural colours; portrait and inscr. in black; background colours given.

239 55. 1 c. yellow 10 10
240 – 2 c. grey 20 30
204 – 3 c. green 90 40
241 – 4 c. pale grey 65 30
242 – 5 c. buff 40 10
243 – 10 c. stone 50 10
244 – 15 c. stone 60 10
209 – 25 c. slate .. .. 2·50 30
210 – 50 c. grey .. .. 2·50 35
211 – $1 blue .. .. 6·00 75
212 – $2 stone .. .. 8·00 3·00
213 – $5 grey .. .. 23·00 13·00

Birds: 2 c. Red-legged Honeycreeper. 3 c. Northern Jacana. 4 c. Great Kiskadee. 5 c. Scarlet-rumped Tanager. 10 c. Scarlet Macaw. 15 c. Slaty-tailed Trogon. 25 c. Red-footed Booby. 50 c. Keel-billed Toucan. $1, Magnificent Frigate Bird. $2, Rufous-tailed Jacamar. $5, Montezuma Oropendola.

1963. Freedom from Hunger. As T **28** of Aden.

214. 22 c. green 30 15

1963. Cent of Red Cross. As T **33** of Antigua.

215. 4 c. red and black 10 10
216. 22 c. red and blue 30 35

1964. New Constitution. Nos. 202, 204, 205 207 and 209 optd. **SELF GOVERNMENT 1964.**

217. 55. 1 c. yellow 10 10
218. – 3 c. green 20 10
219. – 4 c. pale grey 20 10
220. – 10 c. stone 20 10
221. – 25 c. slate 30 30

1965. Cent of I.T.U. As T **36** of Antigua.

222. 2 c. red and green .. 10 10
223. 50 c. yellow and purple .. 35 25

1965. I.C.Y. As T **37** of Antigua.

224. 1 c. purple and turquoise .. 10 10
225. 22 c. green and lavender .. 15 10

1966. Churchill Commem. As T **38** of Antigua.

226. 1 c. blue 10 10
227. 4 c. green 10 10
228. 22 c. brown 25 10
229. 25 c. violet 30 25

1966. Dedication of new Capital Site. Nos. 202, 204/5, 207 and 209 optd. **DEDICATION OF SITE NEW CAPITAL 9th OCTOBER 1965.**

230. 55. 1 c. yellow 10 10
231. – 3 c. green 20 10
232. – 4 c. pale grey 20 10
233. – 10 c. stone 25 10
234. – 25 c. slate 35 30

58. Citrus Grove.

1966. Stamp Cent. Multicoloured.

235. 5 c. Type **58** 10 10
236. 10 c. Half Moon Cay .. 10 10
237. 22 c. Hidden Valley Falls 10 10
238. 25 c. Maya Ruins, Xunantunich 15 10

59. Sailfish.

1967. Int. Tourist Year.

246. 59. 5 c. blue, black & yellow 10 10
247. – 10 c. brown, black & red 10 10
248. – 22 c. orge., blk. and grn. 15 10
249. – 25 c. blue, black & yell. 15 15

Designs: 10 c. Red brocket. 22 c. Jaguar. 25 c. Tarpon.

60. " Schomburgkia tibicinis.

61. Monument of Belizean Patriots.

1968. 20th Anniv. of Economic Commission for Latin America. Multicoloured.

250. 5 c. Type **60** 20 10
251. 10 c. " Maxillaria tenuifolia " 25 10
252. 22 c. " Bletia purpurea " .. 30 10
253. 25 c. " Sobralia macrantha " 40 20

1968. Human Rights Year. Multicoloured.

254. 22 c. Type **61** 10 10
255. 50 c. Monument at Site of New Capital 10 10

63. Jew Fish.

1968. Wildlife.

276. – ½ c. mult. and blue .. 10 10
277. – ½ c. mult. and yellow 30 35
256. 63. 1 c. blk., brn. and yell. 10 10
257. – 2 c. blk., grn. and yell. 10 10
258. – 3 c. blk., brn. and lilac 10 10
259. – 4 c. multicoloured .. 10 20
260. – 5 c. black and red .. 10 20
261. – 10 c. multicoloured .. 15 10
262. – 15 c. multicoloured .. 30 25
263. – 25 c. multicoloured .. 30 25
264. – 50 c. multicoloured .. 70 80
265. – $1 multicoloured .. 2·00 1·25
266. – $2 multicoloured .. 2·50 2·00
267. – $5 multicoloured .. 9·00 6·50

Designs: ½ c. (Nos. 276 and 277) Crana Fish. 2 c. White-lipped peccary. 3 c. Grouper. 4 c. Collared anteater. 5 c. Bonefish. 10 c. Paca. 15 c. Dolphin. 25 c. Kinkajou. 50 c. Mutton Snapper. $1, Tayra. $2, Great Barracuda. $5, Puma.

64. " Rhyncholaelia digbyana ".

1969. " Orchids of Belize " (1st series). Multicoloured.

268. 5 c. Type **64** 35 10
269. 10 c. " Cattleya bowringiana " 40 10
270. 22 c. " Lycaste cochleatum " 65 10
271. 25 c. "Coryanthes speciosum" 85 50

See also Nos. 287/90.

65. Ziricote Tree.

1969. Indigenous Hardwoods (1st series). Multicoloured.

272. 5 c. Type **65** 10 10
273. 10 c. Rosewood 10 10
274. 22 c. Mayflower 15 10
275. 25 c. Mahogany 15 20

See also Nos. 291/4, 315/8 and 333/7.

66. "The Virgin and Child" (Bellini).

69. Santa Maria.

1969. Christmas. Paintings. Multicoloured.

279. 5 c. Type **66** 10 10
280. 15 c. Type **66** 10 10
281. 22 c. " The Adoration of the Magi " (Veronese) .. 10 10
282. 25 c. As No. 281 .. .. 10 10

1970. Population Census. Nos. 260/3 optd. **POPULATION CENSUS 1970**

283. 5 c. multicoloured .. 10 10
284. 10 c. multicoloured .. 10 10
285. 15 c. multicoloured .. 15 10
286. 25 c. multicoloured .. 15 10

1970. "Orchids of Belize" (2nd series). As T **64**. Multicoloured.

287. 5 c. Black Orchid .. 30 10
288. 15 c. White Butterfly Orchid 45 10
289. 22 c. Swan Orchid .. 60 10
290. 25 c. Butterfly Orchid .. 60 30

1970. Indigenous Hardwoods (2nd series). Multicoloured.

291. 5 c. Type **69** 15 10
292. 15 c. Nargusta 20 10
293. 22 c. Cedar 25 10
294. 25 c. Sapodilla 30 25

70. " The Nativity " (A. Hughes).

1970. Christmas. Multicoloured.

295. ½ c. Type **70** 10 10
296. 5 c. " The Mystic Nativity " (Botticelli) 10 10
297. 10 c. Type **70** 10 10
298. 15 c. As 5 c. 10 10
299. 22 c. Type **70** 15 10
300. 50 c. As 5 c. 25 30

71. Legislative Assembly House.

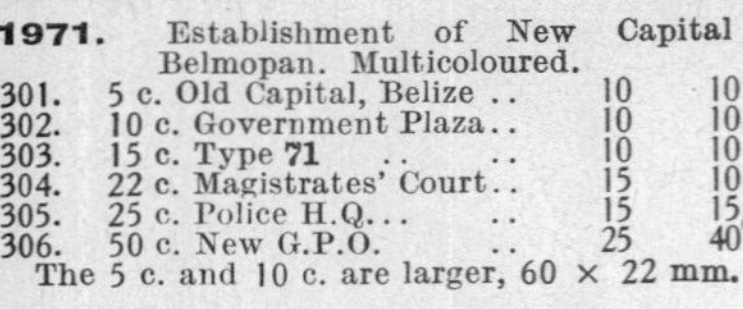

1971. Establishment of New Capital Belmopan. Multicoloured.

301.	5 c. Old Capital, Belize ..	10	10
302.	10 c. Government Plaza ..	10	10
303.	15 c. Type **71**	10	10
304.	22 c. Magistrates' Court ..	15	10
305.	25 c. Police H.Q.	15	15
306.	50 c. New G.P.O.	25	40

The 5 c. and 10 c. are larger, 60 × 22 mm.

72. "Tabebuia chrysantha".

1971. Easter. Flowers. Multicoloured.

307.	½ c. Type **72**	10	10
308.	5 c. "Hymenocallis littorallis"	10	10
309.	10 c. "Hippeastrum equestre"	10	10
310.	15 c. Type **72**	10	10
311.	22 c. As 5 c.	10	10
312.	25 c. As 10 c.	15	20

1971. Racial Equality Year. Nos. 261 and 264 optd. **RACIAL EQUALITY YEAR-1971.**

313.	10 c. multicoloured ..	15	10
314.	50 c. multicoloured ..	25	20

74. Tubroos.

1971. Indigenous Hardwoods (3rd series). Multicoloured.

315.	5 c Type **74**	25	10
316.	15 c. Yemeri	35	30
317.	26 c. Billywebb	55	35
318.	50 c. Logwood	1·10	1·25

75. Hawksworth and Belcan Bridges.

1971. Bridges of the World. Multicoloured.

320.	½ c. Type **75**	10	10
321.	5 c. Narrows Bridge, N.Y. and Quebec Bridge ..	10	10
322.	26 c. London Bridge (1871) and reconstructed, Arizona (1971) ..	20	10
323.	50 c. Belize Mexican Bridge and Swing Bridge ..	30	35

76. "Petrae volubis". **77.** Seated Figure.

1972. Easter. Wild Flowers. Multicoloured.

324.	6 c. Type **76**	15	10
325.	15 c. Yemeri	25	30
326.	26 c. Mayflower ..	50	45
327.	50 c. Tiger's Claw ..	80	70

1972. Mayan Artefacts. Multicoloured.

328.	3c. Type **77**	10	10
329.	6c. Priest in "dancing" pose	15	10
330.	16 c. Sun God's Head (horiz.)	25	15
331.	26c. Priest and Sun God ..	40	20
332.	50c. Full-front figure ..	70	1·10

78. Banak.

1972. Indigenous Hardwoods (4th series). Multicoloured.

333.	3 c. Type **78**	10	10
334.	5 c. Quamwood	10	10
335.	16 c. Waika Chewstick ..	25	15
336.	26 c. Mamee-Apple ..	45	20
337.	50 c. My Lady	80	1·10

1972. Royal Silver Wedding. As T **52** of Ascension, but with Orchids of Belize in background.

341.	26 c. green	25	10
342.	50 c. violet	40	40

80. Baron Bliss Day.

1973. Festivals of Belize. Multicoloured.

343	3 c. Type **80**	10	10
344	10 c. Labour Day ..	15	10
345	26 c. Carib Settlement Day	20	15
346	50 c. Pan American Day ..	35	60

POSTAGE DUE STAMPS

D 1.

1923.

~~D 1~~ D 1.	1 c. black	50	5·50
D 4	2 c. black	1·25	3·00
D 5	4 c. black	50	3·50

For later issues see **BELIZE.**

BRITISH INDIAN OCEAN TERRITORY

A Crown Colony, established 8th November 1965, comprising the Chagos Archipelago (previously administered by Mauritius) and Aldabra, Farquhar and Desroches, previously administered by Seychelles to which country they were returned on 29th June 1976.

The Chagos Archipelego has no indigenous population, but stamps were provided from 1990 for use by civilian workers at the U.S. Navy base on Diego Garcia.

1968. 100 cents = 1 rupee.
1990. 100 pence = 1 pound.

1968. Nos. 196/200, 202/4 and 206/12 of Seychelles optd. **B.I.O.T.**

1. **24.**	5 c. multicoloured ..	10	10
2. –	10 c. multicoloured ..	10	10
3. –	15 c. multicoloured ..	10	15
4. –	20 c. multicoloured ..	15	15
5. –	25 c. multicoloured ..	15	15
6. –	40 c. multicoloured ..	15	20
7. –	45 c. multicoloured ..	20	30
8. –	50 c. multicoloured ..	20	30
9. –	75 c. multicoloured ..	20	35
10. –	1 r. multicoloured ..	30	35
11. –	1 r. 50 multicoloured ..	1·75	1·50
12. –	2 r. 25 multicoloured ..	3·75	3·75
13. –	3 r. 50 multicoloured ..	4·00	4·50
14. –	5 r. multicoloured ..	5·50	7·50
15. –	10 r. multicoloured ..	13·00	15·00

2. Lascar.

1968. Marine Life. Multicoloured.

16.	5 c. Type **2**	30	60
17.	10 c. Hammerhead Shark (vert.)	30	50
18.	15 c. Tiger Shark	30	50
19.	20 c. Bat Ray	30	50
20.	25 c. Butterfly Fish (vert.)	80	1·00
20a.	30 c. Robber Crab	3·00	2·75
21.	40 c. Caranx	40	40
22.	45 c. Garfish (vert.) ..	2·25	2·50
23.	50 c. Barracuda	45	30
23a.	60 c. Spotted Pebble Crab ..	3·00	3·25
24.	75 c. Parrot Fish	2·50	2·75
24a.	85 c. Dorade (" Elegatis bipinnulatus ")	4·50	3·50
25.	1 r. Giant Hermit Crab ..	1·00	35
26.	1 r. 50 Humphead	2·50	2·50
27.	2 r. 25 Rock Cod	7·00	8·50
28.	3 r. 50 Black Marlin ..	4·00	3·75
29.	5 r. black, green and blue (Whale Shark) (vert.) ..	7·50	6·50
30.	10 r. Lion Fish	7·50	8·00

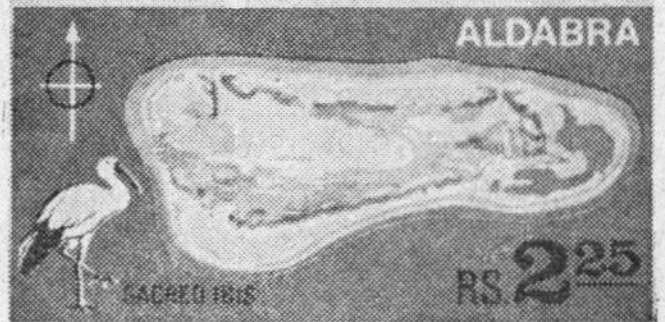

3. Sacred Ibis and Aldabra Coral Atoll.

1969. Coral Atolls.

31. **3.**	2 r. 25 multicoloured ..	1·25	35

4. Outrigger Canoe.

1969. Ships of the Islands. Multicoloured

32.	45 c. Type **4**	65	75
33.	75 c. Pirogue	65	80
34.	1 r. M.V. " Nordvaer " ..	70	90
35.	1 r. 50 " Isle of Farquhar "	80	1·00

5. Giant Land Tortoise.

1971. Aldabra Nature Reserve. Mult.

36.	45 c. Type **5**	2·50	2·00
37.	75 c. Aldabra Lily	3·00	2·50
38.	1 r. Aldabra Snail	3·50	2·75
39.	1 r. 50 Western Reef Heron	8·50	5·00

6. Arms of Royal Society and White-throated Rail.

1971 Opening of Royal Society Research Station, Aldabra.

40. **6.**	3 r. 50 multicoloured ..	13·00	8·50

7. Staghorn Coral.

1972. Coral. Multicoloured.

41.	40 c. Type **7**	3·00	2·00
42.	60 c. Brain coral	3·50	2·50
43.	1 r. Mushroom coral ..	3·50	3·00
44.	1 r. 75 Organ Pipe coral ..	4·50	4·00

1972. Royal Silver Wedding. As T **52** of Ascension, but with White-throated Rail and Sacred Ibis in background.

45.	95 c. green	65	40
46.	1 r. 50 violet	65	40

9. " Christ on the Cross ".

1973. Easter. Multicoloured.

47.	45 c. Type **9**	25	40
48.	75 c. " Joseph and Nicodemus burying Jesus " ..	35	55
49.	1 r. Type **9**	35	60
50.	1 r. 50 As 75 c.	40	70

10. Upsidedown Jellyfish.

1973. Wildlife (1st series). Multicoloured.

53	50 c. Type **10** ..	3·00	3·00
54	1 r. "Hypolimnas misippus" and "Belenois aldabrensis" (butterflies) ..	3·00	3·00
55	1 r. 50 "Nephila Madagascariensis" (spider)	3·50	3·00

See also Nos. 58/61, 77/80 and 86/9.

11. M.V. "Nordvaer".

1974. 5th Anniv. of "Nordvaer" Travelling Post Office. Multicoloured.

56.	85 c. Type **11**	50	75
57.	2 r. 50 "Nordvaer" off shore	75	1·25

12. Auger Shells.

1974. Wildlife (2nd series). Shells. Mult.

58.	45 c. Type **12**	1·50	1·00
59.	75 c. Green Turban ..	1·60	1·25
60.	1 r. Drupe Snail	2·00	1·50
61.	1 r. 50 Helmet Shell ..	2·25	1·75

13. Aldabra Drongo.

1975. Birds. Multicoloured.

62.	5 c. Type **13**	90	1·75
63.	10 c. Black coucal	90	1·75
64.	20 c. Mascarene fody ..	90	1·75
65.	25 c. White tern	90	2·00
66.	30 c. Crested tern	90	2·00
67.	40 c. Brown booby	90	2·00
68.	50 c. Common noddy (horiz.)	90	2·25
69.	60 c. Grey heron	90	2·50
70.	65 c. Blue-faced booby (horiz.)	90	2·50
71.	95 c. Madagascar white eye (horiz.)	1·00	2·50
72.	1 r. Green heron (horiz.) ..	1·25	2·50
73.	1 r. 75 Lesser frigate bird (horiz.)	2·00	3·75
74.	3 r. 50 White-tailed tropic bird (horiz.)	2·75	3·75
75.	5 r. Souimanga sunbird (horiz.)	4·00	5·00
76.	10 r. Madagascar turtle-dove (horiz.)	8·00	9·00

14. "Grewia salicifola".

1975. Wildlife (3rd series). Seashore Plants. Multicoloured.

77.	50 c. Type **14**	40	70
78.	65 c. "Cassia aldabrensis"	45	80
79.	1 r. "Hypoestes aldabrensis"	60	1·00
80.	1 r. 60 "Euphorbia pyrifolia"	75	1·10

15. Map of Aldabra.

1975. 10th Anniv. of Territory. Maps. Mult.

81.	50 c. Type **15**	60	65
82.	1 r. Desroches	75	85
83.	1 r. 50 Farquhar	85	1·00
84.	2 r. Diego Garcia	95	1·25

16. "Utetheisa pulchella"(moth).

1976. Wildlife (4th series). Mult.

86	65 c. Type **16**	60	1·10
87	1 r. 20 "Dysdercus fasciatus" (bug) ..	75	1·25
88	1 r. 50 "Sphex torridus" (wasp)	80	1·40
89	2 r. "Oryctes rhinoceros" (beetle)	85	1·40

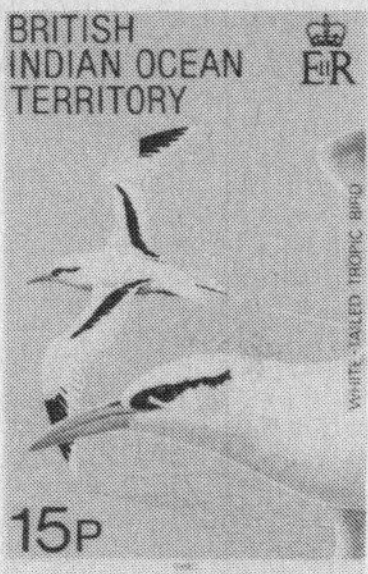

17 White-tailed Tropic Bird

1990. Birds. Multicoloured.

90	15p. Type **17**	30	35
91	20p. Turtle dove	40	45
92	24p. Greater frigate bird ..	50	55
93	30p. Little green heron ..	60	65
94	34p. Greater sand plover ..	70	75
95	41p. Crab plover	80	85
96	45p. Crested tern	90	95
97	54p. Lesser crested tern ..	1·10	1·25
98	62p. Fairy tern	1·25	1·40
99	71p. Red-footed booby ..	1·40	1·50
100	80p. Indian mynah ..	1·60	1·75
101	£1 Madagascar fody ..	2·00	2·10

18 1974 Wildlife 1 r. 50 Stamp

1990. "Stamp World London 90" International Stamp Exhibition. Multicoloured.

102	15p. Type **18**	50	50
103	20p. 1976 Wildlife 2 r. stamp	60	60
104	34p. 1975 Diego Garcia map 2 r. stamp	95	95
105	54p. 1969 "Nordvaer" 1 r. stamp	1·50	1·50

1990. 90th Birthday of Queen Elizabeth the Queen Mother. As T **134** of Ascension.

106	24p. multicoloured	75	75
107	£1 black and ochre ..	2·75	2·75

DESIGNS—21 × 36 mm. 24p. Lady Elizabeth Bowes-Lyon, 1923. 29 × 37 mm. £1 Queen Elizabeth and her daughters, 1940.

19 Territory Flag

1990. 25th Anniv of British Indian Ocean Territory. Multicoloured.

108	20p. Type **19**	70	70
109	24p. Coat of Arms ..	80	80

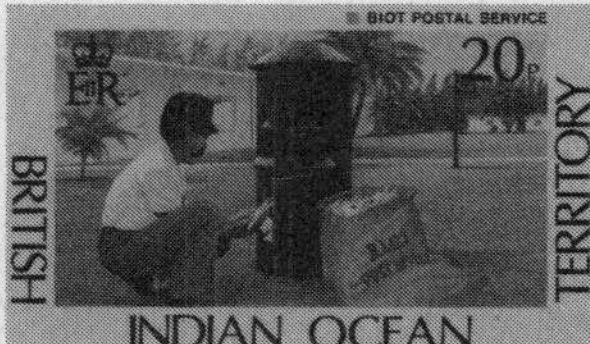

20 Postman emptying Pillar Box

1991. British Indian Ocean Territory Administration. Multicoloured.

111	20p. Type **20**	60	60
112	24p. Commissioner inspecting guard of Royal Marines	70	70
113	34p. Policemen outside station	1·10	1·10
114	54p. Customs officers boarding yacht ..	1·75	1·75

21 "Experiment" (E.I.C. survey brig), 1786

1991. Visiting Ships. Multicoloured.

115	20p. Type **21**	40	45
116	24p. "Pickering" (American brig), 1819 ..	50	55
117	34p. "Emden" (German cruiser), 1914	70	75
118	54p. H.M.S. "Edinburgh" (destroyer), 1988 ..	1·10	1·25

1992. 40th Anniv of Queen Elizabeth II's Accession. As T **143** of Ascension. Mult.

119	15p. Catholic chapel, Diego Garcia	30	35
120	20p. Planter's house, Diego Garcia	40	45
121	24p. Railway tracks on wharf, Diego Garcia ..	50	55
122	34p. Three portraits of Queen Elizabeth ..	70	75
123	54p. Queen Elizabeth II	1·10	1·25

BRITISH LEVANT

Stamps used at Br. post offices in the Turkish Empire. These offices closed in 1914. The stamps were again in use after 1918, during the British Occupation of Turkey.

Stamps of Great Britain surcharged or overprinted.

I. TURKISH CURRENCY.

40 paras = 1 piastre.

80 PARAS

(1.)

1885. Surch as T **1.**

1.	**64.**	40 par. on 2½d. purple ..	65·00	75
2.	**62.**	80 par. on 5d. green ..	£180	9·50
3a	**58.**	12 pi. on 2s. 6d. lilac ..	38·00	22·00

1887. Surch as T **1.**

4	74	40 par. on 2½d. pur. on bl.	1·75	10
5	78	80 par. on 5d. pur. & blue	9·00	25
6	81	4 pi. on 10d. pur. & red ..	28·00	10·00

1893. Handstamped surcharge.

7.	**71.**	40 par. on ½d. red ..	£400	£100

1902. Surch. as T **1.**

29	–	30 par. on 1½d. pur. & grn.	4·25	55
8	86.	40 par. on 2½d. blue ..	4·50	10
9	–	80 par. on 5d. pur. & blue	3·00	85
13	86.	1 pi. on 2½d. blue ..	3·25	10
30	–	2 pi. on 5d. purple & blue	3·25	1·50
10	–	4 pi. on 10d. purple & red	8·50	4·00
21	–	5 pi. on 1s. green and red	3·75	6·00
11	–	12 pi. on 2s. 6d. purple ..	25·00	32·00
12	–	24 pi. on 5s red	30·00	48·00

1906. Surch. **1 Piastre.**

15.	–	1 pi. on 2d. green and red	£1300	£600

1 PIASTRE
10 PARAS

(6.)

1909. Surch. as T **6.**

17.	–	1 pi. 10 par. on 3d. purple on yellow	7·00	18·00
18.	–	1 pi. 30 par. on 4d. green and brown	6·00	14·00
19.	–	1 pi. 30 par. on 4d. orge.	8·50	20·00
20.	**83.**	2 pi. 20 par. on 6d. purple	15·00	38·00

1910. Surch. in two lines.

22.	–	1¼ pi. on 3d. pur. on yell.	40	1·00
23.	–	1¾ pi. on 4d. orange ..	40	60
24.	83.	2½ pi. on 6d. purple ..	90	65

1913. Surch. in one or two lines.

41	**105.**	30 par. on ½d. green ..	30	4·00
35	–	30 par. on 1½d. brown	3·00	6·00
36a	**104.**	1 pi. on 2½d. blue ..	1·00	15
37.	**106.**	1¼ pi. on 3d. violet ..	1·40	4·25
42.	104.	1½ pi. on 1d. red ..	30	10
38b.	**106.**	1¾ pi. on 4d. grey-grn.	2·50	5·00
43.	**104.**	3¾ pi on 2½d. blue ..	60	25
39.	**108.**	4 pi. on 10d. blue ..	5·00	12·00
44.	**106.**	4½ pi. on 3d. violet ..	1·25	2·75
40.	**108.**	5 pi. on 1s. brown ..	19·00	45·00
45.	107.	7½ pi. on 5d. brown ..	30	10
46.	**108.**	15 pi. on 10d. blue ..	45	15
47.		18¾ pi. on 1s. brown ..	3·75	3·75
48.	**109.**	45 pi. on 2s 6d. brown	20·00	40·00
49.		90 pi. on 5s. red ..	25·00	30·00
50.		180 pi. on 10s blue ..	45·00	40·00

II. BRITISH CURRENCY.

1905. Optd. **LEVANT.**

L 1.	88.	½d. green	1·50	15
L 2.		1d. red	1·25	15
L 3.	–	1½d. purple and green	4·50	1·50
L 4a.		2d. green and red ..	2·00	6·00
L 5.		2½d. blue	7·50	17·00
L 6.		3d. purple and yellow	5·50	13·00
L 7.		4d. green and brown ..	7·00	16·00
L 8		5d. purple and blue ..	14·00	25·00
L 9	**83.**	6d. purple	11·00	25·00
L 10.		1s green and red ..	25·00	30·00

1911. Optd. **LEVANT.**

L 12.	**98.**	½d. green	40	90
L 14.	**101.**	½d. green	25	10
L 16.	**105.**	½d. green	15	25
L 13.	**99.**	1d. red	40	3·75
L 15.	**102.**	1d. red	25	15
L 17.	**104.**	1d. red	15	1·75
L 18.	**106.**	2d. orange ..	1·25	16·00
L 19.		3d. violet	7·50	10·00
L 20.		4d. green	4·25	13·00
L 21.	**107.**	5d. brown	9·00	19·00
L 22a.		6d. purple	15·00	8·00
L 23.	**108.**	1s. brown	10·00	6·50
L 24.	**109.**	2s. 6d. brown	35·00	65·00

BRITISH FIELD OFFICE IN SALONICA

Levant

(S 1.)

1916. King George V stamps of Great Britain optd. with S **1.**

S 1.	**105.**	½d. green	22·00	80·00
S 2.	**104.**	1d. red	22·00	80·00
S 3.	**106.**	2d. orange	85·00	£180
S 4.		3d. violet	75·00	£180
S 5.		4d. green	85·00	£180
S 6.	**107.**	6d. purple	55·00	£140
S 7.	**108.**	9d. black	£250	£450
S 8.		1s. brown	£200	£400

The above stamps were overprinted at Salonica during the war of 1914–18.

BRITISH OCCUPATION OF ITALIAN COLONIES

Issues for use in Italian colonies occupied by British Forces. Middle East Forces overprints were used in Cyrenaica, Dodecanese Islands, Eritrea, Italian Somaliland and Tripolitania.

MIDDLE EAST FORCES

12 pence = 1 shilling.
20 shillings = 1 pound.

1942. Stamps of Gt. Britain optd. **M.E.F.**

M11 128 1d. red 60 10
M12 2d. orange 60 10
M 3 2½d. blue 15 15
M 4 3d. violet 15 10
M 5 129 5d. brown 15 10
M16 6d. purple 30 10
M17 130 9d. olive 75 15
M18 1s. brown 50 10
M19 131 2s. 6d. .. .. 6·00 30
M20 5s. red .. .. 11·00 17·00
M21 10s. blue (No. 478a) .. 14·00 8·00

Prices. Our prices for Nos. M1/21 in used condition are for stamps with identifiable postmarks of the territories in which they were issued. These stamps were also used in the United Kingdom with offical sanction, from the summer of 1950 onwards, and with U K. postmarks are worth about 25 per cent less.

POSTAGE DUE STAMPS.

1942. Postage Due stamps of Gt. Britain overprinted **M.E.F.**

MD 1. D 1. ½d. green .. .. 25 2·75
MD 2. 1d. red .. .. 30 2·25
MD 3. 2d. black .. .. 1·25 1·00
MD 4. 3d. violet .. .. 50 2·75
MD 5. 1s. blue .. .. 2·50 5·50

CYRENAICA

1000 milliemes = 1 Egyptian pound.

24. Mounted Warrior. 25.

1950.

136. 24. 1 m. brown 15 40
137. 2 m. red 30 40
138. 3 m. yellow 30 40
139. 4 m. green .. .. 1·00 2·25
140. 5 m. grey 40 55
141. 8 m. orange 40 45
142. 10 m. violet 45 45
143. 12 m. red 45 45
144. 20 m. blue 50 50
145. 25. 50 m. blue and brown .. 1·90 2·75
146. 100 m. red and black .. 6·00 8·50
147. 200 m. violet and blue .. 9·50 23·00
148. 500 m. yellow and green .. 32·00 55·00

POSTAGE DUE STAMPS

D 26.

1950.

D 149. D 26. 2 m. brown .. .. 40·00 48·00
D 150. 4 m. green .. .. 40·00 48·00
D 151. 8 m. red .. .. 40·00 48·00
D 152. 10 m. orange .. .. 40·00 48·00
D 153. 20 m. yellow .. .. 40·00 48·00
D 154. 40 m. blue .. .. 40·00 48·00
D 155. 100 m. brown .. .. 40·00 48·00

ERITREA

100 cents = 1 shilling.

BRITISH MILITARY ADMINISTRATION

1948. Stamps of Great Britain surch. **B.M.A. ERITREA** and value in cents or shillings.

E 1. 128. 5 c. on ½d. green .. 30 65
E 2. 10 c. on 1d. red .. 40 1·75
E 3. 20 c. on 2d. orange .. 45 2·25
E 4. 25 c. on 2½d. blue .. 30 60
E 5. 30 c. on 3d. violet .. 85 3·00
E 6. 129. 40 c. on 5d. brown .. 30 2·50
E 7. 50 c. on 6d. purple .. 30 60
E 7a. 130. 65 c. on 8d. red .. 5·00 2·00
E 8. 75 c. on 9d. olive .. 50 75
E 9. 1 s. on 1s. brown .. 50 50
E 10. 131. 2 s. 50 on 2s. 6d. green 5·00 10·00
E 11. 5 s. on 5s. red .. 5·00 13·00
E 12. – 10 s. on 10s. bright blue (No. 478a) .. 10·00 17·00

BRITISH ADMINISTRATION

1950. Stamps of Great Britain surch. **B.A. ERITREA** and value in cents or shillings.

E 13. 128. 5 c. on ½d. green .. 30 3·75
E 26. 5 c. on ½d. orange .. 30 50
E 14. 10 c. on 1d. red .. 30 1·50
E 27. 10 c. on 1d. blue .. 30 35
E 15. 20 c. on 2d. orange .. 30 70
E 28. 20 c. on 2d. brown .. 25 25
E 16. 25 c. on 2½d. blue .. 25 60
E 29. 25 c. on 2½d. red .. 30 25
E 17. 30 c. on 3d. violet .. 30 70
E 18. 129. 40 c. on 5d. brown .. 40 80
E 19. 50 c. on 6d. purple .. 30 20
E 20. 130. 65 c. on 8d. red .. 40 1·00
E 21. 75 c. on 9d. olive .. 30 25
E 22. 1 s. on 1s. brown .. 30 15
E 23. 131. 2 s. 50 on 2s. 6d. green 2·25 4·50
E 24. 5 s. on 5s. red .. 5·50 9·00
E 25. – 10 s. on 10s. blue (No. 478a) .. 30·00 35·00

1951. Nos. 509/11 of Great Britain surch. **B.A. ERITREA and value in cents or shillings.**

E 30. 147. 2 s. 50 on 2s. 6d. green 5·00 8·00
E 31. – 5 s. on 5s. red .. 14·00 16·00
E 32. – 10 s. on 10s. blue .. 14·00 16·00

POSTAGE DUE STAMPS

1948. Postage Due stamps of Great Britain surch. **B.M.A. ERITREA** and new value in cents or shillings.

ED 1. D 1. 5 c. on ½d. green .. 9·00 18·00
ED 2. 10 c. on 1d. red .. 7·50 17·00
ED 3. 20 c. on 2d. black .. 7·00 12·00
ED 4. 30 c. on 3d. violet .. 8·00 11·00
ED 5. 1s. on 1s. blue .. 15·00 20·00

1950. Postage Due stamps of Great Britain surch. **B.A. ERITREA** and new value in cents or shillings.

ED 6. D 1. 5 c. on ½ d. green 10·00 24·00
ED 7. 10 c. on 1d. red .. 8·00 14·00
ED 8. 20 c. on 2d. black 9·00 12·00
ED 9. 30 c. on 3d. violet 9·00 12·00
ED 10. 1s. on 1s. blue .. 14·00 20·00

SOMALIA

BRITISH OCCUPATION

1943. Stamps of Gt. Britain optd. **E.A.F.** (East African Forces).

S 1. 128. 1d. pale red 60 40
S 2. 2d. pale orange 60 90
S 3. 2½d light blue .. .. 30 1·75
S 4. 3d. pale violet 40 15
S 5. 129. 5d. brown 40 40
S 6. 6d. purple 30 90
S 7. 130. 9d. olive .. .. 80 2·00
S 8. 1s. brown 60 15
S 9. 131. 2s. 6d. green .. .. 5·00 4·25

PRICES. Our prices for Nos. S 1/9 in used condition are for stamps with identifiable postmarks of the territories in which they were issued. These stamps were also used in the United Kingdom, with official sanction, from the summer of 1950, and with U.K. postmarks are worth about 25 per cent less.

BRITISH MILITARY ADMINISTRATION.

1948. Stamps of Great Britain surch. **B.M.A. SOMALIA** and new value in cents and shillings.

S 10. 128. 5 c. on ½d. pale green 20 1·25
S 11. 15 c. on 1½d. pale brn. 55 7·00
S 12. 20 c. on 2d. pale orge. 20 2·25
S 13. 25 c. on 2½d. light blue 20 2·00
S 14. 30 c. on 3d. pale violet 1·75 9·00
S 15. 129. 40 c. on 5d. brown .. 30 20
S 16. 50 c. on 6d. purple .. 30 2·00
S 17. 130. 75 c. on 9d. olive .. 2·00 9·00
S 18. 1s. on 1s. brown .. 1·25 20
S 19. 131. 2s. 50 c. on 2s. 6d. grn. 3·00 13·00
S 20. 5s. on 5s. red .. 6·00 20·00

BRITISH ADMINISTRATION

1950. Stamps of Great Britain surch. **B.A. SOMALIA** and value in cents and shillings.

S 21. 128. 5 c. on ½d. pale green 20 85
S 22. 15 c. on 1½d. pale brn. 60 8·00
S 23. 20 c. on 2d. pale orge. 60 2·75
S 24. 25 c. on 2½d. light blue 40 2·75
S 25. 30 c. on 3d. pale violet 1·00 3·00
S 26. 129. 40 c. on 5d. brown .. 55 85
S 27. 50 c. on 6d. purple .. 40 1·00
S 28. 130. 75 c. on 9d. olive .. 1·00 4·50
S 29. 1s. on 1s. brown .. 60 1·50
S 30. 131. 2s. 50 on 2s. 6d. grn. 4·00 14·00
S 31. 5s. on 5s. red .. 7·50 17·00

TRIPOLITANIA

BRITISH MILITARY ADMINISTRATION

1948. Stamps of Great Britain surch. **B.M.A. TRIPOLITANIA** and value in " **M.A.L.** " (Military Administration lire).

T 1. 128. 1 l. on ½d. pale green 25 80
T 2. 2 l. on 1d. pale red .. 20 25
T 3. 3 l. on 1½d. pale brown 20 50
T 4. 4 l. on 2d. pale orange 25 50
T 5. 5 l. on 2½d. light blue 25 20
T 6. 6 l. on 3d. pale violet 20 40
T 7. 129. 10 l. on 5d. brown .. 20 25
T 8. 12 l. on 6d. purple .. 25 20
T 9. 130. 18 l. on 9d. olive .. 50 65
T 10. 24 l. on 1s. brown .. 50 65
T 11. 131. 60 l. on 2s. 6d. green .. 1·75 4·50
T 12. 120 l. on 5s. red .. 5·50 14·00
T 13. – 240 l. on 10s. bright blue (No. 478a) .. 11·00 55·00

BRITISH ADMINISTRATION

1950. As Nos. T1/13 but surch. **B.A. TRIPOLITANIA** and value in M.A.L.

T 14. 128. 1 l. on ½d. pale green 40 4·25
T 27. 1 l. on ½d. orange .. 20 1·75
T 15. 2 l. on 1d. pale red .. 50 40
T 28. 2 l. on 1d. blue .. 20 90
T 16. 3 l. on 1½d. pale brn. 35 3·75
T 29. 3 l. on 1½d. green .. 25 2·50
T 17. 4 l. on 2d. pale orange 25 3·50
T 30. 4 l. on 2d. brown .. 20 1·25
T 18. 5 l. on 2½d. light blue 25 70
T 31. 5 l. on 2½d. red .. 20 2·50
T 19. 6 l. on 3d. pale violet 25 1·25
T 20. 129. 10 l. on 5d. brown .. 25 1·25
T 21. 12 l. on 6d. purple .. 25 50
T 22. 130. 18 l. on 9d. olive .. 35 1·60
T 23. 24 l. on 1s. brown .. 45 3·00
T 24. 131. 60 l. on 2s. 6d. green 3·75 9·50
T 25. 120 l. on 5s. red .. 11·00 19·00
T 26. – 240 l. on 10s. bright blue (No. 478a) .. 13·00 27·00

1951. Nos. 509/11 of Great Britain surch. **B.A. TRIPOLITANIA** and value in **M.A.L.**

T 32. 147. 60 l. on 2s. 6d. green 3·50 12·00
T 33. – 120 l. on 5s. red .. 7·50 16·00
T 34. – 240 l. on 10s. blue .. 17·00 27·00

POSTAGE DUE STAMPS

1948. Postage Due stamps of Great Britain surch. **B.M.A. TRIPOLITANIA** and value in M.A.L.

TD 1. D 1. 1 l. on ½d. green .. 3·50 23·00
TD 2. 2 l. on 1d. red .. 2·50 23·00
TD 3. 4 l. on 2d. black .. 5·50 15·00
TD 4. 6 l. on 3d. violet .. 7·50 20·00
TD 5. 24 l. on 1s. blue .. 26·00 65·00

1950. As Nos. TD 1/5 but surch. **B.A. TRIPOLITANIA** and value in M.A.L.

TD 6. D 1. 1 l. on ½d. green .. 6·00 30·00
TD 7. 2 l. on 1d. red .. 2·50 17·00
TD 8. 4 l. on 2d. black .. 2·75 18·00
TD 9. 6 l. on 3d. violet .. 13·00 48·00
TD 10. 24 l. on 1s. blue .. 29·00 70·00

BRITISH POSTAL AGENCIES IN EASTERN ARABIA

British stamps were surcharged for use in the area of the Persian Gulf.

The stamps were used in Muscat from 1st April 1948 to 29th April 1966; in Dubai from 1st April 1948 to 6th January 1961; In Qatar: Doha from August 1950, Umm Said from February 1956 to 31st March 1957; and in Abu Dhabi from 30th March 1963 (Das Island from December 1960) to 29th March 1964.

Certain of them were placed on sale in Kuwait Post Offices in 1951 and in 1953 due to shortages of stamps with "KUWAIT" overprint; and they can all be found commercially used from that state and from Bahrain.

1948. 12 pies = 1 anna; 16 annas = 1 rupee.
1957. 100 naye paise = 1 rupee.

Stamps of Great Britain surcharged in Indian currency.

1948. King George VI.

16. 128. ½ a. on ½d. pale green .. 75 90
35. ½ a. on ½d. orange .. 30 2·50
17. 1 a. on 1d. pale red .. 75 20
36. 1 a. on 1d. blue .. 30 1·25
18. 1½a. on 1½d. pale brown 75 20
37. 1½ a. on 1½d. green .. 1·50 7·50
19. 2 a. on 2d. pale orange .. 60 45
38. 2 a. on 2d. brown .. 30 3·75
20. 2½ a. on 2½d. light blue 80 1·40
39. 2½ a. on 2½d. red .. 30 7·50
21. 3 a. on 3d. pale violet .. 80 10
40. 129. 4 a. on 4d. blue .. 30 1·75
22. 6 a. on 6d. purple .. 80 10
23. 130. 1 r. on 1s. brown .. 2·75 50
24. 131. 2 r. on 2s. 6d. green .. 6·50 16·00

1948. Royal Silver Wedding.

25. 137. 2½ a. on 2½d. blue .. 70 40
26. 138. 15 r. on £1 blue .. 28·00 35·00

1948. Olympic Games.

27. 139. 2½ a. on 2½d. blue .. 35 70
28. 140. 3 a. on 3d. violet .. 45 90
29. – 6 a. on 6d. purple .. 45 90
30. – 1 r. on 1s. brown .. 75 1·50

1949. 75th Anniv. of U.P.U.

31. 143. 2½ a. on 2½d. blue .. 60 1·25
32. 144. 3 a. on 3d. violet .. 60 1·25
33. – 6 a. on 6d. purple .. 60 1·10
34. – 1 r. on 1s. brown .. 1·75 1·40

1951. Pictorial.

41. 147. 2 r. on 2s. 6d. green .. 22·00 4·00

1952. Queen Elizabeth.

42 154. ½ a. on ½d. orange .. 10 10
43 1 a. on 1d. blue .. 10 10
44 1½ a. on 1½d. green .. 10 10
45 2 a. on 2d. brown .. 10 10
46 155. 2½ a. on 2½d. red .. 10 10
47 3 a. on 3d. lilac .. 10 10
48 4 a. on 4d. blue .. 20 10
49 157. 6 a. on 6d. purple .. 55 75
50 160. 12 a. on 1s. 3d. green .. 35 10
51 1 r. on 1s. 6d. blue .. 2·00 30

1953. Coronation.

52. 161. 2½ a. on 2½d. red .. 1·75 95
53. – 4 a. on 4d. blue .. 1·75 95
54. 163. 12 a. on 1s. 3d. green .. 3·25 95
55. – 1 r. on 1s. 6d. blue .. 4·50 45

1955. Pictorials.

56. 166. 2 r. on 2s. 6d. brown .. 3·25 70
57. – 5 r. on 5s. red .. 9·00 2·00

1957. Value in naye paise, Queen Elizabeth II stamps surch **NP** twice (once only on 75 n. p.) and value.

65. 157. 1 n.p. on 5d. brown .. 10 20
66. 154. 3 n.p. on ½d. orange .. 20 50
81. 5 n.p. on 1d. blue .. 50 40
67. 6 n.p. on 1d. blue .. 20 50
68. 9 n.p. on 1½d. green .. 20 30
83. 10 n.p. on 1½d. green .. 50 40
69. 12 n.p. on 2d. pale brown 30 35
85. 155. 15 n.p. on 2½d. red .. 25 10
71. 20 n.p. on 3d. lilac .. 20 10
72. 25 n.p. on 4d. blue .. 70 1·50
87. 30 n.p. on 4½d. brown .. 40 40
73. 157. 40 n.p. on 6d. purple .. 30 10
89. 158. 50 n.p. on 9d. olive .. 80 80
90. 160. 75 n.p. on 1s. 3d. green 1·25 90

1957. World Scout Jubilee Jamboree.

76. 170. 15 n.p. on 2½d. red .. 25 60
77. 171. 25 n.p. on 4d. blue .. 30 60
78. – 75 n.p. on 3d. green .. 35 65

BRITISH POST OFFICES IN CHINA

Stamps for use in Weihaiwei, and the neighbouring islands, leased to Great Britain from 1898 to 1 October 1930, when they were returned to China. The stamps were also used in the Treaty ports from 1917 until 1922.

100 cents = 1 dollar.

1917. Stamps of Hong Kong (King George V) optd. **CHINA.**

1 24. 1 c. brown 50 75
2 2 c. green 25 15
3 4 c. red 50 10
4 6 c. orange .. .. 1·00 45
5 8 c. grey .. .. 2·00 60
6 10 c. blue .. .. 1·00 10
7 12 c. purple on yellow .. 1·75 1·75
8 20 c. purple and olive .. 3·25 30
9 25 c. purple .. 4·00 12·00
11 30 c. purple and orange .. 10·00 3·50
12b 50 c. black on green .. 7·50 2·50
13 $1 purple and blue on blue 25·00 1·75
14 $2 red and black .. 70·00 35·00
15 $3 green and purple .. £110 85·00
16 $5 green and red on green £120 85·00
17 $10 purple & black on red £400 £200

BRITISH POST OFFICES IN CRETE

40 paras = piastre.

1.

2.

1898.

1. 1. 20 par. violet £350 £225

1898.

2. 2. 10 par. blue .. .. 8·00 12·00
4. 10 par. brown .. .. 8·00 15·00
3. 20 par. green .. .. 9·00 12·00
5. 20 par. red .. .. 14·00 15·00

BRITISH POST OFFICE IN SIAM

Used at Bangkok. Stamps of Straits Settlements, specially overprinted, were used for a time.

100 cents = 1 dollar.

1882. Stamps of Straits Settlements optd. **B**

On issue of 1867.

1. 19. 32 c. on 2 a. yellow .. £6500 £7500

On issues of 1867–83.

14 5 2 c. brown .. .. £100 90·00
12 9 2 c. on 32 c. red (No. 60) £700 £900
15 5 2 c. red .. .. 30·00 25·00
16 4 c. red £130 £100
17 4 c. brown .. .. 50·00 45·00
4 18 5 c. brown £110 £110
18 5 c. blue .. .. £110 70·00
5 5 6 c. lilac .. .. 75·00 35·00
20 8 c. orange .. .. 50·00 38·00
21 19 10 c. grey .. .. 60·00 45·00
8 5 12 c. blue £500 £225
22 12 c. purple .. .. £120 85·00
9 24 c. green .. .. £225 65·00
10 8 30 c. red £7000 £4000
11 9 96 c. grey £1700 £1100

BRITISH VIRGIN ISLANDS

A group of the Leeward Is., Br. W. Indies. Used general issues for Leeward Is. concurrently with Virgin Is. stamps until 1st July, 1956. A Crown Colony.

1951. 100 cents = 1 West Indian dollar.
1962. 100 cents = 1 U.S. dollar.

1. St. Ursula.

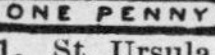

2.

3. 4.

1866.

1. 1. 1d. green .. .. .. 45·00 60·00
16. 3. 4d. red .. .. .. 40·00 60·00
7. 2. 6d. red .. .. .. 60·00 90·00
11. 4. 1s. black and red .. £200 £275

1867. With heavy coloured border.

18. 4. 1s. black and red .. .. 48·00 60·00

6. 8.

1880.

26. 6. ½d. yellow .. .. .. 65·00 80·00
27. ½d. green .. .. .. 3·25 8·00
24. 1d. green .. .. .. 50·00 80·00
29. 1d. red .. .. .. 18·00 23·00
25. 2½d. brown .. .. 80·00 £110
31. 2½d. blue .. .. .. 2·50 9·00

1887.

32 1. 1d. red .. .. .. 2·00 7·00
35 3. 4d. brown .. .. .. 40·00 75·00
38 2. 6d. violet .. .. .. 15·00 48·00
41 4. 1s. brown .. .. .. 50·00 80·00

1888. No. 18 surch. **4D.**

42. 4. 4d. on 1s. black and red .. £110 £150

1899.

43. 8. ½d. green 60 55
44. 1d. red .. .. .. 2·25 2·25
45. 2½d. blue .. .. .. 12·00 4·00
46. 4d. brown .. .. .. 5·00 12·00
47. 6d. violet .. .. .. 4·50 4·50
48. 7d. green .. .. .. 7·00 8·00
49. 1s. yellow .. .. .. 18·00 30·00
50. 5s. blue .. .. .. 65·00 80·00

9.

11.

1904.

54. 9. ½d. purple and green .. 50 40
55. 1d. purple and red .. 85 35
56. 2d. purple and brown .. 3·25 4·50
57. 2½d. purple and blue .. 1·75 2·00
58. 3d. purple and black .. 2·75 3·00
59. 6d. purple and brown .. 2·75 3·00
60. 1s. green and red .. 2·75 4·75
61. 2s. 6d. green and black .. 18·00 40·00
62. 5s. green and blue .. 38·00 60·00

1913.

63 11 ½d. green .. .. .. 75 1·60
68 1d. red .. .. .. 1·75 8·50
70 2d. grey .. .. .. 3·75 10·00
72 2½d. blue .. .. .. 4·00 6·50
73 3d. purple on yellow .. 1·40 4·75
74 6d. purple .. .. .. 2·75 3·75
75 1s. black on green .. 3·25 4·00
76 2s. 6d. blk. & red on blue 35·00 38·00
77 5s. green & red on yellow 32·00 75·00

1917. Optd. **WAR STAMP.**

78c 11 1d. red .. .. .. 20 1·75
79 3d. purple on yellow .. 25 7·00

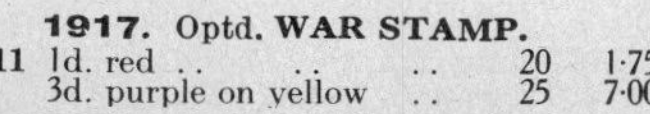

14.

15. King George VI and Badge of Colony.

1922.

86 14 ½d. green 20 75
87 1d. red 20 50
88 1d. violet .. .. .. 70 2·00
90 1½d. red .. .. .. 1·25 2·25
92 2d. grey .. .. .. 60 3·00
95 2½d. blue .. .. .. 80 3·50
94 2½d. orange .. .. 1·25 1·25
96 3d. purple on yellow .. 1·25 4·50
97 5d. purple and olive .. 5·00 26·00
98 6d. purple .. .. 1·25 4·75
99 1s. black on green .. 1·25 7·00
84 2s. 6d. blk. & red on blue 3·75 9·00
101 5s. green & red on yellow 19·00 45·00

1935. Silver Jubilee. As T **13** of Antigua.

103. 1d. blue and red .. 45 90
104. 1½d. blue and grey .. 45 90
105. 2½d. brown and blue .. 55 95
106. 1s. grey and purple .. 3·50 7·00

1937. Coronation. As T **2** of Aden.

107. 1d. red 20 30
108. 1½d. brown 40 80
109. 2½d. blue 45 70

1938.

110a 15 ½d. green 30 30
111a 1d. red 30 30
112 1½d. brown 35 40
113a 2d. grey 40 40
114a 2½d. blue 30 30
115a 3d. orange 30 30
116a 6d. mauve 85 40
117a 1s. brown .. .. .. 1·25 30
118a 2s. 6d. brown .. .. 6·00 3·00
119a 5s. red .. .. .. 9·00 4·00
120 10s. blue .. .. .. 7·00 8·00
121 £1 black .. .. .. 11·00 20·00

1946. Victory. As T **9** of Aden.

122. 1½d. brown 10 10
123. 3d. orange 10 10

1949. Silver Wedding. As T **10/11** of Aden.

124. 2½d. blue 10 10
125. £1 grey .. .. .. 9·00 10·00

1949. 75th Anniv of U.P.U. As T **20/23** of Antigua.

126. 2½d. blue 20 15
127. 3d. orange 40 20
128. 6d. mauve 40 15
129. 1s. olive 40 35

1951. Inauguration of B.W.I. University College. As T **24/25** of Antigua.

130. 3 c. black and red .. 30 15
131. 12 c. black and violet .. 35 25

16. Map.

1951. Restoration of Legislative Council.

132. 16. 6 c. orange 20 50
133. 12 c. purple 20 50
134. 24 c. olive 20 50
135. $1.20 red 45 75

18. Map of Jost Van Dyke.

1952.

136. – 1 c. black 30 40
137. 18. 2 c. green 35 30
138. – 3 c. black and brown .. 30 40
139. – 4 c. red 35 40
140. – 5 c. red and black .. 45 50
141. – 8 c. blue 35 30
142. – 12 c. violet 35 30
143. – 24 c. brown 35 30
144. – 60 c. green and blue .. 2·25 8·00
145. – $1.20 black and blue .. 3·75 6·50
146. – $2.40 green and brown 8·00 6·00
147. – $4.80 blue and red .. 8·00 8·00

DESIGNS—VERT. 1 c. Sombrero lighthouse. 24 c. Badge of Presidency. HORIZ. VIEWS: 3 c. Sheep Industry. 5 c. Cattle Industry. 60 c. Dead Man's Chest (Is.). $1.20, Sir Francis Drake Channel. $2.40, Road Town. HORIZ. MAPS: 4 c. Anegada Is. 8 c. Virgin Gorda Is. 12 c. Tortola Is. $4.80, Virgin Is.

1953. Coronation. As T **13** of Aden.

148. 2 c. black and green .. 15 45

29. Map of Tortola.

30. Brown Pelican.

1956.

149. 29. ½ c. black and purple .. 20 10
150. – 1 c. turquoise and slate 75 20
151. – 2 c. red and black .. 30 10
152. – 3 c. blue and olive .. 30 20
153. – 4 c. brown and turq. .. 35 15
154. – 5 c. black 45 10
155. – 8 c. orange and blue .. 35 40
156. – 12 c. blue and red .. 75 35
157. – 24 c. green and brown .. 55 30
158. – 60 c. blue and orange .. 3·75 4·00
159. – $1.20 green and red .. 1·25 3·50
160. 30. $2.40 yellow and purple 19·00 10·00
161. – $4.80 sepia & turquoise 19·00 13·00

DESIGNS—HORIZ. As Type 13: 1 c. Virgin Islands sloop. 2 c. Nelthrop Red Poll bull. 3 c. Rood Harbour. 4 c. Mountain Travel. 5 c. Badge of the Presidency. 8 c. Beach scene. 12 c. Boat launching. 24 c. White Cedar Tree. 60 c. Bonito (fish). $1.20, Treasury Square. As Type 30: $4.80, Magnificent Frigate Bird.

1962. New Currency. Nos. 149/53, 155/61 surch. in U.S. Currency.

162. 29. 1 c. on ½ c. blk. & purple 30 10
163. – 2 c. on 1 c. turquoise and violet 30 10
164. – 3 c. on 2 c. red and black 30 10
165. – 4 c. on 3 c. blue & olive 30 10
166. – 5 c. on 4 c. brn. & turq. 30 10
167 – 8 c. on 8 c. orange & blue 30 10
168. – 10 c. on 12 c. blue & red 30 10
169. – 12 c. on 24 c. grn. & brn. 30 10
170. – 25 c. on 60 c. blue & orge. 80 45
171. – 70 c. on $1.20 grn. & red 35 45
172. 30. $1.40 on $2.40 lemon & purple .. .. .. 6·00 3·00
173. – $2.80 on $4.80 sepia and turquoise .. .. 6·50 3·00

1963. Freedom from Hunger. As T **28** of Aden.

174. 25 c. violet 20 10

1963. Cent of Red Cross. As T **33** of Antigua.

175. 2 c. red and black 10 10
176. 25 c. red and blue 25 20

1964. 400th Birth Anniv of Shakespeare. As T **34** of Antigua.

177. 10 c. blue 10 10

43. Bonito.

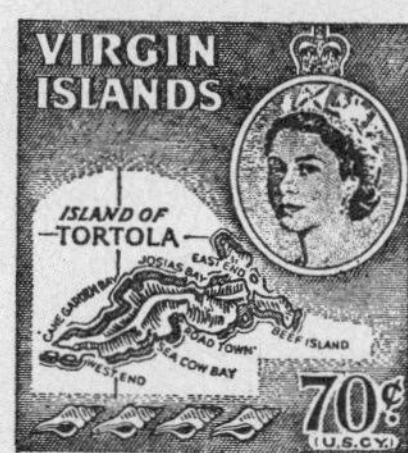
44. Map of Tortola.

1964.

178. 43. 1 c. blue and olive .. 30 30
179. – 2 c. olive and red .. 15 10
180. – 3 c. sepia & turquoise .. 1·75 50
181. – 4 c. black and red .. 40 40
182. – 5 c. black and green .. 35 35
183. – 6 c. black and orange .. 20 35
184. – 8 c. black and mauve .. 20 30
185. – 10 c. lake and lilac .. 40 10
186. – 12 c. green and blue .. 75 55
187. – 15 c. green and black .. 35 70
188. – 25 c. green and purple .. 7·00 55
189. 44. 70 c. black and brown .. 2·25 1·50
190. – $1 green and brown .. 2·75 1·50
191. – $1.40 blue and red .. 11·00 5·50
192. – $2.80 black and purple 11·00 8·00

DESIGNS—HORIZ. As Type **43:** 2 c. Soper's Hole 3 c. Brown Pelican. 4 c. Dead Man's Chest. 5 c. Road Harbour. 6 c. Fallen Jerusalem. 8 c. The Baths, Virgin Gorda. 10 c. Map of Virgin Islands. 12 c. "Youth of Tortola" (Tortola–St. Thomas ferry). 15 c. The Towers, Tortola. 25 c. Beef Island Airfield. VERT. As Type **44:** $1, Virgin Gorda. $1.40, Yachts at anchor. $2.80, Badge of the Colony (27½ × 37½ mm.).

1965. Cent of I.T.U. As T **36** of Antigua.

193. 4 c. yellow and turquoise 10 10
194. 25 c. blue and buff .. 20 15

1965. I.C.Y. As T **37** of Antigua.

195. 1 c. purple and turquoise .. 10 10
196. 25 c. green and lavender .. 30 15

1966. Churchill Commem. As T **38** of Antigua.

197. 1 c. blue 10 10
198. 2 c. green 10 10
199. 10 c. brown 30 10
200. 25 c. violet 60 25

1966. Royal Visit. As T **39** of Antigua.

201. 4 c. black and blue .. 30 10
202. 70 c. black and mauve .. 1·10 45

58. R.M.S. "Atrato", 1866.

1966. Stamp Centenary. Multicoloured.

203. 5 c. Type **58** 15 10
204. 10 c. 1d. and 6d. stamps of 1866 .. .. .. 25 10
205. 25 c. Mail transport, Beef Island, and 6d. stamp of 1866 .. .. .. 40 10
206. 60 c. Landing mail at Road-town, 1866 and 1d. stamp of 1866 .. .. 75 40

1966. Nos. 189 and 191/2 surch.

207. 44. 50 c. on 70 c. blk. & brn. 70 70
208. – $1·50 on $1·40 blue & red 2·00 2·00
209. – $3 on $2·80 blk. & pur. 2·50 2·75

1966. 20th Anniv. of U.N.E.S.C.O. As T **54/6** of Antigua.

210. 2 c. multicoloured .. 10 10
211. 12 c. yellow, violet & olive 20 10
212. 60 c. black, purple & orge. 50 20

63. Map of Virgin Islands.

1967. New Constitution.

213. 63. 2 c. multicoloured .. 10 10
214. 10 c. multicoloured .. 15 10
215. 25 c. multicoloured .. 15 10
216. $1 multicoloured .. 55 25

64. "Mercury" (cable ship) and Bermuda–Tortola Link.

1967. Inauguration of Bermuda–Tortola Telephone Service. Multicoloured.

217. 4 c. Type **64** 10 10
218. 10 c. Chalwell Telecommunications Station .. 10 10
219. 50 c. "Mercury" (cable ship) 30 20

67. Blue Marlin.

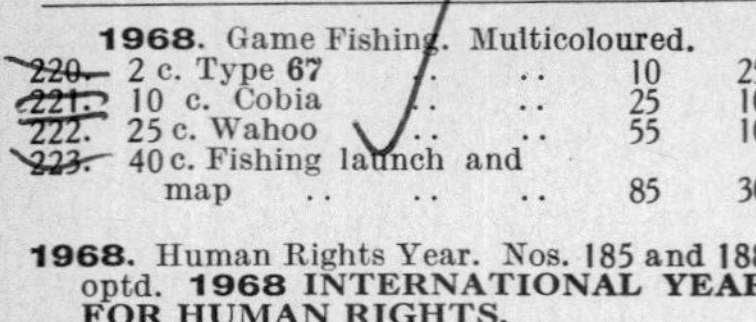

1968. Game Fishing. Multicoloured.
220. 2 c. Type **67** 10 25
221. 10 c. Cobia 25 10
222. 25 c. Wahoo 55 10
223. 40 c. Fishing launch and map 85 30

1968. Human Rights Year. Nos. 185 and 188 optd. **1968 INTERNATIONAL YEAR FOR HUMAN RIGHTS.**
224. 10 c. lake and lilac 15 10
225. 25 c. green and purple .. 25 20

72. Dr. Martin Luther King, Bible, Sword and Armour Gauntlet.

1968. Martin Luther King. Commem.
226. **72.** 4 c. multicoloured .. 15 15
227. 25 c. multicoloured .. 25 15

73. DHC-6 Twin Otter.

1968. Opening of "Beef Island" Airport Extension. Multicoloured.
228. 2 c. Type **73** 10 20
229. 10 c. HS "748" Airliner 10 10
230. 25 c. HS "Heron" .. 20 10
231. $1 Royal Engineers' Cap badge 65 70

77. Long John Silver and Jim Hawkins.

1969. 75th Death Anniv. of Robert Louis Stevenson.
232. **77.** 4 c. blue, yellow & red .. 25 10
233. – 10 c. multicoloured .. 30 10
234. – 40 c. brown, black & blue 50 20
235. – $1 multicoloured .. 75 50
DESIGNS—HORIZ. 10 c. Jim Hawkins escaping from the Pirates. $1, Treasure Trove. VERT. 40 c. The Fight with Israel Hands.

82. Yachts in Road Harbour, Tortola.

1969. Tourism. Multicoloured.
236. 2 c. Tourist and Rock Grouper (fish) .. 15 20
237. 10 c. Type **82** 20 10
238. 20 c. Sun-bathing at Virgin Gorda National Park .. 30 10
239. $1 Tourist and Pipe Organ cactus, at Virgin Gorda 75 75
Nos. 236 and 239 are vert.

85. Carib Canoe.

1970.
240. **85.** ½ c. buff, brn. and sepia 10 35
241. – 1 c. blue and green .. 15 30
242. – 2 c. orge., brn. and slate 25 50
243. – 3 c. red, blue and sepia 25 35
244. – 4 c. turq., blue and brn. 25 35
245. – 5 c. green, pink & black 30 10
246. – 6 c. violet, mauve & grn. 40 55
247. – 8 c. green, yellow & sepia 50 1·00
248. – 10 c. blue and brown .. 50 15
249. – 12 c. yellow, red & brn. 65 50
250. – 15 c. grn., orge. and brn. 3·00 75
251. – 25 c. grn., blue and pur. 3·75 1·25
252. – 50 c. mauve, grn. & brn. 2·25 1·50
253. – $1 salmon, grn. & brn. 3·00 3·50
254. – $2 buff, slate and grey 5·00 6·00
255. – $3 ochre, blue and sepia 5·00 6·50
256. – $5 violet and grey .. 8·00 9·00
DESIGNS: 1 c. "Santamariagallante" (Columbus' flagship). "Elizabeth Bonaventure" (Drake's flagship). 3 c. Dutch Buccaneer, c. 1660. 4 c. "Thetis". 1827 (after etching by E. W. Cooke). 5 c. Henry Morgan's ship (17th-cent.). 6 c. H.M.S. "Boreas" (Capt. Nelson, 1784). 8 c. H.M.S. "Eclair" 1804. 10 c. H.M.S. "Formidable", 1782. 12 c. H.M.S. "Nymph", 1778. 15 c. "Windsor Castle", Post Office Packet, 1807. 25 c. H.M.S. "Astrea", 1808. 50 c. Wreck of R.M.S. "Rhone", 1860. $1, Tortola Sloop. $2, H.M.S. "Frobisher". $3, Merchant Tanker "Booker Viking", 1967. $5, Hydrofoil "Sun Arrow".

102. "A Tale of Two Cities".

1970. Death Cent. of Charles Dickens.
257. **102.** 5 c. black, red and grey 10 10
258. – 10 c. black, blue & green 20 10
259. – 25 c. blk., grn. and yell. 30 20
DESIGNS: 10 c. "Oliver Twist". 25 c. "Great Expectations".

103. Hospital Visit.

1970. Cent. of British Red Cross. Mult.
260. 4 c. Type **103** 15 10
261. 10 c. First Aid class .. 25 10
262. 25 c. Red Cross and Coat of arms 45 20

104. Mary Read.

1970. Piiates. Multicoloured.
263. ½ c. Type **104** 10 10
264. 10 c. George Lowther .. 35 10
265. 30 c. Edward Teach (Blackbeard) 85 20
266. 60 c. Henry Morgan .. 1·25 60

105. Children and "UNICEF".

1971. 25th Anniv. of U.N.I.C.E.F.
267. **105.** 15 c. multicoloured .. 10 10
268. 30 c. multicoloured .. 20 25

1972. Royal Visit of Princess Margaret. Nos. 244 and 251 optd. **VISIT OF H.R.H. THE PRINCESS MARGARET 1972.**
269. 4 c. bl. chalky bl. and brn. 15 10
270. 25 c. green, blue and plum 25 30

107. Seamen of 1800.

1972. "Interpex" Stamp Exhib., New York. Naval Uniforms. Multicoloured.
271. ½ c. Type **107** 10 10
272. 10 c. Boatswain, 1787-1807 35 10
273. 30 c. Captain, 1795-1812 85 45
274. 60 c. Admiral, 1787-95 .. 1·50 1·25

1972. Royal Silver Wedding. As T **52** of Ascension, but with Sailfish and the Yacht "Sir Winston Churchill" in background.
275. 15 c. blue 20 15
276. 25 c. turquoise 20 15

109. Blue Marlin.

1972. Game Fish. Multicoloured.
277. ½ c. Type **109** 10 15
278. ½ c. Wahoo 15 15
279. 15 c. Allison Tuna .. 35 25
280. 25 c. White Marlin .. 40 30
281. 50 c. Sailfish .. 90 80
282. $1 Dolphin .. .. 1·75 1·75

110. J. C. Lettsom.

1973. "Interpex 1973" (Quakers). Mult.
284. ½ c. Type **110** 10 10
285. 10 c. Lettsom house (horiz.) 15 10
286. 15 c. Dr. W. Thornton .. 20 10
287. 30 c. Dr. Thornton and Capitol, Washington (horiz. 25 20
288. $1 William Penn (horiz.) .. 70 85

111. Green-throated Carib and Antillean Crested Hummingbird.

1973. 1st Issue of Coinage. Coins and local scenery. Multicoloured.
289. 1 c. Type **111** .. 10 10
290. 5 c. "Zenaida Dove" (5 c. coin) .. 40 10
291. 10 c. "Ringed Kingfisher" (10 c. coin) 55 10
292. 25 c. "Mangrove Cuckoo" (25 c. coin) 75 15
293. 50 c. "Brown Pelican" (50 c. coin) 85 1·00
294. $1 "Magnificent Frigate-bird ($1 coin) .. 1·25 1·75

1973. Royal Wedding. As T **47** of Anguilla. Multicoloured. Background colours given.
301. 5 c. brown 10 10
302. 50 c. blue 20 15

112. "Virgin and Child" (Pintoricchio).

1973. Christmas. Multicoloured.
303. ½ c. Type **112** 10 10
304. 3 c. "Virgin and Child" (Lorenzo di Credi) .. 10 10
305. 25 c. "Virgin and Child" (Crivelli) 15 10
306. 50 c. "Virgin and Child with St. John" (Luini) 30 40

113. Crest of the "Canopus" (French).

1974. "Interpex 1974" (Naval Crests). Multicoloured.
307. 5 c. Type **113** .. 15 10
308. 18 c. U.S.S. "Saginaw" 30 25
309. 25 c. H.M.S. "Rothesay" 35 30
310. 50 c. H.M.C.S. "Ottawa" 50 60

114. Christopher Columbus.

1974. Historical Figures.
312. **114.** 5 c. orange and black .. 20 10
313. – 10 c. blue and black .. 35 10
314. – 25 c. violet and black .. 50 25
315. – 40 c. brn. & deep brn. 70 75
PORTRAITS: 10 c. Sir Walter Raleigh. 25 c. Sir Martin Frobisher. 40 c. Sir Francis Drake.

115. Trumpet Triton.

1974. Seashells. Multicoloured.
317. 5 c. Type **115** .. 30 15
318. 18 c. West Indian Murex .. 60 30
319. 25 c. Bleeding Tooth .. 75 35
320. 75 c. Virgin Islands Latirus 1·75 1·75

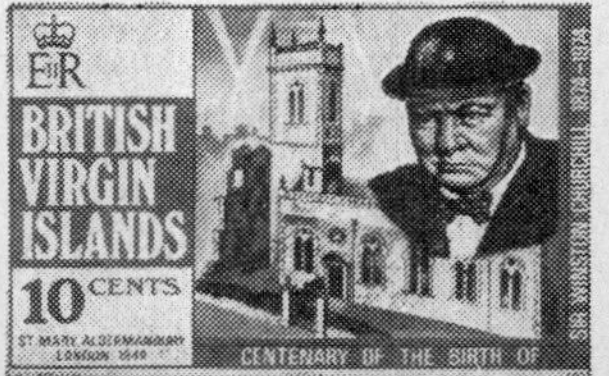

116. Churchill and St. Mary, Aldermanbury, London.

1974. Birth Centenary of Sir Winston Churchill. Multicoloured.

322.	10 c. Type **116**	15	10
323.	50 c. St. Mary, Fulton, Missouri	35	50

117. H.M.S. " Boreas ".

1975. " Interpex 1975 " Stamp Exhibition, New York. Ships' Figure-heads. Mult.

325.	5 c. Type **117**	15	10
326.	18 c. " Golden Hind " ..	40	15
327.	40 c. H.M.S. " Superb " ..	60	20
328.	85 c. H.M.S. " Formidable"	1·25	1·00

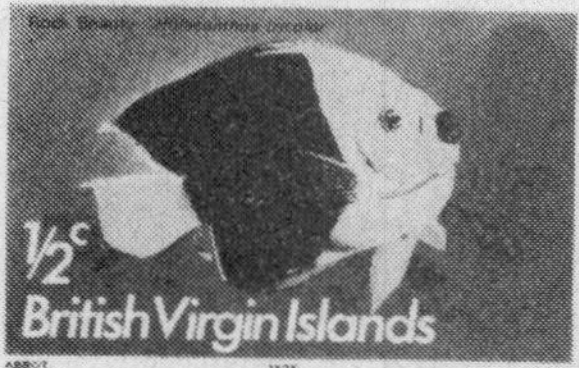

118. Rock Beauty.

1975. Fishes. Multicoloured.

330.	½ c. Type **118**	15	30
331.	1 c. Squirrelfish	30	40
332.	3 c. Queen Triggerfish ..	40	40
333.	5 c. Blue Angelfish ..	30	20
334.	8 c. Stoplight Parrotfish ..	30	25
335.	10 c. Queen Angelfish ..	30	25
336.	12 c. Nassau Grouper ..	40	30
337.	13 c. Blue Tang	40	30
338.	15 c. Sergeant Major ..	40	35
339.	18 c. Jewfish	60	70
340.	20 c. Bluehead Wrasse ..	60	70
341.	25 c. Grey Angelfish ..	60	60
342.	60 c. Glasseye Snapper ..	1·25	1·50
343.	$1 Blue Chromis	1·75	1·75
344.	$2·50 French Angelfish ..	3·50	4·50
345.	$3 Queen Parrotfish ..	4·25	5·00
346.	$5 Four-eye Butterfly Fish	8·00	7·50

119. St. George's Parish School (First meeting-place, 1950).

1975. 25th Anniv. of Legislative Council Restoration. Multicoloured.

347.	5 c. Type **119**	10	10
348.	25 c. Legislative Council Building	25	10
349.	40 c. Mace and gavel ..	35	15
350.	75 c. Commemorative scroll	55	65

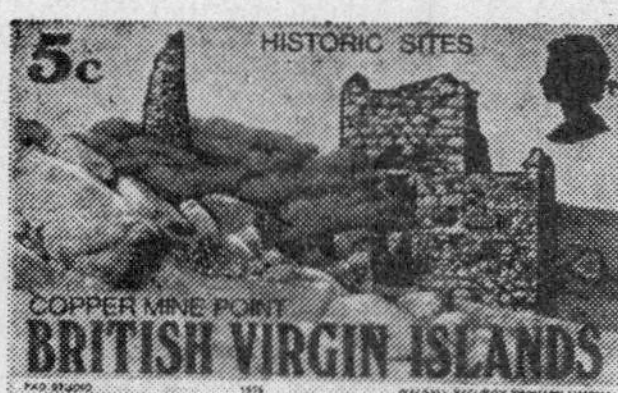

120. Copper Mine Point.

1976. Historic Sites. Multicoloured.

351.	5 c. Type **120**	10	10
352.	18 c. Pleasant Valley ..	20	10
353.	50 c. Callwood Distillery ..	40	30
354.	75 c. The Dungeon ..	60	65

121. Massachusetts Brig " Hazard ".

1976. Bicent of American Revolution. Mult.

355.	8 c. Type **121**	50	15
356.	22 c. American Privateer "Spy"	1·00	45
357.	40 c. Continental Navy frigate "Raleigh" ..	1·50	1·00
358.	75 c. Frigate "Alliance" and H.M.S. "Trepassy"	2·00	1·90

122. Government House, Tortola.

1976. Fifth Anniv. of Friendship Day with U.S. Virgin Is. Multicoloured.

360.	8 c. Type **122**	10	10
361.	15 c. Government House, St. Croix (vert.) ..	10	10
362.	30 c. Flags (vert.) ..	15	10
363.	75 c. Government seals ..	30	40

123. Royal Visit, 1966.

1977. Silver Jubilee. Multicoloured.

364.	8 c. Type **123**	10	10
365.	30 c. The Holy Bible ..	15	15
366.	60 c. Presentation of Holy Bible	25	40

124. Chart of 1739.

1977. 18th-Century Maps. Multicoloured.

367.	8 c. Type **124**	30	10
368.	22 c. French Map, 1758 ..	55	30
369.	30 c. Map from English and Danish surveys, 1775 ..	75	65
370.	75 c. Map of 1779 ..	1·25	1·50

1977. Royal Visit. As Nos. 364/6 inscr. " SILVER JUBILEE ROYAL VISIT ".

371.	5 c. Type **123**	10	10
372.	25 c. The Holy Bible ..	15	10
373.	50 c. Presentation of Holy Bible	30	25

125. Divers checking Equipment.

1978. Tourism. Multicoloured.

374.	½ c. Type **125** ..	10	10
375.	5 c. Cup coral on wreck of "Rhone"	15	10
376.	8 c. Sponge formation on wreck of "Rhone" ..	20	10
377.	22 c. Cup coral and sponges	50	15
378.	30 c. Sponges inside cave ..	60	20
379.	75 c. Marine life	1·10	85

126. Fire Coral.

1978. Corals. Multicoloured.

380.	8 c. Type **126**	25	15
381.	15 c. Staghorn coral ..	40	30
382.	40 c. Brain coral	75	85
383.	75 c. Elkhorn coral ..	1·50	1·60

127. Iguana.

1978. 25th Anniv. of Coronation.

384. –	50 c. brown, green and silver	25	40
385. –	50 c. multicoloured ..	25	40
386. **127.**	50 c. brown, green and silver	25	40

DESIGNS: No. 384, Plantagenet Falcon. No. 385, Queen Elizabeth II.

128. Lignum Vitae.

1978. Flowering Trees. Multicoloured.

387.	8 c. Type **128**	15	10
388.	22 c. Ginger Thomas ..	25	15
389.	40 c. Dog Almond ..	35	20
390.	75 c. White Cedar ..	60	70

129. " Eurema lisa ".

1978. Butterflies. Multicoloured.

392	5 c. Type **129**	25	10
393	22 c. "Agraulis vanillae" ..	75	20
394	30 c. "Heliconius charithonia"	85	30
395	75 c. "Hemiargus hanno" ..	1·25	1·25

130. Spiny Lobster.

1978. Wildlife Conservation. Multicoloured.

397.	5 c. Type **130**	15	10
398.	15 c. Large Iguana (vert.) ..	30	10
399.	22 c. Hawksbill Turtle ..	50	15
400.	75 c. Black Coral (vert.) ..	1·10	90

131. Strawberry Cactus.

1979. Native Cacti. Multicoloured.

402.	½ c. Type **131**	10	10
403.	5 c. Snowy cactus ..	15	10
404.	13 c. Barrel cactus ..	25	20
405.	22 c. Tree cactus	40	35
406.	30 c. Prickly Pear ..	45	40
407.	75 c. Dildo cactus ..	80	1·00

132. West Indian Girl.

1979. International Year of the Child. Multicoloured.

408.	5 c. Type **132**	10	10
409.	10 c. African boy	10	10
410.	13 c. Asian girl	10	10
411.	$1 European boy ..	50	85

133. 1956 Road Harbour 3 c. Definitive Stamp.

1979. Death Centenary of Sir Rowland Hill.

413. **133.**	5 c. deep blue, blue and green	10	10
414. –	13 c. blue and mauve ..	10	10
415. –	75 c. blue and purple ..	45	50

DESIGN—HORIZ. 13 c. 1880 2½d. red-brown. 75 c. Great Britain 1910 unissued 2d. Tyrian plum.

134. Pencil Urchin.

1979. Underwater Life. Multicoloured.

417	½ c. Calcified Algae ..	20	40
418	1 c. Purple-tipped Sea Anemone	25	45
419	3 c. Common Starfish ..	30	45
420a	5 c. Type **134**	30	30
421	8 c. Triton's Trumpet ..	50	40
422	10 c. Christmas Tree Worms	30	40
423a	13 c. Flamingo Tongue Snail	55	40
424	15 c. Spider Crab	40	40
425	18 c. Sea Squirts	70	75
426	20 c. True Tulip	55	55
427	25 c. Rooster Tail Conch ..	1·00	1·00
428a	30 c. Fighting Conch ..	85	65
429	60 c. Mangrove Crab ..	1·75	1·50
430	$1 Coral Polyps	2·50	2·75
431	$2.50 Peppermint Shrimp	3·50	4·25
432	$3 West Indian Murex ..	4·00	4·75
433	$5 Carpet Anemone ..	7·75	8·50

135. Rotary Athletics Meeting, Tortola.

1980. 75th Anniv. of Rotary International. Multicoloured.

434.	8 c. Type **135**	10	10
435.	22 c. Paul P. Harris (founder)	15	10
436.	60 c. Mount Sage, Tortola ("Creation of National Park")	40	40
437.	$1 Rotary anniversary emblem	70	75

136. Brown Booby.

1980. "London 1980" International Stamp Exhibition. Birds. Multicoloured.

439.	20 c. Type **136**	20	20
440.	25 c. Magnificent Frigate-Bird	25	25
441.	50 c. White-tailed Tropic-Bird	40	40
442.	75 c. Brown Pelican ..	55	55

1980. Caribbean Commonwealth Parliamentary Association Meeting, Tortola. Nos. 414/15 optd. **CARIBBEAN COMMONWEALTH PARLIAMENTARY ASSOCIATION MEETING, TORTOLA, 11—19 JULY 1980.**

444.	13 c. blue and red ..	15	10
445.	75 c. deep blue and blue..	40	40

138. Sir Francis Drake.

1980. Sir Francis Drake Commemoration. Multicoloured.

446.	8 c. Type **138**	40	10
447.	15 c. Queen Elizabeth I ..	60	15
448.	30 c. Drake receiving knighthood	75	30
449.	75 c. "Golden Hind" and coat of arms	1·50	80

139. Jost Van Dyke.

1980. Island Profiles. Multicoloured.

451.	2 c. Type **139**	10	10
452.	5 c. Peter Island	10	10
453.	13 c. Virgin Gorda ..	15	10
454.	22 c. Anegada	20	10
455.	30 c. Norman Island ..	30	15
456.	$1 Tortola	85	1·00

MINIMUM PRICE

The minimum price quoted is 10p which represents a handling charge rather than a basis for valuing common stamps. For further notes about prices see introductory pages.

140. Dancing Lady.

1981. Flowers. Multicoloured.

458.	5 c. Type **140**	15	10
459.	20 c. Love in the Mist ..	40	25
460.	22 c. "Pitcairnia angustifolia"	40	25
461.	75 c. Dutchman's Pipe ..	1·40	1·40
462.	$1 Maiden Apple ..	1·60	1·60

141. Wedding Bouquet from British Virgin Islands.

1981. Royal Wedding. Multicoloured.

463.	10 c. Type **141**	10	10
464.	35 c. Prince Charles and Queen Elizabeth the Queen Mother in Garter robes	30	15
465.	$1.25 Prince Charles and Lady Diana Spencer ..	80	80

142. Stamp Collecting.

1981. 25th Anniv. of Duke of Edinburgh Award Scheme. Multicoloured.

466.	10 c. Type **142**	10	10
467.	15 c. Athletics	10	10
468.	50 c. Camping	25	25
469.	$1 Duke of Edinburgh ..	40	45

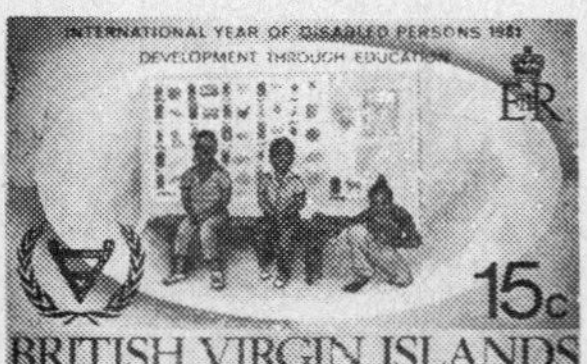
143. "Development through Education".

1981. International Year for Disabled Persons. Multicoloured.

470.	15 c. Type **143**	20	20
471.	20 c. Fort Charlotte Children's Centre	30	30
472.	30 c. "Developing cultural awareness"	40	40
473.	$1 Fort Charlotte Children's Centre" (different) ..	1·25	1·25

144. Detail from "The Adoration of the Shepherds" (Rubens).

1981. Christmas.

474. **144.**	5 c. multicoloured ..	10	10
475. –	15 c. multicoloured ..	20	10
476. –	30 c. multicoloured ..	40	15
477. –	$1 multicoloured ..	1·00	1·10

DESIGNS: 15 c. to $1. Further details from "The Adoration of the Shepherds" by Rubens.

145. Green-throated Caribs and Erythrina.

1982. Hummingbirds. Multicoloured.

479.	15 c. Type **145**	40	15
480.	30 c. Green-throated Carib and Bougainvillea ..	65	45
481.	35 c. Antillean Crested Hummingbirds and "Granadilla passiflora"	75	55
482.	$1.25 Antillean Crested Hummingbirds and Hibiscus	2·50	2·75

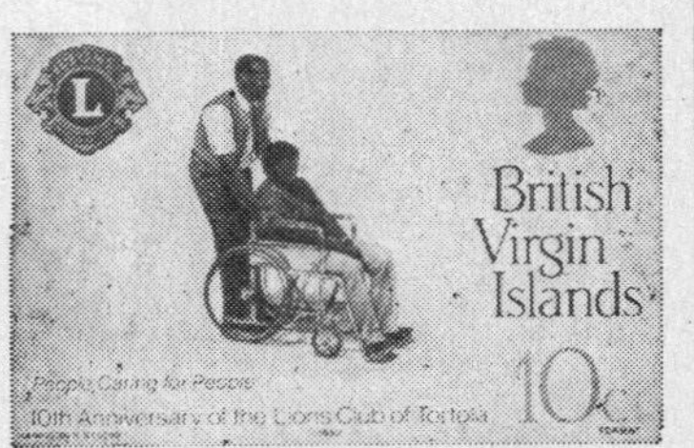
146. "People caring for People".

1982. 10th Anniv. of Lions Club of Tortola. Multicoloured.

483.	10 c. Type **146**	20	15
484.	20 c. Tortola Headquarters	40	20
485.	30 c. "We Serve" ..	50	30
486.	$1.50 "Lions" Symbol ..	1·90	1·75

147. Princess at Victoria and Albert Museum, November, 1981.

1982. 21st Birthday of Princess of Wales. Multicoloured.

488.	10 c. British Virgin Islands coat of arms	15	10
489.	35 c. Type **147**	30	30
490.	50 c. Bride and groom proceeding into Vestry	50	50
491.	$1.50 Formal portrait ..	1·25	1·60

148. Douglas "DC–3".

1982. 10th Anniv. of Air BVI. Multicoloured.

492.	10 c. Type **148**	20	15
493.	15 c. Britten-Norman "Islander"	25	20
494.	60 c. Hawker Siddeley "748"	90	75
495.	75 c. Runway scene ..	1·10	90

149. Scouts Raising Flag.

1982. 75th Anniv. of Boy Scout Movement and 50th Anniv. of Scouting in B.V.I. Multicoloured.

496.	8 c. Type **149**	20	10
497.	20 c. Cub Scout	45	25
498.	50 c. Sea Scout	85	55
499.	$1 First camp, Brownsea Island, and portrait of Lord Baden-Powell ..	1·50	1·50

150. Legislature in Session.

1983. Commonwealth Day. Mult.

500.	10 c. Type **150**	10	10
501.	30 c. Tourism	25	20
502.	35 c. Satellite view of Earth showing Virgin Islands ..	25	25
503.	75 c. B.V.I. and Commonwealth flags	70	90

151. Florence Nightingale.

1983. Nursing Week. Multicoloured.

504.	10 c. Type **151**	40	15
505.	30 c. Staff nurse and assistant nurse	75	45
506.	60 c. Public Health nurses testing blood pressure (horiz.)	1·40	95
507.	75 c. Peebles Hospital (horiz.)	1·75	1·25

152. Frame Construction.

1983. Traditional Boat-building. Multicoloured.

508.	15 c. Type **152**	30	25
509.	25 c. Planking	45	40
510.	50 c. Launching	80	70
511.	$1 Maiden Voyage ..	1·50	1·40

153. Grumman "Goose" Seaplane.

1983. Bicentenary of Manned Flight. Mult.

513.	10 c. Type **153**	20	15
514.	30 c. De Havilland "Heron"	45	45
515.	60 c. EMB "110P1 Bandeirante"	85	85
516.	$1.25, British Aerospace "HS 748"	1·50	1·60

154. "Madonna and Child with the Infant Baptist".

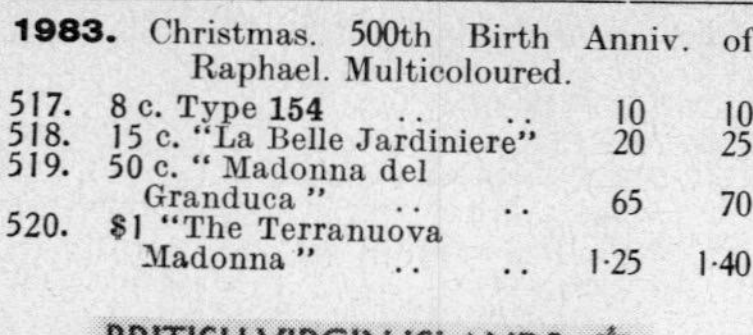

1983. Christmas. 500th Birth Anniv. of Raphael. Multicoloured.
517. 8 c. Type **154** 10 10
518. 15 c. "La Belle Jardiniere" 20 25
519. 50 c. "Madonna del Granduca" 65 70
520. $1 "The Terranuova Madonna" .. .. 1·25 1·40

155. Local Tournament.

1984. 60th Anniv of World Chess Federation. Multicoloured.
522. 10 c. Type **155** 70 30
523. 35 c. "Staunton" chess pieces (vert.) .. .. 1·40 80
524. 75 c. Winning position, 1980 Olympiad (vert.) .. 2·75 2·50
525. $1 B.V.I. Gold Medal from 1980 Olympiad .. .. 3·25 3·25

156. Port Purcell.

1984. 250th Anniv. of "Lloyd's List" (newspaper). Multicoloured.
526. 15 c. Type **156** 25 30
527. 25 c. Boeing "747" .. 45 50
528. 50 c. Loss of R.M.S. "Rhone" 90 95
529. $1 M.S. "Booker Viking" 1·50 1·60

158. Running.

1984. Olympic Games, Los Angeles. Mult.
531. 15 c. Type **158** 30 30
532. 15 c. Runner 30 30
533. 20 c. Wind-surfing .. 35 35
534. 20 c. Surfer 35 35
535. 30 c. Sailing 50 50
536. 30 c. Yacht 50 50

159. Steel Band.

1984. 150th Anniv. of Abolition of Slavery. Multicoloured.
538. 10 c. Type **159** 20 25
539. 10 c. Dancing girls .. 20 25
540. 10 c. Men in traditional costumes 20 25
541. 10 c. Girl in traditional costume 20 25
542. 10 c. Festival Queen .. 20 25
543. 30 c. Green and yellow dinghies 40 45
544. 30 c. Blue and red dinghies 40 45
545. 30 c. White and blue dinghies 40 45
546. 30 c. Red and yellow dinghies 40 45
547. 30 c. Blue and white dinghies 40 45

DESIGNS: Various aspects of Emancipation Festival.

Nos. 543/7 form a composite design, the sail colours of the dinghies being described.

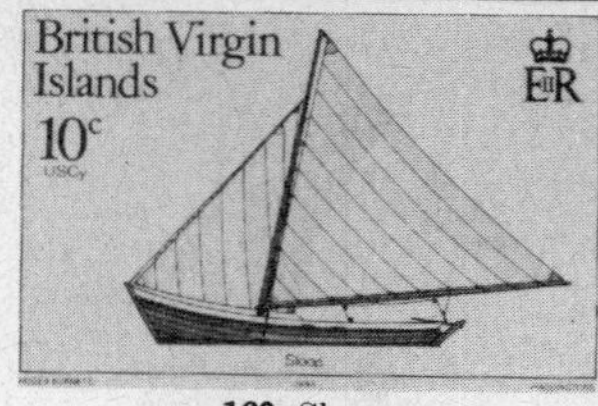

160. Sloop.

1984. Boats. Multicoloured.
548. 10 c. Type **160** 30 20
549. 35 c. Fishing boat 85 65
550. 60 c. Schooner .. .. 1·40 1·10
551. 75 c. Cargo boat .. .. 1·60 1·40

161. One Cent Coin and Aerial View.

1985. New Coinage. Coins and Local Scenery. Multicoloured.
553. 1 c. Type **161** 10 10
554. 5 c. Five cent coin and boulders on beach .. 10 10
555. 10 c. Ten cent coin and scuba diving .. 20 20
556. 25 c. Twenty-five cent coin and yachts 45 45
557. 50 c. Fifty cent coin and jetty .. .. .. 90 1·00
558. $1 One dollar coin and beach at night .. .. 1·75 2·00

162. Red-billed Tropic Bird.

1985. Birds of the British Virgin Islands. Multicoloured
560 1 c. Type **162** 15 20
561 2 c. Yellow-crowned night heron 15 20
562 5 c. Mangrove cuckoo .. 20 20
563 8 c. Northern mockingbird 20 20
647 10 c. Grey kingbird .. 20 15
565 12 c. Red-necked pigeon .. 20 20
649 15 c. Least bittern .. 30 30
567 18 c. Smooth-billed ani .. 30 30
651 20 c. Clapper rail 35 35
652 25 c. American kestrel .. 40 40
570 30 c. Pearly-eyed thrasher 50 55
654 35 c. Bridled quail dove .. 50 50
572 40 c. Green heron 55 60
573 50 c. Scaly-breasted ground dove 70 80
574 60 c. Little blue heron .. 80 1·00
658 $1 Audubon's shearwater 1·50 1·60
576 $2 Blue-faced booby .. 2·75 2·25
660 $3 Cattle egret .. .. 3·75 4·00
578 $5 Zenaida dove .. .. 7·00 6·50

163. The Queen Mother at Festival of Remembrance

1985. Life and Times of Queen Elizabeth the Queen Mother. Multicoloured.
579. 10 c. Type **163** 15 20
580. 10 c. At Victoria Palace Theatre, 1984 .. .. 15 20
581 25 c. At the engagement of the Prince of Wales, 1981 35 40
582. 25 c. Opening Celia Johnson Theatre, 1985 .. 35 40
583. 50 c. The Queen Mother on her 82nd birthday .. 70 75
584. 50 c. At the Tate Gallery, 1983 .. .. .. 70 75
585. 75 c. At the Royal Smithfield Show, 1983 .. .. 1·10 1·25
586. 75 c. Unveiling Mountbatten Statue, 1983 .. 1·10 1·25

164. Seaside Sparrow.

1985. Birth Bicentenary of John J. Audubon (ornithologist). Designs showing original paintings. Multicoloured.
588. 5 c. Type **164** 40 15
589. 30 c. Passenger Pigeon .. 1·00 60
590. 50 c. Yellow-breasted Chat 1·25 1·25
591. $1 American Kestrel .. 2·00 2·00

165. S.V. "Flying Cloud".

1986. Visiting Cruise Ships. Multicoloured.
592. 35 c. Type **165** .. .. 1·50 85
593. 50 c. M.V. "Newport Clipper" .. .. .. 2·00 1·25
594. 75 c. M.V. "Cunard Countess' .. .. 2·50 2·00
595. $1 M.V. "Sea Goddess.. .. 2·75 2·50

1986. Inaugural Flight of Miami–Beef Island Air Service. Nos. 581/2 and 585/6 optd. **MIAMI B.V.I. INAUGURAL FLIGHT.**
596. 25 c. At the engagement of the Prince of Wales, 1981 35 40
597. 25 c. Opening Celia Johnson theatre, 1985 .. 35 40
598. 75 c. At the Royal Smithfield Show, 1983 .. 1·10 1·25
599. 75 c. Unveiling Mountbatten statue, 1983 .. .. .. 1·10 1·25

167. Queen Elizabeth II in 1958. (Illustration reduced, actual size 60 × 40 mm.).

1986. 60th Birthday of Queen Elizabeth II. Multicoloured.
600. 12 c. Type **167** 15 20
601. 35 c. At a Maundy Service 40 45
602. $1.50 Queen Elizabeth .. 1·90 2·00
603. $2 During a visit to Canberra, 1982 (vert.) .. 2·00 2·75

168. Miss Sarah Ferguson.

1986. Royal Wedding. Multicoloured.
605. 35 c. Type **168** 50 55
606. 35 c. Prince Andrew and Miss Sarah Ferguson .. 50 55
607. $1 Prince Andrew in morning dress (horiz.) .. 1·25 1·50
608. $1 Miss Sarah Ferguson (different) (horiz.) .. 1·25 1·50

169. Harvesting Sugar Cane.

1986. History of Rum Making. Multicoloured.
610. 12 c. Type **169** 65 35
611. 40 c. Bringing sugar cane to mill .. .. .. 1·25 1·00
612. 60 c. Rum distillery .. 1·75 1·75
613. $1 Delivering barrels of rum to ship .. .. 2·75 3·00

170. C.S. "Sentinel".

1986. 20th Anniv. of Cable and Wireless Caribbean Headquarters, Tortola. Mult.
615. 35 c. Type **170** 55 65
616. 35 c. C.S. "Retriever" (1961) 55 65
617. 60 c. C.S. "Cable Enterprise" (1964) .. 1·00 1·25
618. 60 c. C.S. "Mercury" (1962) 1·00 1·25
619. 75 c. C.S. "Recorder" (1955) .. .. .. 1·25 1·40
620. 75 c. C.S. "Pacific Guardian" (1984) .. 1·25 1·40
621. $1 S.S. "Great Eastern" (1860's) .. .. 1·50 1·75
622. $1 C.S. "Cable Venture" .. 1·50 1·75

172. 18th-century Spanish Galleon.

1987. Shipwrecks. Multicoloured.
625. 12 c. Type **172** 60 30
626. 35 c. H.M.S. "Astrea", 1808 1·25 85
627. 75 c. R.M.S. "Rhone", 1867 2·00 2·00
628. $1.50 S.S. "Rocus", 1929 .. 3·50 3·75

173. Outline Map and Flag of Montserrat.

1987. 11th Meeting of Organisation of Eastern Caribbean States. Each showing outline map and flag. Multicoloured.

630.	10 c. Type **173**	35	35
631.	15 c. Grenada	40	40
632.	20 c. Dominica	45	45
633.	25 c. St. Kitts-Nevis	50	50
634.	35 c. St. Vincent and Grenadines	70	70
635.	50 c. British Virgin Islands	90	90
636.	75 c. Antigua and Barbuda	1·25	1·25
637.	$1 St. Lucia	1·75	1·75

174. Spider Lily.

1987. Opening of Botanical Gardens. Multicoloured.

638.	12 c. Type **174**	60	30
639.	35 c. Barrel cactus	1·25	80
640.	$1 Wild plantain	2·25	2·50
641.	$1.50 Little butterfly orchid	5·00	5·00

175. Early Mail Packet and 1867 1s. Stamp.

1987. Bicentenary of Postal Services. Multicoloured.

662	10 c. Type **175**	40	30
663	20 c. Map and 1889 1d. stamp	70	55
664	35 c. Road Town Post Office and Customs House, c. 1913, and 1867 4d. stamp	1·25	80
665	$1.50 Mail plane and 1964 25 c. definitive	3·50	3·75

1988. 500th Birth Anniv of Titian (artist). As T **238** of Antigua. Multicoloured.

667	10 c. "Salome"	25	25
668	12 c. "Man with the Glove"	30	30
669	20 c. "Fabrizio Salvaresio"	40	40
670	25 c. "Daughter of Roberto Strozzi"	50	50
671	40 c. "Pope Julius II"	70	70
672	50 c. "Bishop Ludovico Beccadelli"	75	75
673	60 c. "King Philip II"	85	85
674	$1 "Empress Isabella of Portugal"	1·50	1·50

176 Aircraft over Sir Francis Drake Channel and Pawn

1988. 1st British Virgin Islands Open Chess Tournament. Multicoloured.

676	35 c. Type **176**	1·50	1·00
677	$1 Jose Capablanca (former World Champion) and king	3·25	3·25

177 Hurdling

1988. Olympic Games, Seoul. Multicoloured.

679	12 c. Type **177**	20	20
680	20 c. Windsurfing	30	30
681	75 c. Basketball	95	95
682	$1 Tennis	1·40	1·40

178 Swimmer ("Don't Swim Alone")

1988. 125th Anniv of International Red Cross.

684	**178**	12 c. black, red & blue	40	30
685	–	30 c. black, red & blue	75	60
686	–	60 c. black, red & blue	1·25	1·25
687	–	$1 black, red and blue	2·00	2·00

DESIGNS: 30 c. Swimmers ("No swimming during electrical storms"); 60 c. Beach picnic ("Don't eat before swimming"); $1 Boat and equipment ("Proper equipment for boating").

179 Princess Alexandra

1988. Visit of Princess Alexandra. Designs showing different portraits.

689	**179**	40 c. multicoloured	1·25	75
690	–	$1.50 multicoloured	3·00	3·25

180 Brown Pelican in Flight

1988. Wildlife (1st series). Aquatic Birds. Multicoloured.

692	10 c. Type **180**	50	30
693	12 c. Brown pelican perched on post	60	35
694	15 c. Brown pelican	70	50
695	35 c. Brown pelican swallowing fish	1·50	1·50

181 Anegada Rock Iguana

1988. Wildlife (2nd series). Endangered Species. Multicoloured.

697	20 c. Type **181**	45	35
698	40 c. Virgin gorda dwarf gecko	85	70
699	60 c. Hawksbill turtle	1·25	95
700	$1 Humpback whale	1·75	2·00

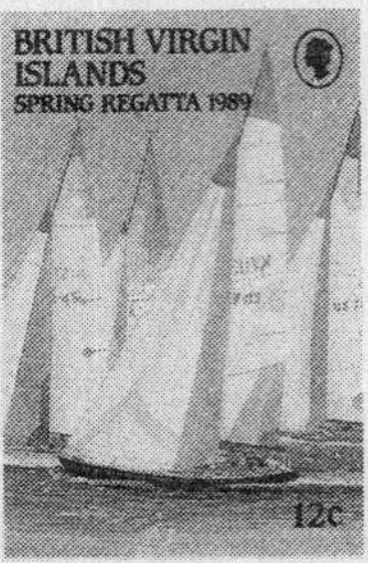

182 Yachts at Start

1989. Spring Regatta. Multicoloured.

702	12 c. Type **182**	15	20
703	40 c. Yacht tacking (horiz)	45	50
704	75 c. Yachts at sunset	85	90
705	$1 Yachts rounding buoy (horiz)	1·10	1·25

1989. 500th Anniv (1992) of Discovery of America by Columbus (1st issue). Pre-Columbian Arawak Society. As T **247** of Antigua. Multicoloured.

707	10 c. Arawak in hammock	10	15
708	20 c. Making fire	25	30
709	25 c. Making implements	30	35
710	$1.50 Arawak family	1·75	1·90

See also Nos. 741/4 and 793/6.

183 "Apollo 11" Emblem

1989. 20th Anniv of First Manned Landing on Moon. Multicoloured.

712	15 c. Type **183**	15	20
713	30 c. Edwin Aldrin deploying scientific experiments	35	40
714	65 c. Aldrin and U.S. flag on Moon	75	80
715	$1 "Apollo 11" capsule after splashdown	1·10	1·25

184 Black Harry and Nathaniel Gilbert preaching to Slaves

1989. Bicentenary of Methodist Church in British Virgin Islands. Multicoloured.

717	12 c. Type **184**	15	20
718	25 c. Methodist school exercise book	30	35
719	35 c. East End Methodist Church, 1810	40	45
720	$1.25 Revd. John Wesley (founder of Methodism) and church youth choir	1·40	1·50

185 Player tackling

1989. World Cup Football Championship, Italy, 1990. Multicoloured.

722	5 c. Type **185**	10	10
723	10 c. Player dribbling ball	10	15
724	20 c. Two players chasing ball	25	30
725	$1.75 Goalkeeper diving for ball	2·00	2·10

186 Princess Alexandra and Sunset House

1990. "Stamp World London 90" Int. Stamp Exhibition. Royal Visitors. Mult.

727	50 c. Type **186**	60	65
728	50 c. Princess Margaret and Government House	60	65
729	50 c. Hon. Angus Ogilvy and Little Dix Bay Hotel	60	65
730	50 c. Princess Diana with Princes William and Harry and Necker Island Resort	60	65

187 Audubon's Shearwater

1990. Birds. Multicoloured.

732	5 c. Type **187**	10	10
733	12 c. Red-necked pigeon	15	20
734	20 c. Moorhen	25	30
735	25 c. Green heron	30	35
736	40 c. Yellow warbler	45	50
737	60 c. Smooth-billed ani	70	75
738	$1 Antillean crested hummingbird	1·10	1·25
739	$1.25 Black-faced grassquit	1·40	1·50

1990. 500th Anniv (1992) of Discovery of America by Columbus (2nd issue). New World Natural History–Fishes. As T **260** of Antigua. Multicoloured.

741	10 c. Blue tang (horiz)	10	15
742	35 c. Glasseye (horiz)	40	45
743	50 c. Slippery dick (horiz)	60	65
744	$1 Porkfish (horiz)	1·10	1·25

188 Queen Elizabeth the Queen Mother

1990. 90th Birthday of Queen Elizabeth the Queen Mother.

746	**188**	12 c. multicoloured	15	20
747	–	25 c. multicoloured	30	35
748	–	60 c. multicoloured	70	75
749	–	$1 multicoloured	1·10	1·25

DESIGNS: 25, 60 c., $1 Recent photographs.

189 Footballers

1990. World Cup Football Championship, Italy.
751 **189** 12 c. multicoloured .. 15 20
752 – 20 c. multicoloured .. 25 30
753 – 50 c. multicoloured .. 60 65
754 – $1.25 multicoloured .. 1·40 1·50
DESIGNS: 20, 50 c., $1.25 Footballers.

190 Judo

1990. Olympic Games, Barcelona (1992). Mult.
756 12 c. Type **190** 15 20
757 40 c. Yachting 45 50
758 60 c. Hurdling 70 75
759 $1 Show jumping .. 1·10 1·25

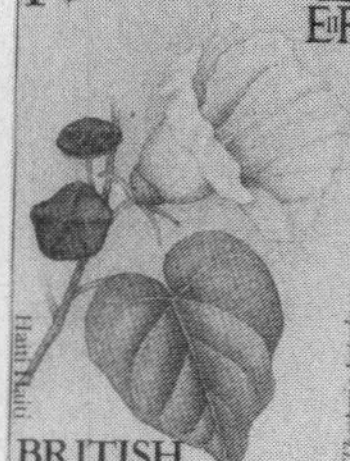

191 Tree-fern, Sage Mountain National Park **192** Haiti Haiti

1991. 30th Anniv of National Parks Trust. Multicoloured.
761 10 c. Type **191** 10 15
762 25 c. Coppermine ruins, Virgin Gorda (horiz) .. 30 35
763 35 c. Ruined windmill, Mount Healthy .. 40 45
764 $2 The Baths (rock formation), Virgin Gorda (horiz) .. .. .. 2·25 2·40

1991. Flowers. Multicoloured.
765 1 c. Type **192** 10 10
766 2 c. Lobster claw .. 10 10
767 5 c. Frangipani .. 10 10
768 10 c. Autograph tree .. 10 15
769 12 c. Yellow allamanda .. 15 20
770 15 c. Lantana .. 15 20
771 20 c. Jerusalem thorn .. 25 30
772 25 c. Turk's cap .. 30 35
773 30 c. Swamp immortelle .. 35 40
774 35 c. White cedar .. 40 45
775 40 c. Mahoe tree 45 50
776 45 c. Pinguin .. 50 55
777 50 c. Christmas orchid .. 60 65
778 70 c. Lignum vitae .. 80 85
779 $1 African tulip tree .. 1·10 1·25
780 $2 Beach morning glory .. 2·25 2·40
781 $3 Organ pipe cactus .. 3·50 3·75
782 $5 Tall ground orchid .. 5·75 6·00

193 "Phoebis sennae"

1991. Butterflies. Multicoloured.
784 5 c. Type **193** 10 10
785 10 c. "Dryas iulia" 10 10
786 15 c. "Junonia evarete" .. 15 20
787 20 c. "Dione vanillae" .. 25 30
788 25 c. "Battus polydamus" 30 35
789 30 c. "Eurema lisa" .. 35 40
790 35 c. "Heliconius charitonius" 40 45
791 $1.50 "Siproeta stelenes" 1·75 1·90

194 "Victoria" in Pacific (Magellan, 1519–21)

1991. 500th Anniv (1992) of Discovery of America by Columbus (3rd issue). History of Exploration. Multicoloured.
793 12 c. Type **194** 10 10
794 50 c. La Salle on the Mississipi, 1682 .. 60 65
795 75 c. John Cabot landing in Nova Scotia, 1497–98 .. 85 90
796 $1 Cartier discovering the St. Lawrence, 1534 .. 1·10 1·25

195 "Cottage with Decrepit Barn and Stooping Woman" (Van Gogh)

1991. Death Centenary (1990) of Vincent Van Gogh (artist). Multicoloured.
798 15 c. Type **195** 15 20
799 30 c. "Paul Gauguin's Armchair" (vert) .. 35 40
800 75 c. "Breton Women" .. 85 90
801 $1 "Vase with Red Gladioli" (vert) .. 1·10 1·25

196 "The Virgin and Child Enthroned" (detail, Q. Massys)

1991. Christmas. Religious Paintings by Quinten Massys. Multicoloured.
803 15 c. Type **196** 15 20
804 30 c. "The Virgin and Child Enthroned" (different detail) 35 40
805 60 c. "Adoration of the Magi" (detail) 70 75
806 $1 "Virgin in Adoration" 1·10 1·25

197 "Agaricus bisporus"

1992. Fungi. Multicoloured.
808 12 c. Type **197** 10 10
809 30 c. "Lentinus edodes" (horiz) 35 40
810 45 c. "Hyrocybe acutoconica" 50 55
811 $1 "Gymnopilus chrysopellus" (horiz) .. 1·10 1·25

1992. 40th Anniv of Queen Elizabeth II Accession. As T **292** of Antigua. Mult.
813 12 c. Little Dix Bay, Virgin Goda .. 10 10
814 45 c. Deadchest Bay, Peter Island 50 55
815 60 c. Pond Bay, Virgin Goda 70 75
816 $1 Cane Garden Bay, Tortola .. .. 1·10 1·25

OFFICIAL STAMPS

1985. Nos. 418/21 and 423/33 optd. **OFFICIAL.**
O 1. 1 c. Purple-tipped Sea Anemone 25 40
O 2. 3 c. Common Starfish .. 35 40
O 3. 5 c. Type **134** 35 20
O 4. 8 c. Triton's Trumpet (shell) 45 20
O 5. 13 c. Flamingo Tongue Snail 60 40
O 6. 15 c. Spider Crab .. 65 55
O 7. 18 c. Sea Squirts .. 70 60
O 8. 20 c. True Tulip (shell) .. 70 60
O 9. 25 c. Rooster Tail Conch (shell) 80 70
O10. 30 c. Fighting Conch (shell) 90 80
O11. 60 c. Mangrove Crab .. 2·00 2·00
O12. $1 Coral Polyps .. 2·75 3·00
O13. $2.50 Peppermint Shrimp .. 4·75 5·50
O14. $3 West Indian Murex (shell) .. .. 6·50 7·50
O15. $5 Carpet Anemone .. 9·50 12·00

1986. Nos. 560/78 optd. **OFFICIAL.**
O 16 1 c. Type **162** 20 30
O 17 2 c. Yellow-crowned night heron 30 35
O 18 5 c. Mangrove cuckoo .. 30 35
O 19 8 c. Northern mocking-bird 40 40
O 20 10 c. Grey kingbird .. 40 40
O 21 12 c. Red-necked pigeon 50 50
O 22 15 c. Least bittern .. 50 50
O 23 18 c. Smooth-billed ani .. 60 60
O 24 20 c. Clipper rail .. 60 60
O 25 25 c. American kestrel .. 60 60
O 26 30 c. Pearly-eyed thrasher 70 70
O 27 35 c. Bridled quail dove 70 70
O 28 40 c. Green heron .. 1·00 1·00
O 29 50 c. Scaly-breasted ground dove .. .. 1·50 1·50
O 30 60 c. Little blue heron .. 1·75 1·75
O 31 $1 Audubon's shear-water .. .. 2·75 2·75
O 32 $2 Blue-faced booby .. 4·75 5·00
O 33 $3 Cattle egret .. 6·50 7·50
O 34 £4 Zenaida dove .. 8·50 9·50

1991. Nos. 767/8, 771, 773/9 and 781 optd **OFFICIAL.**
O35 5 c. Frangipani
O36 10 c. Autograph tree
O37 20 c. Jerusalem thorn
O38 30 c. Swamp immortelle
O39 35 c. White cedar
O40 40 c. Mahoe tree
O41 45 c. Pinguin
O42 50 c. Christmas orchid
O43 70 c. Lignum vitae
O44 $1 African tulip tree
O45 $3 Organ pipe cactus

Nos. O35/45 were used on mail from the Philatelic Bureau and were not sold unused.

BRUNEI

A Sultanate on the N. Coast of Borneo.
100 cents = 1 dollar.

1. Star and Local Scene.

1895.
1. **1.** ½ c. brown .. .. .. 1·00 10·00
2. 1 c. brown .. .. .. 1·00 9·00
3. 2 c. black .. .. .. 3·50 9·00
4. 3 c. blue .. .. .. 3·00 8·50
5. 5 c. green .. .. .. 6·00 10·00
6. 8 c. purple .. .. 8·50 13·00
7. 10 c. red .. .. .. 7·50 15·00
8. 25 c. green .. .. 18·00 28·00
9. 50 c. green .. .. 18·00 50·00
10. $1 green .. .. .. 20·00 70·00

1906. Stamps of Labuan optd. **BRUNEI,** or surch. also.
11. **18.** 1 c. black and purple .. 18·00 28·00
12. 2 c. on 3 c. black & brown 1·50 4·50
13. 2 c. on 8 c. black & orange 20·00 55·00
14. 3 c. black and brown .. 20·00 55·00
15. 4 c. on 12 c. black & yellow 1·25 4·25
16. 5 c. on 16 c. green & brown 27·00 40·00
17. 8 c. black and orange .. 8·50 17·00
18. 10 c. on 16 c. green & brn. 6·00 16·00
19. 25 c. on 16 c. green & brn. 90·00 £120
20. 30 c. on 16 c. green & brn. 80·00 £110
21. 50 c. on 16 c. green & brn. 80·00 £110
22. $1 on 8 c. black & orange 80·00 £110

5. View on Brunei River.

1907.
23. **5.** 1 c. black and green .. 2·25 7·00
24. 2 c black and red .. .. 2·50 4·50
25. 3 c. black and brown .. 9·00 18·00
26. 4 c. black and mauve .. 6·00 10·00
27. 5 c. black and blue .. 30·00 55·00
28. 8 c. black and orange .. 5·50 23·00
29. 10 c. black and green .. 4·50 7·00
30. 25 c. blue and brown .. 20·00 30·00
31. 30 c. violet and black .. 13·00 22·00
32. 50 c. green and brown .. 13·00 22·00
33. $1 red and grey .. .. 45·00 75·00

1908.
35 **5** 1 c. green 25 75
60 1 c black 30 35
79 1 c. brown 50 60
36 2 c. black and brown .. 80 1·25
61 2 c. brown .. .. 90 3·00
62 2 c. green 30 30
80 2 c. grey 40 75
37 3 c. red .. .. .. 1·40 75
63 3 c. green .. .. .. 80 4·50
39 4 c. red 75 75
65 4 c. orange 65 50
40 5 c. black and orange .. 6·50 7·00
82 5 c. orange 60 80
67 5 c. grey .. .. .. 6·50 3·75
68 5 c. brown .. .. 1·25 15
41 8 c. blue and indigo .. 6·00 11·00
71 8 c. blue .. .. .. 4·25 5·00
72 8 c. black .. .. .. 2·25 55
84 8 c. red 40 40
42 10 c. purple on yellow .. 1·25 85
85 10 c. violet 30 10
86 15 c. blue 30 30
87 25 c. lilac 55 40
76 30 c. purple and orange 4·50 12·00
88 30 c. black and orange .. 45 50
77 50 c. black on green .. 7·00 13·00
89 50 c. black 50 30
46 $1 black and red on blue 20·00 48·00
90 $1 black and red .. 1·25 60
47 $5 red on green .. .. 70·00 £140
91 $5 green and red .. 16·00 14·00
92 $10 black and purple .. 27·00 32·00
48 $25 black on red .. £450 £850

1922. Optd. **MALAYA-BORNEO EXHIBITION 1922.**
51. **5.** 1 c. green .. .. .. 1·75 17·00
52. 2 c. black and brown .. 3·75 20·00
53. 3 c. red .. .. .. 5·00 32·00
54. 4 c. red .. .. .. 4·00 40·00
55. 5 c. orange .. .. 7·50 55·00
56. 10 c. purple on yellow .. 6·50 55·00
57. 25 c. lilac .. .. .. 14·00 80·00
58. 50 c. black on green .. 45·00 £150
59. $1 black and red on blue .. 70·00 £190

7. Native Houses, Water Village.

1924.

81. 7. 3 c. green .. .. 75 1·75
83. 6 c. black .. .. 90 2·00
70. 6 c. red .. .. 3·75 9·00
74. 12 c. blue .. .. 4·50 8·00

8. Sultan Ahmed Tajudin and Water Village.

1949. Silver Jubilee of H.H. the Sultan.

93. 8. 8 c. black and red .. 55 60
94. 25 c. purple and orange .. 55 50
95. 50 c. black and blue .. 70 80

1949. 75th Anniv of U.P.U. As T **20/23** of Antigua.

96. 8 c. red 65 80
97. 15 c. blue .. .. .. 1·25 90
98. 25 c. mauve .. .. .. 1·25 90
99. 50 c. black .. .. .. 1·50 90

9. Sultan Omar Ali Saifuddin.

1952. Dollar values as T **8**, but with arms instead of portrait inset.

100 9 1 c. black 10 30
119a 2 c. black and orange .. 20 10
102 3 c. black and brown .. 10 10
103 4 c. black and green .. 10 10
104 6 c. black and grey .. 10 10
105 8 c. black and red .. 20 10
106 10 c. black and sepia .. 15 10
125 12 c. black and violet .. 75 10
126 15 c. black and blue .. 30 10
109 25 c. black and purple .. 90 10
110 50 c. black and blue .. 50 10
111 8 $1 black and green .. 1·25 60
112 $2 black and red .. 4·50 2·00
113a $5 black and purple .. 9·00 3·00

11. Brunei Mosque and Sultan Omar.

1958. Opening of the Brunei Mosque.

114. 11. 8 c. black and green .. 10 45
115. 15 c. black and red .. 10 15
116. 35 c. black and lilac .. 20 70

12. "Protein Foods".

1963. Freedom from Hunger.

117. 12. 12 c. sepia .. .. 2·00 90

13. I.T.U. Emblem.

1965. Centenary of I.T.U.

132. 13. 4 c. mauve and brown .. 35 10
133. 75 c. yellow and green .. 1·00 75

14. I.C.Y. Emblem.

1965. Int. Co-operation Year.

134. 14. 4 c. purple and turquoise 20 10
135. 15 c. green and lavender 55 35

15. Sir Winston Churchill and St. Paul's Cathedral in Wartime.

1966. Churchill Commem. Designs in black, red and gold and with background in colours given.

136. 15. 3 c. blue 30 15
137. 10 c. green .. .. 1·25 20
138. 15 c. brown .. .. 1·50 35
139. 75 c. violet .. .. 3·00 2·00

16. Footballer's Legs, Ball and Jules Rimet Cup.

1966. World Cup Football Championships.

140. 16. 4 c. multicoloured .. 20 15
141. 75 c. multicoloured .. 75 60

17. W.H.O. Building.

1966. Inauguration of W.H.O. Headquarters, Geneva.

142. 17. 12 c. black, grn. & blue 35 20
143. 25 c. blk., pur. & ochre 55 35

18. "Education".

1966. 20th Anniv. of U.N.E.S.C.O.

144. 18. 4 c. multicoloured .. 35 10
145. – 15 c. yell., violet & olive 75 45
146. – 75 c. blk., pur. and orge. 2·25 2·75

DESIGNS: 15 c. "Science". 75 c. "Culture".

21. Religious Headquarters Building.

1967. 1400th Anniv. of Revelation of the Koran.

147. 21. 4 c. multicoloured .. 10 10
148. 10 c. multicoloured .. 15 10
149. – 25 c. multicoloured .. 20 20
150. – 50 c. multicoloured .. 35 50

Nos. 149/50 have sprigs of laurel flanking the main design (which has a smaller circle) in place of flagpoles.

22. Sultan of Brunei, Mosque and Flags.

1968. Installation of Y.T.M. Seri Paduka Duli Pengiran Temenggong. Multicoloured.

151. 4 c. Type 22 .. .. 15 25
152. 12 c. Sultan of Brunei, Mosque and Flags (different) 40 65
153. 25 c. Type 22 .. .. 50 1·10

No. 152 is horiz.

23. Sultan of Brunei.

1968. Birthday of Sultan

154. 23. 4 c. multicoloured .. 10 15
155. 12 c. multicoloured .. 20 25
156. 25 c. multicoloured .. 30 50

24. Sultan of Brunei.

1968. Coronation of Sultan of Brunei.

157. 24. 4 c. multicoloured .. 15 15
158. 12 c. multicoloured .. 25 30
159. 25 c. multicoloured .. 40 45

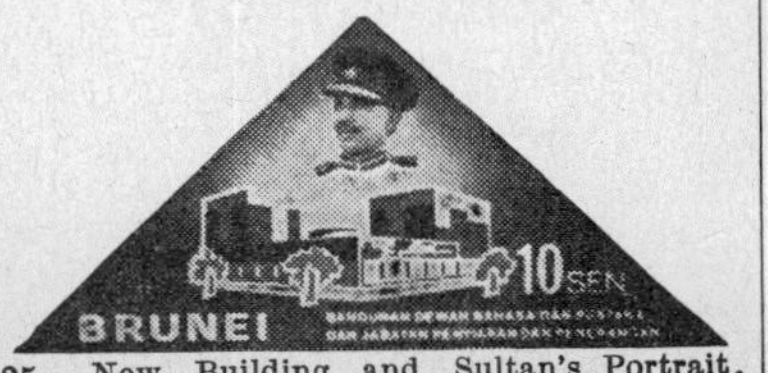

25. New Building and Sultan's Portrait.

1968. Opening of Hall of Language and Literature Bureau. Multicoloured.

160. 10 c. Type 25 .. .. 15 50
161. 15 c. New Building and Sultan's portrait (48½ × 22 mm.) .. 20 30
162. 30 c. As 15 c. 40 60

27. Human Rights Emblem and struggling Man.

1968. Human Rights Year.

163. 27. 12 c. blk., yell. & grn... 10 15
164. 25 c. blk., yell. & bl. .. 15 20
165. 75 c. blk., yell. & pur... 45 1·00

28. Sultan of Brunei and W.H.O. Emblem.

1968. 20th Anniv. of World Health Organization.

166. 28. 4 c. yell., blk. and blue .. 10 25
167. 15 c. yell., blk. & violet 25 35
168. 25 c. yell., blk. & olive .. 35 65

29. Deep Sea Oil-Rig, Sultan of Brunei and inset portrait of Pengiran Di-Gadong.

1969. Installation (9th May, 1968) of Pengiran Shar-bandar as Y.T.M. Seri Paduka Duli Pengiran Di-Gadong Sahibol Mal.

169. 29. 12 c. multicoloured .. 35 25
170. 40 c. multicoloured .. 70 70
171. 50 c. multicoloured .. 80 80

30. Aerial View of Parliament Buildings.

1969. Opening of Royal Audience Hall and Legislative Council Chamber.

172. 30. 12 c. multicoloured .. 15 15
173. 25 c. multicoloured .. 25 30
174. – 50 c. red and violet .. 50 60

DESIGN: 50 c. Elevation of new buildings.

32. Youth Centre and Sultan's Portrait.

1969. Opening of New Youth Centre.

175. 32. 6 c. multicoloured .. 15 20
176. 10 c. multicoloured .. 20 10
177. 30 c. multicoloured .. 55 45

33. Soldier, Sultan and Badge.

1971. 10th Anniv. of Royal Brunei Malay Regiment. Multicoloured.

178.	10 c. Type **33**	45	30
179.	15 c. Helicopter, Sultan and Arms (horiz.)	55	55
180.	75 c. "Pahlawan" (patrol boat), Sultan and Arms (horiz.)	2·50	4·25

34. Badge, and Officer in Full-dress Uniform.

1971. 50th Anniv. of Royal Brunei Police Force. Multicoloured.

181.	10 c. Type **34**	50	30
182.	15 c. Badge and Patrol Constable	70	80
183.	50 c. Badge and Traffic Constable	2·25	4·25

35. Perdana Wazir, Sultan of Brunei and View of Water Village.

1971. Installation of the Yang Teramat Malia as the Perdana Wazir.

184.	**35.**	15 c. multicoloured	40	50
185.	–	25 c. multicoloured	70	1·00
186.	–	50 c. multicoloured	1·40	2·75

Nos. 185/6 show various views of Brunei Town.

36. Pottery.

1972. Opening of Brunei Museum. Mult.

187.	10 c. Type **36**	25	10
188.	12 c. Straw-work	30	20
189.	15 c. Leather-work	35	20
190.	25 c. Gold-work	1·00	1·10
191.	50 c. Museum Building (58×21 mm.)	2·00	2·50

37. Modern Building, Queen Elizabeth and Sultan of Brunei.

1972. Royal Visit. Each design with portrait of Queen and Sultan. Multicoloured.

192.	10 c. Type **37**	20	20
193.	15 c. Native houses	30	30
194.	25 c. Mosque	75	1·00
195.	50 c. Royal Assembly Hall	2·00	3·00

38. Secretariat Building.

1972. Renaming of Brunei Town as Bandar Seri Begawan.

196.	**38.**	10 c. multicoloured	20	15
197.	–	15 c. green, yell. & blk.	25	15
198.	–	25 c. blue, yell. & black	40	45
199.	–	50 c. red, blue and black	80	1·10

VIEWS: 15 c. Darul Hana Palace. 25 c. Old Brunei Town. 50 c. Town and Water Village.

39. Blackburn "Beverley" parachuting supplies.

1972. Opening of R.A.F. Museum, Hendon. Multicoloured.

200.	25 c. Type **39**	1·50	1·25
201.	75 c. Blackburn "Beverley" landing	3·00	3·25

1972. Royal Silver Wedding. As T **52** of Ascension, but with Girl with Traditional Flower-pot, and Boy with Bowl and Pipe in background.

210.	12 c. red	10	10
211.	75 c. green	20	50

41. Interpol H.Q., Paris.

1973. 50th Anniv. of Interpol.

212.	**41.**	25 c. grn., pur. & black	1·25	1·25
213.	–	50 c. blue, ultramarine and red	1·25	1·25

DESIGN: 50 c. Different view of the H.Q.

42. Sultan, Princess Anne and Capt. Phillips.

1973. Royal Wedding.

214.	**42.**	25 c. multicoloured	10	10
215.		50 c. multicoloured	15	25

HAVE YOR READ THE NOTES AT THE BEGINNING OF THIS CATALOGUE?
These often provide answers to the enquiries we receive.

43. Churchill Painting.

44. Sultan Sir Hassanal Bolkiah Mu'izzaddin Waddaulah.

1973. Opening of Churchill Memorial Building. Multicoloured.

216.	12 c. Type **43**	10	15
217.	50 c. Churchill statue	30	85

1975. Multicoloured. Background colours given.

218	**44**	4 c. green	10	10
219		5 c. blue	10	10
220		6 c. green	40	10
221		10 c. lilac	10	10
222		15 c. brown	20	10
223		20 c. stone	20	10
224		25 c. green	30	15
225		30 c. blue	30	15
226		35 c. grey	35	20
227		40 c. purple	35	20
228		50 c. brown	40	20
229		75 c. green	60	1·00
256		$1 orange	90	1·25
257		$2 yellow	2·25	3·50
258		$5 silver	4·00	8·50
233		$10 gold	8·00	18·00

45. Aerial View of Airport.

1974. Inauguration of Brunei Int. Airport. Multicoloured

234.	50 c. Type **45**	75	1·00
235.	75 c. Sultan in Army uniform, and airport (48×36 mm.)	1·25	1·50

46. U.P.U. Emblem and Sultan.

1974. Cent. Universal Postal Union.

236.	**46.**	12 c. multicoloured	20	20
237.		50 c. multicoloured	40	1·00
238.		75 c. multicoloured	50	1·25

47. Sir Winston Churchill.

1974. Birth. Cent. of Sir Winston Churchill.

239.	**47.**	12 c. blk., blue and gold	20	20
240.	–	75 c. blk., grn. & gold	35	70

DESIGN: 75 c. Churchill smoking cigar (profile).

48. Boeing "737" and R.B.A. Crest.

1975. Inauguration of Royal Brunei Airlines. Multicoloured.

241.	12 c. Type **48**	30	25
242.	35 c. '737' over Bander Seri Begawan Mosque	80	1·00
243.	75 c. '737' in flight	1·75	2·00

1976. Surch.

263.	**44.**	10 c. on 6 c. brown	85	50

50. Royal Coat of Arms.

1977. Silver Jubilee. Multicoloured.

264.	10 c. Type **50**	15	20
265.	20 c. Imperial State Crown	20	35
266.	75 c. Queen Elizabeth (portrait by Annigoni)	45	75

51. The Moment of Crowning.

1978. 25th Anniv. of Coronation. Mult.

267.	10 c. Type **51**	10	10
268.	20 c. Queen in Coronation regalia	15	20
269.	75 c. Queen's departure from Abbey	50	80

52. Royal Crest.

1978. 10th Anniv. of Coronation of Sultan.

270.	**52.**	10 c. black, red & yellow	10	10
271.	–	20 c. multicoloured	15	20
272.	–	75 c. multicoloured	50	75

DESIGNS: 20 c. Coronation. 75 c. Sultan's Crown.

53. Human Rights Emblem and Struggling Man.

1978. Human Rights Year.

274.	**53.**	10 c. blk., yell. and red	10	10
275.		20 c. blk., yell. & violet	20	20
276.		75 c. blk., yell. & bistre	50	75

Type **53** is similar to the design used for the previous Human Rights issue in 1968.

54. Smiling Children.

1979. International Year of the Child.
277. 54. 10 c. multicoloured .. 10 10
278. – $1 black and green .. 65 1·00
DESIGN: $1, I.Y.C. emblem.

55. Earth Satellite Station.

1979. Telisai Earth Satellite Station Multicoloured.
279. 10 c. Type 55 .. .. 10 10
280. 20 c. Satellite and antenna 15 20
281. 75 c. Television camera, telex machine and telephone .. .. .. 40 1·25

56. Hegira Symbol.

1979. Moslem Year 1400 A.H. Commemoration.
282. 56. 10 c. black, yell. & green 10 15
283. 20 c. black, yell. & blue 15 25
284. 75 c. black, yell. & lilac 45 1·25

57. Installation Ceremony. 58. Royal umbrella and sash

1980. 1st Anniv. of Prince Sufri Bolkiah's Installation as First Wazir. Multicoloured. Blue borders.
286. 10 c. Type 57 .. .. 15 10
287. 75 c. Wazir Sufri 50 65

1980. 1st Anniv. of Prince Jefri Bolkiah's Installation as Second Wazir. Designs similar to T 57 Multicoloured. Green borders.
288. 10 c. Installation ceremony 15 10
289. 75 c. Wazir Jefri 45 60

1981. Royal Regalia (1st series). Mult.
290. 10 c. Type 58 .. .. 15 15
291. 15 c. Sword and shield .. 20 20
292. 20 c. Lance and sheath .. 25 35
293. 30 c. Betel leaf container 35 55
294. 50 c. Coronation Crown (39 × 22 mm.) .. .. 60 1·75
See Nos. 298/303, 314/19 and 320/5.

59. I.T.U. and W.H.O. Emblems.

1981. World Telecommunciations and Health Day.
296. 59. 10 c. black and red .. 30 20
297. 75 c. black, blue & violet 1·25 2·10

60. Shield and Broadsword.

1981. Royal Regalia (2nd series). Mult.
298. 10 c. Type 60 .. 10 10
299. 15 c. Blunderbuss and Pouch 15 15
300. 20 c. Crossed lances and sash .. 20 20
301. 30 c. Sword, shield and sash .. 30 45
302. 50 c. Forked lance .. 50 1·00
303. 75 c. Royal Drum (29 × 45 mm.) .. 70 1·75

61. Prince Charles as Colonel of the Welsh Guards.

1981. Royal Wedding. Multicoloured.
304. 10 c. Wedding bouquet from Brunei 35 15
305. $1 Type 61 .. .. 1·10 1·25
306. $2 Prince Charles and Lady Diana Spencer .. 1·40 2·25

62. Fishing.

1981. World Food Day. Multicoloured.
307. 10 c. Type 62 .. .. 30 15
308. $1 Farm produce and machinery .. .. 2·10 2·50

63. Blind Man and Braille Alphabet.

1981. International Year for Disabled Persons. Multicoloured.
309. 10 c. Type 63 .. .. 35 15
310. 20 c. Deaf people and sign language 80 45
311. 75 c. Disabled person and wheelchairs .. .. 2·00 2·75

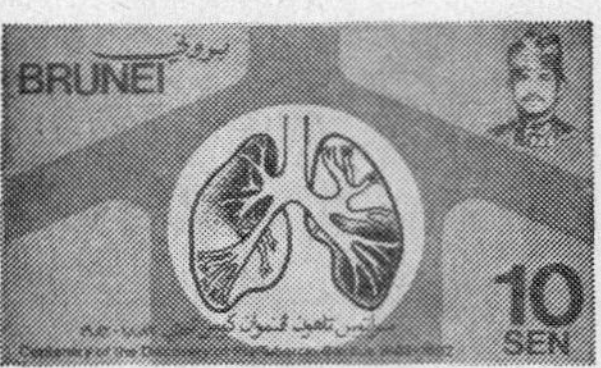

64. Drawing of Infected Lungs.

1982. Centenary of Robert Koch's Discovery of Tubercle Bacillus. Multicoloured.
312. 10 c. Type 64 .. .. 30 25
313. 75 c. Magnified tubercle bacillus and microscope 1·10 2·00

1982. Royal Regalia (3rd series). As T 60. Multicoloured.
314. 10 c. Ceremonial Ornament 10 10
315. 15 c. Silver Betel caddy .. 15 15
316. 20 c. Traditional Flower-pot 20 20
317. 30 c. Solitary Candle .. 30 45
318. 50 c. Golden Pipe .. .. 50 1·10
319. 75 c. Royal Chin Support (28 × 45mm.) .. .. 70 2·00

1982. Royal Regalia (4th series). As T 60. Multicoloured.
320. 10 c. Royal Mace 20 10
321. 15 c. Ceremonial Shield and Spears 30 15
322. 20 c. Embroidered Ornament 40 20
323. 30 c. Golden-tasseled Cushion 55 65
324. 50 c. Ceremonial Dagger and Sheath .. .. 90 1·75
325. 75 c. Religious Mace (28 × 45 mm.) .. .. .. 1·25 2·25

65. Brunei Flag.

1983. Commonwealth Day.
326. 65. 10 c. multicoloured .. 15 15
327. – 20 c. blue, black & buff 20 20
328. – 75 c. blue, black & green 45 55
329. – $2 blue, black & yellow 1·10 1·75
DESIGNS: 20 c. Brunei Mosque. 75 c. Machinery. $2 Sultan of Brunei.

66. "Postal Service".

1983. World Communications Year.
330. 66. 10 c. multicoloured .. 10 10
331. – 75 c. yellow, brn. & blk. 50 60
332. – $2 multicoloured .. 1·40 2·00
DESIGNS: 75 c. "Telephone Service"; $2 "Communications".

67. Football.

1983. Official Opening of the Negara Hassanal Bolkiah Stadium. Multicoloured.
333. 10 c. Type 67 .. .. 30 10
334. 75 c. Athletics .. .. 1·10 1·10
335. $1 View of stadium (44 × 27 mm.) .. .. 1·40 1·90

68. Fishermen and Crustacea.

1983. Fishery Resources. Multicoloured.
336. 10 c. Type 68 .. 15 15
337. 50 c. Fishermen with net .. 50 65
338. 75 c. Fishing Trawler .. 70 1·00
339. $1 Fishing with hook and tackle .. .. .. 90 1·40

69. Royal Assembly Hall.

1984. Independence.
340. 69. 10 c. brown & orange .. 10 10
341. – 20 c. pink and red .. 15 20
342. – 35 c. pink and purple .. 30 35
343. – 50 c. lt. blue and blue .. 40 50
344. – 75 c. lt. green & green .. 55 70
345. – $1 grey and brown .. 75 1·00
346. – $3 multicoloured .. 2·25 3·75
DESIGNS—(34 × 25 mm.). 20 c. Government Secretariat Building. 35 c. New Supreme Courts. 50 c. Natural gas well. 75 c. Omar Ali Saifuddin Mosque. $1 Sultan's Palace. (68 × 29 mm.). $3 Brunei flag and map of South-East Asia.

70. Natural Forests and Enrichment Planting.

1984. Forestry Resources. Multicoloured.
349. 10 c. Type 70 .. .. 35 20
350. 50 c. Forests and water resources .. .. 85 1·00
351. 75 c. Recreation forests .. 1·25 1·75
352. $1 Forests and wildlife .. 1·75 2·50

71. Sultan Omar Saifuddin 50 c. Stamp of 1952.

1984. "Philakorea" International Stamp Exhibition, Seoul. Multicoloured.
353. 10 c. Type 71 .. .. 10 10
354. 75 c. Brunei River view 10 c. stamp of 1907 .. 55 80
355. $2 Star and view ½ c. stamp of 1895 .. .. 1·50 2·25

72. United Nations Emblem.

1985. Admission of Brunei to World Organizations (1st issue).
357. 72. 50 c. black, gold & blue 40 50
358. – 50 c. multicoloured .. 40 50
359. – 50 c. multicoloured .. 40 50
360. – 50 c. multicoloured .. 40 50
DESIGNS: No. 358, Islamic Conference Organization logo. 359, Commonwealth logo. 360, A.S.E.A.N. emblem.
See also Nos. 383/6.

73. Young People and Brunei Flag.

1985. International Youth Year. Mult.

362. 10 c. Type **73** 20 15
363. 75 c. Young people at work 1·00 1·75
364. $1 Young people serving the community . . . . 1·25 2·25

74. Palestinian Emblem.

1985. International Palestinian Solidarity Day.

365. **74.** 10 c. multicoloured . . 20 15
366. 50 c. multicoloured . . 65 85
367. $1 multicoloured . . 1·10 1·75

75. Early and Modern Scout Uniforms.

1985. National Scout Jamboree. Mult.

368. 10 c. Type **75** 20 10
369. 20 c. Scout on tower signalling with flag . . 30 35
370. $2 Jamboree emblem . . 1·75 3·00

76. Sultan Sir Hassanal Bolkiah Mu'izzaddin Waddaulah.

1985.

371. **76.** 10 c. multicoloured . . 10 15
372. 15 c. multicoloured . . 10 15
373. 20 c. multicoloured . . 15 20
374. 25 c. multicoloured . . 15 20
375. 35 c. multicoloured . . 25 30
376. 40 c. multicoloured . . 25 30
377. 50 c. multicoloured . . 35 40
378. 75 c. multicoloured . . 50 55
379. $1 multicoloured . . 70 75
380. $2 multicoloured . . 1·40 1·50
381. $5 multicoloured . . 3·50 3·75
382. $10 multicoloured . . 6·75 7·00

Nos. 379/82 are larger, size 32 × 39 mm.

1986. Admission of Brunei to World Organizations (2nd issue). As T **72**.

383. 50 c. black, gold and green 40 60
384. 50 c. black, gold & mauve 40 60
385. 50 c. black, gold and red . . 40 60
386. 50 c. black, gold and blue 40 60

DESIGNS: No. 383, World Meteorological Organization emblem. 384, International Telecommunication Union emblem. 385, Universal Postal Union emblem. 386, International Civil Aviation Organization emblem.

78. Soldiers on Assault Course and Helicopter.

1986. 25th Anniv. of Brunei Armed Forces. Multicoloured.

388. 10 c. Type **78** 60 75
389. 20 c. Operating computer 70 85
390. 50 c. Anti-aircraft missile, helicopter and missile boat . . . . . . 90 1·25
391. 75 c. Army commanders and parade . . . . 1·00 1·40

Nos. 388/91 were printed together, se-tenant, forming a composite design.

79. Tunggul Charok Buritan, Alam Bernaga (Alam Besar), Pisang-Pisang and Sandaran.

1986. Royal Ensigns (1st series).

392. **79.** 10 c. blk., yell. & red 20 10
393. – 75 c. multicoloured . . 80 80
394. – $2 blk., yell. & grn. . . 1·75 2·25

DESIGNS: 75 c. Ula-Ula Besar, Sumbu Layang and Payong Haram. $2 Panji-Panji, Chogan Istiadat (Chogan Di-Raja) and Chogan Ugama.

1986. Royal Ensigns (2nd series). As T **79**.

395. 10 c. multicoloured . . 20 10
396. 75 c. black, red and yellow 80 80
397. $2 multicoloured . . . . 1·75 2·25

DESIGNS: 10 c. Dadap, Tunggul Kawan, Ambal, Payong Ubor-Ubor, Sapu-Sapu Ayeng and Rawai Lidah. 75 c. Payong Tinggi and Payong Ubor-Ubor Tiga Ringkat. $2 Lambang Duli Yang Maha Mulia and Mahligai.

80. Stylised Peace Doves.

1986. International Peace Year. Multicoloured.

398. 50 c. Type **80** 65 65
399. 75 c. Stylised hands and "1986" 80 80
400. $1 International Peace Year emblem and arms of Brunei . . . . 1·00 1·00

81. Drug Addict in Cage and Syringe (poster by Othman bin Ramboh).

1987. National Anti-drug Campaign. Children's Posters. Multicoloured.

401. 10 c. Type **81** 25 15
402. 75 c. Drug addict and noose (Arman bin Mohd. Zaman) . . . . 80 1·25
403. $1 Blindfolded drug addict and noose (Abidin bin Hj. Rashid) . . . . 1·00 1·75

82. Cannon ("badil").

1987. Brassware (1st series). Multicoloured.

404. 50 c. Type **82** 40 40
405. 50 c. Lamp ("pelita") . . 40 40
406. 50 c. Betel container ("langguai") 40 40
407. 50 c. Water jug ("kiri") . . 40 40

See also Nos. 434/7.

83. Map showing Member Countries.

1987. 20th Anniv. of Association of South East Asian Nations. Multicoloured.

408. 20 c. Type **83** 15 15
409. 50 c. Dates and figures "20" 30 35
410. $1 Flags of member states 60 65

84. Brunei Citizens.

1987. 25th Anniv. (1986) of Language and Literature Bureau. Multicoloured.

411. 10 c Type **84** 15 15
412. 50 c. Flame emblem and hands holding open book 30 35
413. $2 Scenes of village life . . 1·25 1·40

Nos. 411/13 were printed together, se-tenant, forming a composite design taken from a mural.

85. "Artocarpus odoratissima".

1987. Local Fruits (1st series). Multicoloured.

414. 50 c. Type **85** 30 35
415. 50 c. "Canarium odontophyllum mig" 30 35
416. 50 c. "Litsea garciae" . . 30 35
417. 50 c. "Mangifera foetida lour" 30 35

See also Nos 421/4, 459/62 and 480/2.

86. Modern House.

1987. International Year of Shelter for the Homeless.

418. **86.** 50 c. multicoloured . . 30 35
419. – 75 c. multicoloured . . 45 50
420. – $1 multicoloured . . 60 65

DESIGNS: 75 c., $1 Modern Brunei housing projects.

1988. Local Fruits (2nd series). As T **85**. Multicoloured.

421. 50 c. "Durio spp." . . 30 35
422. 50 c. "Durio oxleyanus" . . 30 35
423. 50 c. "Durio graveolens" (blue background) . . 30 35
424. 50 c. "Durio graveolens" (white background) . . 30 35

87. Wooden Lathe.

1988. Opening of Malay Technology Museum. Multicoloured.

425. 10 c. Type **87** 10 10
426. 75 c. Crushing sugar cane 45 50
427. $1 Bird scarer 60 65

88 Patterned Cloth.

1988. Handwoven Material (1st series). Mult.

428 10 c. Type **88** 10 10
429 20 c. Jong Sarat cloth . . 10 10
430 25 c. Si Pugut cloth . . 15 20
431 40 c. Si Pugut Bunga Berlapis cloth 25 30
432 75 c. Si Lobang Bangsi Bungs Belitang Kipas cloth 45 50

See also Nos 442/6.

1988. Brassware (2nd series). As T **82**. Mult.

434 50 c. Lidded two-handled pot ("periok") . . 30 35
435 50 c. Candlestick ("lampong") 30 35
436 50 c. Shallow circular dish with stand ("gangsa") . . 30 35
437 50 c. Repousse box with lid ("celapa") 30 35

89 Sultan reading Proclamation

1988. 20th Anniv of Sultan's Coronation. Multicoloured.

438 20 c. Type **89** 10 10
439 75 c. Sultan reading from Koran 45 50
440 $2 In Coronation robes (26 × 63 mm) . . . . 1·25 1·40

1988. Handwoven Material (2nd series). As T **88**. Multicoloured.

442 10 c. Beragi cloth . . 10 10
443 20 c. Bertabur cloth . . 10 10
444 25 c. Sukma Indra cloth . . 15 20
445 40 c. Si Pugut Bunga cloth 25 30
446 75 c. Beragi Si Lobang Bangsi Bunga Cendera Kesuma cloth 45 50

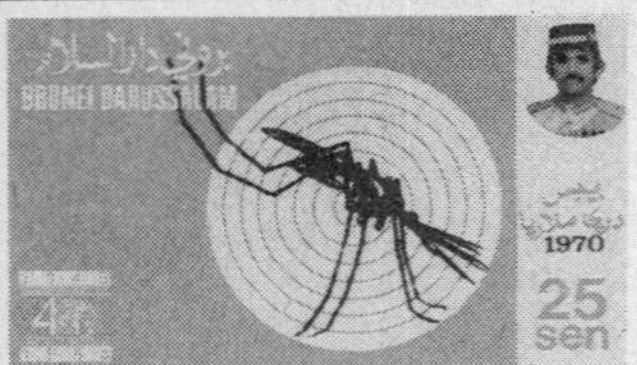

90 Malaria-carrying Mosquito

1988. 40th Anniv of W.H.O. Multicoloured.

448	25 c. Type **90**	20	20
449	35 c. Man with insecticide spray and sample on slide	25	25
450	$2 Microscope and magnified malaria cells	1·40	1·40

91 Sultan and Council of Ministers

1989. 5th Anniv of National Day. Mult.

451	20 c. Type **91**	15	15
452	30 c. Guard of honour ..	25	25
453	60 c. Firework display (27 × 55 mm)	40	40
454	$2 Congregation in mosque	1·40	1·40

92 Dove escaping from Cage

1989. "Freedom of Palestine". Multicoloured.

456	20 c. Type **92**	10	15
457	75 c. Map and Palestinian flag	50	55
458	$1 Dome of the Rock, Jerusalem	65	70

1989. Local Fruits (3rd series). As T **85**. Multicoloured.

459	60 c. "Daemonorops fissa"	55	75
460	60 c. "Eleiodoxa conferta"	55	75
461	60 c. "Salacca zalacca" ..	55	75
462	60 c. "Calamus ornatus" ..	55	75

93 Oil Pump

1989. 60th Anniv of Brunei Oil and Gas Industry. Multicoloured.

463	20 c. Type **93**	15	15
464	60 c. Loading tanker ..	50	50
465	90 c. Oil well at sunset ..	70	80
466	$1 Pipe laying	75	90
467	$2 Oil terminal	1·40	1·75

94 Museum Building and Exhibits

1990. 25th Anniv of Brunei Museum. Mult.

468	30 c. Type **94**	25	30
469	60 c. Official opening, 1965	55	70
470	$1 Brunei Museum ..	85	1·10

95 Letters from Malay Alphabet

1990. International Literacy Year. Mult.

471	15 c. Type **95**	15	10
472	90 c. English alphabet ..	85	90
473	$1 Literacy Year emblem and letters	95	1·00

96 Tarsier in Tree

1990. Endangered Species. Western Tarsier. Multicoloured.

474	20 c. Western Tarsier on branch	20	20
475	60 c. Western Tarsier feeding	55	60
476	90 c. Type **96**	90	1·00

97 Symbolic Family

1990. Worldwide Campaign against AIDS. Multicoloured.

477	20 c. Type **97**	20	20
478	30 c. Sources of infection	40	45
479	90 c. "AIDS" headstone surrounded by skulls ..	90	95

1990. Local Fruits (4th series). As T **85**. Multicoloured.

480	60 c. "Willoughbea" sp. (brown fruit)	55	65
481	60 c. Ripe "Willoughbea" sp. (yellow fruit) ..	55	65
482	60 c. "Willoughbea angustifolia"	55	65

98 Proboscis Monkey on Ground

1991. Endangered Species. Proboscis Monkey. Multicoloured.

483	15 c. Type **98**	15	15
484	20 c. Head of monkey ..	20	20
485	50 c. Monkey sitting on branch	50	55
486	60 c. Female monkey with baby climbing tree ..	60	70

99 Junior School Classes

1991. Teachers' Day. Multicoloured.

487	60 c. Type **99**	55	60
488	90 c. Secondary school class	85	90

100 Young Brunei Beauty

1991. Fishes. Brunei Beauty. Multicoloured.

489	30 c. Type **100**	30	30
490	60 c. Female fish	55	60
491	$1 Male fish	95	1·00

101 Graduate with Family

1991. Happy Family Campaign. Mult.

492	20 c. Type **101**	15	20
493	60 c. Mothers with children	40	45
494	90 c. Family	60	65

102 Symbolic Heart and Trace

1992. World Health Day.

495	**102**	20 c. multicoloured ..	15	20
496	–	50 c. multicoloured ..	35	40
497	–	75 c. multicoloured ..	50	55

DESIGNS: 50 c., 70 c. (48 × 27 mm) Heart and heartbeat trace.

103 Map of Cable System

1992. Launching of Singapore–Borneo–Philippines Fibre Optic Submarine Cable System. Multicoloured.

498	20 c. Type **103**	15	20
499	30 c. Diagram of Brunei connection	25	30
500	90 c. Submarine cable ..	60	65

JAPANESE OCCUPATION OF BRUNEI

These stamps were valid throughout British Borneo (i.e Brunei, Labuan, North Borneo and Sarawak.

100 cents = 1 dollar.

府政國帝本日大

(**1**) ("Imperial Japanese Government")

1942. Stamps of Brunei optd with T **1**.

J 1	**5**	1 c. black	5·00	15·00
J 2		2 c. green	28·00	85·00
J 3		2 c. orange	2·50	6·00
J 4		3 c. green	23·00	65·00
J 5		4 c. orange	3·00	10·00
J 6		5 c. brown	3·00	10·00
J 7	**7**	6 c. grey	50·00	£120
J 8		6 c. red	£550	£550
J 9	**5**	8 c. black	£600	£850
J10	**7**	8 c. red	3·00	10·00
J11	**5**	10 c. purple on yellow ..	7·00	18·00
J12	**7**	12 c. blue	8·00	18·00
J13		15 c. blue	8·00	18·00
J14	**5**	25 c. lilac	17·00	32·00
J15		30 c. purple and orange	90·00	£180
J16		50 c. black on green ..	32·00	42·00
J17		$1 black and red on blue	48·00	60·00
J18		$5 red on green ..	£800	
J19		$25 black on red ..	£850	

1944. Stamps of Brunei surch with Japanese characters reading "Imperial Japanese Post $3".

J20	**5**	$3 on 1 c. black	£3000	£2250

BUNDI

A state of Rajasthan, India. Now uses Indian stamps.

12 pies = 1 anna; 16 annas = 1 rupee.

8. Native Dagger. 11. Raja protecting Sacred Cows.

1894. Imperf.

12.	8.	½ a. grey	1·25	1·50
13.		1 a. red	1·40	1·50
14.		2 a. green	6·50	7·50
8.		4 a. green	25·00	32·00
15.		8 a. red	4·50	7·50
16.		1 r. yellow on blue	8·50	16·00

1898. As T **8**, but dagger point to left.

17a.	8.	4 a. green	7·00	10·00

1914. Roul. or perf.

26a	11	¼ a. blue	1·60	4·00
38		½ a. black	1·25	2·75
28a		1 a. red	3·75	5·50
20a		2 a. green	1·60	7·00
21		2½ a. yellow	4·50	15·00
31		3 a. brown	4·50	14·00
32		4 a. green	3·50	18·00
33		6 a. blue	8·00	30·00
42		8 a. orange	9·00	32·00
43		10 a. olive	16·00	35·00
44		12 a. green	6·00	35·00
25		1 r. lilac	15·00	48·00
46		2 r. brown and black	40·00	85·00
47		3 r. blue and brown	70·00	£140
48		4 r. green and red	£150	£250
49		5 r. red and green	£160	£275

20. 21. Maharao Rajah Bahadur Singh.

1941. Perf.

79.	20.	3 p. blue	75	2·50
80.		6 p. blue	90	2·75
81.		1 a. red	1·00	3·00
82.		2 a. brown	4·00	8·00
83.		4 a. green	6·00	24·00
84.		8 a. green	10·00	70·00
85.		1 r. blue	19·00	85·00

1947.

86.	21.	¼ a. green	55	13·00
87.		½ a. violet	45	13·00
88.		1 a. green	45	13·00
89.	–	2 a. red	1·00	25·00
90.	–	4 a. orange	1·25	35·00
91.	–	8 a. blue	2·25	
92.	–	1 r. brown	10·00	

DESIGNS: 2 a., 4 a. Rajah in Indian dress. 8 a., 1 r. View of Bundi.

OFFICIAL STAMPS

बूंदी

सरविस

(01)

A. Type O 1

B/C Optd. **BUNDI SERVICE.**

1918. Optd.

			A.	B/C
O 6	11.	¼ a. blue	1·10	1·60
O 16		½ a. black	3·50	2·50
O 8b		1 a. red	7·00	7·00
O 18		2 a. green	4·50	8·00
O 2		2½ a. yellow	2·00	5·50
O 3		3 a. brown	2·50	14·00
O 19		4 a. green	8·00	26·00
O 11		6 a. blue	11·00	60·00
O 20		8 a. orange	14·00	24·00
O 21		10 a. olive	30·00	48·00
O 22		12 a. green	32·00	50·00
O 5		1 r. lilac	32·00	32·00
O 24		2 r. brown and black	£225	£180
O 25		3 r. blue and brown	£250	£200
O 26		4 r. green and red	£275	£300
O 27		5 r. red and green	£275	£300

Prices for Nos. O 1/27 are for unused examples. Used examples are generally worth a small premium over the prices quoted.

1941. Optd. **SERVICE.**

O 53.	20.	3 p. blue	2·25	4·50
O 54.		6 p. blue	5·00	6·00
O 55.		1 a. red	5·00	6·50
O 56.		2 a. brown	7·00	8·50
O 57.		4 a. green	24·00	65·00
O 58.		8 a. green	65·00	£140
O 59.		1 r. blue	90·00	£160

For later issues see **RAJASTHAN**.

BURMA

A territory in the east of India. Formerly part of the Indian Empire, but separated from it on 1 April 1937. Japanese forces were in occupation from 1942 to 1945 and Independence was established in 1948.

1937. 12 pies = 1 anna. 16 annas = 1 rupee.
1953. 100 pyas = 1 kyat (rupee).

1937. Stamps of India (King George V) optd. **BURMA.**

1.	55.	3 p. grey	30	10
2.	79.	½ a. green	30	10
3.	80.	9 p. green	30	10
4.	81.	1 a. brown	30	10
5.	59.	2 a. red	30	10
6.	61.	2½ a. orange	30	10
7.	62.	3 a. red	65	30
8.	83.	3½ a. blue	65	10
9.	63.	4 a. olive	70	10
10.	64.	6 a. bistre	60	35
11.	65.	8 a. mauve	1·50	10
12.	66.	12 a. red	2·00	85
13.	67.	1 r. brown and green	7·00	65
14.		2 r. red and orange	11·00	6·00
15.		5 r. blue and violet	24·00	9·00
16.		10 r. green and red	48·00	27·00
17.		15 r. blue and olive	£130	80·00
18.		25 r. orange and blue	£250	£150

2. King George VI and "Chinthes". 3. King George VI and "Nagas".

4. Royal Barge.

8. King George VI and Peacock.

1938. King George VI.

18a.	2.	1 p. orange	1·00	60
19.		3 p. violet	10	20
20.		6 p. blue	10	10
21.		9 p. green	1·00	80
22.	3.	1 a. brown	10	10
23.		1½ a. green	20	55
24.		2 a. red	45	10
25.	4.	2 a. 6 p. red	75	45
26.	–	3 a. mauve	2·25	60
27.	–	3 a. 6 p. blue	1·25	3·25
28.	3.	4 a. blue	35	10
29.	–	8 a. green	1·75	30
30.	8.	1 r. purple and blue	5·00	20
31.		2 r. brown and purple	6·00	85
32.	–	5 r. violet and red	38·00	11·00
33.	–	10 r. brown and green	48·00	35·00

DESIGNS—HORIZ. As Type **4**: 3 a. Burma teak. 3 a. 6 p. Burma Rice. 8 a. Irrawaddy. VERT. As Type **3**: 5 r., 10 r. King George VI and "Nats".

1940. Cent. of First Adhesive Postage Stamp. Surch. **COMMEMORATION POSTAGE STAMP 6TH MAY, 1840,** and value in figures and letters.

34.	4.	1 a. on 2 a. 6 p. red	1·50	35

For Japanese issues see "Japanese Occupation of Burma".

1945. British Military Administration. Stamps of 1938 optd. **MILY ADMN.**

35.	2.	1 p. orange	10	10
36.		3 p. violet	10	30
37.		6 p. blue	10	30
38.		9 p. green	10	30
39.	3.	1 a. brown	10	10
40.		1½ a. green	10	15
41.		2 a. red	10	15
42.	4.	2 a. 6 p. red	20	60
43.	–	3 a. mauve	60	20
44.	–	3 a. 6 p. blue	10	70
45.	3.	4 a. blue	10	25
46.	–	8 a. green	10	40
47.	8.	1 r. purple and blue	15	50
48.		2 r. brown and purple	20	80
49.	–	5 r. violet and red	20	80
50.	–	10 r. brown and green	50	80

1946. British Civil Administration. As 1938, but colours changed.

51.	2.	3 p. brown	10	65
52.		6 p. violet	10	10
53.		9 p. green	10	60
54.	3.	1 a. blue	10	10
55.		1½ a. orange	10	10
56.		2 a. red	10	30
57.	4.	2 a. 6 p. blue	10	80
57a.	–	3 a. blue	1·75	85
57b.	–	3 a. 6 p. black and blue	10	60
58.	3.	4 a. purple	10	30
59.	–	8 a. mauve	1·50	65
60.	8.	1 r. violet and mauve	50	15
61.		2 r. brown and orange	2·50	1·25
62.	–	5 r. green and brown	2·50	4·25
63.	–	10 r. red and violet	2·50	7·00

14. Burman.

1946. Victory.

64.	14.	9 p. green	10	10
65.	–	1½ a. vio. (Burmese woman)	10	10
66.	–	2 a. red (Chinthe)	15	10
67.	–	3 a. 6 p. blue (Elephant)	15	10

ကြားဖြတ်
အစိုးရ။

(18. Trans. "Interim Government").

1947. Stamps of 1946 optd. with T **18** or with larger opt. on large stamps.

68.	2.	3 p. brown	50	20
69.		6 p. violet	10	25
70.		9 p. green	10	25
71.	3.	1 a. blue	10	25
72.		1½ a. orange	55	10
73.		2 a. red	20	15
74.	4.	2 a. 6 p. blue	70	40
75.	–	3 a. blue	55	50
76.	–	3 a. 6 p. black and blue	10	40
77.	3.	4 a. purple	50	30
78.	–	8 a. mauve	90	50
79.	8.	1 r. violet and mauve	1·00	30
80.		2 r. brown and orange	1·00	1·25
81.	–	5 r. green and brown	1·50	2·50
82.	–	10 r. red and violet	1·60	2·50

OFFICIAL STAMPS

1937. Stamps of India (King George V) optd. **BURMA SERVICE.**

O 1.	55.	3 p. grey	10	10
O 2.	79.	½ a. green	35	10
O 3.	80.	9 p. green	30	30
O 4.	81.	1 a. brown	30	10
O 5.	59.	2 a. red	30	35
O 6.	61.	2½ a. orange	85	65
O 7.	63.	4 a. olive	60	10
O 8.	64.	6 a. bistre	1·25	3·00
O 9.	65.	8 a. mauve	70	30
O 10.	66.	12 a. red	1·00	2·00
O 11.	67.	1 r. brown and green	6·00	1·50
O 12.		2 r. red and orange	15·00	13·00
O 13.		5 r. blue and violet	48·00	28·00
O 14.		10 r. green and red	£110	70·00

1939. Stamps of 1938 optd. **SERVICE.**

O 15.	2.	3 p. violet	10	20
O 16.		6 p. blue	10	20
O 17.		9 p. green	4·50	40
O 18.	3.	1 a. brown	10	15
O 19.		1½ a. green	4·50	40
O 20.		2 a. red	70	20
O 21.	4.	2 a. 6 p. red	8·50	3·25
O 22.	3.	4 a. blue	5·50	45
O 23.	–	8 a. green (No. 29)	16·00	3·00
O 24.	8.	1 r. purple and blue	16·00	3·00
O 25.		2 r. brown and purple	21·00	4·00
O 26.	–	5 r. violet & red (No. 32)	48·00	23·00
O 27.	–	10 r. brn. & grn. (No. 33)	85·00	29·00

1946. Stamps of 1946 optd. **SERVICE.**

O 28.	2.	3 p. brown	30	70
O 29.		6 p. violet	35	65
O 30.		9 p. green	10	1·25
O 31.	3.	1 a. blue	10	90
O 32.		1½ a. orange	10	15
O 33.		2 a. red	10	80
O 34.	4.	2 a. 6 p. blue	35	1·50
O 35.	3.	4 a. purple	10	60
O 36.	–	8 a. mauve (No. 59)	15	90
O 37.	8.	1 r. violet and mauve	50	1·75
O 38.		2 r. brown and orange	3·50	8·00
O 39.	–	5 r. green & brn. (No. 62)	7·00	16·00
O 40.	–	10 r. red and violet (No. 63)	9·50	25·00

1947. Interim Govt. Nos. O 28, etc., optd. with T **18** or with large opt. on larger stamps.

O 41.	2.	3 p. brown	10	40
O 42.		6 p. violet	20	10
O 43.		9 p. green	20	70
O 44.	3.	1 a. blue	1·25	55
O 45.		1½ a. orange	1·75	20
O 46.		2 a. red	1·25	15
O 47.	4.	2 a. 6 p. blue	3·25	1·75
O 48.	3.	4 a. purple	1·50	35
O 49.	–	8 a. mauve	2·25	1·25
O 50.	8.	1 r. violet and mauve	5·00	1·25
O 51.		2 r. brown and orange	11·00	10·00
O 52.	–	5 r. green and brown	11·00	14·00
O 53.	–	10 r. red and violet	13·00	23·00

For issues after Independence see Volume 1.

JAPANESE OCCUPATION OF BURMA

1942. 12 pies = 1 anna; 16 annas = 1 rupee.
1942. 100 cents = 1 rupee.

(1.) (3.)

Note.—There are various types of the Peacock overprint. Our prices, as usual in this Catalogue, are for the cheapest type.

1942. Postage stamps of Burma of 1937 (India types) optd. as T **1.**

J 22.	55.	3 p. grey	2·75	11·00
J 23.	80.	9 p. green	17·00	40·00
J 24.	59.	2 a. red	60·00	£110
J 2.	83.	3½ a. blue	32·00	

1942. Official stamp of Burma of 1937 (India type) optd. as T **1.**

J 3.	64.	6 a. bistre	55·00	

1942. Postage stamps of Burma, 1938, optd. as T **1** or with T **3** (rupee values).

J 25	1.	1 p. orange	90·00	£130
J 12		3 p. violet	10·00	32·00
J 27		6 p. blue	18·00	38·00
J 14		9 p. green	10·50	28·00
J 29	3.	1 a. brown	7·50	18·00
J 30		1½ a. green	13·00	30·00
J 16		2 a. red	9·50	26·00
J 17		4 a. blue	22·00	38·00
J 18	8.	1 r. purple and blue	£190	
J 19		2 r. brown and purple	£120	

1942. Official stamps of Burma of 1939 optd. with T **1.**

J 7.	1.	3 p. violet	12·00	35·00
J 8.		6 p. blue	9·00	25·00
J 9.	3.	1 a. brown	8·50	18·00
J 35.		1½ a. green	75·00	£110
J 10.		2 a. red	13·00	35·00
J 11.		4 a. blue	12·00	30·00

(6a.) ("Yon Thon" = "Official use".)

1942. Official stamp of Burma of 1939 optd. with T **6a.**

J 44.	–	8a. green (No. O 23)	60·00	

7.

1942. Yano Seal.

J 45.	7.	(1a.) red	35·00	50·00

8. Farmer.

1942.

J 46.	8.	1 a. red	14·00	14·00

1942. Stamps of Japan surch. in figures.

J 47.	–	¼ a. on 1 s. brn. (No. 317)	15·00	20·00
J 48.	84.	½ a. on 2 s. red ..	15·00	20·00
J 49.	–	¾ a. on 3 s. grn. (No. 319)	32·00	35·00
J 50.	–	1 a. on 5 s. red No. 396)	24·00	28·00
J 51.	–	3 a. on 7 s. grn. (No. 323)	42·00	48·00
J 52.	–	4 a. on 4 s. grn. (No. 320)	28·00	32·00
J 53.	–	8 a. on 8 s. vio. (No. 324)	£130	£140
J 54.	–	1 r. on 10 s. red (No. 325)	15·00	20·00
J 55.	–	2 r. on 20 s. blue (No. 328)	38·00	38·00
J 56.	–	5 r. on 30 s. bl. (No. 330)	12·00	17·00

1942. No. 386 of Japan commemorating the fall of Singapore, surch. in figures.

J 56g.	–	4 a. on 4 s. + 2 s. green and red	£110	£120

(New currency. 100 cents = 1 rupee.)

1942. Handstamped with new value.

J 57.	5.	5 c. on 1 a. red (No. J 46)	8·50	12·00

1942. Nos. J 47/53 with anna surcharges obliterated, and handstamped with new value in figures.

J 58.	–	1 c. on ¼ a. on 1 s. brown	29·00	29·00
J 59.	84.	2 c. on ½ a. on 2 s. red ..	29·00	29·00
J 60.	–	3 c. on ¾ a. on 3 s. green	32·00	32·00
J 61.	–	5 c. on 1 a. on 5 s. red	42·00	48·00
J 62.	–	10 c. on 3 a. on 7 s. green	60·00	65·00
J 63.	–	15 c. on 4 a. on 4 s. green	24·00	26·00
J 64.	–	20 c. on 8 a. on 8 s. violet	£150	£140

1942. Stamps of Japan surch. in cents only in figures.

J 65.	–	1 c. on 1 s. brn. (No. 317)	12·00	15·00
J 66.	84.	2 c. on 2 s. red ..	26·00	26·00
J 67.	–	3 c. on 3 s. grn. (No. 319)	24·00	26·00
J 68.	–	5 c. on 5 s. red (No. 396)	30·00	30·00
J 69.	–	10 c. on 7 s. grn. (No. 323)	28·00	32·00
J 70.	–	15 c. on 4 s. grn. (No. 320)	12·00	15·00
J 71.	–	20 c. on 8 s. vio. (No. 324)	80·00	70·00

14. Burma State Crest.

1943. Perf. or Imperf.

J 72.	14.	5 c. red	10·00	12·00

15. Farmer.

1943.

J 73.	15.	1 c. orange	70	1·25
J 74.		2 c. green	60	90
J 75.		3 c. blue	60	75
J 77.		5 c. red	70	1·25
J 78.		10 c. brown	1·25	1·50
J 79.		15 c. mauve	30	70
J 80.		20 c. lilac	30	65
J 81.		30 c. green	30	70

16. Soldier carving word "Independence".

17. Rejoicing Peasant.

18. Boy with National Flag.

1943. Independence Day. Perf. or roul.

J 82a.	16.	1 c. orange	90	1·50
J 83a.	17.	3 c. blue	90	1·50
J 84a.	18.	5 c. red	90	1·50

19. Burmese Woman.

20. Elephant carrying Log.

21. Watch Tower, Mandalay.

1943.

J 85.	19.	1 c. orange	5·50	8·00
J 86.		2 c. green	30	1·00
J 87.		3 c. violet	50	1·50
J 88.	20.	5 c. red	45	50
J 89.		10 c. blue	55	75
J 90.		15 c. orange	45	80
J 91.		20 c. green	35	1·25
J 92.		30 c. brown	35	1·25
J 93.	21.	1 r. orange	30	1·00
J 94.		2 r. violet	30	2·00

22. Bullock Cart.

23. Shan Woman.

ဗမာနိုင်ငံတော်

၂၀ ဆင့်။

(24. "Burma State" and value).

1943. Shan States issue.

J 95.	22.	1 c. brown	11·00	16·00
J 96.		2 c. green	11·00	16·00
J 97.		3 c. violet	2·75	4·25
J 98.		5 c. blue	2·00	4·25
J 99.	23.	10 c. blue	8·00	13·00
J 100.		20 c. red	14·00	12·00
J 101.		30 c. brown	10·00	16·00

1944. Optd. with T **24.**

J 102.	22.	1 c. brown	1·25	2·75
J 103.		2 c. green	30	75
J 104.		3 c. violet	1·00	2·75
J 105.		5 c. blue	65	75
J 106.	23.	10 c. blue	1·60	1·60
J 107.		20 c. red	30	1·25
J 108.		30 c. brown	30	1·25

BUSHIRE

An Iranian seaport. Stamps issued during the Br. occupation in the 1914–18 War.

20 chahis = 1 kran, 10 krans = 1 toman.

1915. Portrait stamps of Iran (1911) optd. **BUSHIRE Under British Occupation.**

1.	57.	1 ch. orange and green ..	20·00	25·00
2.		2 ch. brown and red ..	22·00	21·00
3.		3 ch. green and grey ..	23·00	30·00
4.		5 ch. red and brown ..	£225	£225
5.		6 ch. lake and green ..	19·00	18·00
6.		9 ch. lilac and brown ..	22·00	25·00
7.		10 ch. brown and red ..	24·00	24·00
8.		12 ch. blue and green ..	30·00	35·00
9.		24 ch. green & purple ..	45·00	35·00
10.		1 kr. red and blue ..	45·00	25·00
11.		2 kr. red and green ..	£130	£110
12.		3 kr. black and lilac ..	£140	£150
13.		5 kr. blue and red ..	70·00	65·00
14.		10 kr. red and brown ..	60·00	60·00

1915. Coronation issue of Iran optd. **BUSHIRE Under British Occupation.**

15.	66.	1 ch. blue and red ..	£300	£300
16.		2 ch. red and blue ..	£5000	£5500
17.		3 ch. green	£375	£400
18.		5 ch. red	£3750	£4000
19.		6 ch. red and green ..	£3000	£3250
20.		9 ch. violet and brown ..	£475	£500
21.		10 ch. brown and green	£800	£850
22.		12 ch. blue	£900	£1000
23.		24 ch. black and brown ..	£375	£400
24.	67.	1 kr. black, brn. & silver	£350	£375
25.		2 kr. red, blue and silver	£300	£325
26.		3 kr. black, lilac & silver	£425	£450
27.		5 kr. slate, brown & silver	£400	£425
28.	–	1 t. black, violet and gold	£350	£400
29.	–	3 t. red, lake and gold ..	£2250	£2250

BUSSAHIR (BASHAHR)

A state in the Punjab, India. Now uses Indian stamps.

12 pies = 1 anna; 16 annas = 1 rupee.

1.

1895. Various frames. Imperf., perf. or roul.

9	1.	¼ a. pink	22·00	65·00
10		½ a. grey	14·00	65·00
11		1 a. red	14·00	65·00
12		2 a. yellow	20·00	65·00
13		4 a. violet	15·00	70·00
14		8 a. brown	15·00	70·00
15		12 a. green	40·00	75·00
16		1 r. blue	24·00	70·00

1896. Similar types, but inscriptions on white ground and inscr. "POSTAGE" instead of "STAMP".

27.	1.	¼ a. violet	5·00	8·00
31.		¼ a. red	1·25	3·00
25.		½ a. blue	2·50	10·00
26.		1 a. olive	9·00	16·00
38.		1 a. red	1·25	5·00
41.		2 a. yellow	18·00	32·00
36.		4 a. red	21·00	48·00

CAICOS ISLANDS

Separate issues for these Islands, part of the Turks and Caicos Islands group, first appeared in 1981.

100 cents = 1 dollar.

1981. Nos. 514, 518, 520, 523 and 525/7 of Turks and Caicos Islands optd. **CAICOS ISLANDS.**

1.	1 c. Indigo Hamlet	10	10
2.	5 c. Spanish Grunt	10	10
3.	8 c. Foureye Butterflyfish ..	10	10
4.	20 c. Queen Angelfish ..	25	30
5.	50 c. Fairy Basslet	65	70
6.	$1 Clown Wrasse	1·00	1·25
7.	$2 Stoplight Parrotfish ..	2·50	2·75

1981. Royal Wedding. Nos. 653/5 of Turks and Caicos Islands optd. A. **Caicos Islands.** B. **CAICOS ISLANDS.**

		A		B	
8.	35 c. Prince Charles and Lady Diana Spencer	25	25	1·25	1·25
9.	65 c. Kensington Palace	40	40	2·00	2·00
10.	90 c. Prince Charles as Colonel of Welsh Guards	50	50	2·25	2·25

1981. Royal Wedding. Booklet stamps. As Nos. 657/9 of Turks and Caicos Islands, but each inscr. "Caicos Islands". Mult. Self-adhesive.

12.	20 c. Lady Diana Spencer ..	80	60
13.	$1 Prince Charles	3·75	2·75
14.	$2 Prince Charles and Lady Diana Spencer	10·00	6·00

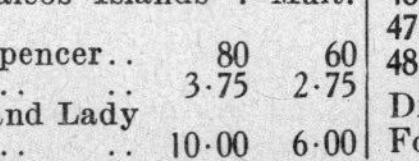

4. Conch and Lobster Fishing, South Caicos.

1983. Multicoloured.

15.	8 c. Type **4**	15	15
16.	10 c. Hawksbill Turtle, East Caicos	20	20
17.	20 c. Arawak Indians and idol, Middle Caicos ..	30	40
18.	35 c. Boat-building, North Caicos	55	60
19.	50 c. Marine biologist at work, Pine Cay	75	75
20.	95 c. Boeing "707" airliner at new airport, Providenciales	1·50	1·60
21.	$1.10 Columbus's "Pinta", West Caicos	2·00	1·75
22.	$2 Fort George Cay	3·50	3·00
23.	$3 Pirates Anne Bonny and Calico Jack at Parrot Cay	6·00	4·75

5. Goofy and Patch.

1983. Christmas. Multicoloured.

30.	1 c. Type **5**	10	10
31.	1 c. Chip and Dale	10	10
32.	2 c. Morty	10	10
33.	2 c. Morty and Ferdie ..	10	10
34.	3 c. Goofy and Louie ..	10	10
35.	3 c. Donald Duck, Huey, Dewey and Louie	10	10
36.	50 c. Uncle Scrooge	1·50	90
37.	70 c. Mickey Mouse and Ferdie	2·00	1·25
38.	$1.10 Pinocchio, Jiminy Cricket and Figaro ..	2·50	1·90

6. "Leda and the Swan".

1984. 500th Birth. Anniv. of Raphael. Multi.

40.	35 c. Type **6**	70	50
41.	50 c. "Study of Apollo for Parnassus"	90	70
42.	95 c. "Study of two figures for the battle of Ostia" ..	1·75	1·25
43.	$1.10 "Study for the Madonna of the Goldfinch"	2·00	1·50

7. High Jump.

1984. Olympic Games, Los Angeles.

45.	7.	4 c. multicoloured ..	10	10
46.	–	25 c. multicoloured ..	20	20
47.	–	65 c. blk., deep bl. & bl.	50	50
48.	–	$1.10 multicoloured ..	85	85

DESIGNS: 25 c. Archery. 65 c. Cycling. $1.10 Football.

8. Horace Horsecollar and Clarabelle Cow.

1984. Easter. Walt Disney Cartoon Characters. Multicoloured.

50. 35 c. Type **8** 60 60
51. 45 c. Mickey and Minnie Mouse, and Chip 75 75
52. 75 c. Gyro Gearloose, Chip 'n Dale .. .. .. 1·25 1·25
53. 85 c. Mickey Mouse, Chip 'n Dale .. .. .. 1·40 1·40

1984. Universal Postal Union Congress Hamburg. Nos. 20/1 optd. **UNIVERSAL POSTAL UNION 1874–1984** and emblem.

55. 95 c. Boeing "707" airliner at new airport, Providenciales .. .. .. 1·00 1·25
56. $1.10 Columbus's "Pinta", West Caicos .. .. 1·25 1·50

1984. "Ausipex" International Stamp Exhibition, Melbourne. No. 22 optd. **AUSIPEX 1984.**

57. $2 Fort George Cay .. 2·40 2·50

11. Seamen sighting American Manatees.

1984. 492nd Anniv. of Columbus's First Landfall. Multicoloured.

58. 10 c. Type **11** 30 15
59. 70 c. Columbus's fleet .. 1·75 1·10
60. $1 First landing in West Indies .. .. .. 2·25 1·60

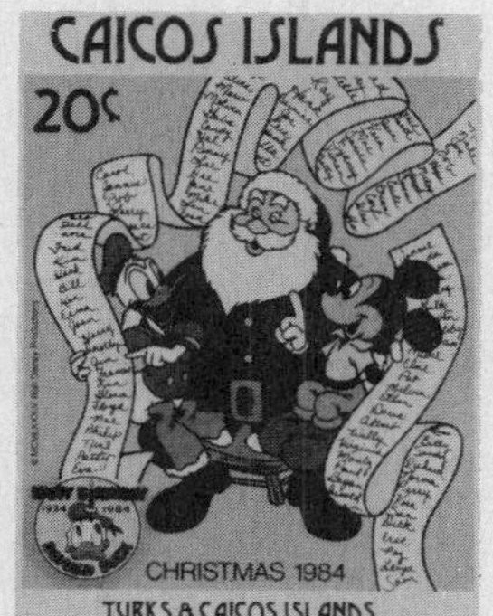

12. Donald Duck and Mickey Mouse with Father Christmas.

1984. Christmas. Walt Disney Cartoon Characters. Multicoloured.

62. 20 c. Type **12** 70 40
63. 35 c. Donald Duck opening refrigerator .. .. 1·00 65
64. 50 c. Mickey Mouse, Donald Duck and toy train .. 1·25 90
65. 75 c. Donald Duck and parcels .. .. .. 1·75 1·25
66. $1.10 Donald Duck and carol singers .. .. 2·25 1·75

13. Thick-billed Vireo.

1985. Birth Bicentenary of John J. Audubon (ornithologist). Multicoloured.

68. 20 c. Type **13** .. .. 1·00 40
69. 35 c. Black-faced Grassquit 1·40 65
70. 50 c. Pearly-eyed Thrasher 1·75 90
71. $1 Greater Antillean Bullfinch .. .. 2·25 1·75

14. Two Children learning to Read and Write (Education)

1985. International Youth Year. 40th Anniv. of United Nations. Multicolour.

73. 16 c. Type **14** 20 25
74. 35 c. Two children on playground swings (Health) .. 50 55
75. 70 c. Boy and girl (Love) .. 1·00 1·10
76. 90 c. Three children (Peace) 1·25 1·40

15. Air Caicos "DC-3" on Ground

1985. 40th Anniv. of International Civil Aviation Organization. Multicoloured.

78. 35 c. Type **15** 75 55
79. 75 c. Air Caicos Convair "440" .. .. .. 1·50 1·25
80. 90 c. TCNA "Islander" .. 1·75 1·40

16. The Queen Mother visiting Foundation for the Disabled, Leatherhead

1985. Life and Times of Queen Elizabeth the Queen Mother. Multicoloured.

82. 35 c Type **16** 50 55
83. 65 c. With Princess Anne (horiz) 90 95
84. 95 c. At Epsom, 1961 .. 1·40 1·60

1985. 150th Birth Anniv. of Mark Twain (author). Designs as T **118** of Anguilla, showing Walt Disney cartoon characters in scenes from "Tom Sawyer, Detective". Multicoloured.

86. 8 c. Huckleberry Finn (Goofy) and Tom Sawyer (Mickey Mouse) reading reward notice 30 10
87. 35 c. Huck and Tom meeting Jake Dunlap .. .. 1·00 55
88. 95 c. Huck and Tom spying on Jubiter Dunlap .. 2·00 1·40
89. $1.10 Huck and Tom with hound (Pluto) .. .. 2·25 1·60

1985. Birth Bicentenaries of Grimm Brothers (folklorists). Designs as T **119** of Anguilla, showing Walt Disney cartoon characters in scenes from "Six Soldiers of Fortune". Mult.

91. 16 c. The Soldier (Donald Duck) with his meagre pay 20 25
92. 25 c. The Soldier meeting the Strong Man (Horace Horsecollar) 30 35
93. 65 c. The Soldier meeting the Marksman (Mickey Mouse) 85 90
94. $1.35 The Fast Runner (Goofy) winning the race against the Princess (Daisy Duck) .. .. 1·75 1·90

CAMEROONS

BRITISH OCCUPATION

12 pence = 1 shilling;
20 shillings = 1 pound.

Former German colony occupied by British and French troops during 1914–16. The country was divided between them and the two areas were administered under the League of Nations mandate from 1922. The British section was administered as part of Nigeria until 1960. (see Southern Cameroons). For German and French issues see Volume 1.

1915. "Yacht" key-types of German Kamerun surch. **C.E.F.** and value in English currency.

1. N. ½d. on 3 pf. brown .. 4·25 12·00
2. ½d. on 5 pf. green .. 1·25 5·50
3. 1d. on 10 pf. red .. 1·25 4·00
4. 2d. on 20 pf. blue .. 3·25 11·00
5. 2½d. on 25 pf. black and red on yellow .. 9·00 24·00
6. 3d. on 30 pf. black and orange on buff .. 9·00 24·00
7. N. 4d. on 40 pf. black & red 9·00 24·00
8. 6d. on 50 pf. black and purple on buff .. 9·00 24·00
9. 8d. on 80 pf. black and red on rose .. 9·00 24·00
10. O. 1s. on 1 m. red .. £120 £325
11. 2s. on 2 m. blue .. £120 £325
12. 3s. on 3 m. black .. £120 £325
13. 5s. on 5 m. red & black £150 £350

CANADA

A British dominion consisting of the former province of Canada with Br. Columbia, New Brunswick, Newfoundland, Nova Scotia, and Prince Edward Is.

1851. 12 pence = 1 shilling (Canadian).
1859. 100 cents = 1 dollar.

4.

1. Beaver.

2. Prince Albert.

5.

6. Jacques Cartier. **3.**

1851. Imperf.

17 **4.** ½d. red £600 £375
5 **1.** 3d. red £950 £160
2 **2.** 6d. purple £7500 £900
12 **5.** 7½d. green £7000 £1500
14 **6.** 10d. blue £6500 £1100
4 **3.** 12d. black £60000 £40000

1858. Perf.

25 **4.** ½d. red £1300 £500
26 **1.** 3d. red £2250 £300
27a **2.** 6d. purple £5500 £1700

1859. Values in cents. Perf.

29 **4.** 1 c. red .. .. .. £160 22·00
44. 2 c. red £375 £110
31 **1.** 5 c. red .. .. .. £160 10·00
37. **2.** 10 c. violet .. .. £500 35·00
36. 10 c. brown .. .. £550 35·00
41. **5.** 12½ c. green .. .. £375 38·00
42. **6** 17 c. blue .. .. .. £600 60·00

DOMINION OF CANADA

13.

14.

1868. Various frames.

54 13 ½ c. black .. .. 38·00 30·00
55 14 1 c. brown .. .. £300 35·00
56 1 c. yellow .. .. £650 60·00
48 2 c. green .. .. £250 30·00
49 3 c. red .. .. .. £550 20·00
72 5 c. olive .. .. £700 65·00
59b 6 c. brown .. .. £550 32·00
60 12½ c. blue .. .. £350 32·00
83 15 c. purple .. .. 60·00 16·00
76b 15 c. blue .. .. £130 25·00

27.

21.

1870. Various frames.

77 **27.** ½ c. black .. .. 5·00 3·75
62d **21.** 1 c. yellow .. .. 15·00 15
78a 2 c. green .. .. 28·00 30
79 3 c. red .. .. .. 20·00 10
80 5 c. grey .. .. 42·00 30
81 6 c. brown .. .. 28·00 7·00
117 – 8 c. grey .. .. 65·00 3·00
82b **21.** 10 c. mauve .. .. £120 14·00

On 8 c. head is to left.

28.

1893.

115. **28.** 20 c. red .. .. £160 40·00
116. 50 c. blue .. .. £225 24·00

30.

31.

1897. Jubilee.

121. **30.** ½ c. black .. .. 42·00 45·00
122. 1 c. orange .. .. 7·00 1·50
124. 2 c. green .. .. 10·00 3·75
126. 3 c. red .. .. .. 5·50 80
128. 5 c. blue .. .. 24·00 9·00
129. 6 c. brown .. .. 75·00 75·00
130. 8 c. violet .. .. 32·00 25·00
131. 10 c. purple .. .. 50·00 35·00
132. 15 c. slate .. .. 80·00 80·00
133. 20 c. red .. .. 80·00 80·00
134. 50 c. blue .. .. £120 95·00
136. $1 red £400 £400
137. $2 violet £700 £275
138. $3 bistre £800 £600
139. $4 violet £800 £600
140. $5 green £800 £600

1897. Maple-leaves in four corners.

141. **31.** ½ c. black .. .. 4·00 3·00
143. 1 c. green .. .. 16·00 30
144. 2 c. violet .. .. 15·00 60
145. 3 c. red .. .. 20·00 35
146. 5 c. blue .. .. 55·00 70
147. 6 c. brown .. .. 55·00 16·00
148. 8 c. orange .. .. 70·00 5·00
149. 10 c. purple .. .. £120 55·00

1898. As T **31** but figures in lower corners.

150. ½ c. black .. .. 1·50 85
151. 1 c. green .. .. 20·00 15
154. 2 c. purple .. .. 22·00 10
155. 2 c. red .. .. 26·00 10
156. 3 c. red .. .. 30·00 20
157. 5 c. blue .. .. 75·00 70
159. 6 c. brown .. .. 70·00 32·00
160. 7 c. yellow .. .. 48·00 10·00
161. 8 c. orange .. .. 80·00 19·00
163. 10 c. purple .. .. £160 11·00
165. 20 c. olive .. .. £325 45·00

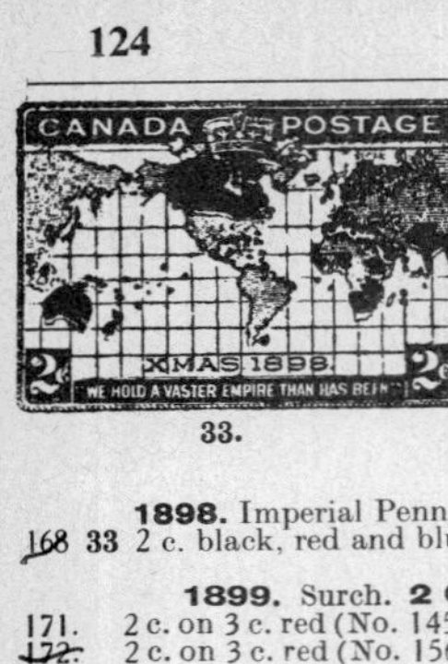

33.

35. King Edward VII.

1898. Imperial Penny Postage.

168	33	2 c. black, red and blue	20·00	3·00

1899. Surch. **2 CENTS.**

171.		2 c. on 3 c. red (No. 145) ..	11·00	4·50
172.		2 c. on 3 c. red (No. 156) ..	13·00	2·50

1903.

175	35.	1 c. green	14·00	15
176		2 c. red	12·00	10
178		5 c. blue	55·00	90
180		7 c. olive	55·00	1·00
182		10 c. purple	85·00	4·50
185		20 c. olive	£200	16·00
187		50 c. mauve	£325	60·00

36. King George V and Queen Mary, when Prince and Princess of Wales.

1908. Tercent. of Quebec. Dated "1608 1908".

188.	36.	½ c. brown	3·25	2·00
189.	–	1 c. green	7·00	1·25
190.	–	2 c. red	10·00	60
191.	–	5 c. blue	40·00	10·00
192.	–	7 c. olive	45·00	30·00
193.	–	10 c. violet	55·00	40·00
194.	–	15 c. orange	75·00	50·00
195.	–	20 c. brown	£100	60·00

DESIGNS: 1 c. Cartier and Champlain. 2 c. King Edward VII and Queen Alexandra. 5 c. Champlain's House in Quebec. 7 c. Gen. Montcalm and Wolfe. 10 c. Quebec in 1700. 15 c. Champlain's departure for the West. 20 c. Cartier's arrival before Quebec.

44.

1912.

197	44	1 c. green	4·50	20
200		2 c. red	4·00	10
224		3 c. brown	3·50	20
205b		5 c. blue	55·00	50
209		7 c. yellow	18·00	1·50
211		10 c. purple	75·00	1·10
212		20 c. olive	28·00	85
215		50 c. deep brown ..	40·00	2·25

1915. Optd. **WAR TAX** diagonally.

225.	44.	5 c. blue	£100	£160
226.		20 c. olive	50·00	75·00
227.		50 c. deep brown ..	70·00	95·00

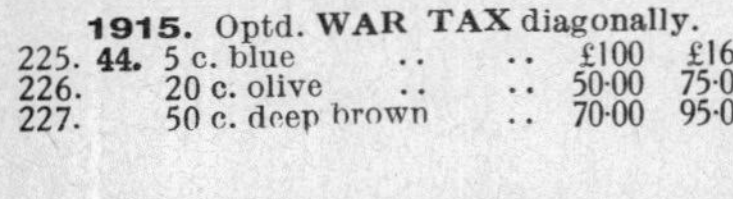

46.

47.

1915.

228.	46.	1 c. green	2·75	10
229.		2 c. red	3·00	20

1916.

233	47	2 c. + 1 c. red	8·00	55
239		2 c. + 1 c. brown ..	2·25	10

48. Quebec Conference, 1864, from painting "The Fathers of the Confederation", by Robert Harris.

1917. 50th Anniv. of Confederation.

244.	48.	3 c. brown	16·00	55

1922.

246.	44.	1 c. yellow	2·50	15
247.		2 c. green	2·25	10
248.		3 c. red	2·25	10
249.		4 c. yellow	7·00	1·25
250.		5 c. violet	5·00	75
251.		7 c. brown	10·00	6·00
252.		8 c. blue	17·00	7·00
253.		10 c. blue	18·00	70
254.		10 c. brown	17·00	70
255.		$1 orange	50·00	3·75

1926. Surch. **2 CENTS** in one line.

264.	44.	2 c. on 3 c. red ..	29·00	48·00

1926. Surch. **2 CENTS** in two lines.

265.	44.	2 c. on 3 c. red ..	10·00	15·00

51. Sir J. A. Macdonald.

DESIGNS — HORIZ. As Type **52**: 3 c. Parliament Buildings, Ottawa. 12 c. Map of Canada, 1867–1927. VERT. As Type **51**: 5 c. Sir W. Laurier.

52. "The Fathers of the Confederation".

1927. 60th Anniv. of Confederation. I. Commemoration Issue. Dated "1867 1927".

266.	51.	1 c. orange	1·75	75
267.	52.	2 c. green	1·50	10
268.	–	3 c. red	3·75	2·50
269.	–	5 c. violet	2·75	1·75
270.	–	12 c. blue	12·00	1·75

56. Darcy McGee.

57. Sir W. Laurier and Sir J. A. Macdonald.

II. Historical Issue.

271.	56.	5 c. violet	2·75	90
312.	–	10 c. olive	2·50	10
272.	57.	12 c. green	9·50	3·75
273.	–	20 c. red	11·00	6·00

DESIGNS—HORIZ. As Type **57**: 20 c. R. Baldwin and L. H. Lafontaine. VERT. As Type **56**: 10 c. Sir Georges Etienne Cartier.

59.

1928. Air.

274.	59.	5 c. brown	2·50	1·00

60. King George V.

DESIGNS—HORIZ. 12 c. Quebec Bridge. 20 c. Harvesting with horses. 50 c. "Bluenose" (fishing schooner). $1 Parliament Buildings, Ottawa.

61. Mt. Hurd and Indian Totem Poles.

1928.

275.	60.	1 c. orange	1·60	30
276.		2 c. green	65	10
277.		3 c. red	13·00	8·00
278.		4 c. yellow	13·00	3·50
279.		5 c. violet	3·75	1·50
280.		8 c. blue	7·50	1·50
281.	61.	10 c. green	6·00	40
282.	–	12 c. black	13·00	3·50
283.	–	20 c. red	24·00	3·75
284.	–	50 c. blue	90·00	25·00
285.	–	$1 olive	£100	32·00

66.

67. Parliamentary Library, Ottawa.

68. The Old Citadel, Quebec.

1930.

288	66.	1 c. orange	35	35
300d		1 c. green	75	10
289		2 c. green	60	10
301		2 c. red	70	30
302b		2 c. brown	70	10
303		3 c. red	90	10
290		4 c. yellow	5·50	1·50
291		5 c. violet	2·50	1·25
304		5 c. blue	5·00	10
292		8 c. blue	5·50	7·00
305		8 c. red	5·00	1·50
293	67.	10 c. olive	7·00	30
294	68.	12 c. black	7·50	1·75
[illegible]		13 c. violet	32·00	1·00
295	–	20 c. red	14·00	20
296	–	50 c. blue	80·00	9·50
297	–	$1 olive	90·00	16·00

DESIGNS—HORIZ. 20 c. Harvesting with tractor. 50 c. Acadian Memorial Church, Grand Pre, Nova Scotia. $1, Mt. Edith Cavell.

72. Mercury and Western Hemisphere.

1930. Air.

310.	72.	5 c. brown	12·00	9·00

1932. Air. Surch. **6** and bars

313.	59.	6 c. on 5 c. brown ..	1·50	1·25

1932. Surch. **3** between bars.

314a.	66.	3 c. on 2 c. red ..	75	10

76. King George V. 77. Duke of Windsor when Prince of Wales.

78. Allegory of British Empire.

1932. Ottawa Conf. (a) Postage.

315.	76.	3 c. red	70	50
316.	77.	5 c. blue	6·00	2·00
317.	78.	13 c. green	7·00	4·50

(b) Air. Surch. **6 OTTAWA CONFERENCE 6 1932** between bars.

318.	72.	6 c. on 5 c. brown ..	10·00	8·50

80. King George V.

1932.

319.	80.	1 c. green	60	10
320.		2 c. brown	70	10
321b.		3 c. red	85	10
322.		4 c. brown	35·00	5·50
323.		5 c. blue	9·00	10
324.		8 c. orange	18·00	1·50

81. Parliament Buildings, Ottawa.

1933. U.P.U. Congress (Preliminary Meeting).

329.	81.	5 c. blue	3·75	1·50

1933. Optd. **WORLD'S GRAIN EXHIBITION & CONFERENCE REGINA 1933.**

330.	–	20 c. red (No. 295) ..	20·00	4·75

83. S.S. "Royal William" (after S. Skillett).

1933. Cent. of 1st Transatlantic Steamboat Crossing.

331.	83.	5 c. blue	6·00	1·25

84. Jacques Cartier approaching Land.

1934. 4th Cent. of Discovery of Canada.

332.	84.	3 c. blue	2·00	70

85. U.E.L. Statue, Hamilton.

1934. 150th Anniv. of Arrival of United Empire Loyalists.

333.	85.	10 c. olive	9·50	3·00

86. Seal of New Brunswick.

1934. 150th Anniv. of New Brunswick.

334.	86.	2 c. brown	75	1·00

87. Queen Elizabeth II when Princess.

88. King George VI when Duke of York.

89. King George V and Queen Mary.

1935. Silver Jubilee. Dated "1910–1935".

335.	87.	1 c. green	55	40
336.	88.	2 c. brown	60	30
337.	89.	3 c. red	1·75	15
338.	–	5 c. blue	3·00	2·00
339.	–	10 c. green	2·50	1·50
340.	–	13 c. blue	5·00	1·50

Designs—vert. 5 c. Duke of Windsor when Prince of Wales. horiz. 10 c. Windsor Castle. 13 c. "Britannia".

Designs—horiz. 13 c. Confederation, Charlottetown, 1864. 20 c. Niagara Falls. 50 c. Parliament Buildings, Victoria, B.C. $1, Champlain Monument, Quebec.

93. King George V.

94. Royal Canadian Mounted Policeman.

1935.

341.	93.	1 c. green	30	10
342.		2 c. brown	50	10
343.		3 c. red	60	10
344.		4 c. yellow	1·50	60
345.		5 c. blue	1·00	10
346.		8 c. orange	1·00	1·40
347.	94.	10 c. red	3·50	15
348.	–	13 c. violet	3·75	20
349.	–	20 c. green	10·00	35
350.	–	50 c. violet	25·00	3·00
351.	–	$1 blue	38·00	3·25

99. Daedalus.

1935. Air.

355.	99.	6 c. brown	1·60	40

100. King George VI and Queen Elizabeth.

1937. Coronation.

356.	100.	3 c. red	70	30

101. King George VI. 102. Memorial Chamber Parliament Buildings, Ottawa.

104. Fort Garry Gate, Winnipeg.

1937.

357.	101.	1 c. green	80	10
358.		2 c. brown	1·00	10
359.		3 c. red	1·25	10
360.		4 c. yellow	3·00	85
361.		5 c. blue	3·00	10
362.		8 c. orange	3·00	90
363.	102.	10 c. red	6·00	10
364.	–	13 c. blue	14·00	20
365.	104.	20 c. brown	22·00	5·50
366.	–	50 c. green	50·00	5·50
367.	–	$1 violet	70·00	5·50

Designs—horiz. 13 c. Halifax Harbour. 50 c. Vancouver Harbour. $1, Chateau de Ramezay, Montreal.

107. Seaplane over S.S. "Distributor" on Mackenzie River.

1938. Air.

371.	107.	6 c. blue	5·50	30

108. Queen Elizabeth II when Princess and Princess Margaret.

1939. Royal Visit.

372.	108.	1 c. black and green	90	10
373.	–	2 c. black and brown	50	30
374.	–	3 c. black and red	40	10

Designs—horiz. 3 c. King George VI and Queen Elizabeth. vert. 2 c. National War Memorial, Ottawa.

111. King George VI in naval uniform. 112. King George VI in military uniform.

114. Grain Elevator. 115. Farm Scene.

121. Air Training Camp.

1942. War Effort.

375.	111.	1 c. green (postage)	75	10
376.	112.	2 c. brown	1·50	10
377.	–	3 c. red	1·00	30
378.	–	3 c. purple	70	10
379.	114.	4 c. grey	3·50	55
380.	112.	4 c. red	45	10
381.	111.	5 c. blue	2·50	10
382.	115.	8 c. sepia	4·00	40
383.	–	10 c. brown	4·00	10
384.	–	13 c. green	3·75	4·25
385.	–	14 c. green	9·50	30
386.	–	20 c. brown	10·00	15
387.	–	50 c. violet	20·00	1·75
388.	–	$1 blue	55·00	3·50
399.	121.	6 c. blue (air)	6·50	2·50
400.		7 c. blue	1·25	10

Designs—As Type 112: 3 c. King George VI. As Type 121. vert. 10 c. Parliament Buildings. horiz. 13 c., 14 c. Ram tank. 20 c. Corvette. 50 c. Munitions factory. $1, H.M.S. Cossack" (destroyer).

122. Ontario Farm Scene.

1946. Re-conversion to Peace-time.

401.	122.	8 c. brown (postage)	1·00	90
402.	–	10 c. green	1·25	10
403.	–	14 c. brown	3·50	30
404.	–	20 c. grey	2·50	10
405.	–	50 c. green	14·00	1·25
406.	–	$1 purple	29·00	1·25
407.	–	7 c. blue (air)	2·50	10

Designs: 10 c. Great Bear Lake. 14 c. St. Maurice River Power station. 20 c. Combine harvester. 50 c. Lumbering in Br. Columbia. $1, "Abegweit" (train ferry). 7 c. Canada Geese in flight.

129. Alexander Graham Bell and "Fame". 130. "Canadian Citizenship".

1947. Birth Cent. of Graham Bell (inventor of the telephone).

408.	129.	4 c. blue	10	10

1947. Advent of Canadian Citizenship and 80th Anniv. of Confederation.

409.	130.	4 c. blue	10	10

131. Queen Elizabeth II when Princess.

1948. Princess Elizabeth's Wedding.

410.	131.	4 c. blue	10	10

132. Queen Victoria. Parliament Building, Ottawa, and King George VI.

1948. Cent. of Responsible Government.

411.	132.	4 c. grey	10	10

133. Cabot's Ship "Matthew".

1949. Entry of Newfoundland into Canadian Confederation.

412.	133.	4 c. green	10	10

134. "Founding of Halifax, 1749" (after C. W. Jeffries).

1949. Halifax Bicent.

413.	134.	4 c. violet	10	10

135. King George VI.

1949. Portraits of King George VI.

414.	135.	1 c. green	10	10
415.	–	2 c. brown	15	20
415a.	–	2 c. olive	30	10
416.	–	3 c. purple	20	10
417.	–	4 c. lake	15	10
417b.	–	4 c. red	40	10
418.	–	5 c. blue	80	10

1950. As Nos. 414/8 but without "POSTES POSTAGE".

424.	1 c. green	10	15
425.	2 c. brown	10	30
426.	3 c. purple	10	55
427.	4 c. red	10	10
428.	5 c. blue	25	80

153. Canada Goose.

142. Drying Furs.

141. Oil Wells in Alberta.

1950.

443.	153.	7 c. blue	30	10
432.	142.	10 c. purple	30	10
441.	–	20 c. grey	65	10
431.	141.	50 c. green	7·00	50
433.	–	$1 blue	45·00	3·50

Designs: 20 c. Forestry products. $1, Fisherman.

145. Mackenzie King.

1951. Canadian Prime Ministers.

434.	–	3 c. green (Borden)	10	30
444.	–	3 c. purple (Abbott)	15	10
435.	145.	4 c. red	10	10
445.	–	4 c. red (A. Mackenzie)	15	10
475.	–	4 c. violet (Thompson)	15	10
483.	–	4 c. violet (Bennett)	10	15
476.	–	5 c. blue (Bowell)	15	10
484.	–	5 c. blue (Tupper)	10	10

146. Mail Trains, 1851 and 1951.

149. Reproduction of 3d., 1851.

Designs—As Type 146: 5 c. S.S. "City of Toronto" and S.S. "Prince George". 7 c. Mail coach and aeroplane.

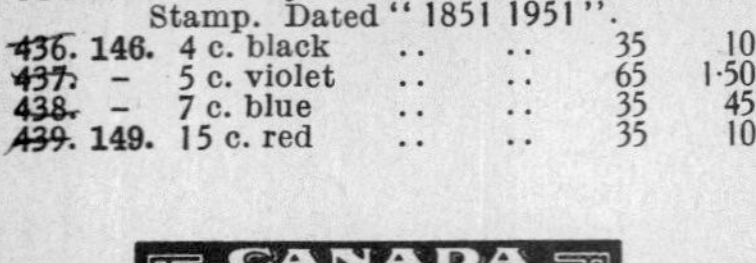

1951. Centenary of First Canadian Postage Stamp. Dated "1851 1951".
~~436.~~ 146. 4 c. black 35 10
~~437.~~ – 5 c. violet .. .. 65 1·50
~~438.~~ – 7 c. blue 35 45
~~439.~~ 149. 15 c. red 35 10

150. Queen Elizabeth II when Princess and Duke of Edinburgh.

1951. Royal Visit.
~~440.~~ 150. 4 c. violet 10 10

152. Red Cross Emblem.

1952. 18th Int. Red Cross Conf., Toronto.
~~442.~~ 152. 4 c. red and blue .. 15 10

165. Eskimo Hunter.

160. Textile Industry.

164. Northern Gannet. **154.** Pacific Coast Indian House and Totem Pole.

1953.
~~477.~~ 165. 10 c. brown 15 10
~~474.~~ 164. 15 c. black 40 10
~~488.~~ – 20 c. green 30 10
~~489.~~ – 25 c. red 35 10
~~462.~~ 160. 50 c. green .. .. 1·00 10
~~446.~~ 154. $1 black .. .. 7·50 20
DESIGNS—As Type **160**—HORIZ. 20 c. Pulp and paper industry. VERT. 25 c. Chemical industry.

155. Polar Bear. **158.** Queen Elizabeth II.

1953. National Wild Life Week.
~~447.~~ 155. 2 c. blue 10 10
~~448.~~ – 3 c. sepia (Elk) 10 10
~~449.~~ – 4 c. slate (American Bighorn) .. 15 10

1953.
~~450.~~ 158. 1 c. brown 10 10
~~451.~~ 2 c. green 15 10
~~452.~~ 3 c. red 15 15
~~453.~~ 4 c. violet 20 10
~~454.~~ 5 c. blue 20 10

159. Queen Elizabeth II. **161.**

1953. Coronation.
~~461.~~ 159. 4 c. violet 10 10

1954.
~~463.~~ 161. 1 c. brown 10 10
~~464.~~ 2 c. green 15 10
~~465.~~ 3 c. red 40 10
~~466.~~ 4 c. violet 30 10
~~467.~~ 5 c. blue 30 10
468. 6 c. orange .. .. 1·00 30

1954. National Wild Life Week. As T **155**.
472. 4 c. slate (Walrus) .. 35 10
473. 5 c. blue (American Beaver) 35 10

166. Musk-ox. **168.** Dove and Torch.

167. Whooping Cranes.

1955. National Wild Life Week.
~~478.~~ 166. 4 c. violet 20 10
~~479.~~ 167. 5 c. blue 60 10

1955. 10th Anniv. of I.C.A.O.
~~480.~~ 168. 5 c. blue 10 10

169. Pioneer Settlers.

1955. 50th Anniv. of Alberta and Saskatchewan Provinces.
~~481.~~ 169. 5 c. blue 15 15

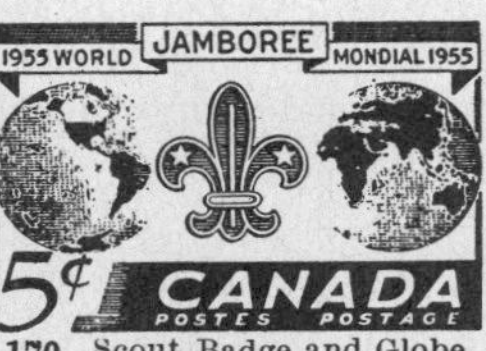

170. Scout Badge and Globe.

1955. 8th World Scout Jamboree.
~~482.~~ 170. 5 c. brown and green .. 20 10

173. Ice-Hockey Players.

1956. Ice-hockey Commem.
~~485.~~ 173. 5 c. blue 15 15

1956. National Wild Life Week. As T **155**.
486. 4 c. violet (Reindeer) .. 20 15
487. 5 c. blue (Mountain goat) 20 10

178. **183.** Great Northern Diver.

181. Hunting.

1956. Fire Prevention Week.
~~490.~~ 178. 5 c. red and black .. 30 10

1957. Outdoor Recreation.
~~491.~~ – 5 c. blue (Fishing) .. 25 10
492. – 5 c. blue (Swimming) 25 10
~~493.~~ 181. 5 c. blue 25 10
~~494.~~ – 5 c. blue (Skiing) .. 25 10

1957. National Wild Life Week.
~~495.~~ 183. 5 c. black 20 10

184. Thompson with Sextant, and North American Map.

1957. Death Cent. of David Thompson (explorer).
~~496.~~ 184. 5 c. blue 15 20

185. Parliament Buildings, Ottawa. **187.** Miner.

1957. 14th U.P.C. Congress, Ottawa.
~~497.~~ 185. 5 c. slate 15 10
~~498.~~ – 15 c. slate .. .. 30 1·00
DESIGN—HORIZ. ($33\frac{1}{2} \times 22$ mm.): 15 c. Globe within posthorn.

1957. Mining Industry.
499. 187. 5 c. black 35 10

188. Queen Elizabeth II and Duke of Edinburgh. **190.** Microscope.

189. "A Free Press".

1957. Royal Visit.
~~500.~~ 188. 5 c. black 30 10

1958. The Canadian Press.
~~501.~~ 189. 5 c. black 15 30

1958. Int. Geophysical Year.
~~502.~~ 190. 5 c. blue 20 10

191. Miner Panning for Gold.

1958. Centenary of British Columbia.
~~503.~~ 191. 5 c. turquoise 20 10

192. La Verendrye statue.

1958. La Verendrye (explorer). Commem.
~~504.~~ 192. 5 c. blue 20 10

193. Samuel de Champlain and Heights of Quebec.

1958. 350th Anniv. of Founding of Quebec by Samuel de Champlain.
~~505.~~ 193. 5 c. brown and green 30 10

194. Nurse.

1958. National Health.
506. 194. 5 c. purple 30 10

195. "Petroleum 1858-1958".

1958. Cent. of Canadian Oil Industry.
507. 195. 5 c. red and olive .. 30 10

196. Speaker's Chair and Mace.

1958. Bicent. of First Elected Assembly.
~~508.~~ 196. 5 c. slate 20 10

197. The "Silver Dart".

1959. 50th Anniv. of First Flight of the "Silver Dart" in Canada.
509. 197. 5 c. black and blue .. 20 10

198. Globe showing N.A.T.O. Countries.

1959. 10th Anniv. of N.A.T.O.
510. **198.** 5 c. blue 40 10

199. 200.

1959. "Associated Country Women of the World" Commem.
511. **199.** 5 c. black & olive .. 15 10

1959. Royal Visit.
512. **200.** 5 c. red 30 10

201. Maple Leaf linked with American Eagle.

1959. Opening of St. Lawrence Seaway.
513. **201.** 5 c. blue and red .. 20 10

202. Maple Leaves.

1959. Bicentenary of Battle of Quebec.
514. **202.** 5 c. green and red .. 30 10

203. Girl Guides Badge. 204. Dollard des Ormeaux.

1960. Golden Jubilee of Canadian Girl Guides Movement.
515. **203.** 5 c. blue and brown.. 20 10

1960. Tercent. of Battle of Long Sault.
516. **204.** 5 c. blue and brown.. 20 10

205. Surveyor, Bulldozer and Compass Rose. 206. E. Pauline Johnson.

1961. Northern Development.
517. **205.** 5 c. green and red .. 15 10

1961. Birth Centenary of E. Pauline Johnson (Mohawk poetess).
518. **206.** 5 c. green and red .. 15 10

207. Arthur Meighen (statesman).

1961. Arthur Meighen Commem.
519. **207.** 5 c. blue 15 10

208. Engineers and Dam.

1961. Colombo Plan.
520. **208.** 5 c. brown and blue .. 30 10

209. "Resources for Tomorrow". 210. "Education".

1961. Natural Resources.
521. **209.** 5 c. green and brown.. 15 10

1962. Education Year.
522. **210.** 5 c. black and brown 15 10

211. Lord Selkirk and Farmer.

1962. 150th Anniv. of Red River Settlement.
523. **211.** 5 c. brown & green .. 20 10

212. Talon bestowing gifts on married couple. 213. British Columbia and Vancouver Is. 2½d. stamp of 1860, and Parliament Bldgs., B.C.

1962. Jean Talon Commem.
524. **212.** 5 c. blue 20 10

1962. Centenary of Victoria, B.C.
525. **213.** 5 c. red and black .. 30 10

214. Highway (map version) and Provincial Arms.

1962. Opening of Trans-Canada Highway.
526. **214.** 5 c. black and brown 15 10

215. Queen Elizabeth II and Wheat (agriculture) Symbol. 216. Sir Casimir Gzowski.

1962. Different symbols in top left corner.
527. **215.** 1 c. brown 10 10
528. 2 c. green 15 10
529. 3 c. violet 15 10
530. 4 c. red 15 10
531. 5 c. blue 15 10

SYMBOLS: 1 c. Crystals (Mining). 2 c. Tree (Forestry). 3 c. Fish (Fisheries). 4 c. Electricity pylon (Industrial power). 5 c. Wheat (Agriculture).

1963. 150th Birth Anniv. of Sir Casimir Gzowski (engineer).
535. **216.** 5 c. purple 10 10

217. "Export Trade".

1963.
536. **217.** $1 red .. .. .. 8·00 1·75

218. Frobisher and barque "Gabriel".

1963. Sir Martin Frobisher Commem.
537. **218.** 5 c. blue .. 20 10

219. Horseman and Map.

1963. Bicent. of Quebec—Trois-Rivieres—Montreal Postal Service.
538. **219.** 5 c. brown and green 15 10

220. Canada Geese. 221. Jet Airliner (composite) and Uplands Airport, Ottawa.

1963.
540. **221.** 7 c. blue 35 65
540a. 8 c. blue 50 30
539. **220.** 15 c. blue .. .. 1·25 10

222. "Peace on Earth".

1964. "Peace".
541. **222.** 5 c. ochre, blue & turq. 15 10

223. Maple Leaves.

1964. "Canadian Unity".
542. **223.** 5 c. lake and blue .. 10 10

224. White Trillium and Arms of Ontario.

1964. Provincial Badges.
543. **224.** 5 c. green, brown & orge. 40 20
544. – 5 c. green, brown & yell. 40 20
545. – 5 c. red, green & violet 30 20
546. – 5 c. blue, red & green.. 30 20
547. – 5 c. purple, green & brn. 30 20
548. – 5 c. brown, green & mve. 30 20
549. – 5 c. lilac, green & pur. 50 20
550. – 5 c. green, yellow & red 30 20
551. – 5 c. sepia, orange & grn. 30 20
552. – 5 c. black, red & green 30 20
553. – 5 c. drab, green & yell. 30 20
554. – 5 c. blue, green and red 30 20
555. – 5 c. red and blue .. 30 20

FLOWERS AND ARMS OF: No. 544, Madonna Lily, Quebec. No. 545, Purple Violet, New Brunswick. No. 546, Mayflower, Nova Scotia. No. 547, Dogwood, British Columbia. No. 548, Prairie Crocus, Manitoba. No. 549, Lady's Slipper, Prince Edward Island. No. 550, Wild Rose, Alberta. No. 551, Prairie Lily, Saskatchewan. No. 552, Pitcher Plant, Newfoundland. No. 553, Mountain Avens, Northwest Territories. No. 554, Fireweed, Yukon Territory. No. 555, Maple Leaf, Canada.

1964. Surch.
556. **221.** 8 c. on 7 c. blue .. 15 15

238. Fathers of the Confederation Memorial, Charlottetown.

1964. Cent. of Charlottetown Conf.
557. **238.** 5 c. black 10 10

239. Maple Leaf and Hand with Quill Pen.

1964. Cent. of Quebec Conf.
558. **239.** 5 c. red and brown 15 10

240. Queen Elizabeth II. 241. "Canadian Family".

1964. Royal Visit.
559. **240.** 5 c. purple 15 10

1964. Christmas.
560. **241.** 3 c. red 10 10
561. 5 c. blue 10 10

242. Co-operation.

1965. Int. Co-operation Year.
562. **242.** 5 c. green 35 10

243. Sir W. Grenfell.

1965. Birth Centenary of Sir Wilfred Grenfell (missionary).
563. **243.** 5 c. green 20 10

244. National Flag.

1965. Inauguration of National Flag.
564. **244.** 5 c. red and blue .. 15 10

245. Sir Winston Churchill.

246. Peace Tower, Parliament Bldgs., Ottawa.

1965. Churchill Commem.

565. 245. 5 c. brown 15 10

1965. Inter-Parliamentary Union Conf., Ottawa.

566. 246. 5 c. green 10 10

247. Parliament Buildings, Ottawa, 1865.

1965. Centenary of Proclamation of Ottawa as Capital.

567. 247. 5 c brown 10 10

248. "Gold, Frankincense and Myrrh".

249. "Alouette 2" over Canada.

1965. Christmas.

568. 248. 3 c. green 10 10
569. 5 c. blue 10 10

1966. Launching of Canadian Satellite, "Alouette 2".

570. 249. 5 c. blue 15 10

250. La Salle.

251. Road Signs.

1966. 300th Anniv. of La Salle's Arrival in Canada.

571. 250. 5 c. green 15 10

1966. Highway Safety.

572. 251. 5 c. yellow, blue & blk. 15 10

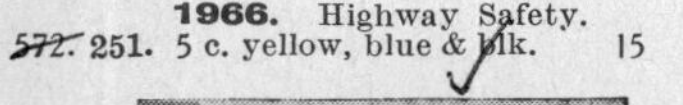

252. Canadian Delegation and Houses of Parliament.

1966. Cent. of London Conference.

573. 252. 5 c. brown 10 10

253. Douglas Point Nuclear Power Station.

1966. Peaceful Uses of Atomic Energy.

574. 253. 5 c. blue 10 10

254. Parliamentary Library, Ottawa.

255. "Praying Hands", after Dürer.

1966. Commonwealth Parliamentary Assn. Conf., Ottawa.

575. 254. 5 c. purple 10 10

1966. Christmas.

576. 255. 3 c. red 10 10
577. 5 c. orange 10 10

256. Flag, and Canada on Globe.

257. Queen Elizabeth, Northern Lights and Dog-team.

262. "Alaska Highway" (A. Y. Jackson).

1967. Canadian Centennial.

578. 256. 5 c. red and blue .. 10 10

1967.

579 257. 1 c. brown 10 10
580 – 2 c. green 10 10
581 – 3 c. purple 20 10
582 – 4 c. red 20 10
583 – 5 c. blue 20 10
601 – 6 c. red 45 10
607 – 6 c. black 50 10
609 – 7 c. green 30 10
584 262. 8 c. purple 35 30
610 – 8 c. black 30 10
585 – 10 c. olive 30 10
586 – 15 c. purple 30 10
587 – 20 c. blue 80 10
588 – 25 c. green .. .. 1·25 10
589 – 50 c. brown .. .. 1·50 10
590 – $1 red .. .. .. 3·50 10

DESIGNS—As Type **257**—Queen Elizabeth and: 2 c. Totem Pole. 3 c. Combine-harvester and Oil Derrick. 4 c. Ship in Lock. 5 c. (No. 583), Harbour Scene. 6 c. (Nos. 606/7), 7 c. "Transport". 8 c. (No. 610), Library of Parliament. As Type **262.** 10 c. "The Jack Pine" (T. Thomson). 15 c. "Bylot Island" (L. Harris). 20 c. "Quebec Ferry" (J. W. Morrice). 25 c. "The Solemn Land" (J. E. H. MacDonald). 50 c. "Summer's Stores" (Grain elevators, J. Ensor). $1, "Oilfield" (near Edmonton, H. G. Glyde).

269. Canadian Pavilion.

1967. World Fair, Montreal.

611. 269. 5 c. blue and red .. 10 10

270. Allegory of "Womanhood" on Ballot-box.

271. Queen Elizabeth. II and Centennial Emblem.

1967. 50th Anniv. of Women's Franchise.

612. 270. 5 c. purple and black 10 10

1967. Royal Visit.

613. 271. 5 c. plum and brown.. 15 10

272. Athletic.

1967. Pan-American Games, Winnipeg.

614. 272. 5 c. red 10 10

273. "World News".

1967. 50th Anniv. of Canadian Press.

615. 273. 5 c blue 10 10

274. Governor-General Vanier.

1967. Vanier Commem.

616. 274. 5 c. black 10 10

275. People of 1867, and Toronto, 1967.

1967. Cent. of Toronto as Capital City of Ontario.

617. 275. 5 c. green and red .. 10 10

276. Carol Singers.

277. Grey Jays.

1967. Christmas.

618. 276. 3 c. red 10 10
619. 5 c. green 10 10

1968. Wild Life.

620. 277. 5 c. multicoloured .. 30 10

See also Nos. 638/40.

278. Weather Map and Instruments.

1968. 20th Anniversary of First Meteorological Readings.

621. 278. 5 c. multicoloured. .. 15 10

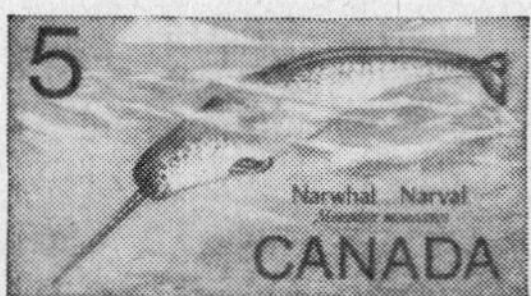

279. Narwhal.

1968. Wild Life.

622. 279. 5 c. multicoloured .. 15 10

280. Globe, Maple Leaf and Rain Gauge.

1968. Int. Hydrological Decade.

623. 280. 5 c. multicoloured .. 10 10

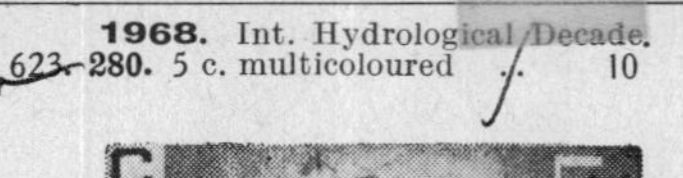

281. The "Nonsuch".

1968. 300th Anniversary of Voyage of the "Nonsuch".

624. 281. 5 c. multicoloured .. 20 10

282. Lacrosse Players.

1968. Lacrosse.

625. 282. 5 c. multicoloured .. 15 10

283. Front Page of "The Globe", George Brown and Legislative Building.

1968. 150th Birth Anniversary of George Brown (politician and journalist).

626. 283. 5 c. multicoloured .. 10 10

284. H. Bourassa (politician and journalist).

286. Armistice Monument, Vimy.

285. John Macrae. Battlefield and First Lines of "In Flanders Fields".

1968. Birth Centenary of Henri Bourassa.

627. 284. 5 c. blk, red & cream 10 10

1968. 50th Death Anniversary of John Macrae (soldier and poet).

628. 285. 5 c. multicoloured .. 10 10

1968. 50th Anniversary of 1918 Armistice.

629. 286. 15 c. black 30 40

287. Eskimo Family (carving).

1968. Christmas.

630. 287. 5 c. black and blue .. 10 10
631. – 6 c. black and ochre.. 10 10

DESIGN: 6 c. "Mother and Child" (carving).

289. Curling.

1969. Curling.
632. **289.** 6 c. black, blue and red 15 10

290. Vincent Massey. **292.** Globe and Tools.

291. "Return from the Harvest Field" (Suzor-Cote).

1969. Vincent Massey, First Canadian-born Governor-General.
633. **290.** 6 c. sepia and ochre .. 10 10

1969. Birth Centenary of Marc Aurele de Foy Suzor-Cote (painter).
634. **291.** 50 c. multicoloured .. 70 2·00

1969. 50th Anniversary of Int. Labour Organization.
635. **292.** 6 c. green 10 10

293. Vickers Vimy Aircraft over Atlantic Ocean.

1969. 50th Anniversary of 1st Non-stop Transatlantic Flight.
636. **293.** 15 c. brn., grn. & blue 40 55

294. Sir William Osler (J. S. Sargent). **295.** White-throated Sparrow.

1969. 50th Death Anniversary of Sir William Osler (physician).
637. **294.** 6 c. blue and brown .. 20 10

1969. Birds. Multicoloured.
638. 6 c. Type **295** 25 10
639. 10 c. Savannah Sparrow .. 65 80
640. 25 c. Hermit Thrush .. 1·90 2·50
The 10 c. and 25 c. are horiz.

298. Flags of Winter and Summer Games. **300.** Sir Isaac Brock and Memorial Column.

299. Outline of Prince Edward Island showing Charlottetown.

1969. Canadian Games.
641. **298.** 6 c. green, red & blue .. 10 10

1969. Bicent. of Charlottetown as Capital of Prince Edward Is.
642. **299.** 6 c. brown, blk. & blue 20 10

1969. Birth Bicent. of Sir Isaac Brock.
643. **300.** 6 c. orge., bis. & brn. 10 10

301. Children of the World in Prayer.

1969. Christmas.
644. **301.** 5 c. multicoloured .. 10 10
645. 6 c. multicoloured .. 10 10

302. Stephen Butler Leacock, Mask and "Mariposa".

1969. Birth Centenary of Stephen Butler Leacock (humorist).
646. **302.** 6 c. multicoloured .. 10 10

303. Symbolic Cross-roads.

1970. Centenary of Manitoba.
647. **303.** 6 c. blue, yellow & red 15 10

304. "Enchanted Owl" (Kenojuak).

1970. Centenary of Northwest Territories.
648. **304.** 6 c. red and black .. 10 10

305. Microscopic View of Inside of Leaf.

1970. Int. Biological Programme.
649. **305.** 6 c. green, yellow & blue 15 10

306. Expo 67 Emblem and stylized Cherry Blossom.

1970. World Fair, Osaka. Expo 70. Mult.
650. 25 c. Type **306** (red) .. 1·40 1·25
651. 25 c. Dogwood (violet) .. 1·40 1·25
652. 25 c. White Trillium (grn.) 1·40 1·25
653. 25 c. White Garden Lily (bl.) 1·40 1·25
NOTE: Each stamp shows a stylized Cherry Blossom, in a different colour, given above in brackets.

310. Henry Kelsey.

1970. 300th Birth Anniversary of Henry Kelsey (explorer).
654. **310.** 6 c. multicoloured .. 10 10

311. "Towards Unification".

1970. 25th Anniversary of U.N.
655. **311.** 10 c. blue 30 30
656. 15 c. mauve and lilac 40 35

312. Louis Riel (Metis leader). **313.** Mackenzie's Inscription, Dean Channel.

1970. Louis Riel Commem.
657. **312.** 6 c. blue and red .. 10 10

1970. Sir Alexander Mackenzie (explorer).
658. **313.** 6 c. brown 15 10

314. Sir Oliver Mowat (statesman).

1970. Sir Oliver Mowat Commem.
659. **314.** 6 c. red and black .. 10 10

315. "Isles of Spruce" (A. Lismer).

1970. 50th Anniversary of "Group of Seven" (artists).
660. **315.** 6 c. multicoloured .. 10 10

316. "Horse-drawn Sleigh" (D. Niskala). **328.** Sir Donald A. Smith.

1970. Christmas. Multicoloured.
661. 5 c. Type **316** .. 40 20
662. 5 c. "Stable and Star of Bethlehem" .. 40 20
663. 5 c. "Snowmen" .. 40 20
664. 5 c. "Skiing" .. 40 20
665. 5 c. "Santa Claus" .. 40 20
666. 6 c. "Santa Claus" (different) .. 40 20
667. 6 c. "Christ in Manger" 40 20
668. 6 c. "Toy Shop" .. 40 20
669. 6 c. "Christmas Tree" .. 40 20
670. 6 c. "Church" .. 40 20
671. 10 c. "Christ in Manger" (37×20 mm.) .. 30 30
672. 15 c. "Trees and Sledge" (37×20 mm.) .. 45 60

1970. 150th Birth Anniversary of Sir Donald Alexander Smith.
673. **328.** 6 c. yell., brn. & grn. 10 10

329. "Big Raven" (E. Carr). **330.** Laboratory Equipment.

1971. Birth Centenary of Emily Carr (painter).
674. **329.** 6 c. multicoloured .. 20 20

1971. 50th Anniv. of Discovery of Insulin.
675. **330.** 6 c. multicoloured .. 30 20

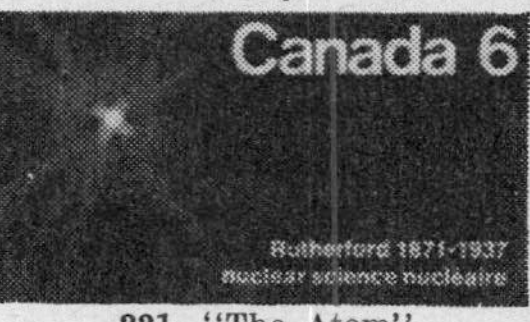

331. "The Atom".

1971. Birth Centenary of Lord Rutherford (scientist).
676. **331.** 6 c. yellow, red & brn. 20 10

332. Maple "Keys". **333.** Louis Papineau.

1971. "The Maple Leaf in Four Seasons". Multicoloured.
677. 6 c. Type **332** (spring) .. 20 15
678. 6 c. Green leaves (summer) 20 15
679. 7 c. Autumn leaves .. 20 15
680. 7 c. Withered leaves and snow (winter) .. 20 15

1971. Death Centenary of Louis-Joseph Papineau (politician).
681. **333.** 6 c. multicoloured .. 15 15

334. Chart of Coppermine River.

1971. Bicentenary of Samuel Hearne's Expedition to the Coppermine River.
682 **334** 6 c. brown, red & buff 30 30

335. "People" and Computer Tapes.

1971. Centenary of 1st Canadian Census.
683. **335.** 6 c. blue, red & black 20 10

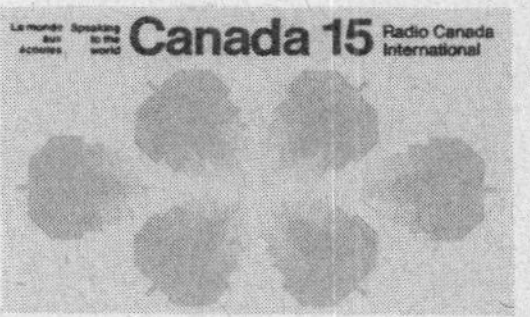

336. Maple Leaves.

1971. Radio Canada International.
684. **336.** 15 c. red, yell. & blk. 50 1·00

337. "B. C.".

1971. Centenary of British Columbia's Entry into the Confederation.

685. **337.** 7 c. multicoloured .. 15 10

338. "Indian Encampment on Lake Huron" (Kane).

1971. Death Cent. of Paul Kane (painter).

686. **338.** 7 c. multicoloured .. 20 10

339. "Snowflake".

340. Pierre Laporte (Quebec Cabinet Minister).

1971. Christmas.

687. **339.** 6 c. blue 10 10
688. 7 c. green 15 10
689. – 10 c. silver and red .. 55 90
690. – 15 c. silver, pur. & lav. 85 1·10

Design: 10 c., 15 c. "Snowflake" design similar to Type **339** but square (26 × 26 mm.)

1971. 1st Anniversary of Assassination of Pierre Laporte.

691. **340.** 7 c. black on buff .. 15 10

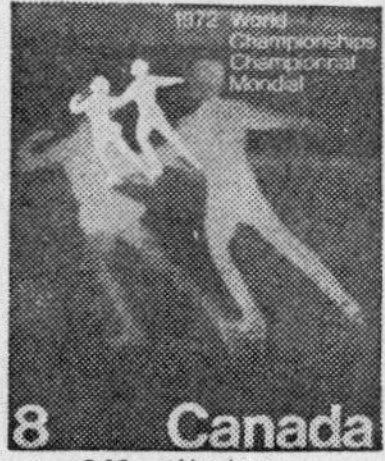

341. Skaters.

1972. World Figure Skating Championships, Calgary.

692. **341.** 8 c. purple 15 10

342. J. A. MacDonald. **343.** Forest, Central Canada.

344. Vancouver.

1972.

693 **342** 1 c. orange 10 10
694 – 2 c. green 10 10
695 – 3 c. brown 10 10
696 – 4 c. black 10 10
697 – 5 c. mauve 10 10
698 – 6 c. red 10 10
699 – 7 c. brown 10 15
700 – 8 c. blue 15 10
701 – 10 c. brown 30 10
702b **343** 10 c. green, turquoise and orange .. 30 10
703b – 15 c. blue and brown 30 10
704a – 20 c. orge., vio. & bl. 30 10
705b – 25 c. ultram. & bl. .. 40 10
706b – 50 c. grn., bl. & brn. 40 10
709a **344** $1 multicoloured .. 70 30
708 – $2 multicoloured .. 1·50 2·00

Designs: As Type **342** (1 to 7 c. show Canadian Prime Ministers). 2 c. W. Laurier. 3 c. R. Borden. 4 c. W. L. Mackenzie King. 5 c. R. B. Bennett. 6 c. L. B. Pearson. 7 c. Louis St. Laurent. 8 and 10 c. Queen Elizabeth II. As Type **343**. 15 c. American bighorn. 20 c. Prairie landscape from the air. 25 c. Polar Bears. 50 c. Seashore, Eastern Canada. As Type **344**. $2 Quebec.

345. Heart.

1972. World Health Day.

719. **345.** 8 c. red 15 10

346. Frontenac and Fort Saint-Louis, Quebec.

1972. 300th Anniversary of Governor Frontenac's Appointment to New France.

720. **346.** 8 c. red, brown & blue 15 15

347. Plains Indians' Artefacts.

347a. Buffalo Chase.

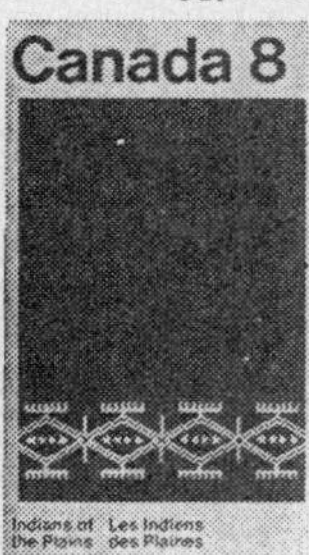

348. Thunderbird and Tribal Pattern.

348a. Dancer in Ceremonial Costume.

1972. Canadian Indians.

(a) Horiz. designs showing Artefacts as T **347** or Scenes from Indian Life as T **347a.**

721. **347.** 8 c. multicoloured .. 40 10
722. **347a.** 8 c. brn., yell. and blk. 40 10
723. – 8 c. multicoloured .. 40 10
724. – 8 c. multicoloured .. 40 10
725. – 8 c. multicoloured .. 40 10
726. – 8 c. brn., yell. and blk. 40 10
727. – 8 c. multicoloured .. 40 10
728. – 8 c. multicoloured .. 40 10
729. – 10 c. multicoloured .. 40 20
730. – 10 c. red, brown and black 40 20

Tribes: Nos. 721/2, Plains Indians. Nos. 723/4, Algonkians. Nos. 725/6, Pacific Coast Indians. Nos. 727/8, Subarctic Indians. Nos. 729/30, Iroquoians.

(b) Vert designs showing Costumes as T **348a** or Thunderbird and pattern as T**348**.

731. **348a.** 8 c. orange, red & black 40 15
732. **348.** 8 c. multicoloured .. 40 15
733. – 8 c. red, violet & black 40 10
734. – 8 c. green, brn. & blk. 40 10
735. – 8 c. red and black .. 40 10
736. – 8 c. multicoloured .. 40 10
737. – 8 c. green, brn. & blk. 40 10
738. – 8 c. multicoloured .. 40 10
739. – 10 c. brn., orge. & blk. 40 20
740. – 10 c. multicoloured .. 40 20

Tribes: Nos. 731/2, Plains Indians. Nos. 733/4, Algonkians. Nos. 735/6, Pacific Coast Indians. Nos. 737/8, Subarctic Indians. Nos. 739/40, Iroquoians.

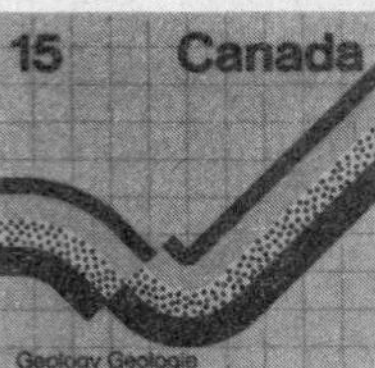

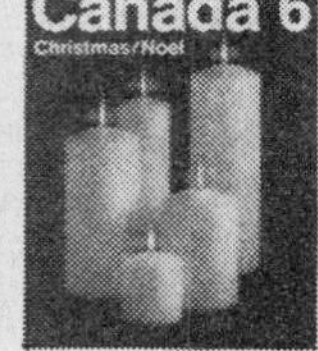

349. Earth's Crust. **350.** Candles.

1972. Earth Sciences.

741. – 15 c. multicoloured .. 1·00 1·40
742. – 15 c. grey, blue & blk. 1·00 1·40
743. **349.** 15 c. multicoloured .. 1·00 1·40
744. – 15 c. grn., orge. & blk 1·00 1·40

Designs and events: No. 741 Photogrammetric surveying (12th Congress of Int. Society of Photogrammetry). No. 742, "Siegfried" lines (6th Conf. of Int. Cartographic Assn). No. 743 (24th Int. Geological Congress). No. 744, Diagram of village at road-intersection (22nd Int. Geographical Congress).

1972. Christmas. Multicoloured.

745. 6 c. Type **350** 15 10
746. 8 c. Type **350** 20 10
747. 10 c. Candles with fruits and pine boughs (horiz.) 60 35
748. 15 c. Candles with prayer-book, caskets and vase (horiz.) 80 75

Nos. 747/8 are size 36 × 20 mm.

351. "The Blacksmith's Shop" (Krieghoff).

1972. Death Centenary of Cornelius Krieghoff (painter).

749. **351.** 8 c. multicoloured .. 30 15

352. F. de Montmorency-Laval.

1973. 350th Birth Anniversary of Monsignor de Laval (1st Bishop of Quebec).

750. **352.** 8 c. blue, gold & silver 20 30

353. Commissioner French and Route of the March West.

1973. Centenary of Royal Canadian Mounted Police.

751. **353.** 8 c. brn., orge. & red .. 35 15
752. – 10 c. multicoloured .. 1·25 1·75
753. – 15 c. multicoloured .. 1·75 2·00

Designs: 10 c. Spectrograph. 15 c. Mounted policeman.

354. Jeanne Mance.

1973. 300th Death Anniv. of Jeanne Mance (nurse).

754. **354.** 8 c. multicoloured .. 20 30

355. Joseph Howe. **356.** "Mist Fantasy" (MacDonald).

1973. Death Centenary of Joseph Howe (Nova Scotian politician).

755. **355.** 8 c. gold and black .. 20 30

1973. J. E. H. MacDonald (artist). Birth Cent.

756. **356.** 15 c. multicoloured .. 30 55

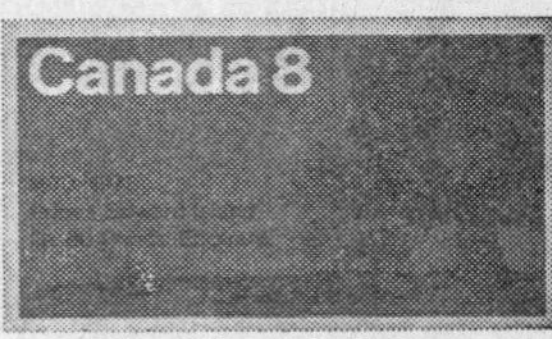

357. Oaks and Harbour.

1973. Centenary of Prince Edward Island's Entry into the Confederation.

757. **357.** 8 c. orange and red .. 20 30

358. Scottish Settlers.

1973. Bicentenary of Arrival of Scottish Settlers at Pictou, Nova Scotia.

758. **358.** 8 c. multicoloured .. 25 20

359. Queen Elizabeth II.

1973. Royal Visit and Commonwealth Heads of Government Meeting, Ottawa.

759. **359.** 8 c. multicoloured .. 25 20
760. 15 c. multicoloured .. 1·00 1·90

360. Nellie McClung. **361.** Emblem of 1976 Olympics.

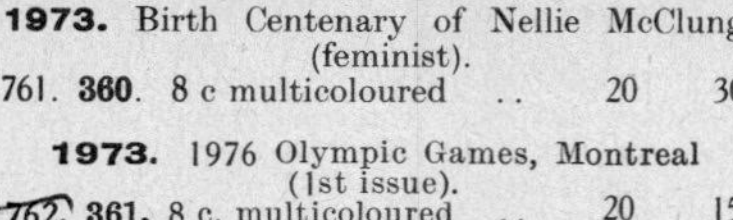

1973. Birth Centenary of Nellie McClung (feminist).

761. **360.** 8 c multicoloured .. 20 30

1973. 1976 Olympic Games, Montreal (1st issue).

762. **361.** 8 c. multicoloured .. 20 15
763. 15 c. multicoloured .. 35 1·25

See also Nos. 768/71, 772/4, 786/9, 798/802, 809/11, 814/16, 829/32, 833/7 and 842/4.

362. Ice-skate.

1973. Christmas. Multicoloured.

764. 6 c. Type **362** 15 10
765. 8 c. Bird decoration .. 20 10
766. 10 c. Santa Claus (20 × 36 mm.) .. .. .. 70 1·25
767. 15 c. Shepherd (20 × 36 mm.) 80 1·50

363. Diving.

1974. 1976 Olympic Games, Montreal. (2nd issue). "Summer Activities". Each blue.

768. 8 c. Type **363** 20 25
769. 8 c. "Jogging" 20 25
770. 8 c. Cycling 20 25
771. 8 c. Hiking 20 25

1974. 1976 Olympic Games, Montreal. (3rd issue). As Type **361** but smaller (20 × 36½ mm.).

772. **361.** 8 c. + 2 c. multicoloured 15 25
773. 10 c. + 5 c. multicoloured 25 60
774. 15 c. + 5 c. multicoloured 30 80

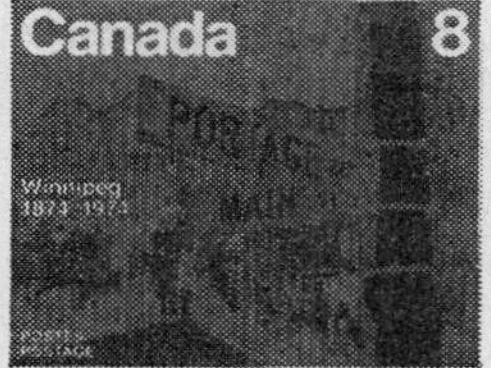

364. Winnipeg Signpost, 1872.

1974. Winnipeg Centennial.

775. **364.** 8 c. multicoloured .. 20 15

365. Postmaster and Customer.

1974. Centenary of Canadian Letter Carrier Delivery Service. Multicoloured.

776. 8 c. Type **365** 55 45
777. 8 c. Postman collecting mail 55 45
778. 8 c. Mail handler 55 45
779. 8 c. Mail sorters 55 45
780. 8 c. Postman making delivery 55 45
781. 8 c. Rural delivery by car 55 45

366. "Canada's Contribution to Agriculture".

1974. Centenary of "Agricultural Education". Ontario Agricultural College.

782. **366.** 8 c. multicoloured .. 20 20

367. Telephone Development.

1974. Centenary of Invention of Telephone by Alexander Graham Bell.

783. **367.** 8 c. multicoloured .. 20 20

368. Bicycle Wheel.

1974. World Cycling Championships, Montreal.

784. **368.** 8 c. black, red & silver 20 30

369. Mennonite Settlers.

1974. Centenary of Arrival of Mennonites in Manitoba.

785. **369.** 8 c. multicoloured 20 20

1974. 1976 Olympic Games, Montreal (4th issue). "Winter Activities". As T **363.** Each red.

786. 8 c. Snow-shoeing .. 50 40
787. 8 c. Skiing 50 40
788. 8 c. Skating 50 40
789. 8 c. Curling 50 40

370. Mercury, Winged Horses and U.P.U. Emblem.

1974. Centenary of U.P.U.

790. **370.** 8 c. violet, red & blue 15 15
791. 15 c. red, violet & blue 50 1·50

371. "The Nativity" (J. P. Lemieux).

1974. Christmas. Multicoloured.

792. 6 c. Type **371** 10 10
793. 8 c. "Skaters in Hull" (H. Masson) 10 10
794. 10 c. "The Ice Cone, Montmorency Falls" (R. C. Todd) 20 65
795. 15 c. "Village in the Laurentian Mountains" (C. A. Gagnon) 30 90

No. 793 is smaller 34 × 31 mm.

372. Marconi and St. John's Harbour, Newfoundland.

1974. Birth Centenary of Guglielmo Marconi (radio pioneer).

796. **372.** 8 c. multicoloured .. 20 20

373. Merritt and Welland Canal.

1974. William Merritt Commemoration.

797. **373.** 8 c. multicoloured .. 20 30

374. Swimming.

1975. 1976 Olympic Games, Montreal (5th issue). Multicoloured.

798. 8 c. + 2 c. Type **374** .. 25 40
799. 10 c. + 5 c. Rowing .. 30 80
800. 15 c. + 5 c. Sailing .. .. 35 1·00

375. "The Sprinter".

1975. 1976 Olympic Games, Montreal (6th issue). Multicoloured.

801. $1 Type **375** .. .. 2·25 3·25
802. $2 "The Diver" (vert.) .. 2·75 4·75

376. "Anne of Green Gables" (Lucy Maud Montgomery).

1975. Canadian Writers (1st series). Mult.

803. 8 c. Type **376** 20 10
804. 8 c. "Maria Chapdelaine" (Louis Hemon) .. 20 10

See also Nos. 846/7, 940/1 and 1085/6.

377. Marguerite Bourgeoys (founder of the Order of Notre Dame).

378. S. D. Chown (founder of United Church of Canada).

1975. Canadian Celebrities.

805. **377.** 8 c. multicoloured .. 50 30
806. – 8 c. multicoloured .. 50 30
807. **378.** 8 c. multicoloured .. 30 40
808. – 8 c. multicoloured .. 30 40

DESIGNS—As Type **377**. No. 806, Alphonse Desjardins (leader of Credit Union movement). As Type **378**. No. 808, Dr. J. Cook (first moderator of Presbyterian Church in Canada).

MINIMUM PRICE

The minimum price quoted is 10p which represents a handling charge rather than a basis for valuing common stamps. For further notes about prices see introductory pages.

379. Pole-vaulting.

1975. 1976 Olympics (7th issue). Mult.

809. 20 c. Type **379** 35 50
810. 25 c. Marathon-running .. 50 80
811. 50 c. Hurdling .. .. 60 1·25

380. "Untamed" (photo by Walt Petrigo).

1975. Centenary of Calgary.

812. **380.** 8 c. multicoloured .. 20 30

381. I.W.Y. Symbol. **382.** Fencing

1975. International Women's Year.

813. **381.** 8 c. grey, brn. and blk. 20 30

1975. Olympic Games, Montreal (1976) (8th issue). Multicoloured.

814. 8 c. + 2 c. Type **382** .. 30 45
815. 10 c. + 5 c. Boxing .. .. 35 1·00
816. 15 c. + 5 c. Judo .. .. 40 1·25

383. "Justice-Justitia" (Statue by W. S. Allward).

1975. Centenary of Canadian Supreme Court.

817. **383.** 8 c. multicoloured .. 20 30

384. "The William D. Lawrence".

1975. Canadian Ships (1st series). Coastal Vessels.

818. **384.** 8 c. brown and black .. 70 40
819. – 8 c. green and black .. 70 40
820. – 8 c. green and black .. 70 40
821. – 8 c. brown and black .. 70 40

DESIGNS: No. 819, "Beaver". No. 820, "Neptune". No. 821, "Quadra".

See also Nos. 851/4, 902/5 and 931/4.

385. "Santa Claus" (G. Kelly).

1975. Christmas. Multicoloured.

822. 6 c. Type **385** .. 10 10
823. 6 c. " Skater " (B. Cawsey) 10 10
824. 8 c. " Child " (D. Hebert) 10 10
825. 8 c. " Family " (L. Caldwell) 10 10
826. 10 c. " Gift " (D. Lovely) 20 50
827. 15 c. " Trees " (R. Kowalski) (horiz.) 30 75

386. Text, Badge and Bugle.

1975. Royal Canadian Legion. 50th Anniv.

828. **386.** 8 c. multicoloured .. 20 20

387. Basketball. **388.** Games Symbol and Snow Crystal.

1976. Olympic Games, Montreal (9th issue). Multicoloured.

829. 8 c.+2 c. Type **387** .. 30 40
830. 10 c.+5 c. Gymnastics .. 35 1·00
831. 20 c.+5 c. Soccer .. 45 1·25

1976. 12th Winter Olympic Games, Innsbruck.

832. **388.** 20 c. multicoloured .. 20 40

389. " Communications Arts ".

1976. Olympic Games, Montreal (10th issue). Multicoloured.

833. 20 c. Type **389** 25 25
834. 25 c. Handicrafts 35 65
835. 50 c. Performing Arts .. 40 1·10

390. Place Ville Marie and Notre-Dame Church.

1976. Olympic Games, Montreal (11th issue). Multicoloured.

836. $1 Type **390** .. .. 2·50 5·50
837. $2 Olympic stadium and flags .. .. .. 3·00 6·50

391. Flower and Urban Sprawl.

1976. HABITAT. U.N. Conf. on Human Settlements, Vancouver.

838. **391.** 20 c. multicoloured .. 20 30

392. Benjamin Franklin and Map.

1976. Bicent. of American Revolution.

839. **392.** 10 c. multicoloured .. 20 35

393. Wing Parade before Mackenzie Building.

1976. Centenary of Royal Military College. Multicoloured.

840. 8 c. Colour party and Memorial Arch .. 15 20
841. 8 c. Type **393** 15 20

394. Transfer of Olympic Flame by Satellite.

1976. Olympic Games, Montreal (12th issue). Multicoloured.

842. 8 c. Type **394** 10 10
843. 20 c. Carrying the Olympic flag 15 40
844. 25 c. Athletes with medals 25 60

395. Archer.

1976. Disabled Olympics.

845. **395.** 20 c. multicoloured .. 20 30

396. " Sam McGee " (Robert W. Service).

1976. Canadian Writers (2nd series). Mult.

846. 8 c. Type **396** 15 20
847. 8 c. " Le Survenant " (Germaine Guevremont) 15 20

397. " Nativity " (F. Mayer).

1976. Christmas. Stained-glass Windows. Multicoloured.

848. 8 c. Type **397** 10 10
849. 10 c. " Nativity " (G. Maile & Son) 10 10
850. 20 c. " Nativity " (Yvonne Williams) 20 50

398. " Northcote ".

1976. Canadian Ships (2nd series). Inland Vessels.

851. **398.** 10 c. light brown, brown and black 30 30
852. – 10 c. blue and black .. 30 30
853. – 10 c. blue and black .. 30 30
854. – 10 c. light green, green and black 30 30

DESIGNS: No. 852, " Chicora ". No. 853, " Passport ". No. 854, " Athabasca ".

399. Queen Elizabeth II.

1977. Silver Jubilee.

855. **399.** 25 c. multicoloured .. 25 50

400. Bottle Gentian. **401.** Queen Elizabeth II (bas-relief by J. Huta).

402. Houses of Parliament. **403.** Trembling Aspen.

404. Prairie Town Main Street.

405. Fundy National Park.

1977.

856 **400.** 1 c. multicoloured .. 10 10
870 **402.** 1 c. blue .. .. 90 2·00
857 – 2 c. multicoloured .. 10 10
858 – 3 c. multicoloured .. 10 10
859 – 4 c. multicoloured .. 10 10
860 – 5 c. multicoloured .. 10 10
871 **402.** 5 c. lilac 35 15
861 – 10 c. multicoloured .. 15 10
867 **401.** 12 c. bl., grey & blk. 15 10
872 **402.** 12 c. blue 20 10
866 – 12 c. multicoloured .. 15 30
868 **401.** 14 c. red, grey & blk. 20 10
873 **402.** 14 c. red 15 10
875 **403.** 15 c. multicoloured .. 15 10
866a – 15 c. multicoloured .. 15 15
869 **401.** 17 c. blk., grey & grn. 40 10
874 **402.** 17 c. green 30 10
876 – 20 c. multicoloured .. 15 10
877 – 25 c. multicoloured .. 15 10
878 – 30 c. multicoloured .. 20 10
869b **401.** 30 c. deep purple, grey and purple .. 50 50
869c 32 c. blk., grey & bl. 45 45
879 – 35 c. multicoloured .. 25 10
883 **404.** 50 c. multicoloured .. 85 60
883a – 60 c. multicoloured .. 65 45
881 – 75 c. multicoloured .. 85 90
882 – 80 c. multicoloured .. 85 60
884 **405.** $1 multicoloured .. 90 50
884b – $1 multicoloured .. 85 45
884c – $1.50 multicoloured 2·50 2·25
885 – $2 multicoloured .. 1·50 45
885b $2 multicoloured .. 3·25 90
885c – $5 multicoloured .. 5·50 2·00
885d – $5 multicoloured .. 5·50 3·00

DESIGNS: As Type **400**, 2 c. Red Columbine. 3 c. Canada Lily. 4 c. Hepatica. 5 c. Shooting Star. 10 c. Franklin's Lady's Slipper Orchid. 12 c. Jewelweed. 15 c. (No. 866a) Canada Violet. As Type **403**, 20 c. Douglas Fir. 25 c. Sugar Maple. 30 c. Red Oak. 35 c. White Pine. As Type **404**. 60 c. Ontario City street. 75 c. Eastern City street. 80 c. Maritimes street. As Type **405**. $1 Glacier. $1.50 Waterton Lakes. $2 (No. 885) Kluane. $2 (No. 885b) Banff. $5 (No. 885c) Point Pelee. $5 (No. 885d) La Mauricie.

406. Puma.

1977. Endangered Wildlife (1st series).

886. **406.** 12 c. multicoloured .. 20 20

See also Nos. 906, 936/7, 976/7 and 1006/7.

407. " April in Algonquin Park ".

1977. Birth Centenary of Tom Thomson (painter). Multicoloured.

887. 12 c. Type **407** 15 10
888. 12 c. " Autumn Birches " 15 10

408. Crown and Lion.

1977. Anniversaries. Multicoloured.

889. 12 c. Type **408** 15 15
890. 12 c. Order of Canada .. 15 15

EVENTS: No. 889, First Canadian-born Governor-General 25th Anniversary. No. 890, Order of Canada. 10th Anniv.

409. Peace Bridge, Niagara River.

1977. 50th Anniv. of Opening of Peace Bridge.

891. **409.** 12 c. multicoloured .. 15 15

410. Sir Sandford Fleming (engineer).

1977. Famous Canadians.

892. **410.** 12 c. blue 15 10
893. – 12 c. brown 15 10

DESIGN: No. 893, Joseph E. Bernier (explorer) and C.G.S. " Arctic ".

411. Peace Tower, Parliament Buildings, Ottawa.

1977. 23rd Commonwealth Parliamentary Conf. Centre.

894. **411.** 25 c. multicoloured .. 20 30

412. Hunter Braves following Star.

1977. Christmas. Canada's first carol " Jesous Ahatonhia ". Multicoloured.

895. 10 c. Type **412** 10 10
896. 12 c. Angelic choir .. 10 10
897. 25 c. Christ Child and " Chiefs from afar " .. 20 45

413. Seal Hunter (soapstone sculpture).

1977. Canadian Eskimos "Inuits" (1st series). Hunting. Multicoloured.
898. 12 c. Type **413** 15 15
899. 12 c. "Fisherman's Dream" (Pitaloosee) 15 15
900. 12 c. "Disguised Hunter" (L. Pitsiulak and S. Karpik 15 15
901. 12 c. "Hunters of Old" (Parr) 15 15
See also Nos. 924/7, 958/61 and 989/92.

414. Pinky (fishing boat).

1977. Canadian Ships (3rd series). Sailing Craft. Multicoloured.
902. 12 c. Type **414** 15 15
903. 12 c. Five-masted schooner 15 15
904. 12 c. Tern schooner 15 15
905. 12 c. Mackinaw boat .. 15 15

415. Peregrine Falcon.

1978. Endangered Wildlife (2nd series).
906. **415.** 12 c. multicoloured .. 30 20

416. Pair of 1851 12 d. Black Stamps.

1978. "CAPEX '78" International Philatelic Exhibition, Toronto.
907. **416.** 12 c. black and sepia .. 10 10
914. – 14 c. blue, grey & pale grey 15 10
915. – 30 c. red, grey & pale grey 20 35
916. – $1.25 violet, grey and pale grey .. .. 80 1·10
DESIGNS: 14 c. Pair of 1855 10d. Cartier stamps. 30 c. Pair of 1857 ½d. red stamps. $1.25, Pair of 1851 6d. Prince Albert stamps.

417. Games Emblem.

1978. 11th Commonwealth Games, Edmonton (1st issue). Multicoloured.
908. 14 c. Type **417** 10 10
909. 30 c. Badminton 20 40
See Nos. 918/21.

418. "Captain Cook". (Nathaniel Dance).

1978. Bicent. of Cook's 3rd Voyage. Mult.
910. 14 c. Type **418** 20 15
911. 14 c. "Nootka Sound" (J. Webber) 20 15

419. Hardrock Silver Mine, Cobalt, Ontario.

1978. Resource Development. Mult.
912. 14 c. Type **419** 15 15
913. 14 c. Giant excavators, Athabasca Tar Sands .. 15 15

1978. 11th Commonwealth Games, Edmonton (2nd issue). As T **417**. Multicoloured.
918. 14 c. Games stadium .. 10 15
919. 14 c. Running 10 15
920. 30 c. Alberta legislature building 25 30
921. 30 c. Bowls 25 30

420. Prince's Gate (Exhibition entrance).

1978. Centenary of National Exhibition.
922. **420.** 14 c. multicoloured .. 15 30

421. Marguerite d'Youville.

1978. Marguerite d'Youville (founder of Grey Nuns) Commem.
923. **421.** 14 c. multicoloured .. 15 20

1978. Canadian Eskimos ("Inuits") (2nd series). Travel. As T **413**. Multicoloured.
924. 14 c. Woman on foot (painting by Pitseolak) .. 15 15
925. 14 c. "Migration" (soapstone sculpture of sailing umiak by Joe Talurinili) 15 15
926. 14 c. Aeroplane (stonecut and stencilprint by Pudlo) 15 15
927. 14 c. Dogteam and dogsled (ivory sculpture by Abraham Kingmeatook) .. 15 15

422. "The Madonna of the Flowering Pea" (Cologne School).

1978. Christmas. Paintings. Multicoloured.
928. 12 c. Type **422** 10 10
929. 14 c. "The Virgin and Child with St. Anthony and Donor" (detail, Hans Memling) 10 10
930. 30 c. "The Virgin and Child" (Jacopo di Cione) .. 25 50

423. "Chief Justice Robinson".

1978. Canadian Ships (4th series). Ice Vessels. Multicoloured.
931. 14 c. Type **423** 35 35
932. 14 c. "St. Roch" 35 35
933. 14 c. "Northern Light" 35 35
934. 14 c. "Labrador" .. 35 35

424. Carnival Revellers.

1978. Quebec Carnival.
935. **424.** 14 c. multicoloured .. 20 20

425. Eastern Spiny Soft-shelled Turtle.

1979. Endangered Wildlife (3rd series). Multicoloured.
936. 17 c. Type **425** 20 10
937. 35 c. Bowhead Whale .. 40 60

426. Knotted Ribbon round Woman's Finger.

1979. Postal Code Publicity. Multicoloured.
938. 17 c. Type **426** 15 10
939. 17 c. Knotted string round man's finger 15 10

427. Scene from "Fruits of the Earth" by Frederick Philip Grove.

1979. Canadian Writers (3rd series). Multicoloured.
940. 17 c. Type **427** 15 15
941. 17 c. Scene from "Le Vaisseau d'Or" by Emile Nelligan 15 15

428. Charles-Michel de Salaberry (military hero).

1979. Famous Canadians. Multicoloured.
942. 17 c. Type **428** 25 15
943. 17 c. John By (engineer) .. 25 15

430. Paddling Kayak.

1979. Canoe-Kayak Championships.
956. **430.** 17 c. multicoloured .. 15 30

431. Hockey Players.

1979. Women's Field Hockey Championship, Vancouver.
957. **431.** 17 c. black, yell. & green 15 30

1979. Canadian Eskimos (3rd series). Shelter and the Community. As T **413**. Multicoloured.
958. 17 c. "Summer Tent" (print by Kiakshuk) .. 15 15
959. 17 c. "Five Eskimos building an Igloo" (soapstone sculpture by Abraham) 15 15
960. 17 c. "The Dane" (print by Kalvak) 15 15
961. 17 c. "Inuit drum dance" (soapstone sculptures by Madeleine Isserkut and Jean Mapsalak) .. 15 15

432. Toy Train.

1979. Christmas. Multicoloured.
962. 15 c. Type **432** 10 10
963. 17 c. Hobby-horse .. 10 10
964. 35 c. Rag doll (vert.) .. 25 50

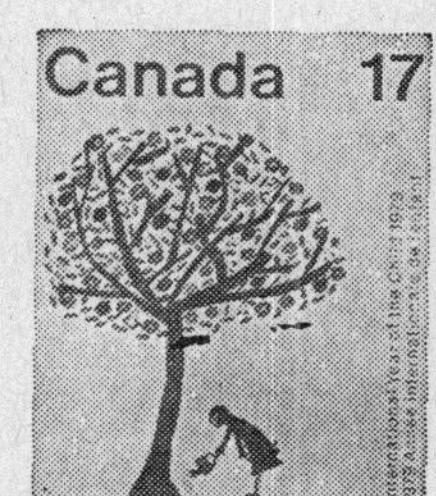

433. Child watering Tree of Life (painting by Marie-Annick Viatour).

1979. International Year of the Child.
965. **433.** 17 c. multicoloured .. 15 30

434. Canadair "CL–215".

1979. Canadian Aircraft (1st series). Flying Boats. Multicoloured.
966. 17 c. Type **434** 15 15
967. 17 c. Curtiss "HS–2L" .. 15 15
968. 35 c. Vickers "Vedette" 30 35
969. 35 c. Consolidated "Canso" 30 35
See also Nos. 996/9, 1050/3 and 1026/9.

435. Map of Arctic Islands.

1980. Centenary of Arctic Islands Acquisition.
970. **435.** 17 c. multicoloured .. 15 30

436. Skier.

1980. Winter Olympic Games, Lake Placid.
971. **436.** 35 c. multicoloured .. 30 65

437. " A Meeting of the School Trustees " (Robert Harris).

1980. Centenary of Royal Canadian Academy of Arts. Multicoloured.
972. 17 c. Type **437** 20 15
973. 17 c. " Inspiration " (Philippe Hebert) .. 20 15
974. 35 c. " Sunrise on the Saguenay " (Lucius O'Brien) 30 35
975. 35 c. Thomas Fuller's design sketch for the original Parliament Buildings .. 30 35

438. Atlantic Whitefish (" Coregonus Canadensis ").

1980. Endangered Wildlife (4th series). Multicoloured.
976. 17 c. Type **438** 15 15
977. 17 c. Prairie Chicken .. 15 15

439. Garden Flowers.

1980. International Flower Show, Montreal.
978. **439.** 17 c. multicoloured .. 15 20

440. " Helping Hand ".

1980. Rehabilitation.
979. **440.** 17 c. gold and blue .. 15 20

441. Opening Bars of " O Canada ".

1980. Centenary of "O Canada" (National Song). Multicoloured.
980. 17 c. Type **441** 15 15
981. 17 c. Galixa Lavallee, Adolphe-Basile Routhier & Robert Stanley Weir (composer and writers) 15 15

442. John G. Diefenbaker (statesman).

1980. John G. Diefenbaker Commemoration.
982. **442.** 17 c. blue 15 20

443. Emma Albani (singer).

1980. Famous Canadians. Multicoloured.
983. 17 c. Type **443** 15 15
984. 17 c. Healy Willan (composer) 15 15
985. 17 c. Ned Hanlan (oarsman) (horiz.) 15 15

444. Alberta.

1980. 75th Anniv. of Alberta and Saskatchewan (provinces). Multicoloured.
986. 17 c. Type **444** 15 15
987. 17 c. Wheat fields, Saskatchewan 15 15

445. Uraninite Molecular Structure.

1980. Uranium Resources.
988. **445.** 35 c. multicoloured .. 30 30

1980. Canadian Eskimos (" Inuits ") (4th series). Spirits. Designs as T **413.** Mult.
989. 17 c. " Return of the Sun " (print, Kenojouak) .. 15 15
990. 17 c. " Sedna " (sculpture, Ashoona Kiawak) .. 15 15
991. 35 c. " Shaman " (print, Simon Tookoome) .. 25 30
992. 35 c. " Bird Spirit " (sculpture, Doris Hagiolok) .. 25 30

446. " Christmas Morning " (J. S. Hallam).

1980. Christmas. Multicoloured.
993. 15 c. Type **446** 10 10
994. 17 c. " Sleigh Ride " (Joseph Hallam) .. 15 10
995. 35 c. " McGill Cab Stand " (Kathleen Morris) .. 30 45

447. Avro Canada " CF-100 ".

1980. Canadian Aircraft (2nd series). Mult.
996. 17 c. Type **447** 15 15
997. 17 c. Avro " Lancaster " 15 15
998. 35 c. Curtiss " JN-4 Canuck " 30 35
999. 35 c. Hawker " Hurricane " 30 35

448. Emmanuel-Persillier Lachapelle.

1980. Dr. E.-P. Lachapelle (founder, Notre-Dame Hospital, Montreal) Commemoration.
1000. **448.** 17 c. brown, deep brown and blue 15 15

449. Mandora (18th century).

1981. " The Look of Music " Exhibition, Vancouver.
1001. **449.** 17 c. multicoloured .. 15 15

450. Henrietta Edwards.

1981. Feminists. Multicoloured.
1002. 17 c. Type **450** 15 15
1003. 17 c. Louise McKinney .. 15 15
1004. 17 c. Idola Saint-Jean .. 15 15
1005. 17 c. Emily Stowe .. 15 15

451. Vancouver Marmot.

1981. Endangered Wildlife (5th series). Multicoloured.
1006. 17 c. Type **451** 15 10
1007. 35 c. American bison .. 35 30

452. Kateri Tekawitha.

1981. 17th-century Canadian Women. Statues by Emile Brunet.
1008. **452.** 17 c. brown and green 15 15
1009. – 17 c. dark blue & blue 15 15
DESIGN: No. 1009, Marie de l'Incarnation.

453. " Self Portrait " (Frederick H. Varley).

1981. Canadian Paintings. Multicoloured.
1010. 17 c. Type **453** 15 10
1011. 17 c. " At Baie Saint-Paul " (Marc-Aurele Fortin) (horiz.) 15 10
1012. 35 c. " Untitled No. 6 " (Paul-Emile Borduas) 30 30

454. Canada in 1867.

1981. Canada Day. Maps showing **evolution** of Canada from Confederation to **present** day. Multicoloured.
1013. 17 c. Type **454** 15 15
1014. 17 c. Canada in 1873 .. 15 15
1015. 17 c. Canada in 1905 .. 15 15
1016. 17 c. Canada since 1949 15 15

355. Frere Marie-Victorin.

1981. Canadian Botanists. **Multicoloured.**
1017. 17 c. Type **455** 15 15
1018. 17 c. John Macoun .. 15 15

456. The Montreal Rose.

1981. Montreal Flower Show.
1019. **456.** 17 c. multicoloured .. 15 20

457. Drawing of Niagara-on-the-Lake.

1981. Bicent. of Niagara-on-the-Lake (town).
1020. **457.** 17 c. multicoloured .. 15 20

458. Acadian Community.

1981. Centenary of First Acadia (community) Convention.
1021. **458.** 17 c. multicoloured .. 15 20

459. Aaron R. Mosher.

1981. Birth Centenary of Aaron R. Mosher (founder of Canadian Labour Congress).
1022. **459.** 17 c. multicoloured .. 15 20

460. Christmas Tree, 1781.

1981. Christmas. Bicentenary of First Illuminated Christmas Tree in Canada.

1023.	15 c. Type **460**	20	15
1024.	15 c. Christmas Tree, 1881	20	15
1025.	15 c. Christmas Tree, 1981	20	15

461. De Havilland " Tiger Moth ".

1981. Canadian Aircraft (3rd series). Mult.

1026.	17 c. Type **461**	20	15
1027.	17 c. Canadair " CL-41 (Tutor) "	20	15
1028.	35 c. Avro " Canada " jetliner	35	35
1029.	35 c. De Havilland Canada " Dash 7 "	35	35

462. Canadian Maple Leaf Emblem.

1981.

1030.	**462.** A (30 c.) red	20	30

No. 1030 was printed before a new first class domestic letter rate had been agreed, " A " representing the face value of the stamp, later decided to be 30 c.

1982. As T **462** but including face values.

1033	**462**	5 c. red	10	10
1033d		8 c. blue	80	75
1034		10 c. green	75	55
1036		30 c. red	35	30
1032		30 c. red, grey & blue	30	30
1036a		32 c. red	1·00	1·00
1032b		32 c. red, brn. & stone	45	45

463. 1851 3 d. Stamp.

1982. " Canada 82 " International Philatelic Youth Exhibition, Toronto. Stamps on Stamps. Multicoloured.

1037.	30 c. Type **463**	25	25
1038.	30 c. 1908 Centenary of Quebec 15 c. commemorative	25	25
1039.	35 c. 1935 10 c.	25	30
1040.	35 c. 1928 10 c.	25	30
1041.	60 c. 1929 50 c.	50	75

464. Jules Leger.

1982. Jules Leger (politician) Commemoration.

1043.	**464.** 30 c. multicoloured ..	20	20

465. Stylised drawing of Terry Fox.

1982. Cancer victim Terry Fox's " Marathon of Hope " (Trans-Canada fund-raising run) Commemoration.

1044.	**465.** 30 c. multicoloured ..	20	20

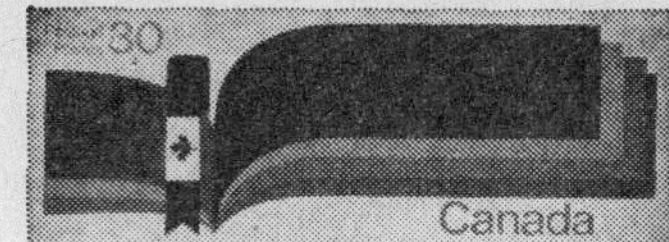

466. Stylised Open Book.
(Illustration reduced. Actual size 57 × 20 mm.)

1982. Patriation of Constitution.

1045.	**466.** 30 c. multicoloured ..	20	20

467. Male and Female Salvationists with Street Scene.

1982. Centenary of Salvation Army in Canada.

1046.	**467.** 30 c. multicoloured ..	20	20

469. Regina Legislature Building.

1982. Centenary of Regina.

1048.	**469.** 30 c. multicoloured ..	20	20

470. Finish of Race.

1982. Centenary of Royal Canadian Henley Regatta.

1049.	**470.** 30 c. multicoloured ..	20	25

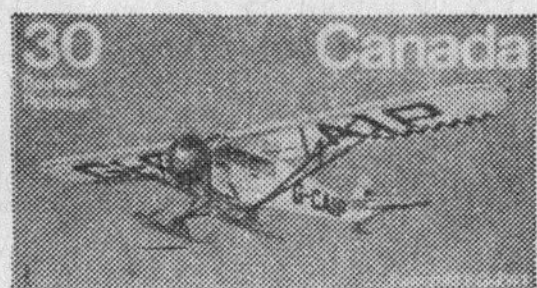

471. Fairchild " FC-2W1 ".

1982. Bush Aircraft. Multicoloured.

1050.	30 c. Type **471**	35	20
1051.	30 c. De Havilland Canada " Beaver " ..	35	20
1052.	60 c. Fokker " Super Universal "	65	75
1053.	60 c. Noorduyn " Norseman "	65	75

472. Decoy.

475. Mary, Joseph and Baby Jesus.

1982. Heritage Artefacts.

1054.	**472.**	1 c. black, light brn. and brown ..	10	10
1055.	–	2 c. black, blue and green ..	10	10
1056.	–	3 c. black, blue and deep blue ..	10	10
1057.	–	5 c. black, pink and brown	10	10
1058.	–	10 c. black, blue and turquoise ..	10	10
1059.	–	20 c. black, light brn. and brown ..	20	10
1060.	–	25 c. multicoloured ..	35	10
1061.	–	37 c. black, green & deep green ..	50	40
1062.	–	39 c. black, grey and violet	1·00	30
1063.	–	42 c. multicoloured ..	45	25
1064.	–	48 c. dp. brown, brn. and pink	70	55
1065.	–	50 c. black, light blue and blue	1·10	20
1066.	–	55 c. multicoloured ..	55	40
1067.	–	64 c. deep grey, black and grey	80	65
1068.	–	68 c. black, light brown and brown	1·00	55
1069.	–	72 c. multicoloured ..	75	65

DESIGNS—VERT. 2 c. Fishing Spear. 3 c. Stable Lantern. 5 c. Bucket. 10 c. Weathercock. 20 c. Skates. 25 c. Butter stamp. HORIZ. 37 c. Plough. 39 c. Settle-bed. 42 c. Linen chest. 48 c. Cradle. 50 c. Sleigh. 55 c. Iron kettle. 64 c. Kitchen Stove. 68 c. Spinning Wheel. 72 c. Hand-drawn cart.

1982. Christmas. Nativity Scenes.

1080.	30 c. Type **475**	20	10
1081.	35 c. The Shepherds ..	25	35
1082.	60 c. The Three Wise Men	45	70

476. Globes forming Symbolic Designs.

1983. World Communications Year.

1083.	**476.** 32 c. multicoloured ..	30	25

477. Map of World showing Canada.

1983. Commonwealth Day.

1084.	**477.** $2 multicoloured ..	1·75	2·25

478. Scene from Novel " Angeline de Montbrun " by " Laure Conan " (Felicite Angers).

1983. Canadian Writers (4th series).

1085.	32 c. Type **478**	25	20
1086.	32 c. Woodcut illustrating " Sea-gulls " (poem by E. J. Pratt)	25	20

479. St. John Ambulance Badge and "100".

1983. Cent. of St. John Ambulance in Canada.

1087.	**479.** 32 c. red, yell. & brn.	30	20

480. Victory Pictogram.

1983. " Universiade 83 " World University Games, Edmonton.

1088.	**480.** 32 c. multicoloured ..	25	15
1089.	– 64 c. multicoloured ..	50	70

481. Fort William, Ontario.

1983. Canada Day. Forts (1st series). Mult.

1090.	32 c. Fort Henry, Ontario (44 × 22 mm.) ..	35	50
1091.	32 c. Type **481**	35	50
1092.	32 c. Fort Rodd Hill, British Columbia ..	35	50
1093.	32 c. Fort Wellington, Otnario (28 × 22 mm.)	35	50
1094.	32 c. Fort Prince of Wales, Manitoba (28 × 22 mm.)	35	50
1095.	32 c. Halifax Citadel, Nova Scotia (44 × 22 mm.) ..	35	50
1096.	32 c. Fort Chambly, Quebec	35	50
1097.	32 c. Fort No. 1, Point Levis, Quebec ..	35	50
1098.	32 c. Coteau-du-Lac Fort, Quebec (28 × 22 mm.)	35	50
1099.	32 c. Fort Beausejour, New Brunswick (28 × 22 mm.)	35	50

See also Nos. 1153/62.

482. Scouting Poster by Marc Fournier (aged 12).

1983. Scouting in Canada (75th Anniv.) and World Scout Jamboree, Alberta, (15th Anniversary).

1100.	**482.** 32 c. multicoloured ..	30	30

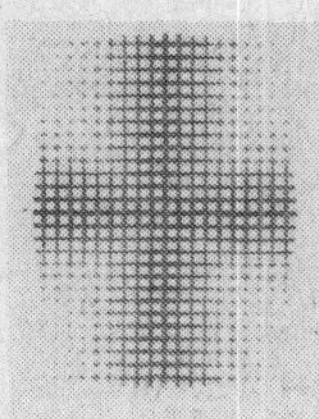

483. Cross Symbol.

1983. 6th Assembly of the World Council of Churches, Vancouver.

1101.	**483.** 32 c. green & lilac ..	30	20

484. Sir Humphrey Gilbert (founder).

1983. 400th Anniv. of Newfoundland.

1102.	**484.** 32 c. multicoloured ..	30	20

485. " NICKEL " Deposits.

1983. Centenary of Discovery of Sudbury Nickel Deposits.

1103.	**485.** 32 c. multicoloured ..	30	20

486. Josiah Henson and Escaping Slaves.

1983. Nineteenth-century Social Reformers. Multicoloured.

1104. 32 c. Type **486** 25 25
1105. 32 c. Father Antoine Labelle and rural village (32 × 26 mm.) 25 25

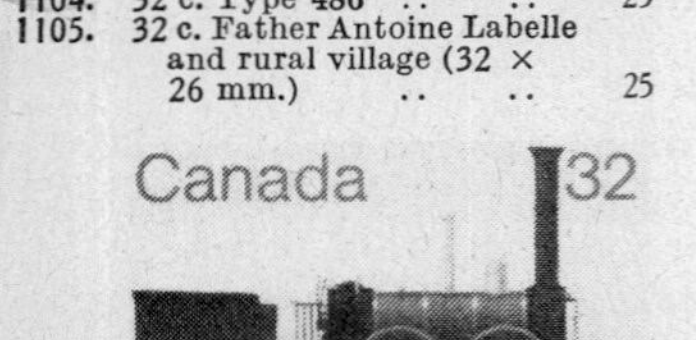

487. Type 0–4–0, "Dorchester" Locomotive.

1983. Railway Locomotives (1st series). Mult.

1106. 32 c. Type **487** 70 35
1107. 32 c. Type 4–4–0, "Toronto" 70 35
1108. 37 c. Type 0–6–0, "Samson" 70 70
1109. 64 c. Type 4–4–0, "Adam Brown" .. 1·00 1·25

See also Nos. 1132/5, 1175/8 and 1213/16.

488. School Coat of Arms.

1983. Centenary of Dalhousie Law School.

1110. **488.** 32 c. multicoloured .. 30 30

489. City Church.

1983. Christmas. Churches. Multicoloured.

1111. 32 c. Type **489** 40 10
1112. 37 c. Family walking to Church 55 35
1113. 64 c. Country Chapel .. 90 1·50

490. Royal Canadian Regiment and British Columbia Regiment.

1983. Canadian Army Regiments. Mult.

1114. 32 c. Type **490** 50 35
1115. 32 c. Royal Winnipeg Rifles & Royal Canadian Dragoons 50 35

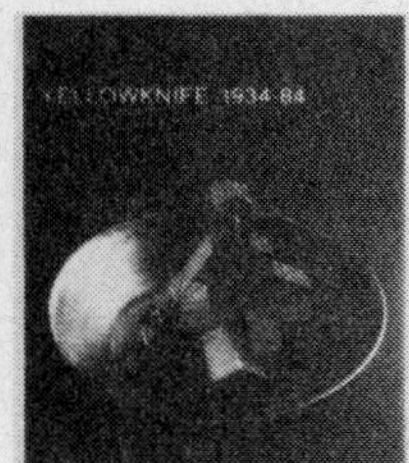

491. Gold Mine in Prospecting Pan.

1984. 50th Anniversary of Yellowknife.

1116. **491.** 32 c. multicoloured .. 30 30

492. Montreal Symphony Orchestra.

1984. 50th Anniversary of Montreal Symphony Orchestra.

1117. **492.** 32 c. multicoloured .. 35 30

493. Jacques Cartier.

1984. 450th Anniversary of Jacques Cartier's Voyage to Canada.

1118. **493.** 32 c. multicoloured .. 35 30

494. U.S.C.S. "Eagle".

1984. Tall Ships Visit.

1119. **494.** 32 c. multicoloured .. 35 30

495. Service Medal.

1984. 75th Anniversary of Canadian Red Cross Society.

1120. **495.** 32 c. multicoloured .. 35 30

496. Oared Galleys.

1984. Bicentenary of New Brunswick.

1121. **496.** 32 c. multicoloured .. 35 30

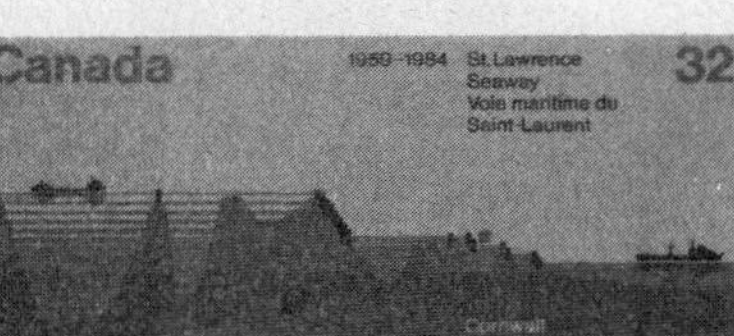

497. St. Lawrence Seaway. (Illustration reduced. Actual size 52 × 22mm.).

1984. 25th Anniv. of St. Lawrence Seaway.

1122. **497.** 32 c. multicoloured .. 45 30

499. Loyalists of 1784.

1984. Bicentenary of Arrival of United Empire Loyalists.

1124. **499.** 32 c. multicoloured .. 30 30

500. St. John's Basilica.

1984. Bicentenary of Roman Catholic Church in Newfoundland.

1125. **500.** 32 c. multicoloured .. 30 25

501. Coat of Arms of Pope John Paul II.

1984. Papal Visit.

1126. **501.** 32 c. multicoloured .. 40 20
1127. 64 c. multicoloured .. 85 1·10

502. Louisbourg Lighthouse, 1734.

1984. Canadian Lighthouses (1st series). Multicoloured.

1128. 32 c. Type **502** 85 85
1129. 32 c. Fisgard Lighthouse, 1860 .. .. 85 85
1130. 32 c. Ile Verte Lighthouse, 1809 .. .. 85 85
1131. 32 c. Gibraltar Point Lighthouse, 1808 .. 85 85

See also Nos. 1166/9.

503. Type 0–6–0, "Scotia", Locomotive.

1984. Railway Locomotives (2nd series). Mult.

1132. 32 c. Type **503** 75 30
1133. 32 c. Type 4-4-0, "Countess of Dufferin" .. 75 30
1134. 37 c. Type 2-6-0, GT Class "E3" 80 60
1135. 64 c. Type 4-6-0, CP Class "D10a" .. .. 1·25 1·25

504. "The Annunciation" (Jean Dallaire).

1984. Christmas. Religious Paintings. Mult.

1137. 32 c. Type **504** 30 10
1138. 37 c. "The Three Kings" (Simone Bouchard) .. 35 35
1139. 64 c. "Snow in Bethlehem" (David Milne) .. 60 80

505. Pilots of 1914–18, 1939–45 and 1984.

1984. 60th Anniv. of Royal Canadian Air Force.

1140. **505.** 32 c. multicoloured .. 35 30

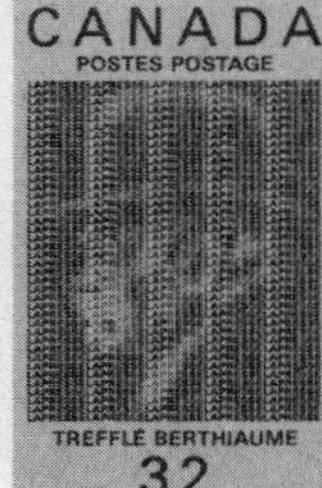

506. Treffle Berthiaume (editor).

1984. Centenary of "La Presse" (newspaper).

1141. **506.** 32 c. brown, red and light brown .. 35 30

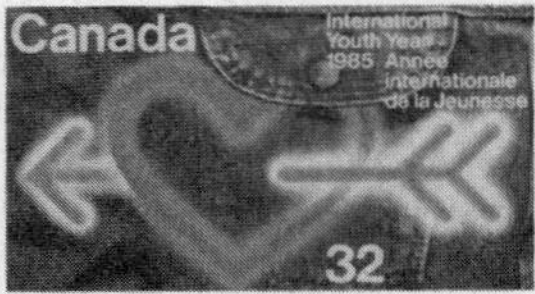

507. Heart and Arrow.

1985. International Youth Year.

1142. **507.** 32 c. multicoloured .. 30 30

508. Astronaut in Space, and Planet Earth.

1985. Canadian Space Programme.

1143. **508.** 32 c. multicoloured .. 40 30

509. Emily Murphy.

1985. Women's Rights Activists. Multicoloured.

1144. 32 c. Type **509** 40 40
1145. 32 c. Therese Casgrain .. 40 40

510. Gabriel Dumont (Métis leader) and Battle of Batoche, 1885.

1985. Centenary of the North-West Rebellion.

1146. **510.** 32 c. blue, red and grey 30 30

511. Rear View, Parliament Building, Ottawa.

512. Queen Elizabeth II.

512a. Queen Elizabeth II in 1984 (from photo by Karsh).

1985.

1147b	–	1 c. green	30	40
1148	–	2 c. green	10	10
1149	–	5 c. brown ..	20	20
1150a	–	6 c. brown ..	30	10
1150b	–	6 c. purplle ..	30	35
1151	511	34 c. black ..	85	80
1155		34c. multicoloured	50	10
1158		34 c. brown ..	1·75	1·75
1161	512	34 c. black and blue	45	30
1152	511	36 c. purple ..	1·10	1·00
1156		36 c. multicoloured	30	40
1159		36 c. red	80	80
1162	512	36 c. purple ..	1·25	60
1153	511	37 c. blue	60	40
1157	–	37 c. multicoloured	75	35
1162a	512a	37 c. multicoloured	1·25	30
1154	511	38 c. blue	50	60
1157c	–	38 c. multicoloured	35	40
1162b	512a	38 c. multicoloured	35	40
1160b	511	38 c. green ..	40	40
1162c	512a	39 c. multicoloured	1·00	35
1162d		40 c. multicoloured	40	45
1162e		42 c. multicoloured	40	45

DESIGNS: 1 c, 5 c, 6 c. (1150b) East Block, Parliament Building. 2, 6 c. (1150) West Block, Parliament Building. 37 c. (1157) Front view Parliament Building. 38 c. (1157c) Side view, Parliament Building.

1985. Canada Day. Forts (2nd series). As T **481**. Multicoloured.

1163. 34 c. Lower Fort Garry, Manitoba 50 55
1164. 34 c. Fort Anne, Nova Scotia 50 55
1165. 34 c. Fort York, Ontario 50 55
1166. 34 c. Castle Hill, Newfoundland 50 55
1167. 34 c. Fort Whoop Up, Alberta 50 55
1168. 34 c. Fort Erie, Ontario 50 55
1169. 34 c. Fort Walsh, Saskatchewan 50 55
1170. 34 c. Fort Lennox, Quebec 50 55
1171. 34 c. York Redoubt, Nova Scotia 50 55
1172. 34 c. Fort Frederick, Ontario 50 55

Nos. 1163 and 1168 measure 44 × 22 mm. and Nos. 1166/7 and 1171/2 28 × 22 mm.

513. Louis Hébert (apothecary). **514.** Parliament Buildings and Map of World.

1985. 45th International Pharmaceutical Sciences Congress of Pharmaceutical Federation, Montreal.

1173. **513.** 34 c. multicoloured .. 45 35

1985. 74th Conference of Inter-Parliamentary Union, Ottawa.

1174. **514.** 34 c. multicoloured .. 45 35

515. Guide and Brownie Saluting.

1985. 75th Anniv. of Girl Guide Movement.

1175. **515.** 34 c. multicoloured .. 45 35

516. Sisters Islets Lighthouse.

1985. Canadian Lighthouses (2nd series). Multicoloured.

1176. 34 c. Type **516** .. .. 1·00 1·10
1177. 34 c. Pelee Passage Lighthouse .. .. 1·00 1·10
1178. 34 c. Haut-fond Prince Lighthouse .. .. 1·00 1·10
1179. 34 c. Rose Blanche Lighthouse, Cains Island .. .. .. 1·00 1·10

517. Santa Claus in Reindeer-drawn Sleigh.

1985. Christmas. Santa Claus Parade. Mult.

1181. 32 c. Canada Post's parade float 45 20
1182. 34 c. Type **517** 60 10
1183. 39 c. Acrobats and horse-drawn carriage .. 70 70
1184. 68 c. Christmas tree pudding and goose on float .. .. .. 1·25 1·25

1985. Railway Locomotives (3rd series). As T **503.** Multicoloured.

1185. 34 c. Class "K2" .. 65 40
1186. 34 c. Class "P2a" .. 65 40
1187. 39 c. Class "O10a" .. 75 75
1188. 68 c. Class "H4D" .. 1·10 1·10

518. Naval Personnel of 1910, 1939–45 and 1985.

1985. 75th Anniv. of Royal Canadian Navy.

1189. **518.** 34 c. multicoloured .. 65 35

519. "The Old Holton House, Montreal" (James Wilson Morrice).

1985. 125th Anniv. of Montreal Museum of Fine Arts.

1190. **519.** 34 c. multicoloured .. 40 35

520. Map of Alberta showing Olympic Sites. (Illustration reduced, actual size 52 × 25 mm.).

1986. Winter Olympic Games, Calgary (1988) (1st issue).

1191. **520.** 34 c. multicoloured .. 40 40

See also Nos. 1216/17, 1236/7, 1258/9 and 1281/4.

521. Canada Pavilion.

1986. "Expo '86" World Fair, Vancouver (1st issue). Multicoloured.

1192. 34p. Type **521** 60 45
1193. 39p. Early telephone, dish aerial and satellite 65 1·10

See also Nos. 1196/7.

522. Molly Brant. **523.** Aubert de Gaspé and Scene from "Les Anciens Canadiens"

1986. 250th Birth Anniv. of Molly Brant (Iroquois leader).

1194. **522.** 34 c. multicoloured .. 40 40

1986. Birth Bicentenary of Philippe Aubert de Gaspé (author).

1195. **523.** 34 c. multicoloured .. 40 40

1986. "Expo '86" World Fair, Vancouver (2nd issue). As T **521.** Multicoloured.

1196. 34 c. Expo Centre, Vancouver (vert.) .. 45 40
1197. 68 c. Early and modern trains .. 1·00 1·10

524. Canadian Field Post Office and Cancellation, 1944.

1986. 75th Anniv. of Canadian Forces Postal Service.

1198. **524.** 34 c. multicoloured .. 65 40

525. Great Blue Heron.

1986. Birds of Canada. Multicoloured.

1199. 34 c. Type **525** 85 95
1200. 34 c. Snow goose .. 85 95
1201. 34 c. Great horned owl .. 85 95
1202. 34 c. Spruce grouse .. 85 95

526. Railway Rotary Snowplough.

1986. Canada Day. Science and Technology. Canadian Inventions (1st series). Mult.

1203. 34 c. Type **526** 75 85
1204. 34 c. Space shuttle "Challenger" launching satellite with Canadarm 75 85
1205. 34 c. Pilot wearing anti-gravity flight suit and "Spitfire" 75 85
1206. 34 c. Variable-pitch propeller and Avro "504K" airplane .. 75 85

See also Nos. 1241/4 and 1292/5.

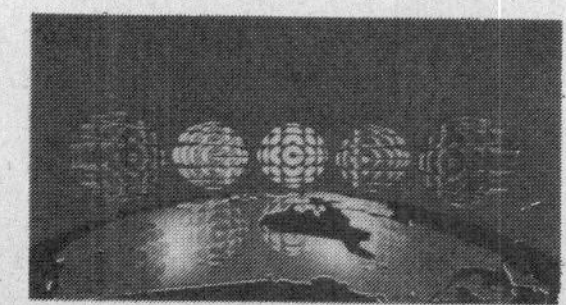

527. C.B.C. Logos over Map of Canada.

1986. 50th Anniv. of Canadian Broadcasting Corporation.

1207. **527.** 34 c. multicoloured .. 40 45

528. Ice Age Artefacts, Tools and Settlement.

1986. Exploration of Canada (1st series). Discoverers. Multicoloured.

1208. 34 c. Type **528** 35 55
1209. 34 c. Viking ships .. 35 55
1210. 34 c. John Cabot's "Matthew" 1497, compass and fish .. 35 55
1211. 34 c. Henry Hudson cast adrift, 1611 .. .. 35 55

See also Nos. 1232/5, 1285/8 and 1319/22.

529. Crowfoot (Blackfoot Chief) and Indian Village.

1986. Founders of the Canadian West. Multicoloured.

1213. 34 c. Type **529** 35 55
1214. 34 c. James Macleod of the North West Mounted Police and Fort Macleod 35 55

530. Peace Dove and Globe.

1986. International Peace Year.

1215. **530.** 34 c. multicoloured .. 40 45

531. Ice Hockey. **532.** Angel with Crown.

1986. Winter Olympic Games, Calgary (1988) (2nd issue). Multicoloured.

1216. 34 c. Type **531** .. .. 75 1·00
1217. 34 c. Biathlon .. .. 75 1·00

1986. Christmas. Multicoloured.

1218. 29 c. Angel singing carol (36 × 22 mm.) 30 15
1219. 34 c. Type **532** 40 25
1220. 39 c. Angel playing lute 50 65
1221. 68 c. Angel with ribbon 75 1·40

533. John Molson with Theatre Royal, Montreal, "Accommodation" (paddle-steamer) and Railway Train.

1986. 150th Death Anniv. of John Molson (businessman).

1222. **533.** 34 c. multicoloured .. 50 50

1986. Railway Locomotives (4th series). As T **503**, but size 60 × 22 mm. Multicoloured
1223. 34 c. Class "V-1-a" .. 90 90
1224. 34 c. Class "Tla" .. 90 90
1225. 39 c. Class "U-2-a" .. 1·00 90
1226. 68 c. Class "Hlc" .. 1·75 2·00

534. Toronto's First Post Office.

1987. "Capex '87" International Stamp Exhibition, Toronto. Post Offices.
1227. 34 c. Type **534** 40 20
1228. 36 c. Nelson-Miramichi, New Brunswick .. 50 35
1229. 42 c. Saint-Ours, Quebec 60 45
1230. 72 c. Battleford, Saskatchewan .. 90 85

535. Etienne Brule exploring Lake Superior.

1987. Exploration of Canada (2nd series). Pioneers of New France. Multicoloured.
1232. 34 c. Type **535** 65 45
1233. 34 c. Radisson and Des Groseilliers with British and French flags 65 45
1234. 34 c. Jolliet and Father Marquette on the Mississippi 65 45
1235. 34 c. Jesuit missionary preaching to Indians 65 45

1987. Winter Olympic Games, Calgary (1988) (3rd issue). As T **531.** Multicoloured.
1236. 36 c. Speed skating .. 50 40
1237. 42 c. Bobsleighing .. 75 60

536. Volunteer Activities.

1987. National Volunteer Week.
1238. **536.** 36 c. multicoloured .. 30 35

537. Canadian Coat of Arms.

1987. 5th Anniv. of Canadian Charter of Rights and Freedoms.
1239. **537.** 36 c. multicoloured .. 35 35

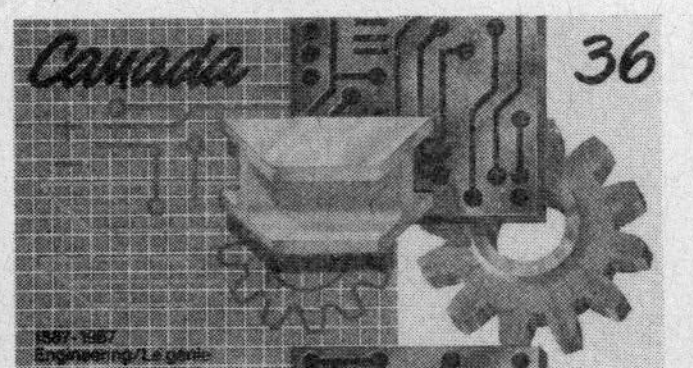

538. Steel Girder, Gear Wheel and Microchip.

1987. Centenary of Engineering Institute of Canada.
1240. **538.** 36 c. multicoloured .. 35 40

539. R. A. Fessenden (AM Radio).

1987. Canada Day. Science and Technology. Canadian Inventors (2nd series). Mult.
1241. 36 c. Type **539** 35 35
1242. 36 c. C. Fenerty (newsprint pulp) 35 35
1243. 36 c. G.-E. Desbarats and W. Leggo (halftone engraving) .. 35 35
1244. 36 c. F. N. Gisborne (first North American undersea telegraph) .. 35 35

540. "Segwun".

1987. Canadian Steamships. Multicoloured.
1245. 36 c. Type **540** .. .. 1·00 1·25
1246. 36 c. "Princess Marguerite" (52 × 22 mm.) .. .. 1·00 1·25

541. Figurehead from "Hamilton", 1813.

1987. Historic Shipwrecks. Multicoloured.
1247. 36 c. Type **541** 45 45
1248. 36 c. "Hull of San Juan", 1565 .. .. .. 45 45
1249. 36 c. Wheel from "Breadalbane", 1853 .. 45 45
1250. 36 c. Bell from "Ericsson", 1892 .. 45 45

542. Air Canada Boeing "767" and Globe.

1987. 50th Anniv. of Air Canada.
1251. **542.** 36 c. multicoloured .. 30 35

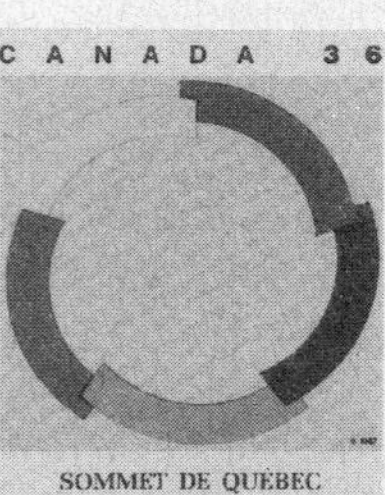

543. Summit Symbol.

1987. 2nd International Francophone Summit, Quebec.
1252. **543.** 36 c. multicoloured .. 30 35

544. Commonwealth Symbol.

1987. Commonwealth Heads of Government Meeting, Vancouver.
1253. **544.** 36 c. multicoloured .. 35 40

545. Poinsettia.

1987. Christmas. Christmas Plants. Mult.
1254. 31 c. Decorated Christmas tree and presents 30 35
1255. 36 c. Type **545** 35 40
1256. 42 c. Holly wreath .. 40 45
1257. 72 c. Mistletoe and decorated tree 65 70

1987. Winter Olympic Games, Calgary (1988) (4th issue). As T **531.** Multicoloured.
1258. 36 c. Cross-country skiing 35 40
1259. 36 c. Ski-jumping .. 35 40

546. Football, Grey Cup and Spectators. **547.** Flying Squirrel.

548a. Runnymede Library, Toronto.

1987. 75th Grey Cup Final (Canadian football championship), Vancouver.
1260. **546.** 36 c. multicoloured .. 35 40

1988. Canadian Mammals and Architecture. Multicoloured.
(a) As T **547.**
1261 1 c. Type **547** .. 10 10
1262 2 c. Porcupine 10 10
1263 3 c. Muskrat 10 10
1264 5 c. Varying hare .. 10 10
1265 6 c. Red fox 10 10
1266 10 c. Striped skunk .. 10 10
1267 25 c. American beaver .. 25 30
1268 43 c. Lynx (26 × 20 mm) 90 50
1269 44 c. Walrus (27 × 21 mm) 45 45
1270 45 c. Pronghorn (27 × 21 mm) 35 40
1270c 46 c. Wolverine (27 × 21 mm) 45 50
1271 57 c. Killer whale (26 × 20 mm) .. .. .. 1·25 70
1272 59 c. Musk ox (27 × 21 mm) 65 60
1273 61 c. Wolf (27 × 21 mm) 50 55
1273b 63 c. Harbour porpoise (27 × 21mm) 65 70
1274 74 c. Wapiti (26 × 20 mm) 1·40 85
1275 76 c. Brown bear (27 × 21 mm) 80 75
1276 78 c. White whale (27 × 21 mm) 90 80
1276c 80 c. Peary caribou (27 × 21) 80 85

(b) As T **548a**.
1277 $1 Type **548a** .. .. 1·00 1·10
1278 $2 McAdam Railway Station, New Brunswick .. .. .. 2·00 2·10
1279 $5 Bonsecours Market, Montreal .. .. 5·00 5·25

1988. Winter Olympic Games, Calgary (5th issue). As T **531.** Multicoloured.
1281. 37 c. Slalom skiing .. 50 40
1282. 37 c. Curling 50 40
1283. 43 c. Figure skating .. 65 45
1284. 74 c. Luge .. .. 1·00 70

549. Trade Goods, Blackfoot Encampment and Page from Anthony Henday's Journal.

1988. Exploration of Canada (3rd series). Explorers of the West. Multicoloured.
1285. 37 c. Type **549** 35 40
1286. 37 c. Discovery and map of George Vancouver's voyage 35 40
1287. 37 c. Simon Fraser's expedition portaging canoes 35 40
1288. 37 c. John Palliser's surveying equipment and view of prairie .. 35 40

550 "The Young Reader" (Ozias Leduc)

1988. Canadian Art (1st series).
1289 **550** 50 c. multicoloured .. 50 70
See also Nos. 1327, 1384 and 1421.

551 Duck landing on Marsh

1988. Wildlife and Habitat Conservation. Multicoloured.
1290 37 c. Type **551** 50 40
1291 37 c. Moose feeding in marsh 50 40

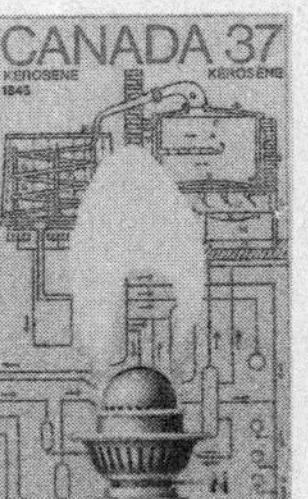

552 Kerosene Lamp and Diagram of Distillation Plant

1988. Canada Day. Science and Technology. Canadian Inventions (3rd series). Mult.
1292 37 c. Type **552** 35 40
1293 37 c. Ears of Marquis wheat 35 40
1294 37 c. Electron microscope and magnified image .. 35 40
1295 37 c. Patient under "Cobalt 60" cancer therapy 35 40

553 "Papilio brevicauda"

1296 37 c. Type **553** 40 40
1297 37 c. "Lycaeides idas" .. 40 40
1298 37 c. "Oeneis macounii" 40 40
1299 37 c. "Papilio glaucus" .. 40 40

554 St. John's Harbour Entrance and Skyline

1988. Centenary of Incorporation of St. John's, Newfoundland.
1300 **554** 37 c. multicoloured .. 35 40

555 Club Members working on Forestry Project and Rural Scene

1988. 75th Anniv of 4-H Clubs.
1301 **555** 37 c. multicoloured .. 35 40

556 Saint-Maurice Ironworks

1988. 250th Anniv of Saint-Maurice Ironworks, Quebec.
1302 **556** 37 c. black, orge & brn 35 40

557 Tahltan Bear Dog

1988. Canadian Dogs. Multicoloured.
1303 37 c. Type **557** 40 40
1304 37 c. Nova Scotia duck tolling retriever .. 40 40
1305 37 c. Canadian eskimo dog 40 40
1306 37 c. Newfoundland .. 40 40

558 Baseball, Glove and Pitch

1988. 150th Anniv of Baseball in Canada. Multicoloured.
1307 **558** 37 c. multicoloured .. 35 40

559 Virgin with Inset of Holy Child

1988. Christmas. Icons. Multicoloured.
1308 32 c. Holy Family (36 × 21 mm) 30 35
1309 37 c. Type **559** 35 40
1310 43 c. Virgin and Child .. 40 45
1311 74 c. Virgin and Child (different) 70 75

On No. 1308 the left-hand third of the design area is taken up by the bar code.

No. 1309 also commemorates the Millenium of Ukrainian Christianity.

560 Bishop Inglis and Nova Scotia Church

1988. Bicentenary of Consecration of Charles Inglis (first Canadian Anglican bishop) (1987).
1312 **560** 37 c. multicoloured .. 35 40

561 Frances Ann Hopkins and "Canoe Manned by Voyageurs"

1988. 150th Birth Anniv of Frances Ann Hopkins (artist).
1313 **561** 37 c. multicoloured .. 35 40

562 Angus Walters and "Bluenose" (schooner)

1988. 20th Death Anniv of Angus Walters (yachtsman).
1314 **562** 37 c. multicoloured .. 35 40

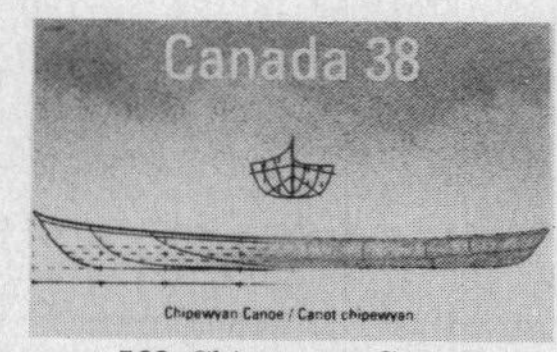

563 Chipewyan Canoe

1989. Small Craft of Canada (1st series). Native Canoes. Multicoloured.
1315 38 c. Type **563** 50 50
1316 38 c. Haida canoe .. 50 50
1317 38 c. Inuit kayak .. 50 50
1318 38 c. Micmac canoe .. 50 50

See also Nos. 1377/80 and 1428/31.

564 Matonabbee and Hearne's Expedition

1989. Exploration of Canada (4th issue). Explorers of the North. Multicoloured.
1319 38 c. Type **564** 55 55
1320 38 c. Relics of Franklin's expedition and White Ensign 55 55
1321 38 c. Joseph Tyrrell's compass, hammer and fossil 55 55
1322 38 c. Vilhjalmur Stefansson, camera on tripod and sledge dog team 55 55

565 Construction of Victoria Bridge, Montreal and William Notman

1989. Canada Day. "150 Years of Canadian Photography". Designs showing early photograph and photographer. Multicoloured.
1323 38 c. Type **565** 50 50
1324 38 c. Plains Indian village and W. Hanson Boorne 50 50
1325 38 c. Horse-drawn sleigh and Alexander Henderson 50 50
1326 38 c. Quebec street scene and Jules-Ernest Livernois 50 50

566 Tsimshian Ceremonial Frontlet, c. 1900

1989. Canadian Art (2nd issue).
1327 **566** 50 c. multicoloured .. 55 60

567 Canadian Flag and Forest

1989. Self-adhesive. Multicoloured.
1328 38 c. Type **567** 90 80
1328b 39 c. Canadian flag and prairie 55 35
1328c 40 c. Canadian flag and sea 45 35
1328d 42 c. Canadian flag over mountains 40 45

568 Archibald Lampman

1989. Canadian Poets. Multicoloured.
1329 38 c. Type **568** 40 45
1330 38 c. Louis-Honore Frechette 40 45

569 "Clavulinopsis fusiformis"

1989. Mushrooms. Multicoloured.
1331 38 c. Type **569** 50 45
1332 38 c. "Boletus mirabilis" 50 45
1333 38 c. "Cantharellus cinnabarinus" .. 50 45
1334 38 c. "Morchella esculenta" 50 45

570 Night Patrol, Korea

1989. 75th Annivs of Canadian Regiments. Multicoloured.
1335 38 c. Type **570** (Princess Patricia's Canadian Light Infantry) .. 70 70
1336 38 c. Trench raid, France, 1914–18 (Royal 22e Regiment) 70 70

571 Globe in Box

1989. Canada Export Trade Month.
1337 **571** 38 c. multicoloured .. 40 45

572 Film Director

1989. Arts and Entertainment.
1338 **572** 38 c. brown, deep brown and violet .. 40 45
1339 – 38 c. brown, deep brown and green .. 40 45
1340 – 38 c. brown, deep brown and mauve 40 45
1341 – 38 c. brown, deep brown and blue .. 40 45

DESIGNS: No. 1339, Actors; No. 1340, Dancers; No. 1341, Musicians.

573 "Snow II" (Lawren S. Harris)

1989. Christmas. Paintings of Winter Landscapes. Multicoloured.
1342 33 c. "Champ-de-Mars, Winter" (William Brymner) (35 × 21 mm) 35 40
1343 38 c. "Bend in the Gosselin River" (Marc-Aurele Suzor-Cote) (21 × 35 mm) 40 45
1344 44 c. Type **573** 45 50
1345 76 c. "Ste. Agnes" (A. H. Robinson) 80 85
On No. 1342 the left-hand third of the design area is taken up by a bar code.

574 Canadians listening to Declaration of War, 1939

1989. 50th Anniv of Outbreak of Second World War (1st issue).
1346 **574** 38 c. blk, silver & pur 40 45
1347 – 38 c. black, silver and grey 40 45
1348 – 38 c. blk, silver & grn 40 45
1349 – 38 c. black, silver & bl 40 45
DESIGNS: No. 1347, Army mobilization; No. 1348, British Commonwealth air crew training.
See also Nos. 1409/12 and 1456/9.

575 Canadian Flag **576**

1989.
1350 **575** 1 c. multicoloured .. 10 10
1351 – 5 c. multicoloured .. 10 10
1352 – 39 c. multicoloured 50 35
1354 **576** 39 c. multicoloured 40 35
1357 – 39 c. purple .. 40 75
1353 – 40 c. multicoloured 40 45
1355 – 40 c. multicoloured 40 45
1358 – 40 c. blue 40 45
1356 – 42 c. multicoloured 40 45
DESIGNS: Nos. 1351/3, 1357/8 as T **575** but different folds in flag. As T **576** No. 1355, Flag over forest.
No. 1356, As T **576** but with different background.

577 Norman Bethune in 1937, and performing Operation, Montreal

1990. Birth Centenary of Dr. Norman Bethune (surgeon). Multicoloured.
1375 39 c. Type **577** 45 50
1376 39 c. Bethune in 1939, and treating wounded Chinese soldiers .. 45 50

1990. Small Craft of Canada (2nd series). Early Work Boats. As T **563**. Multicoloured.
1377 39 c. Fishing dory .. 50 55
1378 39 c. Logging pointer .. 50 55
1379 39 c. York boat .. 50 55
1380 39 c. North canoe .. 50 55

578 Maple Leaf Mosaic

1990. Multiculturalism.
1381 **578** 39 c. multicoloured .. 35 40

579 Mail Van (facing left)

1990. "Moving the Mail". Multicoloured.
1382 39 c. Type **579** 45 55
1383 39 c. Mail van (facing right) 45 55

1990. Canadian Art (3rd series). As T **550**. Multicoloured.
1384 50 c. "The West Wind" (Tom Thomson) .. 55 65

580 Amerindian and Inuit Dolls

1990. Dolls. Multicoloured.
1385 39 c. Type **580** 55 60
1386 39 c. 19th-century settlers' dolls 55 60
1387 39 c. Commercial dolls, 1917–36 .. .. 55 60
1388 39 c. Commercial dolls, 1940–60 .. .. 55 60

581 Canadian Flag and Fireworks

1990. Canada Day.
1389 **581** 39 c. multicoloured .. 45 50

582 "Stromatolites" (fossil algae)

1990. Prehistoric Canada (1st series). Primitive Life. Multicoloured.
1390 39 c. Type **582** 60 60
1391 39 c. "Opabinia regalis" (soft invertebrate) .. 60 60
1392 39 c. "Paradoxides davidis" (trilobite) .. 60 60
1393 39 c. "Eurypterus remipes" (sea scorpion) 60 60
See also Nos. 1417/20.

583 Acadian Forest

1990. Canadian Forests. Multicoloured.
1394 39 c. Type **583** 60 60
1395 39 c. Great Lakes-St. Lawrence forest .. 60 60
1396 39 c. Pacific Coast forest 60 60
1397 39 c. Boreal forest .. 60 60

584 Clouds and Rainbow

1990. 150th Anniv of Weather Observing in Canada.
1398 **584** 39 c. multicoloured .. 40 50

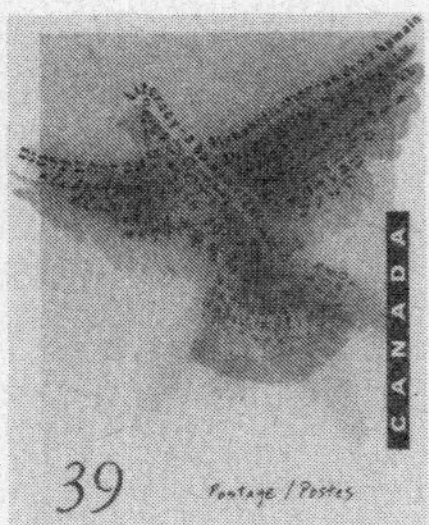

585 "Alphabet" Bird

1990. International Literacy Year.
1399 **585** 39 c. multicoloured .. 40 50

586 Sasquatch

1990. Legendary Creatures. Multicoloured.
1400 39 c. Type **586** 60 60
1401 39 c. Kraken 60 60
1402 39 c. Werewolf 60 60
1403 39 c. Ogopogo 60 60

587 Agnes Macphail

588 "Virgin Mary with Christ Child and St. John the Baptist" (Norval Morrisseau)

1990. Birth Centenary of Agnes Macphail (first woman elected to Parliament).
1404 **587** 39 c. multicoloured .. 40 50

1990. Christmas. Native Art.
1405 – 34 c. multicoloured .. 30 35
1406 **588** 39 c. multicoloured .. 35 40
1407 – 45 c. multicoloured .. 40 45
1408 – 78 c. black, red & grey 70 75
DESIGNS—35 × 21 mm. 34 c. "Rebirth" (Jackson Beardy). As T **588**. 45 c. "Mother and Child" (Inuit sculpture, Cape Dorset); 78 c. "Children of the Raven" (Bill Reid).
No. 1405 includes a bar code in the design.

1990. 50th Anniv of Second World War (2nd issue). As T **574**.
1409 39 c. black, silver & green 55 55
1410 39 c. black, silver & brown 55 55
1411 39 c. black, silver & brown 55 55
1412 39 c. black, silver & mve 55 55
DESIGNS: No. 1409, Canadian family at home, 1940; 1410, Packing parcels for the troops; 1411, Harvesting; 1412, Testing anti-gravity flying suit.

589 Jennie Trout (first woman physician) and Women's Medical College, Kingston

1991. Medical Pioneers. Multicoloured.
1413 40 c. Type **589** 50 50
1414 40 c. Wilder Penfield (neurosurgeon) and Montreal Neurological Institute 50 50
1415 40 c. Frederick Banting (discoverer of insulin) and University of Toronto medical faculty 50 50
1416 40 c. Harold Griffith (anesthesiologist) and Queen Elizabeth Hospital, Montreal .. 50 50

1991. Prehistoric Canada (2nd series). Primitive Vertebrates. As T **582**. Mult.
1417 40 c. "Eusthenopteron foordi" (fish fossil) .. 50 50
1418 40 c. "Hylonomus lyelli" (land reptile) 50 50
1419 40 c. Fossil conodonts .. 50 50
1420 40 c. "Archaeopteris halliana" (early tree) .. 50 50

1991. Canadian Art (4th series). As T **550**. Multicoloured.
1421 50 c. "Forest, British Columbia" (Emily Carr) 50 55

590 Blue Poppies and Butchart Gardens, Victoria

1991. Public Gardens. Multicoloured.
1422 40 c. Type **590** 40 45
1423 40 c. Marigolds and International Peace Garden, Boissevain .. 40 45
1424 40 c. Lilac and Royal Botanical Gardens, Hamilton 40 45
1425 40 c. Roses and Montreal Botanical Gardens .. 40 45
1426 40 c. Rhododendrons and Halifax Public Gardens 40 45

591 Maple Leaf

1991. Canada Day.
1427 **591** 40 c. multicoloured .. 40 45

1991. Small Craft of Canada (3rd series). As T **563**. Multicoloured.
1428 40 c. Verchere rowboat .. 40 45
1429 40 c. Touring kayak .. 40 45
1430 40 c. Sailing dinghy .. 40 45
1431 40 c. Cedar strip canoe .. 40 45

592 South Nahanni River

1991. Canadian Rivers. Multicoloured.

No.	Description	Unused	Used
1432	40 c. Type **592**	40	45
1433	40 c. Athabasca River ..	40	45
1434	40 c. Boundary Waters, Voyageur Waterway ..	40	45
1435	40 c. Jacques-Cartier River	40	45
1436	40 c. Main River ..	40	45

593 "Leaving Europe"

1991. Centenary of Ukrainian Immigration. Panels from "The Ukrainian Pioneer" by William Kurelek. Multicoloured.

No.	Description	Unused	Used
1437	40 c. Type **593**	40	45
1438	40 c. "Canadian Winter"	40	45
1439	40 c. "Clearing the Land"	40	45
1440	40 c. "Harvest" ..	40	45

594 Ski Patrol rescuing Climber

1991. Emergency Services. Multicoloured.

No.	Description	Unused	Used
1441	40 c. Type **594**	40	45
1442	40 c. Police at road traffic accident	40	45
1443	40 c. Firemen on extending ladder ..	40	45
1444	40 c. Rescue helicopter and lifeboat	40	45

595 "The Witched Canoe"

1991. Canadian Folktales. Multicoloured.

No.	Description	Unused	Used
1445	40 c. Type **595**	40	45
1446	40 c. "The Orphan Boy"	40	45
1447	40 c. "Chinook"	40	45
1448	40 c. "Buried Treasure"	40	45

596 Grant Hall Tower

1991. 150th Anniv of Queen's University, Kingston.

No.	Type	Description	Unused	Used
1449	**596**	40 c. multicoloured ..	40	45

597 North American Santa Claus

1991. Christmas. Multicoloured.

No.	Description	Unused	Used
1450	35 c. British Father Christmas (35 × 21 mm)	35	40
1451	40 c. Type **597**	40	45
1452	46 c. French Bonhomme Noel	45	50
1453	80 c. Dutch Sinterklaas ..	80	85

598 Players Jumping for Ball

1991. Basketball Centenary. Multicoloured.

No.	Type	Description	Unused	Used
1454	**598**	40 c. multicoloured ..	40	45

1991. 50th Anniv of Second World War (3rd issue). As T **574**.

No.	Description	Unused	Used
1456	40 c. black, silver and blue	40	45
1457	40 c. black, silver & brown	40	45
1458	40 c. black, silver and lilac	40	45
1459	40 c. black, silver & brown	40	45

DESIGNS: No. 1456, Women's services, 1941; 1457, Armament factory; 1458, Cadets and veterans; 1459, Defence of Hong Kong.

599 McIntosh Apple

1991. Fruit and Nut Trees. Multicoloured.

No.	Description	Unused	Used
1467	48 c. Type **599**	50	55
1468	65 c. Black walnut ..	65	70
1469	84 c. Stanley plum ..	90	95

600 Ski Jumping

1992. Winter Olympic Games, Albertville. Multicoloured.

No.	Description	Unused	Used
1482	42 c. Type **600**	40	45
1483	42 c. Figure skating ..	40	45
1484	42 c. Ice hockey ..	40	45
1485	42 c. Bobsleighing ..	40	45
1486	42 c. Alpine skiing ..	40	45

OFFICIAL STAMPS

1949. Optd. **O.H.M.S.**

No.	Type	Description	Unused	Used
O 1.	**111.**	1 c. green (postage) ..	1·00	1·75
O 2.	**112.**	2 c. brown	8·00	10·00
O 3.	–	3 c. purple (No. 378) ..	1·00	1·10
O 4.	**112.**	4 c. red	1·25	30
O 5.	–	10 c. green (No. 402)	2·50	15
O 6.	–	14 c. brown (No. 403)	4·00	80
O 7.	–	20 c. grey (No. 404) ..	8·50	60
O 8.	–	50 c. green (No. 405)	£160	£100
O 9.	–	$1 purple (No. 406) ..	50·00	45·00
O 10.	–	7 c. blue (No. 407) (air)	18·00	5·00

1949. Optd. **O.H.M.S.**

No.	Type	Description	Unused	Used
O 11.	**135.**	1 c. green	30	40
O 12.	–	2 c. brown (No. 415)	35	55
O 13.	–	3 c. purple (No. 416)	40	45
O 14.	–	4 c. red (No. 417) ..	55	10
O 15.	–	5 c. blue (No. 418) ..	1·00	75
O 16.	**141.**	50 c. green	26·00	24·00

1950. Optd. **G.**

No.	Type	Description	Unused	Used
O 17.	**135.**	1 c. green (postage) ..	30	10
O 18.	–	2 c. brown (No. 415)	60	40
O 19.	–	2 c. olive (No. 415a)	75	10
O 20.	–	3 c. purple (No. 416)	50	10
O 21.	–	4 c. red (No. 417) ..	1·00	20
O 22.	–	4 c. red (No. 417a) ..	1·00	10
O 23.	–	5 c. blue (No. 418) ..	1·00	30
O 32.	**153.**	7 c. blue	1·00	75
O 24.	–	10 c. green (No. 402)	1·50	10
O 30.	**142.**	10 c. purple	80	10
O 25.	–	14 c. brown (No. 403)	5·50	1·75
O 26.	–	20 c. grey (No. 404)	9·00	20
O 33.	–	20 c. grey (No. 441)	80	10
O 27.	**141.**	50 c. green	7·00	6·50
O 28.	–	$1 purple (No. 406)	50·00	42·00
O 31.	–	$1 blue (No. 433) ..	55·00	55·00
O 29.	–	7 c. blue (No. 407) (air)	15·00	6·00

1953. 1st Queen Elizabeth II stamps optd. **G.**

No.	Type	Description	Unused	Used
O 35.	**158.**	1 c. brown	15	10
O 36.		2 c. green	20	10
O 37.		3 c. red	20	10
O 38.		4 c. violet	30	10
O 39.		5 c. blue	30	10

1953. Pictorial stamps optd. **G.**

No.	Type	Description	Unused	Used
O 45.	**165.**	10 c. brown	25	10
O 46.	–	20 c. green (No. 488)	40	10
O 40.	**160.**	50 c. green	2·00	50
O 34.	**154.**	$1 black	7·00	7·00

1955. 2nd Queen Elizabeth II stamps optd. **G.**

No.	Type	Description	Unused	Used
O 41.	**161.**	1 c. brown	15	20
O 42.		2 c. green	15	10
O 43.		4 c. violet	30	10
O 44.		5 c. blue	15	10

1963. 3rd Queen Elizabeth II stamps optd. **G.**

No.	Type	Description	Unused	Used
O 47.	**215.**	1 c. brown	30	2·50
O 48.		2 c. green	30	2·25
O 49.		4 c. red	30	1·75
O 50.		5 c. blue	30	55

OFFICIAL SPECIAL DELIVERY STAMPS

1950. Optd. **O.H.M.S.**

No.	Type	Description	Unused	Used
OS 1.	–	10 c. green (No. S 15) ..	12·00	12·00

1950. Optd. **G.**

No.	Type	Description	Unused	Used
OS 2.	–	10 c. green (No. S 15) ..	18·00	18·00

POSTAGE DUE STAMPS

D 1. D 2.

1906.

No.	Type	Description	Unused	Used
D 1	**D 1.**	1 c. violet	6·00	2·50
D 4		2 c. violet	8·50	90
D 5		4 c. violet	45·00	50·00
D 6		5 c. violet	12·00	1·75
D 8		10 c. violet	28·00	13·00

1930.

No.	Type	Description	Unused	Used
D 9.	**D 2.**	1 c. violet	8·00	10·00
D 10.		2 c. violet	7·00	85
D 11.		4 c. violet	15·00	8·00
D 12.		5 c. violet	13·00	17·00
D 13.		10 c. violet	65·00	26·00

D 3. D 4.

1933.

No.	Type	Description	Unused	Used
D 14.	**D 3.**	1 c. violet	7·00	11·00
D 15.		2 c. violet	5·00	3·00
D 16.		4 c. violet	10·00	7·50
D 17.		10 c. violet	17·00	20·00

1935.

No.	Type	Description	Unused	Used
D 18.	**D 4.**	1 c. violet	40	10
D 19.		2 c. violet	40	10
D 20.		3 c. violet	2·50	7·00
D 21.		4 c. violet	80	10
D 22.		5 c. violet	1·00	35
D 23.		6 c. violet	1·50	4·50
D 24.		10 c. violet	60	10

D 5.

1967.

(a) Size 21 × 17 mm.

No.	Type	Description	Unused	Used
D 25.	**D 5.**	1 c. red	1·25	2·50
D 26.		2 c. red	1·00	80
D 27.		3 c. red	1·00	3·50
D 28.		4 c. red	2·25	1·25
D 29.		5 c. red	3·50	3·25
D 30.		6 c. red	1·60	3·50
D 31.		10 c. red	2·00	2·50

(b) Size 20 × 15½ mm.

No.	Type	Description	Unused	Used
D 32	**D 5.**	1 c. red	30	30
D 33		2 c. red	25	1·75
D 34		3 c. red	1·00	1·75
D 35		4 c. red	85	75
D 36a		5 c. red	50	2·00
D 37		6 c. red	1·75	3·00
D 38		8 c. red	75	60
D 39a		10 c. red	60	80
D 40		12 c. red	1·25	65
D 41		16 c. red	70	2·50
D 42		20 c. red	60	1·75
D 43		24 c. red	60	2·50
D 44		50 c. red	1·00	2·75

REGISTRATION STAMPS

R 1.

1875.

No.	Type	Description	Unused	Used
R 1.	**R 1.**	2 c. orange	55·00	1·00
R 6.		5 c. green	60·00	1·00
R 8.		8 c. blue	£325	£225

SPECIAL DELIVERY STAMPS

S 1.

1898.

No.	Type	Description	Unused	Used
S2	**S 1**	10 c. green	40·00	4·50

S 2.

1922.

No.	Type	Description	Unused	Used
S 4.	**S2.**	20 c. red	30·00	2·50

S 3. Mail-carrying, 1867 and 1927.

1927. 60th Anniversary of Confederation.

No.	Type	Description	Unused	Used
S 5.	**S 3.**	20 c. orange	8·00	7·00

S 4.

1930.

S 6. S 4. 20 c. red .. .. 35·00 4·00

1932. As Type S 4, but inscr. "CENTS" instead of "TWENTY CENTS".

S 7. – 20 c. red .. .. .. 42·00 11·00

S 5. Allegory of Progress.

1935.

S 8. S 5. 20 c. red .. .. 3·50 1·25

S 6. Canadian Coat of Arms.

1938.

S 9. S 6. 10 c. green .. .. 10·00 55

S 10. 20 c. red .. .. 35·00 23·00

1939. Surch. **10 10** and bars.

S 11. S 6. 10 c. on 20 c. red .. 5·50 7·50

S 8. Coat of Arms and Flags.

S 9. Trans-Canada Plane.

1942.

S 12. S 8. 10 c. green (postage).. 1·75 20

S 13. S 9. 16 c. blue (air) .. 1·75 20

S 14. 17 c. blue .. .. 1·75 30

1946.

S 15. 10 c. green (postage) .. 1·25 20

S 17. 17 c. blue (air) .. .. 3·00 2·50

DESIGNS: 10 c. as Type S **8**, but with wreath of leaves. 17 c. as Type S **9**, but with four-engined transatlantic 'plane.

CAPE OF GOOD HOPE

Formerly a Br. Colony, later the southernmost province of the Union of S. Africa.
12 pence = 1 shilling;
20 shillings = 1 pound.

1. " Hope ".

1853. Imperf.

18 1. 1d. red £100 £225

19 4d. blue .. .. .. £100 42·00

20 6d. lilac £150 £450

8a 1s. green £225 £500

3.

1861. Imperf.

13. 3. 1d. red £13000 £2000

14. 4d. blue £9000 £1500

4. " Hope " seated, with vine and ram. (with outer frame-line).

6. (No outer frame-line).

1864. With outer frame line. Perf.

23. 4. 1d. red .. .. .. 75·00 9·00

24. 4d. blue .. .. .. 90·00 2·00

52a. 6d. purple .. .. .. 2·75 15

53a. 1s. green .. .. .. 17·00 30

1868. Surch.

32. 4. 1d. on 6d. violet .. .. £275 45·00

33. 1d. on 1s. green .. .. 35·00 25·00

34. 6. 3d. on 4d. blue .. .. 70·00 90

27. 4. 4d. on 6d. violet .. .. £120 11·00

1880. No outer frame line.

48. 6. ½d. black .. .. .. 1·00 10

49. 1d. red .. .. .. 1·00 10

36. 3d. pink .. .. .. £130 11·00

40. 3d. claret .. .. .. 5·50 90

51. 4d. blue .. .. .. 3·25 15

66. 5s. orange .. .. .. 42·00 3·50

1880. Surch. **THREEPENCE.**

35. 6. 3d. on 4d. red .. .. 38·00 1·50

1880. Surch. **3.**

37. 6. " 3 " on 3d. red .. .. 32·00 75

1882. Surch. **One Half-penny** and bar.

42. 6. ½d. on 3d. red .. .. 3·50 2·00

1882.

59. 6. ½d. green 85 10

60. 2d. brown .. .. .. 1·25 10

56. 2½d. olive .. .. .. 1·50 10

61a. 2½d. blue .. .. .. 1·50 10

62. 3d. mauve .. .. .. 2·00 40

63. 4d. olive .. .. .. 3·25 45

64. 1s. green .. .. .. 20·00 50

65. 1s. yellow .. .. .. 5·50 35

On the 2½d. stamps the value is in a white square at upper right-hand corner as well as at foot.

1891. Surch. **2½d.**

55a. 6. 2½d. on 3d. mauve .. 90 20

1893. Surch. **ONE PENNY** and bar.

57a. 6. 1d. on 2d. brown 70 10

17. " Hope " standing. Table Bay in background.

1893.

67. 17. ½d. green 30 10

58. 1d. red 45 10

68. 3d. mauve .. .. .. 3·00 50

18. Table Mountain and Bay and Arms of the Colony.

19.

1900.

69. 18. 1d. red 35 10

1902. Various frames.

70. 19. ½d. green 40 10

71. 1d. red 40 10

72. 2d. brown .. .. .. 2·25 55

73. 2½d. blue .. .. .. 2·50 4·50

74. 3d. purple .. .. .. 2·25 30

75. 4d. green .. .. .. 3·00 55

76. 6d. mauve .. .. .. 3·00 30

77. 1s. yellow .. .. .. 5·50 40

78. 5s. orange .. .. .. 35·00 6·50

CAYES OF BELIZE

A chain of several hundred islands, coral atolls, reefs and sandbanks stretching along the eastern seaboard of Belize.

The following issues for the Cayes of Belize fall outside the criteria for full listing as detailed on page viii.

100 cents = 1 dollar.

1984.

Marine Life, Map and Views, 1, 2, 5, 10, 15, 25, 75 c., $3, $5.
Lloyd's List (newspaper). 250th Anniv. 25, 75 c., $1, $2.
Olympic Games, Los Angeles. 10, 15, 75 c., $2.
90th Anniv. of "Caye Service" Local Stamps. 10, 15, 75 c., $2.

1985.

Birth Bicentenary of John J. Audubon (ornithologist). 25, 75 c., $1, $3.
Shipwrecks. $1 × 4.

CAYMAN ISLANDS

A group of islands in the Br. W. Indies. A dependency of Jamaica until August 1962, when it became a Crown Colony.

1900. 12 pence = 1 shilling;
20 shillings = 1 pound.
1969. 100 cents = 1 Jamaica dollar.

1.

2.

1900.

1a. 1. ½d. green .. .. .. 1·50 7·00

2. 1d. red .. .. .. 2·25 75

1902.

8 2 ½d. green .. .. .. 1·50 3·50

4 1d. red .. .. .. 5·50 6·50

10 2½d. blue .. .. .. 3·50 2·75

13 4d. brown and blue .. 18·00 27·00

11 6d. brown .. .. 16·00 35·00

14 6d. olive and red .. .. 18·00 38·00

12 1s. orange .. .. 30·00 48·00

15 1s. violet and green .. 30·00 45·00

16 5s. red and green £170 £250

1907. Surch. **One Halfpenny.**

17. 2. ½d. on 1d. red .. .. 29·00 55·00

1907. Surch.

18. 2. "½d." on 5s. red & green £225 £300

19. "1d." on 5s. red & green £225 £300

35. "2½d." on 4d. brn. & blue £1600 £2250

11.

8.

1907.

38. 11. ¼d. brown 30 20

25. 8. ½d. green .. .. .. 70 1·75

26. 1d. red 60 55

27. 2½d. blue .. .. .. 2·75 3·00

28. 3d. purple on yellow .. 2·25 6·50

29. 4d. black & red on yellow 48·00 50·00

30. 6d. purple .. .. 4·50 23·00

31. 1s. black on green .. 4·25 14·00

32. 5s. green & red on yellow 35·00 55·00

34. 10 s. green & red on green £180 £275

12.

19.

1912.

40 12 ¼d. brown 30 30

41 ½d. green .. .. 50 2·00

42 1d. red .. .. 1·75 75

43 2d. grey .. .. 50 2·50

44 2½d. blue .. .. 7·00 7·50

45a 3d. purple on yellow .. 1·75 4·50

46 4d. black & red on yell 75 3·50

47 6d. purple .. .. 2·25 5·00

48a 1s. black on green .. 1·75 2·75

49 2s. purple & blue on bl 7·50 27·00

50 3s. green and violet .. 17·00 45·00

51 5s. green & red on yell 65·00 £100

52a 10s. green & red on grn 80·00 £120

1917. Surch. **1½d.** with **WAR STAMP** in two lines.

54. 12. 1½d. on 2½d blue .. .. 40 3·00

1917. Optd. or surch as last, but with **WAR STAMP** in one line.

57. 12. ½d. green 20 95

58. 1½d. on 2d. grey .. 90 3·75

56. 1½d. on 2½d. blue .. 20 40

59. 1½d. on 2½d. orange .. 25 80

1921.

69 19 ¼d. brown 30 60

70 ½d. green 40 25

71 1d. red 70 85

72 1½d. brown .. .. 1·50 20

73 2d. grey .. .. .. 1·75 3·25

74 2½d. blue 50 45

75 3d. purple on yellow .. 50 75

62 4d. red on yellow .. 80 3·75

76 4½d. green .. .. .. 1·25 3·00

77 6d. red .. .. .. 5·50 18·00

63 1s. black on green .. 1·25 7·00

80 2s. violet on blue .. .. 7·50 12·00

81 3s. violet .. .. .. 17·00 15·00

82 5s. green on yellow .. 22·00 35·00

83 10s. red on green .. 48·00 65·00

20. Kings William IV and George V.

1932. Centenary of "Assembly of Justices and Vestry".

84. 20. ¼d. brown 50 90

85. ½d. green .. .. .. 1·50 4·50

86. 1d. red .. .. .. 1·50 3·50

87. 1½d. orange .. .. 1·50 1·00

88. 2d. grey .. .. .. 1·50 1·75

89. 2½d. blue .. .. .. 1·50 1·00

90. 3d. green .. .. .. 1·75 2·75

91. 6d. purple .. .. .. 6·00 12·00

92. 1s. black and brown .. 13·00 20·00

93. 2s. black and blue .. 38·00 55·00

94. 5s. black and green .. 80·00 £110

95. 10s. black and red .. £250 £350

1935. Silver Jubilee. As T **13** of Antigua.

96. ½d. black and green .. 15 20

97. 2½d. brown and blue .. 60 1·00

98. 6d. blue and olive .. 1·00 1·25

99. 1s. grey and purple .. 2·75 3·75

21. Cayman Islands.

1935.

100. 21. ¼d. black and brown .. 15 50

101. – ½d. blue and green .. 60 30

102. – 1d. blue and red .. 2·25 50

103. – 1½d. black and orange .. 1·25 60

104. – 2d. blue and purple .. 1·25 80

105. – 2½d. blue and black .. 3·00 60

106. 21. 3d. black and green .. 2·00 80

107. – 6d. purple and black .. 8·50 3·00

108. – 1s. blue and orange .. 4·00 4·50

109. – 2s. blue and black .. 40·00 30·00

110. – 5s. green and black .. 42·00 48·00

111. – 10s. black and red .. 65·00 75·00

DESIGNS—HORIZ. ½d., 2d., 1s. Cat boat. 1d., 2s. Red-footed Booby birds. 2½d., 6d., 5s. Hawksbill turtles. VERT. 1½d., 10s. Conch shells and coconut palms.

1937. Coronation. As T **2** of Aden.

112. ½d. green 30 15

113. 1d. red 50 15

114. 2½d. blue 95 35

26. Beach View.

DESIGNS—HORIZ. ½d., 1s. Caribbean Dolphin. 1d., 3d. Map of Islands. 2½d., 5s. "Rembro" (schooner).

30. Hawksbill Turtles.

1938.

115 26 ¼d. orange 10 45
116 – ½d. green 35 40
117 – 1d. red 15 40
118 26 1½d. black 10 10
119a 30 2d. violet 40 30
120 – 2½d. blue 15 20
120a – 2½d. orange .. .. 1·50 30
121 – 3d. orange 15 15
121a – 3d. blue .. .. 1·00 30
122a 30 6d. olive 75 45
123a – 1s. brown .. .. 2·00 50
124a 26 2s. green .. .. 18·00 7·00
125 – 5s. red .. .. 23·00 12·00
126a 30 10s. brown .. .. 16·00 8·50

1946. Victory. As T 9 of Aden.

127. 1½d. black 10 10
128. 3d. yellow 10 10

1948. Silver Wedding. As T 10/11 of Aden.

129. ½d. green 10 10
130. 10s. blue .. .. .. 10·00 6·50

1949. U.P.U. As T 20/23 of Antigua.

131. 2½d. orange 20 15
132. 3d. blue 60 20
133. 6d. olive 60 30
134. 1s. brown 60 30

31. Cat Boat.

1950.

135. 31. ¼d. blue and red .. 15 60
136. – ½d. violet and green .. 10 90
137. – 1d. olive and blue .. 60 75
138. – 1½d. green and brown .. 30 75
139. – 2d. violet and red .. 80 1·50
140. – 2½d. blue and black .. 50 60
141. – 3d. green and blue .. 1·40 1·25
142. – 6d. brown and blue .. 1·00 1·25
143. – 9d. red and green .. 2·25 2·00
144. – 1s. brown and orange .. 3·00 2·75
145. – 2s. violet and purple .. 7·00 5·50
146. – 5s. olive and violet .. 8·50 6·50
147. – 10s. black and red .. 9·50 8·50

DESIGNS: ½d. Coconut grove, Cayman Brac. 1d. Green turtle. 1½d. Making thatch rope. 2d. Cayman seamen. 2½d. Map. 3d. Parrot fish. 6d. Bluff, Cayman Brac. 9d. Georgetown Harbour. 1s. Turtle in "crawl". 2s. "Ziroma" (schooner). 5s. Boat-building. 10s. Government offices, Grand Cayman.

Portrait faces right on ½d., 2d., 2½d., 4d., 1s. and 10s. values and left on others. The £1 shows a larger portrait of the Queen (vert.).

44. South Sound Lighthouse, Grand Cayman.

1953. As 1950 issue but with portrait of Queen Elizabeth II as in T 44.

148 ¼d. blue and red .. 45 30
149 ½d. violet and green .. 10 20
150 1d. olive and blue .. 60 20
151 1½d. green and brown .. 15 15
152 2d. violet and red .. 2·00 55
153 2½d. blue and black .. 3·00 40
154 3d. green and blue .. 3·50 30
155 4d. black and blue .. 1·50 15
156 6d. brown and blue .. 1·50 20
157 9d. red and green .. 1·75 15
158 1s. brown and orange .. 2·75 10
159 2s. violet and purple .. 7·50 4·50
160 5s. olive and violet .. 8·50 3·50
161 10s. black and red .. 11·00 7·00
161a £1 blue .. .. .. 24·00 9·50

1953. Coronation. As T 13 of Aden.

162. 1d. black and green .. 10 50

46. Arms of the Cayman Is.

1959. New Constitution.

163. 46. 2½d. black and blue .. 10 30
164. 1s. black and orange .. 30 10

48. Cat Boat.

1962. Portrait as in T 48.

165. – ¼d. green and red .. 15 35
166. 48. 1d. black and olive .. 20 10
167. – 1½d. yellow and purple 1·50 45
168. – 2d. blue and brown .. 35 30
169. – 2½d. violet & turquoise 40 40
170. – 3d. blue and red .. 20 10
171. – 4d. green and purple .. 80 40
172. – 6d. turquoise and sepia 2·50 30
173. – 9d. blue and purple .. 1·25 30
174. – 1s. sepia and red .. 50 10
175. – 1s. 3d. turq. and brown 1·50 1·50
176. – 1s. 9d. turquoise & violet 6·00 70
177. – 5s. plum and green .. 4·50 2·00
178. – 10s. olive and blue .. 8·00 7·00
179. – £1 red and black .. 14·00 13·00

DESIGNS—VERT. ¼d. Cuban Amazon. 9d. Angler with Kingfish. 10s. Arms. £1, Queen Elizabeth II. HORIZ. 1½d. "Schomburgkia thomsoniana" (orchid). 2d. Cayman Is. map. 2½d. Fisherman casting net. 3d. West Bay Beach. 4d. Green Turtle. 6d. "Lydia E. Wilson" (schooner). 1s. Iguana. 1s 3d. Swimming pool, Cayman Brac. 1s 9d. Water Sports. 5s. Fort George.

1963. Freedom from Hunger. As T 28 of Aden.

180. 1s. 9d. red 30 10

1963. Cent of Red Cross. As T 33 of Antigua.

181. 1d. red and black 15 20
182. 1s 9d. red and blue .. 70 75

1964. 400th Birth Anniv of Shakespeare. As T 34 of Antigua.

183. 6d. purple 10 10

1965. Cent of I.T.U. As T 36 of Antigua.

184. 1d. blue and purple .. 15 10
185. 1s 3d. purple and green .. 40 25

1965. I.C.Y. As T 37 of Antigua.

186. 1d. purple and turquoise 10 10
187. 1s. green and lavender .. 40 25

1966. Churchill Commem. As T 38 of Antigua.

188. ¼d. blue 10 20
189. 1d. green 15 10
190. 1s. brown 35 10
191. 1s. 9d. violet 55 35

1966. Royal Visit. As T 39 of Antigua.

192. 1d. black and blue .. 50 10
193. 1s. 9d. black and mauve .. 1·50 45

1966. World Cup Football Championship. As T 40 of Antigua.

194. 1½d. multicoloured .. 10 10
195. 1s. 9d. multicoloured .. 40 25

1966. Inauguration of W.H.O. Headquarters, Geneva. As T 41 of Antigua.

196. 2d. black, green and blue 25 10
197. 1s 3d. blk., pur. & ochre .. 55 45

62. Telephone and Map.

1966. Int. Telephone Links.

198. 62. 4d. multicoloured .. 15 10
199. 9d. multicoloured .. 15 10

1966. 20th Anniv. of U.N.E.S.C.O. As T 54/6 of Antigua.

200. 1d. multicoloured .. 15 10
201. 1s. 9d. yellow, violet & olive 45 10
202. 5s. black, purple & orange 1·25 55

63. BAC 1-11 Airliner over Cayman Schooner.

1966. Opening of Cayman Jet Service.

203. 63. 1s. black, blue and green 20 15
204. 1s. 9d. purple, bl. & grn. 20 15

64. Water-skiing.

1967. Int. Tourist Year. Multicoloured.

205. 4d. Type 64 .. .. 15 10
206. 6d. Skin diving 15 15
207. 1s. Sport fishing 15 15
208. 1s. 9d. Sailing 20 20

68. Former Slaves and Emblem.

1968. Human Rights Year.

209. 68. 3d. green, black & gold 10 10
210. 9d. brown, gold & green 10 10
211. 5s. ultram., gold & green 30 25

69. Long-Jumping.

1968. Olympic Games, Mexico. Multicoloured.

212. 1s. Type 69 .. .. 10 10
213. 1s. 3d. High-jumping .. 15 15
214. 2s. Pole-vaulting 15 15

72. "The Adoration of the Shepherds" (Fabritius).

1968. Christmas. Multicoloured.

215. ¼d. Type 72 .. .. 10 10
221. ¼d. Type 72 .. .. 10 10
216. 1d. "The Adoration of the Shepherds" (Rembrandt) 10 10
217. 6d. Type 72 .. .. 15 10
218. 8d. As 1d. 15 15
219. 1s. 3d. Type 72 .. .. 20 20
220. 2s. As 1d. 20 20

No. 215 has brown background and No. 221 a bright purple one.

74. Grand Cayman Thrush.

1969. Multicoloured.

237 ¼d. Type 74 .. .. 20 30
223 1d. Brahmin Cattle .. 10 10
224 2d. Blowholes on the coast 10 10
225 2½d. Map of Grand Cayman 15 10
226 3d. Georgetown scene .. 15 10
227 4d. Royal "Poinciana" .. 30 10
228 6d. Cayman Brac and Little Cayman on Chart .. 30 10
229 8d. Motor vessels at berth 30 10
230 1s. Basket making .. 20 10
231 1s. 3d. Beach scene .. 35 1·00
232 1s. 6d. Straw rope making 40 1·00
233 2s. Barracuda .. .. 1·00 80
234 4s. Government House .. 35 80
235 10s. Arms of the Cayman Islands .. .. .. 1·00 1·75
236 £1 black, ochre and red (Queen Elizabeth II) .. 2·00 2·50

Nos. 235/6 are vert.

1969. Decimal Currency. Nos. 222/36 surch. Multicoloured.

238. 74. ¼ c. on ¼d. 10 40
239. – 1 c. on 1d. 10 10
240. – 2 c. on 2d. 10 10
241. – 3 c. on 4d. 10 10
242. – 4 c. on 2½d. 10 10
243. – 5 c. on 6d. 10 10
244. – 7 c. on 8d. 10 10
245. – 8 c. on 3d. 15 10
246. – 10 c. on 1s. 25 10
247. – 12 c. on 1s. 3d. .. 35 50
248. – 15 c. on 1s. 6d. .. 45 50
249. – 20 c. on 2s. .. .. 1·25 1·50
250. – 40 c. on 4s. 45 80
251. – $1 on 10s. .. .. 1·50 1·60
252. – $2 on £1 .. .. 2·00 3·25

90. "Madonna and Child" (Vivarini).

1969. Christmas. Multicoloured. Background colours given.

253. 90. ¼ c. red 10 10
254. ¼ c. mauve 10 10
255. ¼ c. green 10 10
256. ¼ c. blue 10 10
257. – 1 c. blue 10 10
258. 90. 5 c. red 10 10
259. – 7 c. green 10 10
260. 90. 12 c. green 15 10
261. – 20 c. purple 20 20

DESIGNS: 1 c., 7 c., 20 c. "The Adoration of the Kings" (Gossaert).

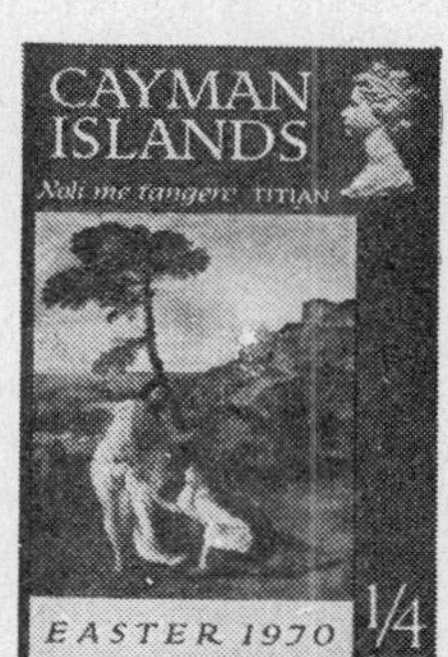

92. "Noli me tangere" (Titian).

1970. Easter. Multicoloured; frame colours given.

262. 92. ¼ c. red 10 10
263. ¼ c. green 10 10
264. ¼ c. brown 10 10
265. ¼ c. violet 10 10
266. 10 c. blue 20 10
267. 12 c. brown 20 10
268. 40 c. plum 25 25

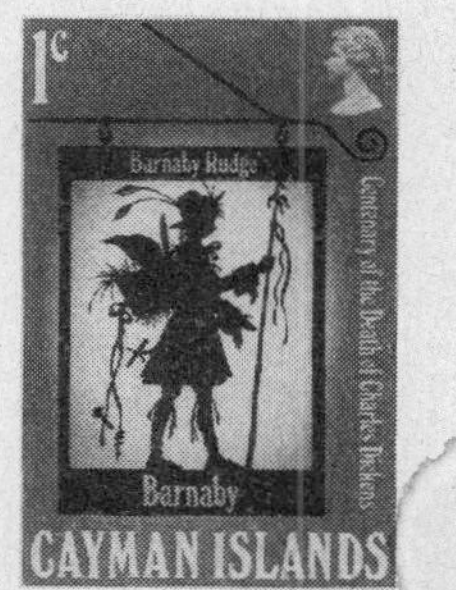

93. Barnaby ("Barnaby Rudge").

1970. Death Centenary of Charles Dickens.

269. **93.** 1 c. blk., grn. & yellow 10 10
270. – 12 c. black, brown & red 10 10
271. – 20 c. black, brn. & gold 15 10
272. – 40 c. black, ultram. & blue 20 25

DESIGNS: 12 c. Sairey Gamp ("Martin Chuzzlewit"). 20 c. Mr. Micawber and David ("David Copperfield"). 40 c. The "Marchioness" ("The Old Curiosity Shop").

97. Grand Cayman Thrush.

1970. Decimal Currency. Designs as Nos. 222/36, but with values inscr. in decimal currency as in T **97**.

273. ½ c. multicoloured .. 10 10
274. 1 c. multicoloured .. 10 10
275. 2 c. multicoloured .. 10 10
276. 3 c. multicoloured .. 20 10
277. 4 c. multicoloured .. 20 10
278. 5 c. multicoloured .. 35 10
279. 7 c. multicoloured .. 30 10
280. 8 c. multicoloured .. 30 10
281. 10 c. multicoloured .. 30 10
282. 12 c. multicoloured .. 90 45
283. 15 c. multicoloured .. 1·25 1·00
284. 20 c. multicoloured .. 2·50 1·25
285. 40 c. multicoloured .. 85 75
286. $1 multicoloured .. 1·75 2·50
287. $2 black, ochre and red 2·75 4·00

98. The Three Wise Men.

1970. Christmas.

288. **98.** ¼ c. green, grey and emer. 10 10
289. – 1 c. black, yell. and grn. 10 10
290. **98.** 5 c. grey, orange and red 10 10
291. – 10 c. black, yell. and red 10 10
292. **98.** 12 c. grey, green and blue 15 10
293. – 20 c. black, yell. and grn. 20 15

DESIGN: 1 c., 10 c., 20 c. Nativity Scene and Globe.

100. Grand Cayman Terrapin.

1971. Turtles. Multicoloured.

294. 5 c. Type **100** 30 25
295. 7 c. Green turtle 35 25
296. 12 c. Hawksbill turtle .. 55 30
297. 20 c. Turtle farm .. .. 1·00 1·40

101. "Dendrophylax fawcetti". **102.** "Adoration of the Kings" (French 15th cent.).

1971. Orchids. Multicoloured.

298. ¼ c. Type **101** 10 30
299. 2 c. "Schomburgkia thomsoniana" 40 40
300. 10 c. "Vanilla claviculata" 90 70
301. 40 c. "Oncidium variegatum" 2·75 3·50

1971. Christmas. Multicoloured.

302. ¼ c. Type **102** 10 10
303. 1 c. "The Nativity" (Parisian, 14th cent.) .. 10 10
304. 5 c. "Adoration of the Magi" (Burgundian, 15th cent.) 10 10
305. 12 c. Type **102** 20 10
306. 15 c. As 1 c. 20 20
307. 20 c. As 5 c. 25 30

103. Turtle and Telephone Cable.

1972. Co-Axial Telephone Cable.

309. **103.** 2 c. multicoloured .. 10 10
310. 10 c. multicoloured .. 10 10
311. 40 c. multicoloured .. 25 40

104. Court House Building.

1972. New Government Buildings. Mult.

312. 5 c. Type **104** 10 10
313. 15 c. Legislative Assembly Building 10 10
314. 25 c. Type **104** 15 15
315. 40 c. As 15 c. 20 30

1972. Royal Silver Wedding. As T **52** of Ascension but with Hawksbill Turtle and Conch Shell in background.

317. 12 c. violet 15 10
318. 30 c. green 15 20

106. $1 Coin and Note.

1972. 1st Issue of Currency. Multicoloured.

319. 3 c. Type **106** 15 10
320. 6 c. $5 Coin and note .. 15 10
321. 15 c. $10 Coin and note .. 30 20
322. 25 c. $25 Coin and note .. 40 35

107. "The Way of Sorrow".

1973. Easter. Stained-Glass Windows. Multicoloured.

324. 10 c. Type **107** 10 10
325. 12 c. "Christ Resurrected" 15 10
326. 20 c. "The Last Supper" (horiz.) 20 15
327. 30 c. "Christ on the Cross" (horiz.) 25 25

108. "The Nativity" (Sforza Book of Hours).

1973. Christmas.

329. **108.** 3 c. multicoloured .. 10 10
330. – 5 c. multicoloured .. 10 10
331. **108.** 9 c. multicoloured .. 15 10
332. – 12 c. multicoloured .. 15 10
333. **108.** 15 c. multicoloured .. 15 15
334. – 25 c. multicoloured .. 20 25

DESIGN: 5, 12, 25 c. "The Adoration of the Magi" (Breviary of Queen Isabella).

1973. Royal Wedding. As Type **47** of Anguilla. Background colour given. Mult.

335. 10 c. green 10 10
336. 30 c. mauve 15 10

109. White-winged Dove.

1974. Birds (1st series). Multicoloured.

337. 3 c. Type **109** .. .. 1·40 20
338. 10 c. Vitelline Warbler .. 2·00 20
339. 12 c. Antillean Grackle 2·00 25
340. 20 c. West Indian Red-bellied Woodpecker .. 3·25 65
341. 30 c. Stripe-headed Tanager 5·00 1·50
342. 50 c. Yucatan Vireo .. 7·00 2·75

See also Nos. 383/8.

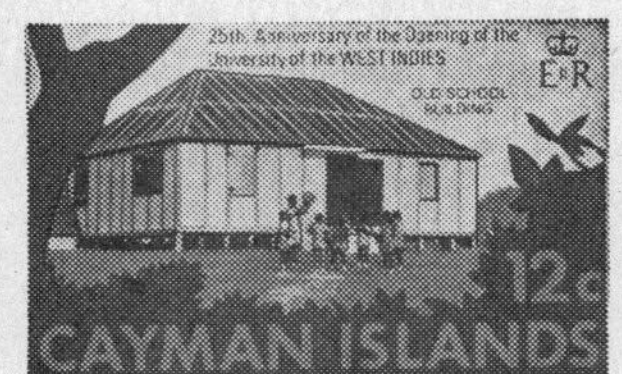

110. Old School Building.

1974. 25th Anniv. of University of West Indies. Multicoloured.

343. 12 c. Type **110** 10 10
344. 20 c. New Comprehensive School 15 10
345. 30 c. Creative Arts Centre, Mona 15 25

111. Hermit Crab and Staghorn Coral.

1974. Size 41½ × 27 mm or 27 × 41½ mm. Mult.

364 1 c. Type **111** .. .. 1·25 1·50
412 3 c. Treasure-chest and lion's paw .. .. 85 1·00
348 4 c. Treasure and spotted scorpion-fish .. 50 60
349 5 c. Flintlock pistol and brain coral .. 2·00 60
350 6 c. Blackbeard and green turtle 35 80
415 8 c. As 9 c. .. .. 2·25 1·25
351 9 c. Jewelled pomander and pork-fish .. 3·00 4·00
416 10 c. Spiny lobster & treasure 1·25 1·75
353 12 c. Jewelled sword and dagger and sea-fan .. 35 60
354 15 c. Cabrit's murex and treasure 40 90
417 20 c. Queen Conch & treasure 3·25 3·00
356 25 c. Hogfish and treasure 45 70
357 40 c. Gold chalice and sea-whip .. .. 1·50 1·00
358 $1 Coat of arms .. 2·75 3·25
359 $2 Queen Elizabeth II .. 4·00 8·00

For smaller designs see Nos. 445/52.

112. Sea Captain and Ship (Shipbuilding).

1974. Local Industries. Multicoloured.

360. 8 c. Type **112** 10 10
361. 12 c. Thatcher and cottage 10 10
362. 20 c. Farmer and plantation 20 20

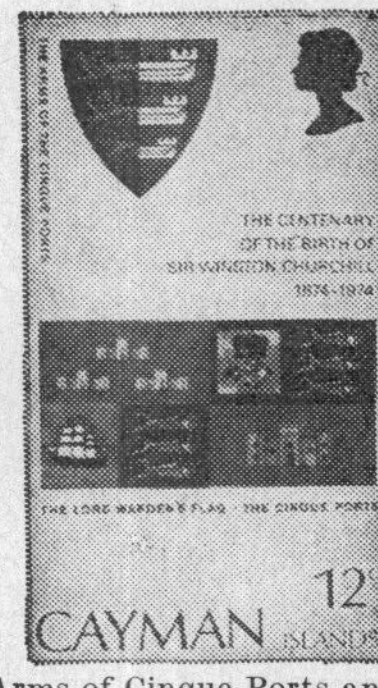

113. Arms of Cinque Ports and Lord Warden's Flag.

1974. Birth Centenary of Sir Winston Churchill. Multicoloured.

380. 12 c. Type **113** 15 10
381. 50 c. Churchill's coat of arms 45 70

1975. Birds (2nd series). As T **109**. Mult.

383 3 c. Common flicker .. 60 45
384 10 c. Black-billed whistling duck 90 45
385 12 c. Yellow warbler .. 1·00 55
386 20 c. White-bellied dove .. 1·75 1·60
387 30 c. Magnificent frigate bird .. .. 2·75 2·75
388 50 c. Cuban amazon .. 3·25 4·00

114. "The Crucifixion".

1975. Easter. French Pastoral Staffs.

389. **114.** 15 c. multicoloured .. 10 15
390. – 35 c. multicoloured .. 20 30

DESIGN: 35 c. Pastoral staff similar to Type **114**.

115. Israel Hands.

1975. Pirates. Multicoloured.

392. 10 c. Type **115** 20 10
393. 12 c. John Fenn 20 10
394. 20 c. Thomas Anstis .. 40 35
395. 30 c. Edward Low .. 55 55

1975. Christmas. "Virgin and Child with Angels". As T **114**.

396. 12 c. multicoloured .. 10 10
397. 50 c. multicoloured .. 30 30

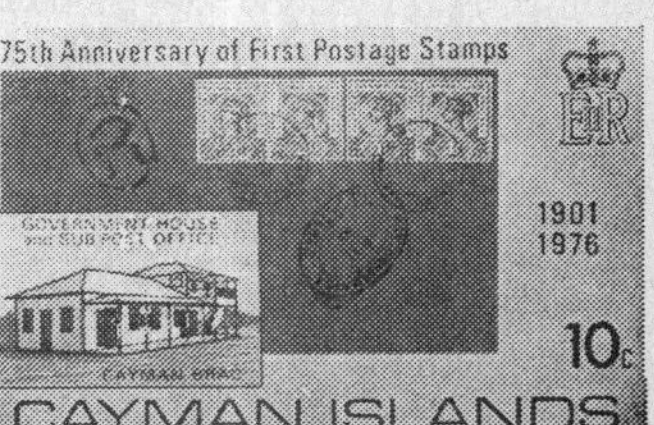

116. Registered Cover, Government House and Sub-Post Office.

1975. 75th Anniv. of First Cayman Islands Postage Stamp. Multicoloured.

399.	10 c. Type **116**	10	10
400.	20 c. ½d. stamp and 1890–94 postmark	15	15
401.	30 c. 1d. stamp and 1908 surcharge	25	25
402.	50 c. ½d. and 1d. stamps	40	50

117. Seals of Georgia, Delaware and New Hampshire. (Illustration reduced. Actual size 58×22 mm.)

1976. Bicent. of American Revolution. Mult.

404.	10 c. Type **117**	40	15
405.	15 c. S.Carolina, New Jersey and Maryland seals	60	20
406.	20 c. Virginia, Rhode Is. and Massachusetts seals	70	25
407.	25 c. New York, Connecticut and N. Carolina seals	70	35
408.	30 c. Pennsylvania seal, Liberty Bell and U.S. Great Seal	85	40

118. Racing Dinghies.

1976. Olympic Games, Montreal. **Mult.**

410.	20 c. Type **118**	15	10
411.	50c. Racing dinghy	45	50

119. Queen Elizabeth II and Westminster Abbey.

1977. Silver Jubilee. Multicoloured.

427.	8 c. The Prince of Wales' visit, 1973	10	20
428.	30 c. Type **119**	15	40
429.	50 c. Preparation of the Anointing (horiz.)	30	75

120. Scuba Diving.

1977. Tourism. Multicoloured.

430.	5 c. Type **120**	10	10
431.	10 c. Exploring a wreck	15	10
432.	20 c. Fairy Basslet (fish)	45	20
433.	25 c. Sergeant majors (fish)	55	35

121. "Composia fidelissima" (moth).

1977. Butterflies and Moths. Multicoloured.

435	5 c. Type **121**	35	10
436	8 c. "Heliconius charithonia"	40	15
437	10 c. "Danaus gilippus"	40	15
438	15 c. "Agraulis vanillae"	70	30
439	20 c. "Junonia evarete"	85	35
440	30 c. "Anartia jatrophae"	1·00	50

122. Cruise Liner "Southward".

1978. New Harbour and Cruise Ships. Mult.

441.	3 c. Type **122**	15	10
442.	5 c. Cruise liner "Renaissance"	20	10
443.	30 c. New harbour (vert.)	70	25
444.	50 c. Cruise liner "Daphne" (vert.)	90	55

1978. As Nos. 346/59, 349, 352, 355, and357/9, but designs smaller, 40×26 mm. or 26×40 mm.

445.	1 c. Type **111**	80	90
446.	3 c. Treasure chest and lion's paw	80	50
447.	5 c. Flintlock pistol and brain coral	1·50	2·25
448.	10 c. Spiny lobster and treasure	1·60	60
449.	20 c. Queen Conch and treasure	3·25	1·25
450.	40 c. Gold chalice and sea-whip	11·00	14·00
451.	$1 Coat of arms (vert.)	8·00	8·00
452.	$2 Queen Elizabeth II (vert.)	7·00	15·00

123. "The Crucifixion" (Durer).

1978. Easter and 450th Death Anniv. of Durers.

459. **123.**	10 c. mauve and black	15	10
460. –	15 c. yellow and black	25	15
461. –	20 c. turquoise & black	30	20
462. –	30 c. lilac and black	45	35

DESIGNS: 15 c. "Christ at Emmaus". 20 c. "The Entry into Jerusalem". 30 c. "Christ washing Peter's Feet".

124. "Explorers" Singing Game. **125.** Yale of Beaufort.

1978. 3rd International Council Meeting of Girls' Brigade. Multicoloured.

464.	3 c. Type **124**	15	10
465.	10 c. Colour party	25	10
466.	20 c. Girls and Duke of Edinburgh Award interests	50	20
467.	50 c. Girls using domestic skills	1·00	80

1978. 25th Anniv. of Coronation.

468. **125.**	30 c. green, mauve and silver	15	25
469. –	30 c. multicoloured	15	25
470. –	30 c. green, mauve and silver	15	25

DESIGNS: No. 469, Queen Elizabeth II. No. 470, Screech Owl.

126. Four Eyed Butterfly Fish.

1978. Fish (1st series). Multicoloured.

471.	3 c. Type **126**	15	10
472.	5 c. Grey Angel Fish	20	10
473.	10 c. Squirrel Fish	35	10
474.	15 c. Parrot Fish	45	30
475.	20 c. Spanish Hogfish	50	35
476.	30 c. Queen Angel Fish	60	50

127. Lockheed "Lodestar".

1979. 25th Anniv. of Owen Roberts Airfield. Multicoloured.

477.	3 c. Type **127**	15	10
478.	5 c. Consolidated "PBY"	15	10
479.	10 c. Vickers "Viking"	20	10
480.	15 c. B.A.C. "1-11" on tarmac	30	20
481.	20 c. Piper "Cheyenne" HS "125" and Bell "47"	40	30
482.	30 c. B.A.C. "1-11" over airfield	60	45

128. Trumpetfish.

1979. Fishes (2nd series). Multicoloured.

483.	1 c. Type **128**	10	10
484.	3 c. Nassau Grouper	15	10
485.	5 c. French Angelfish	15	10
486.	10 c. Schoolmaster Snappers	20	10
487.	20 c. Banded Butterflyfish	35	25
488.	50 c. Blackbar Soldierfish	70	70

129. 1900 1d. Stamp.

1979. Death Centenary of Sir Rowland Hill.

489. **129.**	5 c. blk., carm. and blue	10	10
490. –	10 c. multicoloured	10	10
491. –	20 c. multicoloured	20	20

DESIGNS: 10 c. Great Britain 1902 3d. purple on lemon. 20 c. 1955 £1 blue.

130. The Holy Family and Angels.

1979. Christmas. Multicoloured.

493.	10 c. Type **130**	15	10
494.	20 c. Angels appearing to Shepherds	20	10
495.	30 c. Nativity	30	20
496.	40 c. The Magi	40	30

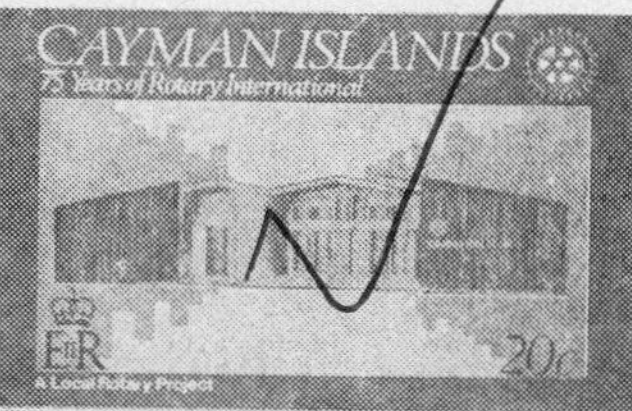

131. Local Rotary Project.

1980. 75th Anniv. of Rotary International.

497. **131.**	20 c. blue, black & yell.	20	15
498. –	30 c. blue, black & yell.	25	20
499. –	50 c. blue, yell. & black	35	30

DESIGNS—VERT: 30 c. Paul P. Harris (founder). 50 c. Rotary anniversary emblem.

132. Walking Mail Carrier.

1980. "London 1980" International Stamp Exhibition. Multicoloured.

500.	5 c. Type **132**	10	10
501.	10 c. Delivering mail by cat boat	15	10
502.	15 c. Mounted mail carrier	20	10
503.	30 c. Horse-drawn wagonette	30	15
504.	40 c. Postman on bicycle	30	15
505.	$1 Motor transport	65	55

133. Queen Elizabeth the Queen Mother at the Derby, 1976.

1980. 80th Birthday of The Queen Mother.

506. **133.**	20 c. multicoloured	20	25

134. Atlantic Spiny Oyster.

1980. Shells. (1st series). Multicoloured.

507.	5 c. Type **134**	20	10
508.	10 c. West Indian Murex	20	10
509.	30 c. Triton	50	35
510.	50 c. Murex-line vase shell	65	65

See also Nos. 565/8 and 582/5.

135. Lantana.

1980. Flowers (1st series). Multicoloured.

511.	5 c. Type **135**	10	10
512.	15 c. "Bauhinia"	25	10
513.	30 c. "Hibiscus Rosa"	35	10
514.	$1 "Milk and Wine Lily"	1·00	75

See also Nos. 541/4.

136. Juvenile Tarpon and Fire Sponge.

1980. Multicoloured.

515.	3 c. Type **136**	40	50
516.	5 c. Mangrove root oyster	50	50
517.	10 c. Mangrove crab	40	40
518.	15 c. Lizard and "Phyciodes phaon" (butterfly)	50	60
519.	20 c. Louisiana heron	1·50	1·25
520.	30 c. Red mangrove flower	70	80
521.	40 c. Red mangrove seeds	75	80
522.	50 c. Waterhouse's leaf-nosed bat	1·25	1·50
523.	$1 Black-crowned night heron	4·00	4·25
524.	$2 Coat of Arms	3·00	3·75
525.	$5 Queen Elizabeth II	5·00	6·50

137. Eucharist.

1981. Easter. Multicoloured.

526.	3 c. Type **137**	10	10
527.	10 c. Crown of thorns ..	10	10
528.	20 c. Crucifix	20	10
529.	$1 Lord Jesus Christ ..	70	80

138. Wood Slave.

1981. Reptiles and Amphibians. Multicoloured.

530.	20 c. Type **138**	30	20
531.	30 c. Cayman Iguana ..	45	35
532.	40 c. Lion Lizard	55	45
533.	50 c. Terrapin ("Hickatee")	65	55

139. Prince Charles.

1981. Royal Wedding. Multicoloured.

534.	20 c. Wedding bouquet from Cayman Islands ..	25	10
535.	30 c. Type **139**	40	10
536.	$1 Prince Charles and Lady Diana Spencer	1·00	1·00

140. Disabled Scuba Divers.

1981. International Year of Disabled Persons. Multicoloured.

537.	5 c. Type **140**	10	10
538.	15 c. Old School for the Handicapped	30	20
539.	20 c. New School for the Handicapped	35	25
540.	$1 Disabled people in wheel-chairs, by the sea ..	1·60	1·25

1981. Flowers (2nd series). As T **135**. **Mult.**

541.	3 c. " Bougainvillea " ..	10	10
542.	10 c. " Morning Glory "	20	10
543.	20 c. " Wild Amaryllis "	45	25
544.	$1 " Cordia "	1·75	1·75

141. Dr. Robert Koch and Microscope.

1982. Centenary of Robert Koch's Discovery of Tubercle Bacillus. Multicoloured.

545.	15 c. Type **141**	25	25
546.	30 c. Koch looking through microscope (vert.) ..	45	45
547.	40 c. Microscope (vert.) ..	70	70
548.	50 c. Dr. Robert Koch (vert.)	80	80

142. Bride and Groom walking down Aisle.

1982. 21st Birthday of Princess of Wales. Multicoloured.

549.	20 c. Cayman Islands coat of arms	35	35
550.	30 c. Lady Diana Spencer in London, June, 1981 ..	45	45
551.	40 c. Type **142**	55	55
552.	50 c. Formal portrait ..	65	70

143. Pitching Tent.

1982. 75th Anniv. of Boy Scout Movement. Multicoloured.

553.	3 c. Type **143**	10	10
554.	20 c. Scouts camping ..	40	40
555.	30 c. Cub Scouts and Leaders	55	55
556.	50 c. Boating skills ..	85	85

144. " Madonna and Child with the Infant Baptist ".

1982. Christmas. Raphael Paintings. Mult.

557.	3 c. Type **144**	10	10
558.	10 c. " Madonna of the Tower "	20	20
559.	20 c. " Ansidei Madonna "	35	35
560.	30 c. " Madonna and Child "	50	50

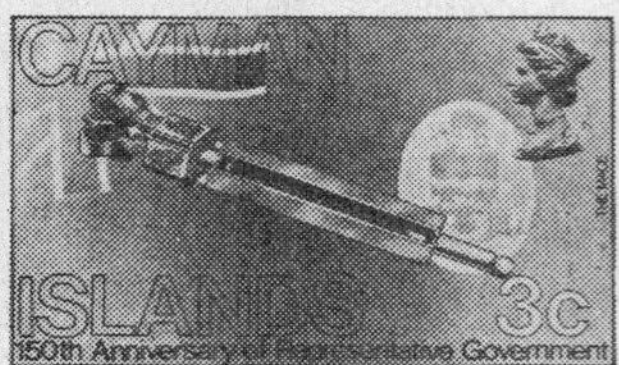

145. Mace.

1982. 150th Anniv. of Representative Government. Multicoloured.

561.	3 c. Type **145**	10	10
562.	10 c. Old Courthouse ..	20	20
563.	20 c. Commonwealth Parliamentary Association coat of arms	35	35
564.	30 c. Legislative Assembly building	50	60

1983. Shells (2nd series). As T **134**. Mult.

565.	5 c. "Natica canrena" ..	15	10
566.	10 c. "Cassis tuberosa" ..	25	20
567.	20 c. "Strombus gallus" ..	45	40
568.	$1 "Cypraecassis testiculus"	1·75	1·75

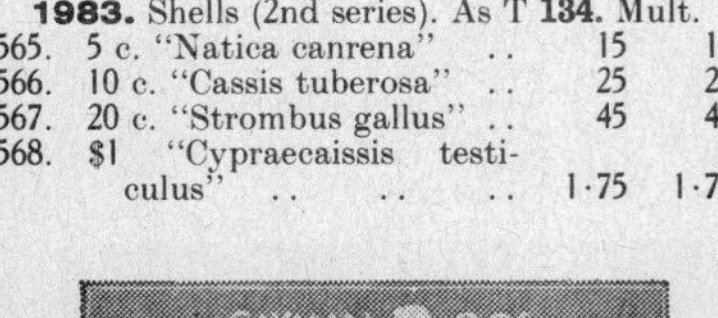

146. Legislative Building, Cayman Brac.

1983. Royal Visit. Multicoloured.

569.	20 c. Type **146**	45	35
570.	30 c. Legislative Building, Grand Cayman	60	50
571.	50 c. Duke of Edinburgh (vert.)	1·25	90
572.	$1 Queen Elizabeth II (vert.)	2·00	2·00

147. Satellite View of Earth.

1983. Commonwealth Day. Multicoloured.

574.	3 c. Type **147**	10	10
575	15 c. Cayman Islands and Commonwealth flags ..	25	30
576.	20 c. Fishing	30	35
577.	40 c. Portrait of Queen Elizabeth II	60	65

148. MRCU " Cessna " Aircraft.

1983. Bicentenary of Manned Flight. Multicoloured.

578.	3 c. Type **148**	15	10
579.	10 c. Consolidated " PBY Catalina "	30	20
580.	20 c. Boeing " 727-200 " ..	55	40
581.	40 c. Hawker Siddeley " HS 748 "	80	1·10

1984. Shells (3rd series). As Type **134**. **Mult.**

582.	3 c. " Natica floridana " ..	25	20
583.	10 c. " Conus austini " ..	45	25
584.	30 c. " Colubraia obscura "	90	80
585.	50 c. " Turbo cailletii " ..	1·25	1·50

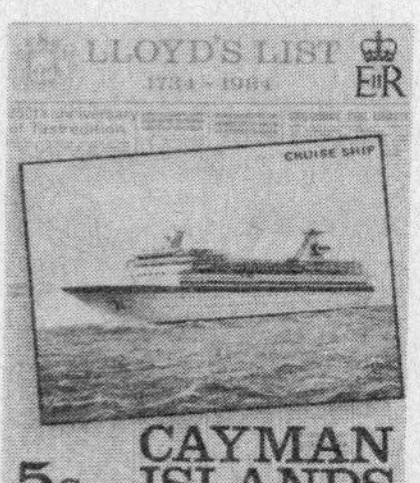

149. "Song of Norway" (cruise liner).

1984. 250th Anniv. of "Lloyd's List" (newspaper). Multicoloured.

586.	5 c. Type **149**	15	10
587.	10 c. View of old harbour	25	25
588.	25 c. Wreck of R.M.S. "Ridgefield"	50	55
589.	50 c. Schooner "Goldfield"	1·00	1·10

1984. Universal Postal Union Congress, Hamburg. No. 589 optd. **U.P.U. CONGRESS HAMBURG 1984.**

591.	50 c. Schooner "Goldfield"	1·00	1·50

151. Snowy Egret.

1984. Birds of the Cayman Islands (1st series). Multicoloured.

592.	5 c. Type **151**	55	15
593.	10 c. Bananaquit	65	25
594.	35 c. Belted kingfisher ..	2·00	1·25
595.	$1 Brown booby	4·00	4·25

See also Nos. 627/30.

152. Couple on Beach at Sunset.

1984. Christmas. Local Festivities. Mult.

596.	5 c. Type **152**	15	20
597.	5 c. Family and schooner	15	20
598.	5 c. Carol singers	15	20
599.	5 c. East End bonfire ..	15	20
600.	25 c. Yachts	55	55
601.	25 c. Father Christmas in power-boat	55	55
602.	25 c. Children on beach ..	55	55
603.	25 c. Beach party	55	55

Nos 596/9 and 600/3 were each printed together, se-tenant, the four designs of each value forming a composite picture of a beach scene at night (5 c.) or in the daytime (25 c.).

153. "Schomburgkia thomsoniana (var. minor)".

1985. Orchids. Multicoloured.

605.	5 c. Type **153**	40	10
606.	10 c. "Schomburgkia thomsoniana"	65	20
607.	25 c. "Encyclia plicata" ..	1·40	70
608.	50 c. "Dendrophylax fawcettii"	1·60	2·00

154. Freighter Aground.

1985. Shipwrecks. Multicoloured.

609.	5 c. Type **154**	45	20
610.	25 c. Submerged sailing ship	1·25	75
611	35 c. Wrecked trawler ..	1·50	1·50
612	40 c. Submerged wreck on its side	1·75	2·00

155. Athletics.

1985. International Youth Year. Mult.

613.	5 c. Type **155**	10	10
614.	15 c. Students in library ..	25	30
615.	25 c. Football (vert.) ..	45	50
616.	50 c. Netball (vert.) ..	85	90

156. Morse Key (1935).

1985. 50th Anniv. of Telecommunications System. Multicoloured.

617. 5 c. Type **156** 10 10
618. 10 c. Hand cranked telephone 20 20
619. 25 c. Tropospheric scatter dish (1966) 45 55
620. 50 c. Earth station dish aerial (1979) .. .. 85 1·10

1986. 60th Birthday of Queen Elizabeth II. As T **110** of Ascension. Multicoloured.

621. 5 c. Princess Elizabeth at wedding of Lady May Cambridge, 1931 .. 10 10
622. 10 c. In Norway, 1955 .. 15 20
623. 25 c. Queen inspecting Royal Cayman Islands Police, 1983 .. .. 45 50
624. 50 c. During Gulf tour, 1979 85 90
625. $1 At Crown Agents Head Office, London, 1983 .. 1·75 1·90

157. Magnificent Frigate Bird.

1986. Birds of the Cayman Islands (2nd series). Multicoloured.

627. 10 c. Type **157** 45 20
628. 25 c. Black-billed whistling duck (vert.) 85 75
629. 35 c. La Sagra's flycatcher (vert.) .. .. .. 95 1·10
630. 40 c. Yellow-faced grass-quit .. .. .. 1·10 1·60

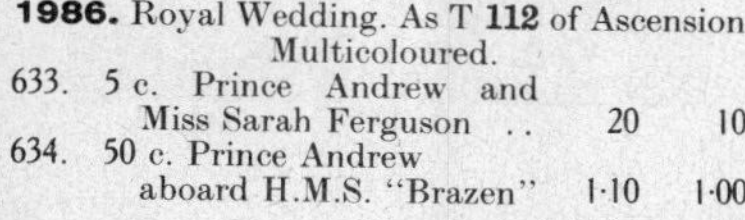

1986. Royal Wedding. As T **112** of Ascension. Multicoloured.

633. 5 c. Prince Andrew and Miss Sarah Ferguson .. 20 10
634. 50 c. Prince Andrew aboard H.M.S. "Brazen" 1·10 1·00

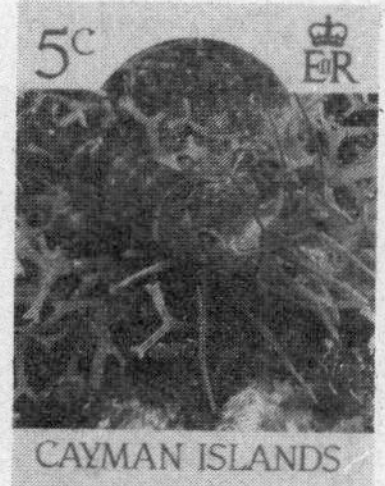

158. Red Coral Shrimp.

1986. Marine Life. Multicoloured.

635 5 c. Type **158** 10 10
696 10 c. Yellow crinoid .. 15 20
637 15 c. Hermit crab 20 25
638 20 c. Tube dwelling anemone 30 35
639 25 c. Christmas tree worm 35 40
640 35 c. Spiny puffer fish .. 50 55
641 50 c. Orangeball anemone 70 75
642 60 c. Basket starfish .. 80 85
643 75 c. Flamingo tongue snail 1·00 1·10
644 $1 Sea anemone .. .. 1·40 1·50
645 $2 Diamond blenny .. 2·75 3·00
646 $4 Flaming scallop .. 5·50 5·75

159. Golf.

1987. Tourism. Multicoloured.

647. 10 c. Type **159** 40 30
648. 15 c. Sailing 60 40
649. 25 c. Snorkelling 75 55
650. 35 c. Paragliding 85 75
651. $1 Game fishing .. .. 2·25 3·00

HAVE YOU READ THE NOTES AT THE BEGINNING OF THIS CATALOGUE?
These often provide answers to the enquiries we receive.

160. Ackee.

1987. Cayman Islands Fruits. Multicoloured.

652. 5 c. Type **160** 10 10
653. 25 c. Breadfruit 45 45
654. 35 c. Pawpaw 60 60
655. $1 Soursop .. .. .. 1·60 2·50

161. Lion Lizard.

1987. Lizards. Multicoloured.

656. 10 c. Type **161** 25 20
657. 50 c. Iguana 90 90
658. $1 Anole .. .. .. 1·75 1·75

162. Poinsettia.

1987. Flowers. Multicoloured.

659. 5 c. Type **162** 25 10
660. 25 c. Periwinkle 80 50
661. 35 c. Yellow allamanda .. 90 80
662. 75 c. Blood lily .. .. 1·75 2·25

163. "Hemiargus ammon" and "Strymon martialis".

1988. Butterflies. Multicoloured.

663 5 c. Type **163** 30 15
664 25 c. "Phocides pigmalion" 70 55
665 50 c. "Anaea troglodyta" 1·10 1·25
666 $1 "Papilio andraemon" .. 1·75 2·25

164 Green Heron

1988. Herons. Multicoloured.

667 5 c. Type **164** 40 15
668 25 c. Louisiana Heron .. 1·00 50
669 50 c. Yellow-crowned night heron .. .. .. 1·40 1·40
670 $1 Little blue heron .. 1·75 2·25

165 Cycling

1988. Olympic Games, Seoul. Multicoloured.

671 10 c. Type **165** 15 20
672 50 c. Cayman Airways airliner and national team 70 75
673 $1 Sailing .. .. 1·40 1·50

166 Princess Alexandra

1988. Visit of Princess Alexandra. Mult.

675 5 c. Type **166** 20 10
676 $1 Princess Alexandra in evening dress .. .. 1·75 1·50

167 Georgetown Post Office and Cayman Postmark on Jamaica Id., 1889

1989. Centenary of Cayman Islands Postal Service. Multicoloured.

677 **167** 5 c. multicoloured .. 15 15
678 – 25 c. green, black & bl 55 55
679 – 35 c. multicoloured .. 70 70
680 – $1 multicoloured .. 1·75 1·75

DESIGNS: 25 c. "Orinoco" (mail steamer) and 1900 ½d. stamp; 35 c. G.P.O., Grand Cayman and "London 1980" $1 stamp; $1 Cayman Airways plane and 1966 1s. Jet Service stamp.

168 Captain Bligh ashore in West Indies

1989. Captain Bligh's Second Breadfruit Voyage, 1791-93. Multicoloured.

681 50 c. Type **168** .. .. 1·50 1·50
682 50 c. H.M.S. "Providence" (sloop) at anchor .. 1·50 1·50
683 50 c. Breadfruit in tubs and H.M.S. "Assistant" (transport) .. .. 1·50 1·50
684 50 c. Sailors moving tubs of breadfruit .. .. 1·50 1·50
685 50 c. Midshipman and stores .. .. .. 1·50 1·50

Nos. 681/5 were printed together, se-tenant, forming a composite design.

169 Panton House

1989. Architecture. Designs showing George Town buildings. Multicoloured.

686 5 c. Type **169** 10 15
687 10 c. Town hall and clock tower 15 20
688 25 c. Old Court House .. 40 50
689 35 c. Elmslie Memorial Church 55 65
690 $1 Post Office .. .. 1·50 2·00

170 Map of Grand Cayman, 1773, and Surveying Instruments

1989. Island Maps and Survey Ships. Mult.

691 5 c. Type **170** 25 20
692 25 c. Map of Cayman Islands, 1956, and surveying instruments 80 70
693 50 c. H.M.S. "Mutine", 1914 .. .. .. 1·40 1·40
694 $1 H.M.S. "Vidal", 1956 2·25 2·50

171 French Angel Fish

1990. Angel Fishes. Multicoloured.

707 10 c. Type **171** 35 30
708 25 c. Grey angel fish .. 70 60
709 50 c. Queen angel fish .. 1·40 1·40
710 $1 Rock beauty .. .. 2·25 2·25

1990. 90th Birhday of Queen Elizabeth the Queen Mother. As T **134** of Ascension.

711 50 c. multicoloured .. 1·00 1·00
712 $1 black and blue .. 2·00 2·00

DESIGNS—21 × 36 mm. 50 c. Silver Wedding photograph, 1948. 29 × 37 mm. $1 King George VI and Queen Elizabeth with Winston Churchill, 1940.

172 "Danaus eresimus"

1990. "Expo 90" International Garden and Greenery Exhibition, Osaka. Butterflies. Multicoloured.

713 5 c. Type **172** 20 20
714 25 c. "Brephidium exilis" 55 55
715 35 c. "Phyciodes phaon" 70 70
716 $1 "Agraulis vanillae" .. 1·90 1·90

173 Goes Weather Satellite

1991. International Decade for Natural Disaster Reduction. Multicoloured.

717	5 c. Type **173**	20	15
718	30 c. Meteorologist tracking hurricane ..	60	60
719	40 c. Damaged buildings ..	75	75
720	$1 U.S. Dept of Commerce weather reconnaisance Lockheed WP-3D Orion	2·25	2·25

174 Angels and "Datura candida"

1991. Christmas. Multicoloured.

721	5 c. Type **174**	10	10
722	30 c. Mary and Joseph going to Bethlehem and "Allamanda cathartica"	40	45
723	40 c. Adoration of the Kings and "Euphorbia pulcherrima" ..	55	60
724	60 c. Holy Family and "Guaiacum officinale"	80	85

175 Coconut Palm

1991. Island Scenes. Multicoloured.

725	5 c. Type **175**	10	10
726	15 c. Beach scene (horiz) ..	20	25
727	20 c. Poincianas in bloom (horiz)	30	35
728	30 c. Blowholes (horiz) ..	35	40
729	40 c. Police band (horiz) ..	50	55
730	50 c. Cruise liner at George Town	70	75
731	60 c. The Bluff, Cayman Brac (horiz) ..	80	85
732	80 c. Coat of arms ..	1·00	1·10
733	90 c. View of Hell (horiz)	1·00	1·10
734	$1 Game fishing (horiz) ..	1·40	1·50
735	$2 Cruise ships in harbour	2·75	3·00
736	$8 Queen Elizabeth II ..	11·00	11·50

1992. 40th Anniv of Queen Elizabeth II's Accession. As T **143** of Ascension. Mult.

737	5 c. Cayman's house ..	10	10
738	20 c. Sunset over islands ..	30	35
739	30 c. Beach	40	45
740	40 c. Three portraits of Queen Elizabeth ..	60	65
741	$1 Queen Elizabeth II ..	1·40	1·50

CEYLON

An island to the S. of India formerly under British administration, then a self-governing Dominion. The island became a Republic within the Commonwealth on 22 May 1972 and was renamed Sri Lanka (q.v.).

1857. 12 pence = 1 shilling;
20 shillings = 1 pound.
1872. 100 cents = 1 rupee.

2.

3.

1.

8.

1857. Imperf.

4.	**2.**	½d. lilac	£160	£140
5.	**1.**	1d. blue	£600	19·00
7.		2d. green	£150	50·00
9.	**3.**	4d. red	£50000	£4500
10.	**1.**	5d. brown	£1500	£150
11.		6d. brown	£1800	£130
13.	**3.**	8d. brown	£1900	£1500
14.		9d. brown	£27000	£900
15.	**1.**	10d. orange	£800	£250
16.		1s. violet	£4500	£200
17.	**3.**	1s. 9d. green	£700	£800
19.		2s. blue	£5000	£1100

The prices of these imperf. stamps vary greatly according to condition. The above prices are for fine copies with four margins. Poor to medium specimens are worth much less.

1861. Perf.

71	2	½d. lilac	19·00	17·00
94	1	1d. blue	50·00	4·00
78		2d. green	32·00	6·00
98		2d. yellow	26·00	5·00
100	3	4d. red	26·00	8·00
27	1	5d. brown	75·00	8·00
101		5d. green	32·00	6·00
104		6d. brown	35·00	7·00
89	3	8d. brown	40·00	20·00
110		9d. brown	20·00	6·00
111a	1	10d. orange	24·00	5·00
114		1s. violet	60·00	5·50
117	3	2s. blue	60·00	11·00

1866. The 3d. has portrait in circle.

119.	**8.**	1d. blue	9·50	4·50
120.	–	3d. red	42·00	20·00

9.

10.

30.

1872. Various frames.

256	9	2 c. brown	1·00	30
147		2 c. green	1·25	15
122	10	4 c. grey	26·00	90
148		4 c. purple	1·40	30
246		4 c. red	6·50	6·50
258		4 c. yellow	1·00	2·00
150	–	8 c. yellow	2·75	6·00
126	–	16 c. violet	50·00	2·75
127	–	24 c. green	28·00	2·00
128	–	32 c. grey	85·00	12·00
129	–	36 c. blue	70·00	13·00
130	–	48 c. red	60·00	5·00
131	–	64 c. brown	£160	50·00
132	–	96 c. grey	£140	26·00
201	30	1 r. 12 red	16·00	14·00
138		2 r. 50 red	£425	£275
249		2 r. 50 purple on red ..	20·00	40·00

1882. Nos. 127 and 131 surch. in words and figures.

142.	–	16 c. on 24 c. green ..	16·00	6·50
143.	–	20 c. on 64 c. brown ..	8·50	3·50

1885. As Nos. 148/132 surch **Postage & Revenue** and value in words.

177.	5 c. on 4 c. purple ..		
178.	5 c. on 4 c. red	10·00	2·75
179.	5 c. on 8 c. yellow ..	28·00	5·50
180.	5 c. on 16 c. violet ..	40·00	8·50
154.	5 c. on 24 c. green ..	£1000	80·00
182.	5 c. on 24 c. purple ..	—	£500
155.	5 c. on 32 c. grey ..	45·00	14·00
156.	5 c. on 36 c. blue ..	85·00	8·00
157.	5 c. on 48 c. red ..	£400	26·00
158.	5 c. on 64 c. brown ..	45·00	4·50
159.	5 c. on 96 c. grey ..	£225	45·00

1885. As Nos. 126/249 surch. with new value in words.

184	10 c. on 16 c. violet ..	£2500	£500
162	10 c. on 24 c. green ..	£275	65·00
185	10 c. on 24 c. purple ..	8·50	5·00
163	10 c. on 36 c. blue ..	£300	£140
174	10 c. on 64 c. brown ..	35·00	55·00
186	15 c. on 16 c. violet ..	7·00	5·50
165	20 c. on 24 c. green ..	30·00	12·00
166	20 c. on 32 c. grey ..	24·00	20·00
167	25 c. on 32 c. grey ..	9·50	4·25
168	28 c. on 48 c. red ..	26·00	4·75
169	30 c. on 36 c. blue ..	8·00	7·00
170	56 c. on 96 c. grey ..	12·00	9·00
176	1 r. 12 on 2 r. 50 red ..	50·00	30·00

1885. Surch. **REVENUE AND POSTAGE 5 CENTS.**

187.	–	5 c. on 8 c. lilac (as No. 150a) ..	5·50	70

1885. As Nos. 126/32 surch. in words and figures.

188.	10 c. on 24 c. purple ..	8·50	4·50
189.	15 c. on 16 c. yellow ..	32·00	5·00
190.	28 c. on 32 c. grey ..	11·00	2·50
191.	30 c. on 36 c. olive ..	25·00	12·00
192.	56 c. on 96 c. grey ..	30·00	7·00

1885. Surch. **1 R. 12 C.**

193.	**30.**	1 r. 12 on 2 r. 50 red ..	26·00	60·00

39.

28.

43.

1886.

245.	**39.**	3 c. brown and green ..	1·25	45
257.		3 c. green	1·25	55
195.	**28.**	5 c. purple	1·10	10
259.	**39.**	6 c. red and black ..	75	45
260.		12 c. olive and red ..	2·50	4·75
197.		15 c. olive	2·50	65
261.		15 c. blue	4·25	1·25
198.		25 c. brown	1·25	1·00
199.		28 c. grey	8·50	1·40
247a.		30 c. mauve and brown	3·50	1·50
262.		75 c. black and brown ..	4·25	4·00
263.	**43.**	1 r. 50 red	15·00	32·00
264.		2 r. 25 blue	28·00	32·00

1887. Nos. 148/9 surch.

A. Surch. **TWO CENTS.**

202.	**10.**	2 c. on 4 c. purple ..	70	30
203.		2 c. on 4 c. red	60	30

B. Surch. **TWO.**

204.	**10.**	2 c. on 4 c. purple ..	60	20
205.		2 c. on 4 c. red	1·60	20

C. Surch. **2 Cents** and bar.

206.	**10.**	2 c. on 4 c. purple ..	30·00	24·00
207.		2 c. on 4 c. red	1·60	75

D. Surch. **Two Cents and bar.**

208.	**10.**	2 c. on 4 c. purple ..	35·00	16·00
209.		2 c. on 4 c. red	1·60	70

E. Surch. **2 Cents** without bar.

210.	**10.**	2 c. on 4 c. purple ..	30·00	20·00
211.		2 c. on 4 c. red	3·50	60

1890. Surch. **POSTAGE Five Cents REVENUE.**

233.	**39.**	5 c. on 15 c. olive ..	1·00	1·00

1891. Surch. **FIFTEEN CENTS.**

239.	**39.**	15 c. on 25 c. brown ..	5·50	8·50
240.		15 c. on 28 c. grey ..	5·50	8·50

1892. Surch. **3 Cents** and bar.

241.	**10.**	3 c. on 4 c. purple ..	50	1·50
242.		3 c. on 4 c. red	1·00	5·00
243.	**39.**	3 c. on 28 c. grey ..	1·10	1·60

1899. Surch. **Six Cents.**

250.	**39.**	6 c. on 15 c. olive ..	45	45

1899. Surch. with value and bar.

254.	**30.**	1 r. 50 on 2 r. 50 grey ..	20·00	35·00
255.		2 r. 25 on 2 r. 50 yellow	27·00	60·00

44.

45.

1903. Various frames.

277.	**44.**	2 c. brown	55	10
278.	**45.**	3 c. green (A)	75	15
293.		3 c. green (B)	85	75
279.		4 c. orange and blue ..	35	50
268.	–	5 c. purple }	1·50	30
289.	–	5 c. purple } see	1·50	10
281.	–	6 c. red .. } footnote	1·10	15
291.	–	6 c. red .. }	70	10
294.	**45.**	10 c. olive and red ..	1·50	80
282.		12 c. olive and red ..	1·50	1·75
283.		15 c. blue	90	50
284.		25 c. brown	6·00	3·75
295.		25 c. grey	2·50	70
285.		30 c. violet and green ..	2·50	1·50
296.		50 c. brown	4·00	7·00
286.		75 c. blue and orange ..	5·25	8·00
297.		1 r. purple on yellow ..	7·50	10·00
287.		1 r. 50 grey	15·00	10·00
298.		2 r. red on yellow ..	15·00	27·00
288.		2 r. 25 brown and green	18·00	27·00
299.		5 r. black on green ..	35·00	65·00
300.		10 r. black on red ..	60·00	£140

(A) has value in shaded tablet; (B) in white tablet as in Type **45.**

Nos. 268 and 281 have the value in words; Nos. 289 and 291 in figures.

52.

57.

1912.

301	**52.**	1 c. brown	40	10
308		2 c. orange	30	20
339		3 c. green	45	1·00
355		3 c. grey	15	20
340		5 c. purple	10	15
341		6 c. red	35	75
356		6 c. violet	15	15
357		9 c. red on yellow ..	30	35
343		10 c. olive	60	40
360d		12 c. red	80	1·50
315		15 c. blue	1·50	1·25
359		15 c. green on yellow ..	1·25	1·25
360f		20 c. blue	55	45
346		25 c. yellow and blue ..	80	1·25
360h		30 c. green and violet	1·40	1·25
348		50 c. black and red ..	1·00	80
322a		1 r. purple on yellow	1·25	2·75
323a		2 r. black & red on yell.	2·00	8·00
324a		5 r. black on green ..	11·00	25·00
325		10 r. pur. & blk. on red	42·00	50·00
352		20 r. blk. & red on blue	65·00	65·00

Large type, as Bermuda T **15.**

327.	50 r. purple	£300
328.	100 r. black	£1300
360.	100 r. purple and blue ..	£1200

1918. Optd. **WAR STAMP** or surch. **ONE CENT** and bar also

335.	**52.**	1 c. on 5 c. purple ..	30	25
330.		2 c. orange	15	40
331.		3 c. green	10	20
333.		5 c. purple	20	30

1918. Surch. **ONE CENT** and bar.

337.	**52.**	1 c. on 5 c. purple ..	15	25

1926. Surch. with new value and **bar.**

361.	**52.**	2 c. on 3 c. grey ..	50	1·00
362.		5 c. on 6 c violet ..	50	40

1927.

363.	**57.**	1 r. purple	1·75	1·25
364.		2 r. green and red ..	3·75	2·75
365.		5 r. green and purple ..	12·00	17·00
366.		10 r. green and orange ..	28·00	70·00
367.		20 r. purple and blue ..	65·00	£140

60. Adam's Peak.

1935. King George V.

368.	–	2 c. black and red ..	25	25
369.	**60.**	3 c. black and green ..	35	30
370.	–	6 c. black and blue ..	30	25
371.	–	9 c. green and orange ..	65	40
372.	–	10 c. black and purple ..	1·00	90
373.	–	15 c. brown and green ..	1·00	50
374.	–	20 c. black and blue ..	1·75	1·60
375.	–	25 c. blue and brown ..	1·25	75
376.	–	30 c. red and green ..	3·00	1·25
377.	–	50 c. black and violet ..	3·75	50
378.	–	1 r. violet and brown ..	8·00	6·00

DESIGNS—VERT. 2 c. Tapping rubber. 6 c. Colombo Harbour. 9 c. Plucking tea. 20 c. Coconut palms. HORIZ. 10 c. Hill paddy (rice). 15 c. River scene. 25 c. Temple of the Tooth, Kandy. 30 c. Ancient irrigation tank. 50 c. Indian elephants. 1 r. Trincomalee.

1935. Silver Jubilee. As T 13 of Antigua.

379. 6 c. blue and grey .. 45 30
380. 9 c. green and blue .. 70 50
381. 20 c. brown and blue .. 3·75 1·50
382. 50 c. grey and purple .. 5·00 3·75

1937. Coronation. As T 2 of Aden.

383. 6 c. red 55 10
384. 9 c. green .. .. 1·50 1·50
385. 20 c. blue .. .. 2·50 2·50

70. Sigiriya (Lion Rock).

1938. As 1935 issue but with portrait of King George VI and "POSTAGE & REVENUE" omitted.

386b – 2 c. black and red .. 30 10
387e 60. 3 c. black and green .. 20 15
387f – 5 c. green and orange .. 20 10
388 – 6 c. black and blue .. 20 10
389 70. 10 c. black and blue .. 60 10
390 – 15 c. green and brown 50 10
391 – 20 c. black and blue .. 1·75 10
392a – 25 c. blue and brown .. 60 10
393 – 30 c. red and green .. 6·00 75
394e – 50 c. black and violet .. 1·40 15
395 – 1 r. blue and brown .. 6·00 35
396 – 2 r. black and red .. 4·00 1·00
396a – 2 r. black and violet .. 11·00 1·25

DESIGNS—VERT. 5 c. Coconut palms. 20 c. Plucking tea. 2 r. Ancient Guard-stone, Anuradhapura. Others, same as for corresponding values of 1935 issue.

1938. As T 57, but head of King George VI to right.

397a. 5 r. green and purple .. 11·00 1·25

1940. Surch. with new value and bars.

398. – 3 c. on 6 c. black & blue (No. 388) 10 10
399. – 3 c. on 20 c. black & blue (No. 391) 50 40

1946. Victory. As T 9 of Aden.

400. 6 c. blue 10 10
401. 15 c. brown 10 30

75. Parliament Building.

1947. New Constitution.

402. 75. 6 c. black and blue .. 10 15
403. – 10 c. black, orge. & red 10 20
404. – 15 c. green and purple .. 10 30
405. – 25 c. yellow and green .. 10 15

DESIGNS—VERT. 10 c. Adam's Peak. 25 c. Anuradhapura. HORIZ. 15 c. Temple of the Tooth.

79. Lion Flag of Dominion.

80. D. S. Senanayake.

1949. 1st Anniv. of Independence.

406. 79. 4 c. red, yellow & brown 10 20
407. 80. 5 c. brown and green .. 10 10
408. 79. 15 c. red, yellow & orge. 25 15
409. 80. 25 c. brown and blue .. 15 15

No. 408 is larger (28×22 mm.).

82. Globe and Forms of Transport.

1949. 75th Anniv. of U.P.U. Inscr. as in T 45. Designs show globe.

410. 82. 5 c. brown and green .. 75 10
411. – 15 c. blk. & red (horiz.) 1·40 60
412. – 25 c. blk. & blue (vert.) 1·40 35

85. Kandyan Dancer.

88. Sigiriya (Lion Rock).

90. Ruins at Madirgiriya.

1950.

413. 85. 4 c. purple and red .. 10 10
414. – 5 c. green 10 10
415. – 15 c. green and violet .. 1·25 25
416. 88. 30 c. red and yellow .. 30 20
417. – 75 c. blue and orange .. 65 10
418. 90. 1 r. blue and brown .. 1·25 10

DESIGNS—VERT. As Types 85 and 88: 5 c. Kiri Vehera, Polonnaruwa. 15 c. Vesak orchid. As Type 90: 75 c. Octagon Library, Temple of the Tooth.

94. Coconut Trees.

99. Tea Plantation.

1951.

419 – 2 c. brown & turquoise 10 20
420 – 3 c. black and violet .. 10 30
421 – 6 c. sepia and green .. 10 10
422 94 10 c. green and grey .. 75 25
423 – 25 c. orange and blue 10 10
424 – 35 c. red and green .. 1·50 60
425 – 40 c. brown .. .. 1·25 25
426 – 50 c. slate 30 10
427 99 85 c. black & turquoise 50 10
428 – 2 r. blue and brown .. 4·50 40
429 – 5 r. brown and orange 4·75 50
430 – 10 r. brown and buff .. 14·00 4·25

DESIGNS—As Type 94. VERT. 2 c. Sambars, Ruhuna National Park. 3 c. Ancient Guard-stone, Anuradhapura. 6 c. Harvesting rice. 25 c. Sigiriya fresco. 35 c. Star orchid. HORIZ. 40 c. Rubber plantation. 50 c. Outrigger canoe. As Type 99. HORIZ. 2 r. River Gal Dam. VERT. 5 r. Bas-relief, Anuradhapura. 10 r. Harvesting rice.

103. Ceylon. Mace and Symbols of Progress.

1952. Colombo Plan Exn.

431. 103. 5 c. green 10 10
432. 15 c. blue 20 15

104. Queen Elizabeth II.

106. King Coconuts.

105. Ceremonial Procession.

1953. Coronation.

433. 104. 5 c. green 40 10

1954. Royal Visit.

434. 105. 10 c. blue 15 10

1954.

435. 106. 10 c. orge., brn. & buff 10 10

107. Farm Produce.

1955. Royal Agricultural and Food Exn.

436. 107. 10 c. brown and orange 10 10

108. Sir John Kotelawala and House of Representatives.

1956. Prime Minister's 25 years of Public Service.

437. 108. 10 c. green 10 10

109. Arrival of Vijaya in Ceylon.

110. Lampstand and Dharmachakra.

DESIGNS—VERT. 10 c. Hand of Peace and Dharmachakra. HORIZ. 15 c. Dharmachakra encircling the globe.

1956. Buddha Jayanti. Inscr. "2500".

438. 109. 3 c. blue and grey .. 15 10
439. 110. 4 c.+2 c. yellow & blue 15 35
440. – 10 c.+5 c. red, yellow and grey 15 30
441. – 15 c. blue 15 10

113. Mail Transport.

114. Stamp of 1857.

1957. Stamp Centenary.

442. 113. 4 c. red and turquoise .. 30 15
443. – 10 c. red and blue .. 30 10
444. 114. 35 c. brn., yell. and blue 30 20
445. – 85 c. brn., yell. and grn. 70 85

1958. Nos. 439/40 with premium obliterated with bars.

446. 110. 4 c. yellow and blue .. 10 10
447. – 10 c. red, yellow & grey 10 10

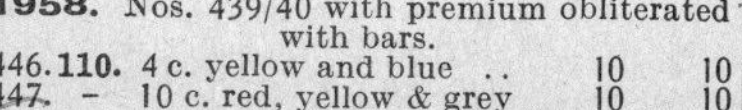

117. Kandyan Dancer.

1958. As Nos. 413 and 419, etc., and 435, but with inscriptions changed as in T 117.

448 2 c. brown and turquoise .. 10 10
449 3 c. black and violet .. 10 35
450 4 c. purple and red .. 10 10
451 5 c. green 10 10
452 6 c. sepia and green .. 10 35
453 10 c. orange, brown & buff 10 10
454 15 c. green and violet .. 2·25 40
455 25 c. orange and blue .. 10 10
456 30 c. red and yellow .. 15 50
457 35 c. red and green .. 3·00 15
459 50 c. slate 30 10
460a 75 c. blue and orange .. 45 30
461 85 c. black and turquoise 3·75 2·25
462 1 r. blue and brown .. 40 10
463 2 r. blue and brown .. 75 10
464 5 r. brown and orange .. 1·25 10
465 10 r. brown and buff .. 3·50 70

118 "Human Rights".

1958. 10th Anniv. of Declaration of Human Rights.

466. 118. 10 c. red, brn. and pur. 10 10
467. 85 c. red, turq. and grn. .. 30 45

119. Portraits of Founders and University Buildings.

1959. Institution of Pirivona Universities.

468. 119. 10 c. orange and blue .. 10 10

120. "Uprooted Tree".

121. S.W.R.D. Bandaranaike.

1960. World Refugee Year.

469. 120. 4 c. brown and gold .. 10 30
470. 25 c. violet and gold .. 10 15

1961. Prime Minister Bandaranaike Commem.

471. 121. 10 c. blue & turquoise 10 10

See also Nos. 479 and 481.

122. Ceylon Scout Badge.

123. Campaign Emblem.

1962. Golden Jubilee of Ceylon Boy Scouts Association.

472. 122. 35 c. buff and blue .. 15 10

1962. Malaria Eradication.

473. 123. 25 c. red and drab .. 10 10

124 "DH85 Leopard-Moth" and "Comet" Airliner

1963. Airmail Services. 25th Anniv.
474. 124. 50 c. black and blue .. 15 30

125. "Produce" and Campaign Emblem.

1963. Freedom from Hunger.
475. 125. 5 c. red and blue .. 20 60
476. – 25 c. brown and olive .. 80 30

(126.)

1963. No. 450 surch. with T **126**.
477. 2 c. on 4 c. purple and red 10 10

127. "Rural Life".

1963. Golden Jubilee of Ceylon Co-operative Movement (1962)
478. 127. 60 c. red and black .. 15 30

1963. Design similar to T **121**, but smaller (21 × 26 mm.) and with inscription rearranged at top.
479. 10 c. blue 10 10
481. 10 c. violet and grey .. 10 10
No. 481 has a decorative pattern at foot instead of the inscription.

129. Terrain, Indian Elephant and Tree.

1963. National Conservation Week.
480. 129. 5 c. sepia and blue .. 10 20

131. Anagarika Dharmapala (Buddhist missionary).

1964. Birth Cent. of A. Dharmapala (founder of Maha Bodhi Society).
482. 131. 25 c. sepia and yellow 10 10

135. D. S. Senanayake.

143. Ceylon Jungle Fowl.

138. Ruins at Madirigiriya.

1964.
485. – 5 c. multicoloured .. 40 60
486. 135. 10 c. green 10 10
487. – 10 c. green 10 10
488. – 15 c. multicoloured .. 90 30
489. 138. 20 c. purple and buff .. 10 15
494. 143. 60 c. multicoloured .. 1·25 50
495. – 75 c. multicoloured .. 1·25 50
497. – 1 r. brown and green .. 1·00 10
499. – 5 r. multicoloured .. 1·75 1·75
500. – 10 r. multicoloured .. 8·50 1·75
DESIGNS: As Type **143**. HORIZ. 5 c. Grackle. 15 c. Peacock. 75 c. Asian Black-headed Oriole. 5 r. Girls transplanting Rice (23 × 36 mm.). VERT. As Type **135**. 10 c. (No. 487). Similar portrait; but larger head and smaller inscriptions. 1 r. Tea Plantation (as Type **99**, but larger, 21 × 35 mm.). 10 r. Map of Ceylon (23 × 36 mm.).

150. Exhibition Buildings and Cogwheels.

1964. Industrial Exn.
501. – 5 c. multicoloured .. 10 25
502. 150. 5 c. multicoloured .. 10 25
No. 501 is inscribed "INDUSTRIAL EXHIBITION" in Sinhala and Tamil, No. 502 in Sinhala and English.

151. Trains of 1864 and 1964.

1964. Centenary of Ceylon Railways.
503. – 60 c. blue, purple & green 1·25 20
504. 151. 60 c. blue, purple & green 1·25 20
No. 503 is inscribed "RAILWAY CENTENARY" in Sinhala and Tamil, No. 504 in Sinhala and English.

152. I.T.U. Emblem and Symbols.

1965. Centenary of I.T.U.
505. 152. 2 c. blue and red .. 15 65
506. 30 c. brown and red .. 1·50 45

153. I.C.Y. Emblem.

1965. Int. Co-operation Year.
507. 153. 3 c. blue and red .. 30 50
508. 50 c. black, red & gold .. 1·50 50

154. Town Hall, Colombo.

1965. Cent. of Colombo Municipal Council.
509. 154. 25 c. green and sepia 10 10

1965. No. 481 surch.
510. 5 c. on 10 c. violet and grey 10 10

157. Kandy and Council Crest.

1966. Cent. of Kandy Municipal Council.
512. 157. 25 c. multicoloured .. 10 10

158. W.H.O. Building.

1966. Inaug. of W.H.O. Headquarters, Geneva.
513. 158. 4 c. multicoloured .. 75 1·50
514. 1 r. multicoloured .. 3·50 1·50

160. Rice Paddy and Map of Ceylon.

1966. Int. Rice Year. Multicoloured.
515. 6 c. Type **160** 20 50
516. 30 c. Rice Paddy and Globe 30 15

161. U.N.E.S.C.O. Emblem.

1966. 20th Anniv. of U.N.E.S.C.O.
517. 161. 3 c. multicoloured .. 40 30
518. 50 c. multicoloured .. 2·25 30

162. Water-resources Map.

1966. Int. Hydrological Decade.
519. 162. 2 c. brown, yellow & blue 10 65
520. – 2 r. multicoloured .. 60 1·25

163. Devotees at Buddhist Temple.

1967. Poya Holiday System. Multicoloured.
521. 5 c. Type **163** 10 20
522. 20 c. Mihintale 10 10
523. 35 c. Sacred Bo-tree Anuradhapura 10 15
524. 60 c. Adam's Peak 10 10

167. Galle Fort and Clock Tower.

1967. Cent. of Galle Municipal Council.
525. 167. 25 c. multicoloured .. 30 20

168. Field Research.

1967. Cent. of Ceylon Tea Industry. Mult.
526. 4 c. Type **168** 15 40
527. 40 c. Tea-tasting equipment 45 40
528. 50 c. Leaves and bud .. 45 20
529. 1 r. Shipping tea 80 10

172. Elephant Ride.

1967. Int. Tourist Year.
530. 172. 45 c. multicoloured .. 80 30

173. Ranger, Jubilee Emblem and Flag.

1967. Golden Jubilee of Ceylon Girl Guides' Assn.
532. 173. 3 c. multicoloured .. 10 10
533. 25 c. multicoloured .. 25 10

174. Col. Olcott and Buddhist Flag.

1967. 60th Death Anniv. of Colonel Olcott (theosophist).
534. 174. 15 c. multicoloured .. 15 15

175. Independence Hall.

1968. 20th Anniv. of Independence. Mult.
535. 5 c. Type **175** 10 35
536. 1 r. Lion Flag and Sceptre 20 10

177. Sir D. B. Jayatilleke.

1968. Birth Centenary of Sir Baron Jayatilleke (scholar and statesman)
537. 177. 25 c. brown 10 10

178. Institute of Hygiene.

1968. 20th Anniv. of World Health Organization.
538. 178. 50 c. multicoloured .. 10 10

179. Aircraft over Terminal Building.

1968. Opening of Colombo Airport.
539. **179.** 60 c. multicoloured .. 10 10

181. Open Koran and "1400".

1968. 1400th Anniv. of Koran.
541. **181.** 25 c. multicoloured .. 10 10

182. Human Rights Emblem.

1968. Human Rights Year.
542. **182.** 2 c. multicoloured .. 10 10
543. – 20 c. multicoloured .. 10 10
544. – 40 c. multicoloured .. 10 10
545. – 2 r. multicoloured .. 45 2·25

183. All Ceylon Buddhist Congress Headquarters.

1968. Golden Jubilee of All Ceylon Buddhist Congress.
546. **183.** 5 c. multicoloured .. 10 30

184. E. W. Perera (patriot). **185.** Symbols of Strength in Savings.

1969. Perera Commem.
547. **184.** 60 c. brown 10 10

1969. Silver Jubilee of National Savings Movement.
548. **185.** 3 c. multicoloured .. 10 10

186. Seat of Enlightenment under Sacred Bodhi Tree. **188.** A. E. Goonesinghe.

1969. Vesak Day. Inscr. "Wesak".
549. **186.** 4 c. multicoloured .. 10 20
550. – 6 c. multicoloured .. 10 20
551. **186.** 35 c. multicoloured .. 10 10
DESIGN: 6 c. Buduresmala (Six-fold Buddha-Rays).

1969. Goonesinghe Commem.
552. **188.** 15 c. multicoloured .. 10 10

189. I.L.O. Emblem.

1969. 50th Anniv. of Int. Labour Organization.
553. **189.** 5 c. black and blue .. 10 10
554. – 25 c. black and red .. 10 10

190. Convocation Hall, University of Ceylon.

1969. Educational Cent. Multicoloured.
555. 4 c. Type **190** 10 30
556. 35 c. Lamp of learning, globe and flags (horiz.) 10 10
557. 50 c. Uranium atom .. 15 10
558. 60 c. Symbols of scientific education 15 10

194. Ath Pana (Elephant Lamp).

1969. Archaeological Cent. Multicoloured.
559. 6 c. Type **194** 10 40
560. 1 r. Rock fortress of Sigiriya 25 10

196. Leopard.

1970. Wild Life Conservation. Multicoloured.
561. 5 c. Water buffalo.. .. 15 60
562. 15 c. Slender loris 50 30
563. 50 c. Spotted deer .. .. 70 1·25
564. 1 r. Type **196** .. .. 90 1·75

197. Emblem and Symbols.

1970. Asian Productivity Year.
565. **197.** 60 c. multicoloured .. 10 10

198. New U.P.U. H.Q. Building.

1970. New U.P.U. Headquarters Building.
566. **198.** 50 c. orge., blk. & blue 10 10
567. – 1 r. 10 red, black and blue 55 30

199. Oil Lamp and Caduceus.

1970. Cent. of Colombo Medical School.
568 **199** 5 c. multicoloured .. 15 40
569 45 c. multicoloured .. 25 40

200. Victory March and S.W.R.D. Bandaranaike.

1970. Establishment of United Front Government.
570. **200.** 10 c. multicoloured .. 10 10

201. U.N. Emblem and Dove of Peace.

1970. 25th Anniv. of United Nations.
571. **201.** 2 r. multicoloured .. 75 1·40

202. Keppetipola Dissawa.

1970. 152nd Death Anniv. of Keppetipola Dissawa (Kandyan patriot).
572. **202.** 25 c. multicoloured .. 10 10

203. Ola Leaf Manuscript.

1970. Int. Education Year.
573. **203.** 15 c. multicoloured .. 30 40

204. C. H. De Soysa. **205.** D. E. H. Pedris (patriot).

1971. 135th Birth Anniv. of C. H. De Soysa (philanthropist).
574. **204.** 20 c. multicoloured .. 10 30

1971. D. E. H. Pedris. Commemoration.
575. **205.** 25 c. multicoloured .. 10 35

206. Lenin. **207.** Ananda Rajakaruna

1971. Lenin Commemoration.
576. **206.** 40 c. multicoloured .. 15 30

1971. Poets and Philosophers.
577. **207.** 5 c. blue 10 15
578. – 5 c. brown 10 15
579. – 5 c. orange 10 15
580. – 5 c. blue 10 15
581. – 5 c. brown 10 15
PORTRAITS: No. 578, Arumuga Navalar. No. 579, Rev. S. Mahinda. No. 580, Ananda Coomaraswamy. No. 581, Cumaratunga Munidasa.

1971. Surch. in figures.
582. **186.** 5 c. on 4 c. multicoloured 1·25 1·50
583. **190.** 5 c. on 4 c. multicoloured 10 55
584. **200.** 15 c. on 10 c. mult. .. 10 10
585. – 25 c. on 6 c. multi-coloured (No. 550) 15 50
586. **194.** 25 c. on 6 c. mult. .. 15 50

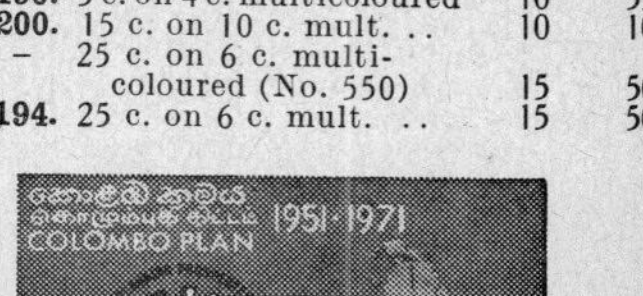

209. Colombo Plan Emblem and Ceylon.

1971. 20th Anniv. of Colombo Plan.
587. **209.** 20 c. multicoloured .. 15 20

210. Globe and C.A.R.E. Package.

1971. 20th Anniv. of Co-operative for American Relief Everywhere.
588. **210.** 50 c. blue, violet & lilac.. .. .. 35 30

211. W.H.O. Emblem and Heart.

1972. World Health Day.
589. **211.** 25 c. multicoloured .. 45 45

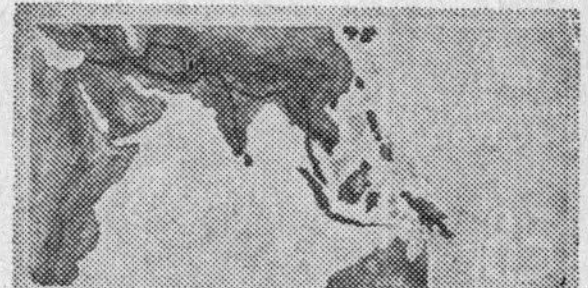

212. Map of Asia and U.N. Emblem.

1972. 25th Anniv. of E.C.A.F.E.
590. **212.** 85 c. multicoloured .. 1·75 1·75

OFFICIAL STAMPS

1895. Stamps of Queen Victoria optd. **On Service.**
O 1. **9.** 2 c. green .. .. 5·50 25
O 8. 2 c. brown .. .. 2·25 60
O 2. **39.** 3 c. brown and green 8·00 40
O 9. 3 c. green .. .. 7·50 60
O 3. **28.** 5 c. purple .. .. 1·25 20
O 4. **29.** 15 c. olive .. .. 8·50 30
O 10. 15 c. blue .. .. 12·00 60
O 5. 25 c. brown .. .. 10·00 80
O 6. 30 c. mauve and brown 11·00 30
O 11. 75 c. black and brown 5·50 4·00
O 7. **30.** 1 r. 12 red .. .. 50·00 45·00

1903. Stamps of King Edward VII optd. **On Service.**
O 12. **44.** 2 c. brown .. .. 5·00 70
O 13. **45.** 3 c. green .. .. 3·00 2·00
O 14. – 5 c. purple (No. 268) 7·50 80
O 15. **45.** 15 c. blue .. .. 18·00 2·50
O 16. 25 c. brown .. .. 19·00 15·00
O 17. 30 c. violet and green 6·50 1·50

For later issues see **SRI LANKA**.

CHAMBA

An Indian "convention" state of the Punjab. Stamps of India optd.

12 pies = 1 anna; 16 annas = 1 rupee.

1886. Queen Victoria. Optd **CHAMBA STATE** in two lines.

No.	Type	Description	Unused	Used
1	**23.**	½ a. turquoise	10	25
2	–	1 a. purple	20	40
4	–	1½ a. brown	60	4·00
5	–	2 a. blue	35	65
7	–	2½ a. green	14·00	40·00
9	–	3 a. orange	40	2·00
10	–	4 a. green (No. 96) ..	60	2·25
12	–	6 a. brown (No. 80) ..	1·25	3·00
15	–	8 a. mauve	1·25	4·50
16	–	12 a. purple on red ..	1·75	4·00
17	–	1 r. grey (No. 101) ..	19·00	55·00
18	**37.**	1 r. green and red ..	1·60	4·25
19	**38.**	2 r. red and brown ..	50·00	£110
20		3 r. brown and green ..	55·00	£100
21		5 r. blue and violet ..	65·00	£140

1900. Queen Victoria. Optd **CHAMBA STATE** in two lines.

No.	Type	Description	Unused	Used
22	**40.**	3 p. red	10	20
23		3 p. grey	15	65
25	**23.**	½ a. green	15	60
26	–	1 a. red	10	30
27	–	2 a. lilac	10	20
			5·00	13·00

1903. King Edward VII. Optd **CHAMBA STATE** in two lines.

No.	Type	Description	Unused	Used
28	**41.**	3 p. grey	10	50
30	–	½ a. green (No. 122) ..	10	20
31	–	1 a. red (No. 123) ..	15	20
32	–	2 a. lilac	30	80
34	–	3 a. orange	70	2·00
35	–	4 a. olive	90	3·50
36	–	6 a. bistre	1·40	5·50
37	–	8 a. mauve	1·25	4·50
39	–	12 a. purple on red ..	1·75	6·00
40	–	1 r. green and red ..	2·00	7·00

1907. King Edward VII. Optd **CHAMBA STATE** in two lines.

No.	Type	Description	Unused	Used
41.	–	½ a. green (No. 149) ..	20	90
42.	–	1 a. red (No. 150) ..	25	90

1913. King George V. Optd **CHAMBA STATE** in two lines.

No.	Type	Description	Unused	Used
43	**55.**	3 p. grey	10	30
44	**56.**	½ a. green	10	30
46	**57.**	1 a. red	10	50
55		1 a. brown	15	80
56	**58.**	1½ a. brown (No. 163) ..	14·00	50·00
57		1½ a. brown (No. 165) ..	30	2·75
58		1½ a. red	60	5·50
47	**59.**	2 a. lilac	30	1·50
59	**61.**	2½ a. blue	50	2·75
60		2½ a. orange	70	4·25
48	**62.**	3 a. orange	85	2·25
61		3 a. blue	1·10	4·25
49	**63.**	4 a. olive	65	1·60
50	**64.**	6 a. bistre	65	2·00
51	**65.**	8 a. mauve	90	3·50
52	**66.**	12 a. red	1·40	7·00
53	**67.**	1 r. brown and green ..	4·00	7·50

1921. No. 192 of India optd. **CHAMBA.**

No.	Type	Description	Unused	Used
54.	**57.**	9 p. on 1 a. red	80	7·50

1927. Stamps of India (King George V) optd. **CHAMBA STATE** in one line.

No.	Type	Description	Unused	Used
62.	**55.**	3 p. grey	10	35
63.	**56.**	½ a. green	10	45
76.	**79.**	½ a. green	30	2·00
64.	**80.**	9 p. green	45	2·50
65.	**57.**	1 a. brown	15	10
77.	**81.**	1 a. brown	40	40
66.	**82.**	1¼ a. mauve	30	1·00
67.	**58.**	1½ a. red	80	1·75
68.	**70.**	2 a. lilac	30	55
78.	**59.**	2 a. red	30	5·50
69.	**61.**	2½ a. orange	40	3·50
70.	**62.**	3 a. blue	60	3·50
80.		3 a. red	1·00	3·00
71.	**71.**	4 a. green	40	1·40
81.	**63.**	4 a. olive	80	2·50
72.	**64.**	6 a. bistre	24·00	75·00
73.	**65.**	8 a. mauve	60	3·50
74.	**66.**	12 a. red	85	4·75
75.	**67.**	1 r. brown and green ..	2·25	7·50

1938. Stamps of India (King George VI Nos. 247/64) optd. **CHAMBA STATE.**

No.	Type	Description	Unused	Used
82.	**91.**	3 p. slate	1·75	3·75
83.		½ a. brown	60	2·25
84.		9 p. green	1·75	8·00
85.		1 a. red	90	65
86.	**92.**	2 a. red	1·40	3·75
87.	–	2½ a. violet	1·50	7·00
88.	–	3 a. green	4·00	9·00
89.	–	3½ a. blue	2·25	9·00
90.	–	4 a. brown	6·00	5·50
91.	–	6 a. green	7·50	19·00
92.	–	8 a. violet	6·50	15·00
93.	–	12 a. red	3·25	20·00
94.	**93.**	1 r. slate and brown ..	16·00	24·00
95.		2 r. purple and brown ..	28·00	85·00
96.		5 r. green and blue ..	50·00	£140
97.		10 r. purple and red ..	£110	£275
98.		15 r. brown and green ..	£225	£425
99.		25 r. slate and purple ..	£325	£550

1942. Stamps of India (King George VI) optd. **CHAMBA.**

(a) On issue of 1938.

No.	Type	Description	Unused	Used
100.	**91.**	½ a. brown	6·50	8·00
101.		1 a. red	9·00	9·00
102.	**93.**	1 r. slate and brown ..	19·00	25·00
103.		2 r. purple and brown ..	24·00	80·00
104.		5 r. green and blue ..	55·00	£120
105.		10 r. purple and red ..	90·00	£225
106.		15 r. brown and green ..	£225	£375
107.		25 r. slate and purple ..	£325	£500

(b) On issue of 1940.

No.	Type	Description	Unused	Used
108.	**100a.**	3 p. slate	40	1·75
109.		½ a. mauve	60	1·00
110.		9 p. green	50	3·50
111.		1 a. red	90	1·25
112.	**101.**	1½ a. violet	60	2·75
113.		2 a. red	1·40	3·50
114.		3 a. violet	2·00	5·50
115.		3½ a. blue	2·50	12·00
116.	**102.**	4 a. brown	3·00	4·75
117.		6 a. green	7·50	18·00
118.		8 a. violet	8·50	22·00
119.		12 a. purple	15·00	30·00
120.	–	14 a. purple (No. 277) ..	4·00	3·00

OFFICIAL STAMPS

Stamps of India optd.

1886. Queen Victoria. Optd **SERVICE CHAMBA STATE**.

No.	Type	Description	Unused	Used
O 1	**23.**	½ a. turquoise ..	10	10
O 3	–	1 a. purple	25	25
O 5	–	2 a. blue	45	70
O 7	–	3 a. orange	1·25	4·00
O 8	–	4 a. green (No. 96) ..	45	1·40
O 10	–	6 a. brown (No. 80) ..	1·50	4·00
O 13	–	8 a. mauve	70	1·25
O 14	–	12 a. purple on red ..	7·00	20·00
O 15	–	1 r. grey (No. 101) ..	11·00	42·00
O 16	**37.**	1 r. green and red ..	4·75	12·00

1902. Queen Victoria. Optd **SERVICE CHAMBA STATE**.

No.	Type	Description	Unused	Used
O 17.	**40.**	3 p. grey	15	40
O 18.	**23.**	½ a. green	15	1·25
O 20.	–	1 a. red	30	40
O 21.	–	2 a. lilac	6·00	13·00

1903. King Edward VII. Optd **SERVICE CHAMBA STATE**.

No.	Type	Description	Unused	Used
O 22.	**41.**	3 p. grey	15	15
O 24.		½ a. green (No. 122) ..	10	10
O 25.		1 a. red (No. 123) ..	15	20
O 27.	–	2 a. lilac	40	40
O 28.	–	4 a. olive	1·50	4·75
O 29.	–	8 a. mauve	1·60	5·00
O 31.	–	1 r. green and red ..	1·25	3·50

1907. King Edward VII. Optd **SERVICE CHAMBA STATE**.

No.	Type	Description	Unused	Used
O 32.	–	½ a. green (No. 149) ..	20	50
O 33.	–	1 a. red (No. 150) ..	50	40

1913. King George V Official stamps optd **CHAMBA STATE.**

No.	Type	Description	Unused	Used
O 34.	**55.**	3 p. grey	20	40
O 36.	**56.**	½ a. green	10	10
O 38.	**57.**	1 a. red	10	10
O 47.		1 a. brown	40	40
O 40.	**59.**	2 a. lilac (No. O 83) ..	75	3·75
O 41.	**63.**	4 a. olive (No. O 86) ..	75	2·50
O 42.	**65.**	8 a. mauve	1·25	3·75
O 43.	**67.**	1 r. brown and green ..	2·75	8·00

1914. King George V Official stamps optd. **SERVICE CHAMBA STATE.**

No.	Type	Description	Unused	Used
O 44.	**59.**	2 a. lilac (No. 166) ..	6·00	
O 45.	**63.**	4 a. olive (No. 210) ..	9·00	

1921. No. O 97 of India optd. **CHAMBA.**

No.	Type	Description	Unused	Used
O 46.	**57.**	9 p. on 1 a. red ..	15	1·50

1927. King George V Postage stamps optd. **CHAMBA STATE SERVICE.**

No.	Type	Description	Unused	Used
O 48.	**55.**	3 p. grey	20	25
O 49.	**56.**	½ a. green	30	15
O 61.	**79.**	½ a. green	30	30
O 50.	**80.**	9 p. green	35	3·00
O 51.	**57.**	1 a. brown	10	10
O 62.	**81.**	1 a. brown	50	30
O 52.	**82.**	1¼ a. mauve	1·50	40
O 53.	**70.**	2 a. lilac	40	40
O 63.	**59.**	2 a. red	1·25	80
O 54.	**71.**	4 a. olive	40	40
O 65.	**63.**	4 a. green	85	1·00
O 55.	**65.**	8 a. mauve	1·40	4·00
O 56.	**66.**	12 a. red	1·25	7·00
O 57.	**67.**	1 r. brown and green ..	6·00	11·00
O 58.		2 r. red and orange ..	12·00	
O 59.		5 r. blue and violet ..	28·00	
O 60.		10 r. green and red ..	38·00	

1938. King George VI Postage stamps of India optd. **CHAMBA STATE SERVICE.**

No.	Type	Description	Unused	Used
O 66.	**91.**	9 p. green	3·75	8·50
O 67.		1 a. red	2·75	1·00
O 68.	**93.**	1 r. slate and brown ..	£650	£750
O 69.		2 r. purple and brown	45·00	£130
O 70.		5 r. green and blue ..	70·00	£200
O 71.		10 r. purple and red ..	£130	£325

1940. Official stamps of India optd. **CHAMBA.**

No.	Type	Description	Unused	Used
O 72.	O **20.**	3 p. grey	60	40
O 73.		½ a. brown	6·50	1·75
O 74.		½ a. purple	60	60
O 75.		9 p. green	1·00	1·50
O 76.		1 a. red	60	50
O 77.		1 a. 3 p. brown ..	25·00	10·00
O 78.		1½ a. violet	3·50	2·00
O 79.		2 a. orange	2·50	1·50
O 80.		2½ a. violet	1·25	7·00
O 81.		4 a. brown	2·75	4·00
O 82.		8 a. violet	5·50	11·00

1942. King George VI Postage stamps of India optd. **CHAMBA SERVICE.**

No.	Type	Description	Unused	Used
O 83.	**93.**	1 r. slate and brown ..	28·00	60·00
O 84.		2 r. purple and brown	40·00	£100
O 85.		5 r. green and blue ..	80·00	£170
O 86.		10 r. purple and red ..	£140	£300

CHARKHARI

A state of Central India. Now uses Indian stamps.

12 pies = 1 anna; 16 annas = 1 rupee.

1. 2.

1894. Imperf. No gum.

No.	Type	Description	Unused	Used
5a	**1.**	¼ a. purple	1·75	2·50
6		½ a. purple	2·25	3·50
7a		1 a. green	4·00	4·50
8a		2 a. green	7·00	8·00
9a		4 a. green	6·00	9·00

1909. Perf. or imperf.

No.	Type	Description	Unused	Used
15a.	**2.**	1 p. brown	1·75	35·00
16.		1 p. blue	30	45
33.		1 p. violet	11·00	65·00
32.		1 p. green	35·00	85·00
25.		½ a. red	70	80
35.		½ a. brown	1·50	15·00
34.		½ a. olive	30	6·50
36.		½ a. black	40·00	85·00
18a.		1 a. green	95	1·10
40.		1 a. brown	2·25	15·00
41.		1 a. red	50·00	55·00
19.		2 a. blue	2·00	3·00
43.		2 a. grey	28·00	42·00
20.		4 a. green	2·75	4·00
44.		4 a. red	4·00	12·00
21.		8 a. red	3·50	12·00
22.		1 r. brown	7·00	16·00

4.

1912. Imperf.

No.	Type	Description	Unused	Used
28.	**4.**	1 p. violet	8·00	6·00

5.

1922. Imperf.

No.	Type	Description	Unused	Used
29.	**5.**	1 a. violet	60·00	75·00

6. Imlia Palace.

DESIGNS—HORIZ. ½ a. The Lake. 2 a. Industrial school. 4 a. Bird's-eye view of city. 8 a. Fort. 1 r. Guest House. 2 r. Palace Gate. 3 r. Temples at Rainpur. 5 r. Goverdhan Temple.

1931. Perf.

No.	Type	Description	Unused	Used
45.	–	½ a. green	40	10
46.	7.	1 a. sepia	40	10
47.	–	2 a. violet	30	10
48.	–	4 a. olive	30	10
49.	–	8 a. mauve	35	10
50.	–	1 r. green and red ..	1·10	15
51.	–	2 r. red and brown ..	1·25	20
52.	–	3 r. brown and green ..	2·50	25
53.	–	5 r. blue and lilac ..	3·00	45

1940. Nos. 21/2 surch.

No.	Type	Description	Unused	Used
54.	**2.**	½ a. on 8 a. red ..	24·00	75·00
55.		1 a. on 1 r. brown ..	55·00	£120
56.		"1 ANNA" on 1 r. brown	£325	£375

CHINA EXPEDITIONARY FORCE

Stamps used by Indian military forces in China.

12 pies = 1 anna; 16 annas = 1 rupee.
Stamps of India optd. **C.E.F.**

1900. Queen Victoria.

No.	Type	Description	Unused	Used
C 1.	**40.**	3 p. red	20	35
C 2.	**23.**	½ a. green	30	30
C 3.	–	1 a. purple	1·25	75
C 11.	–	1 a. red	21·00	6·00
C 4.	–	2 a. blue	1·75	3·00
C 5.	–	2½ a. green	2·25	6·50
C 6.	–	3 a. orange	2·50	9·00
C 7.	–	4 a. green (No. 96) ..	2·00	4·75
C 8.	–	8 a. mauve	2·00	7·50
C 9.	–	12 a. purple on red ..	4·50	12·00
C 10.	**37.**	1 r. green and red ..	5·50	8·50

1904. King Edward VII.

No.	Type	Description	Unused	Used
C 12.	**41.**	3 p. grey	1·25	2·00
C 13.	–	1 a. red (No. 123) ..	1·26	60
C 14.	–	2 a. lilac	6·00	1·50
C 15.	–	2½ a. blue	2·50	5·00
C 16.	–	3 a. orange	3·00	4·00
C 17.	–	4 a. olive	7·00	11·00
C 18.	–	8 a. mauve	6·00	7·00
C 19.	–	12 a. purple on red ..	9·00	19·00
C 20.	–	1 r. green and red ..	9·00	22·00

1909. King Edward VII.

No.	Type	Description	Unused	Used
C 21.		½ a. green (No. 149) ..	1·40	50
C 22.		1 a. red (No. 150) ..	1·00	25

1913. King George V.

No.	Type	Description	Unused	Used
C 23.	**55.**	3 p. grey	1·00	7·00
C 24.	**56.**	½ a. green	1·00	2·25
C 25.	**57.**	1 a. red	1·40	1·00
C 26.	**58.**	1½ a. brown (No. 163)	11·00	35·00
C 27.	**59.**	2 a. lilac	3·50	24·00
C 28.	**61.**	2½ a. blue	5·50	13·00
C 29.	**62.**	3 a. orange	14·00	60·00
C 30.	**63.**	4 a. olive	10·00	90·00
C 32.	**65.**	8 a. mauve	14·00	£160
C 33.	**66.**	12 a. red	14·00	80·00
C 34.	**67.**	1 r. brown and green	42·00	£140

CHRISTMAS ISLAND

Situated in the Indian Ocean about 600 miles S. of Singapore. Formerly part of the Straits Settlements and then of the Crown Colony of Singapore, it was transferred to Australian administration on 15 October, 1958.

1958. 100 cents = 1 dollar (Malaysian).
1968. 100 cents = 1 dollar (Australian).

1. Queen Elizabeth II.

2. Map.

1958. Type of Australia with opt. and value in black.

No.	Type	Description	Unused	Used
1.	**1.**	2 c. orange	55	30
2.		4 c. brown	60	30
3.		5 c. mauve	60	20
4.		6 c. blue	1·50	20
5.		8 c. sepia	3·00	50
6.		10 c. violet	2·50	30
7.		12 c. red	3·50	1·50
8.		20 c. blue	3·00	1·50
9.		50 c. green	4·50	1·50
10.		$1 turquoise	6·00	1·50

1963.

No.	Type	Description	Unused	Used
11.	**2.**	2 c. orange	55	30
12.	–	4 c. brown	50	20
13.	–	5 c. purple	50	20
14.	–	6 c. blue	40	20
15.	–	8 c. black	2·50	40
16.	–	10 c. violet	40	20
17.	–	12 c. red	40	30
18.	–	20 c. blue	1·00	35
19.	–	50 c. green	2·00	35
20.	–	$1 yellow	5·50	60

DESIGNS—VERT. 4 c. Moonflower. 5 c. Robber Crab. 8 c. Phosphate train. 10 c. Raising phosphate. HORIZ. 6 c. Island scene. 12 c. Flying Fish cove. 20 c. Loading cantilever. 50 c. Christmas Island Frigate bird. LARGER. (35 × 21 mm.): $1, White-tailed Tropic bird.

1965. 50th Anniv. of Gallipoli Landing. As T **184** of Australia, but slightly larger (22 × 34½ mm.).

No.	Type	Description	Unused	Used
21.		10 c. brown, blk. & green	30	35

12. Golden Striped Grouper.

1968. Fishes. Multicoloured.

22.	1 c. Type **12**	45	30
23.	2 c. Moorish Idol	60	20
24.	3 c. Forceps Fish	60	30
25.	4 c. Queen Triggerfish ..	60	20
26.	5 c. Regal Angelfish ..	75	20
27.	9 c. Surgeon Fish ..	2·00	40
28.	10 c. Scorpion Fish ..	1·50	20
28a.	15 c. Saddleback Butterfly	12·00	7·00
29.	20 c. Clown Butterfly ..	4·00	55
29a.	30 c. Ghost Pipefish ..	12·00	7·00
30.	50 c. Blue Lined Surgeon ..	10·00	3·00
31.	$1 Meyers Butterfly ..	15·00	5·00

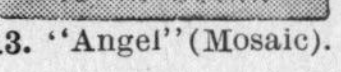

13. "Angel" (Mosaic). **14.** "The Ansidei Madonna" (Raphael).

1969. Christmas.

32. **13.**	5 c. multicoloured ..	20	20

1970. Christmas. Paintings. Multicoloured.

33.	3 c. Type **14**	20	15
34.	5 c. "The Virgin and Child, St. John the Baptist and an Angel" (Morando) ..	20	15

15. "The Adoration of the Shepherds" (ascr. to the School of Seville).

1971. Christmas. Multicoloured.

35.	6 c. Type **15**	50	50
36.	20 c. "The Adoration of the Shepherds" (Reni) ..	1·00	1·00

16. H.M.S. "Flying Fish", 1887.

1972. Ships. Multicoloured.

37.	1 c. "Eagle", 1714	25	35
38.	2 c. H.M.S. "Redpole", 1890	30	40
39.	3 c. M.V. "Hoi Houw", 1959	30	40
40.	4 c. "Pigot", 1771	40	45
41.	5 c. S.S. "Valetta", 1968 ..	40	45
42.	6 c. Type **16**	40	45
43.	7 c. "Asia", 1805"	40	45
44.	8 c. T.S.S. "Islander", 1929-60	45	50
45.	9 c. H.M.S. "Imperieuse", 1888	65	50
46.	10 c. H.M.S. "Egeria", 1857	55	50
47.	20 c. "Thomas", 1615 ..	85	70
48.	25 c. H.M.S. "Gordon", 1864	1·25	85
49.	30 c. "Cygnet", 1688 ..	1·50	85
50.	35 c. S.S. "Triadic", 1945–73	1·75	90
51.	50 c. H.M.S. "Amethyst", 1857	2·25	1·75
52.	$1 "Royal Mary", 1643 ..	3·00	2·25

17. Angel of Peace.

1972. Christmas. Multicoloured.

53.	3 c. Type **17**	65	65
54.	3 c. Angel of Joy	65	65
55.	7 c. Type **17**	75	75
56.	7 c. As No. 54	75	75

18. Virgin and Child, and Map.

1973. Christmas.

57. **18.**	7 c. multicoloured ..	1·00	35
58.	25 c. multicoloured ..	3·00	1·25

19. Mary and Holy Child within Christmas Star.

1974. Christmas.

59. **19.**	7 c. mauve and grey ..	60	75
60.	30 c. orge., yell. & grey ..	1·75	2·50

20. "The Flight into Egypt".

1975. Christmas.

61. **20.**	10 c. yell., brn. & gold ..	50	35
62.	35 c. pink, blue & gold ..	1·50	1·40

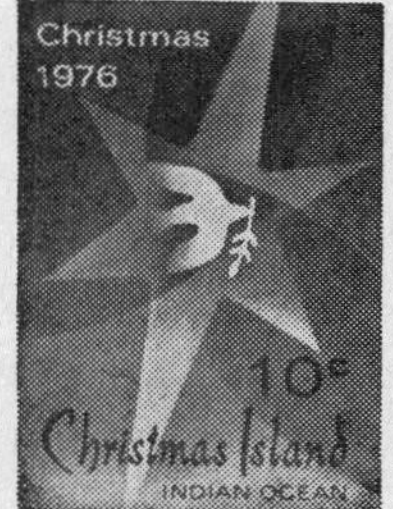

21. Dove of Peace and Star of Bethlehem.

1976. Christmas.

63. **21.**	10 c. red, yellow & mauve	65	65
64. –	10 c. red, yellow & mauve	65	65
65. **21.**	35 c. violet, blue & green	70	70
66. –	35 c. violet, blue & green	70	70

DESIGNS: Nos. 64 and 66 are "mirror-images" of Type **21**.

22. William Dampier (explorer).

1977. Famous Visitors. Multicoloured.

67	1 c. Type **22**	15	30
68	2 c. Capt. de Vlamingh (explorer)	20	30
69	3 c. Vice-Admiral MacLear	30	30
70	4 c. Sir John Murray (oceanographer) ..	30	40
71	5 c. Admiral Aldrich ..	30	20
72	6 c. Andrew Clunies Ross (first settler) ..	30	40
73	7 c. J. J. Lister (naturalist)	30	20
74	8 c. Admiral of the Fleet Sir William May ..	35	40
75	9 c. Henry Ridley (botanist)	40	30
76	10 c. George Clunies Ross (phosphate miner) ..	55	30
77	20 c. Capt. Joshua Slocum (yachtsman)	50	40
78	45 c. Charles Andrews (naturalist)	85	45
79	50 c. Richard Hanitsch (biologist)	95	60
80	75 c. Victor Purcell (scholar)	85	85
81	$1 Fam Choo Beng (educator)	1·25	1·25
82	$2 Sir Harold Spencer-Jones (astronomer)	2·50	2·25

23. Australian Coat of Arms on Map of Christmas Island.

1977. Silver Jubilee.

83. **23.**	45 c. multicoloured ..	60	70

24. "A Partridge in A Pear Tree".

1977. Christmas. "The Twelve Days of Christmas". Multicoloured.

84.	10 c. Type **24**	15	25
85.	10 c. "Two turtle doves"	15	25
86.	10 c. "Three French hens"	15	25
87.	10 c. "Four calling birds"	15	25
88.	10 c. "Five gold rings" ..	15	25
89.	10 c. "Six geese a-laying"	15	25
90.	10 c. "Seven swans a-swimming"	15	25
91.	10 c. "Eight maids a-milking"	15	25
92.	10 c. "Nine ladies dancing"	15	25
93.	10 c. "Ten Lords a-leaping"	15	25
94.	10 c. "Eleven pipers piping"	15	25
95.	10 c. "Twelve drummers drumming"	15	25

25. Abbott's Booby.

1978. 25th Anniv. of Coronation.

96. –	45 c. black and blue ..	60	95
97. –	45 c. multicoloured ..	60	95
98. **25.**	45 c. black and blue ..	60	95

DESIGNS: No. 96, White Swan of Bohun. No. 97, Queen Elizabeth II.

26. "Christ Child".

1978. Christmas. Scenes from "The Song of Christmas". Multicoloured.

99.	10 c. Type **26**	15	20
100.	10 c. "Herald Angels" ..	15	20
101.	10 c. "Redeemer" ..	15	20
102.	10 c. "Israel"	15	20
103.	10 c. "Star"	15	20
104.	10 c. "Three Wise Men"	15	20
105.	10 c. "Manger"	15	20
106.	10 c. "All He Stands For"	15	20
107.	10 c. "Shepherds Come"	15	20

27. Chinese Children.

1979. International Year of the Child. Children of different races. Multicoloured, colours of inscr. given.

108.	20 c. green (Type **27**) ..	45	45
109.	20 c. turquoise (Malay children)	45	45
110.	20 c. lilac (Indian children)	45	45
111.	20 c. red (European children)	45	45
112.	20 c. yellow ("Oranges and Lemons")	45	45

28. 1958 2 c. Definitive.

1979. Death Centenary of Sir Rowland Hill. Multicoloured.

113.	20 c. Type **28**	30	40
114.	20 c. 1963 2 c. Map definitive	30	40
115.	20 c. 1965 50th Anniv. of Gallipoli Landing 10 c. commemorative ..	30	40
116.	20 c. 1968 4 c. Queen Triggerfish definitive ..	30	40
117.	20 c. 1969 Christmas 5 c. value	30	40

29. Wise Men following Star.

1979. Christmas. Multicoloured.

118.	20 c. Type **29**	20	30
119.	55 c. Virgin and Child ..	45	70

30. 9th Green.

1980. 25th Anniv. of Christmas Island Golf Club. Multicoloured.

120.	20 c. Type **30**	60	45
121.	55 c. Clubhouse	70	80

31. Surveying.

1980. Phosphate Industry (1st series). Multicoloured.

122.	15 c. Type **31**	15	20
123.	22 c. Drilling for samples	20	25
124.	40 c. Sample analysis ..	30	40
125.	55 c. Mine planning ..	40	50

See also Nos. 126/9, 136/9 and 140/3.

1980. Phosphate Industry (2nd series). As T **31**. Multicoloured.

126.	15 c. Jungle clearing ..	15	15
127.	22 c. Overburden removal	20	20
128.	40 c. Open cut mining ..	30	25
129.	55 c. Restoration	35	30

32. Angel with Harp.

1980. Christmas. Multicoloured.

130.	15 c. Type **32**	15	25
131.	15 c. Angel with wounded soldier	15	25
132.	22 c. Virgin and Child	20	30
133.	22 c. Kneeling couple	20	30
134.	60 c. Angel with harp (different)	45	45
135.	60 c. Angel with children	45	45

1981. Phosphate Industry (3rd series). As T **31**. Multicoloured.

136.	22 c. Screening and Stockpiling	20	20
137.	28 c. Train loading	25	25
138.	40 c. Railing	40	40
139.	60 c. Drying	55	55

1981. Phosphate Industry (4th series). As T **31**. Multicoloured.

140.	22 c. Crushing	30	20
141.	28 c. Conveying	40	25
142.	40 c. Bulk storage	60	40
143.	60 c. Ship loading	55	55

33. " Cryptoblepharus egeriae ".

1981. Reptiles. Multicoloured.

144.	24 c. Type **33**	25	25
145.	30 c. " Emoia Nativitata "	30	30
146.	40 c. " Lepidodactylus listeri "	45	45
147.	60 c. " Cyrtodactylus sp. nov."	65	65

34. Scene from Carol " Away in a Manger ".

1981. Christmas.

148.	**34.**	18 c. silver, dp. bl. and bl.	50	50
149.	–	24 c. multicoloured	55	55
150.	–	40 c. multicoloured	65	65
151.	–	60 c. multicoloured	75	75

DESIGNS: 24 c. to 60 c. show various scenes from carol " Away in a Manger ".

35. Eastern Reef Heron.

1982 Birds. Multicoloured.

152.	1 c. Type **35**	35	20
153.	2 c. Common Noddy	35	20
154.	3 c. White-bellied Swiftlet	35	45
155.	4 c. Christmas Island Imperial Pigeon	35	45
156.	5 c. Christmas Island White eye	40	45
157.	10 c. Island Thrush	35	45
158.	25 c. Red-tailed Tropic Bird	75	40
159.	30 c. Emerald Dove	50	50
160.	40 c. Brown Booby	60	45
161.	50 c. Red-footed Booby	55	45
162.	65 c. Christmas Island Frigate Bird	55	55
163.	75 c. White-tailed Tropic Bird	65	65
164.	80 c. Australian Kestrel (vert.)	1·00	65
165.	$1 Indonesian Hawk-Owl (vert.)	1·50	90
166.	$2 Australian Goshawk	1·50	3·25
167.	$4 Abbott's Booby (vert.)	3·00	3·50

36. Joseph.

1982. Christmas. Origami Paper Sculptures. Multicoloured.

168.	27 c. Type **36**	30	30
169.	50 c. Angel	45	45
170.	75 c. Mary and baby Jesus	65	65

37. "Mirror" Dinghy and Club House.

1983. 25th Anniv. of Christmas Island Boat Club. Multicoloured.

171.	27 c. Type **37**	35	35
172.	35 c. Ocean-going yachts	40	40
173.	50 c. Fishing launch and cargo ship (horiz.)	50	50
174.	75 c. Dinghy-racing and cantilever (horiz.)	70	70

38. Maps of Christmas Island and Australia, Eastern Grey Kangaroo and Whitetailed Tropic Bird.

1983. 25th Anniv. of Australian Territory. Multicoloured.

175.	24 c. Type **38**	20	20
176.	30 c. Christmas Island and Australian flag	30	30
177.	85 c. Maps of Christmas Island and Australia, and Boeing " 727 "	70	70

39. Candle and Holly.

1983. Christmas. Candles. Multicoloured.

178.	24 c. Type **39**	20	20
179.	30 c. Six gold candles	30	30
180.	85 c. Candles	70	70

40. Feeding on Leaf.

1984. Red Land Crab. Multicoloured.

181.	30 c. Type **40**	30	30
182.	40 c. Migration	40	40
183.	55 c. Development stages	50	50
184.	85 c. Adult female and young	70	70

41. "Leucocoprinus fragilissimus".

1984. Fungi. Multicoloured.

185.	30 c. Type **41**	55	30
186.	40 c. "Microporus xanthopus"	65	40
187.	45 c. "Trogia anthidepas"	75	45
188.	55 c. "Haddowia longipes"	85	60
189.	85 c. "Phillipsia domingensis"	1·00	75

42. Run-out.

1984. 25th Anniv. of Cricket on Christmas Island. Multicoloured.

190.	30 c. Type **42**	70	60
191.	40 c. Bowled-out	80	70
192.	50 c. Batsman in action	1·00	90
193.	85 c. Fielder diving for catch	1·25	1·25

44. Robber Crab.

1985. Crabs (1st series). Multicoloured.

195.	30 c. Type **44**	65	50
196.	40 c. Horn-eyed ghost crab	75	60
197.	55 c. Purple hermit crab	90	75
198.	85 c. Little nipper	1·25	1·00

1985. Crabs (2nd Series). As T **44**. Mult.

199.	33 c. Blue crab	70	40
200.	45 c. Tawny hermit crab	80	60
201.	60 c. Red nipper	95	75
202.	90 c. Smooth-handed ghost crab	1·40	1·10

1985. Crabs (3rd series). As T **44**. Mult.

203.	33 c. Red crab	70	55
204.	45 c. Mottled crab	85	85
205.	60 c. Rock hopper crab	1·10	1·25
206.	90 c. Yellow nipper	1·50	1·75

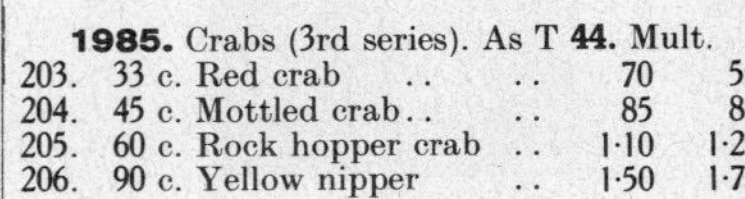

45. "Once in Royal David's City"

1985. Christmas Carols. Multicoloured.

207.	27 c. Type **45**	70	70
208.	33 c. "While Sheperds Watched Their Flocks by Night"	80	80
209.	45 c. "Away in a Manger"	95	95
210.	60 c. "We Three Kings of Orient Are"	1·10	1·10
211.	90 c. "Hark the Herald Angels Sing"	1·40	1·40

46. Halley's Comet over Christmas Island.

1986. Appearance of Halley's Comet. Multicoloured.

212.	33 c. Type **46**	55	55
213.	45 c. Edmond Halley	70	80
214.	60 c. Comet and ship loading phosphate	85	1·00
215.	90 c. Comet over Flying Fish Cove	1·25	1·50

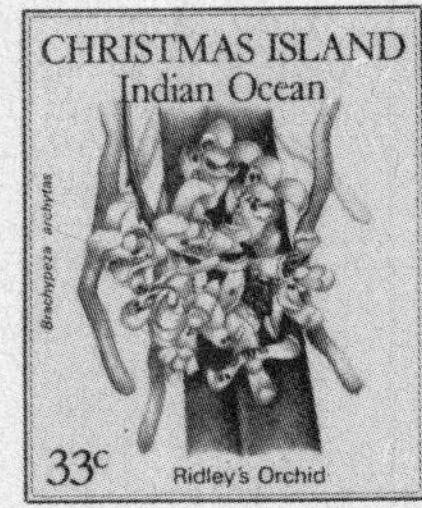

47. Ridley's Orchid.

1986. Native Flowers. Multicoloured.

216.	33 c. Type **47**	50	50
217.	45 c. Hanging flower	65	75
218.	60 c. Hoya	75	90
219.	90 c. Sea hibiscus	1·10	1·40

1986. Royal Wedding. As T **112** of Ascension. Multicoloured.

220.	33 c. Prince Andrew and Miss Sarah Ferguson	45	35
221.	90 c. Prince Andrew piloting helicopter, Digby, Canada, 1985	95	1·40

48. Father Christmas and Reindeer in Speed Boat.

1986. Christmas. Multicoloured.

222.	30 c. Type **48**	55	40
223.	36 c. Father Christmas and reindeer on beach	65	50
224.	55 c. Father Christmas fishing	1·00	1·00
225.	70 c. Playing golf	1·50	1·60
226.	$1 Sleeping in hammock	1·75	2·00

49. H.M.S. "Flying Fish" and Outline Map of Christmas Island.

1987. Centenary of Visits by H.M.S. "Flying Fish" and H.M.S. "Egeria". Mult.

227.	36 c. Type **49**	80	60
228.	90 c. H.M.S. "Egeria" and outline map	1·60	2·40

50. Blind Snake.

1987. Wildlife. Multicoloured.

229	1 c. Type **50**	30	30
230	2 c. Blue-tailed skink	30	30
231	3 c. Insectivorous bat	35	35
232	5 c. Grasshopper	35	35
233	10 c. Christmas Island fruit bat	35	35
234	25 c. Gecko	45	45
235	30 c. "Mantis religiosa" (mantid)	55	55
236	36 c. Indonesian hawk owl	90	90
237	40 c. Bull mouth helmet shell	55	55
237a	41 c. Nudibranch ("Phidiana sp.")	55	60
238	50 c. Textile cone shell	65	65
239	65 c. Brittle stars	65	70
240	75 c. Royal angelfish	65	75
241	90 c. "Appias paulina" (butterfly)	1·75	1·75
242	$1 "Hypolimnas misippus" (butterfly)	1·75	1·75
243	$2 Shrew	2·50	2·50
244	$5 Green turtle	4·50	5·00

1988. Bicentenary of Australian Settlement. Arrival of First Fleet. As Nos. 1105/9 of Australia, but each inscribed "CHRISTMAS ISLAND Indian Ocean" and "AUSTRALIA BICENTENARY".

246.	37 c. Aborigines watching arrival of Fleet, Botany Bay	90	90
247.	37 c. Aboriginal family and anchored ships	90	90
248.	37 c. Fleet arriving at Sydney Cove	90	90
249.	37 c. Ship's boat	90	90
250.	37 c. Raising the flag, Sydney Cove, 26 January 1788	90	90

Nos. 246/50 were printed together, se-tenant, forming a composite design.

52 Captain William May

1988. Cent of British Annexation. Mult.

251	37 c. Type **52**	35	40
252	53 c. Annexation ceremony	50	55
253	95 c. H.M.S. "Imperieuse" firing salute	90	95
254	$1.50 Building commemorative cairn	1·40	1·50

53 Pony and Trap, 1910

1988. Cent of Permanent Settlement. Mult.

255	37 c. Type **53**	45	40
256	55 c. Phosphate mining, 1910	60	55
257	70 c. Steam locomotive, 1914	85	70
258	$1 Arrival of first aircraft, 1957	1·25	1·00

54 Beach Toys

1988. Christmas. Toys and Gifts. Mult.

259	32 c. Type **54**	40	35
260	39 c. Flippers, snorkel and mask	50	40
261	90 c. Model soldier, doll and soft toys	1·10	90
262	$1 Models of racing car, lorry and jet aircraft	1·25	1·00

55 Food on Table ("Good Harvesting")

1989. Chinese New Year. Multicoloured.

263	39 c. Type **55**	45	40
264	70 c. Decorations ("Prosperity")	80	70
265	90 c. Chinese girls ("Good Fortune")	1·10	90
266	$1 Lion dance ("Progress Every Year")	1·25	1·00

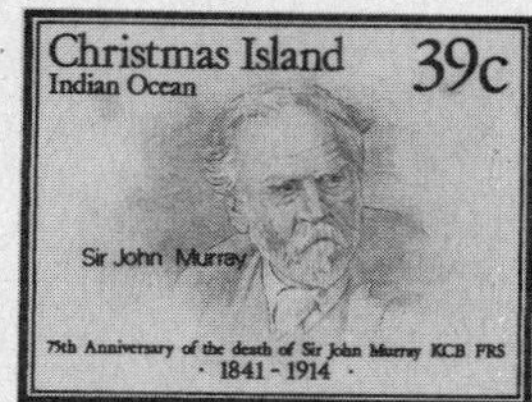

56 Sir John Murray

1989. 75th Death Anniv of Sir John Murray (oceanographer). Multicoloured.

267	39 c. Type **56**	50	50
268	80 c. Map of Christmas Island showing Murray Hill	95	95
269	$1 Oceanographic equipment	1·25	1·25
270	$1.10 H.M.S. "Challenger" (survey ship)	1·50	1·50

57 Four Children

1989. Malay Hari Raya Festival. Mult.

271	39 c. Type **57**	50	50
272	55 c. Man playing tambourine	70	70
273	80 c. Girl in festival costume	1·00	1·00
274	$1.10 Christmas Island Mosque	1·40	1·40

58 "Huperzia phlegmaria"

1989. Ferns. Multicoloured.

275	41 c. Type **58**	40	45
276	65 c. "Asplenium polydon"	60	65
277	80 c. Common bracken	75	80
278	$1.10 Birds-nest fern	1·00	1·10

MINIMUM PRICE

The minimum price quoted is 10p which represents a handling charge rather than a basis for valuing common stamps. For further notes about prices see introductory pages.

59 Virgin Mary and Star

61 First Sighting, 1615

1989. Christmas. Multicoloured.

279	36 c. Type **59**	35	40
280	41 c. Christ Child in manger	40	45
281	80 c. Shepherds and star	75	80
282	$1.10 Three Wise Men following star	1·00	1·10

1989. "Melbourne Stampshow '89". Nos. 237a and 242 optd with Stampshow logo.

283	41 c. Nudibranch ("Phidiana" sp.)	40	45
284	$1 "Hypolimnas misippus" (butterfly)	1·00	1·00

1990. 375th Anniv of Discovery of Christmas Island. Multicoloured.

285	41 c. Type **61**	50	50
286	$1.10 Second sighting and naming, 1643	1·40	1·40

62 Miniature Tractor pulling Phosphate

1990. Christmas Island Transport. Mult.

287	1 c. Type **62**	10	10
288	2 c. Phosphate train	10	10
289	3 c. Diesel railcar (vert)	10	10
290	5 c. Loading road train	10	10
291	10 c. Trishaw (vert)	10	15
292	15 c. Terex truck	15	20
293	25 c. Articulated bus	25	30
294	30 c. Railway passenger rake (vert)	30	35
295	40 c. Passenger barge (vert)	35	40
296	50 c. Kolek (outrigger canoe)	45	50
297	65 c. Flying Doctor aircraft and ambulance	60	65
298	75 c. Commercial van	70	75
299	90 c. Vintage lorry	85	90
300	$1 Water tanker	90	95
301	$2 Traction engine	1·90	2·00
302	$5 Steam locomotive and flat car	4·50	4·75

63 Male Abbott's Booby

1990. Abbott's Booby. Multicoloured.

303	10 c. Type **63**	30	30
304	20 c. Juvenile male	50	50
305	29 c. Female with egg	55	55
306	41 c. Pair with chick	70	70

64 1977 Famous Visitors 9 c. Stamp

1990. Centenary of Henry Ridley's Visit. Multicoloured.

308	41 c. Type **64**	55	55
309	75 c. Ridley (botanist) in rainforest	85	95

65 "Corymborkus veratrifolia"

1990. Christmas. Flowers. Multicoloured.

311	38 c. Type **65**	50	60
312	43 c. "Hoya aldrichii"	55	65
313	80 c. "Quisqualis indica"	95	1·10
314	$1.20 "Barringtonia racemosa"	1·50	1·60

66 "Islander" (freighter), 1898

1991. Centenary of First Phosphate Mining Lease. Multicoloured.

316	43 c. Type **66**	60	60
317	43 c. Miners loading rail wagons, 1908	60	60
318	85 c. Shay steam locomotive No. 4, 1925	1·00	1·00
319	$1.20 Extracting phosphate, 1951	1·40	1·40
320	$1.70 Land reclamation, 1990	1·90	1·90

Nos. 316/20 were printed together, se-tenant, forming a composite forest design.

67 Teaching Children Road Safety

1991. Christmas Island Police Force. Mult.

321	43 c. Type **67**	60	60
322	43 c. Traffic control	60	60
323	90 c. Airport customs	1·40	1·40
324	$1.20 Police launch "Fregata Andrews" towing rescued boat	1·75	1·75

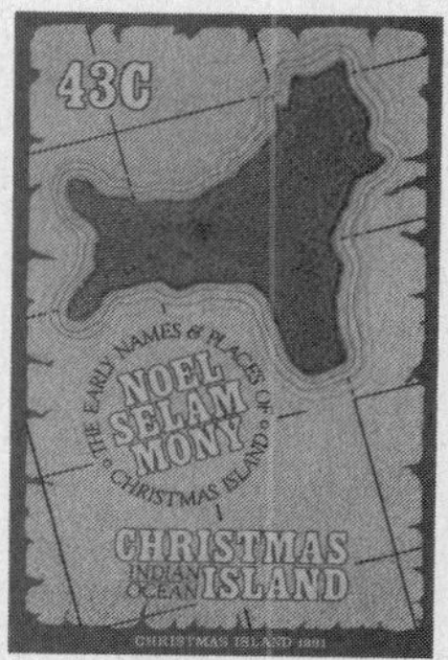

68 Map of Christmas Island, 1991

1991. Maps of Christmas Island. Mult.

326	43 c. Type **68**	55	55
327	75 c. Goos Atlas, 1666	95	95
328	$1.10 De Manevillette, 1745	1·40	1·40
329	$1.20 Comberford, 1667	1·50	1·50

HAVE YOU READ THE NOTES AT THE BEGINNING OF THIS CATALOGUE?

These often provide answers to the enquiries we receive.

69 "Bruguiera gymnorrhiza"

1991. Local Trees. Multicoloured.

330 43 c. Type **69** 55 55
331 70 c. "Syzygium operculatum" 90 90
332 85 c. "Ficus microcarpa" 1·10 1·10
333 $1.20 "Arenga listeri" .. 1·50 1·50

70 "Family round Christmas Tree" (S'ng Yen Luiw)

1991. Christmas. Children's Paintings. Mult.

334 38 c. Type **70** 35 40
335 38 c. "Opening Presents" (Liew Ann Nee) .. 35 40
336 38 c. "Beach Party" (Foo Pang Chuan) 35 40
337 38 c. "Christmas Walk" (Too Lai Peng) .. 35 40
338 38 c. "Santa Claus and Christmas Tree" (Jesamine Wheeler) .. 35 40
339 43 c. "Santa Claus fishing" (Ho Puay Ha) .. 40 45
340 $1 "Santa Claus in Boat" (Ng Hooi Hua) .. 90 95
341 $1.20 "Santa Claus surfing" (Yani Kawi) .. 1·10 1·25

71 Discussing Evacuation, 1942

1992. 50th Anniv of Partial Evacuation. Multicoloured.

342 45 c. Type **71** 40 45
343 45 c. Families waiting to embark .. 40 45
344 $1.05 Ferrying evacuees to "Islander" .. 95 1·0
345 $1.20 Departure of "Islander" (freighter) 1·10 1·25

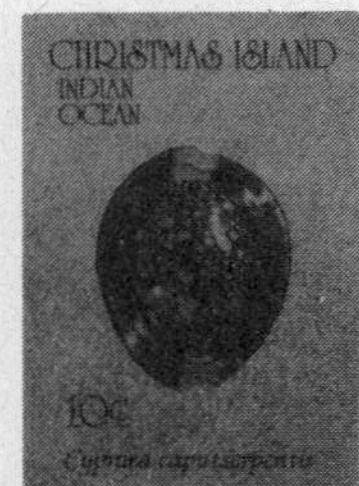

72 "Cypraea caputserpentis"

1992. Shells. Multicoloured.

350 10 c. Type **72** 10 15
351 20 c. "Chlamys pallium" .. 20 25
352 30 c. "Drupa ricinus" .. 30 35
353 45 c. "Turbo petholatus" 40 45
354 60 c. "Conus capitaneus" 55 60
355 80 c. "Lambis chiragra" .. 75 80
356 $1 "Vasum ceramicum" .. 90 95
357 $2 "Tonna perdix" .. 1·90 2·00

COCHIN

A state of S.W. India. Now uses Indian stamps.

1892. 6 puttans = 5 annas. Later as India.

1. Emblems of State.

1892. Value in "puttans".

1 **1.** ½ put. orange .. .. 1·25 1·40
2 1 put. purple .. .. 1·50 1·00
3 2 put. violet .. .. 1·00 1·25

3. 5.

1893. Value in "pies" or "puttans". With or without gum.

16. **3.** 3 pies, blue 30 10
17. ½ put. green (smaller) .. 75 10
18. **5.** 1 put. red .. .. 1·25 10
19. **3.** 2 put. violet .. .. 1·40 20

1909. Surch. **2.** No gum.

22. **3.** "2" on 3 pies, mauve .. 15 30

8. Raja Sir Sri Rama Varma I. 10. Maharaja Sir Sri Rama Varma II.

1911. Value in "pies" or "annas".

26. **8.** 2 p. brown 30 10
27. 3 p. blue 30 10
28. 4 p. green 90 10
29. 9 p. red .. .. 1·10 10
30. 1 a. orange .. .. 1·60 10
31. 1½ a. purple .. .. 3·75 40
32. 2 a. grey .. .. 7·50 40
33. 3 a. red .. .. 28·00 32·00

1918. Various frames.

35b. **10.** 2 p. brown 75 10
36. 4 p. green 95 10
37. 6 p. brown .. .. 1·00 10
38. 8 p. brown .. .. 1·40 10
39. 9 p. red .. .. 7·00 15
40. 10 p. blue .. .. 1·40 10
41. 1 a. orange .. .. 5·00 30
42. 1½ a. purple .. .. 2·25 10
43. 2 a. grey .. .. 3·75 10
44. 2¼ a. green .. .. 3·75 50
45. 3 a. red .. .. 11·00 35

1922. Surch. with figure and words.

46. **8.** 2 p. on 3 p. blue .. 40 30

1928. Surch. in words in English and native characters and **ANCHAL & REVENUE.**

50. **10.** 1 a. on 2¼ a. green .. 5·00 12·00

1932. Surch. in figures and words both in English and in native characters.

51. **10.** 3 p. on 4 p. green .. 1·00 75
52. 3 p. on 8 p. brown .. 1·00 1·40
53. 9 p. on 10 p. blue .. 1·50 1·25

18. Maharaja Sir Sri Rama Varma III. 26. Maharaja Sri Kerala Varma I.

1933.

54. **18.** 2 p. brown 50 10
55. 4 p. green 60 10
56. 6 p. red 70 10
57. 1 a. orange 70 10
58. 1 a. 8 p. red .. .. 3·00 2·25
59. 2 a. grey .. .. 1·75 10
60. 2¼ a. green .. .. 1·50 10
61. 3 a. orange .. .. 3·00 40
62. 3 a. 4 p. violet .. .. 1·50 1·25
63. 6 a. 8 p. sepia .. .. 1·75 4·50
64. 10 a. blue .. .. 3·00 5·50

1934. Surch. with figure and words.

65. **10.** 6 p. on 8 p. brown .. 75 50
66. 6 p. on 10 p. blue .. 1·75 65

1939. Optd. **ANCHAL.**

75. **18.** 1 a. orange .. .. 1·50 15

1939. Surch. in words only.

72. **18.** 3 p. on 1 a. 8 p. red .. £110 50·00
74. 6 p. on 1 a. 8 p. red .. 2·00 12·00

1943. Surch. **SURCHARGED** and value in words.

77. **18.** 3 p. on 4 p. green .. 5·00 1·25
73. 3 p. on 1 a. 8 p. red .. 2·00 4·50
76. 1 a. 3 p. on 1 a. 8 p. red .. 1·00 30

1943. Surch. **ANCHAL SURCHARGED NINE PIES.**

82. **18.** 9 p. on 1 a. orange .. 11·00 1·50

1943. Surch. **ANCHAL** and value in words.

79. **18.** 6 p. on 1 a. orange .. 40·00 24·00
80. 9 p. on 1 a. orange .. 55·00 65·00

1943.

85. **26.** 2 p. brown .. .. 1·00 20
87. 4 p. green .. .. 3·00 1·25
88. 6 p. brown .. .. 1·00 10
89. 9 p. blue .. .. 16·00 1·00
90. 1 a. orange .. .. 20·00 30·00
91. 2¼ a. green .. .. 11·00 40

1944. Surch. with value in words only.

93. **26.** 2 p. on 6 p. brown .. 75 1·25
94. 3 p. on 4 p. green .. 1·25 10
96. 3 p. on 6 p. brown .. 80 15
97. 4 p. on 6 p. brown .. 2·50 5·00

1944. Surch. **SURCHARGED** and value in words.

95. **26.** 3 p. on 4 p. green .. 1·40 10
92c. 1 a. 3 p. on 1 a. orange .. — £2250

1944. Surch. **ANCHAL NINE PIES,**

92a. **26.** 9 p. on 1 a. orange .. 4·00 65

1944. Surch. **ANCHAL SURCHARGED NINE PIES.**

92b. **26.** 9 p. on 1 a. orange .. 1·10 1·00

28. Maharaja Sri Ravi Varma. 29. Maharaja Sri Ravi Varma.

1944.

98a. **28.** 9 p. blue .. .. 4·00 5·50
99. 1 a. 3 p. mauve .. 6·00 4·50
100. 1 a. 9 p. blue .. 10·00 5·00

1946. No gum.

101. **29.** 2 p. brown 75 10
102. 3 p. red 50 10
103. 4 p. green .. .. £1000 65·00
104. 6 p. brown .. .. 14·00 1·75
105. 9 p. blue 50 10
106. 1 a. orange .. .. 5·00 14·00
107. 2 a. black .. .. 55·00 1·75
108. 3 a. red .. .. 35·00 40

For No. 106, overprinted "U.S.T.C." or "T.-C." with or without surcharge, see Travancore-Cochin.

30. Maharaja Sri Kerala Varma II.

1948.

109. **30.** 2 p. brown 75 10
110. 3 p. red 75 10
111. 4 p. green .. .. 3·75 15
112. 6 p. brown .. .. 6·50 10
113. 9 p. blue .. .. 1·10 10
114. 2 a. black .. .. 21·00 30
115. 3 a. orange .. .. 29·00 35
116. 3 a. 4 p. violet £100 £275

31. Chinese Nets.

1949.

117. **31.** 2 a. black .. .. 60 2·25
118. – 2¼ a. green (Dutch palace) 60 2·50

SIX PIES

ആറു പൈ

(33.)

1949. Surch. as T **33.**

121. **29.** 3 p. on 9 p. blue .. 4·00 8·00
125. **30.** 3 p. on 9 p. blue .. 2·00 60
126. 6 p. on 9 p. blue .. 1·00 60
119. **28.** 6 p. on 1 a. 3 p. mauve 1·25 90
122. **29.** 6 p. on 1 a. 3 p. mauve 5·00 5·50
120. **28.** 1 a. on 1 a. 9 p. blue .. 75 40
123. **29.** 1 a. on 1 a. 9 p. blue 3·00 50

1949. Surch. **SIX PIES** or **NINE PIES** only.

127. **29.** 6 p. on 1 a. orange .. 48·00 80·00
128. 9 p. on 1 a. orange .. 32·00 70·00

OFFICIAL STAMPS

1913. Optd. **ON G C S.**

O 1. **8.** 3 p. blue .. .. 80·00 10
O 2. 4 p. green .. .. 8·00 10
O 3a. 9 p. red .. .. 13·00 10
O 4. 1½ a. purple .. .. 22·00 10
O 5. 2 a. grey .. .. 13·00 10
O 6. 3 a. red .. .. 28·00 15
O 7. 6 a. violet .. .. 24·00 2·00
O 8. 12 a. blue .. .. 26·00 5·00
O 9. 1½ r. green .. .. 22·00 28·00

1919. Optd. **ON C G S.**

O 10. **10.** 4 p. green .. .. 3·25 10
O 11. 6 p. brown .. .. 5·00 10
O 26. 8 p. brown .. .. 6·00 10
O 13. 9 p. red .. .. 25·00 10
O 27. 10 p. blue .. .. 6·00 10
O 15. 1½ a. purple .. .. 5·50 10
O 28. 2 a. grey .. .. 14·00 10
O 17. 2¼ a. green .. .. 8·00 10
O 29. 3 a. red .. .. 8·00 15
O 19. 6 a. violet .. .. 24·00 50
O 19a. 12 a. blue .. .. 15·00 2·75
O 19b. 1½ r. green .. .. 22·00 50·00

1923. Official stamps surch. in figures and words.

O 32 **10.** 6 p on 8 p. brown .. 1·75 10
O 33 6 p. on 10 p. blue .. 4·00 10
O 20b **8.** 8 p. on 9 p. red .. £110 15
O 21 **10.** 8 p. on 9 p. red .. 70·00 10
O 23 **8.** 10 p. on 9 p. red .. £400 7·00
O 22 **10.** 10 p. on 9 p. red .. 65·00 30

1933. Optd. **ON C G S.**

O 34. **18.** 4 p. green .. .. 1·75 10
O 35. 6 p. red .. .. 1·75 10
O 52. 1 a. orange .. .. 1·00 10
O 37. 1 a. 8 p. red .. .. 2·00 10
O 50. 2 a. grey .. .. 6·00 30
O 39. 2¼ a. green .. .. 4·00 10
O 53. 3 a. orange .. .. 2·75 35
O 41. 3 a. 4 p. violet .. 1·50 15
O 42. 6 a. 8 p. sepia .. 1·50 15
O 43. 10 a. blue .. .. 1·50 20

1943. Official stamp surch. **NINE PIES.**

O 57. **10.** 9 p. on 1½ a. purple .. £180 10·00

1943. Official stamps surch. **SURCHARGED** and value in words.

O 63. **18.** 3 p. on 4 p. green .. 60·00 32·00
O 58. 3 p. on 1 a. 8 p. red .. 1·00 30
O 66. 1 a. 3 p. on 1 a. orange .. £140 75·00
O 61. 1 a. 9 p. on 1 a. 8 p. red 70 30

1943. Official stamps surch. in words.

O 62. **18.** 3 p. on 4 p. green .. 11·00 2·75
O 64. 3 p. on 1 a. orange .. 1·75 50
O 65. 9 p. on 1 a. orange .. £140 35·00
O 59. 9 p. on 1 a. 8 p. red .. 90·00 21·00
O 60. 1 a. 9 p. on 1 a. 8 p. red 80 80

1944. Optd. **ON C G S.**

O 68 **26.** 4 p. green .. .. 8·00 75
O 69b 6 p. brown 60 10
O 70 1 a. orange .. .. £1100 40·00
O 71 2 a. black .. .. 1·25 20
O 72 2¼ a. green .. .. 1·50 30
O 73 3 a. red .. .. 2·25 40

1944. Official stamps surch. **SURCHARGED** and value in words.

O 75. **26.** 3 p. on 4 p. green .. 3·00 30
O 78. 9 p. on 6 p. brown .. 1·50 15
O 80. 1 a. 3 p. on 1 a. orange 2·25 10

1944. Official stamps surch. in words.

O 74 **26** 3 p. on 4 p. green .. 1·00 10
O 76 3 p. on 1 a. orange .. 8·00 1·40
O 77 9 p. on 6 p. brown .. 4·00 35
O 80 1 a. 3 p. on 1 a. orange 2·25 10

1944. Optd. **ON C G S.**

O 81. **28.** 9 p. blue 75 10
O 82. 1 a. 3 p. mauve .. 45 15
O 83. 1 a. 9 p. blue .. 35 15

1948. Optd. **ON C.G.S.**

O 84. **29.** 3 p. red 30 10
O 85. 4 p. green .. .. 13·00 4·00
O 86. 6 p. brown .. .. 3·00 20
O 87. 9 p. blue 75 10
O 88. 1 a. 3 p. mauve .. 1·25 20
O 89. 1 a. 9 p. blue .. 1·40 40
O 90. 2 a. black .. .. 10·00 1·50
O 91. 2¼ a. green .. .. 11·00 1·10

1949. Optd. **ON C.G.S.**

O 92. **30.** 3 p. red 30 10
O 93. 4 p. green 50 15
O 94. 6 p. brown .. .. 1·00 10
O 95. 9 p. blue 50 10
O 96. 2 a. black 60 15
O 97. 2¼ a. green .. .. 1·25 1·75
O 98. 3 a. orange .. .. 1·10 30
O 99. 3 a. 4 p. violet .. 10·00 12·00

1949. Official stamps surch. as T **12.**

O 103. **30.** 6 p. on 3 p. red .. 30 30
O 104. 9 p. on 4 p. green .. 50 50
O 100. **28.** 1 a. on 1 a. 9 p. blue 60 15
O 101. **29.** 1 a. on 1 a. 9 p. blue 9·00 6·00

1949. Optd. **SERVICE.**

O 105. **30.** 3 p. on 9 p. (No. 125) 60 40

For later issues see under Travancore-Cochin

COCOS (KEELING) ISLANDS

Islands in the Indian Ocean formerly administered by Singapore and transferred to Australian administration on 23 November 1955.

1963. 12 pence = 1 shilling;
12 shillings = 1 pound.
1966. 100 cents = 1 dollar (Australia).

5. Jukong (sailboat).

6. White Tern.

1963.

1. – 3d. brown .. .. .. 1·75 1·25
2. – 5d. blue .. .. .. 1·50 65
3. – 8d. red .. .. .. 4·50 1·75
4. – 1s. green .. .. .. 3·00 55
5. 5. 2s. purple .. .. .. 11·00 3·25
6. 6. 2s. 3d. green .. .. 42·00 3·25

DESIGNS—As Type 5. HORIZ. 3d. Copra industry. 1s. Palms. VERT. 8d. Map of islands. As Type 6: 5d. Super Constellation airliner.

1965. 50th Anniv. of Gallipoli Landing. As T **184** of Australia, but slightly larger (22 × 34½ mm.).

7. 5d. brown, black and green 60 45

With the introduction of decimal currency on 14th February, 1966, Australian stamps were used in Cocos Islands until the 1969 issue.

7. Reef Clam.

1969. Decimal Currency. Multicoloured.

8 1 c. Lajonkaines turbo shell (vert) 30 30
9 2 c. Crocus giant clam (vert) 1·00 45
10 3 c. Type **7** 30 15
11 4 c. "Petroscirtes mitrattus" (fish) .. 30 15
12 5 c. "Porites cocosensis" (coral) 35 15
13 6 c. Greater spotted flying fish 75 20
14 10 c. Banded rail .. .. 1·50 50
15 15 c. Java sparrow .. 1·00 30
16 20 c. Red-tailed tropic bird 1·00 30
17 30 c. Sooty tern .. .. 1·25 30
18 50 c. Eastern reef heron (vert) .. .. .. 2·00 30
19 $1 Great frigate bird (vert) 5·00 1·00

9. " Dragon ", 1609.

1976. Ships. Multicoloured.

20. 1 c. Type **9** 30 40
21. 2 c. H.M.S. "Juno", 1857 (horiz.) 30 40
22. 5 c. H.M.S. "Beagle", 1836 (horiz.) 30 40
23. 10 c. H.M.A.S. "Sydney", 1914 (horiz.) 35 40
24. 15 c. S.M.S. "Emden", 1914 (horiz.) 80 55
25. 20 c. "Ayesha", 1907 (horiz.) 85 65
26. 25 c. T.S.S. "Islander", 1927 90 1·00
27. 30 c. M.V. "Cheshire", 1951 1·00 1·00
28. 35 c. Jukong (sailboat) (horiz.) .. .. .. 1·00 1·00
29. 40 c. C.S. "Scotia", 1900 (horiz.) .. .. .. 1·00 1·00
30. 50 c. R.M.S. "Orontes", 1929 .. .. .. 1·40 1·10
31. $1 Royal Yacht "Gothic", 1954 .. .. .. 1·75 1·40

10. Map of Cocos (Keeling) Islands, Union Flag, Stars and Trees.

1979. Inauguration of Independent Postal Service and First Statutory Council. Multicoloured.

32. 20 c. Type **10** 25 30
33. 50 c. Council seal and jukong (sailboat) .. 35 50

11. Bright Yellow Long-nosed Butterfly Fish.

1979. Fishes. Multicoloured.

34. 1 c. Type **11** 30 50
35. 2 c. Clown Butterfly Fish 30 30
36. 5 c. "Anthias sp." 40 60
37. 10 c. Meyer's Butterfly Fish 30 30
38. 15 c. Wrasse 30 30
39. 20 c. Charles' Clown Fish 45 30
39a. 22 c. Yellow-striped Emerald Triggerfish .. 30 30
40. 25 c. "Cheilinus fasciatus" 45 35
40a. 28 c. "Macropharyngodon meleagris" 35 35
41. 30 c. "Chaetodon madagascariensis" 65 45
42. 35 c. Angel Fish .. .. 65 1·25
43. 40 c. Hog Fish 70 90
44. 50 c. Wrasse (different) .. 85 75
45. 55 c. "Anampses meleagrides" 75 75
45a. 60 c. Grouper 75 75
46. $1 Surgeon fish .. .. 1·75 2·75
47. $2 Three-banded Butterfly Fish .. .. .. 2·00 2·75

12. " Peace on Earth ".

1979. Christmas. Multicoloured.

48. 25 c. Type **12** 25 35
49. 55 c. Atoll seascape (" Goodwill ") 40 55

13. Star, Map of Cocos (Keeling) Islands and Island Landscape.

1980. Christmas. Multicoloured.

50. 15 c. Type **13** 10 10
51. 28 c. The Three Kings .. 15 15
52. 60 c. Adoration 40 40

14. " Administered by the British Government, 1857 ".

1980. 25th Anniv. of Territorial Status under Australian Administration. Multicoloured.

53. 22 c. Type **14** 15 15
54. 22 c. Arms of Ceylon .. 15 15
55. 22 c. Arms of Straits Settlements 15 15
56. 22 c. Arms of Singapore .. 15 15
57. 22 c. Arms and flag of Australia 15 15

15. " Eye of the Wind " and Map of Cocos (Keeling) Islands.

1980. " Operation Drake " Round the World Voyage. Multicoloured.

58. 22 c. Type **15** 20 15
59. 28 c. Voyage map (horiz.) .. 20 15
60. 35 c. Sir Francis Drake and " Golden Hind " .. 20 15
61. 60 c. Prince Charles (patron) and " Eye of the Wind " 35 30

16. Aerial view of Animal Quarantine Station.

1981. Opening of Animal Quarantine Station. Multicoloured.

62. 22 c. Type **16** 15 15
63. 45 c. Unloading livestock .. 30 30
64. 60 c. Livestock in pen .. 35 35

17. Consolidated " Catalina " " Guba II " Flying Boat.

1981. Aircraft. Multicoloured.

65. 22 c. Type **17** 25 25
66. 22 c. Consolidated "Liberator" and Avro "Lancastrian" 25 25
67. 22 c. Douglas " DC 4 (Skymaster) " and Lockheed " Constellation " .. 25 25
68. 22 c. Lockheed " Electra " 25 25
69. 22 c. Boeing " 727 " airliners 25 25

18. Prince Charles and Lady Diana Spencer.

1981. Royal Wedding.

70. **18.** 24 c. multicoloured .. 40 20
71. 60 c. multicoloured .. 85 60

19. " Angels we have heard on High ".

1981. Christmas. Scenes and Lines from Carol " Angels we have heard on High ". **Mult.**

72. 18 c. Type **19** 10 10
73. 30 c. " Shepherds why this Jubilee? " 20 20
74. 60 c. " Come to Bethlehem and see Him " 35 35

20. " Pachyseris speciosa " and " Heliofungia actiniformis " (corals).

1981. 150th Anniv. of Charles Darwin's Voyage. Multicoloured.

75. 24 c. Type **20** 35 15
76. 45 c. Charles Darwin in 1853 and " Pavona cactus " (coral) 55 30
77. 60 c. H.M.S. " Beagle ", 1832, and " Lobophyllia hemprichii " (coral) .. 70 35

21. Queen Victoria.

1982. 125th Anniv. of Annexation of Cocos (Keeling) Islands to British Empire. Mult.

79. 24 c. Type **21** 20 15
80. 45 c. Union flag 35 25
81. 60 c. Capt. S. Fremantle (annexation visit, 1857) .. 40 35

22. Lord Baden-Powell.

1982. 75th Anniv. of Boy Scout Movement. Multicoloured.

82. 27 c. Type **22** 30 15
83. 75 c. " 75 " and map of Cocos (Keeling) Islands (vert.) .. .. 1·10 60

23. " Precis villida ".

1982. Butterflies and Moths. Multicoloured.

84 1 c. Type **23** 55 45
85 2 c. "Cephonodes picus" (horiz) 40 40
86 5 c. "Macroglossom corythus" (horiz) .. 75 50
87 10 c. "Chasmina candida" 40 40
88 20 c. "Nagia linteola" (horiz) 40 40
89 25 c. "Eublemma rivula" .. 40 55
90 30 c. "Eurrhyparodes tricoloralis" 40 40
91 35 c. "Hippotion boerhaviae" (horiz) .. .. 1·25 50
92 40 c. "Euploea core" .. 40 50
93 45 c. "Psara hipponalis" (horiz) 50 60
94 50 c. "Danaus chrysippus" (horiz) .. .. .. 55 1·00
95 55 c. "Hypolimas misippus" 60 60
96 60 c. "Spodoptera litura" .. 65 1·00
97 $1 "Achaea janata" .. 2·25 2·00
98 $2 "Panacra velox" (horiz) 2·00 2·75
99 $3 "Utetheisa pulchelloides" (horiz) .. .. .. 2·75 2·75

.24 " Call His Name Immanuel ".

1982. Christmas. Multicoloured.

100. 21 c. Type **24** 20 20
101. 35 c. " I bring you good tidings " 35 35
102. 75 c. " Arise and flee into Egypt " 80 80

25. " God will look after us " (Matt. 1:20).

1983. Christmas. Extracts from New Testament. Multicoloured.

103. 24 c. Type **25** 30 30
104. 24 c. " Our baby King, Jesus " (Matthew. 2:2) .. 30 30
105. 24 c. " Your Saviour is born " (Luke. 2:11) .. 30 30
106. 24 c. " Wise men followed the Star " (Matthew. 2:9–10) 30 30
107. 24 c. " And worship the Lord " (Matthew. 2:11) 30 30

26. Hari Raya Celebration.

1984. Cocos-Malaya Culture. Multicoloured.

108. 45 c. Type **26** 45 25
109. 75 c. Melenggok dancing .. 65 50
110. 85 c. Cocos-Malaya wedding 75 55

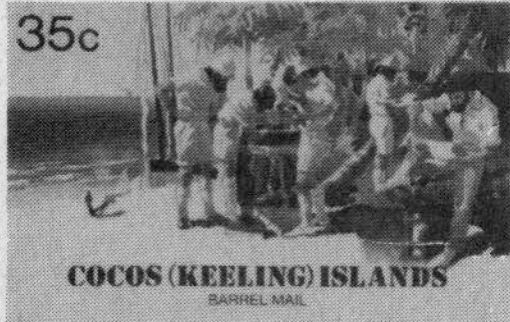

27. Unpacking Barrel.

1984. 75th Anniv. of Cocos Barrel Mail. Mult.

111. 35 c. Type **27** 35 25
112. 55 c. Jukong awaiting mail ship 60 50
113. 70 c. P & O mail ship "Morea" 70 55

28. Captain William Keeling.

1984. 375th Anniv. of Discovery of Cocos (Keeling) Islands. Multicoloured.

115. 30 c. Type **28** 70 40
116. 65 c. "Hector" .. .. 1·50 90
117. 95 c. Mariner's astrolabe .. 1·75 1·25
118. $1.10 Map "circa" 1666 .. 1·90 1·50

29. Malay Settlement, Home Island.

1984. "Ausipex" International Stamp Exhibition, Melbourne. Multicoloured.

119. 45 c. Type **29** 65 50
120. 55 c. Airstrip, West Island 75 60

30. "Rainbow" Fish.

1984. Christmas. Multicoloured.

122. 24 c. Type **30** 40 25
123. 35 c. "Rainbow" butterfly 70 35
124. 55 c. "Rainbow" bird .. 85 55

32. Jukong-building.

1985. Cocos-Malay Culture (2nd series). Handicrafts. Multicoloured.

126. 30 c. Type **32** 65 25
127. 45 c. Blacksmithing .. 90 40
128. 55 c. Woodcarving .. 1·10 50

33. C.S. "Scotia".

1985. Cable-laying Ships. Multicoloured.

129. 33 c. Type **33** .. .. 1·00 35
130. 65 c. C.S. "Anglia" .. 1·60 70
131. 80 c. C.S. "Patrol" .. 2·00 90

34. Red-footed Booby.

1985. Birds of Cocos (Keeling) Islands. Multicoloured.

132. 33 c. Type **34** .. .. 1·50 85
133. 60 c. Rufous night heron (juvenile) (horiz.) .. 1·75 1·10
134. $1 Banded rail (horiz.) .. 2·25 1·50

Nos. 132/4 were issued together se-tenant, forming a composite design.

35. "Trochus maculatus".

1985. Shells and Molluscs. Multicoloured.

135. 1 c. Type **35** 25 25
136. 2 c. "Smaragdia rangiana" 35 35
137. 3 c. "Chama sp." 40 40
138. 4 c. "Cypraea moneta" .. 40 40
139. 5 c. "Drupa morum" .. 40 40
140. 10 c. "Conus miles" .. 45 45
141. 15 c. "Terebra maculata" .. 55 55
142. 20 c. "Fragum fragum" .. 60 60
143. 30 c. "Turbo lajonkaini" .. 75 75
144. 33 c. "Mitra fissurata" .. 75 75
145. 40 c. "Lambis lambis" .. 85 85
146. 50 c. "Tridacna squamosa" 95 95
147. 60 c. "Cypraea histrio" .. 1·25 1·25
148. $1 "Phillidia varicosa" .. 2·00 2·00
149. $2 "Halgerda tessellata" .. 3·25 3·25
150. $3 "Harminoea cymbalum" .. .. 4·25 4·25

37. Charles Darwin, c 1840.

1986. 150th Anniv. of Charles Darwin's Visit. Multicoloured.

152. 33 c. Type **37** 70 50
153. 60 c. Map of H.M.S. "Beagle's" route, Australia to Cocos Islands .. .. .. 1·25 1·25
154. $1 H.M.S. "Beagle" .. 1·75 2·00

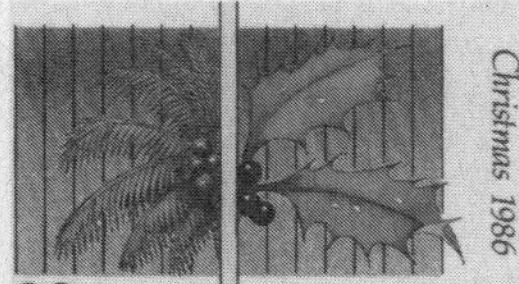

38. Coconut Palm and Holly Sprigs.

1986. Christmas. Multicoloured.

155. 30 c. Type **38** 45 40
156. 90 c. Sea shell and Christmas tree bauble .. 1·25 1·50
157. $1 Tropical fish and bell .. 1·50 1·75

INDEX

Countries can be quickly located by referring to the index at the end of this volume.

39. Jukong.

1987. Sailing Craft. Multicoloured.

158. 36 c. Type **39** .. .. 1·10 1·10
159. 36 c. Ocean racing yachts 1·10 1·10
160. 36 c. "Sarimanok" (replica outrigger) .. .. 1·10 1·10
161. 36 c. "Ayesha" (schooner) 1·10 1·10

Nos. 158/61 were printed together, se-tenant, each strip forming a composite background design.

40. Beach, Direction Island.

1987. Cocos Islands Scenes. Multicoloured.

162. 70 c. Type **40** .. .. 1·25 1·00
163. 90 c. Palm forest, West Island .. .. .. 1·50 1·50
164. $1 Golf course .. .. 2·25 2·50

41. Radio Transmitter and Palm Trees at Sunset.

1987. Communications. Multicoloured.

165. 70 c. Type **41** .. .. 1·25 1·25
166. 75 c. Air liner at terminal 1·50 1·50
167. 90 c. "Intelsat 5" satellite 1·75 1·75
168. $1 Airmail letter and globe 2·00 2·00

42. Batik Printing.

1987. Cocos (Keeling) Islands Malay Industries. Multicoloured.

169. 45 c. Type **42** .. .. 1·00 1·00
170. 65 c. Jukong building .. 1·25 1·25
171. 75 c. Copra production .. 1·50 1·50

43. Hands releasing Peace Dove and Map of Islands.

1987. Christmas. Multicoloured.

172. 30 c. Type **43** 40 30
173. 90 c. Local children at Christmas party .. 1·25 85
174. $1 Island family and Christmas star .. .. 1·50 95

1988. Bicentenary of Australian Settlement. Arrival of First Fleet. As Nos. 1105/9 of Australia but each inscribed "COCOS (KEELING) ISLANDS" and "AUSTRALIA BICENTENARY".

175. 37 c. Aborigines watching arrival of Fleet, Botany Bay .. .. .. 1·00 1·00
176. 37 c. Aboriginal family and anchored ships .. .. 1·00 1·00

177. 37 c. Fleet arriving at Sydney Cove .. .. 1·00 1·00
178. 37 c. Ship's boat .. .. 1·00 1·00
179. 37 c. Raising the flag, Sydney Cove, 26 January 1788 .. .. 1·00 1·00

Nos. 175/9 were printed together, se-tenant, forming a composite design.

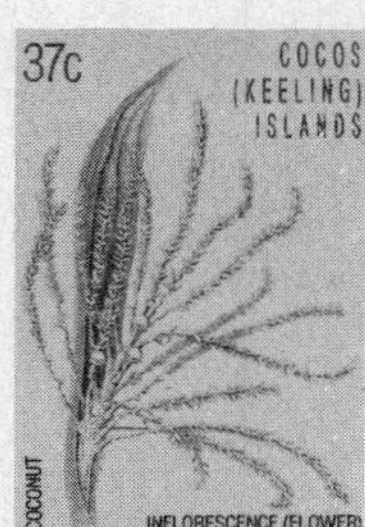

44 Coconut Flower

1988. Life Cycle of the Coconut. Mult.

180 37 c. Type **44** 50 40
181 65 c. Immature nuts .. 75 65
182 90 c. Coconut palm and mature nuts .. .. 1·10 90
183 $1 Seedlings .. .. 1·25 1·00

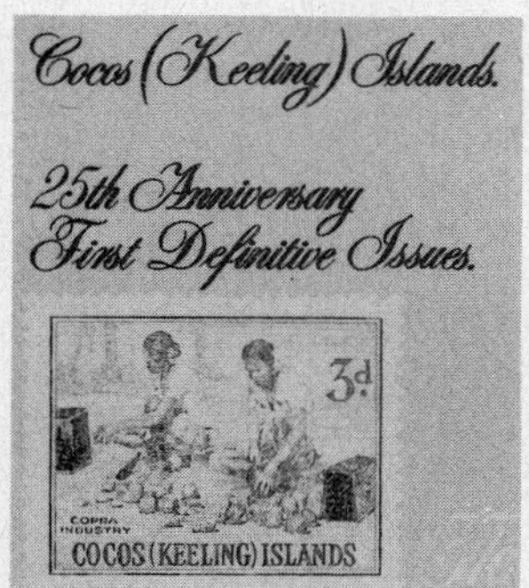

45 Copra 3d. Stamp of 1963

1988. 25th Anniv of First Cocos (Keeling) Islands Stamps. Each showing stamp from 1963 definitive set.

185 **45** 37 c. green, black & blue 70 70
186 – 55 c. green, black & brn 1·00 1·00
187 – 65 c. blue, black & lilac 1·10 1·10
188 – 70 c. red, black and grey 1·25 1·25
189 – 90 c. purple, blk & grey 1·50 1·50
190 – $1 green, black & brown 1·60 1·60

DESIGNS: 55 c. Palms 1s.; 65 c. "Super Constellation" 5d.; 70 c. Map 8d.; 90 c. "Jukong" (sailboat) 2s.; $1 White tern 2s. 3d.

46 "Pisonia grandis"

1988. Flora. Multicoloured.

191 1 c. Type **46** 10 10
192 2 c. "Cocos nucifera" .. 10 10
193 5 c. "Morinda citrifolia" .. 10 10
194 10 c. "Cordia subcordata" 10 15
195 30 c. "Argusia argentea" 25 30
196 37 c. "Calophyllum inophyllum" 35 40
197 40 c. "Barringtonia asiatica" 35 40
198 50 c. "Caesalpinia bonduc" 45 50
199 90 c. "Terminalia catappa" 85 90
200 $1 "Pemphis acidula" .. 90 95
201 $2 "Scaevola sericea" .. 1·90 2·00
202 $3 "Hibiscus tiliaceus" .. 2·75 3·00

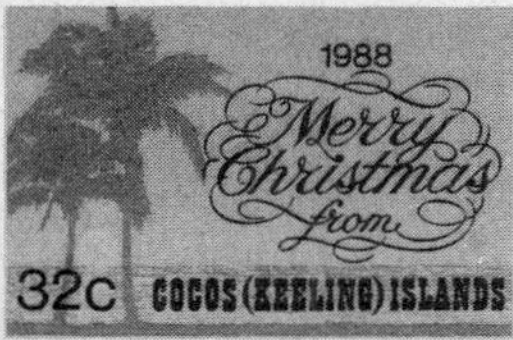

47 Beach at Sunset

1988. Christmas.

204 **47** 32 c. multicoloured .. 70 35
205 90 c. multicoloured .. 1·50 1·25
206 $1 multicoloured .. 1·25 1·25

48 Capt. P. G. Taylor

49 Jukong and Star

1989. 50th Anniv of First Indian Ocean Aerial Survey.

207 **48** 40 c. multicoloured .. 40 45
208 – 70 c. multicoloured .. 65 70
209 – $1 multicoloured .. 95 1·00
210 – $1.10 blue, lilac & black 1·00 1·10

DESIGNS: 70 c. Consolidated Catalina "PBY2" "Guba II" and crew; $1 "Guba II" over Direction Island; $1.10, Unissued Australia 5s. stamp commemorating flight.

1989. Christmas.

211 **49** 35 c. multicoloured .. 45 40
212 80 c. multicoloured .. 90 1·00
213 $1.10 multicoloured .. 1·10 1·25

50 H.M.A.S. "Sydney" (cruiser)

1989. 75th Anniv of Destruction of German Cruiser "Emden". Multicoloured.

214 40 c. Type **50** .. 90 90
215 70 c. "Emden" .. .. 1·25 1·25
216 $1 Steam launch from "Emden" .. .. 1·50 1·50
217 $1.10 H.M.A.S. "Sydney" and crest .. .. 1·50 1·50

51 Xanthid Crab

1990. Cocos Islands Crabs. Multicoloured.

219 45 c. Type **51** 70 70
220 75 c. Ghost crab .. .. 1·00 1·00
221 $1 Red-backed mud crab 1·25 1·25
222 $1.30 Coconut crab (vert) 1·50 1·50

52 Captain Keeling and "Hector", 1609

1990. Navigators of the Pacific.

223 **52** 45 c. mauve 75 75
224 – 75 c. mauve and blue .. 1·10 1·10
225 – $1 mauve and stone .. 1·50 1·50
226 – $1.30 mauve and buff .. 1·75 1·75

DESIGNS: 75 c. Captain Fitzroy and "Beagle", 1836; $1 Captain Belcher and "Samarang", 1846; $1.30 Captain Fremantle and "Juno", 1857.

1990. "New Zealand 1990" International Stamp Exhibition, Auckland. No. 188 optd with logo and **NEW ZEALAND 1990 24 AUG- 2 SEP AUCKLAND**.

228 70 c. red, black and grey .. 90 95

1990. No. 187 surch **$5**.

230 $5 on 65 c. blue, blk & lilac 4·50 4·75

55 Cocos Atoll from West and Star

1990. Christmas. Multicoloured.

231 40 c. Type **55** 45 45
232 70 c. Cocos atoll from south 80 85
233 $1.30 Cocos atoll from east 1·40 1·75

1990. Nos. 140/1, 143 and 146/7 surch **POSTAGE PAID** plus additional words as indicated.

235 (1 c.) on 30 c. "Turbo lajonkaini" (**LOCAL**) .. 10 10
236 (43 c.) on 10 c. "Conus miles" (**MAINLAND**) 40 45
237 70 c. on 60 c. "Cypraea histrio" (**ZONE 1**) .. 65 70
238 80 c. on 50 c. "Tridacna squamosa" (**ZONE 2**) 75 80
239 $1.20 on 15 c. "Terebra maculata" (**ZONE 5**) 1·10 1·25

58 Beaded Sea Star

1991. Starfish and Sea Urchins. Mult.

240 45 c. Type **58** 55 55
241 75 c. Feather star .. 95 95
242 $1 Slate pencil urchin 1·25 1·25
243 $1.30 Globose sea urchin .. 1·60 1·60

59 Cocos Islands

1991. Malay Hari Raya Festival. Mult.

244 45 c. Type **59** 55 55
245 75 c. Island house .. 95 95
246 $1.30 Islands scene .. 1·60 1·60

60 Child praying

1991. Christmas. Multicoloured.

247 38 c. Type **60** 35 40
248 43 c. Child dreaming of Christmas Day .. 40 45
249 $1 Child singing .. 90 95
250 $1.20 Child fascinated by decorations .. .. 1·10 1·25

OFFICIAL STAMPS

1991. No. 182 surch **OFFICIAL PAID MAINLAND**.

O1 (43 c.) on 90 c. Coconut palm and mature nuts † 45

No. O1 was not sold to the public in unused condition.

COOK ISLANDS

A group of islands in the S. Pacific under New Zealand control, including Aitutaki, Niue, Penrhyn and Rarotonga. Granted Self-Government in 1965.

See also issues for Aitutaki and Penrhyn Island.

1892. 12 pence = 1 shilling.
20 shillings = 1 pound.
1967. 100 cents = 1 dollar.

1.

1892.

1. **1.** 1d. black .. .. .. 26·00 30·00
2. 1½d. mauve .. .. .. 38·00 38·00
3. 2½d. blue .. .. .. 38·00 38·00
4. 10d. red £140 £130

3. White Tern or Torea.

2. Queen Makea Takau.

1893.

11ba **3.** ½d. blue .. .. .. 3·50 4·75
28 ½d. green .. .. .. 1·40 3·25
13 **2.** 1d. brown .. .. .. 8·00 12·00
6 1d. blue .. .. .. 6·00 1·50
29 1d. red .. .. .. 2·00 3·00
43 1½d. mauve .. .. 4·75 3·25
15a **3.** 2d. brown .. .. 5·50 6·50
16a **2.** 2½d. red .. .. .. 9·00 9·00
32 2½d. blue .. .. .. 3·75 6·50
9 5d. black .. .. .. 13·00 13·00
18a **3.** 6d. purple .. .. 16·00 19·00
19 **2.** 10d. green .. .. 15·00 24·00
46 **3.** 1s. red .. .. .. 22·00 55·00

1899. Surch. **ONE HALF PENNY.**

21. **2.** ½d. on 1d. blue .. .. 32·00 35·00

1901. Optd. with crown.

22. **2.** 1d. brown £140 £140

1919. New Zealand stamps (King George V.) surch. **RAROTONGA** and value in native language in words.

50 **62** ½d. green 20 50
51 **53** 1d. red 20 60
52 **62** 1½d. brown 25 75
53 2d. yellow 30 70
55 2½d. blue .. .. .. 95 2·00
57 3d. brown .. .. 70 1·50
59 4d. violet .. .. 1·00 4·00
61 4½d. green .. .. 1·10 5·50
63 6d. red .. .. .. 1·50 5·00
65 7½d. brown .. .. 1·25 5·50
66 9d. green .. .. .. 1·75 7·00
68 1s. red .. .. .. 2·75 11·00

9. Captain Cook Landing.

17. Harbour, Rarotonga and Mt. Ikurangi.

1920. Inscr. " RAROTONGA ".

81. **9.** ½d. black and green .. 3·50 3·50
82. – 1d. black and red .. 4·00 1·50
72. – 1½d. black and blue .. 7·00 8·50
83. – 2½d. brown and blue .. 2·25 12·00
73. – 3d. black and brown .. 2·00 5·50
84. **17.** 4d. green and violet .. 3·00 12·00
74. – 6d. brown and orange .. 1·75 8·00
75. – 1s. black and violet .. 5·00 17·00

DESIGNS—VERT. 1d. Wharf at Avarua. 1½d. Capt. Cook (Dance). 2½d. Te Po, Rarotongan chief. 3d. Palm tree. HORIZ. 6d. Huts at Arorangi. 1s. Avarua Harbour.

1921. New Zealand stamps optd. **RAROTONGA.**

76 **F 4.** 2s. blue .. .. .. 26·00 45·00
77 2s. 6d. brown .. .. 18·00 40·00
78 5s. green .. .. .. 26·00 48·00
79 10s. red .. .. .. 48·00 60·00
89 £1 red .. .. .. 75·00 £100

1926. "Admiral" type of New Zealand optd. **RAROTONGA.**

90 **71.** 2s. blue .. .. .. 10·00 38·00
92 3s. mauve .. .. .. 16·00 40·00

1931. No. 77 surch. **TWO PENCE.**

94. 2d. on 1½d. black & blue 1·00 3·75

1931. Arms type of New Zealand optd. **RAROTONGA.**
95. F 6 2s. 6d. brown .. .. .. 7·50 18·00
96. 5s. green .. .. .. 16·00 42·00
97. 10s. red .. .. .. 30·00 65·00
98. £1 pink .. .. .. 60·00 90·00

20. Captain Cook landing.

22. Double Maori Canoe.

1932. Inscr. " COOK ISLANDS ".
106. **20.** ½d. black and green .. 40 1·00
107. – 1d. black and red .. 45 1·00
108. **22.** 2d. black and brown .. 35 30
109. – 2½d. black and blue .. 30 1·25
110. – 4d. black and blue .. 30 35
142. – 6d. black and orange .. 90 60
105. – 1s. black and violet .. 5·00 16·00
DESIGNS—VERT. 1d. Capt. Cook. HORIZ. 2½d. Natives working cargo. 4d. Port of Avarua. 6d. R.M.S. " Monowai ". 1 s. King George V.

1935. Jubilee. As 1932, optd. **SILVER JUBILEE OF KING GEORGE V 1910-1935.**
113. 1d. red 60 70
114. 2½d. blue .. .. .. 75 1·00
115. 6d. green and orange .. 3·00 4·50

1936. Stamps of New Zealand optd **COOK ISLANDS.**
116 **71** 2s. blue .. .. 12·00 35·00
131 **F 6** 2s. 6d. brown .. .. 6·00 9·00
117 **71** 3s. mauve .. .. 13·00 45·00
132 **F 6** 5s. green .. .. 5·50 12·00
133 10s. red .. .. 30·00 45·00
134 £1 pink .. .. 32·00 45·00
135 £3 green .. .. 50·00 £150
98b £5 blue £170 £250

1937. Coronation T **106** of New Zealand optd. **COOK IS'DS.**
124. **106.** 1d. red 35 10
125. 2½d. blue 55 20
126. 6d. orange 55 20

29. King George VI.

30. Native Village.

1938.
143 **29** 1s. black and violet .. 90 1·00
128 **30** 2s. black and orange.. 7·50 6·00
145 – 3s. blue and green .. 15·00 15·00
DESIGN—HORIZ. 3s. Native canoe.

32. Tropical Landscape.

1940.
130. **32.** 3d. on 1½d. black & pur. 10 15

1946. Peace. Peace stamps of New Zealand of 1946 optd. **COOK ISLANDS.**
146. **132.** 1d. green 10 10
147. – 2d. purple 10 15
148. – 6d. brown and red .. 15 15
149. **139.** 8d. black and red .. 15 15

34. Ngatangila Channel, Rarotonga.

1949.
150. **34.** ½d. violet and brown .. 10 55
151. – 1d. brown and green .. 1·75 1·25
152. – 2d. brown and red .. 60 1·25
153. – 3d. green and blue .. 50 1·25
154. – 5d. green and violet .. 70 1·00
155. – 6d. black and red .. 1·25 1·75
156. – 8d. olive and orange .. 40 3·00
157. – 1s. blue and brown .. 4·25 3·00
158. – 2s. brown and red .. 3·00 6·50
159. – 3s. blue and green .. 4·75 8·50
DESIGNS—HORIZ. 1d. Capt. Cook and map of Hervey Is. 2d. Rarotonga and Rev. John Williams. 3d. Aitutaki and palm trees. 5d. Rarotonga Airfield. 6d. Penrhyn village. 8d. Native hut. VERT. 1s. Map and statue of Capt. Cook. 2s. Native hut and palms. 3s. M.V. "Matua".

1953. Coronation. As Types of New Zealand but inscr. " COOK ISLANDS ".
160. **164.** 3d. brown .. .. 1·00 55
161. **166.** 6d. grey .. .. 1·25 95

1960. No. 154 surch. **1/6.**
162. 1s. 6d. on 5d. green & violet 15 30

45. Tiare Maori.

52. Queen Elizabeth II.

55. Rarotonga.

1963.
163. **45.** 1d. green and yellow .. 35 10
164. – 2d. red and yellow .. 10 10
165. – 3d. yell., green & violet 45 10
166. – 5d. blue and black .. 3·50 30
167. – 6d. red, yellow and green 1·00 20
168. – 8d. black and blue .. 1·25 45
169. – 1s. yellow and green .. 40 20
170. **52.** 1s. 6d. violet .. .. 2·75 2·00
171. – 2s. brown and blue .. 75 75
172. – 3s. black and green .. 1·25 1·00
173. **55.** 5s. brown and blue .. 8·50 3·25
DESIGNS—As Type **45.** VERT. 2d. Fishing God. 8d. Skipjack Tuna. HORIZ. 3d. Frangipani (plant). 5d. Love tern. 6d. Hibiscus. 1s. Oranges. As Type **55:** 2s. Island scene. 3s. Administration Centre, Mangalia.

56. Eclipse and Palm.

1965. Solar Eclipse Observation, Manuae Island.
174. **56.** 6d. black, yellow & blue 10 10

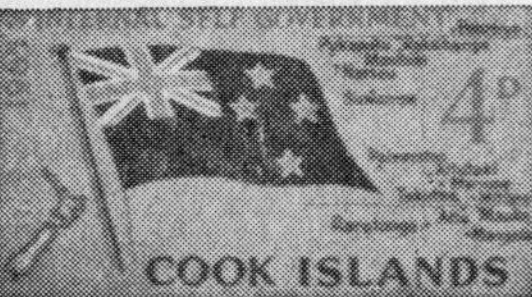
57. N.Z. Ensign and Map.

1965. Internal Self-Government.
175. **57.** 4d. red and blue .. 10 10
176. – 10d. multicoloured .. 10 10
177. – 1s. multicoloured .. 10 10
178. – 1s. 9d. multicoloured .. 30 40
DESIGNS: 10d. London Missionary Society Church. 1s. Proclamation of Cession, 1900. 1s. 9d. Nikao School.

1966. Churchill Commem. Nos. 171/3 and 175/7 optd. **In Memoriam SIR WINSTON CHURCHILL 1874-1965.**
179. **57.** 4d. red and blue .. 75 30
180. – 10d. multicoloured .. 1·50 45
181. – 1s. multicoloured .. 1·50 65
182. – 2s. brown and blue .. 1·50 1·25
183. – 3s. black and green .. 1·50 1·25
184. **55.** 5s. brown and blue .. 2·00 1·75

1966. Air. Various stamps optd. **Airmail** and aeroplane or surch. in addition.
185. – 6d. red, yellow & green (No. 167) .. .. 1·25 20
186. – 7d. on 8d. black & blue (No. 168) .. .. 1·25 25
187. – 10d. on 3d. green & violet (No. 165) .. .. 1·00 15
188. – 1s. yellow and green (No. 169) .. .. 1·00 15
189. **52.** 1s. 6d. violet .. .. 1·25 1·25
190. – 2s. 3d. on 3s. black and green (No. 172) .. 1·00 65
191. **55.** 5s. brown and blue .. 1·50 1·50
192. – 10s. on 2s. brown and blue (No. 171) .. 1·75 6·50
193. – £1 pink (No. 143) .. 9·00 16·00

63. " Adoration of the Magi " (Fra Angelico).

1966. Christmas. Multicoloured.
194. 1d. Type **63** 15 10
195. 2d. " The Nativity " (Memling) 15 10
196. 4d. " Adoration of the Wise Men " (Velazquez) .. 15 15
197. 10d. " Adoration of the Wise Men " (H. Bosch) .. 15 15
198. 1s. 6d. " Adoration of the Shepherds " (J. de Ribera) 25 20

68. Tennis and Queen Elizabeth II.

1967. 2nd South Pacific Games, Noumea. Multicoloured.
199. ½d. Type **68** (postage) .. 10 10
200. 1d. Basketball and Games Emblem 10 10
201. 4d. Boxing and Cook Islands Team Badge 10 10
202. 7d. Football and Queen Elizabeth II 10 10
203. 10d. Running and Games Emblem (air) 10 10
204. 2s. 3d. Running and Cook Islands' Team Badge .. 15 10

1967. Decimal currency. Various stamps surch.
205. **45.** 1 c. on 1d. .. .. 45 1·10
206. – 2 c. on 2d. (No. 164) .. 10 10
207. – 2½ c. on 3d. (No. 165) .. 20 10
209. **57.** 3 c. on 4d. 15 10
210. – 4 c. on 5d. (No. 166) .. 1·00 20
211. – 5 c. on 6d. (No. 167) .. 15 10
212. **56.** 5 c. on 6d. .. .. 2·50 40
213. – 7 c. on 8d. (No. 168) .. 15 10
214. – 10 c. on 1s. (No. 169) .. 15 10
215. **52.** 15 c. on 1s. 6d.. .. 2·00 1·00
216. – 30 c. on 3s. (No. 172) .. 14·00 4·50
217. **55.** 50 c. on 5s. .. .. 3·50 1·25
218. – $1 and 10s. on 10d. (No. 176) .. .. 14·00 6·50
219. – $2 on £1 (No. 134) .. 70·00 80·00
220. – $6 on £3 (No. 135) .. £110 £120
221. – $10 on £5 (No. 136) .. £150 £160

75. Village Scene, Cook Islands 1d. Stamp of 1892 and Queen Victoria (from "Penny Black").

1967. 75th Anniv. of 1st Cook Island Stamps. Multicoloured.
222. 1 c. (1d.) Type **75** 10 10
223. 3 c. (4d.) Post Office, Avarua, Rarotonga and Queen Elizabeth II 15 10
224. 8 c. (10d.) Avarua, Rarotonga, and Cook Islands 10d. stamp of 1892 .. 30 10
225. 18 c. (1s. 9d.) M.S. "Moana Roa", "DC-3" aircraft, map and Captain Cook 1·40 25
The face values are expressed in decimal currency and in the sterling equivalent.

79. Hibiscus.

81. Queen Elizabeth and Flowers.

1967. Flowers. Multicoloured.
227. ½ c. Type **79** 10 10
228. 1 c. " Hibiscus syriacus " 10 10
229. 2 c. Frangipani 10 10
230. 2½ c. " Clitoria ternatea " 20 10
231. 3 c. " Suva Queen " .. 40 10
232. 4 c. Water Lily (wrongly inscr. "Walter Lily") .. 55 70
233. 4 c. Water Lily .. .. 1·50 10
234. 5 c. " Bauhinia bipinnata rosea " 35 10
235. 6 c. Yellow Hibiscus .. 30 10
236. 8 c. " Allamanda cathartica " 30 10
237. 9 c. Stephanotis 30 10
238. 10 c. " Poinciana regia flamboyant " 30 10
239. 15 c. Frangipani 40 10
240. 20 c. Thunbergia .. .. 1·75 60
241. 25 c. Canna Lily .. .. 1·00 15
242. 30 c. " Euphorbia pulcherrima poinsettia " .. 65 50
243. 50 c. "Gardenia taitensis" 1·00 55
244. $1 Queen Elizabeth II 1·75 80
245. $2 Queen Elizabeth II 3·50 1·50
246. $4 Type **81** .. .. 3·00 3·50
247. $6 As No. 246 .. .. 3·50 5·00
247c. $8 As No. 246 .. .. 8·00 12·00
248. $10 As No. 246 .. .. 8·00 12·00

97. " Ia Orana Maria ".

1967. Gaugin's Polynesian Paintings.
249. **97.** 1 c. multicoloured .. 10 10
250. – 3 c. multicoloured .. 10 10
251. – 5 c. multicoloured .. 15 10
252. – 8 c. multicoloured .. 15 10
253. – 15 c. multicoloured .. 35 10
254. – 22 c. multicoloured .. 40 15
DESIGNS: 3 c. " Riders on the Beach ". 5 c. " Still Life with Flowers " and inset portrait of Queen Elizabeth. 8 c. " Whispered Words ". 15 c. " Maternity ". 22 c. " Why are you angry? ".

98. " The Holy Family " (Rubens).

1967. Christmas. Renaissance Paintings.
256. **98.** 1 c. multicoloured .. 10 10
257. – 3 c. multicoloured .. 10 10
258. – 4 c. multicoloured .. 10 10
259. – 8 c. multicoloured .. 15 10
260. – 15 c. multicoloured .. 30 10
261. – 25 c. multicoloured .. 35 10
DESIGNS: 3 c. " The Epiphany " (Durer). 4 c. " The Lucca Madonna " (J. Van Eyck). 8 c. " The Adoration of the Shepherds " (J. da Bassano). 15 c. " The Nativity " (El Greco). 25 c. " The Madonna and Child " (Correggio).

1968. Hurricane Relief. Nos. 231, 233, 251, 238, 241 and 243/4 optd. **HURRICANE RELIEF** plus value.
262. 3 c.+1 c. multicoloured .. 15 10
263. 4 c.+1 c. multicoloured .. 15 10
264. 5 c.+2 c. multicoloured .. 15 10
265. 10 c.+2 c. multicoloured 15 10
266. 25 c.+5 c. multicoloured 25 10
267. 50 c.+10 c. multicoloured 35 15
268. $1+10 c. multicoloured .. 60 30
On No. 264 silver blocking obliterates the design area around the lettering.

100. " Matavai Bay, Tahiti " (J. Barralet).

1968. Bicentenary of Captain Cook's 1st Voyage of Discovery.

No.	Description	Unused	Used
269. 100.	½ c. multicoloured (post.)	10	10
270. –	1 c. multicoloured ..	15	10
271. –	2 c. multicoloured ..	40	35
272. –	4 c. multicoloured ..	40	35
273. –	6 c. multicoloured (air)	90	65
274. –	10 c. multicoloured ..	1·25	75
275. –	15 c. multicoloured ..	1·50	90
276. –	25 c. multicoloured ..	1·75	1·25

DESIGNS—VERT. 1 c. " Island of Huaheine" (John Cleveley). 2 c. " Town of St. Peter and St. Paul, Kamchatka " (J. Webber). 4 c. " The Ice Islands " (Antarctica: W. Hodges). HORIZ. 6 c. " Resolution and Discovery " (J. Webber). 10 c. " The Island of Tahiti " (W. Hodges). 15 c. " Karakakooa, Hawaii " (J. Webber). 25 c. " The Landing at Middleburg " (W. Hodges).

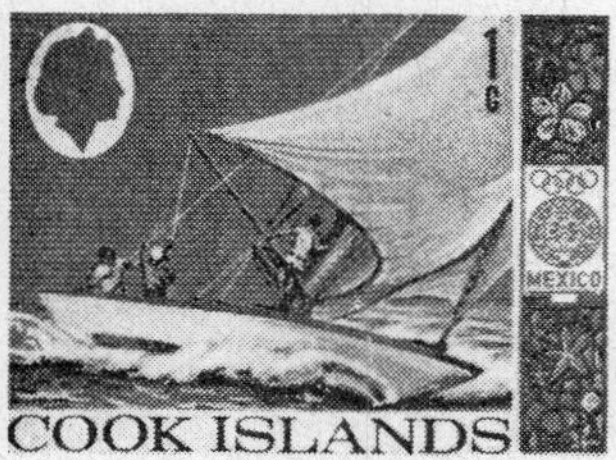

102. Sailing.

1968. Olympic Games, Mexico. Multicoloured.

No.	Description	Unused	Used
277.	1 c. Type **102**	10	10
278.	5 c. Gymnastics	10	10
279.	15 c. High-jumping ..	15	10
280.	20 c. High-diving ..	15	10
281.	30 c. Cycling	15	10
282.	50 c. Hurdling	20	15

103. " Madonna and Child " (Titian).

1968. Christmas. Multicoloured.

No.	Description	Unused	Used
283.	1 c. Type **103** ..	10	10
284.	4 c. "The Holy Family of the Lamb " (Raphael)	10	10
285.	10 c. " The Madonna of the Rosary " (Murillo) ..	25	10
286.	20 c. " Adoration of the Magi " (Memling) ..	30	10
287.	30 c. " Adoration of the Magi " (Ghirlandaio) ..	35	10

104. Camp-fire Cooking.

1969. Diamond Jubilee of New Zealand Scout Movement and 5th National (New Zealand) Jamboree. Multicoloured.

No.	Description	Unused	Used
289.	½ c. Type **104** ..	10	10
290.	1 c. Descent by rope ..	10	10
291.	5 c. Semaphore	10	10
292.	10 c. Tree-planting ..	15	10
293.	20 c. Constructing a shelter	25	10
294.	30 c. Lord Baden-Powell and island scene ..	40	15

105. High Jumping.

1969. 3rd. South Pacific Games, Port Moresby. Multicoloured.

No.	Description	Unused	Used
295.	½ c. Type **105**	10	10
296.	½ c. Footballer	10	10
297.	1 c. Basketball	15	10
298.	1 c. Weightlifter	15	10
299.	4 c. Tennis-player	15	10
300	4 c. Hurdler	15	15
301.	10 c. Javelin-thrower ..	20	15
302.	10 c. Runner	40	25
303.	15 c. Golfer	60	35
304.	15 c. Boxer	60	35

106. Flowers, Map and Captain Cook. (Illustration reduced. Actual size 72 × 26 mm.).

1969. South Pacific Conf., Noumea. Mult.

No.	Description	Unused	Used
306.	5 c. Premier Albert Henry	55	15
307.	10 c. Type **106**	1·00	55
308.	25 c. Flowers, map and arms of New Zealand ..	1·10	75
309.	30 c. Queen Elizabeth II, map and flowers ..	1·10	85

107. " Virgin and Child with Saints Jerome and Dominic " (Lippi).

1969. Christmas. Multicoloured.

No.	Description	Unused	Used
310.	1 c. Type **107**	10	10
311.	4 c. " The Holy Family " (Fra. B. Della Porta) ..	10	10
312.	10 c. " Virgin and Child with Saints " (Memling)	15	10
313.	20 c. " Virgin and Child with Saints" (Robert Campin)	25	10
314.	30 c. " Virgin and Child " (Corregio)	25	15

108. "The Resurrection of Christ " (Raphael).

1970. Easter.

No.	Description	Unused	Used
316. 108.	4 c. multicoloured ..	10	10
317. –	8 c. multicoloured ..	10	10
318. –	20 c. multicoloured ..	15	10
319. –	25 c. multicoloured ..	20	10

DESIGNS: " The Resurrection of Christ " by Dirk Bouts (8 c.), Altdorfer (20 c.), Murillo (25 c.).

1970. "Apollo 13". Nos. 233, 236, 239/40, 242, and 245/6, optd. **KIA ORANA APOLLO 13 ASTRONAUTS Te Atua to Tatou Irinakianga.**

No.	Description	Unused	Used
321.	4 c. multicoloured ..	10	10
322.	8 c. multicoloured ..	10	10
323.	15 c. multicoloured ..	10	10
324.	20 c. multicoloured ..	15	15
325.	30 c. multicoloured ..	20	20
326.	$2 multicoloured	60	90
327.	$4 multicoloured	1·25	2·75

110. The Royal Family.

1970. Royal Visit to New Zealand. Mult.

No.	Description	Unused	Used
328.	5 c. Type **110**	65	30
329.	30 c. Captain Cook and H.M.S. " Endeavour "	2·75	1·75
330.	$1 Royal Visit Commem. Coin	4·00	3·00

1970. 5th Anniv. of Self-Government Nos. 328/30, optd. **FIFTH ANNIVERSARY SELF-GOVERNMENT AUGUST 1970.**

No.	Description	Unused	Used
332. 110.	5 c. multicoloured ..	40	15
333. –	30 c. multicoloured ..	1·25	35
334. –	$1 multicoloured ..	2·00	90

On No. 332, the opt. is arranged in one line around the frame of the stamp.

1970. Surch.

No.	Description	Unused	Used
335. 81.	$4 on $8 multicoloured	4·00	3·00
336.	$4 on $10 multicoloured	1·50	1·75

115. Mary, Joseph, and Christ in Manger.

1970. Christmas. Multicoloured.

No.	Description	Unused	Used
337.	1 c. Type **115**	10	10
338.	4 c. Shepherds and Apparition of the Angel	10	10
339.	10 c. Mary showing Child to Joseph	15	10
340.	20 c. The Wise Men bearing Gifts	20	10
341.	30 c. Parents wrapping Child in swaddling clothes	25	15

1971. Surch. **PLUS 20c. UNITED KINGDOM SPECIAL MAIL SERVICE.**

No.	Description	Unused	Used
343.	30 c. + 20 c. (No. 242) ..	40	50
344.	50 c. + 20 c. (No. 243) ..	1·50	1·75

The premium of 20 c. was to prepay a private delivery service fee in Great Britain during the postal strike. The mail was sent by air to a forwarding address in the Netherlands. No. 343 was intended for ordinary airmail ½ oz. letters, and No. 344 included registration fee.

117. Wedding of Princess Elizabeth and Prince Philip.

1971. Royal Visit of Duke of Edinburgh. Multicoloured.

No.	Description	Unused	Used
345.	1 c. Type **117**	30	50
346.	4 c. Queen Elizabeth, Prince Philip, Prince Charles and Princess Anne at Windsor	75	1·10
347.	10 c. Prince Philip sailing	1·00	1·25
348.	15 c. Prince Philip in polo gear	1·00	1·25
349.	25 c. Prince Philip in Naval uniform, and Royal Yacht, "Britannia"	1·50	2·00

1971. Fourth South Pacific Games, Tahiti, Nos. 238, 241 and 242 optd. **Fourth South Pacific Games Papeete** and emblem or surch. also.

No.	Description	Unused	Used
351.	10 c. multicoloured ..	10	10
352.	10 c. + 1 c. multicoloured ..	10	10
353.	10 c. + 3 c. multicoloured ..	10	10
354.	25 c. multicoloured ..	15	10
355.	25 c. + 1 c. multicoloured ..	15	10
356.	25 c. + 3 c. multicoloured ..	15	10
357.	30 c. multicoloured ..	15	10
358.	30 c. + 1 c. multicoloured ..	15	10
359.	30 c. + 3 c. multicoloured ..	15	10

The stamps additionally surcharged 1 c. or 3 c. helped to finance the Cook Islands' team at the games.

1971. Nos. 230, 233, 236/7 and 239 surch.

No.	Description	Unused	Used
360.	10 c. on 2½ c. multicoloured	15	25
361.	10 c. on 4 c. multicoloured	15	25
362.	10 c. on 8 c. multicoloured	15	25
363.	10 c. on 9 c. multicoloured	15	25
364.	10 c. on 15 c. multicoloured	15	25

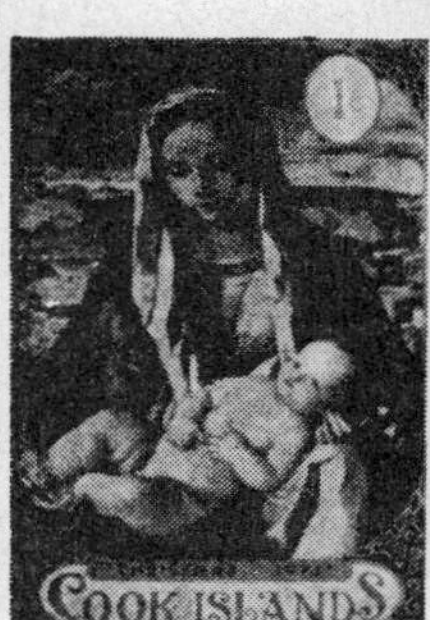

121. " Virgin and Child " (Bellini). 123. St. John.

1971. Christmas.

No.	Description	Unused	Used
365. 121.	1 c. multicoloured ..	10	10
366. –	4 c. multicoloured ..	10	10
367. –	10 c. multicoloured ..	25	10
368. –	20 c. multicoloured ..	50	10
369. –	30 c. multicoloured ..	50	20

DESIGNS: Various paintings of the " Virgin and Child " by Bellini. Similar to Type **121**.

1972. 25th Anniv. of South Pacific Commission. No. 244 optd. **SOUTH PACIFIC COMMISSION FEB. 1947–1972.**

No.	Description	Unused	Used
372.	$1 multicoloured	40	75

1972. Easter. Multicoloured.

No.	Description	Unused	Used
373.	5c. Type **123**	10	10
374.	10c. Christ on the Cross ..	10	10
375.	30c. Mary, Mother of Jesus	25	25

1972. Hurricane Relief.

(a). Nos. 239, 241 and 243 optd. **HURRICANE RELIEF PLUS** premium.

No.	Description	Unused	Used
379.	15c. + 5c. multicoloured ..	20	20
380.	25c. + 5c. multicoloured ..	20	20
382.	50c. + 10c. multicoloured ..	25	25

(b). Nos. 373/5 optd. **Hurricane Relief Plus** premium.

No.	Description	Unused	Used
377.	5c. + 2c. multicoloured ..	10	10
378.	10c. + 2c. multicoloured ..	15	15
381.	30c. + 5c. multicoloured ..	20	20

126. Rocket heading for Moon. 127. (Illustration reduced. Actual size 62 × 30 mm.)

1972. The Apollo Moon Exploration Flights. Multicoloured.

No.	Description	Unused	Used
383.	5 c. Type **126**	15	10
384.	5 c. Type **127**	15	10
385.	10 c. } Astronauts on Moon	20	10
386.	10 c. }	20	10
387.	25 c. } Moon Rover and	25	15
388.	25 c. } astronauts working	25	15
389.	30 c. } Splashdown and	25	15
390.	30 c. } helicopter	25	15

These were issued in horizontal se-tenant pairs of each value, forming one composite design.

1972. Hurricane Relief. Nos. 383/390 surch. **HURRICANE RELIEF Plus** and premium.

No.	Description	Unused	Used
392.	5 c. + 2 c. multicoloured ..	10	10
393.	5 c. + 2 c. multicoloured ..	10	10
394.	10 c. + 2 c. multicoloured	10	10
395.	10 c. + 2 c. multicoloured	10	10
396.	25 c. + 2 c. multicoloured	15	15
397.	25 c. + 2 c. multicoloured	15	15
398.	30 c. + 2 c. multicoloured	15	15
399.	30 c. + 2 c. multicoloured	15	15

129. High-jumping.

1972. Olympic Games, Munich. Mult.

401.	10 c. Type **129**	15	10
402.	25 c. Running	30	15
403.	30 c. Boxing	30	20

130. " The Rest on the flight into Egypt " (Caravaggio).

1972. Christmas. Multicoloured.

406.	1 c. Type **130**	10	10
407.	5 c. " Madonna of the Swallow " (Guercino) ..	25	10
408.	10 c. " Madonna of the Green Cushion " (Solario)	30	10
409.	20 c. " Madonna and Child " (di Credi) ..	45	20
410.	30 c. " Madonna and Child " (Bellini) ..	70	30

131. Marriage Ceremony.

1972. Royal Silver Wedding. Each black and silver.

413.	5 c. Type **131**	25	15
414.	10 c. Leaving Westminster Abbey	60	40
415.	15 c. Bride and Bridegroom (40 × 41 mm.) ..	75	50
416.	30 c. Family group (67 × 40 mm.)	1·10	80

132. Taro Leaf.

1973. Silver Wedding Coinage.

417. **132**	1 c. gold, mauve & black	10	10
418. –	2 c. gold, blue & black ..	10	10
419. –	5 c. silver, green & black	10	10
420. –	10 c. silver, blue & black	25	10
421. –	20 c. silver, grn. & black	35	10
422. –	50 c. silver, mauve & blk.	65	15
423. –	$1 silver, blue & black ..	1·10	30

DESIGNS—HORIZ. (37 × 24 mm.). 2 c. Pineapple. 5 c. Hibiscus. (46 × 30 mm.). 10 c. Oranges. 20 c. White Tern. 50 c. Skipjack Tuna. VERT. (32 × 55 mm.). $1, Tangaroa.

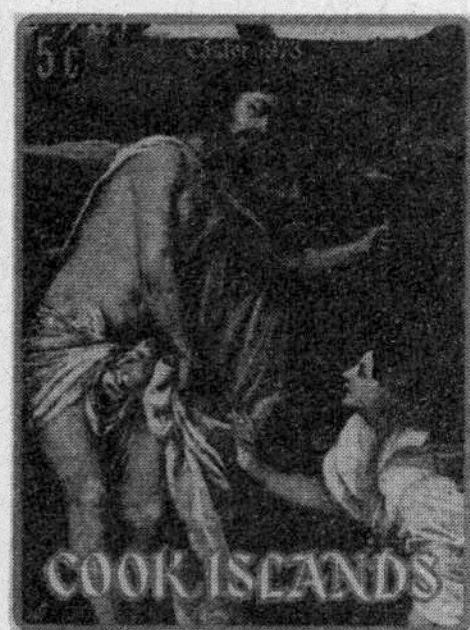

133. " Noli me Tangere " (Titian).

1973. Easter. Multicoloured.

424.	5 c. Type **133**	15	10
425.	10 c. " The Descent from the Cross " (Rubens) ..	20	10
426.	30 c. " The Lamentation of Christ " (Durer) ..	25	10

134. Queen Elizabeth II in Coronation Regalia.

1973. 20th Anniversary of Queen Elizabeth's Coronation.

429.	**134.** 10 c. multicoloured ..	65	1·25

1973. 10th Anniv. of Treaty Banning Nuclear Testing. Nos. 234, 236, 238 and 240/42 optd. **TENTH ANNIVERSARY CESSATION OF NUCLEAR TESTING TREATY.**

431.	5 c. multicoloured	10	10
432.	8 c. multicoloured	10	10
433.	10 c. multicoloured ..	10	10
434.	20 c. multicoloured ..	15	15
435.	25 c. multicoloured ..	20	15
436.	30 c. multicoloured ..	20	15

136. Tipairua.

1973. Maori Exploration of the Pacific. Sailing Craft. Multicoloured.

437.	½ c. Type **136**	10	10
438.	1 c. Wa'a Kaulua ..	10	10
439.	1½ c. Tainui	15	10
440.	5 c. War canoe ..	40	10
441.	10 c. Pahi ..	60	15
442.	15 c. Amatasi ..	1·00	30
443.	25 c. Vaka ..	1·25	50

137. The Annunciation.

1973. Christmas. Scenes from a 15th-cent. Flemish " Book of Hours ". Multicoloured.

444.	1 c. Type **137**	10	10
445.	5 c. The Visitation ..	10	10
446.	10 c. Annunciation to the Shepherds	10	10
447.	20 c. Epiphany	15	10
448.	30 c. The Slaughter of the Innocents	20	15

138. Princess Anne.

1973. Royal Wedding. Multicoloured.

450.	25 c. Type **138**	20	10
451.	30 c. Capt. Mark Phillips	25	10
452.	50 c. Princess Anne and Capt. Phillips	30	15

139. Running.

1974. British Commonwealth Games, Christchurch. Multicoloured.

455.	1 c. Diving (vert.) ..	10	10
456.	3 c. Boxing (vert.) ..	10	10
457.	5 c. Type **139**	10	10
458.	10 c. Weightlifting ..	10	10
459.	30 c. Cycling	20	25

140. " Jesus carrying the Cross " (Raphael).

1974. Easter. Multicoloured.

461.	5 c. Type **140**	10	10
462.	10 c. " The Holy Trinity " (El Greco)	15	10
463.	30 c. " The Deposition of Christ " (Caravaggio) ..	25	20

141. Helmet Shell.

142. Queen Elizabeth II.

1974. Sea-shells. Multicoloured.

466.	½ c. Type **141**	30	10
467.	1 c. Vase Shell	30	10
468.	1½ c. Cockle Shell ..	30	10
469.	2 c. "Terebellum terebellum"	30	10
470.	3 c. Bat Volutes ..	45	10
471.	4 c. Conch Shell ..	50	10
472.	5 c. Triton Shell ..	50	10
473.	6 c. Snake-head (ovries) ..	50	45
474.	8 c. Helmet Shell (different)	60	10
475.	10 c. Auger Shell ..	60	10
476.	15 c. Mitre Shell ..	70	15
477.	20 c. Naticacid Shell ..	1·00	15
478.	25 c. Scallop Shell ..	1·00	30
479.	30 c. Soldier Cone Shell ..	1·00	20
480.	50 c. Cloth of Gold Cone Shell	6·00	2·50
481.	60 c. Olive Shell ..	6·00	2·50
482.	$1 Type **142**	2·50	3·00
483.	$2 Type **142**	2·50	2·25
484.	$4 Queen Elizabeth II and sea shells	3·50	4·50
485.	$6 As $4	11·00	7·00
486.	$8 As $4	11·00	8·00
487.	$10 As $4	12·00	9·00

Nos. 484/7 are larger, 60 × 39 mm.

MINIMUM PRICE

The minimum price quoted is 10p which represents a handling charge rather than a basis for valuing common stamps. For further notes about prices see introductory pages.

143. Footballer and Australasian Map.

1974. World Cup Football Championships, West Germany. Multicoloured.

488.	25 c. Type **143**	15	10
489.	50 c. Map and Munich Stadium	30	25
490.	$1 Footballer, stadium and World Cup	50	45

144. Obverse and Reverse of Commemorative $2.50 Silver Coin.

1974. Bicentenary of Capt. Cook's Second Voyage of Discovery.

492. **144.**	$2.50 silver, blk. & vio.	13·00	7·00
493. –	$7.50 silver, blk. & grn.	27·00	13·00

DESIGN: $7.50, As Type **144** but showing $7.50 coin.

145. Early Stamps of Cook Islands.

1974. Centenary of U.P.U. Multicoloured.

495.	10 c. Type **145**	15	15
496.	25 c. Old landing strip, Rarotonga, and stamp of 1898	30	40
497.	30 c. Post Office, Rarotonga, and stamp of 1920 ..	30	40
498.	50 c. U.P.U. emblem and stamps	40	65

146. "Madonna of the Goldfinch" (Raphael).

1974. Christmas. Multicoloured.

500.	1 c. Type **146**	10	10
501.	5 c. " The Sacred Family " (Andrea del Sarto) ..	10	10
502.	10 c. " The Virgin adoring the Child " (Correggio)	15	10
503.	20 c. " The Holy Family " (Rembrandt)	25	20
504.	30 c. " The Virgin and Child " (Rogier Van Der Weyden)	30	30

147. Churchill and Blenheim Palace.

1974. Birth Centenary of Sir Winston Churchill. Multicoloured.

506. 5 c. Type **147** 25 15
507. 10 c. Churchill and Houses of Parliament 40 15
508. 25 c. Churchill and Chartwell 80 30
509. 30 c. Churchill and Buckingham Palace 90 35
510. 50 c. Churchill and St. Paul's Cathedral .. .. 1·25 65

148. Vasco Nunez de Balboa and Discovery of Pacific Ocean (1513).

1975. Pacific Explorers. Multicoloured.

513. 1 c. Type **148** 10 10
514. 5 c. Fernando de Magallanes and map (1520) .. 35 20
515. 10 c. Juan Sebastian de Elcano and "Vitoria".. (1520) 60 20
516. 25 c. Friar Andres de Urdancta & ship (1564-67) 1·50 75
517. 30 c. Miguel Lopez de Legazpi and ship (1564-67) 1·60 80

149. "Apollo" Capsule.

1975. "Apollo-Soyuz" Space Project. Mult.

518. 25 c. Type **149** 30 15
519. 25 c. "Soyuz" capsule .. 30 15
520. 30 c. "Soyuz" crew .. 35 15
521. 30 c. "Apollo" crew .. 35 15
522. 50 c. Cosmonaut within "Soyuz" 40 25
523. 50 c. Astronauts within "Apollo" 40 25

These were issued in horiz. se-tenant pairs of each value, forming one composite design.

150. $100 Commemorative Gold Coin.

1975. Bicent. of Captain Cook's 2nd Voyage.

525. **150.** $2 brown, gold & vio. 6·50 2·75

151. Cook Island's Flag and Map.

1975. 10th Anniv. of Self-Government.

526. 5 c. Type **151** 20 10
527. 10 c. Premier Sir Albert Henry and flag (vert.).. 30 10
528. 25 c. Rarotonga and flag.. 70 30

152. "Madonna by the Fireside" (R. Campin).

1975. Christmas. Multicoloured.

529. 6 c. Type **152** 10 10
530. 10 c. "Madonna in the Meadow" (Raphael) .. 15 10
531. 15 c. "Madonna of the Oak" (atrib. Raphael) 20 10
532. 20 c. "Adoration of the Shepherds" (J. B. Maino) 25 15
533. 35 c. "The Annunciation" (Murillo) 30 20

153. "Entombment of Christ" (Raphael).

1976. Easter. Multicoloured.

536. 7 c. Type **153** 20 10
537. 15 c. "Pieta" (Veronese) 30 15
538. 35 c. "Pieta" (El Greco) 40 25

154. Benjamin Franklin and H.M.S. "Resolution".

1976. Bicent. of American Revolution. Mult.

541. $1 Type **154** .. .. 6·00 1·50
542. $2 Capt. Cook and H.M.S. "Resolution" .. .. 8·00 2·50

1976. Visit of Queen Elizabeth to U.S.A. Nos. 541/2 optd. **Royal Visit July 1976.**

544. **154.** $1 multicoloured .. 3·50 1·50
545. – $2 multicoloured .. 5·50 2·50

156. Hurdling.

1976. Olympic Games, Montreal. Mult.

547. 7 c. Type **156** 10 10
548. 7 c. Type **156** 10 10
549. 15 c. Hockey 15 15
550. 15 c. Hockey 15 15
551. 30 c. Fencing 25 15
552. 30 c. Fencing 25 15
553. 35 c. Football 30 20
554. 35 c. Football 30 20

157. "The Visitation".

1976. Christmas. Renaissance sculptures. Multicoloured.

556. 6 c. Type **157** 10 10
557. 10 c. "Adoration of the Shepherds" 10 10
558. 15 c. "Adoration of the Shepherds" (different) 15 10
559. 20 c. "The Epiphany" .. 20 20
560. 35 c. "The Holy Family" 25 25

158. Obverse and Reverse of $5 Mangaia Kingfisher Coin.

1976. National Wildlife and Conservation Day.

563. **158.** $1 multicoloured .. 3·50 1·25

159. Imperial State Crown.

1977. Silver Jubilee. Multicoloured.

564. 25 c. Type **159** 90 75
565. 25 c. The Queen with regalia 90 75
566. 50 c. Westminster Abbey 1·50 1·50
567. 50 c. Coronation coach .. 1·50 1·50
568. $1 The Queen and Prince Philip .. .. .. 3·50 3·25
569. $1 Royal Visit, 1974 .. 3·50 3·25

160. "Christ on the Cross".

1977. Easter. 400th Birth Anniv. of Rubens. Multicoloured.

571. 7 c. Type **160** 30 10
572. 15 c. "Christ on the Cross" 45 15
573. 35 c. "The Deposition of Christ" 80 30

161. "Virgin and Child" (Memling).

1977. Christmas. Multicoloured.

576. 6 c. Type **161** 10 10
577. 10 c. "Madonna and Child with Saints and Donors" (Memling) 10 10
578. 15 c. "Adoration of the Kings" (Geertgen) .. 20 10
579. 20 c. "Virgin and Child with Saints" (Crivelli) 25 15
580. 35 c. "Adoration of the Magi" (16th Cent. flemish school).. .. 30 20

162. Obverse and Reverse of $5 Cook Islands Swiftlet Coin.

1977. National Wildlife and Conservation Day.

583. **162.** $1 multicoloured .. 1·40 1·50

163. Captain Cook and H.M.S. "Resolution" (from paintings by N. Dance and H. Roberts).

1978. Bicentenary of Discovery of Hawaii Multicoloured.

584. 50 c. Type **163** .. .. 1·50 60
585. $1 Earl of Sandwich and Cook landing at Owhyhee (from paintings by Thomas Gainsborough and J. Cleveley) .. .. 2·00 1·00
586. $2 Obverse and reverse of $200 coin and Cook monument, Hawaii .. .. 3·25 1·75

164. "Pieta" (Van der Weyden).

1978. Easter. Paintings from the National Gallery, London. Multicoloured.

588. 15 c. Type **164** 30 15
589. 35 c. "The Entombment" (Michelangelo) 40 30
590. 75 c. "The Supper at Emmaus" (Caravaggio) 65 55

165. Queen Elizabeth II.

1978. 25th Anniv. of Coronation. Mult.

593. 50 c. Type **165** 30 30
594. 50 c. The Lion of England 30 30
595. 50 c. Imperial State Crown 30 30
596. 50 c. Statue of Tangaroa (god) 30 30
597. 70 c. Type **165** 35 35
598. 70 c. Sceptre with Cross.. 35 35
599. 70 c. St. Edward's Crown 35 35
600. 70 c. Rarotongan staff god 35 35

1978. Nos. 466, 468, 473/4 and 478/82 surch.

602. 5 c. on $1\frac{1}{2}$ c. "Corculum cardissa" 30 10
603. 7 c. on $\frac{1}{2}$ c. Type **141** .. 35 15
604. 10 c. on 6 c. "Cypraea caputserpentis" .. 40 15
605. 10 c. on 8 c. "Bursa granularis" 40 15
606. 15 c. on $\frac{1}{2}$ c. Type **141** .. 40 20
607. 15 c. on 25 c. "Gloripallium pallium".. .. 40 20
608. 15 c. on 30 c. "Conus miles" 40 20
609. 15 c. on 50 c. "Conus textile" 40 20
610. 15 c. on 60 c. "Oliva sericea" 40 20
611. 17 c. on $\frac{1}{2}$ c. Type **141** .. 50 25
612. 17 c. on 50 c. "Conus textile" 50 25

1978. 250th Birth Anniv. of Captain James Cook. Nos. 584/6 optd. **1728. 250th ANNIVERSARY OF COOK'S BIRTH. 1978.**

613. 50 c. Type **163** 1·50 75
614. $1 Earl of Sandwich and Cook landing at Owhyhee 2·00 1·00
615. $2, $200 commemorative coin and Cook monument, Hawaii 3·00 2·00

168. Obverse and Reverse of Pitcairn Warblers $5 Coin.

1978. National Wildlife and Conservation Day.

617. **168.** $1 multicoloured 2·00 1·00

169. " The Virgin and Child " (Van Der Weyden).

1978. Christmas. Paintings. Multicoloured.

618. 15 c. Type **169** 30 10
619. 17 c. " The Virgin and Child " (Crivelli) 30 15
620. 35 c. " The Virgin and Child " (Murillo) 45 30

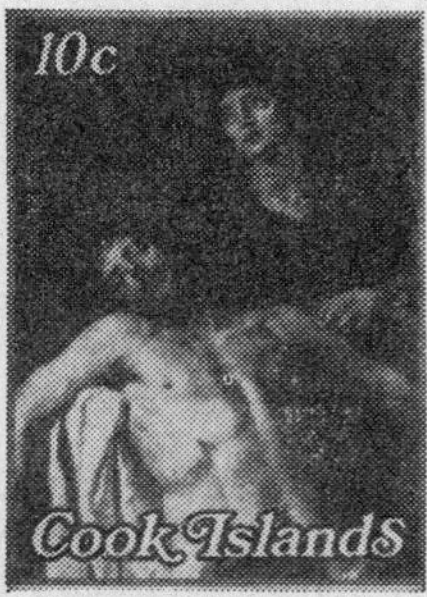

170. Virgin with Body of Christ.

1979. Easter. Details of Painting " Descent " by Gasper de Crayer. Multicoloured.

623. 10 c. Type **170** 15 10
624. 12 c. St. John 20 15
625. 15 c. Mary Magdalene 25 20
626. 20 c. Weeping angels 25 20

171. " Captain Cook " (James Weber).

1979. Death Bicent of Captain Cook. Mult.

628. 20 c. Type **171** 45 20
629. 30 c. H.M.S. "Resolution" 70 35
630. 35 c. H.M.S. "Endeavour" 80 45
631. 50 c. "Death of Captain Cook" (George Carter) 85 60

172. Post-Rider.

1979. Death Centenary of Sir Rowland Hill. Multicoloured.

633. 30 c. Type **172** 35 25
634. 30 c. Mail coach 35 25
635. 30 c. Automobile 35 25
636. 30 c. Railway train 35 25
637. 35 c. " Cap-Horniers " (sailing ship) 40 25
638. 35 c. River steamer 40 25
639. 35 c. " Deutschland " (liner) 40 25
640. 35 c. " United States " (liner) 40 25
641. 50 c. Balloon " Neptune " 50 30
642. 50 c. Junkers " F13 " (aeroplane) 50 30
643. 50 c. " Graf Zeppelin " 50 30
644. 50 c. " Concorde " 50 30

1979. Nos. 466, 468 and 481 **surch.**

646. 6 c. on ½ c. Type **141** 15 15
647. 10 c. on 1½ c. " Corculum cardissa " 20 20
648. 15 c. on 60 c. " Oliva sericea " 30 30

174. Brother and Sister.

1979. International Year of the Child. Multicoloured.

649. 30 c. Type **174** 25 25
650. 50 c. Boy with tree drum 40 40
651. 65 c. Children dancing 50 50

175. "Apollo 11" Emblem.

1979. 10th Anniv. of "Apollo 11" Moon Landing. Multicoloured.

653. 30 c. Type **175** 35 40
654. 50 c. " Apollo 11 " crew 45 60
655. 60 c. Neil Armstrong on the Moon 55 70
656. 65 c. Splashdown recovery 60 75

176. Obverse and reverse of $5 Rarotongan Fruit Dove Coin.

1979. National Wildlife and Conservation Day.

658. **176.** $1 multicoloured 2·75 2·25

177. Glass Christmas Tree Ornaments.

1979. Christmas. Multicoloured.

659. 6 c. Type **177** (postage) 10 10
660. 10 c. Hibiscus and star 10 10
661. 12 c. Poinsettia, bells and candle 10 10
662. 15 c. Poinsettia leaves and Tiki (god) 15 15
663. 20 c. Type **177** (air) 15 15
664. 25 c. As No. 660 20 20
665. 30 c. As No. 661 25 25
666. 35 c. As No. 662 30 30

1980. Christmas. As Nos. 659/66 but with charity premium.

667. 6 c.+2 c. Type **177** (postage) 10 10
668. 10 c.+2 c. Hibiscus and star 15 15
669. 12 c.+2 c. Flower, bells and candle 15 20
670. 15 c.+2 c. Flowers and carving 15 20
671. 20 c.+4 c. Type **177** (air) 15 25
672. 25 c.+4 c. As No. 660 15 25
673. 30 c.+4 c. As No. 661 20 30
674. 35 c.+4 c. As No. 662 25 35

178. " Flagellation ".

1980. Easter. Illustrations by Gustav Dore. Each gold and brown.

675. 20 c. Type **178** 15 20
676. 20 c. " Crown of Thorns " 15 20
677. 30 c. " Jesus Insulted " 25 30
678. 30 c. " Jesus Falls " 25 30
679. 35 c. " The Crucifixion " 25 30
680. 35 c. " The Descent from the Cross " 25 30

179. Dove with Olive Twig.

1980. 75th Anniv. of Rotary International. Multicoloured.

683. 30 c. Type **179** 35 35
684. 35 c. Hibiscus flower 40 40
685. 50 c. Ribbons 50 50

1980. " Zeapex 80 " International Stamp Exhibition, Auckland. Nos. 633/44 optd. **ZEAPEX STAMP EXHIBITION — AUCKLAND 1980** and New Zealand 1865 1s. Stamp.

687. 30 c. Type **172** 30 30
688. 30 c. Mail coach 30 30
689. 30 c. Automobile 30 30
690. 30 c. Railway train 30 30
691. 35 c. " Cap-Horniers " (sailing ship) 35 35
692. 35 c. River steamer 35 35
693. 35 c. " Deutschland " (liner) 35 35
694. 35 c. " United States " (liner) 35 35
695. 50 c. Balloon " Neptune " 65 45
696. 50 c. Junkers " F13 " (aeroplane) 65 45
697. 50 c. " Graf Zeppelin " 65 45
698. 50 c. " Concorde " 65 45

181. Queen Elizabeth the Queen Mother.

1980. 80th Birthday of The Queen Mother.

701. **181.** 50 c. multicoloured 1·40 90

182. Satellites orbiting Moon.

1980. 350th Death Anniv. of Johannes Kepler (astronomer) and 75th Death Anniv. of Jules Verne (writer). Multicoloured.

703. 12 c. Type **182** 50 35
704. 12 c. " Apollo " orbiting Moon 50 35
708. 20 c. } Jules Verne and dif- 45 35
709. 20 c. } ferent scenes from 45 35
710. 30 c. } " From the Earth 55 45
711. 30 c. } to the Moon " (vert.) 55 45
705. 50 c. Space station 1·00 80
706. 50 c. Astronaut on Moon 1·00 80

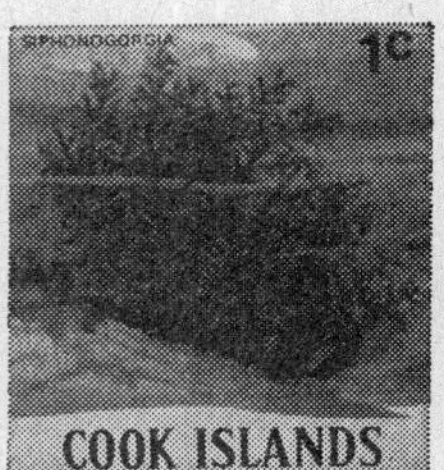

184. " Siphonogorgia ".

1980. Corals (1st series). Multicoloured.

713. 1 c. Type **184** 20 10
714. 1 c. " Pavona praetorta " 20 10
715. 1 c. " Stylaster echinatus " 20 10
716. 1 c. " Tubastraea " 20 10
717. 3 c. " Millepora alcicornis " 25 10
718. 3 c. "Junceella gemmacea " 25 10
719. 3 c. " Fungia fungites " 25 10
720. 3 c. "Heliofungia actiniformis" 25 10
721. 4 c. " Distichopora violacea" 25 10
722. 4 c. " Stylaster " 25 10
723. 4 c. " Gonipora " 25 10
724. 4 c. " Caulastraea echinuata" 25 10
725. 5 c. " Ptilosarcus gurneyi " 25 15
726. 5 c. " Stylophora pistillata " 25 15
727. 5 c. " Melithaea squamata " 25 15
728. 5 c. " Porites andrewsi " 25 15
729. 6 c. "Lobophyllia bemprichii" 25 15
730. 6 c. "Palauastrea ramosa" 25 15
731. 6 c. " Bellonella indica " 25 15
732. 6 c. " Pectinia alcicornis" 25 15
733. 8 c. "Sarcophyton digitatum " 25 15
734. 8 c. " Melithaea albitincta " 25 15
735. 8 c. " Plerogyra sinuosa " 25 15
736. 8 c. " Dendrophyllia gracilis " 25 15
737. 10 c. As Type **184** 30 15
738. 10 c. As No. 714 30 15
739. 10 c. As No. 715 30 15
740. 10 c. As No. 716 30 15
741. 12 c. As No. 717 30 15
742. 12 c. As No. 718 30 15
743. 12 c. As No. 719 30 15
744. 12 c. As No. 720 30 15
745. 15 c. As No. 721 30 20
746. 15 c. As No. 722 30 20
747. 15 c. As No. 723 30 20
748. 15 c. As No. 724 30 20
749. 20 c. As No. 725 35 30
750. 20 c. As No. 726 35 30
751. 20 c. As No. 727 35 30
752. 20 c. As No. 728 35 30
753. 25 c. As No. 729 35 30
754. 25 c. As No. 730 35 30
755. 25 c. As No. 731 35 30
756. 25 c. As No. 732 35 30
757. 30 c. As No. 733 40 30
758. 30 c. As No. 734 40 30
759. 30 c. As No. 735 40 30
760. 30 c. As No. 736 40 30
761. 35 c. Type **184** 45 35
762. 35 c. As No. 714 45 35
763. 35 c. As No. 715 45 35
764. 35 c. As No. 716 45 35
765. 50 c. As No. 717 65 55
766. 50 c. As No. 718 65 55
767. 50 c. As No. 719 65 55
768. 50 c. As No. 720 65 55
769. 60 c. As No. 721 75 65
770. 60 c. As No. 722 75 65
771. 60 c. As No. 723 75 65
772. 60 c. As No. 724 75 65
773. 70 c. As No. 725 1·25 75
774. 70 c. As No. 726 1·25 75
775. 70 c. As No. 727 1·25 75
776. 70 c. As No. 728 1·25 75
777. 80 c. As No. 729 1·25 80
778. 80 c. As No. 730 1·25 80
779. 80 c. As No. 731 1·25 80
780. 80 c. As No. 732 1·25 80
781. $1 As No. 733 2·00 1·00
782. $1 As No. 734 2·00 1·00
783. $1 As No. 735 2·00 1·00
784. $1 As No. 736 2·00 1·00
785. $2 As No. 723 7·50 3·50
786. $3 As No. 720 8·50 4·50
787. $4 As No. 726 4·50 6·50
788. $6 As No. 715 6·00 8·50
789. $10 As No. 734 18·00 20·00

Nos. 761/74 are 30 × 40 mm., and Nos. 785/9, which include a portrait of Queen Elizabeth II in each design, are 55 × 35 mm.

See also Nos. 966/992.

185. Annunciation.

1980. Christmas. Scenes from 13th-century French Prayerbook. Multicoloured.

801.	15 c. Type **185**	20	15
802.	30 c. The Visitation	30	25
803.	40 c. The Nativity	40	30
804.	50 c. The Epiphany	50	40

186. " The Crucifixion " (from book of Saint-Amand).

1981. Easter. Illustrations from 12th-century French Prayer Books. Multicoloured.

807.	15 c. Type **186**	20	20
808.	25 c. " Placing in Tomb " (from book of Ingeburge)	30	30
809.	40 c. " Mourning at the Sepulchre " (from book of Ingeburge)	40	40

187. Prince Charles.

1981. Royal Wedding. Multicoloured.

812.	$1 Type **187**	1·50	1·50
813.	$2 Prince Charles and Lady Diana Spencer	2·75	2·75

188. Footballers.

1981. World Cup Football Championship, Spain (1982). Designs showing footballers. Multicoloured.

815.	20 c. Type **188**	30	20
816.	20 c. Figures to right of stamps	30	20
817.	30 c. Figures to left	40	30
818.	30 c. Figures to right	40	30
819.	35 c. Figures to left	40	35
820.	35 c. Figures to right	40	35
821.	50 c. Figures to left	50	45
822.	50 c. Figures to right	50	45

The two designs of each value were printed together, se-tenant, in horizontal pairs throughout the sheet, forming composite designs.

1981. International Year for Disabled Persons. Nos. 812/13 surch **+5 c.**

824.	$1+5 c. Type **187**	2·50	2·50
825.	$2+5 c. Prince Charles and Lady Diana Spencer	4·50	5·00

190. " Holy Virgin with Child ".

1982. Christmas. Details of Paintings by Rubens. Multicoloured.

827.	8 c. Type **190**	40	10
828.	15 c. " Coronation of St. Catherine "	45	20
829.	40 c. " Adoration of the Shepherds "	65	50
830.	50 c. " Adoration of the Magi "	75	60

191. Princess of Wales (inscr. " 21st Birthday ").

1982. 21st Birthday of Princess of Wales. Multicoloured.

833.	$1.25 Type **191**	1·25	1·25
834.	$1.25 As Type **191**, but inscr. " 1 July 1982 "	1·25	1·25
835.	$2.50 Princess (inscr. " 21st Birthday ") (different)	1·75	1·75
836.	$2.50 As No. 835, but inscr. " 1 July 1982 "	1·75	1·75

1982. Birth of Prince William of Wales (1st issue). Nos. 812/13 optd.

838.	$1 Type **187**	3·50	2·25
839.	$1 Type **187**	3·50	2·25
840.	$2 Prince Charles and Lady Diana Spencer	6·00	5·00
841.	$2 Prince Charles and Lady Diana Spencer	6·00	5·00

OPTS: Nos. 838 and 840, **" ROYAL BIRTH 21 JUNE 1982 "**. Nos. 839 and 841, **" PRINCE WILLIAM OF WALES "**.

1982. Birth of Prince William of Wales (2nd issue). As Nos. 833/6 but with changed inscriptions. Multicoloured.

843.	$1.25 As Type **191**, inscr. " Royal Birth "	1·25	1·25
844.	$1.25 As Type **191**, inscr. " 21 June 1982 "	1·25	1·25
845.	$2.50 As No. 835, inscr. " Royal Birth "	1·75	1·75
846.	$2.50 As No. 835, inscr. " 21 June 1982 "	1·75	1·75

193. " Serenade ".

1982. Norman Rockwell (painter) Commem. Multicoloured.

848.	5 c. Type **193**	25	10
849.	10 c. " The Hikers "	25	15
850.	20 c. " The Doctor and the Doll "	40	25
851.	30 c. " Home from Camp "	50	30

194. Franklin D. Roosevelt.

1982. Air. American Anniversaries. Mult.

852.	60 c. Type **194**	1·25	70
853.	80 c. Benjamin Franklin	1·50	80
854.	$1·40 George Washington	1·75	1·25

ANNIVERSARIES: 60 c. Roosevelt birth centenary. 80 c. "Articles of Peace" negotiations bicentenary. $1.40, Washington 250th birth anniv.

195. " Virgin with Garlands " (detail Rubens) and Princess Diana with Prince William.

1982. Christmas.

856.	**195.**	35 c. multicoloured	70	40
857.	–	48 c. multicoloured	90	60
858.	–	60 c. multicoloured	1·10	75
859.	–	$1.70 multicoloured	1·75	1·60

DESIGNS: 48 c. to $1.70, Different details from Ruben's painting " Virgin with Garlands ".

197. Statue of Tangaroa.

1983. Commonwealth Day. Multicoloured.

862.	60 c. Type **197**	55	60
863.	60 c. Rarotonga oranges	55	60
864.	60 c. Rarotonga airport	55	60
865.	60 c. Prime Minister Sir Thomas Davis	55	60

198. Scouts using Map and Compass.

1983. 75th Anniv. of Boy Scout Movement and 125th Birth Anniv. of Lord Baden-Powell (founder). Multicoloured.

866.	12 c. Type **198**	50	20
867.	12 c. Hiking	50	20
868.	36 c. Campfire cooking	80	40
869.	36 c. Erecting tent	80	40
870.	48 c. Hauling on rope	95	55
871.	48 c. Using bos'n's chair	95	55
872.	60 c. Digging hole for sapling	1·00	70
873.	60 c. Planting sapling	1·00	70

1983. 15th World Scout Jamboree, Alberta, Canada. Nos. 866/73 optd **XV WORLD JAMBOREE** (Nos. 875, 877, 879, 881) or optd **" ALBERTA, CANADA 1983 "** (others).

875.	12 c. Type **198**	20	20
876.	12 c. Hiking	20	20
877.	36 c. Campfire cooking	40	40
878.	36 c. Erecting tent	40	40
879.	48 c. Hauling on rope	55	55
880.	48 c. Using bos'n's chair	55	55
881.	60 c. Digging hole for sapling	70	70
882.	60 c. Planting sapling	70	70

1983. Various stamps surch.

884	–	18 c. on 8 c. mult (No. 733)	40	40
885	–	18 c. on 8 c. mult (No. 734)	40	40
886	–	18 c. on 8 c. mult (No. 735)	40	40
887	–	18 c. on 8 c. mult (No. 736)	40	40
888	–	36 c. on 15 c. mult (No. 745)	70	70
889	–	36 c. on 15 c. mult (No. 746)	70	70
890	–	36 c. on 15 c. mult (No. 747)	70	70
891	–	36 c. on 15 c. mult (No. 748)	70	70
892	–	36 c. on 30 c. mult (No. 757)	70	70
893	–	36 c. on 30 c. mult (No. 758)	70	70
894	–	36 c. on 30 c. mult (No. 759)	70	70
895	–	36 c. on 30 c. mult (No. 760)	70	70
896	184	36 c. on 35 c. mult	70	70
897	–	36 c. on 35 c. mult (No. 762)	70	70
898	–	36 c. on 35 c. mult (No. 763)	70	70
899	–	36 c. on 35 c. mult (No. 764)	70	70
900	–	48 c. on 25 c. mult (No. 753)	90	90
901	–	48 c. on 25 c. mult (No. 754)	90	90
902	–	48 c. on 25 c. mult (No. 755)	90	90
903	–	48 c. on 25 c. mult (No. 756)	90	90
904	–	72 c. on 70 c. mult (No. 773)	1·25	1·25
905	–	72 c. on 70 c. mult (No. 774)	1·25	1·25
906	–	72 c. on 70 c. mult (No. 775)	1·25	1·25
907	–	72 c. on 70 c. mult (No. 776)	1·25	1·25
908	–	96 c. on $1.40 mult (No. 854)	1·50	1·50
909	–	96 c. on $2 mult (No. 813)	8·50	5·50
910	–	96 c. on $2.50 mult (No. 835)	3·00	3·00
911	–	96 c. on $2.50 mult (No. 836)	3·00	3·00
912	–	$5.60 on $6 mult (No. 788)	15·00	13·00
913	–	$5.60 on $10 mult (No. 789)	15·00	13·00

202. Union Flag.

1983. Cook Islands Flags and Ensigns. Mult.

914.	6 c. Type **202** (postage)	15	10
915.	6 c. Group Federal flag	15	10
916.	12 c. Rarotonga ensign	15	10
917.	12 c. Flag of New Zealand	15	10
918.	15 c. Cook Islands' flag (1973–79)	20	15
919.	15 c. Cook Islands' National flag	20	15
920.	20 c. Type **202** (air)	30	25
921.	20 c. Group Federal flag	30	25
922.	30 c. Rarotonga ensign	40	30
923.	30 c. Flag of New Zealand	40	30
924.	35 c. Cook Islands' flag	45	35
925.	35 c. Cook Islands' National flag	45	35

203. Dish Aerial, Satellite Earth Station.

1983. World Communications Year.

927.	36 c. multicoloured	30	35
928.	48 c. multicoloured	45	45
929.	60 c. multicoloured	55	60
930.	96 c. multicoloured	85	90

DESIGNS: 48 to 96 c. Various satellites.

204. " La Belle Jardiniere ".

1983. Christmas. 500th Birth Anniv. of Raphael. Multicoloured.

No.	Description	Unused	Used
932.	12 c. Type **204**	20	20
933.	18 c. "Madonna and Child with five Saints" ..	40	40
934.	36 c. "Madonna and Child with St. John" ..	65	65
935.	48 c. "Madonna of the Fish"	75	75
936.	60 c. "Madonna of the Baldacchino" ..	95	95

205. Montgolfier Balloon, 1783.

1984. Bicentenary (1983) of Manned Flight. Multicoloured.

No.	Description	Unused	Used
939.	36 c. Type **205**	30	35
940.	48 c. Ascent of Adorne, Strasbourg 1784 ..	40	45
941.	60 c. Balloon driven by sails, 1785	55	60
942.	72 c. Ascent of man on horse, 1798	70	75
943.	96 c. Aerial acrobatics of Godard, 1850	85	90

206. Cuvier's Beaked Whale.

1984. Save the Whale. Multicoloured.

No.	Description	Unused	Used
946.	10 c. Type **206**	45	45
947.	18 c. Risso's Dolphin ..	65	65
948.	20 c. True's Beaked Whale	65	65
949.	24 c. Long Finned Pilot Whale	70	70
950.	30 c. Narwhal	80	80
951.	36 c. White Whale ..	95	95
952.	42 c. Common Dolphin ..	1·25	1·25
953.	48 c. Commerson's Dolphin	1·40	1·40
954.	60 c. Bottle-Nosed Dolphin	1·60	1·60
955.	72 c. Sowerby's Beaked Whale	1·75	1·75
956.	96 c. Common Porpoise ..	2·00	2·00
957.	$2 Boutu	2·75	2·75

207. Athens, 1896.

1984. Olympic Games, Los Angeles. Mult.

No.	Description	Unused	Used
958.	18 c. Type **207**	15	20
959.	24 c. Paris, 1900	20	25
960.	36 c. St. Louis, 1904 ..	30	35
961.	48 c. London, 1948 ..	40	45
962.	60 c. Tokyo, 1964 ..	45	50
963.	72 c. Berlin, 1936	55	60
964.	96 c. Rome, 1960	75	80
965.	$1.20 Los Angeles, 1930 ..	90	95

INDEX

Countries can be quickly located by referring to the index at the end of this volume.

208. "Siphonogorgia".

1984. Corals (2nd series). Multicoloured.

No.	Description	Unused	Used
966.	1 c. Type **208**	10	10
967.	2 c. "Millepora alcicornis"	10	10
968.	3 c. "Distichopora violacea"	10	10
969.	5 c. "Ptilosarcus gurneyi"	10	10
970.	10 c. "Lobophyllia bemprichii"	10	10
971.	12 c. "Sarcophyton digitatum"	10	10
972.	14 c. "Pavona praetorta"	10	10
973.	18 c. "Junceella gemmacea"	10	15
974.	20 c. "Stylaster"	10	15
975.	24 c. "Stylophora pistillata"	15	20
976.	30 c. "Palauaster ramosa"	20	25
977.	36 c. "Melithaea albitincta"	25	30
978.	40 c. "Stylaster echinatus"	25	30
979.	42 c. "Fungia fungites" ..	30	35
980.	48 c. "Gonipora"	30	35
981.	50 c. "Melithaea squamata"	35	40
982.	52 c. "Bellonella indica" ..	35	40
983.	55 c. "Plerogyra sinuosa"	35	40
984.	60 c. "Tubastraea" ..	40	45
985.	70 c. "Heliofungia actiniformis"	45	50
986.	85 c. "Caulastraea echinulata"	55	60
987.	96 c. "Porites andrewsi" ..	65	70
988.	$1.10 "Pectinia alcicornis"	75	80
989.	$1.20 "Dendrophyllia gracilis"	80	85
990.	$3.60 on $2 "Gonipora" (55 × 35 mm)	2·40	2·50
991.	$4.20 on $3 "Heliofungia actiniformis" (55 × 35 mm)	2·75	3·00
992.	$5 on $4 "Stylophora pistillata" (55 × 35 mm)	3·25	3·50
993.	$7.20 on $6 "Stylaster echinatus" (55 × 35 mm)	4·75	5·00
994.	$9.60 on $10 "Melithaea albitincta" (55 × 35 mm)	6·25	6·50

1984. Olympic Gold Medal Winners. Nos. 963/5 optd.

No.	Description	Unused	Used
995.	72 c. Berlin, 1936 (optd. **Equestrian Team Dressage Germany**)	60	65
996.	96 c. Rome, 1960 (optd. **Decathlon Daley Thompson Great Britain**) ..	80	85
997.	$1.20 Los Angeles, 1930 (optd. **Equestrian Team Dressage Germany**) ..	1·00	1·10

211. Capt. Cook's Cottage, Melbourne.

1984. "Ausipex" International Stamp Exhibition, Melbourne. Multicoloured.

No.	Description	Unused	Used
998.	36 c. Type **211**	90	90
999.	48 c. "H.M.S. 'Endeavour' careened for Repairs" (Sydney Parkinson) ..	1·40	1·40
1000.	60 c. "Cook's landing at Botany Bay" (E. Phillips Fox)	2·00	2·00
1001.	$2 "Capt. James Cook" (John Webber)	3·25	3·25

1984. Birth of Prince Henry. Nos. 812 and 833/6 variously optd. or surch also (No. 1007).

No.	Description	Unused	Used
1003.	$1.25 Optd. **Commemorating-15 Sept. 1984** (No. 833)	1·75	1·10
1004.	$1.25 Optd. **Birth H.R.H. Prince Henry** (No. 834)	1·75	1·10
1005.	$2.50 Optd. **Commemorating-15 Sept. 1984** (No. 835)	3·00	2·00
1006.	$2.50 Optd. **Birth H.R.H. Prince Henry** (No. 836)	3·00	2·00
1007.	$3 on $1 Optd. **Royal Birth Prince Henry 15 Sept. 1984** (No. 812)	6·00	4·00

213. "Virgin on Throne with Child" (Giovanni Bellini)

1984. Christmas. Multicoloured

No.	Description	Unused	Used
1008.	36 c. Type **213**	35	35
1009.	48 c. "Virgin and Child" (anonymous, 15th century)	45	45
1010.	60 c. "Virgin and Child with Saints" (Alvise Vivarini)	50	50
1011.	96 c. "Virgin and Child with Angels" (H. Memling)	80	80
1012.	$1.20 "Adoration of Magi" (G. Tiepolo)	95	95

214. Downy Woodpecker.

1985. Birth Bicentenary of John J. Audubon (ornithologist). Designs showing original paintings. Multicoloured.

No.	Description	Unused	Used
1015.	30 c. Type **214**	1·00	60
1016.	55 c. Black-throated Blue Warbler	1·40	1·00
1017.	65 c. Yellow-throated Warbler	1·50	1·25
1018.	75 c. Chestnut-sided Warbler	1·60	1·50
1019.	95 c. Dickcissel	1·75	1·60
1020.	$1.15 White-crowned Sparrow	1·90	1·75

215. "The Kingston Flyer" (New Zealand).

1985. Famous Trains. Multicoloured.

No.	Description	Unused	Used
1022.	20 c. Type **215**	85	50
1023.	55 c. Class "640" (Italy)	1·25	85
1024.	65 c. "Gotthard" type (Switzerland)	1·50	90
1025.	75 c. Union Pacific No. 6900 (U.S.A.)	1·75	1·10
1026.	95 c. "Super Continental" type (Canada) ..	2·00	1·25
1027.	$1.15 "TGV" type (France)	2·25	1·50
1028.	$2.20 "The Flying Scotsman" (Great Britain)	3·25	2·50
1029.	$3.40 "The Orient Express"	3·50	3·75

216. "Helena Fourment". (Peter Paul Rubens)

1985. International Youth Year. Mult.

No.	Description	Unused	Used
1030.	55 c. Type **216**	85	85
1031.	65 c. "Vigee-Lebrun and Daughter" (E. Vigee-Lebrun)	1·10	1·10
1032.	75 c. "On the Terrace" (Renoir)	1·25	1·25
1033.	$1.30 "Young Mother Sewing" (M. Cassatt)	1·75	1·75

217. "Lady Elizabeth, 1908". (Mabel Hankey)

1985. Life and Times of Queen Elizabeth the Queen Mother. Designs showing paintings. Multicoloured.

No.	Description	Unused	Used
1035.	65 c. Type **217**	50	55
1036.	75 c. "Duchess of York, 1923" (Savely Sorine)	60	65
1037.	$1.15 "Duchess of York, 1925" (Philip de Laszlo)	90	95
1038.	$2.80 "Queen Elizabeth, 1938" (Sir Gerald Kelly)	2·10	2·25

218 Albert Henry (Prime Minister, 1965–78).

1985. 20th Anniv. of Self-Government. Multicoloured.

No.	Description	Unused	Used
1040.	30 c. Type **218**	35	30
1041.	50 c. Sir Thomas Davis (Prime Minister, 1978–Apr. 1983 and from Nov. 1983)	55	45
1042.	65 c. Geoffrey Henry (Prime Minister, Apr.–Nov. 1983)	65	55

219. Golf.

1985. South Pacific Mini Games, Rarotonga. Multicoloured.

1044. 55 c. Type **219** .. .. 2·00 2·00
1045. 65 c. Rugby .. .. 2·25 2·25
1046. 75 c. Tennis .. .. 2·50 2·50

220. Sea Horse, Gearwheel and Leaves.

1985. Pacific Conferences, Rarotonga.

1048. **220.** 55 c. blk., gold & red 45 50
1049. 65 c. blk., gold & vio. 50 55
1050. 75 c. blk., gold & grn. 60 65

No. 1048 shows the South Pacific Bureau for Economic Co-operation logo and is inscribed "S.P.E.C. Meeting, 30 July–1 Aug 1985, Rarotonga". No. 1049 also shows the S.P.E.C. logo, but is inscribed "South Pacific Forum, 4–6 Aug 1985, Rarotonga". No. 1050 shows the Pacific Islands Conference logo and the inscription "Pacific Islands Conference, 7–10 Aug 1985, Rarotonga".

221. "Madonna of the Magnificat".

1985. Christmas. Virgin and Child Paintings by Botticelli. Multicoloured.

1052. 55 c. Type **221** 80 60
1053. 65 c. "Madonna with Pomegranate" .. 85 65
1054. 75 c. "Madonna and Child with Six Angels" 1·00 75
1055. 95 c. "Madonna and Child with St. John" 1·40 95

222. "The Eve of the Deluge" (John Martin).

1986. Appearance of Halley's Comet. Paintings. Multicoloured.

1058. 55 c. Type **222** .. .. 1·00 1·00
1059. 65 c. "Lot and his Daughters" (Lucas van Leyden) .. .. 1·10 1·10
1060. 75 c. "Auspicious Comet" (from treatise c 1857) .. .. .. 1·25 1·25
1061. $1.25 "Events following Charles I" (Herman Saftleven) .. .. 2·00 2·00
1062. $2 "Ossian receiving Napoleonic Officers" (Anne Louis Girodet-Trioson) .. .. 2·75 2·75

223. Queen Elizabeth II.

1986. 60th Birthday of Queen Elizabeth II. Designs showing formal portraits.

1065. **223.** 95 c. multicoloured .. 1·25 1·25
1066. – $1.25 multicoloured 1·50 1·50
1067. – $1.50 multicoloured 1·75 1·75

224. U.S.A. 1847 Franklin 5. c. Stamp and H.M.S. "Resolution" at Rarotonga.

1986. "Ameripex '86" International Exhibition, Chicago. Multicoloured.

1069. $1 Type **224** .. .. 2·25 2·25
1070. $1.50 Chicago .. .. 2·75 2·75
1071. $2 1975 definitive $2, Benjamin Franklin and H.M.S. "Resolution" .. .. .. 3·25 3·25

225. Head of Statue of Liberty.

1986. Centenary of Statue of Liberty. Multicoloured.

1072. $1 Type **225** 75 75
1073. $1.25 Hand and torch of Statue 90 90
1074. $2.75 Statue of Liberty 2·00 2·00

226. Miss Sarah Ferguson.

1986. Royal Wedding. Multicoloured.

1075. $1 Type **226** .. .. 1·00 1·00
1076. $2 Prince Andrew .. .. 1·75 1·75
1077. $3 Prince Andrew and Miss Sarah Ferguson (57 × 31 mm.) .. .. 2·50 2·50

228. "Holy Family with St. John the Baptist and St. Elizabeth".

1986. Christmas. Paintings by Rubens. Multicoloured.

1080. 55 c. Type **228** 50 50
1081. $1.30 "Virgin with the Garland" .. .. 1·25 1·25
1082. $2.75 "Adoration of the Magi" (detail).. 2·50 2·50

1986. Visit of Pope John Paul II to South Pacific. Nos. 1080/2 surch. **FIRST PAPAL VISIT TO SOUTH PACIFIC POPE JOHN PAUL II NOV 21–24 1986.**

1085 55 c. + 10 c. Type **228** .. 1·25 1·25
1086 $1.30 + 10 c. "Virgin with the Garland" .. 1·75 1·75
1087 $2.75 + 10 c. "Adoration of the Magi" (detail) .. 3·00 3·00

1987. Various stamps surch.

(a) On Nos. 741/56, 761/76, and 787/8

1090. 10 c. on 15 c. "Distichopora violacea" .. 10 10
1091. 10 c. on 15 c. "Stylaster" 10 10
1092. 10 c. on 15 c. "Gonipora" 10 10
1093. 10 c. on 15 c. "Caulastraea echinulata" .. 10 10
1094. 10 c. on 25 c. "Lobophyllia bemprichii" .. 10 10
1095. 10 c. on 25 c. "Palauastrea ramosa" .. 10 10
1096. 10 c. on 25 c. "Bellonella indica" 10 10
1097. 10 c. on 25 c. "Pectinia alcicornis" 10 10
1098. 18 c. on 12 c. "Millepora alcicornis" 15 15
1099. 18 c. on 12 c. "Junceella gemmacea" .. 15 15
1100. 18 c. on 12 c. "Fungia fungites" 15 15
1101. 18 c. on 12 c. "Heliofungia actiniformis" .. 15 15
1102. 18 c. on 20 c. "Ptilosarcus qurneyi" .. 15 15
1103. 18 c. on 20 c. "Stylophora pistillata" .. 15 15
1104. 18 c. on 20 c. "Melithaea squamata" 15 15
1105. 18 c. on 20 c. "Porites andrewsi" 15 15
1106. 55 c. on 35 c. Type **184** .. 40 45
1107. 55 c. on 35 c. "Pavona praetorta" 40 45
1108. 55 c. on 35 c. "Stylaster echinatus" 40 45
1109. 55 c. on 35 c. "Tubastraea" 40 45
1110. 65 c. on 50 c. As No. 1098 45 50
1111. 65 c. on 50 c. As No. 1099 45 50
1112. 65 c. on 50 c. As No. 1100 45 50
1113. 65 c. on 50 c. As No. 1101 45 50
1114. 65 c. on 60 c. As No. 1090 45 50
1115. 65 c. on 60 c. As No. 1091 45 50
1116. 65 c. on 60 c. As No. 1092 45 50
1117. 65 c. on 60 c. As No. 1093 45 50
1118. 75 c. on 70 c. As No. 1102 55 60
1119. 75 c. on 70 c. As No. 1103 55 60
1120. 75 c. on 70 c. As No. 1104 55 60
1121. 75 c. on 70 c. As No. 1105 55 60
1122. $6.40 on $4 "Stylophora pistillata" .. .. 4·50 4·75
1123. $7.20 on $6 "Stylaster echinatus" .. .. 5·00 5·25

(b) On Nos. 812/13.

1124. $9.40 on $1 Type **187** .. 15·00 16·00
1125. $9.40 on $2 Prince Charles and Lady Diana Spencer .. 15·00 16·00

(c) On Nos. 835/6.

1126. $9.40 on $2.50 Princess of Wales (inscr. "21st Birthday") .. .. 15·00 16·00
1127. $9.40 on $2.50 As No. 1126, but inscr. "1 July 1982" .. .. .. 15·00 16·00

(d) On Nos. 966/8, 971/2, 975, 979/80, 982 and 987/9.

1128. 5 c. on 1 c. Type **208** .. 10 10
1129. 5 c. on 2 c. "Millepora alcicornis" 10 10
1130. 5 c. on 3 c. "Distichopora violacea" 10 10
1131. 5 c. on 12 c. "Sarcophyton digitatum" .. 10 10
1132. 5 c on 14 c. "Pavona praetorta" 10 10
1133. 18 c. on 24 c. "Stylophora pistillata" .. 15 15
1134. 55 c. on 52 c. "Bellonella indica" 40 45
1135. 65 c. on 42 c. "Fungia fungites" 45 50
1136. 75 c. on 48 c. "Gonipora" 55 60
1137. 95 c. on 96 c. "Porites andrewsi" 70 75
1138. 95 c. on $1.10 "Pectinia alcicornis" 70 75
1139. 95 c. on $1.20 "Dendrophyllia gracilis" .. 70 75

(e) On Nos. 998/1001.

1140. $1.30 on 36 c. Type **211** 1·40 1·50
1141. $1.30 on 48 c. "The 'Endeavour' careened for Repairs" (Sydney Parkinson) .. .. 1·40 1·50
1142. $1.30 on 60 c. "Cook's landing at Botany Bay" (E. Phillips Fox) 1·40 1·50
1143. $1.30 on $2 "Capt. James Cook" (John Webber) 1·40 1·50

(f) On Nos. 1065/7.

1144. **223.** $2.30 on 95 c. mult. 7·00 7·50
1145. – $2.80 on $1.25 mult. 7·00 7·50
1146. – $2.80 on $1.50 mult. 7·00 7·50

(g) On Nos. 1075/7.

1147. $2.80 on $1 Type **226** .. 6·00 6·50
1148. $2.80 on $2 Prince Andrew .. .. 6·00 6·50
1149. $2.80 on $3 Prince Andrew and Miss Sarah Ferguson (57 × 31 mm.) .. .. 6·00 6·50

1987. Various stamps surch.

1150. $2.80 on $2 "Gonipora" (No. 785) .. .. 2·10 2·25
1151. $5 on $3 "Heliofungia actiniformis" (No. 786) 4·00 4·25
1152. $9.40 on $10 "Melithaea albitincta" (No. 789) .. 7·50 7·75
1153. $9.40 on $1 Type **187** (No. 838) .. 7·50 7·75
1154. $9.40 on $1 Type **187** (No. 839) .. 7·50 7·75
1155. $9.40 on $2 Prince Charles and Lady Diana Spencer (No. 840) .. .. .. 7·50 7·75
1156. $9.40 on $2 Prince Charles and Lady Diana Spencer (No. 841) .. .. 7·50 7·75

1987. Hurricane Relief. Various stamps surch. **HURRICANE RELIEF + 50c.**

(a) On Nos. 1035/8.

1158. 65 c. + 50 c. Type **217** .. 80 85
1159. 75 c. + 50 c. "Duchess of York, 1923" (Savely Sorine) 85 90
1160. $1.15 + 50 c. "Duchess of York, 1925" (Philip de Laszlo) .. .. 1·10 1·25
1161. $2.80 + 50 c. "Queen Elizabeth, 1938" (Sir Gerald Kelly) .. .. 2·25 2·40

(b) On Nos. 1058/62.

1163. 55 c. + 50 c. Type **222** .. 75 80
1164. 65 c. + 50 c. "Lot and his Daughters" (Lucas van Leyden) 80 85
1165. 75 c. + 50 c. "Auspicious Comet" (from treatise c. 1587) 85 90
1166. $1.50 + 50 c. "Events following Charles I" (Herman Saftleven) .. 1·25 1·40
1167. $2 + 50 c. "Ossian receiving Napoleonic Officers" (Anne Louis Girodet-Trioson) .. 1·75 2·00

(c) On Nos. 1065/7.

1168. **223.** 95 c. + 50 c. mult. .. 1·00 1·10
1169. – $1.25 + 50 c. mult. .. 1·25 1·40
1170. – $1.50 + 50 c. mult. .. 1·40 1·50

(d) On Nos. 1069/71.

1172. $1 + 50 c. Type **224** .. 1·00 1·10
1173. $1.50 + 50 c. Chicago .. 1·40 1·50
1174. $2 + 50 c. 1975 definitive $2, Benjamin Franklin and H.M.S. "Resolution" .. .. 1·75 1·90

(e) On Nos. 1072/4.

1175. $1 + 50 c. Type **225** .. 1·00 1·10
1176. $1.25 + 50 c. Hand and torch of Statue .. 1·25 1·40
1177. $2.75 + 50 c. Statue of Liberty .. .. 2·25 2·40

(f) On Nos. 1075/7.
1178. $1+50 c. Type **226** .. 1·00 1·25
1179. $2+50 c. Prince Andrew 1·75 1·90
1180. $3+50 c. Prince Andrew and Miss Sarah Ferguson (57×31 mm.) 2·40 2·50

(g) On Nos. 1080/2.
1181. 55 c.+50 c. Type **228** .. 75 80
1182. $1.30+50 c. "Virgin with the Garland" .. .. 1·25 1·40
1183. $2.75+50 c. "The Adoration of the Magi" (detail) .. 2·25 2·40

(h) On Nos. 1122, 1134/7 and
1186. 55 c.+25 c. on 52 c. "Bellonella indica" .. 55 60
1187. 65 c.+25 c. on 42 c. "Fungia fungites" .. 65 70
1188. 75 c.+25 c. on 48 c. "Gonipora" 70 75
1189. 95 c.+25 c. on 96 c. "Porites andrewsi" .. 85 90
1190. $2.80+50 c. on $2 "Gonipora" .. .. 2·25 2·40
1191. $5+50 c. on $3 "Heliofungia actiniformis" .. 3·75 4·00
1192. $6.40+50 c. on $4 "Stylophora pistillata" 4·75 5·00

1987. Royal Ruby Wedding. Nos. 484 and 787 optd. **ROYAL WEDDING FORTIETH ANNIVERSARY.**
1193. $4 Queen Elizabeth II and sea shells .. .. 3·75 3·75
1194. $4 Queen Elizabeth II and "Stylophora pistillata" .. .. 3·75 3·75

233. "The Holy Family" (Rembrandt).

1987. Christmas. Different paintings of the Holy Family by Rembrandt.
1195. **233.** $1.25 multicoloured 1·50 1·50
1196. – $1.50 multicoloured 1·75 1·75
1197. – $1.95 multicoloured 2·25 2·25

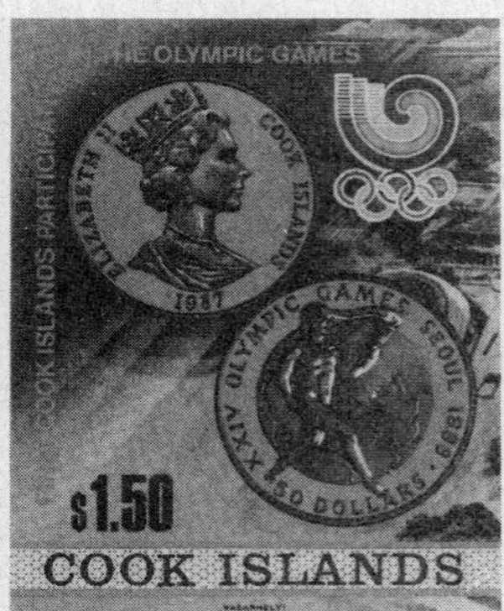

234 Olympic Commemorative $50 Coin

1988. Olympic Games, Seoul. Multicoloured.
1200 $1.50 Type **234** .. .. 1·40 1·50
1201 $1.50 Olympic torch and Seoul Olympic Park .. 1·40 1·50
1202 $1.50 Steffi Graf playing tennis and Olympic medal .. .. .. 1·40 1·50
Nos. 1200/2 were printed together, se-tenant, forming a composite design.

1988. Olympic Tennis Medal Winners, Seoul. Nos.1200/2 optd.
1204 $1.50 Type **234** (optd **MILOSLAV MECIR CZECHOSLOVAKIA GOLD MEDAL WINNER MEN'S TENNIS**) .. .. 1·10 1·25
1205 $1.50 Olympic torch and Seoul Olympic Park (optd **TIM MAYOTTE UNITED STATES GABRIELA SABATINI ARGENTINA SILVER MEDAL WINNERS**) .. 1·10 1·25
1206 $1.50 Steffi Graf playing tennis and Olympic medal (optd **GOLD MEDAL WINNER STEFFI GRAf WEST GERMANY**) 1·10 1·25

236 "Virgin and Child"

1988. Christmas.
1208 **236** 70 c. multicoloured .. 1·00 1·00
1209 – 85 c. multicoloured .. 1·25 1·25
1210 – 95 c. multicoloured .. 1·40 1·40
1221 – $1.25 multicoloured .. 1·60 1·60
DESIGNS: 85 c.; 95 c.; $1.25 Various versions of the "Virgin and Child" by Durer.

237 "Apollo 11" leaving Earth

1989. 20th Anniv of First Manned Landing on Moon. Multicoloured.
1213 40 c. Type **237** 40 40
1214 40 c. Lunar module over Moon 40 40
1215 55 c. Aldrin stepping onto Moon 55 55
1216 55 c. Astronaut on Moon 55 55
1217 65 c. Working on lunar surface 65 65
1218 65 c. Conducting experiment 65 65
1219 75 c. "Apollo 11" leaving Moon 70 70
1220 75 c. Splashdown in South Pacific 70 70

238 Rarotonga Flycatcher

1989. Endangered Birds of the Cook Islands. Multicoloured.
1222 15 c. Type **238** 45 45
1223 20 c. Pair of Rarotonga flycatchers 45 45
1224 65 c. Pair of Rarotongan fruit doves .. .. 1·10 1·10
1225 70 c. Rarotongan fruit dove .. .. .. 1·10 1·10

239 Villagers

1989. Christmas. Details from "Adoration of the Magi" by Rubens. Mult.
1227 70 c. Type **239** 65 65
1228 85 c. Virgin Mary .. 80 80
1229 95 c. Christ Child .. 85 85
1230 $1.50 Boy with gift .. 1·50 1·50

240 Revd. John Williams and L.M.S. Church

1990. Christianity in the Cook Islands. Multicoloured.
1232 70 c. Type **240** 65 65
1233 85 c. Mgr. Bernardine Castanie and Roman Catholic Church .. 80 80
1234 95 c. Elder Osborne Widstoe and Mormon Church 85 85
1235 $1.60 Dr. J. E. Caldwell and Seventh Day Adventist Church .. 1·50 1·50

241 "Woman writing a Letter" (Terborch)

1990. 150th Anniv of the Penny Black. Designs showing paintings. Multicoloured.
1237 85 c. Type **241** 70 70
1238 $1.15 "George Gisze" (Holbein the Younger) 90 90
1239 $1.55 "Mrs. John Douglas" (Gainsborough) .. .. 1·25 1·25
1240 $1.85 "Portrait of a Gentleman" (Durer) .. 1·60 1·60

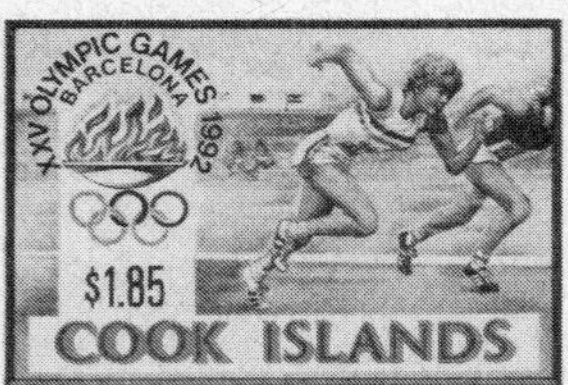

242 Sprinting

1990. Olympic Games, Barcelona, and Winter Olympic Games, Albertville (1992). Mult.
1242 $1.85 Type **242** .. .. 1·90 1·90
1243 $1.85 Cook Islands $50 commemorative coin 1·90 1·90
1244 $1.85 Skiing .. .. 1·90 1·90

243 Queen Elizabeth the Queen Mother

1990. 90th Birthday of Queen Elizabeth the Queen Mother.
1245 **243** $1.85 multicoloured .. 1·25 1·40

244 "Adoration of the Magi" (Memling)

1990. Christmas. Religious Paintings. Mult.
1247 70 c. Type **244** 65 65
1248 85 c. "Holy Family" (Lotto) 75 75
1249 95 c. "Madonna and Child with Saints John and Catherine" (Titian) .. 90 90
1250 $1.50 "Holy Family" (Titian) .. .. 1·40 1·40

247 Columbus (engraving by Theodoro de Bry)

1991. 500th Anniv (1992) of Discovery of America by Columbus.
1254 **247** $1 multicoloured .. 85 85

1991. 65th Birthday of Queen Elizabeth II. No. 789 optd **65TH BIRTHDAY**.
1255 $10 "Melithaea albitincta" 8·50 8·75

249 "Adoration of the Child" (G. delle Notti)

1991. Christmas. Religious Paintings. Mult.
1256 70 c. Type **249** 45 50
1257 85 c. "The Birth of the Virgin" (B. Murillo) .. 55 60
1258 $1.15 "Adoration of the Shepherds" (Rembrandt) 75 80
1259 $1.50 "Adoration of the Shepherds" (L. le Nain) 1·00 1·10

250 Red-breasted Maori Wrasse

1992. Reef Life. Multicoloured.
1261 5 c. Type **250** 10 10
1262 10 c. Blue sea star .. 10 10
1263 15 c. Black and gold angelfish 10 10
1264 20 c. Spotted pebble crab 10 10
1265 25 c. Black-tipped cod .. 15 20
1266 30 c. Spanish dancer .. 25 30
1267 50 c. Royal angelfish .. 35 40
1268 80 c. Squirrel fish .. 55 60

OFFICIAL STAMPS

1975. Nos. 228, etc., optd. **O H.M.S.** or surch. also.

No.	Description		Unused	Used
O 1.	1 c. multicoloured	..		
O 2.	2 c. multicoloured	..		
O 3.	3 c. multicoloured	..		
O 4.	4 c. multicoloured	..		
O 5.	5 c. on 2½ c. multicoloured			
O 6.	8 c. multicoloured	..		
O 7.	10 c. on 6 c. multicoloured			
O 8.	18 c. on 20 c. multicoloured			
O 9.	25 c. on 9 c. multicoloured			
O 10.	30 c. on 15 c. multicoloured			
O 11.	50 c. multicoloured	..		
O 12.	$1 multicoloured ..	..		
O 13.	$2 multicoloured ..	..		
O 14.	$4 multicoloured ..	..		
O 15.	$6 multicoloured ..	..		
O 1/15	.. .. Set of 15		†	30·00

These stamps were only sold to the public cancelled to order and not in unused condition. They were made available to overseas collectors in mint condition during 1980.

1978. Nos. 466/7, 474, 478/81, 484/5, 542 and 568/9 optd. **O.H.M.S.** or surch also.

No.	Type	Description	Unused	Used
O 16.	–	1 c. multicoloured (No. 467) ..	30	10
O 17.	141.	2 c. on ½ c. multicoloured	30	10
O 18.		5 c. on ½ c. multicoloured	30	10
O 19.	–	10 c. on 8 c. multicoloured (No. 474) ..	35	10
O 20.	–	15 c. on 50 c. multicoloured (No. 480) ..	45	10
O 21.	–	18 c. on 60 c. multicoloured (No. 481) ..	45	15
O 22.	–	25 c. multicoloured (No. 478) ..	50	20
O 23.	–	30 c. multicoloured (No. 479) ..	50	25
O 24.	–	35 c. on 60 c. multicoloured (No. 481) ..	65	30
O 25.	–	50 c. multicoloured (No. 480) ..	1·00	35
O 26.	–	60 c. multicoloured (No. 481) ..	1·10	45
O 27.	–	$1 multicoloured (No. 568) ..	3·75	1·25
O 28.	–	$1 multicoloured (No. 569) ..	3·75	1·25
O 29.	–	$2 multicoloured (No. 542) ..	4·75	3·00
O 30.	–	$4 multicoloured (No. 484) ..	7·50	3·25
O 31.	–	$6 multicoloured (No. 485) ..	9·50	6·00

These stamps were only sold to the public cancelled-to-order and not in unused condition.

1985. Nos. 786/8, 862/5, 969/74, 976, 978, 981, 984/6 and 988/9 optd **O.H.M.S.** or surch also.

No.	Description	Unused	Used
O 32	5 c. "Ptilosarcus gurneyi"	10	10
O 33	10 c. "Lobophyllia bemprichii" ..	10	10
O 34	12 c. "Sarcophyton digitatum" ..	10	10
O 35	14 c. "Pavona praetorta"	10	10
O 36	18 c. "Junceella gemmacea"	10	15
O 37	20 c. "Stylastet" ..	10	15
O 38	30 c. "Palauastrea ramosa"	20	25
O 39	40 c. "Stylaster echinatus"	25	30
O 40	50 c. "Melithaea squamata" ..	35	40
O 41	55 c. on 85 c. "Caulastraea echinulata"	35	40
O 42	60 c. "Tubastraea" ..	40	45
O43	70 c. "Heliofungia actiniformis"	45	50
O 46	75 c. on 60 c. Type **197** ..	50	55
O 47	75 c. on 60 c. Rarotonga oranges	50	55
O 48	75 c. on 60 c. Rarotonga airport	50	55
O 49	75 c. on 60 c. Prime Minister Sir Thomas Davis	50	55
O 44	$1.10 "Pectinia alcicornis"	75	80
O 45	$2 on $1.20 "Dendrophyllia gracilis" ..	1·25	1·40
O 50	$5 on $3 "Heliofungia actiniformis"	3·25	3·50
O 51	$9 on $4 "Stylophora pistillata"	6·00	6·25
O 52	$14 on $6 "Stylaster echinatus"	9·25	9·50
O 53	$18 on $10 "Melithaea albitincta"	12·00	12·50

CYPRUS

An island in the E. Mediterranean. A Br. colony which became a republic within the Br. Commonwealth in 1960.

1880. 12 pence = 1 shilling.
1881. 40 paras = 1 piastre. 180 piastres = 1 pound.
1955. 1000 mils = 1 pound.
1983. 100 cents = 1 pound.

1880. Stamps of Gt. Britain (Queen Victoria) optd. **CYPRUS.**

No.	Type	Description	Unused	Used
1.	**7.**	½d. red	95·00	95·00
2.	**5.**	1d. red	7·50	27·00
3.	**41.**	2½d. mauve	1·75	5·00
4.	–	4d. green (No. 153) ..	£120	£170
5.	–	6d. grey (No. 161) ..	£500	£650
6.	–	1s. green (No. 150) ..	£6000	£450

1881. Stamps of Gt. Britain (Queen Victoria), surch. with new values.

No.	Type	Description	Unused	Used
9	**5**	½d. on 1d. red	45·00	60·00
10		30 par. on 1d. red ..	90·00	80·00

7.

13.

1881.

No.	Type	Description	Unused	Used
31	**7.**	½ pi. green	2·50	30
40		½ pi. green and red ..	4·00	40
32		30 par. mauve ..	2·50	2·00
41		30 par. mauve and green	2·00	55
33		1 pi. red	7·00	80
42		1 pi. red and blue ..	4·00	45
34		2 pi. blue	10·00	80
43		2 pi. blue and purple ..	4·50	45
35a		4 pi. olive	16·00	14·00
44		4 pi. olive and purple ..	9·50	3·00
21		6 pi. grey	32·00	15·00
45		6 pi. olive and green ..	6·50	7·50
46		9 pi. brown and red ..	15·00	8·00
22		12 pi. brown	£160	32·00
47		12 pi. brown and black ..	12·00	45·00
48		18 pi. grey and brown ..	48·00	38·00
49		45 pi. purple and blue ..	£110	£120

1882. Surch.

No.	Type	Description	Unused	Used
25.	**7.**	½ pi. on ½ pi. green ..	£110	6·50
24.		30 par. on 1 pi. red ..	£1400	£100

1903. As T **7** but portrait of King Edward VII.

No.	Description	Unused	Used
60.	5 par. brown and black ..	30	20
61.	10 par. orange and green ..	1·50	25
62.	½ pi. green and red ..	2·50	15
51.	30 par. violet and green ..	3·25	80
64.	1 pi. red and blue	1·50	30
65.	2 pi. blue and purple ..	3·75	70
66.	4 pi. olive and purple ..	9·00	6·00
67.	6 pi. olive and green ..	8·50	5·50
68.	9 pi. brown and red ..	15·00	6·50
57.	12 pi. brown and black ..	12·00	24·00
70.	18 pi. black and brown ..	25·00	8·00
71.	45 pi. purple and blue ..	60·00	90·00

1912. As T **7** but portrait of King George V.

No.	Description	Unused	Used
74b.	10 par. orange and green	2·25	40
86.	10 par. grey and yellow ..	8·00	9·00
75.	½ pi. green and red ..	1·50	20
76.	30 par. violet and green ..	1·50	20
88.	30 par. green	4·25	40
77.	1 pi. red and blue	3·75	1·25
90	1 pi. violet and red ..	3·00	2·75
91.	1½ pi. yellow and black ..	3·25	3·75
78.	2 pi. blue and purple ..	4·75	90
93.	2 pi. red and blue	9·00	22·00
94.	2¾ pi. blue and purple ..	8·50	14·00
79.	4 pi. olive and purple ..	2·75	2·75
80.	6 pi. olive and green ..	2·75	5·00
81.	9 pi. brown and red ..	18·00	13·00
82.	12 pi. brown and black ..	8·00	14·00
83.	18 pi. black and brown .	20·00	18·00
84.	45 pi. purple and blue ..	55·00	90·00
100.	10s. green and red on yell.	£350	£500
101.	£1 purple and black on red	£1000	£1200

1924.

No.	Type	Description	Unused	Used
103.	**13.**	¼ pi. grey and brown ..	30	15
104.		½ pi. black	1·25	4·00
118.		½ pi. green	1·75	1·25
105.		¾ pi. green	1·00	50
119.		¾ pi. black	1·75	10
106.		1 pi. purple and brown ..	65	20
107.		1½ pi. orange and black	90	3·50
120.		1½ pi. red	2·25	30
108.		2 pi. red and green ..	1·75	5·50
121.		2 pi. yellow and black ..	4·00	3·25
122.		2½ pi. blue	1·75	30
109.		2¾ pi. blue and purple ..	1·75	1·75
110.		4 pi. olive and purple ..	2·00	1·50
111.		4½ pi. blk. & orge. on grn.	2·25	3·00
112.		6 pi. brown and green ..	2·25	3·50
113.		9 pi. brown and purple ..	2·75	3·00
114.		12 pi. brown and black ..	5·00	28·00
115.		18 pi. black and orange	16·00	4·50
116.		45 pi. purple and blue ..	25·00	28·00
117.		90 pi. green & red on yell.	60·00	90·00
102.		£1 purple & black on red	£325	£400
117a.		£5 black on yellow ..	£3500	£5000

14. Silver coin of Amathus, 6th-Cent. BC.

1928. 50th Anniv. of British Rule. Dated "1878 1928".

No.	Type	Description	Unused	Used
123.	**14.**	¾ pi. violet	1·25	40
124.	–	1 pi. black and blue ..	1·25	65
125.	–	1½ pi. red	2·75	2·00
126.	–	2½ pi. blue	1·75	2·00
127.	–	4 pi. brown	5·00	7·00
128.	–	6 pi. blue	5·00	15·00
129.	–	9 pi. purple	5·00	10·00
130.	–	18 pi. black and brown ..	16·00	17·00
131.	–	45 pi. violet and blue ..	32·00	45·00
132.	–	£1 blue and brown ..	£225	£300

DESIGNS—VERT. 1 pi. Philosophor Zeno. 2½ pi. Discovery of body of St. Barnabas. 4 pi. Cloister, Abbey of Bella Paise. 9 pi. Tekke of Umm Haram. 18 pi. Statue of Richard I, Westminster. 45 pi. St. Nicholas Cathedral, Famagusta (now Lala Mustafa Pasha Mosque). £1 King George V. HORIZ. 1½ pi. Map of Cyprus. 6 pi. Badge of Cyprus.

24. Ruins of Vouni Palace.

30. St. Sophia Cathedral, Nicosia (now Selimiye Mosque).

1934.

No.	Type	Description	Unused	Used
133.	**24.**	¼ pi. blue and brown ..	25	50
134.	–	½ pi. green	45	40
135.	–	¾ pi. black and violet ..	70	10
136	–	1 pi. black and brown ..	70	80
137.	–	1½ pi. red	70	45
138.	–	2½ pi. blue	1·25	80
139.	**30.**	4½ pi. black and red ..	3·00	2·25
140.	–	6 pi. black and blue ..	6·00	11·00
141.	–	9 pi. brown and violet ..	3·00	3·25
142.	–	18 pi. black and green ..	35·00	26·00
143.	–	45 pi. green and black ..	48·00	38·00

The ½ pi. to 2½ pi. values have a medallion portrait of King George V.

DESIGNS—HORIZ. ½ pi. Small Marble Forum, Salamis. ¾ pi. Church of St. Barnabas and St. Hilarion, Peristerona. 1 pi. Roman theatre, Soli; 1½ pi. Kyrenia Harbour. 2½ pi. Kolossi Castle. 45 pi. Forest scene, Troodos. VERT. 6 pi. Bayraktar Mosque, Nicosia. 9 pi. Queen's Window. St. Hilarion Castle. 18 pi. Buyuk Kahn, Nicosia.

1935. Silver Jubilee. As T **13** of Antigua.

No.	Description	Unused	Used
144.	¾ pi. blue and grey ..	55	15
145.	1½ pi. blue and red ..	2·25	2·50
146.	2½ pi. brown and blue	3·75	1·50
147.	9 pi. grey and purple ..	8·00	4·75

1937. Coronation. As T **2** of Aden.

No.	Description	Unused	Used
148.	¾ pi. grey	75	20
149.	1½ pi. red	1·25	80
150.	2½ pi. blue	3·50	1·75

36. Map of Cyprus.

37. Othello's Tower, Famagusta.

38. King George VI.

1938.

No.	Type	Description	Unused	Used
151.	–	¼ pi. blue and brown ..	10	10
152.	–	½ pi. green	15	10
152a.	–	½ pi. violet	1·50	20
153.	–	¾ pi. black and violet ..	5·00	20
154.	–	1 pi. orange	30	10
155.	–	1½ pi. red	4·50	1·50
155a.	–	1½ pi. violet	20	30
155ab.	–	1½ pi. green	1·75	30
155b.	–	2 pi. black and red ..	20	10
156.	–	2½ pi. blue	10·00	4·00
156a.	–	3 pi. blue	35	15
156b.	–	4 pi. blue	3·00	30
157.	**36.**	4½ pi. grey	30	10
158.	–	6 pi. black and blue ..	45	70
159.	**37.**	9 pi. black and purple ..	50	15
160.	–	18 pi. black and olive ..	3·50	85
161.	–	45 pi. green and black ..	12·00	2·25
162.	**38.**	90 pi. mauve and black	23·00	3·50
163.	–	£1 red and blue ..	40·00	17·00

DESIGNS: 2 pi. Peristerona Church. 3 pi., 4 pi. Kolossi Castle. All other values except 4½ pi., 9 pi., 90 pi. and £1 have designs as 1934 issue but portrait of King George VI.

1946. Victory. As T **9** of Aden.

No.	Description	Unused	Used
164.	1½ pi. violet	15	10
165.	3 pi. blue	15	15

1948. Silver Wedding. As T **10/11** of Aden.

No.	Description	Unused	Used
166.	1½ pi. violet	30	20
167.	£1 blue	42·00	35·00

1949. U.P.U. As T **20/23** of Antigua.

No.	Description	Unused	Used
168.	1½ pi. violet	60	55
169.	2 pi. red	80	85
170.	3 pi. blue	85	90
171.	9 pi. purple	1·00	1·00

1953. Coronation. As Type **13** of Aden.

No.	Description	Unused	Used
172.	1½ pi. black and green ..	35	10

39. Carobs. **42.** Copper Pyrites Mine.

49. St. Hilarion Castle.

53. Arms of Byzantium, Lusignan, Ottoman Empire and Venice.

1955.

No.	Type	Description	Unused	Used
173.	**39.**	2 m. brown	10	40
174.	–	3 m. violet	10	15
175.	–	5 m. orange	10	10
176.	**42.**	10 m. brown and green	30	10
177.	–	15 m. olive and blue ..	1·40	35
178.	–	20 m. brown and blue ..	25	15
179.	–	25 m. turquoise ..	50	35
180.	–	30 m. black and lake ..	35	10
181.	–	35 m. brown & turquoise	30	45
182.	–	40 m. green and brown	40	60
183.	**49.**	50 m. blue and brown ..	30	30
184.	–	100 m. mauve and green	6·50	40
185.	–	250 m. blue and brown	7·00	4·00
186.	–	500 m. slate and purple	26·00	9·50
187.	**53.**	£1 lake and slate ..	26·00	20·00

DESIGNS—As Type **39**: 3 m. Grapes. 5 m. Oranges. As Type **42**: 15 m. Troodos Forest. 20 m. Beach of Aphrodite. 25 m. Ancient coin of Paphos. 30 m. Kyrenia. 35 m. Harvest in Messaoria. 40 m. Famagusta harbour. As Type **49**: 100 m. Hala Sultan Tekke. 250 m. Kanakaria Church. As Type **53**: 500 m. Coins of Salamis Paphos, Citium and Idalium.

ΚΥΠΡΙΑΚΗ ΔΗΜΟΚΡΑΤΙΑ KIBRIS CUMHURIYETI

(54.)

55. Map of Cyprus.

1960. Nos 173/87 optd. as T **54** (" CYPRUS REPUBLIC " in Greek and Turkish).

188. **39.** 2 m. brown 20 20
189. – 3 m. violet 20 15
190. – 5 m. orange 35 10
191. **42.** 10 m. brown and green 30 10
192. – 15 m. olive and blue .. 75 10
193. – 20 m. brown and blue .. 40 30
194. – 25 m. turquoise 80 45
195. – 30 m. black and lake .. 1·25 10
196. – 35 m. brown & turquoise 1·50 20
197. – 40 m. green and brown 2·00 65
198. **49.** 50 m. blue and brown .. 2·00 40
199. – 100 m. mauve & green 9·00 40
200. – 250 m. blue and brown 25·00 2·00
201. – 500 m. slate and purple 40·00 15·00
202. **53.** £1 lake and slate .. 60·00 42·00

1960. Constitution of Republic.

203. **55.** 10 m. sepia and green .. 30 10
204. 30 m. blue and brown .. 40 10
205. 100 m. purple and slate 1·25 65

56. Doves.

1962. Europa.

206. **56.** 10 m. purple and mauve 10 10
207. 40 m. blue and cobalt .. 20 10
208. 100 m. emerald & green 20 15

57. Campaign Emblem.

1962. Malaria Eradication.

209. **57.** 10 m. black and green .. 20 10
210. 30 m. black and brown 25 10

63. St Barnabas' Church.

1962.

211. – 3 m. brown and orange 10 30
212. – 5 m. purple and green .. 10 10
213. – 10 m. black and green .. 15 10
214. – 15 m. black and purple 20 15
215. **63.** 25 m. brown & chestnut 30 20
216. – 30 m. dp. blue & lt. blue 20 10
217. – 35 m. green and blue .. 35 10
218. – 40 m. black and blue .. 1·25 1·25
219. – 50 m. bronze and bistre 50 10
220. – 100 m. brown and bistre 3·50 30
221 – 250 m. black and brown 8·00 2·00
222. – 500 m. brown and green 17·00 9·00
223. – £1 bronze and grey .. 22·00 23·00

DESIGNS—VERT. 3 m. Iron Age jug. 5 m. Grapes. 10 m. Bronze head of Apollo. 15 m. Selimiye Mosque, Nicosia. 35 m. Head of Aphrodite. 100 m. Hala Sultan Tekke. 500 m. Mouflon. HORIZ. 30 m. Temple of Apollo Hylates. 40 m. Skiing, Troodos. 50 m. Salamis Gymnasium. 250 m. Bella Paise Abbey. £1, St. Hilarion Castle.

72. Europa " Tree ".

1963. Europa.

224. **72.** 10 m. blue and black .. 75 15
225. 40 m. red and black .. 3·25 2·00
226. 150 m. green and black 6·00 3·75

73. Harvester.

75. Wolf Cub in Camp.

1963. Freedom from Hunger.

227. **73.** 25 c. ochre, sepia & blue 50 25
228. – 75 m. grey, black & lake 2·75 1·00

DESIGN: 75 m. Demeter, Goddess of Corn.

1963. 50th Anniv. of Cyprus Scout Movement and 3rd Commonwealth Scout Conference, Platres. Multicoloured.

229. 3 m. Type **75** 10 15
230. 20 m. Sea Scout 35 10
231. 150 m. Scout with Mouflon 1·00 1·25

79. Children's Centre, Kyrenia.

The 10 m. is vert.

1963. Centenary of Red Cross. Multicoloured.

232. 10 m. Nurse tending child 50 15
233. 100 m. Type **79** 3.50 3.50

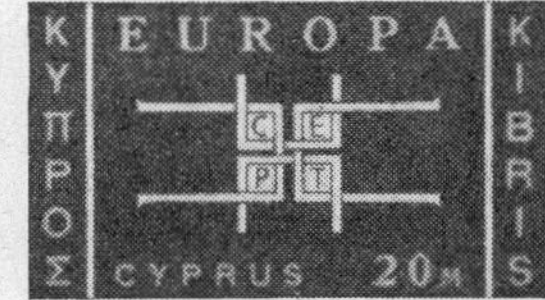

80. " Co-operation " (emblem).

1963. Europa.

234. **80.** 20 m. buff, blue & violet 1·25 40
235. 30 m. grey, yell. & blue 1·50 40
236. 150 m. buff, blue & brown 6·00 7·50

1964. U.N. Security Council's Cyprus Resolutions, March, 1964. Nos. 213, etc., optd. with U.N. emblem and **1964.**

237. 10 m. black and green .. 15 10
238. 30 m. deep blue & light blue 15 10
239. 40 m. black and blue .. 15 15
240. 50 m. bronze and bistre .. 15 10
241. 100 m. brown and bistre .. 20 40

82. Soli Theatre.

1964. 400th Birth Anniv. of Shakespeare. Multicoloured.

242. 15 m. Type **82** 35 15
243. 35 m. Curium Theatre .. 35 15
244. 50 m. Salamis Theatre .. 35 15
245. 100 m. Othello Tower, and scene from " Othello " .. 1·00 1·25

86. Running.

89. Europa " Flower ".

1964. Olympic Games, Tokyo.

246. **86.** 10 m. brown, blk. & yell. 15 10
247. – 25 m. brown, bl. & slate 25 10
248. – 75 m. brn., blk. & chest. 35 55

DESIGNS—HORIZ. 25 m. Boxing. 75 m. Charioteers.

1964. Europa.

249. **89.** 20 m. brown and ochre 50 10
250. 30 m. ultramarine & bue 60 10
251. 150 m. olive and green .. 3·25 3·50

90. Dionysus and Acme.

1964. Cyprus Wines. Multicoloured.

252. 10 m. Type **90** 25 10
253. 40 m. Silenus (satyr) .. 55 30
254. 50 m. Commandaria Wine 65 10
255. 100 m. Wine factory .. 1·75 85

Nos. 253/4 are vert.

94. Pres. Kennedy.

1965. Pres. Kennedy Commem.

256. **94.** 10 m. blue 10 10
257. 40 m. green 15 15
258. 100 m. red 20 15

95. "Old Age".

DESIGNS—As Type **95**: 45 m. " Accident ". LARGER (23 × 48 mm.): 75 m. " Maternity ".

1965. Social Insurance Law.

259. **95.** 30 m. drab and green .. 20 10
260. – 45 m. green, blue and ultramarine .. 20 10
261. – 75 m. brown and flesh .. 80 1·25

98. I.T.U. Emblem and Symbols.

1965. Centenary of I.T.U.

262. **98.** 15 m. black, brn. & yell. 50 20
263. 60 m. blk., grn. & lt.-grn. 2·75 1·50
264. 75 m. blk., indigo & blue 3·00 1·75

99. I.C.Y. Emblem.

1965. Int. Co-operation Year.

265. **99.** 50 m. brown and green 1·00 10
266. 100 m. purple and green 1·50 30

100. Europa "Sprig".

1965. Europa.

267. **100.** 5 m. black, brn. & orge. 15 10
268. 45 m. black, brown & grn. 1·25 1·25
269. 150 m. black, brn. & grey 2·25 2·75

1966. U.N. General Assembly's Cyprus Resolution, Nos. 211, 213, 216 and 221 optd. **U.N. Resolution on Cyprus 18 Dec. 1965.**

270. 3 m. brown and orange .. 10 25
271. 10 m. black and green .. 10 10
272. 30 m. dp. blue and lt. blue 20 15
273. 250 m. black and brown .. 45 1·75

102. Discovery of St. Barnabas' Body.

1966. 1900th Death Anniv. of St Barnabas.

274. **102.** 15 m. multicoloured .. 15 10
275. – 25 m. drab, blk. & blue 15 10
276. – 100 m. multicoloured .. 35 1·25

DESIGNS—HORIZ. 25 m. St. Barnabas' Chapel. VERT. 100 m. St. Barnabas (icon).

1966. No. 211 surch.

278. – 5 m. on 3 m. brown and orange 10 10

107. General K. S. Thimayya and U.N. Emblem.

1966. Gen. Thimayya Commem.

279. **107.** 50 m. black and brown 10 10

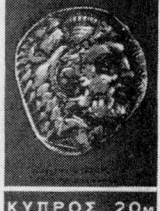

108. Europa "Ship".

113. Silver Coin of Evagoras I.

109. Stavrovouni Monastery.

1966. Europa.

280. **108.** 20 m. green and blue .. 30 10
281. 30 m. purple and blue 30 10
282. 150 m. bistre and blue 1·10 1·90

1966. Multicoloured.

283. 3 m. Type **109** 30 30
284. 5 m. Church of St. James, Trikomo 10 10
285. 10 m. Zeno of Citium (marble bust) 10 20
286. 15 m. Ancient ship (painting) 15 10
287. 20 m. Type **113** 90 75
288. 25 m. Sleeping Eros (marble statue) 30 10
289. 30 m. St. Nicholas' Cathedral, Famagusta 50 40
290. 35 m. Gold sceptre from Curium 50 50
291. 40 m. Silver dish of 7th century 70 40
292. 50 m. Silver coin of Alexander the Great .. 90 10
293. 100 m. Vase, 7th Centenary B.C. .. .. .. 2·75 15
294. 250 m. Bronze ingot-stand 2·00 20
295. 500 m. "The Rape of Ganymede" (mosaic) .. .. 3·50 1·25
296. £1 Aphrodite (marble statue) .. .. .. 6·50 5·50

DESIGNS—As Type **109**—VERT. 5 m. and 10 m. As Type **113**—HORIZ. 15 m., 25 m. and 50 m. VERT. 30 m., 35 m., 40 m. and 100 m. Nos. 294/6 are as Type **113** but larger, 28 × 40 mm.

123. Power Station, Limassol. **124.** Cogwheels.

1967. 1st Development Programme. Mult.

297. 10 m. Type **123** 10 10
298. 15 m. Arghaka-Maghounda Dam 15 10
299. 35 m. Troodos Highway .. 20 10
300. 50 m. Hilton Hotel, Nicosia 20 10
301. 100 m. Famagusta Harbour 25 50
Nos. 298/301 are vert.

1967. Europa.

302. **124.** 20 m. olive, green and light green 35 10
303. 30 m. violet, lilac & mve. 35 10
304. 150 m. sepia, brn. & chest. 1·00 1·25

125. Throwing the Javelin.

1967. Athletic Games, Nicosia. Multicoloured.

305. 15 m. Type **125** 20 10
306. 35 m. Running 20 30
307. 100 m. High-jumping .. 30 50

127. Ancient Monuments.

1967. Int. Tourist Year. Multicoloured.

309. 10 m. Type **127** 10 10
310. 40 m. Famagusta Beach 15 60
311. 50 m. "Comet" at Nicosia Airport 15 10
312. 100 m. Skier and Youth Hostel 20 65

128. St. Andrew Mosaic.

1967. Cent. of St. Andrew's Monastery.

313. **128.** 25 m. multicoloured .. 10 10

129. "The Crucifixion" (icon).

1967. Cyprus Art Exn., Paris.

314. **129.** 50 m. multicoloured .. 10 10

130. The Three Magi.

1967. 20th Anniv. of U.N.E.S.C.O.

315. **130.** 75 m. multicoloured .. 15 20

131. Human Rights Emblem over Stars.

1968. Human Rights Year. Multicoloured.

316. 50 m. Type **131** 10 10
317. 90 m. Human Rights and U.N. Emblems .. 30 50

134. Europa "Key".

1968. Europa.

319. **134.** 20 m. multicoloured .. 20 10
320. 30 m. multicoloured .. 20 10
321. 150 m. multicoloured .. 45 1·25

135. U.N. Children's Fund. Symbol and Boy drinking Milk.

1968. 21st Anniv. of U.N.I.C.E.F.

322. **135.** 35 m. brn., red & blk. 10 10

136. Aesculapius. **137.** Throwing the Discus.

1968. 20th Anniv. of W.H.O.

323. **136.** 50 m. blk., grn. & olive 10 10

1968. Olympic Games, Mexico. Multicoloured.

324. 10 m. Type **137** 10 10
325. 25 m. Sprint finish .. 10 10
326. 100 m. Olympic Stadium (horiz.) 20 75

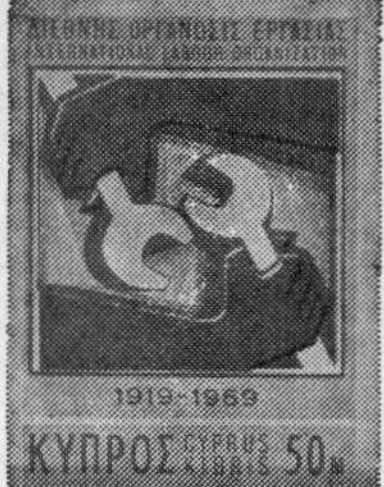

138. I.L.O. Emblem.

1969. 50th Anniv. of Int. Labour Organization.

327. **138.** 50 m. brown and blue 15 30
328. 90 m. brn., blk. & grey 15 20

139. Mercator's Map of Cyprus, 1554.

1969. 1st Int. Congress of Cypriot Studies.

329. **139.** 35 m. multicoloured .. 10 20
330. – 50 m. multicoloured .. 10 10
DESIGN: 50 m. Blaeu's map of Cyprus, 1635.

141. Europa Emblem.

1969. Europa.

331. **141.** 20 m. multicoloured .. 20 10
332. 30 m. multicoloured .. 20 10
333. 150 m. multicoloured .. 70 1·50

142. Common Roller.

1969. Birds of Cyprus. Multicoloured.

334. 5 m. Type **142** 50 15
335. 15 m. Audouin's gull .. 70 15
336. 20 m. Cyprus warbler .. 75 15
337. 30 m. Jay 80 15
338. 40 m. Hoopoe .. .. 1·00 30
339. 90 m. Eleonora's falcon .. 2·25 4·00
Nos. 337/339 are vert.

143. "The Nativity", (12th-century wall painting).

1969. Christmas. Multicoloured.

340. 20 m. Type **143** 10 10
341. 45 m. "The Nativity" (14th cent. wall paintings) .. 15 20

146. Mahatma Gandhi.

1970. Birth Cent. of Mahatma Gandhi.

343. **146.** 25 m. bl., drab & blk. 15 10
344. 75 m. brown, drab and black 20 45

147. " Flaming Sun ".

1970. Europa.

345. **147.** 20 m. brown, yell. & orge. 20 10
346. 30 m. blue, yell. & orge. 20 10
347. 150 m. pur., yell. & orge. 70 1·50

148. Gladioli.

1970. Nature Conservation Year. Mult.

348. 10 m. Type **148** 10 10
349. 50 m. Poppies 15 10
350. 90 m. Giant Fennel .. 40 1·50

149. I.E.Y. Emblem. **152.** Virgin and Child.

1970. International Events.

351. **149.** 5 m. black and brown .. 10 10
352. – 15 m. multicoloured .. 10 10
353. – 75 m. multicoloured .. 15 35
DESIGNS AND EVENTS: 5 m. Int. Education Year. HORIZ. 15 m. Mosaic (50th General Assembly of Int. Vine and Wine Office). 75 m. Globe, Dove and U.N. Emblem (United Nations 25th Anniv.).

1970. Christmas. Wall-painting from Church of Panayia Podhythou, Galaba. Mult.

354. 25 m. Archangel (facing right) 15 15
355. 25 m. Type **152** 15 15
356. 25 m. Archangel (facing left) 15 15
357. 75 m. Virgin and Child between Archangels (42 × 30 mm.) 20 35

153. Cotton Napkin.

1971. Multicoloured.

358 3 m. Type **153** 20 40
359 5 m. St. George and Dragon (19th-cent bas-relief) 10 10
360 10 m. Woman in festival costume 15 20
361 15 m. Archaic Bichrome Kylix (cup) (horiz) .. 20 10
362 20 m. A pair of donors (St. Mamas Church) .. 30 30
363 25 m. "The Creation" (6th-cent mosaic) 30 10

364 30 m. Athena and horse-drawn chariot (4th-cent B.C. terracotta) (horiz) 30 10
365 40 m. Shepherd playing pipe (14th-cent fresco) .. 1·00 80
366 50 m. Hellenistic head (3rd-cent B.C.) 80 10
367 75 m. "Angel" (mosaic detail), Kanakaria Church .. .. .. 1·75 50
368 90 m. Mycenaean silver bowl (horiz) .. .. 2·50 1·25
369 250 m. Moufflon (detail of 3rd-cent mosaic) (horiz) 2·75 40
370 500 m. Ladies and sacred tree (detail 6th-cent amphora) (horiz) .. 1·25 70
371 $1 Horned god from Emkomi (12th-cent bronze statue) .. .. 2·50 1·00

SIZES: 24 × 37 or 37 × 24 10 m. to 90 m., 41 × 28 or 28 × 41 250 m. to £1.

154. Europa Chain.

1971. Europa.
372. **154.** 20 m. blue, ultram. & blk. 20 10
373. 30 m. grn., myrtle & blk. 20 10
374. 150 m. yell., grn. & blk. 70 1·75

155. Archbishop Kyprianos.

1971. 150th Anniv. of Greek War of Independence. Multicoloured.
375. 15 m. Type **155** 10 10
376. 30 m. "Taking the Oath" (horiz.) 10 10
377. 100 m. Bishop Germanos, flag and freedom-fighters 20 50

156. Kyrenia Castle.

1971. Tourism. Multicoloured.
378. 15 m. Type **156** 10 10
379. 25 m. Gourd on sunny beach (vert.) 10 10
380. 60 m. Mountain scenery (vert.) 20 60
381. 100 m. Church of St. Evalios, Lambousa .. 20 65

157. Madonna and Child in Stable.

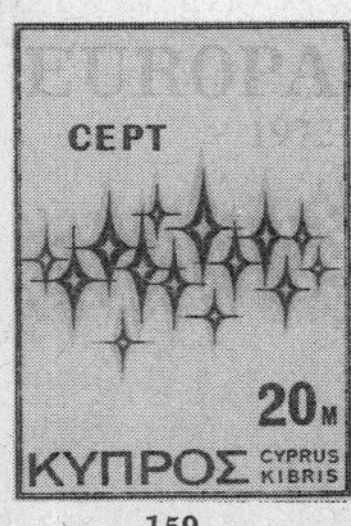

159. "Communications".

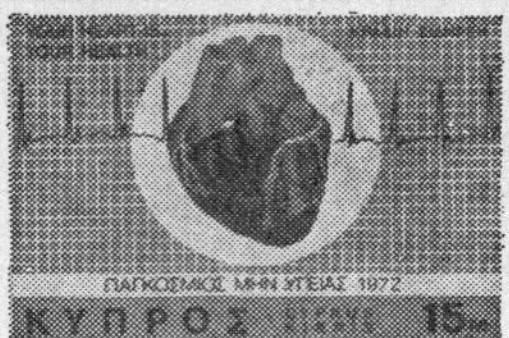

158. Heart.

1971. Christmas. Multicoloured.
382. 10 m. Type **157** 10 10
383. 50 m. The Three Wise Men 15 35
384. 100 m. The Shepherds .. 20 35

1972. World Heart Month.
385. **158.** 15 m. multicoloured .. 10 10
386. 50 m. multicoloured .. 20 45

1972. Europa.
387. **159.** 20 m. orge., brn. & brn. 30 15
388. 30 m. orge., ultram. & bl. 30 15
389. 150 m. orange, myrtle and green .. .. 1·75 2·75

160. Archery.

1972. Olympic Games. Multicoloured.
390. 10 m. Type **160** 10 10
391. 40 m. Wrestling 15 10
392. 100m. Football 35 70

161. Stater of Marion.

1972. Ancient Coins of Cyprus (1st series).
393. **161.** 20 m. blue, blk. & silver 20 10
394. – 30 m. blue, blk. & silver 25 10
395. – 40 m. brn., blk. & silver 30 20
396. – 100 m. pink, blk. & silver 90 1·00

COINS: 30 m. Stater of Paphos. 40 m. Stater of Lapithos. 100 m. Stater of Idalion.

See also Nos. 486/9.

162. Bathing the Child Jesus.

1972. Christmas. Detail of mural in Holy Cross Church, Agiasmati. Multicoloured.
397. 10 m. Type **162** 10 10
398. 20 m. The Magi 10 10
399. 100 m. The Nativity .. 15 30

163. Mount Olympus, Troodos.

1973. 29th Int. Ski Federation Congress. Multicoloured.
401. 20 m. Type **163** 10 10
402. 100 m. Congress emblem .. 25 35

INDEX

Countries can be quickly located by referring to the index at the end of this volume.

164. Europa "Posthorn".

1973. Europa.
403. **164.** 20 m. multicoloured .. 35 10
404. 30 m. multicoloured .. 35 10
405. 150 m. multicoloured .. 1·40 2·50

165. Archbishop's Palace, Nicosia.

1973. Traditional Architecture. Mult.
406. 20 m. Type **165** 10 10
407. 30 m. House of Hajigeorgajis Cornessios, Nicosia (vert.) 10 10
408. 50 m. House at Gourri, 1850 (vert.) 15 10
409. 100 m. House at Rizokarpaso, 1772 .. .. .. 40 75

1973. No. 361 surch.
410. 20 m. on 15 m. multicoloured 15 15

167. Scout Emblem.

1973. Anniversaries.
411. **167.** 10 m. green and brown 20 10
412. – 25 m. blue and lilac .. 20 10
413. – 35 m. grn., cream & grn. 25 25
414. – 50 m. blue and indigo .. 30 10
415. – 100 m. brown & sepia .. 70 65

DESIGNS AND EVENTS—VERT. 10 m. (Cyprus Boy Scouts. 60th anniv.). 50 m. Airline emblem (Cyprus Airways. 25th anniv.). 100 m. Interpol emblem (Interpol. 50th anniv.). HORIZ. 25 m. Outlines of Cyprus and the E.E.C. (Association of Cyprus with "Common Market"). 35 m. F.A.O. emblem (F.A.O. 10th anniv.).

168. Archangel Gabriel.

1973. Christmas. Murals from Araka Church. Multicoloured.
416. 10 m. Type **168** 10 10
417. 20 m. Madonna and Child 10 10
418. 100 m. Araka Church (horiz.) 45 65

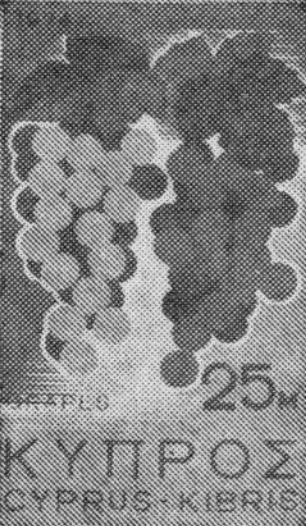

169. Grapes.

170. "The Rape of Europa" (Silver Stater of Marion).

1974. Products of Cyprus. Multicoloured.
419. 25 m. Type **169** 10 15
420. 50 m. Grapefruit 15 50
421. 50 m. Oranges 15 50
422. 50 m. Lemons 15 50

1974. Europa.
423. **170.** 10 m. multicoloured .. 15 10
424. 40 m. multicoloured .. 40 30
425. 150 m. multicoloured .. 1·50 2·50

171. Title Page of A. Kyprianos' "History of Cyprus" (1788).

1974. 2nd Int. Congress of Cypriot Studies. Multicoloured.
426. 10 m. Type **171** 10 10
427. 25 m. Solon (philosopher) in mosaic (horiz.) .. 15 10
428. 100 m. "St. Neophytos" (wall painting) 60 75

1974. Obligatory Tax. Refugee Fund. No. 359 surch. **REFUGEE FUND** in English, Greek and Turkish.
430. 10 m. on 5 m. multicoloured 10 10

1974. U.N. Security Council Resolution 353. Nos. 360, 365, 366 and 369 optd. with **SECURITY COUNCIL RESOLUTION 353 20 JULY 1974.**
431. 10 m. multicoloured .. 20 10
432. 40 m. multicoloured .. 40 50
433. 50 m. multicoloured .. 40 10
434. 250 m. multicoloured .. 70 2·50

174. "Refugees".

1974. Obligatory Tax. Refugee Fund.
435. **174.** 10 m. black and grey 10 10

175. "Virgin and Child between Two Angels" Stavios Church.

1974. Christmas. Church Wall-paintings. Multicoloured.
436. 10 m. Type **175** 10 10
437. 50 m. "Adoration of the Magi", Ayios Neophytos Monastery (vert.) .. 20 10
438. 100 m. "Flight into Egypt", Ayios Neophytos Monastery .. 25 45

176. Larnau–Nicosia Mail-coach, 1878.

1975. International Events.
439. **176.** 20 m. multicoloured .. 35 10
440. – 30 m. blue and orange .. 40 65
441. **176.** 50 m. multicoloured .. 40 15
442. – 100 m. multicoloured .. 60 1·25

DESIGNS AND EVENTS—HORIZ. 20 m., 50 m. Universal Postal Union. Cent. VERT. 30 m. "Disabled Persons" (8th European Meeting of International Society for the Rehabilitation of Disabled Persons). 100 m. Council flag (25th Anniv. of Council of Europe).

177. " The Distaff " (M. Kashalos).

1975. Europa. Multicoloured.
443. 20 m. Type **177** 35 50
444. 30 m. " Nature Morte " (C. Savva) 35 60
445. 150 m. " Virgin and Child of Liopetri " (G. P. Georghiou) .. .. 50 1·00

178. Red Cross Flag over Map.

1975. International Events. Multicoloured.
446. 25 m. Type **178** 25 10
447. 30 m. Nurse and Lamp (horiz.) 25 10
448. 75 m. Woman's Steatite idol (horiz.) 35 90

EVENTS: 25 m. 25th anniv. of Red Cross. 30 m. International Nurses' Day. 75 m. International Women's Year.

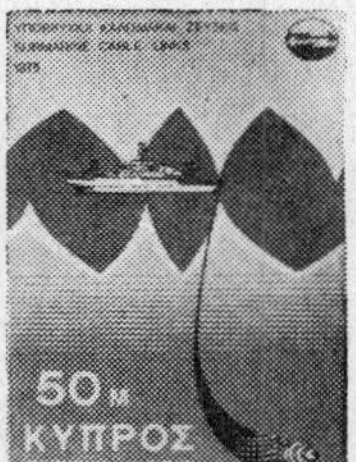

179. Submarine Cable Links.

1976. Telecommunications Achievements.
449. **179.** 50 m. multicoloured .. 40 10
450. – 100 m. yell., vio. & lilac 50 90

DESIGN—HORIZ. 100 m. International subscriber dialling.

1976. Surch.
451. **153.** 10 m. on 3 m. mult. .. 15 10

181. Human-figured Vessel, 19th-Century.

1976. Europa. Multicoloured.
452. 20 m. Type **181** 25 10
453. 60 m. Composite vessel, 2100–2000 B.C. .. 70 70
454. 100 m. Byzantine goblet .. 1·25 1·60

182. Self-help housing.

1976. Economic Reactivation. Mult.
455. 10 m. Type **182** 10 10
456. 25 m. Handicrafts .. 20 20
457. 30 m. Reafforestation .. 20 20
458. 60 m. Air Communications 35 55

183. Terracotta Statue of Youth. **184.** Olympic Symbol.

1976. Cypriot Treasures.
459. **183.** 5 m. multicoloured .. 10 35
460. – 10 m. multicoloured .. 10 30
461. – 20 m. red, yell. & blk. 20 35
462. – 25 m. multicoloured .. 20 10
463. – 30 m. multicoloured .. 25 10
464. – 40 m. grn., brn. & blk. 35 35
465. – 50 m. light brown, brown and black 35 10
466. – 60 m. multicoloured .. 45 10
467. – 100 m. multicoloured 50 20
468. – 250 m. blue, grey & blk. 70 1·00
469. – 500 m blk., brn. & grn. 80 1·75
470. – £1 multicoloured .. 1·25 2·25

DESIGNS—VERT. 10 m. Limestone head (23 × 34 mm.). 20 m. Gold necklace from Lambousa (24 × 37 mm.). 25 m. Terracotta warrior (24 × 37 mm.). 30 m. Statue of a priest of Aphrodite (24 × 37 mm.). 250 m. Silver dish from Lambousa (28 × 41 mm.). 500 m. Bronze stand (28 × 41 mm.). £1, Statue of Artemis (28 × 41 mm.). HORIZ. 40 m. Bronze tablet (37 × 24 mm.). 50 m. Mycenaean crater (37 × 24 mm.). 60 m. Limestone sarcophagus (37 × 24 mm.). 100 m. Gold bracelet from Lambousa. (As Type **183**).

1976. Olympic Games, Montreal.
471. **184.** 20 m. red, blk. & yell. 10 10
472. – 60 m. multicoloured (horiz.) 20 30
473. – 100 m. multicoloured (horiz.) 30 35

DESIGNS: 60 m. and 100 m. Olympic Symbols (different).

185. " George Washington " (G. Stuart).

1976. Bicent. of American Revolution.
474. **185.** 100 m. multicoloured 40 30

186. Children in Library.

1976. International Events.
475. **186.** 40 m. multicoloured .. 20 15
476. – 50 m. brown and black 20 10
477. – 80 m. multicoloured .. 45 60

DESIGNS AND EVENTS: 40 m. Type **186**. (Promotion of Children's Books). 50 m. Low-cost housing (HABITAT Conference, Vancouver). 80 m. Eye protected by hands (World Health Day).

187. Archangel Michael.

188. " Cyprus 74 ", (wood engraving by A. Tassos).

1976. Christmas. Multicoloured.
478. 10 m. Type **187** 15 10
479. 15 m. Archangel Gabriel .. 15 10
480. 150 m. The Nativity .. 60 80

Designs show icons from Ayios Neophytis Monastry.

1977. Refugee Fund.
481. **188.** 10 m. black 20 10

See also Nos. 634 and 729.

189. "View of Prodhrornos" (A. Diamantis).

1977. Europa. Multicoloured.
482. 20 m. Type **189** 20 10
483. 60 m. "Springtime at Monagroulli" (T. Kanthos) 40 55
484. 120 m. "Old Port, Limassol" (V. Ioannides) 70 1·25

190. Overprinted 500 m. Stamp of 1960.

1977. Silver Jubilee.
485. **190.** 120 m. multicoloured 30 30

191. Bronze Coin of Emperor Trajan.

1977. Ancient Coins of Cyprus (2nd series).
486. **191.** 10 m. blk., gold & blue 15 10
487. – 40 m. blk., silver & blue 30 30
488. – 60 m. blk., silver & orge. 35 35
489. – 100 m. blk., gold & grn. 50 95

DESIGNS: 40 m. Silver tetradrachm of Demetrios Poliorcetes. 60 m. Silver tetradrachm of Ptolemy VIII. 100 m. Gold Octadrachm of Arsinoe II.

192. Archbishop Makarios in Ceremonial Robes.

1977. Death of Archbishop Makarios. Mult.
490. 20 m. Type **192** 15 10
491. 60 m. Archbishop in doorway 20 10
492. 250 m. Head and shoulders portrait .. .. .. 50 1·10

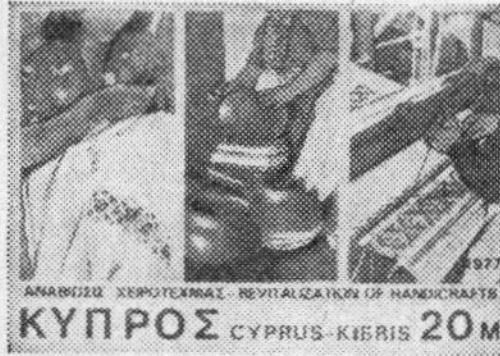

193. Embroidery, Pottery and Weaving.

1977. Anniversaries and Events. Mult.
493. 20 m. Type **193** 10 10
494. 40 m. Map of Mediterranean 15 20
495. 60 m. Gold medals .. 20 20
496. 80 m. Sputnik .. 20 85

DESIGNS COMMEMORATE: 20 m. Revitalisation of handicrafts. 40 m. " Man and the Biosphere " Programme in the Mediterranean region. 60 m. Gold medals won by Cypriot students in the Orleans Gymnasiade. 80 m. 60th Anniv. of Russian Revolution.

194. " Nativity ".

1977. Christmas. Children's Paintings. Mult.
497. 10 m. Type **194** 10 10
498. 40 m. " The Three Kings " 10 10
499. 150 m. " Flight into Egypt " 25 80

195. Demetrios Libertis.

1978. Cypriot Poets.
500. **195.** 40 m. brown & bistre 10 10
501. – 150 m. grey, blk. & red 30 80

DESIGN: 150 m. Vasilis Michaelides.

196. Chrysorrhogiatissa Monastery Courtyard.

1978. Europa. Architecture. Multicoloured.
502. 25 m. Type **196** 15 10
503. 75 m. Kolossi Castle .. 35 35
504. 125 m. Municipal Library, Paphos .. .. .. 50 1·00

197. Archbishop of Cyprus, 1950–1977.

1978. Archbishop Makarios Commem. Mult.
505. 15 m. Type **197** 15 20
506. 25 m. Exiled in Seychelles, 9 March 1956—28 March 1957 .. .. .. 15 20
507. 50 m. President of the Republic 1960–1977 .. 20 25
508. 75 m. " Soldier of Christ " 20 30
509. 100 m. " Fighter for Freedom " 25 35

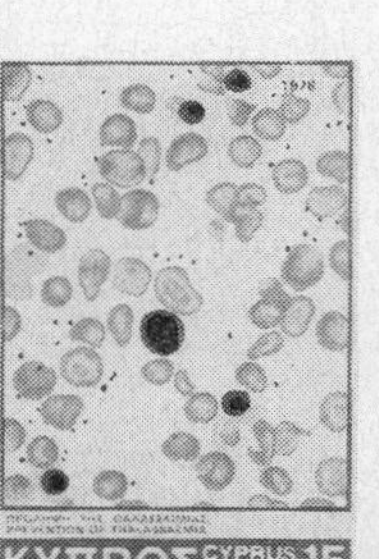

198. Affected Blood Corpuscles (Prevention of Thalassaemia).

199. Icon Stand.

1978. Anniversaries and Events.
511. 198. 15 m. multicoloured .. 10 10
512. – 35 m. multicoloured .. 15 10
513. – 75 m. black and grey .. 20 30
514. – 125 m. multicoloured 35 80
DESIGNS—VERT. 35 m. Aristotle (sculpture) (2300th Death Anniv.). HORIZ 75 m. " Heads " (Human Rights). 125 m. Wright brothers and " Flyer " (75th Anniv. of Powered Flight).

1978. Christmas.
515. 199. 15 m. multicoloured .. 10 10
516. – 35 m. multicoloured .. 15 10
517. – 150 m. multicoloured 40 60
DESIGNS: 35 m., 150 m. Different icon stands.

200. Aphrodite (statue from Soli).

1979. Goddess Aphrodite (1st issue). Mult.
518. 75 m. Type **200** 25 10
519. 125 m. Aphrodite on shell (detail from Botticelli's " Birth of Venus ") .. 35 25
See also Nos. 584/5.

201. Van, Larnaca–Nicosia Mail-coach and Envelope.

1979. Europa. Communications. Multicoloured.
520. 25 m. Type **201** .. 15 10
521. 75 m. Radar, satellite and early telephone .. 25 15
522. 125 m. Aircraft, ship and envelopes 35 60

202. Peacock wrasse.

1979. Flora and Fauna. Multicoloured.
523. 25 m. Type **202** 15 10
524. 50 m. Black partridge. (vert.) 45 20
525. 75 m. Cedar (vert.) .. 45 20
526. 125 m. Mule. 50 60

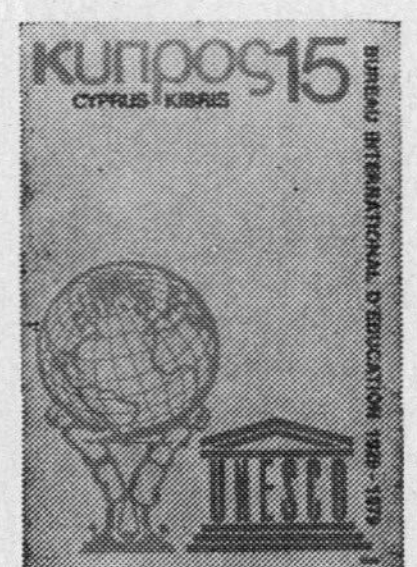

203. I.B.E. and U.N.E.S.C.O. Emblems.

1979. Anniversaries and Events.
527. **203.** 15 m. multicoloured .. 10 10
528. – 25 m. multicoloured .. 10 10
529. – 50 m. blk., brn. & ochre 20 15
530. – 75 m. multicoloured .. 25 10
531. – 100 m. multicoloured 30 20
532. – 125 m. multicoloured 30 40
DESIGNS AND COMMEMORATIONS—VERT. 15 m. Type **203** (International Bureau of Education. 50th anniv.). 125 m. Rotary International emblem and " 75 " (75th anniv.). HORIZ. 25 m. Graphic design of dove and stamp album (Cyprus Philatelic Society. 20th anniv.). 50 m. Lord Kitchener and map of Cyprus (Cyprus Survey Cent.). 75 m. Child's face (International Year of the Child). 100 m. Graphic design of footballers (U.E.F.A. European Football Association) (25th anniv.).

204. " Jesus " (from Church of the Virgin Mary, Arakas, Lagoudhera).

1979. Christmas. Icons. Multicoloured.
533. 15 m. Type **204** 10 10
534. 35 m. " Nativity " (Church of St. Nicholas, Famagusta District) (29 × 41 mm.) 10 10
535. 150 m. " Holy Mary " (Church of the Virgin Mary, Arakas) 25 30

205. 1880 ½d. Stamp with " 969 " (Nicosia) Postmark.

1980. Centenary of Cyprus Stamp. Multicoloured.
536. 40 m. Type **205** 10 10
537. 125 m. 1880 2½ d. stamp with " 974 " (Kyrenia) postmark 15 15
538. 175 m. 1880 1s. stamps with " 942 " (Larnaca) postmark 15 20

206. St. Barnabas (patron saint of Cyprus).

208. Gold Necklace, Arsos (7th cent. BC).

207. Sailing.

1980. Europa. Personalities. Multicoloured.
540. 40 m. Type **206** 10 10
541. 125 m. Zeno of Citium (founder of Stoic philosophy) 20 20

1980. Olympic Games, Moscow. Multicoloured.
542. 40 m. Type **207** 10 10
543. 125 m. Swimming .. 20 20
544. 200 m. Gymnastics .. 25 25

1980. Archaeological Treasures.
545. **208.** 10 m. multicoloured .. 30 35
546. – 15 m. multicoloured .. 30 35
547. – 25 m. multicoloured .. 30 10
548. – 40 m. multicoloured .. 40 30
549. – 50 m. multicoloured .. 40 10
550. – 75 m. multicoloured .. 50 40
551. – 100 m. multicoloured 75 15
552. – 125 m. multicoloured 75 15
553. – 150 m. multicoloured 90 15
554. – 175 m. multicoloured 90 40
555. – 200 m. multicoloured 90 30
556. – 500 m. multicoloured 1·50 1·00
557. – £1 multicoloured .. 2·00 1·25
558. – £2 multicoloured .. 3·75 2·00
DESIGNS—HORIZ. 15 m. Bronze Cow, Vouni Palace (5th cent. BC). 40 m. Gold finger-ring, Enkomi (13th cent. BC). 500 m. Stone Bowl, Khirokitia (6th millennium BC). VERT. 25 m. Amphora, Salamis (6th cent. BC). 50 m. Bronze Cauldron, Salamis (8th cent. BC), 75 m. Funerary Stele, Marion (5th cent. BC). 100 m. Jug (15–14th cent. BC). 125 m. Warrior (Terracotta) (6–5th cent. BC). 150 m. Lions attacking Bull (bronze relief), Vouni Palace (5th cent. BC). 175 m. Faience Rhyton, Kition (13th cent. BC). 200 m. Bronze statue of Ingot God, Enkomi (12th cent. BC). £1, Ivory Plaque, Salamis (7th cent. BC). £2, " Leda and the Swan " (mosaic), Kouklia (3rd cent. AD).

209. Cyprus Flag.

1980. 20th Anniv. of Republic of Cyprus. Multicoloured.
559. 40 m. Type **209** 10 10
560. 125 m. Signing Treaty of Establishment (41 × 29 mm.) 20 15
561. 175 m. Archbishop Makarios 35 25

210. Head and Peace Dove.

1980. International Day of Solidarity with Palestinian People.
562. **210.** 40 m. black and grey .. 20 20
563. – 125 m. black and grey 35 35
DESIGN: 125 m. Head and dove with olive branch.

211. Pulpit, Tripiotis Church, Nicosia. **212.** Folk Dancing.

1980. Christmas. Multicoloured.
564. 25 m. Type **211** 10 10
565. 100 m. Holy Doors, Panayia Church Paralimni 15 15
565. 125 m. Pulpit, Ayios Lazaros Church, Larnaca 15 15

1981. Europa. Folklore, showing folk-dancing from painting by T. Photiades.
567. **212.** 40 m. multicoloured .. 40 10
568. – 175 m. multicoloured 1·00 60

213. Self-portrait. **214.** " Ophrys kotschyi ".

1981. 500th Anniv. of Leonardo da Vinci's Visit. Multicoloured.
569. 50 m. Type **213** 40 10
570. 125 m. "The Last Supper" (50 × 25 mm.) 70 40
571. 175 m Lace (Cyprus) and Milan Cathedral .. 95 60

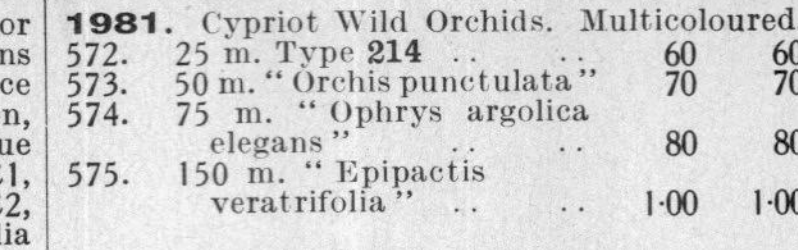
1981. Cypriot Wild Orchids. Multicoloured.
572. 25 m. Type **214** 60 60
573. 50 m. " Orchis punctulata " 70 70
574. 75 m. " Ophrys argolica elegans " 80 80
575. 150 m. " Epipactis veratrifolia " .. .. 1·00 1·00

215. Heinrich von Stephan.

1981. Commemorations.
576. **215.** 25 m. dark green, green and blue 20 10
577. – 40 m. multicoloured .. 25 10
578. – 125 m. blk., red & grn. 50 25
579. – 150 m. multicoloured 60 30
580. – 200 m. multicoloured 60 35
DESIGNS AND COMMEMORATIONS: 25 m., Type **137** (150th birth anniv. of Heinrich von Stephan (founder of U.P.U.). 40 m. Stylised man holding dish of food (World Food Day). 125 m., Stylised hands (International Year for Disabled People). 150 m. Stylised building and flower (European Campaign for Urban Renaissance). 200 m. Prince Charles, Lady Diana Spencer and St. Paul's Cathedral (Royal Wedding).

216. " The Lady of the Angels " (from Church of the Transfiguration of Christ, Palekhori).

1981. Christmas. Murals from Nicosia District Churches. Multicoloured.
581. 25 m. Type **216** 20 10
582. 100 m. "Christ Pantokrator" (Church of Madonna of Arakas, Lagoudera) (vert.) .. 60 20
583. 125 m. "Baptism of Christ" (Church of Our Lady of Assinou, Nikitari) .. 70 30

217. " Louomene " (Aphrodite bathing) (statue, 250 B.C.).

1982. Aphrodite (Greek goddess of love and beauty) Commemoration. (2nd issue). Mult.
584. 125 m. Type **217** 80 45
585. 175 m. " Anadyomene " (Aphrodite emerging from the waters) (Titian) .. 95 65

218. Naval Battle with Greek Fire.

1982. Europa. Historic Events. Multicoloured.
586. 40 m. Type **218** 60 10
587. 175 m. Conversion of Roman Proconsul Sergius Paulus to Christianity, Paphos, 45 A.D. .. .. 1·50 1·75

219. " XP " (monogram of Christ) (mosaic).

1982. World Cultural Heritage. Mult.

588. 50 m. Type **219** 30 10
589. 125 m. Head of priest-king of Paphos (sculpture) (24 × 37 mm.) 60 40
590. 225 m. Theseus (Greek god) (mosaic) .. .. .. 1·00 70

1982. No. 550 surch. **100.**

591. 100 m. on 75 m. Funerary stele, Marion (5th-century B.C.) 50 40

221. Cyprus and Stylised " 75 ".

1982. 75th Anniv. of Boy Scout Movement. Multicoloured.

592. 100 m. Type **221** .. 40 20
593. 125 m. Lord Baden-Powell 45 30
594. 175 m. Camp-site 55 55

222. Holy Communion, The Bread.

1982. Christmas.

595. **222.** 25 m. multicoloured .. 10 10
596. – 100 m. gold and black 30 15
597. – 250 m. multicoloured 70 75

DESIGN—VERT. 100 m. Holy Chalice. HORIZ. 250 m. Holy Communion, The Wine.

223. Cyprus Forest Industries' Sawmill.

1983. Commonwealth Day. Multicoloured.

598. 50 m. Type **223** 10 10
599. 125 m. "Ikarios and the Discovery of Wine" (3rd-cent. mosaic) .. 25 25
600. 150 m. Folk-dancers, Commonwealth Film and Television Festival, 1980 30 35
601. 175 m. Royal Exhibition Building, Melbourne (Commonwealth Heads of Government Meeting, 1981) 35 40

224. Cyprosyllabic Inscription (6th cent. B.C.).

1983. Europa. Multicoloured.

602. 50 m. Type **224** 60 10
603. 200 m. Copper ore, ingot (Enkomi 1400–1250 B.C.) and bronze jug (2nd cent. A.D.) .. .. 1·75 2·00

225. "Pararge aegeria".

1983. Butterflies. Multicoloured.

604 60 m. Type **225** 25 20
605 130 m. "Aricia agestis" .. 45 35
606 250 m. "Glaucopsyche melanops" 85 85

1983. Nos. 545/56 surch.

607. 1 c. on 10 m. Type **208** .. 35 40
608. 2 c. on 15 m. Bronze cow, Vouni Palace (5th-cent. B.C.) (horiz.) 35 40
609. 3 c. on 25 m. Amphora, Salamis (16th-cent. B.C.) 35 20
610. 4 c. on 40 m. Gold finger-ring, Enkomi (13th-cent. B.C.) (horiz.) 40 20
611. 5 c. on 50 m. Bronze cauldron, Salamis (8th-cent. B.C.) 50 50
612. 6 c. on 75 m. Funerary stele, Marion (5th-cent. B.C.) .. 50 20
613. 10 c. on 100 m. Jug (15–14th-cent. B.C.) 60 40
614. 13 c. on 125 m. Warrior (Terracotta) (6–5th-cent. B.C.) 70 50
615. 15 c. on 150 m. Lions attacking bull (bronze relief), Vouni Palace 5th-cent. B.C.) (horiz.) .. 85 55
616. 20 c. on 200 m. Bronze statue of Ingot God, Enkomi (12th-cent. B.C.) .. 85 65
617. 25 c. on 175 m. Faience rhyton, Kition (13th-cent. B.C.) .. .. 95 1·10
618. 50 c. on 500 m. Stone bowl, Khirokitia (6th-millennium B.C.) (horiz.) .. 1·50 2·00

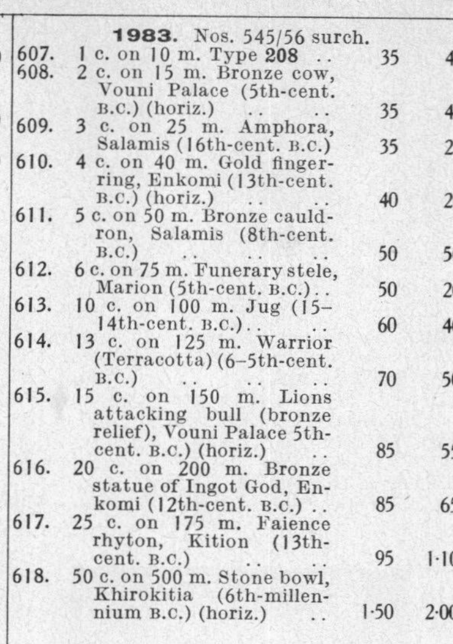

227. View of power station.

1983. Anniversaries and Events. Mult.

619. 3 c. Type **227** 10 10
620. 6 c. W.C.Y. logo 20 15
621. 13 c. "Sol Olympia" (liner) and "Polys" (tanker) .. 40 30
622. 15 c. Human Rights emblem and map of Europe 45 35
623. 20 c. Nicos Kazantzakis .. 55 45
624. 25 c. Makarios in church .. 65 65

COMMEMORATIONS: 3 c. 30th anniv. of Cyprus Electricity Authority. 6 c. World Communications Year. 13 c. 25th anniv. of International Maritime Organization. 15 c. 35th anniv. of Universal Declaration of Human Rights. 20 c. Birth centenary. 25 c. 70th birth anniv.

228. St. Lazaros Church, Larnaca.

1983. Christmas. Multicoloured.

625. 4 c. Type **228** 20 10
626. 13 c. St. Varvara church, Kaimakli, Nicosia .. 55 35
627. 20 c. St. Ioannis church, Larnaca 90 70

229. Waterside Cafe, Larnaca.

1984. Old Engravings. Each brown and black.

628. 6 c. Type **229** 15 10
629. 20 c. Bazaar at Larnaca (39 × 25 mm.) 50 65
630. 30 c. Famagusta Gate, Nicosia (39 × 25 mm.) .. 80 1·25

230. C.E.P.T. 25th Anniversary Logo.

1984. Europa.

632. **230.** 6 c. light green, green and black 75 10
633. 15 c. light blue, blue and black .. .. 1·50 1·75

1984. Obligatory Tax. Refugee Fund. As T **188** but new value and dated "1984".

634. 1 c. black 10 10

231. Running.

1984. Olympic Games, Los Angeles. Multicoloured.

635. 3 c. Type **231** 20 10
636. 4 c. Olympic column .. 20 10
637. 13 c. Swimming 55 60
638. 20 c. Gymnastics .. .. 80 1·00

232. Prisoners-of-War.

1984. 10th Anniv. of Turkish Landings in Cyprus. Multicoloured.

639. 15 c. Type **232** 40 45
640. 20 c. Map and burning buildings 50 55

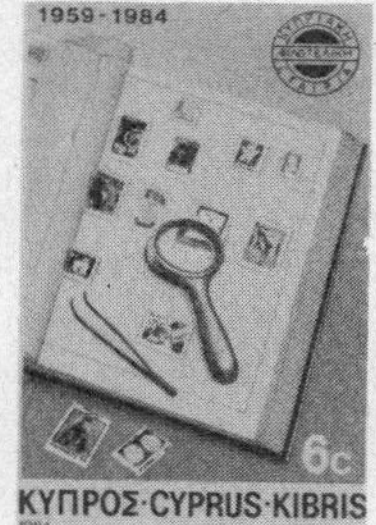

233. Open Stamp Album (25th Anniv. of Cyprus Philatelic Society).

1984. Anniversaries and Events. Mult.

641. 6 c. Type **233** 40 10
642. 10 c. Football in motion (horiz.) (Cyprus Football Association—50th anniv.) 55 30
643. 15 c. "Dr. George Papanicolaou" (medical scientist—birth cent.) .. 75 70
644. 25 c. Antique map of Cyprus and ikon (horiz.) (International Symposia on Cartography and Medieval Paleography) 1·25 1·50

234. St. Mark (miniature from 11th-century Gospel).

1984. Christmas. Illuminated Gospels. Multicoloured.

645. 4 c. Type **234** 35 10
646. 13 c. Beginning of St. Mark's Gospel .. .. 1·00 75
647. 20 c. St. Luke (miniature from 11th-cent. Gospel) 1·50 1·75

235. Autumn at Platania, Troodos Mountains.

1985. Cyprus Scenes and Landscapes. Multicoloured.

648. 1 c. Type **235** 20 40
649. 2 c. Ayia Napa Monastery 20 40
650. 3 c. Phini Village—panoramic view .. 20 30
651. 4 c. Kykko Monastery .. 20 30
652. 5 c. Beach at Makronissos, Ayia Napa 20 20
653. 6 c. Village street, Omodhos (vert.) .. 30 20
654. 10 c. Panoramic sea view 45 30
655. 13 c. Windsurfing 55 30
656. 15 c. Beach at Protaras .. 65 40
657. 20 c. Forestry for development (vert.) 80 50
658. 25 c. Sunrise at Protaras (vert.) .. .. .. 1·00 1·00
659. 30 c. Village house, Pera .. 1·25 1·25
660. 50 c. Apollo Hylates Sanctuary, Curium .. 2·00 1·75
661. £1 Snow on Troodos Mountains (vert.) .. 3·50 3·00
662. £5 Personification of Autumn, House of Dionysos, Paphos (vert.) 13·00 15·00

236. Clay Idols of Musicians (7/6th Century B.C.)

1985. Europa. European Music Year. Mult.

663. 6 c. Type **236** .. .. 1·25 20
664. 15 c. Violin, lute, flute and score from the "Cyprus Suite" .. .. .. 2·00 1·40

237. Cyprus Coat of Arms (25th Anniv. of Republic).

238. "The Visit of the Madonna to Elizabeth" (Lambadistis Monastery, Kalopanayiotis).

1985. Anniversaries and Events.

665. **237.** 4 c. multicoloured .. 40 15
666. – 6 c. multicoloured .. 45 15
667. – 13 c. multicoloured .. 1·00 70
668. – 15 c. black olive-black and orange .. 1·50 1·75
669. – 20 c. multicoloured .. 1·50 2·00

DESIGNS—HORIZ. (43 × 30 mm). 6 c. "Barn of Liopetri" (detail) (Pol. Georghiou) (30th Anniv. of EOKA Campaign). 13 c. Three profiles (International Youth Year). 15 c. Solon Michaelides (composer and conductor) (European Music Year). VERT. (as T **237**)—20 c. U.N. Building, New York, and flags (40th Anniv. of United Nations Organisation).

1985. Christmas. Frescoes from Cypriot Churches. Multicoloured.

670. 4 c. Type **238** 35 10
671. 13 c. "The Nativity" (Lambadistis Monastery, Kalopanayiotis) .. 1·25 65
672. 20 c. "Candlemas-day" (Asinou Church) .. 1·75 1·75

239. Figure from Hellenistic Spoon Handle.

1986. New Archaeological Museum Fund. Multicoloured.

673. 15 c. Type **239** .. .. 1·00 45
674. 20 c. Pattern from early Ionian helmet and foot from statue .. .. 1·25 75
675. 25 c. Roman statue of Eros and Psyche .. .. 1·50 95
676. 30 c. Head of statue .. 1·75 1·10

No. 676 also commemorates the 50th anniversary of the Department of Antiquities.

240. Cyprus Mouflon and Cedars.

1986. Europa. Protection of Nature and the Environment. Multicoloured.

678. 7 c. Type **240** .. .. 1·00 15
679. 17 c. Greater flamingos at Larnaca Salt Lake .. 2·50 2·50

241. "Chlamys pesfelis".

1986. Sea Shells. Multicoloured.

680. 5 c. Type **241** 40 15
681. 7 c. "Charonia variegata" 45 15
682. 18 c. "Murex brandaris" .. 1·00 1·00
683. 25 c. "Cypraea spurca" .. 1·50 1·75

1986. Nos. 653 and 655 surch.

684. 7 c. on 6 c. Village street, Omodhos (vert.) .. 50 30
685. 18 c. on 13 c. Windsurfing 1·40 60

243. Globe, Outline Map of Cyprus and Swallows (Overseas Cypriots' Year).

1986. Anniversaries and Events. Mult.

686. 15 c. Type **243** .. .. 1·25 45
687. 18 c. Halley's Comet over Cyprus beach (40 × 23 mm.) .. 1·50 1·75
688. 18 c. Comet's tail over sea and Edmond Halley (40 × 23 mm.) .. .. 1·50 1·75

Nos. 687/8 were printed together, se-tenant, forming a composite design.

244. Pedestrian Crossing.

1986. Road Safety Campaign. Multicoloured.

689. 5 c. Type **244** .. .. 1·00 30
690. 7 c. Motor cycle crash helmet .. .. .. 1·10 30
691. 18 c. Hands fastening car seat belt .. .. .. 2·25 2·75

245. "The Nativity" (Church of Panayia tou Araka).

1986. Christmas. International Peace Year. Details of Nativity frescoes from Cypriot churches. Multicoloured.

692. 5 c. Type **245** 45 15
693. 15 c. Church of Panayia tou Moutoulla .. .. 1·50 90
694. 17 c. Church of St. Nicholas tis Steyis .. 1·75 1·10

246. Church of Virgin Mary, Asinou.

1987. Troodos Churches on the World Heritage List. Multicoloured.

695. 15 c. Type **246** .. .. 1·00 1·00
696. 15 c. Fresco of Virgin Mary, Moutoulla's Church .. .. .. 1·00 1·00
697. 15 c. Church of Virgin Mary, Podithou .. 1·00 1·00
698. 15 c. Fresco of Three Apostles, St. Ioannis Lampadistis Monastery 1·00 1·00
699. 15 c. Annunciation fresco, Church of the Holy Cross, Pelentriou .. 1·00 1·00
700. 15 c. Fresco of Saints, Church of the Cross, Ayiasmati .. 1·00 1·00
701. 15 c. Fresco of Archangel Michael and Donor, Pedoula's Church of St. Michael .. .. 1·00 1·00
702. 15 c. Church of St. Nicolaos, Steyis.. 1·00 1·00
703. 15 c. Fresco of Prophets, Church of Virgin Mary, Araka .. .. 1·00 1·00

247. Proposed Central Bank of Cyprus Building.

1987. Europa. Modern Architecture.

704. **247.** 7 c. multicoloured .. 1·00 10
705. – 18 c. blk., grey & grn. 2·00 2·00

DESIGN: 18 c. Headquarters complex, Cyprus Telecommunications Authority.

248. Remains of Ancient Ship and Kyrenia Castle.

1987. Voyage of "Kyrenia II" (replica of ancient ship). Multicoloured.

706. 2 c. Type **248** 30 20
707. 3 c. "Kyrenia II" under construction, 1982–5 .. 30 20
708. 5 c. "Kyrenia II" at Paphos, 1986 .. .. 55 30
709. 17 c. "Kyrenia II" at New York, 1986 .. .. 1·40 1·10

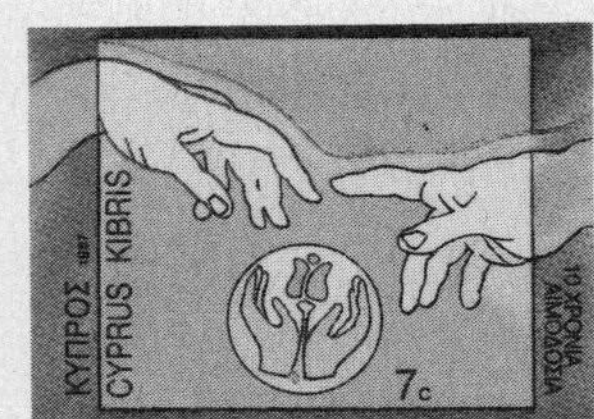

249. Hands (from Michelangelo's "Creation") and Emblem.

1987. Anniversaries and Events. Mult.

710. 7 c. Type **249** (10th anniv. of Blood Donation Co-ordinating Committee) 60 25
711. 15 c. Snail with flowered shell and countryside (European Countryside Campaign) .. 1·40 1·25
712. 20 c. Symbols of ocean bed and Earth's crust ("Troodos '87" Ophiolites and Oceanic Lithosphere Symposium) 1·75 2·00

250. Nativity Crib.

1987. Christmas. Traditional Customs. Mult.

713. 5 c. Type **250** 35 15
714. 15 c. Door knocker decorated with foliage .. 1·10 85
715. 17 c. Bowl of fruit and nuts 1·25 1·10

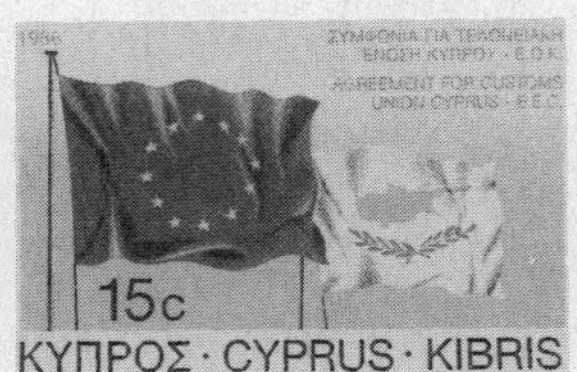

251 Flags of Cyprus and E.E.C.

1988. Cypriot–E.E.C. Customs Union. Mult.

716 15 c. Type **251** .. 90 90
717 18 c. Outline maps of Cyprus and E.E.C. countries .. .. 1·10 1·10

252 Intelpost Telefax Terminal (Illustration reduced, actual size 48 × 33 mm)

1988. Europa. Transport and Communications. Multicoloured.

718 7 c. Type **252** 65 65
719 7 c. Car driver using mobile telephone .. 65 65
720 18 c. Nose of Cyprus Airways airliner and flamingos .. .. 1·25 1·25
721 18 c. Airliner in flight and flamingos .. .. 1·25 1·25

253 Sailing

1988. Olympic Games, Seoul. Multicoloured.

722 5 c. Type **253** 30 20
723 7 c. Athletes at start .. 35 40
724 10 c. Shooting 40 50
725 20 c. Judo .. .. 90 1·40

254 Conference Emblem

1988. Non-Aligned Foreign Ministers' Conference, Nicosia.

726 **254** 1 c. black, blue & grn 10 10
727 – 10 c. multicoloured .. 45 30
728 – 50 c. multicoloured .. 2·25 2·25

DESIGNS: 10 c. Emblem of Republic of Cyprus; 50 c. Nehru, Tito, Nasser and Makarios.

1988. No. 651 surch **15 c.**

730 15 c. on 4 c. Kykko Monastery 70 40

256 "Presentation of Christ at the Temple" (Church of Holy Cross tou Agiasmati)

1988. Christmas. Designs showing frescoes from Cypriot churches. Multicoloured

731 5 c. Type **256** 35 15
732 15 c. "Virgin and Child" (St. John Lampadistis Monastery) .. 90 70
733 17 c. "Adoration of the Magi" (St. John Lampadistis Monastery) 1·25 80

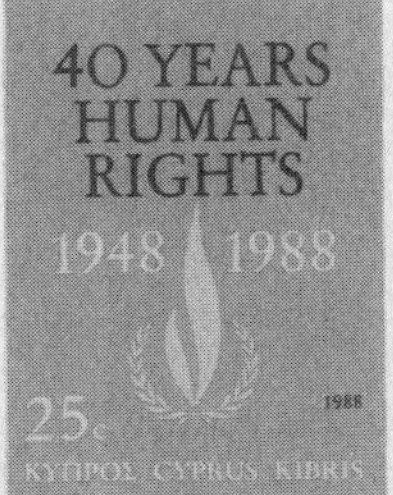

257 Human Rights Logo

1988. 40th Anniv of Universal Declaration of Human Rights.

734 **257** 25 c. lt blue, dp bl & bl 90 1·25

258 Basketball

1989. 3rd Small European States' Games, Nicosia. Multicoloured.

No.	Description	Mint	Used
735	1 c. Type **258**	20	15
736	5 c. Javelin	45	50
737	15 c. Wrestling	60	65
738	18 c. Athletics	1·25	1·40

259 Lingri Stick Game

1989. Europa. Children's Games. Mult.

No.	Description	Mint	Used
740	7 c. Type **259**	25	35
741	7 c. Ziziros	25	35
742	18 c. Sitsia	50	70
743	18 c. Leapfrog	50	70

260 "Universal Man"

1989. Bicentenary of the French Revolution.

No.	Description	Mint	Used
744	**260** 18 c. multicoloured	60	60

261 Stylized Human Figures

1989. Centenary of Interparliamentary Union (15 c.) and 9th Non-Aligned Summit Conference, Belgrade (30 c.). Multicoloured.

No.	Description	Mint	Used
745	15 c. Type **261**	50	40
746	30 c. Conference logo	1·00	1·10

1989. Obligatory Tax. Refugee Fund. As No. 634 but with upper and lower inscriptions redrawn and differently dated.

No.	Description	Mint	Used
747	1 c. black and grey	30	30

262 Worker Bees tending Larvae

1989. Bee-keeping. Multicoloured.

No.	Description	Mint	Used
748	3 c. Type **262**	15	10
749	10 c. Bee on rock-rose flower	40	30
750	15 c. Bee on lemon flower	60	40
751	18 c. Queen and worker bees	65	50

263 Outstretched Hand and Profile (aid for Armenian earthquake victims)

1989. Anniversaries and Events. Mult.

No.	Description	Mint	Used
752	3 c. Type **263**	15	10
753	5 c. Airmail envelope (Cyprus Philatelic Society F.I.P. membership)	20	20
754	7 c. Crab symbol and daisy (European Cancer Year)	35	30
755	17 c. Vegetables and fish (World Food Day)	65	65

264 Winter (detail from "Four Seasons")

1989. Roman Mosaics from Paphos. Mult.

No.	Description	Mint	Used
756	1 c. Type **264**	10	10
757	2 c. Personification of Crete (32 × 24 mm)	10	10
758	3 c. Centaur and Maenad (24 × 32 mm)	10	10
759	4 c. Poseidon and Amymone (32 × 24 mm)	10	15
760	5 c. Leda	10	15
761	7 c. Apollon	15	20
762	10 c. Hermes and Dionysos (24 × 32 mm)	25	30
763	15 c. Cassiopeia	35	40
764	18 c. Orpheus (32 × 24 mm)	45	50
765	20 c. Nymphs (24 × 32 mm)	50	55
766	25 c. Amazon (24 × 32 mm)	60	65
767	40 c. Doris (32 × 24 mm)	1·00	1·10
768	50 c. Heracles and the Lion (39 × 27 mm)	1·25	1·40
769	£1 Apollon and Daphne (39 × 27 mm)	2·50	2·75
770	£3 Cupid (39 × 27 mm)	7·50	7·75

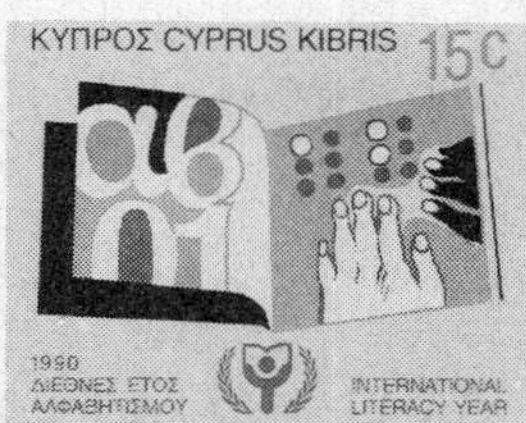

265 Hands and Open Book (International Literacy Year)

1990. Anniversaries and Events. Mult.

No.	Description	Mint	Used
771	15 c. Type **265**	50	50
772	17 c. Dove and profiles (83rd Inter-Parliamentary Conference, Nicosia)	60	60
773	18 c. Lions International emblem (Lions Europa Forum, Limassol)	70	70

266 District Post Office, Paphos

1990. Europa. Post Office Buildings. Mult.

No.	Description	Mint	Used
774	7 c. Type **266**	35	25
775	18 c. City Centre Post Office, Limassol	65	1·00

267 Symbolic Lips (25th anniv of Hotel and Catering Institute) (¾ size illustration)

1990. European Tourism Year. Multicoloured.

No.	Description	Mint	Used
776	5 c. Type **267**	20	20
777	7 c. Bell tower, St. Lazarus Church (1100th anniv)	25	25
778	15 c. Butterflies and woman	40	40
779	18 c. Birds and man	50	50

268 Sun (wood carving)

1990. 30th Anniv of Republic. Multicoloured.

No.	Description	Mint	Used
780	15 c. Type **268**	40	45
781	17 c. Bulls (pottery design)	50	50
782	18 c. Fishes (pottery design)	60	60
783	40 c. Tree and birds (wood carving)	1·25	1·25

269 "Chionodoxa lochiae"

1990. Endangered Wild Flowers. Book illustrations by Elektra Megaw. Mult.

No.	Description	Mint	Used
785	2 c. Type **269**	15	15
786	3 c. "Pancratium maritimum"	15	15
787	5 c. "Paeonia mascula"	20	20
788	7 c. "Cyclamen cyprium"	25	25
789	15 c. "Tulipa cypria"	45	45
790	18 c. "Crocus cyprius"	65	75

270 "Nativity"

1990. Christmas. 16th-Century Icons. Mult.

No.	Description	Mint	Used
791	5 c. Type **270**	20	20
792	15 c. "Virgin Hodegetria"	50	50
793	17 c. "Nativity" (different)	70	70

271 Archangel

1991. 6th-century Mosaics from Kanakaria Church. Multicoloured.

No.	Description	Mint	Used
794	5 c. Type **271**	15	15
795	15 c. Christ Child	45	45
796	17 c. St. James	55	55
797	18 c. St. Matthew	60	60

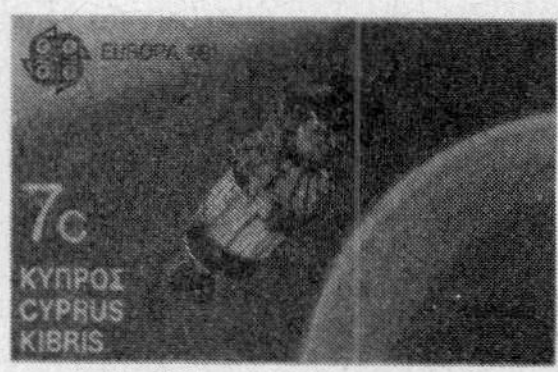

272 "Ulysses" Spacecraft

1991. Europa. Europe in Space. Mult.

No.	Description	Mint	Used
798	7 c. Type **272**	25	20
799	18 c. "Giotto" and Halley's Comet	70	80

273 Young Cyprus Wheatear

1991. Cyprus Wheatear. Multicoloured.

No.	Description	Mint	Used
800	5 c. Type **273**	15	15
801	7 c. Adult bird in autumn plumage	20	20
802	15 c. Adult male in breeding plumage	45	45
803	30 c. Adult female in breeding plumage	90	90

274 Mother and Child with Tents

1991. 40th Anniv of U.N. Commission for Refugees. Each dp brown, brown and silver.

No.	Description	Mint	Used
804	5 c. Type **274**	10	15
805	15 c. Three pairs of legs	35	40
806	18 c. Three children	45	50

1991. Obligatory Tax. Refugee Fund. As No. 747 but inscr "1991".

No.	Description	Mint	Used
807	1 c. black and grey	10	10

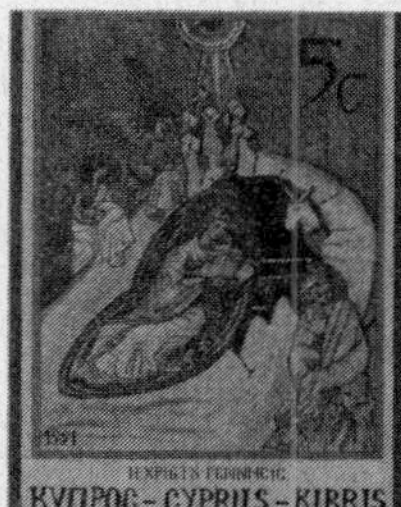

275 The Nativity

1991. Christmas. Multicoloured.

No.	Description	Mint	Used
808	5 c. Type **275**	10	10
809	15 c. Saint Basil	35	40
810	17 c. Baptism of Jesus	40	45

TURKISH CYPRIOT POSTS

After the inter-communal clashes during December 1963, a separate postal service was established on 6 January 1964, between some of the Turkish Cypriot areas, using handstamps inscribed "KIBRIS TURK POSTALARI". During 1964, however, an agreement was reached between representatives of the two communities for the restoration of postal services. This agreement, to which the United Nations representatives were a party, was ratified in November 1966 by the Republic's Council of Ministers. Under the scheme postal services were provided for the Turkish Cypriot communities in Famagusta, Limassol, Lefka and Nicosia, staffed by Turkish Cypriot employees of the Cypriot Department of Posts.

On 8 April 1970, 5 m. and 15 m. locally-produced labels, originally designated "Social Aid Stamps", were issued by the Turkish Cypriot community and these can be found on commercial covers. These local stamps are outside the scope of this catalogue.

On 29 October 1973 Nos. 1/7 were placed on sale, but were again used only on mail between the Turkish Cypriot areas.

Following the intervention by the Republic of Turkey in July 1974 these stamps replaced issues of the Republic of Cyprus in that part of the island, north and east of the Attila Line, controlled by the Autonomous Turkish Cypriot Administration.

1974. 1000 mhls = 1 pound.
1978. 100 kurus = 1 lira.

1. 50th Anniversary Emblem.

1974. 50th Anniv. of Republic of Turkey.
1. – 3 m. multicoloured .. 30·00 30·00
2. – 5 m. multicoloured .. 60 40
3. – 10 m. multicoloured .. 50 20
4. 1. 15 m. red and black .. 2·50 1·50
5. – 20 m. multicoloured .. 70 20
6. – 50 m. multicoloured .. 2·00 1·50
7. – 70 m. multicoloured .. 16·00 16·00

DESIGNS—VERT. 3 m. Woman sentry. 10 m. Man and woman with Turkish flags. 20 m. Ataturk statue, Kyrenia Gate, Nicosia. 50 m. "The Fallen". HORIZ. 5 m. Military parade, Nicosia. 70 m. Turkish flag and map of Cyprus.

These were first issued in 1973 for local use.

1975. Proclamation of the Turkish Federated State of Cyprus. Nos. 3 and 5 surch. **KIBRIS TURK FEDERE DEVLETI 13.2.1975.**
8. 30 m. on 20 m. multicoloured 1·00 1·00
9. 100 m. on 10 m. multicoloured 1·50 2·25

3. Namik Kemal's Bust, Famagusta.

1975. Multicoloured.
10. 3 m. Type **3** 15 20
11. 10 m. Ataturk Statue, Nicosia 15 10
12. 15 m. St. Hilarion Castle .. 25 20
13. 20 m. Ataturk Square, Nicosia 35 20
14. 25 m. Famagusta Beach .. 35 25
15. 30 m. Kyrenia Harbour .. 45 10
16. 50 m. Lala Mustafa Pasha Mosque, Famagusta (vert.) 60 10
17. 100 m. Interior, Kyrenia Castle 1·25 75
18. 250 m. Castle walls, Kyrenia 2·25 2·25
19. 500 m. Othello Tower, Famagusta (vert.) .. 4·50 4·00

See also Nos. 36/8.

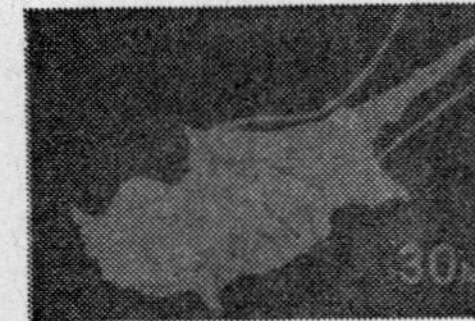

4. Map of Cyprus.

1975. "Peace in Cyprus". Multicoloured.
20. 30 m. Type **4** 75 15
21. 50 m. Map, laurel and broken chain 85 20
22. 150 m. Map and laurel-sprig on globe (vert.) .. .. 2·25 1·00

MINIMUM PRICE

The minimum price quoted is 10p which represents a handling charge rather than a basis for valuing common stamps. For further notes about prices see introductory pages.

5. "Pomegranates" (I. V. Guney).

1975. Europa. Paintings. Multicoloured.
23. 90 m. Type **5** 80 60
24. 100 m. "Harvest Time" (F. Direkoglu) 80 60

1976. Nos. 16/17 surch.
25. 10 m. on 50 m. multicoloured 50 70
26. 30 m. on 100 m. multicoloured 50 80

7. "Expectation" (ceramic statuette).

9. Olympic Symbol "Flower".

8. Carob.

1976. Europa. Multicoloured.
27. 60 m. Type **7** 40 50
28. 120 m. "Man in Meditation" 50 75

1976. Export Products. Fruits. Mult.
29. 10 m. Type **8** 25 10
30. 25 m. Mandarin 35 10
31. 40 m. Strawberry 40 15
32. 60 m. Orange 50 30
33. 80 m. Lemon .. .. 55 1·10

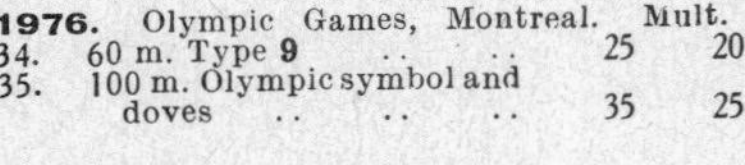

1976. Olympic Games, Montreal. Mult.
34. 60 m. Type **9** 25 20
35. 100 m. Olympic symbol and doves 35 25

10. Kyrema Harbour.

1976. Multicoloured.
36. 5 m. Type **10** 30 10
37. 15 m. St. Hilarion Castle.. 40 10
38. 20 m. Ataturk Square, Nicosia 40 10

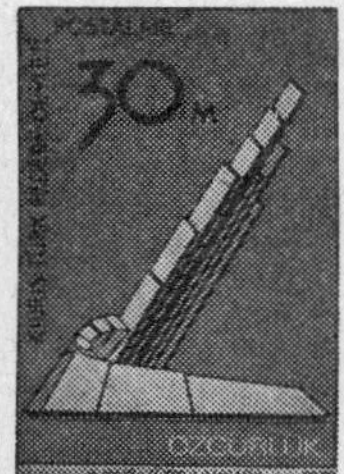

11. Liberation Monument, Karaeglanoglu (Ay. Georghios).

1976. Liberation Monument.
47. 11. 30 m. blue, pink and black 15 20
48. – 150 m. red, pink and black 35 45

DESIGN: 150 m. Liberation Monument (different view).

12. Hotel, Salamis Bay.

1977. Europa. Multicoloured.
49. 80 m. Type **12** 30 65
50. 100 m. Kyrenia Port .. 35 65

13. Pottery.

1977. Handicrafts. Multicoloured.
51. 15 m. Type **13** 10 10
52. 30 m. Pottery (vert.) .. 10 10
53. 125 m. Basketware .. 30 50

14. Arap Ahmet Pasha Mosque, Nicosia.

1977. Turkish Buildings in Cyprus. Mult.
54. 20 m. Type **14** 10 10
55. 40 m. Paphos Castle (horiz.) 10 10
56. 70 m. Bekir Pasha aqueducts (horiz.) 15 20
57. 80 m. Sultan Mahmut library (horiz.) 15 25

15. Namik Kemal (bust) and House, Famagusta.

1977. Namik Kemal (patriotic poet). Mult.
58. 30 m. Type **15** 15 15
59. 140 m. Namik Kemal (portrait) (vert.) 35 50

16. Old Man and Woman.

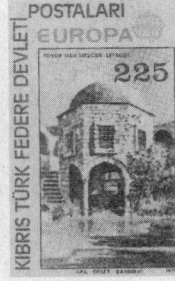

17. Oratory in Buyuk Han, Nicosia.

1978. Social Security.
60. 16. 150 k. black, yell. & blue 10 10
61. – 275 k. blk., orge. and grn. 15 15
62. – 375 k. black, blue & orge. 25 20

DESIGNS: 275 k. Injured man with crutch. 375 k. Woman with family.

1978. Europa. Multicoloured.
63. 225 k. Type **17** 30 20
64. 450 k. Cistern in Selimiye Mosque, Nicosia.. .. 45 35

18. Motorway Junction.

1978. Communications. Multicoloured.
65. 75 k. Type **18** 10 10
66. 100 k. Hydrofoil "Ugur" .. 10 10
67. 650 k. Boeing "720" at Ercan Airport 25 25

19. Dove with laurel branch.

1978. National Oath.
68. 19. 150 k. yell., violet & blk. 10 10
69. – 225 k. black, red & yellow 10 10
70. – 725 k. black, blue & yell. 20 20

DESIGNS—VERT. 225 k. "Taking the Oath". HORIZ. 725 k. Symbolic dove.

20. Kemal Ataturk.

1978. Ataturk Commemoration.
71. 20. 75 k. pale turquoise and deep turquoise .. 10 10
72. 450 k. pink and brown.. 15 15
73. 650 k. blue and light blue 20 25

1979. Nos. 30/3 surch.
74. 50 k. on 25 m. Mandarin.. 10 10
75. 1 l. on 40 m. Strawberry .. 15 10
76. 3 l. on 60 m. Orange .. 15 10
77. 5 l. on 80 m. Lemon .. 35 15

23. Postage Stamp and Map of Cyprus.

1979. Europa. Communications. Mult.
79. 2 l. Type **23** 10 10
80. 3 l. Postage stamps, building and map 10 10
81. 8 l. Telephones, Earth and satellite 20 30

24. Microwave Antenna.

1979. 50th Anniversary of International Consultative Radio Committee.
82. 24. 2 l. multicoloured .. 20 10
83. 5 l. multicoloured .. 20 10
84. 6 l. multicoloured .. 25 15

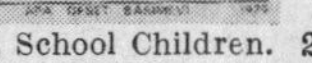

25. School Children.

26. Lala Mustafa Pasha Mosque, Magusa.

1979. International Year of the Child. Multicoloured.

85. 1½ l. Type **25** 20 15
86. 4½ l. Children and globe (horiz.) 30 20
87. 6 l. College children .. 40 20

1980. Islamic Commemorations. Multicoloured.

88. 2½ l. Type **26** 10 10
89. 10 l. Arap Ahmet Pasha Mosque, Lefkosa .. 35 15
90. 20 l. Mecca and Medina .. 50 20

COMMEMORATIONS: 2½ l. 1st Islamic Conference in Turkish Cyprus. 10 l. General Assembly of World Islam Congress. 20 l. Moslem Year 1400 AH.

27. Ebu-Su'ud Efendi (philosopher).

1980. Europa. Personalities. Multicoloured.

91. 5 l. Type **27** 20 10
92. 30 l. Sultan Selim II .. 90 40

28. Omer's Shrine, Kyrenia.

1980. Ancient Monuments.

93. **28.** 2½ l. blue and stone .. 10 10
94. – 3½ l. green and pink .. 10 10
95. – 5 l. brown on green .. 10 10
96. – 10 l. mauve and green .. 20 10
97. – 20 l. blue and yellow .. 35 25

DESIGNS: 3½ l. Entrance gate, Famagusta. 5 l. Funerary monuments (16th-cent.), Famagusta. 10 l. Bella Paise Abbey, Kyrenia. 20 l. Selimiye Mosque, Nicosia.

29. Cyprus 1880 6d. Stamp. 30. Dome of the Rock.

1980. Cyprus Stamp Centenary.

98. **29.** 7½ l. blk., brn. and grn. 10 10
99. – 15 l. brown, dull blue and blue 15 15
100. – 50 l. black, red and grey 50 55

DESIGNS—HORIZ: 15 l. Cyprus 1960 Constitution of the Republic 30 m. commemorative stamp. VERT. 50 l. Social Welfare stamp, 1970.

1980. Palestinian Solidarity. Multicoloured.

101. 15 l. Type **30** 25 15
102. 35 l. Dome of the Rock (horiz.) 65 30

31. Extract from World Muslim Congress Statement in Turkish.

1981. Day of Solidarity with Islamic Countries.

103. **31.** 1 l. buff, red and brown 15 15
104. – 35 l. pale grn., blk. & grn. 55 60

DESIGN: 35 l. Extract in English.

32. "Ataturk".

1981. Ataturk Stamp Exhibition, Lefkosa.

105. **32.** 10 l. multicoloured .. 25 35

33. Folk-dancing.

1981. Europa. Folklore. Multicoloured.

106. 10 l. Type **33** 35 15
107. 30 l. Folkdancing (different) 60 35

35. Wild Convolvulus.

1981. Flowers. Multicoloured.

109. 1 l. Type **35** 10 10
110. 5 l. Persian cyclamen (horiz.) 10 10
111. 10 l. Spring mandrake (horiz.) 10 10
112. 25 l. Corn poppy 10 10
113. 30 l. Wild arum (horiz.) .. 15 10
114. 50 l. Sage-leaved rock rose 30 15
115. 100 l. "Cistus salviaefolius L." 60 20
116. 150 l. Giant fennel (horiz.) 1·10 70

36. Stylised Disabled Person in Wheelchair.

1981. Commemorations. Multicoloured.

117. 7½ l. Type **36** 25 20
118. 10 l. Heads of people of different races, peace dove and barbed wire (vert.) 40 35
119. 20 l. People of different races reaching out from globe, with dishes (vert.) 55 50

COMMEMORATIONS: 7½ l. International Year for Disabled Persons. 10 l. Anti-apartheid publicity. 20 l. World Food Day.

37. Turkish Cypriot and Palestinian Flags.

1981. Palestinian Solidarity.

120. **37.** 10 l. multicoloured .. 25 20

38. Prince Charles and Lady Diana Spencer.

1981. Royal Wedding.

121. **38.** 50 l. multicoloured .. 4·00 4·00

40. Buffavento Castle.

1982. Tourism. Multicoloured.

123. 5 l. Type **40** 10 10
124. 10 l. Windsurfing 15 10
125. 15 l. Kantara Castle .. 20 10
126. 30 l. Shipwreck (300 B.C.) 45 30

Nos. 124/6 are horiz.

41. "Wedding" (A. Orek).

1982. Paintings (1st series). Multicoloured.

127. 30 l. Type **41** 15 25
128. 50 l. "Carob Pickers" (O. Nazim Selenge) (vert.) .. 30 70

See also Nos. 132/3, 157/8, 176/7, 185/6, 208/9, 225/7, 248/50, 284/5 and 315/16.

42. Cross of Lorraine, Koch and Bacillus (Cent. of Koch's Discovery of Tubercle Bacillus).

1982. Anniversaries and Events. Mult.

129. 10 l. Type **42** 30 20
130. 30 l. Spectrum on football pitch (World Cup Football Championships, Spain 55 45
131. 70 l. "75" and Lord Baden-Powell (75th Anniv. of Boy Scout movement and 125th birth anniv.) (vert.) .. 1·10 1·40

43. "Calloused Hands" (Salih Oral).

1983. Paintings (2nd series). Multicoloured.

132. 30 l. Type **43** 70 70
133. 35 l. "Malya-Limassol Bus" (Emin Cizenel) 70 70

45. First Turkish Cypriot 10 m. Stamp.

1983. Anniversaries and Events. Mult.

135. 15 l. Type **45** 30 30
136. 20 l. "Turkish Achievements in Cyprus" (horiz.) 30 30
137. 25 l. "Liberation Fighters" 35 35
138. 30 l. Dish aerial and telegraph pole (horiz.) .. 45 45
139. 50 l. Dove and envelopes (horiz.) 85 85

EVENTS: 15, 20, 25 l. T.M.T. (Turkish Cypriot Resistance Organization) 25th Anniv. 30, 50 l. World Communications Year.

46. European Bee Eater.

1983. Birds of Cyprus. Multicoloured.

140. 10 l. Type **46** 50 65
141. 15 l. Goldfinch 55 70
142. 50 l. European Robin .. 75 95
143. 65 l. Golden Oriole .. 85 1·10

1983. Establishment of Republic. Nos. 109, 111/12 and 116 optd. **Kuzey Kibris Turk Cumhuriyeti 15.11.1983,** or surch. also.

144. 10 l. "Mandragara officinarum" 15 15
145. 15 l. on 1 l. "Convolvulus althaeoides" 15 15
146. 25 l. "Papaver rhoeas" .. 20 20
147. 150 l. "Ferula communis" 1·00 1·75

48. C.E.P.T. 25th Anniversary Logo.

1984. Europa.

148. **48.** 50 l. yellow, brown and black .. .. 1·50 1·50
149. 100 l. light blue, blue and black .. .. 1·50 1·50

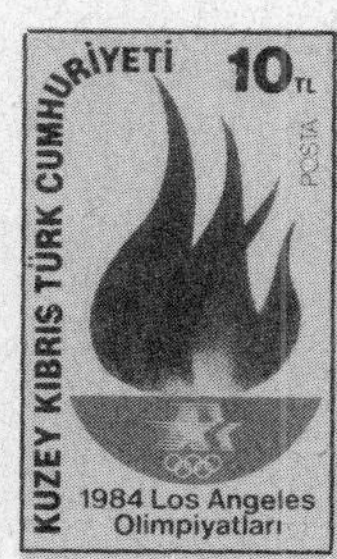

49. Olympic Flame.

1984. Olympic Games, Los Angeles. Mult.

150. 10 l. Type **49** 10 10
151. 20 l. Olympic events within rings (horiz.) 15 15
152. 70 l. Martial arts event (horiz.) 30 65

50. Ataturk Cultural Centre.

1984. Opening of Ataturk Cultural Centre, Lefkosa.

153. **50.** 120 l. stone, black and brown .. .. 90 1·00

52. Turkish Cypriot Flag and Map.

1984. 10th Anniv. of Peace Operation. Mult.

154. 20 l. Type **52** 40 20

155. 70 l. Turkish Cypriot flag within book .. .. 85 1·25

53. Burnt and Replanted Forests.

1984. World Forestry Resources.

156. **53.** 90 l. multicoloured .. 1·00 1·25

54. "Old Turkish Houses, Nicosia" (Cevdet Cagdas).

1984. Paintings (3rd series). Multicoloured.

157. 20 l. Type **54** 35 30

158. 70 l. "Scenery" (Olga Rauf) .. .. .. 75 1·10

55. Kemal Ataturk, Flag and Crowd.

1984. 1st Anniv. of Turkish Republic of Northern Cyprus. Multicoloured.

159. 20 l. Type **55** 20 15

160. 70 l. Legislative Assembly voting for Republic (horiz.) 50 70

56. Taekwondo Bout.

1984. International Taekwondo Championship, Girne.

161. **56.** 10 l. black, brown and grey 35 15

162. – 70 l. multicoloured .. 1·10 1·40

DESIGN: 70 l. Emblem and flags of competing nations.

MORE DETAILED LISTS
are given in the Stanley Gibbons Catalogues referred to in the country headings.
For lists of current volumes see Introduction.

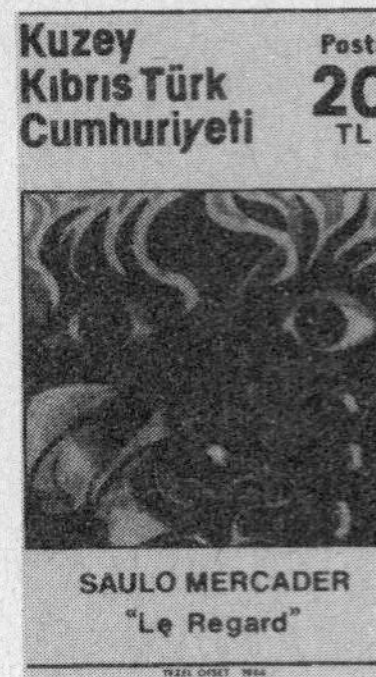

57. "Le Regard".

1984. Exhibition by Saulo Mercader (artist). Multicoloured.

163. 20 l. Type **57** 30 20

164. 70 l. "L'equilibre de L'esprit" (horiz.) .. 1·10 1·40

58. Musical Instruments and Music.

1984. Visit of Nurnberg Chamber Orchestra.

165. **58.** 70 l. multicoloured .. 1·25 1·25

59. Dr. Fazil Kucuk (politician). **61.** George Frederick Handel.

60. Goat.

1985. 1st Death Anniv. of Dr. Fazil Kucuk (politician). Multicoloured.

166. 20 l. Type **59** 30 20

167. 70 l. Dr. Fazil Kucuk reading newspaper .. .. 95 1·10

1985. Domestic Animals. Multicoloured.

168. 100 l. Type **60** 55 30

169. 200 l. Cow and calf 90 70

170. 300 l. Ram .. .. .. 1·25 1·25

171. 500 l. Donkey .. .. 2·00 2·50

1985. Europa. Composers.

172. **61.** 20 l. purple, green and light green .. .. 1·25 1·25

173. – 20 l. pur., brn. & pink 1·25 1·25

174. – 100 l. purple, blue and light blue .. .. 1·75 1·75

175. – 100 l. purple, brown and light brown .. 1·75 1·75

DESIGNS: No. 173, Giuseppe Domenico Scarlatti. 174, Johann Sebastian Bach. 175, Buhurizade Mustafa Itri Efendi.

1985. Paintings (4th series). As T **54**. Multicoloured.

176. 20 l. "Village Life" (Ali Atakan) 45 30

177. 50 l. "Woman carrying Water" (Ismet V. Güney) .. .. .. 1·25 1·50

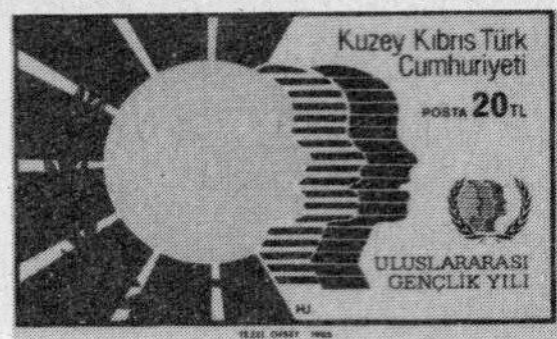

62. Heads of Three Youths.

1985. International Youth Year. Mult.

178. 20 l. Type **62** 40 20

179. 100 l. Dove and globe .. 1·40 1·60

63. Parachutist (Aviation League).

1985. Anniversaries and Events.

180. **63.** 20 l. multicoloured .. 30 15

181. – 50 l. black, brn. & bl. 65 50

182. – 100 l. brown .. .. 1·00 1·00

183. – 100 l. multicoloured .. 1·00 1·00

184. – 100 l. multicoloured .. 1·00 1·00

DESIGNS:—VERT. No. 181, Louis Pasteur (Centenary of Discovery of Rabies vaccine); 182, İsmet İnönü (Turkish statesman) (birth centenary (1984)). HORIZ.—183, "40" in figures and symbolic flower (40th anniv of United Nations Organization); 184, Patient receiving blood transfusion (Prevention of Thalassaemia).

1986. Paintings (5th series) As T **54.** Multicoloured.

185. 20 l. "House with Arches" (Gonen Atakol) 45 20

186. 100 l. "Ataturk Square" (Yalkin Muhtaroglu) .. 1·60 90

65. Karagoz Show Puppets.

1986. Karagoz Folk Puppets.

188. **65.** 100 l. multicoloured .. 1·50 65

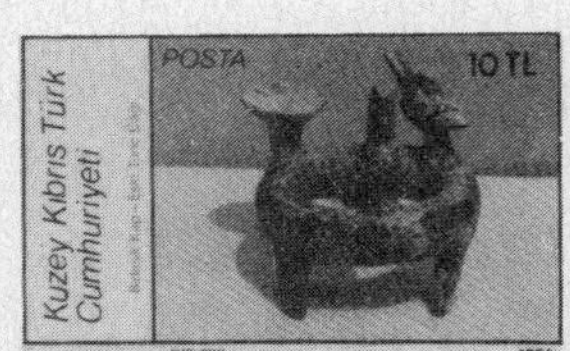

66. Old Bronze Age Composite Pottery.

1986. Archaeological Artefacts. Cultural Links with Anatolia. Multicoloured.

189. 10 l. Type **66** 30 10

190. 20 l. Late Bronze Age bird jug (vert.) 50 10

191. 50 l. Neolithic earthenware pot 75 30

192. 100 l. Roman statue of Artemis (vert.) .. .. 1·25 75

67. Soldiers, Defence Force Badge and Ataturk (10th anniv. of Defence Forces).

1986. Anniversaries and Events. Mult.

193. 20 l. Type **67** 45 10

194. 50 l. Woman and two children (40th anniv. of Food and Agriculture Organization) 55 30

195. 100 l. Football and world map (World Cup Football Championship, Mexico) (horiz.) .. .. 1·25 60

196. 100 l. Orbit of Halley's Comet and "Giotto" space probe (horiz.) .. 1·25 60

68. Guzelyurt Dam and Power Station.

1986. Modern Development (1st series). Mult.

197. 20 l. Type **68** 60 20

198. 50 l. Low cost housing project, Lefkosa .. 75 40

199. 100 l. Kyrenia Airport .. 1·40 1·00

See also Nos. 223/4 and 258/63.

69. Prince Andrew and Miss Sarah Ferguson.

1986. 60th Birthday of Queen Elizabeth II and Royal Wedding. Multicoloured.

200. 100 l. Queen Elizabeth II 90 40

201. 100 l. Type **69** 90 40

70. Locomotive No. 11 and Trakhoni Station.

1986. Cyprus Railway. Multicoloured.

202. 50 l. Type **70** .. .. 1·25 75

203. 100 l. Locomotive No. 1 .. 1·75 1·50

1987. Nos. 94, 96/7 and 113 optd. **Kuzey Kibris Turk Cumhuriyeti** or surch also (No. 205).

204. 10 l. mauve and green .. 25 25

205. 15 l. on $3\frac{1}{2}$ l. green and pink 25 25

206. 20 l. blue and yellow .. 25 25

207. 30 l. multicoloured .. 30 30

1987. Paintings (6th series). As T **54**. Mult.

208. 50 l. "Shepherd" (Feridun Isiman) 60 60

209. 125 l. "Pear Woman" (Mehmet Uluhan) .. 1·00 1·25

72. Modern House (architect A. Vural Behaeddin).

1987. Europa. Modern Architecture. Mult.
210. 50 l. Type **72** 40 20
211. 200 l. Modern house (architect Necdet Turgay) .. .. .. 1·25 1·50

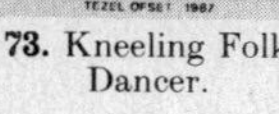

73. Kneeling Folk Dancer.
74. Regimental Colour (1st Anniv. of Infantry Regiment).

1987. Folk Dancers. Multicoloured.
212. 20 l. Type **73** 15 10
213. 50 l. Standing male dancer 20 10
214. 200 l. Standing female dancer 70 45
215. 1000 l. Woman's headdress 2·75 2·40

1987. Anniversaries and Events. Mult.
216. 50 l. Type **74** 35 30
217. 50 l. Pres. Denktash and Turgut Ozal (1st anniv. of Turkish Prime Minister's visit) (horiz.) 35 30
218. 200 l. Emblem and Crescent (5th Islamic Summit Conference, Kuwait) .. .. .. 1·10 1·10
219. 200 l. Emblem and laurel leaves (Membership of Pharmaceutical Federation) (horiz.) .. 1·10 1·10

75. Ahmet Belig Pasha (Egyptian judge).

1987. Turkish Cypriot Personalities.
220. **75.** 50 l. brown and yellow 20 15
221. – 50 l. multicoloured .. 20 15
222. – 125 l. multicoloured .. 50 35
DESIGNS: 50 l. (No. 221) Mehmet Emin Pasha (Ottoman Grand Vizier). 125 l. Mehmet Kamil Pasha (Ottoman Grand Vizier).

76. Tourist Hotel, Girne.

1987. Modern Development (2nd series). Mult.
223. 150 l. Type **76** 75 40
224. 200 l. Dogu Akdeniz University .. .. 1·00 55

1988. Paintings (7th series). As T **54**. Mult.
225 20 l. "Woman making Pastry" (Ayhan Mentes) (vert) 25 15
226 50 l. "Chair Weaver" (Osman Guvenir) .. 35 20
227 150 l. "Woman weaving a Rug" (Zekai Yesiladali) (vert) 85 85

77 "Piyale Pasha" (tug)

1988. Europa. Transport and Communications. Multicoloured.
228 200 l. Type **77** 75 30
229 500 l. Dish aerial and antenna tower, Selvilitepe (vert) .. 1·50 95
No. 229 also commemorates the 25th anniv of Bayrak Radio and Television Corporation.

78 Lefkosa

1988. Tourism. Multicoloured.
230 150 l. Type **78** 35 30
231 200 l. Gazi-Magusa .. 45 40
232 300 l. Girne 65 55

79 Bulent Ecevit

1988. Turkish Prime Ministers. Multicoloured.
233 50 l. Type **79** 15 15
234 50 l. Bulent Ulusu .. 15 15
235 50 l. Turgut Ozal 15 15

80 Red Crescent Members on Exercise

1988. Civil Defence.
236 **80** 150 l. multicoloured .. 30 30

81 Hodori the Tiger (Games mascot) and Fireworks

1988. Olympic Games, Seoul. Multicoloured.
237 200 l. Type **81** 40 35
238 250 l. Athletics 50 50
239 400 l. Shot and running track with letters spelling "SEOUL" .. 70 85

82 Sedat Simavi (journalist)

85 Girl with Doll

1988. Anniversaries and Events.
240 **82** 50 l. green 15 15
241 – 100 l. multicoloured .. 20 20
242 – 300 l. multicoloured .. 50 50
243 – 400 l. multicoloured .. 70 70
244 – 400 l. multicoloured .. 70 70
245 – 600 l. multicoloured .. 90 90
DESIGNS: HORIZ—No. 241, Stylised figures around table and flags of participating countries (International Girne Conferences); 244, Presidents Gorbachev and Reagan signing treaty (Summit Meeting). VERT—No. 242, Cogwheels as flowers (North Cyprus Industrial Fair); 243, Globe (125th anniv of International Red Cross); 245, "Medical Services" (40th anniv of W.H.O.).

1989. Paintings (8th series). As T **54**. Mult.
248 150 l. "Dervis Pasa Mansion, Lefkosa" (Inci Kansu) 35 20
249 400 l. "Gamblers' Inn, Lefkosa" (Osman Gvenir) 75 45
250 600 l. "Mosque, Paphos" (Hikmet Ulucam) (vert) 1·10 70

1989. Europa. Children's Games. Mult.
251 600 l. Type **85** 90 90
252 1000 l. Boy with kite .. 1·50 1·50

86 Meeting of Presidents Vassiliou and Denktash

1989. Cyprus Peace Summit, Geneva, 1988.
253 **86** 500 l. red and black .. 55 60

87 Chukar Partridge

1989. Wildlife. Multicoloured.
254 100 l. Type **87** 10 15
255 200 l. Cyprus hare .. 20 25
256 700 l. Black partridge .. 75 80
257 2000 l. Red fox .. .. 2·10 2·25

88 Road Construction

1989. Modern Development (3rd series). Mult.
258 100 l. Type **88** 10 15
259 150 l. Laying water pipeline (vert) 15 20
260 200 l. Seedling trees (vert) 20 25
261 450 l. Modern telephone exchange (vert) .. 50 75
262 650 l. Steam turbine power station (vert) .. .. 70 1·00
263 700 l. Irrigation reservoir 75 1·25

89 Unloading Freighter at Quayside (15th anniv of Gazi Magusa Free Port)

1989. Anniversaries.
264 **89** 100 l. multicoloured .. 10 15
265 – 450 l. black, blue & red 50 55
266 – 500 l. black, yell & grey 55 60
267 – 600 l. black, red & blue 65 70
268 – 1000 l. multicoloured .. 1·10 1·25
DESIGNS—VERT (26 × 47 mm). 450 l. Airmail letter and stylized bird (25th anniv of Turkish Cypriot postal service). HORIZ (as T **89**). 500 l. Newspaper and printing press (centenary of "Saded" newspaper); 600 l. Statue of Aphrodite, lifebelt and seabird (30th anniv of International Maritime Organization); 1000 l. Soldiers (25th anniv of Turkish Cypriot resistance).

90 Erdal Inonu

1989. Visit of Professor Erdal Inonu (Turkish politician).
269 **90** 700 l. multicoloured .. 75 80

91 Mule-drawn Plough

1989. Traditional Agricultural Implements. Multicoloured.
270 150 l. Type **91** 15 20
271 450 l. Ox-drawn threshing sledge 50 55
272 550 l. Olive press (vert) .. 60 65

92 Smoking Ashtray and Drinks

1990. World Health Day. Multicoloured.
273 200 l. Type **92** 10 10
274 700 l. Smoking cigarette and heart 25 30

93 Yenierenkoy Post Office

1990. Europa. Post Office Buildings. Mult.
275 1000 t. Type **93** 40 45
276 1500 t. Ataturk Meydani Post Office 55 60

94 Song Thrush
96 Amphitheatre, Soli

95 Two Football Teams

1990. World Environment Day. Birds. Multicoloured.
278 150 l. Type **94** 10 10
279 300 l. Blackcap 10 15
280 900 l. Black redstart .. 30 35
281 1000 l. Chiff-chaff .. 40 45

1990. World Cup Football Championship, Italy. Multicoloured.

282	300 l. Type **95**	15	15
283	1000 l. Championship symbol, globe and ball	60	65

1990. Paintings (9th series). As T **54**. Mult.

284	300 l. "Abstract" (Filiz Ankacc)	15	15
285	1000 l. Wooden sculpture (S. Tekman) (vert)	60	65

1990. Tourism. Multicoloured.

286	150 l. Type **96**	10	10
287	1000 l. Swan mosaic, Soli	60	65

97 Kenan Evren and Rauf Denktas

1990. Visit of President Kenan Evren of Turkey.

288	**97**	500 l. multicoloured	40	45

98 Road Signs and Heart wearing Seat Belt

1990. Traffic Safety Campaign. Mult.

289	150 l. Type **98**	20	15
290	300 l. Road signs, speeding car and spots of blood	30	20
291	1000 l. Traffic lights and road signs	90	65

99 Yildirim Akbulut

100 "Rosularia cypria"

1990. Visit of Turkish Prime Minister Yildrim Akbulut.

292	**99**	1000 l. multicoloured	60	65

1990. Plants. Multicoloured.

293	150 l. Type **100**	10	10
294	200 l. "Silene fraudratrix"	10	10
295	300 l. "Scutellaria sibthorpii"	10	15
296	600 l. "Sedum lampusae"	20	25
297	1000 l. "Onosma caespitosum"	40	45
298	1500 l. "Arabis cypria"	55	60

101 Kemal Ataturk at Easel (wood carving)

1990. International Literacy Year. Mult.

299	300 l. Type **101**	10	15
300	750 l. Globe, letters and books	30	35

1991. Nos. 189, 212 and 293 surch.

301	**66**	250 l. on 10 l. mult	10	10
302	**73**	250 l. on 20 l. mult	10	10
303	**100**	500 l. on 150 l. mult	10	15

103 "Ophrys lapethica"

1991. Orchids (1st series). Multicoloured.

304	250 l. Type **103**	10	10
305	500 l. "Ophrys kotschyi"	10	15

See also Nos. 311/14.

105 Kucuk Medrese Fountain, Lefkosa

1991. Fountains. Multicoloured.

307	250 l. Type **105**	10	10
308	500 l. Cafer Pasa fountain, Magusa	10	15
309	1500 l. Sarayonu Square fountain, Lefkosa	30	35
310	5000 l. Arabahmet Mosque fountain, Lefkosa	1·00	1·10

1991. Orchids (2nd series). As T **103**. Multicoloured.

311	100 l. "Serapias levantina"	10	10
312	500 l. "Dactylorhiza romana"	10	15
313	2000 l. "Orchis simia"	40	45
314	3000 l. "Orchis sancta"	60	65

1991. Paintings (10th series). As T **54**. Multicoloured.

315	250 l. "Hindiler" (S. Cizel) (vert)	10	10
316	500 l. "Dusme" (A. Mene) (vert)	10	15

107 Symbolic Roots (Year of Love to Yunus Emre)

1991. Anniversaries and Events.

317	**107**	250 l. yell, blk & mve	10	10
318	–	500 l. multicoloured	10	15
319	–	500 l. multicoloured	10	15
320	–	1500 l. multicoloured	30	35

DESIGNS—VERT. No. 318, Mustafa Cagatay commemoration; 319, University building (5th anniv of Eastern Mediterranean University). HORIZ. No. 320, Mozart (death bicent).

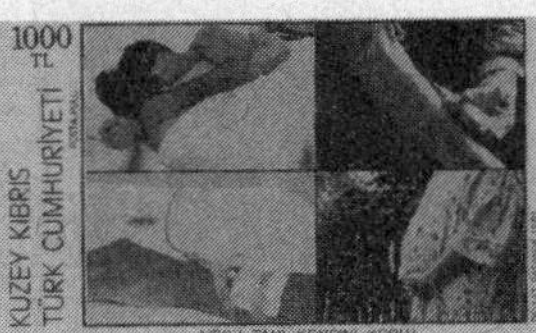

108 Four Sources of Infection

1991. "AIDS" Day.

321	**108**	1000 l. multicoloured	20	25

109 Lighthouse, Gazimagusa

1991. Lighthouses. Multicoloured.

322	250 l. Type **109**	10	10
323	500 l. Ancient lighthouses, Girne harbour	10	15
324	1500 l. Modern lighthouse, Girne harbour	30	35

110 Elephant and Hippopotamus Fossils, Karaoglanoglu

1991. Tourism. Multicoloured.

325	250 l. Type **110**	10	15
326	500 l. Roman fish ponds, Lambusa	10	15
327	1500 l. Roman remains, Lambusa	30	35

DHAR

A state of Central India. Now uses Indian stamps.

4 pice = 1 anna.

1.

2.

1897. Imperf.

1.	**1.**	$\frac{1}{2}$ pice black on red	80	80
3.		$\frac{1}{4}$ a. black on orange	1·00	1·75
4.		$\frac{1}{2}$ a. black on mauve	1·10	1·90
5.		1 a. black on green	2·75	5·00
6.		2 a. black on yellow	15·00	30·00

1898. Perf.

7b.	**2.**	$\frac{1}{2}$ a. red	90	2·25
8.		1 a. purple	90	2·25
10.		2 a. green	3·25	12·00

DOMINICA

Until 31 December, 1939, one of the Leeward Is., but then transferred to the Windward Is. Used Leeward Is. stamps concurrently with Dominican issues from 1903 to above date.

1874. 12 pence = shilling;
20 shillings = 1 pound.
1949. 100 cents = 1 West Indian dollar.

1.

1874.

15	1	$\frac{1}{2}$d. yellow	1·00	4·00
20		$\frac{1}{2}$d. green	50	3·00
5		1d. lilac	4·50	1·50
22a		1d. red	2·50	2·75
16		$2\frac{1}{2}$d. brown	£130	2·00
23		$2\frac{1}{2}$d. blue	3·75	3·00
7		4d. blue	95·00	2·50
24		4d. grey	2·00	2·75
8		6d. green	£140	20·00
25		6d. orange	5·50	17·00
9		1s. mauve	£120	28·00

1882. No. 5 bisected and surch. with small $\frac{1}{2}$.

10.	**1.**	$\frac{1}{2}$(d.) on half 1d. lilac	£140	30·00

1882. No. 5 bisected and surch. with **large** $\frac{1}{2}$.

11.	**1.**	$\frac{1}{2}$(d.) on half 1d. lilac	28·00	12·00

1883. No. 5 bisected and surch. **HALF PENNY** vert.

14.	**1.**	$\frac{1}{2}$d. on half 1d. lilac	38·00	20·00

1886. Nos. 8 and 3 surch. in words and bar.

17.	**1.**	$\frac{1}{2}$d. on 6d. green	4·00	3·50
18.		1d. on 6d. green	£16000	£11000
19.		1d. on 1s. mauve	13·00	13·00

9. View of Roseau from the Sea.

10.

1903.

37	~~9.~~	$\frac{1}{2}$d. green	1·25	2·00
~~38~~		1d. grey and red	2·00	25
29		2d. green and brown	2·50	4·00
30		$2\frac{1}{2}$d. grey and blue	4·50	4·50
31		3d. purple and black	8·00	2·75
32		6d. grey and brown	4·25	13·00
43		1s. mauve and green	3·75	27·00
34		2s. black and purple	17·00	25·00
45		2s. 6d. green and orange	20·00	45·00
46	**10.**	5s. black and brown	55·00	75·00

1908.

48a. 9. 1d. red 1·00 40
64. 1½d. orange 3·50 8·50
65. 2d. grey 2·75 3·25
66. 2½d. blue 1·25 8·00
51. 3d. purple on yellow 1·75 3·50
52a. 6d. purple 3·50 14·00
53. 1s. black on green 1·40 2·75
53a. 2s. pur. and blue on blue 20·00 45·00
70. 2s. 6d. black & red on blue 24·00 55·00

1914. As T 10, but portrait of King George V.
54. 5 s. red and green on yellow 45·00 65·00

1916. Surch. **WAR TAX ONE HALF-PENNY.**
55. 9. ½d. on ½d. green 10 75

1918. Optd. **WAR TAX** in small letters.
56. 9. ½d. green 50 4·00

1918. Optd. **WAR TAX** in large letters.
57. 9. ½d. green 10 30
58. 3d. purple on yellow 20 2·00

1919. Surch. **WAR TAX 1½D.**
59. 9. 1½d. on 2½d. orange 10 55

1920. Surch. **1½D.**
60. 9. 1½d. on 2½d. orange 1·25 3·75

16.

1923.

71. 16. ½d. black and green 65 30
72. 1d. black and violet 1·25 40
73. 1d. black and red 5·50 80
74. 1½d. black and red 90 30
75. 1½d. black and brown 5·50 50
76. 2d. black and grey 85 40
77. 2½d. black and yellow 70 5·50
78. 2½d. black and blue 2·25 1·00
79. 3d. black and blue 70 8·00
80. 3d. black & red on yellow 1·00 1·00
81. 4d. black and brown 75 4·00
82. 6d. black and mauve 1·75 3·50
83. 1s. black on green 1·40 2·25
84. 2s. black & blue on blue 3·50 11·00
85. 2s. 6d. blk. & red on blue 9·50 13·00
86. 3s. black & purple on yell. 2·50 8·00
87. 4s. black and red on green 5·50 11·00
90. 5s. black & green on yell. 7·50 35·00
91. £1 black and purple on red £250 £300

1935. Silver Jubilee. As T 13 of Antigua.
92. 1d. blue and red 75 20
93. 1½d. blue and grey 1·00 40
94. 2½d. brown and blue 1·40 75
95. 1s. grey and purple 1·50 3·25

1937. Coronation. As T 2 of Aden.
96. 1d. red 40 10
97. 1½d. brown 40 10
98. 2½d. blue 60 75

17. Fresh Water Lake. 21. King George VI.

1938.

99. 17. ½d. brown and green 10 15
100. – 1d. black and red 20 20
101. – 1½d. green and purple 20 45
102. – 2d. red and black 40 35
103a. – 2½d. purple and blue 20 50
104. – 3d. olive and brown 30 40
104a. – 3½d. blue and mauve 1·25 45
105. 17. 6d. green and violet 50 50
105a. 7d. green and brown 1·25 50
106. – 1s. violet and olive 1·00 50
106a. – 2s. grey and purple 3·00 4·25
107. 17. 2s. 6d. black and red 5·50 4·00
108. – 5s. blue and brown 5·00 3·50
108a. – 10s. black and orange 8·50 12·00

DESIGNS—As Type 17: 1d., 3d., 2s., 5s. Layou River. 1½d., 2½d., 3½d. Picking Limes. 2d., 1s., 10s. Boiling Lake.

1940.
109a. 21 ¼d. brown 10 10

1946. Victory. As Type 9. of Aden.
110. 1d. red 10 10
111. 3½d. blue 10 10

1948. Silver Wedding. As T 10/11 of Aden.
112. 1d. red 15 10
113. 10s. brown 6·00 12·00

1949. U.P.U. As T 20/23 of Antigua.
114. 5 c. blue 15 15
115. 6 c. brown 30 20
116. 12 c. purple 30 30
117. 24 c. olive 30 30

1951. Inauguration of B.W.I. University College. As T 24/25 of Antigua.
118. 3 c. green and violet 40 20
119. 12 c. green and red 45 15

23. Drying Cocoa.

1951. New Currency.

120. – ½ c. brown 10 15
121. 23. 1 c. black and red 10 10
122. – 2 c. brown and green 10 10
123. – 3 c. green and purple 10 30
124. – 4 c. orange and sepia 20 15
125. – 5 c. black and red 50 15
126. – 6 c. olive and brown 60 15
127. – 8 c. green and blue 35 30
128. – 12 c. black and green 30 60
129. – 14 c. blue and purple 55 60
130. – 24 c. purple and red 30 30
131. – 48 c. green and orange 1·00 3·25
132. – 60 c. red and black 1·00 2·00
133. – $1.20 green and black 4·00 2·25
134. – $2.40 orange and black 20·00 18·00

DESIGNS: ½c. As Type 21, but with portrait as Type 22. HORIZ. (as Type 22). 2 c., 60 c. Carib baskets. 3 c., 48 c. Lime plantation. 4 c. Picking oranges. 5 c. Bananas. 6 c. Botanical Gardens. 8 c. Drying vanilla beans. 12 c., $1.20, Fresh Water Lake. 14 c. Layou River, 24 c. Boiling Lake. VERT. $2.40, Picking oranges.

1951. New Constitution. Stamps of 1951 optd. **NEW CONSTITUTION 1951.**
135. 3 c. green and violet 15 30
136. 5 c. black and red 15 20
137. 8 c. green and blue 15 15
138. 14 c. blue and violet 15 15

1953. Coronation. As T 13 of Aden.
139. 2 c. black and green 10 10

1954. As Nos. 120/34 but with portrait of Queen Elizabeth II.

140. ½ c. brown 10 10
141. 1 c. black and red 10 10
142. 2 c. brown and green 10 10
143. 3 c. green and purple 60 20
144. 3 c. black and red 1·50 55
145. 4 c. orange and brown 15 10
146. 5 c. black and red 60 20
147. 5 c. blue and brown 8·00 50
148. 6 c. green and brown 15 10
149. 8 c. green and blue 15 10
150. 10 c. green and brown 1·00 50
151. 12 c. black and green 50 10
152. 14 c. blue and purple 30 10
153. 24 c. purple and red 30 10
154. 48 c. green and orange 1·25 5·00
155. 48 c. brown and violet 1·25 80
156. 60 c. red and black 50 75
157. $1.20 green and black 9·50 5·50
158. $2.40 orange and black 11·00 11·00

DESIGNS (New)—HORIZ. Nos. 144, 155, Mat-making. No. 147, Canoe making. No. 150, Bananas.

1958. British Caribbean Federation. As T 25 of Antigua.
159. 3 c. green 15 10
160. 6 c. blue 20 20
161. 12 c. red 20 10

40. Seashore at Rosalie.

1963.

162. 40. 1 c. green, blue and sepia 10 10
163 – 2 c. blue 30 10
164 – 3 c. brown and blue 30 20
165 – 4 c. grn., sep. & violet 10 10
166 – 5 c. mauve 30 10
167 – 6 c. green, bistre & violet 10 10
168 – 8 c. green, sepia & black 10 10
169 – 10 c. sepia and pink 10 10
170 – 12 c. green, blue & sepia 10 10
171 – 14 c. multicoloured 30 10
172 – 15 c. yellow, green & brn. 40 10
173 – 24 c. multicoloured 3·50 10
174 – 48 c. green, blue & black 60 25
175 – 60 c. orange, green & blk. 75 50
176 – $1.20 multicoloured 5·00 70
177 – $2.40 blue, turq. & brown 3·25 2·00
178 – $4.80 green, blue & brown 8·00 13·00

DESIGNS—VERT. 2 c., 5 c. Queen Elizabeth II (after Annigoni). 14 c. Traditional costume. 24 c. Imperial amazon. $2.40, Trafalgar Falls. $4.80, Coconut palm. HORIZ.. 3 c. Sailing canoe. 4 c. Sulphur springs. 6 c. Road making. 8 c. Dug-out canoe. 10 c. Crapaud (frog). 12 c. Scotts Head. 15 c. Bananas. 48 c. Goodwill. 60 c. Cocoa tree. $1.20, Coat of Arms.

1963. Freedom from Hunger. As T 28 of Aden.
179. 15 c. violet 15 10

1963. Cent of Red Cross. As T 33 of Antigua.
180. 5 c. red and black 15 20
181. 15 c. red and blue 30 45

1964. 400th Birth Anniv of Shakespeare. As T 34 of Antigua.
182. 15 c. purple 10 10

1965. Cent of I.T.U. As T 36 of Antigua.
183. 2 c. green and blue 10 10
184. 48 c. turquoise and grey 30 20

1965. I.C.Y. As T 37 of Antigua.
185. 1 c. purple and turquoise 10 20
186. 15 c. green and lavender 20 10

1966. Churchill Commem. As T 38 of Antigua.
187. 1 c. blue 10 10
188. 5 c. green 10 10
189. 15 c. brown 20 10
190. 24 c. violet 30 20

1966. Royal Visit. As T 39 of Antigua.
191. 5 c. black and blue 75 10
192. 15 c. black and mauve 1·25 20

1966. World Cup Football Championship. As T 40 of Antigua.
193. 5 c. multicoloured 10 10
194. 24 c. multicoloured 30 10

1966. Inauguration of W.H.O. Headquarters, Geneva. As T 41 of Antigua.
195. 5 c. black, green and blue 10 15
196. 24 c. black, purple & ochre 20 15

1966. 20th Anniv. of U.N.E.S.C.O. As T 54/6 of Antigua.
197. 5 c. red, yellow and orange 10 15
198. 15 c. yellow, violet & olive 25 10
199. 24 c. black, purple & orge. 25 15

56. Children of Three Races.

1967. National Day. Multicoloured.
205. 5 c. Type 56 10 10
206. 10 c. The "Santa Maria" and Motto 10 10
207. 15 c. Hands holding Motto Ribbon 10 15
208. 24 c. Belaire Dancing 10 15

57. John F. Kennedy.

1968. Human Rights Year. Multicoloured.
209. 1 c. Type 57 10 10
210. 10 c. Cecil E. A. Rawle 10 10
211. 12 c. Pope John XXIII 25 10
212. 48 c. Florence Nightingale 25 15
213. 60 c. Albert Schweitzer 25 15

1968. Associated Statehood. Nos. 162, etc. optd. **ASSOCIATED STATEHOOD.**
214. 1 c. grn., blue and sepia 10 10
215. 2 c. blue 10 10
216. 3 c. brown and blue 10 10
217. 4 c. green, sepia and violet 10 10
218. 5 c. mauve 10 10
219. 6 c. green, bistre and violet 10 10
220. 8 c. green, sepia and black 10 10
221. 10 c. sepia and pink 35 10
222. 12 c. green, blue and brown 10 10
224. 14 c. multicoloured 10 10
225. 15 c. yellow, green & brn. 10 10
226. 24 c. multicoloured 1·50 10
227. 48 c. green, blue and black 55 90
228. 60 c. orange, green and blk. 90 70
229. $1.20 multicoloured 1·00 1·75
230. $2.40 blue, turq. & brown 2·00 2·25
231. $4.80 green, blue & brown 2·00 3·75

1968. National Day. Nos. 162/4, 171a and 176 optd. **NATIONAL DAY 3 NOVEMBER 1968.**
232. 1 c. grn., blue and sepia 10 10
233. 2 c. blue 10 10
234. 3 c. brown and blue 10 10
235. 14 c. multicoloured 10 10
236. $1.20 multicoloured 30 40

60. Forward shooting at Goal.

1968. Olympic Games, Mexico. Multicoloured.
237. 1 c. Type 60 10 10
238. 1 c. Goalkeeper attempting to save ball 10 10
239. 5 c. Swimmers preparing to dive 10 10
240. 5 c. Swimmers diving 10 10
241. 48 c. Javelin-throwing 15 15
242. 48 c. Hurdling 15 15
243. 60 c. Basketball 15 15
244. 60 c. Basketball players 15 15

61. "The Small Cowper Madonna" (Raphael).

1968. Christmas.
245. 61. 5 c. multicoloured 10 10

62. "Venus and Adonis" (Rubens).

1969. 20th Anniv. of World Health Organization.
246. 62. 5 c. multicoloured 20 10
247. – 15 c. multicoloured 20 10
248. – 24 c. multicoloured 20 10
249. – 50 c. multicoloured 30 30

DESIGNS: 15 c. "The Death of Socrates" (J.—L. David). 24 c. "Christ and the Pilgrims of Emmaus" (Velasquez). 50 c. "Pilate washing his hands" (Rembrandt).

66. Picking Oranges.

1969. Tourism. Multicoloured.
250. 10 c. Type 66 10 10
251. 10 c. Woman, child and ocean scene 10 10
252. 12 c. Fort Yeoung Hotel 15 10
253. 12 c. Red-necked Amazon 15 10
254. 24 c. Calypso band 15 10
255. 24 c. Women dancing 15 15
256. 48 c. Underwater life 20 25
257. 48 c. Skin-diver and turtle 20 25

67. "Strength in Unity" Emblem and Fruit trees.

1969. 1st Anniv. of C.A.R.I.F.T.A (Caribbean Free Trade Area). Multicoloured.
258. 5 c. Type 67 10 10
259. 8 c. "HS 748" aircraft, emblem and island 10 10
260. 12 c. Chart of Caribbean Sea and emblem 10 10
261. 24 c. Steamship unloading, tug and emblem 15 10

71. "Spinning" (J. Millet).

1969. 50th Anniv. of International Labour Organization. Multicoloured.

No.	Description		
262.	15 c. Type **71**	10	10
263.	30 c. "Threshing" (J. Millet)	15	15
264.	38 c. "Flax-pulling" (J. Millet)	15	15

72. Mahatma Gandhi weaving and Clock Tower, Westminster.

1969. Birth Cent. of Mahatma Gandhi. Mult.

No.	Description		
265.	6 c. Type **72**	30	10
266.	38 c. Gandhi, Nehru and Mausoleum ..	50	15
267.	$1.20 Gandhi and Taj Mahal	1·40	40

NOTE: All stamps are incorrectly inscribed "Ghandi".

75. "Saint Joseph".

1969. National Day. Multicoloured.

No.	Description		
268.	6 c. Type **75**	10	10
269.	8 c. "Saint John" ..	10	10
270.	12 c. "Saint Peter" ..	10	10
271.	60 c. "Saint Paul" ..	30	50

79. Queen Elizabeth II.

80. Purple-throated Carib and Flower.

1969. Centres multicoloured; colours of "D" given.

No.	Type	Description		
272.	79.	½ c. black and silver ..	10	40
273.	80.	1 c. black and yellow ..	30	40
274.	–	2 c. black and yellow ..	15	10
275.	–	3 c. black and yellow ..	75	60
276.	–	4 c. black and yellow ..	75	60
277.	–	5 c. black and yellow ..	1·00	30
278.	–	6 c. black and brown ..	1·00	75
279.	–	8 c. black and brown ..	20	10
280.	–	10 c. black and yellow ..	20	10
281.	–	12 c. black and yellow ..	20	10
282.	–	15 c. black and blue ..	20	10
283.	–	25 c. black and red ..	30	10
284.	–	30 c. black and olive ..	1·50	70
285.	–	38 c. black and purple ..	5·00	1·75
286.	–	50 c. black and brown ..	50	45
287.	–	60 c. black and yellow ..	55	80
288.	–	$1.20 black and yellow	1·00	1·75
289.	–	$2.40 black and gold ..	1·75	3·00
290.	–	$4.80 black and gold ..	3·00	6·00

DESIGNS—HORIZ. As Type **80**: 2 c. Poinsettia. 3 c. Red-necked pigeon. 4 c. Imperial amazon. 5 c. "Battus polydamas" (butterfly). 6 c. "Dryas julia" (butterfly). 8 c. Shipping bananas. 10 c. Portsmouth Harbour. 12 c. Copra processing plant. 15 c. Straw workers. 25 c. Timber plant. 30 c. Pumice mine. 38 c. Grammar school and playing fields. 50 c. Roseau Cathedral. 60 c. Government Headquarters (38 × 26½ mm). $1.20, Melville Hall airport (40 × 27 mm). $2.40, Coat of arms (39½ × 26 mm). VERT. $4.80, As Type **79** but larger (26 × 39 mm).

99. "The Virgin and the Child with St. John" (Perugino).

1969. Christmas. Paintings. Multicoloured.

No.	Description		
291.	6 c. "Virgin and Child with St John" (Lippi) ..	10	10
292.	10 c. "Holy Family with Lamb" (Raphael) ..	10	10
293.	15 c. Type **99** ..	10	10
294.	$1.20 "Madonna of the Rose Hedge" (Botticelli)	35	40

101. Astronaut's First Step onto the Moon.

1970. Moon Landing. Multicoloured.

No.	Description		
296.	½ c. Type **101**	10	10
297.	5 c. Scientific experiment on the Moon and flag ..	10	10
298.	8 c. Astronauts collecting rocks	10	10
299.	30 c. Module over Moon ..	20	15
300.	50 c. Moon plaque	30	25
301.	60 c. Astronauts	30	30

107. Giant Green Turtle.

1970. Flora and Fauna. Multicoloured.

No.	Description		
303.	6 c. Type **107**	30	15
304.	24 c. Flying fish ..	50	40
305.	38 c. Anthurium lily ..	60	65
306.	60 c. Imperial and Red-necked parrots ..	2·25	1·75

108. 18th-Century National Costume.

1970. National Day. Multicoloured.

No.	Description		
308.	5 c. Type **108**	10	10
309.	8 c. Carib basketry ..	10	10
310.	$1 Flag and Chart of Dominica	30	40

109. Scrooge and Marley's Ghost.

1970. Christmas and Death Cent. of Charles Dickens. Scenes from "A Christmas Carol". Multicoloured.

No.	Description		
312.	2 c. Type **109**	10	10
313.	15 c. Fezziwig's Ball ..	10	10
314.	24 c. Scrooge and his Nephew's Party ..	10	10
315.	$1.20 Scrooge and the Ghost of Christmas Present	55	60

110. "The Doctor" (Sir Luke Fildes).

1970. Cent. of British red Cross. Mult.

No.	Description		
317.	8 c. Type **110**	10	10
318.	10 c. Hands and Red Cross	10	10
319.	15 c. Flag of Dominica and Red Cross Emblem ..	15	10
320.	50 c. "The Sick Child" (E. Munch)	40	35

111. Marigot School.

1971. Int. Education Year. Multicoloured.

No.	Description		
322.	5 c. Type **111**	10	10
323.	8 c. Goodwill Junior High School	10	10
324.	14 c. University of West Indies (Jamaica) ..	10	10
325.	$1 Trinity College, Cambridge	25	30

112. Waterfall.

1971. Tourism. Multicoloured.

No.	Description		
327.	5 c. Type **112**	10	10
328.	10 c. Boat-building ..	10	10
329.	30 c. Sailing	20	10
330.	50 c. Yacht and motor launch	35	30

113. U.N.I.C.E.F. Symbol in "D".

1971. 25th Anniv. of U.N.I.C.E.F.

No.	Type	Description		
332.	113.	5 c. violet, blk., & gold	10	10
333.		10 c. yell., blk. & gold ..	10	10
334.		38 c. grn., blk. & gold ..	10	10
335.		$1.20 orge., blk. & gold	30	45

114. German Boy Scout.

1971. World Scout Jamboree, Asagiri, Japan. Various designs showing Boy Scouts from the nations listed. Multicoloured.

No.	Description		
337.	20 c. Type **114**	15	10
338.	24 c. Great Britain ..	20	10
339.	30 c. Japan	25	10
340.	$1 Dominica	50	40

115. Groyne at Portsmouth.

1971. National Day. Multicoloured.

No.	Description		
342.	8 c. Type **115**	10	10
343.	15 c. Carnival scene ..	10	10
344.	20 c. Carifta Queen (vert.)	10	10
345.	50 c. Rock of Atkinson (vert.)	20	25

116. Eight Reals Piece, 1761.

1972. Coins.

No.	Type	Description		
347.	116.	10 c. black, sil. & vio.	10	10
348.	–	30 c. black, sil. & grn. ..	15	15
349.	–	35 c. black, sil. & blue ..	20	20
350.	–	50 c. black, silver & red	40	60

DESIGNS—HORIZ. 30 c. Eleven and three bitt pieces, 1798. VERT. 35 c. Two reals and two bitt pieces, 1770. 50 c. Mocos, Pieces-of-eight and eight reals-eleven bitts piece, 1798.

117. Common Opossum.

1972. U.N. Conf. on the Human Environment, Stockholm. Multicoloured.

No.	Description		
352.	½ c. Type **117**	10	10
353.	35 c. Brazilian agouti (rodent)	40	15
354.	60 c. Orchid	2·00	50
355.	$1·20 Hibiscus	2·25	1·60

118. Sprinter.

1972. Olympic Games, Munich. Mult.

No.	Description		
357.	30 c. Type **118**	10	10
358.	35 c. Hurdler	15	15
359.	58 c. Hammer-thrower (vert.)	15	20
360.	72 c. Long-jumper (vert.) ..	25	40

119. General Post Office.

1972. National Day. Multicoloured.

No.	Description		
362.	10 c. Type **119**	10	10
363.	20 c. Morne Diablotin ..	10	10
364.	30 c. Rodney's Rock ..	15	15

1972. Royal Silver Wedding. As T **52** of Ascension, but with Bananas and Sisserou Parrot in background.

No.	Description		
366.	5 c. green	10	10
367.	**$1** green	40	40

121. " The Adoration of the Shepherds " (Caravaggio).

1972. Christmas. Multicoloured.

368. 8 c. Type **121** 10 10
369. 14 c. " The Myosotis Virgin " (Rubens) .. 10 10
370. 30 c. " Madonna and Child " with St. Francesca Romana " (Gentileschi) 15 10
371. $1 " Adoration of the Kings " (Mostaert) .. 40 70

122. Launching of Weather Satellite.

1973. Cent. of I.M.O./W.M.O. Multicoloured.

373. ½ c. Type **122** .. 10 10
374. 1 c. Nimbus satellite .. 10 10
375. 2 c. Radiosonde balloon .. 10 10
376. 30 c. Radarscope (horiz.) 15 15
377. 35 c. Diagram of pressure zones (horiz.) 20 20
378. 50 c. Hurricane shown by satellite (horiz.) .. 30 35
379. $1 Computer weather-map (horiz.) 60 65

123. Going to Hospital.

1973. 25th Anniv. W.H.O. Multicoloured.

381. ½ c. Type **123** 10 10
382. 1 c. Maternity care .. 10 10
383. 2 c. Smallpox inoculation 10 10
384. 30 c. Emergency service 20 15
385. 35 c. Waiting for the doctor 25 15
386. 50 c. Medical examination 30 25
387. $1 Travelling doctor .. 45 60

124. Cyrique Crab.

1973. Flora and Fauna. Multicoloured.

389. ½ c. Type **124** 10 10
390. 22 c. Blue Land-crab .. 35 10
391. 25 c. Bread Fruit .. 35 15
392. $1.20 Sunflower .. 1·50 2·00

125. Princess Anne and Captain Mark Philips.

1973. Royal Wedding.

394. **125** 25 c. multicoloured .. 10 10
395. – $2 multicoloured .. 30 30

DESIGN: $2 As Type **125**, but with different frame.

126. " Adoration of the Kings " (Brueghel).

1973. Christmas. " The Adoration of the Shepherds " by the artists listed. Mult.

397. ½ c. Type **126** 10 10
398. 1 c. Botticelli " Adoration of the Magi " 10 10
399. 2 c. Durer " Adoration of the Magi " 10 10
400. 12 c. Botticelli " Mystic Nativity " 15 10
401. 22 c. Rubens " Adoration of the Magi " 20 10
402. 35 c. Durer " The Nativity " 20 10
403. $1 Giorgione " Adoration of the Shepherds " .. 55 55

127. Carib Basket-weaving.

1973. National Day. Multicoloured.

405. 5 c. Type **127** 10 10
406. 10 c. Staircase of the Snake 10 10
407. 50 c. Miss Caribbean Queen 1973 .. .. 15 15
408. 60 c. Miss Carifta Queen 1973 15 15
409. $1 Dance Group 25 30

Nos. 407/8 are vert.

128. University Centre Dominica.

1973. 25th Anniv. West Indies University. Multicoloured.

411. 12 c. Type **128** 10 10
412. 30 c. Graduation ceremony 10 10
413. $1 University coat of arms 25 35

129. Dominica 1d. Stamp of 1874 and Map.

1974. Stamp Centenary. Multicoloured.

415. ½ c. Type **129** 10 10
416. 1 c. 6d. stamp of 1874 and posthorn 10 10
417. 2 c. 1d. stamp of 1874 and arms 10 10
418. 10 c. Type **129** 15 10
419. 50 c. As 1 c. 55 30
420. $1.20 As 2 c. 85 70

130. Footballer and Flag of Brazil.

1974. World Cup Football Championship, West Germany. Multicoloured.

422. ½ c. Type **130**. 10 10
423. 1 c. West Germany 10 10
424. 2 c. Italy 10 10
425. 30 c. Scotland 30 10
426. 40 c. Sweden 30 10
427. 50 c. Netherlands 35 15
428. $1 Yugoslavia 65 40

131. Indian Hole.

1974. National Day. Multicoloured.

430. 10 c. Type **131** 10 10
431. 40 c. Teachers' Training College 10 10
432. $1 Bay Oil distillery plant, Petite Savanne 30 45

132. Churchill with "Colonist".

1974. Birth Cent. of Sir Winston Churchill. Multicoloured.

434. ½ c. Type **132** 10 10
435. 1 c. Churchill and Eisenhower 10 10
436. 2 c. Churchill and Roosevelt 10 10
437. 20 c. Churchill and troops on assault-course .. 15 10
438. 45 c. Painting at Marrakesh 25 10
439. $2 Giving the "V" sign .. 80 1·00

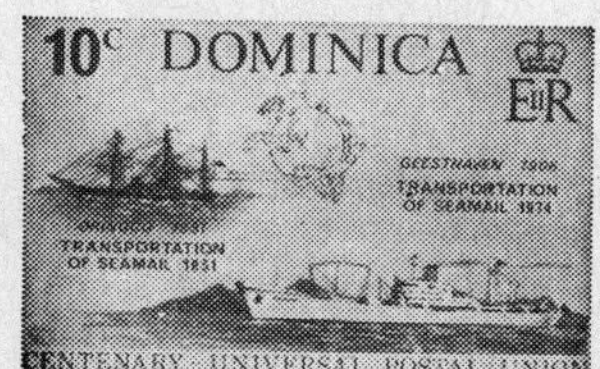

133. Mailboats " Orinoco " (1851) and " Geesthaven " (1974).

1974. Cent. of Universal Postal Union. Mult.

441. 10 c. Type **133** 15 10
442. $2 Mailplanes—De Havilland " 4 " (1918) and Boeing " 747 " (1974) .. 65 1·00

134. " The Virgin and Child " (Tiso).

1974. Christmas. Multicoloured.

444. ½ c. Type **134** 10 10
445. 1 c. " Madonna and Child " (Costa) 10 10
446. 2 c. "The Nativity" (school of Rimini, 14th Cent.) .. 10 10
447. 10 c. " The Rest on the flight into Egypt " (Romanelli) 15 10
448. 25 c. " The Adoration of the Shepherds " (de Sermoneta) 20 10
449. 45 c. " The Nativity " (Guido Reni) 25 10
450. $1 " The Adoration of the Magi " (Caselli) .. 45 40

135. Trigger Fish.

1975. Fishes. Multicoloured.

452. ½ c. Type **135** 10 10
453. 1 c. Cola 10 10
454. 2 c. Sailfish 10 10
455. 3 c. Vayway 10 10
456. 20 c. Bechine .. .. 1·00 50
457. $2 Grouper .. .. .. 4·25 2·75

136. "Myscelia antholia".

1975. Dominican Butterflires. Multicoloured.

459 ½ c. Type **136** 10 15
460 1 c. "Lycorea ceres" .. 10 15
461 2 c. "Anaea manthesia" ("Sierone nemesis") .. 15 15
462 6 c. "Battus polydamas" 50 15
463 30 c. "Anartia lytrea" .. 1·50 60
464 40 c. "Morpho peleides" .. 1·75 65
465 $2 "Dryas julia" .. .. 3·50 3·00

137. R.M.S. " Yare ".

1975. " Ships tied to Dominica's History ". Multicoloured.

467. ½ c. Type **137** 10 10
468. 1 c. R.M.S. " Thames " .. 10 10
469. 2 c. S.S. " Lady Nelson " 10 10
470. 20 c. S.S. " Lady Rodney " 45 35
471. 45 c. M.V. " Statesman " 70 55
472. 50 c. M.V. " Geestecape " 80 65
473. $2 M.V. " Geestestar " .. 4·50 3·25

138. " Women in Agriculture ".

1975. International Women's Year. Mult.

475. 10 c. Type **138** .. 10 10
476. $2 " Women in Industry and Commerce " .. 40 60

139. Miss Caribbean Queen, 1975.

1975. National Day. Multicoloured.

477. 5 c Type **139** 10 10
478. 10 c. Public Library (horiz.) 10 10
479. 30 c. Citrus Factory (horiz.) 10 10
480. $1 National Day Trophy .. 25 50

140. " Virgin and Child " (Mantegna).

1975. Christmas. "Virgin and Child" paintings by artists named. Multicoloured.

No.	Description	Unused	Used
482.	½ c. Type **140**	10	10
483.	1 c. Fra Filippo Lippi	10	10
484.	2 c. Bellini	10	10
485.	10 c. Botticelli	10	10
486.	25 c. Bellini	10	10
487.	45 c. Correggio	15	10
488.	$1 Durer	30	50

141. Hibiscus.

1975. Multicoloured.

No.	Description	Unused	Used
490.	½ c. Type **141**	10	20
491.	1 c. African tulip	15	20
492.	2 c. Castor-oil tree	15	20
493.	3 c. White cedar flower	15	20
494.	4 c. Egg plant	15	20
495.	5 c. Gare	20	20
496.	6 c. Ochro	20	30
497.	8 c. Zenaida dove	1·00	30
498.	10 c. Screw pine	20	10
499.	20 c. Mango longue	30	15
500.	25 c. Crayfish	35	15
501.	30 c. Common opossum	70	45
502.	40 c. Bay leaf groves	75	45
503.	50 c. Tomatoes	55	40
504.	$1 Lime factory	75	55
505.	$2 Ram distillery	2·50	2·75
506.	$5 Bay oil distillery	4·25	4·50
507.	$10 Queen Elizabeth II (vert.)	10·00	15·00

Nos. 502/7 are larger, 28 × 44 mm. ($10) or 44 × 28 (others).

142. American Infantry.

1976. Bicent. of American Revolution. Mult.

No.	Description	Unused	Used
508.	½ c. Type **142**	10	10
509.	1 c. British three-decker, 1782	10	10
510.	2 c. George Washington	10	10
511.	45 c. British sailors	75	30
512.	75 c. British ensign	1·25	65
513.	$2 Admiral Hood	3·00	2·00

143. Rowing.

1976. Olympic Games, Montreal. Mult.

No.	Description	Unused	Used
515.	½ c. Type **143**	10	10
516.	1 c. Shot putting	10	10
517.	2 c. Swimming	10	10
518.	40 c. Relay	15	10
519.	45 c. Gymnastics	15	10
520.	60 c. Sailing	20	20
521.	$2 Archery	55	80

144. Ringed Kingfisher.

1976. Wild Birds. Multicoloured.

No.	Description	Unused	Used
523.	½ c. Type **144**	10	15
524.	1 c. Mourning dove	15	15
525.	2 c. Green heron	15	15
526.	15 c. Blue-winged hawk (vert.)	1·00	45
527.	30 c. Blue-headed hummingbird (vert.)	1·50	70
528.	45 c. Bananaquit (vert.)	2·25	1·00
529.	$2 Imperial amazon (vert.)	8·50	8·50

1976. West Indian Victory in World Cricket Cup. As Nos. 559/60 of Barbados.

No.	Description	Unused	Used
531.	15 c. Map of the Caribbean	1·00	1·25
532.	25 c. Prudential Cup	1·00	1·50

145. Viking Spacecraft System.

1976. Viking Space Mission. Multicoloured.

No.	Description	Unused	Used
533.	½ c. Type **145**	10	10
534.	1 c. Launching pad (horiz.)	10	10
535.	2 c. Titan IIID and Centaur DII	10	10
536.	3 c. Orbiter and lander capsule	10	10
537.	45 c. Capsule, parachute unopened	30	15
538.	75 c. Capsule, parachute opened	40	25
539.	$1 Lander descending (horiz.)	50	35
540.	$2 Space vehicle on Mars (horiz.)	80	60

146. "Virgin and Child with Saints Anthony of Padua and Roch" (Giorgione).

1976. Christmas. "Virgin and Child" paintings by artists named. Multicoloured.

No.	Description	Unused	Used
542.	½ c. Type **146**	10	10
543.	1 c. Bellini	10	10
544.	2 c. Mantegna	10	10
545.	6 c. Mantegna (different)	10	10
546.	25 c. Memling	10	10
547.	45 c. Correggio	15	10
548.	$3 Raphael	70	1·00

147. Island Craft Co-operative.

1976. National Day. Multicoloured.

No.	Description	Unused	Used
550.	10 c. Type **147**	10	10
551.	50 c. Harvesting Bananas	15	10
552.	$1 Boxing Plant	30	35

148. Common Sundial.

1976. Shells. Multicoloured.

No.	Description	Unused	Used
554.	½ c. Type **148**	10	10
555.	1 c. Flame Helmet	10	10
556.	2 c. Mouse Cone	10	10
557.	20 c. Caribbean Vase	45	10
558.	40 c. West Indian Fighting Conch	70	25
559.	50 c. Short Coral Shell	70	25
560.	$3 Apple Murex	3·50	2·75

149. The Queen Crowned and Enthroned.

1977. Silver Jubilee. Multicoloured.

No.	Description	Unused	Used
562.	½ c. Type **149**	10	10
563.	1 c. Imperial State Crown	10	10
564.	45 c. The Queen and Princess Anne	15	10
565.	$2 Coronation Ring	25	30
566.	$2.50 Ampulla and Spoon	30	40

150. Joseph Haydn.

1977. 150th Death Anniv. of Ludwig van Beethoven. Multi.

No.	Description	Unused	Used
568.	½ c. Type **150**	10	10
569.	1 c. Scene from "Fidelio"	10	10
570.	2 c. Maria Casentini (dancer)	10	10
571.	15 c. Beethoven and pastoral scene	15	10
572.	30 c. "Wellington's Victory"	25	10
573.	40 c. Henriette Sontag (singer)	35	10
574.	$2 The young Beethoven	1·50	1·25

151. Hiking.

1977. Caribbean Scout Jamboree, Jamaica. Multicoloured.

No.	Description	Unused	Used
576.	½ c. Type **151**	10	10
577.	1 c. First-aid	10	10
578.	2 c. Camping	10	10
579.	45 c. Rock climbing	35	15
580.	50 c. Canoeing	40	20
581.	$3 Sailing	2·00	1·75

152. Holy Family.

1977. Christmas. Multicoloured.

No.	Description	Unused	Used
583.	½ c. Type **152**	10	10
584.	1 c. Angel and Shepherds	10	10
585.	2 c. Holy Baptism	10	10
586.	6 c. Flight into Egypt	10	10
587.	15 c. Three Kings with gifts	15	10
588.	45 c. Holy Family in the Temple	30	10
589.	$3 Flight into Egypt (different)	1·00	70

1977. Royal Visit. Nos. 562/66 optd. **ROYAL VISIT W.I. 1977.**

No.	Description	Unused	Used
591.	½ c. Type **149**	10	10
592.	1 c. Imperial State Crown	10	10
593.	45 c. The Queen and Princess Anne	15	10
594.	$2 Coronation Ring	30	30
595.	$2·50 Ampulla and Spoon	35	35

154. "Sousouelle Souris".

1978. "History of Carnival". Multicoloured.

No.	Description	Unused	Used
597.	½ c. Type **154**	10	10
598.	1 c. Sensay costume	10	10
599.	2 c. Street musicians	10	10
600.	45 c. Douiette band	15	10
601.	50 c. Pappy Show wedding	15	10
602.	$2 Masquerade band	45	60

155. Colonel Charles Lindbergh and "Spirit of St. Louis".

1978. Aviation Annivs. Multicoloured.

No.	Description	Unused	Used
604.	6 c. Type **155**	15	10
605.	10 c. "Spirit of St. Louis", New York, 20th May 1927	20	10
606.	15 c. Lindbergh and map of Atlantic	25	10
607.	20 c. Lindbergh reaches Paris, 21st May 1927	30	10
608.	40 c. "LZ1", Lake Constance, 1900	35	20
609.	60 c. Count F. von Zeppelin and "LZ 2" 1906	45	30
610.	$3 "LZ127 Graf Zeppelin" 1928	95	1·10

156. Queen receiving Homage.

1978. 25th Anniv. of Coronation. Multi.

No.	Description	Unused	Used
612.	45 c. Type **156**	15	10
613.	$2 Balcony scene	30	30
614.	$2.50 Queen and Prince Philip	40	40

157. Wilbur Wright's Aeroplane.

1978. 75th Anniv. of First Powered Flight. Multicoloured.

No.	Description	Unused	Used
616.	30 c. Type **157**	15	15
617.	40 c. "Flyer", 1908	20	20
618.	60 c. "Flyer I"	25	25
619.	$2 "Flyer I" (different)	85	85

158. "Two Apostles".

1978. Christmas. Paintings by Rubens. Multicoloured.

No.	Description	Unused	Used
621.	20 c. Type **158**	10	10
622.	45 c. "Descent from the Cross"	15	10
623.	50 c. "St. Ildefonso receiving the Chasuble"	15	10
624.	$3 "Assumption of the Virgin"	55	80

MINIMUM PRICE

The minimum price quoted is 10p which represents a handling charge rather than a basis for valuing common stamps. For further notes about prices see introductory pages.

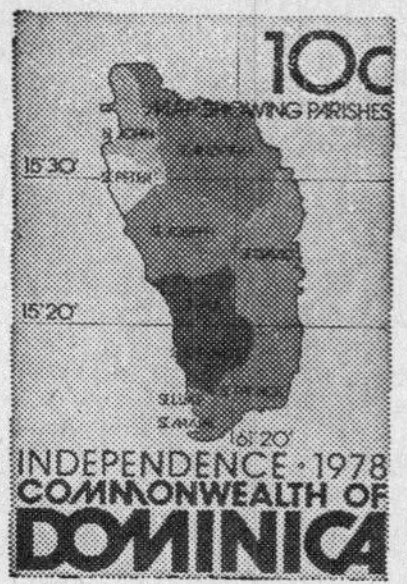

159. Map showing Parishes.

1978. Independence. Multicoloured.

626. 10 c. Type **159** 10 10
627. 25 c. " Sabinea carinalis " (national flower) .. 15 10
628. 45 c. New National flag .. 25 15
629. 50 c. Coat of arms .. 25 15
630. $2 Prime Minister Patrick John 70 70

1978. Nos. 490/507 optd. **INDEPENDENCE 3rd NOVEMBER 1978.**

632. ½ c. Type **57** 30 10
633. 1 c. African tulip 35 10
634. 2 c. Castor-oil tree .. 35 10
635. 3 c. White cedar flower .. 40 15
636. 4 c. Egg plant 40 15
637. 5 c. Gare 40 15
638. 6 c. Ochro 40 15
639. 8 c. Zenaida dove .. .. 1·00 20
640. 10 c. Screw pine 50 15
641. 20 c. Mango longue .. 60 15
642. 25 c. Crayfish 70 20
643. 30 c. Common opossum .. 70 20
644. 40 c. Bay leaf groves .. 70 25
645. 50 c. Tomatoes 80 30
646. $1 Lime Factory 80 65
647. $2 Rum distillery .. .. 1·25 1·00
648. $5 Bay oil distillery .. 2·50 2·25
649. $10 Queen Elizabeth II .. 5·50 4·50

161. Sir Rowland Hill.

1979. Death Cent. of Sir Rowland Hill. Multicoloured.

650. 25 c. Type **161** 20 10
651. 45 c. G.B. 1840 Twopenny Blue 25 10
652. 50 c. Dominica 1874 1d. stamp 25 10
653. $2 Maltese Cross handstamps 65 65

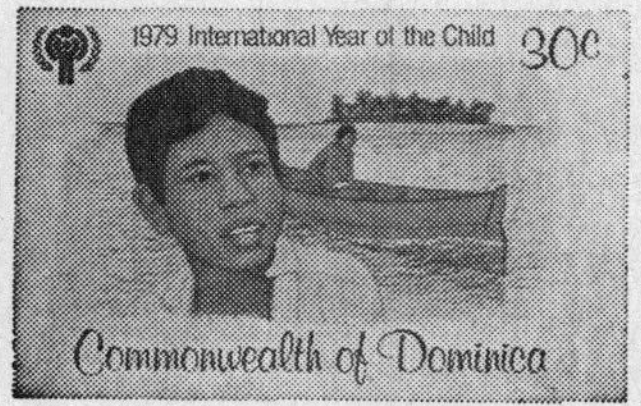

162. Children and Canoe.

1979. International Year of the Child. Multicoloured.

655. 30 c. Type **162** 30 15
656. 40 c. Children with bananas 40 25
657. 50 c. Children playing cricket 85 40
658. $3 Child feeding rabbits .. 1·75 1·50

163. Grouper.

1979. Marine Wildlife. Multicoloured.

660. 10 c. Type **163** 25 10
661. 30 c. Striped dolphin .. 50 15
662. 50 c. White-tailed Tropic-Bird .. .. .. 1·25 25
663. 60 c. Brown Pelican .. 1·25 30
664. $1 Long-finned pilot whale 1·50 45
665. $2 Brown Booby .. .. 2·25 80

164. H.M.S. "Endeavour".

1979. Death Bicentenary of Captain Cook. Multicoloured.

667. 10 c. Type **164** 35 10
668. 50 c. H.M.S. " Resolution " (Second Voyage) .. 80 45
669. 60 c. H.M.S. " Discovery " (Third Voyage) .. 90 55
670. $2 Detail of Cook's chart of New Zealand, 1770 .. 1·40 1·10

165. Cooking at Camp-fire.

1979. 50th Anniv. of Girl Guide Movement in Dominica. Multicoloured.

672. 10 c. Type **165** 20 10
673. 20 c. Pitching emergency rain tent 25 10
674. 50 c. Raising Dominican flag 35 10
675. $2.50 Singing and dancing to accordian .. .. 1·00 80

166. Colvillea.

1979. Flowering Trees. Multicoloured.

677. 20 c. Type **166** 20 10
678. 40 c. " Lignum Vitae " .. 30 15
679. 60 c. Dwarf Poinciana .. 45 25
680. $2 Fern Tree .. .. 1·00 90

167. Cathedral of the Assumption, Roseau.

1979. Christmas. Cathedrals. Multicoloured.

682. 6 c. Type **167** 10 10
683. 45 c. St. Paul's, London (vert.) 15 10
684. 60 c. St. Peter's, Rome .. 15 10
685. $3 Notre Dame, Paris (vert.) 55 60

1979. Hurricane Relief. Nos. 495, 502 and 506/7 optd. **HURRICANE RELIEF.**

687. 5 c. Gare 10 10
688. 40 c. Bay Leaf Groves .. 10 10
689. $5 Bay Oil Distillery .. 1·25 1·50
690. $10 Queen Elizabeth II .. 2·00 2·25

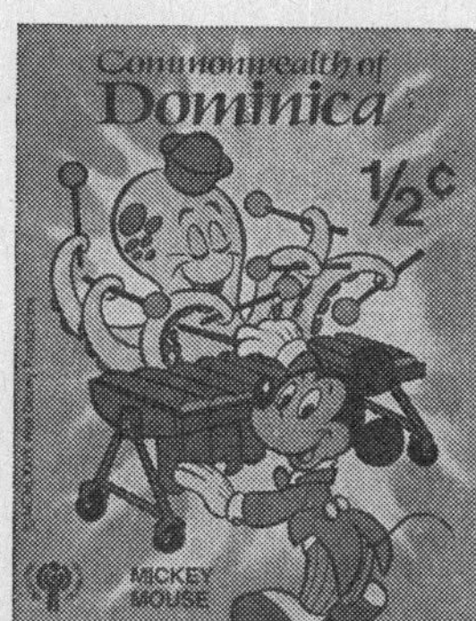

169. Mickey Mouse and Octopus playing Xylophone.

1979. International Year of the Child. Walt Disney Characters. Multicoloured.

691. ½ c. Type **169** 10 10
692. 1 c. Goofy playing guitar on rocking-horse 10 10
693. 2 c. Mickey Mouse playing violin and Goofy on bagpipes 10 10
694. 3 c. Donald Duck playing drum with a pneumatic drill 10 10
695. 4 c. Minnie Mouse playing saxophone 10 10
696. 5 c. Goofy one-man band 10 10
697. 10 c. Horace Horsecollar blowing Dale from French horn 10 10
698. $2 Huey, Dewey and Louie playing bass .. .. 2·75 1·25
699. $2.50 Donald Duck at piano and Huey playing trumpet 3·00 1·50

170. Hospital Ward.

1980. 75th Anniv. of Rotary International. Multicoloured.

701. 10 c. Type **170** 10 10
702. 20 c. Electro-cardiogram 15 10
703. 40 c. Mental hospital site 20 15
704. $2.50 Paul Harris (founder) 55 70

1980. " London 1980 " International Stamp Exhibition. Optd. **LONDON 1980.**

706. **161.** 25 c. multicoloured .. 25 10
707. – 45 c. multicoloured .. 30 15
708. – 50 c. brown, blue & red 30 15
709. – $2 brown, red & yellow 80 60

171. Shot Putting.

1980. Olympic Games, Moscow. Mult.

710. 30 c. Type **171** 20 10
711. 40 c. Basketball 35 15
712. 60 c. Swimming 35 20
713. $2 Gymnastics 70 65

172. " Supper at Emmaus " (Caravaggio).

1980. Famous Paintings. Multicoloured.

715. 20 c. Type **172** 10 10
716. 25 c. " Portrait of Charles I Hunting " (Van Dyck) (vert.) 10 10
717. 30 c. " The Maids of Honour " (Velazquez) (vert.) 15 10
718. 45 c. " The Rape of the Sabine Women " (Poussin) 15 10
719. $1 " Embarkation for Cythera " (Watteau) .. 35 35
720. $5 " Girl before a Mirror " (Picasso) (vert.) .. 1·50 1·50

173. Scene from " Peter Pan ".

1980. Christmas. Scenes from "Peter Pan". Multicoloured.

722. ½ c. Type **173** (Tinker Bell) 10 10
723. 1 c. Wendy sewing back Peter's shadow 10 10
724. 2 c. Peter introduces the mermaids 10 10
725. 3 c. Wendy and Peter with lost boys 10 10
726. 4 c. Captain Hook, Pirate Smee and Tiger Lily .. 10 10
727. 5 c. Peter with Tiger Lily and her father 10 10
728. 10 c. Captain Hook captures Peter and Wendy 10 10
729. $2 Peter fights Captain Hook .. .. .. 1·25 80
730. $2.50 Captain Hook in crocodile's jaws .. 1·50 95

174. Queen Elizabeth the Queen Mother in Doorway.

1980. 80th Birthday of The Queen Mother.

732. **174.** 40 c. multicoloured .. 50 40
733. $2.50 multicoloured .. 1·60 1·50

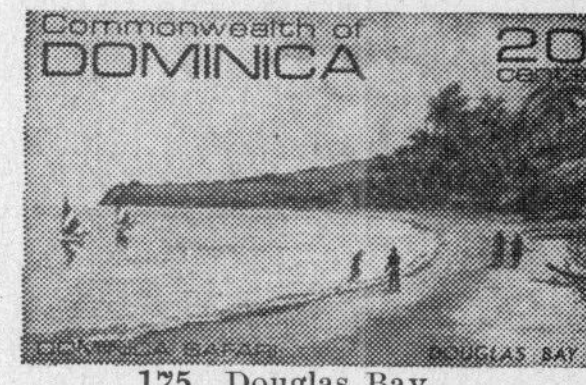

175. Douglas Bay.

1981. " Dominica Safari ". Multicoloured.

735. 20 c. Type **175** 10 10
736. 30 c. Valley of Desolation 15 15
737. 40 c. Emerald Pool (vert.) 20 20
738. $3 Indian River (vert.) .. 1·40 1·60

1981. Walt Disney's Cartoon Character, Pluto. As T **169**. Multicoloured.

740. $2 Pluto and Fifi .. .. 1·25 1·25

176. Forest Thrush.

1981. Birds. Multicoloured.

742. 20 c. Type **176** 55 20
743. 30 c. Wied's crested flycatcher 65 25
744. 40 c. Blue-hooded euphonia 75 35
745. $5 Lesser Antillean pewee 3·50 4·25

177. Windsor Castle.

1981. Royal Wedding. Multicoloured.

747. 40 c. Prince Charles and Lady Diana Spencer .. 20 10
748. 60 c. Type **177** 25 15
749. $4 Prince Charles flying helicopter .. .. 1·00 1·00

178. Lady Diana Spencer.

1981. Royal Wedding. Multicoloured.

751. 25 c. Type **178** 20 35
752. $2 Prince Charles .. 70 1·00
753. $5 Prince Charles and Lady Diana Spencer .. .. 1·75 2·50

1981. Christmas. Scenes from Walt Disney's cartoon film "Santa's Workshop". As T **169**.

754. ½ c. multicoloured .. 10 10
755. 1 c. multicoloured .. 10 10
756. 2 c. multicoloured .. 10 10
757. 3 c. multicoloured .. 10 10
758. 4 c. multicoloured .. 10 10
759. 5 c. multicoloured .. 10 10
760. 10 c. multicoloured .. 10 10
761. 45 c. multicoloured .. 75 30
762. $5 multicoloured .. .. 3·50 2·50

179. Ixora.

1981. Plant Life. Multicoloured.

764 1 c. Type **179** 10 30
765 2 c. Flamboyant 10 30
766 4 c. Poinsettia 15 10
767 5 c. Bois Caribe (national flower of Dominica) .. 15 10
768 8 c. Annatto or Roucou .. 20 10
769 10 c. Passion Fruit .. 30 10
770 15 c. Breadfruit or Yampain 55 15
771 20 c. Allamanda or Buttercup 40 15
772 25 c. Cashew Nut .. 40 15
773 35 c. Sousop or Couassol .. 45 30
774 40 c. Bougainvillea .. 45 30
775 45 c. Anthurium 50 35
776 60 c. Cacao or Cocoa .. 1·00 35
777 90 c. Pawpaw Tree or Papay 70 60
778 $1 Coconut Palm .. 1·00 80
779 $2 Coffee Tree or Cafe .. 1·00 2·00
780 $5 Heliconia or Lobster Claw .. .. .. 3·25 4·00
781 $10 Banana/Fig .. .. 5·00 8·00

Nos. 769, 770, 776, 778, 780 and 781 come with or without imprint date.

180. Curb Slope for Wheelchairs.

1981. International Year of Disabled People. Multicoloured.

782. 45 c. Type **180** 70 25
783. 60 c. Bus with invalid step 80 35
784. 75 c. Motor car controls adapted for handicapped 90 40
785. $4 Bus with wheelchair ramp .. .. .. 2·50 2·50

181. " Olga Picasso in an Armchair ".

1981. Birth Centenary of Picasso. Mult.

787. 45 c. Type **181** 65 25
788. 60 c. " Bathers " 75 35
789. 75 c. " Woman in Spanish Costume " 90 40
790. $4 " Detail of Dog and Cock " .. .. 2·50 2·50

HAVE YOU READ THE NOTES AT THE BEGINNING OF THIS CATALOGUE?
These often provide answers to the enquiries we receive.

1982. World Cup Football Championship, Spain. Walt Disney Cartoon Characters. As T **169**. Multicoloured.

792. ½ c. Goofy chasing ball with butterfly net .. 10 10
793. 1 c. Donald Duck with ball in beak 10 10
794. 2 c. Goofy as goalkeeper .. 10 10
795. 3 c. Goofy looking for ball 10 10
796. 4 c. Goofy as park attendant puncturing ball with litter spike 10 10
797. 5 c. Pete and Donald Duck playing 10 10
798. 10 c. Donald Duck after kicking rock instead of ball 10 10
799. 60 c. Donald Duck feeling effects of a hard game and Daisy Duck dusting ball 75 55
800. $5 Goofy hiding ball under his jersey from Mickey Mouse .. .. 3·25 2·75

182. " Golden Days ".

1982. Norman Rockwell (painter) Commemoration. Multicoloured.

802. 10 c. Type **182** 10 10
803. 25 c. " The Morning News " 15 10
804. 45 c. " The Marbles Champ " 30 30
805. $1 " Speeding Along " .. 55 55

183. Elma Napier (first woman elected to B.W.I. Legislative Council).

1982. Decade for Women. Multicoloured.

806. 10 c. Type **183** 10 10
807. 45 c. Margaret Mead (anthropologist) .. 30 30
808. $1 Mabel (Cissy) Caudeiron (folk song composer and historian) 55 55
809. $4 Eleanor Roosevelt .. 2·25 2·25

184. George Washington and Independence Hall, Philadelphia.

1982. 250th Birth Anniv. of George Washington. Birth Centenary of Franklin D. Roosevelt. Multicoloured.

811. 45 c. Type **184** .. 40 25
812. 60 c. Franklin D. Roosevelt and Capitol Washington D.C. .. 50 35
813. 90 c. Washington at Yorktown (detail " The Surrender of Corwallis " by Trumbull) 70 55
814. $2 Construction of dam from W. Groppers' mural commemorating Roosevelt's " New Deal " .. 1·50 1·60

185. "Anaea dominicana".

1982. Butterflies. Multicoloured.

816 15 c. Type **185** .. .. 1·00 35
817 45 c. "Heliconius charithonia" .. .. 1·75 65
818 60 c. "Hypolimnas misippus" .. .. 2·00 1·25
819 $3 "Biblis hyperia" .. 4·50 5·00

186. Prince and Princess of Wales.

1982. 21st Birthday of Princess of Wales. Multicoloured.

821. 45 c. Buckingham Palace 30 30
822. $2 Type **186** 90 90
823. $4 Princess of Wales .. 1·60 1·60

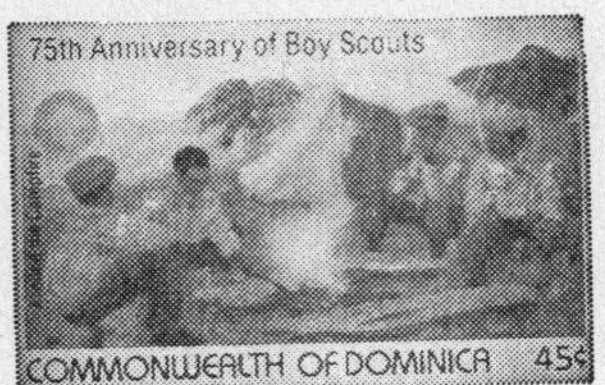

187. Scouts around Campfire.

1982. 75th Anniv. of Boy Scout Movement. Multicoloured.

825. 45 c. Type **187** .. .. 1·25 50
826. 60 c. Temperature study, Valley of Desolation .. 1·75 1·00
827. 75 c. Learning about native birds .. .. 2·00 1·10
828. $3 Canoe trip along Indian River .. .. .. 3·75 4·50

1982. Birth of Prince William of Wales. Nos. 821/3 optd. **ROYAL BABY 21.6.82.**

830. 45 c. Buckingham Palace 30 30
831. $2 Type **186** .. .. 1·10 1·10
832. $4 Princess of Wales .. 1·90 1·90

188. " Holy Family of Francis I ".

1982. Christmas. Raphael Paintings. Mult.

834. 25 c. Type **188** 15 10
835. 30 c. " Holy Family of the Pearl " 20 15
836. 90 c. " Canigiani Holy Family " 55 55
837. $4 " Holy Family of the Oak Tree " .. .. 1·90 1·90

189. Cuvier's Beaked Whale.

1983. Save the Whales. Multicoloured.

839. 45 c. Type **189** .. .. 1·00 65
840. 60 c. Humpback Whale .. 1·25 1·00
841. 75 c. Black Right Whale .. 1·40 1·25
842. $3 Melon-headed Whale .. 3·25 4·00

190. Banana Export.

1983. Commonwealth Day. Multicoloured.

844. 25 c. Type **190** 15 15
845. 30 c. Road building .. 15 20
846. 90 c. Community nursing 40 45
847. $3 Tourism–handicrafts .. 1·25 1·50

191. Map and Satellite Picture of Hurricane.

1983. World Communications Year. Mult.

848. 45 c. Type **191** 20 25
849. 60 c. Aircraft-to-ship transmission 30 35
850. 90 c. Satellite communications 40 45
851. $2 Shortwave radio .. 95 1·00

192. " Mayo-Mercury " Composite.

1983. Bicentenary of Manned Flight. Multi.

853. 45 c. Type **192** 40 30
854. 60 c. Macchi " M.39 " seaplane 60 60
855. 90 c. Fairey " Swordfish " biplane 85 85
856. $4 Zeppelin " LZ3 " .. 2·75 3·00

193. Duesenberg " SJ ", 1935.

1983. Classic Motor Cars. Multicoloured.

858. 10 c. Type **193** 10 10
859. 45 c. Studebaker " Avanti ", 1962 .. .. .. 25 25
860. 60 c. Cord " 812 " 35 35
861. 75 c. MG " TC ", 1945 .. 40 40
862. 90 c. Camaro " 350 SS ", 1967 .. .. .. 45 45
863. $3 Porsch " 356 ", 1948 .. 1·40 1·50

194. " Charity ".

1983. Christmas. 500th Birth Anniv. of Raphael. Multicoloured.

865. 45 c. Type **194** 55 30
866. 60 c. " Hope " 70 50
867. 90 c. " Faith " 80 60
868. $4 " The Cardinal Virtues " 2·50 3·00

195. Plumbeous Warbler.

1984. Birds. Multicoloured.

870. 5 c. Type **195** 50 20
871. 45 c. Imperial amazon .. 1·25 45
872. 60 c. Blue-headed hummingbird .. .. 1·50 90
873. 90 c. Red-necked amazon 2·00 2·00

196. Donald Duck.

1984. Easter. Multicoloured.

875. ½ c. Type **196** 10 10
876. 1 c. Mickey Mouse 10 10
877. 2 c. Tortoise and Hare .. 10 10
878. 3 c. Brer Rabbit and Brer Bear 10 10
879. 4 c. Donald Duck (different) 10 10
880. 5 c. White Rabbit 10 10
881. 10 c. Thumper 10 10
882. $2 Pluto .. .. .. 2·75 2·25
883. $4 Pluto (different) .. 3·75 3·50

197. Gymnastics.

1984. Olympic Games, Los Angeles. Multicoloured.

885. 30 c. Type **197** 20 25
886. 45 c. Javelin-throwing .. 30 35
887. 60 c. High diving 40 45
888. $4 Fencing .. .. .. 2·00 2·50

198. "Atlantic Star".

1984. Shipping. Multicoloured.

890. 45 c. Type **198** .. .. 1·25 60
891. 60 c. "Atlantic" (liner) .. 1·50 1·00
892. 90 c. Carib fishing boat .. 2·00 1·25
893. $4 "Norway" (liner) .. 4·25 5·50

1984. Universal Postal Union Congress, Hamburg. Nos. 769 and 780 optd. **19th UPU CONGRESS HAMBURG.**

895. 10 c. Passion Fruit .. 10 10
896. $5 Heliconia or Lobster Claw .. .. .. 3·25 3·50

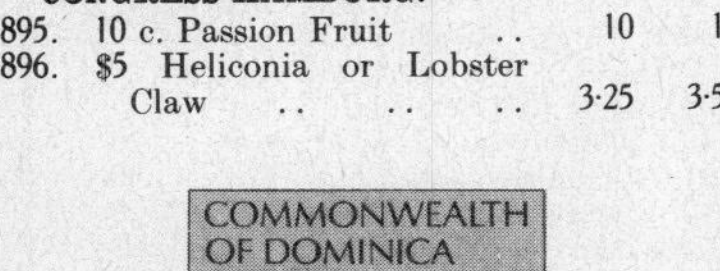

200. "Guzmania lingulata".

1984. "Ausipex" International Stamp Exhibition, Melbourne. Bromeliads. Mult.

897. 45 c. Type **200** 30 35
898. 60 c. "Pitcairnia angustifolia" 40 55
899. 75 c. "Tillandsia fasciculata" 50 75
900. $3 "Aechmea smithiorum" 2·00 3·25

201. "The Virgin and Child with Young St. John" (Correggio).

1984. 450th Death Anniv. of Correggio (painter). Multicoloured.

902. 25 c. Type **201** 40 20
903. 60 c. "Christ bids Farewell to the Virgin Mary" .. 70 40
904. 90 c. "Do not Touch Me" 1·00 60
905. $4 "The Mystical Marriage of St. Catherine" .. 2·75 2·75

202. "Before the Start" (Edgar Degas).

1984. 150th Birth Anniv. of Edgar Degas (painter). Multicoloured.

907. 30 c. Type **202** 40 25
908. 45 c. "Race on the Racecourse" 60 35
909. $1 "Jockeys at the Flagpole" .. .. .. 1·00 65
910. $3 "Racehorses at Longchamp" .. .. .. 2·25 2·25

203. Tabby.

1984. Cats. Multicoloured.

912 10 c. Type **203** 20 10
913 15 c. Calico shorthair .. 20 10
914 20 c. Siamese 30 15
915 25 c. Manx 30 20
916 45 c. Abyssinian 55 30
917 60 c. Tortoise-shell longhair 70 40
918 $1 Cornish rex .. .. 1·25 75
919 $2 Persian .. .. 1·75 2·00
920 $3 Himalayan .. .. 2·50 3·25
921 $5 Burmese .. .. 3·75 5·50

204. Avro "748".

1984. 40th Anniv. of International Civil Aviation Organisation. Multicoloured.

923. 30 c. Type **204** 55 20
924. 60 c. Twin "Otter" .. 1·00 40
925. $1 "Islander" .. .. 1·50 80
926. $3 "Casa" .. .. .. 3·00 3·00

MORE DETAILED LISTS
are given in the Stanley Gibbons Catalogues referred to in the country headings.
For lists of current volumes see Introduction.

205. Donald Duck, Mickey Mouse and Goofy with Father Christmas.

1984. Christmas. Walt Disney Cartoon Characters. Multicoloured.

928. 45 c. Type **205** 90 30
929. 60 c. Donald Duck as Father Christmas with toy train .. .. .. 1·10 50
930. 90 c. Donald Duck as Father Christmas in sleigh .. 1·60 75
931. $2 Donald Duck and nephews in sledge .. 2·25 1·75
932. $4 Donald Duck in snow with Christmas tree .. 3·00 2·75

206. Mrs. M. Bascom presenting Trefoil to Chief Guide Lady Baden-Powell.

1985. 75th Anniv. of Girl Guide Movement. Multicoloured.

934. 35 c. Type **206** 50 30
935. 45 c. Lady Baden-Powell inspecting Dominican brownies 70 35
936. 60 c. Lady Baden-Powell with Mrs. M. Bascom and Mrs. A. Robinson (guide leaders) .. 85 55
937. $3 Lord and Lady Baden-Powell (vert.) .. .. 2·25 2·75

1985. Birth Bicentenary of John J. Audubon (ornithologist) (1st issue). As T **198** of Antigua. Multicoloured.

939. 45 c. Clapper rail 65 30
940. $1 Black and white warbler (vert.) .. .. .. 1·25 80
941. $2 Broad-winged hawk (vert.) .. .. .. 1·75 2·00
942. $3 Ring-necked duck .. 2·25 2·50

See also Nos. 1013/16.

207. Student with Computer.

1985. Duke of Edinburgh's Award Scheme. Multicoloured.

944. 45 c. Type **207** 35 30
945. 60 c. Assisting doctor in hospital 55 40
946. 90 c. Two youths hiking .. 75 65
947. $4 Family jogging .. 2·75 3·25

208. The Queen Mother visiting Sadlers Wells Opera.

1985. Life and Times of Queen Elizabeth the Queen Mother. Multicoloured.

949. 60 c. Type **208** 50 40
950. $1 Fishing in Scotland .. 70 60
951. $3 On her 84th birthday .. 1·90 2·00

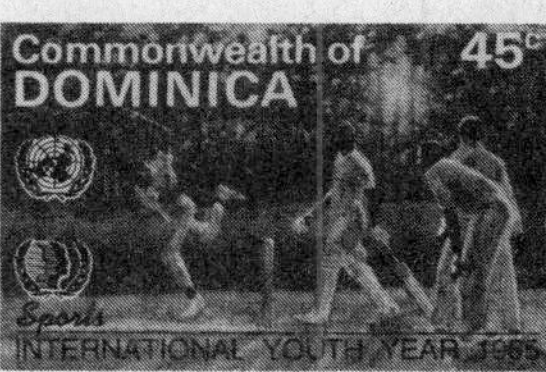

209. Cricket Match ("Sports").

1985. International Youth Year. Mult.

953. 45 c. Type **209** .. .. 2·00 80
954. 60 c. Bird-watching "Environmental Study" .. 2·25 1·00
955. $1 Stamp collecting ("Education") .. .. 2·50 1·75
956. $3 Boating ("Leisure") .. 3·25 4·50

1985. 300th Birth Anniv. of Johann Sebastian Bach (composer). As T **206** of Antigua. Mult.

958. 45 c. Cornet .. .. 1·25 40
959. 60 c. Coiled trumpet .. 1·50 60
960. $1 Piccolo .. .. .. 2·00 1·00
961. $3 Violoncello piccolo .. 3·75 3·50

1985. Royal Visit. As T **207** of Antigua. Multicoloured.

963. 60 c. Flags of Great Britain and Dominica .. .. 1·00 55
964. $1 Queen Elizabeth II (vert.) .. .. .. 1·75 1·50
965. $4 Royal Yacht "Britannia" .. .. 4·50 5·00

1985. 150th Birth Anniv. of Mark Twain (author). As T **118** of Anguilla showing Walt Disney cartoon characters in scenes from "Tom Sawyer". Multicoloured.

967. 20 c. "The glorious whitewasher" 25 15
968. 60 c. "Aunt Polly's home dentistry" 60 40
969. $1 "Aunt Polly's pain killer" 80 60
970. $1.50, Mickey Mouse balancing on fence .. 1·25 85
971. $2 "Lost in the cave with Becky" .. .. .. 1·50 1·25

1985. Birth Bicentenaries of Grimm Brothers (folklorists). Designs as T **119** of Anguilla showing Walt Disney cartoon characters in scenes from "Little Red Cap". Mult.

973. 10 c. Little Red Cap (Daisy Duck) meeting the Wolf 15 10
974. 45 c. The Wolf at the door 40 30
975. 90 c. The Wolf in Grandmother's bed 80 75
976. $1 The Wolf lunging at Little Red Cap .. .. 1·00 85
977. $3 The Woodsman (Donald Duck) chasing the Wolf 2·50 3·25

1985. 40th Anniv. of United Nations Organization. Designs as T **208** of Antigua showing United Nations (New York) stamps. Multicoloured.

979. 45 c. Lord Baden-Powell and 1984 International Youth Year 35 c. .. 1·00 40
980. $2 Maimonides (physician) and 1966 W.H.O. Building 11 c. .. .. 3·75 2·25
981. $3 Sir Rowland Hill (postal reformer) and 1976 25th anniv. of U.N. Postal Administration 13 c. .. 3·75 2·50

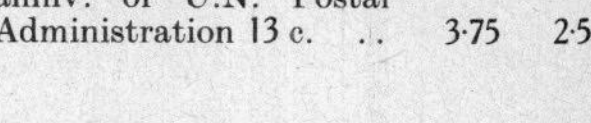

210. Two Players competing for Ball.

1986. World Cup Football Championship, Mexico. Multicoloured.

983. 45 c. Type **210** .. .. 1·00 35
984. 60 c. Player heading ball .. 1·10 55
985. $1 Two players competing for ball (different) .. 1·40 80
986. $3 Player with ball .. 3·25 3·00

211. Police in Rowing Boat pursuing River Pirates, 1890.

1986. Centenary of Statue of Liberty. Multicoloured.

988. 15 c. Type **211** 65 30
989. 25 c. Police patrol launch, 1986 .. .. .. 95 35
990. 45 c. Hoboken Ferry Terminal c 1890 .. .. 1·10 45
991. $4 Holland Tunnel entrance and staff, 1986 3·50 4·00

1986. Appearance of Halley's Comet (1st issue). As T **123** of Anguilla. Multicoloured.

993. 5 c. Nasir al Din al Tusi (Persian astronomer) and Jantal Mantar Observatory, Delhi .. 10 10
994. 10 c. Bell "X-1" Rocket Plane breaking sound barrier for first time, 1947 .. .. .. 10 10
995. 45 c. Halley's Comet of 1531 (from "Astronomicum Caesareum", 1540) 35 30
996. $4 Mark Twain and quotation, 1910 .. 2·25 2·50

See also Nos. 1032/5.

1986. 60th Birthday of Queen Elizabeth II. As T **125** of Anguilla. Mult.

998. 2 c. Wedding photograph, 1947 .. 10 15
999. $1 Queen meeting Pope John Paul II, 1982 .. 70 70
1000. $4 Queen on Royal Visit, 1971 .. .. .. 2·25 2·40

212. Mickey Mouse and Pluto mounting Stamps in Album.

1986. "Ameripex" International Stamp Exhibition, Chicago. Showing Walt Disney cartoon characters. Multicoloured.

1002. 25 c. Type **212** 60 40
1003. 45 c. Donald Duck examining stamp under magnifying glass 80 65
1004. 60 c. Chip n'Dale soaking and drying stamps .. 1·10 85
1005. $4 Donald Duck as scoutmaster awarding merit badges to Nephews .. .. 3·50 4·00

213. William I. **214.** "Virgin at Prayer".

1986. 500th Anniv. (1985) of Succession of House of Tudor. to English throne. Mult.

1007. 10 c. Type **213** 30 15
1008. 40 c. Richard II 70 40
1009. 50 c. Henry VIII 80 50
1010. $1 Charles II .. .. 1·40 1·00
1011. $2 Queen Anne .. .. 2·25 2·50
1012. $4 Queen Victoria .. 3·25 3·50

1986. Birth Bicentenary (1985) of John J. Audubon (ornithologist) (2nd issue). As T **198** of Antigua showing original paintings. Multicoloured.

1013. 25 c. Black-throated diver .. .. .. 1·00 45
1014. 60 c. Great blue heron (vert.) .. .. .. 1·50 95
1015. 90 c. Yellow-crowned night heron (vert.) .. 1·75 1·25
1016. $4 Common shoveler .. 4·00 5·00

1986. Royal Wedding. As T **213** of Antigua. Multicoloured.

1018. 45 c. Prince Andrew and Miss Sarah Ferguson 35 30
1019. 50 c. Prince Andrew .. 45 35
1020. $4 Prince Andrew climbing aboard aircraft .. .. 2·25 2·50

1986. World Cup Football Championship Winners, Mexico. Nos. 983/6 optd. **WINNERS Argentina 3 W. Germany 2.**

1022. 45 c. Type **210** .. .. 1·00 45
1023. 60 c. Player heading ball 1·25 85
1024. $1 Two players competing for ball .. .. 1·75 1·50
1025. $3 Player with ball .. 4·25 4·75

1986. Christmas. Paintings by Dürer. Multicoloured.

1027. 45 c. Type **214** .. 60 35
1028. 60 c. "Madonna and Child" 90 55
1029. $1 "Madonna of the Pear" .. .. 1·25 1·00
1030. $3 "Madonna and Child with St. Anne" .. 3·25 4·25

1986. Appearance of Halley's Comet (2nd issue). Nos. 993/6 optd. as T **218** of Antigua.

1032. 5 c. Nasir al Din al Tusi (Persian astronomer) and Jantal Mantar Observatory, Delhi .. 10 10
1033. 10 c. Bell "X-1" Rocket Plane breaking sound barrier for first time, 1947 .. .. .. 10 10
1034. 45 c. Halley's Comet of 1531 (from "Astronomicum Caesareum", 1540) 20 30
1035. $4 Mark Twain and quotation, 1910 .. 1·75 2·25

215. Broad-winged Hawk.

1987. Birds of Dominica. Multicoloured

1037 1 c. Type **215** .. 15 20
1241 2 c. Ruddy quail dove .. 15 20
1242 5 c. Red-necked pigeon 20 15
1243 10 c. Green heron .. 20 15
1244 15 c. Moorhen 20 15
1245 20 c. Ringed kingfisher .. 20 20
1246 25 c. Brown pelican .. 20 20
1247 35 c. White-tailed tropic bird 30 25
1248 45 c. Red-legged thrush 35 30
1249 60 c. Purple-throated carib 50 40
1047 90 c. Magnificent frigate bird 75 60
1251 $1 Brown trembler .. 60 50
1252 $2 Black-capped petrel .. 1·25 1·25
1253 $5 Barn owl .. .. 4·25 4·25
1254 $10 Imperial parrot .. 7·50 8·50

1987. America's Cup Yachting Championship. As T **222** of Antigua. Multicoloured.

1052. 45 c. "Reliance", 1903 .. 30 25
1053. 60 c. "Freedom", 1980 .. 35 30
1054. $1 "Mischief", 1881 .. 55 55
1055. $3 "Australia", 1977 .. 1·50 1·75

1987. Birth Centenary of Marc Chagall (artist). As T **225** of Antigua. Multicoloured.

1057. 25 c. "Artist and His Model" 15 15
1058. 35 c. "Midsummer Night's Dream" .. 15 20
1059. 45 c. "Joseph the Shepherd" 20 25
1060. 60 c. "The Cellist" .. 25 30
1061. 90 c. "Woman with Pigs" 40 45
1062. $1 "The Blue Circus" .. 45 50
1063. $3 "For Vava" .. .. 1·40 1·50
1064. $4 "The Rider" .. .. 1·75 1·90

216. Morch Poulsen's Triton.

1987. Sea Shells.

1066. **216.** 35 c. multicoloured .. 20 20
1067. – 45 c. vio., blk. & red 25 25
1068. – 60 c. multicoloured .. 30 30
1069. – $5 multicoloured .. 2·40 2·40

DESIGNS: 45 c. Swainson globe purple sea snail. 60 c. Banded tulip. $5 Lamarck deltoid rock shell.

No. 1066 is inscribed "TIRITON" in error.

217. "Cantharellus cinnabarinus".

1987. "Capex '87" International Stamp Exhibition, Toronto. Mushrooms of Dominica. Multicoloured.

1071. 45 c. Type **217** 55 40
1072. 60 c. "Boletellus cubensis" 75 70
1073. $2 "Eccilia cystiophorus" .. 2·25 2·00
1074. $3 "Xerocomus guadelupae" .. 2·75 2·75

218. Discovery of Dominica, 1493.

1987. 500th Anniv (1992) of Discovery of America by Columbus (1st issue). Mult.

1076. 10 c. Type **218** 35 20
1077. 15 c. Caribs greeting Columbus's fleet .. 40 20
1078. 45 c. Claiming the New World for Spain .. 55 35
1079. 60 c. Wreck of "Santa Maria" 70 40
1080. 90 c. Fleet leaving Spain 85 70
1081. $1 Sighting the New World 95 80
1082. $3 Trading with Indians 2·00 2·50
1083. $5 Building settlement .. 3·00 3·75

See Nos. 1221/5, 1355/62 and 1406/13.

1987. Milestones of Transportation. As T **226** of Antigua. Multicoloured.

1085. 10 c. H.M.S. "Warrior" (first ironclad warship), 1860 .. .. 30 30
1086. 15 c. "MAGLEV-MLU 001" (fastest passenger train), 1979 .. .. 40 40
1087. 25 c. "Flying Cloud" (fastest clipper passage New York–San Francisco) (vert.) .. 50 50
1088. 35 c. First elevated railway, New York, 1868 (vert.) 60 60
1089. 45 c. "Tom Thumb" (first U.S. passenger locomotive), 1830 .. 60 60
1090. 60 c. "Spray" (Slocum's solo circumnavigation), 1895-8 (vert.) 65 65
1091. 90 c. "Sea-Land Commerce" (fastest Pacific passage), 1973 (vert.) 80 80
1092. $1 First cable cars, San Francisco, 1873 .. 90 90
1093. $3 "Orient Express", 1883 .. .. .. 2·25 2·25
1094. $4 "Clermont" (first commercial steam boat), 1807 .. .. 2·50 2·50

219. "Virgin and Child with St. Anne" (Durer).

1987. Christmas. Religious Paintings. Mult.

1095. 20 c. Type **219** 30 15
1096. 25 c. "Virgin and Child" (Murillo) 30 15
1097. $2 "Madonna and Child" (Foppa) .. .. 1·50 1·50
1098. $4 "Madonna and Child" (Da Verona) .. .. 2·75 3·25

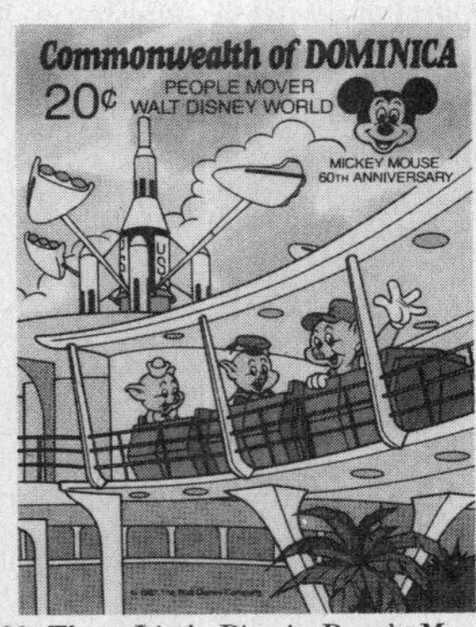

220. Three Little Pigs in People Mover, Walt Disney World.

1987. 60th Anniv. of Mickey Mouse (Walt Disney cartoon character). Multicoloured. Showing cartoon characters in trains.

1100. 20 c. Type **220** 20 20
1101. 25 c. Goofy driving horse tram, Disneyland .. 20 20
1102. 45 c. Donald Duck in "Roger E. Broggie", Walt Disney World .. 35 35
1103. 60 c. Goofy, Mickey Mouse, Donald Duck and Chip n'Dale aboard "Big Thunder Mountain" train, Disneyland 45 45
1104. 90 c. Mickey Mouse in "Walter E. Disney", Disneyland 70 70
1105. $1 Mickey and Minnie Mouse, Goofy, Donald and Daisy Duck in monorail, Walt Disney World 80 80
1106. $3 Dumbo flying over "Casey Jr" .. .. 2·00 2·00
1107. $4 Daisy Duck and Minnie Mouse in "Lilly Belle", Walt Disney World .. .. .. 2·50 2·50

1988. Royal Ruby Wedding. As T **234** of Antigua.

1109 45 c. multicoloured .. 55 25
1110 60 c. brown, black & green 70 45
1111 $1 multicoloured .. 90 80
1112 $3 multicoloured .. 2·00 2·50

DESIGNS: 45 c. Wedding portrait with attendants, 1947; 60 c. Princess Elizabeth with Prince Charles, c. 1950; $1 Princess Elizabeth and Prince Philip with Prince Charles and Princess Anne, 1950; $3 Queen Elizabeth.

221 Kayak Canoeing

1988. Olympic Games, Seoul. Multicoloured.
1114 45 c. Type **221** 55 35
1115 60 c. Taekwon-do .. 65 50
1116 $1 High diving .. 90 85
1117 $3 Gymnastics on bars 2·00 2·50

222 Carib Indian

1988. "Reunion '88" Tourism Programme. Multicoloured.
1119 10 c. Type **222** 10 10
1120 25 c. Mountainous interior (horiz) 15 15
1121 35 c. Indian River .. 15 20
1122 60 c. Belaire dancer and tourists 25 35
1123 90 c. Boiling Lake .. 40 55
1124 $3 Coral reef (horiz) .. 1·40 2·00

1988. Stamp Exhibitions. Nos. 1092/3 optd.
1126 $1 First cable cars, San Francisco, 1873 (optd **FINLANDIA 88**, Helsinki) 45 50
1127 $3 "Orient Express", 1883 (optd **INDEPENDENCE 40**, Israel) 1·25 1·40

223 White-tailed Tropic Bird

1988. Dominica Rain Forest Flora and Fauna. Multicoloured.
1129 45 c. Type **223** 40 40
1130 45 c. Blue-throated euphonia 40 40
1131 45 c. Smooth-billed ani .. 40 40
1132 45 c. Scaly-breasted thrasher 40 40
1133 45 c. Purple-throated carib 40 40
1134 45 c. "Marpesia petreus" and "Strymon maesites" (butterflies) .. 40 40
1135 45 c. Trembler 40 40
1136 45 c. Imperial parrot .. 40 40
1137 45 c. Mangrove cuckoo .. 40 40
1138 45 c. "Dynastes hercules" (beetle) 40 40
1139 45 c. "Historis odius" (butterfly) 40 40
1140 45 c. Red-necked parrot 40 40
1141 45 c. Tillandsia (plant) .. 40 40
1142 45 c. Bananaquit and "Polystacha luteola" (plant) 40 40
1143 45 c. False chameleon .. 40 40
1144 45 c. Iguana 40 40
1145 45 c. "Hypolimnas misippus" (butterfly) .. 40 40
1146 45 c. Green-throated carib 40 40
1147 45 c. Heliconia (plant) .. 40 40
1148 45 c. Agouti 40 40
Nos. 1129/48 were printed together, se-tenant, forming a composite design.

224 Battery Hens

1988. 10th Anniv of International Fund for Agricultural Development. Mult.
1149 45 c. Type **224** 40 30
1150 60 c. Pig 55 45
1151 90 c. Cattle 75 75
1152 $3 Black belly sheep .. 1·75 2·00

225 Gary Cooper

1988. Entertainers. Multicoloured.
1154 10 c. Type **225** 30 20
1155 35 c. Josephine Baker .. 40 35
1156 45 c. Maurice Chevalier .. 45 35
1157 60 c. James Cagney .. 50 40
1158 $1 Clark Gable 70 60
1159 $2 Louis Armstrong .. 1·10 1·10
1160 $3 Liberace .. .. 1·60 1·75
1161 $4 Spencer Tracy .. 2·00 2·50

1988. Flowering Trees. As T **242** of Antigua. Multicoloured.
1163 15 c. Sapodilla 10 10
1164 20 c. Tangerine 10 10
1165 25 c. Avocado pear .. 10 10
1166 45 c. Amherstia 20 25
1167 90 c. Lipstick tree .. 40 45
1168 $1 Cannonball tree .. 45 50
1169 $3 Saman .. .. 1·25 1·40
1170 $4 Pineapple .. .. 1·60 1·75

1988. 500th Birth Anniv of Titian (artist). As T **238** of Antigua. Multicoloured.
1172 25 c. "Jacopo Strada" .. 10 15
1173 35 c. "Titian's Daughter Lavinia" 15 20
1174 45 c. "Andrea Navagero" 20 25
1175 60 c. "Judith with Head of Holoferenes" .. 25 30
1176 $1 "Emilia di Spilimbergo" 45 50
1177 $2 "Martyrdom of St. Lawrence" 80 85
1178 $3 "Salome" .. .. 1·25 1·40
1179 $4 "St. John the Baptist" 1·60 1·75

226 Imperial Parrot

1988. 10th Anniv of Independence. Mult.
1181 20 c. Type **226** 35 15
1182 45 c. Dominica 1874 1d. stamp and landscape (horiz) 40 25
1183 $2 1978 Independence 10 c. stamp and landscape (horiz) .. .. 1·00 1·25
1184 $3 Carib Wood (national flower) .. .. 1·50 2·00

227 Pres. and Mrs. Kennedy

1988. 25th Death Anniv of John F. Kennedy (American statesman). Multicoloured.
1186 20 c. Type **227** 10 10
1187 25 c. Kennedy sailing .. 10 10
1188 $2 Outside Hyannis Port house .. .. 80 1·00
1189 $4 Speaking in Berlin (vert) .. .. .. 1·60 2·00

228 Donald Duck's Nephews decorating Christmas Tree

1988. Christmas. "Mickey's Christmas Mall". Walt Disney Cartoon Characters. Mult.
1191 60 c. Type **228** 35 35
1192 60 c. Daisy Duck outside clothes shop 35 35
1193 60 c. Winnie the Pooh in shop window .. 35 35
1194 60 c. Goofy with parcels 35 35
1195 60 c. Donald Duck as Father Christmas .. 35 35
1196 60 c. Mickey Mouse contributing to collection 35 35
1197 60 c. Minnie Mouse .. 35 35
1198 60 c. Chip n'Dale with peanut 35 35
Nos. 1191/8 were printed together, se-tenant, forming a composite design.

229 Raoul Wallenberg (diplomat) and Swedish Flag

1988. 40th Anniv of Universal Declaration of Human Rights.
1200 **229** $3 multicoloured .. 1·25 1·40

230 Greater Amberjack

1988. Game Fishes. Multicoloured.
1202 10 c. Type **230** 15 10
1203 15 c. Blue marlin .. 15 10
1204 35 c. Cobia 25 20
1205 45 c. Dolphin fish .. 35 25
1206 60 c. Cero 45 40
1207 90 c. Mahogany snapper 65 55
1208 $3 Yellowfin tuna .. 2·00 2·50
1209 $4 Rainbow parrotfish .. 2·50 3·00

231 Leatherback Turtle

1988. Insects and Reptiles. Multicoloured.
1211 10 c. Type **231** 30 15
1212 25 c. "Danaus plexippus" (butterfly) 70 25
1213 60 c. Green anole (lizard) 80 55
1213 $3 "Mantis religiosa" (mantid) .. .. 2·50 3·00

1989. Olympic Medal Winners, Seoul. Nos. 1114/17 optd.
1216 45 c. Type **221** (optd **Men's c-1,500m O. Heukrodt DDR**) .. 25 30
1217 60 c. Taekwon-do (optd **Women's Flyweight N. Y. Choo S. Korea**) 40 45
1218 $1 High diving (optd **Women's Platform Y. Xu China**) .. 1·25 1·40
1219 $3 Gymnastics on bars (optd **V. Artemov USSR**) .. .. 1·90 2·10

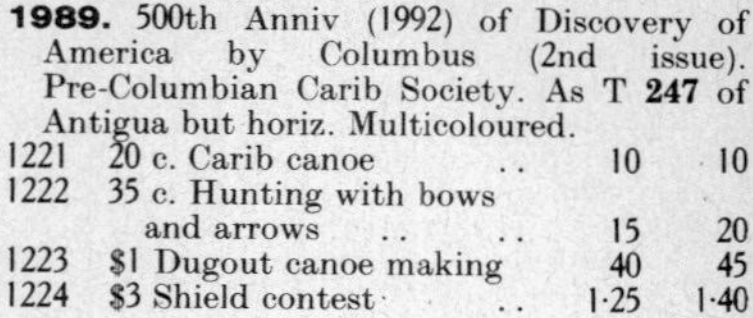
1989. 500th Anniv (1992) of Discovery of America by Columbus (2nd issue). Pre-Columbian Carib Society. As T **247** of Antigua but horiz. Multicoloured.
1221 20 c. Carib canoe .. 10 10
1222 35 c. Hunting with bows and arrows 15 20
1223 $1 Dugout canoe making 40 45
1224 $3 Shield contest .. 1·25 1·40

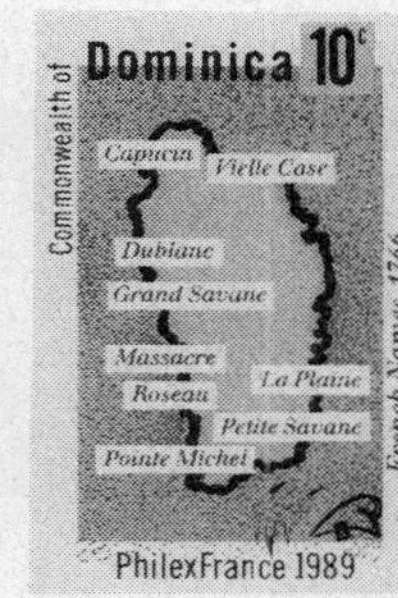

233 Map of Dominica, 1766

1989. "Philexfrance '89" International Stamp Exhibition, Paris. Multicoloured.
1226 10 c. Type **233** 10 10
1227 35 c. French coin of 1653 (horiz) 15 20
1228 $1 French warship, 1720 (horiz) 40 45
1229 $4 Coffee plant (horiz) .. 1·75 1·90

1989. Japanese Art. Paintings by Taikan. As T **250** of Antigua but vert. Multicoloured.
1231 10 c. "Lao-tzu" (detail) .. 10 10
1232 20 c. "Red Maple Leaves" (panels 1 and 2) .. 10 10
1233 45 c. "King Wen Hui learns a Lesson from his Cook" (detail) .. 20 25
1234 60 c. "Red Maple Leaves" (panels 3 and 4) .. 25 30
1235 $1 "Wild Flowers" (detail) 40 45
1236 $2 "Red Maple Leaves" (panels 5 and 6) .. 85 90
1237 $3 "Red Maple Leaves" (panels 7 and 8) .. 1·25 1·40
1238 $4 "Indian Ceremony of Floating Lamps on the River" (detail) .. 1·75 1·90

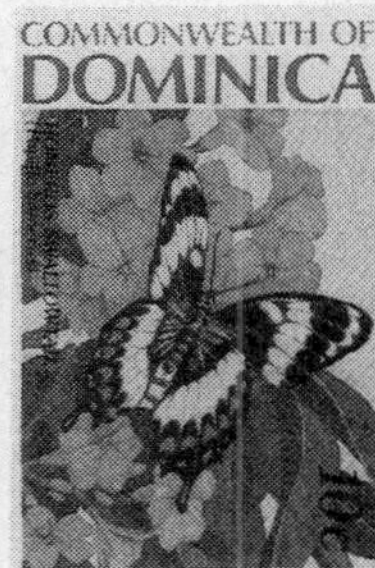

234 "Papilio homerus"

1989. Butterflies. Multicoloured.
1255 10 c. Type **234** 10 10
1256 15 c. "Morpho peleides" 10 10
1257 25 c. "Dryas julia" .. 10 15
1258 35 c. "Parides gundlachianus" 15 20
1259 60 c. "Danaus plexippus" 25 30
1260 $1 "Agraulis vanillae" .. 40 45
1261 $3 "Phoebis avellaneda" 1·25 1·40
1262 $5 "Papilio andraemon" 2·10 2·25

235 "Oncidium pusillum"

1989. Orchids. Multicoloured.

1264 10 c. Type **235** 10 10
1265 35 c. "Epidendrum cochleata" 15 20
1266 45 c. "Epidendrum ciliare" 20 25
1267 60 c. "Cyrtopodium andersonii" .. 25 30
1268 $1 "Habenaria pauciflora" 40 45
1269 $2 "Maxillaria alba" .. 85 90
1270 $3 "Selenipedium palmifolium" .. 1·25 1·40
1271 $4 "Brassavola cucullata" 1·75 1·90

236 "Apollo 11" Command Module in Lunar Orbit

1989. 20th Anniv of First Manned Landing on Moon. Multicoloured.

1273 10 c. Type **236** 10 10
1274 60 c. Neil Armstrong leaving lunar module .. 25 30
1275 $2 Edwin Aldrin at Sea of Tranquillity 85 90
1276 $3 Astronauts Armstrong and Aldrin with U.S. flag .. .. .. 1·25 1·40

237 Brazil v. Italy Final, 1970

1989. World Cup Football Championship, Italy. Multicoloured.

1278 $1 Type **237** 40 45
1279 $1 England v. West Germany, 1966 .. .. 40 45
1280 $1 West Germany v. Holland, 1974 .. .. 40 45
1281 $1 Italy v. West Germany, 1982 .. .. 40 45

Nos. 1278/81 were printed together, se-tenant, forming a composite central design of a football surrounded by flags of competing nations.

238 George Washington and Inauguration, 1789

1989. "World Stamp Expo '89" International Stamp Exhibition, Washington. Bicentenary of the U.S. Presidency. Multicoloured.

1283 60 c. Type **238** 25 30
1284 60 c. John Adams and Presidential Mansion, 1800 .. .. .. 25 30
1285 60 c. Thomas Jefferson, Graff House, Philadelphia and Declaration of Independence 25 30
1286 60 c. James Madison and U.S.S. "Constitution" defeating H.M.S. "Guerriere", 1812 .. 25 30
1287 60 c. James Monroe and freed slaves landing in Liberia 25 30
1288 60 c. John Quincy Adams and barge on Erie Canal 25 30
1289 60 c. Millard Fillmore and Perry's fleet off Japan 25 30
1290 60 c. Franklin Pierce, Jefferson Davis and San Xavier Mission, Tucson 25 30
1291 60 c. James Buchanan, "Buffalo Bill" Cody carrying mail and Wells Fargo Pony Express stamp 25 30
1292 60 c. Abraham Lincoln and U.P.U. Monument, Berne 25 30
1293 60 c. Andrew Johnson, polar bear and Mt. McKinley, Alaska .. 25 30
1294 60 c. Ulysses S. Grant and Golden Spike Ceremony, 1869 .. 25 30
1295 60 c. Theodore Roosevelt and steam shovel excavating Panama Canal 25 30
1296 60 c. William H. Taft and Admiral Peary at North Pole 25 30
1297 60 c. Woodrow Wilson and Curtis "Jenny" on first scheduled airmail flight, 1918 .. .. 25 30
1298 60 c. Warren G. Harding and airship U.S.S. "Shenandoah" at Lakehurst 25 30
1299 60 c. Calvin Coolidge and Lindbergh's "Spirit of St. Louis" on trans-Atlantic flight .. 25 30
1300 60 c. Mt. Rushmore National Monument .. 25 30
1301 60 c. Lyndon B. Johnson and Earth from Moon as seen by "Apollo 8" crew 25 30
1302 60 c. Richard Nixon and visit to Great Wall of China 25 30
1303 60 c. Gerald Ford and "Gorch Fock" at Bicentenary of Revolution celebrations 25 30
1304 60 c. Jimmy Carter and Pres. Sadat of Egypt with Prime Minister Begin of Israel .. 25 30
1305 60 c. Ronald Reagan and space shuttle "Columbia" 25 30
1306 60 c. George Bush and Grumman "Avenger" (fighter-bomber) .. 25 30

1989. Mickey Mouse in Hollywood (Walt Disney cartoon characters). As T **267** of Antigua. Multicoloured.

1308 20 c. Mickey Mouse reading script 10 10
1309 35 c. Mickey Mouse giving interview 15 20
1310 45 c. Mickey and Minnie Mouse with newspaper and magazines .. 20 25
1311 60 c. Mickey Mouse signing autographs .. 25 30
1312 $1 Trapped in dressing room 40 45
1313 $2 Mickey and Minnie Mouse with Pluto in limousine 85 90
1314 $3 Arriving at Awards ceremony .. .. 1·25 1·40
1315 $4 Mickey Mouse accepting award .. 1·75 1·90

1989. Christmas. Paintings by Botticelli. As T **259** of Antigua. Multicoloured.

1317 20 c. "Madonna in Glory with Seraphim" .. 10 10
1318 25 c. "The Annunciation" .. 10 15
1319 35 c. "Madonna of the Pomegranate" .. 15 20
1320 45 c. "Madonna of the Rosegarden" 20 25
1321 60 c. "Madonna of the Book" 25 30
1322 $1 "Madonna under a Baldachin" 40 45
1323 $4 "Madonna and Child with Angels" .. .. 1·75 1·90
1324 $5 "Bardi Madonna" .. 2·10 2·25

240 Lady Olave Baden-Powell and Agatha Robinson (Guide leaders)

1989. 60th Anniv of Girl Guides in Dominica.

1326 **240** 60 c. multicoloured .. 25 30

241 Jawaharlal Nehru

1989. Birth Centenary of Jawaharlal Nehru (Indian statesman).

1328 **241** 60 c. multicoloured .. 25 30

242 Cocoa Damselfish

1990. Tropical Fishes. Multicoloured.

1330 45 c. Type **242** 20 25
1331 45 c. Stinging jellyfish .. 20 25
1332 45 c. Dolphin fish .. 20 25
1333 45 c. Queen angelfish .. 20 25
1334 45 c. French angelfish .. 20 25
1335 45 c. Blue-striped grunt .. 20 25
1336 45 c. Pork fish 20 25
1337 45 c. Hammerhead shark 20 25
1338 45 c. Spadefish 20 25
1339 45 c. Great barracuda .. 20 25
1340 45 c. Stingray 20 25
1341 45 c. Black grunt 20 25
1342 45 c. Two-spotted butter-flyfish 20 25
1343 45 c. Dog snapper .. 20 25
1344 45 c. Southern puffer .. 20 25
1345 45 c. Four-eyed butter-flyfish 20 25
1346 45 c. Lane snapper .. 20 25
1347 45 c. Green moray .. 20 25

Nos. 1330/47 were printed together, se-tenant, forming a composite design.

243 St. Paul's Cathedral, London, c. 1840

1990. 150th Anniv of the Penny Black and "Stamp World London 90" International Stamp Exhibition.

1348 **243** 45 c. green and black 20 25
1349 – 50 c. blue and black 20 25
1350 – 60 c. blue and black 25 30
1351 – 90 c. green and black 40 45
1352 – $3 blue and black .. 1·25 1·40
1353 – $4 blue and black .. 1·75 1·90

DESIGNS: 50 c. British Post Office "accelerator" carriage, 1830; 60 c. St. Paul's and City of London; 90 c. Travelling post office, 1838; $3 "Hen and chickens" delivery cycle, 1883; $4 London skyline.

1990. 500th Anniv (1992) of Discovery of America by Columbus (3rd issue). New World Natural History—Seashells. As T **260** of Antigua. Multicoloured.

1355 10 c. Reticulated cowrie-helmet 10 10
1356 20 c. West Indian chank 10 10
1357 35 c. West Indian fighting conch 15 20
1358 60 c. True tulip .. 25 30
1359 $1 Sunrise tellin .. 40 45
1360 $2 Crown cone .. 85 90
1361 $3 Common dove shell .. 1·25 1·40
1362 $4 Atlantic fig shell .. 1·75 1·90

244 Blue-headed Hummingbird

1990. Birds. Multicoloured.

1364 10 c. Type **244** 10 10
1365 20 c. Black-capped petrel 10 10
1366 45 c. Red-necked amazon 20 25
1367 60 c. Black swift .. 25 30
1368 $1 Troupial 40 45
1369 $2 Common noddy .. 85 90
1370 $4 Lesser Antillean pewee 1·75 1·90
1371 $5 Little blue heron .. 2·10 2·25

1990. 90th Birthday of Queen Elizabeth the Queen Mother. As T **266** of Antigua.

1373 20 c. multicoloured .. 10 10
1374 45 c. multicoloured .. 20 25
1375 60 c. multicoloured .. 25 30
1376 $3 multicoloured .. 1·25 1·40

DESIGNS: 20 c. to $3 Recent photographs of Queen Mother.

1990. Olympic Games, Barcelona (1992). As T **268** of Antigua. Multicoloured.

1378 45 c. Type **245** 20 25
1379 60 c. Fencing 25 30
1380 $2 Swimming 85 90
1381 $3 Yachting .. .. 1·25 1·40

245 Barnes, England

1990. World Cup Football Championship, Italy. Multicoloured.

1383 15 c. Type **245** 10 10
1384 45 c. Romario, Brazil .. 20 25
1385 60 c. Franz Beckenbauer, West Germany manager 25 30
1386 $4 Lindenberger, Austria 1·75 1·90

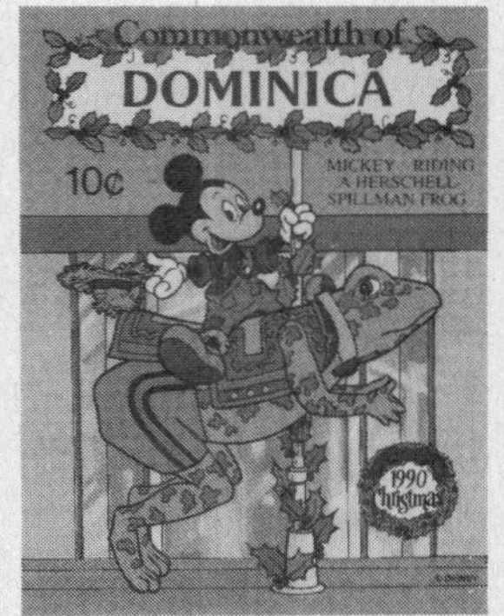

246 Mickey Mouse riding Herschell-Spillman Frog

1990. Christmas. Walt Disney cartoon characters and American carousel animals. Multicoloured.

1388 10 c. Type **246** 10 10
1389 15 c. Huey, Duey and Louie on Allan Herschell elephant .. 10 10
1390 25 c. Donald Duck on Allan Herschell polar bear 10 15
1391 45 c. Goofy on Dentzel goat 20 25
1392 $1 Donald Duck on Zalar giraffe 40 45
1393 $2 Daisy Duck on Herschell-Spillman stork 85 90
1394 $4 Goofy on Dentzel lion 1·75 1·90
1395 $5 Daisy Duck on Stein and Goldstein palomino stander .. .. 2·10 2·25

247 Glion–Roches De Naye Locomotive, 1890

1991. Cog Railways. Multicoloured.

1397 10 c. Type **247** 10 10
1398 35 c. Electric railcar on Mt Pilatus 15 20
1399 45 c. Cog railway line to Schynige Platte .. 20 25
1400 60 c. Bugnli Viaduct, Furka–Oberalp line (vert) 25 30
1401 $1 Jungfrau train, 1910 .. 40 45
1402 $2 Testing Pike's Peak railcar, Switzerland, 1983 .. .. .. 85 90
1403 $4 Brienz–Rothorn steam train, 1991 .. .. 1·75 1·90
1404 $5 Arth–Rrigi steam locomotive, 1890 .. 2·10 2·25

1991. 500th Anniv (1992) of Discovery of America by Columbus (4th issue). History of Exploration. As T **194** of British Virgin Islands. Multicoloured.

1406 10 c. Gil Eannes sailing south of Cape Bojador, 1433–34 .. .. 10 10
1407 25 c. Alfonso Baldaya sailing south to Cape Blanc, 1436 .. .. 10 10
1408 45 c. Bartolomeu Dias in Table Bay, 1487 .. 20 25
1409 60 c. Vasco da Gama on voyage to India, 1497–99 .. .. 25 30
1410 $1 Vallarte the Dane off African coast 40 45
1411 $2 Aloisio Cadamosto in Cape Verde Islands, 1456–58 .. .. 85 90
1412 $4 Diogo Gomes on River Gambia, 1457 .. 1·75 1·90
1413 $5 Diogo Cao off African coast, 1482–85 .. .. 2·10 2·25

248 Donald Duck as Shogun's Guard

1991. "Philanippon '91" International Stamp Exhibition, Tokyo. Multicoloured.

1415 10 c. Type **248** 10 10
1416 15 c. Mickey Mouse as Kabuki actor 10 10
1417 25 c. Minnie and Mickey Mouse as bride and groom 10 10
1418 45 c. Daisy Duck as geisha (vert) 20 25
1419 $1 Mickey Mouse in Sokutai court dress (vert) 40 45
1420 $2 Goofy as Mino farmer (vert) 85 90
1421 $4 Pete as Shogun (vert) 1·75 1·90
1422 $5 Donald Duck as Samurai .. .. 2·10 2·25

249 "Craterellus cornucopioides"

1991. Fungi. Multicoloured.

1424 10 c. Type **249** 10 10
1425 15 c. "Coprinus comatus" 10 10
1426 45 c. "Morchella esculenta" 20 25
1427 60 c. "Cantharellus cibarius" 25 30
1428 $1 "Lepista nuda" .. 40 45
1429 $2 "Suillus luteus" .. 85 90
1430 $4 "Russula emetica" .. 1·75 1·90
1431 $5 "Armillaria mellea" .. 2·10 2·25

1991. 65th Birthday of Queen Elizabeth II. As T **280** of Antigua. Multicoloured.

1433 10 c. Queen and Prince William on Buckingham Palace Balcony, 1990 .. .. .. 10 10
1434 60 c. The Queen at Westminster Abbey, 1988 .. 25 30
1435 $2 The Queen and Prince Philip in Italy, 1990 .. 85 90
1436 $4 The Queen at Ascot, 1986 .. .. .. 1·75 1·90

1991. 10th Wedding Anniv of the Prince and Princess of Wales. As T **280** of Antigua. Multicoloured.

1438 15 c. Prince and Princess of Wales in West Germany, 1987 .. 10 10
1439 40 c. Separate photographs of Prince, Princess and sons .. 20 25
1440 $1 Separate photographs of Prince William and Prince Henry 40 45
1441 $5 Prince Charles at Caister and Princess Diana in Thailand .. 2·10 2·25

1991. Death Cent (1990) of Vincent Van Gogh (artist). As T **278** of Antigua. Mult.

1443 10 c. "Thatched Cottages" (horiz) 10 10
1444 25 c. "The House of Pere Eloi" (horiz) 10 10
1445 45 c. "The Midday Siesta" (horiz) 20 25
1446 60 c. "Portrait of a Young Peasant" 25 30
1447 $1 "Still Life: Vase with Irises against a Yellow Background" 40 45
1448 $2 "Still Life: Vase with Irises" (horiz) .. 85 90
1449 $4 "Blossoming Almond Tree" (horiz) .. .. 1·75 1·90
1450 $5 "Irises" (horiz) .. 2·10 2·25

250 Ariel, Flounder and Sebastian

1991. International Literacy Year. Scenes from Disney cartoon film "The Little Mermaid". Multicoloured.

1452 10 c. Type **250** 10 10
1453 25 c. King Triton 10 10
1454 45 c. Sebastian playing drums 20 25
1455 60 c. Flotsam and Jetsam taunting Ariel .. 25 30
1456 $1 Scuttle, Flounder and Ariel with pipe .. 40 45
1457 $2 Ariel and Flounder discovering book .. 85 90
1458 $4 Prince Eric and crew 1·75 1·90
1459 $5 Ursula the Sea Witch 2·10 2·25

251 Empire State Building, New York

1991. World Landmarks. Mutlicoloured.

1461 10 c. Type **251** 10 10
1462 25 c. Kremlin, Moscow (horiz) 10 10
1463 45 c. Buckingham Palace, London (horiz) .. 20 25
1464 60 c. Eiffel Tower, Paris 25 30
1465 $1 Taj Mahal, Agra (horiz) 40 45
1466 $2 Opera House, Sydney (horiz) 85 90
1467 $4 Colosseum, Rome (horiz) .. .. 1·75 1·90
1468 $5 Pyramids, Giza (horiz) 2·10 2·25

252 Japanese Aircraft leaving Carrier "Akagi"

1991. 50th Anniv of Japanese Attack on Pearl Harbor. Multicoloured.

1470 10 c. Type **252** 10 10
1471 15 c. U.S.S. "Ward" and flying boat attacking midget submarine .. 10 10
1472 45 c. Second wave of aircraft leaving carriers .. 20 25
1473 60 c. Japanese Zero attacking Kaneche naval airfield 25 30
1474 $1 Three destroyers sinking midget submarine 40 45
1475 $2 U.S.S. "Nevada" under attack 85 90
1476 $4 U.S.S. "Arizona" sinking 1·75 1·90
1477 $5 Japanese aircraft .. 2·10 2·25

253 "Eurema venusta"

1991. Butterflies. Multicoloured.

1479 1 c. Type **253** 10 10
1480 2 c. "Agraulis vanillae" .. 10 10
1481 5 c. "Danaus plexippus" 10 10
1482 10 c. "Biblis hyperia" .. 10 10
1483 15 c. "Dryas julia" .. 10 10
1484 20 c. "Phoebis agarithe" 10 10
1485 25 c. "Junonia genoveva" 10 10
1486 35 c. "Battus polydamas" 15 20
1487 45 c. "Leptotes cassius" 20 25
1488 60 c. "Anaea dominicana" 25 30
1489 90 c. "Hypolimnas misippus" 40 45
1490 $1 "Urbanus proteus" .. 40 45
1491 $2 "Phoebis sennae" .. 85 90
1492 $5 "Cynthia cardui" ("Vanessa cardui") .. 2·10 2·25
1493 $10 "Marpesia petreus" .. 4·25 4·50
1494 $20 "Anartia jatrophae" 8·50 9·00

1991. Birth Centenary (1990) of Charles De Gaulle (French statesman). As T **283** of Antigua.

1495 45 c. brown 20 25

DESIGN—VERT. 45 c. De Gaulle in uniform.

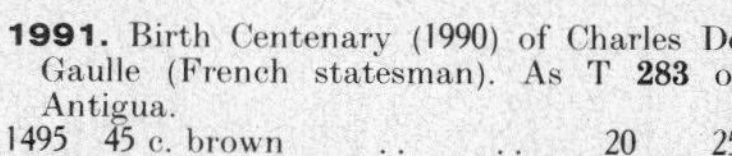

254 Symbolic Cheque

1992. 40th Anniv of Credit Union Bank.

1497 **254** 10 c. grey and black 10 10
1498 – 60 c. multicoloured .. 25 30

DESIGN—HORIZ. 60 c. Credit Union symbol.

APPENDIX

The following stamps have either been issued in excess of postal needs, or have not been made available to the public in reasonable quantities at face value.

1978-79.

History of Aviation. $16 × 30, each embossed on gold foil.

DUNGARPUR

A state of Rajasthan. Now uses Indian stamps.

12 pies = 1 anna, 16 annas = 1 rupee.

1. State Arms.

1933.

1. **1.** $\frac{1}{4}$ a. yellow .. .. — 65·00
2. $\frac{1}{4}$ a. red .. .. .. — £150
3. $\frac{1}{4}$ a. brown .. .. — £130
4. 1 a. blue .. .. — 65·00
5. 1 a. red .. .. .. — £450
6. 1 a. 3 p. violet .. .. — 90·00
7. 2 a. green .. .. — £110
8. 4 a. red .. .. .. — £160

2. Maharawal Sir Shri Lakshman Singh Bahadur.

1932. T **2** (various frames).

9. **2.** $\frac{1}{4}$ a. orange .. .. £170 26·00
10. $\frac{1}{2}$ a. red .. .. £110 24·00
11. 1 a. blue .. .. £110 16·00
12. 1 a. 3 p. mauve .. £225 75·00
13. $1\frac{1}{2}$ a. violet .. .. £225 85·00
14. 2 a. green £275 £150
15. 4 a. brown .. .. £225 60·00

DUTTIA (DATIA)

A state of Central India. Now uses Indian stamps.

12 pies = 1 anna, 16 annas = 1 rupee.

1. Ganesh.

2.

1893. Imperf.

1. **1.** $\frac{1}{4}$ a. black on orange .. £1900
2. $\frac{1}{2}$ a. black on green .. £2250
4. 2 a. black on yellow .. £1700
5. 4 a. black on red .. £1300

Stamps of Type **1** come with the circular handstamp as shown on Type **2**. Examples of Nos. 1/2 without handstamp are worth slightly less than the prices quoted.

1893. Imperf.

6. **2.** $\frac{1}{2}$ a. black on green .. 13·00 75·00
3. 1 a. red £1900
7. 1 a. black .. .. .. 50·00 95·00
8. 2 a. black on yellow .. 17·00 80·00
10. 4 a. black on red .. .. 15·00 70·00

1896. Imperf.

5a. **2.** $\frac{1}{2}$ a. black on green .. £3750
5b. 2 a. blue on yellow .. £2250

Nos. 5a/b are as Type **2**, but have rosettes in lower corners.

3.

4.

1897. Imperf.

12. **3.** $\frac{1}{2}$ a. black on green .. 50·00
13. 1 a. black £110
14. 2 a. black on yellow .. 60·00
15. 4 a. black on red .. 55·00

1899. Imperf., roul. or perf.

16c. 4. ½ a. red .. .. .. 1·25 4·50
38. ½ a. blue .. .. .. 1·00 4·50
37. ½ a. black .. .. .. 3·50 8·00
17. ½ a. black on green .. 1·40 4·50
30. ½ a. green .. .. .. 2·75 10·00
35. ½ a. blue .. .. .. 1·00 5·00
39. ½ a. pink .. .. .. 1·25 6·00
18. 1 a. black .. .. .. 1·10 4·50
31. 1 a. purple .. .. .. 3·50 11·00
36. 1 a. pink .. .. .. 1·40 6·50
19b. 2 a. black on yellow .. 1·75 6·50
32. 2 a. brown .. .. .. 7·00 16·00
33. 2 a. lilac .. .. .. 5·00 16·00
20. 4 a. black on red .. .. 1·40 6·50
34. 4 a. brown .. .. .. 60·00

FALKLAND ISLANDS

A Br. colony in the S. Atlantic.

1878. 12 pence = 1 shilling;
20 shillings = 1 pound.
1971. 100 (new) pence = 1 pound.

3.

6.

1878.

17a 3. ½d. green .. .. .. 2·00 1·25
23 1d. red to brown .. .. 5·00 1·00
26 2d. purple .. .. .. 5·00 11·00
30 2½d. blue .. .. .. 16·00 6·50
32 4d. black .. .. .. 14·00 20·00
3 6d. green .. .. .. 45·00 45·00
34 6d. yellow .. .. .. 27·00 32·00
35 9d. red .. .. .. 22·00 48·00
38 1s. brown .. .. .. 27·00 35·00
41 – 2s. 6d. blue £200 £250
42 6. 5s. red £180 £200

DESIGN: 2s. 6d. As Type 6, but different frame.

1891. No. 11 bisected diagonally and each half surch. ½d.

14. 3. ½d. on half of 1d. brown .. £425 £225

7.

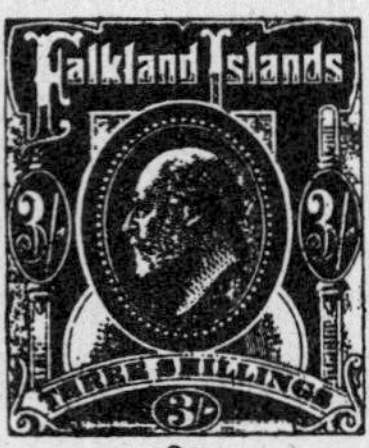
8.

1904.

43. 7. ½d. green .. .. .. 2·00 85
59. 1d. red .. .. .. 75 1·75
50. 2d. purple .. .. .. 9·50 24·00
52. 2½d. blue .. .. .. 26·00 7·00
54. 6d. orange .. .. .. 32·00 48·00
55. 1s. brown .. .. .. 38·00 30·00
57. 8. 3s. green £120 £130
58. 5s. red £140 £140

1912. As T 7/8 but portrait of King George V.

60 ½d. green .. .. .. 1·75 2·50
74 1d. red .. .. .. 3·00 80
75b 2d. purple .. .. .. 5·50 3·00
63c 2½d. blue .. .. .. 5·50 14·00
77 2½d. purple on yellow .. 3·75 26·00
64 6d. orange .. .. .. 11·00 17·00
65 1s. brown .. .. .. 26·00 27·00
66 3s. green .. .. .. 55·00 70·00
67 5s. red .. .. .. 60·00 85·00
67b 5s. purple .. .. .. 65·00 85·00
68 10s. red on green £140 £200
69 £1 black on red £350 £400

1918. As 1912, optd. WAR STAMP.

70b. ½d. green .. .. .. 50 6·50
71c. 1d. red .. .. .. 50 3·50
72a. 1s. brown .. .. .. 6·00 32·00

1928. No. 75b surch 2½d.

115 2½d. on 2d. purple £650 £700

13. Fin Whale and Gentoo Penguins.

1929.

116. 13. ½d. green .. .. .. 60 1·00
117. 1d. red 70 35
118. 2d. grey 70 70
119. 2½d. blue .. .. .. 70 1·00
120. 4d. orange .. .. .. 5·50 12·00
121. 6d. purple .. .. .. 6·00 6·50
122. 1s. black on green .. .. 11·00 17·00
123. 2s. 6d. red on blue .. 22·00 25·00
124. 5s. green on yellow .. 40·00 55·00
125. 10s. red on green .. .. 70·00 95·00
126. £1 black on red £350 £450

15. Romney Marsh Ram.

1933. Centenary of British Occupation. Inscr. "1833–1933".

127. 15. ½d. black and green .. 1·50 3·75
128. – 1d. black and red .. 3·25 1·25
129. – 1½d. black and blue .. 5·50 7·50
130. – 2d. black and brown .. 7·00 14·00
131. – 3d. black and violet .. 9·00 7·50
132. – 4d. black and orange .. 10·00 12·00
133. – 6d. black and grey .. 40·00 45·00
134. – 1s. black and olive .. 30·00 45·00
135. – 2s. 6d. black and violet £100 £130
136. – 5s. black and yellow .. £500 £650
137. – 10s. black and brown .. £550 £650
138. – £1 black and red .. £1300 £1800

DESIGNS—HORIZ. 1d. Iceberg. 1½d. Whale-catcher. 2d. Port Louis. 3d. Map of Falkland Is. 4d. S. Georgia. 6d. Fin Whale. 1s. Government House, Stanley. VERT. 2s. 6d. Battle Memorial. 5s. King Penguin. 10s. Arms. £1, King George V.

1935. Silver Jubilee. As T 13 of Antigua.

139. 1d. blue and red .. 1·75 40
140. 2½d. brown and blue .. 3·75 1·25
141. 4d. green and blue .. 3·75 1·25
142. 1s. grey and purple .. 4·00 1·25

1937. Coronation. As T 2 of Aden.

143. ½d. green 30 10
144. 1d. red 40 20
145. 2½d. blue 80 35

27. Whales' Jaw Bones.

1938.

146. 27. ½d. black and green .. 15 30
147a. A. 1d. black and red .. 3·00 30
148. B. 1d. black and violet .. 90 75
149. 2d. black and violet .. 1·00 40
150a. A. 2d. black and red .. 75 30
151. C. 2½d. black and blue .. 45 30
152. D. 2½d. black and blue .. 2·25 3·50
153. C. 3d. black and blue .. 2·25 1·25
154. D. 4d. black and purple .. 1·75 50
155. E. 6d. black and brown .. 4·50 3·50
156. 6d. black .. .. .. 2·75 4·50
157. F. 9d. black and blue .. 4·00 50
158a. G. 1s. blue .. .. .. 8·00 2·50
159. H. 1s. 3d. black and red .. 1·50 1·10
160. I. 2s. 6d. black .. .. 45·00 6·50
161. J. 5s. blue and orange .. 80·00 35·00
162. K. 10s. black and orange .. 50·00 27·00
163. L. £1 black and violet .. 90·00 45·00

DESIGNS—HORIZ. A, Black-necked swan. B, Battle memorial. C, Flock of sheep. D, Magellan goose. E, R.R.S. "Discovery II". F, R.R.S. "William Scoresby". G, Mount Sugar Top. H, Turkey vultures. I, Gentoo penguins. J, Southern sealion. K, Deception Is. L, Arms of the colony.

1946. Victory. As T 9 of Aden.

164. 1d. mauve 30 15
165. 3d. blue 30 15

1948. Silver Wedding. As T 10/11 of Aden.

166. 2½d. blue .. .. .. 2·00 70
167. £1 mauve .. .. .. 90·00 55·00

1949. U.P.U. As T 20/23 of Antigua.

168. 1d. violet .. .. .. 1·50 75
169. 3d. blue .. .. .. 4·50 1·50
170. 1s. 3d. green .. .. 5·50 2·25
171. 2s. blue .. .. .. 5·50 5·00

39. Sheep.

1952.

172. 30. ½d. green 70 70
173. – 1d. red 80 40
174. – 2d. violet .. .. .. 3·25 1·50
175. – 2½d. black and blue .. 95 50
176. – 3d. blue .. .. .. 1·00 75
177. – 4d. purple .. .. .. 6·50 2·50
178. – 6d. brown .. .. .. 12·00 1·00
179. – 9d. yellow .. .. .. 7·50 4·50
180. – 1s. black .. .. .. 12·00 80
181. – 1s. 3d. orange .. .. 4·00 11·00
182. – 2s. 6d. olive .. .. 12·00 10·00
183. – 5s. purple .. .. .. 6·00 6·50
184. – 10s. grey .. .. .. 14·00 30·00
185. – £1 black .. .. .. 22·00 30·00

DESIGNS—HORIZ. 1d. R.M.S. "Fitzroy". 2d. Magellan goose. 2½d. Map. 4d. Auster aircraft. 6d. M.S.S. "John Biscoe". 9d. View of "Two Sisters". 1s 3d. Kelp goose and gander. 10s. Sea-lion and female. £1, Hulk of "Great Britain". VERT. 3d Arms. 1s. Gentoo penguins. 2s 6d. Sheep shearing. 5s. Memorial.

1953. Coronation. As T 13 of Aden.

186. 1d. black and red .. 1·00 1·25

1955. As 1952 issue but with portrait of Queen Elizabeth II.

187. ½d. green .. .. .. 70 1·25
188. 1d. red .. .. .. 1·25 60
189. 2d. violet .. .. .. 2·75 4·50
190. 6d. brown .. .. .. 5·50 60
191. 9d. yellow .. .. .. 23·00 17·00
192. 1s. black .. .. .. 3·50 1·25

54. Austral Thrush.

1960. Birds.

227. 54. ½d. black and green .. 30 30
194. – 1d. black and red .. 1·25 30
195. – 2d. black and blue .. 2·25 60
196. – 2½d. black and bistre .. 1·50 20
197. – 3d. black and olive .. 80 15
198. – 4d. black and red .. 1·25 50
199. – 5½d. black and violet .. 1·50 1·00
200. – 6d. black and sepia .. 1·50 15
201. – 9d. black and red .. 1·50 80
202. – 1s. black and purple .. 80 15
203. – 1s. 3d. black and blue .. 9·00 8·50
204. – 2s. black and brown .. 27·00 1·50
205. – 5s. black and turquoise 24·00 8·50
206. – 10s. black and purple .. 45·00 11·00
207. – £1 black and yellow .. 48·00 25·00

BIRDS: 1d. Southern black-backed gull. 2d. Gentoo penguins. 2½d. Long-tailed meadow lark. 3d. Magellan goose. 4d. Falkland Is. flightless steamer ducks. 5½d. Rock-hopper penguins. 6d. Black-browed albatross. 9d. Silver grebe. 1s. Magellanic oystercatcher. 1s. 3d. Chilean teal. 2s. Kelp geese. 5s. King cormorants. 10s. Common Caracara. £1 Black-necked swan.

69. Morse Key.

1962. 50th Anniversary of Establishment of Radio Communication.

208. 69. 6d. red and orange .. 1·00 30
209. – 1s. green and olive .. 1·25 35
210. – 2s. violet and blue .. 1·25 40

DESIGNS: 1s. One-valve receiver. 2s. Rotary Spark transmitter.

1963. Freedom from Hunger. As T 28 of Aden.

211. 1s. blue .. .. .. 13·00 85

1963. Cent of Red Cross. As T 33 of Antigua.

212. 1d. red and black .. .. 4·00 50
213. 1s. red and blue .. .. 17·00 4·50

1964. 400th Birth Anniv of Shakespeare. As T 34 of Antigua.

214. 6d. black .. .. .. 1·00 30

72. H.M.S. "Glasgow".

1964. 50th Anniv. of Battle of the Falkland Islands.

215. 72. 2½d. black and red .. 6·00 2·25
216. – 6d. black and blue .. 1·00 25
217. – 1s. black and red .. 1·75 60
218. – 2s. black and blue .. 2·50 75

DESIGNS—HORIZ. 6d. H.M.S. "Kent". 1s. H.M.S. "Invincible". VERT. 2s. Battle Memorial.

1965. Cent of I.T.U. As T 36 of Antigua.

219. 1d. light blue & deep blue 85 20
220. 2s. lilac and yellow .. 12·00 1·50

1965. I.C.Y. As T 37 of Antigua.

221. 1d. purple and turquoise .. 1·50 20
222. 1s. green and lavender .. 7·50 1·10

1966. Churchill Commem. As T 38 of Antigua.

223. ½d. blue 65 30
224. 1d. green .. .. .. 2·25 15
225. 1s. brown .. .. .. 6·50 80
226. 2s. violet .. .. .. 8·00 1·25

76. Globe and Human Rights Emblem.

1968. Human Rights Year.

228. 76. 2d. multicoloured .. 50 15
229. 6d. multicoloured .. 55 15
230. 1s. multicoloured .. 60 15
231. 2s. multicoloured .. 70 30

77. Dusty Miller.

1968. Flowers Multicoloured.

232. ½d. Type 77 .. .. 15 40
233. 1½d. Pig Vine 20 15
234. 2d. Pale Maiden 30 15
235. 3d. Dog Orchid .. .. 1·25 15
236. 3½d. Sea Cabbage 30 15
237. 4½d. Vanilla Daisy 50 50
238. 5½d. yellow, brown and grn. (Arrowleaf Marigold) .. 50 80
239. 6d. red, black and green (Diddle Dee) 50 20
240. 1s. Scurvy Grass 60 50
241. 1s. 6d. Prickly Burr .. 4·50 8·50
242. 2s. Fachine .. .. 5·50 6·50
243. 3s. Lavender .. .. 9·00 5·50
244. 5s. Felton's Flower .. 24·00 13·00
245. £1 Yellow Orchid .. 13·00 2·00

Nos. 233, 236, 238/40 and 244 are horiz.

91. DHC—2 Beaver Floatplane.

1969. 21st Anniv. of Government Air Services. Multicoloured.

246. 2d. Type 91 .. .. 35 30
247. 6d. "Norseman" 40 35
248. 1s. "Auster" 50 35
249. 2s. Arms of the Falkland Islands .. .. 1·75 70

92. Holy Trinity Church, 1869.

1969. Centenary of Bishop Stirling's Consecretation.

250. 92. 2d. black, grey & green 40 30
251. – 6d. black, grey and red 50 30
252. – 1s. black, grey & lilac .. 55 30
253. – 2s. multicoloured .. 80 55

DESIGNS: 6d. Christ Church Cathedral, 1969. 1s. Bishop Stirling. 2s. Bishop's Mitre.

96. Mounted Volunteer.

1970. Golden Jubilee of Defence Force. Multicoloured.
254. 2d. Type **96** .. .. 1·90 50
255. 6d. Defence Post .. .. 2·00 50
256. 1s. Corporal in No. 1 Dress uniform .. .. .. 2·25 50
257. 2s. Badge .. .. .. 4·00 75
Nos. 255 and 257 are horiz.

97. S.S. "Great Britain" (1843).

1970. S.S. "Great Britain" Restoration. Stamps show S.S. "Great Britain" in year given Multicoloured.
258. 2d. Type **97** .. .. 1·75 40
259. 4d. 1845 .. .. .. 2·00 80
260. 9d. 1876 .. .. .. 2·00 80
261. 1s. 1886 .. .. .. 2·00 80
262. 2s. 1970 .. .. .. 2·25 90

1971. Decimal Currency. Nos. 232/44 surch.
263. ½p. on ½d. multicoloured 25 20
264. 1p. on 1½d. multicoloured 30 15
265. 1½p. on 2d. multicoloured 30 15
266. 2p. on 3d. multicoloured 50 20
267. 2½p. on 3½d. multicoloured 30 20
268. 3p. on 4½d. multicoloured 30 20
269. 4p. on 5½d. yellow, brown and green 30 20
270. 5p. on 6d. red, blk. & grn. 30 20
271. 6p. on 1s. multicoloured .. 5·50 2·50
272. 7½p. on 1s. 6d. mult. .. 8·00 3·25
273. 10p. on 2s. multicoloured .. 8·50 3·00
274. 15p. on 3s. multicoloured .. 6·50 2·75
275. 25p. on 5s. multicoloured .. 7·00 3·25

1972. Decimal Currency. Nos. 232/44 inscr. in decimal currency.
276. ½p. multicoloured .. 35 1·75
277. 1p. multicoloured .. 30 40
278. 1½p. multicoloured .. 30 1·00
279. 2p. multicoloured .. 8·50 1·25
280. 2½p. multicoloured .. 35 1·00
281. 3p. multicoloured .. 35 1·00
282. 4p. yellow, brown & green 40 50
283. 5p. red, black and green .. 40 55
295. 6p. multicoloured .. 2·00 2·25
285. 7½p. multicoloured .. 1·50 4·00
286. 10p. multicoloured .. 7·50 4·50
287. 15p. multicoloured .. 4·50 5·00
288. 25p. multicoloured .. 4·50 6·00

1972. Royal Silver Wedding. As T **52** of Ascension but with Romney Marsh Sheep and Giant Sea Lions in background.
289. 1p. green 30 25
290. 10p. blue 70 85

1973. Royal Wedding. As Type **47** of Anguilla. Background colour given. Mult.
291. 5p. mauve 25 10
292. 15p. brown 40 20

101. South American Fur Seal.

1974. Tourism. Multicoloured.
296. 2p. Type **101** .. .. 2·25 1·00
297. 4p. Trout-fishing .. .. 3·00 1·25
298. 5p. Rockhopper penguins 7·00 2·25
299. 15p. Long-tailed meadow lark .. .. .. 10·00 3·25

MORE DETAILED LISTS

are given in the Stanley Gibbons Catalogues referred to in the country headings.
For lists of current volumes see Introduction.

102. 19th-century Mail-coach.

1974. U.P.U. Multicoloured.
300. 2p. Type **102** 25 25
301. 5p. Packet ship, 1841 .. 35 45
302. 8p. First U.K. aerial post, 1911 .. .. .. 40 55
303. 16p. Ship's catapult mail, 1920's 60 75

103. Churchill and Houses of Parliament.

1974. Birth Cent. of Sir Winston Churchill. Multicoloured.
304. 16p. Type **103** .. .. 1·40 1·40
305. 20p. Churchill and warships 1·90 1·60

104. H.M.S. "Exeter".

1974. 35th Anniv. of Battle of the River Plate. Multicoloured.
307. 2p. Type **104** .. .. 2·50 1·60
308. 6p. H.M.N.Z. "Achilles" 4·00 3·00
309. 8p. "Admiral Graf Spee" 4·50 4·25
310. 16p. H.M.S. "Ajax" .. 7·50 10·00

105. Seal and Flag Badge.

1975. 50th Anniv. of Heraldic Arms. Mult.
311. 2p. Type **105** 50 35
312. 7½p. Coat of arms, 1925 .. 1·00 1·00
313. 10p. Coat of arms, 1948 .. 1·10 1·25
314. 16p. Arms of the Dependencies, 1952 .. .. 1·75 1·60

106. ½p Coin and Trout.

1975. New Coinage. Multicoloured.
316. 2p. Type **106** 85 45
317. 5½p. 1p Coin and Gentoo penguin .. .. .. 1·00 90
318. 8p 2p Coin and Magellan goose .. .. .. 1·10 1·25
319. 10p. 5p Coin and Black-browed albatross .. 1·40 1·40
320. 16p. 10p Coin and Southern sealion .. 1·75 1·75

107. Gathering Sheep.

1976. Sheep Farming Industry. Mult.
321. 2p. Type **107** 45 30
322. 7½p. Shearing .. .. 1·10 75
323. 10p. Dipping .. .. 1·40 95
324. 20p. Shipping .. .. 2·00 1·60

108. The Queen Awaiting Anointment.

1977. Silver Jubilee. Multicoloured.
325. 6p. Visit of Prince Philip 1957 1·50 95
326. 11p. The Queen, ampulla and anointing spoon .. 80 75
327. 33p. Type **108** .. .. 1·00 1·25

109. Map of Falkland Islands.

1977. Telecommunications. Multicoloured.
328. 3p. Type **109** 35 15
329. 11p. Ship to shore communications 75 40
330. 40p. Telex and telephone service .. .. .. 2·50 1·40

110. "A.E.S." 1957–74.

1978. Mail Ships. Multicoloured.
331. 1p. Type **110** 20 20
332. 2p. "Darwin" 1957–73 .. 30 20
333. 3p. "Merak-N" 1951–52 .. 25 30
334. 4p. "Fitzroy" 1936–57 .. 20 30
335. 5p. "Lafonia" 1936–41 .. 30 30
336. 6p. "Fleurus" 1924–33 .. 30 30
337. 7p. "Falkland" 1914–34 .. 30 50
338. 8p. "Oravia" 1900–12 .. 35 40
339. 9p. "Memphis" 1890–97 .. 35 35
340. 10p. "Black Hawk" 1873–80 .. .. .. 35 35
341. 20p. "Foam" 1863–72 .. 1·25 1·60
342. 25p. "Fairy" 1857–61 .. 1·25 2·00
343. 50p. "Amelia" 1852–54 .. 2·25 2·75
344. £1 "Nautilus" 1846–48 .. 2·50 4·50
345. £3 "Hebe" 1842–46 .. 5·50 9·50
Nos. 331/45 come with and without date imprint.

111. Short "Hythe" at Stanley.

1978. 26th Anniv. of 1st Direct Flight, Southampton–Port Stanley. Multicoloured.
346. 11p. Type **111** .. .. 2·00 1·25
347. 33p. Route map and Short flying boat .. .. 2·50 1·75

112. Red Dragon of Wales.

113. First Fox Bay P.O. and 1d. Stamp of 1878.

1978. 25th Anniv. of Coronation. Mult.
348. **112.** 25p. brn., blue & silver 1·00 1·00
349. – 25p. multicoloured .. 1·00 1·00
350. – 25p. brn., blue & silver 1·00 1·00
DESIGNS: No. 349, Queen Elizabeth II No. 350, Hornless ram.

1978. Centenary of First Falkland Is. Postage Stamp. Multicoloured.
351. 3p. Type **113** 20 20
352. 11p. Second Stanley P.O. and 4d. stamp of 1878 35 40
353. 15p. New Island P.O. and 6d. stamp of 1878 .. 40 50
354. 22p. First Stanley P.O. and 1s. stamp of 1878 .. 70 65

114. "Macrocystis pyrifera".

1979. Kelp and Seaweed. Multicoloured.
355. 3p. Type **114** 20 15
356. 7p. "Durvillea sp." .. 40 25
357. 11p. "Lessonia sp." (horiz.) 50 30
358. 15p. "Callophyllis sp." (horiz.) 70 35
359. 25p. "Iradaea sp." .. 90 55

115. Britten-Norman "Islander" over Falkland Islands.

1979. Opening of Stanley Airport. Mult.
360. 3p. Type **115** 30 20
361. 11p. Fokker "F27" over South Atlantic 70 60
362. 15p. Fokker "28" over Airport 80 60
363. 25p. Cessna "172 (Skyhawk)", Britten-Norman "Islander", Fokker "F27" and "F28" over runway .. .. 1·50 80

116. Sir Rowland Hill and 1953 Coronation 1d. commemorative.

1979. Death Centenary of Sir Rowland Hill. Multicoloured.
364. 3p. Type **116** 25 25
365. 11p. 1878 1d. stamp (vert.) 50 70
366. 25p. Penny Black .. 75 85

Falkland Islands
3p
117. Mail Drop by "Beaver" Aircraft.

1979. Centenary of Accession to the U.P.U. Multicoloured.

368.	3 p. Type **117**	20	20
369.	11p. Mail by horseback ..	45	55
370.	25p. Mail by schooner "Gwendolin"	75	1·00

118. Peale's Porpoise.

1980. Dolphins and Porpoises. Multicoloured.

371.	3p. Type **118**	30	25
372.	6p. Commerson's Dolphin (horiz.) ..	40	40
373.	7p. Hour-glass Dolphin (horiz.) ..	40	40
374.	11p. Spectacled Porpoise	70	65
375.	15p. Dusky Dolphin (horiz.)	80	75
376.	25p. Killer Whale (horiz.)	1·25	1·25

119. 1878 Falkland Islands Postmark.

1980. "London 1980" International Stamp Exhibition.

377.	**119.**	11p. blk., gold and blue	30	35
378.	–	11p. blk., gold and yell.	30	35
379.	–	11p. blk., gold and green	30	35
380.	–	11p. blk., gold and pur.	30	35
381.	–	11p. black, gold and red	30	35
382.	–	11p. blk., gold and flesh	30	35

Postmarks: No. 378, 1915 New Island. No. 379, 1901 Falkland Islands. No. 380, 1935 Port Stanley. No. 381, 1952 Port Stanley first overseas airmail. No. 382, 1934 Fox Bay.

120. Queen Elizabeth the Queen Mother at Ascot, 1971.

1980. 80th Birthday of Queen Mother.

383.	**120.**	11p. multicoloured ..	40	30

121. Forster's Caracara.

1980. Birds of Prey. Multicoloured.

384.	3p. Type **121**	30	25
385.	11p. Red-backed buzzard	70	60
386.	15p. Common caracara ..	85	75
387.	25p. Peregrine falcon ..	1·25	1·00

122. Stanley.

1981. Early Settlements. Multicoloured.

388.	3p. Type **122**	20	15
389.	11p. Port Egmont ..	40	35
390.	25p. Port Louis	80	65
391.	33p. Mission House, Keppel Island	1·10	80

123. Sheep.

1981. Farm Animals. Multicoloured.

392.	3p. Type **123**	20	25
393.	11p. Cattle	35	55
394.	25p. Horse	70	95
395.	33p. Dogs	1·00	1·25

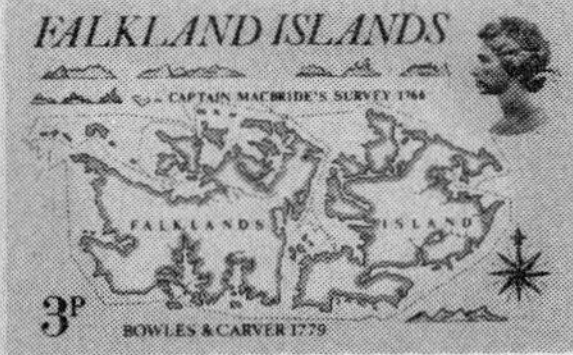

124. Bowles and Carver, 1779.

1981. Early Maps.

396.	**124.**	3p. multicoloured ..	20	20
397.	–	10p. multicoloured ..	40	45
398.	–	13p. multicoloured ..	55	60
399.	–	15p. multicoloured ..	55	65
400.	–	25p. multicoloured ..	70	75
401.	–	26p. black, pink & stone	70	75

Maps: 10p. J. Hawkesworth, 1773. 13p. Eman Bowen, 1747. 15p. T. Boutflower, 1768. 25p. Philippe de Pretot, 1771. 26p. Bellin "Petite Atlas Maritime", Paris, 1764.

125. Wedding Bouquet from Falkland Islands.

1981. Royal Wedding. Multicoloured.

402.	10p. Type **125**	45	40
403.	13p. Prince Charles riding	55	50
404.	52p. Prince Charles and Lady Diana Spencer ..	1·00	1·00

126. "Handicrafts".

1981. 25th Anniv. of Duke of Edinburgh Award Scheme. Multicoloured.

405.	10p. Type **126**	30	20
406.	13p. "Camping"	50	30
407.	15p. "Canoeing" ..	55	40
408.	26p. Duke of Edinburgh	75	60

127. "The Adoration of the Holy Child" (16th-century Dutch Artist).

1981. Christmas. Paintings. Multicoloured.

409.	3p. Type **127**	20	20
410.	13p. "The Holy Family in an Italian Landscape" (17th-century Genoan artist) ..	35	45
411.	26p. "The Holy Virgin" (Reni)	55	75

128. Falkland Herring.

1981. Shelf Fishes. Multicoloured.

412.	5p. Type **128**	15	15
413.	13p. Rock Cod (vert.) ..	30	30
414.	15p. Patagonian Hake ..	35	35
415.	25p. Southern Blue Whiting	60	65
416.	26p. Grey-tailed Skate (vert.)	60	65

129. "Lady Elizabeth," 1913.

1982. Shipwrecks. Multicoloured.

417.	5p. Type **129**	30	50
418.	13p. "Capricorn", 1882	40	70
419.	15p. "Jhelum", 1870 ..	45	85
420.	25p. "Snowsquall", 1864	75	1·10
421.	26p. "St. Mary", 1890 ..	75	1·10

130. Charles Darwin.

1982. 150th Anniv. of Charles Darwin's Voyage. Multicoloured.

422.	5p. Type **130**	20	20
423.	17p. Darwin's microscope	50	55
424.	25 p. Falkland Islands Wolf	65	75
425.	34p. H.M.S. "Beagle" ..	85	95

131. Falkland Islands Coat of Arms.

1982. 21st Birthday of Princess of Wales. Multicoloured.

426.	5p. Type **131**	15	20
427.	17p. Princess at Royal Opera House, Covent Garden, November 1981	40	50
428.	37p. Bride and groom in doorway of St. Paul's ..	75	90
429.	50p. Formal portrait ..	1·00	1·25

132. Map of Falkland Islands. (Illustration reduced. Actual size 60 × 35 mm).

1982. Rebuilding Fund.

430.	**132.**	£1 + £1 multicoloured ..	3·50	4·75

1982. Commonwealth Games, Brisbane. Nos. 335 and 342 optd. **1st PARTICIPATION COMMONWEALTH GAMES 1982.**

431.	5p. "Lafonia", 1936–41	15	30
432.	25p. "Fairy", 1857–61 ..	60	1·10

134. Blackish Cinclodes.

1982. Birds of the Passerine Family. Mult.

433.	5p. Type **134**	15	15
434.	10p. Black-chinned siskin	25	25
435.	13p. Short-billed marsh wren	30	30
436.	25p. Black-throated finch	35	35
437.	25p. Correndera pipit ..	50	50
438.	34p. Dark-faced ground-tyrant	65	65

135. Raising Flag, Port Louis, 1833.

1983. 150th Anniv. of British Administration. Multicoloured.

439.	1p. Type **135**	20	20
440.	2p. Chelsea pensioners and barracks, 1849 (horiz.) ..	30	30
441.	5p. Development of wool trade, 1874	30	30
442.	10p. Ship-repairing trade, 1850–1890 (horiz.) ..	60	60
443.	15p. Government House, early 20th century (horiz.)	70	70
444.	20p. Battle of Falkland Islands, 1914	90	90
445.	25p. Whalebone Arch (horiz.) ..	90	90
446.	40p. Contribution to War effort, 1939–45	1·40	1·40
447.	50p. Duke of Edinburgh's visit, 1957 (horiz.) ..	1·75	1·75
448.	£1 Royal Marine uniforms	2·50	2·50
449.	£2 Queen Elizabeth II ..	3·75	4·50

136. 1933 British Administration Centenary 3d. Commemorative.

1983. Commonwealth Day. Multicoloured.

450.	5p. Type **136**	15	15
451.	17p. 1933 British Administration Centenary ½d. commemorative ..	35	45
452.	34p. 1933 British Administration Centenary 10s. commemorative (vert.)	70	80
453.	50p. 1983 British Administration 150th anniversary £2 commemorative (vert.)	1·00	1·25

137. British Army advancing across East Falkland.

1983. First Anniv. of Liberation. Mult.
454. 5p. Type **137** 15 25
455. 13p. S.S. "Canberra" and M.V. "Norland" at San Carlos 30 45
456. 17p. R.A.F. Hawker "Harrier" fighter .. 35 55
457. 50p. H.M.S. "Hermes" (aircraft carrier) .. 1·00 1·25

138. Diddle Dee.

1983. Native Fruits. Multicoloured.
459. 5p. Type **138** 20 20
460. 17 p. Tea Berry 45 50
461. 25p. Mountain Berry .. 70 65
462. 34p. Native Strawberry .. 85 80

139. Britten-Norman "Islander."

1983. Bicentenary of Manned Flight. Multicoloured.
463. 5p. Type **139** 15 20
464. 13p. " DHC-2 Beaver " .. 35 45
465. 17p. " Noorduyn Norseman " 40 50
466. 50p. " Auster " .. .. 1·00 1·25

1984. Nos. 443 and 445 surch.
467. 17p. on 15p. Government House, early 20th century 60 45
468. 22p. on 25p. Whalebone Arch, 1933 .. .. 65 55

141. "Araneus cinnabarinus" (juvenile spider).

1984. Insects and Spiders. Multicoloured.
469 1p. Type **141** 20 30
470 2p. "Alopophion occidentalis" (fly) 50 70
471 3p. "Pareuxoina falklandica" (moth) 30 30
472 4p. "Lissopterus quadrinotatus" (beetle) .. 20 30
473 5p. "Issoria cytheris" (butterfly) 20 30
474 6p. "Araneus cinnabarinus" (adult spider) 20 30
475 7p. "Trachysphyrus penai" (fly) 20 30
476 8p. "Caphornia ochricraspia" (moth) 20 30
477 9p. "Caneorhinus biangulatus" (weevil) 20 30
478 10p. "Syrphus octomaculatus" (fly) 20 30
479 20p. "Malvinius compressiventris" (weevil) .. 1·50 75
480 25p. "Metius blandus" (beetle) 75 90
481 50p. "Parudenus falklandicus" (cricket) .. 1·00 1·50
482 £1 "Emmenomma beauchenieus" (spider) 1·75 2·25
483 £3 "Cynthia carye" (butterfly) .. .. 5·00 6·00
No. 470 comes with or without imprint date.

142. "Wavertree".

1984. 250th Anniv. of "Lloyd's List" (newspaper). Multicoloured.
484. 6p. Type **142** 40 25
485. 17p. Port Stanley 80 50
486. 22p. R.M.S. "Oravia" stranded 85 55
487. 52p. "Cunard Countess" .. 1·50 1·25

143. Ship, Aircraft and U.P.U. Logo.

1984. Universal Postal Union Congress, Hamburg.
488. **143.** 22p. multicoloured .. 50 65

144. Great Grebe.

1984. Grebes. Multicoloured.
489. 17p. Type **144** 85 70
490. 22p. Silver grebe .. .. 1·00 90
491. 52p. White-tufted grebe .. 2·25 2·25

145. Black-browed Albatross.

1984. Nature Conservation. Multicoloured.
492. 6p. Type **145** 90 55
493. 17p. Tussock grass .. 1·10 80
494. 22p. Dusky Dolphin and Southern Sea Lion .. 1·40 1·00
495. 52p. "Notothenia" (fish) and krill .. .. .. 2·00 2·00

146. Technical Drawing of "Wren" Class Locomotive.

1985. 70th Anniv. of Camber Railway. Each black, brown and light brown.
497. 7p. Type **146** 35 30
498. 22p. Sail-propelled trolley 70 65
499. 27p. Locomotive at work 85 75
500. 54p. "Falkland Islands Express" passenger train (76 × 25 mm.) .. .. 1·50 1·50

147. Construction Workers' Camp.

1985. Opening of Mount Pleasant Airport. Multicoloured.
501. 7p. Type **147** 50 30
502. 22p. Building construction 1·00 80
503. 27p. Completed airport .. 1·25 95
504. 54p. Airliner over runway 1·60 1·75

148. The Queen Mother on 84th Birthday.

1985. Life and Times of Queen Elizabeth the Queen Mother. Multicoloured.
505 7p. Attending reception at Lancaster House .. 25 20
506 22p. With Prince Charles, Mark Phillips and Princess Anne at Falklands Memorial Service 60 50
507 27p. Type **148** 70 60
508 54p. With Prince Henry at his christening (from photo by Lord Snowdon) 1·25 1·25

149. Captain J. McBride and H.M.S. "Jason", 1765.

1985. Early Cartographers. Multicoloured.
510. 7p. Type **149** 60 30
511. 22p. Commodore J. Byron and H.M.S. "Dolphin" and "Tamar", 1765 .. 90 70
512. 27p. Vice-Admiral R. FitzRoy and H.M.S. "Beagle", 1831 .. .. 95 75
513. 54p. Admiral Sir B. J. Sullivan and H.M.S. "Philomel", 1842 .. 1·60 1·50

1985. Early Naturalists. As T **35** of British Antarctic Territory. Multicoloured.
514. 7p. Philibert Commerson and Commerson's dolphin 75 35
515. 22p. Rene Primevere Lesson and "Lessonia" sp. (kelp) .. .. 1·25 80
516. 27p. Joseph Paul Gaimard and Common diving petre 1·60 1·25
517. 54p. Charles Darwin and "Calceolaria darwinii" .. 1·90 2·00

150. Painted Keyhole Limpet.

1986. Seashells. Multicoloured.
518. 7p. Type **150** 65 35
519. 22p. Magellanic Volute .. 1·25 80
520. 27p. Patagonian Scallop .. 1·40 90
521. 54p. Rough Thorn Drupe 2·25 1·60

1986. 60th Birthday of Queen Elizabeth II. As T **110** of Ascension. Multicoloured.
522 10p. With Princess Margaret at St. Paul's, Walden Bury, Welwyn, 1932 .. .. .. 35 25
523 24p. Queen making Christmas television broadcast, 1958 .. .. 65 55
524 29p. In robes of Order of the Thistle, St. Giles Cathedral, Edinburgh, 1962 .. .. .. 75 60
525 45p. Aboad Royal Yacht "Britannia", U.S.A., 1976 .. .. .. 1·25 95
526 58p. At Crown Agents Head Office, London, 1983 .. .. .. 1·40 1·25

151. S.S. "Great Britain" crossing Atlantic, 1845.

1986. "Ameripex '86" International Stamp Exhibition, Chicago. Centenary of Arrival of S.S. "Great Britain" in Falkland Islands. Multicoloured.
527. 10p. Type **151** 40 30
528. 24p. Beached at Sparrow Cove, 1937 .. .. 75 65
529. 29p. Refloated on pontoon, 1970 .. .. 85 70
530. 58p. Undergoing restoration, Bristol, 1986 .. 1·40 1·25

152. Head of Rockhopper Penguin.

1986. Rockhopper Penguins. Multicoloured.
532. 10p. Type **152** 60 30
533. 24p. Rockhopper Penguins at sea .. .. 1·00 60
534. 29p. Courtship display .. 1·10 65
535. 58p. Adult with chick .. 1·75 1·25

153. Prince Andrew and Miss Sarah Ferguson presenting Polo Trophy, Windsor.

1986. Royal Wedding. Multicoloured.
536. 17p. Type **153** 65 40
537. 22p. Prince Andrew and Duchess of York on wedding day 75 50
538. 29p. Prince Andrew in battledress at opening of Fox Bay Mill 90 60

154. Survey Party, Sapper Hill.

1987. Bicentenary of Royal Engineers' Royal Warrant. Multicoloured.
539. 10p. Type **154** 80 35
540. 24p. Mine clearance by robot .. .. .. 1·40 75
541. 29p. Boxer Bridge, Stanley 1·60 90
542. 58p. Unloading mail, Mount Pleasant Airport 2·25 1·40

155. Southern Sea Lion.

1987. Seals. Multicoloured.

543.	10p. Type **155**	40	25
544.	24p. Falkland fur seal	1·00	55
545.	29p. Southern elephant seal	1·10	65
546.	58p. Leopard seal	1·90	1·25

156. "Suillus luteus".

1987. Fungi. Multicoloured.

547.	10p. Type **156**	1·00	75
548.	24p. "Mycena" sp.	1·75	1·25
549.	29p. "Camarophyllus adonis"	2·00	1·75
550.	58p. "Gerronema schusteri"	2·75	2·75

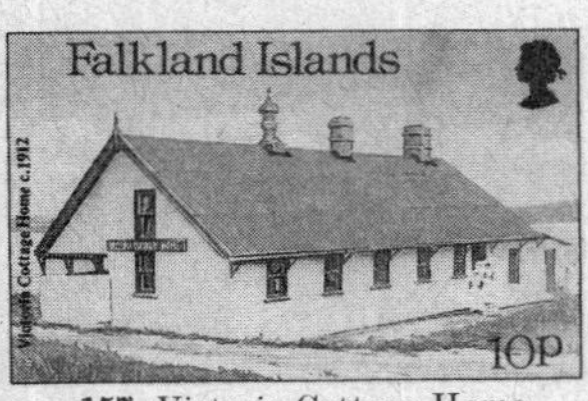

157. Victoria Cottage Home, c. 1912.

1987. Local Hospitals. Multicoloured.

551.	10p. Type **157**	30	25
552.	24p. King Edward VII Memorial Hospital, c 1914	65	55
553.	29p. Churchill Wing, King Edward VII Memorial Hospital, c. 1953	75	60
554.	58p. Prince Andrew Wing, New Hospital, 1987	1·25	1·25

158 Morris Truck, Fitzroy, 1940

1988. Early Vehicles. Multicoloured.

555	10p. Type **158**	30	25
556	24p. Citroen "Kegresse" half-track, San Carlos, 1929	65	55
557	29p. Ford one ton truck, Port Stanley, 1933	75	60
558	58p. Ford "Model T" car, Darwin, 1935	1·25	1·25

159 Kelp Goose

1988. Falkland Islands Geese. Multicoloured.

559	10p. Type **159**	60	35
560	24p. Magellan ("Upland") goose	1·00	60
561	29p. Ruddy-headed goose	1·10	70
562	58p. Ashy-headed goose	1·75	1·40

1988. 300th Anniv of Lloyd's of London. Multicoloured. As T **123** of Ascension.

563	10p. Silver from Lloyd's Nelson Collection	25	25
564	24p. Falkland Islands hydroponic market garden (horiz)	55	55
565	29p. "A.E.S." (freighter) (horiz)	60	60
566	58p. "Charles Cooper" (full-rigged sailing ship), 1866	1·25	1·25

160 "Padua" (barque)

1989. Cape Horn Sailing Ships. Multicoloured

567	1p. Type **160**	10	10
568	2p. "Priwall" (barque) (vert)	15	15
569	3p. "Passat" (barque)	15	15
570	4p. "Archibald Russell" (barque) (vert)	10	10
571	5p. "Pamir" (barque) (vert)	10	15
572	6p. "Mozart" (barquentine)	20	20
573	7p. "Pommern" (barque)	15	20
574	8p. "Preussen" (full-rigged ship)	15	20
575	9p. "Fennia" (barque)	30	30
576	10p. "Cassard" (barque)	20	25
577	20p. "Lawhill" (barque)	40	45
578	25p. "Garthpool" (barque)	50	55
579	50p. "Grace Harwar" (full-rigged ship)	1·00	1·10
580	£1 "Criccieth Castle" (full-rigged ship)	2·50	2·75
581	£3 "Cutty Sark" (full-rigged ship) (vert)	6·00	6·25
582	£5 "Flying Cloud" (full-rigged ship)	10·00	10·50

161 Southern Right Whale

1989. Baleen Whales. Multicoloured.

583	10p. Type **161**	45	30
584	24p. Minke whale	90	70
585	29p. Humpback whale	1·10	75
586	58p. Blue whale	1·90	1·50

162 "Gymkhana" (Sarah Gilding)

1989. Sports Associations' Activities. Children's drawings. Multicoloured.

587	5p. Type **162**	20	20
588	10p. "Steer Riding" (Karen Steen)	30	30
589	17p. "Sheep Shearing" (Colin Shepherd)	45	45
590	24p. "Sheepdog Trials" (Rebecca Edwards)	60	70
591	29p. "Horse Racing" (Dilys Blackley)	70	80
592	45p. "Sack Race" (Donna Newell)	1·00	1·10

163 Vice-Admiral Sturdee and H.M.S. "Invincible" (battle cruiser)

1989. 75th Anniv of Battle of the Falkland Islands and 50th Anniv of Battle of the River Plate. Multicoloured.

593	10p. Type **163**	30	30
594	24p. Vice-Admiral Graf von Spee and "Scharnhorst" (German cruiser)	70	75
595	29p. Commodore Harwood and H.M.S. "Ajax" (cruiser)	80	85
596	58p. Captain Langsdorff and "Admiral Graf Spee" (German pocket battleship)	1·50	1·60

164 Southern Sea Lions on Kidney Island

1990. Nature Reserves and Sanctuaries. Mult.

597	12p. Type **164**	35	35
598	26p. Black-browed albatrosses on Beauchene Island	70	70
599	31p. Penguin colony on Bird Island	80	80
600	62p. Tussock grass on Elephant Jason Island	1·40	1·40

165 Spitfire Mk. I "Falkland Islands I"

1990. "Stamp World London 90" International Stamp Exhibition, London. Presentation Spitfires. Multicoloured.

601	12p. Type **165**	40	35
602	26p. Spitfire Mk. I "Falkland Islands VII"	80	70
603	31p. Cockpit and wing of "Falkland Islands I"	90	80
604	62p. Squadron scramble, 1940	1·40	1·40

1990. 90th Birthday of Queen Elizabeth the Queen Mother. As T **134** of Ascension.

606	26p. multicoloured	75	65
607	£1 black and red	2·50	2·75

DESIGNS—21 × 36 mm. 26p. Queen Mother in Dover. 29 × 37 mm. £1 On bridge of liner "Queen Elizabeth", 1946.

166 Black-browed Albatrosses

1990. Black-browed Albatross. Multicoloured.

608	12p. Type **166**	35	35
609	26p. Female with egg	70	70
610	31p. Adult and chick	85	85
611	62p. Black-browed albatross in flight	1·60	1·75

MINIMUM PRICE

The minimum price quoted is 10p which represents a handling charge rather than a basis for valuing common stamps. For further notes about prices see introductory pages.

167 "Gavilea australis"

1991. Orchids. Multicoloured.

629	12p. Type **167**	40	40
630	26p. Dog orchid	75	75
631	31p. "Chlorea gaudichaudii"	90	90
632	62p. Yellow orchid	1·75	2·00

168 Heads of Two King Penguins

1991. Endangered Species. King Penguin. Multicoloured.

633	2p. Type **168**	15	15
634	6p. Female incubating egg	20	25
635	12p. Female with two chicks	35	35
636	20p. Penguin underwater	60	65
637	31p. Parents feeding their chick	80	85
638	62p. Courtship dance	1·50	1·60

169 ½d and 2½d Stamps of September 1891

1991. Cent of Bisected Surcharges. Mult.

639	12p. Type **169**	35	35
640	26p. Cover of March 1891 franked with strip of five ½d. bisects	70	70
641	31p. Unsevered pair of ½d. surcharge	85	85
642	62p. "Isis" (mail ship)	1·50	1·60

170 Map of Re-enactment Voyages and "Eye of the Wind" (cadet ship)

1991. 500th Anniv of Discovery of America by Columbus. Re-enactment Voyages. Mult.

643	14p. Type **170**	25	30
644	29p. Compass rose and "Soren Larsen" (cadet ship)	50	55
645	34p. "Santa Maria", "Pinta" and "Nina"	60	65
646	68p. Columbus and "Santa Maria"	1·25	1·40

1992. 40th Anniv of Queen Elizabeth II's Accession. As T **143** of Ascension. Mult.

647 7p. "Stanley through the Narrows" (A. Asprey) .. 15 20
648 14p. "Hill Cove" (A. Asprey) 30 35
649 29p. "San Carlos Water" (A. Asprey) 60 65
650 34p. Three portraits of Queen Elizabeth .. 70 75
651 68p. Queen Elizabeth II .. 1·40 1·50

171 Laying Foundation Stone, 1890

1992. Centenary of Christ Church Cathedral, Stanley. Multicoloured.

652 14p. Type **171** 30 35
653 29p. Interior of Cathedral, 1920 .. .. .. 60 65
654 34p. Bishop's chair .. 70 75
655 68p. Cathedral in 1900 (horiz) .. .. .. 1·40 1·50

POSTAGE DUE STAMPS

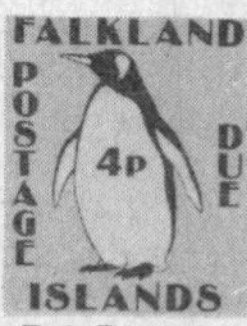

D **1** Penguin

1991.

D1 D **1** 1p. red and mauve .. 10 10
D2 2p. orange & lt orange 10 10
D3 3p. ochre and yellow .. 10 10
D4 4p. green & light green 10 10
D5 5p. blue and light blue 10 15
D6 10p. deep blue and blue 20 25
D7 20p. violet and lilac .. 40 45
D8 50p. green & lt green 1·00 1·10

FALKLAND ISLANDS DEPENDENCIES

Four groups of Islands situated between the Falkland Is. and the South Pole. In 1946 the four groups ceased issuing separate issues which were replaced by a single general issue. From 1963 the stamps of Br. Antarctic Territory were used in all these islands except South Georgia and South Sandwich for which separate stamps were issued inscribed "SOUTH GEORGIA" from 1963 until 1980.

Under the new constitution effective on 3 October 1985, South Georgia and South Sandwich Islands ceased to be dependencies of the Falkland Islands.

1944. 12 pence = 1 shilling.
20 shillings = 1 pound.
1971. 100 (new) pence = 1 pound.

GRAHAM LAND

1944. Stamps of Falkland Is. of 1938 optd **GRAHAM LAND DEPENDENCY OF.**

A 1. **27.** ½d. black and green .. 30 1·00
A 2. – 1d. black and violet .. 30 1·00
A 3. – 2d. black and red .. 40 1·00
A 4. – 3d. black and blue .. 30 1·00
A 5. – 4d. black and purple .. 1·75 1·25
A 6. – 6d. black and brown .. 8·50 2·25
A 7. – 9d. black and blue .. 1·50 1·00
A 8. – 1s. blue .. .. 1·50 1·00

SOUTH GEORGIA

1944. Stamps of Falkland Is. of 1938 optd. **SOUTH GEORGIA DEPENDENCY OF.**

B 1. **27.** ½d. black and green .. 30 1·00
B 2. – 1d. black and violet .. 30 1·00
B 3. – 2d. black and red .. 40 1·00
B 4. – 3d. black and blue .. 30 1·00
B 5. – 4d. black and purple .. 1·75 1·25
B 6. – 6d. black and brown .. 8·50 2·25
B 7. – 9d. black and blue .. 1·50 1·00
B 8. – 1s. blue.. .. .. 1·50 1·00

SOUTH ORKNEYS

1944. Stamps of Falkland Is. of 1938 optd. **SOUTH ORKNEYS DEPENDENCY OF.**

C 1. **27.** ½d. black and green .. 30 1·00
C 2. – 1d. black and violet .. 30 1·00
C 3. – 2d. black and red .. 40 1·00
C 4. – 3d. black and blue .. 30 1·00
C 5. – 4d. black and purple .. 1·75 1·25
C 6. – 6d. black and brown .. 8·50 2·25
C 7. – 9d. black and blue .. 1·50 1·00
C 8. – 1s. blue .. .. 1·50 1·00

SOUTH SHETLANDS

1944. Stamps of Falkland Is. of 1938 optd. **SOUTH SHETLAND DEPENDENCY OF.**

D 1. **27.** ½d. black and green .. 30 1·00
D 2. – 1d. black and violet .. 30 1·00
D 3. – 2d. black and red .. 40 1·00
D 4. – 3d. black and blue .. 30 1·00
D 5. – 4d. black and purple .. 1·75 1·25
D 6. – 6d. black and brown .. 8·50 2·25
D 7. – 9d. black and blue .. 1·50 1·00
D 8. – 1s. blue .. .. 1·50 1·00

GENERAL ISSUES

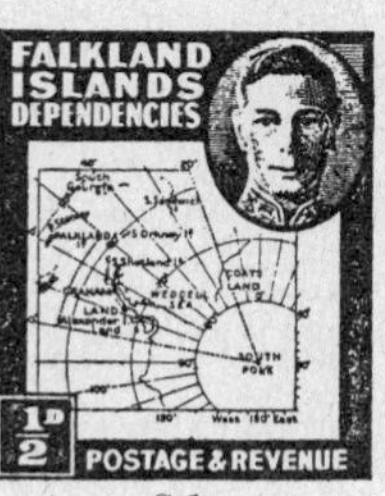

G **1**.

1946.

G 1 G **1.** ½d. black and green .. 1·00 2·00
G 2 1d. black and violet .. 1·00 1·75
G 3 2d. black and red .. 1·00 2·50
G 1la 2½d. black and blue .. 9·50 7·00
G 4 3d. black and blue .. 1·00 3·50
G 5 4d. black and red .. 2·25 4·25
G 6 6d. black and orange .. 4·25 4·50
G 7 9d. black and brown .. 1·75 2·75
G 8 1s. black and purple .. 2·00 4·00

1946. Victory. As T **9** of Aden.

G 17. 1d. violet 50 15
G 18. 3d. blue.. .. .. 50 15

1949. Silver Wedding. As T **10/11** of Aden.

G 19. 2½d. blue .. .. 1·00 75
G 20. 1s. blue .. .. .. 5·50 1·75

1949. U.P.U. As T **20/23** of Antigua.

G 21. 1d. violet .. .. 2·00 1·25
G 22. 2d. red .. .. .. 6·50 2·50
G 23. 3d. blue.. .. .. 8·00 1·25
G 24. 6d. orange .. .. 12·00 3·00

1953. Coronation. As T **13** of Aden.

G 25. 1d. black and violet .. 1·50 1·25

G **3**. "Trepassey", 1945-47.

1954. Ships.

G 26. – ½d. black and green .. 30 65
G 27. G **3**. 1d. black and sepia 75 65
G 28. – 1½d. black and olive 75 65
G 29. – 2d. black and red .. 90 20
G 30. – 2½d. black and yellow 90 15
G 31. – 3d. black and blue .. 90 15
G 32. – 4d. black and purple 2·50 30
G 33. – 6d. black and lilac .. 2·50 35
G 34. – 9d. black .. .. 2·50 40
G 35. – 1s. black and brown.. 2·50 40
G 36. – 2s. black and red .. 15·00 9·00
G 37. – 2s. 6d. black & turq. 15·00 6·00
G 38. – 5 s. black and violet 32·00 6·50
G 39. – 10s. black and blue .. 48·00 18·00
G 40. – £1 black .. .. £110 48·00

SHIPS—VERT. ½d. "John Biscoe". 6d. "Discovery". 9d. "Endurance". 2s. 6d. "Francais". 5s. "Scotia". £1, "Belgica". HORIZ. 1½d. "Wyatt Earp". 2d. "Eagle". 2½d. "Penola". 3d. "Discovery II". 4d. "William Scoresby". 1s. "Deutschland". 2s. "Pourquoi pas?". 10s. "Antarctic".

1956. Trans-Antarctic Expedition. Nos. G 27, G 30/1 and G 33 optd. **TRANS-ANTARCTIC EXPEDITION 1955-1958.**

G 41. G **3**. 1d. black and sepia .. 10 30
G 42. – 2½d. black and yellow 40 30
G 43. – 3d. black and blue .. 40 30
G 44. – 6d. black and lilac .. 40 30

For later issues see **BRITISH ANTARCTIC TERRITORIES** and **SOUTH GEORGIA.**

ISSUES FOR SOUTH GEORGIA AND SOUTH SANDWICH ISLANDS.

In 1980 stamps were again inscribed "FALKLAND ISLANDS DEPENDENCIES" for use in the above area.

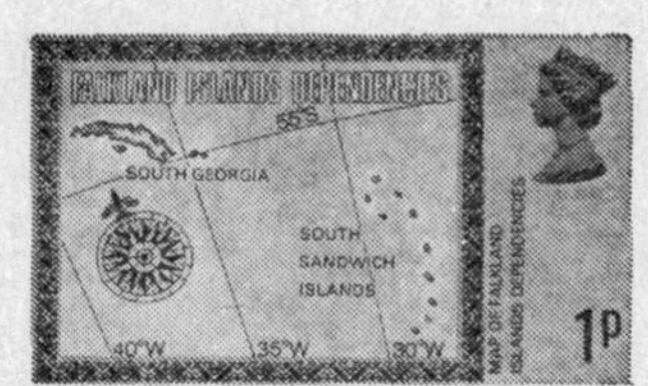

14. Map of Falkland Islands Dependencies.

1980. Multicoloured.

74 1p. Type **14** 25 30
75 2p. Shag Rocks 25 30
76 3p. Bird and Willis Islands 25 30
77 4p. Gulbrandsen Lake .. 25 30
78 5p. King Edward Point .. 30 30
79 6p. Sir Ernest Shackleton's Memorial Cross, Hope Point 30 30
80 7p. Sir Ernest Shackleton's grave, Grytviken .. 30 30
81 8p. Grytviken Church .. 30 30
82 9p. Coaling Hulk "Louise" at Grytviken 30 35
83 10p. Clerke Rocks 50 35
84 20p. Candlemas Island .. 2·00 1·25
85 25p. Twitcher Rock and Cook Island, Southern Thule .. .. .. 2·00 1·50
86 50p. R.R.S. "John Biscoe II" in Cumberland Bay 1·50 2·00
87 £1 R.R.S. "Bransfield" in Cumberland Bay .. 2·00 2·75
88 £3 H.M.S. "Endurance" in Cumberland Bay .. 5·00 6·50

These stamps come with or without date imprint.

15. Magellanic Clubmoss.

1981. Plants. Multicoloured.

89. 3p. Type **15** 25 25
90. 6p. Alpine Cat's-tail .. 30 30
91. 7p. Greater Burnet .. 30 30
92. 11p. Antarctic Bedstraw .. 50 40
93. 15p. Brown Rush 70 55
94. 25p. Antarctic Hair Grass 1·00 80

16. Wedding Bouquet from Falkland Islands Dependencies.

1981. Royal Wedding. Multicoloured.

95. 10p. Type **16** 30 40
96. 13p. Prince Charles dressed for Skiing 40 50
97. 52p. Prince Charles and Lady Diana Spencer .. .. 1·00 1·00

17. Introduced Reindeer during Calving, Spring.

1982. Reindeer. Multicoloured.

98. 5p. Type **17** 45 60
99. 13p. Bull at rut, Autumn 65 80
100. 25p. Reindeer and mountains, Winter .. .. 1·10 1·25
101. 26p. Reindeer feeding on tussock, late Winter .. 1·10 1·25

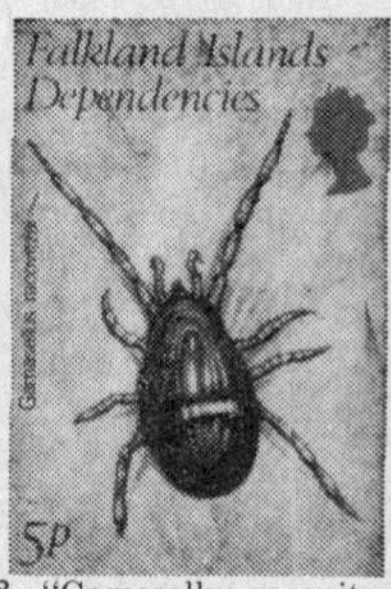

18. "Gamasellus racovitzai" (tick).

1982. Insects. Multicoloured.

102 5p. Type **18** 20 25
103 10p. "Alaskozetes antarcticus" (mite) .. 30 35
104 13p. "Cryptopygus antarcticus" (spring-tail) .. 35 40
105 15p. "Notiomaso australis" (spider) 40 45
106 25p. "Hydromedion sparsutum" (beetle) .. 65 70
107 26p. "Parochlus steinenii" (midge) 65 70

19. Lady Diana Spencer at Tidworth, Hampshire, July 1981.

1982. 21st Birthday of Princess of Wales. Multicoloured.

108. 5p. Falkland Islands Dependencies coat of arms 10 15
109. 17p. Type **19** 30 35
110. 37p. Bride and groom on steps of St. Pauls .. 75 80
111. 50p. Formal portrait .. 1·00 1·10

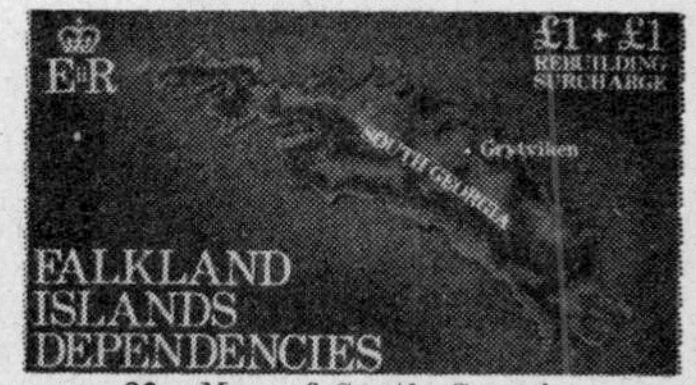

20. Map of South Georgia. (Illustration reduced. Actual size 60 × 35 mm).

1982. Rebuilding Fund.

112.	20.	£1+£1 multicoloured ..	3·50	4·50

21. Westland " Whirlwind ".

1983. Bicentenary of Manned Flight. Mult.

113.	5p. Type 21	30	20
114.	13p. Westland " Wasp " ..	55	45
115.	17p. Saunders-Roe " Walrus "	60	50
116.	50p. Auster	1·40	1·25

22. " Euphausia superba ".

1983. Crustacea. Multicoloured.

117.	5p. Type 22	20	20
118.	17p. " Glyptonotus antarcticus "	50	50
119.	25p. " Epimeria monodon "	60	60
120.	34p. " Serolis pagenstecheri "	90	80

23. Zavodovski Island.

1984. Volcanoes of South Sandwich Islands. Multicoloured.

121.	6p. Type 23	70	50
122.	17p. Mt Michael, Saunders Island	1·50	75
123.	22p. Bellingshausen Island	1·60	85
124.	52p. Bristol Island ..	2·25	1·60

24. Grey-headed Albatross.

1985. Albatrosses. Multicoloured.

125.	7p. Type 24	85	45
126.	22p. Black-browed Albatross	1·50	75
127.	27p. Wandering Albatross	1·60	85
128.	54p. Light-mantled Sooty Albatross	2·00	1·50

25. The Queen Mother.

1985. Life and Times of Queen Elizabeth the Queen Mother. Multicoloured.

129.	7p. At Windsor Castle on Princess Elizabeth's 14th Birthday, 1940	20	25
130.	22p. With Princess Anne, Lady Sarah Armstrong-Jones and Prince Edward at Trooping the Colour	50	60
131.	27p. Type 25	60	70
132.	54p. With Prince Henry at his christening (from photo by Lord Snowdon)	1·25	1·25

1985. Early Naturalists. As T **35** of British Antarctic Territory. Multicoloured.

134.	7p. Dumont d'Urville and "Durvillea antarctica" (kelp)	75	50
135.	22p. Johann Reinhold Forster and King Penguin	1·50	1·00
136.	27p. Johann Georg Adam Forster and Tussock Grass	1·60	1·25
137.	54p. Sir Joseph Banks and Dove Prion	2·25	2·25

For later issues see **SOUTH GEORGIA** and **SOUTH SANDWICH ISLANDS.**

FARIDKOT

A state of the Punjab, India. Now uses Indian stamps.

1 folus = 1 paisa = ¼ anna. Later, as India.

N 1. (1 folus).

N 2. (1 paisa).

1879. Imperf.

N 5.	1.	1 f. blue	1·00	1·50
N 6.	2.	1 p. blue	1·50	3·75

1887. Stamps of India (Queen Victoria) optd. **FARIDKOT STATE.**

17.	40.	3 p. red	50	12·00
1.	23.	½ a. turquoise	20	30
2.	–	1 a. purple	35	85
4.	–	2 a. blue	1·50	2·25
7.	–	3 a. orange	1·00	1·75
8.	–	4 a. green (No. 96) ..	2·00	4·50
11.	–	6 a. brown (No. 80) ..	1·75	6·50
12.	–	8 a. mauve	3·25	12·00
14.	–	12 a. purple on red ..	25·00	£150
15.	–	1 r. grey	22·00	£130
16.	37.	1 r. green and red ..	17·00	26·00

OFFICIAL STAMPS

1886. Stamps of India (Queen Victoria) optd. **SERVICE FARIDKOT STATE.**

O 1	23.	½ a. turquoise	15	30
O 3	–	1 a. purple	45	55
O 5	–	2 a. blue	70	5·00
O 6	–	3 a. orange	3·25	3·25
O 8	–	4 a. green (No. 96) ..	1·40	5·50
O 11	–	6 a. brown (No. 80) ..	10·00	13·00
O 12	–	8 a. mauve	2·50	7·50
O 14	–	1 r. grey	23·00	65·00
O 15	37.	1 r. green and red ..	42·00	£160

FEDERATED MALAY STATES

A Br. protectorate in S.E. Asia, comprising the States of Negri Sembilan (with Sungei Ujong), Pahang, Perak and Selangor.

Separate issues for each of these states appeared in 1936.

100 cents = $1 (Straits).

1900. Stamps of Negri Sembilan optd. **FEDERATED MALAY STATES** and bar.

1.	3.	1 c. purple and green ..	40	3·00
2.		2 c. purple and brown ..	22·00	45·00
3.		3 c. purple and black ..	1·90	3·25
4.		5 c. purple and yellow ..	65·00	£110
5.		10 c. purple and orange ..	2·00	12·00
6.		20 c. green and olive ..	50·00	65·00
7.		25 c. green and red ..	£140	£170
8.		50 c. green and black ..	60·00	80·00

1900. Stamps of Perak optd. **FEDERATED MALAY STATES** and bar.

9.	31.	5 c. purple and yellow ..	10·00	45·00
10.		10 c. purple and orange ..	55·00	60·00
11.	32.	$1 green	£110	£130
12.		$2 green and red	90·00	£120
13.		$5 green and blue	£200	£275
14.		$25 green and orange ..	£3750	

3.

4.

1900.

15a	3.	1 c. black and green ..	30	30
29		1 c. green	1·25	20
30		1 c. brown	2·25	90
53		1 c. black	50	20
55		2 c. green	45	10
54		2 c. brown	4·00	2·25
16b		3 c. black and brown ..	1·25	20
58		3 c. brown	60	40
34		3 c. red	2·00	10
35		3 c. grey	1·00	20
57		3 c. green	1·50	1·75
36d		4 c. black and red ..	3·50	25
38		4 c. red	80	15
60		4 c. orange	55	10
18		5 c. green & red on yellow	1·50	2·00
61		5 c. mauve on yellow ..	75	20
62		5 c. brown	1·60	10
63		6 c. orange	55	45
64		6 c. red	80	10
41b		8 c. black and blue ..	5·00	3·50
42		8 c. blue	13·00	1·25
43b		10 c. black and mauve ..	7·00	25
44		10 c. blue	6·00	80
66		10 c. black and blue ..	2·00	75
67		10 c. purple on yellow ..	3·50	40
68		12 c. blue	1·25	10
45		20 c. mauve and black ..	1·50	35
70		25 c. purple and mauve ..	2·50	75
71		30 c. purple and orange ..	3·25	95
72		35 c. red on yellow ..	3·75	12·00
73		35 c. red and purple ..	12·00	12·00
74		50 c. black and orange ..	13·00	4·50
75		50 c. black on green ..	4·00	2·00
76a	4.	$1 green	10·00	22·00
77	3.	$1 black and red on blue ..	10·00	2·50
78	4.	$2 green and red ..	10·00	48·00
79	3.	$2 green & red on yellow	27·00	26·00
80	4.	$5 green and blue ..	60·00	85·00
81	3.	$5 green and red on green	£120	£130
82	4.	$25 green and orange ..	£650	£300

POSTAGE DUE STAMPS

D 1.

1924.

D 1.	D 1.	1 c. violet	3·50	7·00
D 2.		2 c. black	1·75	2·00
D 3.		4 c. green	2·25	4·25
D 4.		8 c. red	4·25	14·00
D 5.		10 c. orange	7·75	11·00
D 6.		12 c. blue	8·50	18·00

FIJI

A Br. colony in the S. Pacific which became independent within the Commonwealth during October 1970.

1870. 12 pence = 1 shilling;
20 shillings = 1 pound.
1969. 100 cents = 1 dollar.

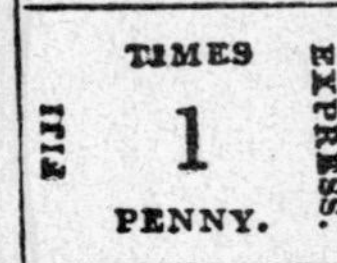

1.

2.

1870.

5.	1.	1d. black on pink	£750	£1400
6.		3d. black on pink	£1200	£1800
7.		6d. black on pink	£800	£1500
8.		9d. black on pink	£1300	£2000
9.		1s. black on pink	£800	£1000

1871.

10.	2.	1d. blue	70·00	£120
11.		3d. green	£150	£250
12.		6d. red	£160	£275

1872. Surch. in words.

13a	2.	2 c. on 1d. blue	25·00	40·00
14		6 c. on 3d. green ..	55·00	55·00
15		12 c. on 6d. red	75·00	75·00

(5.) (8.)

1874. Optd. as T **5.**

16.	2.	2 c. on 1d. blue	£650	£180
17.		6 c. on 3d. green	£950	£450
18.		12 c. on 6d. red	£470	£170

1875. Nos. 17 and 18 surch. **2d.**

22.	2.	2d. on 6 c. on 3d. green ..	£375	£130
27.		2d. on 12 c. on 6d. red ..	£900	£475

1876. Optd. with T **8,** and the 3d. surch. in words also.

31.	2.	1d. blue	13·00	22·00
29.		2d. on 3d. green ..	35·00	48·00
34.		4d. on 3d. mauve ..	65·00	30·00
33.		6d. red	42·00	32·00

10.

12.

1878. Surcharges on Nos. 36 and 41/2 in words.

35	10	1d. blue	3·50	4·00
40		2d. green	7·00	90
36		2d. on 3d. green ..	4·00	7·00
54		4d. mauve	6·00	7·00
41		4d. on 1d. mauve ..	18·00	11·00
42		4d. on 2d. mauve ..	55·00	9·00
59a		6d. red	6·50	4·50
67	12	1s. brown	23·00	8·50
69		5 s. red and black ..	50·00	35·00

1891. Surch. in figures or words.

72a.	10.	½d. on 1d. blue	35·00	60·00
70.		2½d. on 2d. green ..	48·00	48·00
73.		5d. on 4d. mauve ..	45·00	65·00
74a.		5d. on 6d. red	55·00	60·00

20.

21. Native Canoe.

1891.

99	20	½d. grey	1·00	2·50
87	21	1d. black	2·50	3·00
101		1d. mauve	3·25	50
89		2d. green	4·75	80
103a	10	2½d. brown	5·00	5·00
85	21	5d. blue	7·00	7·50

23.

1903.

104	23.	½d. green	1·75	1·50
105		1d. purple & black on red	6·00	55
119		1d. red	2·00	10
106		2d. purple and orange ..	1·50	1·25
107		2½d. purple & blue on blue	14·00	15·00
120		2½d. blue	3·50	5·50
108		3d. purple	1·25	4·00
109		4d. purple and black ..	1·25	2·50
110		5d. purple and green ..	1·25	5·00
111		6d. purple and red ..	1·50	2·50
121		6d. purple	5·50	12·00
112		1s. green and red ..	10·00	22·00
122		1s. black on green ..	4·00	10·00
113		5s. green and black ..	25·00	60·00
123		5s. green and red on yell.	38·00	48·00
114		£1 black and blue ..	£325	£350
124		£1 purple and blk. on red	£325	£375

1912. As T **23,** but portrait of King George V.

125	¼d. brown	20	30
126	½d. green	40	55
127	1d. red	1·90	10
231	1d. violet	1·00	10
232	1½d. red	4·00	3·25
128	2d. grey	80	10
129	2½d. blue	3·50	3·50
130	3d. purple on yellow ..	2·75	3·50
234	3d. blue	90	1·25
235	4d. black & red on yellow	5·00	7·00
236	5d. purple and olive ..	1·50	2·00
237	6d. purple	1·75	1·25
238	1s. black on green ..	2·50	6·00
239	2s. purple and blue on blue	25·00	48·00
240	2s. 6d. black & red on blue	10·00	32·00
136	5s. green and red on yellow	29·00	40·00
137	£1 purple and black on red	£250	£275

1916. Nos. 126/7 optd **WAR STAMP.**

138.	½d. green	30	1·50
139a.	1d. red	60	75

1935. Silver Jubilee. As T **13** of Antigua.
242. 1½d. blue and red .. 45 2·50
243. 2d. blue and grey .. 1·00 35
244. 3d. brown and blue .. 2·50 2·50
245. 1s. grey and purple .. 4·50 3·50

1937. Coronation. As T **2** of Aden.
246. 1d. violet 70 45
247. 2d. grey 80 45
248. 3d. blue 80 45

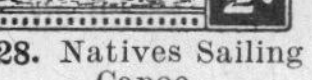

28. Natives Sailing Canoe. **29.** Native Village.

32. Government Offices.

1938.
249. **28.** ½d. green 10 20
250. **29.** 1d. brown and blue .. 15 10
252. – 1½d. red 50 90
254. – 2d. brown and green .. 16·00 16·00
255. **32.** 2d. green and mauve .. 40 30
256a – 2½d. brown and green .. 40 30
257 – 3d. blue 60 15
258 – 5d. blue and red .. 42·00 9·00
259 – 5d. green and red .. 15 15
261b – 6d. black .. .. 1·25 40
261c – 8d. red 40 25
262 – 1s. black and yellow .. 35 20
263 – 1s. 5d. black and red .. 15 10
263a. – 1s. 6d. blue .. .. 3·00 1·00
264 – 2s. violet and orange .. 1·25 30
265 – 2s. 6d. green and brown 1·25 70
266 – 5s. green and purple .. 2·00 70
266a – 10s. orange and green .. 30·00 40·00
266b – £1 blue and red .. 45·00 48·00
DESIGNS—HORIZ. As Type **32**: 1½d. Canakan (canoe). 2d. (No. 254), 2½d., 6d. Map of Fiji Is. HORIZ. As Type **29**: 3d. Canoe and Arms. 8d., 1s. 5d., 1s. 6d. Arms. 2 s. Suva Harbour. 2s. 6d. River scene. 5s. Chief's hut. VERT. As Type **29**: 5d. (Nos. 258/9) Sugar cane. 1s. Spearing fish. 10s. Paw-Paw tree. £1, Police bugler.

1941. No. 254 surch.
267. – 2½d. on 2d. brn. & green 30 10

1946. Victory. As T **9** of Aden.
268. 2½d. green 10 15
269. 3d. blue 10 10

1948. Silver Wedding. As T **10/11** of Aden.
270. 2½d. green 40 30
271. 5s. blue .. .. .. 14·00 5·00

1949. U.P.U. As T **20/23** of Antigua.
272. 2d. purple 55 30
273. 3d. blue .. .. .. 90 1·00
274. 8d. red .. .. .. 90 1·00
275. 1s. 6d. blue .. .. .. 1·10 1·00

43. Children Bathing.

1951. Health stamps. Inscr. "HEALTH".
276. **43.** 1d.+1d. brown .. 10 30
277. – 2d.+1d. green .. 20 30
DESIGN—VERT. 2d. Rugby footballer.

1953. Coronation. As T **13** of Aden.
278. 2½d. black and green .. 50 30

1953. Royal Visit. As No. 261c but with portrait of Queen Elizabeth II and inscr "ROYAL VISIT 1953".
279 8d. red 15 10

46. Queen Elizabeth II (after Annigoni).

48. Loading Copra.

1954. Queen Elizabeth II. (I) inscr. "FIJI". (II) inscr. "Fiji".
280 **28.** ½d. green 15 30
298 **46.** ½d. green 15 30
281 1d. turquoise (I) .. 40 10
299 1d. blue (II) .. .. 1·00 60
282 1½d. sepia (I) 40 10
300 1½d. sepia (II) .. .. 1·00 30
283 **32.** 2d. green and mauve .. 1·00 30
312 **46.** 2d. red (I) 45 15
284 2½d. violet (I) 70 10
302 2½d. orange brown (I) .. 1·25 2·00
285 **48.** 3d. brown and purple .. 1·00 15
287 – 6d. black (As No. 261) 75 30
303 A. 6d. red and black .. 1·00 10
288 – 8d. red (As No. 261d) 1·00 75
316 B. 10d. brown and red .. 60 40
289 – 1s. black & yell. (As 262) 70 10
306 C. 1s. blue .. .. 1·50 10
290 D. 1s. 6d. blue and green 15·00 90
291 E. 2s. black and red .. 5·50 20
292a – 2s. 6d. grn. & brn. (As 265) 50 10
320 F. 2s. 6d. black and purple 75 25
293 G. 5s. ochre and blue .. 22·00 1·00
294 – 10s. orange and green (As 266a) .. 11·00 20·00
309 H. 10s. green and sepia .. 8·00 3·50
295 – £1 blue and red (As 266b) .. 42·00 18·00
325 I. £1 black and orange .. 16·00 11·00
DESIGNS—HORIZ. As Type **48**: A, Fijian beating lali. B, Yaqona ceremony. C, Location map. D, Sugar cane train. E, Preparing bananas for export. F, Nadi Airport. G, Gold industry. H, Cutting sugar-cane. I, Arms of Fiji.

52. River Scene.

1954. Health stamps.
296. **52.** 1½d.+½d. brown & grn. 10 20
297. – 2½d.+½d. orge. & black 10 10
DESIGN: 2½d. Queen's portrait and Cross of Lorraine inscr. "FIJI WAR MEMORIAL" and "ANTI-TUBERCULOSIS CAMPAIGN".

56. Hibiscus.

DESIGNS — HORIZ. 1s. 6d. International date line. 4s. Kandavu parrot. 5s. Orange dove. VERT. 2s. White orchid. SMALLER (23×28 mm.): 3d. Queen Elizabeth II.

1959.
313 – 3d. multicoloured .. 25 10
304 **56** 8d. multicoloured .. 50 25
315 – 9d. multicoloured .. 90 65
318 – 1s. 6d. multicoloured .. 3·50 90
319 – 2s. yell., grn. & copper 14·00 1·75
308 – 4s. multicoloured .. 1·55 1·75
323 – 5s. red, yellow and grey 13·00 35

1963. Royal Visit. Optd. **ROYAL VISIT 1963.**
326. – 3d. mult. (No. 313) .. 10 10
327. C. 1s. blue (No. 317) .. 10 10

1963. Freedom from Hunger. As T **28** of Aden.
328. – 2s. blue .. .. .. 4·75 70

69. Running.

1963. 1st South Pacific Games, Suva, Inscr. as in T **69**.
329. **19.** 3d. brn., yellow & black 25 10
330. – 9d. brown, violet & black 35 30
331. – 1s. brown, green & black 35 10
332. – 2s. 6d. brown, blue & blk. 90 40
DESIGNS—VERT. 9d. Throwing the discus. 1s. Hockey. HORIZ. 2s. 6d. High-jumping.

1963. Cent of Red Cross. As T **33** of Antigua.
333. 2d. red and black 50 10
334. 2s. red and blue .. .. 2·50 90

1963. Opening of COMPAC (Trans-Pacific Telephone Cable). No. 317 optd. **COMPAC CABLE IN SERVICE DECEMBER 1963** and ship.
335. C. 1s. blue 25 10

74. Jamborette Emblem. **76.** Flying-boat "Aotearoa".

1964. 50th Anniv. of Fijian Scout Movement.
336. **74.** 3d. multicoloured 10 15
337. – 1s. violet and brown .. 10 15
DESIGN: 1s. Scouts of three races.

1964. 25th Anniv. of 1st Fiji–Tonga Airmail Service.
338. **76.** 3d. black and red .. 20 10
339. – 6d. red and blue .. 30 20
340. – 1s. black and turquoise 35 20
DESIGNS—VERT. 6d. Fiji Airways "Heron". HORIZ. (37½×25 mm.): 1s. "Aotearoa" and map.

1965. Cent of I.T.U. As T **36** of Antigua.
341. 3d. blue and red .. 50 10
342. 2s. yellow and bistre .. 1·25 25

1965. I.C.Y. As T **37** of Antigua.
343. 2d. purple and turquoise .. 30 10
344. 2s. 6d. green and lavender 70 25

1966. Churchill Commem. As T **38** of Antigua.
345. 3d. blue 70 10
346. 9d. green 90 40
347. 1s. brown 90 10
348. 2s. 6d. violet .. .. 1·00 50

1966. World Cup Football Championship. As T **40** of Antigua.
349. 2d. multicoloured .. 20 10
350. 2s. multicoloured .. 50 20

79. H.M.S. "Pandora" approaching Split Island, Rotuma.

1966. 175th Anniv. of Discovery of Rotuma. Multicoloured.
351. 3d. Type **79** 15 10
352. 10d. Rotuma Chiefs .. 15 10
353. 1s. 6d. Rotumans welcoming H.M.S. "Pandora" .. 25 15

1966. Inauguration of W.H.O. Headquarters, Geneva. As T **41** of Antigua.
354. 6d. black, green and blue 1·00 20
355. 2s. 6d. black, pur. & ochre 2·50 55

82. Running.

1966. 2nd South Pacific Games.
356. **82.** 3d. black, brown & green 10 10
357. – 9d. black, brown & blue 15 15
358. – 1s. multicoloured 15 15
DESIGNS: VERT. 9d. Putting the shot. HORIZ. 1s. Diving.

85. Military Forces Band.

1967. Int. Tourist Year. Multicoloured.
360. 3d. Type **85** 10 10
361. 9d. Reef diving 10 10
362. 1s. Beqa Fire Walkers .. 10 10
363. 2s. "Oriana" (cruise liner) at Suva 40 15

89. Bligh (bust), H.M.S. "Providence" and Chart.

1967. 150th Death Anniv. of Admiral Bligh.
364. **89.** 4d. multicoloured .. 10 10
365. – 1s. multicoloured .. 10 10
366. – 2s. 6d. multicoloured .. 15 15
DESIGNS—(As Type **89**): 2s. 6d. Bligh's Tomb. (54×20 mm.) 1s. "Bounty's longboat being chased in Fiji waters".

92. Simmonds "Spartan" Seaplane.

1968. 40th Anniv. of Kingsford Smith's Pacific Flight via Fiji.
367. **92.** 2d. black and green .. 10 10
368. – 6d. blue, black and lake 10 10
369. – 1s. violet and green .. 15 10
370. – 2s. brown and blue .. 20 15
DESIGNS: 6d. HS "748" and airline insignias. 1s. "Southern Cross" and Crew. 2s. Lockheed "Altair" Monoplane.

96. Bure Huts.

1968.
371. ½d. multicoloured 10 10
372. 1d. blue, red & yellow .. 10 10
373. 2d. blue, brown & ochre .. 10 10
374. 3d. green, blue & ochre .. 35 10
375. 4d. multicoloured 80 15
376. 6d. multicoloured 25 10
377. 9d. multicoloured 15 15
378. 10d. blue, orange & brown 1·25 20
379. 1s. blue and red 20 10
380. 1s. 6d. multicoloured .. 4·25 3·50
381. 2s. turq., black & red .. 1·00 2·00
382. 2s. 6d. multicoloured .. 1·00 75
383. 3s. multicoloured .. .. 4·50 5·50
384. 4s. ochre, black and olive 5·00 2·75
385. 5s. multicoloured .. .. 4·00 2·50
386. 10s. brown, black & ochre 3·50 3·50
387. £1 multicoloured .. .. 3·50 7·50
DESIGNS—HORIZ. (As T **96**) ½d. Type **96**. 1d. Passion flowers. 2d. Pearly nautilus. 4d. "Psilogramma jordana" (moth). 6d. Angel fish 9d. Bamboo raft. 10d. "Asota woodfordi" (moth). 3s. Golden cworie shell (33×22 mm). 2s. Sea snake. 2s. 6d. Outrigger canoes. 5s. Bamboo orchids. £1, Queen Elizabeth and Arms of Fiji. VERT. (23×33 mm). 3d. Eastern reef heron. 1s. Black marlin. 1s. 6d. Orangebreasted honey-eaters. 4s. Mining industry. 10s. Ceremonial whale's tooth.

WHEN YOU BUY AN ALBUM LOOK FOR THE NAME "STANLEY GIBBONS"
It means Quality combined with Value for Money.

113. Map of Fiji, W.H.O. Emblem and Nurses.

1968. 20th Anniv. of W.H.O. Multicoloured.

388. 3d. Type **113**. 10 10
389. 9d. Transferring Patient to Medical Ship "Vuniwai" 10 10
390. 3s. Recreation 20 20

116. Passion Flowers.

1969. Decimal Currency. Designs as T **96** etc., but with values inscr. in decimal currency as in T **116**.

391.**116.** 1 c. bl., red & yell. .. 10 10
392. – 2 c. bl., brn. & ochre (As 373) 10 10
393. – 3 c. green, blue & ochre (As 374) 30 10
394. – 4 c. multicoloured (As 375) .. .. .. 1·25 10
395. – 5 c. multicoloured (As 376) 20 10
396. **96.** 6 c. multicoloured .. 10 10
397. – 8 c. multicoloured (As 377) 10 10
398. – 9 c. blue, orange and brown (As 378) .. 1·25 70
399. – 10 c. blue & red (As 379) 20 10
400. – 15 c. mult. (As 380) .. 6·50 3·00
401. – 20 c. turq., blk. & red (As 381) 75 80
402. – 25 c. mult. (As 382) .. 75 30
403. – 30 c. mult. (As 383) .. 6·50 2·25
404. – 40 c. ochre, blk. & olive (As 384) .. .. 5·00 3·25
405. – 50 c. mult. (As 385) .. 4·50 30
406. – $1 brn., blk. & ochre (As 386) .. .. 4·00 60
407. – $2 mult. (As 387) .. 4·00 5·00

117. Fijian Soldiers overlooking the Solomon Islands.

1969. 25th Anniv. of Fijian Military Forces' Solomons Campaign.

408.**117.** 3 c. multicoloured .. 15 10
409. – 10 c. multicoloured .. 20 10
410. – 25 c. multicoloured .. 30 20

DESIGNS: 10 c. Regimental flags and soldiers in full dress and battledress. 25 c. Sofanaia Sukanaivala and Victoria Cross.

120. Javelin Throwing.

1969. 3rd South Pacific Games, Port Moresby.

411.**120.** 4 c. blk., brown & red .. 10 10
412. – 8 c. black, grey & blue 10 10
413. – 20 c. multicoloured .. 20 20

DESIGNS: 8 c. Yachting. 20 c. Games medal and winner's rostrum.

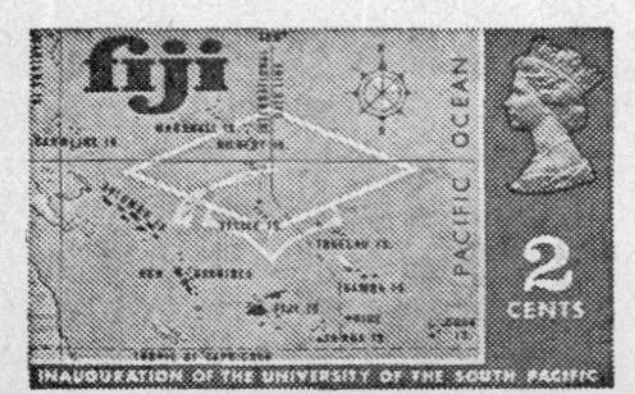

123. Map of South Pacific and "Mortar-board."

1969. Inauguration of University of the South Pacific. Multicoloured.

414. 2 c. Type **123** 10 15
415. 8 c. R.N.Z.A.F. Badge and "Sunderland" Flying-Boat over Laucala Bay (Site of University) .. 15 10
416. 25 c. Science Students at work 25 15

1970. Royal Visit. Nos. 392, 399 and 402 optd. **ROYAL VISIT 1970.**

417. 2 c. blue, brown and ochre 10 20
418. 10 c. blue and red .. 10 10
419. 25 c. multicoloured .. 20 10

127. Chaulmugra Tree, Makogai.

1970. Closing of Leprosy Hospital, Makogai.

420.**127.** 2 c. multicoloured .. 10 10
421. – 10 c. green and black .. 10 10
422. – 10 c. blue, blk. & mauve 10 10
423. – 30 c. multicoloured .. 20 40

DESIGNS: 10 c. (No. 421) "Cascade" (Semisi Maya). 10 c. (No. 422) "Sea urchins" (Semisi Maya). 30 c. Makogai Hospital. Nos. 421/2 are vert.

131. Abel Tasman and Log, 1643.

1970. Explorers and Discoverers.

424.**131.** 2 c. blk., brn. & turq. 40 25
425. – 3 c. multicoloured .. 1·00 25
426. – 8 c. multicoloured .. 1·00 15
427. – 25 c. multicoloured .. 1·00 15

DESIGNS: 3 c. Captain Cook and H.M.S. "Endeavour", 1774. 8 c. Captain Bligh and Longboat, 1789. 25 c. Fijian and Ocean-going Canoe.

135. King Cakobau and Cession Stone.

1970. Independence. Multicoloured.

428. 2 c. Type **135**. 10 10
429. 3 c. Children of the World 10 10
430. 10 c. Prime Minister and Fijian Flag 10 10
431. 25 c. Dancers in Costume 20 20

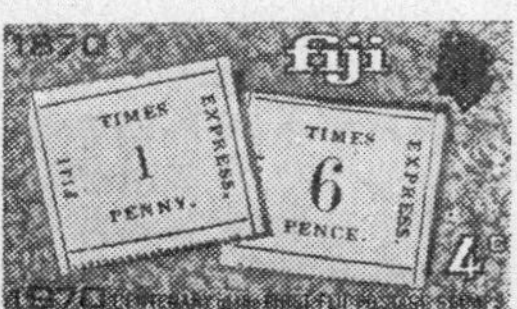

139. 1d. and 6d. Stamps of 1870.

1970. Stamp Cent. Multicoloured.

432. 4 c. Type **139** 10 10
433. 15 c. Fijian Stamps of all Reigns (61 × 21 mm.) .. 15 15
434. 20 c. "Fiji Times" Office and modern G.P.O. .. 15 15

140. Grey-backed White-eye. 142. Women's Basketball.

1971. Birds and Flowers. Multicoloured.

435 1 c. "Cirrhopetalum umbellatum" 15 20
436 2 c. Cardinal honeyeater .. 10 10
437 3 c. "Calanthe furcata" .. 35 20
438 4 c. "Bulbophyllum sp. nov." 35 20
439 5 c. Type **140** 35 10
510 6 c. "Phaius tancarvilliae" 1·25 10
441 8 c. Blue-headed flycatcher 35 10
442 10 c. "Acanthephippium vitiense" 40 10
513 15 c. "Dendrobium tokai" 1·50 60
444 20 c. Slaty flycatcher .. 90 30
445 25 c. Yellow-faced honey-eater .. .. 1·50 20
516 30 c. "Dendrobium gordonii" .. .. 5·50 95
517 40 c. Masked shining parrot .. .. 3·00 60
448 50 c. White-throated pigeon .. 3·25 50
449 $1 Collared lory .. 4·00 1·25
520 $2 "Dendrobium platygastrium" .. 5·50 3·50

The 25c. to $2 are larger ($22\frac{1}{2} \times 35\frac{1}{2}$ mm.).

1971. 4th South Pacific Games, Tahiti.

451.**142.** 8 c. multicoloured .. 10 10
452. – 10 c. blue, blk. and brn. 10 10
453. – 25 c. grn., blk. and brn. 30 25

DESIGNS: 10 c. Running. 25 c. Weightlifting.

143. Community Education.

1972. 25th Anniv. of South Pacific Commission. Multicoloured.

454. 2 c. Type **143** 10 10
455. 4 c. Public Health 10 10
456. 50 c. Economic Growth .. 35 65

144. "Native Canoe".

1972. South Pacific Festival of Arts, Suva.

457.**144.** 10 c. blk., orge. and bl. 10 10

145. Flowers, Conch and Ceremonial Whale's Tooth.

1972. Royal Silver Wedding. Multicoloured. Background colours given.

474.**145.** 10 c. green 20 10
475. 25 c. purple 30 10

1972. Hurricane Relief. Nos. 400 and 403 surch. **HURRICANE RELIEF +** and premium.

476. 15 c. + 5 c. multicoloured .. 15 15
477. 30 c. + 10 c. multicoloured 15 15

147. Line Out.

1973. Diamond Jubilee of Rugby Union. Multicoloured.

478. 2 c. Type **147** 15 10
479. 8 c. Body tackle 25 10
480. 25 c. Conversion 65 30

148. Forestry Development.

1973. Development Projects. Multicoloured.

481. 5 c. Type **148** 10 10
482. 8 c. Rice irrigation scheme 10 10
483. 10 c. Low income housing 10 10
484. 25 c. Highway construction 15 20

149. Christmas.

1973. Festivals of Joy. Multicoloured.

485. 3 c. Type **149** 10 10
486. 10 c. Diwali 10 10
487. 20 c. Id-ul-Fitar 15 10
488. 25 c. Chinese New Year .. 15 10

150. Athletics.

1974. Commonwealth Games, Christchurch, New Zealand. Multicoloured.

489. 3 c. Type **150** 15 10
490. 8 c. Boxing 15 10
491. 50 c. Bowling 50 65

151. Bowler.

1974. Centenary of Cricket. Multicoloured.

492. 3 c. Type **151** 50 25
493. 25 c. Batsman and wicket-keeper .. .. 1·75 35
494. 40 c. Fielder (horiz.) .. 2·50 90

152. Fiji Postman.

1974. Cent. of Universal Postal Union. Multicoloured.

495. 3 c. Type **152** 10 10
496. 8 c. Loading mail onto "Fijian Princess" .. 10 10
497. 30 c. Fijian post office and mailbus 20 20
498. 50 c. Modern aircraft .. 35 60

153. Cubs lighting Fire.

1974. 1st National Scout Jamboree, Lautoka. Multicoloured.

499.	3 c. Type **153**	15	10
500.	10 c. Scouts reading map	20	10
501.	40 c. Scouts and Fijian flag (vert.)	65	1·00

154. Cakobau Club and Flag.

1974. Cent. of Deed of Cession and 4th Anniv. of Independence. Multicoloured.

502.	3 c. Type **154**	10	10
503.	8 c. King Cakobau and Queen Victoria	10	10
504.	50 c. Raising the Royal Standard at Nasova Ovalau	30	55

155. " Diwali " (Hindu Festival).

1975. " Festivals of Joy ". Multicoloured.

521.	3 c. Type **155**	10	10
522.	15 c. " Id-Ul-Fitar " (Muslim Festival)	10	10
523.	25 c. Chinese New Year	15	15
524.	30 c. Christmas	20	30

156. Steam Locomotive No. 21.

1976. Sugar Trains. Multicoloured.

526	4 c. Type **156**	25	10
527	15 c. Diesel loco No. 8	70	30
528	20 c. Diesel loco No. 1	80	40
529	30 c. Free passenger train	95	70

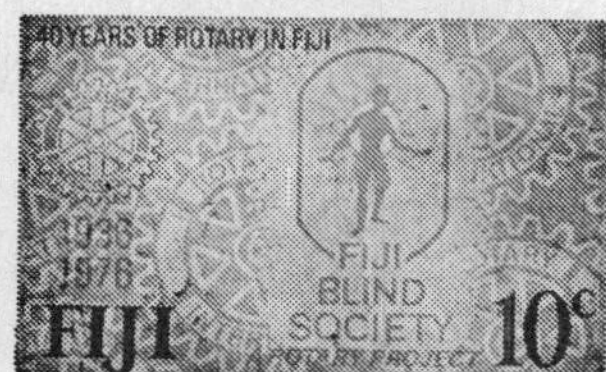

157. Fiji Blind Society and Rotary Symbols.

1976. 40th Anniv. of Rotary in Fiji.

530. **157.**	10 c. blue, grn. & blk.	15	10
531. –	25 c. multicoloured	40	50

DESIGN: 25 c. Ambulance and Rotary Symbol.

158. D.H. " Drover ".
(Illustration reduced, Actual size 57 × 21 mm).

1976. 25th Anniv. of Air Services. Mult.

532.	4 c. Type **158**	40	20
533.	15 c. B.A.C. " 1–11 "	1·00	1·00
534.	25 c. H.S. " 748 "	2·00	1·25
535.	30 c. Britten-Norman " Trislander "	2·25	2·75

159. The Queen's Visit to Fiji, 1970.

1977. Silver Jubilee. Multicoloured.

536.	10 c. Type **159**	10	10
537.	25 c. King Edward's Chair	15	10
538.	30 c. The Queen wearing cloth of gold supertunica	25	15

160. Map of the World.

1977. E.E.C./A.C.P.* Council of Ministers Conference. Multicoloured.

539.	4 c. Type **160**	10	10
540.	30 c. Map of Fiji group	30	65

* A.C.P. = African, Caribbean, Pacific Group.

161. " Hibiscus rosa-sinensis ".

1977. 21st Anniversary of Fiji Hibiscus Festival.

541. **161**	4 c. multicoloured	10	10
542. –	15 c. multicoloured	15	10
543. –	30 c. multicoloured	25	15
544. –	35 c. multicoloured	40	35

Nos. 542/44 show different varieties of " Hibiscus rosa-sinensis ".

162. Drua.

1977. Canoes. Multicoloured.

545.	4 c. Type **162**	10	5
546.	15 c. Tabilai	20	20
547.	25 c. Takai	25	25
548.	40 c. Camakua	35	70

163. White Hart of Richard II.

1978. 25th Anniv. of Coronation. Mult.

549. **163.**	25 c. brn., green & silver	20	25
550. –	25 c. multicoloured	20	25
551. –	25 c. brn., green & silver	20	25

DESIGNS: No. 550, Queen Elizabeth II. No. 551, Banded iguana.

164. Defence Force surrounding Plane, Suva.

1978. Aviation Annivs. Multicoloured.

552.	4 c. Type **164**	15	10
553.	15 c. " Southern Cross " prior to leaving Naselai Beach	25	30
554.	25 c. Wright " Flyer "	50	55
555.	30 c. Bristol " F2B "	50	70

The 25 c. value commemorates the 75th Anniv. of Powered Flight, the 30 c. the 60th Anniv. of R.A.F. and the other values the 50th Anniv. of First Trans-Pacific Flight by Kingsford-Smith.

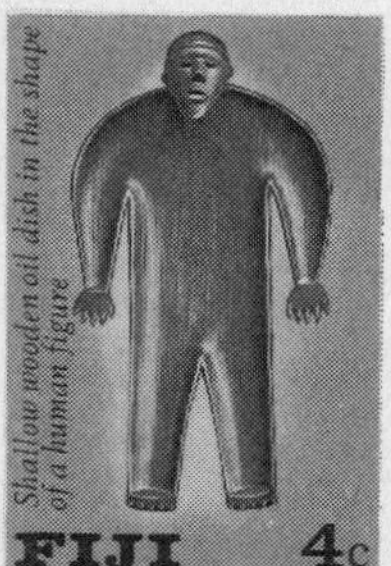

165. Shallow Wooden Oil Dish in Shape of Human Figure.

1978. Fijian Artifacts. Multicoloured.

556.	4 c. Type **165**	10	10
557.	15 c. Necklace of cachalot teeth (horiz.)	10	10
558.	25 c. Double water bottle (horiz.)	15	10
559.	30 c. Finely carved Ula or throwing club	15	15

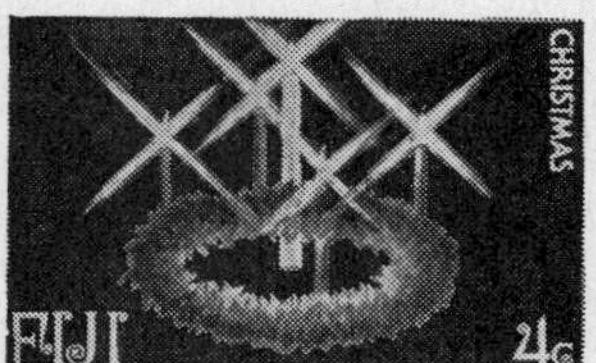

166. Advent Crown with Candles (Christmas).

1978. Festivals. Multicoloured.

560.	4 c. Type **166**	10	10
561.	15 c. Lamps (Diwali)	10	10
562.	25 c. Coffee pot, cups and fruit (Id-Ul-Fitar)	10	10
563.	40 c. Lion (Chinese New Year)	25	40

167. Banded Iguana.

1979. Endangered Wildlife. Multicoloured.

564.	4 c. Type **167**	10	10
565.	15 c. Tree Frog	30	10
566.	25 c. Long-legged Warbler	50	20
567.	30 c. Pink-billed Parrot Finch	65	55

168. Women with Dholak.

1979. Centenary of Arrival of Indians. Multicoloured.

568.	4 c. Type **168**	10	10
569.	15 c. Men sitting round tanoa	10	10
570.	30 c. Farmer and sugar cane plantation	15	10
571.	40 c. Sailing ship " Leonidas "	40	25

169. Soccer.

1979. 6th South Pacific Games. Multicoloured.

572.	4 c. Type **169**	10	10
573.	15 c. Rugby Union	25	10
574.	30 c. Lawn tennis	55	35
575.	40 c. Weightlifting	60	45

170. Indian Child and Map of Fiji.

1979. International Year of the Child. Multicoloured.

576.	4 c. + 1 c. Type **170**	10	10
577.	15 c. + 2 c. European child	15	15
578.	30 c. + 3 c. Chinese child	15	15
579.	40 c. + 4 c. Fijian child	15	20

171. Old Town Hall, Suva.

1979. Architecture. Multicoloured.

719	1 c. Type **171**	10	10
720	2 c. Dudley Church, Suva	10	10
721	3 c. Fiji International Telecommunications Building, Suva	10	10
722	4 c. Lautoka Mosque	10	10
583	5 c. As 4 c.	10	10
584	6 c. General Post Office, Suva	10	10
724	8 c. Public School, Levuka	10	10
725	10 c. Fiji Visitors Bureau, Suva	10	10
586	12 c. Public School, Bureau, Levuka	10	10
587a	15 c. Colonial War Memorial Hospital, Suva	10	15
588	18 c. Labasa sugar mill	15	20
730	20 c. Rewa Bridge, Nausori	15	20
590a	30 c. Sacred Heart Cathedral, Suva (vert.)	25	30
591	35 c. Grand Pacific Hotel, Suva	30	35
592	45 c. Shiva Temple, Suva	35	40
593	50 c. Serua Island Village	40	40
735	$1 Solo Rock lighthouse (30 × 46 mm)	80	85
595	$2 Baker Memorial Hall, Nauson (46 × 30 mm.)	1·60	1·75
595a	$5 Government House (46 × 30 mm.)	4·00	4·25

Nos. 580/95a come with or without date imprint.

172. " Southern Cross ", 1873.

1980. " London 1980 " International Stamp Exhibition. Multicoloured.

596.	6 c. Type **172**	15	10
597.	20 c. " Levuka ", 1910	15	10
598.	45 c. " Matua ", 1936	30	35
599.	50 c. " Oronsay ", 1951	30	40

173. Sovi Bay.

1980. Tourism. Multicoloured.

600.	6 c. Type **173**	10	10
601.	20 c. Evening scene, Yanuca Island	15	15
602.	45 c. Dravuni Beach ..	20	40
603.	50 c. Wakaya Island ..	20	45

174. Official Opening of Parliament 1979.

1980. 10th Anniv. of Independence. Multi.

604.	6 c. Type **174**	10	10
605.	20 c. Fiji coat of arms (vert.)	15	10
606.	45 c. Fiji flag	20	20
607.	50 c. Queen Elizabeth II (vert.)	25	35

175. " Coastal Scene " (painting, Semisi Maya).

1981. International Year for Disabled Persons. Multicoloured.

608.	6 c. Type **175**	10	10
609.	35 c. " Underwater Scene " (Semisi Maya)	45	30
610.	50 c. Semisi Maya (disabled artist) at work (vert.) ..	55	40
611.	60 c. " Peacock " (Semisi Maya) (vert.)	60	45

176. Prince Charles Sailing.

1981. Royal Wedding. Multicoloured.

612.	6 c. Wedding bouquet from Fiji	10	10
613.	45 c. Type **176**	45	15
614.	$1 Prince Charles and Lady Diana Spencer ..	75	60

177. Operator Assistance Centre.

1981. Telecommunications. Multicoloured.

615.	6 c. Type **177**	10	10
616.	35 c. Microwave station	55	50
617.	50 c. Satellite earth station	75	75
618.	60 c. Cable ship "Retriever"	90	90

178. " Eat Fiji Foods ".

1981. World Food Day.

619. **178.**	20 c. multicoloured ..	30	15

179. Ratu Sir Lala Sukuna (first Speaker, Legislative Council).

1981. Commonwealth Parliamentary Association Conference, Suva.

620. **179.**	6 c. black, buff and brown	10	10
621. –	35 c. multicoloured ..	30	30
622. –	50 c. multicoloured ..	45	45

DESIGNS: 35 c. Mace of the House of Representatives. 50 c. Suva Civic Centre.

180. Bell " P–39 (Airacobra) ".

1981. World War II Aircraft. Multicoloured.

624.	6 c. Type **180** ..	35	10
625.	18 c. Consolidated " PBY-5 " (Catalina)	70	25
626.	35 c. Curtiss " P-40 (Warhawk) "	80	40
627.	60 c. Short " Singapore "	1·10	85

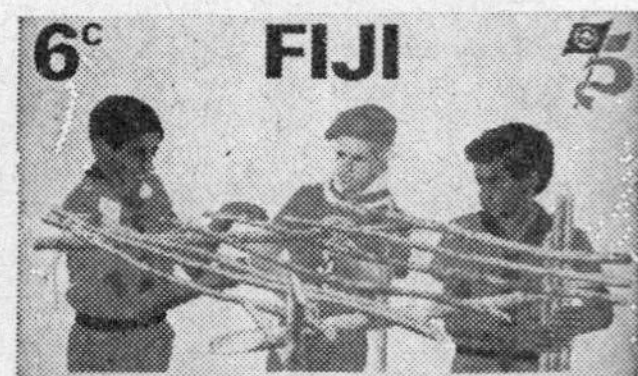

181. Scouts constructing Shelter.

1982. 75th Anniv. of Boy Scout Movement. Multicoloured.

628.	6 c. Type **181**	15	10
629.	20 c. Scouts sailing (vert.)	50	30
630.	45 c. Scouts by campfire ..	85	50
631.	60 c. Lord Baden-Powell (vert.)	1·00	1·00

182. Fiji Soldiers at U.N. Checkpoint.

1982. Disciplined Forces. Multicoloured.

632.	12 c. Type **182** ..	25	10
633.	30 c. Soldiers engaged on rural development ..	50	45
634.	40 c. Police patrol	70	60
635.	70 c. "Kiro" (minesweeper)	1·00	1·10

183. Footballers and Fiji Football Association Logo.

1982. World Cup Football Championship, Spain.

636. **183.**	6 c. red, black and yel.	10	10
637. –	18 c. multicoloured ..	25	20
638. –	50 c. multicoloured ..	70	60
639. –	90 c. multicoloured ..	1·10	1·25

DESIGNS: 18 c. Footballers and World Cup emblem. 50 c. Football and Bernabeu Stadium. 90 c. Footballers and Naranjito (mascot.)

184. Bride and Groom leaving St. Paul's.

1982. 21st Birthday of Princess of Wales. Multicoloured.

640.	20 c. Fiji coat of arms ..	25	25
641.	35 c. Lady Diana Spencer at Broadlands, May 1981	35	35
642.	45 c. Type **184**	50	50
643.	$1 Formal portrait ..	1·25	1·25

185. Prince Philip.

1982. Royal Visit. Multicoloured.

644.	6 c. Type **185**	10	10
645.	45 c. Queen Elizabeth II ..	65	1·40

186. Baby Jesus with Mary and Joseph.

1982. Christmas. Multicoloured.

647.	6 c. Type **186**	10	10
648.	20 c. Three Wise Men presenting gifts ..	30	20
649.	35 c. Carol-singing ..	45	35

187. Red-throated Lorikeet.

1983. Parrots. Multicoloured.

651.	20 c. Type **187**	90	15
652.	40 c. Blue-crowned Lory ..	1·25	40
653.	55 c. Masked Shining Parrot	1·40	70
654.	70 c. Red Shining Parrot ..	1·50	1·25

188. Bure in Traditional Village.

1983. Commonwealth Day. Multicoloured.

655.	8 c. Type **188**	10	10
656.	25 c. Barefoot firewalkers	20	15
657.	50 c. Sugar industry ..	30	35
658.	80 c. Kava " Yagona " ceremony	55	70

189. First Manned Balloon Flight, 1783.

1983. Bicentenary of Manned Flight. Mult.

659.	8 c. Type **189**	10	10
660.	20 c. Wright brothers' " Flyer "	25	30
661.	25 c. Douglas " Super DC 3 "	35	40
662.	40 c. De Havilland " Comet "	55	60
663.	50 c. Boeing " 747 " ..	65	70
664.	58 c. Space Shuttle ..	75	80

190. Nawanawa.

1983. Flowers (1st series). Multicoloured.

665.	8 c. Type **190**	10	10
666.	25 c. Rosawa	35	30
667.	40 c. Warerega	55	50
668.	$1 Saburo	1·25	1·40

See also Nos. 680/3.

191. Fijian beating Lali and Earth Satellite Station.

1983. World Communications Year.

669. **191.**	50 c. multicoloured ..	50	70

192. " Dacryopinax spathularia ".

1984. Fungi. Multicoloured.

670.	8 c. Type **192**	40	10
671.	15 c. " Podoscypha involula "	60	25
672.	40 c. " Lentinus squarrosulus "	1·00	70
673.	50 c. " Scleroderma flavidum " (horiz.) ..	1·25	80
674.	$1 " Phillipsia domingensis " (horiz.)	1·60	1·75

193. "Tui Lau" on Reef.

1984. 250th Anniv. of "Lloyd's List" (newspaper). Multicoloured.

675.	8 c. Type **193**	30	10
676.	40 c. S.S. "Tofua" ..	85	65
677.	55 c. S.S. "Canberra" ..	1·00	85
678.	60 c. Suva wharf	1·10	95

1984. Flowers (2nd series). As T **190**. Mult.

680.	15 c. Drividrivi	25	25
681.	20 c. Vesida	35	35
682.	50 c. Vuga	80	80
683.	70 c. Qaiqi	1·10	1·10

INDEX

Countries can be quickly located by referring to the index at the end of this volume.

195. Prize Bull, Yalavou Cattle Scheme.

1984. "Ausipex" International Stamp Exhibition, Melbourne. Multicoloured.

No.	Description	Unused	Used
684.	8 c. Type **195**	15	10
685.	25 c. Wailoa Power Station	40	40
686.	40 c. Air Pacific Boeing "737" airliner	65	65
687.	$1 Container ship "Fua Kavenga"	1·60	1·60

196. The Stable at Bethlehem.

1984. Christmas. Children's Paintings. Multicoloured.

No.	Description	Unused	Used
688.	8 c. Type **196**	10	10
689.	20 c. Outrigger canoe ..	30	20
690.	25 c. Father Christmas and Christmas tree ..	35	25
691.	40 c. Going to church ..	60	60
692.	$1 Decorating Christmas tree (vert.)	1·50	1·60

197. "Danaus plexippus".

1985. Butterflies. Multicoloured.

No.	Description	Unused	Used
693	8 c. Type **197**	60	10
694	25 c. "Hypolimnas bolina"	1·10	50
695	40 c. "Lampides boeticus" (vert)	1·50	80
696	$1 "Precis villida" (vert)	2·00	2·75

198. Outrigger Canoe off Toberua Island.

1985. "Expo '85" World Fair, Japan. Mult.

No.	Description	Unused	Used
697.	20 c. Type **198**	50	30
698.	25 c. Wainivula Falls ..	85	40
699.	50 c. Mana Island	95	70
700.	$1 Sawa-I-Lau Caves ..	1·25	1·40

199. With Prince Charles at Garter Ceremony.

1985. Life and Times of Queen Elizabeth the Queen Mother. Multicoloured.

No.	Description	Unused	Used
701.	8 c. With Prince Andrew on her 60th Birthday ..	10	10
702.	25 c. Type **199**	35	40
703.	40 c. The Queen Mother at Epsom Races	50	65
704.	50 c. With Prince Henry at his christening (from photo by Lord Snowdon)	65	90

200. Horned Squirrel Fish.

1985. Shallow Water Marine Fishes. Multicoloured.

No.	Description	Unused	Used
706.	40 c. Type **200**	85	55
707.	50 c. Yellow-banded Goatfish	1·00	70
708.	55 c. Fairy Cod	1·00	75
709.	$1 Peacock Rock Cod ..	1·75	2·25

201. Collared Petrel.

1985. Seabirds. Multicoloured.

No.	Description	Unused	Used
710.	15 c. Type **201**	75	30
711.	20 c. Lesser Frigate Bird ..	85	35
712.	50 c. Brown Booby ..	1·60	1·60
713.	$1 Crested Tern	2·75	3·25

1986. 60th Birthday of Queen Elizabeth II. As T **110** of Ascension. Multicoloured.

No.	Description	Unused	Used
714.	20 c. With Duke of York at Royal Tournament, 1936	30	30
715.	25 c. Royal Family on Palace balcony after Princess Margaret's wedding, 1960 ..	35	35
716.	40 c. Queen inspecting guard of honour, Suva, 1982	55	55
717.	50 c. In Luxembourg, 1976	65	85
718.	$1 At Crown Agents Head Office, London, 1983 ..	1·10	1·60

202. Children and "Peace for Fiji and the World" Slogan

1986. International Peace Year. Mult.

No.	Description	Unused	Used
736.	8 c. Type **202**	15	10
737.	40 c. Peace dove and houses	60	75

203. Halley's Comet in Centaurus Constellation and Newton's Reflector.

1986. Appearance of Halley's Comet. Multicoloured.

No.	Description	Unused	Used
738.	25 c. Type **203**	75	40
739.	40 c. Halley's Comet over Lomaiviti	95	65
740.	$1 "Giotto" spacecraft photographing comet nucleus	1·75	2·50

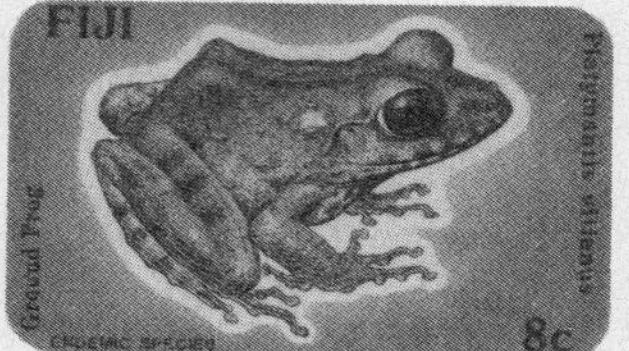

204. Ground Frog.

1986. Reptiles and Amphibians. Mult.

No.	Description	Unused	Used
741.	8 c. Type **204**	45	10
742.	20 c. Burrowing snake ..	70	30
743.	25 c. Spotted gecko ..	80	35
744.	40 c. Crested iguana ..	1·00	80
745.	50 c. Blotched skink ..	1·25	1·50
746.	$1 Speckled skink	1·75	2·50

205. Gatawaka. **206.** Weasel Cone.

1986. Ancient War Clubs. Multicoloured.

No.	Description	Unused	Used
747.	25 c. Type **205**	70	35
748.	40 c. Siriti	90	60
749.	50 c. Bulibuli	1·10	1·25
750.	$1 Culacula	1·90	2·50

1987. Cone Shells of Fiji. Multicoloured.

No.	Description	Unused	Used
751.	15 c. Type **206**	70	25
752.	20 c. Pertusus cone ..	80	30
753.	25 c. Admiral cone ..	85	35
754.	40 c. Leaden cone	1·25	70
755.	50 c. Imperial cone ..	1·40	1·25
756.	$1 Geography cone ..	1·90	2·25

209. Traditional Fijian House.

1987. International Year of Shelter for the Homeless. Multicoloured.

No.	Description	Unused	Used
759.	55 c. Type **209**	45	50
760.	70 c. Modern bungalows ..	55	60

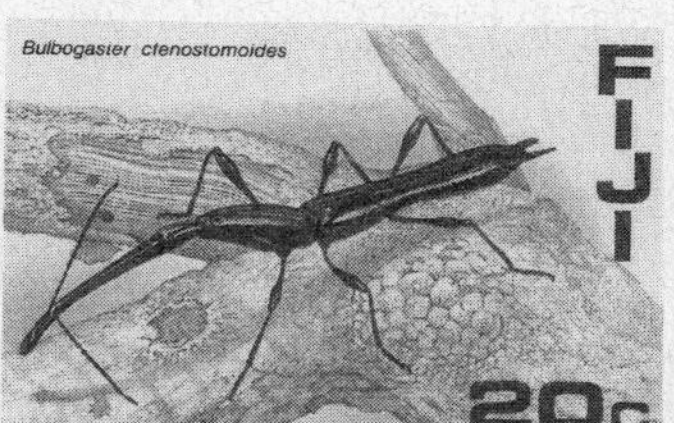

210. "Bulbogaster ctenostomoides" (stick-inscet).

1987. Fijian Insects. Multicoloured.

No.	Description	Unused	Used
761	20 c. Type **210**	35	30
762	25 c. "Paracupta flaviventris" (beetle) ..	40	35
763	40 c. "Cerambyrhynchus schoenherri" (beetle) ..	55	45
764	50 c. "Rhinoscapha lagopyga" (weevil) ..	65	60
765	$1 "Xixuthrus heros" (beetle)	1·00	1·10

POSTAGE DUE STAMPS

D 1.

D 3.

1917.

No.	Type	Description	Unused	Used
D 5a	D 1.	½d. black	£550	£225
D 2		1d. black	£250	65·00
D 3		2d. black	£200	55·00
D 4		3d. black	£250	70·00
D 5		4d. black	£600	£325

1918.

No.	Type	Description	Unused	Used
D 6.	D 3.	½d. black	2·25	13·00
D 7.		1d. black	2·50	4·50
D 8.		2d. black	2·50	7·50
D 9.		3d. black	3·00	23·00
D 10.		4d. black	5·50	17·00

D 4.

1940.

No.	Type	Description	Unused	Used
D 11.	D 4.	1d. green	4·50	40·00
D 12.		2d. green	6·00	40·00
D 13.		3d. green	8·50	50·00
D 14.		4d. green	11·00	50·00
D 15.		5d. green	12·00	50·00
D 16.		6d. green	14·00	60·00
D 17.		1s. red	19·00	80·00
D 18.		1s. 6d. red	20·00	£120

Fiji left the Commonwealth in 1987. Subsequent issues are listed in volume 1.

GAMBIA

A Br. colony and protectorate on the W. coast of Africa. Granted full internal self-government on 4 October 1963, and achieved independence on 18 February 1965. Became a republic within the Commonwealth on 24 April 1970.

1869. 12 pence = 1 shilling;
20 shillings = 1 pound.
1971. 100 bututs = 1 dalasy.

1.

2.

1869. Imperf.

No.	Type	Description	Unused	Used
5	1	4d. brown	£350	£180
8		6d. blue	£300	£180

1880. Perf.

No.	Type	Description	Unused	Used
11	1.	½d. orange	3·75	8·50
12		1d. purple	2·50	4·50
13		2d. red	18·00	9·50
14b		3d. blue	42·00	25·00
30		4d. brown	2·25	2·00
17		6d. blue	70·00	45·00
19		1s. green	£180	£100

1886.

No.	Type	Description	Unused	Used
21	1	½d. green	70	80
23		1d. red	3·25	3·75
25		2d. orange	1·40	5·00
27		2½d. blue	1·75	1·50
29		3d. grey	2·00	9·00
34		6d. green	10·00	26·00
35		1s. violet	2·75	14·00

1898.

No.	Type	Description	Unused	Used
37.	2.	½d. green	1·75	1·75
38.		1d. red	1·25	75
39.		2d. orange and mauve ..	2·75	3·50
40.		2½d. blue	1·40	1·50
41.		3d. purple and blue ..	6·00	12·00
42.		4d. brown and blue ..	4·75	16·00
43.		6d. green and red ..	8·00	15·00
44.		1s. mauve and green ..	15·00	32·00

1902. As T **2**, but portrait of King Edward VII.

No.	Description	Unused	Used
57	½d. green	1·25	25
46	1d. red	1·00	55
47	2d. orange and mauve ..	3·25	20
74	2d. grey	1·40	4·00
60	2½d. blue	2·00	3·00
61	3d. purple and blue ..	4·50	2·00
75	3d. purple on yellow ..	2·75	1·50
50	4d. brown and blue ..	3·00	14·00
76	4d. black and red on yellow	80	65
63	5d. grey and black ..	8·00	12·00
77	5d. orange and purple ..	1·00	1·25
51	6d. green and red ..	3·25	9·50
78	6d. purple	1·50	1·25
65	7½d. green and red ..	5·00	18·00

79 7½d. brown and blue .. 1·25 2·50
80 10d. green and red .. 1·75 6·50
67 1s. mauve nad green .. 15·00 38·00
81 1s. black on green .. 1·50 7·50
53 1s. 6d. green & red on yell 5·50 15·00
82 1s. 6d. violet and green .. 7·00 24·00
54 2s. grey and orange .. 27·00 45·00
83 2s. purple and blue on blue 4·25 15·00
55 2s. 6d. purple & brn on yell 15·00 45·00
84 2s. 6d. black & red on blue 20·00 18·00
56 3s. red and green on yellow 16·00 45·00
85 3s. yellow and green .. 20·00 38·00

1906. Surch. in words.
69. ½d. on 2s. 6d. (No. 55) .. 40·00 60·00
70. 1d. on 3s. (No. 56) .. 55·00 35·00

1912. As T 2, but portrait of King George V.
86 ½d. green 45 70
87 1d. red 55 35
88 1½d. olive and green .. 30 30
89 2d. grey 45 75
112 2½d. blue .. .. .. 50 3·50
91 3d. purple on yellow .. 25 30
92c 4d. black & red on yellow 1·50 5·00
93 5d. orange and purple .. 50 1·25
94 6d. purple 50 90
95 7½d. brown and blue .. 80 3·75
96a 10d. green and red .. 1·50 13·00
97 1s. black on green .. 45 1·00
98 1s. 6d. violet and green .. 4·00 8·50
99 2s. purple & blue on blue 2·25 6·00
100 2s. 6d. black & red on blue 2·50 11·00
101 3s. yellow and green .. 7·00 16·00
117 4s. black and red .. 40·00 60·00
102 5s. green & red on yellow 40·00 60·00

9. 10.

1922.
122. 9. ½d. blk. and green .. 45 40
124. 1d. black and brown .. 60 10
125. 1½d. black and red .. 70 10
126. 2d. black and grey .. 70 80
127. 2½d. black and orange 80 5·50
128. 3d. black and blue .. 75 10
118. 4d. black & red on yell. 1·25 1·50
130. 5d. black and olive .. 2·00 10·00
131. 6d. black and red .. 90 15
119. 7½d. black & pur. on yell. 1·50 6·50
133. 10d. black and blue .. 4·00 16·00
134. 10. 1s. black & pur. on yell. 2·25 25
135. 1s. 6d. black and blue .. 7·00 12·00
136. 2s. black & pur. on blue 3·00 3·00
137. 2s. 6d. black and green 3·75 9·50
138. 3s. black and purple .. 10·00 32·00
140. 4s. black and brown .. 3·75 16·00
141. 5s. black & grn. on yell. 8·00 26·00
142. 10s. black and olive .. 55·00 75·00

1935. Silver Jubilee. As T 13 of Antigua.
143. 1½d. blue and red .. 50 30
144. 3d. brown and blue .. 55 70
145. 6d. blue and olive .. 90 90
146. 1s. grey and purple .. 1·75 90

1937. Coronation. As T 2 of Aden.
147. 1d. brown 20 10
148. 1½d. red 20 15
149. 3d. blue 55 35

11. Elephant (from Colony Badge).

1938.
150. 11. ½d. black and green .. 15 20
151. 1d. purple and brown 20 20
152a. 1½d. pink and red .. 30 40
152b. 1½d. blue and black .. 30 50
153. 2d. blue and black .. 80 1·40
153a. 2d. pink and red .. 30 40
154. 3d. blue 20 10
154a. 5d. green and purple .. 35 30
155. 6d. olive and red .. 30 20
156. 1s. blue and purple .. 65 10
156a. 1s. 3d. purple and blue 1·00 60
157. 2s. red and blue .. 3·25 2·75
158. 2s. 6d. brown and green 7·00 1·75
159. 4s. red and purple .. 12·00 2·00
160. 5s. blue and red .. 12·00 3·50
161. 10s. orange and black .. 12·00 6·00

1946. Victory. As T 9 of Aden.
162. 1½d. black 10 10
163. 3d. blue 10 10

1948. Silver Wedding. As T 10/11 of Aden.
164. 1½d. black 25 10
165. £1 mauve .. .. 12·00 11·00

1949. U.P.U. As T 20/23 of Antigua.
166. 1½d. black 20 30
167. 3d. blue 60 30
168. 6d. mauve 60 30
169. 1s. violet 65 20

1953. Coronation. As T 13 of Aden.
170. 1½d. black and blue .. 10 30

12. Tapping for Palm Wine.

1953. Queen Elizabeth II.
171. 12. ½d. red and green .. 30 20
172. – 1d. blue and brown .. 40 15
173. – 1½d. brown and black .. 20 30
174. – 2½d. black and red .. 45 60
175. – 3d. blue and lilac .. 35 10
176. – 4d. black and blue .. 60 1·25
177. 12. 6d. brown and purple .. 35 10
178. – 1s. brown and green .. 60 10
179. – 1s. 3d. ultram. and blue 6·00 20
180. – 2s. blue and red .. 2·75 2·25
181. – 2s. 6d. green and brown 3·00 1·00
182. – 4s. blue and brown .. 3·00 1·25
183. – 5s. brown and blue .. 2·00 1·50
184. – 10s. blue and green .. 8·00 6·50
185. – £1 green and black .. 8·50 9·00

DESIGNS—HORIZ. 1d., 1s. 3d. Cutter (sailing ship). 1½d., 5s. Wollof woman. 2½d., 2s. Barra canoe. 3d., 10s. S.S. "Lady Wright". 4d., 4s. James Island. 1s., 2s. 6d. Woman hoeing. £1 as Type 11.

20. Queen Elizabeth II and Palm.

1961. Royal Visit.
186. 20. 2d. green and purple .. 10 10
187. – 3d. turquoise and sepia 15 10
188. – 6d. blue and red .. 15 15
189. 20. 1s. 3d. violet and green 20 50

DESIGN: 3d., 6d. Queen Elizabeth II and West African map.

1963. Freedom from Hunger. As T 28 of Aden.
190. 1s. 3d. red 40 15

1963. Cent of Red Cross. As T 33 of Antigua.
191. 2d. red and black 15 10
192. 1s. 3d. red and blue .. 40 35

22. Beautiful Sunbird.

1963. Queen Elizabeth II. Multicoloured.
193. ½d. Type 22 .. .. 15 30
194. 1d. Yellow-mantled Whydah 20 20
195. 1½d. Cattle Egret 80 60
196. 2d. Senegal Parrot .. 80 40
197. 3d. Rose-ringed Parakeet .. 1·25 20
198. 4d. Violet Starling .. 60 50
199. 6d. Village Weaver .. 1·25 10
200. 1s. Rufous-crowned Roller 60 10
201. 1s. 3d. Red-eyed Dove .. 8·50 1·40
202. 2s. 6d. Double-spurred Francolin .. .. 7·00 2·25
203. 5s. Palm-nut Vulture .. 5·50 2·75
204. 10s. Orange-cheeked Waxbill .. .. 12·00 7·00
205. £1 African Emerald Cuckoo 22·00 14·00

1963. New Constitution. Nos. 194, 197 and 200/1 optd. SELF GOVERNMENT 1963.
206. 1d. multicoloured .. 10 15
207. 3d. multicoloured .. 15 10
208. 1s. multicoloured 15 10
209. 1s. 3d. multicoloured .. 20 25

1964. 400th Birth Anniv of Shakespeare. As T 34 of Antigua.
210. 6d. blue 10 10

36. Gambia Flag and River.

1965. Independence. Multicoloured.
211. ½d. Type 36 .. .. 10 10
212. 2d. Arms 10 10
213. 7½d. Type 36 .. .. 10 10
214. 1s. 6d. Arms 10 10

1965. Nos. 193/205 optd. **INDEPENDENCE 1965.** Multicoloured.
215 ½d. Type 22 .. .. 30 30
216 1d. Yellow-mantled whydah 30 10
217 1½d. Cattle egret 40 30
218 2d. Senegal parrot .. 40 15
219 3d. Rose-ringed parakeet 50 15
220 4d. Violet starling .. 50 30
221 6d. Village weaver .. 50 10
222 1s. Rufous-crowned roller 60 10
223 1s. 3d. Red-eyed dove .. 60 10
224 2s. 6d. Double-spurred francolin 60 15
225 5s. Palm-nut vulture .. 60 40
226 10s. Orange-cheeked waxbill .. .. .. 1·25 1·50
227 £1 African emerald cuckoo 3·25 6·00

39. I.T.U. Emblem and Symbols.

1965. Centenary of I.T.U.
228. 39. 1d silver and blue .. 15 10
229. 1s 6d. gold and violet 45 15

40. Sir Winston Churchill and Houses of Parliament.

1966. Churchill Commem.
230. 40. 1d. multicoloured .. 10 10
231. 6d. multicoloured .. 20 10
232. 1s. 6d. multicoloured .. 40 30

41. Red-cheeked Cordon-bleu.

1966. Birds. Multicoloured.
233. ½d. Type 41 .. .. 40 20
234. 1d. White-faced Whistling Duck 30 15
235 1½d. Red-throated Bee Eater 30 20
236. 2d. Lesser Pied Kingfisher 2·75 30
237. 3d. Golden Bishop 30 10
238. 4d. African Fish Eagle .. 50 30
239. 6d. Yellow-bellied Green Pigeon 40 10
240. 1s. Blue-bellied Roller .. 40 10
241. 1s. 6d. African Pigmy Kingfisher 85 30
242. 2s. 6d. Spur-winged Goose 95 70
243. 5s. Cardinal Woodpecker .. 1·00 75
244. 10s. Violet Turaco .. .. 1·25 2·75
245. £1 Pin-tailed Whydah (Size 25 × 39½ mm.) .. 1·25 5·50

54. Arms, Early Settlement and Modern Buildings.

1966. 150th Anniversary of Bathurst.
246. 54. 1d. silver, brown & orge. 10 10
247. 2d. silver, brown & blue 10 10
248. 6d. silver, brown & grn. 10 10
249. 1s. 6d. silver, brn. & pur. 15 15

55. I.T.Y. Emblem and Hotels.

1967. Int. Tourist Year.
250. 55. 2d. silver, brown & green 10 10
251. 1s. silver, brown & orge. 10 10
252. 1s. 6d. silver, brn. & mve. 15 15

56. Handcuffs.

1968. Human Rights Year. Multicoloured.
253. 1d. Type 56 .. .. 10 10
254. 1s. Fort Bullen 10 10
255. 5s. Methodist Church .. 30 30

59. Queen Victoria, Queen Elizabeth II and 4d. stamp of 1869.

1969. Gambia Stamp Centenary.
256. 59. 4d. sepia and ochre .. 15 10
257. 6d. blue and green .. 15 10
258. – 2s. 6d. multicoloured .. 35 55

DESIGN: 2s. 6d. Queen Elizabeth II with 4d. and 6d. stamps of 1869.

61. Catapult-Ship "Westfalen" launching Dornier "Wal".

1969. 35th Anniv. of Pioneer Air Service. Multicoloured.
259. 2d. Type 61 .. .. 30 15
260. 1s. Dornier "Wal" flying-boat 35 15
261. 1s. 6d. "Graf Zeppelin" airship 45 80

63. Athlete and Gambian Flag.

1970. 9th British Commonwealth Games, Edinburgh.
262. 63. 1d. multicoloured .. 10 10
263. 1s. multicoloured .. 10 10
264. 5s. multicoloured .. 30 30

64. President Sir Dawda Kairaba Jawara and State House.

1970. Republic Day. Multicoloured.
265. 2d. Type 64 .. .. 10 10
266. 1s. President Sir Dawda Jawara 15 10
267. 1s. 6d. President and flag of Gambia .. 20 15

The 1s. and 1s. 6d. are both vertical designs.

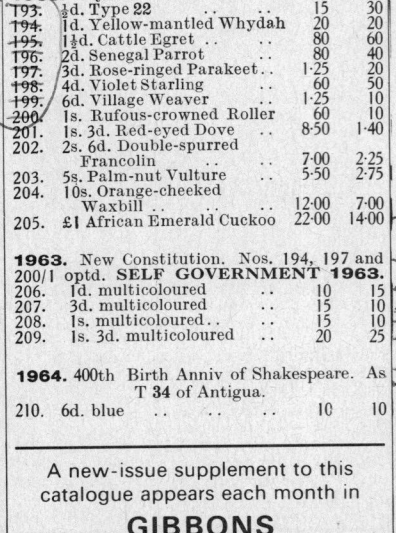

65. Methodist Church, Georgetown.

1971. 150th Anniversary of Establishment of Methodist Mission. Multicoloured.

268. 2d. Type **65** 10 10
269. 1s. Map of Africa and Gambian flag (vert.) 15 10
270. 1s. 6d. John Wesley and scroll 15 15

66. Yellowfin Tunny.

1971. New Currency. Fishes. Multicoloured.

271. 2 b. Type **66** 10 30
272. 4 b. Peters' Mormyrid 10 15
273. 6 b. Tropical Flying Fish 15 30
274. 8 b. African Sleeper Goby 15 30
275. 10 b. Yellowtail Snapper 20 15
276. 13 b. Rock Hind 20 30
277. 25 b. Gymnallabes 35 30
278. 38 b. Tiger Shark 55 45
279. 50 b. Electric Catfish 70 55
280. 63 b. Black Synbranchus 80 1·00
281. 1 d. 25 Smalltooth Sawfish 1·75 2·00
282. 2 d. 50 Barracuda 4·00 4·25
283. 5 d. Brown Bullhead 5·50 6·50

67. Mungo Park in Scotland.

1971. Birth Cent. of Mungo Park. Mult.

284. 4 b. Type **67** 10 10
285. 25 b. Dug-out canoe 20 10
286. 37 b. Death of Mungo Park, Busa Rapids 30 35

68. Radio Gambia.

1972. 10th Anniv. of Radio Gambia.

287. **68.** 4 b. brown and black 10 10
288. – 25 b. blue, orge. & blk. 10 20
289. **68.** 37 b. green and black 20 35

DESIGN: 25 b. Broadcast-area map.

69. High-jumping.

1972. Olympic Games, Munich.

290. **69.** 4 b. multicoloured 10 10
291. 25 b. multicoloured 15 15
292. 37 b. multicoloured 15 20

70. Manding Woman.

1972. Int. Conf. on Manding Studies. Mult.

293. 2 b. Type **70** 10 10
294. 25 b. Musician playing the Kora 15 15
295. 37 b. Map of Mali Empire 25 25

71. Children carrying Fanal.

1972. Fanals (Model Boats). Multicoloured.

296. 2 b. Type **71** 10 10
297. 1 d. 25 Fanal with lanterns 30 45

72. Groundnuts.

1973. Freedom from Hunger Campaign.

298. **72.** 2 b. multicoloured 10 10
299. 25 b. multicoloured 15 10
300. 37 b. multicoloured 25 20

73. Planting and Drying Rice.

1973. Agriculture (1st series). Multicoloured.

301. 2 b. Type **73** 10 10
302. 25 b. Guinea Corn 20 15
303. 37 b. Rice 25 25

74. Oil Palm.

1973. Agriculture (2nd series). Mult.

304. 2 b. Type **74** 10 10
305. 25 b. Limes 30 30
306. 37 b. Oil Palm (fruits) 40 40

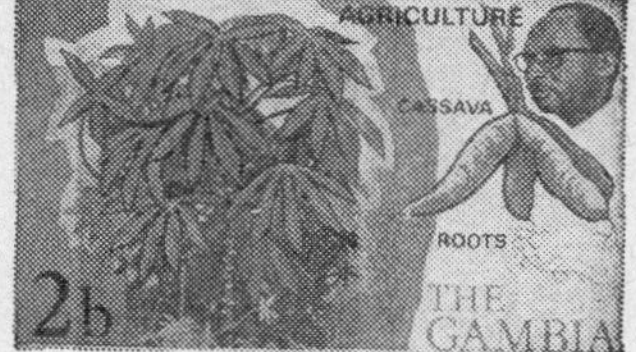

75. Cassava.

1973. Agriculture (3rd series). Multicoloured.

307. 2 b. Type **75** 10 10
308. 50 b. Cotton 40 25

76. O.A.U. Emblem.

1973. 10th Anniversary of O.A.U.

309. **76.** 4 b. multicoloured 10 10
310. 25 b. multicoloured 15 10
311. 37 b. multicoloured 15 15

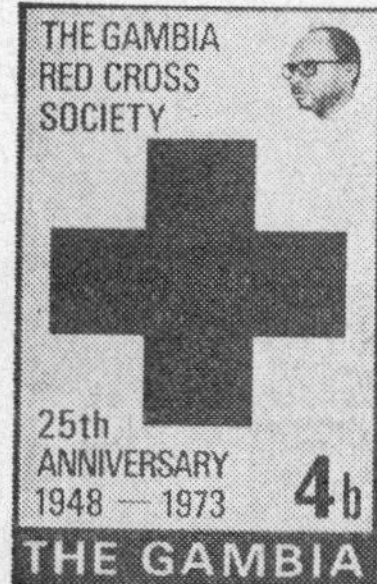

77. Red Cross.

1973. 25th Anniv. of Gambian Red Cross.

312. **77.** 4 b. red and black 10 10
313. 25 b. red black & blue 15 15
314. 37 b. red, black & green 20 20

78. Arms of Banjul.

1973. Change of Bathurst's Name to Banjul.

315. **78.** 4 b. multicoloured 10 10
316. 25 b. multicoloured 15 15
317. 37 b. multicoloured 15 20

79. U.P.U. Emblem.

1974. Centenary of U.P.U.

318. **79.** 4 b. multicoloured 10 10
319. 37 b. multicoloured 20 30

80. Churchill as Harrow Schoolboy.

1974. Birth Centenary of Sir Winston Churchill. Multicoloured.

320. 4 b. Type **80** 10 10
321. 37 b. Churchill as 4th Hussars officer 25 10
322. 50 b. Churchill as Prime Minister 40 35

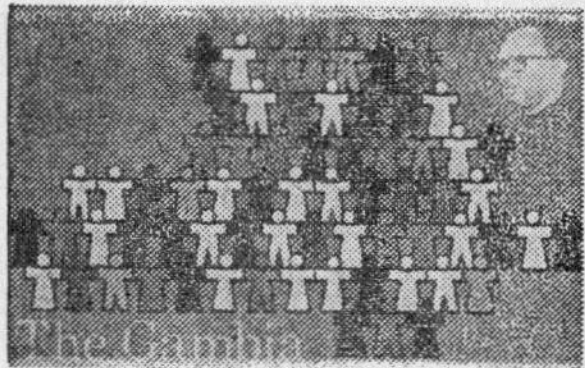

81. " Different Races ".

1974. World Population Year. Multicoloured.

323. 4 b. Type **81** 10 10
324. 37 b. " Multiplication and Division of Races " 15 15
325. 50 b. " World Population " 20 25

82. Dr. Schweitzer and River Scene.

1975. Birth Centenary of Dr. Albert Schweitzer. Multicoloured.

326. 10 b. Type **82** 15 10
327. 50 b. Surgery scene 35 25
328. 1 d. 25 River journey 75 55

83. Dove of Peace.

1975. 10th Anniv. of Independence. Mult.

329. 4 b. Type **83** 10 10
330. 10 b. Gambian flag 10 10
331. 50 b. Gambian arms 15 10
332. 1 d. 25 Map of The Gambia 35 40

84. Development Graph.

1975. 10th Anniversary of African Development Bank. Multicoloured.

333. 10 b. Type **84** 10 10
334. 50 b. Symbolic plant 20 15
335. 1 d. 25 Bank emblem and symbols 55 60

85. " Statue of David " (Michelangelo).

1975. 500th Birth Anniv. of Michelangelo. Multicoloured.

336. 10 b. Type **85** 10 10
337. 50 b. " Madonna of the Steps " 25 10
338. 1 d. 25 " Battle of the Centaurs " (horiz.) 50 60

86. School Building.

1975. Centenary of Gambia High School. Multicoloured.

- **339.** 10 b. Type **86** 10 10
- **340.** 50 b. Pupil with scientific apparatus 15 10
- **341.** 1 d. 50 School crest .. 35 35

87. " Teaching ".

1975. International Women's Year. Mult.

- **342.** 4 b. Type **87** 10 10
- **343.** 10 b. " Planting rice " .. 10 10
- **344.** 50 b. " Nursing " 35 15
- **345.** 1 d. 50 " Directing traffic " 85 35

88. Woman playing Golf.

1975. 11th Anniversary of Independence. Multicoloured.

- **346.** 10 b. Type **88** 25 10
- **347.** 50 b. Man playing golf .. 90 20
- **348.** 1 d. 50 President playing golf .. .. .. 2·00 70

89. American Militiaman.

1976. Bicent. of American Revolution. Mult.

- **349.** 25 b. Type **89** 30 10
- **350.** 50 b. Soldier of the Continental Army 50 20
- **351.** 1 d. 25 Independence Declaration 80 60

90. Mother and Child.

1976. Christmas.

- **353. 90.** 10 b. multicoloured .. 10 10
- **354.** 50 b. multicoloured .. 15 10
- **355.** 1 d. 25 multicoloured .. 50 45

91. Serval Cat.

1976. Abuko Nature Reserve (1st series). Multicoloured.

- **356.** 10 b. Type **91** 35 10
- **357.** 20 b. Bushbuck 80 20
- **358.** 50 b. Sitatunga (deer) .. 1·25 40
- **359.** 1 d. 25 Leopard .. .. 2·75 1·25

See also Nos. 400/3, 431/4 and 460/3.

92. Festival Emblem and Gambian Weaver.

1977. 2nd World Black and African Festival of Arts and Culture, Nigeria.

- **361. 92.** 25 b. multicoloured .. 15 10
- **362.** 50 b. multicoloured .. 20 15
- **363.** 1 d. 25 multicoloured .. 50 70

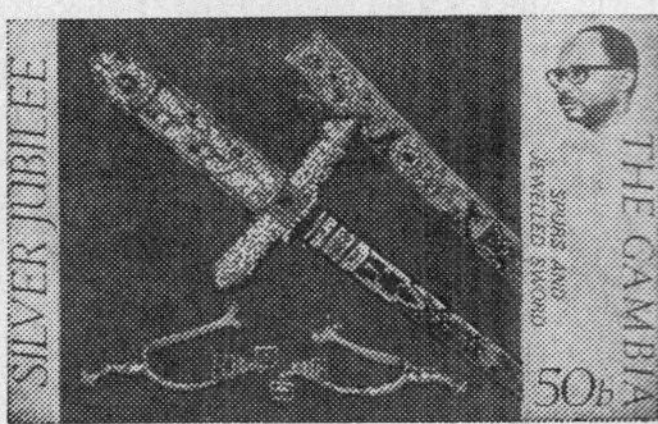

93. The Spurs and Jewelled Sword.

1977. Silver Jubilee. Multicoloured.

- **365.** 25 b. The Queen's visit, 1961 .. .. 70 60
- **366.** 50 b. Type **93** 40 40
- **367.** 1 d. 25 Oblation of the Sword 75 75

94. Stone Circles, Kuntaur.

1977. Tourism. Multicoloured.

- **368.** 25 b. Type **94** 10 10
- **369.** 50 b. Ruined Fort, James Island 20 20
- **370.** 1 d. 25 Mungo Park Monument 70 70

95. Widow of Last Year.

1977. Flowers and Shrubs. Multicoloured.

- 371 2 b. Type **95** 10 15
- 372 4 b. White Water-lily .. 10 30
- 373 6 b. Fireball Lily 10 30
- 374 8 b. Cocks-comb 10 15
- 375 10 b. Broad Leaved Ground Orchid .. .. 1·00 30
- 376 13 b. Fibre Plant (yellow background) 15 40
- 376a 13 b. Fibre Plant (grey background) .. .. 3·00 3·00
- 377 25 b. False Kapok .. 15 15
- 378 38 b. Baobab 25 55
- 379 50 b. Coral Tree 35 35
- 380 63 b. Gloriosa Lily .. 40 70
- 381 1 d. 25 Bell-flowered Mimosa .. .. 70 1·25
- 382 2 d. 50 Kindin Dolo .. 75 1·25
- 383 5 d. African Tulip Tree .. 1·25 2·00

Nos. 373/78 and 381/2 are vert. designs.

96. Endangered Animals.

1977. Banjul Declaration.

- **384. 96.** 10 b. black and blue .. 15 10
- **385.** – 25 b. multicoloured .. 40 10
- **386.** – 50 b. multicoloured .. 65 20
- **387.** – 1 d. 25 black and red .. 1·40 75

DESIGNS: 25 b. Extract from Declaration. 50 b. Declaration in full. 1 d. 25, Endangered insects and flowers.

97. " Flight into Egypt ".

1977. 400th Birth Anniv. of Rubens. Mult.

- **388.** 10 b. Type **97** 10 10
- **389.** 25 b. " The Education of the Virgin " 15 10
- **390.** 50 b. " Clara Serena Rubens " 35 20
- **391.** 1 d. " Madonna with Saints " 60 70

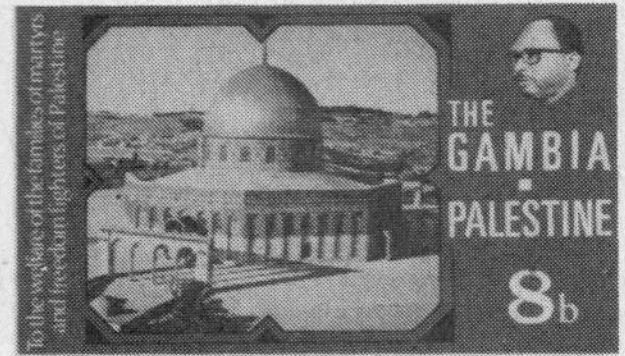

98. Dome of the Rock, Jerusalem.

1978. Palestinian Welfare.

- **392. 98.** 8 b. multicoloured .. 50 15
- **393.** 25 b. multicoloured .. 2·00 85

99. Walking on a Greasy Pole.

1978. 13th Anniv. of Independence. Mult.

- **394.** 10 b. Type **99** 10 10
- **395.** 50 b. Pillow fighting .. 15 10
- **396.** 1 d. Long boat rowing .. 35 45

100. Lion.

1978. 25th Anniversary of Coronation.

- **397.** – 1 d. black, brown & yell. 35 60
- **398.** – 1 d. multicoloured .. 35 60
- **399. 100.** 1 d. black, brn. & yell 35 60

DESIGNS: No. 397, White Greyhound of Richmond. No. 398, Queen Elizabeth II.

101. Verreaux's Eagle Owl.

1978. Abuko Nature Reserve (2nd series). Multicoloured.

- **400.** 20 b. Type **101** .. .. 1·50 30
- **401.** 25 b. Lizard buzzard .. 1·50 30
- **402.** 50 b. African Harrier hawk 2·50 1·25
- **403.** 1 d. 25 Long-crested eagle 3·50 3·50

102. M.V. " Lady Wright ".

1978. Launching of River Vessel " Lady Chilel Jawara ". Multicoloured.

- **404.** 8 b. Type **102** 15 10
- **405.** 25 b. Sectional view of " Lady Chilel Jawara " 40 25
- **406.** 1 d. " Lady Chilel Jawara " 1·25 1·10

103. Police Service.

1979. 14th Anniv. of Independence. Mult.

- **407.** 10 b. Type **103** 45 10
- **408.** 50 b. Fire Service .. 75 25
- **409.** 1 d. 25 Ambulance Service 1·25 80

1979. Nos. 376 and 380/1 surch.

- **410.** 25 b. on 13 b. Fibre Plant 20 35
- **411.** 25 b. on 63 b. Gloriosa Lily 15 20
- **412.** 25 b. on 1 d. 25, Bell-flowered Mimosa .. 15 20

105. " Ramsgate Sands " (detail showing children playing on beach).

1979. International Year of the Child. " Ramsgate Sands " (William Powell Frith). Multicoloured.

- **413.** 10 b. Type **105** 10 10
- **414.** 25 b. Detail showing child paddling (vert.) .. 20 10
- **415.** 1 d. Complete painting (60 × 23 mm.) 60 60

106. 1883 2½d. Stamp.

1979. Death Centenary of Sir Rowland Hill. Multicoloured.

- **416.** 10 b. Type **106** 10 10
- **417.** 25 b. 1869 4d. stamp .. 15 10
- **418.** 50 b. 1965 Independence 7½d. commemorative .. 20 20
- **419.** 1 d. 25 1935 Silver Jubilee 1½d. commemorative .. 40 50

107. Satellite Earth Station under Construction.

1979. Abuko Satellite Earth Station. Mult.
421. 25 b. Type **107** 20 10
422. 50 b. Satellite Earth Station (completed) .. 30 20
423. 1 d. "Intelsat" satellite 65 60

108. "Apollo 11" leaving Launch Pad.

1979. 10th Anniv. of Moon Landing. Mult.
424. 25 b. Type **108** 20 10
425. 38 b. "Apollo 11" in Moon orbit 25 20
426. 50 b. Splashdown .. 30 40
430. 2 d. Lunar module on Moon 1·50 1·75

Nos. 424/6 also exist self-adhesive from booklet panes. No. 430 only exists in this form.

109. "Acraea zetes".

1980. Abuko Nature Reserve (3rd series). Butterflies. Multicoloured.
431 25 b. Type **109** 35 20
432 50 b. "Precis hierta" .. 55 40
433 1 d. "Graphium leonidas" 85 80
434 1 d. 25 "Charaxes jasius" 90 85

110. Steam Launch "Vampire".

1980. "London 1980" International Stamp Exhibition. Multicoloured.
436. 10 b. Type **110** 15 10
437. 25 b. T.S.S. "Lady Denham" 20 10
438. 50 b. T.S.C.M.Y. "Mansa Kila Ba" 30 20
439. 1 d. 25 T.S.S. "Prince of Wales" 50 60

Nos. 438 and 439 are larger, 50×28 mm.

111. Queen Elizabeth the Queen Mother.

1980. 80th Birthday of The Queen Mother.
440. **111.** 67 b. multicoloured .. 30 35

INDEX
Countries can be quickly located by referring to the index at the end of this volume.

112. Phoenician Trading Vessel.

1980. Early Sailing Vessels. Multicoloured.
441. 8 b. Type **112** 10 10
442. 67 b. Egyptian sea-going vessel 25 20
443. 75 b. Portuguese caravel .. 30 30
444. 1 d. Spanish galleon .. 50 50

113. "Madonna and Child" (Francesco de Mura).

1980. Christmas. Multicoloured.
445. 8 b. Type **113** 10 10
446. 67 b. "Praying Madonna with Crown of Stars" (workshop of Correggio) 25 25
447. 75 b. "La Zingarella" (workshop replica of Correggio painting) .. 25 30

114. New Atlantic Hotel.

1981. World Tourism Conference, Manila. Multicoloured.
448. 25 b. Type **114** 15 10
449. 75 b. Ancient stone circles 40 40
450. 85 b. Conference emblem 50 50

115. 1979 Abuko Satellite Earth Station 50 b. Commemorative.

1981. World Telecommunications Day.
451. **115.** 50 b. multicoloured .. 55 30
452. – 50 b. multicoloured .. 55 30
453. – 85 b. black and brown 80 55

DESIGNS: No. 452, 1975 Schweitzer Birth Cent. 50 b. Commemorative. No. 453, I.T.U. and W.H.O. emblems.

116. Prince Charles in Naval Uniform.

1981. Royal Wedding. Multicoloured.
454. 75 b. Wedding bouquet from Gambia 30 20
455. 1 d. Type **116** 35 30
456. 1 d. 25 Prince Charles and Lady Diana Spencer .. 40 35

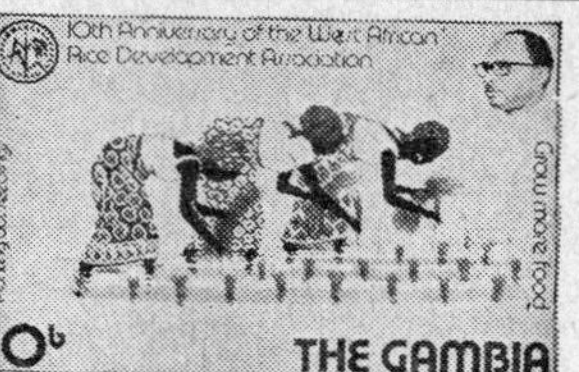

117. Planting-out Seedlings.

1981. 10th Anniversary of West African Rice Development Association. Mult.
457. 10 b. Type **117** 10 10
458. 50 b. Care of the Crops .. 35 35
459. 85 b. Winnowing and drying 55 55

118. Bosc's Monitor.

1981. Abuko Nature Reserve (4th series). Reptiles. Mult.
460. 40 b. Type **118** 45 20
461. 60 b. Dwarf Crocodile .. 70 35
462. 80 b. Royal Python .. 90 50
463. 85 b. Chameleon 95 55

119. Examination Room.

1982. 30th Anniversary of West African Examinations Council. Multicoloured.
464. 60 b. Type **119** 50 30
465. 85 b. First High School .. 65 45
466. 1 d. 10 Council's office .. 85 55

1982. No. 454 surch. **60 B.**
467. 60 b. on 75 b. Wedding bouquet from Gambia .. 2·50 2·50

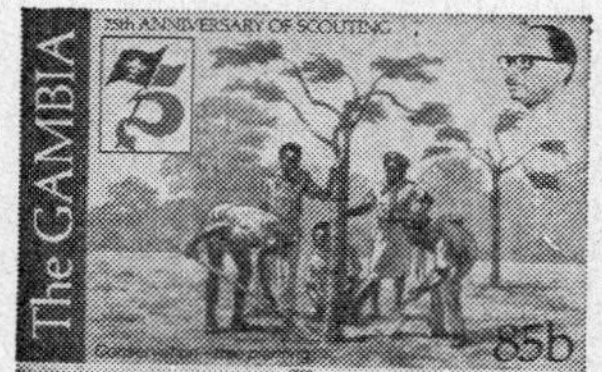

121. Tree-planting ("Conservation").

1982. 75th Anniv. of Boy Scout Movement. Multicoloured.
468. 85 b. Type **121** .. .. 1·50 1·00
469. 1 d. 25 Woodworking .. 1·75 1·75
470. 1 d. 27 Lord Baden-Powell 1·75 2·00

122. Gambia Football Team.

1982. World Cup Football Championship, Spain. Multicoloured.
471. 10 b. Type **122** 15 10
472. 1 d. 10 Gambian team practice 85 70
473. 1 d. 25 Bernabeu Stadium, Madrid 90 75
474. 1 d. 55 FIFA World Cup .. 95 80

123. Gambia Coat of Arms.

1982. 21st Birthday of Princess of Wales. Multicoloured.
476. 10 b. Type **123** 10 10
477. 85 b. Princess at City Hall, Cardiff, October 1981 .. 40 30
478. 1 d. 10 Bride and groom returning to Buckingham Palace 50 45
479. 2 d. 50 Formal portrait .. 1·25 1·25

124. Vegetable Garden at Yundum Experimental Farm.

1982. Economic Community of West African States Development. Multicoloured.
480. 10 b. Type **124** 25 15
481. 60 b. Banjul/Kaolack microwave tower .. .. 1·25 90
482. 90 b. Soap factory, Denton Bridge, Banjul .. 1·40 1·40
483. 1 d. 25 Control tower, Yundum Airport .. 1·60 2·00

125. "Kassina cassinoides".

1982. Frogs. Multicoloured.
484. 10 b. Type **125** 40 15
485. 20 b. "Hylarana galamensis" .. 55 20
486. 85 b. "Euphlyctis occipitalis" .. 1·00 80
487. 2 d. "Kassina senegalensis" 2·00 2·50

126. Satellite View of Gambia.

1983. Commonwealth Day. Multicoloured.
488. 10 b. Type **126** 10 10
489. 60 b. Batik cloth 30 45
490. 1 d. 10 Bagging groundnuts 50 65
491. 2 d. 10 Gambia flag .. 90 1·25

127. Blessed Anne Marie Javouhey (foundress of Order).

1983. Centenary of Sisters of St. Joseph of Cluny's Work in Gambia. Multicoloured.
492. 10 b. Type **127** 10 10
493. 85 b. Bathurst Hospital, nun and school children (horiz.) 45 50

128. Canoes.

1983. River Craft. Multicoloured.

494.	1 b. Type **128**	10	20
495.	2 b. Upstream ferry	15	20
496.	3 b. Dredger	15	20
497.	4 b. "Sir Dawda" (harbour launch)	20	20
498.	5 b. Cargo liner	20	20
499.	10 b. "Lady Dale" (60 ft. launch)	20	10
500.	20 b. Container ship	30	20
501.	30 b. Large sailing canoe	30	20
502.	40 b. "Lady Wright" (passenger and cargo ferry)	30	25
503.	50 b. Container ship (different)	35	25
504.	75 b. Fishing boats	40	25
505.	1 d. Tug with groundnut barges	45	35
506.	1 d. 25, Groundnut canoe	55	35
507.	2 d. 50, "Banjul" (car ferry)	1·00	1·25
508.	5 d. "Bintang Bolong" (ferry)	1·60	2·00
509.	10 d. "Lady Chilel Jawara" (passenger and cargo ferry)	2·75	3·25

129. Osprey in Tree.

1983. The Osprey. Multicoloured.

510.	10 b. Type **129**	75	20
511.	60 b. Osprey	1·50	85
512.	85 b. Osprey with catch	1·75	1·50
513.	1 d. 10 In flight	2·00	2·00

130. Local Ferry.

1983. World Communications Year. Mult.

514.	10 b. Type **130**	10	10
515.	85 b. Telex operator	45	50
516.	90 b. Radio Gambia	45	50
517.	1 d. 10 Loading mail into aircraft	60	65

131. "St. Paul preaching at Athens" (detail).

1983. 500th Birth Anniversary of Raphael.

518.	**131.**	**60 b. multicoloured**	**35**	**40**
519.	**–**	**85 b. multicoloured**	**45**	**50**
520.	**–**	**1 d. multicoloured**	**50**	**55**

Nos. 519/20 show different details of "St. Paul preaching at Athens".

132. Early Balloon and Siege of Paris Cover.

1983. Bicentenary of Manned Flight. Mult.

522.	60 b. Type **132**	35	40
523.	85 b. Lufthansa aircraft and flown cover	45	50
524.	90 b. Junkers aircraft and Hans Bertram cover	45	50
525.	1 d. 25 Lunar Module and H. E. Sieger's space cover	65	70
526.	4 d. "Graf Zeppelin" (airship)	2·00	2·50

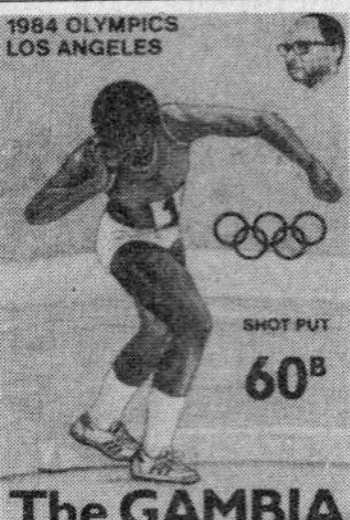

133. Shot-putting.

1984. Olympic Games Los Angeles (1st issue). Multicoloured.

527.	60 b. Type **133**	25	30
528.	85 b. High jumping (horiz.)	35	40
529.	90 b. Wrestling	35	40
530.	1 d. Gymnastics	40	45
531.	1 d. 25 Swimming (horiz.)	50	55
532.	2 d. Diving	80	85

See also Nos. 555/8.

134. Goofy.

1984. Easter. Multicoloured.

534.	1 b. Type **134**	10	10
535.	2 b. Mickey Mouse	10	10
536.	3 b. Huey, Dewey and Louie	10	10
537.	4 b. Goofy (different)	10	10
538.	5 b. Donald Duck	10	10
539.	10 b. Chip 'n' Dale	10	10
540.	60 b. Pluto	35	35
541.	90 b. Scrooge McDuck	50	50
542.	5 d. Morty and Ferdie	2·25	2·40

Nos. 534/42 show Walt Disney cartoon characters painting eggs.

135. Young Crocodiles hatching.

1984. The Nile Crocodiles. Multicoloured.

544.	4 b. Type **135**	10	10
545.	6 b. Adult carrying young	10	10
546.	90 b. Adult	1·00	1·25
547.	1 d. 50 Crocodile at riverbank	1·90	2·50

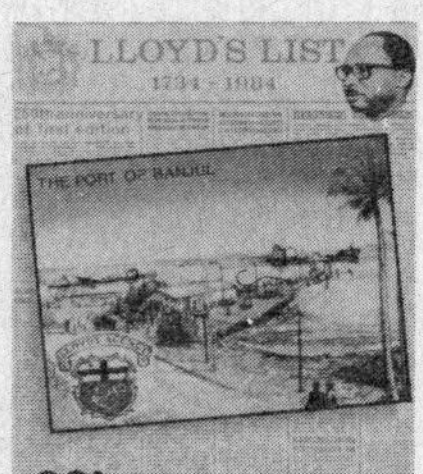

136. Port Banjul.

1984. 250th Anniv. of "Lloyd's List" (newspaper). Multicoloured.

549.	60 b. Type **136**	50	30
550.	85 b. Bulk carrier	60	40
551.	90 b. Sinking of the "Dagomba"	60	55
552.	1 d. 25 19th century frigate	1·10	85

1984. Universal Postal Union Congress Hamburg. Nos. 507/8 optd. **19th UPU CONGRESS HAMBURG.**

553.	2 d. 50 Banjul (car ferry)	1·00	1·10
554.	5 d. Bintang Bolong (ferry)	2·00	2·25

138. Sprinting.

1984. Olympic Games, Los Angeles (2nd issue). Multicoloured.

555.	60 b. Type **138**	25	30
556.	85 b. Long jumping	35	40
557.	90 b. Long-distance running	35	40
558.	1 d. 25 Triple jumping	50	55

139. "Graf Zeppelin".

1984. 50th Anniversary of Gambia-South America Trans-Atlantic Flights. Mult.

559.	60 b. Type **139**	80	60
560.	85 b. Dornier "Wal" on S.S. "Westfalen"	1·10	90
561.	90 b. Dornier "DO 18"	1·10	1·00
562.	1 d.25 Dornier "Wal"	1·40	1·50

140. Pink Shrimp.

1984. Marine Life. Multicoloured.

563.	55 b. Type **140**	25	25
564.	75 b. Atlantic Loggerhead Turtle	40	35
565.	1 d. 50 Portuguese Man-of-War	70	70
566.	2 d. 35 Fiddler Crab	95	1·25

141. "Antanartia hippomene".

1984. Butterflies. Multicoloured.

568.	10 b. Type **141**	20	20
569.	85 b. "Pseudacraea eurytus"	70	70
570.	90 b. "Charaxes lactitinctus"	70	70
571.	3 d. "Graphium pylades"	1·75	2·75

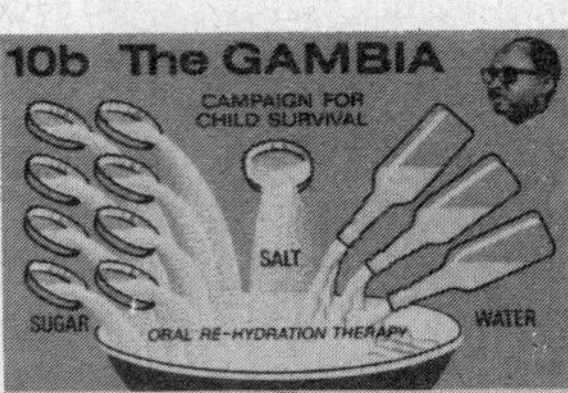

142. Oral Re-hydration Therapy.

1985. Campaign for Child Survival.

573.	**142.**	10 b. blk., bl. and brn.	10	10
574.	–	85 b. multicoloured	35	40
575.	–	1 d. 10 multicoloured	45	50
576.	–	1 d. 50 multicoloured	60	65

DESIGNS: 85 b. Growth monitoring. 1 d. 10, Health care worker with women and babies ("Promotion of breast feeding"). 1 d. 50, Universal immunisation.

143. Women at Market.

1985. Women and Development. Mult.

577.	60 b. Type **143**	25	30
578.	85 b. Type **143**	35	40
579.	1 d. Woman office worker	40	45
580.	1 d. 25 As 1 d.	50	55

144. Turkey Vulture.

1985. Birth Bicentenary of John J. Audubon (ornithologist). Designs showing original paintings. Multicoloured.

581.	60 b. Type **144**	1·00	45
582.	85 b. American Anhinga	1·25	95
583.	1 d. 50 Green Heron	1·50	1·75
584.	5 d. Wood Duck	2·75	3·25

145. The Queen Mother.

1985. Life and Times of Queen Elizabeth the Queen Mother. Multicoloured.

586.	85 b. The Queen Mother and King George VI reviewing Home Guard	25	30
587.	3 d. Type **145**	80	85
588.	5 d. The Queen Mother with posy	1·40	1·50

1985. 150th Birth Anniversary of Mark Twain (author). Designs as T **118** of Anguilla showing Walt Disney cartoon characters in scenes from "Life on the Mississippi". Multicoloured.

590.	1 d. 50 Mickey Mouse steering the "Calamity Jane"	40	45
591.	2 d. Mickey and Minnie Mouse at antebellum mansion	55	60
592.	2 d. 50 Donald Duck and Goofy heaving the lead	65	70
593.	3 d. Poker game aboard the "Gold Dust"	80	85

1985. Birth Bicentenaries of Grimm Brothers (folklorists). As T **119** of Anguilla, but vert, showing Walt Disney cartoon characters in scenes from "Faithful John". Multicoloured.

595.	60 b. The King (Mickey Mouse) and portrait of the Princess (Minnie Mouse)	30	25
596.	85 b. The King showing the Princess his treasures	35	30
597.	2 d. 35, Faithful John (Goofy) playing trumpet	75	75
598.	5 d. Faithful John turned to stone	1·75	1·75

MINIMUM PRICE

The minimum price quoted is 10p which represents a handling charge rather than a basis for valuing common stamps. For further notes about prices see introductory pages.

1985. Olympic Gold Medal Winners, Los Angeles. Nos. 527/32 optd.

600. 60 b. Type **133** (optd. **GOLD MEDALLIST CLAUDIA LOCH WEST GERMANY**) 25 25
601. 85 b. High jumping (optd. **GOLD MEDALLIST ULRIKE MEYFARTH WEST GERMANY**) .. 30 30
602. 90 b. Wrestling (optd. **GOLD MEDALLIST PASQUALE PASSARELLI WEST GERMANY**) 30 30
603. 1 d. Gymnastics (optd. **GOLD MEDALLIST LI NING CHINA**) 35 35
604. 1 d. 25, Swimming (optd. **GOLD MEDALLIST MICHAEL GROSS WEST GERMANY**) 45 45
605. 2 d. Diving (optd. **GOLD MEDALLIST SYLVIE BERNIER CANADA**) .. 60 65

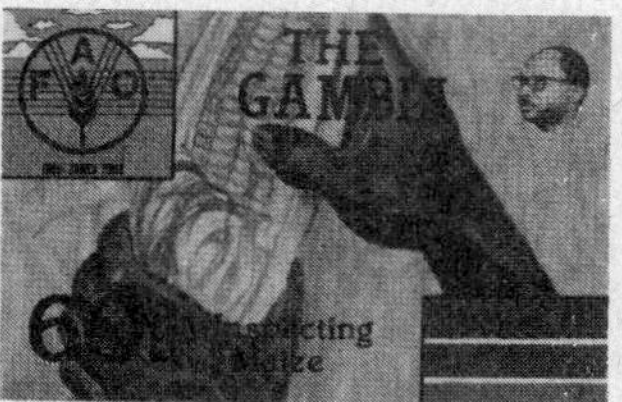

147. Inspecting Maize.

1985. United Nations Anniversaries. Mult.

607. 60 b. Type **147** 40 35
608. 85 b. Football match, Independence Stadium, Banjul 50 40
609. 1 d. 10 Rice fields 60 50
610. 2 d. Central Bank of The Gambia 85 75
611. 3 d. Cow and calf .. .. 1·50 1·40
612. 4 d. Banjul harbour .. 2·00 2·00
613. 5 d. Gambian fruits .. 2·25 2·25
614. 6 d. Oyster Creek Bridge .. 2·50 2·75

Nos. 607, 609, 611 and 613 commemorate the 40th anniversary of the Food and Agriculture Organization and Nos. 608, 610, 612 and 614 the 40th anniversary of the United Nations Organization.

148. Fishermen in Fotoba, Guinea.

1985. 50th Anniv. of Diocese of The Gambia and Guinea. Multicoloured.

615. 60 b. Type **148** 30 30
616. 85 b. St. Mary's Primary School, Banjul 30 40
617. 1 d. 10 St. Mary's Cathedral Banjul .. 35 65
618. 1 d. 50 Mobile dispensary at Christy Kunda .. 50 85

149. "Virgin and Child" (Dieric Bouts).

1985. Christmas. Religious Paintings. Mult.

619. 60 b. Type **149** 20 25
620. 85 b. "The Annunciation" (Robert Campin) 25 30
621. 1 d. 50 "Adoration of the Shepherds" (Gerard David) 45 50
622. 5 d. "The Nativity" (Gerard David) .. .. 1·60 1·75

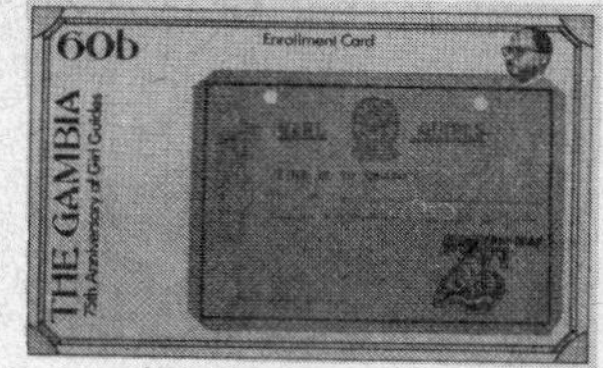

150. Enrolment Card.

1985. 75th Anniv. of Girl Guide Movement. Multicoloured.

624. 60 b. Type **150** 40 30
625. 85 b. 2nd Bathurst Company centre .. 50 35
626. 1 d. 50 Lady Baden-Powell (vert.) 70 80
627. 5 d. Miss Rosamond Fowlis (Gambian Guide Association leader) (vert.) .. 2·00 3·00

151. Girl and Village Scene.

1985. International Youth Year. Mult.

629. 60 b. Type **151** 25 30
630. 85 b. Youth and wrestling bout 30 35
631. 1 d. 10 Girl and Griot storyteller 40 65
632. 1 d. 50 Youth and crocodile pool 50 80

1986. Appearance of Halley's Comet. As T **123** of Anguilla. Multicoloured.

634. 10 b. Maria Mitchell (astronomer) and Kitt Peak National Observatory, Arizona 20 15
635. 20 b. Neil Armstrong, first man on Moon, 1969 .. 30 20
636. 75 b. "Skylab 4" and Comet Kohoutek, 1973 .. 60 50
637. 1 d. N.A.S.A.'s infra-red astronomical satellite and Halley's Comet .. 70 60
638. 2 d. Comet of 1577 from Turkish painting .. 1·10 1·10
639. 10 d. N.A.S.A.'s International Cometary Explorer .. .. 3·50 4·25

1986. 60th Birthday of Queen Elizabeth II. As T **125** of Anguilla.

641. 1 d. black and yellow .. 25 30
642. 2 d. 50 multicoloured .. 65 70
643. 10 d. multicoloured .. 2·50 2·75

DESIGNS: No. 641, Duke of York and family, Royal Tournament, 1936. 642, Queen attending christening, 1983. 643, In West Germany, 1978.

152. Two Players competing for Ball.

1986. World Cup Football Championship, Mexico. Multicoloured.

645. 75 b. Type **152** 50 50
646. 1 d. Player kicking ball .. 70 70
647. 2 d. 50 Player kicking ball (different) .. .. 1·50 1·50
648. 10 d. Player heading ball 3·75 4·25

153. Mercedes "500" (1986).

1986. "Ameripex" International Stamp Exhibition, Chicago. Centenary (1985) of First Benz Motor Car. Multicoloured.

650. 25 b. Type **153** 15 10
651. 75 b. Cord "810" (1935) .. 40 40
652. 1 d. Borgward "Isabella Coupe" (1957) 60 60
653. 1 d. 25 Lamborghini "Countach" (1985/6) .. 70 70
654. 2 d. Ford "Thunderbird" (1955) .. .. .. 1·25 1·25
655. 2 d. 25 Citroen "DS19" (1956) .. .. .. 1·40 1·40
656. 5 d. Bugatti "Atlante" (1936) .. .. .. 2·50 2·50
657. 10 d. Horch "853" (1936) .. 4·50 4·50

The 25 b. value is inscribed "MECEDES" and the 10 d. "LARL BENZ".

1986. Centenary of Statue of Liberty (1st issue). Multicoloured. As T **211** of Dominica, showing Statue of Liberty and immigrants to the U.S.A..

659. 20 b. John Jacob Astor (financier) 10 10
660. 1 d. Jacob Riis (journalist) 40 50
661. 1 d. 25 Igor Sikorsky (aeronautics engineer) .. 50 60
662. 5 d. Charles Boyer (actor) 2·00 2·50

See also Nos. 705/9.

1986. Royal Wedding. As T **213** of Antigua. Multicoloured.

664. 1 d. Prince Andrew and Miss Sarah Ferguson .. 40 45
665. 2 d. 50 Prince Andrew .. 1·00 1·40
666. 4 d. Prince Andrew as helicopter pilot .. .. 1·60 2·00

1986. World Cup Football Championship Winners, Mexico. Nos. 645/8 optd. **WINNERS Argentine 3 W. Germany 2.**

668. 75 b. Type **152** 30 40
669. 1 d. Player kicking ball .. 40 55
670. 2 d. 50 Player kicking ball (different) .. .. 1·00 1·25
671. 10 d. Player heading ball 4·25 4·75

154. Minnie Mouse (Great Britain).

1986. Christmas. Designs showing Walt Disney cartoon characters posting letters in various countries. Multicoloured.

673. 1 d. Type **154** 75 50
674. 1 d. 25 Huey (U.S.A.) .. 80 60
675. 2 d. Huey, Dewey and Louie (France) .. 1·25 85
676. 2 d. 35 Kanga and Roo (Australia) .. .. 1·40 90
677. 5 d. Goofy (Germany) .. 2·25 2·00

Nos. 673/7 also show the emblem of "Stockholmia '86" International Stamp Exhibition.

1986. Appearance of Halley's Comet (2nd issue). Nos. 634/9 optd as T **218** of Antigua.

679. 10 b. Maria Mitchell (astronomer) and Kitt Peak National Observatory, Arizona 20 10
680. 20 b. Neil Armstrong, first man on Moon, 1969 .. 30 10
681. 75 b. "Skylab 4" and Comet Kohoutek, 1973 .. 50 20
682. 1 d. N.A.S.A.'s infra-red astronomical satellite and Halley's Comet .. 55 25
683. 2 d. Comet of 1577 from Turkish painting .. 90 50
684. 10 d. N.A.S.A.'s International Cometary Explorer .. .. .. 3·00 2·50

155. Bugarab and Tabala.

1987. Manding Musical Instruments. Mult.

686. 75 b. Type **155** 15 20
687. 1 d. Balaphong and fiddle 15 25
688. 1 d. 25 Bolongbato and konting (vert.) 20 30
689. 10 d. Antique and modern koras (vert.) .. .. 1·60 2·00

156. "Snowing".

1987. Birth Centenary of Marc Chagall (artist). Multicoloured.

691. 75 b. Type **156** 15 15
692. 85 b. "The Boat" 20 20
693. 1 d. "Maternity" 20 20
694. 1 d. 25 "The Flute Player" 25 25
695. 2 d. 35 "Lovers and the Beast" 45 45
696. 4 d. "Fishes at Saint Jean" 70 70
697. 5 d. "Entering the Ring" 85 85
698. 10 d. "Three Acrobats" .. 1·75 1·75

157. "America", 1851.

1987. America's Cup Yachting Championship. Multicoloured.

700. 20 b. Type **157** 10 10
701. 1 d. "Courageous", 1974 .. 25 25
702. 2 d. 50 "Volunteer", 1887 55 55
703. 10 d. "Intrepid", 1967 .. 1·90 1·90

158. Arm of Statue of Liberty.

159. "Lantana camara".

1987. Centenary of Statue of Liberty (1986) (2nd issue). Multicoloured.

705. 1 b. Type **158** 10 10
706. 2 b. Launch passing Statue (horiz.) 10 10
707. 3 b. Schooner passing Statue (horiz.) 10 10
708. 5 b. Aircraft carrier and "Queen Elizabeth 2" (horiz.) 10 10
709. 50 b. Checking Statue for damage 10 10
710. 75 b. Cleaning in progress 15 15
711. 1 d. Working on Statue .. 15 20
712. 1 d. 25 Statue and fireworks 20 25
713. 10 d. Statue illuminated .. 1·60 1·75
714. 12 d. Statue and fireworks 1·90 2·00

1987. Flowers of Abuko Nature Reserve. Multicoloured.

715. 75 b. Type **159** 15 15
716. 1 d. "Clerodendrum thomsoniae" 15 20
717. 1 d. 50 "Haemanthus multiflorus" 25 30
718. 1 d. 70 "Gloriosa simplex" 25 30
719. 1 d. 75 "Combretum microphyllum" 30 35
720. 2 d. 25 "Eulophia quineensis" 35 40
721. 5 d. "Erythrina senegalensis" 80 85
722. 15 d. "Dichrostachys glomerata" .. .. 2·40 2·50

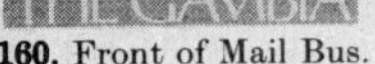

160. Front of Mail Bus. **161.** Basketball.

1987. "Capex '87" International Stamp Exhibition, Toronto and 10th Anniv. of Gambia Public Transport Corporation. Mail Buses. Multicoloured.

724. 20 b. Type **160** 10 10
725. 75 b. Bus in Banjul (horiz.) 15 20
726. 1 d. Passengers queueing for bus (horiz.) .. 15 20
727. 10 d. Two buses on rural road .. .. .. 1·60 2·50

1987. Olympic Games, Seoul (1988) (1st issue). Multicoloured.

729. 50 b. Type **161** 25 20
730. 1 d. Volleyball 40 35
731. 3 d. Hockey (horiz.) .. 95 85
732. 10 d. Handball (horiz.) .. 2·25 2·25
See also Nos. 779/82.

162. "A Partridge in a Pear Tree".

1987. Christmas. Multicoloured. Designs showing a Victorian couple in scenes from carol "The Twelve Days of Christmas".

734. 20 b. Type **162** 10 10
735. 40 b. "Two turtle doves" 10 10
736. 60 b. "Three French hens" 10 10
737. 75 b. "Four calling birds" 15 15
738. 1 d. "Five golden rings" .. 15 20
739. 1 d. 25 "Six geese a-laying" 20 25
740. 1 d. 50 "Seven swans a-swimming" 25 30
741. 2 d. "Eight maids a-milking" 30 35
742. 3 d. "Nine ladies dancing" 50 55
743. 5 d. "Ten lords a-leaping" 80 85
744. 10 d. "Eleven pipers piping" .. .. .. 1·60 1·75
745. 12 d. "Twelve drummers drumming" .. .. 1·90 2·00

163. Campfire Singsong.

1987. World Scout Jamboree, Australia. Multicoloured.

747. 75 b. Type **163** .. 25 15
748. 1 d. Scouts examining African katydid .. 30 25
749. 1 d. 25 Scouts watching Red-tailed tropic bird .. 45 30
750. 12 d. Scouts helping bus passenger .. .. 2·50 3·00

1987. 60th Anniv. of Mickey Mouse (Walt Disney cartoon character). As T **220.** of Dominica. Multicoloured.

752. 60 b. Morty and Ferdie examining Trevithick's locomotive, 1804 .. 10 10
753. 75 b. Clarabelle Cow in "Empire State Express", 1893 .. .. 15 15
754. 1 d. Donald Duck inspecting Stephenson's "Rocket", 1829 .. 15 20
755. 1 d. 25 Piglet and Winnie the Pooh with Santa Fe Railway locomotive, 1920 .. .. .. 20 25
756. 2 d. Donald and Daisy Duck with Class "GG-1", Pennsylvannia Railway, 1933 .. .. .. 30 35
757. 5 d. Mickey Mouse in "Stourbridge Lion", 1829
758. 10 d. Goofy in "Best Friend of Charleston", 1830 .. .. .. 80 85 / 1·60 1·75
759. 12 d. Brer Bear and Brer Rabbit with Union Pacific No M10001, 1934 1·90 2·00

164 Common Duiker and Acacia

1988. Flora and Fauna. Multicoloured.

761 50 b. Type **164** 15 10
762 75 b. Red-billed hornbill and casuarina (vert) .. 20 15
763 90 b. West African dwarf crocodile and rice .. 20 20
764 1 d. Leopard and papyrus (vert) 20 20
765 1 d.25 Crested crane and millet 30 25
766 2 d. Waterbuck and baobab tree (vert) .. 35 35
767 3 d. Oribi and Senegal palm 50 55
768 5 d. Hippopotamus and papaya (vert) 80 85

165 Wedding Portrait, 1947

1988. Royal Ruby Wedding.

770 **165** 75 b. brn, blk & orge 25 15
771 – 1 d. brown, black & bl 30 20
772 – 3 d. multicoloured 70 80
773 – 10 d. multicoloured .. 2·00 2·50

DESIGNS: 1 d. Engagement photograph; 3 d. Wedding portrait, 1947 (different); 10 d. Queen Elizabeth II and Prince Philip (photo by Karsh),1986.

1988. Stamp Exhibitions. Nos. 689, 703, 722 and 726 optd.

775 1 d. Passengers queuing for bus (optd **Independence 40**, Israel) .. 15 20
776 10 d. Antique and modern koras (optd **FINLANDIA 88**, Helsinki) .. .. 1·60 1·75
777 10 d. "Intrepid" (yacht), 1967 (optd **Praga '88**, Prague) .. 1·60 1·75
778 15 d. "Dichrostachys glomerata" (optd **OLYMPHILEX '88**, Seoul) .. .. 2·40 2·50

1988. Olympic Games, Seoul (2nd issue). As T **161**. Multicoloured.

779 1 d. Archery 15 20
780 1 d.25 Boxing 20 25
781 5 d. Gymnastics .. 80 85
782 10 d. Start of 100 metre race (horiz) .. .. 1·60 1·75

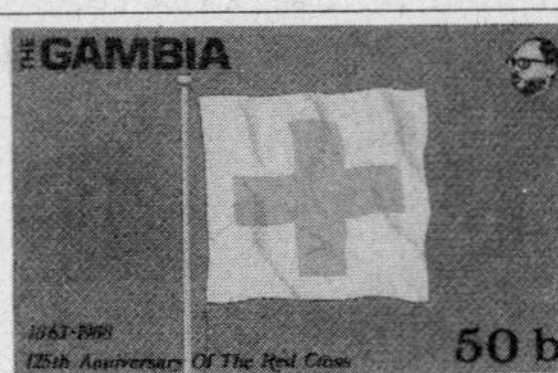

166 Red Cross Flag

1988. Anniversaries and Events. Mult.

784 50 b. Type **166** (125th anniv) 25 25
785 75 b. "Friendship 7" spacecraft (25th anniv of first American manned Earth orbit) 30 30
786 1 d. British Airways "Concorde" (10th anniv of "Concorde" London –New York service) .. 50 50
787 1 d.25 "Spirit of St. Louis" (60th anniv of first solo transatlantic flight) .. 50 50
788 2 d. "X-15" (20th anniv of fastest aircraft flight) .. 60 60
789 3 d. Bell "X-1" rocket plane (40th anniv of first supersonic flight) .. 75 75
790 10 d. English and Spanish galleons (400th anniv of Spanish Armada) .. 2·25 2·25
791 12 d. "Titanic" (75th anniv of sinking) .. 2·75 2·75

1988. 500th Birth Anniv of Titian (artist). As T **238** of Antigua. Multicoloured.

793 25 b. "Emperor Charles V" 10 10
794 50 b. "St. Margaret and the Dragon" .. 10 10
795 60 b. "Ranuccio Farnese" 10 15
796 75 b. "Tarquin and Lucretia" 15 15
797 1 d. "The Knight of Malta" 15 20
798 5 d. "Spain succouring Faith" 80 85
799 10 d. "Doge Francesco Venier" .. .. 1·60 1·75
800 12 d. "Doge Grimani before the Faith" (detail) .. 1·90 2·00

167 John Kennedy sailing

1988. 25th Death Anniv of President John F. Kennedy. Multicoloured.

802 75 b. Type **167** 15 15
803 1 d. Kennedy signing Peace Corps legislation, 1962 .. .. .. 15 20
804 1 d.25 Speaking at U.N., New York (vert) .. 20 25
805 12 d. Grave and eternal flame, Arlington National Cemetery (vert) 1·90 2·00

168 "LZ 7" "Deutschland" (first regular air passenger service), 1910

1988. Milestones of Transportation. Mult.

807 25 b. Type **168** 10 10
808 50 b. Stephenson's "Locomotion" (first permanent public railway), 1825 .. 10 10
809 75 b. G.M. "Sun Racer" (first world solar challenge), 1987 .. 15 15
810 1 d. Sprague's "Premiere" (first operational electric tramway), 1888 .. 15 20
811 1 d.25 "Gold Rush" Bicycle (holder of man-powered land speed record), 1986 .. .. 20 25
812 2 d.50 Robert Goddard and rocket launcher (first liquid fuel rocket), 1925 40 45
813 10 d. "Orukter Amphibolos" (first steam traction engine), 1805 .. .. 1·60 1·75
814 12 d. "Sovereign of the Seas" (largest cruise liner), 1988 .. .. 1·90 2·00

169 Emmett Kelley **170** Prince Henry the Navigator and Caravel

1988. Entertainers. Multicoloured.

816 20 b. Type **169** 10 10
817 1 d. Gambia National Ensemble .. 25 25
818 1 d.25 Jackie Gleason .. 30 30
819 1 d.50 Laurel and Hardy 40 40
820 2 d.50 Yul Brynner .. 65 65
821 3 d. Cary Grant 80 80
822 10 d. Danny Kaye .. 2·25 2·50
823 20 d. Charlie Chaplin .. 4·00 4·50

1988. Exploration of West Africa. Mult.

825 50 b. Type **170** 30 30
826 75 b. Jesse Ramsden's sextant, 1785 .. .. 35 35
827 1 d. 15th-century hourglass 45 45
828 1 d.25 Prince Henry the Navigator and Vasco da Gama 60 60
829 2 d.50 Vasco da Gama and ship 90 90
830 5 d. Mungo Park and map of Gambia River (horiz) 1·75 1·75
831 10 d. Map of West Africa, 1563 (horiz) .. .. 2·50 2·50
832 12 d. Portuguese caravel (horiz) .. .. .. 3·00 3·00

171 Projected Space Plane and Ernst Mach (physicist)

1988. 350th Anniv of Publication of Galileo's "Discourses". Space Achievements. Mult.

834 50 b. Type **171** 15 10
835 75 b. OAO III astronomical satellite and Niels Bohr (physicist) 20 15
836 1 d. Space shuttle, projected space station and Robert Goddard (physicist) (horiz) .. 25 20
837 1 d.25 Jupiter probe, 1979, and Edward Barnard (astronomer) (horiz) .. 30 25
838 2 d. Hubble Space Telescope and George Hale (astronomer) .. 45 35
839 3 d. Earth-to-Moon laser measurement and Albert Michaelson (physicist) (horiz) 65 55
840 10 d. HEAO-2 "Einstein" orbital satellite and Albert Einstein (physicist) .. .. 1·75 2·00
841 20 d. "Voyager" (first non-stop round-the-world flight), 1987, and Wright Brothers (aviation pioneers) (horiz) .. 3·50 3·75

HAVE YOU READ THE NOTES AT THE BEGINNING OF THIS CATALOGUE?
These often provide answers to the enquiries we receive.

172 Passing Out Parade

1989. Army Day. Multicoloured.

No.	Description	Unused	Used
843	75 b. Type **172**	10	10
844	1 d. Standards of The Gambia Regiment	10	15
845	1 d.25 Side drummer in ceremonial uniform (vert)	15	20
846	10 d. Marksman with Atlantic Shooting Cup (vert)	1·25	1·40
847	15 d. Soldiers on assault course (vert)	1·75	1·90
848	20 d. Gunner with 105 mm field gun	2·40	2·50

173 Mickey Mouse, 1928

1989. 60th Birthday of Mickey Mouse. Mult.

No.	Description	Unused	Used
849	2 d. Type **173**	25	30
850	2 d. Mickey Mouse, 1931	25	30
851	2 d. Mickey Mouse, 1936	25	30
852	2 d. Mickey Mouse, 1955	25	30
853	2 d. Mickey Mouse, 1947	25	30
854	2 d. Mickey Mouse as magician, 1940	25	30
855	2 d. Mickey Mouse with palette, 1960	25	30
856	2 d. Mickey Mouse as Uncle Sam, 1976	25	30
857	2 d. Mickey Mouse, 1988	25	30

Nos. 849/57 were printed together, se-tenant, forming a composite design.

174 "Le Coup de Lance" (detail)

1989. Easter. Religious Paintings by Rubens. Multicoloured.

No.	Description	Unused	Used
859	50 b. Type **174**	10	10
860	75 b. "Flagellation of Christ"	10	10
861	1 d. "Lamentation for Christ"	10	15
862	1 d. 25, "Descent from the Cross"	15	20
863	2 d. "Holy Trinity"	25	30
864	5 d. "Doubting Thomas"	60	65
865	10 d. "Lamentation over Christ"	1·25	1·40
866	12 d. "Lamentation with Virgin and St. John"	1·40	1·50

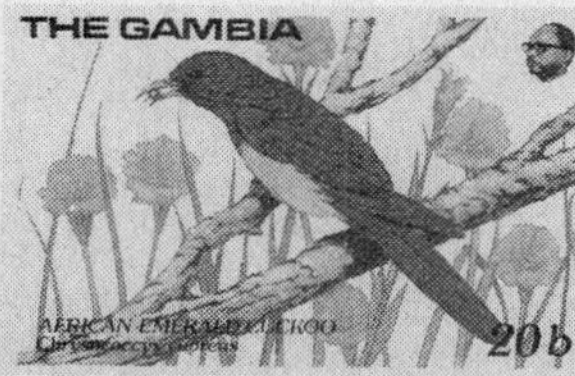

175 African Emerald Cuckoo

1989. West African Birds. Multicoloured.

No.	Description	Unused	Used
868	20 b. Type **175**	10	10
869	60 b. Grey-headed bush shrike	10	10
870	75 b. Crowned crane	10	10
871	1 d. Secretary bird	10	15
872	2 d. Red-billed hornbill	25	30
873	5 d. Superb sunbird	60	65
874	10 d. Little owl	1·25	1·40
875	12 d. Bateleur	1·40	1·50

176 "Druryia antimachus"

1989. Butterflies of Gambia. Multicoloured.

No.	Description	Unused	Used
877	50 b. Type **176**	10	10
878	75 b. "Euphaedra neophron"	10	10
879	1 d. "Aterica rabena"	10	15
880	1 d. 25 "Salamis parhassus"	15	20
881	5 d. "Precis rhadama"	60	65
882	10 d. "Papilio demodocus"	1·25	1·40
883	12 d. "Charaxes etesipe"	1·40	1·50
884	15 d. "Danaus formosa"	1·75	1·90

177 Nigerian Steam Locomotive, 1959

1989. African Steam Locomotives. Mult.

No.	Description	Unused	Used
886	50 b. Type **177**	10	10
887	75 b. Garratt Class "14A"	10	10
888	1 d. British-built locomotive, Sudan	10	15
889	1 d. 25 American built locomotive, 1925	15	20
890	5 d. Scottish-built locomotive, 1955	60	65
891	7 d. Scottish-built locomotive, 1926	85	90
892	10 d. East African Railways British-built tank locomotive	1·25	1·40
893	12 d. American-built locomotive, Ghana	1·40	1·50

1989. "Philexfrance '89" International Stamp Exhibition, Paris. Nos. 686/9 optd **PHILEXFRANCE '89**.

No.	Description	Unused	Used
895	75 b. Type **155**	10	10
896	1 d. Balaphong and fiddle	10	15
897	1 d. 25, Bolongbato and konting (vert)	15	20
898	10 d. Antique and modern koras (vert)	1·25	1·40

1989. Japanese Art. As T **250** of Antigua. Multicoloured.

No.	Description	Unused	Used
900	50 b. "Sparrow and Bamboo" (Hiroshige) (vert)	10	10
901	75 b. "Peonies and a Canary" (Hokusai) (vert)	10	10
902	1 d. "Crane and Marsh Grasses" (Hiroshige) (vert)	10	15
903	1 d. 25, "Crossbill and Thistle" (Hokusai) (vert)	15	20
904	2 d. "Cuckoo and Azalea" (Hokusai) (vert)	25	30
905	5 d. "Parrot on a Pine Branch" (Hiroshige) (vert)	60	65
906	10 d. "Mandarin Ducks in a Stream" (Hiroshige) (vert)	1·25	1·40
907	12 d. "Bullfinch and Drooping Cherry" (Hokusai) (vert)	1·40	1·50

179 Rialto Bridge, Venice

1989. World Cup Football Championship, Italy (1990). Designs showing landmarks and players. Multicoloured.

No.	Description	Unused	Used
909	75 b. Type **179**	10	10
910	1 d. 25 The Baptistery, Pisa	15	20
911	7 d. Casino, San Remo	85	90
912	12 d. Colosseum, Rome	1·40	1·50

180 "Vitex doniana"

1989. Medicinal Plants. Multicoloured.

No.	Description	Unused	Used
914	20 b. Type **180**	10	10
915	50 b. "Ricinus communis"	10	10
916	75 b. "Palisota hirsuta"	10	10
917	1 d. "Smilax kraussiana"	10	15
918	1 d. 25 "Aspilia africana"	15	20
919	5 d. "Newbouldia laevis"	60	65
920	8 d. "Monodora tenuifolia"	95	1·00
921	10 d. "Gossypium arboreum"	1·25	1·40

181 Lookdown Fish

1989. Fishes. Multicoloured.

No.	Description	Unused	Used
923	20 b. Type **181**	10	10
924	75 b. Boarfish	10	10
925	1 d. Grey triggerfish	10	15
926	1 d. 25 Skipjack tuna	15	20
927	2 d. Bermuda chub	25	30
928	4 d. Atlantic manta	50	55
929	5 d. Striped mullet	60	65
930	10 d. Ladyfish	1·25	1·40

1989. "World Stamp Expo '89" International Stamp Exhibition, Washington. As T **256** of Antigua, but showing Walt Disney cartoon characters and American carousel horses. Multicoloured.

No.	Description	Unused	Used
932	20 b. Little Hiawatha on Daniel Muller Indian pony	10	10
933	50 b. Morty on Herschell-Spillman stander	10	10
934	75 b. Goofy on Gustav Dentzel stander	10	10
935	1 d. Mickey Mouse on Daniel Muller armoured stander	10	15
936	1 d. 25, Minnie Mouse on jumper from Smithsonian Collection	15	20
937	2 d. Webby on Illion "American Beauty"	25	30
938	8 d. Donald Duck on Zalar jumper	95	1·00
939	10 d. Mickey Mouse on Parker bucking horse	1·25	1·40

183 Mickey and Minnie Mouse in Pierce-Arrow, 1922

1989. Christmas. Designs showing Walt Disney cartoon characters with cars. Mult.

No.	Description	Unused	Used
942	20 b. Type **183**	10	10
943	50 b. Goofy in Spyker, 1919	10	10
944	75 b. Donald and Grandma Duck with Packard, 1929	10	10
945	1 d. Mickey Mouse driving Daimler, 1920	10	15
946	1 d. 25, Mickey Mouse in Hispano "Suiza", 1924	15	20
947	2 d. Mickey and Minnie Mouse in Opel "Laub-frosch", 1924	25	30
948	10 d. Donald Duck driving Vauxhall "30/98", 1927	1·25	1·40
949	12 d. Goofy with Peerless, 1923	1·40	1·50

184 Charles Nicolle (typhus transmission) and Vaccination

1989. Great Medical Discoveries. Mult.

No.	Description	Unused	Used
951	20 b. Type **184**	10	10
952	50 b. Paul Ehrlich (immunization pioneer) and medical examination	10	10
953	75 b. Selman Waksman (discoverer of streptomycin) and T.B. clinic	10	10
954	1 d. Edward Jenner (smallpox vaccination), and Jenner conducting experiment, 1796	10	15
955	1 d. 25 Robert Koch (developer of tuberculin test) and Gambian using vaccination gun	15	20
956	5 d. Sir Alexander Fleming (discoverer of penicillin) and doctor giving injection	60	65
957	8 d. Max Theiler (developer of yellow fever vaccine) and child clinic	95	1·00
958	10 d. Louis Pasteur (bacteriologist) and health survey	1·25	1·40

185 "Bulbophyllum lepidum"

1989. Orchids. Multicoloured.

No.	Description	Unused	Used
960	20 b. Type **185**	10	10
961	75 b. "Tridactyle tridactylites"	10	10
962	1 d. "Vanilla imperialis"	10	15
963	1 d. 25 "Oeceoclades maculata"	15	20
964	2 d. "Polystachya affinis"	25	30
965	4 d. "Ancistrochilus rothschildianus"	50	55
966	5 d. "Angraecum distichum"	60	65
967	10 d. "Liparis guineensis"	1·25	1·40

186 John Newcombe

1990. Wimbledon Tennis Champions. Mult.

No.	Description		
969	20 b. Type **186**	10	10
970	20 b. Mrs. G. W. Hillyard	10	10
971	50 b. Roy Emerson	10	10
972	50 b. Dorothy Chambers	10	10
973	75 b. Donald Budge	10	10
974	75 b. Suzanne Lenglen	10	10
975	1 d. Laurence Doherty	10	10
976	1 d. Helen Wills Moody	10	10
977	1 d. 25 Bjorn Borg	15	20
978	1 d. 25 Maureen Connolly	15	20
979	4 d. Jean Borotra	50	55
980	4 d. Maria Bueno	50	55
981	5 d. Anthony Wilding	60	65
982	5 d. Louise Brough	60	65
983	7 d. Fred Perry	85	90
984	7 d. Margaret Court	85	90
985	10 d. Bill Tilden	1·25	1·40
986	10 d. Billie Jean King	1·25	1·40
987	12 d. Rod Laver	1·40	1·50
988	12 d. Martina Navratilova	1·40	1·50

187 Lunar Module "Eagle"

1990. 20th Anniv (1989) of First Manned Landing on Moon. Multicoloured.

No.	Description		
990	20 b. Type **187**	10	10
991	50 b. Lift-off of "Apollo 11" (vert)	10	10
992	75 b. Neil Armstrong stepping on to Moon	10	10
993	1 d. Buzz Aldrin and American flag	10	15
994	1 d. 25 "Apollo 11" emblem (vert)	15	20
995	1 d. 75 Crew of "Apollo 11"	20	25
996	8 d. Lunar Module "Eagle" on Moon	95	1·00
997	12 d. Recovery of "Apollo 11" after splashdown	1·40	1·50

188 Bristol Blenheim Mk I

1990. R.A.F. Aircraft of Second World War. Multicoloured.

No.	Description		
999	10 b. Type **188**	10	10
1000	20 b. Fairey Battle	10	10
1001	50 b. Bristol Blenheim Mk IV	10	10
1002	60 b. Vickers-Armstrong Wellington Mk IC	10	10
1003	75 b. Armstrong-Whitworth Whitley Mk V	10	10
1004	1 d. Handley-Page Hampden Mk I	10	15
1005	1 d. 25, Supermarine Spitfire Mk IA and Hawker Hurricane Mk I	15	20
1006	2 d. Avro Manchester	25	30
1007	3 d. Short Stirling Mk I	35	40
1008	5 d. Handley-Page Halifax Mk I	60	65
1009	10 d. Avro Lancaster Mk III	1·25	1·40
1010	12 d. De Havilland Mosquito Mk IV	1·40	1·50

189 White-faced Scops Owl

1990. African Birds. Multicoloured.

No.	Description		
1012	1 d. 25 Type **189**	15	20
1013	1 d. 25 Village weaver	15	20
1014	1 d. 25 Red-throated bee-eater	15	20
1015	1 d. 25 Brown harrier eagle	15	20
1016	1 d. 25 Red bishop	15	20
1017	1 d. 25 Scarlet-chested sunbird	15	20
1018	1 d. 25 Red-billed hornbill	15	20
1019	1 d. 25 Mosque swallow	15	20
1020	1 d. 25 White-faced whistling duck	15	20
1021	1 d. 25 African fish-eagle	15	20
1022	1 d. 25 Eastern white pelican	15	20
1023	1 d. 25 Carmine bee-eater	15	20
1024	1 d. 25 Hadada ibis	15	20
1025	1 d. 25 Blackhead plover	15	20
1026	1 d. 25 Yellow-bellied sunbird	15	20
1027	1 d. 25 African skimmer	15	20
1028	1 d. 25 Woodland kingfisher	15	20
1029	1 d. 25 Jacana	15	20
1030	1 d. 25 African pygmy goose	15	20
1031	1 d. 25 Hammerkop	15	20

Nos. 1012/31 were printed together, forming a composite design of birds at a lake.

190 Penny Black

1990. 150th Anniv of the Penny Black.

No.	Type	Description		
1032	**190**	1 d. 25 black and blue	15	20
1033		12 d. black and red	1·40	1·50

191 Flag and National Assembly Building

1990. 25th Anniv of Independence. Mult.

No.	Description		
1035	1 d. Type **191**	10	15
1036	3 d. Pres. Sir Dawda Jawara	35	40
1037	12 d. Map of Yundum airport and Air Gambia airliner	1·40	1·50

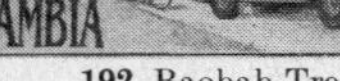

192 Baobab Tree

1990. Gambian Life. Multicoloured.

No.	Description		
1039	5 b. Type **192**	10	10
1040	10 b. Woodcarving, Albert Market, Banjul	10	10
1041	20 b. President Jawara planting seedling (vert)	10	10
1042	50 b. Sailing canoe and map	10	10
1043	75 b. Batik fabric	10	10
1044	1 d. Hibiscus and Bakau beach	10	15
1045	1 d. 25 Bougainvillea and Tendaba Camp	15	20
1046	2 d. Shrimp fishing and sorting	25	30
1047	5 d. Groundnut oil mill, Denton Bridge	60	65
1048	10 d. Handicraft pot and kora (musical instrument)	1·25	1·40
1049	15 d. "Ansellia africana" (orchid) (vert)	1·75	1·90
1050	30 d. "Euriphene gambiae" (butterfly) and ancient stone ring near Georgetown	3·50	3·75

193 Daisy Duck at 10 Downing Street

1990. "Stamp World London 90" International Stamp Exhibition. Walt Disney cartoon characters in England. Mult.

No.	Description		
1051	20 b. Type **193**	10	10
1052	50 b. Goofy in Trafalgar Square	10	10
1053	75 b. Mickey Mouse on White Cliffs of Dover (horiz)	10	10
1054	1 d. Mickey Mouse at Tower of London	10	15
1055	5 d. Mickey Mouse and Goofy at Hampton Court Palace (horiz)	60	65
1056	8 d. Mickey Mouse by Magdalen Tower, Oxford	95	1·00
1057	10 d. Mickey Mouse on Old London Bridge (horiz)	1·25	1·40
1058	12 d. Scrooge McDuck and Rosetta Stone, British Museum (horiz)	1·40	1·50

194 Lady Elizabeth Bowes-Lyon in High Chair

1990. 90th Birthday of Queen Elizabeth the Queen Mother.

No.	Type	Description		
1060	**194**	6 d. black, mve & yell	70	75
1061	–	6 d. black, mve & yell	70	75
1062	–	6 d. black, mve & yell	70	75

DESIGNS: No. 1061, Lady Elizabeth Bowes-Lyon as a young girl; 1062, Lady Elizabeth Bowes-Lyon with wild flowers.

195 Vialli, Italy

1990. World Cup Football Championship, Italy. Multicoloured.

No.	Description		
1064	1 d. Type **195**	10	15
1065	1 d. 25 Cannegia, Argentina	15	20
1066	3 d. Marchena, Costa Rica	35	40
1067	5 d. Shaiba, United Arab Emirates	60	65

1990. Olympic Games, Barcelona. As T **268** of Antigua. Multicoloured.

No.	Description		
1069	1 d. Men's 200 metres	10	15
1070	1 d. 25 Women's rhythmic gymnastics	15	20
1071	3 d. Football	35	40
1072	10 d. Men's marathon	1·25	1·40

1990. Christmas. Paintings by Renaissance Masters. As T **272** of Antigua. Multicoloured.

No.	Description		
1074	20 b. "The Annunciation, with St. Emidius" (detail) (Crivelli) (vert)	10	10
1075	50 b. "The Annunciation" (detail) (Campin) (vert)	10	10
1076	75 b. "The Solly Madonna" (detail) (Raphael) (vert)	10	15
1077	1 d. 25 "The Tempi Madonna" (Raphael) (vert)	15	20
1078	2 d. "Madonna of the Linen Window" (detail) (Raphael) (vert)	25	30
1079	7 d. "The Annunciation, with St. Emidius" (different detail) (Crivelli) (vert)	85	90
1080	10 d. "The Orleans Madonna" (Raphael) (vert)	1·25	1·40
1081	15 d. "Madonna and Child" (detail) (Crivelli) (vert)	1·75	1·90

1990. 350th Death Anniv of Rubens. As T **273** of Antigua. Multicoloured.

No.	Description		
1083	20 b. "The Lion Hunt" (sketch)	10	10
1084	75 b. "The Lion Hunt" (detail)	10	15
1085	1 d. "The Tiger Hunt" (detail)	10	15
1086	1 d. 25 "The Tiger Hunt" (different detail)	15	20
1087	3 d. "The Tiger Hunt" (different detail)	35	40
1088	5 d. "The Boar Hunt" (detail)	60	65
1089	10 d. "The Lion Hunt" (different detail)	1·25	1·40
1090	15 d. "The Tiger Hunt" (different detail)	1·75	1·90

196 Summit Logo

1991. World Summit for Children, New York.

No.	Type	Description		
1092	**196**	1 d. multicoloured	10	15

1991. International Literacy Year. As T **269** of Antigua, but scenes from Disney cartoon film "The Sword in the Stone". Multicoloured.

No.	Description		
1093	3 d. Sir Kay and Wart searching for lost arrow	35	40
1094	3 d. Merlin the Magician	35	40
1095	3 d. Merlin teaching Wart	35	40
1096	3 d. Wart writing on blackboard	35	40
1097	3 d. Wart transformed into bird and Madame Mim	35	40
1098	3 d. Merlin and Madame Mim	35	40
1099	3 d. Madame Mim transformed into dragon	35	40
1100	3 d. Wart pulling sword from stone	35	40
1101	3 d. King Arthur on throne	35	40

197 "Bebearia senegalensis"

1991. Wildlife. Multicoloured.

1103 1 d. Type **197** 10 15
1104 1 d. "Graphium ridleyanus" (butterfly) .. 10 15
1105 1 d. "Precis antilope" (butterfly) 10 15
1106 1 d. "Charaxes ameliae" (butterfly) 10 15
1107 1 d. Addax 10 15
1108 1 d. Sassaby 10 15
1109 1 d. Civet 10 15
1110 1 d. Green monkey .. 10 15
1111 1 d. Spur-winged goose .. 10 15
1112 1 d. Red-billed hornbill .. 10 15
1113 1 d. Osprey 10 15
1114 1 d. Glossy ibis 10 15
1115 1 d. Egyptian plover .. 10 15
1116 1 d. Golden-tailed woodpecker 10 15
1117 1 d. Green woodhoopoe .. 10 15
1118 1 d. Gaboon viper .. 10 15

Nos. 1103/18 were issued together, se-tenant, forming a composite design.

GHANA

Formerly the Br. Colony of Gold Coast. Attained Dominion status on 6 March 1957, and became a republic within the Br. Commonwealth in 1960.

1957. 12 pence = 1 shilling.
20 shillings = 1 pound.
1965. 100 pesewas = 1 cedi.
1967. 100 new pesewas = 1 new cedi.
1972. 100 pesewas = 1 cedi = 0·8 (old) new cedi.

NOTE. CANCELLED REMAINDERS

In 1961 remainders of some issues of 1957 to 1960 were put on the market concelled-to-order in such a way as to be indistinguishable from genuine postally used copies. Our used quotations which are indicated by an asterisk are, therefore, for cancelled-to-order copies.

29. Dr. Kwame Nkrumah, Palm-nut Vulture and Map of Africa.

1957. Independence Commem.

166. **29.** 2d. red 10 10*
167. 2½d. green 10 10*
168. 4d. brown 10 10*
169. 1s. 3d. blue 15 10*

1957. Queen Elizabeth stamps of 1952 of Gold Coast optd. **GHANA INDEPENDENCE 6TH MARCH 1957.**

170. ½d. brown and red .. 10 10*
171. 1d. blue 10 10*
172. 1½d. green 10 10*
173. 2d. brown 30 30
174. 2½d. red .. .. 1·00 1·25*
175. 3d. mauve 10 10*
176. 4d. blue .. .. 3·00 3·25*
177. 6d. black and orange .. 10 10*
178. 1s. black and red .. 10 10*
179. 2s. olive and red .. 45 10*
180. 5s. purple and black .. 50 10*
181. 10s. black and olive .. 60 30*

31. Viking Ship.

1957. Inaug. of Black Star Shipping Line.

182. **31.** 2½d. green 35 20
183. – 1s. 3d. blue 65 90
184. – 5s. purple .. .. 1·00 2·50

DESIGNS—HORIZ. 1s. 3d., Galleon. 5s. M.V. "Volta River".

34. Ambassador Hotel, Accra.

DESIGNS—HORIZ. 2½d. State Opening of Parliament. 1s. 3d., National Monument. VERT. 2s. Ghana Coat of Arms.

1958. 1st Anniv. of Independence. Flag and Coat of Arms in national colours.

185. **34.** ½d. black and red .. 10 10
186. – 2½d. black, red & yellow 10 10
187. – 1s. 3d. black and blue.. 20 10
188. – 2s. yellow and black .. 25 25

38. Map showing the Independent African States.

1958. 1st Conference of Independent African States, Accra. Star in black and yellow.

189. **38.** 2½d. red and yellow .. 10 10
190. 3d. green and brown .. 10 10
191. – 1s. blue, yellow & orge. 10 10
192. – 2s. 6d. pur., yell. & orge.. .. .. 20 25

DESIGN—VERT. 1s., 2s. 6d. Map of Africa and flaming torch.

40. Palm-nut Vulture over Globe.

DESIGNS—HORIZ. As Type **42**: 1s 3d., "Britannia" airliner. As Type **40**: 2s 6d., Palm-nut vulture and jet aircraft.

42. "Stratocruiser" and Yellow-nosed Albatross.

1958. Inaug. of Ghana Airways. Inscr. as in T **40/42.**

193. **40.** 2½d. black, bistre and red 30 10
194. – 1s 3d. multicoloured (air) 55 15
195. **42.** 2s. multicoloured .. 60 30
196. – 2s. 6d. black and bistre 80 60

1958. Prime Minister's Visit to United States and Canada. Optd. **PRIME MINISTER'S VISIT. U.S.A. AND CANADA.**

197. **29.** 2d. red 10 10
198. 2½d. green 10 10
199. 4d. brown 10 10
200. 1s. 3d. blue 15 20

45. **46.** Dr. Nkrumah and Lincoln Statue, Washington.

1958. United Nations Day.

201. **45.** 2½d. brn., grn. and blk. 10 10
202. 1s. 3d. brn., blue & blk. 15 10
203. 2s. 6d. brn., violet & blk. 20 25

1959. 150th Birth Anniv. of Abraham Lincoln.

204. **46.** 2½d. pink and purple .. 15 10
205. 1s. 3d. light blue & blue 20 20
206. 2s. 6d. yellow and olive 30 30

49. Talking Drums and Elephant-horn Blower.

1959. Independence. Inscr. "SECOND ANNIVERSARY OF INDEPENDENCE".

207. – ½d. multicoloured .. 10 10
208. **49.** 2½d. multicoloured .. 10 10
209. – 1s. 3d. multicoloured .. 10 10
210. – 2s. multicoloured .. 25 50

DESIGNS—HORIZ. ½d. Kente cloth and traditional symbols. 2s. Map of Africa, Ghana flag and palms. VERT. 1s. 3d., "Symbol of Greeting".

52. Globe and Flags.

1959. Africa Freedom Day.

211. **52.** 2½d. multicoloured .. 15 10
212. 8½d. multicoloured .. 15 20

54. Nkrumah Statue, Accra.

55. Ghana Timber.

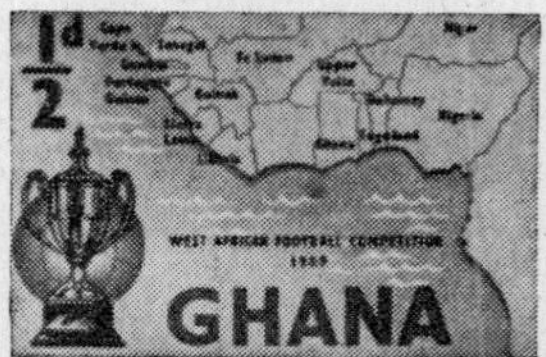

65. Tropical African Cichlid.

1959. Multicoloured.

213 ½d. "God's Omnipotence" (postage) 10 10
213a ½d. "Gye Nyame" .. 30 10
214 1d. Type **54** 10 10
215 1½d. Type **55** 10 10
216 2d. Volta river 10 10
217 2½d. Cocoa bean .. 10 10
218 3d. "God's Omnipotence" 10 10
218a 3d. "Gye Nyame" .. 30 10
219 4d. Diamond and mine .. 1·40 30
220 6d. Red-crowned bishop (bird) 50 10
221 11d. Golden spider lily .. 25 10
222 1s. Shell ginger .. 25 10
223 2s 6d. Giant blue turaco 2·00 15
224 5s. Tiger orchid .. 5·00 50
225 10s. Type **65** .. .. 2·75 70
225a £1 Red-fronted gazelle 11·00 4·75
226 1s. 3d. Pennant-winged nightjar (air) .. .. 1·75 10
227 2s. Crowned cranes .. 1·50 10

SIZES—HORIZ. As Type **54**: ½d. As Type **55**: 2d., 2½d., 3d., 4d., 6d., 1s. 3d., 2s. 6d. As Type **65**: £1. VERT. As Type **55**: 11d., 1s., 2s., 5s. The 3d. is a different symbolic design from the ½d.

68. Gold Cup and West African Map.

1959. West African Football Competition, 1959. Multicoloured.

228. ½d. Type **68** 10 10*
229. 1d. Footballers 10 10*
230. 3d. Goalkeeper saving ball 15 10*
231. 8d. Forward attacking goal 40 10*
232. 2s. 6d. "Kwame Nkrumah" Gold Cup 60 10*

Nos. 229 and 232 are vert. and the rest horiz.

73. Duke of Edinburgh and Arms of Ghana.

1959. Visit of the Duke of Edinburgh

233. **73.** 3d. black and mauve .. 20 10*

74. Ghana Flag and Talking Drums.

1959. U.N. Trusteeship Council. Multicoloured.
234. 3d. Type **74** 10 10*
235. 6d. Ghana flag and U.N. emblem 10 10*
236. 1s. 3d. As 6d. but emblem above flag 25 15*
237. 2s. 6d. "Totem pole" 30 15*
Nos. 235/7 are vert.

78. Eagles in Flight.

1960. 3rd Anniv. of Independence. Mult.
238. ½d. Type **78** 10 10*
239. 3d. Fireworks 10 10*
240. 1s. 3d. "Third Anniversary" 25 10*
241. 2s. "Ship of State" .. 25 15*

82. Flags and Map forming letter "A".

1960. African Freedom Day. Mult.
242. 3d. Type **82** 10 10*
243. 6d. Letter "f" 15 10*
244. 1s. Letter "d" 15 10*

85. Dr. Nkrumah.

1960. Republic Day. Inscr. "REPUBLIC DAY 1st JULY 1960". Multicoloured.
245. 3d. Type **85** 10 10
246. 1s. 3d. Ghana Flag .. 15 10
247. 2s. Torch of Freedom .. 20 10
248. 10s. Ghana Arms 70 70
The 10s. is horiz. and the rest vert.

90. Athlete.

1960. Olympic Games.
249. – 3d. multicoloured .. 10 10
250. – 6d. multicoloured .. 10 10
251. **90.** 1s. 3d. multicoloured .. 15 10
252. 2s. 6d. multicoloured .. 20 20
DESIGN—VERT. 3d., 6d. Olympic torch.

91. Pres. Nkrumah.

1960 Founder's Day. Inscr. as in T **91.**
253. **91.** 3d. multicoloured .. 10 10
254. – 6d. multicoloured .. 10 10
255. – 1s. 3d. multicoloured .. 15 15
DESIGNS—VERT. 6d. Pres. Nkrumah within star. 1s. 3d. Map of Africa and column.

94. U.N. Emblem and Ghana Flag.

1960. Human Rights Day.
256. **94.** 3d. multicoloured .. 10 10
257. – 6d. yellow, black & blue 15 10
258. – 1s. 3d. multicoloured .. 25 15
DESIGNS U.N. Emblem with torch (6d.) or within laurel (1s. 3d.).

97. Talking Drums.

1961. Africa Freedom Day. Inscr. "15th APRIL 1961".
259. **97.** 3d. multicoloured .. 10 10
260. – 6d. red, black and green 15 10
261. – 2s. multicoloured .. 30 25
DESIGNS—VERT. 6d. Map of Africa. HORIZ. 2s. Flags and map.

100. Eagle on Column.

1971. 1st Anniv. of Republic. Inscribed "1st JULY 1961". Multicoloured.
262. 3d. Type **100** 10 10
263. 1s. 3d. "Flower" 10 10
264. 2s. Ghana flags. 20 30

103. Dove with Olive Branch.

DESIGNS—HORIZ 1s. 3d. World map, chain and olive branch. 5s. Rostrum, Conference room.

1961. Belgrade Conf.
265. **103.** 3d. green 10 10
266. – 1s. 3d. blue 20 10
267. – 5s. purple 65 50

106. Pres. Nkrumah and Globe.

1961. Founder's Day Multicoloured.
268. 3d. Type **106** 10 10
269. 1s. 3d. Pres. in Kente cloth 20 10
270. 5s. Pres. in national costume 80 1·25
Nos. 269/70 are vert.

109. Queen Elizabeth II and African Map.

1961. Royal Visit.
271. **109.** 3d. multicoloured .. 15 10
272. 1s. 3d. multicoloured .. 60 15
273. 5s. multicoloured .. 1·75 1·75

110. Ships in Tema Harbour.

1962. Opening of Tema Harbour.
274. **110.** 3d. multicoloured (post.) 15 10
275. – 1s. 3d. multicoloured (air) 40 10
276. – 2s. 6d. multicoloured .. 55 30
DESIGN 1s. 3d., 2s. 6d. Aircraft and ships at Tema.

112. Africa and Peace Dove.

1962. 1st Anniv. of Casablanca Conf.
277. **112.** 3d. multicoloured (post.) 10 10
278. 1s. 3d. multicoloured (air) 20 10
279. 2s. 6d. multicoloured .. 30 30

113. Compass over Africa.
115. Atomic Bomb-burst Skull.

1962. Africa Freedom Day.
280. **113.** 3d. sepia, turq. & purple 10 10
281. 6d. sepia, turq. & brown 10 10
282. 1s. 3d. sepia, turq. & red 10 10

1962. The Accra Assembly.
283. – 3d. black and lake .. 10 10
284. **115.** 6d. black and red .. 15 15
285. – 1s. 3d. turquoise .. 20 15
DESIGNS: 3d. Ghana Star over "five continents". 1s. 3d., Dove of Peace.

117. Patrice Lumumba.

1962. 1st Death Anniv. of Lumumba.
286. **117.** 3d. black and yellow .. 10 10
287. 6d. black, green & lake 10 10
288. 1s. 3d. blk., pink & grn. 15 15

118. Star over Two Columns.

1962. 2nd. Anniv. of Republic. Inscribed "1st JULY 1962". Multicoloured.
289. 3d. Type **118** 10 10
290. 6d. Flaming torch .. 15 15
291. 1s. 3d. Eagle trailing flag .. 25 25
The 1s. 3d. is horiz.

121. President Nkrumah.

DESIGNS: 3d. Nkrumah Medallion. 1s. 3d., President and Ghana Star. 2s. Laying "Ghana" brick.

1962. Founder's Day.
292. **121.** 1d. multicoloured .. 10 10
293. – 3d. multicoloured .. 10 10
294. – 1s. 3d. black and blue .. 25 10
295. – 2s. multicoloured .. 25 20

125. Campaign Emblem.
126. Campaign Emblem.

1962. Malaria Eradication.
296. **125.** 1d. red 10 10
297. 4d. green 20 15
298. 6d. bistre 20 10
299. 1s. 3d. violet 25 20

1963. Freedom from Hunger.
300. **126.** 1d. multicoloured .. 15 10
301. – 4d. sepia, yellow & orge. 75 20
302. – 1s. 3d. ochre, blk. & grn. 1·60 65
DESIGNS—HORIZ. 4d. Emblem in hands. 1s. 3d. World map and emblem.

129. Map of Africa.
133. Red Cross.

1963. Africa Freedom Day.
303. **129.** 1d. gold and red .. 10 10
304. – 4d. red, black & yellow 10 10
305. – 1s. 3d. multicoloured .. 15 10
306. – 2s. 6d. multicoloured .. 25 55
DESIGNS—HORIZ. 4d. Carved stool. VERT. 1s. 3d., Map and bowl of fire. 2s. 6d., Topi and flag.

1963. Centenary of Red Cross. Multicoloured.
307. 1d. Type **133** 35 15
308. 1½d. Centenary emblem .. 45 60
309. 4d. Nurses and child .. 1·50 15
310. 1s. 3d. Emblem, Globe and laurel .. .. 2·75 1·60
The 1½d. and 4d. are horiz.

137. "3rd Anniversary".

1963. 3rd Anniv. of Republic. Multicoloured.

311. 1d. Type **137** 10 10
312. 4d. Three Ghanian flags .. 10 10
313. 1s. 3d. Map, flag and star (vert.) 20 30
314. 2s. 6d. Flag and torch (vert.) 30 50

141. Pres. Nkrumah and Ghana Flag. **145.** Rameses II, Abu Simbel.

1963. Founder's Day.

315. **141.** 1d. multicoloured .. 10 10
316. – 4d. multicoloured .. 10 10
317. – 1s. 3d. multicoloured .. 15 10
318. – 5s. yellow and mauve .. 50 65

DESIGNS—VERT. 4d. As Type **141** but with larger flag behind Pres. Nkrumah. HORIZ. 1s. 3d. Pres. Nkrumah and fireworks. 5s. Native symbol of wisdom.

1963. Preservation of Nubian Monuments. Multicoloured.

319. 1d. Type **145** 10 10
320. 1½d. Rock paintings .. 15 50
321. 2d. Queen Nefertari .. 15 10
322. 4d. Sphinx, Sebua .. 25 15
323. 1s. 3d. Rock Temple, Abu Simbel 70 85

The 1d. and 4d. are vert., the rest horiz.

150. Steam and Diesel Locomotives.

1963. 60th Anniv. of Ghana Railway.

324. **150.** 1d. multicoloured .. 10 10
325. 6d. multicoloured .. 50 10
326. 1s. 3d. multicoloured .. 1·00 60
327. 2s. 6d. multicoloured .. 2·25 2·25

151. Eleanor Roosevelt and "Flame of Freedom".

1963. 5th Anniv. of Declaration of Human Rights. Multicoloured.

328. 1d. Type **151** 10 10
329. 4d. Type **151** 10 10
330. 6d. Eleanor Roosevelt .. 10 10
331. 1s. 3d. Eleanor Roosevelt and emblems (horiz.) .. 10 10

154. Sun and Globe Emblem.

1964. Int. Quiet Sun Years.

332. **154.** 3d. multicoloured .. 10 10
333. 6d. multicoloured .. 15 10
334. 1s. 3d. multicoloured .. 15 10

155. Harvesting Corn on State Farm.

1964. 4th Anniv. of Republic.

335. **155.** 3d. olive, brown & yell. 10 10
336. – 6d. grn., brn & turquoise 10 10
337. – 1s. 3d. red, brn. & salmon 10 10
338. – 5s. multicoloured.. 40 60

DESIGNS: 6d. Oil refinery, Tema. 1s. 3d., "Communal Labour". 5s. Procession headed by flag.

159. Globe and Dove.

1964. 1st Anniv. of African Unity Charter.

339. **159.** 3d. multicoloured .. 10 10
340. – 6d. green and red .. 10 10
341. – 1s. 3d. multicoloured .. 15 10
342. – 5s. multicoloured .. 45 60

DESIGNS—VERT. 6d. Map of Africa and quill pen. 5s. Planting flower. HORIZ. 1s. 3d., Hitched rope on map of Africa.

163. Pres Nkrumah and Hibiscus Flowers.

1964. Founder's Day.

343. **163.** 3d. multicoloured .. 10 10
344. 6d. multicoloured .. 10 10
345. 1s. 3d. multicoloured .. 25 10
346. 2s. 6d. multicoloured .. 30 25

164. Hurdling.

1964. Olympic Games, Tokyo. Multicoloured.

347. 1d. Type **164** 10 10
348. 2½d. Running 10 30
349. 3d. Boxing 10 10
350. 4d. Long-jumping .. 10 10
351. 6d. Football 10 10
352. 1s. 3d. Athlete holding Olympic Torch 15 10
353. 5s. Olympic "Rings" and Flags .. .. .. 65 2·00

Nos. 249/52 are vert.

171. G. Washington Carver (botanist) and Plant.

1964. UNESCO Week.

354. **171.** 6d. blue and green .. 15 10
355. – 1s. 3d. purple and blue 35 10
356. **171.** 5s. sepia and red .. 1·40 2·00

DESIGN: 1s. 3d., Albert Einstein (scientist) and Atomic symbol.

173. African Elephant.

1964. Multicoloured.

357. 1d. Type **173** 30 15
358. 1½d. Secretary bird (horiz.) 45 1·00
359. 2½d. Purple wreath (flower) 45 1·00
360. 3d. Grey parrot 55 30
361. 4d. Blue-naped mousebird (horiz.) 75 50
362. 6d. African tulip tree (horiz.) 45 20
363. 1s 3d. Violet starling (horiz.) .. .. .. 1·50 1·25
364. 2s 6d. Hippopotamus (horiz.) .. .. .. 1·50 4·00

181. I.C.Y. Emblem.

1965. Int. Co-operation Year.

365. **181.** 1d. multicoloured .. 30 20
366. 4d. multicoloured .. 85 45
367. 6d. multicoloured .. 1·00 20
368. 1s. 3d. multicoloured .. 1·60 1·90

182. I.T.U. Emblem and Symbols.

1965. Centenary of I.T.U.

369. **182.** 1d. multicoloured .. 15 15
370. 6d. multicoloured .. 45 15
371. 1s. 3d. multicoloured .. 85 25
372. 5s. multicoloured .. 2·25 2·75

183. Lincoln's Home.

1965. Death Cent. of Abraham Lincoln.

373. **183.** 6d. multicoloured .. 15 10
374. – 1s. 3d. black, red & blue 30 15
375. – 2s. black, brn. & yellow 40 30
376. – 3s. black and red .. 85 1·50

DESIGNS: 1s. 3d., Lincoln's Inaugural Address. 2s. Abraham Lincoln. 5s. Adaption of U.S. 90 c. Lincoln stamp of 1869.

187. Obverse (Pres. Nkrumah) and Reverse of 5 p. Coin.

1965. Introduction of Decimal Currency. Multicoloured designs showing coins expressed in the same denominations as on the stamps.

377. 5 p. Type **187** 20 10
378. 10 p. As Type **187** .. 25 10
379. 25 p. Size 63 × 39 mm. .. 85 1·00
380. 50 p. Size 71 × 43½ mm. .. 1·75 2·25

1965. Nos. 214/27 surch. **Ghana New Currency 19th July, 1965,** and value. Multicoloured.

381. **54.** 1 p. on 1d. (postage) .. 10 10
382. – 2 p. on 2d. 10 10
383. – 3 p. on 3d. (No. 218a) 95 2·50
384. – 4 p. on 4d. .. .. 1·25 30
385. – 6 p. on 6d. 30 10
386. – 11 p. on 11d. 25 10
387. – 12 p. on 1s. 25 10
388. – 30 p. on 2s. 6d. .. 2·25 1·00
389. – 60 p. on 5s. .. .. 4·00 70
390. **65.** ₵1.20 on 10s. .. .. 1·75 2·25
391. – ₵2.40 on £1 .. .. 2·00 6·00
392. – 15 p. on 1s. 3d. (air) .. 2·00 35
393. – 24 p. on 2s. .. .. 2·50 30

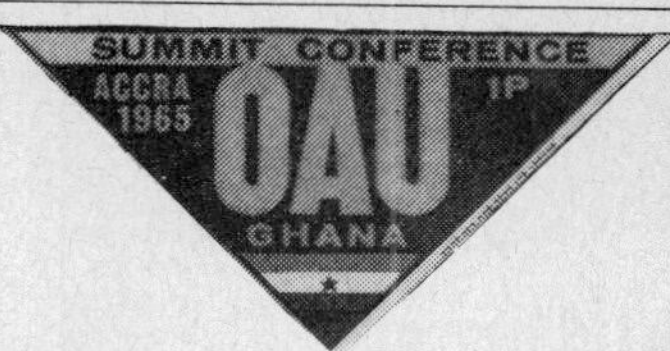

189. "OAU" and Flag (reduced size illustration. Actual size 60 × 30 mm.).

1965. O.A.U. Summit Conf., Accra. **Mult.**

394. 1 p. Type **189** 10 10
395. 2 p. "OAU", Heads & Flag 10 10
396. 5 p. O.A.U. Emblem & Flag 10 10
397. 6 p. African Map and Flag 10 10
398. 15 p. "Sunburst" and Flag 20 25
399. 24 p. "OAU" on Map, and Flag 35 50

Nos. 397/9 are horiz., 37½ × 27½ mm.

195. Goalkeeper saving Ball.

1965. African Soccer Cup Competition. **Mult.**

400. 6 p. Type **195** 10 10
401. 15 p. Player with ball (vert.) 20 20
402. 24 p. Player, ball and Soccer Cup 35 40

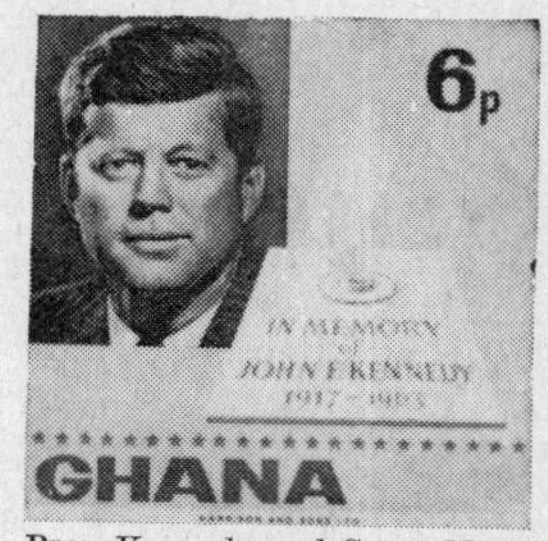

198. Pres. Kennedy and Grave Memorial.

1965. 2nd Death Anniv. of Pres. Kennedy.

403. **198.** 6 p. multicoloured .. 15 10
404. – 15 p. violet, red & green 40 35
405. – 24 p. black and purple .. 50 60
406. – 30 p. dull purple & black 60 75

DESIGNS: 15 p. Pres. Kennedy and Eternal Flame. 24 p. Pres. Kennedy and Memorial Inscription. 30 p. Pres. Kennedy.

202. Section of Dam and Generators.

1966. Volta River Project.

408. **202.** 6 p. multicoloured .. 15 10
409. – 15 p. multicoloured .. 20 15
410. – 24 p. multicoloured .. 25 20
411. – 30 p. black and blue .. 35 50

DESIGNS: 15 p. Dam and Lake Volta. 24 p. Word "GHANA" as Dam. 30 p. "Fertility".

1966. "Black Stars" Victory in African Soccer Cup Competition. Optd. **Black Stars Retain Africa Cup 21st Nov. 1965.**

412. **195.** 6 p. multicoloured .. 10 10
413. – 15 p. multicoloured .. 20 20
414. – 24 p. multicoloured .. 35 35

207. W.H.O. Building and Ghana Flag.

1966. Inauguration of W.H.O. Headquarters, Geneva. Multicoloured.

415. 6 p. Type **207** 40 50
416. 15 p. Type **207** .. .. 75 1·00
417. 24 p. W.H.O. Building and Emblem .. .. .. 1·00 1·75
418. 30 p. W.H.O. Building and Emblem .. .. .. 1·25 3·00

209. Herring.

1966. Freedom from Hunger. Multicoloured.
420. 6 p. Type **209** 15 10
421. 15 p. Flat Fish 35 15
422. 24 p. Spade Fish 65 35
423. 30 p. Red Snapper .. 80 75
424. 60 p. Tuna .. .. 2·00 2·50

214. African " Links " and Ghana Flag.

1966. 3rd Anniv. of African Charter. Mult.
426. 6 p. Type **214** 10 10
427. 15 p. Flags as " Quill " and Diamond (horiz.) .. 25 20
428. 24 p. Ship's Wheel, Map and Cocoa Bean (horiz.) .. 30 25

217. Player Heading Ball, and Jules Rimet Cup.

1966. World Cup Football Championships. Multicoloured.
429. 5 p. Type **217** 15 10
430. 15 p. Goalkeeper clearing ball 40 20
431. 24 p. Player and Jules Rimet Cup (Replica) 55 35
432. 30 p. Players and Jules Rimet Cup (Replica) .. 75 90
433. 60 p. Players with ball .. 1·50 2·50

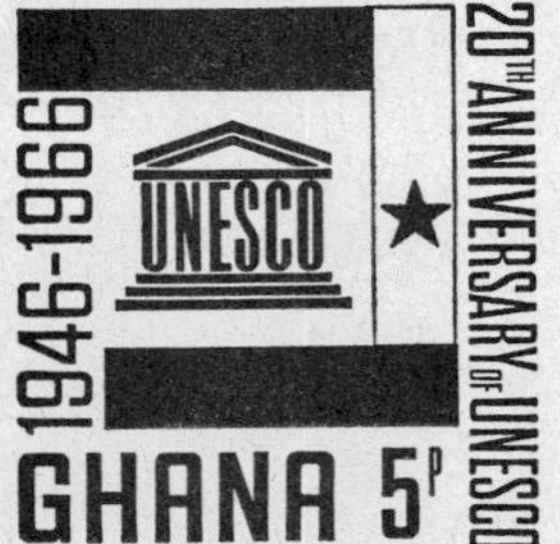

222. U.N.E.S.C.O. Emblem.

1966. 20th Anniv. of U.N.E.S.C.O.
435. **222.** 5 p. multicoloured .. 25 15
436. 15 p. multicoloured .. 50 35
437. 24 p. multicoloured .. 80 80
438. 30 p. multicoloured .. 1·25 1·75
439. 60 p. multicoloured .. 2·25 3·50

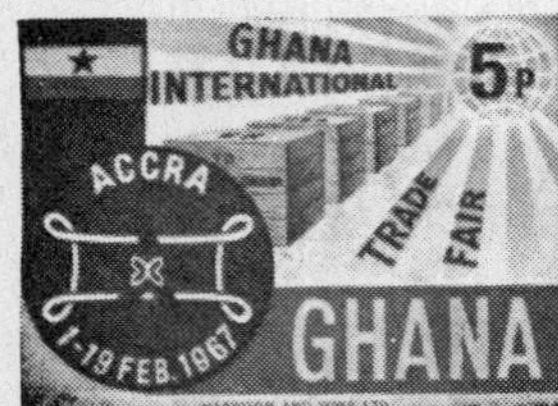

223. Fair Emblem and Crates.

1967. Ghana Trade Fair, Accra. Multicoloured.
441. 5 p. Type **223** 10 10
442. 15 p. Fair Emblem and World Map 15 15
443. 24 p. Shipping and flags .. 25 30
444. 36 p. Fair Emblem and hand-held hoist.. .. 40 80

1967. New Currency. Nos. 216/26 and 393 surch. with new value.
445. 1½ n.p. on 2d. (postage) .. 5·50 3·25
446. 3½ n.p. on 4d. .. .. 1·00 30
447. 5 n.p. on 6d. 35 15
448. 9 n.p. on 11d. 30 15
449. 10 n.p. on 1s. 30 15
450. 25 n.p. on 2s. 6d. .. .. 3·25 2·00
451. 1 n.c. on 10s. .. .. 6·50 11·00
452. 2 n.c. on £1 .. .. 12·00 22·00
453. 12½ n.p. on 1s. 3d. (air) .. 3·00 90
454. 20 n.p. on 24 p. on 2s. .. 3·00 1·75

229. Ghana Eagle and Flag.

1967. 1st Anniv. of 24 February Revolution.
455. **229.** 1 n.p. multicoloured .. 10 15
456. 4 n.p. multicoloured .. 10 10
457. 12½ n.p. multicoloured 40 55
458. 25 n.p. multicoloured .. 85 2·00

230. Maize.

232. The Ghana Mace.

1967. Multicoloured.
460. 1 n.p. Type **230** 10 10
461. 1½ n.p. Forest Kingfisher 90 30
462. 2 n.p. Type **232** 10 10
463. 2½ n.p. Commelina .. 35 10
464. 3 n.p. Mud-fish 20 30
465. 4 n.p. Rufous-crowned Roller .. .. .. 1·50 10
466. 6 n.p. Akosombo Dam .. 15 10
467. 8 n.p. Adomi Bridge .. 15 10
468. 9 n.p. Chameleon 45 10
469. 10 n.p. Tema Harbour .. 15 10
470. 20 n.p. Bush hare (blue) .. 20 10
471. 50 n.p. Black-winged Stilt 3·50 35
472. 1 n.c. Wooden Stool .. 2·25 75
473. 2 n.c. Frangipani .. .. 2·00 3·00
474. 2 n.c. 50 Seat of State .. 3·25 4·00

Sizes—(As Type **230**)—vert. 4 n.p. horiz. 8 n.p. (As Type **232**). vert. 1½ n.p., 2½ n.p., 20 n.p., 2 n.c. and 2 n.c. 50. horiz. 3 n.p., 6 n.p., 9 n.p., 10 n.p., 50 n.p. and 1 n.c.

245. Kumasi Fort.

1967. Castles and Forts.
475. **245.** 4 n.p. multicoloured .. 25 10
476. – 12½ n.p. multicoloured 1·00 1·00
477. – 20 n.p. multicoloured .. 1·40 2·00
478. – 25 n.p. multicoloured .. 1·75 2·50

Designs: 12½ n.p. Christiansborg Castle and British Galleon. 20 n.p. Elimina Castle and Portuguese Galleon. 25 n.p. Cape Coast, Castle and Spanish Galleon.

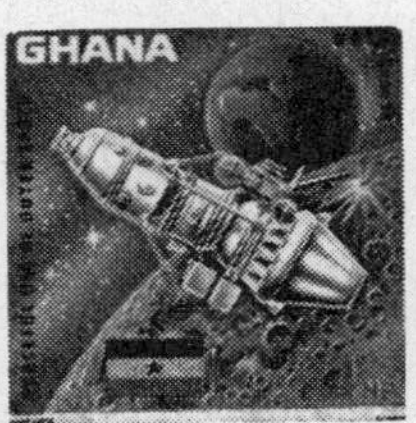

249. "Luna 10".

1967. "Peaceful Use of Outer Space". Mult.
479. 4 n.p. Type **249** 10 10
480. 10 n.p. "Orbiter 1" .. 10 15
481. 12½ n.p. Man in Space .. 20 30

252. Scouts and Camp-fire.

1967. 50th Anniv. of Ghanaian Scout Movement. Multicoloured.
483. 4 n.p. Type **252** 20 10
484. 10 n.p. Scout on march .. 50 20
485. 12½ n.p. Lord Baden-Powell 70 70

255. U.N. Headquarters Building.

1967. U.N. Day (24 October).
487. **255.** 4 n.p. multicoloured .. 15 10
488. 10 n.p. multicoloured 20 15
489. – 50 n.p. mulitcoloured .. 40 70
490. – 2 n.c. 50 multicoloured 1·50 4·00

Design: 50 n.p., 2 n.c. 50, General View of U.N. H.Q., Manhattan.

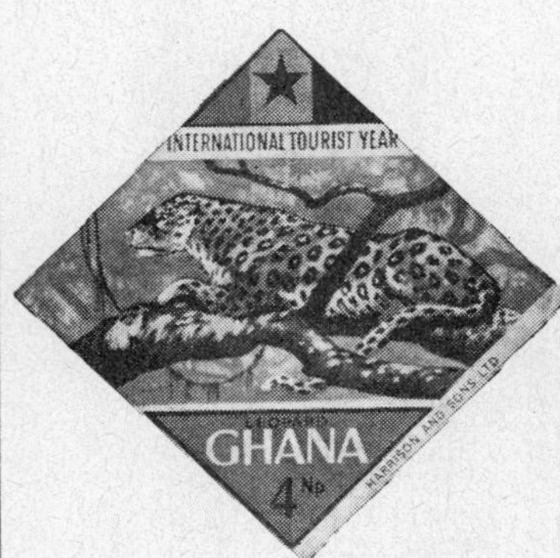

257. Leopard.

1987. International Tourist Year. Mult.
492 4 n.p. Type **257** 50 10
493 12½ n.p. "Papilio demodocus" (butterfly) .. 1·00 1·25
494 20 n.p. Carmine bee eater 2·00 2·75
495 50 n.p. Waterbuck .. 3·00 4·75

261. Revolutionaries entering Accra.

1968. 2nd Anniv. of February Revolution. Multicoloured.
497. 4 n.p. Type **261** 10 10
498. 12½ n.p. Marching Troops 20 20
499. 20 n.p. Cheering People .. 30 40
500. 40 n.p. Victory Celebrations 50 1·25

265. Microscope and Cocoa Beans.

1968. Cocoa Research.
501. **265.** 2½ n.p. multicoloured .. 10 10
502. – 4 n.p. multicoloured .. 10 10
503. **265.** 10 n.p. multicoloured .. 15 15
504. – 25 n.p. multicoloured .. 60 80

Designs: 4 n.p. and 25 n.p. Microscope and Cocoa Tree, Beans and Pods.

267. Kotoka and Flowers.

1968. 1st Death Anniv. of Lt.-Gen. E. K. Kotoka. Multicoloured.
506. 4 n.p. Type **267** 10 10
507. 12½ n.p. Kotoka & Wreath 20 20
508. 20 n.p. Kotoka in Civilian Clothes 35 65
509. 40 n.p. Lt.-Gen. Kotoka .. 50 1·00

271. Tobacco.

1968. Multicoloured.
510. 4 n.p. Type **271** 15 10
511. 5 n.p. North African crested porcupine .. 15 15
512. 12½ n.p. Rubber 50 65
513. 20 n.p. "Cymothoe sangaris" (butterfly) .. 1·00 1·75
514. 40 n.p. "Charaxes ameliae" (butterfly) .. .. 1·75 3·50

276. Surgeons, Flag and W.H.O. Emblem.

1968. 20th Anniv. of W.H.O.
516. **276.** 4 n.p. multicoloured .. 20 10
517. 12½ n.p. multicoloured 40 35
518. 20 n.p. multicoloured .. 70 70
519. 40 n.p. multicoloured .. 1·25 1·50

277. Hurdling.

1969. Olympic Games, Mexico (1968). **Mult.**
521. 4 n.p. Type **277** 10 10
522. 12½ n.p. Boxing 20 30
523. 20 n.p. Torch. Olympic Rings and Flags .. . 40 70
524. 40 n.p. Football .. .. 70 1·50

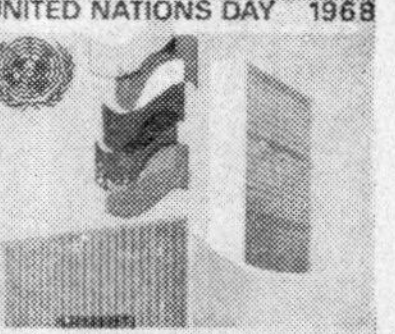

281. U.N. Building.

1969. U.N. Day. Multicoloured.
526. 4 n.p. Type **281** 10 10
527. 12½ n.p. Native school staff and U.N. Emblem 15 20
528. 20 n.p. U.N. Building and Emblem over Ghanaian Flag.. .. 25 35
529. 40 n.p. U.N. Emblem encircled by flags .. 50 90

285. Dr. J. B. Danquah.

1969. Human Rights Year. Multicoloured.

531. 4 n.p. Type **285** 10 10
532. 12½ n.p. Dr. Martin Luther King 20 30
533. 20 n.p. As 12½ n.p. .. 35 60
534. 40 n.p. Type **285** .. .. 55 1·10

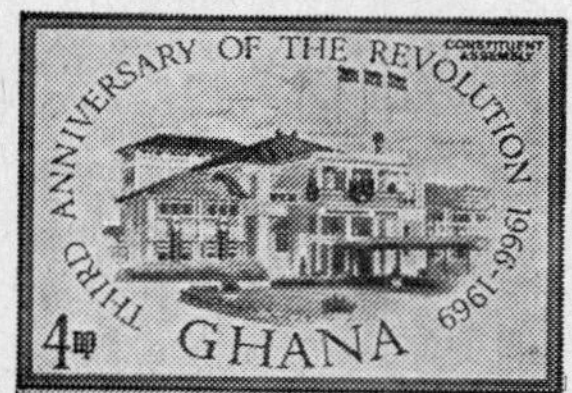

287. Constituent Assembly Building.

1969. 3rd Anniv. of Revolution. Mult.

536. 4 n.p. Type **287** .. 10 10
537. 12½ n.p. Arms of Ghana .. 10 10
538. 20 n.p. As Type **287** 15 15
539. 40 n.p. As 12½ n.p. 20 35

1969. New Constitution. Nos. 460/74 optd. **NEW CONSTITUTION 1969.**

541. **230.** 1 n.p. multicoloured .. 10 40
542. – 1½ n.p. multicoloured .. 60 60
543. **232.** 2 n.p. multicoloured 10 45
544. – 2½ n.p. multicoloured .. 10 45
545. – 3 n.p. multicoloured 45 60
546. – 4 n.p. multicoloured 1·25 30
547. – 6 n.p. multicoloured 15 50
548. – 8 n.p. multicoloured 15 40
549. – 9 n.p. multicoloured 15 50
550. – 10 n.p. multicoloured .. 20 40
551. – 20 n.p. multicoloured .. 35 70
552. – 50 n.p. multicoloured .. 4·00 4·25
553. – 1 n.c. multicoloured .. 2·25 4·50
554. – 2 n.c. multicoloured .. 3·50 7·00
555. – 2 n.c. 50 multicoloured 3·50 8·00

On Nos. 541, 545, 547/50 and 552/3 the overprint is horiz. The rest are vert.

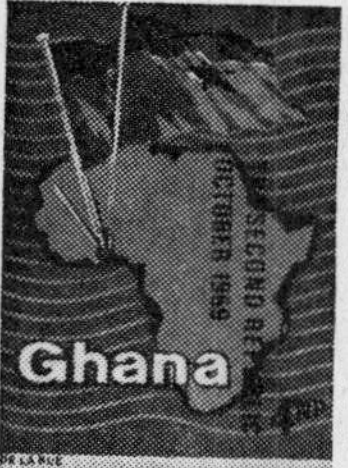

290. Map of Africa and Flags.

1969. Inaug. of 2nd Republic. Multicoloured.

556. 4 n.p. Type **290** 10 10
557. 12½ n.p. Figure "2", Branch and Ghanaian Colours .. 20 10
558. 20 n.p. Hands receiving egg 30 30
559. 40 n.p. Type **290** 60 70

293. I.L.O. Emblem and Cog-wheels.

1970. 50th Anniv. of I.L.O.

560. **293.** 4 np. multicoloured .. 10 10
561. 12½ n.p. multicoloured 20 25
562. 20 n.p. multicoloured .. 30 45

294. Red Cross and Globe.

1970. 50th Anniv. of League of Red Cross Societies. Multicoloured.

564. 4 n.p. Type **294** 25 10
565. 12½ n.p. Henri Dunant and Red Cross emblem .. 45 20
566. 20 n.p. Patient receiving medicine 55 55
567. 40 n.p. Patient having arm bandaged .. .. 80 1·40

Nos. 565/7 are horiz.

298. General Kotoka, "VC-10" and Airport.

1970. Inaug. of Kotoka Airport. Mult.

569. 4 n.p. Type **298** 10 10
570. 12½ n.p. Control Tower and tail of "VC-10" .. 20 15
571. 20 n.p. Aerial view of airport 30 30
572. 40 n.p. Airport and flags .. 60 80

302. Lunar Module landing on Moon.

1970. Moon Landing. Multicoloured.

573. 4 n.p. Type **302** 30 10
574. 12½ n.p. Astronaut's first step onto the Moon .. 85 60
575. 20 n.p. Astronaut with equipment on Moon .. 1·40 1·40
576. 40 n.p. Astronauts .. 3·00 3·00

Nos. 575/6 are horiz.

306. Adult Education.

1970. Int. Education Year. Multicoloured.

578. 4 n.p. Type **306** 10 10
579. 12½ n.p. International education 20 20
580. 20 n.p. "Ntesie" and I.E.Y. symbols .. 35 30
581. 40 n.p. Nursery School .. 60 85

310. Saluting March-Past.

1970. 1st Anniv. of Second Republic. Mult.

582. 4 n.p. Type **310** 10 10
583. 12½ n.p. Busia Declaration 15 15
584. 20 n.p. Doves Symbol .. 25 30
585. 40 n.p. Opening of Parliament 50 65

314. "Crinum ornatum".

1970. Flora and Fauna. Multicoloured.

586. 4 n.p. Type **314** .. 1·00 10
587. 12½ n.p. Lioness .. .. 1·10 35
588. 20 n.p. "Ansellia africana" (flower) .. 1·25 80
589. 40 n.p. African elephant .. 3·50 2·50

315. Kuduo Brass Casket.

1970. Monuments and Archaeological Sites in Ghana. Multicoloured.

590. 4 n.p. Type **315** .. 15 10
591. 12½ n.p. Akan Traditional House 35 20
592. 20 n.p. Larabanga Mosque 60 50
593. 40 n.p. Funerary Clay Head .. .. 90 1·10

316. Trade Fair Building.

1971. Int. Trade Fair, Accra. Multicoloured.

595. 4 n.p. Type **316** 10 10
596. 12½ n.p. Cosmetics and pharmaceutical goods .. 40 20
597. 20 n.p. Vehicles .. 45 25
598. 40 n.p. Construction equipment 80 95
599. 50 n.p. Transport and packing case .. .. 90 1·10

The 50 n.p. is vert.

317. Christ on the Cross.

1971. Easter. Multicoloured.

600. 4 n.p. Type **317** .. 15 10
601. 12½ n.p. Christ & Disciples 25 35
602. 20 n.p. Christ blessing Disciples 40 75

318. Corn Cob.

1971. Freedom From Hunger Campaign.

603. **318.** 4 n.p. multicoloured .. 10 10
604. 12½ n.p. multicoloured 35 60
605. 20 n.p. multicoloured 65 1·10

Remainder stocks of the above stamps were overprinted on the occasion of the death of Lord Boyd Orr and further surcharged 12½, 20 and 60 n.p.

It is understood that 8070 sets from the agency were overprinted locally and returned to New York. Limited remainders of these stamps (only 330 of 60 n.p.) were sold at the G.P.O. We do not list these as they were not freely on sale in Ghana.

319. Guides Emblem and Ghana Flag.

1971. Golden Jubilee of Ghana Girl Guides. Each design includes Guides emblem. Mult.

606. 4 n.p. Type **319** 20 10
607. 12½ n.p. Mrs. E. Ofuatey-Kodjoe (founder) and guides with flags .. 60 50
608. 20 n.p. Guides laying stones 90 90
609. 40 n.p. Camp-fire and tent 1·50 1·75
610. 50 n.p. Signallers .. 1·75 2·00

320. Child-care Centre.

1971. Y.W.C.A. World Council Meeting Accra. Multicoloured.

612. 4 n.p. Type **320** 10 10
613. 12½ n.p. Council Meeting 10 15
614. 20 n.p. School typing class 15 30
615. 40 n.p. Building Fund Day 30 60

321. Firework Display. **322.** Weighing Baby.

1971. Christmas. Multicoloured.

617. 1 n.p. Type **321** 10 20
618. 3 n.p. African Nativity 15 30
619. 6 n.p. The Flight into Egypt 15 30

1971. 25th Anniv. of U.N.I.C.E.F. Mult.

620. 5 n.p. Type **322** 10 10
621. 15 n.p. Mother and child (horiz.) 30 70
622. 30 n.p. Nurse .. .. 40 1·75
623. 50 n.p. Young boy (horiz.) 60 2·50

323. Unity Symbol and Trade Fair Emblem.

1972. All African Trade Fair. Multicoloured.

625. 5 np. Type **323** .. 10 10
626. 15 np. Horn of Plenty .. 20 30
627. 30 np. Fireworks on map of Africa .. 35 70
628. 60 np. "Participating Nations" .. .. 50 1·50
629. 1 nc. As No. 628 .. 80 2·25

On 24 June, 1972, on the occasion of the Belgian International Philatelic Exhibition, Nos. 625/9 were issued overprinted **"BELGICA 72"**. Only very limited supplies were sent to Ghana (we understand not more than 900 sets), and for this reason we do not list them.

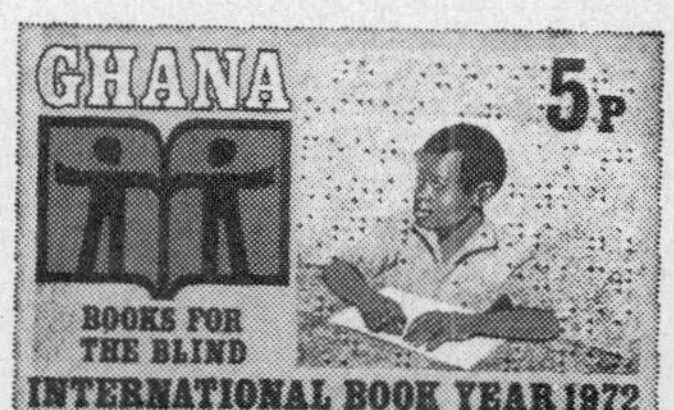

324. Books for the Blind.

1972. Int. Book Year. Multicoloured.

630. 5 p. Type **324** 15 10
631. 15 p. Children's books .. 40 50
632. 30 p. Books for recreation 70 85
633. 50 p. Books for students .. 1·25 2·00
634. 1 c. Book and flame of knowledge (vert.) .. 2·00 2·75

325. "Hypoxis urceolata".

1972. Flora and Fauna. Multicoloured.

636. 5 p. Type **325** 30 10
637. 15 p. Mona monkey .. 65 65
638. 30 p. "Crinum ornatum" .. 3·50 2·50
639. 1 c. De Winton's Tree squirrel .. .. .. 4·50 6·00

326. Football.

1972. Olympic Games, Munich. Mult.

No.	Description		
640.	5 p. Type **326**	10	10
641.	15 p. Running	20	20
642.	30 p. Boxing	40	60
643.	50 p. Long-jumping ..	70	1·40
644.	1 c. High-jumping ..	1·25	2·25

327. Senior Scout and Cub.

1972. 65th Anniv. of Boy Scouts. Mult.

No.	Description		
646.	5 p. Type **327**	30	10
647.	15 p. Scout and tent ..	65	45
648.	30 p. Sea scouts	1·25	1·00
649.	50 p. Leader with cubs ..	1·60	1·75
650.	1 c. Training school ..	3·00	3·25

328. "The Holy Night" (Correggio).

1972. Christmas. Multicoloured.

No.	Description		
652.	1 p. Type **328**	10	10
653.	3 p. "Adoration of the Kings" (Holbein) ..	10	10
654.	15 p. "Madonna of the Passion" (School of Ricco)	30	30
655.	30 p. "King Melchior" ..	55	55
656.	60 p. "King Gaspar", Mary and Jesus ..	90	1·25
657.	1 c. "King Balthasar" ..	1·50	2·25

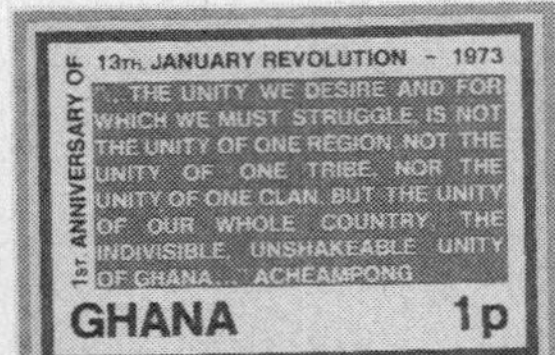

329. Extract from Speech.

1973. 1st Anniv. of 13 January Revolution. Multicoloured.

No.	Description		
659.	1 p. Type **329**	10	10
660.	3 p. Market scene ..	10	10
661.	5 p. Selling bananas (vert.)	10	10
662.	15 p. Farmer with hoe and produce (vert.) ..	20	25
663.	30 p. Market traders ..	30	40
664.	1 c. Farmer cutting palm-nuts	70	1·40

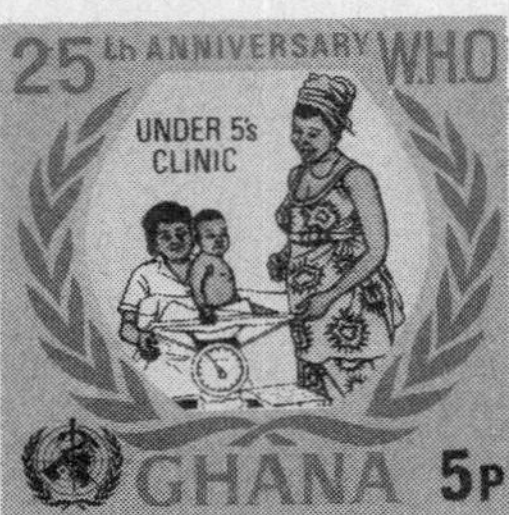

330. Under 5's Clinic.

1973. 25th Anniv. of W.H.O. Multicoloured.

No.	Description		
666.	5 p. Type **330**	10	10
667.	15 p. Radiography ..	25	30
668.	30 p. Immunisation ..	35	50
669.	50 p. Starving child ..	50	1·25
670.	1 c. W.H.O. H.Q., Geneva	1·00	2·25

1973. World Scouting Conference. Nairobi/Addis Ababa. Nos. 646/50 optd. **1st WORLD SCOUTING CONFERENCE IN AFRICA.**

No.	Description		
671. **327.**	5 p. multicoloured ..	10	15
672. –	15 p. multicoloured ..	35	60
673. –	30 p. multicoloured ..	60	1·25
674. –	50 p. multicoloured ..	80	1·75
675. –	1 c. multicoloured ..	1·50	2·75

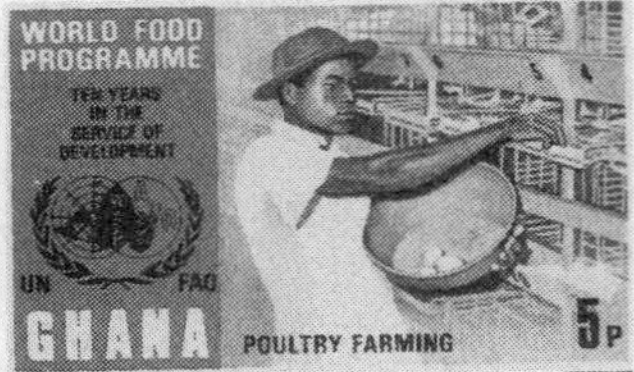

332. Poultry Farming.

1973. 10th Anniv. of World Food Programme. Multicoloured.

No.	Description		
677.	5 p. Type **332**	10	10
678.	15 p. Mechanisation ..	15	15
679.	50 p. Cocoa harvest ..	40	90
680.	1 c. F.A.O. H.Q., Rome ..	60	1·90

333. "Green Alert".

1973. 50th Anniv. of Interpol. Multicoloured.

No.	Description		
682.	5 p. Type **333**	15	10
683.	30 p. "Red Alert" ..	75	80
684.	50 p. "Blue Alert" ..	1·50	1·75
685.	1 c. "Black Alert" ..	3·00	4·00

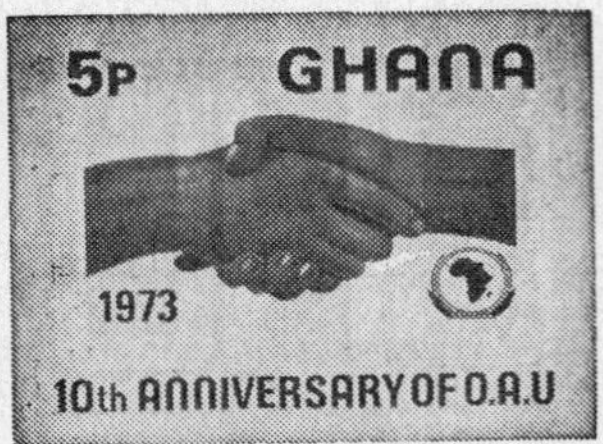

334. Handshake.

1973. 10th Anniv. of O.A.U. Multicoloured.

No.	Description		
686.	5 p. Type **334**	10	10
687.	30 p. Africa Hall Addis Ababa	15	30
688.	50 p. O.A.U. emblem ..	30	80
689.	1 c. "X" in colours of Ghana flag	45	1·25

335. Weather Balloon.

1973. Cent. of I.M.O./W.M.O. Multicoloured.

No.	Description		
690.	5 p. Type **335**	10	10
691.	15 p. Satellite "Tiros" ..	20	20
692.	30 p. Computer weather map	40	65
693.	1 c. Radar screen ..	80	2·25

336. Epiphany Scene.

1973. Christmas. Multicoloured.

No.	Description		
695.	1 p. Type **336**	10	10
696.	3 p. Madonna and Child ..	10	10
697.	30 p. "Madonna and Child" (Murillo) ..	30	75
698.	50 p. "Adoration of the Magi" (Tiepolo) ..	45	1·00

337. "Christ carrying the Cross" (Thomas de Kolozsvar).

1974. Easter.

No.	Description		
700. **337.**	5 p. multicoloured ..	10	10
701. –	30 p. bl., silver & brn.	20	35
702. –	50 p. red, silver & brn.	30	60
703. –	1 c. green, silver & brn.	50	1·25

DESIGNS (from 15th-century English carved alabaster)—30 p. "The Betrayal". 50 p. "The Deposition". 1 c. "The Risen Christ and Mary Magdalene".

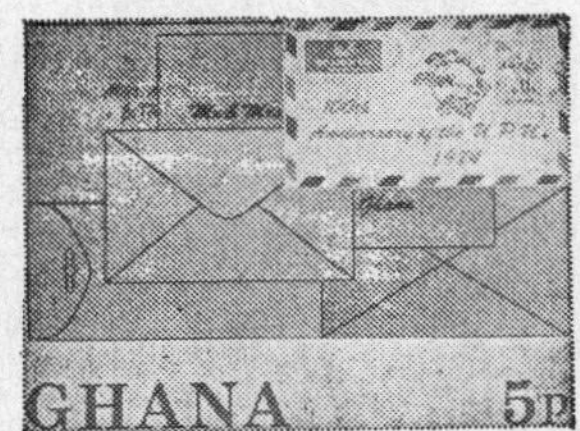

338. Letters.

1974. Centenary of U.P.U. Multicoloured.

No.	Description		
705.	5 p. Type **338**	10	10
706.	9 p. U.P.U. Monument and H.Q.	15	15
707.	50 p. Airmail letter ..	50	1·00
708.	1 c. U.P.U. Monument and Ghana stamp ..	80	1·75

1974. "Internaba 1974" Stamp Exn. As Nos. 705/8 additionally inscr. "INTERNABA 1974".

No.	Description		
710.	5 p. multicoloured ..	10	10
711.	9 p. multicoloured ..	15	15
712.	50 p. multicoloured ..	40	1·00
713.	1 c. multicoloured ..	60	1·75

339. Footballers.

1974. World Cup Football Championships.

No.	Description		
715. **339.**	5 p. multicoloured ..	10	10
716. –	30 p. multicoloured ..	25	50
717. –	50 p. multicoloured ..	35	75
718. –	1 c. multicoloured ..	50	1·50

DESIGNS: As Type **339** showing footballers in action.

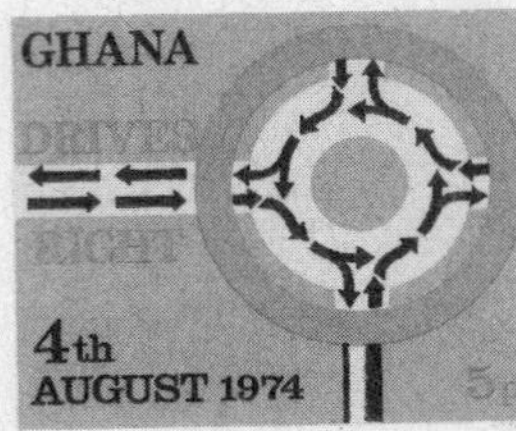

340. Roundabout.

1974. Change to Driving on the Right.

No.	Description		
720. **340.**	5 p. grn., red & blk. ..	10	10
721. –	15 p. pur., red & blk.	25	35
722. –	30 p. multicoloured ..	45	60
723. –	50 p. multicoloured ..	70	1·10
724. –	1 c. multicoloured ..	1·40	2·00

DESIGNS—HORIZ. 15 p. Warning triangle sign. VERT. 30 p. Highway arrow and slogan. 50 p. Warning hands. 1 c. Car on symbolic hands.

1974. West Germany's Victory in World Cup. Nos. 715/18 optd. **WEST GERMANY WINNERS.**

No.	Description		
725.	5 p. multicoloured ..	10	10
726.	30 p. multicoloured ..	35	40
727.	50 p. multicoloured ..	50	55
728.	1 c. multicoloured ..	90	1·25

342. "Planned Family".

1974. World Population Year. Multicoloured.

No.	Description		
730.	5 p. Type **342**	10	10
731.	30 p. Family planning clinic	25	35
732.	50 p. Immunization ..	35	60
733.	1 c. Population census enumeration	60	1·40

343. Angel.

1974. Christmas. Multicoloured.

No.	Description		
734.	5 p. Type **343**	10	10
735.	7 p. The Magi (diamond 47 × 47 mm.)	10	10
736.	9 p. The Nativity ..	10	10
737.	1 c. The Annunciation ..	60	1·40

1975. "Apollo-Soyuz" Space Link. Nos. 715/18 optd. with **Apollo Soyuz July 15, 1975.**

No.	Description		
739. **339.**	5 p. multicoloured ..	10	10
740. –	30 p. multicoloured ..	25	25
741. –	50 p. multicoloured ..	45	55
742. –	1 c. multicoloured ..	70	80

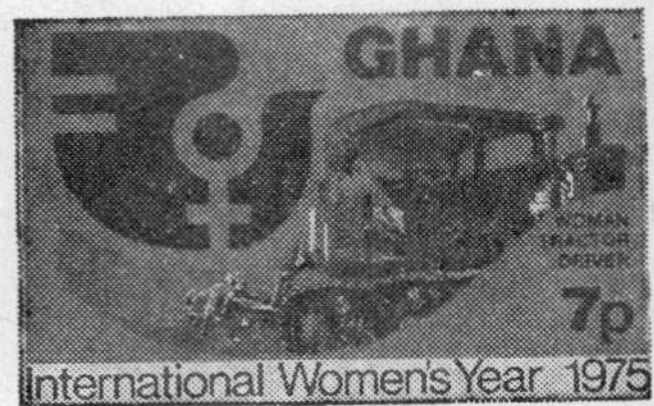

345. Tractor Driver.

1975. International Women's Year. Mult.

No.	Description		
744.	7 p. Type **345**	15	10
745.	30 p. Motor mechanic ..	35	35
746.	60 p. Factory workers ..	60	80
747.	1 c. Cocoa research ..	90	1·40

346. Angel.

1975. Christmas.

No.	Description		
749. **346.**	2 p. multicoloured ..	10	10
750. –	5 p. yellow and green	10	10
751. –	7 p. yellow and green	10	10
752. –	30 p. yellow and green	20	20
753. –	1 c. yellow and green	50	1·00

DESIGNS: 5 p. Angel with harp. 7 p. Angel with lute. 30 p. Angel with viol. 1 c. Angel with trumpet.

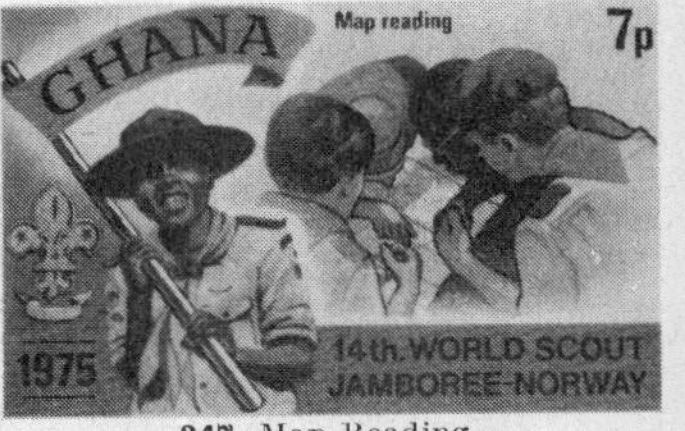

347. Map Reading.

1976. 14th World Scout Jamboree, Norway. Multicoloured.

No.	Description		
755.	7 p. Type **347**	30	1
756.	30 p. Sailing	85	7
757.	60 p. Hiking	1·50	1·7
758.	1 c. Life-saving	2·00	2·5

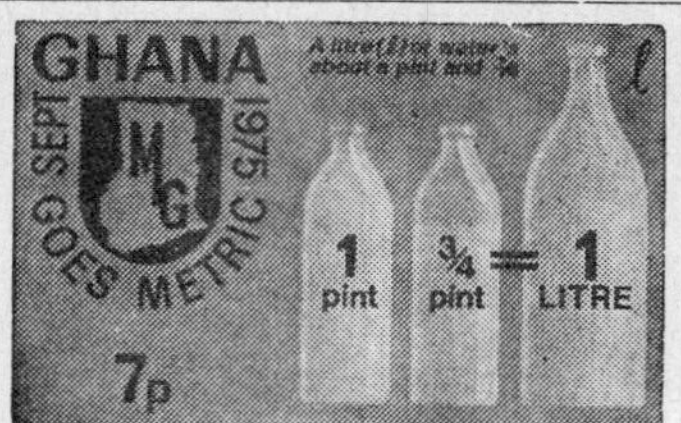

348. Bottles (litre).

1976. Metrication Publicity. Mult.

760. 7 p. Type **348** 15 10
761. 30 p. Scales (kilogramme) 40 40
762. 60 p. Tape measure and bale of cloth (metre) .. 80 1·00
763. 1 c. Ice, thermometer and kettle (temperature) .. 1·25 1·75

349. Fair Site.

1976. Int. Trade Fair, Accra.

764. **349.** 7 p. multicoloured .. 10 10
765. – 30 p. multicoloured .. 20 20
766. – 60 p. multicoloured .. 50 60
767. – 1 c. multicoloured .. 70 1·00

DESIGNS: As Type **349**, showing different views of the Fair.

1976. Interphil Stamp Exn. Nos. 755/8 optd. **"INTERPHIL" 76 BICENTENNIAL EXHIBITION.**

768. **347.** 7 p. multicoloured .. 15 15
769. – 30 p. multicoloured .. 35 50
770. – 60 p. multicoloured .. 55 75
771. – 1 c. multicoloured .. 80 1·25

351. Shot-put.

1976. Olympic Games, Montreal. Mult.

773. 7 p. Type **351** 10 10
774. 30 p. Football 20 25
775. 60 p. Women's 1500 metres 35 50
776. 1 c. Boxing 60 80

352. Supreme Court.

1976. Centenary of Supreme Court.

778. **352.** 8 p. multicoloured .. 10 10
779. – 30 p. multicoloured .. 20 25
780. – 60 p. multicoloured .. 35 50
781. – 1 c. multicoloured .. 60 1·00

DESIGNS: As Type **352** showing different views of the Court Buildings.

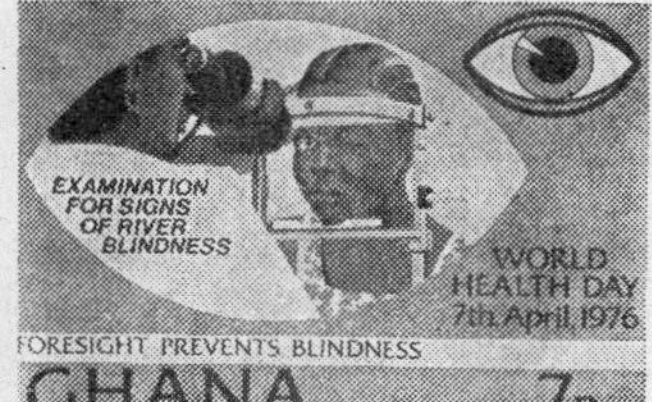

353. Examination for River Blindness.

1976. Prevention of Blindness. Mult.

782. 7 p. Type **353** 45 10
783. 30 p. Entomologist .. 1·25 80
784. 60 p. Checking effects of insecticide .. 2·25 1·75
785. 1 c. Normal eye's view .. 3·25 3·25

354. Fireworks Party, Christmas Eve.

1976. Christmas. Multicoloured.

786. 6 p. Type **354** .. 15 10
787. 8 p. Children and gifts .. 20 15
788. 30 p. Christmas feast .. 60 50
789. 1 c. As 8 p. .. .. 1·50 2·00

355. "Gallows Frame" Telephone and Alexander Graham Bell.

1976. Cent. of Telephone. Multicoloured.

791. 8 p. Type **355** 20 15
792. 30 p. Bell and 1895 telephone 45 45
793. 60 p. Bell and 1929 telephone 90 90
794. 1 c. Bell and 1976 telephone 1·40 1·40

1977. Olympic Winners. Nos. 773/6 optd. **WINNERS** and country name.

796. **351.** 7 p. multicoloured .. 15 15
797. – 30 p. multicoloured .. 40 40
798. – 60 p. multicoloured .. 60 85
799. – 1 c. multicoloured .. 80 1·50

OPTD. 7 p., 30 p. **EAST GERMANY.** 60 p. **USSR.** 1 c. **USA.**

357. Dipo Dancers and Drum Ensemble.

1977. Second World Black and African Festival of Arts and Culture, Nigeria. Multicoloured.

801. 8 p. Type **357** 25 15
802. 30 p. Arts and Crafts .. 70 70
803. 60 p. Acon music and dancing priests .. 1·40 1·40
804. 1 c. African Huts.. .. 2·00 2·25

1977. Prince Charles's Visit to Ghana. Nos. 791/94 optd. **PRINCE CHARLES VISITS GHANA 17th TO 25th MARCH, 1977.**

806. 8 p. Type **355** .. 50 55
807. 30 p. 1895 telephone .. 1·60 1·25
808. 60 p. 1929 telephone .. 2·50 2·25
809. 1 c. 1976 telephone .. 3·25 2·75

359. Olive Colobus Monkey.

1977. Wildlife. Multicoloured.

811. 8 p. Type **359** 45 15
812. 20 p. Temminck's Giant Squirrel .. .. 1·25 80
813. 30 p. Hunting Dog .. 1·75 1·25
814. 60 p. African Manatee (sea cow) .. .. 3·00 2·25

360. "Le Chapeau de Paille" (Rubens—400th Birth Anniv.).

1977. Painters' Anniversaries. Multicoloured.

816. 8 p. Type **360** 15 10
817. 30 p. "Isabella of Portugal" (Titian–500th Birth Anniv.) 40 40
818. 60 p. "Duke and Duchess of Cumberland" (Gainsborough–250th Birth Anniv.) 50 65
819. 1 c. "Rubens and Isabella Brandt" .. .. 85 1·25

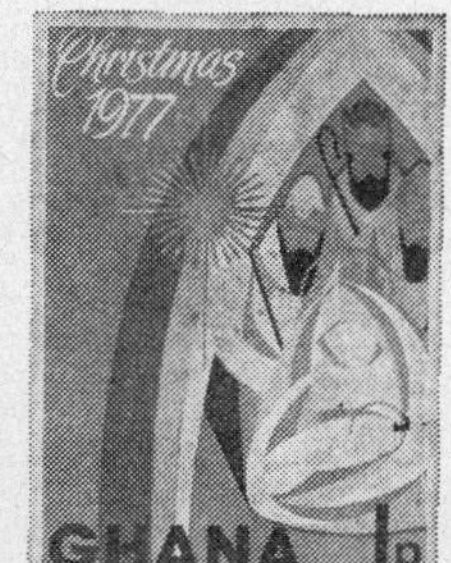

361. The Magi, Madonna and Child.

1977. Christmas. Multicoloured.

821. 1 p. Type **361** 10 10
822. 2 p. Choir, St. Andrew's Anglican Church, Abossey Okai 10 10
823. 6 p. Methodist Church, Wesley, Accra 10 10
824. 8 p. Madonna and Child.. 15 10
825. 30 p. Holy Spirit Cathedral, Accra 50 50
826. 1 c. Ebenezer Presbyterian Church, Osu, Accra .. 1·60 1·60

1978. Referendum. Nos. 821/26 optd. **REFERENDUM 1978 VOTE EARLY.**

828. 1 p. Type **361** 10 10
829. 2 p. Choir, St. Andrew's Anglican Church, Abossey Okai 10 10
830. 6 p. Methodist Church, Wesley, Accra 10 10
831. 8 p. Madonna and Child.. 15 10
832. 30 p. Holy Spirit Cathedral, Accra 50 50
833. 1 c. Ebenezer Presbyterian Church, Accra .. 1·50 1·50

363. Cutting Bananas.

1978. Operation "Feed Yourself". Mult.

835. 2 p. Type **363** 10 10
836. 8 p. Home produce .. 10 10
837. 30 p. Market 35 35
838. 60 p. Fishing 65 60
839. 1 c. Mechanisation .. 1·00 1·25

364. Wright Biplane.

1978. 75th Anniv. of Powered Flight.

840. **364.** 8 p. black, brn. & ochre 20 10
841. – 30 p. black, brn. & grn. 40 30
842. – 60 p. black, brn. & red 60 60
843. – 1 c. black, brn. & blue 1·40 1·10

DESIGNS: 30 p. "Heracles". 60 p D. H. "Comet". 1 c. "Concorde".

1978. "CAPEX 1978" International Stamp Exhibition, Toronto. Nos. 840/3 optd. **"CAPEX 78 JUNE 9–18 1978".**

845. **364.** 8 p. black, brn. & ochre 15 15
846. – 30 p. blk., brn. & grn. 25 25
847. – 60 p. blk., brown & red 50 50
848. – 1 c. blk., brown & blue 1·10 80

366. Players and African Cup Emblem.

1978. Football Championships. Multicoloured.

850. 8 p. Type **366** 20 15
851. 30 p. Players and African Cup Emblem (different) 30 30
852. 60 p. Players and World Cup Emblem 60 60
853. 1 c. Goalkeeper and World Cup Emblem .. .. 1·00 1·00

367. "The Betrayal".

1978. Easter. Drawings by Durer.

855. **367.** 11 p. black and mauve 10 10
856. – 39 p. black and flesh.. 25 30
857. – 60 p. black and yellow 40 45
858. – 1 c. black and green .. 60 65

DESIGNS: 39 p. "The Cruxifixion". 60 p. "The Deposition". 1 c. "The Resurrection".

1978. Football Victories of Ghana and Argentina. Nos. 850/3 optd. **"GHANA WINNERS"** (8, 30 p.) or **ARGENTINA WINS** (others).

859. **366.** 8 p. multicoloured .. 15 15
860. – 30 p. multicoloured .. 30 30
861. – 60 p. multicoloured .. 45 45
862. – 1 c. multicoloured .. 75 75

369. "Bauhinia purpurea".

1978. Flowers. Multicoloured.

864. 11 p. Type **369** 20 10
865. 39 p. "Cassia fistula" .. 65 55
866. 60 p. "Plumeria acutifolia" 85 70
867. 1 c. "Jacaranda mimosifolia .. .. 1·25 1·00

370. Mail Van.

1978. 75th Anniv. of Ghana Railways. Multicoloured.

868. 11 p. Type **370** .. 50 10
869. 39 p. Pay and bank car .. 1·25 65
870. 60 p. Steam locomotive, 1922 .. .. 1·75 1·00
871. 1 c. Diesel locomotive, 1960 2·00 1·40

371. " Orbiter " Spacecraft.

1979. " Pioneer " Venus Space Project. Multicoloured.

872. 11 p. Type **371** 15 10
873. 39 p. " Multiprobe " space craft 35 30
874. 60 p. "Orbiter" and "Multi-probe" spacecraft in Venus orbit 45 45
875. 3 c. Radar chart of Venus 1·40 1·60

372. " O Come All Ye Faithful ".

1979. Christmas. Lines and Scenes from Christmas Carols. Multicoloured.

877. 8 p. Type **372** 10 10
878. 10 p. " O Little Town of Bethlehem " 10 10
879. 15 p. " We Three Kings of Orient Are " 10 10
880. 20 p. " I Saw Three Ships come Sailing By " 10 15
881. 2 c. " Away in a Manger " 65 80
882. 4 c. " Ding Dong Merrily on High " .. .. 1·00 1·40

373. Dr. J. B. Danquah (lawyer and nationalist).

1980. Famous Ghanaians. Multicoloured.

884. 20 p. Type **373** 15 10
885. 65 p. John Mensah Sarbah (nationalist) 30 30
886. 80 p. Dr. J. E. K. Aggrey (educationalist) .. 40 40
887. 2 c. Dr. Kwame Nkrumah (nationalist) .. 65 65
888. 4 c. G. E. (Paa) Grant (lawyer) .. .. 1·40 1·60

374. Tribesman ringing Clack Bells.

1980. Death centenary of Sir Rowland Hill. (1979). Multicoloured.

889. 20 p. Type **374** 15 15
893. 25 p. Type **374** 20 20
894. 50 p. Chieftain with Golden Elephant Staff 45 40
890. 65 p. As 50 p. 45 50
895. 1 c. Signalling with drums 80 75
891. 2 c. As 1 c. .. .. 1·25 1·40
892. 4 c. Chieftain with ivory and gold staff .. .. 2·50 2·75
896. 5 c. As 4 c. .. .. 3·75 3·75

375. Children in Classroom.

1980. International Year of the Child (1979). Multicoloured.

898. 20 p. Type **375** 15 15
899. 65 p. Playing football .. 35 45
900. 2 c. Playing in a boat .. 75 1·00
901. 4 c. Mother and child .. 1·40 1·75

1980. " London 1980 " International Stamp Exhibition. Nos. 889/96 optd. **" LONDON 1980 " 6th - 14th May 1980.**

903. **374.** 20 p. multicoloured .. 15 15
907. – 25 p. multicoloured .. 30 35
908. – 50 p. multicoloured .. 55 65
904. – 65 p. multicoloured .. 45 60
909. – 1 c. multicoloured .. 95 1·40
905. – 2 c. multicoloured .. 1·10 1·60
906. – 4 c. multicoloured .. 2·00 3·00
910. – 5 c. multicoloured .. 3·00 3·75

1980. Papal Visit. Nos. 898/901 optd. **" PAPAL VISIT " 8th - 9th May 1980.**

912. **375.** 20 p. multicoloured .. 30 35
913. – 65 p. multicoloured .. 70 60
914. – 2 c. multicoloured .. 1·25 1·40
915. – 4 c. multicoloured .. 2·25 2·50

378. Parliament House.

1980. 3rd Republic Commemoration. Mult.

917. 20 p. Type **378** 10 10
918. 65 p. Supreme Court .. 20 25
919. 2 c. The Castle 40 70

379. Airliner and Map of West Africa.

1980. 5th Anniv. of Economic Community of West African States. Multicoloured.

921. 20 p. Type **379** 10 10
922. 65 p. Antenna and map .. 15 20
923. 80 p. Cog-wheels and map 20 25
924. 2 c. Corn and map .. 35 50

380. " OAU ".

1980. First Organization of African Unity Summit Conference, Nigeria.

925. **380.** 20 p. multicoloured .. 10 10
926. – 65 p. multicoloured .. 15 20
927. – 80 p. deep red, red and black 20 25
928. – 2 c. multicoloured .. 35 65

DESIGNS: 65 p. Maps of Africa and Ghana and banner. 80 p. Map of Africa. 2 c. Map of Africa, banner and Ghanaian flag.

381. " The Adoration of the Magi ".

1980. Christmas. Paintings by Fra Angelico. Multicoloured.

929. 15 p. Type **381** 10 10
930. 20 p. " The Virgin and Child Enthroned with Four Angels " 10 10
931. 2 c. " The Virgin and Child Enthroned with Eight Angels " 35 80
932. 4 c. " The Annunciation " 60 1·60

382. " Health ".

1980. 75th Anniv. of Rotary International. Multicoloured.

934. 20 p. Type **382** 10 10
935. 65 p. World map 15 30
936. 2 c. Hands 35 85
937. 4 c. Pouring food .. .. 60 1·50

383. Narina Trogon.

1981. Birds. Multicoloured.

939. 20 p. Type **383** 80 15
940. 65 p. White-crowned robin chat .. .. .. 1·75 50
941. 2 c. Swallow-tailed bee eater .. .. .. 2·50 1·25
942. 4 c. Rose-ringed parakeet 4·00 3·25

384. Pope John Paul II, Archbishop of Canterbury and President Limann during Papal Visit.

1981. 1st Anniv. of Papal Visit.

944. **384.** 20 p. multicoloured .. 35 15
945. 65 p. multicoloured .. 75 55
946. 80 p. multicoloured .. 95 70
947. 2 c. multicoloured .. 2·00 2·00

385. Royal Yacht "Britannia".

1981. Royal Wedding. Multicoloured.

948. 20 p. Prince Charles and Lady Diana Spencer .. 15 10
952. 65 p. As 20 p. 25 25
949. 80 p. Prince Charles on visit to Ghana 20 20
953. 1 c. As 80 p. 45 45
955. 2 c. Type **385** .. .. 1·25 1·25
954. 3 c. Type **385** .. .. 1·00 1·40
950. 4 c. Type **385** .. .. 80 1·10
956. 5 c. As 20 p. .. .. 2·50 2·50

386. Earth Satellite Station.

1981. Commissioning of Earth Satellite Station. Multicoloured.

957. 20 p. Type **386** 10 10
958. 65 p. Satellites beaming signals to Earth .. 25 25
959. 80 p. Satellite 30 30
960. 4 c. Satellite orbiting Earth 1·75 1·75

387. Pounding Fufu.

1981. World Food Day. Multicoloured.

962. 20 p. Type **387** 10 10
963. 65 p. Plucking Cocoa .. 25 35
964. 80 p. Preparing Banku .. 35 40
965. 2 c. Garri processing .. 1·00 2·00

388. " The Betrothal of St. Catherine of Alexandria " (Lucas Cranach).

1981. Christmas. Details from Paintings. Multicoloured.

967. 15 p. Type **388** 20 10
968. 20 p. " Angelic Musicians play for Mary and Child " (Aachener Altares) 20 10
969. 65 p. " Child Jesus embracing his Mother " (Gabriel Metsu) 45 25
970. 80 p. " Madonna and Child " (Fra Filippo Lippi) .. 55 30
971. 2 c. " The Madonna with Infant Jesus " (Barnaba da Modena) .. 1·25 80
972. 4 c. " The Immaculate Conception " (Murillo) 1·75 1·40

389. Blind Person.

1982. International Year of Disabled People. Multicoloured.

974. 20 p. Type **389** 10 10
975. 65 p. Disabled person with crutches 35 35
976. 80 p. Blind child reading braille 45 45
977. 4 c. Disabled people helping one another .. 2·25 2·25

390. African Clawless Otter.

1982. Flora and Fauna. Multicoloured.

979. 20 p. Type **390** 15 15
980. 65 p. Bushbuck 40 40
981. 80 p. Aardvark 50 50
982. 1 c. Scarlet Bell Tree .. 60 60
983. 2 c. Glory lilies .. .. 1·25 1·25
984. 4 c. Blue-Pea .. .. 2·25 2·25

HAVE YOU READ THE NOTES AT THE BEGINNING OF THIS CATALOGUE?

These often provide answers to the enquiries we receive.

391. "Precis westermanni".

1982. Butterflies. Multicoloured.

986 20 p. Type **391** 40 15
987 65 p. "Papilio menestheus" 80 45
988 2 c. "Antanartia delius" .. 1·75 2·25
989 4 c. "Charaxes castor" .. 2·50 3·25

392. Scouts planting Tree.

1982. 75th Anniv. of Boy Scout Movement. Multicoloured.

991. 20 p. Type **392** 35 10
992. 65 p. Scouts cooking on campfire 90 35
993. 80 p. Sea Scouts sailing .. 1·25 45
994. 3 c. Scouts observing African elephant .. 2·50 2·00

393. Initial Stages of Construction.

1982. Kpong Hydro-Electric Project. Multicoloured.

996. 20 p. Type **393** 30 10
997. 65 p. Truck removing rubble 35 45
998. 80 p. Hydro-Electric turbines 75 65
999. 2 c. Aerial view of completed plant .. 1·00 1·60

394. Footballers.

1982. World Cup Football Championship, Spain.

1000. **394.** 20 p. multicoloured 10 10
1005. 30 p. multicoloured .. 20 20
1001. – 65 p. multicoloured .. 35 35
1002. – 80 p. multicoloured (Heading) 45 45
1006. – 80 p. multicoloured (Three Footballers) 45 45
1007. – 1 c. multicoloured .. 55 55
1008. – 3 c. multicoloured .. 1·60 1·60
1003. – 4 c. multicoloured .. 2·00 2·00

DESIGNS: 65 p. to 4 c. Scenes showing footballers.

395. The fight against Tuberculosis.

1982. Centenary of Robert Koch's Discovery of Tubercle Bacillus. Multicoloured.

1009. 20 p. Type **395** 50 15
1010. 65 p. Robert Koch .. 1·25 65
1011. 80 p. Robert Koch in Africa .. .. 1·50 1·00
1012. 1 c. Centenary of discovery of Tuberculosis .. 1·75 2·00
1013. 2 c. Robert Koch and Nobel Prize, 1905 .. 2·50 3·00

396. The Three Kings Worship Jesus.

1982. Christmas. Multicoloured.

1014. 15 p. Type **396** 10 10
1015. 20 p. Mary, Joseph and baby Jesus 10 10
1016. 65 p. The Three Kings sight star 30 30
1017. 4 c. Winged Angel .. 1·40 1·75

397. Ghana and Commonwealth Flags with Coat of Arms.

1983. Commonwealth Day. Multicoloured.

1019. 20 p. Type **397** 25 15
1020. 55 p. Satellite view of Ghana 45 40
1021. 80 p. Minerals of Ghana 85 85
1022. 3 c. African fish eagle .. 2·50 3·00

1983. Italy's Victory in World Cup Football Championship (1982). Nos. 1000/8 optd WINNER ITALY 3–1.

1023. 20 p. multicoloured .. 10 10
1028. 30 p. multicoloured .. 15 15
1024. 65 p. multicoloured .. 30 30
1025. 80 p. multicoloured .. 40 40
1029. 80 p. multicoloured .. 50 50
1030. 1 c. multicoloured .. 60 60
1031. 3 c. multicoloured .. 1·50 1·75
1026. 4 c. multicoloured .. 1·90 1·90

1983. No. 470 surch **C1**.

1031a 1 c. on 20 n.p. Bush hare (blue) 15 15

399. Short Fin Pilot Whale.

1983. Coastal Marine Mammals. Mult.

1032. 1 c. Type **399** 65 65
1033. 1 c. 40 Risso's Dolphin .. 65 65
1034. 2 c. 30 False Killer Whale 80 80
1035. 3 c. Spinner Dolphin .. 1·00 1·00
1036. 5 c. Atlantic Humpbacked Dolphin 1·40 1·40

400. "Hemichramis fasciatus" 401. Communication Devices.

1983.

1038. **400.** 5 p. multicoloured .. 10 10
1039. – 10 p. multicoloured 10 10
1040. – 20 p. multicoloured 10 10
1041. – 50 p. grn., orge. and blk. 20 10
1042. – 1 c. orge., bl. and blk. 20 10
1043. – 2 c. multicoloured .. 20 10
1044. – 3 c. multicoloured .. 20 10
1045. – 4 c. multicoloured .. 20 10
1046. – 5 c. multicoloured .. 20 10
1047. – 10 c. multicoloured .. 20 10

DESIGNS—HORIZ. 10 p. "Hemichramis fasciatus" (different). 2 c. Jet airliner. VERT. 20 p. "Haemanthus rupestris". 50 p. Mounted warrior. 1 c. Scorpion. 3 c. White-collared mangabey. 4 c. Demidoff's galago. 5 c. "Kaemferia nigerica". 10 c. Grey-backed camaroptera.

1983. World Communications Year. Mult.

1048. 1 c. Type **401** 15 15
1049. 1 c. 40 Satellite dish aerial 20 20
1050. 2 c. 30 Cable and cable-laying ship 35 35
1051. 3 c. Switchboard operators 40 40
1052. 5 c. Aircraft cockpit and air traffic controllers .. 50 50

402. Children receiving Presents.

1983. Christmas. Multicoloured.

1054. 70 p. Type **402** 15 10
1055. 1 c. Nativity and Star of Bethlehem (vert.) .. 15 10
1056. 1 c. 40 Children celebrating (vert.) 25 20
1057. 2 c. 30 Family praying together (vert.) 30 35
1058. 3 c. Dancing to Bongo drum 40 45

403. Soldiers with Rifles.

1983. Namibia Day.

1060. **403.** 50 p. green and black 10 10
1061. – 1 c. multicoloured .. 10 10
1062. – 1 c. 40 blue, bright blue and black .. 15 15
1063. – 2 c. 30 multicoloured 20 25
1064. – 3 c. multicoloured .. 25 30

DESIGNS: 1 c. Soldiers supported by tank. 1 c. 40, Machete cutting chains. 2 c. 30, Peasant woman. 3 c. Soldiers and artillery support.

1984. (a) Nos. 948/50, 952 and 954 surch.

1065. 1 c. on 20 p. Prince Charles and Lady Diana Spencer .. 4·00 3·00
1066. 9 c. on 65 p. Prince Charles and Lady Diana Spencer .. 5·00 4·00
1067. 9 c. on 80 p. Prince Charles on visit to Ghana .. .. 5·00 4·00
1068. 20 c. on 3 c. Type **385** .. 6·00 6·00
1069. 20 c. on 4 c. Type **385** .. 6·00 6·00

(b) Nos. 991/2 and 994 surch.

1071. 10 c. on 20 p. Type **392** 40 45
1072. 19 c. on 65 p. Scouts cooking on campfire .. 80 85
1073. 30 c. on 3 c. Scouts observing African elephant .. .. 1·25 1·40

(c) Nos. 1000/3, 1005/6 and 1008 surch.

1075. **394.** 1 c. on 20 p. mult. .. 10 10
1076. – 9 c. on 65 p. mult. .. 40 45
1077. – 9 c. on 3 c. mult. .. 40 45
1078. **394.** 10 c. on 30 p. mult. 40 45
1079. – 10 c. on 80 p. mult. 40 45
1080. – 20 c. on 80 p. mult. 85 90
1081. – 20 c. on 4 c. mult. .. 85 90

(d) Nos. 1019–22 surch.

1083. 1 c. on 20 p. Type **397** .. 10 10
1084. 9 c. on 55 p. Satellite view of Ghana .. 40 45
1085. 30 c. on 80 p. Minerals of Ghana .. .. 1·25 1·40
1086. 50 c. on 3 c. African Fish Eagle .. .. .. 2·10 2·25

(e) Nos. 1023/6, 1028/9 and 1031 surch.

1087. **394.** 1 c. on 20 p. mult. .. 10 10
1088. – 9 c. on 65 p. mult. .. 40 45
1089. – 9 c. on 3 c. mult. .. 40 45
1090. **394.** 10 c. on 30 p. mult. 40 45
1091. – 10 c. on 80 p. mult. 40 45
1092. – 20 c. on 80 p. mult. 80 85
1093. – 20 c. on 4 c. mult. .. 80 85

1984. Universal Postal Union Congress, Hamburg. Nos. 1035/6 optd. **19th U.P.U. CONGRESS–HAMBURG** and surch.

1095. 10 c. on 3 c. Spinner Dolphin 40 45
1096. 50 c. on 5 c. Atlantic Humpbacked Dolphin 2·10 2·25

407. Cross and Crown of Thorns.

1984. Easter. Multicoloured.

1098. 1 c. Type **407** 10 10
1099. 1 c. 40 Christ praying .. 10 10
1100. 2 c. 30 The Resurrection 10 10
1101. 3 c. Palm Sunday .. 10 15
1102. 50 c. Christ on the road to Emmaus .. .. 1·90 2·25

408. Women's 400 Metre Race.

1984. Olympic Games, Los Angeles. Multicoloured.

1104. 1 c. Type **408** 10 10
1105. 1 c. 40 Boxing 10 10
1106. 2 c. 30 Field hockey .. 15 15
1107. 3 c. Men's 400 metre hurdles race 15 15
1108. 50 c. Rhythmic gymnastics .. .. .. 2·40 3·25

409. "Amorphophallus johnsonii".

1984. Flowers. Multicoloured.

1110. 1 c. Type **409** 10 10
1111. 1 c. 40 "Pancratium trianthum" 10 10
1112. 2 c. 30 "Eulophia cucullata" 15 15
1113. 3 c. "Amorphophallus abyssinicus" 15 15
1114. 50 c. "Chorophytum togoense" .. .. 3·25 4·50

410. Young Bongo.

1984. Endangered Antelopes. Multicoloured.

1116.	1 c. Type **410**	20	20
1117.	2 c. 30 Bongo bucks fighting	40	40
1118.	3 c. Bongo family	50	50
1119.	20 c. Bongo herd in high grass	2·25	2·75

411. Dipo Girl.

1984. Ghanaian Culture. Multicoloured.

1121.	1 c. Type **411**	10	10
1122.	1 c. 40 Adowa dancer ..	10	10
1123.	2 c. 30 Agbadza dancer	10	15
1124.	3 c. Damba dancer ..	10	15
1125.	50 c. Dipo dancer ..	1·75	3·00

412. The Three Wise Men bringing Gifts. **414.** The Queen Mother attending Church Service.

1984. Christmas. Multicoloured.

1127.	70 p. Type **412**	10	10
1128.	1 c. Choir of angels ..	10	10
1129.	1 c. 40 Mary and shepherds at manger ..	10	10
1130.	2 c. 30 The flight into Egypt	10	10
1131.	3 c. Simeon blessing Jesus	10	15
1132.	50 c. Holy Family and angels	1·75	3·00

1984. Olympic Winners. Nos. 1104/8 optd.

1134.	1 c. Type **408** (optd. **VALERIE BRISCO-HOOKS (U.S.A.)** ..	10	10
1135.	1 c. 40 Boxing (optd. **U.S. WINNERS**)	10	10
1136.	2 c. 30 Field hockey (optd. **PAKISTAN FIELD HOCKEY**) ..	10	10
1137.	3 c. Men's 400 metre hurdles race (optd. **EDWIN MOSES U.S.A.**)	10	10
1138.	50 c. Rhythmic gymnastics (optd. **FRANCE**) ..	1·50	1·60

1985. Life and Times of Queen Elizabeth the Queen Mother. Multicoloured.

1140.	5 c. Type **414**	15	20
1141.	12 c. At Ascot Races ..	40	45
1142.	100 c. At Clarence House on her 84th birthday	3·00	3·25

Stamps as Nos. 1140/2 but with face values of 8 c., 20 c. and 70 c. exist from additional sheetlets with changed background colours.

415. Moslems going to Mosque.

1985. Islamic Festival of Id-el-Fitr. Multicoloured.

1144.	5 c. Type **415**	15	20
1145.	8 c. Moslems at prayer ..	25	30
1146.	12 c. Pilgrims visiting the Dome of the Rock ..	40	45
1147.	18 c. Preaching the Koran	55	60
1148.	50 c. Banda Nkwanta Mosque, Accra, and map of Ghana ..	1·50	1·60

416. Youths clearing Refuse ("Make Ghana Clean").

1985. International Youth Year. Mult.

1149.	5 c. Type **416**	10	10
1150.	8 c. Planting sapling ("Make Ghana Green")	15	15
1151.	12 c. Youth carrying bananas ("Feed Ghana")	20	25
1152.	100 c. Open-air class ("Educate Ghana") ..	1·60	2·25

417. Honda "Interceptor", 1984.

1985. Centenary of the Motorcycle. Mult.

1154.	5 c. Type **417**	45	45
1155.	8 c. DKW 1938	55	55
1156.	12 c. BMW "R 32" 1923	85	85
1157.	100 c. NSU, 1900 ..	4·25	4·75

418. Fork-tailed Flycatcher.

1985. Birth Bicentenary of John J. Audubon (ornithologist). Designs showing original paintings. Multicoloured.

1159.	5 c. Type **418**	60	30
1160.	8 c. Barred Owl	1·50	1·00
1161.	12 c. Black-throated Mango	1·50	1·25
1162.	100 c. White-crowned Pigeon	3·75	4·50

No. 1159 is inscribed "York-tailed Fly Catcher" in error.

419. United Nations Building, New York.

1985. 40th Anniv. of United Nations Organization. Multicoloured.

1164.	5 c. Type **419**	10	10
1165.	8 c. Flags of member nations and U.N. Building	15	15
1166.	12 c. Dove with olive branch	20	25
1167.	18 c. General Assembly	30	35
1168.	100 c. Flags of Ghana and United Nations ..	1·60	1·75

420. Coffee.

1985. 20th Anniv. of United Nations Conference on Trade and Development. Designs showing export products. Multicoloured.

1170.	5 c. Type **420**	10	10
1171.	8 c. Cocoa	15	15
1172.	12 c. Timber	25	25
1173.	18 c. Bauxite	1·00	80
1174.	100 c. Gold	4·50	5·00

421. Growth Monitoring.

1985. U.N.I.C.E.F. Child Survival Campaign. Multicoloured.

1176.	5 c. Type **421**	20	10
1177.	8 c. Oral rehydration therapy	30	20
1178.	12 c. Breast feeding ..	45	30
1179.	100 c. Immunization ..	2·25	3·25

422. Airline Stewardess and Boys with Stamp Album.

1986. "Ameripex" International Stamp Exhibition, Chicago. Multicoloured.

1181.	5 c. Type **422**	10	10
1182.	25 c. Globe and Ghana Airways aircraft ..	45	45
1183.	100 c. Ghana Airways stewardess (vert.) ..	1·75	2·75

423. Kejetia Roundabout, Kumasi.

1986. "Inter-Tourism '86" Conference. Multicoloured.

1185.	5 c. Type **423**	10	10
1186.	15 c. Fort St. Jago, Elmina	30	30
1187.	25 c. Tribal warriors ..	45	45
1188.	100 c. Chief holding audience	1·75	3·00

MINIMUM PRICE

The minimum price quoted is 10p which represents a handling charge rather than a basis for valuing common stamps. For further notes about prices see introductory pages.

424. Tackling.

1987. World Cup Football Championship, Mexico (1986). Multicoloured.

1190.	5 c. Type **424**	15	10
1191.	15 c. Player taking control of ball ..	20	15
1192.	25 c. Player kicking ball	30	25
1193.	100 c. Player with ball ..	1·10	1·25

425. Fertility Doll.

1987. Ghanaian Fertility Dolls. Designs showing different dolls.

1195.	**425.** 5 c. multicoloured ..	10	10
1196.	– 15 c. multicoloured ..	15	15
1197.	– 25 c. multicoloured ..	30	25
1198.	– 100 c. multicoloured	1·00	1·25

426. Children of Different Races, Peace Doves and Sun.

1987. International Peace Year (1986). Multicoloured.

1200.	5 c. Type **426**	10	10
1201.	25 c. Plough, peace dove and rising sun ..	40	25
1202.	100 c. Peace dove, olive branch and globe (vert.)	1·25	1·50

427. Lumber and House under Construction.

1987. "Gifex '87" International Forestry Exposition, Accra. Multicoloured.

1204.	5 c. Type **427**	10	10
1205.	15 c. Planks and furniture	15	15
1206.	25 c. Felled trees ..	30	25
1207.	200 c. Logs and wood carvings	1·90	2·25

1987. Appearance of Halley's Comet (1986). As T **123** of Anguilla. Multicoloured.

1208.	5 c. Mikhail Lomonosov (scientist) and Chamber of Curiosities, St. Petersburg	10	10
1209.	25 c. Lunar probe "Surveyor III", 1966 ..	50	25
1210.	200 c. Wedgwood plaques for Isaac Newton, 1790, and "Apollo 11" Moon landing, 1968	2·75	2·10

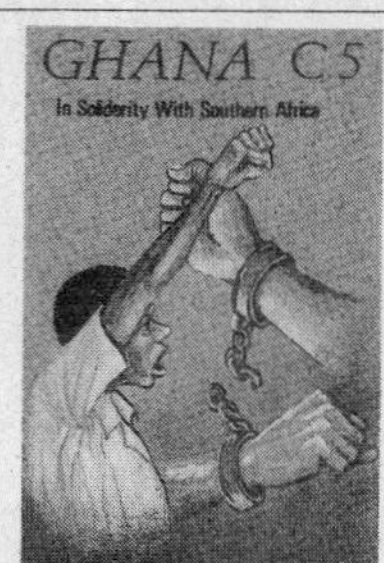

428. Demonstrator and Arms breaking Shackles.

1987. Solidarity with the People of Southern Africa. Multicoloured.

1212. 5 c. Type **428** 10 10
1213. 15 c. Miner and gold bars 15 15
1214. 25 c. Xhosa warriors .. 30 25
1215. 100 c. Nelson Mandela and shackles .. .. 1·00 1·50

429. Aerophones.

1987. Musical Instruments. Multicoloured.

1217. 5 c. Type **429** 10 10
1218. 15 c. Xylophone .. 15 15
1219. 25 c. Chordophones .. 30 25
1220. 100 c. Membranophones 1·00 1·25

430. Woman filling Water Pot at Pump.

1987. International Year of Shelter for the Homeless. Multicoloured.

1222. 5 c. Type **430** 10 10
1223. 15 c. Building house from breeze blocks 10 15
1224. 25 c. Modern village with stream 20 25
1225. 100 c. Modern houses with verandahs .. 70 75

431. Ga Women preparing Kpokpoi for Homowo Festival.

1988. Ghana Festivals. Multicoloured.

1226. 5 c. Type **431** 10 10
1227. 15 c. Efute hunters with deer, Aboakyir festival 10 15
1228. 25 c. Fanti chief dancing at Odwira festival .. 20 25
1229. 100 c. Chief in palanquin, Yam festival 70 75

432. Port Installation.

1988. 5th Anniv. (1987) of 31 December Revolution. Multicoloured.

1230. 5 c. Type **432** 20 15
1231. 15 c. Repairing railway line 35 30
1232. 25 c. Planting cocoa .. 35 30
1233. 100 c. Miners with ore truck .. .. .. 1·50 1·50

433. Nurse giving Injection. **435** Akwadjan Men

434 Fishing

1988. U.N.I.C.E.F. Global Immunization Campaign. Multicoloured.

1234. 5 c. Type **433** 10 10
1235. 15 c. Girl receiving injection 15 15
1236. 25 c. Schoolgirl crippled by polio 30 30
1237. 100 c. Nurse giving oral vaccine to baby .. 90 1·00

1988. 10th Anniv of International Fund for Agricultural Development. Multicoloured.

1238 5 c. Type **434** 10 10
1239 15 c. Women harvesting crops 15 15
1240 25 c. Cattle 30 30
1241 100 c. Village granaries .. 1·00 1·40

1988. Tribal Costumes. Multicoloured.

1242 5 c. Type **435** 10 10
1243 25 c. Bannaa man .. 20 20
1244 250 c. Agwasen woman .. 1·50 1·50

1988. Nos. 460, 464/6, 469/70, 1031a, 1038/42, 1044 and 1046 surch.

1245 – 20 c. on 50 p. green, orange and black (No. 1041) .. 10 10
1246 – 20 c. on 1 c. orge, bl & black (No. 1042) 10 10
1247 – 50 c. on 10 n.p. mult (No. 469) .. 10 15
1248 – 50 c. on 20 n.p. deep blue and blue (No. 470) (surch **C50**) 50 25
1249 – 50 c. on 20 n.p. deep blue and blue (No. 470) (surch **C50.00**) 50 25
1250 – 50 c. on 10 p. mult (No. 1039) .. 10 10
1251 – 50 c. on 1 c. on 20 n.p. deep blue and blue (No. 1031a) (surch **C50**) 50 25
1252 – 50 c. on 1 c. on 20 n.p. dp blue & blue (No. 1031a) (surch **C50.00**) .. 50 25
1254 – 50 c. on 1 c. orange, bl & blk (No. 1042) 50 25
1255a **230** 60 c. on 1 n.p. mult 40 25
1256 – 60 c. on 4 n.p. mult (No. 465) 15 20
1257 – 60 c. on 3 c. mult (No. 1044) .. 15 20
1258 **400** 80 c. on 5 p. mult .. 20 25
1259 – 80 c. on 5 c. mult (No. 1046) .. 75 80
1260 – 100 c. on 3 n.p. mult (No. 464) .. 1·25 1·25
1261 – 100 c. on 20 n.p. deep blue & bl (No. 470) 25 30
1262 – 100 c. on 20 p. mult (No. 1040) .. 25 30
1263 – 100 c. on 3 c. mult (No. 1044) .. 25 30
1264 – 200 c. on 6 n.p. mult (No. 466) .. 1·00 80

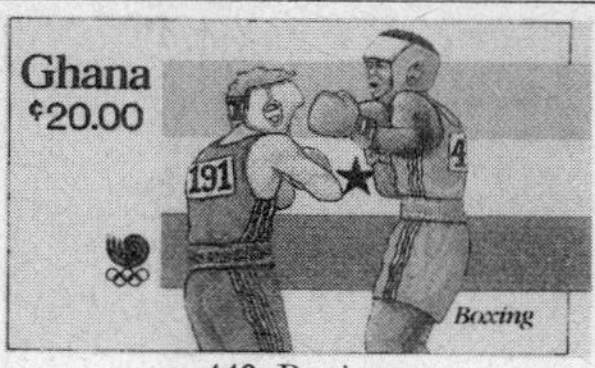

440 Boxing

1988. Olympic Games, Seoul. Multicoloured.

1265 20 c. Type **440** 15 15
1266 60 c. Athletics 45 45
1267 80 c. Discus-throwing .. 60 60
1268 100 c. Javelin-throwing .. 80 80
1269 350 c. Weightlifting .. 2·00 2·00

441 Nutrition Lecture

1988. 125th Anniv of Int. Red Cross. Mult.

1271 20 c. Type **441** 20 15
1272 50 c. Red Cross volunteer with blind woman .. 60 60
1273 60 c. Distributing flood relief supplies 70 70
1274 200 c. Giving first aid .. 1·75 1·75

442 Tropical Forest

1988. Christmas. Multicoloured.

1275 20 c. Type **442** 15 10
1276 60 c. Christ Child (vert) .. 35 35
1277 80 c. Virgin and Child with Star (vert) .. 50 50
1278 100 c. Three Wise Men following Star .. 60 70
1279 350 c. Symbolic Crucifixion (vert) .. 2·00 2·50

443 "African Solidarity"

1989. 25th Anniv (1988) of Organization of African Unity. Multicoloured.

1281 20 c. Type **443** 10 10
1282 50 c. O.A.U. Headquarters, Addis Ababa 15 20
1283 60 c. Emperor Haile Selassie and Ethiopian flag (horiz) 20 25
1284 200 c. Kwame Nkrumah (former Ghanaian President) and flag (horiz) 60 65

444 "Amor"

1989. 500th Birth Anniv of Titian (artist). Multicoloured.

1285 20 c. Type **444** 10 10
1286 60 c. "The Appeal" .. 20 25
1287 80 c. "Bacchus and Ariadne" (detail) .. 25 30
1288 100 c. "Portrait of a Musician" 30 35
1289 350 c. "Philip II seated" 1·00 1·10

1989. Olympic Medal Winners, Seoul. Nos. 1251/5 optd.

1291 20 c. Type **436** (optd **A. ZUELOW DDR 60 KG**) 10 10
1292 20 c. Athletics (optd **G. BORDIN ITALY MARATHON**) .. 20 25
1293 80 c. Discus-throwing (optd **J. SCHULT DDR**) 25 30
1294 10 c. Javelin-throwing (optd **T. KORJUS FINLAND**) 30 35
1295 350 c. Weightlifting (optd **B. GUIDIKOV BULGARIA 75 KG**) 1·00 1·10

1989. Various stamps surch (a) Nos. 949/50 and 952/4.

1297 80 c. on 65 p. Prince Charles and Lady Diana Spencer .. 35 40
1298 100 c. on 80 p. Prince Charles on visit to Ghana 45 50
1299 100 c. on 1 c. Prince Charles on visit to Ghana 45 50
1300 300 c. on 3 c. Type **385** .. 1·25 1·40
1301 500 c. on 4 c. Type **385** .. 2·25 2·50

(b) Nos. 1048/51

1302 60 c. on 1 c. Type **401** .. 25 30
1303 80 c. on 1 c. 40 Satellite dish aerial 35 40
1304 200 c. on 2 c. 30 Cable and cable-laying ship .. 90 95
1305 300 c. on 3 c. Switchboard operators .. .. 1·25 1·40

(c) Nos. 1104/7

1307 60 c. on 1 c. Type **408** .. 25 30
1308 80 c. on 1 c. 40 Boxing .. 35 40
1309 200 c. on 2 c. 30 Hockey 90 95
1310 300 c. on 3 c. Men's 400 metre hurdles race .. 1·25 1·40

(d) Nos. 1134/7

1312 60 c. on 1 c. Type **408** (optd **VALERIE BRISCO-HOOKS (U.S.A.)**) 25 30
1313 80 c. on 1 c. 40 Boxing (optd **U.S. WINNERS**) 35 40
1314 200 c. on 2 c. 30 Field hockey (optd **PAKISTAN (FIELD HOCKEY)**) 90 95
1315 300 c. on 3 c. Men's 400 metre hurdles race (optd **EDWIN MOSES U.S.A.**) .. 1·25 1·40

(e) Nos. 1140/2

1317 80 c. on 5 c. Type **414** .. 35 40
1318 250 c. on 12 c. At Ascot Races .. .. .. 1·10 1·25
1319 300 c. on 100 c. At Clarence House on her 84th birthday .. .. 1·25 1·40

(f) Nos. 1159/61

1321 80 c. on 5 c. Type **418** .. 35 40
1322 100 c. on 8 c. Barred owl 45 50
1323 300 c. on 12 c. Black-throated mango .. 1·25 1·40

(g) Nos. 1190/2

1325 60 c. on 5 c. Type **424** .. 25 30
1326 200 c. on 15 c. Player taking control of ball .. 90 95
1327 300 c. on 25 c. Player kicking ball .. .. 1·25 1·40

(h) As Nos. 1190/2 but with unissued opt
WINNERS Argentina 3 W. Germany 2

1329 60 c. on 5 c. Type **424** .. 25 30
1330 200 c. on 15 c. Player taking control of ball .. 90 95
1331 300 c. on 25 c. Player kicking ball .. .. 1·25 1·40

(i) Nos. 1208/10

1333 60 c. on 5 c. Mikhail Lomonosov (scientist) and Chamber of Curiosities, St. Petersburg 25 30
1334 80 c. on 25 c. Lunar probe "Surveyor 3", 1966 .. 35 40
1335 500 c. on 200 c. Wedgwood plaques for Isaac Newton, 1790, and "Apollo 11" Moon landing, 1968 .. .. 2·25 2·50

(j) As Nos. 1208/10 but with unissued logo opt as T **218** of Antigua

1337 60 c. on 5 c. Mikhail Lomonosov (scientist) and Chamber of Curiosities, St. Petersburg 25 30
1338 80 c. on 25 c. Lunar probe "Surveyor 3", 1966 .. 35 40
1339 500 c. on 200 c. Wedgwood plaques for Isaac Newton, 1790, and "Apollo 11" Moon landing, 1968 .. .. 2·25 2·50

448 French Royal Standard and Field Gun

1989. "Philexfrance 89" International Stamp Exhibition, Paris. Multicoloured.

1341 20 c. Type **448** 20 15
1342 60 c. Regimental standard, 1789, and French infantryman .. 40 35
1343 80 c. Revolutionary standard, 1789, and pistol 50 50
1344 350 c. Tricolour, 1794, and musket .. .. 2·00 2·25

1989. Japanese Art. Portraits. As T **250** of Antigua. Multicoloured.

1346 20 c. "Minamoto- no-Yoritomo" (Fujiwara-no-Takanobu) (vert) .. 10 10
1347 50 c. "Takami Senseki" (Watanabe Kazan) (vert) 15 20
1348 60 c. "Ikkyu Sojun" (study) (Bokusai) (vert) 20 25
1349 75 c. "Nakamura Kuranosuka" (Ogata Korin) (vert) 20 25
1350 125 c. "Portrait of a Lady" (Kyoto branch, Kano school) (vert) .. 35 40
1351 150 c. "Portrait of Zemmui" (anon, 12th-century) (vert) .. 45 50
1352 200 c. "Ono no Komachi the Poetess" (Hokusai) (vert) 60 65
1353 500 c. "Kobo Daisi as a Child" (anon) (vert) .. 1·50 1·60

449 Storming the Bastille

1989. Bicentenary of the French Revolution. Multicoloured.

1355 20 c. Type **449** 10 10
1356 60 c. Declaration of Human Rights .. 20 25
1357 80 c. Storming the Bastille (horiz) 25 30
1358 200 c. Revolution monument (horiz) .. 60 65
1359 350 c. Tree of Liberty (horiz) .. .. 1·00 1·10

450 Spindle Shank

1989. Fungi (1st series). Multicoloured.

1360 20 c. Type **450** 10 10
1361 50 c. Shaggy ink cap .. 15 20
1362 60 c. "Xerocomus subtomentosus" .. 20 25
1363 80 c. Wood belwits .. 25 30
1364 150 c. "Suillus placidus" 45 50
1365 200 c. "Lepista nuda" .. 60 65
1366 300 c. Fairy ring champignon 90 95
1367 500 c. Field mushroom .. 1·50 1·60

See also Nos. 1489/96.

"The course of true love never did run smooth. I:i"

451 "The Course of True Love ...."

1989. 425th Birth Anniv of Shakespeare. Verses and scenes from "A Midsummer Night's Dream". Multicoloured.

1369 40 c. Type **451** 10 15
1370 40 c. "Love looks not with the eye but with the mind" 10 15
1371 40 c. "Nature here shows art" 10 15
1372 40 c. "Things growing are not ripe till their season" 10 15
1373 40 c. "He is defiled that draws a sword on thee" 10 15
1374 40 c. "It is not enough to speak, but to speak true" 10 15
1375 40 c. "Thou art as wise as thou art beautiful" .. 10 15
1376 40 c. Wildcat in wood (face value at left) .. 10 15
1377 40 c. Man 10 15
1378 40 c. Woman with flower 10 15
1379 40 c. King and queen .. 10 15
1380 40 c. Bottom 10 15
1381 40 c. Wildcat in wood (face value at right) .. 10 15
1382 40 c. Woman 10 15
1383 40 c. Leopard 10 15
1384 40 c. Tree trunk and man 10 15
1385 40 c. Meadow flowers .. 10 15
1386 40 c. Mauve flowers .. 10 15
1387 40 c. Plants 10 15
1388 40 c. Lion 10 15
1389 40 c. Fern and flowers .. 10 15

Nos. 1369/89 were printed together, forming a composite design.

1989. Birds. As T **244** of Dominica. Mult.

1390 20 c. Village weaver (horiz) 10 10
1391 50 c. African pied wagtail (horiz) 15 20
1392 60 c. African pygmy kingfisher (inscr "Halcyon malimbicus") (horiz) .. 50 50
1392a 60 c. African pygmy kingfisher (inscr "Ispidina picta") .. 20 25
1393 80 c. Blue-breasted kingfisher (inscr "Ispidina picta") (horiz) .. 70 70
1393a 80 c. Blue-breasted kingfisher (inscr "Halcyon Malimbicus") .. 25 30
1394 150 c. Striped kingfisher 45 50
1395 200 c. Shrika 60 65
1396 300 c. Grey parrot .. 90 95
1397 500 c. Black kite .. 1·50 1·60

452 Command Module "Columbia" orbiting Moon

1989. 20th Anniv of First Manned Landing on Moon. Multicoloured.

1399 20 c. Type **452** 10 10
1400 80 c. Neil Armtrong's footprint on Moon .. 25 30
1401 200 c. Edwin Aldrin on Moon 60 65
1402 300 c. "Apollo 11" capsule on parachutes .. 90 95

453 Desertification of Pasture

1989. World Environment Day. Mult.

1404 20 c. Type **453** 10 10
1405 60 c. Wildlife fleeing bush fire 20 25
1406 400 c. Industrial pollution 1·25 1·40
1407 500 c. Erosion .. .. 1·50 1·60

454 "Bebearia arcadius"

1990. Butterflies. Multicoloured.

1408 20 c. Type **454** 10 10
1409 60 c. "Charaxes laodice" 20 25
1410 80 c. "Euryphura porphyrion" 25 30
1411 100 c. "Neptis nicomedes" 30 35
1412 150 c. "Citrinophila erastus" 45 50
1413 200 c. " Aethiopana honorius" 60 65
1414 300 c. "Precis westermanni" 90 95
1415 500 c. "Cymothoe hypatha" .. .. 1·50 1·60

455 "Cymbium costatum Linne"

1990. Seashells. Multicoloured.

1417 20 c. Type 455 .. .. 10 10
1418 60 c. "Cardium glans" Gmelin 20 25
1419 80 c. "Conus genuanus" Linne 25 30
1420 200 c. "Ancilla tankervillei" Swainson .. 60 65
1421 350 c. "Tectarius coronatus" Valenciennes .. .. .. 1·00 1·10

456 Nehru welcoming President Nkrumah of Ghana

1990. Birth Centenary of Jawaharlal Nehru (Indian statesman). Multicoloured.

1422 20 c. Type **456** 10 10
1423 60 c. Nehru addressing Bandung Conference, 1955 .. .. .. 20 25
1424 80 c. Nehru with garland and flowers (vert) .. 25 30
1425 200 c. Nehru releasing pigeon (vert) 60 65
1426 350 c. Nehru (vert) .. 1·00 1·10

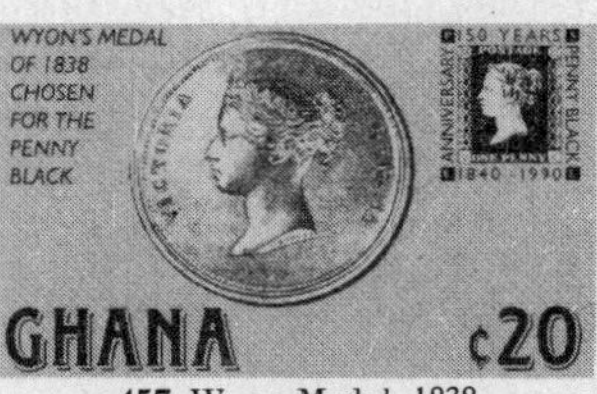

457 Wyon Medal, 1838

1990. 150th Anniv of the Penny Black.

1427 **457** 20 c. black and violet 10 10
1428 – 60 c. black and green 20 25
1429 – 80 c. black and violet 25 30
1430 – 200 c. black and green 60 65
1431 – 350 c. black and green 1·00 1·50
1432 – 400 c. black and red 1·25 1·40

DESIGNS: 60 c. Bath mail coach, 1840; 80 c. Leeds mail coach, 1840; 200 c. Proof of Queen's head engraved by Heath, 1840; 350 c. Master die, 1840; 400 c. London mail coach, 1840.

458 Anniversary Emblem

1990. 10th Anniv (1989) of 4 June Revolution. Multicoloured.

1434 20 c. Type **458** 10 10
1435 60 c. Foodstuffs 20 25
1436 80 c. Cocoa 25 30
1437 200 c. Mining 60 65
1438 350 c. Scales of Justice and sword .. .. 1·00 1·10

459 Map of Africa and Satellite Network

1990. 25th Anniv of Intelsat Satellite System. Multicoloured.

1439 20 c. Type **459** 10 10
1440 60 c. Map of Americas .. 20 25
1441 80 c. Map of Asia and Pacific 25 30
1442 200 c. Map of South America and Africa .. 60 65
1443 350 c. Map of Indian Ocean and Pacific .. 1·00 1·10

460 Housewife using Telephone

1990. 2nd Anniv of Introduction of International Direct Dialling Service. Mult.

1444 20 c. Type **460** 10 10
1445 60 c. Businessman using telephone 20 25
1446 80 c. Man using phonecard telephone 25 30
1447 200 c. Public telephones for internal and IDD services 60 65
1448 350 c. Satellite station .. 1·00 1·10

461 Blue Flycatcher

1990. African Tropical Rain Forest. Mult.

1449 40 c. Type **461** 10 15
1450 40 c. Boomslang (snake) 10 15
1451 40 c. Superb sunbird .. 10 15
1452 40 c. Bateleur 10 15
1453 40 c. Yellow-casqued hornbill 10 15
1454 40 c. "Salamis temora" (butterfly) 10 15
1455 40 c. Potto 10 15
1456 40 c. Leopard 10 15
1457 40 c. Bongo 10 15
1458 40 c. Grey parrot 10 15
1459 40 c. Okapi 10 15
1460 40 c. Gorilla 10 15
1461 40 c. Flap-necked chameleon 10 15
1462 40 c. West African dwarf crocodile 10 15
1463 40 c. Python 10 15
1464 40 c. Giant ground pangolin 10 15
1465 40 c. "Pseudacraea boisduvali" (butterfly) 10 15
1466 40 c. North African crested porcupine .. 10 15
1467 40 c. "Rosy-columned aerangis" (orchid) .. 10 15
1468 40 c. "Cymothoe sangaris" (butterfly) 10 15

Nos. 1449/68 were printed together, se-tenant, forming a composite design.

462 Jupiter

1990. Space Flight of "Voyager 2". Mult.

1470 100 c. Type **462** 30 35
1471 100 c. Neptune and Triton 30 35
1472 100 c. Ariel, moon of Uranus 30 35
1473 100 c. Saturn from "Mimas" 30 35
1474 100 c. Saturn 30 35
1475 100 c. Rings of Saturn .. 30 35
1476 100 c. Neptune 30 35
1477 100 c. Uranus from "Miranda" 30 35
1478 100 c. Volcano on Io .. 30 35

463 "Eulophia guineensis"

1990. Orchids. Multicoloured.

1480 20 c. Type **463** 10 10
1481 40 c. "Eurychone rothschildiana" 10 15
1482 60 c. "Bulbophyllum barbigerum" 20 25
1483 80 c. "Polystachya galeata" 25 30
1484 200 c. "Diaphananthe kamerunensis" .. 60 65
1485 300 c. "Podangis dactyloceras" 90 95
1486 400 c. "Ancistrochilus rothschildianus" .. 1·25 1·40
1487 500 c. "Rangaeris muscicola" .. .. 1·50 1·60

464 "Coprinus atramentarius"

1990. Fungi (2nd series). Multicoloured.

1489 20 c. Type **464** 10 10
1490 50 c. "Marasmius oreades" 15 20
1491 60 c. "Oudemansiella radicata" 20 25
1492 80 c. "Boletus edulis" (cep) 25 30
1493 150 c. "Hebeloma crustuliniforme" 45 50
1494 200 c. "Coprinus micaceus" 60 65
1495 300 c. "Lepiota procera" 90 95
1496 500 c. "Amanita phalloides" .. .. 1·50 1·60

465 Italian and Swedish Players chasing Ball

1990. World Cup Football Championship, Italy. Multicoloured.

1498 20 c. Type **465** 10 10
1499 50 c. Egyptian player penetrating Irish defence 15 20
1500 60 c. Cameroon players celebrating 20 25
1501 80 c. Rumanian player beating challenge .. 25 30
1502 100 c. Russian goalkeeper Dassayev 30 35
1503 150 c. Roger Milla of Cameroon (vert) .. 45 50
1504 400 c. South Korean player challenging opponent .. .. 1·25 1·40
1505 600 c. West German player celebrating .. 1·75 1·90

1990. 350th Death Anniv of Rubens. As T **273** of Antigua, but vert. Multicoloured.

1507 20 c. "Duke of Mantua" 10 10
1508 50 c. "Jan Brant" .. 15 20
1509 60 c. "Portrait of a Young Man" 20 25
1510 80 c. "Michel Ophovius" 25 30
1511 100 c. "Caspar Gevaerts" 30 35
1512 200 c. "Head of Warrior" (detail) 60 65
1513 300 c. "Study of a Bearded Man" .. 90 95
1514 400 c. "Paracelsus" .. 1·25 1·40

466 Manganese Ore

1991. Minerals. Multicoloured.

1516 20 c. Type **466** 10 10
1517 60 c. Iron ore 20 25
1518 80 c. Bauxite ore .. 25 30
1519 200 c. Gold ore 60 65
1520 350 c. Diamond .. .. 1·00 1·10

467 Dance Drums

1991. Tribal Drums. Multicoloured.

1522 20 c. Type **467** 10 10
1523 60 c. Message drums .. 20 25
1524 80 c. War drums .. 25 30
1525 200 c. Dance drums (different) 60 65
1526 350 c. Ceremonial drums 1·00 1·10

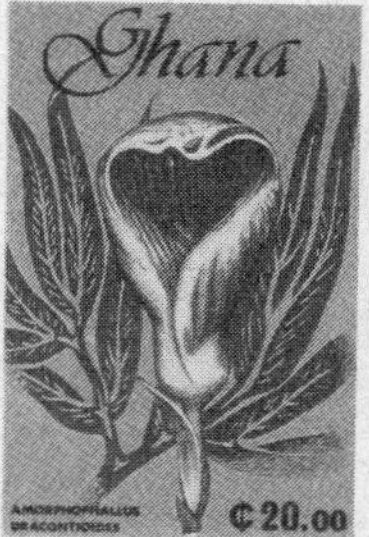

468 "Amorphophallus dracontioides"

1991. Flowers (1st series). Multicoloured.

1528 20 c. Type **468** 10 10
1529 60 c. "Anchomanes difformus" 20 25
1530 80 c. "Kaemferia nigerica" 25 30
1531 200 c. "Aframomum sceptrum" 60 65
1532 350 c. "Amorphophallus flavovirens" .. .. 1·00 1·10

1991. Flowers (2nd series). As T **468** but inscr "GHANA". Multicoloured.

1534 20 c. "Urginea indica" .. 10 10
1535 60 c. "Hymenocallis littoralis" 20 25
1536 80 c. "Crinum jagus" .. 25 30
1537 200 c. "Dipcadi tacazzeanum" 60 65
1538 350 c. "Haremanthus rupestris" .. .. 1·00 1·10

469 Transport and Telecommunication Symbols

1991. 40th Anniv of United Nations Development Programme. Multicoloured.

1540 20 c. Type **469** 10 10
1541 60 c. Agricultural research 20 25
1542 80 c. Literacy 25 30
1543 200 c. Advances in agricultural crop growth .. 60 65
1544 350 c. Industrial symbols 1·00 1·10

470 Drawing of Scout from First Handbook

1991. 50th Death Anniv of Lord Baden-Powell.

1545 **470** 20 c. black and buff .. 10 10
1546 – 50 c. grey, blue & blk 15 20
1547 – 60 c. multicoloured .. 20 25
1548 – 80 c. black and buff .. 25 30
1549 – 100 c. multicoloured 30 35
1550 – 200 c. multicoloured 60 65
1551 – 500 c. multicoloured 1·50 1·60
1552 – 600 c. multicoloured 1·75 1·90

DESIGNS—VERT. 50 c. Lord Baden-Powell; 80 c. Handbook illustration by Norman Rockwell; 500 c. Scout at prayer. HORIZ. 60 c. Hands holding Boy Scout emblem; 100 c. Mafeking Siege 1d. Goodyear stamp and African runner; 200 c. Scouts with Blitz victim, London, 1944; 600 c. Mafeking Siege 1d. Goodyear stamp.

471 Women sorting Fish

1991. Chorkor Smoker (fish smoking process). Multicoloured.

1554 20 c. Type **471** 10 10
1555 60 c. Cleaning the ovens 20 25
1556 80 c. Washing fish .. 25 30
1557 200 c. Laying fish on pallets 60 65
1558 350 c. Stacking pallets over ovens .. .. 1·00 1·10

POSTAGE DUE STAMPS

1958. Postage Due stamps of Gold Coast optd. **GHANA** and bar.

D 9. D **1.** 1d. black 10 20
D 10. 2d. black 10 25
D 11. 3d. black 10 30
D 12. 6d. black 15 45
D 13. 1s. black 20 80

D 3.

1958.

D 14. D **3.** 1d. red 10 20
D 15. 2d. green 10 20
D 16. 3d. orange 10 30
D 17. 6d. blue 10 50
D 18. 1s. violet .. .. 15 1·75

1965. Surch. **Ghana New Currency 19th July, 1965,** and value.

D 19. D **3.** 1 p. on 1d. 10 40
D 20. 2 p. on 2d. 10 40
D 21. 3 p. on 3d. 10 40
D 22. 6 p. on 6d. 10 70
D 23. 12 p. on 1s. .. 15 1·10

1968. Nos. D 20/2 additionally surch.

D 24. D **3.** 1½ n.p. on 2 p. on 2d. 5·50 4·25
D 25. 2½ n.p. on 3 p. on 3d. 1·00 4·00
D 26. 5 n.p. on 6 p. on 6d.. . 1·00

1970. Inscr. in new currency.

D 27. D **3.** 1 n.p. red .. .. 30 1·25
D 28. 1½ n.p. green .. 30 1·50
D 29. 2½ n.p. orange .. 40 1·75
D 30. 5 n.p. blue .. .. 55 2·00
D 31. 10 n.p. violet .. 75 2·50

1980. Currency described as "p".

D 32. D **3.** 2 p. orange .. .. 40 1·00
D 33. 3 p. brown .. .. 40 1·00

GIBRALTAR

A Br. colony at the W. entrance to the Mediterranean.

1886. 12 pence = 1 shilling; 20 shillings = 1 pound.
1971. 100 (new) pence = 1 pound.

1886. Stamps of Bermuda (Queen Victoria) optd. **GIBRALTAR.**

1. 9. ½d. green 6·50 6·00
2. 1d. red 25·00 5·00
3. 2d. purple 75·00 70·00
4. 2½d. blue 90·00 2·75
5. 4d. orange 95·00 85·00
6. 6d. lilac £200 £180
7. 1s. brown £400 £350

2.

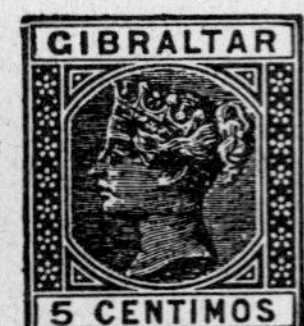

7.

1886. Various frames.

39. 2. ½d. green 1·25 1·25
40. 1d. red 2·00 35
10. 2d. purple 28·00 17·00
42. 2½d. blue 9·00 40
12. 4d. brown 60·00 60·00
13. 6d. lilac 85·00 85·00
14. 1s. brown £180 £180

1889. Surch. with new value in **CENTIMOS.**

15. 2. 5 c. on ½d. green 8·00 13·00
16. 10 c. on 1d. red 7·00 6·50
17. 25 c. on 2d. purple 4·00 5·00
18. 25 c. on 2½d. blue 24·00 1·25
19. 40 c. on 4d. brown 55·00 70·00
20. 50 c. on 6d. lilac 55·00 60·00
21. 75 c. on 1s. brown 55·00 70·00

1889.

22 7 5c. green 2·00 45
23 10 c. red 1·50 45
24 20 c. green and brown 16·00 10·00
25 20 c. green 7·00 25·00
26 25 c. blue 12·00 70
27 40 c. brown 2·50 2·25
28 50 c. lilac 2·00 1·50
29 75 c. green 25·00 32·00
30 1 p. brown 65·00 20·00
31 1 p. brown and blue 3·50 3·25
32 2 p. black and red 7·00 24·00
33 5 p. grey 40·00 75·00

1898. As 1886.

41. 2. 2d. purple and blue 7·00 1·50
43. 4d. brown and green 9·00 8·00
44. 6d. violet and red 23·00 20·00
45. 1s. brown and red 23·00 16·00

8. 9.

1903.

66 8 ½d. green 1·75 80
57b 1d. purple on red 1·50 55
58a 2d. green and red 3·75 2·50
49 2½d. purple & blk. on blue 1·50 60
60a 6d. purple and violet 7·50 8·50
61 1s. black and red 22·00 10·00
62 9 2s. green and blue 48·00 55·00
53 4s. purple and green 60·00 90·00
54 8s. purple & blk. on blue 80·00 £100
55 £1 purple & black on red £475 £550

1907.

67. 8. 1d. red 1·25 45
68. 2d. grey 5·50 9·00
69. 2½d. blue 3·25 1·25
70. 6d. purple £110 £325
71. 1s. black on green 18·00 18·00
72. 9. 2s. purple & blue on blue 35·00 45·00
73. 4s. black and red 65·00 85·00
74. 8s. purple and green £180 £180

1912. As T 8/9, but portrait of King George V. (3d. A. Inscr. "3 PENCE", B. Inscr. "THREE PENCE".)

89 ½d. green 30 35
90 1d. red 1·00 50
91a 1½d. brown 75 30
93 2d. grey 1·25 85
79 2½d. blue 3·25 1·75
95a 3d. blue (A) 1·40 1·50
109 3d. blue (B) 6·50 2·00
97a 6d. purple 1·60 4·50
81 1s. black on green 5·50 6·00
102a 1s. olive and black 10·00 12·00
82 2s. purple & blue on blue 16·00 3·00
103 2s. brown and black 8·00 27·00
104 2s. 6d. green and black 7·00 16·00
83 4s. black and red 26·00 50·00
105 5s. red and black 12·00 40·00
84 8s. purple and green 50·00 60·00
106 10s. blue and black 32·00 50·00
85 £1 purple & black on red £160 £190
107 £1 orange and black £140 £180
108 £5 violet and black £1600 £2750

1918. Optd. **WAR TAX.**

86. ½d. green (No. 89) 30 80

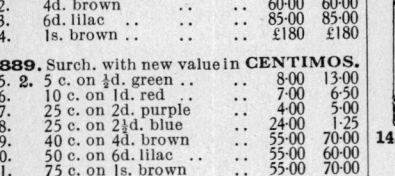

13. The Rock of Gibraltar.

1931.

110. 13. 1d. red 1·25 1·75
111. 1½d. brown 1·00 2·00
112. 2d. grey 2·75 1·00
113. 3d. blue 4·00 3·25

1935. Silver Jubilee. As T 13 of Antigua.

114. 2d. blue and black 1·60 2·50
115. 3d. brown and blue 3·25 3·50
116. 6d. green and blue 7·50 8·00
117. 1s. grey and purple 7·50 8·50

1937. Coronation. As T 2 of Aden.

118. ½d. green 25 10
119. 2d. grey 80 60
120. 3d. blue 2·00 90

14. King George VI.

DESIGNS—HORIZ. 2d. The Rock (North side). 3d., 5d. Europa Point. 6d. Moorish Castle. 1s. Southport Gate. 2s. Eliott Memorial. 5s. Govt. House. 10s. Catalan Bay.

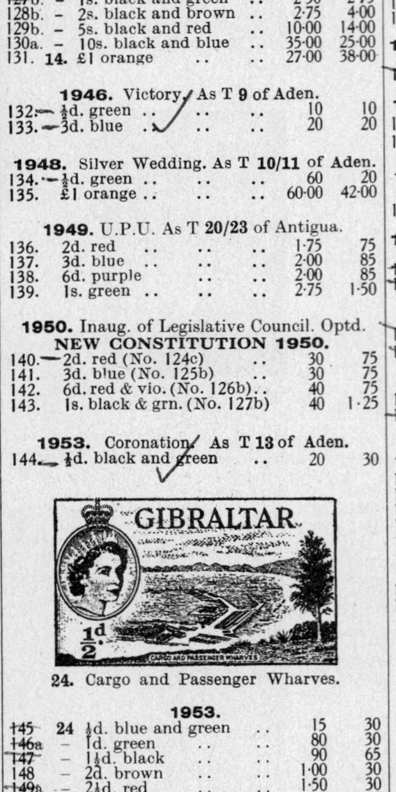

15. Rock of Gibraltar.

1938. King George VI.

121. 14. ½d. green 10 15
122b. 15. 1d. brown 40 55
123. 1½d. red 24·00 75
123b. – 1½d. violet 20 65
124a. – 2d. grey 30 35
124c. – 2d. red 30 35
125b. – 3d. blue 30 30
125c. – 5d. orange 70 1·25
126b. – 6d. red and violet 1·75 1·25
127b. – 1s. black and green 2·50 2·75
128b. – 2s. black and brown 2·75 4·00
129b. – 5s. black and red 10·00 14·00
130a. – 10s. black and blue 35·00 25·00
131. 14. £1 orange 27·00 38·00

1946. Victory. As T 9 of Aden.

132. ½d. green 10 10
133. 3d. blue 20 20

1948. Silver Wedding. As T 10/11 of Aden.

134. ½d. green 60 20
135. £1 orange 60·00 42·00

1949. U.P.U. As T 20/23 of Antigua.

136. 2d. red 1·75 75
137. 3d. blue 2·00 85
138. 6d. purple 2·00 85
139. 1s. green 2·75 1·50

1950. Inaug. of Legislative Council. Optd. **NEW CONSTITUTION 1950.**

140. 2d. red (No. 124c) 30 75
141. 3d. blue (No. 125b) 30 75
142. 6d. red & vio. (No. 126b) 40 75
143. 1s. black & grn. (No. 127b) 40 1·25

1953. Coronation. As T 13 of Aden.

144. ½d. black and green 20 30

24. Cargo and Passenger Wharves.

1953.

145 24 ½d. blue and green 15 30
146a – 1d. green 80 30
147 – 1½d. black 90 65
148 – 2d. brown 1·00 30
149a – 2½d. red 1·50 30
150 – 3d. blue 2·00 10
151 – 4d. blue 2·25 1·25
152 – 5d. purple 35 50
153 – 6d. black and blue 30 30
154a – 1s. blue and brown 30 35
155a – 2s. orange and violet 16·00 1·75
156 – 5s. brown 24·00 12·00
157 – 10s. brown and blue 70·00 35·00
158 – £1 red and yellow 75·00 38·00

DESIGNS—HORIZ. 1d. South view from Straits. 1½d. Tunny fishing industry. 2d. Southport Gate. 2½d. Sailing in the Bay. 3d. Liner. 4d. Coaling wharf. 5d. Airport. 6d. Europa Point. 1s. Straits from Buena Vista. 2s. Rosia Bay and Straits. 5s. Main entrance, Govt. House. VERT. 10s. Tower of Homage, Moorish Castle. £1, Arms of Gibraltar.

1954. Royal Visit. As No. 150 but inscr. "ROYAL VISIT 1954".

159. 3d. blue 15 20

38. Gibraltar Candytuft.

DESIGNS—As Type 38—HORIZ. 1d. Moorish Castle. 2d. St. George's Hall. 3d. The Rock by moonlight. 4d. Catalan Bay. 1s. Barbary ape. 2s. Barbary Partridge. 5s. Blue Rock Thrush. VERT. 2½d. The keys. 6d. Map of Gibraltar. 7d. Air Terminal. 9d. American War Memorial. 10s. Rock lily.

40. Rock and Badge of Gibraltar Regiment.

1960.

160 38 ½d. purple and green 15 30
161 – 1d. black and green 10 10
162 – 2d. blue and brown 15 15
163a – 2½d. black and blue 15 15
164 – 3d. blue and orange 30 10
199 – 4d. brown and turq 30 40
166 – 6d. brown and green 70 35
167 – 7d. blue and red 70 75
168 – 9d. blue and turquoise 50 50
169 – 1s. brown and green 90 30
170 – 2s. brown and blue 13·00 2·00
171 – 5s. blue and green 8·00 5·00
172 – 10s. yellow and blue 14·00 9·00
173 40 £1 black and brown 23·00 14·00

1963. Freedom from Hunger. As T 28 of Aden.

174. 9d. sepia 11·00 2·00

1963. Cent of Red Cross. As T 33 of Antigua.

175. 1d. red and black 50 50
176. 9d. red and blue 12·00 2·75

1964. 400th Birth Anniv of Shakespeare. As T 34 of Antigua.

177. 7d. bistre 40 20

1964. New Constitution. Nos. 164 and 166 optd. **NEW CONSTITUTION 1964.**

178. 3d. blue and orange 15 10
179. 6d. sepia and green 15 20

1965. Cent of I.T.U. As T 36 of Antigua.

180. 4d. green and yellow 5·00 50
181. 2s. green and blue 12·00 2·50

1965. I.C.Y. As T 37 of Antigua.

182. ½d. green and lavender 20 45
183. 4d. purple and turquoise 1·00 80

The value of the ½d. stamp is shown as "1/2".

1966. Churchill Commem. As T 38 of Antigua.

184. ½d. blue 20 40
185. 1d. green 30 10
186. 4d. brown 1·50 10
187. 9d. violet 1·75 1·40

1966. World Cup Football Championship. As T 40 of Antigua.

188. 2½d. multicoloured 75 30
189. 6d. multicoloured 1·00 50

53. Bream.

1966. European Sea Angling Championships. Gibraltar.

190. 53. 4d. red, blue and black 20 10
191. – 7d. red, green and black 20 20
192. – 1s. brown, green & black 20 20

DESIGNS: 7d. Scorpion Fish. 1s Stone Bass.

1966. Inauguration of W.H.O. Headquarters, Geneva. As T 41 of Antigua.

193. 6d. black, green and blue 3·00 1·50
194. 9d. black, purple & ochre 4·00 1·50

56. "Our Lady of Europa".

1966. Centenary of Re-enthronement of "Our Lady of Europa".

195. 56. 2s. blue and black 30 50

1966. 20th Anniv. of U.N.E.S.C.O. As T 54/6 of Antigua.

196. 2d. multicoloured 25 10
197. 7d. yellow, violet & olive 60 10
198. 5s. black, purple & orange 2·50 1·75

57. H.M.S. "Victory".

1967. Multicoloured.

200. ½d. Type 57 10 15
201. 1d. S.S. "Arab" 10 10
202. 2d. H.M.S. "Carmania" 15 10
203. 2½d. M.V. "Mons Calpe" 30 30
204. 3d. S.S. "Canberra" 20 10
205. 4d. H.M.S. "Hood" 30 10
205a. 5d. Cable Ship "Mirror" 2·75 45
206. 6d. Xebec (sailing vessel) 30 30
207. 7d. "Amerigo Vespucci" (training vessel) 30 35
208. 9d. T. V. "Raffaello" 30 50
209. 1s. H.M.S. "Royal Katherine" 25 35
210. 2s. H.M.S. "Ark Royal" 2·25 1·50
211. 5s. H.M.S. "Dreadnought" 3·50 4·00
212. 10s. S.S. "Neuralia" 14·00 16·00
213. £1 "Mary Celeste" (sailing vessel) 14·00 16·00

58. Aerial Ropeway.

1967. Int. Tourist Year. Multicoloured.

214. 7d. Type 58 10 10
215. 9d. Shark fishing (horiz.) 10 10
216. 1s. Skin-diving (horiz.) 15 15

59. Mary, Joseph and Child Jesus.

1967. Christmas. Multicoloured.

217. 2d. Type 59 10 10
218. 6d. Church window (vert.) 10 10

61. Gen. Eliott and Route Map.

1967. 250th Birth Anniv. of General Eliott. Multicoloured.

219. 4d. Type 61 10 10
220. 9d. Heathfield Tower and Monument, Sussex 10 10
221 1s. General Eliott (vert.) 10 10
222. 2s. Eliott directing Rescue Operations 30 15

No. 222 is 55×21 mm.

65. Lord Baden-Powell.

1968. 60th Anniv. of Gibraltar Scout Assn.

223. **65.** 4d. buff and violet .. 15 10
224. – 7d. ochre and green .. 15 10
225. – 9d. blue, orge. & black 20 10
226. – 1s. yellow and green .. 20 15

DESIGNS: 7d. Scout Flag over the Rock. 9d. Tent, Scouts and Salute. 1s. Scout Badges.

66. Nurse and W.H.O. Emblem.

1968. 20th Anniv. of World Health Organization. Multicoloured.

227. 2d. Type **66** 10 10
228. 4d. Doctor and W.H.O. Emblem 10 10

68. King John signing Magna Carta.

70. Shepherd, Lamb and Star.

1968. Human Rights Year.

229. **68.** 1s. orange, brown & gold 15 10
230. – 2s. myrtle and gold .. 15 20

DESIGN: 2s. "Freedom" and Rock of Gibraltar.

1968. Christmas. Multicoloured.

231. 4d. Type **70** 10 10
232. 9d. Mary holding Holy Child 10 10

72. Parliament Houses.

1969. Commonwealth Parliamentary Assn., Conference.

233. **72.** 4d green and gold .. 10 10
234. – 9d. violet and gold .. 10 10
235. – 2s. red, gold and blue .. 15 20

DESIGNS—HORIZ. 9d. Parliamentary Emblem and outline of "The Rock". VERT. 2s. Clock Tower, Westminster (Big Ben) and Arms of Gibraltar.

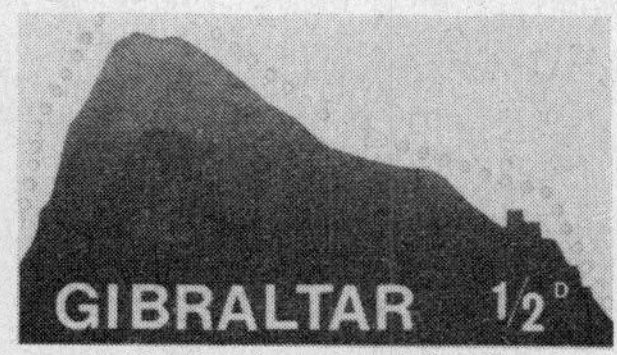

75. Silhouette of Rock, and Queen Elizabeth.

1969. New Constitution.

236. **75.** ½d. gold and orange .. 10 10
237. 5d. silver and green .. 10 10
238. 7d. silver and purple .. 10 10
239. 5s. silver and blue .. 35 70

77. Soldier and Cap Badge, Royal Anglian Regiment, 1969.

1969. Military Uniforms (1st series). Mult.

240. 1d. Royal Artillery Officer, 1758, and modern cap badge 20 10
241. 6d. Type **77** 55 20
242. 9d. Royal Engineers' Artificer, 1786, and modern cap badge .. 75 30
243. 2s. Private, Fox's Marines, 1704, and modern Royal Marines' cap badge .. 4·00 1·60

See also Nos. 248/51, 290/3, 300/303, 313/16, 331/4, 340/3 and 363/6.

80. "Madonna of the Chair" (detail, Raphael).

1969. Christmas. Multicoloured.

244. 5d. Type **80** 10 10
245. 7d. "Virgin and Child" (detail, Morales) .. 15 15
246. 1s. "The Virgin of the Rocks" (detail, Leonardo da Vinci) 15 20

83. Europa Point.

1970. Europa Point.

247. **83.** 2s. multicoloured .. 30 30

1970. Military Uniforms (2nd series). As T **77**. Multicoloured.

248. 2d. Royal Scots Officer (1839) and Cap Badge .. 40 10
249. 5d. South Wales Borderers Private (1763) and Cap Badge 80 10
250. 7d. Queen's Royal Regiment Private (1742) and Cap Badge 90 15
251. 2s. Royal Irish Rangers piper (1969) and Cap Badge .. .. .. 4·50 1·75

88. Stamp and Rock of Gibraltar.

1970. "Philympia 70" Stamp Exhibition, London.

252. **88.** 1s. red and green .. 10 10
253. – 2s. blue and mauve .. 20 25

DESIGN: 2s. Stamp and Moorish Castle. The stamps shown in the designs are well known varieties with values omitted.

90. "The Virgin Mary" (stained-glass window, Gabriel Loire).

1970. Christmas.

254. **90.** 2s. multicoloured .. 30 30

91. Saluting Battery, Rosia.

92. Saluting Battery, Rosia, Modern View.

1971. Decimal Currency. Each value printed se-tenant in two designs showing respectively old and new views.

255. ½p. Type **91** 15 20
256. ½p. Type **92** 15 20
257. 1p. } Prince George of 80 30
258. 1p. } Cambridge Quarters and Trinity Church 80 30
259. 1½p. } The Wellington Bust 20 25
260. 1½p. } Almeda Gardens .. 20 25
317. 2p. } Gibraltar from the 75 1·25
318. 2p. } North Bastion .. 75 1·25
263. 2½p. } Catalan Bay .. 20 25
264. 2½p. } 20 25
265. 3p. } Covent Garden .. 20 15
266. 3p. } 20 15
319. 4p. } The Exchange and 1·00 1·25
320. 4p. } Spanish Chapel .. 1·00 1·25
269. 5p. } Commercial Square 30 20
270. 5p. } and Library .. 30 20
271. 7p. } South Barracks 65 65
272. 7p. } and Rosia Magazine 65 65
273. 8p. } Moorish Mosque 70 70
274. 8p. } and Castle 70 70
275. 9p. } Europa Pass Road .. 70 70
276. 9p. } 70 70
277. 10p. } South Barracks 80 80
278. 10p. } from Rosia Bay .. 80 80
279. 12½p. } Southport Gates .. 1·00 1·25
280. 12½p. } 1·00 1·25
281. 25p. } The Alameda, 1·40 1·40
282. 25p. } Trooping the Guards 1·40 1·40
283. 50p. } Europa Pass Gorge 1·40 2·50
284. 50p. } (vert.) .. .. 1·40 2·50
285. £1 } Prince Edward's 2·75 4·00
286. £1 } Gate (vert.) .. 2·75 4·00

93.

94. Regimental Arms.

1971. Coil Stamps.

287. **93.** ½p. orange 15 30
288. 1p. blue 15 30
289. 2p. green .. .. 65 1·10

1971. Military Uniforms (3rd series). As T **77**. Multicoloured.

290. 1p. The Black Watch (1845) 45 20
291. 2p. Royal Regt. of Fusiliers (1971) 85 30
292. 4p. King's Own Royal Border Regt. (1704) .. 1·75 70
293. 10p. Devonshire and Dorset Regt. (1801) .. 5·00 2·50

1971. Presentation of Colours to the Gibraltar Regiment.

294. **94.** 3p. black, gold and red 30 30

95. Nativity Scene.

1971. Christmas. Multicoloured.

295. 3p. Type **95** 45 35
296. 5p. Mary and Joseph going to Bethlehem 55 40

96. Soldier Artificer, 1773.

1972. Bicentenary of Royal Engineers in Gibraltar. Multicoloured.

297. 1p. Type **96** 40 20
298. 3p. Modern tunneller .. 60 50
299. 5p. Old and new uniforms and badge (horiz.) .. 75 65

1972. Military Uniforms (4th series). As T **77**. Multicoloured.

300. 1p. The Duke of Cornwall's Light Infantry, 1704 .. 60 20
301. 3p. King's Royal Rifle Corps, 1830 .. .. 1·75 50
302. 7p. 37th North Hampshire, Officer, 1825 .. .. 2·50 1·25
303. 10p. Royal Navy, 1972 .. 3·00 2·00

97. "Our Lady of Europa".

1972. Christmas.

304. **97.** 3p. multicoloured .. 10 10
305. 5p. multicoloured .. 10 20

1972. Royal Silver Wedding. As T **52** of Ascension, but with Keys of Gibraltar and "Narcissus niveus" in background.

306. 5p. red 20 20
307. 7p. green 20 20

99. Flags of Member Nations and E.E.C. Symbol.

1973. Britain's Entry into the E.E.C.

308. **99.** 5p. multicoloured .. 40 30
309. 10p. multicoloured .. 60 50

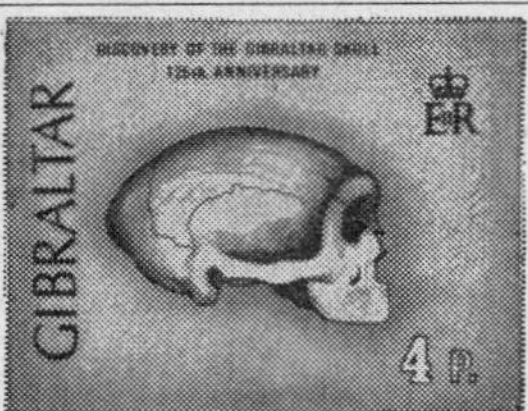

100. Skull.

1973. 125th Anniv. of Gibraltar Skull Discovery. Multicoloured.

310.	4p. Type **100**	1·00	50
311.	6p. Prehistoric man ..	1·00	70
312.	10p. Prehistoric family ..	1·50	1·25

No. 312 is size 40×26 mm.

1973. Military Uniforms (5th series). As T **77.** Multicoloured.

313.	1p. King's Own Scottish Borderers, 1770 ..	40	20
314.	4p. Royal Welch Fusiliers, 1800	1·25	1·40
315.	6p. Royal Northumberland Fusiliers, 1736	2·00	1·50
316.	10p. Grenadier Guards, 1898	3·00	2·50

101. " Nativity " (Danckerts).

1973. Christmas.

321. **101.**	4p. violet and red ..	25	15
322.	6p. mauve and blue ..	35	45

1973. Royal Wedding. As Type **43** of Anguilla. Background colours given. Multicoloured.

323.	6p. blue	10	10
324.	14p. green	20	20

102. Victorian Pillar-box.

1974. Centenary of U.P.U. Multicoloured.

325.	2p. Type **102**	15	20
326.	6p. Pillar-box of George VI	25	30
327.	14p. Pillar-box of Elizabeth II	40	65

Nos. 325/7 also come self-adhesive from booklet panes.

1974. Military Uniforms (6th series). As T **77.** Multicoloured.

331.	4p. East Lancashire Regt., 1742	50	50
332.	6p. Somerset Light Infantry, 1833	70	70
333.	10p. Royal Sussex Regt., 1790	1·00	1·25
334.	16p. R.A.F. officer, 1974	2·25	2·50

103. " Madonna with the Green Cushion " (Solario).

1974. Christmas. Multicoloured.

335.	4p. Type **103**	40	30
336.	6p. "Madonna of the Meadow" (Bellini)	60	60

104. Churchill and Houses of Parliament.

1974. Birth Centenary of Sir Winston Churchill. Multicoloured.

337. **104.**	6p. black, purple and lavender	25	15
338. –	20p. black, brown and red	50	50

DESIGN: 20p. Churchill and "King George V" (battleship).

1975. Military Uniforms (7th series). As Type **77.** Multicoloured.

340.	4p. East Surrey Regt., 1846	30	30
341.	6p. Highland Light Infantry, 1777	50	50
342.	10p. Coldstream Guards 1704	70	80
343.	20p. Gibraltar Regt., 1974	1·25	1·50

105. Girl Guides' Badge.

1975. 50th Anniv. of Gibraltar Girl Guides.

346. **105.**	5p. gold, blue & violet	30	40
347.	7p. gold and brown ..	40	50
343. –	15p. silver, blk. & brn.	65	85

No. 348 is as Type **105** but shows a different badge.

106. Child at Prayer.

1975. Christmas. Multicoloured.

349.	6p. Type **106** ..	40	45
350.	6p. Angel with lute ..	40	45
351.	6d. Child singing carols ..	40	45
352.	6p. Three children ..	40	45
353.	6p. Girl at prayer ..	40	45
354.	6p. Boy and lamb ..	40	45

107. Bruges Madonna.

1975. 500th Birth Anniv. of Michelangelo. Multicoloured.

355.	6p. Type **107**	25	20
356.	9p. Taddei Madonna ..	35	30
357.	15p. Pieta	65	55

Nos. 355/7 also come self-adhesive from booklet panes.

INDEX

Countries can be quickly located by referring to the index at the end of this volume.

108. Bicentennial Emblem and Arms of Gibraltar.

1976. Bicent. of American Revolution.

361. **108.**	25 p. multicoloured ..	50	50

1976. Military Uniforms (8th series). As T **24.** Mult.

363.	1p. Suffolk Regt., 1795 ..	15	15
364.	6p. Northamptonshire Regt. 1779	30	30
365.	12p. Lancashire Fusiliers, 1793	55	55
366.	25p. Ordnance Corps, 1896	1·10	1·10

109. The Holy Family.

1976. Christmas. Multicoloured.

367.	6p. Type **109**	25	15
368.	9p. Madonna and Child ..	30	25
369.	12p. St. Bernard	45	45
370.	20p. Archangel Michael ..	70	80

Nos. 367/70 show different stained-glass windows from St. Joseph's Church, Gibraltar.

110. Queen Elizabeth II, Royal Arms and Gibraltar Arms.

1977. Silver Jubilee. Multicoloured.

371. **110.**	6p. red	25	20
372.	£1 blue	1·75	2·25

111. Toothed Orchid.

1977. Birds, Flowers, Fish and Butterflies. Multicoloured.

374	½p. Type **111**	40	50
375	1p. Red mullet (horiz) ..	10	10
376	2p. "Maculinea arion" (butterfly) (horiz) ..	30	30
377	2½p. Sardinian warbler ..	40	35
378	3p. Giant squill	20	10
379	4p. Grey wrasse (horiz) ..	30	10
380	5p. "Vanessa atalanta" (butterfly) (horiz) ..	50	60
381	6p. Black kite	45	30
382	9p. Shrubby scorpion-vetch	90	70
383	10p. John dory (fish) (horiz)	40	20
384	12p. "Colias crocea" (butterfly) (horiz) ..	1·00	35
384b	15p. Winged asparagus pea	2·25	40
385	20p. Audouin's gull ..	1·25	1·25
386	25p. Barbary nut (iris) ..	1·25	1·50
387	50p. Swordfish (horiz) ..	2·00	95
388	£1 "Papilio machaon" (butterfly) (horiz) ..	4·75	4·00
389	£2 Hoopoe	7·50	10·00
389a	£5 Arms of Gibraltar ..	10·00	10·00

112. " Our Lady of Europa " Stamp.

1977. " Amphilex '77 " Stamp Exn., Amsterdam. Multicoloured.

390.	6p. Type **112**	10	20
391.	12p. " Europa Point " stamp	20	30
392.	25p. " E.E.C. Entry " stamp	30	50

113. " The Annunciation " (Rubens).

1977. Christmas and 400th Birth Anniv. of Rubens. Multicoloured.

393.	3p. Type **113**	10	10
394.	9p. " The Adoration of the Magi "	20	20
395.	12p. " The Adoration of the Magi " (horiz.) ..	25	30
396.	15p. " The Holy Family under the Apple Tree "	30	40

114. Aerial View of Gibraltar.

1978. Gibraltar from Space.

398. **114.**	12p. multicoloured ..	25	40

115. Holyroodhouse.

1978. 25th Anniv. of Coronation. Mult.

400.	6p. Type **115** ..	20	15
401.	9p. St. James' Palace ..	25	15
402.	12p. Sandringham ..	30	25
403.	18p. Balmoral ..	40	40
406.	25p. Windsor Castle ..	70	1·10

Nos. 402/3 also exist as self-adhesive stamps from booklet panes, No. 406 only coming in this form.

116. " Sunderland ", 1938–58.

1978. 60th Anniv. of Royal Air Force. Mult.

407.	3p. Type **116**	15	10
408.	9p. " Cauldron ", 1918 ..	35	35
409.	12p. " Shackleton ", 1953–66	40	40
410.	16p. " Hunter ", 1954–77	45	50
411.	18p. " Nimrod ", 1969–78	50	60

117. " Madonna with Animals ".

1978. Christmas. Paintings by Durer. Multicoloured.

412.	5p. Type **117**	10	10
413.	9p. " The Nativity " ..	15	15
414.	12p. " Madonna of the Goldfinch "	20	25
415.	15p. " Adoration of the Magi "	30	40

118. Sir Rowland Hill and 1d. Stamp of 1886.

1979. Death Cent. of Sir Rowland Hill.

416. **118**	3p. multicoloured ..	15	10
417. –	9p. multicoloured ..	30	15
418. –	12p. multicoloured ..	35	20
419. –	25p. blk., purple & yell.	50	50

DESIGNS: 9p. 1971 1p. coil stamp. 12p. 1840 Post Office Regulations. 25p. " G " cancellation.

119. Posthorn, Dish Antenna and Early Telephone.

1979. Europa. Communications.

420. **119.**	3p. green and pale green	30	10
421.	9p. brown and ochre ..	80	90
422.	12p. blue and violet ..	1·00	1·10

120. African Child.

1979. Christmas. International Year of the Child. Multicoloured.

423.	12p. Type **120**	25	30
424.	12p. Asian child	25	30
425.	12p. Polynesian child ..	25	30
426.	12p. American Indian child	25	30
427.	12p. Nativity and children of different races ..	25	30
428.	12p. European child ..	25	30

121. Early Policeman.

1980. 150th Anniv. of Gibraltar Police Force. Multicoloured.

429.	3p. Type **121**	20	10
430.	6p. Policemen of 1895, early 1900's and 1980..	20	15
431.	12p. Police officer and police ambulance	25	20
432.	37p. Policewoman and police motor cyclist ..	55	80

122. Peter Amigo (Archbishop).

1980. Europa. Personalities. Multicoloured.

433.	12p. Type **122**	20	25
434.	12p. Gustavo Bacarisas (artist)	20	25
435.	12p. John Mackintosh (philanthropist) ..	20	25

123. Queen Elizabeth the Queen Mother.

1980. 80th Birthday of The Queen Mother.

436. **123.**	15 p. multicoloured ..	25	25

124. " Horatio Nelson " (J. F. Rigaud).

1980. 175th Death Anniv. of Nelson Paintings. Multicoloured.

437.	3p. Type **124**.	15	10
438.	9p. " H.M.S. Victory " (horiz.)	25	25
439.	15p. " Horatio Nelson " (Sir William Beechey)..	35	35
440.	40p. " H.M.S. Victory " being towed into Gibraltar (Clarkson Stanfield)(horiz.)	80	1·00

125. Three Kings.

1980. Christmas.

442. **125.**	15p. brown and yellow	25	35
443. –	15p. brown and yellow	25	35

DESIGN: No. 443, Nativity scene.

126. Hercules creating the Mediterranean.

1981. Europa. Multicoloured.

444.	9p. Type **126**	20	15
445.	15p. Hercules and pillars	25	35

127. Dining-room.

1981. 450th Anniv. of The Convent. Mult.

446.	4p. Type **127**.	10	10
447.	14p. King's Chapel ..	20	20
448.	15p. The Convent ..	20	20
449.	55p. Cloister	85	1·10

128. Prince Charles and Lady Diana Spencer.

1981. Royal Wedding.

450. **128.**	£1 multicoloured ..	1·50	1·75

129.

1981. Booklet Stamps.

451. **129.**	1p. black	10	10
452.	4p. blue..	10	10
453.	15p. green	25	30

130. Paper Aeroplane.

1981. 50th Anniv. of Gibraltar Airmail Service. Multicoloured.

454.	14p. Type **130**	20	20
455.	15p. Airmail letters, post box and aircraft tail fin	20	20
456.	55p. Aircraft circling globe	80	90

131. Carol Singers.

1981. Christmas. Children's Drawings. Multicoloured.

457.	15p. Type **131**.	30	15
458.	55p. Postbox (vert.) ..	1·00	85

132. I.Y.D.P. Emblem and Stylised Faces.

1981. International Year for Disabled Persons.

459. **132.**	14p. multicoloured ..	30	30

133. Douglas " DC 3 ".

1982. Aircraft. Multicoloured.

460.	1p. Type **133**	25	30
461.	2p. Vickers " Viking " ..	30	30
462.	3p. Airspeed " Ambassador "	30	30
463.	4p. Vickers " Viscount "	40	15
464.	5p. Boeing " 727 " ..	60	30
465.	10p. Vickers " Vanguard "	75	30
466.	14p. Short " Solent" ..	85	60
467.	15p. Fokker " F.27 (Friendship) "	1·00	30
468.	17p. Boeing " 737 " ..	1·00	45
469.	20p. BAC " One-eleven "	75	40
470.	25p. Lockheed " Constellation "	1·50	1·00
471.	50p. De Havilland " Comet 4B "	2·75	1·75
472.	£1 Saro " Windhover " ..	4·00	2·25
473.	£2 Hawker Siddeley " Trident 2 " ..	4·50	4·75
474.	£4 D.H. " 89A (Dragon Rapide) "	9·00	13·00

134. Crest, H.M.S. " Opossum ".

1982. Naval Crests (1st series). Multicoloured.

475.	½p. Type **134**	10	10
476.	15½p. H.M.S. " Norfolk "	45	50
477.	17p. H.M.S. " Fearless "	50	55
478.	60p. H.M.S. " Rooke " ..	1·25	1·60

See also Nos. 493/6, 510/13, 522/5, 541/4 565/8, 592/5, 616/9, 638/41 and 651/4.

135. "Spitfires" at Gibraltar.

1982. Europa. Operation Torch. Mult.

479.	14p. Type **135**	25	40
480.	17p. General Giraud, General Eisenhower and Gibraltar	35	45

136. Gibraltar Chamber of Commerce Centenary.

1982. Anniversaries. Multicoloured.

481.	½p. Type **136**	10	10
482.	15½p. British Forces Postal Service centenary ..	30	25
483.	60p. 75th anniv. of Gibraltar Scout Association	1·10	1·25

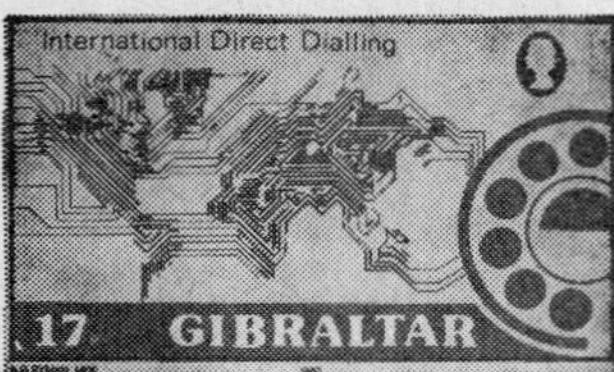

137. Printed Circuit forming Map of World.

1982. International Direct Dialling.

484. **137.** 17p. black, blue and orange 35 35

138. Gibraltar illuminated at Night and Holly.

1982. Christmas. Multicoloured.

485. 14p. Type **138** 45 30
486. 17p. Gibraltar illuminated at night and Mistletoe .. 50 35

139. Yacht Marina.

1983. Commonwealth Day. Multicoloured.

487. 4p. Type **139** 10 10
488. 14p. Scouts and Guides Commonwealth Day Parade 30 35
489. 17p. Flag of Gibraltar (vert.) 35 40
490. 60p. Queen Elizabeth II (from photo by Tim Graham) (vert.) .. .. 1·25 1·40

140. St. George's Hall Gallery.

1983. Europa.

491. **140.** 16p. black and brown 35 35
492. – 19p. black and blue .. 40 40

DESIGN: 19p. Water catchment slope.

1983. Naval Crests (2nd series). Multicoloured. As Type **134.**

493. 4p. H.M.S. "Faulknor" .. 20 10
494. 14p. H.M.S. "Renown" .. 50 35
495. 17p. H.M.S. "Ark Royal" 60 40
496. 60p. H.M.S. "Sheffield" .. 1·75 1·50

141. Landport Gate, 1729.

1983. Fortress Gibraltar in the 18th Century. Multicoloured.

497. 4p. Type **141** 20 10
498. 17p. Koehler Gun, 1782 .. 60 40
499. 77p. King's Bastion, 1779 2·00 1·75

142. "Adoration of the Magi" (Raphael).

1983. Christmas. 500th Birth Anniv. of Raphael. Multicoloured.

501. 4p. Type **142** 20 10
502. 17p. "Madonna of Foligno" (vert.) 70 35
503. 60p. "Sistine Madonna" (vert.) .. .. .. 1·75 1·40

143. 1932 2d. Stamp and Globe.

1984. Europa. Post and Telecommunications. Multicoloured.

504. 17p. Type **143** 35 40
505. 23p. Circuit board and globe 45 50

144. Hockey.

1984. Sports. Multicoloured.

506. 20p. Type **144** 40 50
507. 21p. Basketball 40 50
508. 26p. Rowing 55 70
509. 29p. Football 60 75

1984. Naval Crests (3rd series). As T **134.** Multicoloured.

510. 20p. H.M.S. "Active" .. 1·00 80
511. 21p. H.M.S. "Foxhound" .. 1·00 80
512. 26p. H.M.S. "Valiant" .. 1·25 1·00
513. 29p. H.M.S. "Hood" .. 1·40 1·50

145. Mississippi River Boat Float.

1984. Christmas. Epiphany Floats. Mult.

514. 20p. Type **145** 40 50
515. 80p. Roman Temple float 1·60 2·00

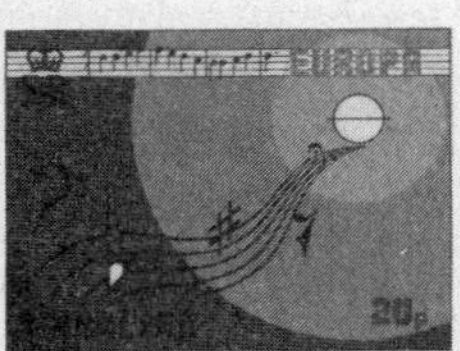

146. Musical Symbols, and Score from Beethoven's 9th (Choral) Symphony.

1985. Europa. European Music Year. Mult.

516. **146.** 20p. multicoloured .. 50 50
517. – 29p. multicoloured .. 75 1·00

DESIGN: The 29p. is as T **146**, but shows different symbols.

147. Globe and Stop Polio Campaign Logo.

1985. Stop Polio Campaign.

518. 26p. multicoloured (Type **147**) 60 60
519. 26p. multicoloured ("ST" visible) 60 60
520. 26p. multicoloured ("STO" visible) 60 60
521. 26p. multicoloured ("STOP" visible) .. 60 60

Each design differs in the position of the logo across the centre of the globe. On No. 518 only the letter "S" is fully visible, on No. 519 "ST", on No. 520 "STO" and on No. 521 "STOP". Other features of the design also differ, so that the word "Year" moves towards the top of the stamp and on No. 521 the upper logo is omitted.

1985. Naval Crests (4th series). As T **134.** Multicoloured.

522. 4p. H.M.S. "Duncan" .. 25 10
523. 9p. H.M.S. "Fury" .. 40 40
524. 21p. H.M.S. "Firedrake" .. 90 90
525. 80p. H.M.S. "Malaya" .. 2·75 3·25

148. I.Y.Y. Logo.

1985. International Youth Year. Mult.

526. 4p. Type **148** 25 10
527. 20p. Hands passing diamond 95 80
528. 80p. 75th anniv. logo of Girl Guide Movement .. 2·50 2·75

149. St. Joseph.

1985. Christmas. Centenary of St. Joseph's Parish Church. Multicoloured.

529. 4p. Type **149** 20 20
530. 4p. St. Joseph's Parish Church 20 20
531. 80p. Nativity crib .. .. 1·75 2·00

150. "Papilio machaon" (butterfly) and The Convent.

1986. Europa. Nature and the Environment. Multicoloured.

532. 22p. Type **150** .. .. 1·00 50
533. 29p. Herring gull and Europa Point .. .. 1·50 2·25

151. 1887 Queen Victoria 6d. Stamp.

1986. Centenary of First Gibraltar Postage Stamps. Designs showing stamps. Mult.

534. 4p. Type **151** 25 10
535. 22p. 1903 Edward VII 2½d. 85 75
536. 32p. 1912 George V 1d. .. 1·25 1·40
537. 36p. 1938 George VI £1 .. 1·40 1·60
538. 44p. 1953 Coronation ½d. (29 × 46 mm) .. .. 1·75 2·00

152. Queen Elizabeth II in Robes of Order of the Bath.

1986. 60th Birthday of Queen Elizabeth II.

540. **152.** £1 multicoloured .. 2·00 3·00

1986. Naval Crests (5th series). As T **134.** Multicoloured.

541. 22p. H.M.S. "Lightning" .. 1·00 75
542. 29p. H.M.S. "Hermione" .. 1·25 1·00
543. 32p. H.M.S. "Laforey" .. 1·50 1·75
544. 44p. H.M.S. "Nelson" .. 1·75 2·25

154. Three Kings and Cathedral of St. Mary the Crowned.

1986. Christmas. International Peace Year. Multicoloured.

546. 18p. Type **154** .. .. 1·00 40
547. 32p. St. Andrew's Church 1·50 1·75

155. Neptune House.

1987. Europa. Architecture. Multicoloured.

563. 22p. Type **155** .. .. 1·25 50
564. 29p. Ocean Heights .. 2·00 1·40

1987. Naval Crests (6th series). As T **134.** Multicoloured.

565. 18p. H.M.S. "Wishart" (destroyer) .. .. 1·25 75
566. 22p. H.M.S. "Charybdis" (cruiser) .. .. 1·40 95
567. 32p. H.M.S. "Antelope" (destroyer) .. .. 1·90 2·25
568. 44p. H.M.S. "Eagle" (aircraft carrier) .. 2·50 3·00

156. 13-inch Mortar, 1783.

1987. Guns. Multicoloured.

569. 1p. Type **156** 10 10
570. 2p. 6-inch coastal gun, 1909 10 10
571. 3p. 8-inch howitzer, 1783 .. 10 10
572. 4p. Bofors "L40/70" AA gun, 1951 .. .. 10 10
573. 5p. 100 ton rifled muzzle-loader, 1882 .. .. 10 15
574. 10p. 5.25-inch heavy AA gun, 1953 .. .. 20 25
575. 18p. 25-pounder gun-how, 1943 .. .. .. 35 40
576. 19p. 64-pounder rifled muzzle-loader, 1873 .. 40 45
577. 22p. 12-pounder gun, 1758 45 50
578. 50p. 10-inch rifled muzzle-loader, 1870 .. .. 1·00 1·10
579. £1 Russian 24-pounder gun, 1854 .. .. 2·00 2·10
580. £3 9.2-inch "Mk.10" coastal gun, 1935 .. 6·00 6·25
581. £5 24-pounder gun, 1779 .. 10·00 10·50

157. Victoria Stadium.

1987. Bicentenary of Royal Engineers' Royal Warrant. Multicoloured.

582. 18p. Type **157** .. .. 1·00 65
583. 32p. Freedom of Gibraltar scroll and casket .. 1·50 1·75
584. 44p. Royal Engineers' badge .. .. .. 1·75 2·50

158. The Three Kings.

1987. Christmas. Multicoloured.

585. 4p. Type **158** 15 10
586. 22p. The Holy Family .. 75 75
587. 44p. The Shepherds .. 1·40 1·60

159. Liner passing Gibraltar.

1988. Europa Transport and Communications. Multicoloured.

588. 22p. Type **159** .. .. 1·25 1·50
589. 22p. Ferry, dish aerial and aircraft .. .. .. 1·25 1·50
590. 32p. Horse-drawn carriage and modern coach .. 1·75 2·00
591. 32p. Car, telephone and Rock of Gibraltar .. 1·75 2·00

1988. Naval Crests (7th series). As T **134**.

592. 18p. multicoloured .. 90 65
593. 22p. black, brown and gold 1·10 90
594. 32p. multicoloured .. 1·50 1·75
595. 44p. multicoloured .. 2·00 2·50

DESIGNS: 18p. H.M.S. "Clyde". 22p. H.M.S. "Foresight". 32p. H.M.S. "Severn". 44p. H.M.S. "Rodney".

160 European Bee Eater

1988. Birds. Multicoloured.

596 4p. Type **160** 30 15
597 22p. Atlantic puffin .. 80 80
598 32p. Honey buzzard .. 1·00 1·25
599 44p. Blue rock thrush .. 1·40 2·00

161 "Zebu" (brigantine)

1988. Operation Raleigh. Multicoloured.

600 19p. Type **161** 55 60
601 22p. Miniature of Sir Walter Raleigh and logo 60 70
602 32p. "Sir Walter Raleigh" (expedition ship) and world map .. .. 85 1·25

162 "Snowman" (Rebecca Falero)

1988. Christmas. Children's Paintings. Mult.

604 4p. Type **162** 15 10
605 22p. "The Nativity" (Dennis Penalver) .. 55 60
606 44p. "Father Christmas" (Gavin Key) (23 × 31 mm) .. .. .. 1·00 1·25

163 Soft Toys and Toy Train

1989. Europa. Children's Toys. Multicoloured.

607 25p. Type **163** .. .. 1·00 60
608 32p. Soft toys, toy boat and doll's house .. 1·25 1·40

164 Port Sergeant with Keys

1989. 50th Anniv of Gibraltar Regiment. Mult.

609 4p. Type **164** 25 10
610 22p. Regimental badge and colours 80 80
611 32p. Drum major .. 1·25 1·50

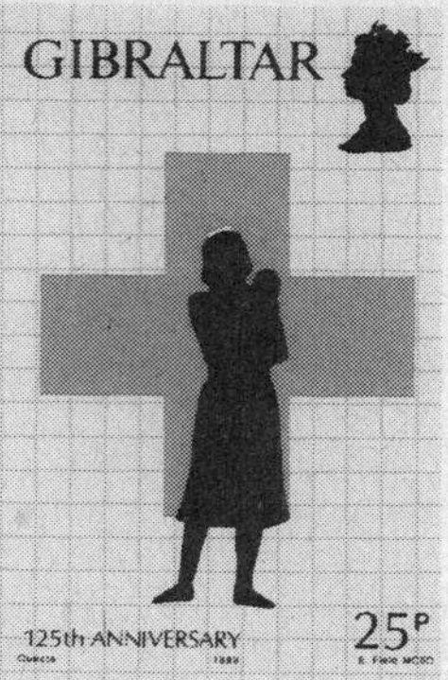

165 Nurse and Baby

1989. 125th Anniv of International Red Cross.

613 **165** 25p. black, red & brn 60 60
614 – 32p. black, red & brn 75 80
615 – 44p. black, red & brn 1·00 1·40

DESIGNS—32p. Famine victims; 44p. Accident victims.

1989. Naval Crests (8th series). As T **134**.

616 22p. multicoloured .. 75 65
617 25p. black and gold .. 85 75
618 32p. gold, black and red .. 1·10 1·40
619 44p. multicoloured .. 1·50 1·75

DESIGNS: 22p. H.M.S. "Blankney"; 25p. H.M.S. "Deptford"; 32p. H.M.S. "Exmoor"; 44p. H.M.S. "Stork".

167 Father Christmas in Sleigh

1989. Christmas. Multicoloured.

622 4p. Type **167** 15 10
623 22p. Shepherds and sheep 60 70
624 32p. The Nativity .. 90 1·10
625 44p. The Three Wise Men 1·40 1·75

168 General Post Office Entrance

1990. Europa. Post Office Buildings Multicoloured.

626 22p. Type **168** 65 70
627 22p. Interior of General Post Office 65 70
628 32p. Interior of South District Post Office .. 1·00 1·25
629 32p. South District Post Office .. .. .. 1·00 1·25

169 19th-century Firemen

1990. 125th Anniv of Gibraltar Fire Service. Multicoloured.

630 4p. Type **169** 20 10
631 20p. Early fire engine (horiz) 70 60
632 42p. Modern fire engine (horiz) .. .. 1·25 1·50
633 44p. Modern fireman in breathing apparatus .. 1·40 1·60

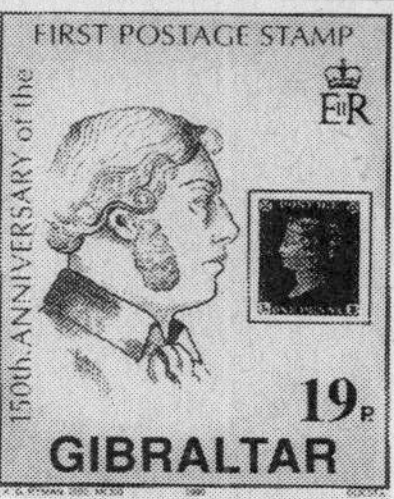

170 Henry Corbould (artist) and Penny Black

1990. 150th Anniv of the Penny Black. Mult.

634 19p. Type **170** 55 50
635 22p. Bath Royal Mail coach 65 60
636 32p. Sir Rowland Hill and Penny Black .. .. 95 1·00

1990. Naval Crests (9th series). As T **134**. Mult.

638 22p. H.M.S. "Calpe" .. 65 60
639 25p. H.M.S. "Gallant" .. 75 75
640 32p. H.M.S. "Wrestler" .. 1·00 1·10
641 44p. H.M.S. "Greyhound" 1·50 1·60

171 Model of Europort Development

1990. Development Projects. Multicoloured.

642 22p. Type **171** 45 50
643 23p. Construction of building material factory .. 45 50
644 25p. Land reclamation .. 50 55

172 Candle and Holly

1990. Christmas. Multicoloured.

645 4p. Type **172** 10 10
646 22p. Father Christmas .. 45 50
647 42p. Christmas tree .. 85 90
648 44p. Nativity crib .. 90 95

173 Space Laboratory and Spaceplane (Columbus Development Programme)

1991. Europa. Europe in Space. Mult.

649 25p. Type **173** 75 60
650 32p. "ERS-1" earth resources remote sensing satellite .. .. 1·00 1·25

1991. Naval Crests (10th series). As T **134**.

651 4p. black, blue and gold .. 15 10
652 21p. multicoloured .. 65 65
653 22p. multicoloured .. 70 70
654 62p. multicoloured .. 2·00 2·25

DESIGNS: 4p. H.M.S. "Hesperus"; 21p. H.M.S. "Forester"; 22p. H.M.S. "Furious"; 62p. H.M.S. "Scylla".

174 Shag

1991. Endangered Species. Birds. Mult.
655 13p. Type **174** 45 50
656 13p. Barbary partridge .. 45 50
657 13p. Egyptian vulture .. 45 50
658 13p. Black stork 45 40

1991. No. 580 surch **£1.05**.
659 £1.05 on £3 9.2-inch "Mk.10" coastal gun, 1935 .. .. .. 2·10 2·25

176 "North View of Gibraltar" (Gustavo Bacarisas)

1991. Local Paintings. Multicoloured.
660 22p.Type **176** 45 50
661 26p. "Parson's Lodge" (Eleana Mifsud) .. 50 55
662 32p. "Governor's Parade" (Jacobo Azagury) .. 65 70
663 42p. "Waterport Wharf" (Rudesindo Mannia) (vert) 85 90

177 "Once in Royal David's City"

1991. Christmas. Carols. Multicoloured.
664 4p. Type **177** 10 10
665 24p. "Silent Night" .. 50 55
666 25p. "Angels We Have Heard on High" .. 50 55
667 49p. "O Come All Ye Faithful" .. .. 1·00 1·10

179 Columbus and "Santa Maria"

1992. Europa. 500th Anniv of Discovery of America by Columbus. Multicoloured.
669 24p. Type **179** 50 55
670 24p. Map of Old World and "Nina" 50 55
671 34p. Map of New World and "Pinta" 70 75
672 34p. Map of Old World and look-out 70 75

Nos. 669/70 and 671/2 were issued together, se-tenant, each pair forming a composite design.

1992. 40th Anniv of Queen Elizabeth II's Accession. As T **143** of Ascension. Mult.
673 4p. Gibraltar from North 10 10
674 20p. R.N. frigate and Gibraltar from south .. 40 45
675 24p. Southport Gates .. 50 55
676 44p. Three portraits of Queen Elizabeth .. 90 95
677 54p. Queen Elizabeth II .. 1·10 1·25

180 Compass Rose, Sail and Atlantic Map

1992. Round the World Yacht Rally. Multicoloured designs, each incorporating compass rose and sail.
678 21p. Type **180** 40 45
679 24p. Map of Indonesian Archipelago (horiz) .. 50 55
680 25p. Map of Indian Ocean (horiz) 50 55

POSTAGE DUE STAMPS.

1956. As Type D 1 of Barbados.
D 1. 1d. green .. .. .. 2·00 2·75
D 2. 2d. brown .. .. .. 2·50 3·75
D 3. 4d. blue .. .. .. 3·00 5·50

1971. As Nos. D1/3, inscr. in decimal currency.
D 4. ½p. green 55 80
D 5. 1p. brown 55 70
D 6. 2p. blue 65 80

D 2.

D 3. Gibraltar Coat of Arms.

1976.
D 7. D 2. 1p. orange 15 25
D 8. 3p. blue 15 40
D 9. 5p. red 20 50
D 10. 7p. violet 25 60
D 11. 10p. green 35 60
D 12. 20p. green 70 95

1984.
D 13. D 3. 1p. black 10 10
D 14. 3p. red 10 10
D 15. 5p. blue 10 15
D 16. 10p. blue 20 25
D 17. 25p. mauve 50 55
D 18. 50p. orange .. .. 1·00 1·10
D 19. £1 green .. .. 2·00 2·10

GILBERT AND ELLICE ISLANDS

A Br. colony in the S. Pacific.
1911. 12 pence = 1 pound;
20 shillings = 1 pound.
1966. 100 cents = $1 Australian.

1911. Stamps of Fiji (King Edward VII) optd. **GILBERT & ELLICE PROTECTORATE.**
1. **23.** ½d. green .. .. .. 4·50 27·00
2. 1d. red .. .. .. 45·00 32·00
3. 2d. grey .. .. .. 6·00 12·00
4. 2½d. blue .. .. .. 12·00 23·00
5. 5d. purple and green .. 30·00 50·00
6. 6d. purple .. .. .. 20·00 38·00
7. 1s. black on green .. .. 17·00 35·00

2. Pandanus pine.

3.

1911.
8. **2.** ½d. green .. .. .. 3·25 9·00
9. 1d. red .. .. .. 2·00 5·50
10. 2d. grey .. .. .. 1·50 5·50
11. 2½d. blue .. .. .. 1·50 7·50

1912.
27. **3.** ½d. green .. .. .. 45 1·25
13. 1d. red .. .. .. 65 2·25
28. 1d. violet .. .. .. 1·25 2·00
29. 1½d. red .. .. .. 75 1·00
30. 2d. grey .. .. .. 2·50 8·50
15. 2½d. blue .. .. .. 1·75 8·50
16. 3d. purple on yellow .. 90 5·50
17. 4d. black & red on yellow 60 3·50
18. 5d. purple and green .. 1·40 7·00
19. 6d. purple .. .. .. 1·25 7·50
20. 1s. black on green .. 1·25 5·50
21. 2s. purple & blue on blue .. 14·00 24·00
22. 2s. 6d. black & red on blue 10·00 23·00
23. 5s. green & red on yellow 22·00 45·00
35. 10s. green & red on green £180 £275
24. £1 purple and black on red £800 £1400

1918. Optd. **WAR TAX.**
26. **3.** 1d. red .. .. .. 30 3·00

1935. Silver Jubilee. As T **13** of Antigua.
36. 1d. blue and black .. 1·75 5·00
37. 1½d. blue and red .. 1·50 2·50
38. 3d. brown and blue .. 5·00 6·50
39. 1s. grey and purple .. 27·00 24·00

1937. Coronation. As T **2** of Aden.
40. 1d. violet 30 20
41. 1½d. red 40 20
42. 3d. blue 55 30

6. Great Frigate Bird.

7. Pandanus Pine.

1939.
43. **6.** ½d. blue and green .. 20 35
44. **7.** 1d. green and purple .. 20 70
45. – 1½d. black and red .. 30 75
46. – 2d. brown and black .. 20 80
47. – 2½d. black and olive .. 20 45
48. – 3d. black and blue .. 45 80
49. – 5d. blue and brown .. 2·25 70
50. – 6d. olive and violet .. 40 40
51. – 1s. black and blue .. 2·50 90
52. – 2s. blue and orange .. 11·00 6·50
53. – 2s. 6d. blue and green .. 13·00 11·00
54. – 5s. red and blue .. 14·00 12·00

DESIGNS: 1½d. Canoe crossing reef. 2d. Canoe and boat-house. 2½d. Native House. 3d. Seascape. 5d. Ellice Is. canoe. 6d. Coconut palms. 1s. Jetty, Ocean Is. 2s. H.M.C.S. "Nimanoa". 2s. 6d. Gilbert Is. canoe. 5s. Coat of arms.

1946. Victory. As T **9** of Aden.
55. 1d. purple 15 15
56. 3d. blue 15 15

1949. Silver Wedding. As T **10/11** of Aden.
57. 1d. violet 40 50
58. £1 red .. .. .. 15·00 17·00

1949. U.P.U. As T **20/23** of Antigua.
59. 1d. purple 55 45
60. 2d. black .. .. .. 1·25 60
61. 3d. blue .. .. .. 1·50 75
62. 1s. blue .. .. .. 2·25 95

1953. Coronation. As T **13** of Aden.
63. 2d. black and grey .. 45 1·25

18. Great Frigate Bird

1956. As 1939 issue but with portrait of Queen Elizabeth II as in T **18** and colours changed.
64. **18.** ½d. black and blue .. 35 60
65. **7.** 1d. olive and violet .. 40 20
66. – 2d. green and purple .. 90 1·00
67. – 2½d. black and green .. 50 60
68. – 3d. black and red .. 50 45
69. – 5d. blue and orange .. 6·00 1·50
70. – 6d. brown and black .. 55 65
71. – 1s. black and olive .. 55 50
72. – 2s. blue and sepia .. 7·00 3·50
73. – 2s. 6d. red and blue .. 8·50 4·50
74. – 5s. blue and green .. 12·00 6·00
75. – 10s. blk. & turq. (as 1½d.) 21·00 14·00

19. Loading Phosphate from Cantilever.

1960. Diamond Jubilee of Phosphate Discovery at Ocean Is. Inscr. "1900 1960".
76. **19.** 2d. green and red .. 50 15
77. – 2½d. black and olive .. 50 15
78. – 1s. black and turquoise .. 60 25

DESIGNS: 2½d. Phosphate rock. 1s. Phosphate-mining.

1963. Freedom from Hunger. As T **28** of Aden.
79. 10d. blue .. .. .. 3·00 30

1963. Red Cross Cent. As T **33** of Antigua.
80. 2d. red and black .. .. 1·50 30
81. 10d. red and blue .. .. 3·50 1·25

23. Eastern Reef Heron in Flight.

1964. First Air Service.
82. – 3d. blue, blk. & light blue 30 10
83. **23.** 1s. light blue, blk. & dp. bl. 55 10
84. – 3s. 7d. green, black & emer. 80 35

DESIGNS—VERT. 3d. D. H. "Heron" aircraft and route map. 3s. 7d. D. H. "Heron" aircraft over Tarawa Lagoon.

1965. Cent of I.T.U. As T **36** of Antigua.
87. 3d. orange and green .. 20 10
88. 2s. 6d. turquoise and purple 80 20

26. Gilbertese Women's Dance.

1965. Multicoloured.
89. ½d. Maneaba and Gilbertese Man blowing Bu Shell .. 10 10
90. 1d. Ellice Islanders Reef-fishing by Flare .. 10 10
91. 2d. Gilbertese Girl weaving Head-garland .. 10 10
92. 3d. Gilbertese Woman performing Ruoia .. 10 10
93. 4d. Gilbertese Man performing Kamei .. 15 10
94. 5d. Gilbertese Girl drawing water 20 10
95. 6d. Ellice Islander performing a Fatele .. 20 10
96. 7d. Ellice Youths performing Spear dance .. 25 10
97. 1s. Gilbertese Girl tending Ikaroa Babai plant .. 40 10
98. 1s. 6d. Ellice islanders dancing a Fatele .. 1·00 65
99. 2s. Ellice Islanders pounding Pulaka .. .. 1·00 1·25
100. 3s. 7d. Type **26** .. .. 2·25 65
101. 5s. Gilbertese Boys playing a Stick Game .. 2·25 80
102. 10s. Ellice Youths beating the Box for the Fatele .. 4·00 1·25
103. £1 Coat of Arms .. .. 4·50 2·50

Nos. 89/99 are vert

1965. I.C.Y. As T **37** of Antigua.

104.	½d. purple and turquoise ..	10	10
105.	3s. 7d. green and lavender	60	15

1966. Churchill Commem. As T **38** of Antigua.

106.	½d. blue	10	10
107.	3d. green	30	10
108.	3s. brown	65	25
109.	3s. 7d. violet	65	25

1966. Decimal Currency. Nos. 89/103 **surch.**

110.	1 c. on 1d.	10	10
111.	2 c. on 2d.	10	10
112.	3 c. on 3d.	10	10
113.	4 c. on ½d.	10	10
114.	5 c. on 6d.	15	10
115.	6 c. on 4d.	15	10
116.	8 c. on 5d.	15	10
117.	10 c. on 1s.	15	10
118.	15 c. on 7d.	80	30
119.	20 c. on 1s. 6d. ..	45	25
120.	25 c. on 2s.	45	20
121.	35 c. on 3s. 7d. ..	1·25	20
122.	50 c. on 5s.	75	35
123.	$1 on 10s.	75	40
124.	$2 on £1	1·50	1·25

1966. World Cup Championship. As T **40** of Antigua.

125.	3 c. multicoloured ..	15	10
126.	35 c. multicoloured ..	45	20

1966. Inauguration of W.H.O. Headquarters, Geneva. As T **41** of Antigua.

127.	3 c. black, green and blue	30	10
128.	12 c. black, purple & ochre	60	40

1966. 20th Anniv. of U.N.E.S.C.O. As T **54/6** of Antigua.

129.	5 c. multicoloured	60	10
130.	10 c. yellow, violet & olive	80	10
131.	20 c. black, purple & orge.	1·75	45

41. H.M.S. "Royalist".

1967. 75th Anniv. of Protectorate.

132. **41.**	3 c. red, blue and green ..	20	15
133. –	10 c. multicoloured ..	10	10
134. –	35 c. sepia, yellow & grn.	25	15

DESIGNS: 10 c. Trading post. 35 c. **Island** family.

1968. Decimal Currency. As Nos. 89/103, but with values inscr. in decimal currency.

135. –	1 c. mult. (as 1d.) ..	10	15
136. –	2 c. mult. (as 2d.) ..	15	10
137. –	3 c. mult. (as 3d.) ..	15	10
138. –	4 c. mult. (as ½d.) ..	15	10
139. –	5 c. mult. (as 6d.) ..	15	10
140. –	6 c. mult. (as 4d.) ..	20	10
141. –	8 c. mult. (as 5d.) ..	20	10
142. –	10 c. mult. (as 1s.) ..	20	10
143. –	15 c. mult. (as 7d.) ..	50	20
144. –	20 c. mult. (as 1s. 6d.) ..	65	15
145. –	25 c. mult. (as 2s.) ..	1·25	20
146. **26.**	35 c. multicoloured ..	1·50	20
147. –	50 c. mult. (as 5s.) ..	1·50	1·25
148. –	$1 mult. (as 10s.) ..	1·50	2·00
149. –	$2 mult. (as £1). ..	4·00	2·00

45. Map of Tarawa Atoll.

1968. 25th Anniv. of Battle of Tarawa.

150.	3 c. Type **45**	15	10
151.	10 c. Marines landing	15	10
152.	15 c. Beach-head assault	20	10
153.	35 c. Raising U.S. and British Flags ..	35	15

46. Young Pupil against outline of Abemama Island.

1969. End of Inaugural Year of South Pacific University.

154. **46.**	3 c. multicoloured ..	10	10
155. –	10 c. multicoloured ..	10	10
156. –	35 c. black, brown & grn.	15	20

DESIGNS: 10 c. Boy and girl students and Tarawa atoll. 35 c. University graduate and South Pacific Islands.

47. "Virgin and Child" in Pacific Setting.

1969. Christmas.

157. –	2 c. multicoloured ..	15	20
158. **47.**	10 c. multicoloured ..	15	10

DESIGN: 2 c. as Type **12** but with grass foreground instead of sand.

48. "Kiss of Life".

1970. Centenary of British Red Cross.

159. **48.**	10 c. multicoloured ..	20	10
160. –	15 c. multicoloured ..	25	10
161. –	35 c. multicoloured ..	45	20

Nos. 160/1 are as Type **48**, but arranged differently.

49. Foetus and Patients.

1970. 25th Anniv. of U.N.

162. **49.**	5 c. multicoloured ..	15	10
163. –	10 c. black, grey & red	15	10
164. –	15 c. multicoloured ..	20	10
165. –	35 c. blue, grn. & black	30	15

DESIGNS: 10 c. Nurse and Surgical Instruments. 15 c. X-ray Plate and Technician. 35 c. U.N. Emblem and Map.

53. Map of Gilbert Islands.

1970. Centenary of Landing in Gilbert Islands by London Missionary Society.

166. **53.**	2 c. multicoloured ..	15	20
167. –	10 c. black and green ..	20	10
168. –	25 c. brown and blue ..	20	10
169. –	35 c. blue, blk. & red	30	20

DESIGNS—VERT. 10 c. Sailing-Ship "John Williams III". 25 c. Rev. S. J. Whitmee. HORIZ. 35 c. M.V. "John Williams VII".

57. "Child with Halo" (T. Collis).

1970. Christmas Sketches. Multicoloured.

170.	2 c. Type **57**	10	15
171.	10 c. "Sanctuary, Tarawa Cathedral" (Mrs. A. Burroughs)	10	10
172.	35 c. "Three Ships inside Star" (Mrs. C. Barnett)	20	20

60. Casting Nets.

1971. Multicoloured.

173.	1 c. Cutting toddy (vert.)	10	10
174.	2 c. Lagoon fishing ..	15	20
175.	3 c. Cleaning pandanus leaves	15	15
176.	4 c. Type **60**	20	25
177.	5 c. Gilbertese canoe ..	35	15
178.	6 c. De-husking coconuts (vert.)	30	35
179.	8 c. Weaving pandanus fronds (vert.)	35	15
180.	10 c. Weaving a basket (vert.)	40	15
181.	15 c. Tiger shark and fisherman (vert.) ..	3·75	1·50
182.	20 c. Beating rolled pandanus leaf	2·00	90
183.	25 c. Loading copra ..	2·00	1·00
184.	35 c. Fishing at night ..	2·00	50
185.	50 c. Local handicrafts (vert.)	1·75	1·25
186.	$1 Weaving coconut screens (vert.)	2·50	2·25
187.	$2 Coat of Arms (vert.) ..	10·00	10·00

61. House of Representatives.

1971. New Constitution. Multicoloured.

188.	3 c. Type **61**	10	20
189.	10 c. Maneaba Betio (Assembly hut) ..	20	10

62. Pacific Nativity Scene.

1971. Christmas.

190. **62.**	3 c. blk., yell. & blue ..	10	10
191. –	10 c. black, gold & blue	10	10
192. –	35 c. black, gold & red ..	25	20

DESIGNS: 10 c. Star and palm leaves. 35 c. Outrigger canoe and star.

MORE DETAILED LISTS are given in the Stanley Gibbons Catalogues referred to in the country headings. For lists of current volumes see Introduction.

63. Emblem and Young Boys.

1971. 25th Anniv. of U.N.I.C.E.F. Mult.

193.	3 c. Type **63**	10	10
194.	10 c. Young boy	15	10
195.	35 c. Young boy's face ..	45	35

Nos. 193/5 include the Unicef Emblem within each design.

64. Flag and Map of South Pacific.

1972. 25th Anniv. of South Pacific Commission. Multicoloured.

196.	3 c. Type **64**	10	20
197.	10 c. Flag and native boats	10	10
198.	35 c. Flags of member nations	15	55

65. "Alveopora".

1972. Coral. Multicoloured.

199.	3 c. Type **65**	25	20
200.	10 c. "Euphyllia" ..	35	10
201.	15 c. "Melithea" ..	55	20
202.	35 c. "Spongodes" ..	1·00	35

66. Star of Peace.

1972. Christmas. Multicoloured.

208.	3 c. Type **66**	10	10
209.	10 c. "The Nativity" ..	10	10
210.	35 c. Baby in "manger" (horiz.)	20	20

1972. Royal Silver Wedding. As T **52** of Ascension, but with Floral Head-dresses in background.

211.	3 c. brown	10	15
212.	35 c. brown	25	15

68. Funafuti ("The Land of Bananas").

1973. Legends of Island Names (1st series). Multicoloured.

213. 3 c. Type **68** 10 15
214. 10 c. Butaritari ("The Smell of the Sea") .. 15 10
215. 25 c. Tarawa ("The Centre of the World") .. 25 20
216. 35 c. Abemama ("The Land of the Moon") .. 30 20

See also Nos. 252/5.

69. Dancer.

1973. Christmas. Multicoloured.

217. 3 c. Type **69** 10 10
218. 10 c. Canoe and lagoon .. 10 10
219. 35 c. Lagoon at evening .. 20 10
220. 50 c. Map of Christmas Island 30 45

1973. Royal Wedding. As Type **47** of Anguilla. Background colours given. Multicoloured.

221. 3 c. green 10 15
222. 35 c. blue 20 15

70. Meteorological Observation.

1973. Cent. of I.M.O./W.M.O. Multicoloured.

223. 3 c. Type **70** 80 30
224. 10 c. Island observing-station 80 20
225. 35 c. Wind-finding radar..
226. 50 c. World weather watch 1·50 40
stations .. .. .. 2·00 1·50

71. Te Mataaua Crest.

1974. Canoe Crests. Multicoloured.

227. 3 c. Type **71** 10 10
228. 10 c. "Te-Nimta-wawa" 15 10
229. 35 c. "Tara-tara-venei-na" 25 10
230. 50 c. "Te Bou-uoua" .. 35 50

72. £1 Stamp of 1924 and Te Koroba (canoe).

1974. Centenary of U.P.U.

232. **72.** 4 c. multicoloured .. 10 10
233. – 10 c. multicoloured .. 10 10
234. – 25 c. multicoloured .. 15 15
235. – 35 c. multicoloured .. 20 20

DESIGNS: 10 c. 5 s. stamp of 1939 and sailing vessel "Kiakia". 25 c. $2 stamp of 1971 and B.A.C. "1–11". 35 c. U.P.U. Emblem.

73. Toy Canoe.

1974. Christmas. Multicoloured.

236. 4 c. Type **73** 10 10
237. 10 c. Toy windmill .. 10 10
238. 25 c. Coconut "ball" .. 15 15
239. 35 c. Canoes and constellation Pleiades 20 15

74. North Front Entrance, Blenheim Palace.

1974. Birth Cent. of Sir Winston Churchill.

240. 4 c. Type **74** 10 10
241. 10 c. Churchill painting .. 10 10
242. 35 c. Churchill's statue, London 25 15

75. Barometer Crab.

243. 4 c. Type **75** 25 15
244. 10 c. "Ranina ranina" .. 35 10
245. 25 c. Pelagic Swimming Crab 70 25
246. 35 c. Ghost Crab 85 45

76. Eyed Cowrie.

1975. Cowrie Shells. Multicoloured.

247. 4 c. Type **76** 40 15
248. 10 c. Sieve Cowrie .. 70 10
249. 25 c. Mole Cowrie .. 1·50 55
250. 35 c. Map Cowrie .. 1·75 75

1975. Legends of Island Names (2nd series). As T **68**. Multicoloured.

252. 4 c. Beru ("The Bud") .. 10 10
253. 10 c. Onotoa ("Six Giants") 10 10
254. 25 c. Abaiang ("Land to the North") 20 15
255. 35 c. Marakei ("Fish-trap floating on eaves") .. 30 20

77. "Christ is Born".

1975. Christmas. Multicoloured.

256. 4 c. Type **77** 10 10
257. 10 c. Protestant Chapel, Tarawa 10 10
258. 25 c. Catholic Church, Ocean Island 20 40
259. 35 c. Fishermen and star .. 25 45

POSTAGE DUE STAMPS

D 1.

1940.

D 1. D 1. 1d. green .. .. 6·00 8·00
D 2. 2d. red .. .. .. 7·00 9·00
D 3. 3d. brown .. .. 9·00 12·00
D 4. 4d. blue .. .. 12·00 20·00
D 5. 4d. olive .. .. 16·00 21·00
D 6. 6d. purple .. .. 16·00 22·00
D 7. 1s. violet .. .. 18·00 32·00
D 8. 1s. 6d. green .. .. 35·00 65·00

GILBERT ISLANDS

On 1st January, 1976 the Gilbert Islands and Tuvalu (Ellice) Islands became separate Crown Colonies. The Islands became independent on 12 July 1979, under the name of Kiribati.

100 cents = $1.

1. Charts of Gilbert Islands and Tuvalu (formerly Ellice) Islands.

1976. Separation of the Islands. Mult.

1. 4 c. Type **1** 50 75
2. 35 c. Maps of Tarawa and Funafuti .. .. .. 1·25 2·00

1976. Nos. 173/87 of Gilbert and Ellice Islands optd. **THE GILBERT ISLANDS.**

3 1 c. Cutting toddy 25 20
5 2 c. Lagoon fishing .. 50 30
12 3 c. Cleaning pandanus leaves 40 50
7 4 c. Type **60** 30 50
13 5 c. Gilbertese canoe .. 50 50
14 6 c. De-husking coconuts .. 50 60
15 8 c. Weaving pandanus fronds 50 60
16 10 c. Weaving a basket .. 50 60
17 15 c. Tiger Shark .. .. 1·50 1·25
18 20 c. Beating a pandanus leaf 1·50 90
19 25 c. Loading copra .. 2·00 1·25
20 35 c. Fishing at night .. 2·00 1·75
21 50 c. Local handicrafts .. 2·50 2·75
22 $1 Weaving coconut screens 8·00 9·00

3. M.V. "Teraaka".

1976. Multicoloured.

23. 1 c. Type **3** 20 15
24. 3 c. M.V. "Tautunu" .. 30 20
25. 4 c. Moorish Idol 30 20
26. 5 c. Hibiscus 30 20
27. 6 c. Eastern Reef Heron .. 35 30
28. 7 c. Tarawa Cathedral .. 30 30
29. 8 c. Frangipani 30 30
30. 10 c. Maneaba building .. 30 30
31. 12 c. Betio Harbour .. 45 45
32. 15 c. Evening scene .. 55 45
33. 20 c. Marakei Atoll .. 35 35
34. 35 c. Tangintebu Chapel .. 35 40
35. 40 c. Flamboyant tree .. 40 45
36. 50 c. "Hypolimnas bolina elliciana," (butterfly) .. 2·25 1·75
37. $1 Ferry "Tabakea" .. 2·00 2·50
38. $2 National flag .. .. 2·25 2·75

4. Church.

1976. Christmas. Children's Drawings. Multicoloured.

39. 5 c. Type **4** 35 15
40. 15 c. Feasting (vert.) .. 50 15
41. 20 c. Maneaba (vert.) .. 55 30
42. 35 c. Dancing 70 45

5. Porcupine Fish Helmet.

1976. Artefacts. Multicoloured.

43. 5 c. Type **5** 35 15
44. 15 c. Shark's Teeth Dagger 50 35
45. 20 c. Fighting Gauntlet .. 55 40
46. 35 c. Coconut Body Armour 70 55

6. The Queen in Coronation Robes.

1977. Silver Jubilee. Multicoloured.

48. 8 c. Prince Charles' visit, 1970 .. .. .. 15 10
49. 20 c. Prince Philip's visit, 1959 .. .. .. 20 15
50. 40 c. Type **6** 30 35

7. Commodore Byron and H.M.S. "Dolphin".

1977. Explorers. Multicoloured.

51. 5 c. Type **7** .. .. 1·00 1·50
52. 15 c. Capt. Fanning and "Betsey" .. .. 1·50 2·75
53. 20 c. Admiral Bellinghausen and "Vostok" .. .. 2·00 3·25
54. 35 c. Capt. Wilkes and "Vincennes" .. .. 3·50 5·75

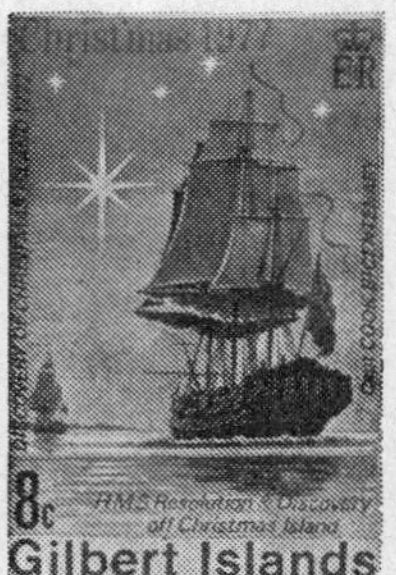

8. H.M.S. "Resolution" and H.M.S. "Discovery".

1977. Christmas and Bicent. of Capt. Cook's Discovery of Christmas Is. Mult.

55. 8 c. Type **8** 55 10
56. 15 c. Logbook entry (horiz.) 70 15
57. 20 c. Capt. Cook 85 20
58. 40 c. Landing party (horiz.) 1·75 60

9. Scout Emblem.

1977. 50th Anniv. of Scouting in the Gilbert Is. Multicoloured.

60. 8 c. Type 9 .. .. .. 20 10
61. 15 c. Patrol meeting (horiz.) 30 20
62. 20 c. Scout making mat (horiz.) 40 20
63. 40 c. Canoeing 50 55

10. Taurus. (The Bull).

1978. The Night Sky over the Gilbert Is.

64. 10. 10 c. black and blue .. 20 15
65. – 20 c. black and red .. 30 30
66. – 25 c. black and green .. 35 35
67. – 45 c. black and orange .. 50 60

DESIGNS: 20 c. Canis Major (the Great Dog). 25 c. Scorpio (the Scorpion). 45 c. Orion (the Giant Warrior).

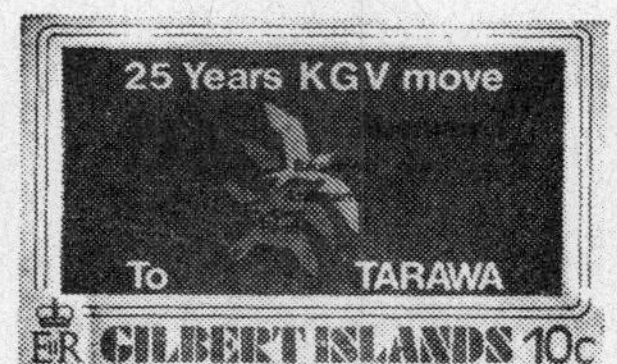

11. Unicorn of Scotland.

1978. 25th Anniv. of Coronation.

68. 11. 45 c. green, violet & silver 30 40
69. – 45 c. multicoloured .. 30 40
70. – 45 c. green, violet & silver 30 40

DESIGNS: No. 69, Queen Elizabeth II. No. 70, Great Frigate Bird.

12. Birds in Flight to Tarawa.

1978. 25th Anniv. of Return of George V School to Tarawa. Multicoloured.

71. 10 c. Type 12 .. .. 10 10
72. 20 c. Tarawa, Abemama and school badge 20 20
73. 25 c. Rejoicing islanders .. 20 20
74. 45 c. King George V School Tarawa and Abemama .. 35 35

13. " Te Kaue ni Maie ".

1978. Christmas. Kaue (traditional head decorations). Multicoloured.

75. 10 c. Type 13 .. .. 15 10
76. 20 c. " Te Itera " 20 15
77. 25 c. " Te Bau " 25 20
78. 45 c. " Te Tai " 35 30

14. H.M.S. "Endeavour".

1979. Bicentenary of Captain Cook's Voyages, 1768–79.

80. 14. 10 c. multicoloured .. 25 15
81. – 20 c. multicoloured .. 40 30
82. – 25 c. black, lilac & green 50 45
83. – 45 c. multicoloured .. 75 80

DESIGNS: 20 c. Green Turtle. 25 c. Quadrant. 45 c. Flaxman/Wedgwood medallion.

For later issues see KIRIBATI.

GOLD COAST

A Br. colony on the W. coast of Africa. For later issues after independence in 1957 see under Ghana.

12 pence = 1 shilling;
20 shillings = 1 pound.

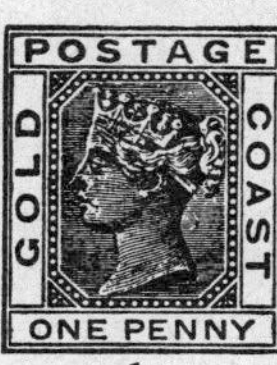

1.

4.

1875.

4 1. ½d. yellow .. .. .. 28·00 22·00
11a ½d. green 65 30
5 1d. blue .. .. .. 1·00 4·00
12a 1d. red 90 30
6 2d. green .. .. .. 48·00 11·00
13b 2d. grey .. .. .. 1·40 50
14 2½d. blue and orange .. 1·25 35
15a 3d. olive .. .. .. 3·75 4·00
16 4d. mauve .. .. .. 2·00 80
17 6d. orange .. .. .. 3·00 2·75
18a 1s. mauve .. .. .. 3·50 1·00
19a 2s. brown .. .. .. 22·00 15·00

1889. Surch. ONE PENNY and bar.

20. 1. 1d. on 6d. orange .. £100 48·00

1889.

26. 4. ½d. mauve and green .. 75 25
27. 1d. mauve and red .. 40 25
27a. 2d. mauve and red .. 24·00 48·00
28. 2½d. mauve and blue .. 4·00 3·00
29. 3d. mauve and orange .. 4·50 1·00
30. 6d. mauve and violet .. 5·50 1·00
31. 1s. green and black .. 5·50 5·50
32. 2s. green and red .. .. 9·00 14·00
22. 5s. mauve and blue .. 45·00 12·00
33. 5s. green and mauve .. 38·00 17·00
23. 10s. mauve and red .. 65·00 15·00
34. 10s. green and brown .. 95·00 35·00
24. 20s. green and red .. £3250
25. 20s. mauve & black on red £150 35·00

1901. Surch. ONE PENNY and bar.

35. 4. 1d. on 2½d. mauve & blue 1·25 3·00
36. 1d. on 6d. mauve & violet 1·25 3·00

1902. As T 4, but with portrait of King Edward VII.

38. ½d. purple and green .. 40 40
39. 1d. purple and red .. 75 15
51. 2d. purple and orange .. 3·50 40
41. 2½d. purple and blue .. 4·00 6·50
42. 3d. purple and orange .. 1·50 1·00
43. 6d. purple and violet .. 1·50 1·00
44. 1s. green and black .. 2·75 2·50
45. 2s. green and red .. .. 10·00 9·50
57. 2s. 6d. green and yellow .. 26·00 60·00
46. 5s. green and mauve .. 17·00 35·00
47. 10s. green and brown .. 38·00 75·00
48. 20s. purple & black on red £100 £120

1907. As last.

59. ½d. green .. .. .. 1·50 30
60. 1d. red 80 10
61. 2d. grey .. .. .. 2·00 30
62. 2½d. blue .. .. .. 3·50 1·75
63. 3d. purple on yellow .. 4·50 45
64a. 6d. purple .. .. .. 3·50 2·50
65. 1s. black and green .. 4·50 40
66. 2s. purple & blue on blue .. 3·50 12·00
67. 2s. 6d. black & red on blue 18·00 35·00
68. 5s. green and red on yellow 40·00 75·00

8.

13. King George V and Christiansborg Castle.

1908.

69. 8. 1d. red 25 10

1913. As T 3 and 8 (1d.) but portraits of King George V.

86 ½d. green 30 30
72 1d. red 20 10
87 1d. brown 30 10
88 1½d. red 30 10
89 2d. grey 30 20
76 2½d. blue 75 35
90 2½d. orange .. .. .. 30 5·50
77a 3d. purple on yellow .. 30 40
91 3d. blue 30 30
94 6d. purple .. .. .. 45 2·00
79b 1s. black on green .. 50 35
96 2s. purple & blue on blue 2·00 3·25
97 2s. 6d. blk. & red on blue 4·00 9·00
98 5s. green & red on yellow 7·00 24·00
83a 10s. green and red on grn. 17·00 55·00
100a 15s. purple and green .. £100 £200
84 20s. purple & black on red £100 80·00
102 £2 green and orange .. £400 £700

1918. Surch. WAR TAX ONE PENNY.

85. 1d. on 1d. red (No. 72) .. 15 25

1928.

103. 13. ½d. green 20 30
104. 1d. brown 20 10
105. 1½d. red .. .. .. 35 1·50
106. 2d. grey 20 10
107. 2½d. orange .. .. .. 90 3·50
108. 3d. blue 55 40
109. 6d. black and purple .. 55 30
110. 1s. black and orange .. 75 75
111. 2s. black and violet .. 8·50 2·50
112. 5s. red and olive .. 22·00 30·00

1935. Silver Jubilee. As T 13 of Antigua.

113. 1d. blue and black .. 50 30
114. 3d. brown and blue .. 2·25 4·25
115. 6d. green and blue .. 2·25 5·50
116. 1s. grey and purple .. 2·25 6·50

1937. Coronation. As T 2 of Aden.

117. 1d. brown 70 40
118. 2d. grey .. .. .. 80 1·00
119. 3d. blue 80 95

14.

15. King George VI and Christiansborg Castle, Accra.

1938.

120. 14. ½d. green 30 30
121. 1d. brown 30 10
122. 1½d. red 35 20
123. 2d. black 35 10
124. 3d. blue 35 10
125. 4d. mauve 50 50
126. 6d. purple 50 10
127. 9d. orange 50 40
128. 15. 1s. black and olive .. 55 10
129. 1s. 3d. brown and blue .. 80 10
130. 2s. blue and violet .. 2·50 3·25
131. 5s. olive and red .. .. 3·25 5·00
132. 10s. black and violet .. 5·00 11·00

1946. Victory. As T 9 of Aden.

133a. 2d. grey 10 10
134a. 4d. mauve 30 80

16. Northern Territories Mounted Constabulary.

DESIGNS—HORIZ. 1d. Christiansborg Castle. 1½d. Emblem of Joint Provincial Council. 2½d. Map showing position of Gold Coast. 3d. Manganese mine. 4d. Lake Bosumtwi. 1s. Breaking cocoa pods. 2s. Trooping the Colour. 5s. Surfboats. VERT. 2d. Talking drums. 6d. Cocoa farmer. 10s. Forest.

1948.

135. 16. ½d. green 20 25
136. – 1d. blue 15 10
137. – 1½d. red .. .. .. 1·25 70
138. – 2d. brown 55 10
139. – 2½d. brown and red .. 2·00 1·25
140. – 3d. blue .. .. .. 3·00 20
141. – 4d. mauve .. .. .. 1·75 1·25
142. – 6d. black and orange .. 30 10
143. – 1s. black and red .. 30 10
144. – 2s. olive and red .. 2·25 1·25
145. – 5s. purple and black .. 12·00 1·75
146. – 10s. black and olive .. 8·00 4·00

1948. Silver Wedding. As T 10/11 of Aden.

147. 1½d. red 20 15
148. 10s. olive .. .. .. 8·00 7·00

1949. U.P.U. As T 20/23 of Antigua.

149. 2d. brown 30 30
150. 2½d. orange .. .. .. 1·00 1·50
151. 3d. blue 75 70
152. 1s. green 75 50

1952. As 1948 but portrait of Queen Elizabeth II. Designs as for corresponding values except where stated.

153. ½d. brown & red (as 2½d.) 10 10
154. 1d. blue 30 10
155. 1½d. green 30 90
156. 2d. brown 30 10
157. 2½d. red (as ½d.) 35 35
158. 3d. mauve 50 10
159. 4d. blue 30 20
160. 6d. black and orange .. 30 10
161. 1s. black and red 30 10
162. 2s. olive and red .. .. 7·50 55
163. 5s. purple and black .. 13·00 2·25
164. 10s. black and olive .. 8·00 11·00

1953. Coronation. As T 13 of Aden.

165. 2d. black and brown .. 10 10

POSTAGE DUE STAMPS

D1.

1923.

D 1. D 1. ½d. black .. .. 14·00 75·00
D 2. 1d. black .. .. 75 1·00
D 5. 2d. black .. .. 2·00 9·00
D 6. 3d. black .. .. 1·50 8·00
D 7. 6d. black .. .. 2·00 10·00
D 8. 1s. black .. .. 2·25 32·00

For later issues see GHANA.

GREAT BRITAIN

Consisting of England, Wales Scotland and Northern Ireland, lying to the N.W. of the European continent.

1840. 12 pence = 1 shilling;
20 shillings = 1 pound sterling.
1971. 100 (new) pence = 1 pound sterling.

1.

3.

1840. Letters in lower corners. Imperf.

2. 1. 1d. black £3000 £150
5. 2d. blue £5500 £300

1841. Imperf.

8. 1. 1d. brown .. .. .. £130 3·50
14. 3. 2d. blue .. .. .. £1000 35·00

In T 3 there are white lines below " POSTAGE " and above " TWO PENCE ".

12. 10.

1847. Imperf.

59. 12. 6d. purple £2500 £375
57. 10. 10d. brown £2250 £550
54. 1s. green £2750 £350

1854. Perf.

29. 1. 1d. brown .. .. .. £100 1·00
40. 1d. red .. .. .. 25·00 1·00
34. 3. 2d. blue .. .. .. £1000 25·00

14.

18.

19.

1855. No letters in corners.

66a. 14. 4d. red .. .. .. £600 38·00
70. 18. 6d. lilac .. .. .. £500 40·00
72. 19. 1s. green £650 £140

7.

5.

8.

6.

1858. Letters in four corners.

48.	**7.**	½d. red	45·00	6·00
43.	**5.**	1d. red	4·50	50
51.	**8.**	1½d. red	£150	18·00
46.	**6.**	2d. blue	£150	6·00

21.

22.

23.

24.

25.

1862. Small white letters in corners.

77	**21.**	3d. red	£700	£100
80	**22.**	4d. red	£500	35·00
84	**23.**	6d. lilac	£650	30·00
87	**24.**	9d. bistre	£1100	£130
90	**25.**	1s. green	£700	65·00

30.

32.

1865. Designs as 1862 and T **30** and **32**, but large white letters in coners.

103	**21**	3d. red	£200	12·00
94	**22**	4d. red	£225	15·00
97	**23**	6d. lilac (with hyphen)	£350	28·00
109		6d. lilac (without hyphen)	£275	25·00
110	**24**	9d. straw	£600	£100
112	**30**	10d. brown	£1000	£130
117	**25**	1s. green	£350	10·00
118	**32**	2s. blue	£950	60·00
121		2s. brown	£6000	£1000

35.

38.

1867.

126.	**35.**	5s. red	£2500	£250
128.	–	10s. green	£18000	£850
129.	–	£1 brown	£22000	£1200
137.	**38.**	£5 orange	£4250	£1200

The 10s. and £1 are as Type **35**, but have different frames.

34.

1872. Large white letters in corners.

123.	**34.**	6d. brown	£350	18·00
125.		6d. grey	£600	75·00

41.

46.

1873. Large coloured letters in corners.

141	**41**	2½d. mauve	£225	14·00
157		2½d. blue	£180	8·00
143	**21**	3d. red	£200	12·00
152	**22**	4d. red	£600	£140
153		4d. green	£400	85·00
160		4d. brown	£180	25·00
161	**34**	6d. grey	£150	22·00
156	**46**	8d. orange	£550	£110
150	**25**	1s. green	£250	28·00
163		1s. brown	£225	45·00

The 3d., 4d. and 1s. are as 1862, and the 6d. as Type **34**, but all with large coloured letters.

52.

53.

1880. Various frames.

164.	**52.**	½d. green	15·00	3·00
187.		½d. blue	8·00	1·50
166.	**53.**	1d. brown	5·00	2·00
167.	–	1½d. brown	80·00	14·00
168.	–	2d. red	95·00	30·00
169.	–	5d. blue	£350	40·00

57.

58.

61.

1881.

173	**57**	1d. lilac	1·00	30

1883. Types, as 1873, surch. **3d.** or **6d.**

159.	**21.**	3d. on 3d. lilac	£225	70·00
162.	**34.**	6d. on 6d. lilac	£200	65·00

1883.

178.	**58.**	2s. 6d lilac	£200	50·00
180.	–	5s. red	£400	75·00
183.	–	10s. blue	£750	£225
185.	**61.**	£1 brown	£10000	£850
212.		£1 green	£2000	£350

The 5s. and 10s. are similar to Type **58**, but have different frames.

62.

63.

1883. Various frames.

188.	**62.**	1½d. purple	55·00	18·00
189.	**63.**	2d. purple	70·00	30·00
190.		2½d. purple	40·00	5·00
191.	**62.**	3d. purple	90·00	40·00
192.		4d. green	£225	90·00
193.		5d. green	£225	90·00
194.	**63.**	6d. green	£225	95·00
195.		9d. green	£475	£200
196.	**62.**	1s. green	£350	£130

71.

72.

73. 74.

75. 76.

77. 78.

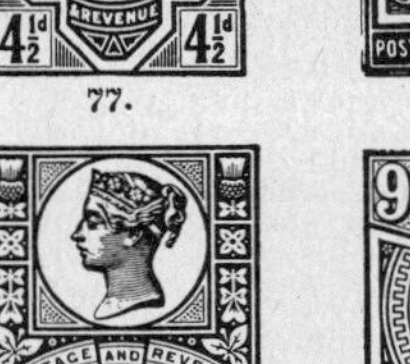
79. 80.

81.

82.

1887.

197.	**71.**	½d. red	1·00	50
213.		½d. green*	1·00	60
198.	**72.**	1½d. purple and green	10·00	4·00
200.	**73.**	2d. green and red	15·00	6·00
201.	**74.**	2½d. purple on blue	10·00	75
202.	**75.**	3d. purple on yellow	15·00	1·50
205a.	**76.**	4d. green and brown	18·00	7·25
206.	**77.**	4½d. green and red	5·00	20·00
207a.	**78.**	5d. purple and blue	18·00	6·00
208.	**79.**	6d. purple on red	18·00	7·50
209.	**80.**	9d. purple and blue	40·00	25·00
210.	**81.**	10d. purple and red	35·00	22·00
211.	**82.**	1s. green	£130	30·00
214.		1s. green and red	45·00	80·00

*** No. 213, in blue, has had the colour changed after issue.**

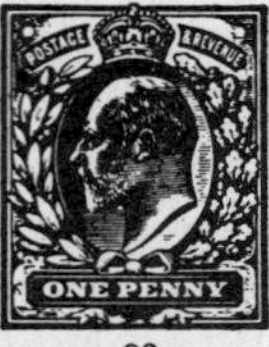
83.

90.

1902. Designs not shown are as 1887 (2s. 6d. to £1 as 1883) but with portrait of King Edward VII.

217	**83**	½d. green	40	30
219		1d. red	40	30
222	–	1½d. purple and green	12·00	4·75
291	–	2d. green and red	10·00	4·50
231	**83**	2½d. blue	4·00	2·50
232	–	3d. purple on yellow	15·00	2·50
236a	–	4d. green and brown	15·00	7·00
240	–	4d. orange	7·50	6·50
294	–	5d. purple and blue	10·00	4·75
246	**83**	6d. purple	12·00	4·00
249	**90**	7d. grey	3·00	6·00
307	–	9d. purple and blue	30·00	22·00
311	–	10d. purple and red	30·00	20·00
314	–	1s. green and red	25·00	8·00
260	–	2s. 6d. purple	90·00	45·00
263	–	5s. red	£100	55·00
319	–	10s. blue	£275	£200
320	–	£1 green	£750	£300

98. (Hair heavy).

99. (Lion unshaded).

1911.

322	**98.**	½d. green	2·50	1·00
327	**99.**	1d. red	2·25	1·00

101. (Hair light). 102. (Lion shaded).

1912.

344	**101**	½d. green	2·75	70
341	**102**	1d. red	1·25	50

104.

105.

106.

107.

108.

109.

1912. Lined background.

418	**105**	½d. green	15	25
419	**104**	1d. red	15	25
420	**105**	1½d. brown	15	25
368	**106**	2d. orange	1·00	50
422	**104**	2½d. blue	3·00	1·25
375	**106**	3d. violet	2·00	75
379		4d. green	4·00	75
381	**107**	5d. brown	3·50	3·00
426a		6d. purple	1·50	50
387		7d. green	6·00	3·75
390		8d. black on yellow	15·00	6·50
392	**108**	9d. black	5·00	2·25
427		9d. green	5·00	2·25
394		10d. blue	9·00	12·00
395		1s. brown	7·50	1·00
450	**109**	2s. 6d. brown	40·00	15·00
451		5s. red	85·00	40·00
452		10s. blue	£200	40·00
403		£1 green	£950	£600

112.

1924. British Empire Exn. Dated "1924".

430.	**112.**	1d. red	5·00	6·00
431.		1½d. brown	7·50	11·00

1925. Dated "1925".

432.	**112.**	1d. red	8·00	17·00
433.		1½d. brown	25·00	50·00

113.

114.

115.

116. St. George and the Dragon.

1929. 9th U.P.U. Congress, London.

434.113.	½d. green	.. ..	1·50	1·50
435.114.	1d. red	.. ..	1·50	1·50
436.	1½d. brown	.. ..	1·00	1·00
437.115.	2½d. blue	.. ..	7·50	9·00
438.116.	£1 black	.. ..	£500	£400

118. 119.

120. 121.

122.

1934. Solid background.

439.118.	½d. green	.. ..	10	25
440.119.	1d. red	.. ..	10	25
441.118.	1½d. brown	.. ..	10	25
442.120.	2d. orange	.. ..	25	25
443.119.	2½d. blue	.. ..	75	60
444.120.	3d. violet	.. ..	75	50
445.	4d. green	.. ..	1·00	55
446.121.	5d. brown	.. ..	3·50	1·50
447.122.	9d. olive	.. ..	6·00	1·60
448.	10d. blue	.. ..	6·00	8·00
449.	1s. brown	.. ..	8·00	50

123.

1935. Silver Jubilee.

453. 123.	½d. green	.. ..	25	20
454.	1d. red	.. ..	50	1·00
455.	1½d. brown	.. ..	25	20
456.	2½d. blue	.. ..	4·00	3·00

Emblems at right differ.

124. King Edward VIII.

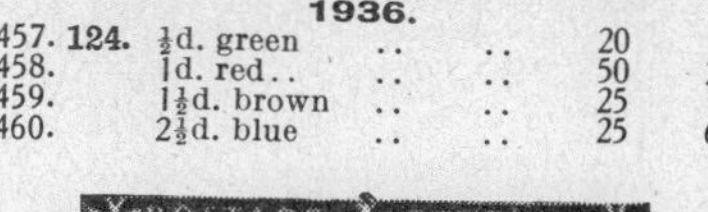

1936.

457. 124.	½d. green	.. ..	20	15
458.	1d. red ..	.. ..	50	20
459.	1½d. brown	.. ..	25	15
460.	2½d. blue	.. ..	25	60

126. King George VI and Queen Elizabeth.

1937. Coronation.

461. 126.	1½d. brown	.. ..	40	25

128. 129.

130. 131. King George VI.

1937.

462. 128.	½d. green	.. ..	10	15
485.	½d. pale green	..	15	10
503.	½d. orange	.. ..	10	15
463.	1d. red	.. ..	10	15
486.	1d. pale red	.. ..	15	10
504.	1d. blue	.. ..	15	15
464.	1½d. brown	.. ..	20	15
487.	1½d. pale brown	..	75	45
505.	1½d. green	.. ..	25	30
465.	2d. orange	.. ..	1·25	35
488.	2d. pale orange	..	50	40
506.	2d. brown	.. ..	25	20
466.	2½d. blue	.. ..	25	15
489.	2½d. light blue	..	15	10
507.	2½d. red	.. ..	20	15
467.	3d. violet	.. ..	6·00	60
490.	3d. pale violet	..	1·90	50
468. 129.	4d. green	.. ..	35	30
508.	4d. blue	.. ..	1·90	1·10
469.	5d. brown	.. ..	2·50	35
470.	6d. purple	.. ..	1·75	25
471. 130.	7d. green	.. ..	5·00	35
472.	8d. red	.. ..	5·00	40
473.	9d. olive	.. ..	6·50	40
474.	10d. blue	.. ..	6·50	45
474a.	11d. plum	.. ..	3·00	1·25
475.	1s. brown	.. ..	7·50	25

1939.

476. 131.	2s. 6d. brown ..	..	40·00	6·50
476a.	2s. 6d. green ..	..	9·00	1·75
477.	5s. red ..	.. ..	18·00	1·00
478. –	10s. deep blue	..	£130	15·00
478a. –	10s. bright blue	..	40·00	3·50
478b. –	£1 brown	.. ..	15·00	19·00

The 10s. and £1 values have the portrait in the centre in an ornamental frame.

134. Queen Victoria and King George VI.

1940. Cent. of First Adhesive Postage Stamps.

479. 134.	½d. green	.. ..	30	20
480.	1d. red	.. ..	90	40
481.	1½d. brown	.. ..	30	30
482.	2d. orange	.. ..	50	40
483.	2½d. blue	.. ..	1·90	80
484.	3d. violet	.. ..	4·00	4·00

135.

1946. Victory Commemoration.

491. 135.	2½d. blue	.. ..	25	15
492. –	3d. violet	.. ..	25	15

DESIGN—HORIZ. 3d. Symbols of Peace and Reconstruction.

137.

138. King George VI and Queen Elizabeth.

1948. Royal Silver Wedding.

493. 137.	2½d. blue	.. ..	30	30
494. 138.	£1 blue	.. ..	32·00	30·00

139. Globe and Laurel Wreath.

140. "Speed".

1948. Olympic Games. Inscr. "OLYMPIC GAMES 1948".

495. 139.	2½d. blue	.. ..	10	10
496. 140.	3d. violet	.. ..	30	30
497. –	6d. purple	.. ..	60	30
498. –	1s. brown	.. ..	1·25	1·50

DESIGNS: 6d. Olympic symbol. 1s. Winged Victory.

143. Two Hemispheres.

144. U.P.U. Monument, Berne.

1949. 75th Anniv. of U.P.U. Inscr. as in T 143/4.

499. 143.	2½d. blue	.. ..	10	10
500. 144.	3d. violet	.. ..	30	40
501. –	6d. purple	.. ..	60	75
502. –	1s. brown	.. ..	1·25	1·50

DESIGNS: 6d. Goddess Concordia, globe and points of compass, 1s. Posthorn and globe.

147. H.M.S. "Victory".

1951.

509. 147.	2s. 6d. green ..	..	8·00	75
510. –	5s. red	.. ..	30·00	1·50
511. –	10s. blue	.. ..	18·00	10·00
512. –	£1 brown	.. ..	40·00	14·00

DESIGNS; 5s. White Cliffs of Dover. 10s. St. George and dragon. £1, Royal Coat of Arms.

152. Festival Symbol.

1951. Festival of Britain.

513. –	2½d. red	.. ..	25	15
514. 152.	4d. blue	.. ..	50	45

DESIGN; 2½d. Britannia, cornucopia and Mercury.

154. 155.

157. 158.

159.
Queen Elizabeth II and National Emblems.

1952.

570 154.	½d. orange	.. ..	10	10
571	1d. blue	.. ..	10	10
517	1½d. green	.. ..	10	15
573	2d. brown	.. ..	10	10
574 155.	2½d. red	.. ..	10	10
575	3d. lilac	.. ..	10	10
576a	4d. blue	.. ..	15	10
577	4½d. brown	.. ..	10	15
578 157.	5d. brown	.. ..	25	20
579	6d. purple	.. ..	25	15
580	7d. green	.. ..	40	20
617b 158.	8d. mauve	.. ..	20	25
582	9d. olive	.. ..	40	15
583	10d. blue	.. ..	1·00	15
553	11d. plum	.. ..	40	1·00
584 159.	1s. bistre	.. ..	40	15
585	1s. 3d. green ..	..	25	15
618a	1s. 6d. blue	.. ..	2·00	1·00

The 4d., 4½d. and 1s. 3d. values are printed with colour tones reversed.

Stamps with either one or two vertical black lines on the back were issued in 1957 in connection with the Post Office automatic facing machine experiment in the Southampton area. Later the lines were replaced by almost invisible phosphor bands on the face, in the above and later issues. They are listed in the Stanley Gibbons British Commonwealth Catalogue.

161.

163.

1953. Coronation. Portraits of Queen Elizabeth II.

532. 161.	2½d. red	.. ..	10	10
533. –	4d. blue	.. ..	30	70
534. 163.	1s. 3d. green ..	..	4·00	4·00
535. –	1s. 6d. blue ..	..	6·75	7·00

DESIGNS: 4d. Coronation and National Emblems. 1s. 6d. Crowns and Sceptres dated "2 JUNE 1953".

166. Carrickfergus Castle.

1955.

595a. **166.** 2s. 6d. brown .. 50 30
596a. – 5s. red .. .. 1·00 60
597a. – 10s. blue .. .. 2·50 3·00
762. – £1 black .. .. 4·00 4·00
CASTLES: 5s. Caernarvon. 10s. Edinburgh. £1, Windsor.

170. Scout Badge and "Rolling Hitch".

171. "Scouts coming to Britain".

1957. World Scout Jubilee Jamboree.
557. **170.** 2½d. red 15 10
558. **171.** 4d. blue 50 40
559. – 1s. 3d. green .. .. 5·00 5·00
DESIGN: 1s. 3d. Globe within a compass.

1957. Inter-Parliamentary Union Confrence. As No. 576a but inscr "46th PARLIAMENTARY CONFERENCE".
560 4d. blue .. .. .. 1·10 1·10

176. Welsh Dragon.

1958. 6th British Empire and Commonwealth Games, Cardiff. Inscr. as in T **176.**
567. **176.** 3d. lilac 15 10
568. – 6d. mauve 25 20
569. – 1s. 3d. green .. .. 2·75 2·00
DESIGNS: 6d. Flag and Games Emblem. 1s. 3d. Welsh Dragon.

180. Postboy of 1660.

181. Posthorn of 1660.

1960. "General Letter Office" Tercent.
619. **180.** 3d. lilac 20 10
620. **181.** 1s. 3d. green .. .. 4·50 4·25

182. Conference Emblem.

1960. 1st Anniversary of European Postal and Telecommunications Conference.
621. **182.** 6d. green and purple 40 60
622. 1s. 6d. brown and blue 6·50 5·50

184. "Growth of Savings".

1961. Cent. of Post Office Savings Bank. Inscr. "POST OFFICE SAVINGS BANK".
623. – 2½d. black and red .. 10 10
624. **184.** 3d. brown and violet .. 10 10
625. – 1s. 6d. red and blue .. 2·50 2·00
DESIGNS—VERT. 2½d. Thrift plant. HORIZ. 1s. 6d. Thrift plant.

186. C.E.P.T. Emblem.

187. Doves and emblem.

1961. Europa.
626. **186.** 2d. orge., pink & brn. 10 10
627. **187.** 4d. buff, mauve & blue 20 10
628. – 10d. turq., green & blue 40 25
DESIGN: 10d. As 4d. but arranged differently.

189. Hammer Beam Roof, Westminster Hall.

1961. 7th Commonwealth Parliamentary Conference.
629. **189.** 6d. purple and gold .. 25 20
630. – 1s. 3d. green and blue 2·75 2·00
DESIGN—VERT. 1s. 3d. Palace of Westminster.

191. "Units of Productivity".

1962. National Productivity Year.
631. **191.** 2½d. green and red .. 20 10
632. – 3d. blue and violet .. 25 10
633. – 1s. 3d. red, blue & grn. 2·50 1·60
DESIGNS: 3d. Arrows over map. 1s. 3d. Arrows in formation.

194. Campaign Emblem and Family.

1963. Freedom from Hunger.
634. **194.** 2½d. red and pink .. 10 10
635. – 1s. 3d. brown and yell. 2·75 2·50
DESIGN: 1s. 3d. Children of three races.

196. "Paris Conference".

1963. Centenary of Paris Postal Conf.
636. **196.** 6d. green and mauve .. 60 40

197. Posy of Flowers.

1963. National Nature Week. Multicoloured.
637. 3d. Type **197** 20 20
638. 4½d. Woodland life .. 40 40

199. Rescue at Sea.

1963. 9th Int. Lifeboat Conference, Edinburgh. Multicoloured.
639. 2½d. Type **199** 10 10
640. 4d. 19th-cent. Lifeboat .. 40 30
641. 1s. 6d. Lifeboatmen .. 4·50 4·00

202. Red Cross.

1963. Red Cross Centenary Congress.
642. **202.** 3d. red and lilac .. 10 10
643. – 1s. 3d. red, blue & grey 3·25 2·75
644. – 1s. 6d. red, bl. & bistre 3·25 2·75
DESIGNS: Nos. 643/4 are as Type **202** but differently arranged.

205. Commonwealth Cable.

1963. COMPAC (Trans-Pacific Telephone Cable). Opening.
645. **205.** 1s. 6d. blue and black 3·25 3·25

206. Puck and Bottom. ("A Midsummer Night's Dream").

210. Hamlet contemplating Yorick's skull ("Hamlet") and Queen Elizabeth II.

1964. Shakespeare Festival.
646. **206.** 3d. multicoloured .. 10 10
647. – 6d. multicoloured .. 20 20
648. – 1s. 3d. multicoloured .. 1·00 1·25
649. – 1s. 6d. multicoloured .. 1·25 1·25
650. **210.** 2s. 6d. slate-purple .. 2·00 2·00
DESIGNS—As Type **206**: 6d. Feste ("Twelfth Night"). 1s. 3d. Balcony Scene ("Romeo and Juliet"). 1s. 6d. "Eve of Agincourt" ("Henry V").

211. Flats near Richmond Park.

1964. 20th Int. Geographical Congress, London. Multicoloured.
651. 2½d. Type **211** 10 10
652. 4d. Shipbuilding yards, Belfast 25 25
653. 8d. Beddgelert Forest Park, Snowdonia 50 50
654. 1s. 6d. Nuclear reactor, Dounreay .. .. 4·00 3·75
The designs represent "Urban development", "Industrial activity", "Forestry" and "Technological development" respectively.

215. Spring Gentian.

1964. 10th Int. Botanical Congress, Edinburgh. Multicoloured.
655. 3d. Type **215** 10 10
656. 6d. Dog Rose 20 20
657. 9d. Honeysuckle .. .. 2·25 2·25
658. 1s. 3d. Fringed Water Lily 3·00 2·10

219. Forth Road Bridge.

1964. Opening of Forth Road Bridge.
659. **219.** 3d. black, blue & violet 15 10
660. – 6d. black, blue & red .. 45 40
DESIGN: 6d. Forth Road and Railway Bridges.

221. Sir Winston Churchill.

1965. Churchill Commem.
661. **221.** 4d. black and drab .. 15 10
662. – 1s. 3d. black and grey 45 30
The 1s. 3d. shows a closer view of Churchill's head.

222. Simon de Montfort's Seal.

1965. 700th Anniversary of Simon de Montfort's Parliament.
663. **222.** 6d. olive 10 10
664. – 2s. 6d. blk., grey & drab 1·25 1·25
DESIGN: ($58\frac{1}{2} \times 21\frac{1}{2}$ mm.): 2s. 6d. Parliament buildings (after engraving by Hollar, 1647).

224. Bandsmen and Banner.

1965. Cent. of Salvation Army. Mult.
665. 3d. Type **224** 10 10
666. 1s. 6d. Three Salvationists 1·00 1·00

226. Lister's Carbolic Spray.

1965. Centenary of Joseph Lister's Discovery of Antiseptic Surgery.
667. **226.** 4d. blue, brown & grey 10 10
668. – 1s. black, purple & blue 1·00 1·25
DESIGN: 1s. Lister and chemical symbols.

228. Trinidad Carnival Dancers.

1965. Commonwealth Arts Festival.
669. **228.** 6d. black and orange .. 10 10
670. – 1s. 6d. black and violet 1·40 1·40
DESIGN: 1s. 6d. Canadian folk-dancers.

230. Flight of Spitfires.

234. Spitfire attacking Stuka Dive-bomber.

1965. 25th Anniv. of Battle of Britain. Inscr. "Battle of Britain 1940".

671 230. 4d. olive and black .. 30 35
672 – 4d. olive and black .. 30 35
673 – 4d. multicoloured .. 30 35
674 – 4d. olive and black .. 30 35
675 234. 4d. olive and black .. 30 35
676 – 4d. multicoloured .. 30 35
677p – 9d. violet, orange and purple 80 80
678p – 1s. 3d. grey, blk. & blue 80 80

DESIGNS: No. 672, Pilot in Hurricane. No. 673, Wing-tips of Spitfire and Messerschmitt "ME-109". No. 674, Spitfires attacking Heinkel "HE-111" bomber. No. 676, Hurricanes over wreck of Dornier "DO-17z2" bomber. 9d. Anti-aircraft artillery in action. 1s. 3d. Air battle over St. Paul's Cathedral.

239. Tower and "Nash" Terrace, Regent's Park.

1965. Opening of Post Office Tower.

679 – 3d. yell., blue & green 10 10
680p 239. 1s. 3d. green and blue 50 50

DESIGN—VERT. 3d. Tower and Georgian Buildings.

240. U.N. Emblem.

1965. 20th Anniv. of U.N.O. and Int. Co-operation Year.

681. 240. 3d. black, orge. & blue 15 20
682. – 1s. 6d. blk., pur. & blue 1·10 90

DESIGN: 1s. 6d. I.C.Y. Emblem.

242. Telecommunications Network.

1965. Centenary of I.T.U. Multicoloured.

683. 9d. Type 242 .. .. 20 20
684. 1s. 6d. Radio waves and switchboard .. .. 1·40 1·10

244. Robert Burns (after Skirving chalk drawing).

1966. Burns Commem.

685. 244. 4d. black, indigo & blue 15 15
686. – 1s. 3d. blk., bl. & orge. 70 70

DESIGN: 1s. 3d. Robert Burns (after Nasmyth portrait).

246. Westminster Abbey.

1966. 900th Anniv. of Westminster Abbey.

687. 246. 3d. black, brown & blue 15 10
688. – 2s. 6d. black 85 90

DESIGN: 2s. 6d. Fan Vaulting, Henry VII Chapel.

248. View near Hassocks, Sussex.

1966. Landscapes.

689 248. 4d. blk., grn. & bl. .. 15 15
690 – 6d. blk., grn. & bl. .. 15 15
691 – 1s. 3d. black, yellow and blue 35 35
692 – 1s. 6d. black, orange & blue 50 50

VIEWS: 6d. Antrim, Northern Ireland. 1s. 3d. Harlech Castle, Wales. 1s. 6d. Cairngorm Mountains, Scotland.

253. Goalmouth Melee.

1966. World Cup Football Competition. Multicoloured.

693. 4d. Players with ball (vert.) 15 10
694. 6d. Type 253 .. .. 20 20
695. 1s. 3d. Goalkeeper saving goal 50 50

255. Black-headed Gull.

1966. British Birds. Multicoloured.

696. 4d. Type 255 .. .. 10 15
697. 4d. Blue tit 10 15
698. 4d. European robin 10 15
699. 4d. Blackbird 10 15

1966. England's World Cup Football Victory. As No. 693 but inscr. "ENGLAND WINNERS".

700. – 4d. multicoloured .. 20 20

260. Jodrell Bank Radio Telescope.

1966. British Technology.

701. 260. 4d. black and lemon .. 15 15
702. – 6d. red, blue & orange 15 15
703. – 1s. 3d. multicoloured .. 30 40
704. – 1s. 6d. multicoloured .. 50 45

DESIGNS: 6d. British Motor-Cars. 1s. 3d. SRN 6 Hovercraft. 1s. 6d. Windscale Reactor.

264.

265.

1966. 900th Anniv. of Battle of Hastings. Multicoloured.

705. 4d. Type 264 .. .. 10 15
706. 4d. Type 265 .. .. 10 15
707. 4d. "Yellow" horse .. 10 15
708. 4d. "Blue" horse .. 10 15
709. 4d. "Purple" horse .. 10 15
710. 4d. "Grey" horse .. 10 15
711. 6d. Norman ship .. 10 10
712. 1s. 3d. Norman horsemen attacking Harold's Troops ($59 \times 22\frac{1}{2}$ mm.) .. 20 20

272. King of the Orient.

1966. Christmas. Multicoloured.

713. 3d. Type 272 .. .. 10 10
714. 1s. 6d. Snowman .. 35 35

274. Sea Freight.

1967. European Free Trade Assn. (EFTA). Multicoloured

715. 9d. Type 274 .. .. 15 15
716. 1s. 6d. Air Freight .. 30 30

276. Hawthorn and Bramble.

1967. British Wild Flowers. Multicoloured.

717p 4d. Type 276 .. .. 10 10
718p 4d. Larger Bindweed and Viper's Buglos(s) .. 10 10
719p 4d. Ox-eye Daisy, Coltsfoot and Buttercup .. 10 10
720p 4d. Bluebell, Red Campion and Wood Anemone .. 10 10
721p 9d. Dog Violet 10 10
722 1s. 9d. Primroses 20 20

282.

1967.

723 282. ½d. brown 10 20
724 1d. olive 10 10
726 2d. brown 10 15
729 3d. violet 10 10
731 4d. sepia 10 10
733 4d. red 10 10
735 5d. blue 10 10
736 6d. purple 20 20
737 7d. green 40 30
738 8d. red 15 30
739 8d. turquoise 45 50
740 9d. green 50 30
741 10d. drab 45 50
742 1s. violet 40 30
743 1s. 6d. blue and indigo 50 30
744 1s. 9d. orange & black 40 30

For decimal issue, see Nos. X841 etc.

284. "Mares and Foals in a Landscape" (George Stubbs).

1967. British Paintings.

748. – 4d. multicoloured .. 10 10
749. 284. 9d. multicoloured .. 20 20
750. – 1s. 6d. multicoloured 35 25

PAINTINGS—VERT. 4d. "Master Lambton" (Sir Thomas Lawrence). HORIZ. 1s. 6d. "Children Coming Out of School" L. S. Lowry).

286. Gipsy Moth IV.

1967. Sir Francis Chichester's World Voyage.

751. 286. 1s. 9d. multicoloured .. 25 25

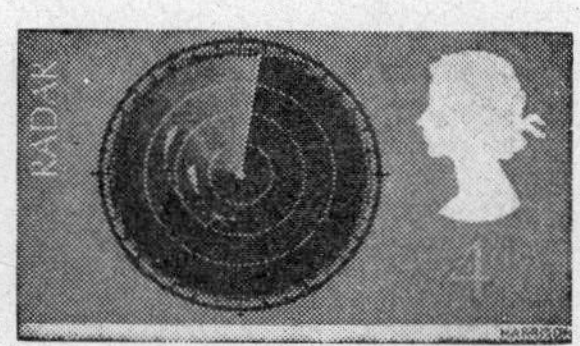

287. Radar Screen.

1967. British Discovery and Invention. Mult.

752 4d. Type 287 .. .. 10 10
753 1s. "Penicillium notatum" 10 10
754 1s. 6d. "VC-10" jet engines 25 15
755 1s. 9d. Television equipment 30 20

292. "Madonna and Child" (Murillo).

1967. Christmas.

756. – 3d. multicoloured .. 10 10
757. 292. 4d. multicoloured .. 10 10
758. – 1s. 6d. multicoloured .. 35 35

PAINTINGS—VERT. 3d. "The Adoration of the Shepherds" (School of Seville). HORIZ. 1s. 6d. "The Adoration of the Shepherds" (Louis Le Nain).

294. Tarr Steps, Exmoor.

1968. British Bridges. Multicoloured.

763. 4d. Type 294 .. .. 10 10
764. 9d. Aberfeldy Bridge .. 10 10
765. 1s. 6d. Menai Bridge .. 20 15
766. 1s. 9d. M4 Viaduct .. 25 30

298. "T U C" and Trades Unionists.

1968. British Annivs. Events described on stamps.

767. 298. 4d. multicoloured .. 10 10
768. – 9d. violet, grey & black 10 10
769. – 1s. multicoloured .. 20 20
770. – 1s. 9d. ochre & brown 25 25

DESIGNS: 9d. Mrs. Emmeline Pankhurst (statue). 1s. Sopwith "Camel" and Lightning Fighters. 1s. 9d. Captain Cook's "Endeavour" and Signature.

302. "Queen Elizabeth I" (Unknown Artist).

1968. British Paintings.

771. 302. 4d. multicoloured .. 10 10
772. – 1s. multicoloured .. 15 15
773. – 1s. 6d. multicoloured .. 20 20
774. – 1s. 9d. multicoloured .. 25 25

PAINTINGS—VERT. 1s. "Pinkie" (Lawrence). 1s. 6d., "Ruins of St. Mary Le Port" (Piper). HORIZ. 1s. 9d., "The Hay Wain" (Constable).

306. Boy and Girl with Rocking Horse.

1968. Christmas. Multicoloured.

775. 4d. Type 306 .. .. 10 10
776. 9d. Girl with Doll's House 15 15
777. 1s. 6d. Boy with Train Set 25 25

Nos. 776/7 are vert.

310. Elizabethan Galleon.

1969. British Ships. Multicoloured.

No.	Type	Description		
778.		5d. R.M.S. "Queen Elizabeth 2"	10	10
779.		9d. Type **310**	10	15
780.		9d. East Indiaman	10	15
781.		9d. "Cutty Sark"	10	15
782.		1s. S.S. "Great Britain" ..	25	25
783.		1s. R.M.S. "Mauretania" ..	25	25

Nos. 778 and 782/3 are 58 × 23 mm.

315. "Concorde" in Flight.

1969. 1st Flight of "Concorde".

No.	Type	Description		
784.	**315.**	4d. multicoloured ..	10	10
785.	–	9d. multicoloured ..	20	20
786.	–	1s. 6d. indigo, grey and blue	30	30

DESIGNS: 9d. Plan and elevation views. 1s. 6d. "Concorde's" nose and tail.

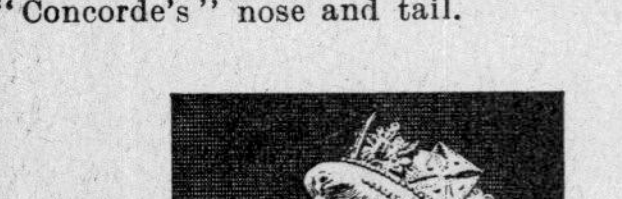

318. Queen Elizabeth II.

1969.

No.	Type	Description		
787.	**318.**	2s. 6d. brown	50	30
788.		5s. lake	2·25	60
789.		10s. blue	7·00	7·50
790.		£1 black	3·00	1·60

For decimal issues see Nos. 829/31b.

No. 790 has an italic "£". For later version with roman "£" see No. 831b.

319. Page from "Daily Mail", and Vickers "Vimy" Aircraft.

1969. Annivs. Events described on stamps.

No.	Type	Description		
791.	**319.**	5d. multicoloured ..	10	10
792.	–	9d. multicoloured ..	20	20
793.	–	1s. claret, red and blue	20	20
794.	–	1s. 6d. multicoloured ..	15	15
795.	–	1s. 9d. turquoise, yellow and sepia	25	25

DESIGNS: 9d. Europa and C.E.P.T. Emblems. 1s. I.L.O. Emblem. 1s. 6d., Flags of N.A.T.O. countries. 1s. 9d., Vickers "Vimy" Aircraft and globe showing Flight.

324. Durham Cathedral.

1969. British Architecture (Cathedrals). Multicoloured.

No.	Type	Description		
796.		5d. Type **324**	10	10
797.		5d. York Minster	10	10
798.		5d. St. Giles' Cathedral, Edinburgh	10	10
799.		5d. Canterbury Cathedral	10	10
800.		9d. St. Paul's Cathedral ..	15	15
801.		1s. 6d. Liverpool Metropolitan Cathedral ..	15	15

332. Queen Eleanor's Gate, Caernarvon Castle.

1969. Investiture of H.R.H. The Prince of Wales.

No.	Type	Description		
802.	–	5d. multicoloured ..	10	10
803.	–	5d. multicoloured ..	10	10
804.	**332.**	5d. multicoloured ..	10	10
805.	–	9d. multicoloured ..	20	10
806.	–	1s. black and gold ..	20	10

DESIGNS: No. 802, The King's Gate, Caernarvon Castle. No. 803, The Eagle Tower, Caernarvon Castle. No. 805, Celtic Cross, Margam Abbey. No. 806, H.R.H. The Prince of Wales.

335. Mahatma Gandhi.

1969. Gandhi Centenary Year.

No.	Type	Description		
807.	**335.**	1s. 6d. multicoloured ..	30	30

336. National Giro "G" Symbol.

1969. Post Office Technology Commem.

No.	Type	Description		
808.	**336.**	5d. multicoloured ..	10	10
809.	–	9d. green, blue & black	15	15
810.	–	1s. green, lav. & black	15	15
811.	–	1s. 6d. pur., blue & blk.	40	40

DESIGNS: 9d. International Subscriber dialling (Telecommunications). 1s. Pulse Code Modulations (Telecommunications). 1s. 6d. Automatic Sorting (Postal Mechanisation).

340. Herald Angel.

1969. Christmas. Multicoloured.

No.	Type	Description		
812.		4d. Type **340**	10	10
813.		5d. The Three Shepherds	10	10
814.		1s. 6d. The Three Kings ..	30	30

343. Fife Harling.

1970. British Rural Architecture. Mult.

No.	Type	Description		
815.		5d. Type **343**	10	10
816.		9d. Cotswold Limestone ..	20	20
817.		1s. Welsh Stucco ..	20	20
818.		1s. 6d. Ulster Thatch ..	35	35

The 1s. and 1s. 6d. are larger (38 × 27 mm.).

347. Signing the Declaration of Arbroath.

1970. Anniversaries. Events described on stamps. Multicoloured.

No.	Type	Description		
819.		5d. Type **347**	10	10
820.		9d. Florence Nightingale attending patients ..	15	15
821.		1s. Signing of International Co-operative Alliance ..	25	15
822.		1s. 6d. Pilgrims and "Mayflower"	30	30
823.		1s. 9d. Sir William and Sir John Herschel, Francis Baily and Telescope ..	30	30

352. Mr Pickwick and Sam ("Pickwick Papers").

357. Queen Elizabeth II.

1970. Literary Annivs. Death Cent. of Charles Dickens (novelist) (5d × 4). Birth Bicent. of William Wordsworth (poet) (1s. 6d.) Multicoloured.

No.	Type	Description		
824.		5d. Type **352**	10	10
825.		5d. Mr. and Mrs. Micawber ("David Copperfield")	10	10
826.		5d. David Copperfield and Betsy Trotwood ("David Copperfield") ..	10	10
827.		5d. "Oliver asking for more" ("Oliver Twist") ..	10	10
828.		1s. 6d. "Grasmere" (from engraving by J. Farrington, R.A.)	20	20

1970. Decimal Currency. Designs as T **318**. but inscr. in decimal currency as T **357**.

No.	Type	Description		
829.	**357.**	10p. red	1·00	75
830.		20p. green	70	15
831.		50p. blue	1·50	40
831b.		£1 black	3·50	75

On No. 831b. the "£" is in roman type.

360. Cyclists.

1970. 9th British Commonwealth Games. Multicoloured.

No.	Type	Description		
832.		5d. Runners	10	10
833.		1s. 6d. Swimmers	50	50
834.		1s. 9d. Type **360**	50	50

361. 1d. Black (1840).

1970. "Philympia 70" Stamp Exn. Mult.

No.	Type	Description		
835.		5d. Type **361**	10	10
836.		9d. 1s. green (1847) ..	35	35
837.		1s. 6d. 4d. red (1855) ..	40	40

364. Shepherds and Apparition of the Angel.

1970. Christmas. Multicoloured.

No.	Type	Description		
838.		4d. Type **364**	10	10
839.		5d. Mary, Joseph, and Christ in the Manger ..	10	10
840.		1s. 6d. The Wise Men bearing Gifts	35	35

367.

1971. Decimal currency. As Nos. 723, etc., but new colours and with decimal figures of value, as in T **367**.

No.	Description		
X841	½p. blue	10	10
X844	1p. red	10	10
X848	1½p. black	20	15
X926	2p. green	10	10
X1001	2p. light green & green	25	25
X851	2½p. mauve	15	10
X929	2½p. red	20	20
X855	3p. blue	20	10
X930	3p. mauve	20	20
X859	3½p. grey	30	15
X931	3½p. brown	45	30
X861	4p. brown	20	20
X933	4p. blue	10	10
X865	4½p. blue	20	25
X866	5p. violet	20	10
X935	5p. brown	10	10
X869	5½p. violet	20	20
X870	6p. green	30	15
X936	6p. yellow	10	15
X872	6½p. blue	30	15
X875	7p. brown	35	20
X937	7p. red	2·00	1·50
X877	7½p. brown	30	25
X879	8p. red	25	15
X881	8½p. green	35	20
X882	9p. yellow and black ..	60	30
X883	9p. violet	45	25
X884	9½p. purple	45	30
X885	10p. brown & lt brown	40	30
X939	10p. brown	15	20
X940	10p. orange	15	15
X890	10½p. yellow	40	30
X891	10½p. blue	60	45
X892	11p. red	60	25
X893	11½p. drab	45	30
X942	11½p. brown	50	45
X943	12p. green	45	40
X898	12½p. green	45	25
X900	13p. brown	50	35
X944	13p. grey	60	45
X945	13½p. brown	65	60
X903	14p. blue	45	40
X905	15p. blue	25	20
X948	15½p. violet	50	40
X949	16p. brown	60	30
X950	16½p. brown	85	75
X951	17p. blue	30	30
X952	17p. green	70	40
X953	17½p. brown	80	80
X954	18p. violet	70	75
X1009	18p. grey	60	60
X913	18p. green	30	35
X956	19p. red	30	35
X957	19½p. grey	2·00	1·50
X958	20p. purple	80	20
X959	20p. green	30	35
X960	20p. black	30	30
X961	20½p. blue	1·10	85
X962	22p. blue	80	45
X963	22p. green	60	55
X964	22p. orange	35	35
X965	23p. red	1·40	60
X966	23p. green	70	40
X967	24p. violet	1·40	85
X968	24p. red	40	45
X969	24p. brown	40	45
X970	25p. purple	90	90
X971	26p. red	90	30
X972	26p. brown	40	40
X973	27p. brown	1·00	85
X974	27p. violet	45	45
X975	28p. violet	75	60
X976	28p. ochre	45	50
X977	28p. grey	45	50
X978	29p. brown	2·50	1·25
X979	29p. mauve	45	50
X980	30p. grey	45	50
X981	31p. purple	1·25	80
X982	31p. blue	50	50
X983	32p. blue	50	55
X984	33p. green	50	50
X985	34p. brown	1·10	80
X986	34p. grey	1·00	80
X987	34p. mauve	55	60
X988	35p. brown	1·25	75
X989	35p. yellow	55	60
X990	37p. red	60	65
X991	39p. mauve	60	65
X994	50p. brown	75	45
X993	75p. black	1·10	1·25
X1019	75p. grey and black ..	6·50	3·50

368. "A Mountain Road" (T. P. Flanagan).

1971. "Ulster '71" Festival. Paintings. Multicoloured.

No.	Type	Description		
881.		3p. Type **368**	10	10
882.		7½p. "Deer's Meadow" (Tom Carr) ..	75	80
883.		9p. "Slieve na brock" (Colin Middleton) ..	75	80

371. John Keats (150th Death Anniv.).

1971. Literary Annivs.

No.	Type	Description		
884.	**371.**	3p. black, gold & blue	10	10
885.	–	5p. black, gold & grn.	75	80
886.	–	7½p. black, gold & brn.	75	80

DESIGNS AND ANNIVERSARIES: 5p. Thomas Gray (Death Bicent.). 7½p. Sir Walter Scott (Birth Bicent.).

374. Servicemen and Nurse of 1921.

1971. British Annivs. Events described on stamps. Multicoloured.

No.	Description		
887.	3p. Type 374	10	10
888.	7½p. Roman Centurion ..	75	75
889.	9p. Rugby Football, 1871	75	75

377. Physical Sciences Building, University College of Wales, Aberystwyth.

1971. British Architecture (Modern University Buildings).

No.	Type	Description		
890.	377.	3p. multicoloured ..	10	10
891.	–	5p. multicoloured ..	20	25
892.	–	7½p. ochre, blk. & brn.	80	80
893.	–	9p. multicoloured ..	1·60	1·60

DESIGNS: 5p. Faraday Building, Southampton University. 7½p. Engineering Department, Leicester University. 9p. Hexagon Restaurant, Essex University.

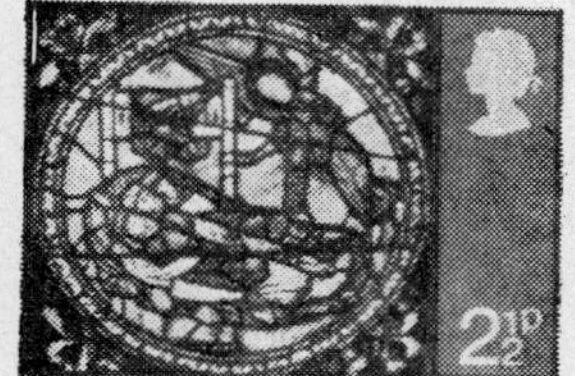

381. "Dream of the Wise Men".

1971. Christmas. Multicoloured.

No.	Description		
894.	2½p. Type 381	10	10
895.	3p. "Adoration of the Magi"	10	10
896.	7½p. "Ride of the Magi"	90	1·00

384. Sir James Clark Ross.

1972. British Polar Explorers. Multicoloured.

No.	Description		
897.	3p. Type 384	10	10
898.	5p. Sir Martin Frobisher	20	20
899.	7½p. Henry Hudson ..	65	65
900.	9p. Capt. Robert Scott..	1·10	1·10

See also Nos. 923/7.

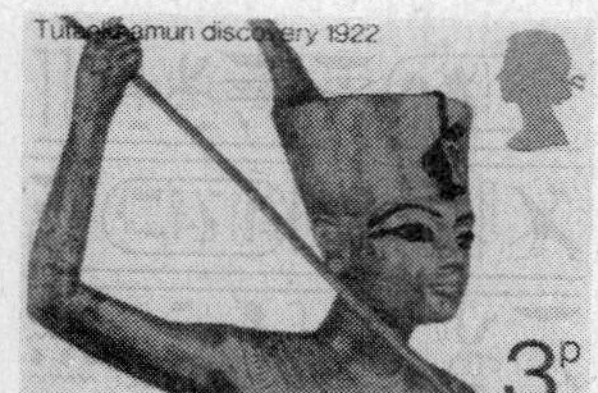

388. Statuette of Tutankhamun.

1972. General Anniversaries. Multicoloured.

No.	Description		
901.	3p. Type 388	10	10
902.	7½p. 19th-Century Coastguard	70	80
903.	9p. Ralph Vaughan Williams (composer) and Score	70	65

ANNIVERSARIES: 3p. Discovery of Tutankhamun's tomb. 50th Anniv. 7½p. Formation of H.M. Coastguard. 150th Anniv. 9p. Birth Cent.

391. St. Andrew's, Greensted-juxta-Ongar, Essex.

1972. British Architecture. Village Churches. Multicoloured.

No.	Description		
904.	3p. Type 391	10	10
905.	4p. All Saints, Earls Barton, Northants.	20	20
906.	5p. St. Andrew's, Letheringsett, Norfolk.. ..	20	25
907.	7½p. St. Andrew's, Helpringham, Lincs.. ..	1·00	1·10
908.	9p. St. Mary the Virgin, Huish Episcopi, Somerset	1·25	1·40

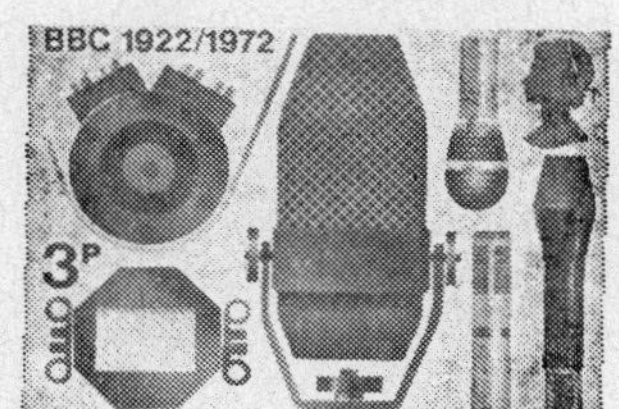

396. Microphones, 1924-69.

1972. Broadcasting Annivs. Multicoloured.

No.	Description		
909.	3p. Type 396	10	10
910.	5p. Horn Loudspeaker ..	15	20
911.	7½p. T.V. Camera, 1972	1·00	1·00
912.	9p. Oscillator and Spark Transmitter, 1897	1·00	1·00

ANNIVERSARIES: Nos. 909/11, Daily Broadcasting by the B.B.C. 50th Anniv. No. 912, Marconi and Kemp's Radio Experiments. 75th Anniv.

400. Angel holding Trumpet.

1972. Christmas. Multicoloured.

No.	Description		
913.	2½p. Type 400	10	15
914.	3p. Angel playing Lute ..	10	15
915.	7½p. Angel playing Harp	90	80

403. Queen Elizabeth and Duke of Edinburgh.

1972. Royal Silver Wedding.

No.	Type	Description		
916.	403.	3p. blk., blue & silver	20	20
917.		20p. blk., purple & silver	80	80

404. "Europe".

1973. Britain's Entry into European Communities.

No.	Type	Description		
919.	404.	3p multicoloured ..	10	10
920.		5p. mult. (blue jig-saw)	25	35
921.		5p. mult. (green jig-saw)	25	35

405. Oak Tree.

1973. Tree Planting Year British Trees (1st issue).

No.	Type	Description		
922.	405.	9 p. multicoloured ..	50	45

See also No. 949.

1973. British Explorers. As Type 384. Mult.

No.	Description		
923.	3p. David Livingstone ..	25	20
924.	3p. H. M. Stanley ..	25	20
925.	5p. Sir Francis Drake ..	30	30
926.	7½p. Sir Walter Raleigh ..	35	30
927.	9p. Charles Sturt	40	40

412. W. G. Grace.

1973. County Cricket 1873-1973. Designs as T 412 showing caricatures of W. G. Grace by Harry Furniss.

No.	Type	Description		
928.	412.	3p. blk., brn. & gold..	10	10
929.	–	7½p. blk., grn. & gold..	1·25	1·40
930.	–	9p. blk., blue & gold	1·50	1·40

414. "Self-portrait" (Reynolds).

1973. British Paintings. 250th Birth Anniv. of Sir Joshua Reynolds, and 150th Death Anniv. of Sir Henry Raeburn. Multicoloured.

No.	Description		
931.	3p. Type 414	10	10
932.	5p. "Self-portrait" (Raeburn)	20	25
933.	7½p. "Nelly O' Brien" (Reynolds) ..	70	70
934.	9p. "Rev. R. Walker (The Skater)" (Raeburn) ..	90	90

418. Court Masque Costumes.

1973. 400th Birth. Anniv. of Inigo Jones (architect and designer). Multicoloured.

No.	Description		
935.	3p. Type 418	10	15
936.	3p. St. Paul's Church, Covent Garden	10	15
937.	5p. Prince's Lodging, Newmarket	40	45
938.	5p. Court Masque Stage Scene	40	45

422. Palace of Westminster, seen from Whitehall.

1973. 19th Commonwealth Parliamentary Conference.

No.	Type	Description		
939.	422.	8p. stone, grey & black	50	60
940.	–	10p. gold and black ..	50	40

DESIGN: 10p. Palace of Westminster, seen from Millbank.

424. Princess Anne and Capt. Mark Phillips.

1973. Royal Wedding.

No.	Type	Description		
941.	424.	3½p. violet and silver..	10	10
942.		20p. brown and silver	90	1·00

425. "Good King Wenceslas".

1973. Christmas. Designs as T 425 showing various scenes from the carol "Good King Wenceslas".

No.	Type	Description		
943.	425.	3p. multicoloured ..	15	15
944.	–	3p. multicoloured ..	15	15
945.	–	3p. multicoloured ..	15	15
946.	–	3p. multicoloured ..	15	15
947.	–	3p. multicoloured ..	15	15
948.	–	3½p. multicoloured ..	15	15

431. Horse Chestnut.

1974. British Trees (2nd issue).

No.	Type	Description		
949.	431.	10p. multicoloured ..	50	50

432. First Motor Fire-engine, 1904.

1974. Bicentenary of Fire Prevention (Metropolis) Act. Multicoloured.

No.	Description		
950.	3½p. Type 432	10	10
951.	5½p. Prize-winning fire-engine, 1863	25	25
952.	8p. First steam fire-engine, 1830	60	65
953.	10p. Fire-engine, 1766 ..	80	85

436. P. & O. Packet, "Peninsular", 1888.

1974. Cent. of Universal Postal Union. Mult.

No.	Description		
954.	3½p. Type 436	10	10
955.	5½p. Farman Biplane, 1911	20	25
956.	8p. Airmail-blue van and postbox, 1930	30	35
957.	10p. Imperial Airways "C" Class Flying-boat, 1937	50	40

440. Robert the Bruce.

1974. Medieval Warriors. Multicoloured.

No.	Description		
958.	4½p. Type 440	10	10
959.	5½p. Owain Glyndwr ..	20	25
960.	8p. Henry the Fifth ..	70	65
961.	10p. The Black Prince ..	70	70

444. Churchill in Royal Yacht Squadron Uniform.

1974. Birth Centenary of Sir Winston Churchill.

962. **444.**	4½p. silver, bl. & grn. ..	15	15
963. –	5½p. silver, brn. & grey	20	25
964. –	8p. silver, red & pink ..	50	50
965. –	10p. silver, brn. & stone	50	50

DESIGNS: 5½p. Prime Minister, 1940. 8p. Secretary for War and Air, 1919. 10p. War Correspondent, South Africa, 1899.

448. " Adoration of the Magi " (York Minster, c. 1355).

1974. Christmas. Church Roof Bosses. Mult.

966.	3½p. Type **448**	10	10
967.	4½p. "The Nativity" (St. Helen's Church, Norwich, c. 1480)	10	10
968.	8p. "Virgin and Child" (Ottery St. Mary Church, c. 1350)	45	45
969.	10p. "Virgin and Child" (Worcester Cathedral, c. 1224)	50	50

452. Invalid in Wheelchair.

1975. Health and Handicap Funds.

970. **452.**	4½p.+1½p. blue & azure	25	25

453. " Peace—Burial at Sea ".

1975. Birth Bicentenary of J. M. W. Turner (painter).

971.	4½p. Type **453**	10	10
972.	5½p. " Snowstorm—Steamer off a Harbour's Mouth "	15	15
973.	8p. " The Arsenal, Venice "	55	55
974.	10p. " St. Laurent " ..	60	60

457. Charlotte Square, Edinburgh.

1975. European Architectural Heritage Year. Multicoloured.

975.	7p. Type **457**	30	30
976.	7p. The Rows, Chester ..	30	30
977.	8p. Royal Observatory, Greenwich	20	25
978.	10p. St. George's Chapel, Windsor	25	25
979.	12p. National Theatre, London	30	35

462. Sailing Dinghies.

1975. Sailing. Multicoloured.

980.	7p. Type **462**	20	20
981.	8p. Racing Keel Yachts ..	30	30
982.	10p. Cruising Yachts ..	35	35
983.	12p. Multihulls	55	55

466. Stephenson's " Locomotion ", 1825.

1975. 150th Anniversary of Public Railways. Multicoloured.

984.	7p. Type **466**	30	35
985.	8p. " Abbotsford ", 1876	30	40
986.	10p. " Caerphilly Castle ", 1923	40	45
987.	12p. High Speed Train, 1975	50	60

470. Palace of Westminster.

1975. 62nd Inter-Parliamentary Union Conference.

988. **470.**	12p. multicoloured ..	50	50

471. Emma and Mr. Woodhouse (" Emma ").

1975. Birth Bicentenary of Jane Austen (novelist). Multicoloured.

989.	8½p. Type **471**	20	20
990.	10p. Catherine Morland (" Northanger Abbey ")	25	25
991.	11p. Mr. Darcy (" Pride and Prejudice ")	40	45
992.	13p. Mary and Henry Crawford (" Mansfield Park ")	55	50

475. Angels with Harp and Lute.

1975. Christmas. Multicoloured.

993.	6½p. Type **475**	20	15
994.	8½p. Angel with Mandolin	20	20
995.	11p. Angel with Horn ..	50	50
996.	13p. Angel with Trumpet	50	55

479. Housewife.

1976. Cent. of Telephone. Multicoloured.

997.	8½p. Type **479**	20	20
998.	10p. Policeman	25	25
999.	11p. District Nurse ..	40	45
1000.	13p. Industrialist ..	55	50

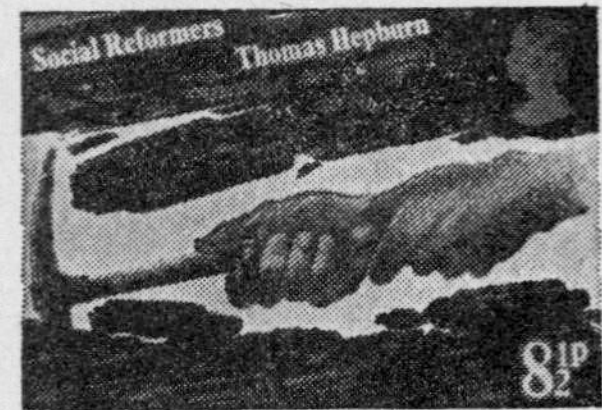

483. Hewing Coal (Thomas Hepburn).

1976. Industrial and Social Reformers. Mult.

1001.	8½p. Type **483**	20	20
1002.	10p. Machinery (Robert Owen)	25	25
1003.	11p. Chimney cleaning (Lord Shaftesbury) ..	40	50
1004.	13p. Hands clutching prison bars (Elizabeth Fry) ..	55	45

487. Benjamin Franklin (bust by Jean-Jacques Caffieri).

1976. Bicentenary of American Revolution.

1005. **487.**	11p. multicoloured ..	50	50

488. " Elizabeth of Glamis ".

1976. Centenary of Royal Nat. Rose Society. Multicoloured.

1006.	8½p. Type **488**	20	20
1007.	10p. " Grandpa Dickson "	30	30
1008.	11p. " Rosa Mundi " ..	45	50
1009.	13p. " Sweet Briar " ..	45	40

492. Archdruid.

1976. British Cultural Traditions. Mult.

1010.	8½p. Type **492**	20	20
1011.	10p. Morris dancing ..	30	30
1012.	11p. Scots piper	45	50
1013.	13p. Welsh harpist ..	45	50

The 8½p. and 13p. commemorate the 800th Anniv. of the Royal National Eisteddfod.

496. Woodcut from " The Canterbury Tales ".

1976. 500th Anniv. of British Printing. Multicoloured.

1014.	8½p. Type **496**	20	20
1015.	10p. Extract from " The Tretyse of Love " ..	25	30
1016.	11p. Woodcut from " The Game and Playe of Chesse "	45	45
1017.	13p. Early Printing Press	50	45

501. Angel with Crown.

1976. Christmas. English Medieval Embroidery. Mult.

1018.	6½p. Virgin and Child ..	15	15
1019.	8½p. Type **501**	20	20
1020.	11p. Angel appearing to Shepherds	50	50
1021.	13p. The Three Kings ..	55	55

504. Lawn Tennis.

1977. Racket Sports. Multicoloured.

1022.	8½p. Type **504**	20	20
1023.	10p. Table tennis ..	30	30
1024.	11p. Squash	45	50
1025.	13p. Badminton	45	40

508.

1977.

1026	**508**	£1 green and olive ..	3·00	20
1026b		£1·30 brown and blue	8·00	8·00
1026c		£1·33 mauve & black	8·00	8·00
1026d		£1·41 brown and blue	7·50	7·50
1026e		£1·50 olive and black	6·00	4·00
1026f		£1·60 brown and blue	6·00	6·00
1027		£2 green and brown	5·50	75
1028		£5 pink and blue ..	13·00	2·00

559. Steroids—Conformational Analysis.

1977. Centenary of Royal Institute of Chemistry. Multicoloured.

1029.	8½p. Type **509**	20	20
1030.	10p. Vitamin C molecular structure	30	30
1031.	11p. Starch chromatography graph	45	50
1032.	13p. Chemical model of salt crystal	45	40

513.

1977. Silver Jubilee. Multicoloured.

1033.	8½p. Type **513**	20	20
1034.	9p. Type **513**	25	25
1035.	10p. " Leaf " initials ..	25	30
1036.	11p. " Star " initials ..	30	35
1037.	13p. " Oak " initials ..	40	40

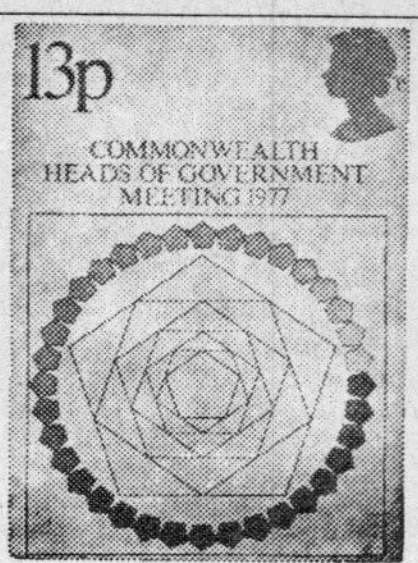

517. " Gathering of Nations ".

1977. Commonwealth Heads of Government Meeting, London.

1038. **517.**	13p. multicoloured ..	50	50

518. West European Hedgehog.

1977. British Wildlife. Multicoloured.

1039.	9p. Type **518**	25	20
1040.	9p. Brown Hare	25	20
1041.	9p. Eurasian Red Squirrel	25	20
1042.	9p. European Otter ..	25	20
1043.	9p. Eurasian Badger ..	25	20

523. " Three French Hens, Two Turtle Doves and a Partridge in a Pear Tree ".

1977. Christmas. " The Twelve Days of Christmas ". Multicoloured.

1044.	7p. Type **523**	15	15
1045.	7p. " Six Geese a-laying, Five Gold Rings, Four Colly Birds "	15	15
1046.	7p. " Eight Maids a-milking, Seven Swans a-Swimming "	15	15
1047.	7p. " Ten Pipers piping; Nine Drummers drumming "	15	15
1048.	7p. " Twelve Lords a-leaping, Eleven Ladies dancing "	15	15
1049.	9p. " A Partridge in a Pear Tree "	20	20

529. Oil—North Sea Production Platform.

1978. Energy Resources. Multicoloured.

1050.	9p. Type **529**	25	20
1051.	10½p. Coal—modern pithead	25	35
1052.	11p. Natural gas—flame rising from sea ..	35	45
1053.	13p. Electricity—nuclear power station and uranium atom	55	40

533. The Tower of London.

1978. British Architecture (Historic Buildings). Multicoloured.

1054.	9p. Type **533**	25	20
1055.	10½p. Holyroodhouse ..	25	30
1056.	11p. Caernarvon Castle ..	45	35
1057.	13p. Hampton Court Palace	50	55

537. State Coach.

1978. 25th Anniv. of Queen's Coronation.

1059. **537.**	9p. gold and blue ..	20	20
1060. –	10½p. gold and red ..	25	30
1061. –	11p. gold and green ..	45	50
1062. –	13p. gold and violet ..	50	40

DESIGNS: 10½p. St. Edward's Crown. 11p. The Sovereign's Orb. 13p. Imperial State Crown.

541. Shire Horse.

1978. Horses. Multicoloured.

1063.	9p. Type **541**	20	25
1064.	10½p. Shetland Pony ..	25	30
1065.	11p. Welsh Pony ..	45	35
1066.	13p. Thoroughbred ..	50	50

545. " Penny-farthing " and 1884 Safety Bicycle.

1978. Centenaries of Cyclists' Touring Club and British Cycling Federation. Mult.

1067.	9p. Type **545**	20	20
1068.	10½p. 1920 Touring bicycles	25	35
1069.	11p. Modern small-wheeled bicycles ..	45	45
1070.	13p. 1978 Road-racers ..	50	40

549. Singing Carols round the Christmas Tree.

1978. Christmas. Carol-singing. Mult.

1071.	7p. Type **549**	20	20
1072.	9p. The Waits	25	25
1073.	11p. 18th-century carol singers	45	50
1074.	13p. " The Boar's Head Carol "	50	45

553. Old English Sheepdog.

1979. Dogs. Multicoloured.

1075.	9p. Type **553**	20	25
1076.	10½p. Welsh springer spaniel	30	35
1077.	11p. West Highland terrier	45	40
1078.	13p. Irish setter	45	40

557. Primrose.

1979. Spring Wild Flowers. Multicoloured.

1079.	9p. Type **557**	20	20
1080.	10½p. Daffodil	30	35
1081.	11p. Bluebell	45	45
1082.	13p. Snowdrop	45	40

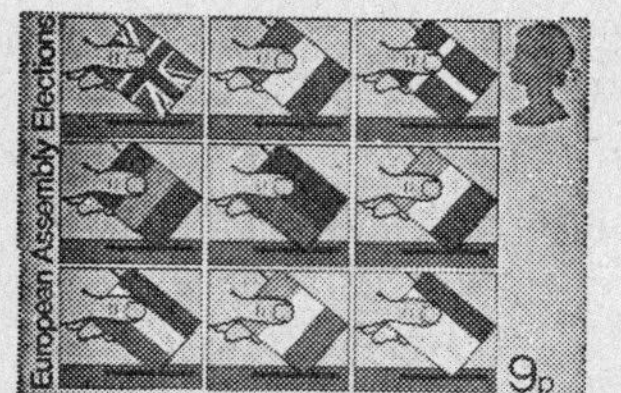

561. Hands placing National Flags into Ballot Boxes.

1979. First Direct Elections to European Assembly.

1083. **561.**	9p. multicoloured ..	20	20
1084. –	10½p. multicoloured	30	35
1085. –	11p. multicoloured ..	45	45
1086. –	13p. multicoloured ..	45	40

DESIGNS: Nos. 1084/6 differ from Type **561** in the position of the hands and flags.

565. " Saddling 'Mahmoud' for the Derby, 1936 " (Sir Alfred Munnings).

1979. Horseracing paintings and Bicentenary of the Derby (9p). Multicoloured.

1087.	9p. Type **565**	25	25
1088.	10½p. " The Liverpool Great National Steeple Chase, 1839 " (aquatint, F. C. Turner) ..	30	30
1089.	11p. " The First Spring Meeting, Newmarket, 1793 " (J. N. Sartorius)	35	50
1090.	13p. " Racing at Dorsett Ferry, Windsor, 1684 " (Francis Barlow) ..	50	55

569. " The Tale of Peter Rabbit " (Beatrix Potter).

1979. International Year of the Child. Multicoloured.

1091.	9p. Type **569**	45	20
1092.	10½p. " The Wind in the Willows " (Kenneth Grahame) ..	50	35
1093.	11p. " Winnie-the-Pooh " (A. A. Milne)	55	40
1094.	13p. " Alice's Adventures in Wonderland " (Lewis Carroll) ..	60	55

573. Sir Rowland Hill.

1979. Death Centenary of Sir Rowland Hill. Multicoloured.

1095.	10p. Type **573**	25	25
1096.	11½p. General Post, c. 1839	30	35
1097.	13p. London Post, c. 1839	35	40
1098.	15p. Uniform Postage, 1840	50	40

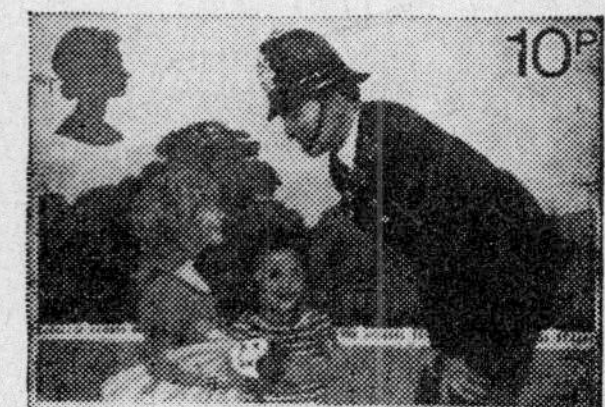

577. Policeman on the Beat.

1979. 150th Anniv. of Metropolitan Police. Multicoloured.

1100.	10p. Type **577**	25	25
1101.	11½p. Policeman directing Traffic ..	30	35
1102.	13p. Mounted Policewoman	35	40
1103.	15p. River Patrol Boat ..	50	40

581. The Three Kings.

1979. Christmas.

1104.	8p. Type **581**	20	20
1105.	10p. Angel appearing to the Shepherds ..	25	25
1106.	11½p. The Nativity ..	30	35
1107.	13p. Mary and Joseph travelling to Bethlehem	40	40
1108.	15p. The Annunciation ..	50	45

586. Common Kingfisher.

1980. Centenary of Wild Bird Protection Act. Multicoloured.

1109.	10p. Type **586**	25	25
1110.	11½p. Dipper	30	35
1111.	13p. Moorhen	55	45
1112.	15p. Yellow Wagtails ..	60	50

590. " Rocket " at Moorish Arch, Liverpool.

1980. 150th Anniv. of Liverpool and Manchester Railway. Multicoloured.

1113.	12p. Type **590** ..	25	25
1114.	12p. First and Second Class carriages at Olive Mount	25	25
1115.	12p. Third Class carriage and sheep truck passing Chat Moss	25	25
1116.	12p. Flat truck carrying horse-drawn carriage and horse-box near Bridgewater Canal	25	25
1117.	12p. Truck and Mailcoach at Manchester	25	25

595. Montage of London Buildings.

1980. " London 1980 " International Stamp Exhibition.

1118. **595.**	50p. brown	1·50	1·50

596. Buckingham Palace.

1980. London Landmarks. Multicoloured.

1120.	10½p. Type **596**	25	25
1121.	12p. The Albert Memorial	30	30
1122.	13½p. Royal Opera House	35	35
1123.	15p. Hampton Court ..	50	45
1124.	17½p. Kensington Palace	60	55

601. Charlotte Bronte (" Jane Eyre ").

1980. Women Novelists. Multicoloured.

1125.	12p. Type **601**	30	30
1126.	13½p. George Eliot (" The Mill on the Floss ") ..	35	35
1127.	15p. Emily Bronte ("Wuthering Heights")	40	45
1128.	17½p. Elizabeth Gaskell (" North and South ")	60	60

605. Queen Elizabeth the Queen Mother.

1980. 80th Birthday of The Queen Mother.

1129. **605.**	12p. multicoloured ..	50	50

606. Sir Henry Wood.

1980. British Conductors. Multicoloured.

1130.	12p. Type **606**	30	30
1131.	13½p. Sir Thomas Beecham	35	40
1132.	15p. Sir Malcolm Sargent	45	45
1133.	17½p. Sir John Barbirolli	55	50

610. Running.

1980. Sport Centenaries. Multicoloured.

1134.	12p. Type **610**	30	30
1135.	13½p. Rugby	35	40
1136.	15p. Boxing	40	40
1137.	17½p. Cricket	60	55

CENTENARIES: 12p. Amateur Athletics Association. 13½p. Welsh Rugby Union. 15p. Amateur Boxing Association. 17½p. England-Australia Test Match.

614. Christmas Tree.

1980. Christmas. Multicoloured.

1138.	10p. Type **614**	25	25
1139.	12p. Candles	30	35
1140.	13½p. Mistletoe and apples	35	40
1141.	15p. Crown, chains and bell	50	45
1142.	17½p. Holly wreath ..	55	50

619. St. Valentine's Day.

1981. Folklore. Multicoloured.

1143.	14p. Type **619**	35	35
1144.	18p. Morris Dancers ..	45	50
1145.	22p. Lammastide ..	60	60
1146.	25p. Medieval Mummers	75	70

623. Blind Man with Guide Dog.

1981. International Year of Disabled Persons. Multicoloured.

1147.	14p. Type **623**	35	35
1148.	18p. Hands spelling "Deaf" in sign language	45	50
1149.	22p. Disabled man in wheel-chair	60	60
1150.	25p. Disabled artist painting with foot	75	70

627. "Aglais urticae".

1981. Butterflies. Multicoloured.

1151	14p. Type **627**	35	35
1152	18p. "Maculinea arion"	50	50
1153	22p. "Inachis io" ..	60	65
1154	25p. "Carterocephalus palaemon"	70	75

631. Glenfinnan. Scotland..

1981. 50th Anniv. of National Trust for Scotland. British Landscapes. Multicoloured.

1155.	14p. Type **631**	40	40
1156.	18p. Derwentwater, England	50	55
1157.	20p. Stackpole Head, Wales	55	60
1158.	22p. Giant's Causeway, N. Ireland	60	60
1159.	25p. St. Kilda, Scotland	75	70

636. Prince Charles and Lady Diana Spencer.

1981. Royal Wedding.

1160. **636.**	14p. multicoloured ..	35	35
1161.	25p. multicoloured ..	90	90

637. " Expeditions ".

1981. 25th Anniv. of Duke of Edinburgh Award Scheme. Multicoloured.

1162.	14p. Type **637**	35	35
1163.	18p. " Skills "	50	50
1164.	22p. " Service "	60	60
1165.	25p. " Recreation " ..	70	70

641. Cockle-dredging.

1981. Fishing Industry. Multicoloured.

1166.	14p. Type **641**	35	35
1167.	18p. Hauling in Trawl Net	50	50
1168.	22p. Lobster Potting ..	60	60
1169.	25p. Hoisting Seine Net	70	65

645. Father Christmas.

1981. Christmas. Children's Pictures. **Mult.**

1170.	11½p. Type **645**	30	30
1171.	14p. Jesus Christ ..	40	40
1172.	18p. Flying Angel ..	50	50
1173.	22p. Joseph and Mary arriving at Bethlehem	60	60
1174.	25p. Three Kings approching Bethlehem ..	70	70

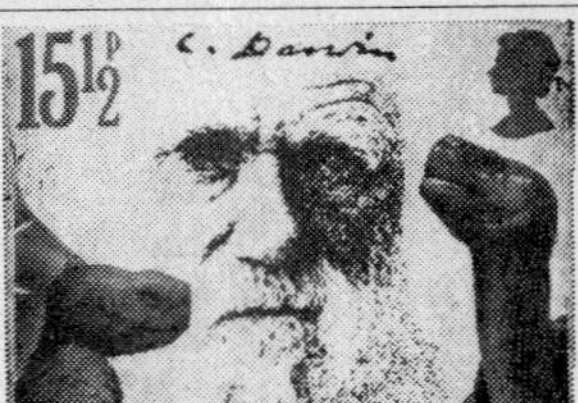

650. Charles Darwin and Giant Tortoises.

1982. Death Centenary of Charles Darwin. Multicoloured.

1175.	15½p. Type **650**	35	35
1176.	19½p. Darwin and Marine Iguanas	60	60
1177.	26p. Darwin and cactus ground finch and large ground finch	70	70
1178.	29p. Darwin and prehistoric skulls ..	75	75

654. Boys' Brigade.

1982. Youth Organizations. Multicoloured.

1179.	15½p. Type **654**	35	35
1180.	19½p. Girls' Brigade ..	70	70
1181.	26p. Boy Scout Movement	90	90
1182.	29p. Girl Guide Movement	1·00	1·00

658. Ballerina.

1982. Europa. British Theatre. **Mult.**

1183.	15½p. Type **658** ..	35	35
1184.	19½p. " Harlequin " ..	70	70
1185.	26p. " Hamlet " ..	90	90
1186.	29p. Opera Singer ..	1·00	1·00

662. Henry VIII and " Mary Rose ".

1982. Maritime Heritage. Multicoloured.

1187.	15½p. Type **662** ..	35	35
1188.	19½p. Admiral Blake and " Triumph "	60	60
1189.	24p. Lord Nelson and H.M.S. " Victory " ..	70	70
1190.	26p. Lord Fisher and H.M.S. " Dreadnought "	80	80
1191.	29p. Viscount Cunningham and H.M.S. " Warspite "	90	80

667. " Strawberry Thief " (William Morris).

1982. British Textiles. Multicoloured.
1192. 15½p. Type **667** .. 35 35
1193. 19½p. Untitled (Steiner and Co.) 70 70
1194. 26p. " Cherry Orchard " (Paul Nash) .. 70 70
1195. 29p. " Chevron " (Andrew Foster) .. 1·00 1·00

671. Development of Communications.
(Illustration reduced: Actual size 70 × 20 mm.)

1982. Information Technology. **Mult.**
1196. 15½p. Type **671** .. 45 50
1197. 26p. Modern Technology Aids 80 85

673. Austin " Seven " and " Metro ".

1982. British Motor Industry. Mult.
1198. 15½p. Type **673** 50 50
1199. 19½p. Ford " Model T " and " Escort " .. 1·00 1·10
1200. 26p. Jaguar " SS1 " and " XJ6 " .. .. 1·10 1·25
1201. 29p. Rolls-Royce " Silver Ghost " and " Silver Spirit " .. .. 1·25 1·40

677. " While Shepherds Watched ".

1982. Christmas. Carols. Multicoloured.
1202. 12½p. Type **677** 30 30
1203. 15½p. " The Holly and the Ivy " 55 55
1204. 19½p. " I Saw Three Ships " 80 80
1205. 26p. " We Three Kings " 80 80
1206. 29p. " Good King Wenceslas " 90 90

682. Salmon.

1983. British River Fishes. Multicoloured.
1207. 15½p. Type **682** 35 35
1208. 19½p. Pike 70 70
1209. 26p. Trout 80 80
1210. 29p. Perch 90 90

686. Tropical Island.

1983. Commonwealth Day. Geographical Regions. Multicoloured.
1211. 15½p. Type **686** 35 35
1212. 19½p. Desert 70 70
1213. 26p. Temperate Farmland 80 80
1214. 29p. Mountain Range .. 90 90

690. Humber Bridge.

1983. Europa. Engineering Achievements. Multicoloured.
1215. 16p. Type **690** 55 55
1216. 20½p. Thames Flood Barrier .. .. 1·25 1·25
1217. 28p. " Iolair " (oilfield emergency support vessel) .. .. .. 1·25 1·25

693. Musketeer and Pikeman, The Royal Scots (1633).

1983. British Army Uniforms. Multicoloured.
1218. 16p. Type **693** 40 40
1219. 20½p. Fusilier and Ensign, The Royal Welsh Fusiliers (mid-18th century) 70 70
1220. 26p. Riflemen, 95th Rifles (The Royal Green Jackets) (1805) 80 80
1221. 28p. Sergeant (khaki service uniform) and Guardsman (full dress), The Irish Guards (1900) 80 80
1222. 31p. Paratroopers, The Parachute Regiment (1983) 90 90

698. 20th-century Garden, Sissinghurst.

1983. British Gardens. **Multicoloured.**
1223. 16p. Type **698** 50 40
1224. 20½p. 19th-century garden, Biddulph Grange .. 60 65
1225. 28p. 18th-century garden, Blenheim .. .. 95 1·00
1226. 31p. 17th-century garden, Pitmedden .. .. 1·00 1·00

702. Merry-go-round.

1983. British Fairs. Multicoloured.
1227. 16p. Type **702** 50 40
1228. 20½p. Big wheel, helter-skelter and performing animals 60 65
1229. 28p. Side shows .. .. 95 1·00
1230. 31p. Early produce fair .. 1·00 1·00

706. " Christmas Post " (pillar-box).

1983. Christmas. Multicoloured.
1231. 12½p. Type **706** 30 30
1232. 16p. " The Three Kings " (chimney pots) .. 45 45
1233. 20½p. " World at Peace " (Blackbird) 70 70
1234. 28p. " Light of Christmas " (street lamp) 90 90
1235. 31p. " Christmas Dove " (hedge sculpture) .. 1·00 1·00

711. Arms of College of Arms.

1984. 500th Anniv. of College Arms. Mult.
1236. 16p. Type **711** 40 40
1237. 20½p. Arms of King Richard III (founder) 70 70
1238. 28p. Arms of Earl Marshal of England .. 1·00 1·00
1239. 31p. Arms of City of London .. .. 1·25 1·25

715. Highland Cow.

1984. Cattle. Multicoloured.
1240. 16p. Type **715** 40 40
1241. 20½p. Chillingham Wild Bull 65 65
1242. 26p. Hereford Bull .. 70 70
1243. 28p. Welsh Black Bull .. 85 85
1244. 31p. Irish Moiled Cow .. 1·00 1·00

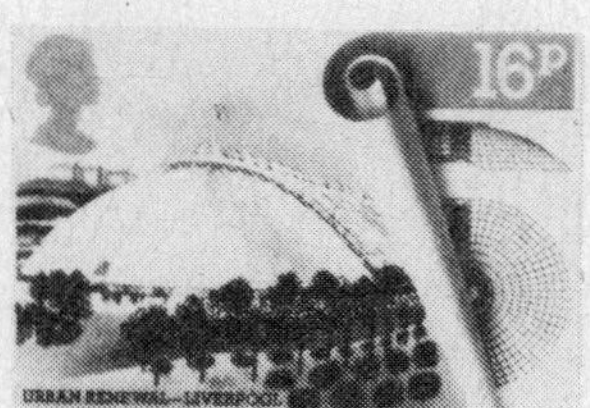

720. Garden Festival Hall, Liverpool.

1984. Urban Renewal. Multicoloured.
1245. 16p. Type **720** 40 40
1246. 20½p. Milburngate Centre, Durham .. 70 70
1247. 28p. Bush House, Bristol 95 95
1248. 31p. Commercial Street development, Perth .. 1·00 1·00

725. Abduction of Europa.

1984. 25th Anniv. of C.E.P.T. (Europa) (Nos. 1249, 1251), and Second Elections to European Parliament (others).
1249. – 16p. grey, bl. & gold 60 60
1250. **725.** 16p. grey, bl., blk. & gold 60 60
1251. – 20½p red, pur. & gold 1·00 1·00
1252. **725.** 20½p. red, pur., blk. & gold .. .. 1·00 1·00

DESIGN: Nos. 1249 and 1251, Bridge (C.E.P.T. 25th Anniversary logo).

MINIMUM PRICE

The minimum price quoted is 10p which represents a handling charge rather than a basis for valuing common stamps. For further notes about prices see introductory pages.

726. Lancaster House.

1984. London Economic Summit Conference.
1253. **726.** 31p. multicoloured .. 1·25 1·25

727. View of Earth from "Apollo 11".

1984. Centenary of Greenwich Meridian. Multicoloured.
1254. 16p. Type **727** 40 40
1255. 20½p. Navigational Chart of the English Channel 65 65
1256. 28p. Greenwich Observatory .. .. .. 1·10 1·10
1257. 31p. Sir George Airey's Transit Telescope .. 1·25 1·25

731. Bath Mail Coach leaving London, 1784.

1984. Bicentenary of First Mail Coach Run, Bath and Bristol to London. Multicoloured.
1258. 16p. Type **731** .. 65 65
1259. 16p. Attack on Exeter Mail, 1816 .. .. 65 65
1260. 16p. Norwich Mail in Thunderstorm, 1827 .. 65 65
1261. 16p. Holyhead and Liverpool Mails, 1828 65 65
1262. 16p. Edinburgh Mail snowbound, 1831 .. 65 65

736. Nigerian Clinic.

1984. 50th Anniv. of British Council. Mult.
1263. 17p. Type **736** 50 50
1264. 22p. Violinist and Acropolis, Athens .. 75 75
1265. 31p. Building project, Sri Lanka .. .. .. 1·10 1·10
1266. 34p. British Council library, Middle East .. 1·25 1·25

740. The Holy Family.

1984. Christmas. Multicoloured.

1267. 13p. Type **740** 30 30
1268. 17p. Arrival in Bethlehem 50 50
1269. 22p. Shepherd and Lamb 70 70
1270. 31p. Virgin and Child .. 1·10 1·10
1271. 34p. Offering of Frankincense .. .. 1·25 1·25

745. "The Flying Scotsman".

1985. Famous Trains. Multicoloured.

1272. 17p. Type **745** 60 60
1273. 22p. "The Golden Arrow" 90 90
1274. 29p. "The Cheltenham Flyer" .. .. .. 1·25 1·25
1275. 31p. "The Royal Scot" .. 1·25 1·25
1276. 34p. "The Cornish Riviera" .. .. 1·60 1·60

750. "Bombus terrestris" (bee).

1985. Insects. Multicoloured.

1277 17p. Type **750** 50 55
1278 22p. "Coccinella septempunctata" (ladybird) .. 70 70
1279 29p. "Decticus verrucivorus" (bush-cricket) .. 90 90
1280 31p. "Lucanus cervus" (stag beetle) .. .. 1·10 1·10
1281 34p. "Anax imperator" (dragonfly) .. .. 1·10 1·10

755. "Water Music" (George Frideric Handel).

1985. Europa. European Music Year. British Composers. 300th Birth Anniv. of Handel. Multicoloured.

1282. 17p. Type **755** 75 75
1283. 22p. "The Planets" Suite (Gustav Holst) .. 1·00 1·00
1284. 31p. "The First Cuckoo" (Frederick Delius) .. 1·60 1·40
1285. 34p. "Sea Pictures" (Edward Elgar) .. 1·60 1·60

759. R.N.L.I. Lifeboat and Signal Flags.

1985. Safety at Sea. Multicoloured.

1286. 17p. Type **759** 50 50
1287. 22p. Beachy Head Lighthouse and chart .. 75 75
1288. 31p. "Marecs A" communications satellite and dish aerials .. 1·10 1·10
1289. 34p. Buoys .. .. 1·25 1·25

763. Datapost Motorcyclist, City of London.

1985. 350 Years of Royal Mail Public Service. Multicoloured.

1290. 17p. Type **763** 50 50
1291. 22p. Rural postbus .. 75 75
1292. 31p. Parcel delivery in winter .. .. .. 1·10 1·10
1293. 34p. Town letter delivery 1·25 1·25

767. King Arthur and Merlin.

1985. Arthurian Legends. Multicoloured.

1294. 17p. Type **767** 50 50
1295. 22p. Lady of the Lake .. 75 75
1296. 31p. Queen Guinevere and Sir Lancelot .. 1·25 1·25
1297. 34p. Sir Galahad .. 1·40 1·40

771. Peter Sellers (from photo by Bill Brandt).

1985. British Film Year. Multicoloured.

1298. 17p. Type **771** 50 50
1299. 22p. David Niven (from photo by Cornell Lucas) 85 90
1300. 29p. Charlie Chaplin (from photo by Lord Snowdon) .. .. 1·40 1·40
1301. 31p. Vivien Leigh (from photo by Angus McBean) .. .. 1·40 1·40
1302. 34p. Alfred Hitchcock (from photo by Howard Carter) .. 1·40 1·40

776. Principal Boy.

1985. Christmas. Pantomime Characters. Multicoloured.

1303. 12p. Type **776** 45 45
1304. 17p. Genie 55 55
1305. 22p. Dame 85 85
1306. 31p. Good fairy .. .. 1·10 1·10
1307. 34p. Pantomime cat .. 1·25 1·25

781. Light Bulb and North Sea Oil Drilling Rig (Energy).

1986. Industry Year. Multicoloured.

1308. 17p. Type **781** 45 45
1309. 22p. Thermometer and pharmaceutical laboratory (Health) 70 70
1310. 31p. Garden hoe and steelworks (Steel) .. 1·10 1·10
1311. 34p. Loaf of bread and cornfield (Agriculture) 1·10 1·10

785. Dr Edmond Halley as Comet.

1986. Appearance of Halley's Comet. Multicoloured.

1312. 17p. Type **785** 45 45
1313. 22p. "Giotto" spacecraft approaching comet .. 90 90
1314. 31p. "Twice in a lifetime" .. .. .. 1·25 1·25
1315. 34p. Comet orbiting sun and planets .. .. 1·25 1·25

789. Queen Elizabeth II in 1928, 1942 and 1952.

1986. 60th Birthday of Queen Elizabeth II. Multicoloured.

1316. 17p. Type **789** 75 75
1317. 17p. Queen Elizabeth II in 1958, 1973 and 1982 75 75
1318. 34p. Type **789** .. .. 1·50 1·50
1319. 34p. As No. 1317 .. 1·50 1·50

791. Barn Owl.

1986. Europa. Nature Conservation. Endangered Species. Multicoloured.

1320. 17p. Type **791** 50 50
1321. 22p. Pine Marten .. 90 90
1322. 31p. Wild Cat .. .. 1·40 1·40
1323. 34p. Natterjack Toad .. 1·40 1·40

795. Peasants working in Fields.

1986. 900th Anniv. of Domesday Book. Multicoloured.

1324 17p. Type **795** 50 50
1325 22p. Freeman working at town trades 90 90
1326 31p. Knights and retainers 1·40 1·40
1327 34p. Lord at Banquet .. 1·40 1·40

799. Athletics.

1986. 13th Commonwealth Games, Edinburgh, and World Hockey Cup for Men, London. Multicoloured.

1328. 17p. Type **799** 45 50
1329. 22p. Rowing 90 60
1330. 29p. Weightlifting .. 1·25 1·25
1331. 31p. Rifle shooting .. 1·25 1·25
1332. 34p. Hockey .. .. 1·25 1·10

No. 1332. also commemorates centenary of Hockey Association.

804. Prince Andrew and Miss Sarah Ferguson (from photo by Gene Nocon).

1986. Royal Wedding.

1333. **804.** 12p. multicoloured .. 60 60
1334. – 17p. multicoloured .. 90 90

DESIGN: 17p. As Type **804** but with naval motif.

806. Stylized Cross on Ballot Paper.

1986. 32nd Commonwealth Parliamentary Association Conference.

1335. **806.** 34p. multicoloured .. 1·50 1·50

807. Lord Dowding and Hawker "Hurricane".

1986. History of Royal Air Force. Multicoloured.

1336. 17p. Type **807** 45 40
1337. 22p. Lord Tedder and Hawker "Typhoon" .. 1·00 90
1338. 29p. Lord Trenchard and De Havilland "DH9A" 1·25 1·10
1339. 31p. Sir Arthur Harris and Avro "Lancaster" 1·40 1·25
1340. 34p. Lord Portal and De Havilland "Mosquito" 1·50 1·25

Nos. 1336/40 were issued to celebrate 50th anniv. of first R.A.F. Commands.

812. The Glastonbury Thorn.

1986. Christmas. Multicoloured.

1341. 12p. Type **812** 75 75
1342. 13p. Type **812** 40 40
1343. 18p. The Tanad Valley Plygain 55 55
1344. 22p. The Hebrides Tribute 75 75
1345. 31p. The Dewsbury Church Knell .. .. 1·00 1·00
1346. 34p. The Hereford Boy Bishop .. .. .. 1·00 1·00

817. North American Blanket Flower.

1987. Flower Photographs by Alfred Lammer. Multicoloured.

1347.	18p. Type **817**	50	50
1348.	22p. Globe thistle	80	80
1349.	31p. "Echeveria"	1·25	1·25
1350.	34p. Autumn crocus	1·40	1·40

821. "Principia Mathematica".

1987. 300th Anniv. of "Principia Mathematica" by Sir Isaac Newton. Multicoloured.

1351.	18p. Type **821**	50	50
1352.	22p. "Motion of Bodies in Ellipses"	80	80
1353.	31p. "Optick Treatise"	1·25	1·25
1354.	34p. "The System of the World"	1·40	1·40

825. Willis Faber and Dumas Building, Ipswich.

1987. Europa. British Architects in Europe.

1355.	18p. Type **825**	50	50
1356.	22p. Pompidou Centre, Paris	80	80
1357.	31p. Staatsgalerie, Stuttgart	1·25	1·25
1358.	34p. European Investment Bank, Luxembourg	1·40	1·40

829. Brigade Members with Ashford Litter, 1887.

1987. Centenary of St. John Ambulance Brigade. Multicoloured.

1359.	18p. Type **829**	50	50
1360.	22p. Bandaging blitz victim, 1940	80	80
1361.	31p. Volunteer with fainting girl, 1965	1·25	1·25
1362.	34p. Transport of transplant organ by "Air Wing", 1987	1·40	1·40

833. Arms of the Lord Lyon King of Arms.

1987. 300th Anniv. of Revival of Order of the Thistle. Multicoloured.

1363.	18p. Type **833**	50	50
1364.	22p. Scottish Heraldic Banner of Prince Charles	80	80
1365.	31p. Arms of Royal Scottish Academy of Painting, Sculpture and Architecture	1·25	1·25
1366.	34p. Arms of Royal Society of Edinburgh	1·40	1·40

837. Crystal Palace, "Monarch of the Glen" (Landseer) and Grace Darling.

1987. 150th Anniv. of Queen Victoria's Accession. Multicoloured.

1367.	18p. Type **837**	50	50
1368.	22p. "Great Eastern", Beeton's "Book of Household Management" and Prince Albert	80	80
1369.	31p. Albert Memorial, ballot box and Disraeli	1·25	1·40
1370.	34p. Diamond Jubilee emblem, newspaper placard for Relief of Mafeking and morse key	1·25	1·40

841. Pot by Bernard Leach.

1987. Studio Pottery. Multicoloured.

1371.	18p. Type **841**	50	50
1372.	26p. Pot by Elizabeth Fritsch	80	80
1373.	31p. Pot by Lucie Rie	1·25	1·25
1374.	34p. Pot by Hans Coper	1·40	1·40

845. Decorating the Christmas Tree.

1987. Christmas. Multicoloured.

1375.	13p. Type **845**	50	50
1376.	18p. Waiting for Father Christmas	60	60
1377.	26p. Sleeping child and Father Christmas in sleigh	90	90
1378.	31p. Child reading	1·10	1·10
1379.	34p. Child playing recorder and snowman	1·10	1·10

850. "Bull-rout" (Jonathan Couch).

1988. Bicentenary of Linnean Society. Archive Illustrations. Multicoloured.

1380.	18p. Type **850**	45	45
1381.	26p. "Yellow Waterlily" (Major Joshua Swatkin)	85	85
1382.	31p. "Bewick's Swan" (Edward Lear)	1·10	1·10
1383.	34p. "Morchella esculenta" (James Sowerby)	1·25	1·25

854. Revd. William Morgan (Bible translator, 1588).

1988. 400th Anniv. of Welsh Bible. Mult.

1384.	18p. Type **854**	45	45
1385.	26p. William Salesbury (New Testament translator, 1567)	85	85
1386.	31p. Bishop Richard Davies (New Testament translator, 1567)	1·10	1·10
1387.	34p. Bishop Richard Parry (editor of Revised Welsh Bible, 1620)	1·25	1·25

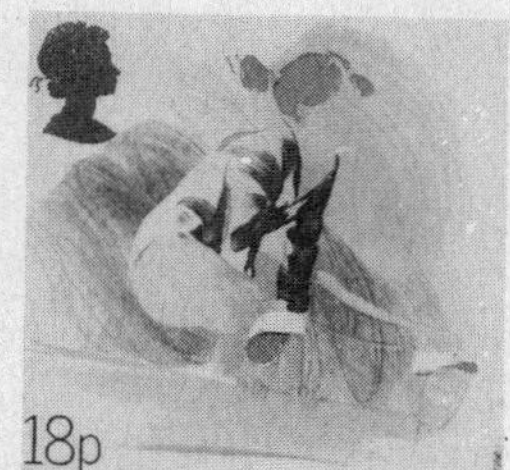

858. Gymnastics (Centenary of British Amateur Gymnastics Association).

1988. Sports Organizations. Multicoloured.

1388.	18p. Type **858**	45	45
1389.	26p. Downhill skiing (Ski Club of Great Britain)	85	85
1390.	31p. Tennis (centenary of Lawn Tennis Association)	1·10	1·10
1391.	34p. Football (centenary of Football League)	1·25	1·25

862. "Mallard" and Mailbags on Pick-up Arms.

1988. Europa. Transport and Mail Services in 1930's. Multicoloured.

1392.	18p. Type **862**	50	50
1393.	26p. Loading trans-atlantic mail on liner "Queen Elizabeth"	80	80
1394.	31p. Glasgow tram No. 1173 and piller box	1·10	1·10
1395.	34p. Imperial Airways Handley Page "HP 24" and airmail van	1·25	1·25

866 Early Settler and Sailing Clipper

1988. Bicent of Australian Settlement. Mult.

1396	18p. Type **866**	60	60
1397	18p. Queen Elizabeth II with British and Australian Parliament Buildings	60	60
1398	34p. W. G. Grace (cricketer) and tennis racquet	1·10	1·10
1399	34p. Shakespeare, John Lennon (entertainer) and Sydney Opera House	1·10	1·10

Stamps in similar designs were also issued by Australia.

870 Spanish Galeasse off The Lizard

1988. 400th Anniv of Spanish Armada. Mult.

1400	18p. Type **870**	65	65
1401	18p. English Fleet leaving Plymouth	65	65
1402	18p. Engagement off Isle of Wight	65	65
1403	18p. Attack of English Fire-ships, Calais	65	65
1404	18p. Armada in storm, North Sea	65	65

Nos. 1400/4 were printed together, se-tenant, forming a composite design.

875 "The Owl and the Pussy-cat"

1988. Death Centenary of Edward Lear (artist and author).

1405	**875**	19p. blk, cream & red	50	50
1406	–	27p. blk, cream & yell	80	80
1407	–	32p. blk, cream & grn	1·10	1·10
1408	–	35p. black, cream & bl	1·25	1·25

DESIGNS: 27p. "Edward Lear as a Bird" (self-portrait); 32p. "Cat" (from alphabet book); 35p. "There was a Young Lady whose Bonnet..." (limerick).

879 Carrickfergus Castle

1988.

1410	**879**	£1 green	1·50	50
1411	–	£1.50 red	2·25	1·00
1412	–	£2 blue	3·00	1·50
1413	–	£5 brown	7·00	3·00

DESIGNS: £1.50, Caernarfon Castle; £2, Edinburgh Castle; £5, Windsor Castle.

For similar designs, but with silhouette Queen's head see Nos. 1611/14.

883 Journey to Bethlehem

1988. Christmas. Christmas Cards. Mult.

1414 14p. Type **883** 35 35
1415 19p. Shepherds and Star 50 50
1416 27p. Three Wise Men .. 80 80
1417 32p. Nativity .. .. 1·10 1·10
1418 35p. The Annunciation .. 1·25 1·25

888 Puffin

1989. Centenary of Royal Society for the Protection of Birds. Multicoloured.

1419 19p. Type **888** 50 50
1420 27p. Avocet .. .. 1·10 1·10
1421 32p. Oystercatcher .. 1·25 1·25
1422 35p. Gannet .. .. 1·10 1·10

892 Rose

1989. Greetings Stamps. Multicoloured.

1423 19p. Type **892** .. .. 3·00 2·00
1424 19p. Cupid .. .. 3·00 2·00
1425 19p. Yachts .. .. 3·00 2·00
1426 19p. Fruit .. .. 3·00 2·00
1427 19p. Teddy bear .. 3·00 2·00

897 Fruit and Vegetables

1989. Food and Farming Year. Multicoloured.

1428 19p. Type **897** 50 50
1429 27p. Meat products .. 80 80
1430 32p. Dairy produce .. 1·10 1·10
1431 35p. Cereal products .. 1·25 1·25

901 Mortar Board

1989. Anniversaries. Multicoloured.

1432 19p. Type **901** (150th Anniv of Public Education in England) 55 55
1433 19p. Cross on Ballot Paper (3rd Direct Elections to European Parliament) 55 55
1434 35p. Posthorn (26th Postal, Telegraph and Telephone International Congress, Brighton) .. 1·10 1·10
1435 35p. Globe (Inter-Parliamentary Union Centenary Conference, London) .. .. 1·10 1·10

905 Toy Train and Airplane

1989. Europa. Games and Toys. Mult.

1436 19p. Type **905** .. 50 50
1437 27p. Building bricks .. 80 80
1438 32p. Dice and board games .. .. 1·10 1·10
1439 35p. Toy robot, boat and doll's house .. .. 1·25 1·25

909 Ironbridge, Shropshire

913

1989. Industrial Archaeology. Multicoloured.

1440 19p. Type **909** 50 50
1441 27p. Tin Mine, St. Agnes Head, Cornwall .. 80 80
1442 32p. Cotton Mills, New Lanark, Strathclyde .. 1·00 1·00
1443 35p. Pontcysyllte Aqueduct, Clwyd .. 1·10 1·10

1989.

1449 **913** (2nd) blue 30 55
1511 – (2nd) deep blue .. 45 45
1447 – (1st) black .. .. 1·00 1·00
1512 – (1st) red 30 35

915 Snowflake (× 10)

1989. 150th Anniv of Royal Microscopical Society. Multicoloured.

1453 19p. Type **915** 50 50
1454 27p. "Calliphora erythrocephala" (fly) (× 5) 85 85
1455 32p. Blood cells (× 500) .. 1·00 1·00
1456 35p. Microchip (× 600) .. 1·00 1·00

919 Royal Mail Coach

1989. Lord Mayor's Show, London. Mult.

1457 20p. Type **919** 60 60
1458 20p. Escort of Blues and Royals 60 60
1459 20p. Lord Mayor's coach 60 60
1460 20p. Coach team passing St. Pauls 60 60
1461 20p. Blues and Royals drum horse 60 60

This issue commemorates the 800th anniversary of the installation of the first Lord Mayor of London.

924 14th-century Peasants from Stained-glass Window

1989. Christmas. 800th Anniv of Ely Cathedral.

1462 **924** 15p. gold, silver & bl 35 35
1463 – 15p.+1p. gold, silver and blue 50 50
1464 – 20p.+1p. gold, silver and red 60 60
1465 – 34p.+1p. gold, silver and green .. 1·10 1·10
1466 – 37p.+1p. gold, silver and green .. 1·10 1·10

DESIGNS: 15p.+1p. Arches and roundels, West Front; 20p.+1p. Octagon Tower; 34p.+1p. Arcade from West Transept; 37p.+1p. Triple arch from West Front.

929 Queen Victoria and Queen Elizabeth II

930 Kitten

1990. 150th Anniv of the Penny Black.

1467 **929** 15p. blue 55 55
1469 20p. black and cream 75 75
1471 29p. mauve .. .. 1·00 1·10
1473 34p. grey .. .. 1·25 1·40
1474 37p. red .. .. 1·40 1·50

1990. 150th Anniv of Royal Society for Prevention of Cruelty to Animals. Mult.

1479 20p. Type **930** 50 50
1480 29p. Rabbit 80 80
1481 34p. Duckling .. .. 1·00 1·00
1482 37p. Puppy .. .. 1·10 1·10

934 Teddy Bear

1990. Greetings Stamps. "Smiles". Multicoloured (except No. 1492).

1483 20p. Type **934** 75 75
1484 20p. Dennis the Menace .. 75 75
1485 20p. Punch 75 75
1486 20p. Cheshire Cat .. 75 75
1487 20p. The Man in the Moon 75 75
1488 20p. The Laughing Policeman 75 75
1489 20p. Clown 75 75
1490 20p. Mona Lisa 75 75
1491 20p. Queen of Hearts .. 75 75
1492 20p. Stan Laurel (comedian) (gold and black) .. 75 75

See also Nos. 1550/9.

944 Alexandra Palace ("Stamp World London 90" Exhibition)

1990. Europa (Nos. 1493 and 1495) and "Glasgow 1990 European City of Culture" (Nos. 1494 and 1496). Multicoloured.

1493 20p. Type **944** 50 50
1494 20p. Glasgow School of Art 50 50
1495 29p. British Philatelic Bureau, Edinburgh .. 1·00 1·00
1496 37p. Templeton Carpet Factory, Glasgow .. 1·10 1·10

948 Export Achievement Award

1990. 25th Anniv of Queen's Awards for Export and Technology. Multicoloured.

1497 20p. Type **948** 55 55
1498 20p. Technological Achievement Award .. 55 55
1499 37p. Type **948** .. .. 1·10 1·10
1500 37p. As No. 1498 .. 1·10 1·10

950 Cycad and Sir Joseph Banks Building

1990. 150th Anniv of Kew Gardens. Mult.

1502 20p. Type **950** 50 50
1503 29p. Stone Pine and Princess of Wales Conservatory 80 80
1504 34p. Willow Tree and Palm House .. .. 1·10 1·25
1505 37p. Cedar Tree and Pagoda .. .. 1·25 1·40

954 Thomas Hardy and Clyffe Clump, Dorset

1990. 150th Birth Anniv of Thomas Hardy (author).

1506 **954** 20p. multicoloured .. 60 70

955 Queen Elizabeth the Queen Mother

1990. 90th Birthday of Queen Elizabeth the Queen Mother. Multicoloured.

1507 20p. Type **955** 50 80
1508 29p. Queen Elizabeth .. 80 80
1509 34p. Elizabeth, Duchess of York .. .. .. 1·10 1·25
1510 37p. Lady Elizabeth Bowes-Lyon .. .. 1·25 1·40

959 Victoria Cross

1990. Gallantry Awards. Multicoloured.

1517 20p. Type **959** 65 65
1518 20p. George Cross .. 65 65
1519 20p. Distinguished Service Cross and Distinguished Service Medal (horiz) .. 65 65
1520 20p. Military Cross and Military Medal (horiz) 65 65
1521 20p. Distinguished Flying Cross and Distinguished Flying Medal (horiz) .. 65 65

964 Armagh Observatory, Jodrell Bank Radio Telescope and La Palma Telescope

1990. Astronomy. Multicoloured.

1522 22p. Type **964** 50 40
1523 26p. Newton's moon and tides diagram with early telescopes .. 80 90
1524 31p. Greenwich Old Observatory and early astronomical equipment 1·00 1·00
1525 37p. Stonehenge, gyroscope and navigating by stars .. .. 1·10 1·10

Nos. 1522/5 commemorate the Centenary of the British Astronomical Association and the Bicentenary of the Armagh Observatory.

968 Building a Snowman

1990. Christmas. Multicoloured.

1526 17p. Type **968** 45 35
1527 22p. Fetching the Christmas tree 55 65
1528 26p. Carol singing .. 80 80
1529 31p. Tobogganing .. 1·00 1·00
1530 37p. Ice skating .. 1·10 1·10

973 "King Charles Spaniel"

1991. Dogs. Paintings by George Stubbs. Multicoloured.

1531 22p. Type **973** 60 60
1532 26p. "A Pointer" .. 70 70
1533 31p. "Two Hounds in a Landscape" 80 80
1534 33p. "A Rough Dog" .. 85 85
1535 37p. "Fino and Tiny" .. 1·00 1·00

978 Thrush's Nest

1991. Greetings Stamps. "Good Luck". Mult.

1536 (1st) Type **978** 60 60
1537 (1st) Shooting star and rainbow 60 60
1538 (1st) Magpies and charm bracelet 60 60
1539 (1st) Black cat 60 60
1540 (1st) Kingfisher with key 60 60
1541 (1st) Duck and frog .. 60 60
1542 (1st) Four-leaf clover in boot and match box .. 60 60
1543 (1st) Pot of gold at end of rainbow 60 60
1544 (1st) Heart-shaped butterflies 60 60
1545 (1st) Wishing well and sixpence 60 60

Nos. 1536/45 were initially sold at 22p. each. It is intended that the price will be increased to reflect future alterations in postage rates. The backgrounds of the stamps form a composite design.

988 Michael Faraday (inventor of electric motor) (birth bicentenary)

1991. Scientific Achievements. Multicoloured.

1546 22p. Type **988** 60 60
1547 22p. Charles Babbage (computer science pioneer) (birth bicent) 60 60
1548 31p. Radar sweep of East Anglia (50th anniv of operational radar network) 85 85
1549 37p. Gloster E28/39 aircraft over East Anglia (50th anniv of first flight of Sir Frank Whittle's jet engine) .. 95 95

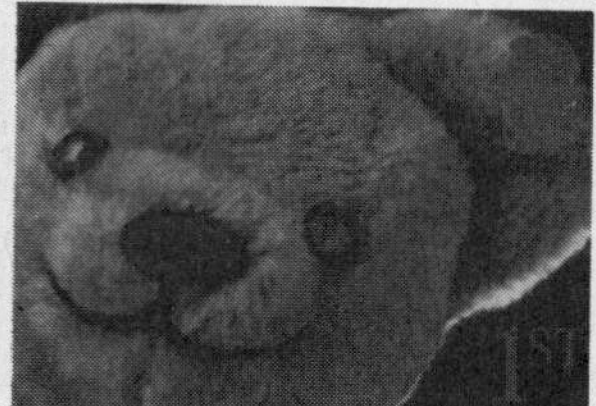

992 Teddy Bear

1991. Greetings Stamps. "Smiles". As Nos. 1483/92, but inscr "1st" as in T **992**. Multicoloured (except No. 1559).

1550 (1st) Type **992** 35 40
1551 (1st) Dennis the Menace 35 40
1552 (1st) Punch 35 40
1553 (1st) Cheshire Cat .. 35 40
1554 (1st) The Man in the Moon 35 40
1555 (1st) The Laughing Policeman 35 40
1556 (1st) Clown 35 40
1557 (1st) Mona Lisa 35 40
1558 (1st) Queen of Hearts .. 35 40
1559 (1st) Stan Laurel (comedian) (gold and black) 35 40

Nos. 1550/9 were initially sold at 22p. each. It is intended that the price will be increased to reflect future alterations in postage rates.

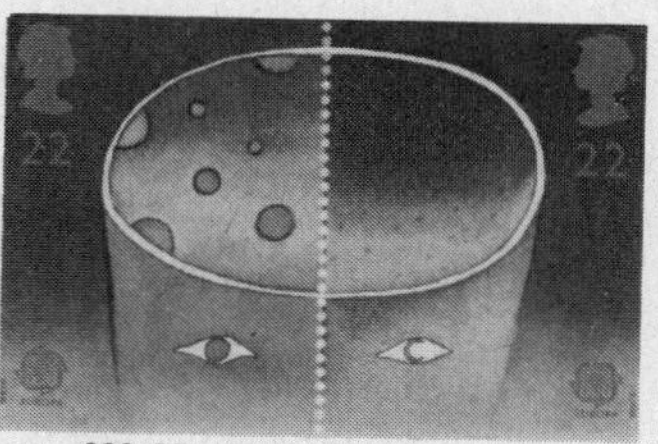

993 Man looking at Space **994**
(¾ size illustration)

1991. Europa. Europe in Space. Mult.

1560 22p. Type **993** 55 55
1561 22p. Type **994** 55 55
1562 37p. Space looking at Man (Queen's head on left) 1·00 1·00
1563 37p. Similar to No. 1562 (Queen's head on right) 1·00 1·00

Stamps of the same value were printed together in horizontal pairs, each pair forming a composite design.

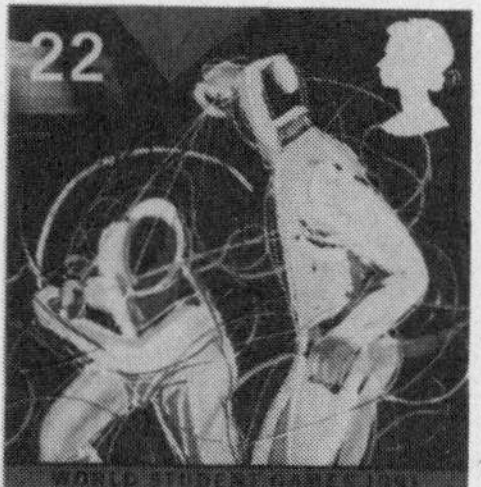

997 Fencing

1991. World Student Games, Sheffield (Nos. 1564/6) and World Cup Rugby Championship (No. 1567).

1564 22p. Type **997** 50 50
1565 26p. Hurdling 70 70
1566 31p. Diving 85 85
1567 37p. Rugby .. .. 1·00 1·00

1001 "Silver Jubilee"

1991. 9th World Congress of Roses, Belfast. Multicoloured.

1568 22p. Type **1001** 50 50
1569 26p. "Mme Alfred Carriere" 60 60
1570 31p. "Rosa moyesii" .. 70 70
1571 33p. "Harvest Fayre" .. 80 80
1572 37p. "Mutabilis" .. 1·00 1·00

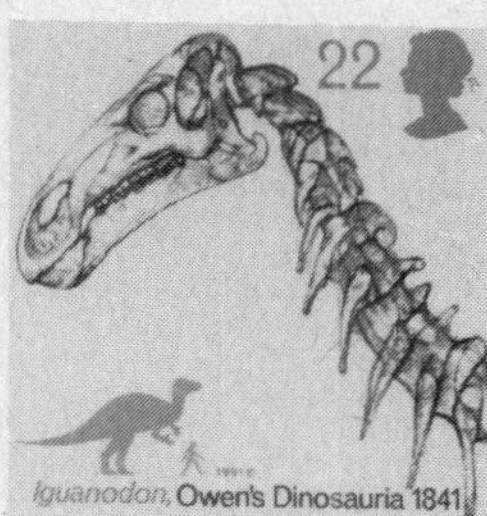

1006 Iguanodon

1991. 150th Anniv of Dinosaurs' Identification by Owen. Multicoloured.

1573 22p. Type **1006** 35 40
1574 26p. Stegosaurus .. 40 45
1575 31p. Tyrannosaurus .. 50 55
1576 33p. Protoceratops .. 50 55
1577 37p. Triceratops .. 60 65

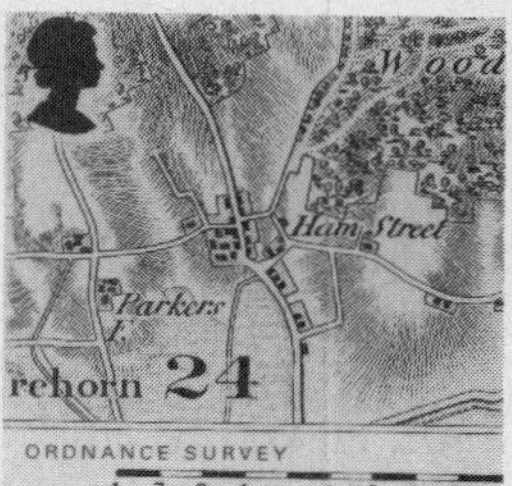

1011 Map of 1816

1991. Bicentenary of Ordnance Survey. Maps of Hamstreet, Kent.

1578 **1011** 24p. black, mauve and cream .. 40 45
1579 – 28p. multicoloured .. 45 50
1580 – 33p. multicoloured .. 50 55
1581 – 39p. multicoloured .. 60 65

DESIGNS: 28p. Map of 1906; 33p. Map of 1959; 39p. Map of 1991

1015 Adoration of the Magi

1991. Christmas. Iluminated Letters from "Acts of Mary and Jesus" Manuscript in Bodleian Library, Oxford. Multicoloured.

1582 18p. Type **1015** 30 35
1583 24p. Mary and Baby Jesus in the Stable 40 45
1584 28p. The Holy Family and Angel 45 50
1585 33p. The Annunciation .. 50 55
1586 39p. The Flight into Egypt 60 65

1020 Fallow Deer in Scottish Forest

1992. The Four Seasons. Wintertime. Mult.

No.	Description	Unused	Used
1587	18p. Type **1020**	30	35
1588	24p. Hare on North Yorkshire Moors	40	45
1589	28p. Fox in the Fens ..	45	50
1590	33p. Redwing and Home Counties village ..	50	55
1591	39p. Welsh mountain sheep in Snowdonia ..	60	65

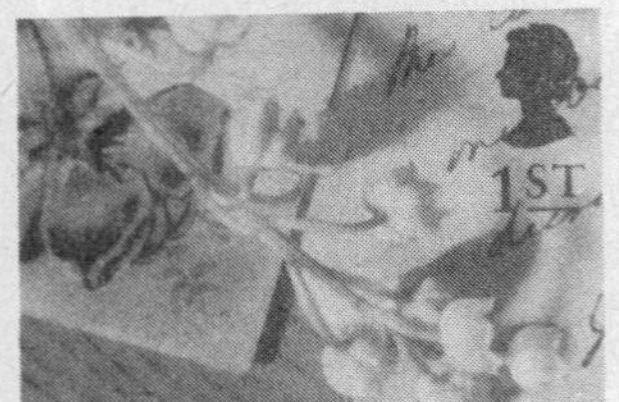

1025 Flower Spray

1992. Greetings Stamps. "Memories". Mult.

No.	Description	Unused	Used
1592	(1st) Type **1025**	40	45
1593	(1st) Double locket ..	40	45
1594	(1st) Key	40	45
1595	(1st) Model car and cigarette cards ..	40	45
1596	(1st) Compass and map ..	40	45
1597	(1st) Pocket watch ..	40	45
1598	(1st) 1858–79 1d. Red stamp and pen ..	40	45
1599	(1st) Pearl necklace ..	40	45
1600	(1st) Marbles ..	40	45
1601	(1st) Bucket, spade and strafish	40	45

Nos. 1592/1601 were issued together, se-tenant, in booklets, the backgrounds forming a compsite design.

1035 Queen Elizabeth in Coronation Robes and Parliamentary Emblem

1992. 40th Anniv of Accession. Mult.

No.	Description	Unused	Used
1602	24p. Type **1035**	40	45
1603	24p. Queen Elizabeth in Garter robes and archiepiscopal arms ..	40	45
1604	24p. Queen Elizabeth with baby Prince Andrew and Royal Arms ..	40	45
1605	24p. Queen Elizabeth at Trooping the Colour and service emblems	40	45
1606	24p. Queen Elizabeth and Commonwealth emblem	40	45

1040 Tennyson in 1888 and "The Beguiling of Merlin" (Sir Edward Burne-Jones)

1992. Death Centenary of Alfred, Lord Tennyson (poet). Multicoloured.

No.	Description	Unused	Used
1607	24p. Type **1040**	40	45
1608	28p. Tennyson in 1864 and "I am Sick of the Shadows" (John Waterhouse)	45	50
1609	33p. Tennyson in 1856 and "April Love" (Arthur Hughes)	50	55
1610	39p. Tennyson as a young man and "Mariana" (Dante Gabriel Rossetti)	60	65

1044 Carrickfergus Castle

1992. Designs as Nos. 1410/13, but showing Queen's head in silhouette as T **1044**.

No.	Type	Description	Unused	Used
1611	**1044**	£1 green and gold †	1·50	1·50
1612	–	£1.50 purple & gold †	2·25	2·25
1613	–	£2 blue and gold † ..	3·00	3·00
1614	–	£5 brown and gold †	7·50	7·50

†The Queen's head on these stamps is printed in optically variable ink which changes colour from gold to green when viewed from different angles.

1045 British Olympic Association Logo (Olympic Games, Barcelona)

1992. Europa. International Events. Mult.

No.	Description	Unused	Used
1615	24p. Type **1045**	40	45
1616	24p. British Paralympic Association symbol (Paralympics '92, Barcelona)	40	45
1617	24p. "Santa Maria" (500th Anniv of discovery of America by Columbus)	40	45
1618	39p. "Kaisei" (cadet sailing ship) (Grand Regatta Columbus, 1992)	60	65
1619	39p. British Pavilion, "EXPO '92", Seville ..	60	65

1050 Pikeman

1992. 350th Anniv of the Civil War. Mult.

No.	Description	Unused	Used
1620	24p. Type **1050**	40	45
1621	28p. Drummer	45	50
1622	33p. Musketeer	50	55
1623	39p. Standard Bearer ..	60	65

1054 "The Yeoman of the Guard"

1992. 150th Birth Anniv of Sir Arthur Sullivan (composer). Gilbert and Sullivan Operas. Multicoloured.

No.	Description	Unused	Used
1624	18p. Type **1054**	35	40
1625	24p. "The Gondoliers" ..	40	45
1626	28p. "The Mikado" ..	40	45
1627	33p. "The Pirates of Penzance"	50	55
1628	39p. "Iolanthe"	60	65

REGIONAL ISSUES

I. CHANNEL ISLANDS

Islands in the English Channel off N.W. coast of France. Occupied by German Forces from June, 1940 to May, 1945, when separate issues for both islands were made. "Regional" issues were introduced from 1958.

C **1.** Gathering Vraic (seaweed).

1948. 3rd Anniversary of Liberation.

No.	Type	Description	Unused	Used
C 1.	C **1.**	1d. red	20	20
C 2.	–	2½d. blue	30	30

DESIGN: 2½d. Islanders gathering vraic.

II. GUERNSEY.

2.

3.

1958.

No.	Type	Description	Unused	Used
6	**2.**	2½d. red	35	40
7p	**3.**	3d. lilac	20	20
9		4d. blue	10	25
10		4d. sepia	15	20
11		4d. red	15	30
12		5d. blue	15	30

For War Occupation issues and issues of independent postal administration from 1967 see GUERNSEY.

III. ISLE OF MAN.

1.

2.

1958.

No.	Type	Description	Unused	Used
1	**1.**	2½d. red	45	80
2	**2.**	3d. lilac	20	10
3p		4d. blue	20	15
5		4d. sepia	20	30
6		4d. red	45	60
7		5d. blue	45	60

3.

1971. Decimal Currency.

No.	Type	Description	Unused	Used
8.	**3.**	2½p. red	20	15
9.		3p. blue	20	15
10.		5p. violet	70	75
11.		7½p. brown	70	90

For issues of independent postal administration from 1973 see ISLE OF MAN.

IV. JERSEY.

8.

9.

1958.

No.	Type	Description	Unused	Used
9.	**8.**	2½d. red	35	50
10p.	**9.**	3d. lilac	20	20
11p.		4d. blue	20	25
12.		4d. sepia	20	25
13.		4d. red	20	30
14.		5d. blue	20	40

For War Occupation issues and issues of independent postal administration from 1969 see JERSEY.

V. NORTHERN IRELAND.

N **1.**

N **2.**

N **3.**

N **4.**

1958.

No.	Type	Description	Unused	Used
NI 1.	N **1.**	**3d. lilac**	20	10
NI 2.		**4d. blue**	20	15
NI 8.		**4d. sepia**	20	20
NI 9.		**4d. red**	20	20
NI 10.		**5d. blue**	20	20
NI 3.	N **2.**	**6d. purple**	20	20
NI 4.		**9d. green**	30	50
NI 5.	N **3.**	**1s. 3d. green** ..	30	50
NI 6.		**1s. 6d. blue**	30	50

1971.

No.	Type	Description	Unused	Used
NI 12	N 4	2½p. mauve ..	75	25
NI 14		3p. blue	20	15
NI 15		3½p. grey	20	20
NI 17		4½p. blue	25	25
NI 18		5p. violet	1·50	1·50
NI 19		5½p. violet ..	20	20
NI 21		6½p. turquoise ..	20	20
NI 22		7p. brown	35	25
NI 23		7½p. brown ..	2·50	2·50
NI 24		8p. red	30	30
NI 25		8½p. green ..	30	30
NI 26		9p. violet	30	30
NI 28		10p. brown ..	35	35
NI 29		10½p. blue ..	40	40
NI 30		11p. red	40	40
NI 34		11½p. drab ..	1·00	60
NI 31		12p. green ..	40	45
NI 36		12½p. green ..	50	40
NI 37		13p. brown ..	60	35
NI 32		13½p. brown ..	70	70
NI 39		14p. blue	40	35
NI 40		15p. blue	45	30
NI 41		15½p. violet ..	1·00	65
NI 42		16p. brown ..	1·00	1·00
NI 44		17p. blue	30	35
NI 45		18p. violet ..	80	80
NI 46		18p. grey ..	80	70
NI 47		18p. green ..	30	35
NI 48		19p. red	60	60
NI 49		19½p. grey ..	2·00	2·00
NI 50		20p. black ..	30	30
NI 51		20½p. blue ..	4·00	4·00
NI 52		22p. blue ..	90	1·10
NI 53		22p. green ..	85	85
NI 54		22p. red	85	40
NI 55		23p. green ..	80	80
NI 56		24p. red	70	70
NI 57		24p. brown ..	40	45
NI 58		26p. red	90	90
NI 59		26p. brown ..	40	45
NI 60a		28p. blue ..	80	80
NI 61		28p. grey ..	45	50
NI 62		31p. purple ..	1·10	1·10
NI 63		32p. blue	1·10	1·10
NI 64		34p. grey ..	1·00	1·00
NI 65		37p. red	60	65
NI 66		39p. mauve ..	60	65

VI. SCOTLAND.

S **1.**

S **2.**

S **3.**

S **4.**

1958.

No.	Type	Description	Unused	Used
S 7	S **1.**	3d. lilac	10	15
S 8		4d. blue	10	15
S 9		4d. sepia	10	10
S 10		4d. red	10	10
S 11		5d. blue	20	10
S 3	S **2.**	6d. purple	20	15
S 4		9d. green	30	30
S 5	S **3.**	1s. 3d. green	30	30
S 6		1s. 6d. blue	35	30

1971. Decimal Currency.

S 14	S 4	2½p. mauve	25	15
S 16		3p. blue	15	15
S 17		3½p. grey	20	20
S 19		4½p. blue	25	20
S 20		5p. violet	1·50	1·50
S 21		5½p. violet	20	20
S 23		6½p. blue	20	20
S 24		7p. brown	25	25
S 25		7½p. brown	2·00	2·00
S 26		8p. red	30	40
S 27		8½p. green	30	30
S 28		9p. violet	30	30
S 29		10p. brown	35	30
S 31		10½p. blue	45	35
S 32		11p. red	45	35
S 36		11½p. drab	85	60
S 33		12p. green	50	30
S 38		12½p. green	50	40
S 39		13p. brown	60	65
S 34		13½p. brown	40	30
S 54		14p. blue	50	30
S 56		15p. blue	70	65
S 41		15½p. violet	70	45
S 42		16p. brown	70	45
S 43		17p. blue	70	1·00
S 44		18p violet	70	65
S 58		17p. blue	30	35
S 44		18p. violet	1·00	90
S 59		18p. grey	1·00	90
S 60		18p. green	30	35
S 61		19p. red	60	45
S 45		19½p. grey	2·00	2·25
S 63		20p. black	60	30
S 46		20½p. blue	3·75	3·75
S 47		22p. blue	80	1·10
S 64		22p. green	80	80
S 65		22p. red	90	40
S 66		23p. green	90	80
S 68		24p. red	70	70
S 69		24p. brown	40	45
S 49		26p. red	90	80
S 71		26p. brown	40	45
S 72		28p. blue	85	75
S 73		28p. grey	45	50
S 51		31p. purple	1·40	1·10
S 75		32p. blue	1·10	90
S 76		34p. grey	1·00	90
S 77		37p. red	60	65
S 78		39p. mauve	60	65

VII. WALES.

W 1. W 2.

W 3. W 4.

1958.

W 1	W 1.	3d. lilac	20	10
W 8		4d. blue	20	10
W 9		4d. sepia	20	10
W 10		4d. red	20	20
W 11		5d. blue	20	10
W 3	W 2.	6d. purple	40	20
W 4		9d. green	30	35
W 5	W 3.	1s. 3d. green	30	30
W 6		1s. 6d. blue	35	30

1971. Decimal Currency.

W 13	W 4	2½p. mauve	20	15
W 15		3p. blue	20	20
W 16		3½p. grey	20	25
W 18		4½p. blue	25	20
W 19		5p. violet	1·50	1·50
W 20		5½p. violet	20	25
W 22		6½p. blue	20	20
W 23		7p. brown	25	25
W 24		7½p. brown	2·00	2·25
W 25		8p. red	30	30
W 26		8½p. green	30	30
W 27		9p. violet	30	30
W 29		10p. brown	35	30
W 30		10½p. blue	40	35
W 31		11p. red	40	45
W 35		11½p. drab	85	60
W 32		10p. green	50	45
W 37		12p. green	60	60
W 38		13p. brown	50	35
W 33		13p. brown	60	70
W 40		14p. blue	45	30
W 41		15p. blue	45	30
W 42		15½p. violet	80	65
W 43		16p. brown	1·50	1·25
W 45		17p. blue	30	35
W 46		18p. violet	80	75
W 47		18p. grey	1·00	45
W 48		18p. green	30	35
W 50		19p. red	60	45
W 51	W 4	19½p. grey	2·00	2·00
W 52		20p. black	60	50
W 53		20½p. blue	3·75	3·75
W 54		22p. blue	1·10	1·10
W 55		22p. green	80	50
W 56		22p. red	35	40
W 57		23p. green	80	50
W 58		24p. red	70	70
W 59		24p. brown	40	45
W 61		26p. red	90	80
W 62		26p. brown	40	45
W 63a		28p. blue	80	75
W 64		28p. grey	45	50
W 65		31p. purple	1·00	70
W 66		32p. blue	1·10	75
W 67		34p. grey	1·00	85
W 68		37p. red	60	65
W 69		39p. mauve	60	65

OFFICIAL STAMPS
(for Government Departments)

ADMIRALTY
Overprinted **ADMIRALTY OFFICIAL.**

1903. Stamps of King Edward VII.

O 107	83.	½d. turquoise	7·00	4·00
O 102	–	1d. red	5·00	2·50
O 103	–	1½d. purple and green	60·00	45·00
O 104	–	2d. green and red	£100	5000
O 105	83.	2½d. blue	£120	40·00
O 106	–	3d. purple on yellow	£100	38·00

ARMY
Overprinted **ARMY OFFICIAL.**

1896. Stamps of Queen Victoria.

O 41.	71.	½d. red	1·50	75
O 42.		½d. green	1·75	4·00
O 43.	57.	1d. lilac	1·50	75
O 44.	74.	2½d. purple on blue	4·00	3·00
O 45.	79.	6d. purple on red	16·00	10·00

1902. Stamps of King Edward VII.

O 48.	83.	½d. turquoise	2·00	65
O 49.		1d. red	1·50	55
O 50.		6d. purple	60·00	32·00

BOARD OF EDUCATION
Overprinted **BOARD OF EDUCATION.**

1902. Stamps of Queen Victoria.

O 81.	78.	5d. purple and blue	£500	£100
O 82.	82.	1s. green and red	£950	£375

1902. Stamps of King Edward VII.

O 83.	83.	½d. turquoise	18·00	6·00
O 84.		1d. red	18·00	5·00
O 85.		2½d. blue	£500	50·00
O 86.	–	5d. purple and blue	£2000	£950
O 87.	–	1s. green and red	£25000	£15000

GOVERNMENT PARCELS
Overprinted **GOVT. PARCELS.**

1883. Stamps of Queen Victoria.

O 61	62	1½d. purple	£100	25·00
O 62	–	6d. green (No. 194)	£750	£275
O 63	–	9d. green (No. 195)	£625	£175
O 64	25	1s. brown (No. 163)	£425	70·00

1887. Stamps of Queen Victoria.

O 69	57	1d. lilac	28·00	8·00
O 65	72	1½d. purple and green	14·00	2·00
O 70	73	2d. green and red	45·00	7·00
O 71	77	4½d. green and red	£100	75·00
O 66	79	6d. purple on red	28·00	10·00
O 67	80	9d. purple and blue	55·00	15·00
O 68	82	1s. green	£120	70·00
O 72		1s. green and red	£160	50·00

1902. Stamps of King Edward VII.

O 74.	83.	1d. red	17·00	6·00
O 75.	–	2d. green and red	65·00	9·00
O 76.	83.	6d. purple	£100	18·00
O 77.	–	9d. purple and blue	£225	50·00
O 78.	–	1s. green and red	£350	85·00

INLAND REVENUE
Overprinted **I. R. OFFICIAL.**
Stamps of Queen Victoria.

1882.

O 1	52.	½d. green	12·00	3·00
O 5		½d. blue	25·00	15·00
O 3	57.	1d. lilac	1·50	65
O 6	–	2½d. purple (No. 190)	£110	35·00
O 4	34.	6d. grey (No. 161)	75·00	20·00
O 7	–	1s. green (No. 196)	£2500	£450
O 9	–	5s. red (No. 181)	£1300	£400
O 10	–	10s. blue (No. 183)	£2250	£475
O 11	61.	£1 brown	£18000	

1888.

O 13.	71.	½d. red	1·50	50
O 17.		½d. green	4·00	3·00
O 14.	74.	2½d. purple on blue	5·00	4·00
O 18.	79.	6d. purple on red	£100	22·00
O 15.	82.	1s. green	£200	20·00
O 19.		1s. green and red	£600	£100
O 16.	61.	£1 green	£3700	£450

1902. Stamps of King Edward VII.

O 20.	83.	½d. turquoise	17·00	1·50
O 21.		1d. red	10·00	70
O 22.		2½d. blue	£400	60·00
O 23.		6d. purple	£85000	£65000
O 24.	–	1s. green and red	£500	65·00
O 25.	–	5s. red	£4000	£1300
O 26.	–	10s. blue	£15000	£9500
O 27.	–	£1 green	£12000	£6000

OFFICE OF WORKS
Overprinted **O.W. OFFICIAL.**

1896. Stamps of Queen Victoria.

O 31.	71.	½d. red	90·00	40·00
O 32.		½d. green	£150	75·00
O 33.	57.	1d. lilac	£150	40·00
O 34.	78.	5d. purple and blue	£750	£150
O 35.	81.	10d. purple and red	£1300	£225

1902. Stamps of King Edward VII.

O 36.	83.	½d. turquoise	£350	80·00
O 37.	–	1d. red	£350	80·00
O 38.	–	2d. green and red	£600	75·00
O 39.	83.	2½d. blue	£700	£200
O 40.	–	10d. purple and red	£5000	£1500

ROYAL HOUSEHOLD
Overprinted **R.H. OFFICIAL.**

1902. Stamps of King Edward VII.

O 91.	83.	½d. turquoise	£150	95·00
O 92.		1d. red	£130	85·00

POSTAGE DUE STAMPS.

D 1.

D 4.

1914.

D 10	D 1.	½d. green	50	30
D 56		½d. orange	10	45
D 11		1d. red	50	30
D 57		1d. blue	10	15
D 12		1½d. brown	35·00	15·00
D 58		1½d. green	90	1·50
D 69		2d. black	40	40
D 60		3d. violet	40	15
D 15		4d. green	8·00	2·00
D 61		4d. blue	40	20
D 62		5d. brown	45	45
D 63		6d. purple	60	30
D 76		8d. red	1·25	75
D 17		1s. blue	5·00	75
D 64		1s. brown	1·40	25
D 65		2s. 6d. purple on yell.	4·00	45
D 66		5s. red on yellow	7·50	70
D 67		10s. blue on yellow	9·00	3·75
D 68		£1 black on yellow	45·00	7·00

On the 2s. 6d. to £1 the inscription reads "TO PAY".

1970. Decimal Currency.

D 77.	–	½p. blue	10	20
D 78.	–	1p. purple	10	15
D 79.	–	2p. green	10	15
D 80.	–	3p. blue	15	15
D 81.	–	4p. brown	15	15
D 82.	–	5p. violet	20	20
D 83.	–	7p. brown	35	45
D 84.	D 4.	10p. red	30	20
D 85.		11p. green	50	60
D 86.		20p. brown	60	50
D 87.		50p. blue	1·50	40
D 88.		£1 black	2·75	60
D 89.		£5 yellow and black	20·00	2·00

DESIGN: ½p. to 7p. similar to Type D **4**, but with "TO PAY" reading vertically upwards at the left.

D 5.

198[illegible]

D 90.	D 5.	1p. red	10	10
D 91.		2p. blue	10	10
D 92.		3p. mauve	10	15
D 93.		4p. blue	10	20
D 94.		5p. brown	10	20
D 95.	–	10p. brown	15	25
D 96.	–	20p. green	30	30
D 97.	–	25p. blue	40	70
D 98.	–	50p. black	75	1·00
D 99.	–	£1 red	1·50	80
D100.	–	£2 blue	3·00	2·00
D101.	–	£5 orange	7·50	1·50

DESIGN: 10p. to £5, As Type D **5** but with "TO PAY" horizontal.

GUERNSEY, ISLE OF MAN and JERSEY are now in Country alphabetical order.

GRENADA

One of the Windward Is., Br. W. Indies. Ministerial Government was introduced on 1 January 1960. Achieved Associated Statehood on 3 March 1967 and Independence during 1974.

1861. 12 pence = 1 shilling;
20 schillings = 1 pound.
1949. 100 cents = 1 West Indian dollar.

1.

5.

1861.

14.	1.	1d. green	55·00	5·00
6.		6d. red	£600	12·00

1875. Surch. **POSTAGE** and value in words.

21.	5.	½d. mauve	10·00	5·50
22.		2½d. lake	40·00	5·50
23.		4d. blue	90·00	8·00
13.		1s. mauve	£650	9·00

1883. Revenue stamp surch. crown and value (in green) optd. **POSTAGE.**

27.	5.	1d. orange	£225	45·00

1883. Revenue stamp as last but optd. **POSTAGE** twice diagonally.

29.	5.	Half of 1d. orange	£170	£120

ONE PENNY
13.

21.

1883.

30.	13.	½d. green	90	60
31.		1d. red	50·00	3·25
32.		2½d. blue	6·50	50
33.		4d. grey	4·50	1·75
34.		6d. mauve	3·50	3·75
35.		8d. brown	8·00	12·00
36.		1s. violet	90·00	55·00

1886. Revenue stamps as No. 27 but surch. **POSTAGE** and value in words or figures.

43.	5.	½d. on 2s. orange	12·00	17·00
37.		1d. on 1½d. orange	30·00	24·00
39.		1d. on 4d. orange	£120	80·00
38.		1d. on 1s. orange	30·00	30·00
41.		4d. on 2s. orange	26·00	16·00

1887. As Type 3, but inscr. "GRENADA POSTAGE & REVENUE" at top.

40.	13.	1d. red	50	20

1890. Revenue stamp as No. 27 but surch. **POSTAGE AND REVENUE 1d.**

45	5	1d. on 2s. orange	45·00	45·00

1891. Surch **POSTAGE AND REVENUE 1d.**

46.	13.	1d. on 8d. brown	9·00	11·00

1891. Surch. **2½d.**

47.	13.	2½d. on 8d. brown	8·00	11·00

1895.

48.	21.	½d. mauve and green	1·25	50
49.		1d. mauve and red	2·75	20
50.		2d. mauve and brown	28·00	32·00
51.		2½d. mauve and blue	5·00	60
52.		3d. mauve and orange	6·50	14·00
53.		6d. mauve and green	5·00	8·00
54.		8d. mauve and black	12·00	24·00
55.		1s. green and orange	14·00	20·00

23. Flagship of Columbus (Columbus named Grenada "La Concepcion").

1898. Discovery of Grenada by Columbus.

56.	23.	2½d. blue	10·00	5·00

1902. As T 21, but portrait of King Edward VII.

57		½d. purple and green	1·25	30
58		1d. purple and red	1·50	20
59		2d. purple and brown	2·25	6·50
60		2½d. purple and blue	2·50	1·25
71		3d. purple and orange	1·75	3·50
72		6d. purple and green	2·00	3·75
63		1s. green and orange	3·25	14·00
64		2s. green and blue	14·00	38·00
65		5s. green and red	35·00	48·00
66		10s. green and purple	95·00	£170

26. Badge of the Colony.

28.

1906.

77. 26. ½d. green 70 20
78. 1d. red 50 10
79. 2d. orange .. .. .. 1·50 3·00
80. 2½d. blue .. .. .. 3·00 1·25
84. 3d. purple on yellow 1·50 1·75
85. 6d. purple .. .. .. 14·00 23·00
86. 1s. black on green .. 2·50 3·75
87. 2s. blue & purple on blue 12·00 12·00
88. 5s. green & red on yellow 42·00 55·00
83. 10s. green & red on green 70·00 £130

1913.

112 28 ½d. green 45 15
113 1d. red 30 20
114 1d. brown 40 15
115 1½d. red .. .. 1·00 60
116 2d. orange 50 15
117 2d. grey .. .. 2·00 1·75
117a 2½d. blue .. .. 1·00 65
118 2½d. grey .. .. 75 5·00
96 3d. purple on yellow .. 40 85
121 3d. blue .. .. 1·00 5·00
123 4d. black & red on yell 50 3·25
124 5d. purple and green .. 85 3·50
97 6d. purple .. .. 90 6·50
126 6d. black and red .. 1·75 2·50
127 9d. purple and black .. 2·25 6·00
98a 1s. black on green .. 70 4·50
129 1s. brown .. .. 3·00 12·00
99 2s. purple & blue on bl 3·00 8·50
131 2s. 6d. blk & red on bl 6·00 14·00
132 3s. green and violet .. 6·00 24·00
133 5s. green & red on yell 12·00 26·00
101 10s. green & red on grn 42·00 55·00

1916. Optd. **WAR TAX.**

111. 28. 1d. red 15 20

31. Grand Anse Beach.

DESIGNS—VERT. 1½d. Grand Etang. 2½d. St. George's.

32. Badge of the Colony.

1934.

135. 31. ½d. green 15 40
136a. 32. 1d. black and brown 65 35
137a. – 1½d. black and red .. 1·25 55
138. 32. 2d. black and orange 70 40
139. – 2½d. blue 30 30
140. 32. 3d. black and olive .. 35 90
141. – 6d. black and purple 70 1·10
142. – 1s. black and brown 80 2·50
143. – 2s. 6d. black and blue 6·50 15·00
144. – 5s. black and violet .. 26·00 32·00

1935. Silver Jubilee. As T 13 of Antigua.

145. ½d. black and green .. 30 20
146. 1d. blue and grey .. 40 60
147. 1½d. blue and red .. 50 45
148. 1s. grey and purple .. 4·00 8·75

1937. Coronation. As T 2 of Aden.

149. 1d. violet 20 15
150. 1½d. red 20 15
151. 2½d. blue 50 30

35. King George VI.

40. Badge of the Colony.

1937.

152b 35 ½d. brown 10 10

1938. As 1934, but with portrait of King George VI.

153b 31 ½d. green 15 40
154 32 1d. black and brown 20 20
155 – 1½d. black and red 40 10
156 32 2d. black and orange 20 20
157 – 2½d. blue 20 15
158ab 32 3d. black and olive .. 30 70
159 6d. black and purple 45 20
160 1s. black and brown 40 30
161 2s. black and blue .. 7·50 1·00
162 5s. black and violet .. 2·00 1·50
163e 10s. black and red .. 20·00 7·00

1946. Victory. As T 9 of Aden.

164. 1½d. red 10 10
165. 3½d. blue 10 10

1948. Silver Wedding. As T **10/11** of Aden.

166. 1½d. red 10 10
167. 10s. grey .. .. 6·00 12·00

1949. U.P.U. As T **20/23** of Antigua.

168. 5 c. blue 15 10
169. 6 c. olive 25 30
170. 12 c. mauve 25 20
171. 24 c. brown 25 20

41. King George VI.

42. Badge of the Colony.

1951.

172. 41. ½ c. black and brown .. 15 1·00
173. 1 c. black and green .. 15 25
174. 2 c. black and brown .. 15 25
175. 3 c. black and red .. 15 10
176. 4 c. black and orange .. 35 40
177. 5 c. black and violet .. 20 10
178. 6 c. black and olive .. 30 50
179. 7 c. black and blue .. 1·00 10
180. 12 c. black and purple 1·50 30
181. 42. 25 c. black and brown .. 2·25 50
182. 50 c. black and blue .. 3·00 40
183. $1·50 black and orange 7·50 3·00
184. $2·50 slate and red .. 4·75 3·50
No. 184 is larger (24½ × 30½ mm.).

1951. Inauguration of B.W.I. University College. As T 24/25 of Antigua.

185. 22. 3 c. black and red .. 15 10
186. 23. 6 c. black and olive .. 15 10

1951. New Constitution. Optd. **NEW CONSTITUTION 1951.**

187. 41. 3 c. black and red .. 10 10
188. 4 c. black and orange .. 10 10
189. 5 c. black and violet .. 10 10
190. 12 c. black and purple .. 10 15

1953. Coronation. As T 13 of Aden.

191. 3 c. black and red .. 10 10

1953. As T 41, but with portrait of Queen Elizabeth II, and T 42, but Royal Cypher changed.

192. 41. ½ c. black and brown .. 10 10
193. 1 c. black and green .. 10 10
194. 2 c. black and brown .. 20 10
195. 3 c. black and red .. 10 10
196. 4 c. black and orange .. 10 10
197. 5 c. black and violet .. 10 10
198. 6 c. black and olive .. 35 15
199. 7 c. black and blue .. 60 10
200. 12 c. black and purple .. 20 10
220 42. 25 c. black and brown .. 45 15
202. 50 c. black and blue .. 3·75 40
203 $1.50 black and orange 8·00 5·50
204 $2.50 slate and red .. 12·00 3·25
No. 204 is larger (24½ × 30½ mm.).

1958. British Caribbean Federation. As T 28 of Antigua.

205. 3 c. green 15 10
206. 6 c. blue 20 20
207. 12 c. red 30 10

48. Queen Victoria, Queen Elizabeth II, Mail Van and Post Office, St. George's.

1961. Grenada Stamp Centenary.

208. 48. 3 c. red and black .. 10 10
209. – 8 c. blue and orange .. 30 15
210. – 25 c. lake and blue .. 30 15
DESIGNS: (incorporating Queen Victoria and Queen Elizabeth II): 8 c. Flagship of Columbus. 25 c. R.M.S.P. "Solent" and Dakota aircraft.

1963. Freedom from Hunger. As T 28 of Aden.

211. 8 c. green 30 15

1963. Cent of Red Cross. As T 33 of Antigua.

212. 3 c. red and black .. 10 15
213. 25 c. red and blue .. 20 15

1965. Cent of I.T.U. As T 36 of Antigua.

221. 2 c. orange and olive .. 10 10
222. 50 c. yellow and red .. 25 20

1965. I.C.Y. As T 37 of Antigua.

223. 1 c. purple and turquoise .. 10 15
224. 25 c. green and lavender .. 20 15

1966. Churchill Commem. As T 38 of Antigua.

225. 1 c. blue 10 15
226. 3 c. green 10 15
227. 25 c. brown 15 10
228. 35 c. violet 25 10

1966. Royal Visit. As T 39 of Antigua.

229. 3 c. black and blue .. 15 15
230. 35 c. black and mauve .. 40 15

52. Hillsborough, Carriacou.

1966. Multicoloured.

231. 1 c. Type 52 .. .. 10 10
232. 2 c. Bougainvillea .. 10 10
233. 3 c. Flamboyant Plant .. 10 10
234. 5 c. Levera Beach .. 15 10
235. 6 c. Careenage (inscr. "CARENAGE"), St. George's .. 10 10
236. 8 c. Annandale Falls .. 15 10
237. 10 c. Cocoa Pods .. 15 10
238. 12 c. Inner Harbour .. 10 10
239. 15 c. Nutmeg 15 10
240. 25 c. St. George's .. 20 10
241. 35 c. Grand Anse Beach .. 30 10
242. 50 c. Bananas 80 80
243. $1 Badge of the Colony .. 2·75 1·00
244. $2 Queen Elizabeth II .. 3·75 2·25
245. $3 Map of Grenada .. 4·00 4·00
Nos. 243/5 are vert. and larger, 25 × 39 mm.

1966. World Cup Football Championship. As T 40 of Antigua.

246. 5 c. multicoloured .. 10 10
247. 50 c. multicoloured .. 25 20

1966. Inauguration of W.H.O. Headquarters, Geneva. As T 41 of Antigua.

248. 8 c. black, green and blue 10 10
249. 25 c. black, purple & ochre 25 20

1966. 20th Anniv. of U.N.E.S.C.O. As T 54/56 of Antigua.

250. 2 c. multicoloured 10 10
251. 15 c. yellow, violet & orge. 15 10
252. 50 c. black, purple & orge. 30 25

1967. Statehood. Nos. 232/3, 236 and 240. optd. **ASSOCIATED STATEHOOD 1967.**

253 2 c. multicoloured .. 10 15
254 3 c. multicoloured .. 10 10
255 8 c. multicoloured .. 15 10
256 25 c. multicoloured .. 15 15

1967. World Fair, Montreal, Nos. 232, 237, 239 and 243/4 surch., or optd. **expo 67 MONTREAL · CANADA** and emblem only.

257. 1 c. on 15 c. multicoloured 10 15
258. 2 c. multicoloured .. 10 15
259. 3 c. on 10 c. multicoloured 10 15
260. $1 multicoloured .. 30 15
261. $2 multicoloured .. 45 20

1967. Nos. 231/45 optd. **ASSOCIATED STATEHOOD.**

262. 52. 1 c. multicoloured .. 10 10
263. – 2 c. multicoloured .. 10 10
264. – 3 c. multicoloured .. 10 10
265. – 5 c. multicoloured .. 10 10
266. – 6 c. multicoloured .. 10 10
267. – 8 c. multicoloured .. 10 10
268. – 10 c. multicoloured .. 10 10
269. – 12 c. multicoloured .. 10 10
270. – 15 c. multicoloured .. 15 10
271. – 25 c. multicoloured .. 20 10
272. – 35 c. multicoloured .. 55 10
273. – 50 c. multicoloured .. 70 20
274. – $1 multicoloured .. 70 60
275. – $2 multicoloured .. 1·25 2·25
276. – $3 multicoloured .. 2·25 2·50

70. Kennedy and Local Flower.

1968. 50th Birth Anniv. of Pres. Kennedy. Multicoloured.

277. 1 c. Type 70 .. .. 10 15
278. 15 c. Type 70 .. .. 10 10
279. 25 c. Kennedy and Strelitzia 10 10
280. 35 c. Kennedy and Roses 10 10
281. 50 c. As 25 c. 15 15
282. $1 As 35 c. 25 30

73. Scout Bugler.

1968. World Scout Jamboree, Idaho. Mult.

283. 1 c. Type 73 .. .. 10 10
284. 2 c. Scouts camping .. 10 10
285. 3 c. Lord Baden-Powell .. 10 10
286. 35 c. Type 73 .. .. 20 10
287. 50 c. As 2 c. 25 20
288. $1 As 3 c. 40 30

76. " Near Antibes ".

1968. Paintings by Sir Winston Churchill. Multicoloured.

289. 10 c. Type 76 .. .. 10 10
290. 12 c. "The Mediterranean" 10 10
291. 15 c. " St. Jean, Cap Ferrat " 15 10
292. 25 c. Type 76 .. .. 15 10
293. 35 c. As No. 291 .. .. 20 10
294. 50 c. Sir Winston painting 30 25

1968. No. 275 surch.

295 $5 on $2 multicoloured .. 1·50 2·25

1968. "Children Need Milk". Surch. **CHILDREN NEED MILK** and value.

(a) Nos. 244/5.

296. 2 c.+3 c. on $2 multicoloured 10 10
297. 3 c.+3 c. on $3 multicoloured 10 10

(b) Nos. 243/4.

298. 1 c.+3 c. on $1 multicoloured 10 40
299. 2 c.+3 c. on $2 multicoloured .. .. 17·00 38·00

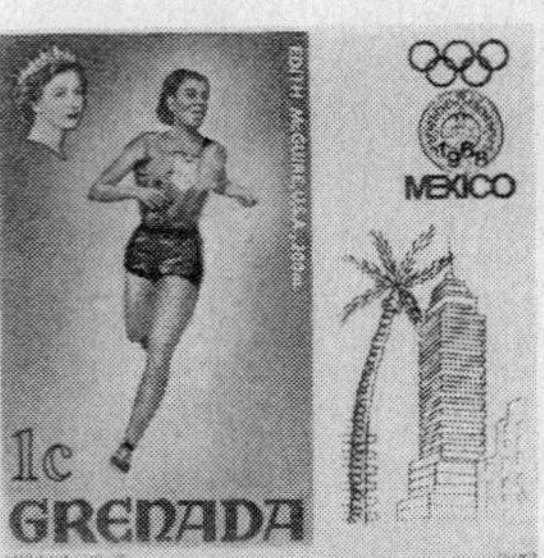

83. Edith McGuire (U.S.A.).

1968. Olympic Games, Mexico.

300. 83. 1 c. brn., blk. and blue .. 10 10
301. – 2 c. multicoloured .. 10 10
302. – 3 c. scarlet, brn. & grn. 10 10
303. 83. 10 c. multicoloured .. 10 10
304. – 50 c. multicoloured .. 25 30
305. – 60 c. red, brn. and orge. 30 35
DESIGNS: 2 c., 50 c. Arthur Wint (Jamaica). 3 c., 60 c. Ferreira de Silva (Brazil).

86. Hibiscus.

102. Kidney Transplant.

1968. Multicoloured.

306 1 c. Type **86** 10 10
307 2 c. Strelitzia 10 10
308 3 c. Bougainvillea 10 10
309 5 c. Rock hind 10 10
310 6 c. Sailfish 10 10
311 8 c. Snapper 10 30
312 10 c. Marine toad 10 10
313 12 c. Turtle 15 10
314 15 c. Tree boa 70 60
314a 15 c. Thunbergia .. 4·25 2·50
315 25 c. Greater Trinidadian murine opossum .. 30 10
316 35 c. Nine-banded armadillo 35 10
317 50 c. Mona monkey .. 45 25
317a 75 c. Yacht in St. Georges Harbour .. .. 8·50 6·50
318 $1 Bananaquit .. .. 2·00 1·50
319 $2 Brown pelican .. 3·00 5·00
320 $3 Magnificent frigate bird .. .. 4·00 4·50
321 $5 Bare-eyed thrush .. 4·00 11·00

Nos. 309, 311/12, 314, 316 and 317a. are horiz. Nos. 318/21 are larger (25½ × 48 mm.).

1968. 20th Anniversary of World Health Organization. Multicoloured.

322. 5 c. Type **102** 10 10
323. 25 c. Heart transplant .. 20 10
324. 35 c. Lung transplant .. 20 10
325. 50 c. Eye transplant .. 25 20

106. "The Adoration of the Kings" (Veronese).

1968. Christmas.

326. **106.** 5 c. multicoloured .. 10 10
327. – 15 c. multicoloured .. 10 10
328. – 35 c. multicoloured .. 10 10
329. – $1 multicoloured .. 30 40

DESIGNS: 15 c. "Madonna and Child with Saints John and Catherine" (Titian). 35 c. "The Adoration of the Kings" (Botticelli). $1, "A Warrior adoring" (Catena).

1969. Caribbean Free Trade Area Exhibition. Nos. 300/5 surch. **VISIT CARIFTA EXPO '69 APRIL 5-30** and value.

330. **83.** 5 c. on 1 c. 10 10
331. – 8 c. on 2 c. 10 10
332. – 25 c. on 3 c. 10 10
333. **83.** 35 c. on 10 c. 10 10
334. – $1 on 50 c. 20 25
335. – $2 on 60 c. 35 40

111. Dame Hylda Bynoe (Governor) and Island Scene.

1969. Carifta Expo '69. Multicoloured.

336. 5 c. Type **111** 10 10
337. 15 c. Premier E. M. Gairy and Island scene .. 10 10
338. 50 c. Type **111** .. 10 15
339. 60 c. Emblems of 1958 and 1967 World Fairs .. 10 20

114. Dame Hylda Bynoe.

1969. Human Rights Year. Multicoloured

340. 5 c. Type **114** .. 10 10
341. 25 c. Dr. Martin Luther King 10 10
342. 35 c. As 5 c. 10 10
343. $1 "Balshazzar's Feast" (Rembrandt) (horiz.) .. 20 25

117. Batsman and Wicket Keeper.

1969. Cricket.

344. **117.** 3 c. yell., brn. and blue 25 35
345. – 10 c. multicoloured .. 30 15
346. – 25 c. brn., ochre & grn. 60 50
347. – 35 c. multicoloured .. 80 65

DESIGNS: 10 c. Batsman playing defensive stroke. 25 c. Batsman sweeping ball. 35 c. Batsman playing on-drive.

129. Astronaut handling Moon Rock.

1969. 1st Man on the Moon. Multicoloured.

348. ½ c. Astronaut handling Moon Rock (different) .. 10 10
349. 1 c. Moon rocket en-route to the moon .. 10 10
350. 2 c. Space Module landing on moon 10 10
351. 3 c. Declaration left on the moon by astronauts .. 10 10
352. 8 c. Module separating from Space Ship 10 10
353. 25 c. Spacecraft after lift-off 15 10
354. 35 c. Spacecraft in orbit .. 15 10
355. 50 c. Final descent of Space Module 20 10
356. $1 Type **129** 35 30

The ½ c. is larger (56 × 36 mm.), and has a different frame design than Type **129**.
The 25, 35 and 50 c. are vert.

130. Gandhi. (Reduced size illustration—actual size 54 × 30½ mm.).

1969. Birth Cent. of Mahatma Gandhi. Mult.

358. 6 c. Type **130** 15 10
359. 15 c. Gandhi (standing) .. 20 10
360. 25 c. Gandhi (walking) .. 30 10
361. $1 Head of Gandhi .. 1·00 60

1969. Christmas. Nos. 326/9 optd. **1969** and surch. (No. 363).

363. – 2 c. on 15 c. multicoloured 10 10
364. **106.** 5 c. multicoloured .. 10 10
365. – 35 c. multicoloured .. 10 10
366. – $1 multicoloured .. 35 70

135. "Blackbeard" (Edward Teach).

1970. Pirates.

367. **135.** 15 c. black 35 10
368. – 25 c. green 50 10
369. – 50 c. lilac 90 20
370. – $1 carmine .. 1·50 75

DESIGNS: 25 c. Anne Bonney. 50 c. Jean Lafitte. $1, Mary Read.

1970. No. 348 surch.

371 5 c. on ½ c. multicoloured 10 10

141/2. "The Last Supper" (detail, Del Sarto). (Illustration reduced. Actual size 64 × 45 mm.).

1970. Easter. Paintings.

372. **141.** 5 c. multicoloured .. 10 10
373. **142.** 5 c. multicoloured .. 10 10
374. – 15 c. multicoloured .. 15 10
375. – 15 c. multicoloured .. 15 10
376. – 25 c. multicoloured .. 20 10
377. – 25 c. multicoloured .. 20 10
378. – 60 c. multicoloured .. 25 30
379. – 60 c. multicoloured .. 25 30

DESIGNS: 15 c. "Christ crowned with Thorns" (detail—Van Dyck). 25 c. "The Passion of Christ" (detail—Memling). 60 c. "Christ in the Tomb" (detail—Rubens).

Each value was issued in sheets containing the two stamps se-tenant. Each design is spread over two stamps as in Type **141/2**.

149. Girl with Kittens in Pram. (Illustration reduced. Actual size 59 × 34 mm.)

1970. Birth Bicentenary of Wordsworth. "Children and Pets". Multicoloured.

381. 5 c. Type **149** 15 10
382. 15 c. Girl with puppy and kitten 20 10
383. 30 c. Boy with fishing-rod and cat 35 15
384. 60 c. Boys and girls with cats and dogs 55 30

153. Parliament of India.

1970. Commonwealth Parliamentary Assn. 7th Regional Conf. Stamps showing Parliaments country given. Multicoloured.

386. 5 c. Type **153** .. 10 10
387. 25 c. Great Britain, Westminster 10 10
388. 50 c. Canada 15 15
389. 60 c. Grenada 15 15

157. Tower of the Sun.

1970. World Fair, Osaka. Multicoloured.

391. 1 c. Type **157** 10 10
392. 2 c. Livelihood and Industry Pavilion .. 10 10
393. 3 c. Flower Painting (1634) 10 10
394. 10 c. "Adam and Eve" (Tintoretto) 15 10
395. 25 c. Organization For Economic Co-operation and Development (O.E.C.D.) Pavilion 35 20
396. 50 c. San Francisco Pavilion 60 20

164. Roosevelt and "Raising U.S. Flag on Iwo Jima". (Illustration reduced. Actual size 60 × 35 mm.).

1970. 25th Anniv. of Ending of World War Two. Multicoloured.

398. ½ c. Type **164** 10 10
399. 5 c. Zhukov and "Fall of Berlin" 30 15
400. 15 c. Churchill and "Evacuation at Dunkirk" .. 60 25
401. 25 c. De Gaulle and "Liberation of Paris" .. 90 45
402. 50 c. Eisenhower and "D-Day Landing" .. 1·25 90
403. 60 c. Montgomery and "Battle of Alamein" .. 1·50 1·75

1970. "Philympia 1970" Stamp Exhibition, London. Nos. 353/6 optd. **PHILYMPIA LONDON 1970.**

405. – 25 c. multicoloured .. 10 10
406. – 35 c. multicoloured .. 10 10
407. – 50 c. multicoloured .. 15 15
408. **129.** $1 multicoloured .. 20 30

170. U.P.U. Emblem, Building and Transport.

1970. U.P.U. Headquarters Building. Mult.

409. 15 c. Type **170** 15 10
410. 25 c. As Type **170**, but modern transport .. 20 10
411. 50 c. Sir Rowland Hill and U.P.U. Building .. 30 15
412. $1 Abraham Lincoln and U.P.U. Building .. 55 50

The 50 c. and $1 are both vert.

171. "The Madonna of the Goldfinch" (Tiepolo).

1970. Christmas. Multicoloured.

414. ½ c. Type **171** 10 10
415. ½ c. "The Virgin and Child with St. Peter and St. Paul" (Bouts) 10 10
416. ½ c. "The Virgin and the Child" (Bellini) 10 10
417. 2 c. "The Madonna of the Basket" (Correggio) .. 10 10
418. 3 c. Type **171** 10 10
419. 35 c. As No. 415 .. .. 30 10
420. 50 c. As 2 c. 45 15
421. $1 As No. 416 .. .. 75 35

172. 19th-Century Nursing.

1970. Cent. of British Red Cross. Multicoloured.

423. 5 c. Type **172** 10 10
424. 15 c. Military Ambulance, 1918 .. .. 20 10
425. 25 c. First-Aid Post, 1941 35 10
426. 60 c. Red Cross Transport, 1970 .. .. 80 60

173. John Dewey and Art Lesson.

1971. Int. Education Year. Multicoloured.
428. 5 c. Type **173** 10 10
429. 10 c. Jean-Jacques Rousseau and "Alphabetisation" .. 15 10
430. 50 c. Maimonides and laboratory .. 50 15
431. $1 Bertrand Russell and mathematics class .. 95 40

174. Jennifer Hosten and outline of Grenada.

1971. Winner of "Miss World" Competition (1970).
433. **174.** 5 c. multicoloured .. 10 10
434. 10 c. multicoloured .. 15 10
435. 15 c. multicoloured .. 15 10
436. 25 c. multicoloured .. 15 10
437. 35 c. multicoloured .. 20 10
438. 50 c. multicoloured .. 45 55

175. French and Canadian Scouts.

1971. 13th World Scout Jamboree, Asagiri, Japan. Multicoloured.
440. 5 c. Type **175** 10 10
441. 35 c. German and American scouts 30 25
442. 50 c. Australian and Japanese scouts 50 50
443. 75 c. Grenada and British scouts 65 75

176. " Napoleon reviewing the Guard ". (E. Detaille).

1971. 150th Death Anniversary of Napoleon Bonaparte. Paintings. Multicoloured.
445. 5 c. Type **176** 15 15
446. 15 c. " Napoleon before Madrid " (Vernet) .. 25 15
447. 35 c. " Napoleon crossing Mt. St. Bernard " (David) 30 15
448. $2 " Napoleon in his study " (David) .. 1·25 1·75

177. 1d. Stamp of 1861 and Badge of Grenada. (Illustration reduced. Actual size 59 × 34 mm.)

1971. 110th Anniv. of the Postal Service. Multicoloured.
450. 5 c. Type **177** 10 15
451. 15 c. 6d. stamp of 1861 and Queen Elizabeth II .. 15 15
452. 35 c. 1d. and 6d. stamps of 1861 and badge of Grenada 30 20
453. 50 c. Scroll and 1d. stamp of 1861 .. .. .. 45 70

178. Apollo splashdown. (Illustration reduced. Actual size 58 × 35 mm.)

1971. Apollo Moon Exploration Series. Multicoloured.
455. 1 c. Type **178** 10 10
456. 2 c. Recovery of "Apollo 13" 10 10
457. 3 c. Separation of Lunar Module from "Apollo 14" 10 10
458. 10 c. Shepard and Mitchell taking samples of moon rock 20 10
459. 25 c. Moon Buggy 55 20
460. $1 "Apollo 15" blast-off (vert.) .. .. .. 1·75 1·50

179. 67th Regt. of Foot, 1787.

1971. Military Uniforms. Multicoloured.
462. ½ c. Type **179** 10 10
463. 1 c. 45th Regt. of Foot, 1792 10 10
464. 2 c. 29th Regt. of Foot, 1794 10 10
465. 10 c. 9th Regt. of Foot, 1801 45 20
466. 25 c. 2nd Regt. of Foot, 1815 85 35
467. $1 70th Regt. of Foot, 1764 2·25 2·00

180. "The Adoration of the Kings" (Memling).

1972. Christmas (1971). Multicoloured.
469. 15 c. Type **180** 10 10
470. 25 c. "Madonna and Child" (Michelangelo) 20 10
471. 35 c. "Madonna and Child" (Murillo) 25 10
472. 50 c. "The Virgin with the Apple" (Memling) .. 30 40

1972. Winter Olympic Games, Sapporo, Japan. Nos. 462/4 surch. **WINTER OLYMPICS FEB. 3-13, 1972 SAPPORO, JAPAN.** Olympic rings and premium. Nos. 476/7 additionally surch. **AIR MAIL.**
474. $2 on 2 c. multicoloured (postage) 60 90
476. 35 c. on ½ c. multicoloured (air) 20 25
477. 50 c. on 1 c. multicoloured 25 35

1972. General Election. Nos. 307/8, 310 and 315 optd. **VOTE FEB. 28 1972.**
478. 2 c. multicoloured .. 10 10
479. 3 c. multicoloured .. 10 10
480. 6 c. multicoloured .. 10 15
481. 25 c. multicoloured .. 15 30

183. King Arthur.

1972. U.N.I.C.E.F. Multicoloured.
482. ½ c. Type **183** 10 10
483. 1 c. Robin Hood 10 10
484. 2 c. Robinson Crusoe (vert.) 10 10
485. 25 c. Type **183** 10 10
486. 50 c. As 1 c. 25 35
487. 75 c. As 2 c. 30 50
488. $1 Mary and her little lamb (vert.) 45 70

1972. "Interpex" Stamp Exhib., New York. Nos. 433/8 optd. **INTERPEX 1972.**
490. **174.** 5 c. multicoloured .. 10 10
491. 10 c. multicoloured .. 10 10
492. 15 c. multicoloured .. 10 10
493. 25 c. multicoloured .. 10 10
494. 35 c. multicoloured .. 15 15
495. 50 c. multicoloured .. 25 30

1972. Nos. 306/8 and 433 surch.
497. – 12 c. on 1 c. multicoloured 30 45
498. – 12 c. on 2 c. multicoloured 30 45
499. – 12 c. on 3 c. multicoloured 30 45
500. **174.** 12 c. on 5 c. multicoloured 30 45

1972. Air. Optd. **AIR MAIL** or surch. in addition.
501. – 5 c. mult. (No. 309) .. 10 10
518. **175.** 5 c. multicoloured .. 30 10
502. – 8 c. mult. (No. 311) .. 15 10
503. – 10 c. mult. (No. 312) .. 15 10
504. – 15 c. mult. (No. 314a) .. 30 20
505. – 25 c. mult. (No. 315) .. 35 20
506. – 30 c. on 1 c. mult. (No. 306) 40 25
507. – 35 c. mult. (No. 316) .. 45 25
519. – 35 c. mult. (No. 441) .. 80 30
508. – 40 c. on 2 c. mult. (No. 307) 50 25
509. – 45 c. on 3 c. mult. (No. 308) 55 35
510. – 50 c. mult. (No. 317) .. 55 35
520. – 50 c. mult. (No. 442) .. 1·00 45
511. – 60 c. on 5 c. mult. (No. 309) 60 40
512. – 70 c. on 6 c. mult. (No. 310) 70 50
521. – 75 c. mult. (No. 443) .. 1·50 70
513. – $1 mult. (No. 318) .. 3·00 60
514. – $1·35 on 8 c. mult. (No. 311) .. .. 3·00 1·25
515. – $2 mult. (No. 319) .. 4·25 3·00
516. – $3 mult. (No. 320) .. 5·00 3·50
517. – $5 mult. (No. 321) .. 6·00 6·50

187. Yachting.

1972. Olympic Games, Munich. Multicoloured.
522. ½ c. Type **187** (postage) .. 10 10
523. 1 c. Show-jumping .. 10 10
524. 2 c. Running (vert. .. 10 10
525. 35 c. As 2 c. 40 20
526. 50 c. As 1 c. 55 40
527. 25 c. Boxing (air) .. 30 15
528. $1 as 25 c. 90 75

1972. Royal Silver Wedding. As T **52** of Ascension, but with Badge of Grenada and Nutmegs in background.
530 8 c. brown 10 10
531. $1 blue 45 55

INDEX

Countries can be quickly located by referring to the index at the end of this volume.

189. Boy Scout Saluting.

1972. 65th Anniv. of Boy Scouts. Mult.
532. ½ c. Type **189** (postage) .. 10 10
533. 1 c. Scouts knotting ropes 10 10
534. 2 c. Scouts shaking hands 10 10
535. 3 c. Lord Baden Powell .. 10 10
536. 75 c. As 2 c. .. .. 1·60 1·40
537. $1 As 3 c. .. .. 1·75 1·90
538. 25 c. Type **189** (air) .. 50 40
539. 25 c. As 1 c. 70 50

190. Madonna and Child.

1972. Christmas. Multicoloured.
541. 1 c. Type **190** 10 10
542. 3 c. The Three Kings .. 10 10
543. 5 c. The Nativity .. 10 10
544. 25 c. Type **190** 15 15
545. 35 c. As 3 c. 20 20
546. $1 As 5 c. 60 60

191. Greater Flamingoes.

1973. National Zoo. Multicoloured.
548. 25 c. Type **191** 70 35
549. 35 c. Brazilian tapir .. 80 45
550. 60 c. Blue and yellow macaws .. .. 1·40 1·00
551. 70 c. Ocelot .. .. 1·50 1·25

192. Class II Racing Yacht.

1973. World Yachting Centre. Multicoloured.
552. 25 c. Type **192** .. 35 15
553. 35 c. Harbour, St. George's 40 15
554. 60 c. Yacht " Bloodhound" 55 55
555. 70 c. St. George's .. 70 75

193. Helios (Greek god) and Earth orbiting the Sun.

1973. Centenary of I.M.O./W.M.O. Greek Gods. Multicoloured.
556. ½ c. Type **193** 10 10
557. 1 c. Poseidon and "Normad" 10 10
558. 2 c. Zeus and radarscope .. 10 10
559. 3 c. Iris and weather balloon 10 10
560. 35 c. Hermes and "ATS-3" satellite 40 10
561. 50 c. Zephyrus and diagram of pressure zones .. 55 25
562. 75 c. Demeter and space photo 75 50
563. $1 Selene and rainfall diagram 80 80

194. Racing Class Yachts.

1973. Carriacou Regatta. Multicoloured.

565.	½c. Type **194**	10	10
566.	1 c. Cruising Class Yacht	10	10
567.	2 c. Open-decked sloops	10	10
568.	35 c. "Mermaid" (sloop)	35	20
569.	50 c. St. George's Harbour	50	35
570.	75 c. Map of Carriacou	70	60
571.	$1 Boat-building	90	80

195. Ignatius Semmelweis (obstetrician).

1973. 25th Anniv. of W.H.O. Multicoloured.

573.	½ c. Type **195**	10	10
574.	1 c. Louis Pasteur	10	10
575.	2 c. Edward Jenner	10	10
576.	3 c. Sigmund Freud	10	10
577.	25 c. Emil Von Behring (bacteriologist)	55	10
578.	35 c. Carl Jung	65	20
579.	50 c. Charles Calmette (bacteriologist)	90	30
580.	$1 William Harvey	1·25	75

196. Princess Anne and Capt. Mark Phillips.

1973. Royal Wedding.

582.**196.**	25 c. multicoloured	10	10
583.	$2 multicoloured	45	55

197. "Virgin and Child" (Maratti).

1973. Christmas. Multicoloured.

585.	½ c. Type **197**	10	10
586.	1 c. "Madonna and Child" (Crivelli)	10	10
587.	2 c. "Virgin and Child with two Angels" (Verrocchio)	10	10
588.	3 c. "Adoration of the Shepherds" (Roberti)	10	10
589.	25 c. "The Holy Family with the Infant Baptist" (Baroccio)	15	10
590.	35 c. "The Holy Family" (Bronzino)	20	10
591.	77 c. "Mystic Nativity" (Botticelli)	30	20
592.	$1 "Adoration of the Kings" (Geertgen)	40	30

1974. Independence. Nos. 306/9, 311/13, 315/16 and 317*a*/21 optd. with **INDEPENDENCE 7TH FEB. 1974.**

594. **86.**	1 c. multicoloured	10	10
595. –	2 c. multicoloured	10	10
596. –	3 c. multicoloured	10	10
597. –	5 c. multicoloured	10	10
598. –	8 c. multicoloured	15	10
599. –	10 c. multicoloured	20	15
600. –	12 c. multicoloured	20	15
601. –	25 c. multicoloured	45	35
602. –	35 c. multicoloured	75	50
603. –	75 c. multicoloured	2·00	1·25
604. –	$1 multicoloured	3·75	1·50
605. –	$2 multicoloured	6·00	3·50
606. –	$3 multicoloured	10·00	5·00
607. –	$5 multicoloured	15·00	9·50

199. Creative Arts Theatre, Jamaica Campus.

1974. 25th Anniv. of University of West Indies. Multicoloured.

608.	10 c. Type **199**	10	10
609.	25 c. Marryshow House	10	10
610.	50 c. Chapel, Jamaica Campus (vert.)	20	10
611.	$1 University arms (vert.)	30	30

200. Nutmeg Pods and Scarlet Mace.

1974. Independence. Multicoloured.

613.	3 c. Type **200**	10	10
614.	8 c. Map of Grenada	10	10
615.	25 c. Prime Minister Eric Gairy	15	10
616.	35 c. Grand Anse beach and flag	15	10
617.	$1 Coat of arms	35	40

201. Footballers (West Germany v. Chile).

1974. World Cup Football Championships, West Germany. Multicoloured.

619.	½ c. Type **201**	10	10
620.	1 c. East Germany v. Australia	10	10
621.	2 c. Yugoslavia v. Brazil	10	10
622.	10 c. Scotland v. Zaire	10	10
623.	25 c. Netherlands v. Uruguay	15	10
624.	50 c. Sweden v. Bulgaria	20	10
625.	75 c. Italy v. Haiti	35	15
626.	$1 Poland v. Argentina	50	25

202. Early U.S. Mail-trains and "Concorde".

1974. Centenary of U.P.U. Multicoloured.

628.	½ c. Type **202**	10	10
629.	1 c. Mailboat "Caesar" (1839) and helicopter	10	10
630.	2 c. Airmail transport	10	10
631.	8 c. Pigeon post (1480) and telephone dial	15	10
632.	15 c. 18th-century bellman and tracking antenna	25	10
633.	25 c. Messenger (1450) and satellite	30	15
634.	35 c. French pillar-box (1850) and mail-boat	65	25
635.	$1 18th-century German postman and mail-train of the future	1·75	1·75

203. Sir Winston Churchill.

1974. Birth Centenary of Sir Winston Churchill.

637. **203.**	35 c. multicoloured	15	10
638.	$2 multicoloured	45	50

204. "Madonna and Child of the Eucharist" (Botticelli).

1974. Christmas. "Madonna and Child" paintings by named artists. Multicoloured.

640.	½ c. Type **204**	10	10
641.	1 c. Niccolo di Pietro	10	10
642.	2 c. Van der Weyden	10	10
643.	3 c. Bastiani	10	10
644.	10 c. Giovanni	10	10
645.	25 c. Van der Weyden	15	10
646.	50 c. Botticelli	25	20
647.	$1 Mantegna	45	50

205. Yachts, Point Saline.

1975. Multicoloured.

649.	½ c. Type **205**	10	10
650.	1 c. Yacht Club race, St. George's	10	10
651.	2 c. Carenage taxi	10	10
652.	3 c. Large working boats	10	10
653.	5 c. Deep-water dock, St. George's	10	10
654.	6 c. Cocoa beans in drying trays	10	10
655.	8 c. Nutmegs	10	10
656.	10 c. Rum distillery, River Antoine Estate, c. 1785	10	10
657.	12 c. Cocoa tree	10	10
658.	15 c. Fishermen at Fontenoy	10	10
659.	20 c. Parliament Building	15	15
660.	25 c. Fort George cannons	20	15
661.	35 c. Pearls Airport	20	15
662.	50 c. General Post Office	25	30
663.	75 c. Caribs Leap, Sauteurs Bay	45	50
664.	$1 Carenage, St. George's	65	70
665.	$2 St. George's harbour by night	1·00	1·50
666.	$3 Grand Anse beach	1·25	2·00
667.	$5 Canoe Bay & Black Bay	1·75	2·75
668.	$10 Sugar-loaf Island	4·50	6·50

Nos. 663/8 are size 45 × 28 mm.

206. Sail-fish.

1975. Big Game Fishing. Multicoloured.

669.	½ c. Type **206**	10	10
670.	1 c. Blue Marlin	10	10
671.	2 c. White Marlin	10	10
672.	10 c. Yellowfin Tuna	10	10
673.	25 c. Wahoo	25	10
674.	50 c. Dolphin	40	15
675.	70 c. Grouper	60	20
676.	$1 Great Barracuda	80	35

207. Granadilla Barbadine.

1975. Flowers. Multicoloured.

678.	½ c. Type **207**	10	10
679.	1 c. Bleeding Heart (Easter Lily)	10	10
680.	2 c. Poinsettia	10	10
681.	3 c. Cocoaflower	10	10
682.	10 c. Gladioli	10	10
683.	25 c. Redhead/Yellowhead	25	10
684.	50 c. Plumbago	45	15
685.	$1 Orange flower	70	25

208. Dove, Grenada Flag and U.N. Emblem.

1975. Grenada's Admission to the U.N. (1974). Multicoloured.

687.	½ c. Type **208**	10	10
688.	1 c. Grenada and U.N. flags	10	10
689.	2 c. Grenada coat of arms	10	10
690.	35 c. U.N. emblem over map of Grenada	15	10
691.	50 c. U.N. buildings and flags	20	15
692.	$2 U.N. emblem and scroll	45	45

CANCELLED REMAINDERS*. Some of the following issues have been remaindered, cancelled to order, at a fraction of their face-value. For all practical purposes these are undistinguishable from genuine postally used copies. Our used quotations which are indicated by an asterisk are the same for cancelled-to-order or postally used copies.

209. Paul Revere's Midnight Ride.

1975. Bicentenary of American Revolution. (1st issue). Multicoloured.

694.	½ c. Type **209** (postage)	10	10*
695.	1 c. Crispus Attucks	10	10*
696.	2 c. Patrick Henry	10	10*
697.	3 c. Franklin visits Washington	10	10*
698.	5 c. Rebel troops	10	10*
699.	10 c. John Paul Jones	10	10*
700.	40 c. "John Hancock" (air) (Copley)	30	10*
701.	50 c. "Ben Franklin" (Roslin)	45	15*
702.	75 c. "John Adams" (Copley)	60	15*
703.	$1 "Lafayette" (Casanova)	75	20*

Nos. 700/3 are vert.

See also Nos. 785/91.

210. "Blood of the Redeemer" (G. Bellini).

1975. Easter. Multicoloured.

No.	Description	Unused	Used
705.	½ c. Type **210**	10	10*
706.	1 c. "Pieta" (Bellini)	10	10*
707.	2 c. "The Entombment" (Van der Weyden)	10	10*
708.	3 c. "Pieta" (Bellini)	10	10*
709.	35 c. "Pieta" (Bellini)	30	10*
710.	75 c. "The Dead Christ" (Bellini)	45	10*
711.	$1 "The Dead Christ supported by Angels" (Procaccini)	55	10*

211. Wildlife Study.

1975. 14th World Scout Jamboree, Norway. Multicoloured.

No.	Description	Unused	Used
713.	½ c. Type **211**	10	10*
714.	1 c. Sailing	10	10*
715.	2 c. Map-reading	10	10*
716.	35 c. First-aid	40	10*
717.	40 c. Physical training	45	10*
718.	75 c. Mountaineering	70	10*
719.	$2 Sing-song	1·60	20*

212. Leafy Jewel Box.

1975. Seashells. Multicoloured.

No.	Description	Unused	Used
721.	½ c. Type **212**	10	10*
722.	1 c. Emerald Nerite	10	10*
723.	2 c. Yellow Cockle	10	10*
724.	25 c. Purple Sea Snail	55	10*
725.	50 c. Turkey Wing	1·00	10*
726.	75 c. West Indian Fighting Conch	1·50	10*
727.	$1 Noble Wentletrap	1·75	15*

213. "Lycorea ceres".

1975. Butterflies. Multicoloured.

No.	Description	Unused	Used
729	½ c. Type **213**	10	10*
730	1 c. "Adelpha cytherea"	10	10*
731	2 c. "Atlides polybe"	10	10*
732	35 c. "Anteos maerula"	50	10*
733	45 c. "Parides neophilus"	55	10*
734	75 c. "Nymula orestes"	85	15*
735	$2 "Euptychia cephus"	1·75	20*

214. Rowing.

1975. Pan-American Games, Mexico City. Multicoloured.

No.	Description	Unused	Used
737.	½ c. Type **214**	10	10*
738.	1 c. Swimming	10	10*
739.	2 c. Show-jumping	10	10*
740.	35 c. Gymnastics	15	10*
741.	45 c. Football	15	10*
742.	75 c. Boxing	25	15*
743.	$2 Cycling	65	20*

215. "The Boy David" (Michelangelo).

1975. 500th Birth Anniv. of Michelangelo. Multicoloured.

No.	Description	Unused	Used
745.	½ c. Type **215**	10	10*
746.	1 c. "Young Man" (detail)	10	10*
747.	2 c. "Moses"	10	10*
748.	40 c. "Prophet Zachariah"	20	10*
749.	50 c. "St. John the Baptist"	20	10*
750.	75 c. "Judith and Holofernes"	35	15*
751.	$2 "Doni Madonna" (detail from "Holy Family")	70	20*

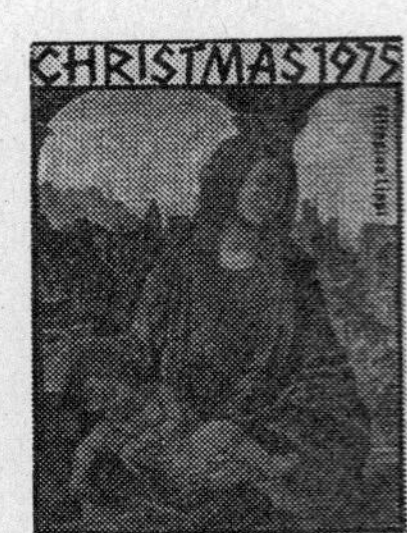

216. "Madonna and Child" (Filippino Lippi).

1975. Christmas. "Virgin and Child" paintings by Artists named. Multicoloured.

No.	Description	Unused	Used
753.	½ c. Type **216**	10	10*
754.	1 c. Mantegna	10	10*
755.	2 c. Luis de Morales	10	10*
756.	35 c. G. M. Morandi	15	10*
757.	50 c. Antonello da Messina	20	10*
758.	75 c. Durer	25	10*
759.	$1 Velasquez	35	10*

217. Bananaquit.

1976. Flora and Fauna. Multicoloured.

No.	Description	Unused	Used
761.	½ c. Type **217**	10	10
762.	1 c. Brazilian Agouti	10	10
763.	2 c. Hawksbill Turtle (horiz.)	10	10
764.	5 c. Dwarf Poinciana	10	10
765.	35 c. Albacore	90	45
766.	40 c. Cardinal's Guard	95	50
767.	$2 Nine-banded Armadillo	3·00	2·25

218. Carnival Time.

1976. Tourism. Multicoloured.

No.	Description	Unused	Used
769.	½ c. Type **218**	10	10
770.	1 c. Scuba diving	10	10
771.	2 c. Cruise Ship "Southward" at St. George's	10	10
772.	35 c. Game fishing	55	20
773.	50 c. St. George's Golf Course	1·50	60
774.	75 c. Tennis	1·75	1·25
775.	$1 Ancient rock carvings at Mount Rich	2·00	1·75

219. "Pieta" (Master of Okolicsno).

1976. Easter. Paintings by Artists named. Multicoloured.

No.	Description	Unused	Used
777.	½ c. Type **219**	10	10
778.	1 c. Correggio	10	10
779.	2 c. Van der Weyden	10	10
780.	3 c. Durer	10	10
781.	35 c. Master of the Holy Spirit	15	10
782.	75 c. Raphael	30	40
783.	$1 Raphael	35	50

220. Sharpshooters.

1976. Bicentenary of American Revolution. (2nd Issue). Multicoloured.

No.	Description	Unused	Used
785.	½ c. Type **220**	10	10
786.	1 c. Defending the Liberty Pole	10	10
787.	2 c. Loading muskets	10	10
788.	35 c. The fight for Liberty	30	15
789.	50 c. Peace Treaty, 1783	50	40
790.	$1 Drummers	1·00	90
791.	$3 Gunboat	2·50	2·50

221. Nature Study.

1976. 50th Anniv. of Girl Guides in Grenada. Multicoloured.

No.	Description	Unused	Used
793.	½ c. Type **221**	10	10
794.	1 c. Campfire cooking	10	10
795.	2 c. First Aid	10	10
796.	50 c. Camping	55	35
797.	75 c. Home economics	85	70
798.	$2 First Aid	2·50	2·50

222. Volleyball.

1976. Olympic Games, Montreal. Mult.

No.	Description	Unused	Used
800.	½ c. Type **222**	10	10
801.	1 c. Cycling	10	10
802.	2 c. Rowing	10	10
803.	35 c. Judo	15	10
804.	45 c. Hockey	20	30
805.	75 c. Gymnastics	35	60
806.	$1 High jump	50	85

223. "Cha-U-Kao at the Moulin Rouge".

1976. 75th Death Anniv. of Toulouse-Lautrec. Multicoloured.

No.	Description	Unused	Used
808.	½ c. Type **223**	10	10
809.	1 c. "Quadrille of the Moulin Rouge"	10	10
810.	2 c. "Profile of a Woman"	10	10
811.	3 c. "Salon in the Rue des Mountains"	10	10
812.	40 c. "The Laundryman"	40	35
813.	50 c. "Marcelle Lender dancing the Bolero"	50	40
814.	$2 "Signor Boileau at the Cafe"	1·25	1·50

1976. West Indian Victory in World Cricket Cup. Nos. 559/60 of Barbados.

No.	Description	Unused	Used
816.	35 c. Map of the Caribbean	1·25	35
817.	$1 The Prudential Cup	2·75	2·75

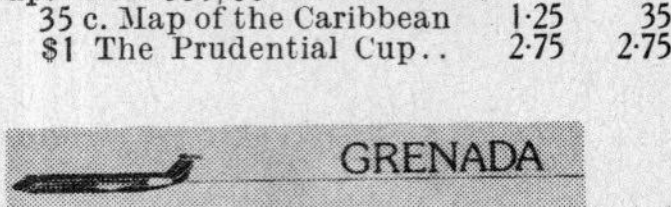

224. Piper "Apache".

1976. Aeroplanes. Multicoloured.

No.	Description	Unused	Used
818.	½ c. Type **224**	10	10
819.	1 c. Beech "Twin Bonanza"	10	10
820.	2 c. D.H. "Twin Otter"	10	20
821.	40 c. Britten Norman "Islander"	70	50
822.	50 c. D.H. "Heron"	75	60
823.	$2 H.S. "748"	2·50	2·75

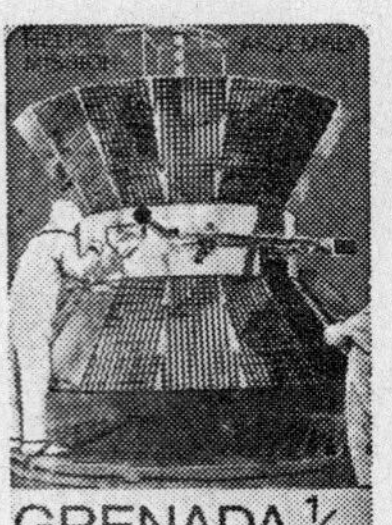

225. Satellite Assembly.

1976. Viking and Helios Space Missions. Multicoloured.

No.	Description	Unused	Used
825.	½ c. Type **225**	10	10
826.	1 c. Helios satellite	10	10
827.	2 c. Helios encapsulation	10	10
828.	15 c. Systems test	10	10
829.	45 c. Viking lander (horiz.)	20	20
830.	75 c. Lander on Mars	35	60
831.	$2 Viking encapsulation	90	1·60

226. S.S. "Geestland".

1976. Ships. Multicoloured.

No.	Description	Unused	Used
833.	½ c. Type **226**	10	10
834.	1 c. M.V. "Federal Palm"	10	10
835.	2 c. H.M.S. "Blake"	10	10
836.	25 c. M.V. "Vistafjord"	35	15
837.	75 c. S.S. "Canberra"	90	80
838.	$1 S.S. "Regina"	1·25	90
839.	$5 S.S. "Arandora Star"	4·50	4·75

227. San Barbara Altarpiece (Botticelli).

1976. Christmas. Multicoloured.

841.	½ c. Type **227**	10	10
842.	1 c. "Annunciation" (Botticelli)	10	10
843.	2 c. "Madonna of Chancellor Rolin" (Jan van Eyck)	10	10
844.	35 c. "Annunciation" (Fra Filippo Lippi) ..	15	10
845.	50 c. "Madonna of the Magnificat" (Botticelli)	20	20
846.	75 c. "Madonna of the Pomegranate" (Botticelli)	30	30
847.	$3 "Madonna with St. Cosmas and other Saints" (Botticelli)	1·00	1·75

228. Alexander Graham Bell and Telephones.

1976. Centenary of First Telephone Transmission. Multicoloured.

849.	½ c. Type **228**	10	10
850.	1 c. Telephone users within globe	10	10
851.	2 c. Telephone satellite ..	10	10
852.	18 c. Telephone viewer and console	15	15
853.	40 c. Satellite and tracking stations	35	45
854.	$1 Satellite transmitting to ships	65	85
855.	$2 Dish aerial and modern telephone	1·10	1·40

229. Coronation Scene.

1977. Silver Jubilee. Multicoloured. (a) Perf.

857.	½ c. Type **229**	10	10
858.	1 c. Sceptre and orb	10	10
859.	35 c. The Queen on horseback	15	10
860.	$2 Spoon and ampulla ..	60	60
861.	$2.50 The Queen and Prince Philip	65	60
	(b) Roul. Self-adhesive.		
863.	35 c. As $2.50	25	25
864.	50 c. As $2	55	70
865.	$1 As 1 c.	1·00	1·50
866.	$3 As 35 c.	2·75	3·75

Nos. 863/6 come from booklets.

230. Water Skiing.

1977. Easter Water Parade. Multicoloured.

867.	½ c. Type **230**	10	10
868.	1 c. Speedboat race ..	10	10
869.	2 c. Row boat race ..	10	10
870.	22 c. Swimming	15	15
871.	35 c. Work Boat race ..	25	20
872.	75 c. Water polo	50	60
873.	$2 Game fishing	1·40	2·00

231. Meeting Place, Grand Anse Beach.

1977. 7th Meeting of Organization of American States.

875. **231.**	35 c. multicoloured ..	10	10
876.	$1 multicoloured ..	25	60
877.	$2 multicoloured ..	40	1·25

232. Rafting.

1977. Caribbean Scout Jamboree, Jamaica. Multicoloured.

878.	½ c. Type **232**	10	10
879.	1 c. Tug-of-war	10	10
880.	2 c. Sea Scouts regatta ..	10	10
881.	18 c. Camp fire	25	15
882.	40 c. Field kitchen ..	50	30
883.	$1 Scouts and sea scouts ..	1·25	1·00
884.	$2 Hiking and map reading	1·75	2·25

233. Angel and Shepherd.

1977. Christmas. Ceiling Panels from Church of St. Martin, Zillis. Multicoloured.

886.	½ c. Type **233**	10	10
887.	1 c. St. Joseph	10	10
888.	2 c. Virgin and Child fleeing to Egypt	10	10
889.	22 c. Angel	10	10
890.	35 c. Magus on horseback	15	10
891.	75 c. Three horses ..	20	30
892.	$2 Virgin and Child ..	50	1·10

1977. Royal Visit. Nos. 857/61 optd. **Royal Visit W.I. 1977.**

894.	½ c. Type **229**	10	10
895.	1 c. Sceptre and Orb ..	10	10
896.	35 c. Queen on horseback	15	10
897.	$2 Spoon and ampulla ..	40	40
898.	$2·50 The Queen and Prince Philip	45	45

235. Christjaan Eijkman (Medicine).

1978. Nobel Prize Winners. Multicoloured.

900.	½ c. Type **235**	10	10
901.	1 c. Sir Winston Churchill (Literature)	10	10
902.	2 c. Woodrow Wilson (Peace)	10	10
903.	35 c. Frederic Passy (Peace)	15	10
904.	$1 Albert Einstein (Physics)	55	40
905.	$3 Carl Bosch (Chemistry)	1·75	1·50

236. Count von Zeppelin and 1st Zeppelin Airship.

1978. 75th Anniv. of 1st Zeppelin Flight and 50th Anniv. of Lindbergh's Transatlantic Flight. Multicoloured.

907.	½ c. Type **236**	10	10
908.	1 c. Lindbergh with "Spirit of St. Louis"	10	10
909.	2 c. Airship "Deutschland"	10	10
910.	22 c. Lindbergh's arrival in France	15	10
911.	75 c. Lindbergh and "Spirit of St. Louis" in flight	40	30
912.	$1 Zeppelin over Alps ..	50	40
913.	$3 Zeppelin over White House	1·25	1·10

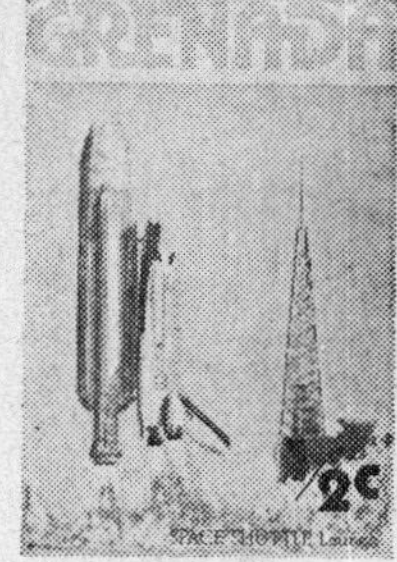

237. Rocket Launching.

1978. Space Shuttle. Multicoloured.

915.	½ c. Type **237**	10	10
916.	1 c. Booster jettison ..	10	10
917.	2 c. External tank jettison	10	10
918.	18 c. Space Shuttle in orbit	15	15
919.	75 c. Satellite placement ..	35	35
920.	$2 Landing approach ..	1·00	1·00

238. Black-headed Gull.

1978. Wild Birds of Grenada. Multicoloured.

922.	½ c. Type **238**	10	10
923.	1 c. Wilson's petrel ..	10	10
924.	2 c. Killdeer	10	10
925.	50 c. White-necked jacobin	1·50	30
926.	75 c. Blue-faced booby ..	2·00	45
927.	$1 Broad-winged hawk ..	3·00	75
928.	$2 Red-necked pigeon ..	4·00	1·75

239. "The landing of Marie de Medici at Marseilles".

1978. 400th Birth Anniv. of Peter Paul Rubens. Multicoloured.

930.	5 c. Type **239**	10	10
931.	15 c. "Rubens and Isabella Brandt"	10	10
932.	18 c. "Marchesa Brigida Spindola-Doria" ..	10	10
933.	25 c. "Ludovicus Nonninus"	10	10
934.	45 c. "Helene Fourment and her Children" ..	15	15
935.	75 c. "Clara Serena Rubens"	25	25
936.	$3 "Le Chapeau de Paille"	60	80

240. Ludwig van Beethoven.

1978. 150th Death Anniv. of Beethoven. Multicoloured.

938.	5 c. Type **240**	10	10
939.	15 c. Woman violinist (horiz.)	15	10
940.	18 c. Musical instruments (horiz.)	20	15
941.	22 c. Piano (horiz.) ..	20	15
942.	50 c. Violins	40	30
943.	75 c. Piano and sonata score	60	45
944.	$3 Beethoven's portrait and home (horiz.) ..	2·25	1·75

241. King Edward's Chair.

1978. 25th Anniv. of Coronation. Mult.

(a) Perf.

946.	35 c. Type **241**	15	10
947.	$2 Queen with regalia ..	50	50
948.	$2.50 St. Edward's Crown	60	50
	(b) Roul. × imperf. Self-adhesive.		
950.	25 c. Queen Elizabeth II taking salute, Trooping the Colour	15	15
951.	35 c. Queen at Maundy Thursday ceremony	15	25
952.	$5 Queen and Prince Philip	2·00	2·75

Nos. 950/2 come from booklets.

243. Goalkeeper reaching for Ball.

1978. World Cup Football Championships, Argentina.

953. **243.**	40 c. multicoloured ..	10	10
954. –	60 c. multicoloured ..	15	20
955. –	90 c. multicoloured ..	25	30
956. –	$2 multicoloured ..	60	60

DESIGNS: 60 c. to $2. Designs similar to Type **243** with goalkeeper reaching for ball.

244. Aerial Phenomena, Germany, 1561 and U.S.A., 1952.

1978. Unidentified Flying Objects Research. Multicoloured.

958.	5 c. Type **244**	15	10
959.	35 c. Various aerial phenomena, 1950	35	25
960.	$3 U.F.O.'s, 1965 ..	2·00	1·75

245. Wright Glider, 1902.

1978. 75th Anniv. of Powered Flight. Mult.

962.	5 c. Type **245**	10	10
963.	15 c. "Flyer I", 1903 ..	10	10
964.	18 c. "Flyer 3"	10	10
965.	22 c. "Flyer 3" from above	15	10
966.	50 c. Orville Wright and "Flyer"	25	20
967.	75 c. "Flyer 3", Pau, France, 1908 ..	35	25
968.	$3 Wilbur Wright and glider	1·10	70

246. Cook and Hawaiian Feast.

1978. 250th Birth Anniv. of Captain James Cook and Bicentenary of Discovery of Hawaii. Multicoloured.

970. 18 c. Type **246** — 55 — 15
971. 35 c. Cook and Hawaiian dance — 75 — 25
972. 75 c. Cook and Honolulu harbour — 1·50 — 1·00
973. $3 Cook's statue and H.M.S. "Resolution" — 3·50 — 3·25

247. "Paumgartner Altarpiece" (detail).

1978. Christmas. Paintings by Durer. Multicoloured.

975. 40 c. Type **247** — 25 — 15
976. 60 c. "The Adoration of the Magi" — 30 — 20
977. 90 c. "Virgin and Child" — 40 — 20
978. $2 "Virgin and Child with St. Anne" (detail) — 75 — 55

248. National Convention and Cultural Centre (interior).

1979. 5th Anniv. of Independence. Mult.

980. 5 c. Type **248** — 10 — 10
981. 18 c. National Convention and Cultural Centre (exterior) — 10 — 10
982. 22 c. Easter Water Parade, 1978 — 10 — 10
983. 35 c. Sir Eric M. Gairy (Prime Minister) — 15 — 10
984. $3 The Cross, Fort Frederick — 60 — 80

249. "Acalypha hispida".

1979. Flowers. Multicoloured.

985. 18 c. Type **249** — 10 — 10
986. 50 c. "Hibiscus rosa sinensis" — 30 — 15
987. $1 "Thunbergia grandiflora" — 55 — 25
988. $3 "Nerium oleander" — 1·60 — 1·10

250. Birds in Flight.

1979. 30th Anniv. of Declaration of Human Rights. Multicoloured.

990. 15 c. Type **250** — 10 — 10
991. $2 Bird in Flight — 55 — 65

251. Children playing Cricket.

1979. International Year of the Child. Multicoloured.

992. 18 c. Type **251** — 20 — 15
993. 22 c. Children playing baseball — 25 — 20
994. $5 Children playing in a tree — 3·75 — 4·50

252. "Around the World in 80 Days".

1979. 150th Birth Anniv. of Jules Verne. Multicoloured.

996. 18 c. Type **252** — 25 — 10
997. 35 c. "20,000 Leagues under the Sea" — 35 — 15
998. 75 c. "From the Earth to the Moon" — 50 — 25
999. $3 "Master of the World" — 1·10 — 80

253. Mail Runner, Africa (early 19th-century).

1979. Death Centenary of Sir Rowland Hill. Multicoloured.

1001. 20 c. Type **253** — 10 — 10
1002. 40 c. Pony Express, America (mid. 19th-century) — 15 — 10
1003. $1 Pigeon post — 35 — 25
1004. $3 Mail coach, Europe (18–19th-century) — 90 — 80

254. "The Pistol of Peace" (vaccination gun), Map of Grenada and Children.

1979. International Year of the Child.

1006. **254.** 5 c. multicoloured — 30 — 20
1007. $1 multicoloured — 1·40 — 1·75

255. Reef Shark.

1979. Marine Wildlife. Multicoloured.

1008. 40 c. Type **255** — 35 — 20
1009. 45 c. Spotted Eagle Ray — 35 — 20
1010. 50 c. Manytooth Conger — 40 — 30
1011. 60 c. Golden Olive — 60 — 35
1012. 70 c. West Indian Murex — 70 — 40
1013. 75 c. Giant Tun — 75 — 40
1014. 90 c. Brown Booby — 1·40 — 60
1015. $1 Magnificent Frigate Bird — 1·50 — 70

256. The Flight into Egypt.

1979. Christmas. Tapestries. Multicoloured.

1017. 6 c. Type **256** — 10 — 10
1018. 25 c. The Flight into Egypt (detail) — 10 — 10
1019. 30 c. Angel (vert.) — 15 — 10
1020. 40 c. Jesus (Doge Marino Grimani) (vert.) — 15 — 15
1021. 90 c. The Annunciation to the Shepherds (vert.) — 40 — 30
1022. $1 The Flight into Egypt (Rome) (vert.) — 45 — 35
1023. $2 The Virgin in Glory (vert.) — 75 — 60

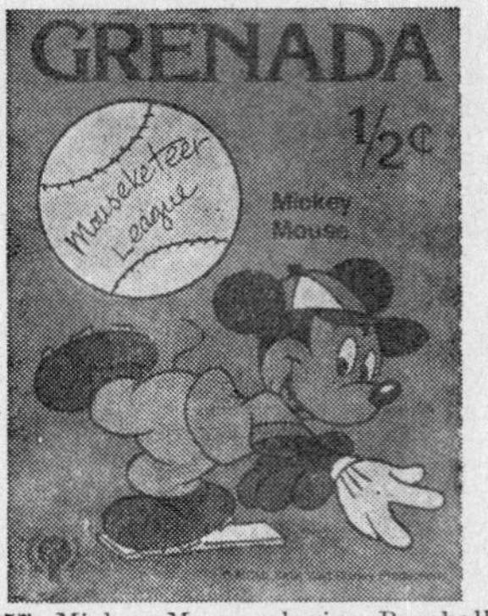

257. Mickey Mouse playing Baseball.

1979. International Year of the Child. Disney Characters. Multicoloured.

1025. ½ c. Type **257** — 10 — 10
1026. 1 c. Donald Duck jumping on springs — 10 — 10
1027. 2 c. Goofy in basketball net — 10 — 10
1028. 3 c. Goofy running down hurdles — 10 — 10
1029. 4 c. Donald Duck playing golf — 10 — 10
1030. 5 c. Mickey Mouse playing cricket — 10 — 10
1031. 10 c. Mickey Mouse playing football — 10 — 10
1032. $2 Mickey Mouse playing tennis — 2·25 — 2·00
1033. $2.50 Minnie Mouse riding horse — 2·25 — 2·00

258. Paul Harris (founder).

1980. 75th Anniv. of Rotary International. Multicoloured.

1035. 6 c. Type **258** — 10 — 10
1036. 30 c. "Health" — 15 — 15
1037. 90 c. "Hunger" — 30 — 30
1038. $2 "Humanity" — 70 — 80

1980. 1st Anniv. of Revolution (1st issue). Nos. 651/2, 654/7, 659/60 and 662/8 optd. **PEOPLE'S REVOLUTION 13TH MARCH 1979.**

1040. 2 c. Carenage taxi — 10 — 10
1041. 3 c. Large working boats — 10 — 10
1042. 6 c. Cocoa beans in drying trays — 10 — 10
1043. 8 c. Nutmegs — 10 — 10
1044. 10 c. Rum distillery, River Antoine Estate, c. 1785 — 10 — 10
1045. 12 c. Cocoa tree — 10 — 10
1046. 20 c. Parliament Building — 10 — 15
1047. 25 c. Fort George Cannons — 30 — 30
1048. 50 c. General Post Office — 30 — 30
1049. 75 c. Carib's Leap, Sauteurs Bay — 50 — 40
1050. $1 Carenage, St. George's — 60 — 60
1051. $2 St. George's Harbour by night — 1·25 — 2·00
1052. $3 Grand Anse beach — 2·00 — 3·25
1053. $5 Canoe Bay and Black Bay — 3·25 — 5·00
1054. $10 Sugar-loaf Island — 4·75 — 7·50

See also Nos. 1065/8.

260. Boxing.

1980. Olympic Games, Moscow. Multicoloured.

1055. 25 c. Type **260** — 10 — 10
1056. 40 c. Cycling — 15 — 10
1057. 90 c. Show-jumping — 20 — 20
1058. $2 Running — 40 — 55

261. Tropical Kingbird.

1980. Wild Birds. Multicoloured.

1060. 20 c. Type **261** — 60 — 15
1061. 40 c. Rufous-breasted Hermit — 75 — 20
1062. $1 Troupial — 1·25 — 1·00
1063. $2 Ruddy Quail Dove — 2·00 — 2·25

1980. "London 1980". International Stamp Exhibition. Nos. 1001/4 optd. **"LONDON 1980".**

1065. **253.** 20 c. Mail runner, Africa — 20 — 20
1066. – 40 c. Pony Express, America — 30 — 30
1067. – $1 Pigeon post — 60 — 60
1068. – $3 Mail coach, Europe — 1·75 — 1·75

263. Free Hot Lunch at Schools.

1980. 1st Anniv. of Revolution (2nd issue). Multicoloured.

1069. 10 c. Type **263** — 10 — 10
1070. 40 c. Canning (agro-industry) — 15 — 20
1071. $1 National Health care — 40 — 45
1072. $2 New housing projects — 75 — 90

264. Jamb Statues, West Portal, Chartres Cathedral.

1980. Famous Works of Art. Multicoloured.

1074. 8 c. Type **264** — 10 — 10
1075. 10 c. "Les Demoiselles d'Avignon" (painting, Picasso) — 10 — 10
1076. 40 c. Winged Victory of Samothrace (statue) — 20 — 20
1077. 50 c. "The Night Watch" (painting, Rembrandt) — 20 — 20
1078. $1 "Portrait of Edward VI as a Child" (painting, Holbein the Younger) — 35 — 45
1079. $3 Portrait head of Queen Nefertiti (carving) — 1·00 — 1·25

265. Carib Canoes.

1980. Shipping. Multicoloured.

1081.	½ c. Type **265**	10	10
1082.	1 c. Boat building	10	10
1083.	2 c. Small working boat	15	10
1084.	4 c. Columbus' "Santa Maria"	30	10
1085.	5 c. West Indiaman barque, c. 1840	30	10
1086.	6 c. R.M.S.P. "Orinoco", c. 1851	30	10
1087.	10 c. Working schooner	30	10
1088.	12 c. Trimaran at Grand Anse anchorage	35	10
1089.	15 c. Spice Island cruising yacht "Petite Amie"	40	10
1090.	20 c. Fishing pirogue	50	10
1091.	25 c. Harbour Police launch	75	15
1092.	30 c. Grand Anse speed-boat	75	20
1093.	40 c. M.V. "Seimstrand"	75	25
1094.	50 c. Three-masted schooner "Ariadne"	50	30
1095.	90 c. M.V. "Geestide"	1·25	50
1096.	$1 M.V. "Cunard Countess"	1·50	70
1097.	$3 Rum-runner	3·25	2·75
1098.	$5 S.S. "Statendam" off St. George's	5·50	5·00
1099.	$10 Coast-guard patrol boat	8·00	8·50

Nos. 1081/99 come with and without date imprint.

1980. Christmas. Scenes from Walt Disney's "Snow White and the Seven Dwarfs". As Type **257**. Multicoloured.

1100.	½ c. Snow White at well	10	10
1101.	1 c. The Wicked Queen	10	10
1102.	2 c. Snow White singing to animals	10	10
1103.	3 c. Snow White doing housework for Dwarfs	10	10
1104.	4 c. The Seven Dwarfs	10	10
1105.	5 c. Snow White with Dwarfs	10	10
1106.	10 c. Witch offering Snow White apple	10	10
1107.	$2.50 Snow White with Prince and Dwarfs	2·75	1·25
1108.	$3 Snow White and Prince	3·25	2·50

1981. 50th Anniv. of Walt Disney's Pluto (cartoon character). As T **257**. Mult.

1110.	$2 Pluto with birthday cake	1·25	1·00

266. Revolution and Grenada Flags. (Illustration reduced. Actual size: 55×28 mm.)

1981. Festival of the Revolution. Mult.

1112.	5 c. Type **266**	10	10
1113.	10 c. Teacher, pupil, book and pencil ("education")	10	10
1114.	15 c. Food processing plant ("industry")	10	10
1115.	25 c. Selection of fruits and farm scene ("agriculture")	15	15
1116.	40 c. Crawfish and boat ("fishing")	20	20
1117.	90 c. "Cunard Countess" arriving at St. George's Harbour ("shipping")	50	50
1118.	$1 Straw-work ("native handicrafts")	60	60
1119.	$3 Map of Caribbean with expanded view of Grenada	1·75	1·75

1981. Easter. Walt Disney Cartoon Characters. As T **257**. Multicoloured.

1120.	35 c. Mickey Mouse and Goofy	25	25
1121.	40 c. Donald Duck, Chip and Daisy Duck	25	25
1122.	$2 Minnie Mouse	1·40	1·25
1123.	$2.50 Pluto and Mickey Mouse	1·60	1·40

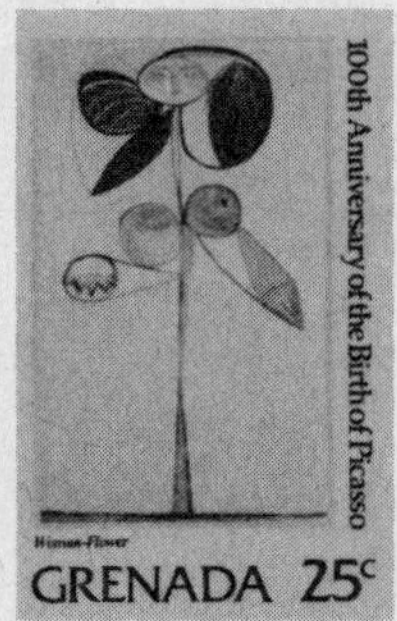

267. "Woman-Flower".

1981. Birth Centenary of Picasso. Mult.

1125.	25 c. Type **267**	15	15
1126.	30 c. "Portrait of Madame"	20	15
1127.	90 c. "Cavalier with Pipe"	45	45
1128.	$4 "Large Heads"	2·00	1·75

268. Prince Charles playing Polo.

1981. Royal Wedding. Multicoloured.

1134.	30 c. Prince Charles and Lady Diana Spencer	20	20
1135.	40 c. Holyrood House	30	30
1130.	50 c. As 30 c.	30	30
1131.	$2 As 40 c.	1·00	1·10
1132.	$4 Type **268**	1·75	2·25

269. Lady Diana Spencer.

1981. Royal Wedding. Booklet stamps. Multicoloured. Self-adhesive.

1136.	$1 Type **269**	50	65
1137.	$2 Prince Charles	75	1·00
1138.	$5 Prince Charles and Lady Diana Spencer	2·00	2·50

270. "The Bath" (Mary Cassatt).

1981. "Decade for Women". Paintings. Multicoloured.

1139.	15 c. Type **270**	10	10
1140.	40 c. "Mademoiselle Charlotte du Val d'Ognes" (Constance Marie Charpentier)	25	20
1141.	60 c. "Self-portrait" (Mary Beale)	40	30
1142.	$3 "Woman in White Stockings" (Suzanne Valadon)	1·50	1·25

1981. Christmas. Horiz. designs as T **257** showing scenes from Walt Disney's cartoon film "Cinderella".

1144.	½ c. multicoloured	10	10
1145.	1 c. multicoloured	10	10
1146.	2 c. multicoloured	10	10
1147.	3 c. multicoloured	10	10
1148.	4 c. multicoloured	10	10
1149.	5 c. multicoloured	10	10
1150.	10 c. multicoloured	10	10
1151.	$2.50 multicoloured	2·75	1·50
1152.	$3 multicoloured	3·00	1·75

271. Landing.

1981. Space Shuttle Project. Multicoloured.

1154.	30 c. Type **271**	20	15
1155.	60 c. Working in space	40	30
1156.	70 c. Lift off	45	35
1157.	$3 Separation	1·40	1·25

272. West German Footballer and Flag.

1981. World Cup Football Championship, Spain (1982). Multicoloured.

1159.	25 c.+10 c. Type **272**	55	30
1160.	40 c.+20 c. Argentinian footballer and flag	70	40
1161.	50 c.+25 c. Brazilian footballer and flag	80	50
1162.	$1+50 c. English footballer and flag	1·25	95

273. General Post Office, St. Georges.

1981. Centenary of U.P.U. Membership. Multicoloured.

1164.	25 c. Type **273**	20	15
1165.	30 c. 1861 1d. stamp	25	20
1166.	90 c. New U.P.U. Headquarters Building 25 c. commemoratives	75	50
1167.	$4 1961 Stamp Centenary 25 c. commemorative	2·25	2·00

274. Artist without Hands.

1982. International Year for the Disabled (1981). Multicoloured.

1169.	30 c. Type **274**	55	15
1170.	40 c. Computer operator without hands	60	20
1171.	70 c. Blind schoolteacher teaching braille	85	35
1172.	$3 Midget playing drums	2·40	1·40

275. Tending Vegetable Patch.

1982. 75th Anniv. of Boy Scout Movement and 125th Birth Anniv. of Lord Baden-Powell. Multicoloured.

1174.	70 c. Type **275**	50	45
1175.	90 c. Map reading	55	50
1176.	$1 Bee keeping	65	60
1177.	$4 Hospital reading	2·25	2·25

276. "Dryas julia".

1982. Butterflies. Multicoloured.

1179	10 c. Type **276**	75	20
1180	60 c. "Phoebis agarithe"	2·00	60
1181	$1 "Anartia amathea"	2·50	1·25
1182	$3 "Battis polydamas"	4·00	4·50

277. "Saying Grace".

1982. Norman Rockwell (painter) Commemoration. Multicoloured.

1184.	15 c. Type **277**	30	10
1185.	30 c. "Card Tricks"	50	15
1186.	60 c. "Pharmacist"	80	25
1187.	70 c. "Pals"	85	35

278. Kensington Palace.

1982. 21st Birthday of Princess of Wales. Multicoloured.

1188.	50 c. Type **278**	35	35
1189.	60 c. Type **278**	40	35
1190.	$1 Prince and Princess of Wales	80	75
1191.	$2 As $1	1·25	1·00
1192.	$3 Princess of Wales	1·75	2·00
1193.	$4 As $3	2·00	2·00

279. Mary McLeod Bethune appointed Director of Negro Affairs, 1942.

1982. Birth Centenary of Franklin D. Roosevelt. Multicoloured.

1195.	10 c. Type **279**	10	10
1196.	60 c. Huddie Ledbetter "Leadbelly" in concert (Works Progress administration)	35	30
1197.	$1.10 Signing bill No. 8802, 1941 (Fair employment committee)	65	55
1198.	$3 Farm Security administration	1·40	1·25

1982. Birth of Prince William of Wales Nos. 1188/93 optd. **ROYAL BABY 21.6.82.**

1200.	50 c. Type **278**	25	30
1201.	60 c. Type **278**	30	35
1202.	$1 Prince and Princess of Wales	50	55
1203.	$2 As $1	95	1·00
1204.	$3 Princess of Wales	1·60	1·75
1205.	$4 As $3	1·75	1·90

280. Apostle and Tormentor.

1982. Easter. Details from Painting "The Way to Calvary" (Raphael). Multicoloured.

1207.	40 c. Type **280**	50	20
1208.	70 c. Captain of the guards (vert.)	75	35
1209.	$1.10 Christ and apostle (vert.)	1·00	45
1210.	$4 Mourners (vert.)	2·75	1·75

HAVE YOU READ THE NOTES AT THE BEGINNING OF THIS CATALOGUE?
These often provide answers to the enquiries we receive.

281. "Orient Express".

1982. Famous Trains of the World. Mult.

1212. 30 c. Type **281** 60 20
1213. 60 c. "Trans-Siberian Express" 80 35
1214. 70 c. "Golden Arrow" 1·00 45
1215. 90 c. "Flying Scotsman" 1·25 55
1216. $1 German Federal Railways 1·50 1·00
1217. $3 German National Railways 3·00 3·00

282. Footballers.

1982. World Cup Football Championship Winners.

1219. **282.** 60 c. multicoloured 35 35
1220. $4 multicoloured 2·00 2·00

1982. Christmas. Scenes from Walt Disney's cartoon film "Robin Hood". As T **257**, but horiz.

1222. ½ c. multicoloured 10 10
1223. 1 c. multicoloured 10 10
1224. 2 c. multicoloured 10 10
1225. 3 c. multicoloured 10 10
1226. 4 c. multicoloured 10 10
1227. 5 c. multicoloured 10 10
1228. 10 c. multicoloured 10 10
1229. $2.50 multicoloured 1·25 1·00
1230. $3 multicoloured 1·40 1·25

283. Killer Whale.

1983. Save the Whales. Multicoloured.

1232. 15 c. Type **283** 75 20
1233. 40 c. Sperm Whale 1·50 45
1234. 70 c. Blue Whale 2·25 1·75
1235. $3 Common Dolphin 3·25 4·00

284. Construction of Ark.

1983. 500th Birth Anniv. of Raphael. Mult.

1237. 25 c. Type **284** 15 15
1238. 30 c. Jacob's vision 15 20
1239. 90 c. Joseph interprets the dreams of his brothers 40 45
1240. $4 Joseph interprets Pharaoh's dreams 1·90 2·00

285. Dentistry, Health Centre.

1983. Commonwealth Day. Multicoloured.

1242. 10 c. Type **285** 10 10
1243. 70 c. Airport runway construction 35 35
1244. $1.10 Tourism 55 55
1245. $3 Boat-building 1·40 1·40

286. Maritime Communications via Satellite.

1983. World Communications Year. Mult.

1246. 30 c. Type **286** 15 15
1247. 40 c. Rural telephone installation 20 20
1248. $2.50 Satellite weather map 1·25 1·25
1249. $3 Airport control room 1·40 1·40

287. Franklin Sport Sedan, 1928.

1983. 75th Anniv. of Model "T" Ford Car. Multicoloured.

1251. 6 c. Type **287** 10 10
1252. 10 c. Delage "D8", 1933 10 10
1253. 40 c. Alvis, 1938 20 25
1254. 60 c. Invicta "S-type" tourer, 1931 30 35
1255. 70 c. Alfa-Romeo "1750 Gran Sport", 1930 35 40
1256. 90 c. Isotta Fraschini, 1930 40 45
1257. $1 Bugatti Royale Type "41" 45 50
1258. $2 B.M.W. "328", 1938 95 1·00
1259. $3 Marmon "V 16", 1931 1·40 1·50
1260. $4 Lincoln "K 8" saloon, 1932 1·90 2·00

288. "Norge" (airship).

1983. Bicentenary of Manned Flight. Mult.

1262. 30 c. Type **288** 50 20
1263. 60 c. Gloster "VI" seaplane 70 45
1264. $1.10 Curtiss "NC-4" flying boat 1·25 1·00
1265. $4 Dornier "Do 18" flying boat 3·00 2·75

289. Morty.

1983. Christmas. Multicoloured.

1267. ½ c. Type **289** 10 10
1268. 1 c. Ludwig von Drake 10 10
1269. 2 c. Gyro Gearloose 10 10
1270. 3 c. Pluto and Figaro 10 10
1271. 4 c. Morty and Ferdie 10 10
1272. 5 c. Mickey Mouse and Goofy 10 10
1273. 10 c. Chip'n Dale 10 10
1274. $2.50 Mickey and Minnie Mouse 2·50 2·00
1275. $3 Donald and Grandma Duck 2·75 2·25

Nos. 1267/75 show Disney cartoon characters in scenes from "It's beginning to look a lot like Christmas" (song).

290. Daisy Duck on Pommel Horse.

1984. Olympic Games, Los Angeles. Mult.
A. Inscr "1984 LOS ANGELES"
B. Inscr "1984 OLYMPICS LOS ANGELES" and Olympic emblem

		A		B	
1277.	½ c. Type **290**	10	10	10	10
1278.	1 c. Mickey Mouse boxing	10	10	10	10
1279.	2 c. Daisy Duck in archery event	10	10	10	10
1280.	3 c. Clarabelle Cow on uneven bars	10	10	10	10
1281.	4 c. Mickey and Minnie Mouse in hurdles race	10	10	10	10
1282.	5 c. Donald Duck with Chip'n'Dale weightlifting	10	10	10	10
1283.	$1 Little Hiawatha in single kayak	90	70	90	70
1284.	$2 The Tortoise and the Hare in marathon	1·50	1·25	1·50	1·25
1285.	$3 Mickey Mouse polevaulting	2·00	1·75	2·00	1·75

291. William I.

1984. English Monarchs. Multicoloured.

1287 $4 Type **291** 2·50 2·75
1288 $4 William II 2·50 2·75
1289 $4 Henry I 2·50 2·75
1290 $4 Stephen 2·50 2·75
1291 $4 Henry II 2·50 2·75
1292 $4 Richard I 2·50 2·75
1293 $4 John 2·50 2·75
1294 $4 "Henry III" 2·50 2·75
1295 $4 Edward I 2·50 2·75
1296 $4 Edward II 2·50 2·75
1297 $4 Edward III 2·50 2·75
1298 $4 Richard II 2·50 2·75
1299 $4 Henry IV 2·50 2·75
1300 $4 Henry V 2·50 2·75
1301 $4 Henry VI 2·50 2·75
1302 $4 Edward IV 2·50 2·75
1303 $4 Edward V 2·50 2·75
1304 $4 Richard III 2·50 2·75
1305 $4 Henry VII 2·50 2·75
1306 $4 Henry VIII 2·50 2·75
1307 $4 Edward VI 2·50 2·75
1308 $4 Jane Grey 2·50 2·75
1309 $$ Mary I 2·50 2·75
1310 $4 Elizabeth I 2·50 2·75
1311 $4 James I 2·50 2·75
1312 $4 Charles I 2·50 2·75
1313 $4 Charles II 2·50 2·75
1314 $4 James II 2·50 2·75
1315 $4 William III 2·50 2·75
1316 $4 Mary II 2·50 2·75
1317 $4 Anne 2·50 2·75
1318 $4 George I 2·50 2·75
1319 $4 George II 2·50 2·75
1320 $4 George III 2·50 2·75
1321 $4 George IV 2·50 2·75
1322 $4 William IV 2·50 2·75
1323 $4 Victoria 2·50 2·75
1324 $4 Edward VII 2·50 2·75
1325 $4 George V 2·50 2·75
1326 $4 Edward VIII 2·50 2·75
1327 $4 George VI 2·50 2·75
1328 $4 Elizabeth II 2·50 2·75

Although inscribed "Henry III" the portrait on No. 1294 is actually of Edward I.

292. Lantana.

1984. Flowers. Multicoloured.

1329. 25 c. Type **292** 20 15
1330. 30 c. Plumbago 25 20
1331. 90 c. Spider Lily 70 60
1332. $4 Giant Alocasia 2·50 3·00

293. Blue Parrot Fish.

1984. Coral Reef Fish. Multicoloured.

1334. 10 c. Type **293** 65 20
1335. 30 c. Flame-back Cherub Fish 1·25 50
1336. 70 c. Painted Wrasse 2·00 2·00
1337. 90 c. Straight-tailed Razor Fish 2·50 2·50

1984. Universal Postal Union Congress, Hamburg. Nos. 1331/2 optd. **19th U.P.U. CONGRESS-HAMBURG.**

1339. 90 c. Spider Lily 60 65
1340. $4 Giant Alocasia 2·50 3·00

295. Freighter.

1984. Ships. Multicoloured.

1342. 40 c. Type **295** 1·25 55
1343. 70 c. "Queen Elizabeth 2" 1·50 1·00
1344. 90 c. Sailing boats 1·90 1·40
1345. $4 "Amerikanis" 6·00 6·50

296. "The Night" (detail) (Correggio).

1984. 450th Death Anniv. of Correggio (painter). Multicoloured.

1347. 10 c. Type **296** 35 15
1348. 30 c. "The Virgin adoring the Child" 60 35
1349. 40 c. "The Mystical Marriage of St. Catherine and St. Sebastian" 1·50 1·00
1350. $4 "The Madonna and the Fruit Basket" 3·50 4·50

297. "L'Absinthe" (Degas).

1984. 150th Birth Anniv. of Edgar Degas (painter). Multicoloured.

1352. 25 c. Type **297** 50 20
1353. 70 c. "Pouting" (horiz.) 1·00 75
1354. $1.10 "The Millinery Shop" 1·60 1·50
1355. $3 "The Bellelli Family" (horiz.) 3·00 3·50

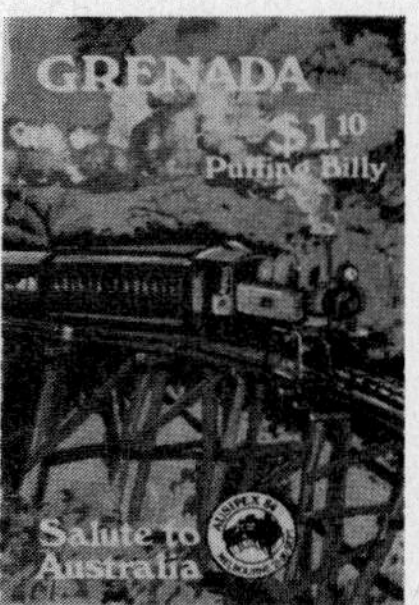

298. Train on "Puffing Billy" Line, Victoria.

1984. "Ausipex" International Stamp Exhibition, Melbourne. Multicoloured.

1357. $1.10 Type **298** 2·00 1·50
1358. $4 Yacht "Australia II" (winner of America's Cup) 4·50 4·50

299. "Locomotion" (1825).

1984. Railway Locomotives. Multicoloured.

1360.	30 c. Type **299**	80	35
1361.	40 c. "Novelty" (1829)	95	40
1362.	60 c. "Washington Farmer" (1836)	1·10	55
1363.	70 c. French Crampton type (1859)	1·25	70
1364.	90 c. Dutch State Railways (1873)	1·50	1·00
1365.	$1.10 "Champion" (1882)	1·75	1·50
1366.	$2 Webb Compound type (1893)	2·25	2·50
1367.	$4 Berlin "No. 74" (1900)	3·75	4·50

1984. Opening of Port Saline International Airport (1st issue). Nos. 1247 and 1249 optd. **OPENING OF PORT SALINE INT'L AIRPORT.**

1369.	40 c. Rural telephone installation	25	30
1370.	$3 Airport control room	1·75	1·90

See also Nos. 1393/5.

301. Donald Duck as Father Christmas looking into Mirror.

1984. Christmas. Walt Disney Cartoon Characters. Multicoloured.

1372.	45 c. Type **301**	1·00	40
1373.	60 c. Donald Duck filling stocking with presents	1·25	45
1374.	90 c. As Father Christmas pulling a sleigh	1·50	75
1375.	$2 As Father Christmas decorating Christmas tree	2·50	2·25
1376.	$4 Donald Duck and nephews singing carols	3·50	3·75

1985. Birth Bicentenary of John J. Audubon (ornithologist) (1st issue). As T **198** of Antigua. Multicoloured.

1378.	50 c. Clapper rail (vert.)	1·00	50
1379.	70 c. Hooded warbler (vert.)	1·25	75
1380.	90 c. Common flicker (vert.)	1·75	1·10
1381.	$4 Bohemian waxwing (vert.)	4·00	4·50

See also Nos. 1480/3.

302. Honda "XL500R".

1985. Centenary of the Motor Cycle. Multicoloured.

1383.	25 c. Type **302**	65	40
1384.	50 c. Suzuki "GS1100ES"	90	70
1385.	90 c. Kawasaki "KZ700"	1·40	1·40
1386.	$4 BMW "K100"	4·00	4·50

303. "Explorer".

1985. 75th Anniv. of Girl Guide Movement. Designs showing work for Guide badges. Multicoloured.

1388.	25 c. Type **303**	20	20
1389.	60 c. "Cook"	45	40
1390.	90 c. "Musician"	60	55
1391.	$3 "Home nurse"	1·75	2·00

304. Avro "748" on Inaugural Flight from Barbados.

1985. Opening of Point Saline International Airport (1984) (2nd issue). Multicoloured.

1393.	70 c. Type **304**	1·50	65
1394.	$1 Pan Am "L1011" on inaugural flight from New York	2·00	1·25
1395.	$4 "Tri-Star" on inaugural flight to Miami	4·25	4·50

305. McDonnell Douglas "DC-8".

1985. 40th Anniv. of International Civil Aviation Organization. Multicoloured.

1397.	10 c. Type **305**	15	15
1398.	50 c. "Super Constellation"	40	35
1399.	60 c. Vickers "Vanguard"	45	45
1400.	$4 De Havilland "Twin Otter"	2·75	3·00

306. Model Boat Racing.

1985. Water Sports. Multicoloured.

1402.	10 c. Type **306**	15	10
1403.	50 c. Scuba diving, Carriacou	35	30
1404.	$1·10, Windsurfers on Grand Anse Beach	75	75
1405.	$4 Windsurfing	2·25	2·50

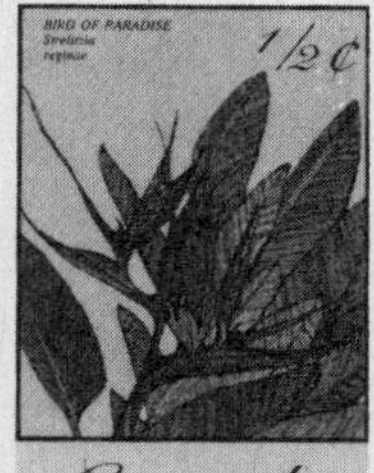

307. Bird of Paradise (flower).

1985. Native Flowers. Multicoloured.

1407	½ c. Type **307**	10	15
1408	1 c. Passion Flower	10	15
1409	2 c. Oleander	10	20
1410	4 c. Bromeliad	10	15
1411	5 c. Anthurium	10	15
1412	6 c. Bougainvillea	10	20
1413	10 c. Hibiscus	10	20
1414	15 c. Ginger	10	20
1415	25 c. Poinsettia	10	20
1416	30 c. Mexican Creeper	10	20
1417	40 c. Angel's Trumpet	15	30
1418	50 c. Amaryllis	20	30
1419	60 c. Prickly Pear	25	40
1420	70 c. Chenille Plant	30	50
1420c	75 c. Cordia	50	75
1421	$1 Periwinkle	40	70
1422	$1·10, Ixora	45	75
1423	$3 Shrimp Plant	1·25	2·00
1424	$5 Plumbago	2·00	3·25
1425	$10 "Lantana camara"	4·00	6·50
1425c	$20 Peregrina	8·50	13·00

308. The Queen Mother at Royal Opera House, London.

1985. Life and Times of Queen Elizabeth the Queen Mother. Multicoloured.

1426.	$1 Type **308**	55	60
1427.	$1·50, The Queen Mother playing snooker at London Press Club (horiz)	80	85
1428.	$2·50, At Epsom Races, 1960	1·40	1·50

Stamps as Nos. 1426/8 but with face values of 90 c., $1 and $3 exist from additional sheetlets with changed background colours.

309. Youth Gardening (Horticulture).

1985. International Youth Year. Mult.

1430.	25 c. Type **309**	20	20
1431.	50 c. Young people on beach (Leisure)	40	30
1432.	$1·10, Girls in classroom (Education)	80	80
1433.	$3 Nurse and young patient (Health Care)	1·75	2·00

1985. 300th Birth Anniv. of Johann Sebastian Bach (composer). As T **206** of Antigua. Mult.

1435.	25 c. Crumhorn	45	20
1436.	70 c. Oboe d'Amore	80	60
1437.	$1 Violin	1·25	1·00
1438.	$3 Harpsichord	2·50	2·75

310. Cub Scouts Camping.

1985. 4th Caribbean Cuboree. Multicoloured.

1440.	10 c. Type **310**	20	15
1441.	50 c. Cub scouts swimming ("Physical Fitness")	45	40
1442.	$1 Stamp collecting	80	80
1443.	$4 Birdwatching	2·75	3·00

1985. Royal Visit. As T **207** of Antigua. Multicoloured.

1445.	50 c. Flags of Great Britain and Grenada	60	35
1446.	$1 Queen Elizabeth II (vert.)	1·25	1·00
1447.	$4 Royal Yacht "Britannia"	3·50	4·25

1985. 150th Birth Anniv. of Mark Twain (author). As T **118** of Anguilla. Designs showing Walt Disney cartoon characters in scenes from "The Prince and the Pauper". Multicoloured.

1449.	25 c. Mortie as Tom meeting the Prince (Ferdie)	20	20
1450.	50 c. Tom and the Prince exchanging clothes	35	30
1451.	$1·10, The Prince with John Cantry	70	65
1452.	$1·50, The Prince knights Mike Hendon (Goofy)	95	85
1453.	$2 Tom and the Whipping Boy	1·40	1·25

1985. Birth Bicentenaries of Grimm Brothers (folklorists). As T **119** of Anguilla, showing Walt Disney cartoon characters in scenes from "The Fisherman and his Wife". Multicoloured.

1455.	30 c. The Fisherman (Goofy) catching enchanted fish	15	20
1456.	60 c. The Fisherman scolded by his Wife (Clarabelle)	35	40
1457.	70 c. The Fisherman's Wife with dream cottage	40	55
1458.	$1 The Fisherman's Wife as King	60	80
1459.	$3 The Fisherman and Wife in their original shack	1·75	2·50

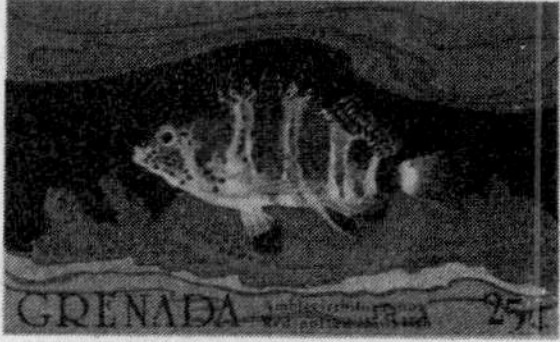

311. Red spotted Hawkfish.

1985. Marine Life. Multicoloured.

1461.	25 c. Type **311**	65	30
1462.	50 c. Spotfin Butterflyfish	1·00	70
1463.	$1·10, Fire Coral and Orange Sponges	1·75	2·00
1464.	$3 Pillar Coral	3·50	4·00

1985. 40th Anniv. of U.N.O. Multicoloured. As T **208** of Antigua showing United Nations (New York) stamps.

1466.	50 c. Mary McLeod Bethune (educationist) and 1975 International Women's Year 10 c.	50	30
1467.	$2 Maimonides (physician) and 1966 W.H.O. 5 c.	2·50	2·00
1468.	$2.50 Alexander Graham Bell (telephone inventor) and 1956 I.T.U. 3 c.	2·75	2·75

312. "Adoration of the Sheperds' (Mantegna).

1985. Christmas. Religious Paintings. Multicoloured.

1470.	25 c. Type **312**	35	15
1471.	60 c. "Journey of the Magi" (Sassetta)	70	55
1472.	90 c. "Madonna and Child enthroned with Saints" (Raphael)	1·00	85
1473.	$4 "Nativity" (Monaco)	3·25	4·00

1986. Centenary of Statue of Liberty (1st issue). Multicoloured. As T **211** of Dominica.

1475.	5 c. Columbus Monument, 1893 (vert.)	15	20
1476.	25 c. Columbus Monument, 1986 (vert.)	30	20
1477.	40 c. Mounted police, Central Park, 1895	1·00	60
1478.	$4 Mounted police, 1986	4·50	4·50

See also Nos. 1644/52.

1986. Birth Bicentenary of John J. Audubon (ornithologist) (2nd issue). Multicoloured. As T **198** of Antigua.

1480.	50 c. Snowy egret	70	45
1481.	90 c. Greater flamingo	1·25	80
1482.	$1.10 Canada goose	1·40	1·00
1483.	$3 Smew	2·25	2·50

1986. Visit of President Reagan. Nos. 1418 and 1424 optd. **VISIT OF PRES REAGAN 20 FEB. 1986.**

1485.	50 c. Amaryllis	25	30
1486.	$5 Plumbago	2·50	3·00

MORE DETAILED LISTS

are given in the Stanley Gibbons Catalogues referred to in the country headings.

For lists of current volumes see Introduction.

314. Methodist Church, St. Georges.

1986. Bicentenary of Methodist Church in Grenada.

1487. **314.** 60 c. multicoloured .. 50 60

315. Player with Ball.

1986. World Cup Football Championship, Mexico. Multicoloured.

1489. 50 c. Type **315** 50 40
1490. 70 c. Player heading ball 70 60
1491. 90 c. Player controlling ball 85 70
1492. $4 Player controlling ball with right foot .. 4·00 3·25

1986. Appearance of Halley's Comet (1st issue). As T **123** of Anguilla. Multicoloured.

1494. 5 c. Clyde Tombaugh (astronomer) and Dudley Observatory, New York 15 15
1495. 20 c. N.A.S.A.—U.S.A.F. "X-24B" Space Shuttle prototype, 1973 .. .. 15 15
1496. 40 c. German comet medal, 1618 .. .. 30 30
1497. $4 Destruction of Sodom and Gomorrah, 1949 B.C. .. .. .. 2·25 2·75

See also Nos. 1533/6 and 1980/3.

1986. 60th Birthday of Queen Elizabeth II. As T **125** of Anguilla.

1499. 2 c. black and yellow .. 10 15
1500. $1.50 multicoloured .. 75 90
1501. $4 multicoloured .. 2·00 2·75

Designs: 2 c. Princess Elizabeth in 1951. $1.50, Queen presenting trophy at polo match, Windsor, 1965. $4 at Epsom, Derby Day, 1977.

1986. "Ameripex" International Stamp Exhibition, Chicago. As T **212** of Dominica, showing Walt Disney cartoon characters playing baseball. Multicoloured.

1503. 1 c. Goofy as pitcher .. 10 10
1504. 2 c. Goofy as catcher .. 10 10
1505. 3 c. Mickey Mouse striking ball and Donald Duck as catcher .. 10 10
1506. 4 c. Huey forcing out Dewey 10 10
1507. 5 c. Chip n'Dale chasing flyball 10 10
1508. 6 c. Mickey Mouse, Donald Duck and Clarabelle in argument 10 10
1509. $2 Minnie Mouse and Donald Duck reading baseball rules .. .. 1·40 1·40
1510. $3 Ludwig von Drake as umpire with Goofy and Pete colliding .. 1·75 2·00

1986. Royal Wedding. As T **213** of Antigua. Multicoloured.

1512. 2 c. Prince Andrew and Miss Sarah Ferguson 10 15
1513. $1.10 Prince Andrew .. 70 70
1514. $4 Prince Andrew with H.M.S. "Brazen's" helicopter .. .. 2·50 3·00

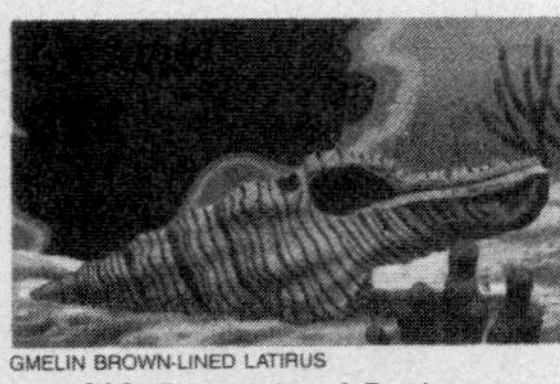

316. Brown-lined Latirus.

1986. Sea Shells. Multicoloured.

1516. 25 c. Type **316** 30 20
1517. 60 c. Lamellose wentletrap 55 45
1518. 70 c. Turkey wing .. 65 50
1519. $4 Rooster tail conch .. 2·50 3·00

317. "Lepiota roseolamellata".

1986. Mushrooms. Multicoloured.

1521. 10 c. Type **317** 40 20
1522. 60 c. "Lentinus bertieri" 1·25 85
1523. $1 "Lentinus retinervis" 2·00 1·25
1524. $4 "Eccilia cystiophorus" .. .. 4·50 4·50

1986. World Cup Football Championship Winners. Mexico. Nos. 1489/92 optd. **WINNERS Argentina 3 W. Germany 2.**

1526. 50 c. Type **315** 30 35
1527. 70 c. Player heading ball 40 45
1528. 90 c. Player controlling ball 50 60
1529. $4 Player controlling ball with right foot .. 2·25 2·75

318. Dove on Rifles and Mahatma Gandhi (Disarmament Week).

1986. International Events. Multicoloured.

1531. 60 c. Type **318** 50 50
1532. $4 Hands passing olive branch and Martin Luther King (International Peace Year) (horiz.) .. .. 2·00 2·50

1986. Appearance of Halley's Comet (2nd issue). Nos. 1494/7 optd with T **218** of Antigua.

1533. 5 c. Clyde Tombaugh (astronomer) and Dudley Observatory, New York 30 30
1534. 20 c. N.A.S.A.—U.S.A.F. "X-24B" Space Shuttle prototype, 1973 .. .. 55 30
1535. 40 c. German comet medal, 1618 .. .. 70 45
1536. $4 Destruction of Sodom and Gomorrah, 1949 B.C. .. .. .. 3·50 4·00

1986. Christmas. Multicoloured. As T **220** of Antigua showing Walt Disney cartoon characters.

1538. 30 c. Mickey Mouse asleep in armchair (vert.) 20 20
1539. 45 c. Young Mickey Mouse with Father Christmas (vert.) .. 30 30
1540. 60 c. Donald Duck with toy telephone 40 35
1541. 70 c. Pluto with pushcart 45 45
1542. $1.10 Daisy Duck with doll 70 75
1543. $2 Goofy as Father Christmas (vert.) .. 1·25 1·50
1544. $2·50 Goofy singing carols at piano (vert.) 1·60 1·75
1545. $3 Mickey Mouse, Donald Duck and nephew riding toy train .. .. .. 2·00 2·25

319. Cockerel and Hen.

1986. Fauna and Flora. Multicoloured.

1547. 10 c. Type **319** 20 10
1548. 30 c. Fish-eating bat .. 35 20
1549. 60 c. Goat 55 35
1550. 70 c. Cow 60 40
1551. $1 Anthurium .. .. 1·50 1·25
1552. $1·10 Royal poinciana .. 1·50 1·25
1553. $2 Frangipani .. .. 2·25 2·50
1554. $4 Orchid .. .. 5·50 6·00

320. Maserati "Biturbo" (1984).

1986. Centenary of Motoring. Multicoloured.

1556. 10 c. Type **320** 20 20
1557. 30 c. AC "Cobra" (1960) 30 30
1558. 60 c. Corvette (1963) .. 50 50
1559. 70 c. Dusenberg "SJ7" (1932) 60 60
1560. 90 c. Porsche (1957) .. 75 75
1561. $1·10 Stoewer (1930) .. 85 85
1562. $2 Volkswagen "Beetle" (1957) .. .. .. 1·40 1·40
1563. $3 Mercedes "600 Limo" (1963) .. .. .. 1·90 2·00

321. Pole Vaulting.

1986. Olympic Games, Seoul, South Korea (1988). Multicoloured.

1565. 10 c.+5 c. Type **321** .. 10 20
1566. 50 c.+20 c. Gymnastics 35 45
1567. 70 c.+30 c. Putting the shot 50 65
1568. $2+$1 High jumping .. 1·50 2·00

The premiums on Nos. 1565/9 were to support the participation of the Grenada team.

1986. Birth Centenary of Marc Chagall (artist). Designs as T **225** of Antigua, showing various paintings.

1570/1609. $1 × 40 multicoloured set of 40 .. .. 16·00 18·00

1987. America's Cup Yachting Championship. As T **222** of Antigua. Multicoloured.

1611. 10 c. "Columbia", 1958 .. 10 10
1612. 60 c. "Resolute", 1920 .. 35 35
1613. $1.10 "Endeavor", 1934 70 75
1614. $4 "Rainbow", 1934 .. 1·90 2·50

322. Virgin Mary and Outline Map of Grenada.

1987. 500th Anniv (1992) of Discovery of America by Christopher Columbus (1st issue). Multicoloured.

1616. 10 c. Type **322** 15 15
1617. 30 c. "Santa Maria" "Pinta" and "Nina" (horiz.) 20 15
1618. 50 c. Columbus and outline map of Grenada 25 30
1619. 60 c. Christopher Columbus 25 30
1620. 90 c. King Ferdinand and Queen Isabella of Spain (horiz.) 40 45
1621. $1.10 Map of Antilles by Columbus 50 60
1622. $2 Caribs with sailing raft (horiz.) .. .. 90 1·25
1623. $3 Columbus in the New World, 1493 (contemporary drawing) .. 1·40 1·60

See also Nos. 2051/4 and 2091/8.

1987. Milestones of Transportation. As T **226** of Antigua. Multicoloured.

1625. 10 c. Cornu's first helicopter, 1907 .. 15 15
1626. 15 c. Monitor and Merrimack (first battle between ironclad warships), 1862 .. 20 20
1627. 30 c. "LZ1" (first Zeppelin), 1900 .. 30 30
1628. 50 c. S.S. "Sirius" (first transatlantic steamship crossing), 1838 .. 35 35
1629. 60 c. Steam locomotive on Trans-Siberian Railway (longest line) 35 35
1630. 70 c. U.S.S. "Enterprise" (largest aircraft carrier), 1960 .. .. 40 40
1631. 90 c. Blanchard's ballon (first ballon across English Channel), 1785 55 55
1632. $1.50 U.S.S. "Holland 1" (first steam-powered submarine), 1900 .. 90 90
1633. $2 S.S. "Oceanic" (first luxury liner), 1871 .. 1·40 1·40
1634. $3 Lamborghini "Countach" (fastest commercial car), 1984 1·75 1·75

323. Black Grouper.

1987. "Capex '87" International Stamp Exhibition, Toronto. Game Fishes. Mult.

1635. 10 c. Type **323** 30 15
1636. 30 c. Blue marlin (horiz.) 40 15
1637. 60 c. White marlin .. 60 45
1638. 70 c. Big eye thresher shark (horiz.) 70 60
1639. $1 Bonefish (horiz.) .. 90 80
1640. $1.10 Wahoo (horiz.) .. 1·00 90
1641. $2 Sailfish (horiz.) .. 1·75 2·00
1642. $4 Albacore (horiz.) .. 2·75 3·00

1987. Centenary of Statue of Liberty (2nd issue). As T **227** of Antigua. Multicoloured.

1644. 10 c. Computer projections of statue and base (horiz.) .. 15 10
1645. 25 c. Statue and fireworks (horiz.) .. 20 15
1646. 50 c. Statue and fireworks (different) (horiz.) 35 35
1647. 60 c. Statue and boats .. 35 35
1648. 70 c. Computer projection of top of statue (horiz.) .. 40 40
1649. $1 Rear view of Statue and fireworks 60 60
1650. $1.10 Aerial view of statue 70 70
1651. $2 Statue and flotilla .. 1·10 1·40
1652. $4 "Queen Elizabeth 2" in New York Harbour 2·00 2·25

324. Alice and the Rabbit Hole.

1987. 50th Anniv. of First Full-Length Disney Cartoon Film. Scenes from various films.

1653/1706. 30 c. × 54 multicoloured
Set of 54 .. .. 6·00 6·50

325. Isaac Newton holding Apple (Law of Gravity).

1987. Great Scientific Discoveries. Mult.

1708. 50 c. Type **325** 55 45
1709. $1.10 John Jacob Berzelius and symbols of chemical elements 95 95
1710. $2 Robert Boyle (law of Pressure and Volume) 1·75 1·75
1711. $3 James Watt and drawing of steam engine .. .. .. 2·40 2·50

No. 1711 is inscribed "RUDOLF DIESEL" in error.

1987. 60th Anniv. of International Social Security Association. Nos. 1413, 1418 and 1423 optd. **International Social Security Association** and Emblem.

1714. 10 c. Hibiscus 10 15
1715. 50 c. Amaryllis 25 30
1716. $3 Shrimp plant .. 1·40 2·00

1987. Bicentenary of U.S. Constitution. As T **232** of Antigua. Multicoloured.

1717. 15 c. Independence Hall, Philadelphia (vert.) .. 10 10
1718. 50 c. Benjamin Franklin (Pennsylvania delegate) (vert.) .. 25 30
1719. 60 c. State Seal, Massachusetts .. 25 30
1720. $4 Robert Morris (Pennsylvania delegate) (vert.) .. 1·75 2·40

328. Goofy in "The Shadow".

1987. "Hafnia '87" International Stamp Exhibition. Walt Disney cartoon characters in scenes from Hans Christian Andersen's fairy tales. Multicoloured.

1722. 25 c. Type **328** 15 15
1723. 30 c. Mother Stork and brood in "The Storks" 15 15
1724. 50 c. King Richard, Robin Hood and Little John (from Robin Hood) in "The Emperor's New Clothes" 25 30
1725. 60 c. Goofy and Pluto in "The Tinderbox" .. 25 30
1726. 70 c. Daisy and Donald Duck in "The Shepherdess and the Chimney Sweep" .. 30 35
1727. $1.50 Mickey and Minnie Mouse in "The Little Mermaid" 70 80
1728. $3 Clarabelle and Goofy in "The Princess and the Pea" .. 1·40 1·75
1729. $4 Minnie Mouse and Pegleg Pete in "The Marsh King's Daughter" .. .. 1·75 2·00

329. "The Annunciation" (Fra Angelico).

1987. Christmas. Religious Paintings. Multicoloured.

1731. 15 c. Type **329** 30 10
1732. 30 c. "The Annunciation" (attr. Hubert van Eyck) .. 45 30
1733. 60 c. "The Adoration of the Magi" (Januarius Zick) 80 60
1734. $4 "The Flight into Egypt" (Gerard David) .. .. .. 3·00 3·50

330. T. Albert Marryshow.

1988. Birth Centenary of T. Albert Marryshow (nationalist).

1736. **330.** 25 c. brown, light brown and red .. 20 20

1988. Royal Ruby Wedding. As T **234** of Antigua. Multicoloured.

1737. 15 c. brown, blk. & bl. .. 20 10
1738. 50 c. multicoloured .. 45 30
1739. $1 brown and black .. 75 60
1740. $4 multicoloured .. 2·25 2·40

Designs: 15 c. Wedding photograph, 1947. 50 c. Queen Elizabeth II with Prince Charles and Princess Anne, c. 1955. $1, Queen with Princess Anne, c. 1957. $4, Queen Elizabeth (from photo by Tim Graham), 1980.

331 Goofy and Daisy Duck lighting Olympic Torch, Olympia

1988. Olympic Games, Seoul. Designs showing Walt Disney cartoon characters. Mult.

1742 1 c. Type **331** 10 10
1743 2 c. Donald and Daisy Duck carrying Olympic torch 10 10
1744 3 c. Donald Duck, Goofy and Mickey Mouse carrying flags of U.S., Korea and Spain .. 10 10
1745 4 c. Donald Duck releasing doves .. 10 10
1746 5 c. Mickey Mouse flying with rocket belt .. 10 10
1747 10 c. Morty and Ferdie carrying banner with Olympic motto .. 10 10
1748 $6 Donald Duck, Minnie Mouse and Hodori the Tiger (mascot of Seoul Games) .. .. 2·75 3·00
1749 $7 Pluto, Hodori and old post office, Seoul .. 3·25 3·75

1988. Stamp Exhibitions. Nos. 1631/4 optd.

1751 90 c. Blanchard's Balloon, 1785 (optd **OLYMPHILEX' 88**, Seoul) 40 45
1752 $1.50 U.S.S. "Holland 1", 1900 (optd **INDEPENDENCE 40**, Israel) .. 60 75
1753 $2 S.S. "Oceanic", 1871 (optd **FINLANDIA 88, Helsinki**) .. 80 1·00
1754 $3 Lamborghini "Countach", 1984 (optd **Praga 88**, Prague) .. 1·25 1·60

332 Scout fishing from Boat

1988. World Scout Jamboree, Australia. Mult.

1755 20 c. Type **332** 20 15
1756 70 c. Scouts hiking through forest (horiz) 70 60
1757 90 c. Practising first aid (horiz) 90 80
1758 $3 Shooting rapids in inflatable canoe .. 2·25 2·50

333 "Santa Maria de Guia" (Columbus), 1498, and Map of Rotary District

1988. Rotary District 405 Conference, St. George's.

1760 **333** $2 multicoloured .. 80 1·00

334 Roseate Tern

1988. Birds. Multicoloured.

1762 10 c. Type **334** 20 15
1763 25 c. Laughing gull .. 30 20
1764 50 c. Osprey 50 35
1765 60 c. Rose-breasted grosbeak 50 35
1766 90 c. Purple gallinule .. 55 45
1767 $1.10 White-tailed tropic bird 60 70
1768 $3 Blue-faced booby .. 1·40 1·75
1769 $4 Common shoveler .. 1·75 2·25

335 Vauxhall Type "OE 30/98", 1925

1988. Cars. Multicoloured.

1771 $2 Type **335** 80 85
1772 $2 Wills "Sainte Claire", 1926 .. .. .. 80 85
1773 $2 Bucciali, 1928 .. 80 85
1774 $2 Irving Napier "Golden Arrow", 1929 .. 80 85
1775 $2 Studebaker "President", 1930 .. 80 85
1776 $2 Thomas "Flyer", 1907 80 85
1777 $2 Isotta-Fraschini "Tipo J", 1908 .. .. 80 85
1778 $2 Fiat 10/14HP, 1910 .. 80 85
1779 $2 Mercer "Type 35 Raceabout", 1911 .. 80 85
1780 $2 Marmon "Model 34 Cloverleaf", 1917 .. 80 85
1781 $2 Tatra "Type 77", 1934 80 85
1782 $2 Rolls-Royce "Phantom III", 1938 .. 80 85
1783 $2 Studebaker "Champion Starlight", 1947 .. 80 85
1784 $2 Porsche "Gmund", 1948 .. .. .. 80 85
1785 $2 Tucker, 1948 .. .. 80 85
1786 $2 Peerless "V-16", 1931 80 85
1787 $2 Minerva "AL", 1931 .. 80 85
1788 $2 Reo "Royale", 1933 .. 80 85
1789 $2 Pierce Arrow "Silver Arrow", 1933 .. .. 80 85
1790 $2 Hupmobile "Aerodynamic", 1934 .. 80 85
1791 $2 Peugeot "404", 1965 .. 80 85
1792 $2 Ford "Capri", 1969 .. 80 85
1793 $2 Ferrari "312T", 1975 .. 80 85
1794 $2 Lotus "T-79", 1978 .. 80 85
1795 $2 Williams-Cosworth "FW07", 1979 .. 80 85
1796 $2 H.R.G. "1500 Sports", 1948 .. .. .. 80 85
1797 $2 Crosley "Hotshot", 1949 .. .. .. 80 85
1798 $2 Volvo "PV444", 1955 80 85
1799 $2 Maserati "Tipo 61", 1960 .. .. .. 80 85
1800 $2 Saab "96", 1963 .. 80 85

1988. 500th Birth Anniv of Titian (artist). As T **238** of Antigua. Multicoloured.

1801 10 c. "Lavinia Vecellio" 10 10
1802 20 c. "Portrait of a Man" 10 10
1803 25 c. "Andrea de Franceschi" 10 15
1804 90 c. "Head of a Soldier" 40 45
1805 $1 "Man with a Flute" .. 45 50
1806 $2 "Lucrezia and Tarquinius" 80 85
1807 $3 "Duke of Mantua with Dog" .. .. .. 1·25 1·40
1808 $4 "La Bella di Tiziano" 1·60 1·75

336 "Graf Zeppelin" over Chicago World's Fair, 1933

1988. Airships. Multicoloured

1810 10 c. Type **336** 10 10
1811 15 c. "LZ-1" over Lake Constance, 1901 (horiz) 10 10
1812 25 c. "Washington" (balloon) and balloon barge, 1862 .. .. 10 15
1813 45 c. "Hindenberg" and Maybach "Zeppelin" car (horiz) 20 25

1814 50 c. Goodyear airship in Statue of Liberty Centenary Race, 1986 .. 20 25
1815 60 c. "Hindenberg" over Statue of Liberty, 1937 (horiz) 25 30
1816 90 c. Aircraft docking experiment with "Hindenberg" 1936 (horiz) 40 45
1817 $2 "Hindenberg" over Olympic Stadium, Berlin, 1936 .. .. 80 1·00
1818 $3 "Hindenberg" over Christ of the Andes Monument, 1937 .. 1·25 1·60
1819 $4 "Hindenberg" and "Bremen" (liner), 1936 (horiz) .. .. 1·60 2·00

337 Tasmanian Wolf, Mickey Mouse and Pluto

1988. "Sydpex '88" National Stamp Exhibition, Sydney and 60th Birthday of Mickey Mouse. Multicoloured.
1821 1 c. Type **337** 10 10
1822 2 c. Mickey Mouse feeding wallabies 10 10
1823 3 c. Mickey Mouse and Goofy with kangaroo .. 10 10
1824 4 c. Mickey and Minnie Mouse riding emus .. 10 10
1825 5 c. Mickey and Minnie Mouse with wombat .. 10 10
1826 10 c. Mickey Mouse and Donald Duck watching platypus 10 10
1827 $5 Mickey Mouse and Goofy photographing kookaburra .. .. 2·50 3·00
1828 $6 Mickey Mouse and Koala on map of Australia .. .. 2·75 3·25

338 Pineapple

1988. 10th Anniv of International Fund for Agricultural Development. Multicolured.
1830 25 c. Type **338** 15 15
1831 75 c. Bananas 40 40
1832 $3 Mace and nutmeg (horiz) .. .. 1·50 2·00

339 Lignum Vitae

1988. Flowering Trees and Shrubs. Mult.
1833 15 c. Type **339** 15 15
1834 25 c. Saman 20 15
1835 35 c. Red frangipani .. 25 20
1836 45 c. Flowering maple .. 30 25
1837 60 c. Yellow poui .. 40 30
1838 $1 Wild chestnut .. 60 60
1839 $3 Mountain immortelle 1·50 2·00
1840 $4 Queen of flowers 1·75 2·25

340 Mickey Mantle (New York Yankees)
(Illustration reduced, actual size 50 × 38mm)

1988. Major League Baseball Players (1st series). Designs showing portraits or league emblems.
1842/1922 30 c. × 81 mult Set of 81 .. .. 8·75 9·00

1988. Christmas. "Mickey's Christmas Eve". As T **246** of Antigua showing Walt Disney cartoon characters. Multicoloured.
1923 $1 Donald Duck's nephew on mantelpiece .. 45 50
1924 $1 Goofy with string of popcorn .. 45 50
1925 $1 Chip n'Dale decorating Christmas tree .. 45 50
1926 $1 Father Christmas in sleigh 45 50
1927 $1 Donald's nephew with stocking 45 50
1928 $1 Donald's nephew unpacking decorations 45 50
1929 $1 Donald Duck with present 45 50
1930 $1 Mickey Mouse with present 45 50

341 Tina Turner

1988. Entertainers. Multicoloured.
1932 10 c. Type **341** 15 15
1933 25 c. Lionel Ritchie .. 20 20
1934 45 c. Whitney Houston .. 30 30
1935 60 c. Joan Armatrading 45 45
1936 75 c. Madonna 55 55
1937 $1 Elton John 70 75
1938 $3 Bruce Springsteen .. 1·90 2·25
1939 $4 Bob Marley .. .. 2·50 3·00
No. 1935 is incorrectly inscribed "JOAN AMMERTRADING".

342 Canada Atlantic Railway No. 2, 1889

1989. North American Railway Locomotives. Multicoloured.
1941 $2 Type **342** .. .. 95 1·00
1942 $2 Virginia & Truckee Railroad "J. W. Bowker" type, 1875 .. 95 1·00
1943 $2 Philadelphia & Reading Railway "Ariel", 1872 .. .. 95 1·00
1944 $2 Chicago & Rock Island Railroad "America" type, 1867 .. .. 95 1·00
1945 $2 Lehigh Valley Railroad Consolidation No. 63, 1866 .. .. .. 95 1·00
1946 $2 Great Western Railway "Scotia", 1860 .. 95 1·00
1947 $2 Grand Trunk Railway "Birkenhead" Class, 1854 .. .. .. 95 1·00
1948 $2 Camden & Amboy Railroad "Monster", 1837 .. .. .. 95 1·00
1949 $2 Baltimore & Ohio Railroad "Grass-hopper" Class, 1834 .. 95 1·00
1950 $2 Baltimore & Ohio Railroad "Tom Thumb", 1829 .. 95 1·00
1951 $2 United Railways of Yucatan "Yucatan", 1925 .. .. .. 95 1·00
1952 $2 Canadian National Railways Class "T2", 1924 .. .. .. 95 1·00
1953 $2 St. Louis–San Francisco Railroad "Light Mikado" class, 1919 .. .. .. 95 1·00
1954 $2 Atlantic Coast Line Railroad "Light Pacific" class, 1919 .. 95 1·00
1955 $2 Edaville Railroad No. 7, 1913 .. .. 95 1·00
1956 $2 Denver & Rio Grande Western Railroad Class "K27", 1903 .. .. 95 1·00
1957 $2 Pennsylvania Railroad Class "E-2" No. 7002, 1902 .. .. .. 95 1·00
1958 $2 Pennsylvania Railroad Class "H6", 1899 .. 95 1·00
1959 $2 Mohawk & Hudson Railroad "De Witt Clinton", 1893 .. .. 95 1·00
1960 $2 St. Clair Tunnel Company No. 598, 1891 95 1·00
1961 $2 Chesapeake & Ohio Railroad Class "M-1" No. 500 steam turbine electric, 1947 .. .. 95 1·00
1962 $2 Rutland Railroad No. 93, 1946 .. .. 95 1·00
1963 $2 Pennsylvania Railroad Class "T1", 1942 .. 95 1·00
1964 $2 Chesapeake & Ohio Railroad Class "H-8", 1942 .. .. .. 95 1·00
1965 $2 Atchison, Topeka & Santa Fe Railway Model "FT" diesel, 1941 95 1·00
1966 $2 Gulf, Mobile & Ohio Railroad Models "S-1" & "S-2", 1940 .. 95 1·00
1967 $2 New York, New Haven & Hartford Railroad Class "15", 1937 .. 95 1·00
1968 $2 Seaboard Air Line Railroad Class "R", 1936 .. .. .. 95 1·00
1969 $2 Newfoundland Railway Class "R-2", 1930 .. 95 1·00
1970 $2 Canadian National Railway No. 9000, 1928 95 1·00

343 Women's Long Jump (Jackie Joyner-Kersee, U.S.A.)

1989. Olympic Gold Medal Winners, Seoul (1988). Multicoloured.
1971 10 c. Type **343** 10 10
1972 25 c. Women's Singles Tennis (Steffi Graf, West Germany) .. 10 15
1973 45 c. Men's 1500 metres (Peter Rono, Kenya) .. 20 25
1974 75 c. Men's 1000 metres single kayak (Greg Barton, U.S.A.) .. 30 35
1975 $1 Women's team foil (Italy) 40 45
1976 $2 Women's 100 metres freestyle swimming (Kristin Otto, East Germany) 85 90
1977 $3 Men's still rings gymnastics (Holger Behrendt, East Germany) .. .. 1·25 1·40
1978 $4 Synchronized swimming pair (Japan) 1·75 1·90

344 Nebulae

1989. Appearance of Halley's Comet (1986) (3rd issue).
1980 **344** 25 c.+5 c. mult .. 10 15
1981 – 75 c.+5 c. blk & grn 35 40
1982 – 90 c.+5 c. mult .. 40 45
1983 – $2+5 c. multicoloured 85 90
DESIGNS: 75 c.+5 c. Marine astronomical experiments; 90 c.+5 c. Moon's surface; $2+5 c. Edmond Halley, Sir Isaac Newton and his book "Principia". (102 × 69 mm). $5+5 c. 17th-century warships and astrological signs.

1989. Japanese Art. Paintings by Hiroshige. As T **250** of Antigua. Multicoloured.
1985 10 c. "Shinagawa on Edo Bay" 10 10
1986 25 c. "Pine Trees on the Road to Totsuka" 10 15
1987 60 c. "Kanagawa on Edo Bay" 25 30
1988 75 c. "Crossing Banyu River to Hiratsuka" .. 30 35
1989 $1 "Windy Shore at Odawara" 40 45
1990 $2 "Snow-Covered Post Station of Mishima" .. 85 90
1991 $3 "Full Moon at Fuchu" 1·25 1·40
1992 $4 "Crossing the Stream at Okitsu" .. .. 1·75 1·90

345 Great Blue Heron

1989. Birds. Multicoloured.
1994 5 c. Type **345** 10 10
1995 10 c. Green heron .. 10 10
1996 15 c. Turnstone .. 10 10
1997 25 c. Blue-winged teal .. 10 15
1998 35 c. Ringed plover (vert) 15 20
1999 45 c. Green-throated carib ("Emerald-throated hummingbird") (vert) 20 25
2000 50 c. Rufous-breasted hermit (vert) 20 25
2001 60 c. Lesser Antillean bullfinch (vert) .. 25 30
2002 75 c. Brown pelican (vert) 30 35
2003 $1 Black-crowned night heron (vert) 40 45
2004 $3 American kestrel ("Sparrow Hawk") (vert) .. .. .. 1·25 1·40
2005 $5 Barn swallow (vert) .. 2·10 2·25
2006 $10 Red-billed tropic bird (vert) .. .. .. 4·25 4·50
2007 $20 Barn owl (vert) .. 8·50 8·75

1989. World Cup Football Championship, Italy (1990) (1st issue). As T **252** of Antigua. Multicoloured.
2008 10 c. Scotland player .. 10 10
2009 25 c. England and Brazil players 10 15
2010 60 c. Paolo Rossi (Italy) 25 30
2011 75 c. Jairzinho (Brazil) .. 30 35
2012 $1 Sweden striker .. 40 45
2013 $2 Pele (Brazil) 85 90
2014 $3 Mario Kempes (Argentina) .. .. 1·25 1·40
2015 $4 Pat Jennings (Northern Ireland) .. 1·75 1·90
See also Nos. 2174/7.

HAVE YOU READ THE NOTES AT THE BEGINNING OF THIS CATALOGUE?
These often provide answers to the enquiries we receive.

346 Xebec and Sugar Cane

1989. "Philexfrance '89" International Stamp Exhibition, Paris. Designs showing French sailing vessels and plantation crops. Mult.

2017 25 c. Type **346** 10 15
2018 75 c. Lugger and cotton 30 35
2019 $1 Full-rigged ship and cocoa 40 45
2020 $4 Ketch and coffee .. 1·75 1·90

347 Alan Shepard and "Freedom 7" Spacecraft, 1961 (first American in Space)

1989. 20th Anniv of First Manned Landing on Moon. Multicoloured.

2022 15 c. Type **347** 10 10
2023 35 c. "Friendship 7" spacecraft, 1962 (first manned earth orbit) .. 15 20
2024 45 c. "Apollo 8" orbiting Moon, 1968 (first manned lunar orbit) .. 20 25
2025 70 c. "Apollo 15" lunar rover, 1972 .. .. 30 35
2026 $1 "Apollo 11" emblem and lunar module "Eagle" on Moon, 1969 40 45
2027 $2 "Gemini 8" and "Agena" rocket, 1966 (first space docking) .. 85 90
2028 $3 Edward White in space, 1965 (first U.S. space walk) .. .. 1·25 1·40
2029 $4 "Apollo 7" emblem .. 1·75 1·90

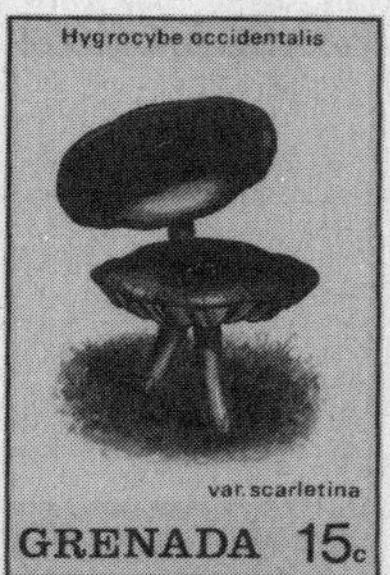

348 "Hygrocybe occidentalis"

1989. Fungi. Multicoloured.

2031 15 c. Type **348** 10 10
2032 40 c. "Marasmius haematocephalus" .. 15 20
2033 50 c. "Hygrocybe hypohaemacta" .. 20 25
2034 70 c. "Lepiota pseudoignicolor" .. 30 35
2035 90 c. "Cookeina tricholoma" 40 45
2036 $1.10 "Leucopaxillus gracillimus" 45 50
2037 $2.25 "Hygrocybe nigrescens" .. .. 95 1·00
2038 $4 "Clathrus crispus" .. 1·75 1·90

349 Y.W.C.A. Logo and Grenada Scenery

1989. Centenary of Young Women's Christian Association. Multicoloured.

2040 50 c. Type **349** 20 25
2041 75 c. Y.W.C.A. logo and town (horiz) 30 35

350 "Historis odius"

1989. Butterflies. Multicoloured.

2042 6 c. Type **350** 10 10
2043 30 c. "Marpesia petreus" 10 15
2044 40 c. "Danaus gilippus" 15 20
2045 60 c. "Dione juno" .. 25 30
2046 $1.10 "Agraulis vanillae" 45 50
2047 $1.25 "Danaus plexippus" 50 55
2048 $4 "Papilio androgeus" 1·75 1·90
2049 $5 "Dryas julia" .. 2·10 2·25

351 Amerindian Hieroglyph

1989. 500th Anniv (1992) of Discovery of America by Columbus (2nd issue). Designs showing different hieroglyphs.

2051 **351** 45 c. brown, blk & bl 20 25
2052 – 60 c. brown, blk & grn 25 30
2053 – $1 black, black & vio 40 45
2054 – $4 dp brn , blk & brn 1·75 1·90

352 Amos leaving Home

1989. "World Stamp Expo '89" International Stamp Exhibition, Washington. Designs showing Walt Disney cartoon characters in scenes from "Ben and Me". Multicoloured.

2056 1 c. Type **352** 10 10
2057 2 c. Meeting of Benjamin Franklin and Amos .. 10 10
2058 3 c. The Franklin stove .. 10 10
2059 4 c. Ben and Amos with bi-focals 10 10
2060 5 c. Amos on page of "Pennsylvania Gazette" 10 10
2061 6 c. Ben working printing press 10 10
2062 10 c. Conducting experiment with electricity .. 10 10
2063 $5 Ben disembarking in England .. .. 2·10 2·25
2064 $6 Ben with Document of Agreement .. .. 2·50 2·25

1990. Christmas. Paintings by Rubens. As T **259** of Antigua. Multicoloured.

2066 20 c. "Christ in the House of Mary and Martha" 10 10
2067 35 c. "The Circumcision" 15 20
2068 60 c. "Trinity adored by Duke of Mantua and Family" 25 30
2069 $2 "Holy Family with St. Francis" 85 90
2070 $3 "The Ildefonso Altarpiece" .. .. 1·25 1·40
2071 $4 "Madonna and Child with Garland and Putti" .. .. 1·75 1·90

353 Alexander Graham Bell and Early Telephone System (150th anniv of invention)

1990. Anniversaries. Multicoloured.

2073 10 c. Type **353** 10 10
2074 25 c. George Washington and Capitol (bicentenary of presidential inauguration) 10 15
2075 35 c. Shakespeare and birthplace, Stratford (425th birth anniv) .. 15 20
2076 75 c. Nehru and Gandhi (birth cent of Nehru) .. 30 35
2077 $1 Dr. Hugo Eckener, Ferdinand von Zeppelin and Zeppelin "Delag" (80th anniv of first passenger Zeppelin) .. 40 45
2078 $2 Charlie Chaplin (birth cent) 85 90
2079 $3 Container ship in Hamburg Harbour (800th anniv) .. .. 1·25 1·40
2080 $4 Friedrich Ebert (first President) and Heidelberg gate (70th anniv of German Republic) .. 1·75 1·90

No. 2080 is inscribed "40th Anniversary of German Republic" in error.

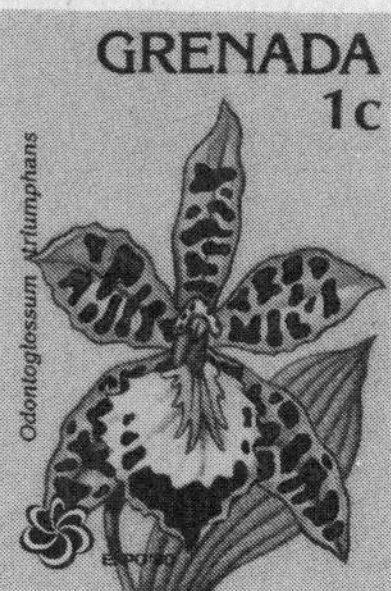

354 "Odontoglossum triumphans"

1990. "EXPO '90" International Garden and Greenery Exhibition, Osaka. Caribbean Orchids. Multicoloured.

2082 1 c. Type **354** 10 10
2083 25 c. "Oncidium splendidum" 10 15
2084 60 c. "Laelia anceps" .. 25 30
2085 75 c. "Cattleya trianaei" 30 35
2086 $1 "Odontoglossum rossii" 40 45
2087 $2 "Brassia gireoudiana" 85 90
2088 $3 "Cattleya dowiana" 1·25 1·40
2089 $4 "Sobralia macrantha" 1·75 1·90

1990. 500th Anniv (1992) of Discovery of America by Columbus (3rd issue). New World Natural History—Butterflies. As T **260** of Antigua. Multicoloured.

2091 15 c. "Marpesia petreus" 10 10
2092 25 c. "Junonia evarete" 10 15
2093 75 c. "Siproeta stelenes" 30 35
2094 90 c. "Historis odius" .. 40 45
2095 $1 "Mestra cana" .. 40 45
2096 $2 "Biblis hyperia" .. 85 90
2097 $3 "Dryas julia" .. 1·25 1·40
2098 $4 "Anartia amathea" .. 1·75 1·90

1990. Local Fauna. As T **254** of Antigua. Multicoloured.

2100 10 c. Caribbean monk seal 10 10
2101 15 c. Little brown bat .. 10 10
2102 45 c. Brown rat 20 25
2103 60 c. Common rabbit .. 25 30
2104 $1 Water opossum .. 40 45
2105 $2 White-nosed ichneumon 85 90
2106 $3 Little big-eared bat (vert) .. .. 1·25 1·40
2107 $4 Mouse opossum .. 1·75 1·90

1990. 50th Anniv of Second World War. As T **274** of Antigua. Multicoloured.

2109 25 c. British tanks during Operation Battleaxe, 1941 .. .. .. 10 10
2110 35 c. Allied tank in southern France, 1944 15 20
2111 45 c. U.S. forces landing on Guadalcanal, 1942 .. 20 20
2112 50 c. U.S. attack in New Guinea, 1943 .. .. 20 20

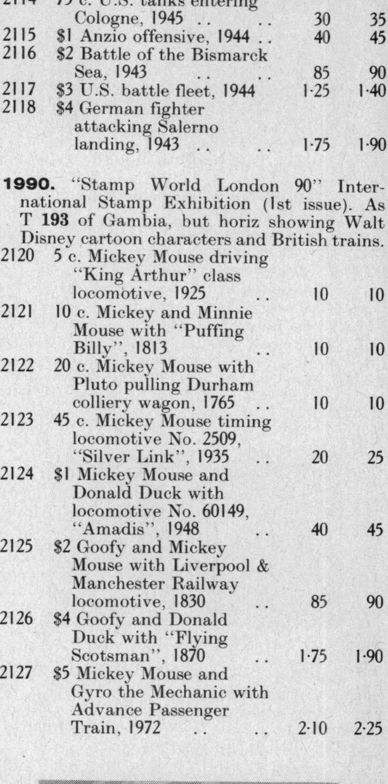
2113 60 c. Hoisting U.S. flag on Leyte, Phillippines, 1944 25 30
2114 75 c. U.S. tanks entering Cologne, 1945 .. .. 30 35
2115 $1 Anzio offensive, 1944 .. 40 45
2116 $2 Battle of the Bismarck Sea, 1943 .. .. 85 90
2117 $3 U.S. battle fleet, 1944 1·25 1·40
2118 $4 German fighter attacking Salerno landing, 1943 .. .. 1·75 1·90

1990. "Stamp World London 90" International Stamp Exhibition (1st issue). As T **193** of Gambia, but horiz showing Walt Disney cartoon characters and British trains.

2120 5 c. Mickey Mouse driving "King Arthur" class locomotive, 1925 .. 10 10
2121 10 c. Mickey and Minnie Mouse with "Puffing Billy", 1813 .. 10 10
2122 20 c. Mickey Mouse with Pluto pulling Durham colliery wagon, 1765 .. 10 10
2123 45 c. Mickey Mouse timing locomotive No. 2509, "Silver Link", 1935 .. 20 25
2124 $1 Mickey Mouse and Donald Duck with locomotive No. 60149, "Amadis", 1948 .. 40 45
2125 $2 Goofy and Mickey Mouse with Liverpool & Manchester Railway locomotive, 1830 .. 85 90
2126 $4 Goofy and Donald Duck with "Flying Scotsman", 1870 .. 1·75 1·90
2127 $5 Mickey Mouse and Gyro the Mechanic with Advance Passenger Train, 1972 .. .. 2·10 2·25

355 U.S. Paratroop Drop over Grenada

1990. 50th Anniv of United States' Airborne Forces.

2129 **355** 75 c. multicoloured .. 30 35

1990. 90th birthday of Queen Elizabeth the Queen Mother. As T **194** of Gambia showing photographs from the 1960s. Multicoloured.

2131 $2 Queen Mother in coat and hat 85 90
2132 $2 Queen Mother in evening dress 85 90
2133 $2 Queen Mother in Garter robes .. 85 90

1990. Olympic Games, Barcelona (1992). As T **268** of Antigua. Multicoloured.

2135 10 c. Men's steeplechase 10 10
2136 15 c. Dressage 10 10
2137 45 c. Men's 200 m. butterfly swimming 20 25
2138 50 c. Men's hockey .. 20 25
2139 65 c. Women's beam gymnastics 25 30
2140 75 c. "Flying Dutchman" class yachting .. 30 35
2141 $2 Freestyle wrestling .. 85 90
2142 $3 Men's springboard diving .. .. .. 1·25 1·40
2143 $4 Women's 1000 m. sprint cycling .. .. 1·75 1·90
2144 $5 Men's basketball .. 2·10 2·25

357 Yellow Goatfish

1990. Coral Reef Fishes. Multicoloured.

2147 10 c. Type **357** 10 10
2148 25 c. Black margate .. 10 10
2149 65 c. Bluehead wrasse .. 25 30
2150 75 c. Pudding wife .. 30 35
2151 $1 Foureye butterflyfish 40 45
2152 $2 Honey damselfish .. 85 90
2153 $3 Queen angelfish .. 1·25 1·40
2154 $5 Cherubfish .. .. 2·10 2·25

358 Tropical Mockingbird

1990. Birds. Multicoloured.

2156 15 c. Type **358** 10 10
2157 25 c. Grey kingbird 10 10
2158 65 c. Bare-eyed thrush .. 25 30
2159 75 c. Antillean crested hummingbird 30 35
2160 $1 House wren 40 45
2161 $2 Purple martin .. 85 90
2162 $4 Hooded tanager .. 1·75 1·90
2163 $5 Scaly-breasted ground dove .. .. .. 2·10 2·25

359 Coral Crab

1990. Crustaceans. Multicoloured.

2165 5 c. Type **359** 10 10
2166 10 c. Smoothtail spiny lobster 10 10
2167 15 c. Flamestreaked box crab 10 10
2168 25 c. Spotted swimming crab 10 10
2169 75 c. Sally lightfoot rock crab 30 35
2170 $1 Spotted spiny lobster 40 45
2171 $3 Longarm spiny lobster 1·25 1·40
2172 $20 Caribbean spiny lobster .. .. 8·50 8·75

360 Cameroon Player

1990. World Cup Football Championship, Italy (2nd issue). Multicoloured.

2174 10 c. Type **360** 10 10
2175 25 c. Michel (Spain) .. 10 10
2176 $1 Brehme (West Germany) 40 45
2177 $5 Nevin (Scotland) .. 2·10 2·25

1990. Christmas. Paintings by Raphael. As T **272** of Antigua. Multicoloured.

2180 10 c. "The Ansidei Madonna" (vert) .. 10 10
2181 15 c. "The Sistine Madonna"(vert) .. 10 10
2182 $1 "The Madonna of the Baldacchino" (vert) .. 40 45
2183 $2 "The Large Holy Family" (detail) (vert) 85 90
2184 $5 "Madonna in the Meadow" (vert) .. 2·10 2·25

1991. 350th Death Anniv of Rubens. As T **273** of Antigua. Multicoloured.

2186 5 c. "The Brazen Serpent" (detail) 10 10
2187 10 c. "The Garden of Love" 10 10
2188 25 c. "Head of Cyrus" (detail) 10 10
2189 75 c. "Tournament in Front of a Castle" .. 30 35
2190 $1 "The Brazen Serpent" (different detail) 40 45
2191 $2 "Judgement of Paris" (detail) 85 90
2192 $4 "The Brazen Serpent" 1·75 1·90
2193 $5 "The Karmesse" (detail) .. .. 2·10 2·25

362 "The Sorcerer's Apprentice"

1991. 50th Anniv of "Fantasia" (cartoon film). Multicoloured.

2195 5 c. Type **362** 10 10
2196 10 c. Dancing mushrooms ("The Nutcracker Suite") 10 10
2197 20 c. Pterodactyls ("The Rite of Spring") .. 10 10
2198 45 c. Centaurs ("The Pastoral Symphony") 20 25
2199 $1 Bacchus and Jacchus ("The Pastoral Symphony") .. 40 45
2200 $2 Dancing ostrich ("Dance of the Hours") 85 90
2201 $4 Elephant ballet ("Dance of the Hours") 1·75 1·90
2202 $5 Diana ("The Pastoral Symphony") .. 2·10 2·25

363 "Adelpha iphicla"

1991. Butterflies. Multicoloured.

2205 5 c. Type **363** 10 10
2206 10 c. "Nymphalidae claudina" 10 10
2207 15 c. "Brassolidae polyxena" 10 10
2208 20 c. "Zebra Longwing" 10 10
2209 25 c. "Marpesia corinna" 10 10
2210 30 c. "Morpho hecuba" .. 10 15
2211 45 c. "Morpho rhetenor" 20 25
2212 50 c. "Dismorphia spio" 20 25
2213 60 c. "Prepona omphale" 25 30
2214 70 c. "Morpho anaxibia" 30 35
2215 75 c. "Marpesia iole" .. 30 35
2216 $1 "Amarynthis meneria" 40 45
2217 $2 "Morpho cisseis" .. 85 90
2218 $3 "Danaidae plexippus" 1·25 1·50
2219 $4 "Morpho achilleana" 1·75 1·90
2220 $5 "Calliona argenissa" 2·10 2·25

1991. 500th Anniv (1992) of Discovery of America by Columbus. History of Exploration. As T **194** of British Virgin Islands. Multicoloured.

2222 5 c. Vitus Bering in Bering Sea, 1728–9 .. 10 10
2223 10 c. De Bougainville off Pacific island, 1766–69 10 10
2224 25 c. Polynesian canoe .. 10 10
2225 50 c. De Mendana off Solomon Islands, 1567–69 20 25
2226 $1 Darwin's H.M.S. "Beagle", 1831–35 .. 40 45
2227 $2 Cook's H.M.S. "Endeavour", 1768–71 85 90
2228 $4 Willem Schouten in LeMaire Strait, 1615–17 1·75 1·90
2229 $5 Tasman off New Zealand, 1642–44 .. 2·10 2·25

1991. "Philanippon '91" International Stamp Exhibition, Tokyo. As T **248** of Dominica showing Walt Disney cartoon characters at Japanese festivals. Multicoloured.

2231 5 c. Minnie Mouse and Daisy Duck at Dolls festival 10 10
2232 10 c. Morty and Ferdie with Boys' Day display 10 10
2233 20 c. Mickey and Minnie Mouse at Star festival 10 10
2234 45 c. Minnie and Daisy folk-dancing .. 20 25
2235 $1 Huey, Dewey and Louie wearing Eboshi headdresses .. 40 45
2236 $2 Mickey and Goofy pulling decorated cart at Gion festival .. 85 90
2237 $4 Minnie and Daisy preparing rice broth, Seven Plants festival .. 1·75 1·90
2238 $5 Huey and Dewey with straw boat at Lanterns festival .. .. 2·10 2·25

1991. Death Centenary (1990) of Vincent van Gogh (artist). As T **195** of British Virgin Islands. Multicoloured.

2240 20 c. "Blossoming Almond Branch in Glass" .. 10 10
2241 25 c. "La Mousme sitting" 10 10
2242 30 c. "Still Life with Red Cabbages and Onions" (horiz) 10 15
2243 40 c. "Japonaiserie: Flowering Plum Tree" 15 20
2244 45 c. "Japonaiserie: Bridge in Rain" .. 20 25
2245 60 c. "Still Life with Basket of Apples" (horiz) 25 30
2246 75 c. "Italian Woman" .. 30 35
2247 $1 "The Painter on his Way to Work" .. 40 45
2248 $2 "Portrait of Pere Tanguy" 85 90
2249 $3 "Still Life with Plaster Statuette, a Rose and Two Novels" .. 1·25 1·40
2250 $4 "Still Life: Bottle, Lemons and Oranges" (horiz) .. .. 1·75 1·90
2251 $5 "Orchard with Blossoming Apricot Trees" (horiz) .. 2·10 2·25

364 "Psilocybe cubensis"

1991. Fungi. Multicoloured.

2253 15 c. Type **364** 10 10
2254 25 c. "Leptonia caeruleo-capitata" 10 10
2255 65 c. "Cystolepiota eriophora" 25 30
2256 75 c. "Chlorophyllum molybdites" 30 35
2257 $1 "Xerocomus hypo-xanthus" 40 45
2258 $2 "Volvariella cubensis" 85 90
2259 $4 "Xerocomus cocco-lobae" .. .. 1·75 1·90
2260 $5 "Pluteus chryso-phlebius" .. .. 2·10 2·25

365 Johannes Kepler (astronomer)

1991. Exploration of Mars. Designs showing astronomers, spacecraft and Martian land-scapes. Multicoloured.

2262/97 75 c.×9, $1.25×9, $2×9, $7×9 .. Set of 36 40·00 42·00

1991. 65th Birthday of Queen Elizabeth II. As T **280** of Antigua. Multicoloured.

2299 15 c. Royal Family on balcony after Trooping the Colour, 1985 .. 10 10
2300 40 c. Queen and Prince Philip at Peterborough, 1988 .. .. .. 20 25
2301 $2 Queen and Queen Mother at Windsor, 1986 .. .. .. 85 90
2302 $4 Queen and Prince Philip on visit to United Arab Emirates 1·75 1·90

1991. 10th Wedding Anniv of the Prince and Princess of Wales. As T **280** of Antigua. Multicoloured.

2304 10 c. Prince and Princess in July 1985 .. 10 10
2305 50 c. Separate photo-graphs of Prince, Princess and sons 20 25
2306 $1 Prince Henry at Trooping the Colour and Prince William in Majorca 40 45
2307 $5 Separate photographs of Prince Charles and Princess Diana .. 2·10 2·25

366 Anglican High School Pupils

1991. 75th Anniv of Anglican High School (10, 25 c.) and 40th Anniv of University of the West Indies (45, 50 c.). Multicoloured.

2309 10 c. Type **366** 10 10
2310 25 c. Artist's impression of new Anglican High School 10 10
2311 45 c. Marryshow House, Grenada 20 25
2312 50 c. University Adminis-trative Building, Barbados 20 25

OFFICIAL STAMPS

1982. Optd. **P.R.G.** (a) Nos. 1085/97 and 1099.

O 1. 5 c. West Indiaman barque, c. 1840 .. .. .. 15 10
O 2. 6 c. R.M.S.P. "Orinoco", c. 1851 .. .. .. 15 10
O 3. 10 c. Working Schooner .. 15 10
O 4. 12 c. Trimaran at Grand Anse anchorage .. 15 10
O 5. 15 c. Spice Island cruising yacht "Petite Amie" 20 15
O 6. 20 c. Fishing pirogue .. 25 15
O 7. 25 c. Harbour police launch 30 20
O 8. 30 c. Grand Anse speedboat 30 25
O 9. 40 c. M.V. "Seimstrand" 35 30
O10. 50 c. Three-masted schooner "Ariadne" 40 30
O11. 90 c. M.V. "Geestide" .. 70 70
O12. $1 M.V. "Cunard Countess" 70 70
O13. $3 Rum-runner .. .. 2·00 3·25
O14. $10 Coast-guard patrol boat .. .. .. 6·00 11·00

(b) Nos. 1130/2. and 113/4.

O 15. 30 c. Prince Charles and Lady Diana Spencer .. 1·75 2·25
O 16. 40 c. Holyrood House .. 2·25 2·75
O 17. 50 c. Prince Charles and Lady Diana Spencer .. 1·25 1·75
O 18. $2 Holyrood House .. 2·75 3·50
O 19. $4 Type **268** .. .. 6·50 8·00

POSTAGE DUE STAMPS

D 1.

1892.

D 8. D **1.** 1d. black .. .. 2·00 3·75
D 9. 2d. black .. .. 5·50 1·75
D 10. 3d. black .. .. 9·00 5·50

1892. Surch. **SURCHARGE POSTAGE** and value.

D 4. **13.** 1d. on 6d. mauve .. 42·00 1·25
D 5. 1d. on 8d. brown .. £275 3·25
D 6. 2d. on 6d. mauve .. 80·00 2·50
D 7. 2d. on 8d. brown .. £550 9·00

1921. As Type D **1** but inscr. "POSTAGE DUE" instead of "SURCHARGE POSTAGE".

D 11. D **1.** 1d. black .. .. 90 1·00
D 12. 1½d. black .. .. 6·00 9·25
D 13. 2d. black .. .. 2·00 1·75
D 14. 3d. black .. .. 2·00 3·50

1952. As last but currency changed.

D 15. D **1.** 2 c. black .. .. 30 3·75
D 16. 4 c. black .. .. 30 7·00
D 17. 6 c. black .. .. 45 8·50
D 18. 8 c. black .. .. 75 8·50

GRENADINES OF GRENADA

The southern part of the group, attached to Grenada. Main islands Petit Martinique and Carriacou.

100 cents = 1 dollar.

1973. Royal Wedding. Nos. 582/3 of Grenada optd. **GRENADINES.**

1. **196.** 25 c. multicoloured .. 20 10
2. $2 multicoloured .. 70 50

1974. Stamps of Grenada optd. **GRENADINES.**

4. 1 c. multicoloured (No. 306) 10 10
5. 2 c. multicoloured (No. 307) 10 10
6. 3 c. multicoloured (No. 308) 10 10
7. 5 c. multicoloured (No. 309) 10 10
8. 8 c. multicoloured (No. 311) 10 10
9. 10 c. multicoloured (No. 312) 10 10
10. 12 c. multicoloured (No. 313) 15 10
11. 25 c. multicoloured (No. 315) 25 10
12. $1 multicoloured (No. 318).. 1·75 45
13. $2 multicoloured (No. 319).. 2·50 1·00
14. $3 multicoloured (No. 320).. 2·50 1·50
15. $5 multicoloured (No. 321).. 3·50 1·75

1974. World Cup Football Championships. As Nos. 619/26 of Grenada inscr. "GRENADA GRENADINES".

16. ½ c. multicoloured 10 10
17. 1 c. multicoloured 10 10
18. 2 c. multicoloured 10 10
19. 10 c. multicoloured 10 10
20. 25 c. multicoloured 10 10
21. 50 c. multicoloured 15 15
22. 75 c. multicoloured 20 20
23. $1 multicoloured 25 25

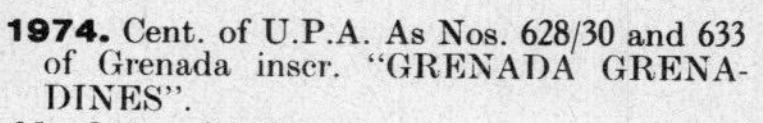

1974. Cent. of U.P.A. As Nos. 628/30 and 633 of Grenada inscr. "GRENADA GRENADINES".

25. 8 c. multicoloured 10 10
26. 25 c. multicoloured 15 10
27. 35 c. multicoloured 15 10
28. $1 multicoloured 50 40

1974. Birth Cent. of Sir Winston Churchill. As Nos. 637/8 of Grenada inscr. "GRENADA GRENADINES".

30. 35 c. multicoloured 15 10
31. $2 multicoloured 40 45

1974. Christmas. As Nos. 640/7 of Grenada, but inscr. "GRENADA GRENADINES" and background colours changed.

33. **204.** ½ c. multicoloured .. 10 10
34. – 1 c. multicoloured .. 10 10
35. – 2 c. multicoloured .. 10 10
36. – 3 c. multicoloured .. 10 10
37. – 10 c. multicoloured .. 10 10
38. – 25 c. multicoloured .. 10 10
39. – 50 c. multicoloured .. 15 15
40. – $1 multicoloured .. 30 25

1975. Big Game Fishing. As Nos. 669/76 of Grenada inscr. "GRENADA GRENADINES" and background colours changed.

42. ½ c. multicoloured .. 10 10
43. 1 c. multicoloured .. 10 10
44. 2 c. multicoloured .. 10 10
45. 10 c. multicoloured .. 10 10
46. 25 c. multicoloured .. 15 10
47. 50 c. multicoloured .. 20 15
48. 70 c. multicoloured .. 25 20
49. $1 multicoloured .. 35 35

1975. Flowers. As Nos. 678/85 of Grenada inscr. "GRENADINES".

51. ½ c. multicoloured 10 10
52. 1 c. multicoloured 10 10
53. 2 c. multicoloured 10 10
54. 3 c. multicoloured 10 10
55. 10 c. multicoloured .. 10 10
56. 25 c. multicoloured .. 10 10
57. 50 c. multicoloured .. 20 15
58. $1 multicoloured 30 20

CANCELLED REMAINDERS. Some of the following issues have been remaindered, cancelled-to-order, at a fraction of their face value. For all practical purposes these are indistinguishable from genuine postally used copies. Our used quotations which are indicated by an asterisk are the same for cancelled-to-order or postally used copies.

3. " Christ Crowned with Thorns " (Titian).

1975. Easter. Paintings showing Crucifixion and Deposition by artists listed. Multicoloured.

60. ½ c. Type **3** 10 10*
61. 1 c. Giotto 10 10*
62. 2 c. Tintoretto 10 10*
63. 3 c. Cranach 10 10*
64. 35 c. Caravaggio 10 10*
65. 75 c. Tiepolo 10 10*
66. $2 Velasquez 30 15*

4. " Dawn " (detail from Medici tomb).

1975. 500th Birth Anniv. of Michelangelo. Multicoloured.

68. ½ c. Type **4** 10 10*
69. 1 c. " Delphic Sibyl " .. 10 10*
70. 2 c. " Giuliano de Medici "
71. 40 c. " The Creation " (detail) 10 10*
.. 25 10*
72. 50 c. " Lorenzo de Medici " 25 10*
73. 75 c. " Persian Sibyl " .. 25 10*
74. $2 " Head of Christ " .. 50 10*

1975. Butterflies. As T **213** of Grenada but inscr "GRENADINES". Multicoloured.

76. ½ c. "Morpho peleides" .. 10 10
77. 1 c. "Danaus eresimus" ("Danaus gilippus") .. 10 10
78. 2 c. "Dismorphia amphione" 10 10
79. 35 c. "Hamadryas feronia" 35 15
80. 45 c. "Philaethria dido" .. 45 15
81. 75 c. "Phoebis argante" .. 70 25
82. $2 "Prepona laertes" 1·40 70

5. Progress " Standard " Badge.

1975. 14th World Scout Jamboree, Norway. Multicoloured.

84. ½ c. Type **5** 10 10*
85. 1 c. Boatman's badge .. 10 10*
86. 2 c. Coxswain's badge .. 10 10*
87. 35 c. Interpreter's badge .. 25 10*
88. 45 c. Ambulance badge .. 25 10*
89. 75 c. Chief Scout's award .. 35 10*
90. $2 Queen's Scout award .. 70 15*

6. The Surrender of Lord Cornwallis.

1975. Bicentenary of American Revolution (1976) (1st issue). Multicoloured.

92. ½ c. Type **6** 10 10*
93. 1 c. Minute-men 10 10*
94. 2 c. Paul Revere's ride .. 10 10*
95. 3 c. Battle of Bunker Hill 10 10*
96. 5 c. Fifer and drummer .. 10 10*
97. 45 c. Backwoodsman .. 50 10*
98. 75 c. Boston Tea Party .. 65 10*
99. $2 Naval engagement .. 1·50 10*
100. $2 George Washington .. 1·50 1·00
101. $2 White House and flags 1·50 1·00

Nos. 100/1 are larger, 35 × 60 mm.

7. Fencing.

1975. Pan-American Games, Mexico City. Multicoloured.

103. ½ c. Type **7** 10 10*
104. 1 c. Hurdling 10 10*
105. 2 c. Pole-vaulting .. 10 10*
106. 35 c. Weightlifting .. 15 10*
107. 45 c. Throwing the javelin 15 10*
108. 75 c. Throwing the discus 15 10*
109. $2 Diving 35 15*

1975. Nos. 649/68 of Grenada additionally inscr. " GRENADINES ".

111. ½ c. Yachts, Port Saline .. 10 20
112. 1 c. Yacht Club race, St. George's 10 15
113. 2 c. Carenage taxi .. 10 15
114. 3 c. Large working boats .. 10 15
115. 5 c. Deep-water dock, St. George's 10 15
116. 6 c. Cocoa beans in drying trays 10 15
117. 8 c. Nutmegs 10 15
118. 10 c. Rum distillery, River Antoine Estate, c. 1785 10 15
119. 12 c. Cocoa tree 10 15
120. 15 c. Fishermen at Fontenoy 10 15
121. 20 c. Parliament Building 10 15
122. 25 c. Fort George cannons 10 15
123. 35 c. Pearls Airport .. 15 15
124. 50 c. General Post Office .. 20 30
125. 75 c. Caribs Leap, Sauteurs Bay 40 50
126. $1 Carenage, St. George's 60 70
127. $2 St. George's Harbour by night .. .. .. 1·25 1·75
128. $3 Grand Anse beach .. 1·75 2·25
129. $5 Canoe Bay and Black Bay .. .. .. 3·00 4·25
130. $10 Sugar-loaf Island .. 5·00 5·50

8. " Virgin and Child " (Durer).

1975. Christmas. " Virgin and Child " paintings by Artists named. Mult.

131. ½ c. Type **8** 10 10*
132. 1 c. Durer 10 10*
133. 2 c. Correggio 10 10*
134. 40 c. Botticelli 10 10*
135. 50 c. Niccolo da Cremona 10 10*
136. 75 c. Correggio 15 10*
137. $2 Correggio 30 15*

9. Bleeding Tooth.

1976. Shells. Multicoloured.

139. ½ c. Type **9** 10 10*
140. 1 c. Wedge Clam 10 10*
141. 2 c. Hawk Wing Conch .. 10 10*
142. 3 c. " Distorsio clathrata " 10 10*
143. 25 c. Scotch Bonnet .. 20 10*
144. 50 c. King Helmet .. 40 10*
145. 75 c. Queen Conch .. 65 15*

10. Cocoa Thrush.

1976. Flora and Fauna. Multicoloured.

147 ½ c. "Lignum vitae" .. 10 10
148 1 c. Type **10** 10 10
149 2 c. "Eurypelma sp." (spider) 10 10
150 35 c. Hooded tanager .. 80 40
151 50 c. "Nyctaginaceae" .. 90 70
152 75 c. Grenada dove .. 2·00 1·50
153 $1 Marine toad .. 2·00 1·75

11. Hooked Sailfish.

1976. Tourism. Multicoloured.

155. ½ c. Type **11** 10 10
156. 1 c. Careened schooner, Carriacou 10 10
157. 2 c. Carriacou Annual Regatta 10 15
158. 18 c. Boat building on Carriacou 15 15
159. 22 c. Workboat race, Carriacou Regatta .. 15 15
160. 75 c. Cruising off Petit Martinique 30 45
161. $1 Water skiing 40 65

12. Making a Camp Fire.

1976. 50th Anniv. of Girl Guides in Grenada. Multicoloured.

163. ½ c. Type **12** 10 10
164. 1 c. First Aid 10 10
165. 2 c. Nature Study .. 10 10
166. 50 c. Cookery 40 50
167. $1 Sketching .. .. 80 1·25

13. " Christ Mocked " (Bosch).

1976. Easter. Multicoloured.

169. ½ c. Type **13** 10 10
170. 1 c. " Christ Crucified " (Antonello da Messina) 10 10
171. 2 c. " Adoration of the Trinity " (Durer) .. 10 10
172. 3 c. " Lamentation of Christ " (Durer) .. 10 10
173. 35 c. " The Entombment " (Van der Weyden) .. 15 10
174. $3 " The Entombment " (Raphael) .. .. 60 1·25

14. Frigate " South Carolina ".

1976. Bicentenary of American Revolution (2nd issue). Multicoloured.

176. ½ c. Type **14** 10 15
177. 1 c. Schooner "Lee" .. 10 15
178. 2 c. H.M.S. "Roebuck" .. 10 15
179. 35 c. "Andrea Doria" .. 60 55
180. 50 c. Sloop "The Providence" .. .. .. 80 1·00
181. $1 American frigate "Alfred" .. .. .. 2·00 2·25
182. $2 Frigate "Confederacy" 3·25 3·75

15. Piper " Apache ".

1976. Aeroplanes. Multicoloured.

184. ½ c. Type **15** 10 10
185. 1 c. Beech " Twin Bonanza " 10 10
186. 2 c. D.H. " Twin Otter " 10 10
187. 40 c. Britten Norman " Islander " 30 40
188. 50 c. D.H. " Heron " .. 40 45
189. $2 H.S. " 748 " .. .. 1·25 2·00

16. Cycling.

1976. Olympic Games, Montreal. Mult.

191. ½ c. Type **16** 10 10
192. 1 c. Pommel horse .. 10 10
193. 2 c. Hurdling 10 10
194. 35 c. Shot putting .. 10 10
195. 45 c. Diving 15 15
196. 75 c. Sprinting 15 20
197. $2 Rowing 35 65

17. " Virgin and Child " (Cima).

1976. Christmas. Multicoloured.

199.	½ c. Type **17**	10	10
200.	1 c. " The Nativity " (Romanino)	10	10
201.	2 c. " The Nativity " (Romanino) (different)	10	10
202.	35 c. " Adoration of the Kings " (Bruegel) ..	10	10
203.	50 c. " Madonna and Child " (Girolamo)	15	20
204.	75 c. " Adoration of the Magi " (Giorgione) (horiz.)	15	25
205.	$2 " Adoration of the Kings " (School of Fra Angelico) (horiz.)	30	70

18. Alexander Graham Bell and First Telephone.

1977. Centenary of First Telephone Transmission. T **18** and similar horiz. designs showing Alexander Graham Bell and telephone. Multicoloured.

207.	½ c. Type **18**	10	10
208.	1 c. 1895 telephone ..	10	10
209.	2 c. 1900 telephone ..	10	10
210.	35 c. 1915 telephone ..	15	10
211.	75 c. 1920 telephone ..	30	40
212.	$1 1929 telephone ..	50	75
213.	$2 1963 telephone ..	75	1·40

19. Coronation Coach.

1977. Silver Jubilee. Multicoloured. (a) Perf.

215.	35 c. Type **19**	10	10
216.	$2 Queen entering Abbey	30	20
217.	$4 Queen crowned ..	55	45

(b) Imperf. × roul. Self-adhesive.

219.	35 c. Royal visit ..	15	20
220.	50 c. Crown of St. Edward	40	80
221.	$2 The Queen and Prince Charles	1·50	1·60
222.	$5 Royal Standard ..	1·60	1·75

Nos. 219/22 come from booklets.

21. "Disrobing of Christ" (Fra Angelico).

1977. Easter. Paintings by artists named. Multicoloured.

223.	½ c. Type **21**	10	10
224.	1 c. Fra Angelico	10	10
225.	2 c. El Greco	10	10
226.	18 c. El Greco	10	10
227.	35 c. Fra Angelico ..	10	10
228.	50 c. Giottino	15	30
229.	$2 Antonello da Messina ..	40	85

22. "The Virgin adoring the Child" (Correggio).

1977. Christmas. Multicoloured.

231.	½ c. Type **22**	10	10
232.	1 c. " Virgin and Child " (Giorgione)	10	10
233.	2 c. " Virgin and Child " (Morales)	10	10
234.	18 c. " Madonna della Tenda " (Raphael) ..	10	10
235.	35 c. " Rest on the Flight into Egypt " (Van Dyck)	10	10
236.	50 c. " Madonna and Child " (Lippi)	15	30
237.	$2 " Virgin and Child " (Lippi) (different) ..	40	85

1977. Royal Visit. Nos. 215/17 optd. **Royal Visit W.I. 1977.**

239.	35 c. Type **19**	15	10
240.	$2 Queen entering Abbey	40	30
241.	$4 Queen crowned ..	70	50

24. Life-saving.

1977. Caribbean Scout Jamboree, Jamaica. Multicoloured.

243.	½ c. Type **24**	10	10
244.	1 c. Overnight hike ..	10	10
245.	2 c. Cubs tying knots ..	10	10
246.	22 c. Erecting a tent ..	15	10
247.	35 c. Gang show limbo dance	25	10
248.	75 c. Campfire cooking ..	50	55
249.	$3 Sea Scout's yacht race	1·75	3·25

25. Blast-off.

1977. Space Shuttle. Multicoloured.

251.	½ c. Type **25**	10	10
252.	1 c. Booster jettison ..	10	10
253.	2 c. External tank jettison	10	10
254.	22 c. Working in orbit ..	15	15
255.	50 c. Shuttle re-entry ..	30	30
256.	$3 Shuttle landing ..	1·25	1·00

26. Alfred Nobel and Physiology/Medicine Medal.

1978. Nobel Prize Awards. Multicoloured.

258.	½ c. Type **26**	10	10
259.	1 c. Physics and Chemistry medal	10	10
260.	2 c. Peace medal (reverse)	10	10
261.	22 c. Nobel Institute, Oslo	15	15
262.	75 c. Peace Prize committee	45	45
263.	$3 Literature medal ..	1·25	1·25

27. German Zeppelin Stamp, 1930.

1978. 75th Anniv. of 1st Zeppelin Flight and 50th Anniv. of Lindbergh's Transatlantic Flight. Multicoloured.

265.	5 c. Type **27**	15	10
266.	15 c. French " Concorde " stamp, 1970	20	10
267.	25 c. Liechtenstein Zeppelin stamp, 1931 ..	25	10
268.	35 c. Panama Lindbergh stamp, 1928	25	10
269.	50 c. Russia Airship stamp, 1931	35	20
270.	$3 Spanish Lindbergh stamp, 1930	1·25	1·10

28. Coronation Ring.

1978. 25th Anniv. of Coronation. Mult. (a) Horiz. designs. Perf.

272.	50 c. Type **28**	20	15
273.	$2 The Orb	50	40
274.	$2.50 Imperial State Crown	55	45

(b) Vert. designs. Roul. × imperf. Self-adhesive.

276.	18 c. Drummer, Royal Regiment of Fusiliers ..	25	35
277.	50 c. Drummer, Royal Anglian Regiment ..	25	45
278.	$5 Drum Major, Queen's Regiment	2·25	3·00

Nos. 276/8 come from booklets.

30. " Le Chapeau de Paille ".

1978. 400th Birth Anniv. of Rubens. Mult.

279.	5 c. Type **30**	10	10
280.	15 c. " Achilles slaying Hector "	10	10
281.	18 c. " Helene Fourment and her Children " ..	10	10
282.	22 c. " Rubens and Isabella Brandt "	15	10
283.	35 c. The Ildefonso Altarpiece	15	10
284.	$3 " Heads of negros " (detail)	80	80

31. Wright " Flyer I ".

1978. 75th Anniv. of Powered Flight.

286.	**31.**	5 c. black, blue & brown	10	10
287.	–	15 c. black, brown & red	10	10
288.	–	18 c. black, brown & red	10	10
289.	–	25 c. black, yell. & green	10	10
290.	–	35 c. black, pink & pur.	15	10
291.	–	75 c. black, lilac & yell.	25	25
292.	–	$3 blk., violet & mve.	75	75

DESIGNS—HORIZ. 25 c. Wright " Flyer ", 1905. 35 c. Wright glider. 75 c. " Flyer I " (different). $3, Wright glider (different). VERT. 15 c. Orville Wright. 18 c. Wilbur Wright.

32. Audubon's Shearwater.

1978. Birds. Multicoloured.

294.	5 c. Type **32**	40	10
295.	10 c. Semipalmated plover	60	10
296.	18 c. Purple-throated carib (horiz.)	85	15
297.	22 c. Red-billed whistling duck (horiz.)	1·00	20
298.	40 c. Caribbean martin (horiz.)	1·25	35
299.	$1 Yellow-tailed tropic-bird	2·25	1·10
300.	$2 Long-billed curlew ..	3·25	1·50

33. Players with Ball.

1978. World Cup Football Championship, Argentina. Multicoloured.

302.	15 c. Type **33**	10	10
303.	35 c. Running with ball ..	20	10
304.	50 c. Player with ball ..	25	20
305.	$3 Heading	80	80

34. Captain Cook and Kalaniopu (King of Hawaii), 1778.

1978. 250th Birth Anniv. of Captain James Cook. Multicoloured.

307.	18 c. Type **34**	45	10
308.	22 c. Cook and native of Hawaii	50	15
309.	50 c. Cook and death scene, 1779	85	30
310.	$3 Cook and offering ceremony	2·25	1·75

35. " Virgin at Prayer ".

1978. Christmas. Paintings by Durer, Multicoloured.

312.	40 c. Type **35**	15	10
313.	60 c. " The Dresden Altarpiece "	15	15
314.	90 c. " Madonna and Child with St. Anne " ..	20	15
315.	$2 " Madonna and Child with Pear "	40	50

36. " Strelitzia reginae ".

1979. Out Island Flowers. Multicoloured.

317.	22 c. Type **36**	15	10
318.	40 c. " Euphorbia pulcherrima "	25	15
319.	$1 " Heliconia humilis " ..	55	30
320.	$3 " Thunbergia alata "	1·25	80

37. Children with Pig.

1979. International Year of the Child. Multicoloured.

322.	18 c. Type 37	10	10
323.	50 c. Children with donkey	25	25
324.	$1 Children with goats ..	30	35
325.	$3 Children fishing ..	1·00	1·10

38. " 20,000 Leagues under the Sea ".

1979. 150th Birth Anniv. of Jules Verne (author). Multicoloured.

327.	18 c. Type 38	20	10
328.	38 c. " From the Earth to the Moon "	30	20
329.	75 c. " From the Earth to the Moon " (different)	55	35
330.	$3 " Five Weeks in a Balloon "	1·25	1·00

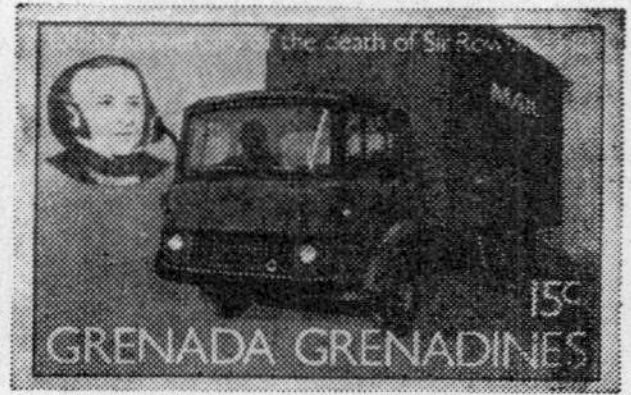

39. Sir Rowland Hill and Mail Van.

1979. Death Centenary of Sir Rowland Hill. Multicoloured.

332.	15 c. Type 39	10	10
333.	$1 Cargo liner	45	35
334.	$2 Diesel mail train ..	85	50
335.	$3 "Concorde"	1·40	80

40. " Virgin and Child " (11th-century Byzantine).

1979. Christmas. Sculptures. Multicoloured.

337.	6 c. Type 40	10	10
338.	25 c. " Presentation in the Temple " (Andre Beauneveu)	10	10
339.	30 c. " Flight to Egypt " (Utrecht, c. 1510) ..	10	10
340.	40 c. " Madonna and Child " (Jacopo della Quercia)	10	10
341.	90 c. " Madonna della Mela " (Luca della Robbia) ..	15	15
342.	$1 " Madonna and Child " (Antonio Rossellino) ..	20	20
343.	$2 " Madonna and Child " (Antwerp, 1700) ..	35	35

41. Great Hammerhead Shark.

1979. Marine Wildlife. Multicoloured.

345.	40 c. Type 41	35	25
346.	45 c. Banded Butterflyfish	35	25
347.	50 c. Permit (fish) ..	35	30
348.	60 c. Threaded Turban (shell)	50	35
349.	70 c. Milk Conch	55	40
350.	75 c. Great Blue Heron ..	65	40
351.	90 c. Coloured Atlantic Natica (shell)	70	50
352.	$1 Red Footed Booby ..	90	55

42. Doctor Goofy.

1979. International Year of the Child. Walt Disney Characters. Multicoloured.

354.	½ c. Type 42	10	10
355.	1 c. Admiral Mickey Mouse	10	10
356.	2 c. Fireman Goofy ..	10	10
357.	3 c. Nurse Minnie Mouse ..	10	10
358.	4 c. Drum Major Mickey Mouse	10	10
359.	5 c. Policeman Donald Duck	10	10
360.	10 c. Pilot Donald Duck ..	10	10
361.	$2 Postman Goofy (horiz.)	1·75	1·00
362.	$2.50 Train driver Donald Duck (horiz.)	2·00	1·00

See also Nos. 434/7.

1980. 1st Anniv. of Revolution. Nos. 116 and 119/29 optd. **PEOPLE'S REPUBLIC 13 MARCH 1979.**

364.	6 c. Cocoa beans in drying trays	10	10
365.	12 c. Cocoa Tree	10	10
366.	15 c. Fishermen at Fontenoy	10	10
367.	20 c. Parliament Building, St. George	10	10
368.	25 c. Fort George cannons	15	10
369.	35 c. Pearls Airport	20	10
370.	50 c. General Post Office ..	35	15
371.	75 c. Caribs Leap, Sauteurs Bay	40	20
372.	$1 Carenage, St. George's	55	30
373.	$2 St. George's Harbour by night	85	70
374.	$3 Grand Anse Beach ..	1·60	1·60
375.	$5 Canoe Bay and Black Bay	2·25	2·50
376.	$10 Sugar-loaf Island ..	3·75	4·25

43. Classroom.

1980. 75th Anniv. of Rotary International. Multicoloured.

377.	6 c. Type 43	10	10
378.	30 c. Different races encircling Rotary emblem ..	20	10
379.	60 c. Rotary executive presenting doctor with cheque	40	20
380.	$3 Nurses attending children	1·50	75

44. Yellow-bellied Seedeater.

1980. Wild Birds. Multicoloured.

382.	25 c. Type 44	50	15
383.	40 c. Blue-hooded Euphonia	55	20
384.	90 c. Yellow Warbler ..	1·25	65
385.	$2 Tropical Mockingbird	1·75	1·25

45. Running.

1980. Olympic Games, Moscow. Multicoloured.

387.	30 c. Type 45	15	15
388.	40 c. Football	15	20
389.	90 c. Boxing	30	35
390.	$2 Wrestling	60	75

1980. " London 1980 " International Stamp Exhibition. Nos. 332/5 optd. **LONDON 1980.**

392.	15 c. Mail van	15	15
393.	$1 Cargo liner	65	35
394.	$2 Diesel mail train ..	1·25	80
395.	$3 "Concorde"	1·90	2·25

47. Longspine Squirrelfish.

1980. Fishes. Multicoloured.

396.	½ c. Type 47	10	10
397.	1 c Blue Chromis	10	10
398.	2 c. Foureye Butterfly Fish	10	10
399.	4 c. Sergeant Major ..	10	10
400.	5 c. Yellowtail Snapper ..	10	10
401.	6 c. Mutton Snapper ..	10	10
402.	10 c. Cocoa Damselfish ..	10	10
403.	12 c. Royal Gramma ..	10	10
404.	15 c. Cherubfish	10	10
405.	20 c. Blackbar Soldierfish	15	10
406.	25 c. Comb Grouper ..	15	15
407.	30 c. Longsnout Butterfly fish	20	20
408.	40 c. Pudding Wife ..	25	25
409.	50 c. Midnight Parrotfish	35	35
410.	90 c. Redspotted Hawkfish	65	55
411.	$1 Hogfish	70	60
412.	$3 Beau Gregory	1·75	2·00
413.	$5 Rock Beauty	2·75	3·00
414.	$10 Barred Hamlet ..	6·00	7·00

1980. Christmas. Scenes from Walt Disney's " Bambi ". As Type 42. Mult.

415.	½ c. Bambi with Mother ..	10	10
416.	1 c. Bambi with quails ..	10	10
417.	2 c. Bambi meets Thumper the rabbit	10	10
418.	3 c. Bambi meets Flower the skunk	10	10
419.	4 c. Bambi and Faline ..	10	10
420.	5 c. Bambi with his father	10	10
421.	10 c. Bambi on ice ..	10	10
422.	$2.50 Faline with foals ..	1·25	85
423.	$3 Bambi and Faline ..	1·25	1·00

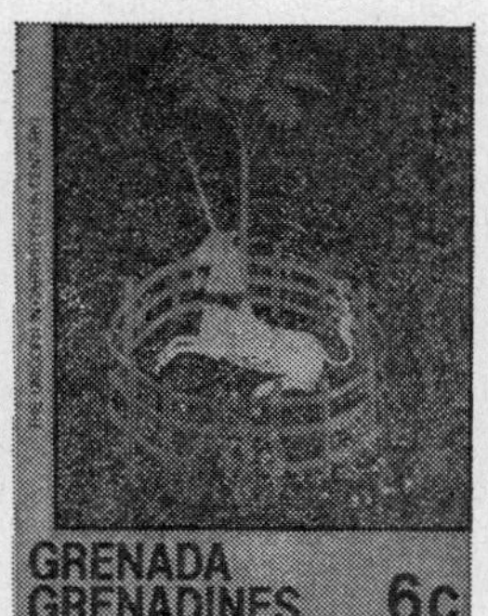

48. " The Unicorn in Captivity " (15th century unknown artist).

1981. Art Masterpieces. Multicoloured.

425.	6 c. Type 48	10	10
426.	10 c. " The Fighting ' Temeraire ' " (Turner) (horiz.)	10	10
427.	25 c. " Sunday Afternoon on the Ile de la Grande-Jatte " (Seurat) (horiz.)	15	15
428.	90 c. " Max Schmitt in a Single Scull " (Eakins) (horiz.)	45	45
429.	$2 " The Burial of the Count of Orgaz " (El Greco) ..	85	85
430.	$3 " Portrait of George Washington " (Stuart)	1·10	1·10

1981. Walt Disney's Pluto (cartoon character). 50th Anniv. As Type 42.

432.	$2 Mickey Mouse serving birthday cake to Pluto ..	90	80

1981. Easter. Walt Disney Cartoon Characters. As T 42. Multicoloured.

434.	35 c. Chip	25	25
435.	40 c. Dewey	25	25
436.	$2 Huey	80	80
437.	$2.50 Mickey Mouse ..	1·10	1·10

49. " Bust of a Woman ". 50. Balmoral Castle.

1981. Birth Centenary of Picasso. Mult.

439.	6 c. Type 49	10	10
440.	40 c. Woman (study for " Les Demoiselles d'Avignon ")	40	15
441.	90 c. " Nude with raised Arms (The Dancer of Avignon) "	70	30
442.	$4 " The Dryad "	2·00	1·25

1981. Royal Wedding. Multicoloured.

448	30 c. Prince Charles and Lady Diana Spencer ..	25	25
444	40 c. As 30 c.	25	25
449	40 c. Type 50	30	30
445	$2 Type 50	60	75
446	$4 Prince Charles as parachutist	1·00	1·25

51. Lady Diana Spencer.

1981. Royal Wedding. Booklet stamps. Multicoloured. Self-adhesive.

450.	$1 Type 51	45	70
451.	$2 Prince Charles ..	70	1·10
452.	$5 Prince Charles and Lady Diana Spencer (horiz.)	2·00	2·50

52. Amy Johnson (1st solo flight, Britain to Australia by Woman, May 1930).

1981. " Decade for Women ". Famous Female Aviators. Multicoloured.

453.	30 c. Type 52	35	15
454.	70 c. Mme. La Baronne de Laroche (1st qualified woman pilot, March 1910)	55	30
455.	$1.10 Ruth Nichols (solo Atlantic flight attempt, June 1931)	85	40
456.	$3 Amelia Earhart (1st North Atlantic solo flight by woman, May 1932).	1·75	1·10

1981. Christmas. Designs as T 42 showing scenes from Walt Disney's cartoon film " Lady and the Tramp ".

458.	½ c. multicoloured ..	10	10
459.	1 c. multicoloured ..	10	10
460.	2 c. multicoloured ..	10	10
461.	3 c. multicoloured ..	10	10
462.	4 c. multicoloured ..	10	10
463.	5 c. multicoloured ..	10	10
464.	10 c. multicoloured ..	10	10
465.	$2.50 multicoloured ..	1·25	1·00
466.	$3 multicoloured	1·50	1·25

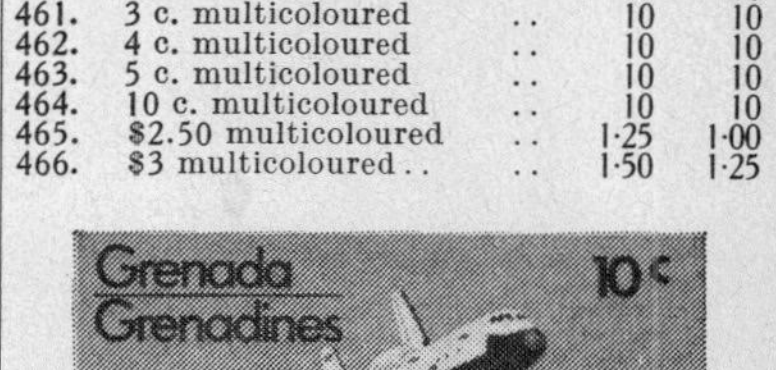

53. " 747 " Carrier.

1981. Space Shuttle Project. Multicoloured.

468.	10 c. Type **53**	30	10
469.	40 c. Re-entry	55	15
470.	$1.10 External tank separation	1·25	45
471.	$3 Touchdown	2·00	1·00

54. Footballer.

1981. World Cup Football Championship, Spain (1982).

473. **54.**	20 c. multicoloured ..	10	10
474. –	40 c. multicoloured ..	20	20
475. –	$1 multicoloured ..	45	45
476. –	$2 multicoloured ..	75	75

DESIGNS: 40 c. to $2 Various designs showing footballers.

55. Mail Van and Stage-coach.

1982. Centenary of U.P.U. Membership. Multicoloured.

478.	30 c. Type **55**	40	15
479.	40 c. U.P.U. emblem ..	45	20
480.	$2.50 "Queen Elizabeth 2" (liner) and sailing ship ..	2·00	90
481.	$4 Airliner and biplane ..	2·75	1·60

56. National Sports Meeting.

1982. 75th Anniv. of Boy Scout Movement and 125th Birth Anniv. of Lord Baden-Powell. Multicoloured.

483.	6 c. Type **56**	15	10
484.	90 c. Sea scouts sailing ..	65	30
485.	$1.10 Handicraft	90	60
486.	$3 Animal tending ..	1·90	1·40

57. "Anartia jatrophae".

1982. Butterflies. Multicoloured.

488	30 c. Type **57**	65	30
489	40 c. "Chioides vintra" ..	70	35
490	$1.10 "Cynthia cardui" ..	1·25	75
491	$3 "Historis odius" ..	2·25	1·60

58. Prince and Princess of Wales.

1982. 21st Birthday of Princess of Wales. Multicoloured.

493.	50 c. Blenheim Palace ..	50	30
494.	60 c. As 50 c.	60	35
495.	$1 Type **58**	70	60
496.	$2 Type **58**	1·50	1·25
497.	$3 Princess of Wales ..	2·00	1·75
498.	$4 As $3	2·25	2·00

59. "New Deal"—Soil Conservation.

1982. Birth Centenary of Franklin D. Roosevelt. Multicoloured.

500.	30 c. Type **59**	25	15
501.	40 c. Roosevelt and George Washington Carver (scientist)	35	15
502.	70 c. Civilian conservation corps (reafforestation) ..	65	35
503.	$3 Roosevelt with Pres. Barclay of Liberia, Casablanca Conference, 1943	2·00	1·25

1982. Birth of Prince William of Wales. Nos. 493/8 optd. **ROYAL BABY 21.6.82.**

505.	50 c. Blenheim Palace ..	40	40
506.	60 c. As 50 c. ..	45	45
507.	$1 Type **58**	60	60
508.	$2 Type **58**	1·25	1·25
509.	$3 Princess of Wales ..	1·75	1·75
510.	$4 As $3	2·00	2·00

60. "Presentation of Christ in the Temple".

1982. Easter. Easter Paintings by Rembrandt. Multicoloured.

512.	30 c. Type **60**	40	15
513.	60 c. "Descent from the Cross"	55	20
514.	$2 "Raising of the Cross"	1·75	1·00
515.	$4 "Resurrection of Christ"	2·75	2·00

61. "Santa Fe".

1982. Famous Trains of the World. Mult.

517.	10 c. Type **61**	50	15
518.	40 c. "Mistral"	1·00	20
519.	70 c. "Rheingold"	1·25	45
520.	$1 "ET 403"	1·50	55
521.	$1·10 Steam locomotive "Mallard"	1·75	70
522.	$2 "Tokaido"	2·00	1·25

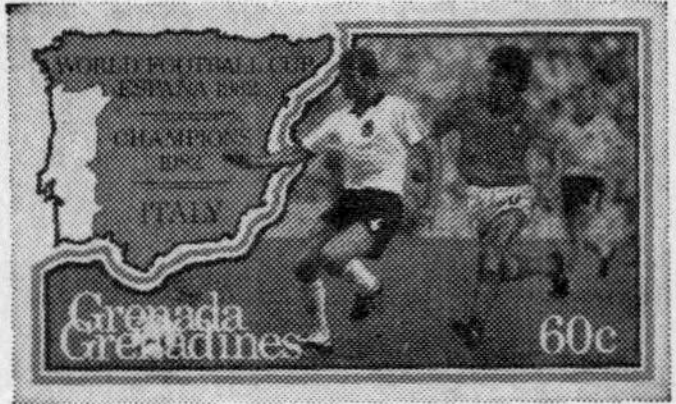

62. Footballers.

1982. World Cup Football Championship Winners.

524. **62.**	60 c. multicoloured ..	35	35
525.	$4 multicoloured ..	1·75	1·75

1982. Christmas. Scenes from Walt Disney's cartoon film "The Rescuers" as **T 42**, but horiz.

527.	½ c. multicoloured ..	10	10
528.	1 c. multicoloured ..	10	10
529.	2 c. multicoloured ..	10	10
530.	3 c. multicoloured ..	10	10
531.	4 c. multicoloured ..	10	10
532.	5 c. multicoloured ..	10	10
533.	10 c. multicoloured ..	10	10
534.	$2.50 multicoloured ..	1·00	1·00
535.	$3 multicoloured ..	1·25	1·25

63. Short-finned Pilot Whale.

1982. Save the Whale. Multicoloured.

537.	10 c. Type **63**	75	30
538.	60 c. Dall's Porpoise ..	1·75	80
539.	$1.10 Humpback Whale ..	2·25	1·40
540.	$3 Bowhead Whale ..	3·50	3·25

64. "David and Goliath".

1983. 500th Birth Anniv. of Raphael. Mult.

542.	25 c. Type **64**	20	15
543.	30 c. "David sees Bath-sheba"	20	20
544.	90 c. Triumph of David"	50	45
545.	$4 "Anointing of Solomon"	1·60	1·75

65. Voice and Visual Communication.

1983. World Communications Year. Mult.

547	30 c. Type **65**	15	15
548	60 c. Ambulance	25	25
549	$1.10 Helicopters ..	45	45
550	$3 Satellite	1·25	1·25

66. Chrysler "Imperial Roadster", 1931.

1983. 75th Anniv. of Model "T" Ford Car. Multicoloured.

552.	10 c. Type **66**	10	10
553.	30 c. Doble steam car, 1925	15	20
554.	40 c. Ford "Mustang" 1965	20	25
555.	60 c. Packard tourer, 1930	30	35
556.	70 c. Mercer "Raceabout" 1913	35	40
557.	90 c. Corvette "Stingray", 1963	40	45
558.	$1.10 Auburn "851 Super-charger Speedster", 1935	50	55
559.	$2.50 Pierce-Arrow "Silver Arrow", 1933	90	1·00
560.	$3 Dusenberg dual cowl phaeton, 1929	1·25	1·40
561.	$4 Mercedes-Benz "SSK", 1928	1·60	1·75

67. Short "Solent" Flying Boat.

1983. Bicentenary of Manned Flight. Mult.

563.	40 c. Type **67**	60	20
564.	70 c. Curtiss "R3C–2" seaplane	75	35
565.	90 c. Hawker "Nimrod" biplane	90	40
566.	$4 Montgolfier balloon ..	2·75	2·75

68. Goofy.

1983. Christmas. Multicoloured.

568.	½ c. Type **68**	10	10
569.	1 c. Clarabelle Cow ..	10	10
570.	2 c. Donald Duck	10	10
571.	3 c. Pluto	10	10
572.	4 c. Morty and Ferdie ..	10	10
573.	5 c. Huey, Dewey and Louie	10	10
574.	10 c. Daisy and Chip'n Dale	10	10
575.	$2.50 Big Bad Wolf ..	2·75	2·75
576.	$5 Mickey Mouse	3·25	3·25

Nos. 568/76 show Disney cartoon characters in scenes from "Jingle Bells" (Christmas carol).

69. Weightlifting.

1984. Olympic Games, Los Angeles. Mult.

578.	30 c. Type **69**	15	15
579.	60 c. Gymnastics	35	35
580.	70 c. Archery	40	40
581.	$4 Sailing	1·75	1·90

70. Frangipani.

1984. Flowers. Multicoloured.

583.	15 c. Type **70**	15	10
584.	40 c. Dwarf Poinciana ..	30	25
585.	70 c. Walking Iris	55	45
586.	$4 Lady's Slipper	2·25	2·50

71. Goofy.

1984. Easter. Multicoloured.

588.	½ c. Type **71**	10	10
589.	1 c. Chip and Dale ..	10	10
590.	2 c. Daisy Duck and Huey	10	10
591.	3 c. Daisy Duck	10	10
592.	4 c. Donald Duck	10	10
593.	5 c. Merlin and Madam Mim	10	10
594.	10 c. Flower	10	10
595.	$2 Minnie and Mickey Mouse	1·25	1·40
596.	$4 Minnie Mouse	2·00	2·25

72. Bobolink.

1984. Songbirds. Multicoloured.

598. 40 c. Type **72** .. .. 1·40 90
599. 50 c. Eastern Kingbird .. 1·60 1·10
600. 60 c. Barn Swallow .. 1·75 1·25
601. 70 c. Yellow Warbler .. 1·75 1·40
602. $1 Rose-breasted Grosbeak 2·00 1·60
603. $1.10 Yellowthroat .. 2·25 2·00
604. $2 Catbird .. .. .. 3·00 3·50

1984. Universal Postal Union Congress, Hamburg. Nos. 585/6 optd. **19th U.P.U. CONGRESS HAMBURG.**

606. 70 c. Walking Iris .. .. 1·00 50
607. $4 Lady's Slipper .. .. 3·50 3·00

74. "Geeststar".

1984. Ships. Multicoloured.

609. 30 c. Type **74** .. .. 1·00 40
610. 60 c. "Daphne" .. .. 1·50 75
611. $1.10 "Southwind" .. 2·00 1·50
612. $4 "Oceanic" .. .. 4·50 4·50

1984. 450th Death Anniv. of Correggio (painter). As T **296** of Grenada. Multicoloured.

614. 10 c. "The Hunt—Blowing the Horn" 10 10
615. 30 c. "St. John the Evangelist" (horiz.) .. 15 15
616. 90 c. "The Hunt—The Deer's Head" 50 50
617. $4 "The Virgin crowned by Christ" (horiz.) .. .. 2·00 2·00

1984. 150th Birth Anniv. of Edgar Degas (painter). As T **297** of Grenada. Multicoloured.

619. 25 c. "The Song of the Dog" 35 15
620. 70 c. "Cafe-concert" .. 60 35
621. $1.10 "The Orchestra of the Opera" .. .. .. 1·25 1·00
622. $3 "The Dance Lesson" .. 2·50 2·25

1984. "Ausipex" International Stamp Exhibition, Melbourne. As T **298** of Grenada. Multicoloured.

624. $1.10 Queen Victoria Gardens, Melbourne .. 50 50
625. $4 Ayers Rock .. .. 2·00 2·00

75. Col. Steven's Model (1825).

1984. Railway Locomotives. Multicoloured.

627. 20 c. Type **75** 65 25
628. 50 c. "Royal George" (1827) .. .. .. 1·00 50
629. 60 c. "Stourbridge Lion" (1829) .. .. .. 1·10 60
630. 70 c. "Liverpool" (1830) .. 1·25 70
631. 90 c. "South Carolina" (1832) .. .. .. 1·50 85
632. $1.10 "Monster" (1836) .. 1·75 1·00
633. $2 "Lafayette" (1837) .. 2·50 1·75
634. $4 "Lion" (1838) .. .. 4·00 3·25

1984. Opening of Port Saline International Airport. Nos. 547 and 549 optd. **OPENING OF PORT SALINE INT'L AIRPORT.**

636. 30 c. Type **65** 20 25
637. $1.10 Helicopters 70 75

1984. Christmas. Walt Disney Cartoon Characters. As T **301** of Grenada. Mult.

639. 45 c. Donald Duck, and nephews knitting Christmas stockings .. 30 30
640. 60 c. Donald Duck and nephews sitting on sofa 40 40
641. 90 c. Donald Duck getting out of bed 55 55
642. $2 Donald Duck putting presents in wardrobe .. 1·25 1·25
643. $4 Nephews singing carols outside Donald Duck's window .. .. 2·25 2·25

1985. Birth Bicentenary of John J. Audubon (ornithologist). As T **198** of Antigua. Mult.

645. 50 c. Blue-winged teal .. 1·00 30
646. 90 c. White ibis .. .. 1·50 60
647. $1.10 Swallow-tailed kite .. 2·00 1·25
648. $3 Moorhen .. .. 2·75 2·50

See also Nos. 736/9.

76. Kawasaki "750" (1972).

1985. Centenary of the Motor Cycle. Mult.

650. 30 c. Type **76** 25 20
651. 60 c. Honda "Goldwing GL1000" (1974) (horiz) .. 45 40
652. 70 c. Kawasaki "Z650" (1976) (horiz) 55 45
653. $4 Honda "CBX" (1977) .. 2·40 2·25

77. Nursing Cadets folding Bandages (Health).

1985. International Youth Year. Mult.

655. 50 c. Type **77** 45 35
656. 70 c. Scuba diver and turtle (Environment) 60 50
657. $1.10, Yachting (Leisure) 1·00 90
658. $3 Boys playing chess (Education) .. .. 3·25 2·25

1985. 40th Anniv. of International Civil Aviation Organization. As T **305** of Grenada. Multicoloured.

660. 5 c. Lockheed "Lodestar" 20 10
661. 70 c. Avro "748" Turbo-prop .. .. .. 1·00 45
662. $1.10, Boeing "727" .. 1·50 85
663. $4 Boeing "707" .. .. 2·75 2·25

78. Lady Baden-Powell (founder) and Grenadian Guide Leaders.

1985. 75th Anniv. of Girl Guide Movement. Multicoloured.

665. 30 c. Type **78**. 25 20
666. 50 c. Guide leader and guides on botany field trip 45 30
667. 70 c. Guide leader and guides camping (vert.) .. 70 45
668. $4 Guides sailing (vert.) .. 2·50 2·25

79. "Chiomara asychis".

1985. Butterflies. Multicoloured.

670 ½ c. Type **79** 10 10
671 1 c. "Anartia amathea" .. 10 10
672 2 c. "Pseudolycaena marsyas" 10 10
673 4 c. "Urbanus proteus" .. 10 10
674 5 c. "Polygonus manueli" .. 10 10
675 6 c. "Battus polydamas" .. 10 10
676 10 c. "Eurema daira" .. 10 10
677 12 c. "Phoebis agarithe" .. 10 10
678 15 c. "Aphrissa statira" .. 10 10
679 20 c. "Strymon simaethis" .. 10 10
680 25 c. "Mestra cana" .. 10 15
681 30 c. "Agraulis vanillae" .. 10 15
682 40 c. "Junonia evarete" .. 15 20
683 60 c. "Dryas julia" .. 25 30
684 70 c. "Philaethria dido" .. 30 35
685 $1.10 "Hamadryas feronia" 45 50
686 $2.50 "Strymon rufofusca" .. .. 1·00 1·10
687 $5 "Appias drusilla" .. 2·10 2·25
688 $10 "Polites dictynna" .. 4·25 4·50
688c $20 "Euptychia cephus" 8·50 8·75

80. The Queen Mother before Prince William's Christening.

81. Scuba Diving.

1985. Life and Times of Queen Elizabeth the Queen Mother. Multicoloured.

689. $1 Type **80** 55 60
690. $1·50 In winner's enclosure at Ascot (horiz) 80 85
691. $2·50 With Prince Charles at Garter ceremony, Windsor Castle .. .. 1·25 1·50

Stamps as Nos 689/91 but with face values of 70 c., $1·10 and $3 exist from additional sheetlets with changed background colours.

1985. Water Sports. Multicoloured.

693. 15 c. Type **81** 20 10
694. 70 c. Boys playing in waterfall 55 45
695. 90 c. Water skiing 65 55
696. $4 Swimming .. .. 2·25 2·25

82. Queen Conch.

1985. Marine Life. Multicoloured.

698. 60 c. Type **82** 50 40
699. 90 c. Porcupine Fish and Fire Coral 65 55
700. $1.10, Ghost Crab 80 70
701. $4 West Indies Spiny Lobster .. .. .. 2·25 2·25

1985. 300th Birth Anniv. of Johann Sebastian Bach (composer). As T **206** of Antigua. Mult.

703. 15 c. Natural trumpet .. 30 10
704. 60 c. Bass viol 65 40
705. $1.10, Flute 90 70
706. $3 Double flageolet .. 1·75 1·75

1985. Royal Visit. As T **207** of Antigua. Multicoloured.

708. 10 c. Arms of Great Britain and Grenada 20 15
709. $1 Queen Elizabeth II (vert.) .. .. .. 1·25 1·25
710. $4 Royal Yacht "Britannia" .. .. 3·75 3·75

1985. 40th Anniv. of United Nations Organization. Designs as T **208** of Antigua showing United Nations (New York) stamps. Multicoloured.

712. $1 Neil Armstrong (first man on Moon) and 1982 Peaceful Uses of Outer Space 20 c. .. .. 1·00 75
713. $2 Gandhi and 1971 Racial Equality Year 13 c. .. 2·50 1·90
714. $2.50, Maimonides (physician) and 1956 World Health Organization 3 c. .. 3·75 2·75

1985. 150th Birth Anniv. of Mark Twain (author). As T **118** of Anguilla showing Walt Disney cartoon characters illustrating scenes from "Letters from Hawaii". Multicoloured.

716. 25 c. Minnie Mouse dancing the hula 15 20
717. 50 c. Donald Duck surfing 30 35
718. $1.50 Donald Duck roasting marshmallow in volcano 90 95
719. $3 Mickey Mouse and Chip'n'Dale canoeing .. 1·75 1·90

1985. Birth Bicentenaries of Grimm Brothers (folklorists). As T **119** of Anguilla, but vert, showing Walt Disney cartoon characters in scenes from "The Elves and the Shoemaker". Multicoloured.

721. 30 c. Mickey Mouse as the unsuccessful Shoemaker 35 35
722. 60 c. Two elves making shoes 60 60
723. 70 c. The Shoemaker discovering the new shoes 70 70
724. $4 The Shoemaker's wife (Minnie Mouse) making clothes for the elves .. 2·75 2·75

83. "Madonna and Child" (Titian).

1985. Christmas. Religious Paintings. Mult.

726. 50 c. Type **83** 45 35
727. 70 c. "Madonna and Child with St. Mary and John the Baptist" (Bugiardini) 55 45
728. $1.10 "Adoration of the Magi" (Di Fredi) .. 90 90
729. $3 "Madonna and Child with Young St. John the Baptist" (Bartolomeo) .. 2·25 2·50

1986. Centenary of Statue of Liberty (1st issue). As T **211** of Dominica. Multicoloured.

731. 5 c. Croton Reservoir, New York (1875) 10 10
732. 10 c. New York Public Library (1986) 10 10
733. 70 c. Old Boathouse, Central Park (1894) .. 35 40
734. $4 Boating in Central Park (1986) .. .. .. 2·00 2·10

See also Nos. 892/903.

1986. Birth Bicentenary of John J. Audubon (ornithologist) (2nd issue). As T **198** of Antigua. Multicoloured.

736. 50 c. Louisiana heron .. 1·25 80
737. 70 c. Black-crowned night heron .. .. .. 1·75 1·00
738. 90 c. American bittern .. 2·00 1·10
739. $4 Glossy ibis .. .. 3·50 4·00

1986. Visit of President Reagan of U.S.A. Nos. 684 and 687, optd. **VISIT OF PRES. REAGAN 20 FEBRUARY 1986.**

741 70 c. "Philaethria dido" .. 1·00 1·00
742 $5 "Appias drusilla" .. 5·00 5·50

85. Two Footballers.

1986. World Cup Football Championship, Mexico. Designs showing footballers.

743. **85.** 10 c. multicoloured .. 20 15
744. – 70 c. multicoloured .. 90 80
745. – $1 multicoloured .. 1·25 95
746. – $4 multicoloured .. 3·75 3·75

1986. Appearance of Halley's Comet (1st issue). As T **123** of Anguilla. Multicoloured.

748. 5 c. Nicholas Copernicus (astronomer) and Earl of Rosse's six foot reflector telescope 10 10
749. 20 c. "Sputnik I" (first satellite) orbiting Earth, 1957 .. .. .. 20 20
750. 40 c. Tycho Brahe's notes and sketch of 1577 Comet 30 30
751. $4 Edmond Halley and 1682 Comet .. .. 2·25 2·75

See also Nos 790/3.
The captions of Nos. 750/1 are transposed.

1986. 60th Birthday of Queen Elizabeth II. As T **125** of Anguilla.

753. 2 c. black and yellow .. 10 15
754. $1·50 multicoloured .. 1·00 1·00
755. $4 multicoloured .. .. 2·25 2·50

DESIGN: 2 c. Princesses Elizabeth and Margaret, Windsor Park, 1933. $1·50, Queen Elizabeth. $4, In Sydney, Australia, 1970.

1986. "Ameripex '86" International Stamp Exhibition, Chicago. As T **212** of Dominica. Multicoloured.

757. 30 c. Donald Duck riding mule in Grand Canyon 45 45
758. 60 c. Daisy Duck, Timothy Mouse and Dumbo on Golden Gate Bridge, San Francisco 70 70
759. $1 Mickey Mouse and Goofy in fire engine and Chicago Watertower .. 1·25 1·25
760. $3 Mickey Mouse as airmail pilot and White House 3·00 3·00

1986. Royal Wedding. As T **213** of Antigua. Multicoloured.

762. 60 c. Prince Andrew and Miss Sarah Ferguson .. 45 45
763. 70 c. Prince Andrew in car 55 55
764. $4 Prince Andrew with naval helicopter .. 2·50 2·50

86. "Hygrocybe firma".

1986. Mushrooms of the Lesser Antilles. Multicoloured.

766. 15 c. Type **86** 60 20
767. 50 c. "Xerocomus coccolobae" .. .. 1·40 60
768. $2 "Volvariella cubensis" 3·00 2·25
769. $3 "Lactarius putidus" .. 4·25 3·50

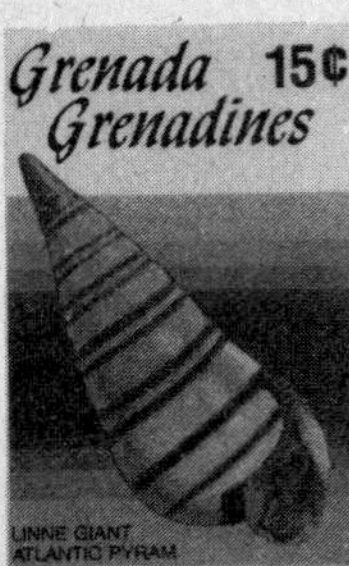

87. Giant Atlantic Pyram.

1986. Sea Shells. Multicoloured.

771. 15 c. Type **87** 60 20
772. 50 c. Beau's murex .. 1·40 60
773. $1.10 West Indian fighting conch .. .. .. 2·25 1·90
774. $4 Alphabet coral shell .. 4·50 4·25

1986. World Cup Football Championship Winners, Mexico. Nos. 743/6 optd. **WINNERS Argentina 3 W. Germany 2.**

776. **85.** 10 c. multicoloured .. 20 20
777. – 70 c. multicoloured .. 65 65
778. – $1 multicoloured .. 85 85
779. – $4 multicoloured .. 2·75 3·00

88. Common Opossum.

1986. Wildlife. Multicoloured.

781. 10 c. Type **88** 20 20
782. 30 c. Giant toad 40 40
783. 60 c. Land tortoise .. 80 80
784. 70 c. Murine opossum (vert.) 85 85
785. 90 c. Burmese mongoose (vert.) 90 90
786. $1.10 Nine-banded armadillo .. .. 1·00 1·00
787. $2 Agouti .. .. .. 1·75 2·00
788. $3 Humpback whale .. 3·50 3·75

1986. Appearance of Halley's Comet (2nd issue). Nos. 748/51 optd with T **218** of Antigua.

790. 5 c. Nicholas Copernicus (astronomer) and Earl of Rosse's six foot reflector telescope 30 25
791. 20 c. "Sputnik I" orbiting Earth, 1957 .. .. 50 35
792. 40 c. Tycho Brahe's notes and sketch of 1577 Comet 65 45
793. $4 Edmond Halley and 1682 Comet .. .. 3·00 3·50

1986. Christmas. As T **220** of Antigua showing Walt Disney cartoon characters. Mult.

795. 25 c. Chip n'Dale with hummingbird 15 15
796. 30 c. Robin delivering card to Mickey Mouse (vert.) 15 20
797. 50 c. Piglet, Pooh and Jose Carioca on beach .. 25 30
798. 60 c. Grandma Duck feeding birds (vert.) .. 30 35
799. 70 c. Cinderella and birds with mistletoe (vert.) .. 35 40
800. $1.50 Huey, Dewey and Louie windsurfing .. 75 80
801. $3 Mickey Mouse and Morty on beach with turtle .. .. .. 1·50 1·75
802. $4 Kittens playing on piano (vert.) .. .. 2·00 2·25

89. Cycling.

1986. Olympic Games, Seoul, South Korea (1988). Multicoloured.

804. 10 c.+5 c. Type **89** .. 25 30
805. 50 c.+20 c. Sailing .. 60 70
806. 70 c.+30 c. Gymnastics .. 75 85
807. $2+$1 Horse trials .. 2·25 2·50

90. Aston-Martin "Volanté" (1984).

1986. Centenary of Motoring. Multicoloured.

809. 10 c. Type **90** 20 20
810. 30 c. Jaguar "Mk V" (1948) 30 30
811. 60 c. Nash "Ambassador" (1956) 45 45
812. 70 c. Toyota "Supra" (1984) 50 50
813. 90 c. Ferrari "Testarrosa" (1985) 65 65
814. $1 BMW "501B" (1955) .. 70 70
815. $2 Mercedes-Benz "280 SL" (1968) .. .. .. 1·25 1·25
816. $3 Austro-Daimler "ADR8" (1932) .. .. 1·75 1·75

1986. Birth Centenary of Marc Chagall (artist). As T **225** of Antigua, showing various paintings.

818/57. $1.10 × 40 multicoloured Set of 40 .. .. 18·00 19·00

1987. America's Cup Yachting Championship. Multicoloured. As T **222** of Antigua.

859. 25 c. "Defender", 1895 .. 40 25
860. 45 c. "Caletea", 1886 .. 55 35
861. 70 c. "Azzurra", 1981 .. 70 55
862. $4 "Australia II", 1983 .. 2·00 2·50

1987. 500th Anniv (1992) of Discovery of America by Christopher Columbus (1st issue). As T **322** of Grenada. Multicoloured.

864. 15 c. Christopher Columbus 20 20
865. 30 c. Queen Isabella of Castile 20 20
866. 50 c. "Santa Maria" .. 35 35
867. 60 c. Claiming the New World for Spain .. 35 35
868. 90 c. Early Spanish map of Lesser Antilles 55 55
869. $1 King Ferdinand of Aragon 60 60
870. $2 Fort La Navidad (drawing by Columbus) 1·25 1·25
871. $3 Galley and Caribs, Hispaniola (drawing by Columbus) .. .. 1·75 1·75

See also Nos. 1191/4 and 1224/31.

1987. Milestones of Transportation. As T **226** of Antigua. Multicoloured.

873. 10 c. Saunders Roe "SR-N1" (first hovercraft), 1959 .. .. .. 10 10
874. 15 c. Bugatti "Royale" (largest car), 1931 .. 15 15
875. 30 c. Aleksei Leonov and "Voskhod II" (first spacewalk), 1965 .. 25 25
876. 50 c. C.S.S. "Hunley" (first submarine to sink enemy ship), 1864 .. .. 35 35
877. 60 c. Rolls Royce "Flying Bedstead" (first VTOL aircraft), 1954 .. .. 40 40
878. 70 c. "Jenny Lind" (first mass produced locomotive class), 1847 .. 45 45
879. 90 c. Duryea "Buggyaut" (first U.S. petrol-driven car), 1893 .. .. 55 55
880. $1.50 Steam locomotive, Metropolitan Railway, London (first underground line), 1863 1·00 1·00
881. $2 S.S. "Great Britain" (first transatlantic crossing by screw-steamship), 1843 .. 1·25 1·25
882. $3 "Budweiser Rocket" (fastest car), 1979 .. 1·75 1·75

1987. "Capex '87" International Stamp Exhibition, Toronto. Game Fishes. As T **323** of Grenada. Multicoloured.

883. 6 c. Yellow chub 15 15
884. 30 c. Kingfish 35 25
885. 50 c. Mako shark 45 45
886. 60 c. Dolphinfish 50 50
887. 90 c. Bonito 65 65
888. $1.10 Cobia 90 90
889. $3 Great tarpon .. .. 2·00 2·25
890. $4 Swordfish .. .. 2·50 2·75

1987. Centenary of Statue of Liberty (1986) (2nd issue). As T **227** of Antigua. Mult.

892. 10 c. Cleaning face of statue 10 10
893. 15 c. Commemorative lapel badges 15 15
894. 25 c. Band playing and statue 25 25
895. 30 c. Band on parade and statue 25 25
896. 45 c. Face of statue .. 40 40
897. 50 c. Cleaning head of statue (horiz.) 45 45
898. 60 c. Models of statue (horiz.) 50 50
899. 70 c. Small boat flotilla (horiz.) 55 55
900. $1 Unveiling ceremony .. 75 75
901. $1.10 Statue and Manhattan skyline .. 80 80
902. $2 Parade of warships .. 1·40 1·40
903. $3 Making commemorative flags .. .. .. 1·75 1·75

1987. Great Scientific Discoveries. As T **325** of Grenada. Multicoloured.

904. 60 c. Newton medal .. 55 40
905. $1 Louis Daguerre (inventor of daguerreotype) 80 65
906. $2 Antoine Lavoisier and apparatus .. .. 1·60 1·75
907. $3 Rudolf Diesel and diesel engine .. .. .. 3·25 3·50

No. 907 is inscribed "JAMES WATT" in error.

1987. Bicentenary of U.S. Constitution. As T **232** of Antigua. Multicoloured.

909. 10 c. Washington addressing delegates, Constitutional Convention 20 15
910. 50 c. Flag and State Seal, Georgia 60 50
911. 60 c. Capitol, Washington (vert.) 60 50
912. $4 Thomas Jefferson (statesman) (vert.) .. 3·00 3·25

1987. "Hafnia '87" International Stamp Exhibition, Copenhagen. Designs As T **328** of Grenada, but horiz., illustrating Hans Christian Andersen's fairy tales. Mult.

914. 25 c. Donald and Daisy Duck in "The Swine-herd" 20 20
915. 30 c. Mickey Mouse, Donald and Daisy Duck in "What the Good Man Does in Always Right" 20 20
916. 50 c. Mickey and Minnie Mouse in "Little Tuk" 35 35
917. 60 c. Minnie Mouse and Ferdie in "The World's Fairest Rose" 35 35
918. 70 c. Mickey Mouse in "The Garden of Paradise" 45 45
919. $1.50 Goofy and Mickey Mouse in "The Naughty Boy" 90 90
920. $3 Goofy in "What the Moon Saw" .. .. 1·75 1·75
921. $4 Alice as "Thumbelina" 2·25 2·25

91. "The Virgin and Child with Saints Martin and Agnes".

1987. Christmas. Religious Paintings by El Greco. Multicoloured.

923. 10 c. Type **91** 20 15
924. 50 c. "St. Agnes" (detail from "The Virgin and Child with Saints Martin and Agnes") 60 50
925. 60 c. "The Annunciation" 60 50
926. $4 "The Holy Family with St. Anne" .. .. 3·50 4·00

1988. Royal Ruby Wedding. As T **234** of Antigua. Multicoloured.

928. 20 c. brown, blk. & grn. .. 20 15
929. 30 c. brown and black .. 25 20
930. $2 multicoloured .. .. 1·40 1·60
931. $3 multicoloured .. .. 2·00 2·25

DESIGNS: 20 c. Queen Elizabeth II with Princess Anne, c. 1957. 30 c. Wedding photograph, 1947. $2, Queen with Prince Charles and Princess Anne, c. 1955. $3, Queen Elizabeth (from photo by Tim Graham), 1980.

1988. Olympic Games, Seoul. Multicoloured. As T **331** of Grenada showing Walt Disney cartoon characters as Olympic competitors.

933 1 c. Minnie Mouse as rhythmic gymnast (horiz) 10 10
934 2 c. Pete and Goofy as pankration wrestlers (horiz) 10 10
935 3 c. Huey and Dewey as synchronized swimmers (horiz) 10 10
936 4 c. Huey, Dewey and Louey in hoplite race (horiz) 10 10
937 5 c. Clarabelle and Daisy Duck playing baseball (horiz) 10 10
938 10 c. Goofy and Donald Duck in horse race (horiz) 10 10
939 $6 Donald Duck and Uncle Scrooge McDuck wind-surfing (horiz) 2·75 3·00
940 $7 Mickey Mouse in chariot race (horiz) 3·25 3·50

92 Scout signalling with Semaphore Flags

1988. World Scout Jamboree, Australia. Mult.

942 50 c. Type **92** 30 35
943 70 c. Canoeing 35 40
944 $1 Cooking over campfire (horiz) 50 55
945 $3 Scouts around campfire (horiz) 1·60 2·00

1988. Birds. As T **334** of Grenada. Mult.

947 20 c. Yellow-crowned night heron 30 25
948 25 c. Brown pelican 30 25
949 45 c. Audubon's shearwater 40 35
950 60 c. Red-footed booby 50 40
951 70 c. Bridled tern 55 45
952 90 c. Red-billed tropic bird 70 60
953 $3 Blue-winged teal 1·75 2·00
954 $4 Sora rail 2·00 2·50

1988. 500th Birth Anniv of Titian (artist). As T **238** of Antigua. Multicoloured.

956 15 c. "Man with Blue Eyes" 10 10
957 30 c. "The Three Ages of Man" (detail) 15 15
958 60 c. "Don Diego Mendoza" 25 30
959 75 c. "Emperor Charles V seated" 35 40
960 $1 "A Young Man in a Fur" 45 50
961 $2 "Tobias and the Angel" 90 95
962 $3 "Pietro Bembo" 1·40 1·50
963 $4 "Pier Luigi Farnese" 1·75 1·90

1988. Airships. As T **336** of Grenada. Multicoloured.

965 10 c. "Hindenberg" over Sugarloaf Mountain, Rio de Janeiro, 1937 (horiz) 10 10
966 20 c. "Hindenberg" over New York, 1937 (horiz) 10 10
967 30 c. U.S. Navy airships on Atlantic escort duty, 1944 (horiz) 15 15
968 40 c. "Hindenberg" approaching Lakehurst, 1937 20 25
969 60 c. "Graf Zeppelin" and "Hindenberg" over Germany, 1936 25 30
970 70 c. "Hindenberg" and "Los Angeles" moored at Lakehurst, 1936 (horiz) 30 35
971 $1 "Graf Zeppelin II" over Dover, 1939 45 50
972 $2 "Deutschland" on scheduled passenger flight, 1912 (horiz) 80 1·00
973 $3 "Graf Zeppelin" over Dome of the Rock, Jerusalem, 1931 (horiz) 1·25 1·50
974 $4 "Hindenberg" over Olympic stadium, Berlin, 1936 (horiz) 1·60 1·75

93 Bambi and his Mother

1988. Disney Animal Cartoon Films.

976/1029 30 c. × 54 multicoloured Set of 54 6·50 8·00

DESIGNS: Scenes from Bambi, Dumbo, Lady and The Tramp, The Aristocats, The Fox and the Hound and 101 Dalmatians.

1988. "Sydpex '88" National Stamp Exhibition, Sydney and 60th Birthday of Mickey Mouse. As T **337** of Grenada. Multicoloured.

1031 1 c. Mickey Mouse conducting at Sydney Opera House 10 10
1032 2 c. Mickey Mouse and Donald Duck at Ayers Rock 10 10
1033 3 c. Goofy and Mickey Mouse on sheep station 10 10
1034 4 c. Goofy and Mickey Mouse at Lone Pine Koala Sanctuary 10 10
1035 5 c. Mickey Mouse, Donald Duck and Goofy playing Australian football 10 10
1036 10 c. Mickey Mouse and Goofy camel racing 10 10
1037 $5 Donald Duck and his nephews bowling 2·40 2·75
1038 $6 Mickey Mouse with America's Cup trophy and "Australia II" (yacht) 2·75 3·25

1988. Flowering Trees and Shrubs. As T **339** of Grenada. Multicoloured.

1040 10 c. Potato tree (vert) 15 15
1041 20 c. Wild cotton 15 15
1042 30 c. Shower of gold (vert) 20 20
1043 60 c. Napoleon's button (vert) 35 30
1044 90 c. Geiger tree 60 55
1045 $1 Fern tree 70 65
1046 $2 French cashew 1·25 1·50
1047 $4 Amherstia (vert) 2·00 2·50

1988. Cars. As T **335** of Grenada. Mult.

1049 $2 Doble "Series E", 1925 1·00 1·00
1050 $2 Alvis "12/50", 1926 1·00 1·00
1051 $2 Sunbeam 3-litre, 1927 1·00 1·00
1052 $2 Franklin "Airman", 1928 1·00 1·00
1053 $2 Delage "D8S", 1929 1·00 1·00
1054 $2 Mors, 1897 1·00 1·00
1055 $2 Peerless "Green Dragon", 1904 1·00 1·00
1056 $2 Pope-Hartford, 1909 1·00 1·00
1057 $2 Daniels "Submarine Speedster", 1920 1·00 1·00
1058 $2 McFarlan 9.3 litre, 1922 1·00 1·00
1059 $2 Frazer Nash "Lemans" replica, 1949 1·00 1·00
1060 $2 Pegaso "Z102", 1953 1·00 1·00
1061 $2 Siata "Spyder V-8", 1953 1·00 1·00
1062 $2 Kurtis-Offenhauser, 1953 1·00 1·00
1063 $2 Kaiser-Darrin, 1954 1·00 1·00
1064 $2 Tracta, 1930 1·00 1·00
1065 $2 Maybach "Zeppelin", 1932 1·00 1·00
1066 $2 Railton "Light Sports", 1934 1·00 1·00
1067 $2 Hotchkiss, 1936 1·00 1·00
1068 $2 Mercedes-Benz "W163", 1939 1·00 1·00
1069 $2 Aston Martin "Vantage V8", 1982 1·00 1·00
1070 $2 Porsche "956", 1982 1·00 1·00
1071 $2 Lotus "Esprit Turbo", 1983 1·00 1·00
1072 $2 McLaren "MP4/2", 1984 1·00 1·00
1073 $2 Mercedes-Benz "190E 2.3-16", 1985 1·00 1·00
1074 $2 Ferrari "250 GT Lusso", 1963 1·00 1·00
1075 $2 Porsche "904", 1964 1·00 1·00
1076 $2 Volvo "P1800", 1967 1·00 1·00
1077 $2 McLaren-Chevrolet "M8D", 1970 1·00 1·00
1078 $2 Jaguar "XJ6", 1981 1·00 1·00

1988. "Mickey's Christmas Parade". As T **246** of Antigua showing Walt Disney cartoon characters. Multicoloured.

1079 $1 Dumbo 45 50
1080 $1 Goofy as Father Christmas 45 50
1081 $1 Minnie Mouse waving from window 45 50
1082 $1 Clarabelle, Mordie and Ferdie watching parade 45 50
1083 $1 Donald Duck's nephews 45 50
1084 $1 Donald Duck as drummer 45 50
1085 $1 Toy soldiers 45 50
1086 $1 Mickey Mouse on wooden horse 45 50

94 Middleweight Boxing (Gold, Henry Maske, East Germany)

1989. Olympic Medal Winners, Seoul (1988). Multicoloured.

1088 15 c. Type **94** 10 10
1089 50 c. Freestyle wrestling (130 kg) (Bronze, Andreas Schroeder, East Germany) 20 25
1090 60 c. Women's team gymnastics (Bronze, East Germany) 25 30
1091 75 c. Platform diving (Gold, Greg Louganis, USA) 30 35
1092 $1 Freestyle wrestling (52 kg) (Gold, Mitsuru Sato, Japan) 40 45
1093 $2 Men's freestyle 4 × 200 metres relay swimming (Bronze, West Germany) 85 90
1094 $3 Men's 5000 metres (Silver, Dieter Baumann, West Germany) 1·25 1·40
1095 $4 Women's heptathlon (Gold, Jackie Joyner-Kersee, U.S.A.) 1·75 1·90

1989. Japanese Art. Paintings by Hiroshige. As T **250** of Antigua. Multicoloured.

1097 15 c. "Crossing the Oi at Shimada by Ferry" 10 10
1098 20 c. "Daimyo and Entourage at Arai" 10 10
1099 45 c. "Cargo Portage through Goyu" 20 25
1100 75 c. "Snowfall at Fujigawa" 30 35
1101 $1 "Horses for the Emperor at Chirifu" 40 45
1102 $2 "Rainfall at Tsuchiyama" 85 90
1103 $3 "An Inn at Ishibe" 1·25 1·40
1104 $4 "On the Shore of Lake Biwa at Otsu" 1·75 1·90

1989. World Cup Football Championship, Italy (1990). As T **252** of Antigua. Mult.

1106 15 c. World Cup trophy 10 10
1107 20 c. Flags of Argentina (winners 1986) and International Federation of Football Associations (FIFA) (horiz) 10 10
1108 45 c. Franz Beckenbauer (West Germany) with World Cup, 1974 20 25
1109 75 c. Flags of Italy (winners 1982) and FIFA (horiz) 30 35
1110 $1 Pele (Brazil) with Jules Rimet trophy 40 45
1111 $2 Flags of West Germany (winners 1974) and FIFA (horiz) 85 90
1112 $3 Flags of Brazil (winners 1970) and FIFA (horiz) 1·25 1·40
1113 $4 Jules Rimet trophy and Brazil players 1·75 1·90

1989. North American Railway Locomotives. As T **342** of Grenada. Multicoloured.

1115 $2 Morris & Essex Railroad "Dover", 1841 85 90
1116 $2 Baltimore & Ohio Railroad "Memmon" No. 57, 1848 85 90
1117 $2 Camden & Amboy Railroad "John Stevens", 1849 85 90
1118 $2 Lawrence Machine Shop "Lawrence", 1853 85 90
1119 $2 South Carolina Railroad "James S. Corry", 1859 85 90
1120 $2 Mine Hill & Schuylkill Haven Railroad Flexible Beam No. 3 type, 1860 85 90
1121 $2 Delaware, Lackawanna & Western Railroad "Montrose", 1861 85 90
1122 $2 Central Pacific Railroad "Pequop" No. 68, 1868 85 90
1123 $2 Boston & Providence Railroad "Daniel Nason", 1863 85 90
1124 $2 Morris & Essex Railroad "Joe Scranton", 1870 85 90
1125 $2 Central Railroad of New Jersey No. 124, 1871 85 90
1126 $2 Baldwin tramway steam locomotive, 1876 85 90
1127 $2 Lackawanna & Bloomsburg Railroad "Luzerne", 1878 85 90
1128 $2 Central Mexicano Railroad No. 150, 1892 85 90
1129 $2 Denver, South Park & Pacific Railroad "Breckenridge" No. 15, 1879 85 90
1130 $2 Miles Planting & Manufacturing Company plantation locomotive "Daisy", 1894 85 90
1131 $2 Central of Georgia Railroad Baldwin "854" No. 1136, 1895 85 90
1132 $2 Savannah, Florida & Western Railroad No. 111, 1900 85 90
1133 $2 Douglas, Gilmore & Company contractors locomotive No. 3, 1902 85 90
1134 $2 Lehigh Valley Coal Company compressed air locomotive No. 900, 1903 85 90
1135 $2 Morgan's Louisiana & Texas Railroad McKeen diesel locomotive, 1908 85 90
1136 $2 Clear Lake Lumber Company Type "B Climax" locomotive No. 6, 1910 85 90
1137 $2 Blue Jay Lumber Company Heisler locomotive No. 10, 1912 85 90
1138 $2 Stewartstown Railroad gasoline locomotive No. 6, 1920s 85 90
1139 $2 Bangor & Aroostock Railroad Class "G" No. 186, 1921 85 90
1140 $2 Hammond Lumber Company No. 6, 1923 85 90
1141 $2 Central Railroad of New Jersey diesel locomotive No. 1000, 1925 85 90
1142 $2 Atchison, Topeka & Santa Fe Railroad "Super Chief" diesel express, 1935 85 90
1143 $2 Norfolk & Western Railroad Class "Y-6", 1948 85 90
1144 $2 Boston & Maine Railroad Budd diesel railcar, 1949 85 90

1989. "Philexfrance '89" International Stamp Exhibition, Paris. As T **251** of Antigua showing Walt Disney cartoon characters in Paris. Multicoloured.

1145 1 c. Mickey Mouse and Donald Duck at Ecole Militaire inflating balloon 10 10
1146 2 c. Mickey and Minnie Mouse on river boat passing Conciergerie 10 10
1147 3 c. Mickey Mouse at Hotel de Ville (vert) 10 10
1148 4 c. Mickey Mouse at Genie of the Bastille monument (vert) 10 10
1149 5 c. Mickey and Minnie Mouse arriving at Opera House 10 10
1150 10 c. Mickey and Minnie Mouse on tandem in Luxembourg Gardens 10 10
1151 $5 Mickey Mouse in aeroplane over L'Arch de la Defense (vert) 2·40 2·75
1152 $6 Mickey Mouse at Place Vendome (vert) 2·75 3·25

95 Launch of "Apollo 11"

1989. 20th Anniv of First Manned Landing on Moon. Multicoloured.

1154 25 c. Type **95** 10 15
1155 50 c. Splashdown (horiz) 20 25
1156 60 c. Modules in space 25 30
1157 75 c. Aldrin setting up experiment (horiz) 30 35
1158 $1 "Apollo 11" leaving Earth orbit (horiz) 40 45
1159 $2 Moving "Apollo 11" to launch site 85 90
1160 $3 Lunar module "Eagle" leaving Moon (horiz) 1·25 1·40
1161 $4 "Eagle" landing on Moon 1·75 1·90

1989. Fungi. As T **348** of Grenada. Mult.

1163 6 c. "Collybia aurea" 10 10
1164 10 c. "Podaxis pistillaris" 10 10
1165 20 c. "Hygrocybe firma" 10 10
1166 30 c. "Agaricus rufoaurantiacus" 10 15
1167 75 c. "Leptonia howellii" 30 35
1168 $2 "Marasmiellus purpureus" 85 90
1169 $3 "Marasmius trinitatis" 1·25 1·40
1170 $4 "Hygrocybe martinicensis" 1·75 1·90

1989. Butterflies. As T **350** of Grenada. Mult.

1172 25 c. "Battus polydamas" (inscr "Papilio androgeus") 10 15
1173 35 c. "Phoebis sennae" 15 20
1174 45 c. "Hamadryas feronia" 20 25
1175 50 c. "Cynthia cardui" 20 25
1176 75 c. "Ascia monuste" 30 35
1177 90 c. "Eurema lisa" 40 45
1178 $2 "Aphrissa statira" 85 90
1179 $3 "Hypolimnas misippus" 1·25 1·40

96 Ethel Barrymore

1989. 425th Birth Anniv of Shakespeare. Shakespearean Actors. Multicoloured.

1181 15 c. Type **96** 10 10
1182 $1.10 Richard Burton 45 50
1183 $2 John Barrymore 85 90
1184 $3 Paul Robeson 1·25 1·40

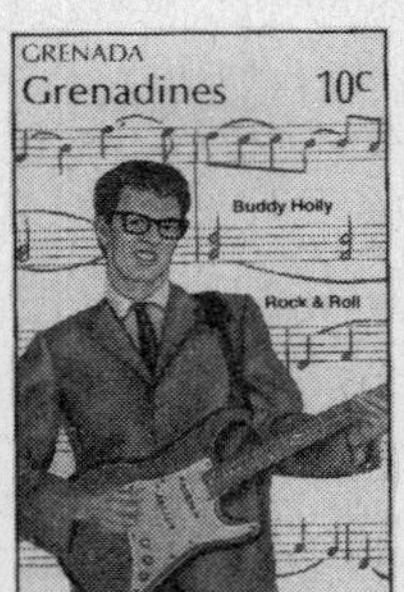

97 Buddy Holly

1989. Musicians. Multicoloured.

1186 10 c. Type **97** 10 10
1187 25 c. Jimmy Hendrix 10 15
1188 75 c. Mighty Sparrow 30 35
1189 $4 Katsutoji Kineya 1·75 1·90

1989. 500th Anniv (1992) of Discovery of America by Columbus (2nd issue). Pre-Columbian Arawak Society. As T **247** of Antigua. Multicoloured.

1191 15 c. Arawaks canoeing 10 10
1192 75 c. Family and campfire 30 35
1193 90 c. Using stone tools 40 45
1194 $3 Eating and drinking 1·25 1·40

1989. "World Stamp Expo '89" International Stamp Exhibition, Washington. Designs showing Walt Disney cartoon characters illustrating proverbs from "Poor Richard's Almanack". As T **352** of Grenada. Mult.

1196 1 c. Uncle Scrooge McDuck with gold coins in sinking boat 10 10
1197 2 c. Robin Hood shooting apple off Friar Tuck 10 10
1198 3 c. Winnie the Pooh with honey 10 10
1199 4 c. Goofy, Minnie Mouse and Donald Duck exercising 10 10
1200 5 c. Pinnochio holding Jimminy Cricket 10 10
1201 6 c. Huey and Dewey putting up wallpaper 10 10
1202 8 c. Mickey Mouse asleep in storm 10 10
1203 10 c. Mickey Mouse as Benjamin Franklin selling "Pennsylvania Gazette" 10 10
1204 $5 Mickey Mouse with chicken, recipe book and egg 2·10 2·25
1205 $6 Mickey Mouse missing carriage 2·50 2·75

1990. Christmas. Paintings by Rubens. As T **259** of Antigua. Multicoloured.

1207 10 c. "The Annunciation" 10 10
1208 15 c. "The Flight of the Holy Family into Egypt" 10 10
1209 25 c. "The Presentation in the Temple" 10 15
1210 45 c. "The Holy Family under the Apple Tree" 20 25
1211 $2 "Madonna and Child with Saints" 85 90
1212 $4 "The Virgin and Child enthroned with Saints" 1·75 1·90
1213 $5 "The Holy Family" 2·10 2·25

1990. "EXPO '90" International Garden and Greenery Exhibition, Osaka. Caribbean Orchids. As T **354** of Grenada. Multicoloured.

1215 15 c. "Brassocattleya" Thalie 10 10
1216 20 c. "Odontocidium" Tigersun 10 10
1217 50 c. "Odontioda" Hambuhren 20 25
1218 75 c. "Paphiopedilum" Delrosi 30 35
1219 $1 "Vuylstekeara" Yokara 40 45
1220 $2 "Paphiopedilum" Geelong 85 90
1221 $3 "Wilsonara" Tigerwood 1·25 1·40
1222 $4 "Cymbidium" Ormoulu 1·75 1·90

1990. 500th Anniv (1992) of Discovery of America by Columbus (3rd issue). New World Natural History—Insects. As T **260** of Antigua. Multicoloured.

1224 35 c. "Dynastes hercules" (beetle) 15 20
1225 40 c. "Chalcolepidius porcatus" (beetle) 15 20
1226 50 c. "Acrocinus longimanus" (beetle) 20 25
1227 60 c. "Battus polydamas" (butterfly) 25 30
1228 $1 "Orthemis ferruginea" (skimmer) 40 45
1229 $2 "Psiloptera variolosa" (beetle) 85 90
1230 $3 "Hypolimas misippus" (butterfly) 1·25 1·40
1231 $4 Scarab beetle 1·75 1·90

1990. Wildlife. As T **254** of Antigua. Mult.

1233 5 c. West Indies giant rice rat 10 10
1234 25 c. Agouti 10 15
1235 30 c. Humpback whale 10 15
1236 40 c. Pilot whale 15 20
1237 $1 Spotted dolphin 40 45
1238 $2 Egyptian mongoose 85 90
1239 $3 Brazilian tree porcupine 1·25 1·40
1240 $4 American manatee 1·75 1·90

1990. 50th Anniv of Second World War. As T **274** of Antigua. Multicoloured.

1242 6 c. British tanks in France, 1939 10 10
1243 10 c. Operation "Crusader", North Africa, 1941 10 10
1244 20 c. Retreat of the Afrika Corps, 1942 10 10
1245 45 c. American landing on Aleutian Islands, 1943 20 25
1246 50 c. U.S. marines landing on Tarawa, 1943 20 25
1247 60 c. U.S. army entering Rome, 1944 25 30
1248 75 c. U.S. tanks crossing River Seine, 1944 30 35
1249 $1 Battle of the Bulge, 1944 40 45
1250 $5 American infantry in Italy, 1945 2·10 2·25
1251 $6 "Enola Gay" dropping atomic bomb on Hiroshima, 1945 2·50 2·75

1990. "Stamp World London 90" International Stamp Exhibition. As T **193** of Gambia showing Walt Disney cartoon characters at Shakespeare sites. Mult.

1253 15 c. Daisy Duck at Ann Hathaway's Cottage (horiz) 10 10
1254 30 c. Minnie and Bill Mouse at Shakespeare's birthplace, Stratford 10 15
1255 50 c. Minnie Mouse in front of Mary Arden's house, Wilmcote 20 25
1256 60 c. Mickey Mouse leaning on hedge in New Place gardens, Stratford (horiz) 25 30
1257 $1 Mickey Mouse walking in New Place gardens, Stratford (horiz) 40 45
1258 $2 Mickey Mouse carrying books in Scholars Lane, Stratford 85 90
1259 $4 Mickey Mouse and Royal Shakespeare Theatre, Stratford 1·75 1·90
1260 $5 Ludwig von Drake teaching Mickey Mouse at the Stratford Grammar School (horiz) 2·10 2·25

1990. 90th Birthday of Queen Elizabeth the Queen Mother. As T **194** of Gambia, showing photographs 1970–79.

1262 $2 Queen Mother wearing pink hat and coat 85 90
1263 $2 Prince Charles and Queen Mother at Garter ceremony 85 90
1264 $2 Queen Mother in blue floral outfit 85 90

1990. Birds. As T **358** of Grenada, but vert. Multicoloured.

1267 25 c. Yellow-bellied seed-eater 10 15
1268 45 c. Carib grackle 20 25
1269 50 c. Black-whiskered vireo 20 25
1270 75 c. Bananaquit 30 35
1271 $1 Collared swift 40 45
1272 $2 Yellow-bellied elaenia 85 90
1273 $3 Blue-hooded euphonia 1·25 1·40
1274 $5 Eared dove 2·10 2·25

1990. Crustaceans. As T **359** of Grenada. Mult.

1276 10 c. Slipper lobster 10 10
1277 25 c. Green reef crab 10 15
1278 65 c. Caribbean lobsterette 25 30
1279 75 c. Blind deep sea lobster 30 35
1280 $1 Flattened crab 40 45
1281 $2 Ridged slipper lobster 85 90
1282 $3 Land crab 1·25 1·40
1283 $4 Mountain crab 1·75 1·90

98 Lineker, England

1990. World Cup Football Championship, Italy. Multicoloured.

1285 15 c. Type **98** 10 10
1286 45 c. Burruchaga, Argentina 20 25
1287 $2 Hysen, Sweden 85 90
1288 $4 Sang Ho, South Korea 1·75 1·90

1990. Olympic Games, Barcelona (1992). As T **268** of Antigua. Multicoloured.

1290 10 c. Boxing 10 10
1291 25 c. Olympic flame 10 15
1292 50 c. Football 20 25
1293 75 c. Discus throwing 30 35
1294 $1 Pole vaulting 40 45
1295 $2 Show jumping 85 90
1296 $4 Women's basketball 1·75 1·90
1297 $5 Men's gymnastics 2·10 2·25

1991. 350th Death Anniv of Rubens. As T **273** of Antigua. Multicoloured.

1299 5 c. "Adam and Eve" (Eve detail) (vert) 10 10
1300 15 c. "Esther before Ahasuerus" (detail) 10 10
1301 25 c. "Adam and Eve" (Adam detail) (vert) 10 10
1302 50 c. "Expulsion from Eden" 20 25
1303 $1 "Cain slaying Abel" (detail) (vert) 40 45
1304 $2 "Lot's Flight" 85 90
1305 $4 "Samson and Delilah" (detail) 1·75 1·90
1306 $5 "Abraham and Melchizedek" 2·10 2·25

1991. Coral Reef Fishes. As T **357** of Grenada. Multicoloured.

1308 15 c. Barred hamlet 10 10
1309 35 c. Squirrelfish 15 20
1310 45 c. Redspotted hawkfish 20 25
1311 75 c. Bigeye 30 35
1312 $1 Spiny puffer 40 45
1313 $2 Smallmouth Grunt 80 85
1314 £3 Harlequin bass 1·25 1·40
1315 $4 Creole fish 1·75 1·90

99 Angel with Star and Lantern

1991. Christmas (1990). Hummel Figurines. Multicoloured.

1317 10 c. Type **99** 10 10
1318 15 c. Christ Child and Angel playing mandolin 10 10
1319 25 c. Shepherd 10 15
1320 50 c. Angel with trumpet and lantern 20 25
1321 $1 Nativity scene 40 45
1322 $2 Christ Child and Angel holding candle 85 90
1323 $4 Angel with baskets 1·75 1·90
1324 $5 Angels singing 2·10 2·25

100 "Brassia maculata"

1991. Orchids. Multicoloured.

1326 5 c. Type **100** 10 10
1327 10 c. "Oncidium lanceanum" 10 10
1328 15 c. "Broughtonia sanguinea" 10 10
1329 25 c. "Diacrium bicornutum" 10 15
1330 35 c. "Cattleya labiata" 15 20
1331 45 c. "Epidendrum fragrans" 20 25
1332 50 c. "Oncidium papilio" 20 25
1333 75 c. "Neocogniauxia monophylla" 30 35
1334 $1 "Epidendrum polybulbon" 40 45
1335 $2 "Spiranthes speciosa" 85 90
1336 $4 "Epidendrum ciliare" 1·75 1·90
1337 $5 "Phais tankervilliae" 2·10 2·25
1339 $10 "Brassia caudata" 4·00 4·25

1991. Butterflies. As T **363** of Grenada. Mult.

1340 20 c. "Dynastor napoleon" 10 10
1341 25 c. "Pieridae callinira" 10 10
1342 30 c. "Anartia amathea" 10 15
1343 35 c. "Heliconiidae dido" 15 20
1344 50 c. "Nymphalidae praeneste" 20 25
1345 75 c. "Dryas julia" 30 35
1346 $3 "Papilionidae paeon" 1·25 1·50
1347 $4 "Morpho cypris" 1·75 1·90

101 Donald and Daisy Duck with Solar-powered Car

1991. Ecology Conservation. Walt Disney cartoon characters. Multicoloured.
1349 10 c. Type **101** 10 10
1350 15 c. Goofy saving water 10 10
1351 25 c. Donald and Daisy on nature hike 10 10
1352 45 c. Donald Duck returning chick to nest 20 25
1353 $1 Donald Duck and balloons 40 45
1354 $2 Minnie Mouse and Daisy Duck on hot day 85 90
1355 $4 Mickey's nephews cleaning beach .. 1·75 1·90
1356 $5 Donald Duck on pedal generator .. .. 2·10 2·25

1991. 500th Anniv (1992) of Discovery of America by Columbus. History of Exploration. As T **194** of British Virgin Islands. Multicoloured.
1358 15 c. Magellan rounding Cape Horn, 1519–21 .. 10 10
1359 20 c. Drake's Golden Hind, 1577–80 .. .. 10 10
1360 50 c. Cook's H.M.S. "Resolution", 1768–71 20 25
1361 60 c. Douglas World Cruiser seaplane, 1924 25 30
1362 $1 "Sputnik 1" satellite, 1957 .. .. 40 45
1363 $2 Gagarin's space flight, 1961 .. .. 85 90
1364 $4 Glenn's space flight, 1962 .. .. .. 1·75 1·90
1365 $5 Space shuttle, 1981 .. 2·10 2·25

1991. "Philanippon '91" International Stamp Exhibition, Tokyo. As T **248** of Dominica showing Walt Disney cartoon characters in Japanese scenes. Multicoloured.
1367 15 c. Minnie Mouse with silkworms 10 10
1368 30 c. Mickey, Minnie, Morty and Ferdie at Torii Gate 10 15
1369 50 c. Donald Duck and Mickey Mouse trying origami 20 25
1370 60 c. Mickey and Minnie diving for pearls .. 25 30
1371 $1 Minnie Mouse in kimono 40 45
1372 $2 Mickey making masks 85 90
1373 $4 Donald and Mickey making paper .. .. 1·75 1·90
1374 $5 Minnie and Pluto making pottery .. 2·10 2·25

102 "Pyrrhoglossum pyrrhum"

1991. Mushrooms. Multicoloured.
1376 5 c. Type **102** 10 10
1377 45 c. "Agaricus purpurellus" 20 25
1378 50 c. "Amanita craseoderma" 20 25
1379 90 c. "Hygrocybe acutoconica" 40 45
1380 $1 "Limacella guttata" .. 40 45
1381 $2 "Lactarius hygrophoroides" 80 90
1382 $4 "Boletellus cubensis" 1·75 1·90
1383 $5 "Psilocybe caerulescens" .. .. 2·10 2·25

103 Queen, Prince Philip, Prince Charles and Prince William at Trooping the Colour, 1990

1991. 65th Birthday of Queen Elizabeth II. Multicoloured.
1385 20 c. Type **103** 10 10
1386 25 c. Queen and Prince Charles at polo match, 1985 .. .. .. 10 10
1387 $2 Queen and Prince Philip at Maundy service, 1989 .. .. 85 90
1388 $4 Queen with Queen Mother on her 87th birthday, 1987 .. 1·75 1·90

1991. 10th Wedding Anniv of Prince and Princess of Wales. As T **103**. Mult.
1390 5 c. Prince and Princess of Wales kissing, 1987 .. 10 10
1391 60 c. Portraits of Prince, Princess and sons .. 25 30
1392 $1 Prince Henry in 1988 and Prince William in 1987 .. .. .. 40 45
1393 $5 Princess Diana in 1990 and Prince Charles in 1988 .. .. .. 2·10 2·25

OFFICIAL STAMPS

1982. Optd. **P.R.G.** (a) Nos. 400/12 and 414.
O 1. 5 c. Yellowtail Snapper .. 10 15
O 2. 6 c. Mutton Snapper .. 10 15
O 3. 10 c. Cocoa Damselfish .. 10 15
O 4. 12 c. Royal Gramma .. 10 15
O 5. 15 c. Cherubfish 10 15
O 6. 20 c. Blackbar Soldierfish 10 20
O 7. 25 c. Comb Grouper .. 10 20
O 8. 30 c. Longsnout Butterflyfish 15 20
O 9. 40 c. Pudding Wife .. 15 25
O10. 50 c. Midnight Parrotfish 20 30
O11. 90 c. Redspotted Hawkfish 40 55
O12. $1 Hogfish 40 60
O13. $3 Beau Gregory .. .. 1·25 2·25
O14. $10 Barred Hamlet .. 4·25 6·00

(b) Nos. 444/6 and 448/9.
O 15. 30 c. Prince Charles and Lady Diana Spencer .. 2·00 2·00
O 16. 40 c. Prince Charles and Lady Diana Spencer .. 1·60 1·60
O 17. 40 c. Type **50** .. .. 2·00 2·75
O 18. $2 Type **50** .. .. 2·50 3·50
O 19. $4 Prince Charles as parachutist .. .. 6·50 8·50

(c) Nos. 473/6.
O20. **54.** 20 c. multicoloured .. 10 20
O21. – 40 c. multicoloured .. 15 25
O22. – $1 multicoloured .. 35 70
O23. – $2 multicoloured .. 70 1·40

GRENADINES OF ST. VINCENT

Part of a group of islands south of St. Vincent which include Bequia, Mustique, Canouan and Union.

100 cents = 1 dollar.

1973. Royal Wedding. As T **47** of Anguilla. Multicoloured. Background colours given
1. 25 c. green 10 10
2. $1 brown 25 15

1974. Nos. 286/300 of St. Vincent optd. **GRENADINES OF.** Multicoloured.
3. 1 c. Green Heron .. 10 10
4. 2 c. Lesser Antillean bullfinches 15 15
25. 3 c. St. Vincent amazon .. 40 30
6. 4 c. Rufous-throated solitaire (vert.) .. 15 10
7. 5 c. Red-necked pigeon (vert.) 15 10
8. 6 c. Bananaquits .. 15 10
9. 8 c. Purple-throated carib .. 15 10
10. 10 c. Mangrove cuckoo (vert.) 15 10
11. 12 c. Common black hawk (vert.) 20 15
12. 20 c. Bare-eyed thrush .. 35 20
13. 25 c. Hooded tanager .. 40 20
14. 50 c. Blue hooded euphonia 70 40
15. $1 Barn owl (vert.) .. 1·50 75
16. $2.50 Yellow-bellied elaenia (vert.) .. .. 2·00 1·25
17. $5 Ruddy quail dove .. 3·50 2·25

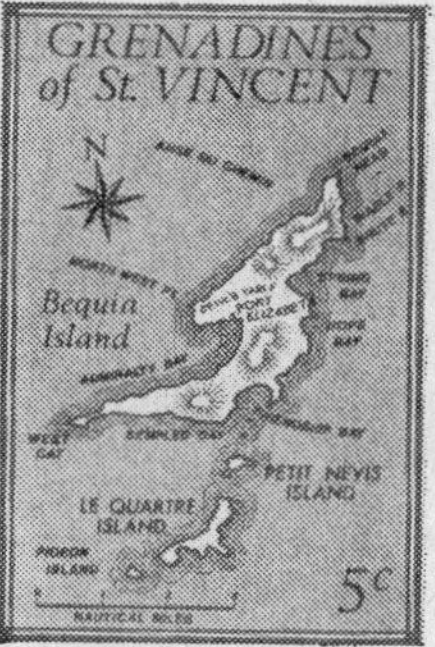

2. Map of Bequia.

1974. Maps (1st series).
18. **2.** 5 c. black, grn. & deep grn. 10 10
19. – 15 c. multicoloured .. 10 10
20. – 20 c. multicoloured .. 10 10
21. – 30 c. black, pink & red .. 10 10
22. – 40 c. blk., violet & purple 10 10
23. – $1 black, ultram. & blue 25 20
MAPS: 15 c. Prune Island. 20 c. Mayreau Island and Tobago Cays. 30 c. Mustique Island. 40 c. Union Island. $1, Canouan Island.
See also Nos. 85/8.

1974. Centenary of U.P.U. As Nos. 392/5 of St. Vincent.
26. 2 c. multicoloured 10 10
27. 15 c. multicoloured 10 10
28. 40 c. multicoloured 10 10
29. $1 multicoloured 25 15

4. Boat-building.

1974. Bequia Island (1st series). Multicoloured.
34. 5 c. Type **4** 15 10
31. 30 c. Careening at Port Elizabeth 10 15
32. 35 c. Admiralty Bay .. 10 15
33. $1 Fishing-boat race .. 20 25
See also Nos. 185/88.

5. Music Volute.

1974. Shells and molluscs. Multicoloured.
35. 1 c. Atlantic Thorny Oyster 10 10
36. 2 c. Zigzag Scallop 10 10
37. 3 c. Reticulated Helmet .. 10 10
38. 4 c. Type **5** 10 10
39. 5 c. Amber Pen Shell .. 10 10
40. 6 c. Angular Triton 10 10
41. 8 c. Flame Helmet 10 10
42. 10 c. Caribbean Olive .. 10 10
43. 12 c. Common Sundial .. 10 10
44. 15 c. Glory of the Atlantic Cone 25 10
45. 20 c. Flame Auger 30 20
46. 25 c. King Venus 40 20
47. 35 c. Long-spined Star-shell 35 25
48. 45 c. Speckled Tellin .. 35 30
49. 50 c. Rooster Tail Conch .. 40 25
50. $1 Green Star Shell .. 1·00 60
51. $2.50 Incomparable Cone .. 2·25 1·25
52. $5 Rough File Clam .. 4·00 2·75
52a. $10 Measled Cowrie .. 10·00 4·00
Nos. 38/42, 45, 47 and 49/50 come with and without an imprint below the design.

1974. Birth Centenary of Sir Winston Churchill. As Nos. 403/6 of St. Vincent, but inscr. "GRENADINES OF ST. VINCENT", and values (Nos. 53/5) and colours changed.
53. **75.** 5 c. multicoloured .. 10 10
54. – 40 c. multicoloured .. 10 10
55. – 50 c. multicoloured .. 15 10
56. – $1 multicoloured .. 25 20

6. Cotton House, Mustique.

1975. Mustique Island. Multicoloured.
57. 5 c. Type **6** 10 10
58. 35 c. "Blue Waters" Endeavour Bay 10 10
59. 45 c. Endeavour Bay .. 10 10
60. $1 "Les Jolies Eaux", Gelliceaux Bay 25 20

7. Danaus plexippus".

1975. Butterflies. Multicoloured.
61 3 c. Type **7** 20 10
62 5 c. "Agraulis vanillae" .. 25 10
63 35 c. "Battus polydamas" 80 10
64 45 c. "Evenus dindymus" and "Junonia evarete" .. 1·00 10
65 $1 "Anartia jatrophae" .. 1·75 35

8. Resort Pavilion.

1975. Petit St. Vincent. Multicoloured.
66. 5 c. Type **8** 10 10
67. 35 c. The Harbour .. 10 10
68. 45 c. The Jetty 15 10
69. $1 Sailing in coral lagoon .. 50 30

9. Ecumenical Church, Mustique.

1975. Christmas. Multicoloured.
70. 5 c. Type **9** 10 10
71. 25 c. Catholic Church, Union Island 10 10
72. 50 c. Catholic Church, Bequia 10 10
73. $1 Anglican Church, Bequia 25 15

10. Sunset Scene.

1976. Union Island (1st series). Multicoloured.
74. 5 c. Type **10** 10 10
75. 35 c. Customs and Post Office, Clifton 10 10
76. 45 c. Anglican Church, Ashton 10 10
77. $1 Mail schooner, Clifton Harbour 25 20
See also Nos. 242/5.

11. Staghorn Coral.

1976. Corals. Multicoloured.
78. 5 c. Type **11** 10 10
79. 35 c. Elkhorn coral 25 10
80. 45 c. Pillar coral 30 10
81. $1 Brain coral 80 20

12. 25 c. Bicentennial Coin.

1976. Bicent. of American Revolution.
82. **12.** 25 c. silver, black and blue 10 10
83. – 50 c. silver, black and red 20 10
84. – $1 silver, black & mauve 25 20
DESIGNS: 50 c. Half-dollar coin. $1, One dollar coin.

1976. Maps (2nd series). As T **2**.
85. 5 c. blk., deep grn. and grn. 10 10
86. 10 c. black, green and blue 10 10
87. 35 c. black, brown and red 20 20
88. 45 c. black, red and orange 25 25

Nos. 85/8 exist in 7 different designs to each value as follows: A, Bequia, B, Canouan, C, Mayreau, D, Mustique, E, Petit St. Vincent, F, Prune, G, Union. To indicate any particular design use the appropriate catalogue No. together with the prefix for the island concerned.

13. Station Hill School and Post Office.

1977. Mayreau Island. Multicoloured.
89. 5 c. Type **13** 10 10
90. 35 c. Church at Old Wall.. 10 10
91. 45 c. La Sourciere Anchorage 10 10
92. $1 Saline Bay 25 15

14. Coronation Crown Coin.

1977. Silver Jubilee. Multicoloured.
93. 25 c. Type **14** 20 10
94. 50 c. Silver Wedding Crown 25 10
95. $1 Silver Jubilee Crown .. 30 15

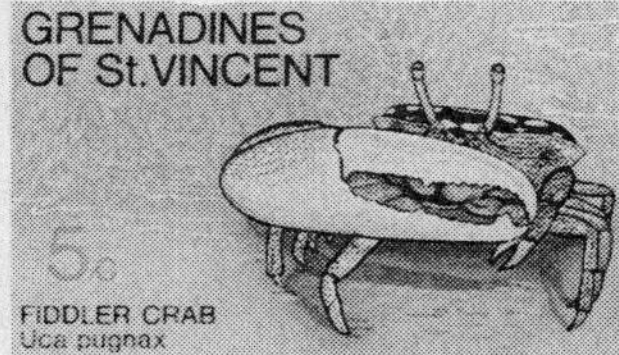

15. Fiddler Crab.

1977. Crustaceans. Multicoloured.
96. 5 c. Type **15** 10 10
97. 35 c. Ghost crab 20 10
98. 50 c. Blue crab 25 10
99. $1.25 Spiny lobster .. 55 40

16. Snorkel Diving.

1977. Prune Island. Multicoloured.
100. 5 c. Type **16** 10 10
101. 35 c. Palm Is. Resort .. 10 10
102. 45 c. Casuarina Beach .. 10 10
103. $1 Palm Is. Beach Club.. 30 30

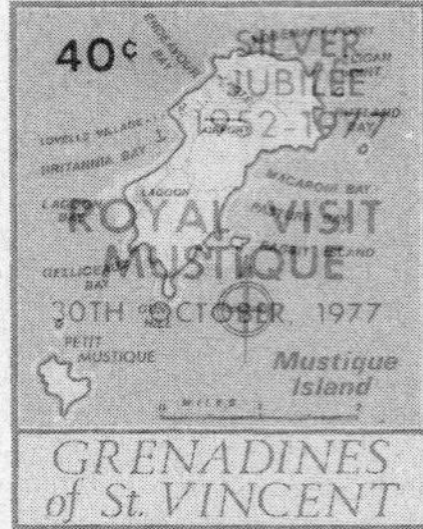

17. Mustique Island.

1977. Royal Visit. Surch. as in T **17**.
104. **17.** 40 c. turquoise and green 20 10
105. $2 ochre and brown .. 65 25

18. The Clinic, Charlestown.

1977. Canouan Island Views (1st series). Multicoloured.
106. 5 c. Type **18** 10 10
107. 35 c. Town Jetty, Charlestown 10 10
108. 45 c. Mail schooner arriving at Charlestown 10 10
109. $1 Grand Bay 30 20

See also Nos. 307/10.

19. Tropical Mockingbird.

1978. Birds and Birds' Eggs. Multicoloured.
110. 1 c. Type **19** 10 10
111. 2 c. Mangrove cuckoo .. 15 10
112. 3 c. Osprey.. .. .. 20 10
113. 4 c. Smooth billed ani .. 20 10
114. 5 c. House wren 20 10
115. 6 c. Bananaquit 20 10
116. 8 c. Carib grackle 20 10
117. 10 c. Yellow-bellied elaenia 20 10
118. 12 c. Collared plover .. 30 10
119. 15 c. Cattle egret 30 10
120. 20 c. Red-footed booby .. 30 10
121. 25 c. Red-billed tropic bird 30 10
122. 40 c. Royal tern 45 15
123. 50 c. Grenada flycatcher .. 45 20
124. 80 c. Purple gallinule .. 70 30
125. $1 Broad-winged hawk .. 75 50
126. $2 Scaly-breasted ground dove 90 75
127. $3 Laughing gull .. .. 1·25 1·00
128. $5 Common noddy .. 2·25 1·25
129. $10 Grey kingbird.. .. 5·00 2·25

1978. 25th Anniv. of Coronation. British Cathedrals. Designs as Nos. 422/5 of Monserrat. Multicoloured.
130. 5 c. Worcester Cathedral 10 10
131. 40 c. Coventry Cathedral 10 10
132. $1 Winchester Cathedral 15 10
133. $3 Chester Cathedral .. 25 35

20. Green Turtle.

1978. Turtles. Multicoloured.
135. 5 c. Type **20** 10 10
136. 40 c. Hawksbill Turtle .. 15 10
137. 50 c. Leatherback Turtle 15 10
138. $1.25 Loggerhead Turtle 40 40

21. Three Kings following Star.

1978. Christmas. Scenes and Verses from the Carol " We Three Kings ". Multicoloured.
139. 5 c. Type **21** 10 10
140. 10 c. King presenting gold 10 10
141. 25 c. King presenting frankincense 10 10
142. 50 c. King presenting myrrh 10 10
143. $2 Kings paying homage to infant Jesus 30 20

22. Sailing Yachts.

1979. National Regatta.
145. **22.** 5 c. multicoloured .. 10 10
146. – 40 c. multicoloured .. 20 10
147. – 50 c. multicoloured .. 25 10
148. – $2 multicoloured .. 75 60
DESIGNS: 40 c. to $2, Various sailing yachts.

1979. Wildlife. As T **114** of St. Vincent. Multicoloured.
149. 20 c. Green Iguana .. 10 10
150. 40 c. Common Opossum .. 15 10
151. $2 Red-legged Tortoise .. 60 65

1979. Death Centenary of Sir Rowland Hill. As T **103** of St. Vincent. Multicoloured.
152. 80 c. Sir Rowland Hill .. 25 15
153. $1 Great Britain 1d. and 4d. stamps of 1858 with " A10 " (Kingstown, St. Vincent) postmark.. 30 25
154. $2 St. Vincent ½d. and 1d. stamps of 1894 with Bequia postmark .. 50 40

1979. International Year of the Child. Designs as Nos. 570/3 of St. Vincent.
156. 6 c. black, silver and blue 10 10
157. 40 c. black, silver & salmon 10 10
158. $1 black, silver and buff.. 20 10
159. $3 black, silver and lilac 45 30

1979. Independence. As T **106** of St. Vincent. Multicoloured.
160. 5 c. National flag and " Ixora salicifolia " (flower) 10 10
161. 40 c. House of Assembly and " Ixora odorata " (flower) 10 10
162. $1 Prime Minister R. Milton Cato and " Ixora javanica " (flower) 20 20

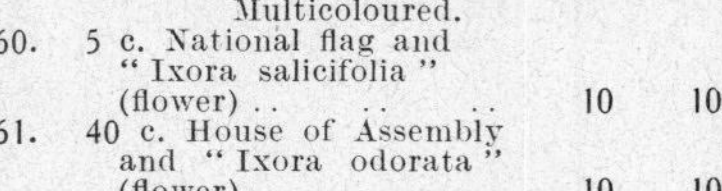

23. False Killer Whale.

1980. Whales and Dolphins. Multicoloured.
163. 10 c. Type **23** 15 10
164. 50 c. Spinner Dolphin .. 40 20
165. 90 c. Bottle-nosed Dolphin 65 40
166. $2 Short-finned Pilot Whale ("Blackfish") .. 1·00 65

1980. " London 1980 " International Stamp Exhibition. As T **110** of St. Vincent. Multicoloured.
167. 40 c. Queen Elizabeth II .. 20 10
168. 50 c. St. Vincent 2 c. stamp of 1965 .. .. .. 20 10
169. $3 First Grenadines stamps 60 80

1980. Sport. As T **112** of St. Vincent. **Mult.**
171. 25 c. Running 10 10
172. 50 c. Sailing 10 10
173. $1 Long-jumping 20 20
174. $2 Swimming 30 30

1980. Hurricane Relief. Nos. 171/4 optd. **HURRICANE RELIEF 50 c.**
175. **22.** 25 c. + 50 c. multicoloured 10 20
176. – 50 c. + 50 c. multicoloured 20 30
177. – $1 + 50 c. multicoloured 25 40
178. – $2 + 50 c. multicoloured 40 60

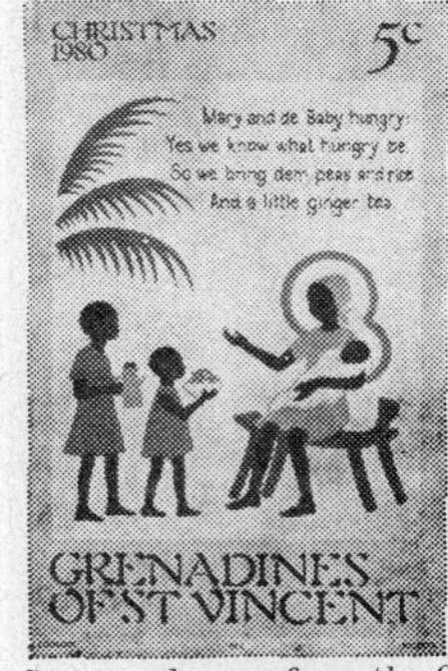

24. Scene and verse from the Carol " De Borning Day ".

1980. Christmas. Multicoloured.
179. 5 c. Type **24** 10 10
180. 50 c. " Mary and de Baby lonely " 10 10
181. 60 c. " Mary and de Baby weary " 10 10
182. $1 " Mary and de Baby rest easy " 15 15
183. $2 " Star above shine in de sky " 25 25

25. Post Office, Port Elizabeth.

1981. Bequia Island (2nd series). Mult.
185. 50 c. Type **25** 15 15
186. 60 c. Moonhole 20 20
187. $1.50 Fishing boats, Admiralty Bay 40 40
188. $2 "The Friendship Rose" (yacht) at jetty 55 55

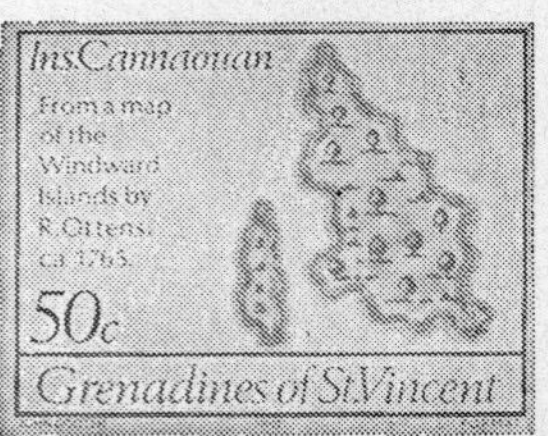

26. Ins. Cannaouan (from map of Windward Islands by R. Ottens, c. 1765).

1981. Details from Early Maps. Mult.
189 50 c. Type **26** 40 30
190 50 c. Cannouan Is. (from chart by J. Parsons, 1861) 40 30
191 60 c. Ins. Moustiques (from map of Windward Islands by R. Ottens, c. 1765) 45 35
192 60 c. Mustique Is. (from chart by J. Parsons, 1861) 45 35
193 $2 Ins. Bequia (from map of Windward Islands by R. Ottens, c. 1765) .. 80 75
194 $2 Bequia Is. (from map surveyed in 1763 by T. Jefferys) 80 75

1981. Royal Wedding. Royal Yachts. As T **26** of Kiribati. Multicoloured.
195. 50 c. " Mary " 15 15
196. 50 c. Prince Charles and Lady Diana Spencer .. 40 40
197. $3 " Alexandra " 30 30
198. $3 As No. 196 .. .. 90 90
199. $3.50 " Britannia " .. 35 35
200. $3.50 As No. 196 .. .. 90 90

27. Bar Jack.

1981. Game Fish. Multicoloured.

204. 10 c. Type **27** 15 10
205. 50 c. Tarpon 25 10
206. 60 c. Cobia 30 10
207. $2 Blue Marlin 90 70

28. H.M.S. "Experiment".

1982. Ships. Multicoloured.

208. 1 c. Type **28** 10 10
209. 3 c. "Lady Nelson" (cargo liner) 10 10
210. 5 c. "Daisy" (brig) 10 10
211. 6 c. Carib canoe 10 10
212. 10 c. "Hairoun Star" (freighter) 10 10
213. 15 c. "Jupiter" (liner) 10 10
214. 20 c. "Christina" (steamer yacht) 10 10
215. 25 c. "Orinoco" (paddle-steamer) 10 15
216. 30 c. H.M.S. "Lively" 10 15
217. 50 c. "Alabama" (Confederate warship) 20 25
218. 60 c. "Denmark" (freighter) 25 30
219. 75 c. "Santa Maria" 30 35
220. $1 "Baffin" (cable ship) 40 45
221. $2 "Queen Elizabeth 2" (liner) 85 90
222. $3 R.Y. "Britannia" 1·25 1·40
223. $5 "Geeststar" (cargo liner) 2·10 2·25
224. $10 "Grenadines Star" (ferry) 4·25 4·40

29. Fruit of Prickly Pear.

1982. Prickly Pear Cactus. Multicoloured.

225. 10 c. Type **29** 15 15
226. 50 c. Prickly Pear flower buds 35 35
227. $1 Flower of Prickly Pear Cactus 60 60
228. $2 Prickly Pear Cactus 1·25 1·25

30. Anne Neville. Princess of Wales, 1470.

1982. 21st Birthday of Princess of Wales. Multicoloured.

229. 50 c. Type **30** 20 20
230. 60 c. Coat of arms of Anne Neville 20 20
231. $6 Diana, Princess of Wales 1·25 1·25

31. Old and New Uniforms.

1982. 75th Anniv. of Boy Scout Movement. Multicoloured.

232. $1.50 Type **31** 60 60
233. $2.50 Lord Baden-Powell 90 90

1982. Birth of Prince William of Wales. Nos. 224/6 optd. **ROYAL BABY** and island name.

234. 50 c. Type **30** 20 20
235. 60 c. Coat of arms of Anne Neville 20 20
236. $6 Diana, Princess of Wales 1·25 1·25

Nos. 229/31 exist overprinted with 5 different island names as follows: A. Bequia, B. Canouan, C. Mayreau. D. Mustique, E. Union Island. To indicate any particular overprint use the appropriate catalogue No. together with the prefix for the island concerned.

33. Silhouette Figures of Mary and Joseph.

1982. Christmas. Silhouette of figures. Multicoloured.

237. 10 c. Type **33** 10 10
238. $1. 50 Animals in stable 45 45
239. $2. 50 Mary and Joseph with baby Jesus 60 60

1983. No. 123 surch.

241. 45 c. on 50 c. Grenada flycatcher 20 25

35. Power Station, Clifton.

1983. Union Island (2nd series). Multicoloured.

242. 50 c. Type **35** 15 15
243. 60 c. Sunrise, Clifton harbour 15 15
244. $1.50 Junior Secondary School, Ashton 40 40
245. $2 Frigate Rock and Conch Shell Beach 55 55

36. British Man-of-war.

1983. Bicent. of Treaty of Versailles. Mult.

246. 45 c. Type **36** 15 15
247. 60 c. American man-of-war 15 15
248. $1.50 Soldiers carrying U.S. flags 45 45
249. $2 British troops in battle 55 55

MORE DETAILED LISTS

are given in the Stanley Gibbons Catalogues referred to in the country headings.
For lists of current volumes see Introduction.

37. Montgolfier Balloon, 1783.

1983. Bicentenary of Manned Flight. Mult.

250. 45 c. Type **37** 15 15
251. 60 c. Ayres "Turbo-thrush Commander" (horiz.) 15 15
252. $1.50 Lebaudy "1" dirigible (horiz.) 45 45
253. $2 Space shuttle "Columbia" 55 55

38. Coat of Arms of James I

1983. Leaders of the World. British Monarchs. Multicoloured.

255. 60 c. Type **38** 25 25
256. 60 c. Henry VIII 25 25
257. 60 c. Coat of Arms of James I 25 25
258. 60 c. James I 25 25
259. 75 c. Henry VIII at Hampton Court 25 25
260. 75 c. Hampton Court 25 25
261. 75 c. James I at Edinburgh Castle 25 25
262. 75 c. Edinburgh Castle 25 25
263. $2.50 The "Mary Rose" 35 25
264. $2.50 Vignette of Henry VIII and Portsmouth harbour 35 25
265. $2.50 James I and the Gunpowder plot 35 25
266. $2.50 Vignette of James I and Gunpowder plot 35 25

39. Quarter Dollar and Half Dollar, 1797.

1983. Old Coinage. Multicoloured.

267. 20 c. Type **39** 10 10
268. 45 c. Nine Bitts, 1811–14 15 15
269. 75 c. Twelve Bitts and six Bitts, 1811–14 25 25
270. $3 Sixty six Shillings, 1798 80 80

40. Class "D 13".

1984. Leaders of the World. Railway Locomotives (1st series). The first design in each pair shows technical drawings and the second the locomotive at work.

271. 5 c. multicoloured 10 10
272. 5 c. multicoloured 10 10
273. 10 c. multicoloured 10 10
274. 10 c. multicoloured 10 10
275. 15 c. multicoloured 15 15
276. 15 c. multicoloured 15 15
277. 35 c. multicoloured 20 20
278. 35 c. multicoloured 20 20
279. 45 c. multicoloured 20 20
280. 45 c. multicoloured 20 20
281. 60 c. multicoloured 25 25
282. 60 c. multicoloured 25 25
283. $1 multicoloured 35 35
284. $1 multicoloured 35 35
285. $2.50 multicoloured 50 50
286. $2.50 multicoloured 50 50

DESIGNS: Nos. 271/2, Class "D 13", U.S.A. 1892. (Type **40**). 273/4, High Speed Train "125", Great Britain (1980) 275/6, Class "T9", Great Britain (1899). 277/8, "Claud Hamilton", Great Britain (1900). 279/80, Class "J", U.S.A. (1941). 281/2, Class "D 16", U.S.A. (1895), 283/4. "Lode Star", Great Britain (1907). 285/6, "Blue Peter", Great Britain (1948).

See also Nos. 311/26, 351/8, 390/7, 412/9, 443/58, 504/19 and 520/35.

41. Spotted Eagle Ray.

1984. Reef Fishes. Multicoloured.

287. 45 c. Type **41** 25 30
288. 60 c. Queen Trigger Fish 30 35
289. $1.50 White Spotted File Fish 75 80
290. $2 Schoolmaster 1·00 1·10

42. R. A. Woolmer.

1984. Leaders of the World. Cricketers (1st series). The first design in each pair shows a head portrait and the second the cricketer in action.

291. 1 c. multicoloured 10 10
292. 1 c. multicoloured 10 10
293. 3 c. multicoloured 10 10
294. 3 c. multicoloured 10 10
295. 5 c. multicoloured 10 10
296. 5 c. multicoloured 10 10
297. 30 c. multicoloured 20 20
298. 30 c. multicoloured 20 20
299. 60 c. multicoloured 40 40
300. 60 c. multicoloured 40 40
301. $1 multicoloured 50 50
302. $1 multicoloured 50 50
303. $2 multicoloured 80 80
304. $2 multicoloured 80 80
305. $3 multicoloured 1·10 1·10
306. $3 multicoloured 1·10 1·10

DESIGNS: Nos. 291/2, R. A. Woolmer (Type **42**). 293/4, K. S. Ranjitsinhji. 295/6, W. R. Hammond. 297/8, D. L. Underwood. 299/300, W. G. Grace. 301/2, E. A. E. Baptiste. 303/4, A. P. E. Knott. 305/6, L. E. G. Ames.

See also Nos. 331/8 and 364/9.

43. Junior Secondary School.

1984. Canouan Island (2nd series). Multicoloured.

307. 35 c. Type **43** 20 20
308. 45 c. Police Station 25 25
309. $1 Post Office 50 50
310. $3 Anglican Church 1·25 1·50

INDEX

Countries can be quickly located by referring to the index at the end of this volume.

1984. Leaders of the World. Railway Locomotives (2nd series). As T **40**. The first design in each pair shows technical drawings and the second the locomotive at work.

311. 1 c. multicoloured 10 10
312. 1 c. multicoloured 10 10
313. 5 c. multicoloured 10 10
314. 5 c. multicoloured 10 10
315. 20 c. multicoloured .. 15 15
316. 20 c. multicoloured .. 15 15
317. 35 c. multicoloured .. 25 25
318. 35 c. multicoloured .. 25 25
319. 60 c. multicoloured .. 40 40
320. 60 c. multicoloured .. 40 40
321. $1 multicoloured 50 50
322. $1 multicoloured 50 50
323. $1.50 multicoloured .. 55 55
324. $1.50 multicoloured .. 55 55
325. $3 multicoloured 80 80
326. $3 multicoloured 80 80

DESIGNS: Nos. 311/12, Class "C62", Japan (1948). 313/14, Class "V", Great Britain (1903). 315/16, "Catch-Me-Who-Can", Great Britain (1808). 317/18, Class "E10", Japan (1948). 319/20, "J. B. Earle", Great Britain (1904). 321/2, "Lyn", Great Britain (1898). 323/4, "Talyllyn", Great Britain (1865). 325/6, "Cardean", Great Britain (1906).

44. Lady of the Night.

1984. Night-blooming Flowers. Mult.

327. 35 c. Type **44** 35 30
328. 45 c. Four o'clock 45 35
329. 75 c. Mother-in-Law's Tongue 60 50
330. $3 Queen of the night .. 2·00 1·75

1984. Leaders of the World. Cricketers (2nd series). As T **42**. The first in each pair listed shows a head portrait and the second the cricketer in action.

331. 5 c. multicoloured 10 10
332. 5 c. multicoloured 10 10
333. 30 c. multicoloured .. 20 20
334. 30 c. multicoloured .. 20 20
335. $1 multicoloured 50 50
336. $1 multicoloured 50 50
337. $2.50 multicoloured .. 1·10 1·10
338. $2.50 multicoloured .. 1·10 1·10

DESIGNS: Nos. 331/2, S. F. Barnes. 333/4, R. Peel. 335/6, H. Larwood. 337/8, Sir John Hobbs.

45. Facel "Vega HK500".

1984. Leaders of the World. Automobiles (1st series). The first design in each pair shows technical drawings and the second paintings.

339. 5 c. black, blue and green 10 10
330. 5 c. multicoloured 10 10
341. 25 c. black, lilac and pink 15 15
342. 25 c. multicoloured .. 15 15
343. 50 c. black, blue and orange 20 20
344. 50 c. multicoloured .. 20 20
345. $3 black, stone and brown 60 60
346. $3 multicoloured 60 60

DESIGNS: Nos. 339/40, Facel "Vega HK500" (Type **45**). 341/2, B.M.W. "328". 343/4, Frazer-Nash "TT Replica 1.5L". 345/6, Buick "Roadmaster Riviera".

See also Nos. 378/85 and 431/42.

46. Three Wise Men and Star.

1984. Christmas. Multicoloured.

347. 20 c. Type **46** 10 10
348. 45 c. Journeying to Bethlehem 20 25
349. $3 Presenting gifts .. 1·00 1·40

1985. Leaders of the World. Railway Locomotives (3rd series). As T **40**. The first in each pair shows technical drawings and the second the locomotive at work.

351. 1 c. multicoloured 10 10
352. 1 c. multicoloured 10 10
353. 15 c. multicoloured .. 10 10
354. 15 c. multicoloured .. 10 10
355. 75 c. multicoloured .. 35 35
356. 75 c. multicoloured .. 35 35
357. $3 multicoloured .. .. 1·00 1·00
358. $3 multicoloured .. .. 1·00 1·00

DESIGNS: Nos. 351/2, P.L.M. "Grosse C", France (1898). 353/4, Class "C12", Japan (1932). 355/6, Class "D50", Japan (1923), 357/8, "Fire Fly", Great Britain (1840).

47. Caribbean King Crab.

1985. Shell Fish. Multicoloured.

360. 25 c. Type **47** 40 15
361. 60 c. Queen Conch .. 55 35
362. $1 White Sea Urchin .. 80 60
363. $3 West Indian Top Shell 1·75 1·90

1985. Leaders of the World. Cricketers (3rd series). As T **42** (55 c., 60 c.), the first in each pair showing a head portrait and the second the cricketer in action, or horiz. designs showing teams ($2).

364. 55 c. multicoloured .. 30 35
365. 55 c. multicoloured .. 30 35
366. 60 c. multicoloured .. 35 40
367. 60 c. multicoloured .. 35 40
368. $2 multicoloured 80 85
369. $2 multicoloured 80 85

DESIGNS—VERT. (As T **42**). Nos. 364/5, M. D. Moxon. 366/7, L. Potter. HORIZ. (59 × 42 mm.). No. 368, Kent team. 369, Yorkshire team.

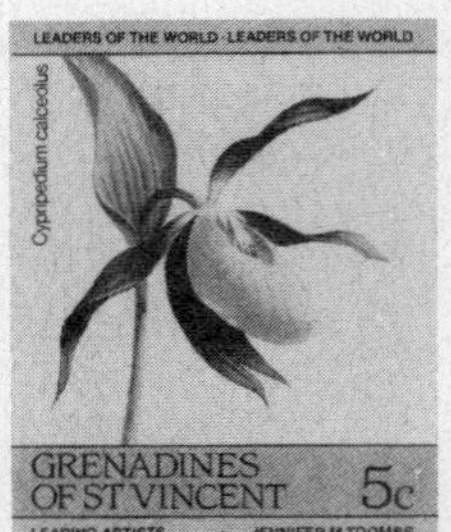

48. "Cypripedium calceolus".

1985. Leaders of the World. Flowers. Multicoloured.

370. 5 c. Type **48** 10 10
371. 5 c. "Gentiana asclepiadea" 10 10
372. 55 c. "Clianthus formosus" 30 35
373. 55 c. "Celmisia coriacea" .. 30 35
374. 60 c. "Erythronium americanum" 35 40
375. 60 c. "Laelia anceps" .. 35 40
376. $2 "Leucadendron discolor" 75 75
377. $2 "Meconopsis horridula" 75 75

1985. Leaders of the World. Automobiles (2nd series). As T **45**. The first in each pair shows technical drawings and the second paintings.

378. 5 c. black, yellow and blue 10 10
379. 5 c. multicoloured 10 10
380. 60 c. black, yellow and orange 25 25
381. 60 c. multicoloured .. 25 25
382. $1 black, green and blue .. 30 30
383. $1 multicoloured 30 30
384. $1.50 black, blue and green 35 35
385. $1.50 multicoloured .. 35 35

DESIGNS: Nos. 378/9, Winton (1903). 380/1, Invicta 4½ litre (1931). 382/3, Daimler "SP250 Dart" (1959). 384/5, Brabham "Repco BT 19" (1966).

49. Windsurfing.

1985. Tourism. Watersports. Multicoloured.

386. 35 c. Type **49** 20 25
387. 45 c. Water-skiing 25 30
388. 75 c. Scuba-diving .. 35 40
389. $3 Deep-sea game fishing 1·50 1·60

1985. Leaders of the World. Railway Locomotives (4th series). As T **40**. The first design in each pair shows technical drawings and the second the locomotive at work.

390. 10 c. multicoloured .. 10 10
391. 10 c. multicoloured .. 10 10
392. 40 c. multicoloured .. 25 30
393. 40 c. multicoloured .. 25 30
394. 50 c. multicoloured .. 25 30
395. 50 c. multicoloured .. 25 30
396. $2.50 multicoloured .. 1·00 1·10
397. $2.50 multicoloured .. 1·00 1·10

DESIGNS: Nos. 390/1, Class "581" 12-car train, Japan (1968). 392/3, Class "231-132BT", Ageria (1936). 394/5, "Class "S." "Slieve Gullion", Great Britain (1913). 396/7, Class "Beattie" Well Tank, Great Britain (1874).

50. Passion Fruits and Blossom.

1985. Fruits and Blossoms. Multicoloured.

398. 30 c. Type **50** 15 20
399. 75 c. Guava 35 40
400. $1 Sapodilla 50 55
401. $2 Mango .. .. 1·00 1·10

51. Queen Elizabeth the Queen Mother.

1985. Leaders of the World. Life and Times of Queen Elizabeth the Queen Mother. Various vertical portraits.

403. **51.** 40 c. multicoloured .. 15 20
404. – 40 c. multicoloured .. 15 20
405. – 75 c. multicoloured .. 25 30
406. – 75 c. multicoloured .. 25 30
407. – $1.10 multicoloured .. 30 35
408. – $1.10 multicoloured .. 30 35
409. – $1.75 multicoloured .. 45 55
410. – $1.75 multicoloured .. 45 55

Each value issued in pairs showing a floral pattern across the bottom of the portraits which stops short of the left-hand edge on the first stamp and of the right-hand edge on the second.

1985. Leaders of the World. Railway Locomotives (5th series). As T **40**. The first design in each pair shows technical drawings and the second the locomotive at work.

412. 35 c. multicoloured .. 20 25
413. 35 c. multicoloured .. 20 25
414. 70 c. multicoloured .. 35 40
415. 70 c. multicoloured .. 35 40
416. $1.20 multicoloured .. 55 65
417. $1.20 multicoloured .. 55 65
418. $2 multicoloured 75 80
419. $2 multicoloured 75 80

DESIGNS: Nos. 412/13, "Coronation" Class, Great Britain (1937). 414/15, Class "E18", Germany (1935). 416/7, "Hayes", type, U.S.A. (1854), 418/19, Class "2120", Japan (1890).

1985. Royal Visit. Nos. 199/200, 222, 287, 398 and 407/8 optd. **CARIBBEAN ROYAL VISIT—1985** or surch. also.

420. **50.** 30 c. multicoloured .. 2·50 2·00
421. **41.** 45 c. multicoloured .. 3·00 2·50
422. – $1.10 multicoloured (No. 407) .. .. 4·50 4·00
423. – $1.10 multicoloured (No. 408) .. .. 4·50 4·00
424. – $1.50 on $3.50 multicoloured (No. 199) .. 3·00 3·00
425. – $1.50 on $3.50 multicoloured (No. 200) .. 9·00 9·00
426. – $3 multicoloured (No. 222) .. .. .. 5·50 5·00

52. Donkey Man.

1985. Traditional Dances. Multicoloured.

427. 45 c. Type **52** 25 30
428. 75 c. Cake Dance (vert.) .. 35 40
429. $1 Bois-Bois Man (vert.) .. 50 55
430. $2 Maypole Dance .. 1·00 1·10

1986. Leaders of the World. Automobiles (3rd series). As T **45**. The first in each pair shows technical drawings and the second paintings.

431. 15 c. blk., lilac & mve. .. 10 10
432. 15 c. multicoloured .. 10 10
433. 45 c. blk., yell. & brn. .. 25 30
434. 45 c. multicoloured .. 25 30
435. 60 c. black, green and blue 25 30
436. 60 c. multicoloured .. 25 30
437. $1 black, brown and green 35 40
438. $1 multicoloured 35 40
439. $1.75 blk., yell. & orge. .. 50 60
440. $1.75 multicoloured .. 50 60
441. $3 multicoloured 75 80
442. $3 multiciloured 75 80

DESIGNS: Nos. 431/2, Mercedes-Benz 4.5 litre (1914). 433/4, Rolls Royce "Silver Wraith" (1954) 435/6, Lamborghini "Countach" (1974). 437/8, Marmon "V-16" (1932). 439/40, Lotus-Ford "49 B" (1968). 441/2, Delage 1.5 litre (1927).

1986. Leaders of the World. Railway Locomotives (6th series). As T **40**. The first in each pair shows technical drawings and the second the locomotive at work.

443. 15 c. multicoloured .. 10 10
444. 15 c. multicoloured .. 10 10
445. 45 c. multicoloured .. 25 30
446. 45 c. multicoloured .. 25 30
447. 60 c. multicoloured .. 30 35
448. 60 c. multicoloured .. 30 35
449. 75 c. multicoloured .. 35 40
450. 75 c. multicoloured .. 35 40
451. $1 multicoloured 40 50
452. $1 multicoloured 40 50
453. $1.50 multicoloured .. 55 70
454. $1.50 multicoloured .. 55 70
455. $2 multicoloured 65 75
456. $2 multicoloured 65 75
457. $3 multicoloured .. .. 80 1·00
458. $3 multicoloured .. .. 80 1·00

DESIGNS: Nos. 443/4, Class "T15", Germany (1897). 445/6, Class "13", Great Britain (1900). 447/8, "Halesworth", Great Britain (1879). 449/50, Class "Problem", Great Britain (1859). 451/2, Class "Western" diesel, Great Britain (1961). 453/4, Drummond's "Bug", Great Britain (1899). 455/6, Class "Clan", Great Britain (1951). 457/8, Class "1800", Japan (1884).

1986. 60th Birthday of Queen Elizabeth II. Multicoloured. As T **167** of British Virgin Islands.

459. 5 c. Queen Elizabeth II .. 10 10
460. $1 At Princess Anne's christening, 1950 .. 40 45
461. $4 Princess Elizabeth .. 1·25 1·50
462. $6 In Canberra, 1982 (vert.) 2·00 2·50

53. Handmade Dolls.

1986. Handicrafts. Multicoloured.

464. 10 c. Type **53** 10 10
465. 60 c. Basketwork 35 35
466. $1 Scrimshaw work .. 55 55
467. $3 Model boat .. .. 1·60 1·60

54. Uruguayan Team.
(Illustration reduced, actual size 67 × 37 mm.).

1986. World Cup Football Championship, Mexico. Multicoloured.

468. 1 c. Type **54** 10 10
469. 10 c. Polish team 10 10
470. 45 c. Bulgarian player (28 × 42 mm.) 25 30
471. 75 c. Iraqi player (28 × 42 mm.) 35 40
472. $1·50 South Korean player (28 × 42 mm.) 75 80
473. $2 Northern Irish player (28 × 42 mm.) .. .. 1·00 1·10
474. $4 Portuguese team .. 2·00 2·10
475. $5 Canadian team .. .. 2·50 2·75

55. "Marasmius pallescens".

1986. Fungi. Multicoloured.

477. 45 c. Type **55** .. .. 1·00 55
478. 60 c. "Leucocoprinus fragilissimus" .. .. 1·25 70
479. 75 c. "Hygrocybe occidentalis" .. .. 1·50 85
480. $3 "Xerocomus hypoxanthus" .. .. 4·00 3·00

1986. Royal Wedding (1st issue). Multicoloured. As T **168** of British Virgin Islands.

481. 60 c. Miss Sarah Ferguson and Princess Diana applauding 30 35
482. 60 c. Prince Andrew at shooting match 30 35
483. $2 Prince Andrew and Miss Sarah Ferguson (horiz.) 1·00 1·10
484. $2 Prince Charles with Prince Andrew, Princess Anne and Princess Margaret on balcony (horiz.) .. .. .. 1·00 1·10

1986. Royal Wedding (2nd issue). Nos. 481/4 optd. **Congratulations to T.R.H. The Duke and Duchess of York.**

486. 60 c. Miss Sarah Ferguson and Princess Diana applauding 30 35
487. 60 c. Prince Andrew at shooting match 30 35
488. $2 Prince Andrew and Miss Sarah Ferguson (horiz.) 1·00 1·10
489. $2 Prince Charles, Prince Andrew, Princess Anne and Princess Margaret on balcony (horiz.) .. 1·00 1·10

57. American Kestrel.

1986. Birds of Prey. Multicoloured.

495. 10 c. Type **57** 30 15
496. 45 c. Common black hawk 75 45
497. 60 c. Peregrine falcon .. 1·00 55
498. $4 Osprey .. .. .. 3·75 4·00

58. Santa playing Steel Band Drums.

1986. Christmas. Multicoloured.

499. 45 c. Type **58** 25 30
500. 60 c. Santa windsurfing .. 30 35
501. $1.25 Santa skiing 60 65
502. $2 Santa limbo dancing .. 1·00 1·10

1987. Railway Locomotives (7th series). As T **40**. The first in each pair shows technical drawings and the second the locomotive at work.

504. 10 c. multicoloured .. 10 10
505. 10 c. multicoloured .. 10 10
506. 40 c. multicoloured .. 20 25
507. 40 c. multicoloured .. 20 25
508. 50 c. multicoloured .. 25 30
509. 50 c. multicoloured .. 25 30
510. 60 c. multicoloured .. 25 30
511. 60 c. multicoloured .. 25 30
512. 75 c. multicoloured .. 35 40
513. 75 c. multicoloured .. 35 40
514. $1 multicoloured 45 50
515. $1 multicoloured 45 50
516. $1.25 multicoloured .. 55 60
517. $1.25 multicoloured .. 55 60
518. $1.50 multicoloured .. 70 75
519. $1.50 multicoloured .. 70 75

DESIGNS: Nos. 504/5, Class "1001", No. 1275, Great Britain (1874). 506/7, Class "4P Garratt", Great Britain (1927). 508/9, "Papyrus", Great Britain (1929). 510/11, Class "V1", Great Britain (1930). 512/13, Class "40" diesel, No. D200, Great Britain (1958). 514/15, Class "42 Warship" diesel, Great Britain (1958). 516/17, Class "P-69" U.S.A. (1902). 518/19, class "60-3 Shay", No. 15, U.S.A. (1913).

1987. Railway Locomotives (8th series). As T **40**. The first in each pair shows technical drawings and the second the locomotive at work.

520. 10 c. multicoloured .. 10 10
521. 10 c. multicoloured .. 10 10
522. 40 c. multicoloured .. 20 25
523. 40 c. multicoloured .. 20 25
524. 50 c. multicoloured .. 25 30
525. 50 c. multicoloured .. 25 30
526. 60 c. multicoloured .. 25 30
527. 60 c. multicoloured .. 25 30
528. 75 c. multicoloured .. 35 40
529. 75 c. multicoloured .. 35 40
530. $1 multicoloured 45 50
531. $1 multicoloured 45 50
532. $1.50 multicoloured .. 70 75
533. $1.50 multicoloured .. 70 75
534. $2 multicoloured 90 95
535. $2 multicoloured 90 95

DESIGNS: Nos. 520/1, Class "142", East Germany (1977). 522/3, Class "120", West Germany (1979). 524/5, Class "X", Australia (1954). 526/7, Class "59", Great Britain (1986). 528/9, New York Elevated Railroad Spuyten Duyvel, U.S.A. (1875). 530/1, Camden & Amboy Railroad Stevens (later John Bull), U.S.A. (1831). 532/3, "Royal Hudson" Class "H1-d", No. 2850, Canada (1938). 534/5, "Pioneer Zephyr" 3-car set, U.S.A. (1934).

59. Queen Elizabeth with Prince Andrew.

1987. Royal Ruby Wedding and 150th Anniv. of Queen Victoria's Accession.

536. **59.** 15 c. multicoloured .. 15 15
537. – 45 c. brown, black and yellow 30 30
538. – $1.50 multicoloured .. 90 90
539. – $3 multicoloured .. 1·75 1·75
540. – $4 multicoloured .. 2·00 2·00

DESIGNS: 45 c. Queen Victoria and Prince Albert, c 1855. $1.50, Queen and Prince Philip after Trooping the Colour, 1977. $3 Queen and Duke of Edinburgh, 1953. $4 Queen in her study, c 1980.

60. Banded Coral Shrimp.

1987. Marine Life. Multicoloured.

542. 45 c. Type **60** 45 45
543. 50 c. Arrow crab and flamingo tongue .. 50 50
544. 65 c. Cardinal fish 70 70
545. $5 Moray eel .. .. 4·00 4·00

61 "Australia IV"

1988. Ocean Racing Yachts. Multicoloured.

547 50 c. Type **61** 50 50
548 65 c. "Crusader II" .. 60 60
549 75 c. "New Zealand K27" 75 75
550 $2 "Italia" .. .. 1·50 1·50
551 $4 "White Crusader" .. 2·50 2·50
552 $5 "Stars and Stripes" .. 3·00 3·00

62 Seine-fishing Boats racing

1988. Bequia Regatta. Multicoloured.

554 5 c. Type **62** 10 10
555 50 c. "Friendship Rose" (motor fishing boat) .. 20 25
556 75 c. Fishing boats racing 30 35
557 $3.50 Yachts racing .. 1·50 1·60

63 "Twin-Otter" making Night Approach
(Illustration reduced, actual size 50 × 38mm)

1988. Mustique Airways. Multicoloured.

559 15 c. Type **63** 10 10
560 65 c. Beech "Baron" aircraft in flight .. 30 35
561 75 c. "Twin-Otter" over forest 30 35
562 $5 Beech "Baron" on airstrip .. .. 2·10 2·25

64 "Sv. Pyotr" in Arctic (Bering)

1988. Explorers. Multicoloured.

564 15 c. Type **64** 10 10
565 75 c. Bering's ships in pack ice 30 35
566 $1 Livingstone's steam launch "Ma-Robert" on Zambesi 45 50
567 $2 Meeting of Livingstone and H. M. Stanley at Ujiji 80 85
568 $3 Speke and Burton at Tabori .. .. 1·25 1·40
569 $3.50 Speke and Burton in canoe on Lake Victoria 1·50 1·60
570 $4 Sighting the New World, 1492 .. 1·60 1·75
571 $4.50 Columbus trading with Indians .. 2·00 2·10

65 Asif Iqbal Razvi

1988. Cricketers of 1988 International Season. Multicoloured.

573 20 c. Type **65** 30 30
574 45 c. R. J. Hadlee .. 50 50
575 75 c. M. D. Crowe .. 70 70
576 $1.25 C. H. Lloyd .. 1·00 1·00
577 $1.50 A. R. Boarder .. 1·25 1·25
578 $2 M. D. Marshall .. 1·75 1·75
579 $2.50 G. A. Hick .. .. 2·00 2·00
580 $3.50 C. G. Greenidge (horiz) .. .. .. 2·50 2·50

66 Pam Shriver

1988. International Tennis Players. Mult.

582 15 c. Type **66** 10 10
583 50 c. Kevin Curran (vert) 20 25
584 75 c. Wendy Turnbull (vert) 30 35
585 $1 Evonne Cawley (vert) 45 50
586 $1.50 Ilie Nastase 60 65
587 $2 Billie Jean King (vert) 80 85
588 $3 Bjorn Borg (vert) 1·25 1·40
589 $3.50 Virginia Wade with Wimbledon trophy (vert) 1·50 1·60

No. 584 is inscribed "WENDY TURNBALL" in error.

67 Mickey and Minnie Mouse visiting Fatehpur Sikri

1989. "India–89" International Stamp Exhibition. Multicoloured. Designs showing Walt Disney cartoon characters in India.

591 1 c. Type **67** 10 10
592 2 c. Mickey and Minnie Mouse aboard "Palace on Wheels" train 10 10
593 3 c. Mickey and Minnie Mouse passing Old Fort, Delhi 10 10
594 5 c. Mickey and Minnie Mouse on camel, Pinjore Gardens, Haryana 10 10
595 10 c. Mickey and Minnie Mouse at Taj Mahal, Agra 10 10
596 25 c. Mickey and Minnie Mouse in Chandni Chowk, Old Delhi 10 10
597 $4 Goofy on elephant with Mickey and Minnie Mouse at Agra Fort, Jaipur 1·60 1·75
598 $5 Goofy, Mickey and Minnie Mouse at Gandhi Memorial, Cape Comorin 2·10 2·25

1989. Japanese Art. As T **250** of Antigua. Multicoloured.

600 5 c. "The View at Yotsuya" (Hokusai) 10 10
601 30 c. "Landscape at Ochanomizu" (Hokuju) 10 15
602 45 c. "Itabashi" (Eisen) 20 25
603 65 c. "Early Summer Rain" (Kunisada) 25 30
604 75 c. "High Noon at Kasumigaseki" (Kuniyoshi) 30 35
605 $1 "The Yoshiwara Embankment by Moonlight" (Kuniyoshi) 40 45
606 $4 "The Bridge of Boats at Sano" (Hokusai) 1·75 1·90
607 $5 "Lingering Snow on Mount Hira" (Kunitora) 2·10 2·25

68 Player with Ball and Mt Vesuvius

1989. World Cup Football Championship, Italy (1st issue). Designs showing players and Italian landmarks. Multicoloured.

609 $1.50 Type **68** 65 70
610 $1.50 Fallen player, opponent kicking ball and Coliseum 65 70
611 $1.50 Player blocking ball and Venice 65 70
612 $1.50 Player tackling and Forum, Rome 65 70
613 $1.50 Two players competing for ball and Leaning Tower, Pisa 65 70
614 $1.50 Goalkeeper and Florence 65 70
615 $1.50 Two players competing for ball and St. Peter's, Vatican 65 70
616 $1.50 Player kicking ball and Pantheon 65 70

Nos. 609/16 were printed together, se-tenant, forming a composite foreground design.

See also Nos. 680/3.

1989. 500th Anniv (1992) of Discovery of America by Columbus. Pre-Columbian Arawak Society. As T **247** of Antigua. Multicoloured.

617 25 c. Arawak smoking Tobacco 10 15
618 75 c. Arawak rolling cigar 30 35
619 $1 Applying body paint 40 45
620 $1.50 Making fire 65 70
621 $1.50 Cassava production 65 70
622 $1.50 Woman baking bread 65 70
623 $1.50 Using stone implement 65 70
624 $4 Arawak priest 1·75 1·90

Nos. 620/4 were printed together, se-tenant, forming a composite design.

70 Command Module "Columbia"

1989. 10th Anniv of First Manned Landing on Moon. Multicoloured.

626 5 c. Type **70** 10 10
627 40 c. Astronaut Neil Armstrong saluting U.S. flag 15 20
628 55 c. "Columbia" above lunar surface 25 30
629 65 c. Lunar module "Eagle" leaving Moon 25 30
630 70 c. "Eagle" on Moon 30 35
631 $1 "Columbia" re-entering Earth's atmosphere 40 45
632 $3 "Apollo 11" emblem 1·25 1·40
633 $5 Armstrong and Aldrin on Moon 2·10 2·25

71 "Marpesia petreus"

1989. Butterflies. Multicoloured.

635 5 c. Type **71** 10 10
636 30 c. "Papilio androgues" 10 15
637 45 c. "Chiorostrymon maesites" 20 25
638 65 c. "Junonia coenia" 25 30
639 75 c. "Eurema gratiosa" 30 35
640 $1 "Hypolimnas misippus" 40 45
641 $4 "Urbanus proteus" 1·75 1·90
642 $5 "Junonia evarete" 2·10 2·25

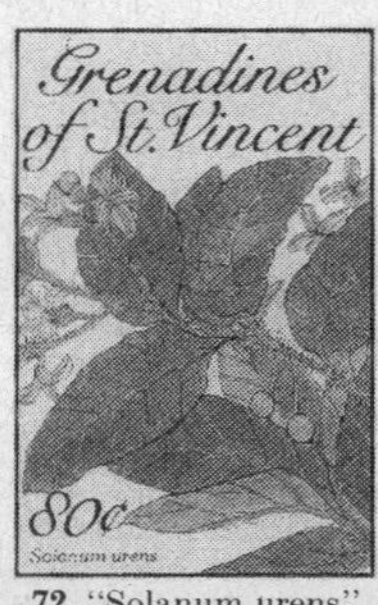

72 "Solanum urens"

1989. Flowers from St. Vincent Botanical Gardens. Multicoloured.

644 80 c. Type **72** 35 40
645 $1.25 "Passiflora andersonii" 50 55
646 $1.65 "Miconia andersonii" 70 75
647 $1.85 "Pitcairnia sulphurea" 80 85

1989. Christmas. As T **183** of Gambia. Mult.

648 5 c. Goofy and Mickey Mouse in Rolls-Royce "Silver Ghost", 1907 10 10
649 10 c. Daisy Duck driving first Stanley Steamer, 1897 10 10
650 15 c. Horace Horsecollar and Clarabelle Cow in Darracq "Genevieve", 1904 10 10
651 45 c. Donald Duck driving Detroit electric coupe, 1914 20 25
652 55 c. Mickey and Minnie Mouse in first Ford, 1896 20 25
653 $2 Mickey Mouse driving Reo "Runabout", 1904 85 90
654 $3 Goofy driving Winton mail truck, 1899 1·25 1·40
655 $5 Mickey and Minnie Mouse in Duryea car, 1893 2·10 2·25

1990. 50th Anniv of Second World War. As T **98** of Grenada Grenadines. Multicoloured.

657 10 c. Destroyer in action, First Battle of Narvik, 1940 10 10
658 15 c. Allied tank at Anzio, 1944 10 10
659 20 c. U.S. carrier under attack, Battle of Midway, 1942 10 10
660 45 c. U.S. bombers over Gustav Line, 1944 20 25
661 55 c. Map showing Allied zones of Berlin, 1945 25 30
662 65 c. German U-boat pursuing convoy, Battle of the Atlantic, 1943 25 30
663 90 c. Allied tank, North Africa, 1943 40 45
664 $3 U.S. forces landing on Guam, 1944 1·25 1·40
665 $5 Crossing the Rhine, 1945 2·10 2·25
666 $6 Japanese battleships under attack, Leyte Gulf, 1944 2·50 2·75

1990. "Stamp World London 90" International Stamp Exhibition (1st issue). Mickey's Shakespeare Company. As T **193** of Gambia showing Walt Disney cartoon characters. Multicoloured.

668 20 c. Goofy as Mark Anthony ("Julius Caesar") 10 10
669 30 c. Clarabelle Cow as the Nurse ("Romeo and Juliet") 10 15
670 45 c. Pete as Falstaff ("Henry IV") 20 25
671 50 c. Minnie Mouse as Portia ("The Merchant of Venice") 20 25
672 $1 Donald Duck as Hamlet ("Hamlet") 40 45
673 $2 Daisy Duck as Ophelia ("Hamlet") 85 90
674 $4 Donald and Daisy Duck as Benedick and Beatrice ("Much Ado About Nothing") 1·75 1·90
675 $5 Minnie Mouse and Donald Duck as Katherine and Petruchio ("The Taming of the Shrew") 2·10 2·25

74 Exhibition Emblem

1990. "Stamp World London 90" International Stamp Exhibition (2nd issue). 150th Anniv of the Penny Black.

677 **74** $1 black, pink & mauve 40 45
678 – $5 black, lilac and blue 2·10 2·25

DESIGN: $5 Negative image of Penny Black.

1990. World Cup Football Championship, Italy (2nd issue). As T **210** of St. Vincent. Multicoloured.

680 25 c. McCleish, Scotland 10 15
681 50 c. Rasul, Egypt 20 25
682 $2 Lindenberger, Austria 85 90
683 $4 Murray, U.S.A. 1·75 1·90

1990. "EXPO 90" International Garden and Greenery Exposition, Osaka. Orchids. As T **213** of St. Vincent. Multicoloured.

685 5 c. "Paphiopedilum" 10 10
686 25 c. "Dendrobium phalaenopsis" and "Cymbidium" hybrid 10 15
687 30 c. "Miltonia candida" hybrid 10 15
688 50 c. "Epidendrum ibaguense" and "Cymbidium" Elliot Rogers 20 25
689 $1 "Rossioglossum grande" 40 45
690 $2 "Phalaenopsis" Elisa Chamg Lou and "Masdevallia coccinea" 85 90
691 $4 "Cypripedium acaule" and "Cypripedium calceolus" 1·75 1·90
692 $5 "Orchis spectabilis" 2·10 2·25

75 Scaly-breasted Ground Dove

1990. Birds of the Caribbean. Multicoloured.

694 5 c. Type **75** 10 10
695 25 c. Purple martin 10 15
696 45 c. Painted bunting 20 25
697 55 c. Blue-hooded euphonia 25 30
698 75 c. Blue-grey tanager 30 35
699 $1 Red-eyed vireo 40 45
700 $2 Palm chat 85 90
701 $3 Northern jacana 1·25 1·40
702 $4 Green-throated carib 1·75 1·90
703 $5 St. Vincent amazon 2·10 2·25

1991. 90th Birthday of Queen Elizabeth the Queen Mother. As T **194** of Gambia.

705 $2 multicoloured 85 90
706 $2 multicoloured 85 90
707 $2 multicoloured 85 90
708 $2 multicoloured 85 90
709 $2 multicoloured 85 90
710 $2 multicoloured 85 90
711 $2 multicoloured 85 90
712 $2 multicoloured 85 90
713 $2 multicoloured 85 90
714 $2 multicoloured 85 90
715 $2 multicoloured 85 90
716 $2 multicoloured 85 90
717 $2 black and lilac 85 90
718 $2 black and lilac 85 90
719 $2 black, green and lilac 85 90
720 $2 multicoloured 85 90
721 $2 black and lilac 85 90
722 $2 multicoloured 85 90
723 $2 multicoloured 85 90
724 $2 multicoloured 85 90
725 $2 multicoloured 85 90
726 $2 multicoloured 85 90
727 $2 multicoloured 85 90
728 $2 multicoloured 85 90
729 $2 multicoloured 85 90
730 $2 multicoloured 85 90
731 $2 multicoloured 85 90

DESIGNS: No. 705, Lady Elizabeth Bowes-Lyon with sister; 706, Young Lady Elizabeth in long dress; 707, Young Lady Elizabeth wearing a hat; 708, Lady Elizabeth leaning on wall; 709, Lady Elizabeth on pony; 710, Studio portrait; 711, Lady Elizabeth in evening dress; 712, Duchess of York in fur-lined cloak; 713, Duchess of York holding rose; 714, Coronation, 1937; 715, King and Queen with Princess Elizabeth at Royal Lodge, Windsor; 716, Queen Elizabeth in blue hat; 717, King George VI and Queen Elizabeth; 718, Queen Elizabeth with Princess Elizabeth; 719, Queen Elizabeth watching sporting fixture; 720, Queen Elizabeth in white evening dress; 721, Princess Anne's christening, 1950; 722, Queen Mother with yellow bouquet; 723, Queen Mother and policewoman; 724, Queen Mother at ceremonial function; 725, Queen Mother in pink coat; 726, Queen Mother in academic robes; 727, Queen Mother in carriage with Princess Margaret; 728, Queen Mother in blue coat and hat; 729, Queen Mother with bouquet; 730, Queen Mother outside Clarence House on her birthday; 731, Queen Mother in turquoise coat and hat.

1991. Death Centenary (1990) of Vincent van Gogh (artist). As T **195** of British Virgin Islands. Multicoloured.

733 5 c. "View of Arles with Irises" 10 10
734 10 c. "Saintes-Maries" (vert) 10 10
735 15 c. "Old Woman of Arles" (vert) 10 10
736 20 c. "Orchard in Blossom, bordered by Cypresses" 10 10
737 25 c. "Three White Cottages in Saintes-Maries" 10 10
738 35 c. "Boats at Saintes-Maries" 15 20
739 40 c. "Interior of a Restaurant in Arles" .. 15 20
740 45 c. "Peasant Women" (vert) 20 25
741 55 c. "Self-portrait" (vert) 20 25
742 60 c. "Pork Butcher's Shop from a Window" (vert) 25 30
743 75 c. "The Night Cafe in Arles" 30 35
744 $1 "2nd Lieut. Millet of the Zouaves" 40 45
745 $2 "The Cafe Terrace, Place du Forum, Arles at Night" (vert) .. 85 90
746 $3 "The Zouave" (vert) .. 1·25 1·50
747 $4 "The Two Lovers" (detail) (vert) .. 1·75 2·00
748 $5 "Still Life" .. .. 2·10 2·25

1991. 65th Birthday of Queen Elizabeth II. As T **280** of Antigua. Multicoloured.

750 15 c. Inspecting the Yeomen of the Guard .. 10 10
751 40 c. Queen Elizabeth II with the Queen Mother at the Derby, 1988 .. 15 20
752 $2 The Queen and Prince Philip leaving Euston, 1986 .. .. .. 85 90
753 $4 The Queen at the Commonwealth Institute, 1987 .. .. 1·75 1·90

1991. 10th Wedding Anniv of Prince and Princess of Wales. As T **280** of Antigua. Multicoloured.

755 10 c. Prince and Princess at polo match, 1987 .. 10 10
756 50 c. Separate family portraits 20 25
757 $1 Prince William and Prince Henry at Kensington Palace, 1991 40 45
758 $5 Portraits of Prince Charles and Princess Diana .. .. .. 2·10 2·25

76 First Japanese Steam Locomotive and Map

1991. "Philanippon '91" International Stamp Exhibition, Tokyo. Japanese Railway Locomotives. Each in black, red and green.

760 10 c. Type **76** 10 10
761 25 c. First imported American steam locomotive 10 15
762 35 c. Class "8620" steam locomotive 15 20
763 50 c. Class "C53" steam locomotive 20 25
764 $1 Class "DD-51" diesel locomotive 40 45
765 $2 Class "RF22327" electric rail car 85 90
766 $4 Class "EF55" electric locomotive .. .. 1·75 1·90
767 $5 Class "EF58" electric locomotive .. .. 2·10 2·25

1991. 50th Death Anniv of Lord Baden-Powell and World Scout Jamboree, Korea. As T **225** of St. Vincent. Multicoloured.

769 $2 Czechoslovakia 1918 20 h. stamp and scout delivering mail (horiz) .. 20 25
770 $4 Scouts and cog train on Snowdon .. .. 1·75 1·90

1991. Birth Centenary (1990) of Charles de Gaulle (French statesman). As T **226** of St. Vincent. Multicoloured.

772 60 c. General De Gaulle in Djibouti, 1959 .. .. 25 30

1991. Bicentenary of Brandenburg Gate. As T **227** of St. Vincent. Multicoloured.

774 45 c. President Gorbachev and photo of Gate .. 20 25
775 65 c. "DIE MAUER MUSS WEG!" slogan 25 30
776 80 c. East German border guard escaping to West 35 40

1991. Death Bicentenary of Mozart. As T **228** of St. Vincent. Multicoloured.

778 $1 "Abduction from the Seraglio" 40 45
779 $3 Dresden, 1749 .. .. 1·25 1·50

77 Japanese Aircraft and Submarines leaving Truk

1991. 50th Anniv of Japanese Attack on Pearl Harbor. Multicoloured.

781 $1 Type **77** 40 45
782 $1 "Akagi" (Japanese aircraft carrier) .. 40 45
783 $1 Nakajima B5 N2 "Kate" aircraft .. 40 45
784 $1 Torpedo bombers attacking Battleship Row 40 45
785 $1 Burning aircraft, Ford Island airfield .. 40 45
786 $1 Doris Miller winning Navy Cross 40 45
787 $1 U.S.S. "West Virginia" and "Tennessee" (battleships) ablaze .. 40 45
788 $1 U.S.S. "Arizona" (battleship) sinking .. 40 45
789 $1 U.S.S. "New Orleans" (cruiser) 40 45
790 $1 President Roosevelt declaring war 40 45

78 Pluto pulling Mickey Mouse in Sledge, 1974

1991. Christmas. Walt Disney Company Christmas Cards. Multicoloured.

791 10 c. Type **78** 10 10
792 55 c. Mickey, Pluto and Donald Duck watching toy band, 1961 .. .. 20 25
793 65 c. "The Same Old Wish", 1942 .. .. 25 30
794 75 c. Mickey, Peter Pan, Donald and Nephews with Merlin the magician, 1963 .. .. 30 35
795 $1.50 Mickey and Donald with leprechauns, 1958 60 65
796 $2 Mickey and friends with book "Old Yeller", 1957 85 90
797 $4 Mickey controlling Pinnochio, 1953 .. 1·75 2·00
798 $5 Cinderella and Prince dancing, 1987 .. 2·10 2·25

1991. Centenary of Trans-Siberian Railway. As T **286** of Antigua. Multicolooured.

800 $1.75 Trans-Siberian logo (horiz) 75 80
801 $1.75 Trans-Siberian steam locomotive 75 80

1991. 700th Anniv of Swiss Confederation. As T **287** of Antigua. Multicoloured.

803 $2 Zurich couple maypole dancing 85 90
804 $2 Man and woman in Vaud traditional costumes 85 90

1991. Centenary of Otto Lilienthal's Gliding Experiments. As T **285** of Antigua. Mult.

806 $1.50 Lilienthal and glider 60 65

OFFICIAL STAMPS.

1982. Nos. 195/200 optd. **OFFICIAL.**

O 1. 50 c. "Mary" 15 20
O 2. 50 c. Prince Charles and Lady Diana Spencer .. 40 45
O 3. $3 "Alexandra" 55 75
O 4. $3 Prince Charles and Lady Diana Spencer .. 1·25 1·25
O 5. $3.50 "Britannia" .. 75 1·00
O 6. $3.50 Prince Charles and Lady Diana Spencer .. 1·50 1·75

APPENDIX

The following stamps have either been issued in excess of postal needs, or have not been made available to the public in reasonable quantities at face value.

BEQUIA

1984.

Leaders of the World. Railway Locomotives (1st series). Two designs for each value, the first showing technical drawings and the second the locomotive at work. 1, 5, 10, 25, 35, 45 c., $1.50 $2, each ×2.

Grenadines of St. Vincent 1982 Ships definitives (Nos. 208/24) optd. **"BEQUIA"**. 1, 3, 5, 6, 10, 15, 20, 25, 30, 50, 60, 75 c., $1, $2, $3, $5, $10.

Leaders of the World. Automobiles (1st series). Two designs for each value, the first showing technical drawings and the second the car in action. 5, 40 c., $1, $1.50, each ×2.

Leaders of the World, Olympic Games, Los Angeles. 1, 10, 60 c., $3, each ×2.

Leaders of the World. Railway Locomotives (2nd series). Two designs for each value, the first showing technical drawings and the second the locomotive at work. 1, 10, 20, 25, 75 c., $1, $2.50, $3, each ×2.

Leaders of the World. Automobiles (2nd series). Two designs for each value, the first showing technical drawings and the second the car in action. 5, 10, 20, 25, 75 c., $1.50, $3, each ×2.

1985.

Leaders of the World. Railway Locomotives (3rd series). Two designs for each value, the first showing technical drawings and the second the locomotive at work. 25, 55, 60 c, $2, each ×2.

Leaders of the World. Dogs. 25, 35, 55 c., $2, each ×2.

Leaders of the World. Warships of the Second World War. Two designs for each value, the first showing technical drawings and the second the ship at sea. 15, 50 c., $1, $1.50, each ×2.

Leaders of the World. Flowers. 10, 20, 70 c., $2.50, each ×2.

Leaders of the World. Automobiles (3rd series). Two designs for each value, the first showing technical drawings and the second the car in action. 5, 25, 50 c., $1, $1.25, $2, each ×2.

Leaders of the World. Railway Locomotives (4th series). Two designs for each value, the first showing technical drawings and the second the locomotive at work. 25, 55, 60, 75 c., $1, $2.50, each ×2.

Leaders of the World. Life and Times of Queen Elizabeth the Queen Mother. Two designs for each value, showing different portraits. 20, 65 c., $1.35, $1.80, each ×2.

Leaders of the World. Automobiles (4th series). Two designs for each value, the first showing technical drawings and the second the car in action. 10, 35, 75 c., $1.15, $1.50, $2, each ×2.

1986

Leaders of the World. Automobiles (5th sereis). Two designs for each value, the first showing technical drawings and the second the car in action. 25, 50, 65, 75 c., $1, $3, each ×2.

60th Birthday of Queen Elizabeth II. 5, 75 c., $2, $8.

World Cup Football Championship, Mexico. 1, 2, 5, 10, 45, 60, 75 c., $1.50, $1.50, $2, $3.50, $6.

Royal Wedding (1st issue). 60 c., $2, each ×2.

Railway Engineers and Locomotives. $1, $2.50, $3, $4.

Royal Wedding (2nd issue) Previous issue optd. "Congratulation T.R.H. The Duke & Duchess of York" 60 c., $2, each ×2.

Automobiles (6th series). Two designs for each value, the first showing technical drawings and the second the car in action. 20, 60, 75, 90 c., $1, $3, each ×2.

1987.

Automobiles (7th series). Two designs for each value, the first showing technical drawings and the second the car in action. 5, 20, 35, 60, 75, 80 c., $1.25, $1.75, each ×2.

Royal Ruby Wedding 15, 75 c., $1, $2.50, $5.

Railway Locomotives (5th series). Two designs for each value, the first showing technical drawings and the second the locomotive at work. 15, 25, 40, 50, 60, 75 c., $1, $2, each ×2.

1988.

Explorers. 15, 50 c., $1.75, $2, $2.50, $3, $3.50, $4.

International Lawn Tennis Players. 15, 45, 80 c., $1.25, $1.75, $2, $2.50, $3.

1989.

"Philexfrance 89" International Stamp Exhibition, Paris. Walt Disney Cartoon Characters. 1, 2, 3, 4, 5, 10 c., $5, $6.

UNION ISLAND

1984.

Leaders of the World. British Monarchs. Two designs for each value, forming a composite picture. 1, 5, 10, 20, 60 c., $3, each ×2.

Leaders of the World. Railway Locomotives (1st series). Two designs for each value, the first showing technical drawings and the second the locomotive at work. 5, 60 c., $1, $2.

Grenadines of St. Vincent 1982 Ships definitives (Nos. 208/24) optd. **"UNION ISLAND"**. 1, 3, 5, 6, 10, 15, 20, 25, 30, 50, 60, 75 c., $1, $2, $3, $5, $10.

Leaders of the World. Cricketers. Two designs for each value, the first showing a portrait and the second the cricketer in action. 1, 10, 15, 55, 60, 75 c., $1.50, $3, each ×2.

Leaders of the World. Railway Locomotives (2nd series). Two designs for each value, the first showing technical drawings and the second the locomotive at work. 5, 10, 20, 25, 75 c., $1, $2.50, $3, each ×2.

1985.

Leaders of the World. Automobiles (1st series). Two designs for each value, the first showing technical drawings and the second the car in action 1, 50, 75 c., $2.50, each ×2.

Leaders of the World. Birth Bicentenary of John J. Audubon (ornithologist). Birds. 15, 50 c., $1, $1.50, each ×2.

Leaders of the World. Railway Locomotives (3rd series). Two designs for each value, the first showing technical drawings and the second the locomotive at work. 5, 50, 60 c., $2, each ×2.

Leaders of the World. Butterflies. 15, 25, 75 c., $2, each ×2.

Leaders of the World. Automobiles (2nd series). Two designs for each value, the first showing technical drawings and the second the car in action. 5, 60 c., $1, $1.50, each ×2.

Leaders of the World. Automobiles (3rd series). Two designs for each value, the first showing technical drawings and the second the car in action. 10, 55, 60, 75, 90 c., $1, $1.50, $2, each ×2.

Leaders of the World. Life and Times of Queen Elizabeth the Queen Mother. Two designs for each value, showing different portraits. 55, 70 c., $1.05, $1.70, each ×2.

1986.

Leaders of the World. Railway Locomotives (4th series). Two designs for each value, the first showing technical drawings and the second the locomotive at work. 15, 30, 45, 60, 75 c., $1.50, $2.50, $3, each ×2.

60th Birthday of Queen Elizabeth II. 10, 60 c., $2, $8.

World Cup Football Championship, Mexico. 1, 10, 30, 75 c., $1, $2.50, $3, $6.

Royal Wedding (1st issue). 60 c., $2, each ×2.

Automobiles (4th series). Two designs for each value, the first showing technical drawings and the second the car in action. 10, 60, 75 c., $1, $1.50, $3, each ×2.

Royal Wedding (2nd issue) Previous issue optd. as Bequia. 60 c., $2, each ×2.

Railway Locomotive (5th series). Two designs for each value, the first showing technical drawings and the second the locomotive at work. 15, 45, 60, 75 c., $1, $2, $3, each ×2.

1987.

Railway Locomotives (6th series). Two designs for each value, the first showing technical drawings and the second the locomotive at work. 15, 25, 40, 50, 60, 75 c., $1, $2, each ×2.

Royal Ruby Wedding. 15, 45 c., $1.50, $3, $4.

Railway Locomotives (7th series). Two designs for each value, the first showing technical drawings the second the locomotive at work. 15, 20, 30, 45, 50, 75 c., $1, $1.50, each ×2.

1989.

"Philexfrance 89" International Stamp Exhibition, Paris. Walt Disney Cartoon Characters. 1, 2, 3, 4, 5, 10 c., $5, $6.

GRIQUALAND WEST

A Br. colony, later annexed to the Cape of Good Hope and now part of South Africa, whose stamps it uses.

12 pence = 1 shilling.
20 shillings = 1 pound.

1874. Stamp of Cape of Good Hope (" Hope " seated) with pen-and-ink surch.

1.	**4.**	1d. on 4d. blue	£600	£1100

1877. Stamps of Cape of Good Hope (" Hope " seated) optd. **G.W.**

2.	**6.**	1d. red	£400	65·00
3.		4d. blue	£300	55·00

1877. Stamps of Cape of Good Hope (" Hope " seated) optd. **G** in various types.

78	**6.**	½d. grey	4·50	6·00
93		1d. red	6·00	3·50
17	**4.**	4d. blue	90·00	16·00
94	**6.**	4d. blue	10·00	3·50
31	**4.**	6d. violet	48·00	15·00
40		1s. green	75·00	13·00
97	**6.**	5s. orange	£225	6·00

GUERNSEY

An island in the English Channel off N.W. coast of France. Occupied by German Forces from June, 1940, to May, 1945. "Regional" issues were introduced from 1958 (see after GREAT BRITAIN); the island's Postal Service was organised as a separate Postal Administration in 1969.

(a) War Occupation Issues.

1.

1941.

1f	1	½d. green	3·00	2·50
2		1d. red	2·25	1·25
3a		2½d. blue	600	4·50

(b) Independent Postal Administration.

4. Castle Cornet and Edward the Confessor.

5. View of Sark.

1969.

13.	**4.**	½d. mauve and black ..	10	10
14.	–	1d. blue and black* ..	10	10
14b.	–	1d. blue and black* ..	50	60
15.	–	1½d. brown and black ..	10	10
16.	–	2d. multicoloured ..	10	10
17.	–	3d. multicoloured ..	15	15
18.	–	4d. multicoloured ..	25	25
19.	–	5d. multicoloured ..	25	15
20.	–	6d. multicoloured ..	30	35
21.	–	9d. multicoloured ..	70	60
22.	–	1s. multicoloured.. ..	55	45
23.	–	1s. 6d. green and black *	40	50
23b.	–	1s. 6d. green & black * ..	6·50	1·90
24.	–	1s. 9d. multicoloured ..	2·50	3·00
25.	–	2s. 6d. violet and black ..	10·00	4·00
26.	**5.**	5s. multicoloured.. ..	4·00	6·00
27.	–	10s. multicoloured ..	35·00	28·00
28a.	–	£1 multicoloured	2·00	2·00

DESIGNS—As Type **4**: 1d. Map and William I. 1½d. Martello Tower and Henry II. 2d. Arms of Sark and King John. 3d. Arms of Alderney and Edward III. 4 d. Guernsey Lily and Henry V. 5d. Arms of Guernsey and Elizabeth I. 6d. Arms of Alderney and Charles II. 9d. Arms of Sark and George III. 1s. Arms of Guernsey and Queen Victoria. 1s. 6d., as 1d. 1s. 9d., Guernsey Lily and Elizabeth I. 2s. 6d., Martello Tower and King John. As Type **5**: 10s. View of Alderney. 20s. View of Guernsey.

*On Nos. 14 and 23 the degree of latitude is inscr. (incorrectly) as 40° 30′ N. On Nos. 14b and 23b it has been corrected to 49° 30′.

19. Isaac Brock as Colonel.

1969. Birth Bicentenary of Sir Isaac Brock. Multicoloured.

29.	4d. Type **19**	30	30
30.	5d. Sir Isaac Brock as Major-General	30	30
31.	1s. 9d. Isaac Brock as Ensign	2·75	2·50
32.	2s. 6d. Arms and flags ..	2·75	2·50

The 2s. 6d., is horiz.

23. Landing Craft entering St. Peter's Harbour.

1970. 25th Anniversary of Liberation.

33.	**23.**	4d. blue	35	50
34.	–	5d. brown, lake and grey	35	50
35.	–	1s. 6d. brn. & buff ..	4·75	3·00

DESIGNS—HORIZ. 5d. British ships entering St. Peter Port. VERT. 1s. 6d., Brigadier Snow reading Proclamation.

26. Guernsey " Toms ".

1970. Agriculture and Horticulture. Mult.

36.	4d. Type **26**	1·00	30
37.	5d. Guernsey cow	1·10	30
38.	9d. Guernsey bull	14·00	3·25
39.	1s. 6d. Freesias	16·00	3·75

32. St. Peter's Church, Sark.

1970. Christmas. Churches (1st series). Mult.

40.	4d. St. Anne's Church, Alderney (horiz.).. ..	50	20
41.	5d. St. Peter's Church (horiz.)	60	25
42.	9d. Type **32**	3·00	2·00
43.	1s. 6d. St. Tugual Chapel, Herm	3·75	2·00

See also Nos. 63/6.

34. Martello Tower and King John.

1971. Decimal currency. Nos. 13, etc., but with new colours and decimal values as T **34.**

44.	½p. mve. & blk. (as No. 13)	10	15
45.	1p. blue & blk (as No. 14b)	10	10
46.	1½p. brn. & blk. (as No. 15)	15	15
47.	2p. mult. (as No. 18) ..	15	15
48.	2½p. mult. (as No. 19) ..	15	10
49.	3p. mult. (as No. 17) ..	20	20
50.	3½p. mult. (as No. 24) ..	25	25
51.	4p. mult. (as No. 16) ..	35	25
52.	5p. grn. & blk.(as No. 14b)	30	25
53.	6p. mult. (as No. 20) ..	30	35
54.	7½p. mult. (as No. 22) ..	40	45
55.	9p. mult. (as No. 21) ..	1·00	1·25
56a.	10p. violet & blk. (as No. 25)	1·00	1·50
57a.	20p. mult. (as No. 26) ..	80	75
58.	50p. mult. (as No. 27) ..	2·00	3·25

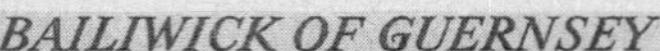

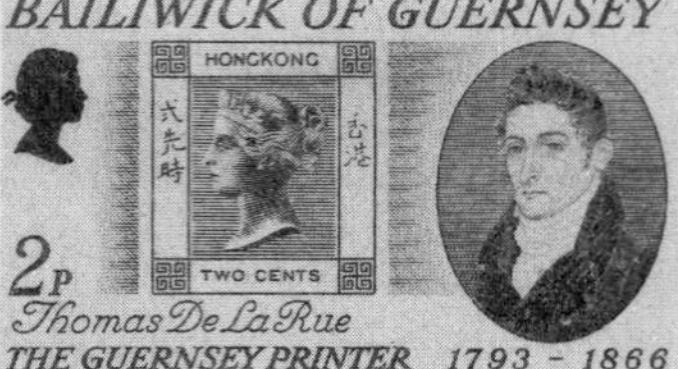

35. Hong Kong 2 c. of 1862.

1971. Thomas De La Rue Commemoration.

59.	**35.**	2p. purple	50	30
60.	–	2½p. red	50	30
61.	–	4p. green..	4·00	3·00
62.	–	7½p. blue..	4·00	3·00

DESIGNS (Each showing portraits of Queen Elizabeth and Thomas De La Rue): 2½p. Great Britain 4d. of 1855–7. 4p. Italy. 5c. of 1862. 7½p. Confederate States 5c. of 1862.

1971. Christmas. Churches (2nd series). As T **32.** Multicoloured.

63.	2p. Ebenezer Church, St. Peter Port (horiz.) ..	45	25
64.	2½p. Church of St. Pierre du Bois (horiz.)	50	25
65.	5p. St. Joseph's Church, St. Peter Port ..	3·25	2·00
66.	7½p. Church of St. Philippe de Torteval	3·50	2·00

37. " Earl of Chesterfield " (1794).

1972. Mail Packet Ships (1st series). Mult.

67.	2p. Type **37**	25	15
68.	2½p. " Dasher " (1827) ..	25	20
69.	7½p. " Ibex " (1891) ..	75	75
70.	9p. " Alberta " (1900) ..	1·00	85

See also Nos. 80/3.

1972. World Conf. of Guernsey Breeders, Guernsey. As No. 38 but size 48 × 29 mm, and additional inscription with face value changed.

71.	5p. multicoloured	1·00	1·00

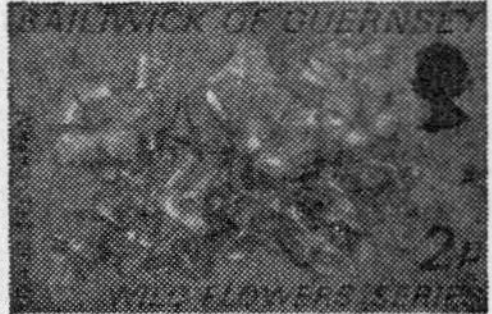

39. Bermuda Buttercup.

1972. Wild Flowers. Multicoloured.

72.	2p. Type **39**	15	20
73.	2½p. Heath Spotted Orchid (vert.)	15	20
74.	7½p. Kaffir Fig	80	80
75.	9p. Scarlet Pimpernel (vert.)	1·10	1·10

40. Angels adoring Christ.

1972. Royal Silver Wedding and Christmas. Stained-glass windows from Guernsey Churches. Multicoloured.

76.	2p. Type **40**	10	10
77.	2½p. The Epiphany ..	15	15
78.	7½p. The Virgin Mary ..	75	75
79.	9p. Christ	80	80

See also Nos. 89/92.

1973. Mail Packet Boats (2nd series). As T **37.** Multicoloured.

80.	2½p. " St. Julien " (1925) ..	10	10
81.	3p. " Isle of Guernsey " (1930)	20	20
82.	7½p. " St. Patrick " (1947)	65	60
83.	9p. " Sarnia " (1961) ..	85	75

41. Supermarine " Sea Eagle ".

1973. 50th Anniv. of Air Service. Mult.

84.	2½p. Type **41**	10	10
85.	3p. Westland " Wessex "..	15	15
86.	5p. De Havilland " Rapide "	25	25
87.	7½p. Douglas " Dakota "..	55	50
88.	9p. Vickers " Viscount " ..	60	55

42. " The Good Shepherd ".

1973. Christmas. Stained-glass windows from Guernsey Churches. Multicoloured.

89.	2½p. Type **42**	10	10
90.	3p. Christ at the well of Samaria	10	10
91.	7½p. St. Dominic	30	30
92.	20p. Mary and the Child Jesus	60	60

43. Princess Anne and Capt. Mark Phillips.

1973. Royal Wedding.

93.	**43.**	25p. multicoloured ..	85	80

44. " John Lockett ", 1875.

1974. 150th Anniv. of Royal National Lifeboat Institution. Multicoloured.

94.	2½p. Type **44**	10	10
95.	3p. " Arthur Lionel ", 1912	10	10
96.	8p " Euphrosyne Kendal ", 1954	45	45
97.	10p. " Arun ", 1972 ..	45	45

45. Private, East Regt., 1815. **46.** Driver, Field Battery Royal Guernsey Artillery, 1848.

1974. Guernsey Militia. Multicoloured.

(a) As Type **45.**

98.	½p. Type **45**	10	10
99.	1p. Officer, 2nd North Regt., 1825	10	10
100.	1½p. Gunner, Guernsey Artillery, 1787	10	10
101.	2p. Gunner, Guernsey Artillery, 1815	10	10
102.	2½p. Corporal, Royal Guernsey Artillery, 1868	10	10
103.	3p. Field Officer, Royal Guernsey Artillery, 1895	10	10
104.	3½p. Sergeant, 3rd Regt., 1867	10	10

105. 4p. Officer, East Regt., 1822 .. .. .. 15 15
105a. 5p. Field Officer, Royal Guernsey Artillery .. 15 15
106. 5½p. Colour-Sergeant of Grenadiers, East Regt., 1833 .. .. .. 20 25
107. 6p. Officer, North Regt., 1832 20 25
107a. 7p. Officer, East Regt., 1822 .. .. .. 25 25
108. 8p. Field Officer, Rifle Company, 1868 .. .. 25 30
109. 9p. Private, 4th West Regt., 1785 .. .. .. 30 35
110. 10p. Field Officer, 4th West Regt., 1824 .. .. 30 35

(b) As Type **46**.

111. 20p. Type **46** 55 55
112. 50p. Officer, Field Battery, Royal Guernsey Artillery, 1868 .. .. 1·50 1·40
113. £1 Cavalry Trooper, Light Dragoons, 1814 (horiz.) 3·00 2·75

47. Badge of Guernsey and U.P.U. Emblem.

1974. Centenary of U.P.U. Multicoloured.

114. 2½p. Type **47** 10 10
115. 3p. Map of Guernsey .. 10 10
116. 8p. U.P.U. Building, Berne, and Guernsey flag .. 45 45
117. 10p. "Salle des Etats" .. 45 45

48. "Cradle Rock".

1974. Renoir Paintings. Multicoloured.

118. 3p. Type **48** 10 10
119. 5½p. "Moulin Huet Bay" .. 15 15
120. 8p. "Au Bord de la Mer" (vert.) 40 40
121. 10p. Self-portrait (vert.) .. 45 45

49. Guernsey Spleenwort.

1975. Guernsey Ferns. Multicoloured.

122. 3½p. Type **49** 10 10
123. 4p. Sand Quillwort .. 10 10
124. 8p. Guernsey Quillwort .. 40 40
125. 10p. Least Adder's Tongue 45 45

50. Victor Hugo House.

1975. Victor Hugo's Exile in Guernsey. Mult.

126. 3½p. Type **50** 10 10
127. 4p. Candie Gardens (vert.) 10 10
128. 8p. United Europe Oak, Hauteville (vert.) .. 40 40
129. 10p. Tapestry Room, Hauteville 50 50

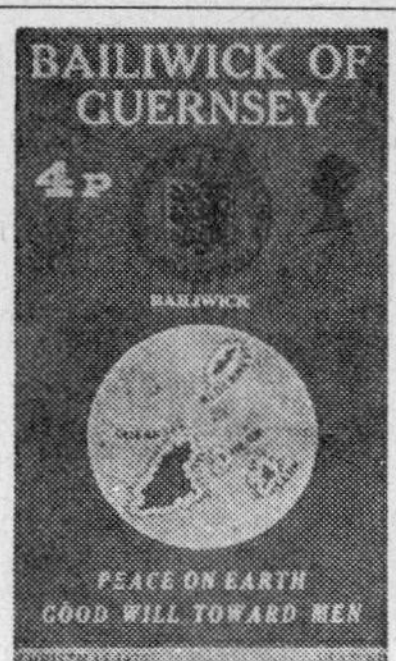

51. Globe and Seal of Bailiwick.

1975. Christmas. Multicoloured.

131. 4p. Type **51** 10 10
132. 6p. Guernsey flag .. 15 15
133. 10p. Guernsey flag and Alderney shield (horiz.) 35 35
134. 12p. Guernsey flag and Sark shield (horiz.) .. 50 50

52. Les Hanois.

1976. Bailiwick Lighthouses. Mult.

135. 4p. Type **52** 10 10
136. 6p. Les Casquets 15 15
137. 11p. Quesnard 40 35
138. 13p. Point Robert .. 45 50

53. Milk Can.

1976. Europa.

139. **53.** 10p. brown and green .. 30 30
140. – 25p. grey and blue .. 70 70

DESIGN: 25p. Christening Cup.

54. Pine Forest, Guernsey.

1976. Bailiwick Views. Multicoloured.

141. 5p. Type **54** 15 10
142. 7p. Herm and Jethou .. 15 15
143. 11p. Grand Greve Bay, Sark (vert.) 40 35
144. 13p. Trois Vaux Bay, Alderney (vert.) .. 40 50

55. Royal Court House, Guernsey.

1976. Christmas. Buildings. Multicoloured.

145. 5p. Type **55** 15 10
146. 7p. Elizabeth College, Guernsey .. 15 15
147. 11p. La Seigneurie, Sark .. 40 35
148. 13p. Island Hall, Alderney 40 50

56. Queen Elizabeth II.

1977. Silver Jubilee. Multicoloured.

149. 7p. Type **56** 20 20
150. 35p. Queen Elizabeth (half-length portrait) .. 80 80

57. Woodland, Talbots Valley.

1977. Europa. Multicoloured.

151. 7p. Type **57** 25 25
152. 25p. Pastureland, Talbots Valley 75 75

58. Statue-menhir, Castel.

1977. Prehistoric Monuments. Multicoloured.

153. 5p. Type **58** 10 10
154. 7p. Megalithic tomb, St. Saviour (horiz.) .. 15 15
155. 11p. Cist, Tourgis (horiz.) 40 35
156. 13p. Statue-menhir, St. Martin 50 50

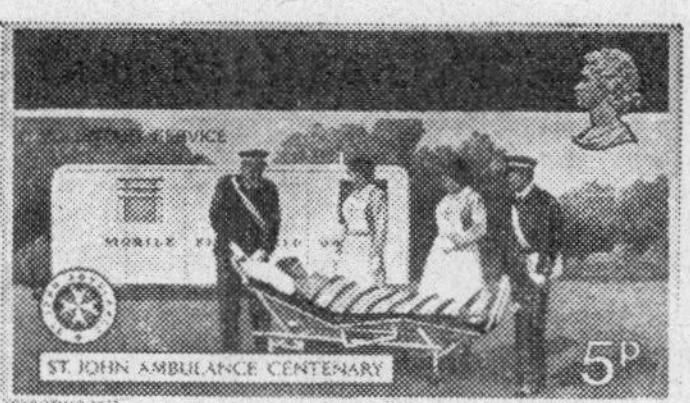

59. Mobile First Aid Unit.

1977. Christmas and St. John Ambulance Centenary. Multicoloured.

157. 5p. Type **59** 10 10
158. 7p. Mobile radar unit .. 15 15
159. 11p. Marine ambulance "Flying Christine II" (vert.) 40 35
160. 13p. Cliff rescue (vert.) .. 50 50

60. View from Clifton, c. 1830.

1978. Old Guernsey Prints (1st series).

161. **60.** 5p. black and green .. 10 10
162. – 7p. black and stone .. 15 15
163. – 11p. black and pink .. 40 35
164. – 13p. black and blue .. 50 50

DESIGNS: 7p. Market Square, St. Peter Port, c. 1838. 11p. Petit-Bo Bay, c. 1839. 13p. The Quay, St. Peter Port, c. 1830.

See also Nos. 249/52.

61. "Prosperity" Memorial.

1978. Europa. Multicoloured.

165. 5p. Type **61** 35 35
166. 7p. Victoria Monument (vert.) 40 40

62. Queen Elizabeth II.

1978. 25th Anniversary of Coronation.

167. **62.** 20p. black, grey & blue 60 60

1978. Royal Visit. As T **62**, but inscr. "VISIT OF H.M. THE QUEEN AND H.R.H. THE DUKE OF EDINBURGH JUNE 28–29, 1978 TO THE BAILIWICK OF GUERNSEY".

168. 7p. black, grey and green 25 25

63. Northern Gannet.

1978. Birds. Multicoloured.

169. 5p. Type **63** 15 15
170. 7p. Firecrest 25 25
171. 11p. Dartford warbler .. 35 35
172. 13p. Spotted redshank .. 40 40

64. Solanum.

1978. Christmas. Multicoloured.

173. 5p. Type **64** 10 10
174. 7p. Christmas Rose .. 20 20
175. 11p. Holly (vert.) .. 40 30
176. 13p. Mistletoe (vert.) .. 50 50

65. One Double Coin, 1830.

67. Pillar-box and Postmark, 1853, and Mail Van and Postmark, 1979.

1979. Coins.

177. 65. ½p. multicoloured .. 10 10
178. – 1p. multicoloured .. 10 10
179. – 2p. multicoloured .. 10 10
180. – 4p. multicoloured .. 10 10
181. – 5p. blk., silver and brn. 15 10
182. – 6p. black, silver and red 15 15
183. – 7p. blk., silver & green 15 20
184. – 8p. blk., silver & brown 20 20
185. – 9p. multicoloured .. 25 20
186. – 10p. multicoloured (green background) 50 50
187. – 10p. multicoloured (orge. background) 35 30
188. – 11p. multicoloured .. 25 30
189. – 11½p. multicoloured .. 25 30
190. – 12p. multicoloured .. 30 30
191. – 13p. multicoloured .. 30 30
192. – 14p. black, silver & blue 30 30
193. – 15p. blk., silver & brn. 35 35
194. – 20p. blk., silver & brn. 50 45
195. – 50p. black, silver & red 1·25 1·25
196. – £1 black, silver & green 2·40 2·40
197. – £2 black, silver and blue 4·75 4·75
198. – £5 multicoloured .. 10·00 10·50

DESIGNS:—VERT. (as Type **65**). 1p. Two doubles, 1899. 2p. Four doubles, 1902. 4p. Eight doubles, 1959. 5p. Three pence, 1956. 6p. Five new pence, 1968. 7p. Fifty new pence, 1969. 8p. Ten new pence, 1970. 9p. Half new penny, 1971. 10p. (both) One new penny, 1971. 11p. Two new pence, 1971. 11½p. Half penny, 1979. 12p. One penny, 1977. 13p. Two pence, 1977. 14p. Five pence, 1977. 15p. Ten pence, 1977. 20p. Twenty-five pence, 1972. (26 × 45 mm.) 50p. William I commemorative 10s., 1966. £5, Seal of the Bailiwick. HORIZ. (45 × 26 mm.) £1, Silver Jubilee crown, 1977. £2, Royal Silver Wedding crown, 1972.

1979. Europa. Communications. Multicoloured.

201. 6p. Type **67** 30 30
202. 8p. Telephone, 1897, and telex machine, 1979 .. 30 30

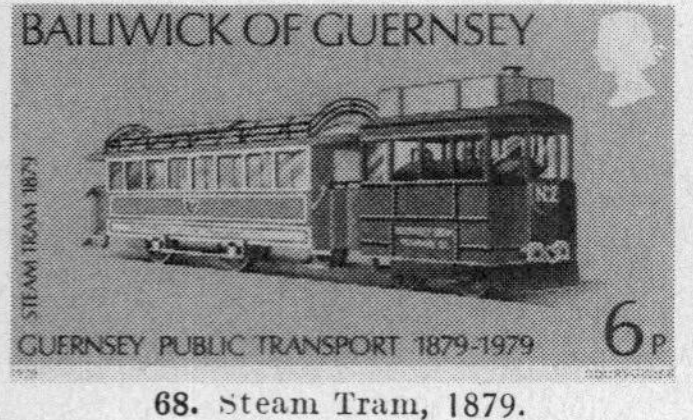

68. Steam Tram, 1879.

1979. History of Public Transport. Mult.

203. 6p. Type **68** 15 15
204. 8p. Electric tram, 1896 .. 20 20
205. 11p. Motor bus, 1911 .. 40 35
206. 13p. Motor bus, 1979 .. 50 45

69. Bureau and Postal Headquarters.

1979. 10th Anniv. of Guernsey Postal Administration. Multicoloured.

207. 6p. Type **69** 15 15
208. 8p. " Mails and telegrams " 25 15
209. 13p. " Parcels " 30 35
210. 15p. " Philately " .. 40 45

70. Major-General Le Marchant.

1980. Europa Personalities. Multicoloured.

212. 10p. Type **70** 35 35
213. 13½p. Admiral Lord de Saumarez 45 45

71. Policewoman with Lost Child.

1980. 60th Anniv. Guernsey Police Force. Multicoloured.

214. 7p. Type **71** 15 15
215. 15p. Motorcycle escort .. 60 45
216. 17½p. Dog-handler .. 65 50

72. Golden Guernsey Goat.

1980. Golden Guernsey Goats. Multicoloured.

217. 7p. Type **72** 20 20
218. 10p. Head of goat .. 40 35
219. 15p. Goat 60 45
220. 17½p. Goat and kids .. 75 60

73. " Sark Cottage ".

1980. Peter Le Lievre Paintings. Multicoloured.

221. 7p. Type **73** 30 20
222. 10p. " Moulin Huet " .. 35 25
223. 13½p. " Boats at Sea " .. 40 30
224. 15p. " Cow Lane " (vert.) 50 40
225. 17½p. " Peter Le Lievre " (vert.) 55 50

74. "Polyommatus icarus".

1981. Butterflies. Multicoloured.

226 8p. Type **74** 25 25
227 12p. "Vanessa atalanta" .. 40 40
228 22p. "Aglais urticae" .. 75 70
229 25p. "Lasionmmata megera" 85 90

75. Sailors paying respect to " Le Petit Bonhomme Andriou " (rock resembling head of a man).

76. Prince Charles.

1981. Europa. Folklore.

230. 75. 12p. gold, brown and light brown 45 45
231. – 18p. gold, blue and light blue 55 55

DESIGN: 18p. Fairies and Guernsey Lily.

1981. Royal Wedding. Multicoloured.

232. 8p. Type **76** 20 20
233. 8p. Prince Charles and Lady Diana Spencer .. 20 20
234. 8p. Lady Diana 20 20
235. 12p. Type **76** 30 30
236. 12p. As No. 233 .. .. 30 30
237. 12p. As No. 234 .. .. 30 30
238. 25p. Royal Family (49 × 32 mm.) 75 75

77. Sark Launch.

1981. Inter-island Transport. Multicoloured.

240. 8p. Type **77** 20 20
241. 12p. "Trislander" aeroplane 40 40
242. 18p. Hydrofoil 60 60
243. 22p. Herm catamaran .. 75 75
244. 25p. "Sea Trent" (coaster) 85 85

78. Rifle Shooting.

1981. International Year for Disabled Persons. Multicoloured.

245. 8p. Type **78** 20 20
246. 12p. Riding 50 40
247. 22p. Swimming 75 65
248. 25p. " Work " 80 70

1982. Old Guernsey Prints (2nd series). Prints from Sketches by T. Compton. As T **60**.

249. 8p. black and blue .. 20 20
250. 12p. black and green .. 50 50
251. 22p. black and brown .. 75 75
252. 25p. black and lilac .. 80 80

DESIGNS: 8p. Jethou. 12p. Fermain Bay. 22p. The Terres. 25p. St. Peter Port.

79. Sir Edgar MacCulloch (founder-president) and Guille-Alles Library, St. Peter Port.

1982. Centenary of La Societe Guernesiaise. Multicoloured.

253 8p. Type **79** 20 20
254 13p. French invasion fleet crossing English Channel, 1066 ("history") 45 45
255 20p. H.M.S. "Crescent", 1793 ("history") .. 55 55
256 24p. "Aeshna sp." ("entomology") 70 70
257 26p. Common snipe caught for ringing ("ornithology") 75 75
258 29p. Samian Bowl, 160–200 A.D. ("archaeology") .. 80 80

The 13p. and 20p. designs also include the Europa C.E.P.T. emblem.

80. " Sea Scouts ".

1982. 75th Anniversary of Boy Scout Movement. Multicoloured.

259. 8p. Type **80** 20 25
260. 13p. " Scouts " 50 50
261. 26p. " Cub Scouts " .. 80 80
262. 29p. " Air Scouts " .. 1·00 1·00

81. Midnight Mass.

1982. Christmas. Multicoloured.

263. 8p. Type **81** 20 20
264. 13p. Exchanging gifts .. 40 40
265. 24p. Christmas meal .. 80 80
266. 26p. Exchanging cards .. 80 80
267. 29p. Queen's Christmas message 85 85

82. Flute Player and Boats.

1982. Centenary of Boys' Brigade. Mult.

268. 8p. Type **82** 25 25
269. 13p. Cymbal player and tug 'o' war 45 45
270. 24p. Trumpet player and bible class 75 75
271. 26p. Drummer and cadets marching 85 85
272. 29p. Boy's Brigade band .. 95 95

83. Building Albert Pier Extension, 1850s.

1983. Europa. Development of St. Peter Port Harbour. Multicoloured.

273. 13p. Type **83** 35 35
274. 13p. St. Peter Port harbour, 1983 .. .. .. 35 35
275. 20p. St. Peter Port, 1680 .. 75 75
276. 20p. Artist's impression of future development scheme 75 75

84. " View at Guernsey " (Renoir).

1983. Centenary of Renoir's Visit to Guernsey. Multicoloured.

277. 9p. Type **84** 25 25
278. 13p. " Children on the Seashore " (25 × 39 mm) .. 45 45
279. 26p. " Marine, Guernsey " 80 80
280. 28p. " La Baie du Moulin Huet a travers les Arbres " 85 85
281. 31p. " Brouillard a Guernsey " 95 95

85. Launching " Star of the West ", 1869, and Capt. J. Lenfestey.

1983. Guernsey Shipping (1st series). Mult.

282. 9p. Type **85** 25 25
283. 13p. Leaving St. Peter Port 40 40
284. 26p. Off Rio Grande Bar .. 80 80
285. 28p. Off St. Lucia 85 85
286. 31p. Map of 1879-80 voyage 95 95

See also Nos. 415/19.

86. Dame of Sark as young Woman.

1984. Birth Centenary of Sibyl Hathaway, Dame of Sark. Multicoloured.

287. 9p. Type **86** 25 25
288. 13p. German occupation, 1940–45 .. .. 40 45
289. 26p. Royal visit, 1957 .. 90 90
290. 28p. Chief Pleas 95 95
291. 31p. The Dame of Sark rose 1·10 1·10

87. C.E.P.T. 25th Anniversary logo.

1984. Europa.

292. 87. 13p. light bl., bl. & blk. 50 50
293. 20½p. green, deep green and black 75 75

88. The Royal Court and St. George's Flag.

1984. Links with the Commonwealth. Mult.

294.	9p. Type **88**	30	30
295.	31p. Castle Cornet and Union flag	1·10	1·10

89. St. Apolline Chapel.

1984. Views. Multicoloured.

296	1p. Little Chapel ..	10	10
297	2p. Fort Grey (horiz) ..	10	10
298	3p. Type **89**	10	10
299	4p. Petit Port (horiz) ..	10	10
300	5p. Little Russel (horiz)	10	10
301	6p. The Harbour, Herm (horiz)	10	15
302	7p. Saints (horiz) ..	15	20
303	8p. St. Saviour	15	20
304	9p. New Jetty (inscr "Cambridge Berth") (horiz)	20	25
305	10p. Belvoir, Herm (horiz)	20	25
306	11p. La Seigneurie, Sark (horiz)	20	25
306b	12p. Petit Bot	25	30
307	13p. St. Saviours reservoir (horiz)	25	30
308	14p. St. Peter Port ..	30	35
309	15p. Havelet	30	35
309c	16p. Hostel of St. John (horiz)	30	35
309d	18p. Le Variouf	35	40
310	20p. La Coupee, Sark (horiz)	40	45
310b	21p. King's Mills (horiz)	40	45
310c	26p. Town Church ..	50	55
311	30p. Grandes Rocques (horiz)	60	65
312	40p. Torteval Church ..	80	85
313	50p. Bordeaux (horiz) ..	1·00	1·10
314	£1 Albecq (horiz) ..	2·00	2·10
315	£2 L'Ancresse (horiz) ..	4·00	4·25

See also Nos. 398/9a.

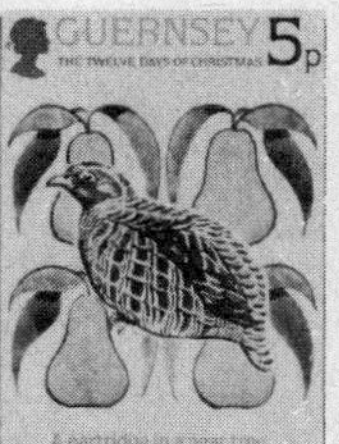

90. "A Partridge in a Pear Tree".

91. Sir John Doyle and Coat of Arms.

1984. Christmas. "The Twelve Days of Christmas". Multicoloured.

316.	5p. Type **90**	20	20
317.	5p. "Two turtle doves" ..	20	20
318.	5p. "Three French hens"	20	20
319.	5p. "Four colly birds" ..	20	20
320.	5p "Five gold rings"	20	20
321.	5p. "Six geese a-laying" ..	20	20
322.	5p. "Seven swans a-swimming"	20	20
323.	5p. "Eight maids a-milking"	20	20
324.	5p. "Nine drummers drumming"	20	20
325.	5p. "Ten pipers piping" ..	20	20
326.	5p. "Eleven ladies dancing"	20	20
327.	5p. "Twelve lords a-leaping"	20	20

1984. 150th Death Anniv. of Lieut-General Sir John Doyle. Multicoloured.

328.	13p. Type **91**	40	40
329.	29p. Battle of Germantown, 1777 (horiz.) ..	1·00	1·00
330.	31p. Reclamation of Braye du Valle, 1806 (horiz.) ..	1·10	1·10
331.	34p. Mail for Alderney, 1812 (horiz.)	1·10	1·10

92. Cuckoo Wrasse.

1985. Fishes. Multicoloured.

332.	9p. Type **92**	40	40
333.	13p. Red Gurnard	60	60
334.	29p. Red Mullet	1·50	1·10
335.	31p. Mackerel	1·50	1·10
336.	34p. Sunfish	1·60	1·25

93. Dove.

1985. 40th Anniv. of Peace in Europe.

337.	**93.**	22p. multicoloured ..	1·00	1·00

94. I.Y.Y. Emblem and Young People of Different Races.

1985. International Youth Year. Mult.

338.	9p. Type **94**	40	40
339.	31p. Girl Guides cooking over campfire	1·00	1·00

95. Stave of Music enclosing Flags.

1985. Europa. European Music Year. Multicoloured.

340.	14p. Type **95**	45	40
341.	22p. Stave of music and musical instruments ..	95	1·00

96. Guide Leader, Girl Guide and Brownie.

1985. 75th Anniv. of Girl Guide Movement.

342	96	34 p. multicoloured ..	1·25	1·25

97. Santa Claus.

1985. Christmas. Gift-bearers. Mult.

343.	5p. Type **97**	25	25
344.	5p. Lussibruden (Sweden)	25	25
345.	5p. King Balthazar ..	25	25
346.	5p. Saint Nicholas (Netherlands)	25	25
347.	5p. La Befana (Italy) ..	25	25
348.	5p. Julenisse (Denmark) ..	25	25
349.	5p. Christkind (Germany)	25	25
350.	5p. King Wenceslas (Czechoslovakia)	25	25
351.	5p. Shepherd of Les Baux (France)	25	25
352.	5p. King Caspar	25	25
353.	5p. Baboushka (Russia) ..	25	25
354.	5p. King Melchior	25	25

98. "Vraicing" (Illustration reduced, actual size 58 × 22 mm.)

1985. Paintings by Paul Jacob Naftel. Multicoloured.

355.	9p. Type **98**	40	40
356.	14p. "Castle Cornet" ..	50	50
357.	22p. "Rocquaine Bay" ..	1·00	1·00
358.	31p. "Little Russel" ..	1·50	1·50
359.	34p. "Seaweed gatherers"	1·60	1·60

99. Squadron off Nargue Island, 1809.

1986. 150th Death Anniv. of Admiral Lord De Saumarez. Multicoloured.

360.	9p. Type **99**	40	40
361.	14p. Battle of the Nile, 1798	60	60
362.	29p. Battle of St. Vincent, 1797	1·50	1·50
363.	31p. H.M.S. "Crescent" off Cherbourg, 1793	1·50	1·50
364.	34p. Battle of the Saints, 1782	1·60	1·60

100. Profile of Queen Elizabeth II (after R. Maklouf).

1986. 60th Birthday of Queen Elizabeth II.

365.	**100.**	60p. multicoloured ..	2·25	2·25

101. Northern Gannet and Nylon Net ("Operation Gannet").

1986. Europa. Nature and Environmental Protection. Multicoloured.

366.	10p. Type **101** ..	45	45
367.	14p. Loose-flowered orchid	65	65
368.	22p. Guernsey elm ..	85	85

102. Prince Andrew and Miss Sarah Ferguson.

1986. Royal Wedding. Multicoloured.

369.	14p. Type **102**	60	60
370.	34p. Prince Andrew and Miss Sarah Ferguson (different) (47 × 30 mm.)	1·40	1·40

103. Bowls.

1986. Sport in Guernsey. Multicoloured.

371.	10p. Type **103**	30	30
372.	14p. Cricket	50	50
373.	22p. Squash	75	75
374.	29p. Hockey	1·10	1·10
375.	31p. Swimming (horiz.) ..	1·25	1·25
376.	34p. Rifle-shooting (horiz.)	1·40	1·40

104. Guernsey Museum and Art Gallery, Candie Gardens.

1986. Centenary of Guernsey Museums. Multicoloured.

377.	14p. Type **104**	60	60
378.	29p. Fort Grey Maritime Museum	1·10	1·10
379.	31p. Castle Cornet ..	1·10	1·10
380.	34p. National Trust of Guernsey Folk Museum	1·40	1·40

105. "While Shepherds Watched their Flocks by Night".

107. Post Office Headquarters.

1986. Christmas. Carols. Multicoloured.

381.	6p. Type **105** ..	25	25
382.	6p. "In The Bleak Mid-Winter"	25	25
383.	6p. "O Little Town of Bethlehem"	25	25
384.	6p. "The Holly and the Ivy"	25	25
385.	6p. "O Little Christmas Tree"	25	25
386.	6p. "Away in a Manger"	25	25
387.	6p. "Good King Wenceslas"	25	25
388.	6p. "We Three Kings of Orient Are" ..	25	25
389.	6p. "Hark the Herald Angels Sing"	25	25
390.	6p. "I Saw Three Ships"	25	25
391.	6p. "Little Donkey" ..	25	25
392.	6p. "Jingle Bells" ..	25	25

1987. Europa. Modern Architecture. Mult.
394. 15p. Type **107** 55 55
395. 15p. Architect's elevation of Post Office Headquarters 55 55
396. 22p. Guernsey Grammar School 80 80
397. 22p. Architect's elevation of Grammar School .. 80 80

1987. Designs as Nos. 306, 306b, 309 and 309a but smaller.
398. 11p. La Seigneurie, Sark (22 × 18 mm.) 30 30
398a. 12p. Petit Bot (18 × 22 mm.) 20 25
399. 15p. Havelet (18 × 22 mm.) 45 45
399a. 16p. Hostel of St. John (22 × 18 mm.) 30 35

108. Sir Edmund Andros and La Plaiderie, Guernsey.

1987. 350th Birth Anniv. of Sir Edmund Andros (colonial administrator). Mult.
400. 15p. Type **108** 45 45
401. 29p. Governor's Palace, Virginia .. .. .. 1·00 1·00
402. 31p. Governor Andros in Boston .. .. .. 1·10 1·10
403. 34p. Map of New Amsterdam (New York), 1661 .. .. 1·40 1·40

109. The Jester's Warning to Young William.

1987. 900th Death Anniv. of William the Conqueror. Multicoloured.
404. 11p. Type **109** 45 45
405. 15p. Hastings battlefield .. 60 60
406. 15p. Norman soldier with pennant 60 60
407. 22p. William the Conqueror 95 95
408. 22p. Queen Matilda and Abbaye aux Dames, Caen 95 95
409. 34p. William's coronation regalia and Halley's comet .. .. .. 1·40 1·40

110. John Wesley preaching on the Quay, Alderney.

1987. Bicentenary of John Wesley's Visit to Guernsey. Multicoloured.
410. 7p. Type **110** 30 30
411. 15p. Wesley preaching at Mon Plaisir, St. Peter Port 45 45
412. 29p. Preaching at Assembly Rooms .. 1·25 1·25
413. 31p. Wesley and La Ville Baudu (early Methodist meeting place) .. .. 1·25 1·25
414. 34p. Wesley and first Methodist Chapel, St. Peter Port .. .. 1·25 1·25

111. "Golden Spur" off St. Sampson Harbour.

1988. Guernsey Shipping (2nd series). "Golden Spur". Multicoloured.
415. 11p. Type **111** 35 35
416. 15 p. "Golden Spur" entering Hong Kong harbour 50 50
417. 29p. Anchored off Macao .. 1·25 1·25
418. 31p. In China Tea Race .. 1·25 1·25
419. 34p. "Golden Spur" and map showing voyage of 1872–74 .. .. .. 1·25 1·25

112 Rowing Boat and Bedford "Rascal" Mail Van

1988. Europa. Transport and Communications. Multicoloured.
420 16p. Type **112** 55 55
421 16p. Rowing boat and "Viscount" mail plane 55 55
422 22p. Postman on bicycle and horse-drawn carriages, Sark .. 85 85
423 22p. Postmen on bicycles and carriage 85 85

Nos. 420/1 and 422/3 were each printed together, se-tenant, the two stamps of each value forming a composite design.

113 Frederick Corbin Lukis and Lukis House, St. Peter Port

1988. Birth Bicentenary of Frederick Corbin Lukis (archaeologist). Multicoloured.
424 12p. Type **113** 40 40
425 16p. Natural history books and reconstructed pot .. 50 50
426 29p. Lukis directing excavation of Le Creux es Faies and prehistoric beaker .. .. .. 1·10 1·10
427 31p. Lukis House Observatory and garden 1·10 1·10
428 34p. Prehistoric artifacts 1·10 1·10

114 Powerboats and Rescue Helicopter off Jethou

1988. World Offshore Powerboat Championships. Multicoloured.
429 16p. Type **114** 60 60
430 30p. Powerboats in Gouliot Passage .. .. 1·10 1·10
431 32p. Start of race at St. Peter Port (vert) .. 1·10 1·10
432 35p. Admiralty chart showing course (vert) .. 1·40 1·40

115 Joshua Gosselin and Herbarium

1988. Bicentenary of Joshua Gosselin's "Flora Sarniensis". Multicoloured.
433 12p. Type **115** 40 40
434 16p. Hares-tail grass .. 55 55
435 16p. Dried hares-tail grass 55 55
436 23p. Variegated catchfly .. 75 75
437 23p. Dried variegated catchfly 75 75
438 35p. Rock sea lavender .. 1·25 1·25

116 Coutances Cathedral, France

118 Outline Map of Guernsey

117 Le Cat (Tip Cat)

1988. Christmas. Ecclesiastical Links. Mult.
439 8p. Type **116** 25 25
440 8p. Interior of Notre Dame du Rosaire Church, Guernsey 25 25
441 8p. Stained glass, St. Sampson's Church, Guernsey 25 25
442 8p. Dol-de-Bretagne Cathedral, France .. 25 25
443 8p. Bishop's throne, Town Church, Guernsey .. 25 25
444 8p. Winchester Cathedral 25 25
445 8p. St. John's Cathedral, Portsmouth 25 25
446 8p. High altar, St. Joseph's Church, Guernsey .. 25 25
447 8p. Mont Saint-Michel, France 25 25
448 8p. Chancel, Vale Church, Guernsey 25 25
449 8p. Lychgate, Forest Church, Guernsey .. 25 25
450 8p. Marmoutier Abbey, France 25 25

1989. Europa. Children's Toys and Games. Multicoloured.
451 12p. Type **117** 40 40
452 16p. Girl with Cobo Alice doll 50 50
453 23p. Le Colimachaon (hopscotch) 80 80

1989. Coil Stamp. No value expressed.
454 **118** (–) blue 30 35
455 (–) green 40 45

No. 454 is inscribed "MINIMUM BAILIWICK POSTAGE PAID" and No. 455 "MINIMUM FIRST CLASS POSTAGE TO UK PAID". They were initially sold at 14p. and 18p. but it is intented this will change in line with future postage rate rises.

119 Guernsey Airways DH86 "Express" and Mail Van

1989. 50th Annivs of Guernsey Airport (Nos. 456, 458, and 460) and 201 Squadron's Affiliation with Guernsey (Nos. 457, 459 and 461). Multicoloured.
456 12p. Type **119** 40 40
457 12p. Supermarine "Southampton" flying boat at mooring .. 40 40
458 18p. B.E.A. DH89 "Rapide" 55 55
459 18p. Sunderland "Mk V" flying boat taking off .. 55 55
460 35p. Air U.K. BAe "146" 1·00 1·00
461 35p. Shackleton "Mk 3" .. 1·00 1·00

120 "Queen Elizabeth II" (June Mendoza)

1989. Royal Visit.
462 **120** 30p. multicoloured .. 1·00 1·00

121 "Ibex" at G.W.R. Terminal, St. Peter Port

1989. Centenary of Great Western Railway Steamer Service to Channel Islands. Mult.
463 12p. Type **121** 30 30
464 18p. "Great Western" (paddle-steamer) in Little Russel 65 65
465 29p. "St. Julien" passing Casquets Light .. 90 90
466 34p. "Roebuck" off Portland .. .. 1·10 1·10
467 37p. "Antelope" and boat train at Weymouth quay 1·25 1·25

122 Two-toed Sloth

1989. 10th Anniv of Guernsey Zoological Trust. Animals of the Rainforest. Mult.
469 18p. Type **122** 90 90
470 29p. Capuchin monkey .. 90 90
471 32p. White-lipped tamarin 90 90
472 34p. Common squirrel-monkey 90 90
473 37p. Common gibbon .. 90 90

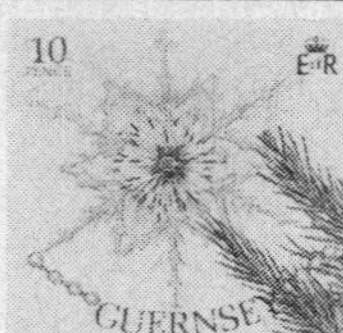

123 Star

1989. Christmas. Christmas Tree Decorations. Multicoloured.

474	10p. Type **123**	30	30
475	10p. Fairy	30	30
476	10p. Candles	30	30
477	10p. Bird	30	30
478	10p. Present	30	30
479	10p. Carol-singer ..	30	30
480	10p. Christmas cracker ..	30	30
481	10p. Bauble	30	30
482	10p. Christmas stocking	30	30
483	10p. Bell	30	30
484	10p. Fawn	30	30
485	10p. Church	30	30

124 Sark Post Office, c. 1890

1990. Europa. Post Office Buildings.

486	**124**	20p. deep brown, sepia and light brown ..	60	60
487	–	20p. multicoloured ..	60	60
488	–	24p. deep brown, sepia and light brown ..	75	75
489	–	24p. multicoloured ..	75	75

DESIGNS: No. 487, Sark Post Office, 1990; 488, Arcade Post Office counter, St. Peter Port, c. 1840; 489, Arcade Post Office counter, St. Peter Port, 1990.

125 Penny Black and Mail Steamer off St. Peter Port, 1840

1990. 150th Anniv of the Penny Black. Mult.

490	14p. Type **125**	45	45
491	20p. Penny Red, 1841, and pillar box of 1853 ..	60	60
492	32p. Bisected 2d., 1940, and German Army band ..	90	90
493	34p. Regional 3d., 1958, and Guernsey emblems	95	95
494	37p. Independent postal administration 1½d., 1969, and queue outside Main Post Office ..	1·00	1·00

126 Lt. Philip Saumarez writing Log Book

1990. 250th Anniv of Anson's Circumnavigation. Multicoloured.

496	14p. Type **126**	45	45
497	20p. Anson's squadron leaving Portsmouth, 1740	60	60
498	29p. Ships at St. Catherine's Island, Brazil	90	90
499	34p. H.M.S. "Tryal" (sloop) dismasted, Cape Horn, 1741	95	95
500	37p. Crew of H.M.S. "Centurion" on Juan Fernandez	1·00	1·00

127 Grey Seal and Pup

1990. Marine Life. Multicoloured.

501	20p. Type **127**	60	60
502	26p. Bottle-nosed dolphin	80	80
503	31p. Basking shark	85	85
504	37p. Common porpoise ..	1·10	1·10

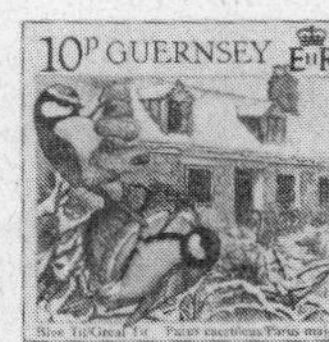

128 Blue Tit and Great Tit

1990. Christmas. Winter Birds. Multicoloured.

505	10p. Type **128**	25	25
506	10p. Snow bunting ..	25	25
507	10p. Common kestrel ..	25	25
508	10p. Common starling ..	25	25
509	10p. Greenfinch	25	25
510	10p. European robin ..	25	25
511	10p. Winter wren ..	25	25
512	10p. Barn owl	25	25
513	10p. Mistle thrush ..	25	25
514	10p. Grey heron	25	25
515	10p. Chaffinch	25	25
516	10p. Common kingfisher ..	25	25

129 Air Raid and 1941 ½d. Stamp

1991. 50th Anniv of First Guernsey Stamps. Multicoloured.

517	37p. Type **129**	1·10	80
518	53p. 1941 1d. stamp ..	1·25	1·25
519	57p. 1941 2½d. stamp ..	1·25	1·25

130 Visit of Queen Victoria to Guernsey, and Discovery of Neptune, 1846

1991. Europa. Europe in Space. Mult.

520	21p. Type **130**	50	50
521	21p. Visit of Queen Elizabeth II and Prince Phillip to Sark, and "Sputnik" (first artificial satellite), 1957	50	50
522	26p. Maiden voyage of "Sarnia" (ferry), and "Vostok 1" (first manned space flight), 1961	60	60
523	26p. Cancelling Guernsey stamps, and first manned landing on Moon, 1969	60	60

131 Children in Guernsey Sailing Trust "GP14" Dinghy

1991. Cent of Guernsey Yacht Club. Mult.

524	15p. Type **131**	30	35
525	21p. Guernsey Regatta ..	40	45
526	26p. Lombard Channel Islands' Challenge race	50	55
527	31p. Rolex Swan Regatta	60	65
528	37p. Old Gaffers' Association gaff-rigged yacht	75	80

132 Pair of Oystercatchers

1991. Nature Conservation. L'Eree Shingle Bank Reserve. Mutlicoloured.

530	15p. Type **132**	30	35
531	15p. Three turnstones ..	30	35
532	15p. Dunlins and turnstones	30	35
533	15p. Curlew and turnstones	30	35
534	15p. Ringed plover with chicks	30	35
535	21p. Gull and wild flowers	40	45
536	21p. Yellow horned poppy	40	45
537	21p. Pair of stone chats and wild flowers ..	40	45
538	21p. Wild flowers on shingle	40	45
539	21p. Sea Kale on shore ..	40	45

Nos. 530/4 and 535/9 were each printed together, se-tenant, with the backgrounds forming composite designs.

133 "Rudolph the Red-nosed Reindeer" (Melanie Sharpe)

1991. Christmas. Children's Paintings. Mult.

540	12p. Type **133**	25	30
541	12p. "Christmas Pudding" (James Quinn)	25	30
542	12p. "Snowman" (Lisa Guille)	25	30
543	12p. "Snowman in Top Hat" (Jessica Ede-Golightly)	25	30
544	12p. "Robins and Christmas Tree" (Sharon Le Page)	25	30
545	12p. "Shepherds and Angels" (Anna Coquelin)	25	30
546	12p. "Nativity" (Claudine Lihou)	25	30
547	12p. "Three Wise Men" (Jonathan Le Noury) ..	25	30
548	12p. "Star of Bethlehem and Angels" (Marcia Mahy)	25	30
549	12p. "Christmas Tree" (Laurel Garfield) ..	25	30
550	12p. "Santa Claus" (Rebecca Driscoll) ..	25	30
551	12p. "Snowman and Star" (Ian Lowe)	25	30

134 Queen Elizabeth II in 1952

1992. 40th Anniv of Accession. Multicoloured.

552	23p. Type **134**	45	50
553	28p. Queen Elizabeth in 1977	55	60
554	33p. Queen Elizabeth in 1986	65	70
555	39p. Queen Elizabeth in 1991	75	80

135 Christopher Columbus

1992. 500th Anniv of Discovery of America by Columbus. Multicoloured.

556	23p. Type **135**	45	50
557	23p. Examples of Columbus's signature ..	45	50
558	28p. "Santa Maria" ..	55	60
559	28p. Map of first voyage	55	60

137 Stock

1992. Horticultural Exports. Multicoloured.

562	3p. Type **137**	10	10
563	4p. Anemones	10	10
564	5p. Gladiolus	10	10
565	10p. Alstroemeria ..	20	25
566	16p. Standard carnation (horiz)	35	40
567	20p. Spray rose	40	45
568	23p. Mixed freesia (horiz)	45	50
569	40p. Spray carnation ..	80	85
570	50p. Single freesia (horiz)	1·00	1·10
571	£1 Floral arrangement (35 × 26½ mm)	2·00	2·10

POSTAGE DUE STAMPS

D 1. Castle Cornet.

1969. Face values in black.

D 1.	**D 1.**	1d. plum	2·50	1·25
D 2.		2d. green	2·50	1·25
D 3.		3d. red	4·00	4·00
D 4.		4d. blue	5·00	5·00
D 5.		5d. ochre	6·00	6·00
D 6.		6d. turquoise	9·00	8·50
D 7.		1s. brown	21·00	20·00

1971. Decimal Currency. Face values in black.

D 8.	**D 1.**	½p. plum	10	10
D 9.		1p. green	10	10
D 10.		2p. red	10	10
D 11.		3p. blue	10	15
D 12.		4p. ochre	15	15
D 13.		5p. blue	15	15
D 14.		6p. violet	20	20
D 15.		8p. orange	25	20
D 16.		10p. brown	30	30
D 17.		15p. grey	40	40

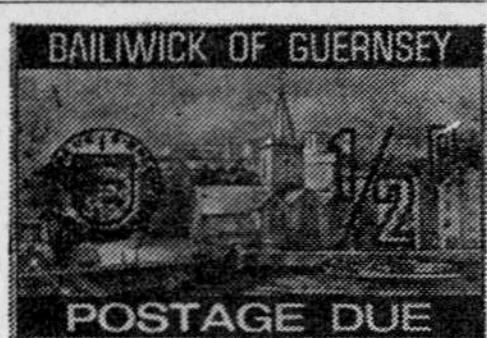

D 2. St. Peter Port.

1977. Face values in black.

D 18.	D 2.	½p. brown	10	10
D 19.		1p. purple	10	10
D 20.		2p. orange	10	10
D 21.		3p. red	10	10
D 22.		4p. blue	10	10
D 23.		5p. green	15	15
D 24.		6p. green	20	20
D 25.		8p. brown	25	25
D 26.		10p. blue	30	30
D 27.		14p. green	35	35
D 28.		15p. violet	35	35
D 29.		16p. red	45	45

D 3. Milking Cow.

1982. Guernsey Scenes, c. 1900.

D 30.	D 3.	1p. blue and green ..	10	10
D 31.	–	2p. brn., lt. brn. & blue	10	10
D 32.	–	3p. green and lilac ..	10	10
D 33.	–	4p. green & orange ..	10	10
D 34.	–	5p. blue and green ..	10	10
D 35.	–	16p. blue & lt. blue..	30	35
D 36.	–	18p. blue and green..	35	40
D 37.	–	20p. green and blue..	40	45
D 38.	–	25p. blue and pink ..	50	55
D 39.	–	30p. green & yellow..	60	65
D 40.	–	50p. brn. and blue ..	1·00	1·10
D 41.	–	£1 lt. brn. & brn. ..	2·00	2·10

DESIGNS: 2p. Vale Mill. 3p. Sark cottage. 4p. Quay-side, St. Peter Port. 5p. Well, Water Lane, Moulin Huet. 16p. Seaweed gathering. 18p. Upper Walk, White Rock. 20p. Cobo Bay. 25p. Saint's Bay. 30p. La Coupee, Sark. 50p. Old Harbour, St. Peter Port. £1, Greenhouses, Doyle Road, St. Peter Port.

C. ALDERNEY

The following issues are provided by the Guernsey Post Office for use on Alderney. They are also valid for postal purposes throughout the rest of the Bailiwick of Guernsey.

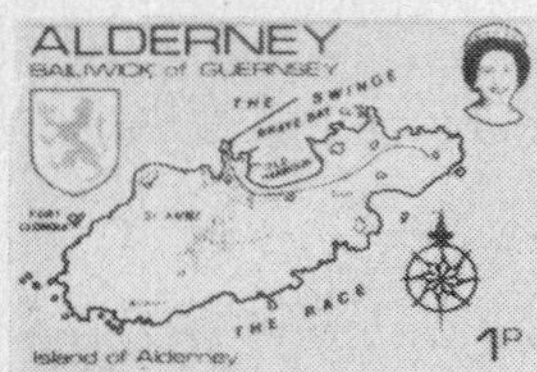

A 1. Island Map.

1983. Island Scenes. Multicoloured.

A 1	1p. Type A 1	10	10
A 2	4p. Hanging Rock ..	10	10
A 3	9p. States' Building, St. Anne	20	25
A 4	10p. St. Anne's Church	20	25
A 5	11p. Yatchs in Braye Bay	20	25
A 6	12p. Victoria St., St. Anne	25	30
A 7	13p. Map of Channnel	25	25
A 8	14p. Fort Clonque ..	30	35
A 9	15p. Corblets Bay and Fort	30	35
A 10	16p. Old Tower, St. Anne	30	35
A 11	17p. Golf course and Essex Castle ..	35	40
A 12	18p. Old Harbour ..	35	40
A 12a	20p. Quesnard Lighthouse (35 × 27 mm)	40	45
A 12b	21p. Braye Harbour (38 × 27mm) ..	45	45
A 12c	23p. Island Hall (38 × 27 mm) ..	45	50

A 2. Oystercatcher.

1984. Birds. Multicoloured.

A 13.	9p. Type A 2	2·00	1·75
A 14.	13p. Turnstone	2·75	2·50
A 15.	26p. Ringed Plover ..	8·00	5·00
A 16.	28p. Dunlin	8·50	5·50
A 17.	31p. Curlew	10·00	6·00

A. 3. Wessex Helicopter of the Queen's Flight.

1985. 50th Anniversary of Alderney Airport. Multicoloured.

A 18.	9p. Type A 3	3·50	2·50
A 19.	13p. Britten-Norman "Trislander"	4·00	3·50
A 20.	29p. De Havilland "Heron"	8·00	4·75
A 21.	31p. De Havilland "Dragon Rapide"	8·50	8·50
A 22.	34p. Saro "Windhover" ..	9·50	6·00

A 4. Royal Engineers, 1890.

1985. Regiments of the Alderney Garrison. Multicoloured.

A 23.	9p. Type A 4	75	75
A 24.	14p. Duke of Albany's Own Highlanders, 1856	1·50	1·25
A 25.	29p. Royal Artillery, 1855	2·00	2·25
A 26.	31p. South Hampshire Regiment, 1810 ..	2·75	2·75
A 27.	34p. Royal Irish Regiment, 1782 ..	3·00	3·00

A. 5 Fort Grosnez.

1986. Alderney Forts. Multicoloured.

A 28.	10 p. Type A 5	1·50	1·50
A 29.	14 p. Fort Tourgis ..	2·25	2·25
A 30.	31 p. Fort Clonque ..	5·25	5·25
A 31.	34 p. Fort Albert	5·50	5·50

A 6. "Liverpool" (full-rigged ship), 1902.

1987. Alderney Shipwrecks. Multicoloured.

A 32.	11p. Type A 6	1·75	1·25
A 33.	15p. "Petit Raymond" (schooner), 1906 ..	2·50	1·60
A 34.	29p. "Maina" (yacht), 1910	4·50	4·50
A 35.	31p. "Burton" (steamer), 1911	5·25	5·00
A 36.	34p. "Point Law" (oil tanker), 1975	6·00	5·50

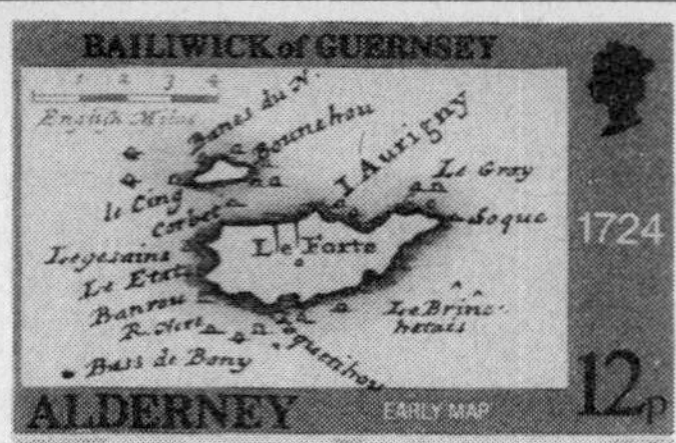

A 7 Moll's Map of 1724

1989. 250th Anniv of Bastide's Survey of Alderney.

A37	A 7	12p. multicoloured ..	45	45
A38	–	18p. black, blue & brn	60	60
A39	–	27p. black, blue & grn	1·10	1·10
A40	–	32p. black, blue & red	1·10	1·10
A41	–	35p. multicoloured ..	1·25	1·25

DESIGNS: 18p. Bastide's survey of 1739; 27p. Goodwin's map of 1831; 32p. General Staff map of 1943; 35p. Ordnance Survey map, 1988.

A 8 H.M.S. "Alderney" (bomb ketch), 1738

1990. Royal Navy Ships named after Alderney.

A42	A 8	14p. black and bistre	45	45
A43	–	20p. black and brown	60	60
A44	–	29p. black and brown	1·10	1·10
A45	–	34p. black and blue	1·10	1·10
A46	–	37p. black and blue ..	1·25	1·25

DESIGNS: 20p. H.M.S. "Alderney" (sixth rate), 1742; 29p. H.M.S. "Alderney" (sloop), 1755; 34p. H.M.S. "Alderney" (submarine), 1945; 37p. H.M.S. "Alderney" (fishery protection vessel), 1979.

A 9 Wreck of H.M.S. "Victory", 1744

1991. Automation of The Casquets Lighthouse. Multicoloured.

A47	21p. Type A 9	50	50
A48	26p. Lighthouse keeper's daughter rowing back to the Casquets	60	60
A49	31p. Helicopter leaving pad on St. Thomas Tower ..	70	70
A50	37p. Migrating birds over lighthouse	1·00	1·00
A51	50p. Trinity House vessel "Patricia" and arms ..	1·40	1·40

GUYANA

Formerly British Guiana, attained independence on 26th May, 1966, and changed its name to Guyana.

100 cents = 1 dollar.

CANCELLED REMAINDERS. In 1969 remainders of some issues were put on the market cancelled-to-order in such a way as to be indistinguishable from genuine postally used copies for all practical purposes. Our quotations which are indicated by an asterisk are the same for cancelled-to-order or postally used copies.

1966. Nos. 331, etc., optd. **GUYANA INDEPENDENCE, 1966.**

393	55.	1 c. black	10	10
379	–	2 c. myrtle	10	10
395	–	3 c. olive and brown ..	10	10
396	–	4 c. violet	10	10
397	–	5 c. red and black ..	10	10
398	–	6 c. green	10	10
384	–	8 c. blue	10	10
400	–	12 c. black and brown ..	10	10
435	–	24 c. black and orange ..	1·25	10
436	–	36 c. red and black ..	30	10
403	–	48 c. blue and brown ..	30	30
404	–	72 c. red and green ..	30	50
405	–	$1 multicoloured ..	35	35
406	–	$2 mauve	1·00	75
407	–	$5 blue and black ..	1·00	1·75

74. Flag and Map.

1966. Independence. Multicoloured.

408.	5 c. Type 74	10	10
409.	15 c. Type 74	10	10
410.	25 c. Arms of Guyana ..	10	10
411.	$1 Arms of Guyana ..	20	25

76. Bank Building.

1966. Opening of Bank of Guyana.

412. 76.	5 c. multicoloured ..	10	10
413.	25 c. multicoloured ..	10	10

77. British Guiana One Cent Stamp of 1856. (¾-size illus.).

1967. World's Rarest Stamp Commem.

414. 77.	5 c. multicoloured ..	10	10*
415.	25 c. multicoloured ..	10	10*

78. Chateau Margot.

1967. 1st Anniv. of Independence. Mult.

416.	6 c. Type 78	10	10*
417.	15 c. Independence Arch ..	10	10*
418.	25 c. Fort Island ..	10	10*
419.	$1 National Assembly ..	20	15

Nos. 418/9 are horiz.

83. "Millie" (Blue and Yellow Macaw). 84. Wicket-keeping.

1967. Christmas.

441. 83. 5 c. yell., bl., blk. & green .. 10 10*
443. 5 c. yell., blue, black & red .. 10 10*
442. 25 c. yell., blue, blk. & vio. .. 15 10*
444. 25 c. yell., blue, blk. & grn. .. 15 10*

1968. M.C.C.'s. West Indies Tour. Mult.

445. 5 c. Type **84** 10 10*
446. 6 c. Batting 10 10*
447. 25 c. Bowling 30 10*

87. Sunfish.

1968. Multicoloured.

448 1 c. Type **87** 10 10
449 2 c. Pirai 10 10
450 3 c. Lukunani 10 10
451 5 c. Hassar 10 10
452 6 c. Patua 20 10
490 10 c. Spix's guan 25 15
491 15 c. Harpy eagle 30 10
492 20 c. Hoatzin 30 20
493 25 c. Guianan cock of the rock 30 10
457 40 c. Great kiskadee 60 20
495 50 c. Brazilian agouti 35 15
459 60 c. White-lipped peccary .. 80 10
460 $1 Paca .. .. .. 1·00 10
461 $2 Nine-banded armadillo .. 1·50 2·00
462 $5 Ocelot .. .. 2·00 3·00

Nos. 453/7 are vert.

102. "Christ of St. John of the Cross" (Salvador Dali).

1968. Easter.

463. 102. 5 c. multicoloured .. 10 10*
464. 25 c. multicoloured .. 10 10*

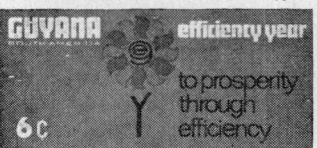

103. "Efficiency Year".

1968. "Savings Bonds and Efficiency". Multicoloured.

465. 6 c. Type **103** 10 10*
466. 25 c. Type **103** 10 10*
467. 30 c. "Savings Bonds" .. 10 10*
468. 40 c. "Savings Bonds" .. 10 10*

105. Open Book, Star and Crescent.

1968. 1400th Anniv. of Holy Quran.

469. 105. 6 c. black, gold & flesh .. 10 10*
470. 25 c. black, gold & lilac 10 10*
471. 30 c. black, gold & green 10 10*
472. 40 c. black, gold & blue 10 10*

107. Broadcasting Greetings.

1968. Christmas.

473. 107. 6 c. brown, black & grn. 10 10*
474. 25 c. brown, violet & grn. 10 10*
475. – 30 c. green & turquoise 10 10*
476. – 40 c. red and turquoise 10 10*

DESIGNS: 30 c. and 40 c. Map showing Radio Link, Guyana – Trinidad.

109. Festival Ceremony.

1969. Hindu Festival of Phagwah. Mult.

477. 6 c. Type **109** 10 10
478. 25 c. Ladies spraying Scent 10 10
479. 30 c. Type **109** 10 10
480. 40 c. As No. 478 .. .. 10 10

111. "Sacrament of the Last Supper" (Dali).

1969. Easter Commemoration.

481. 111. 6 c. multicoloured .. 10 10
482. 25 c. multicoloured .. 10 10
483. 30 c. multicoloured .. 10 10
484. 40 c. multicoloured .. 10 10

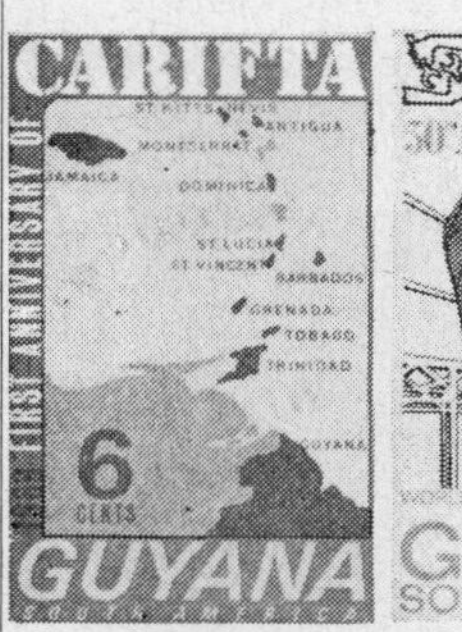

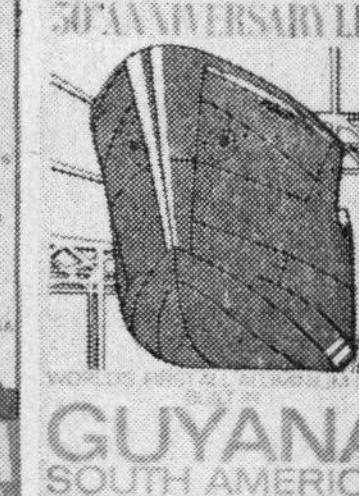

112. Map showing "CARIFTA" Countries. 114. Building "Independence" (first aluminium ship).

1969. 1st Anniv. of "CARIFTA".

500. 112. 6 c. red, blue & turquoise 10 10
501. – 25 c. lemon, brn. & red 10 10

DESIGN—HORIZ. 25 c. "Strength in Unity".

1969. 50th Anniv. of I.L.O.

502. 114. 30 c. blue, black & silver 20 10
503. – 40 c. multicoloured 20 10

DESIGN—HORIZ. 40 c. Bauxite Processing plant.

116. Scouts raising Flag.

1969. 3rd Caribbean Scout Jamboree and Diamond Jubilee of Scouting in Guyana. Multicoloured.

504. 6 c. Type **116** 10 10
505. 8 c. Camp Fire cooking .. 10 10
506. 25 c. As Type **116** .. 10 10
507. 30 c. As 8 c. 10 10
508. 50 c. As Type **116** .. 15 15

118. Gandhi and Spinning Wheel.

1969. Birth Cent. of Mahatma Gandhi.

509. 118. 6 c. black, brn. & olive 15 20
510. 15 c. blk., brn. & lilac 20 25

119. "Mother Sally" Dance Troupe. 121. Forbes Burnham and Map.

1969. Christmas. Unissued stamps optd. as in T **119**. Multicoloured.

511. 5 c. Type **119** 10 10
512. 6 c. City Hall, Georgetown (horiz.) 10 10
513. 25 c. As Type **119** .. 10 10
514. 60 c. As 6 c. 20 25

1970. Republic Day.

515. 121. 5 c. sepia, ochre and blue 10 10
516. – 6 c. multicoloured .. 10 10
517. – 15 c. multicoloured .. 10 10
518. – 25 c. multicoloured .. 10 10

DESIGNS—VERT. 6 c. Rural self-help. HORIZ. 15 c. University of Guyana. 25 c. Guyana House.

125. "The Descent from the Cross".

1970. Easter. Paintings by Rubens. Mult.

519. 5 c. Type **125** 10 10
520. 6 c. "Christ on the Cross" 10 10
521. 15 c. Type **125** 10 10
522. 25 c. As 6 c. 10 10

127. "Peace" and U.N. Emblem.

1970. 25th Anniv. of United Nations. Mult.

523. 5 c. Type **127** 10 10
524. 6 c. U.N. Emblem, Gold-panning and Drilling .. 10 10
525. 15 c. Type **127** 10 10
526. 25 c. As 6 c. 10 10

128. "Mother and Child" (Philip Moore).

1970. Christmas.

527. 128. 5 c. multicoloured .. 10 10
528. 6 c. multicoloured .. 10 10
529. 15 c. multicoloured .. 10 15
530. 25 c. multicoloured .. 10 15

129. National Co-operative Bank.

1971. Republic Day.

531. 129. 6 c. multicoloured .. 10 10
532. 15 c. multicoloured .. 10 10
533. 25 c. multicoloured .. 10 10

130. Racial Equality Symbol.

1971. Racial Equality Year.

534. 130. 5 c. multicoloured .. 10 10
535. 6 c. multicoloured .. 10 10
536. 15 c. multicoloured .. 10 15
537. 25 c. multicoloured .. 10 15

131. Young Volunteer felling Tree (from painting by J. Criswick).

1971. 1st Anniv. of Self-help Road Project.

538. 131. 5 c. multicoloured .. 10 10
539. 20 c. multicoloured .. 15 10
540. 25 c. multicoloured .. 20 10
541. 50 c. multicoloured .. 30 65

132. Yellow Allamanda.

1971. Flowering Plants. Multicoloured.

542 1 c. Pitcher Plant of Mt. Roraima 10 10
543 2 c. Type **132** 10 10
544 3 c. Hanging Heliconia .. 10 10
545 5 c. Annatto tree .. 10 10
546 6 c. Cannon-ball tree .. 10 10
547 10 c. Cattleya .. .. 1·25 10
548a 15 c. Christmas Orchid .. 65 10
549 20 c. "Paphinia cristata" 1·00 20
550 25 c. Marabunta .. 90 3·00
550ab 25 c. Marabunta .. 45 10
551 40 c. Tiger Beard .. 1·50 10
552 50 c. "Guzmania lingulata" .. 40 50
553 60 c. Soldier's Cap .. 40 50
554 $1 "Chelonanthus uliginoides" 40 45
555 $2 "Norantea guianensis" .. 60 1·50
556 $5 "Odontadenia grandiflora" .. .. 1·00 1·50

No. 550 shows the flowers facing upwards and has the value in the centre. No. 550a has the flowers facing downwards with the value to the right.

133. Child praying at Bedside.

1971. Christmas. Multicoloured.

557. 5 c. Type **133** 10 10
558. 20 c. Type **133** 10 10
559. 25 c. Carnival Masquerader (vert.) 10 10
560. 50 c. as 25 c. 20 30

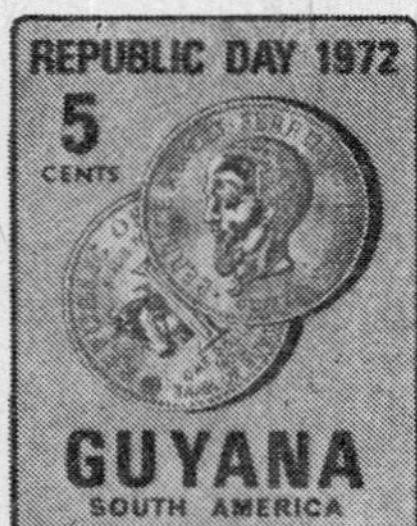

134. Obverse and Reverse of Guyana $1 Coin.

1972. Republic Day.

561. **134.** 5 c. silver, black and red 10 10
562. – 20 c. silver, black and red 15 10
563. **134.** 25 c. silver, black & blue 15 15
564. – 50 c. silver, blk. & grn. 25 30

DESIGN: 20 c., 50 c. Reverse and obverse of Guyana $1 coin.

135. Hands and Irrigation Canal.

1972. Youman Nabi (Mohammed's Birthday).

565. **135.** 5 c. multicoloured .. 10 10
566. 25 c. multicoloured .. 10 10
567. 30 c. multicoloured .. 10 10
568. 60 c. multicoloured .. 20 20

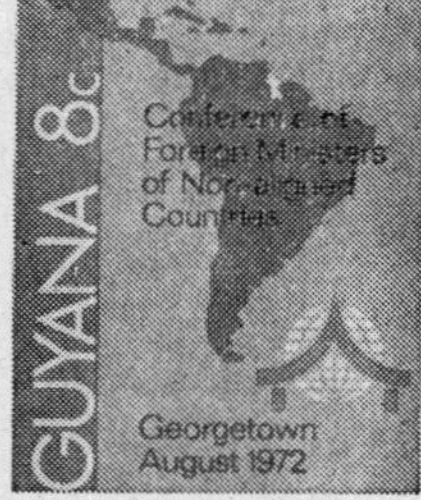

136. Map and Emblem.

1972. Conf. of Foreign Ministers of Non-aligned Countries.

569. **136.** 8 c. multicoloured .. 10 10
570. 25 c. multicoloured .. 10 10
571. 40 c. multicoloured .. 15 15
572. 50 c. multicoloured .. 20 20

137. Hand reaching for Sun.

1972. 1st Caribbean Festival of Arts.

573. **137.** 8 c. multicoloured .. 10 10
574. 25 c. multicoloured .. 10 10
575. 40 c. multicoloured .. 15 20
576. 50 c. multicoloured .. 20 25

138. Joseph, Mary and the Infant Jesus.

1972. Christmas.

577. **138.** 8 c. multicoloured .. 10 10
578. 25 c. multicoloured .. 10 10
579. 40 c. multicoloured .. 15 25
580. 50 c. multicoloured .. 15 25

139. Umana Yana (Meeting-house).

1973. Republic Day. Multicoloured.

581. 8 c. Type **139** 10 10
582. 25 c. Bethel Chapel .. 10 10
583. 40 c. As 25 c. 15 20
584. 50 c. Type **139** 20 20

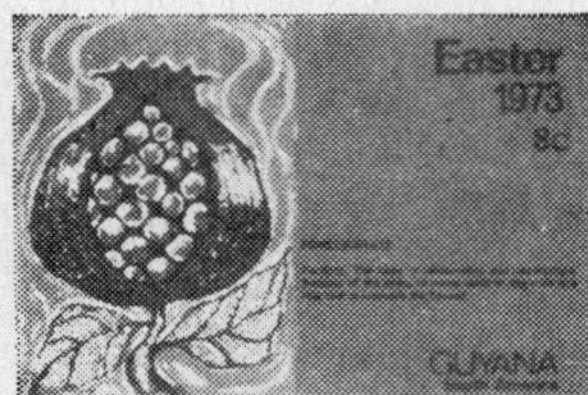

140. Pomegranate.

1973. Easter. Multicoloured.

585. 8 c. Type **140** 10 10
586. 25 c. Cross and map (34×17 mm.) 10 10
587. 40 c. As 25 c. 10 10
588. 50 c. Type **140** 15 15

141. Stylized Blood Cell.

1973. 25th Anniv. of Guyana Red Cross.

589. **141.** 8 c. red and black .. 10 10
590. 25 c. red and purple .. 20 15
591. 40 c. red and blue .. 30 45
592. 50 c. red and green .. 40 70

142. Steel-Band Players.

1973. Christmas. Multicoloured.

593. 8 c. Type **142** 10 10
594. 25 c. Type **142** 15 10
595. 40 c. Virgin and Child stained-glass window .. 30 40
596. 50 c. As 40 c. 30 40

143. Symbol of Progress.

1974. Republic Day. Multicoloured.

597. 8 c. Type **143** 10 10
598. 25 c. Wai-Wai Indian .. 10 10
599. 40 c. Type **143** 15 25
600. 50 c. As 25 c. 15 30

1974. No. 546 surch.

601. 8 c. on 6 c. multicoloured .. 10 10

145. Kite with Crucifixion Motif.

1974. Easter.

602. **145.** 8 c. multicoloured .. 10 10
603. – 25 c. black and green 10 10
604. – 40 c. black and mauve 10 15
605. **145.** 50 c. multicoloured .. 15 25

DESIGN: Nos. 603/4, "Crucifixion" in pre-Columbian style.

146. British Guiana 24 c. Stamp of 1874.

1974. Cent. of Universal Postal Union.

606. **146.** 8 c. multicoloured .. 15 10
607. – 25 c. lt. grn., grn. & blk. 20 10
608. **146.** 40 c. multicoloured .. 20 20
609. – 50 c. grn., brn. and blk. 25 25

DESIGNS—VERT. (42×25 mm.). 25 c., 50 c. U.P.U. emblem and Guyana postman.

147. Guides with Banner.

1974. Golden Jubilee of Girl Guides. Mult.

610. 8 c. Type **147** 15 10
611. 25 c. Guides in camp .. 30 15
612. 40 c. As 25 c. 45 40
613. 50 c. Type **147** 45 45

148. Buck Toyeau.

1974. Christmas. Multicoloured.

615. 8 c. Type **148** 10 10
616. 35 c. Five-fingers and awaras 10 10
617. 50 c. Pawpaw and tangerine 15 10
618. $1 Pineapple and sapodilla 30 60

1975. No. 544 surch.

620. 8 c. on 3 c. multicoloured 10 10

149. Golden Arrow of Courage. **150.** Old Sluice Gate.

1975. Republic Day. Guyana Orders and Decorations. Multicoloured.

621. 10 c. Type **149** 10 10
622. 35 c. Cacique's Crown of Honour 10 15
623. 50 c. Cacique's Crown of Valour 15 20
624. $1 Order of Excellence .. 35 60

1975. Silver Jubilee of International Commission on Irrigation and Drainage. Mult.

625. 10 c. Type **150** 10 10
626. 35 c. Modern sluice gate (horiz.) 10 15
627. 50 c. Type **150** 15 30
628. $1 As 35 c. 35 60

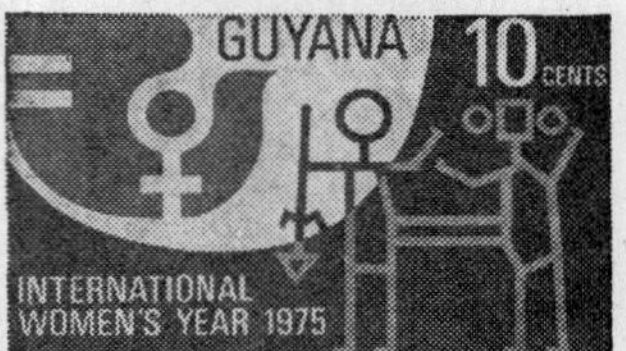

151. I.W.Y. Emblem and Rock Drawing.

1975. International Women's Year. Designs showing different rock drawings.

630. **151.** 10 c. green and yellow .. 10 10
631. – 35 c. violet and blue .. 20 10
632. – 50 c. blue and orange .. 25 15
633. – $1 brown and blue .. 45 45

152. Freedom Monument.

1975. Namibia Day. Multicoloured.

635. 10 c. Type **152** 10 10
636. 35 c. Unveiling of Monument 15 10
637. 50 c. Type **152** 25 10
638. $1 As 35 c. 35 35

MINIMUM PRICE

The minimum price quoted is 10p which represents a handling charge rather than a basis for valuing common stamps. For further notes about prices see introductory pages.

153. G.N.S. Emblem.

1975. 1st Anniv. of National Service.

639. **153.** 10 c. yell., grn. & violet 10 10
640. – 35 c. orge., grn. & violet 10 10
641. – 50 c. blue, grn. & brown 15 15
642. – $1 mve., grn. & light grn. 40 40

Nos. 640/2 are as Type **153** but have different symbols within the circle.

154. Court Building, 1875, and Forester's Badge.

1975. Centenary of Guyanese Ancient Order of Foresters. Multicoloured.

644. 10 c. Type **154** 10 10
645. 35 c. Rock drawing of hunter and quarry .. 10 10
646. 50 c. Crossed axes and bugle-horn 15 10
647. $1 Bow and arrow 40 40

1976. No. 553 surch.

649. 35 c. on 60 c. Soldier's Cap 20 25

156. Shoulder Flash.

1976. 50th Anniv. of St. John Ambulance in Guyana.

650. **156.** 8 c. silver, blk. & mauve 10 10
651. – 15 c. silver, blk. & orge. 10 10
652. – 35 c. silver, blk. & grn. 20 20
653. – 40 c. silver, blk. & blue 25 25

Nos. 651/3 areas Type **156** but show different shoulder flashes.

157. Triumphal Arch.

1976. 10th Anniv. of Independence. Mult.

654. 8 c. Type **157** 10 10
655. 15 c. Stylised Victoria Regia lily 10 10
656. 35 c. "Onward to Socialism" 15 15
657. 40 c. Worker pointing the way 15 15

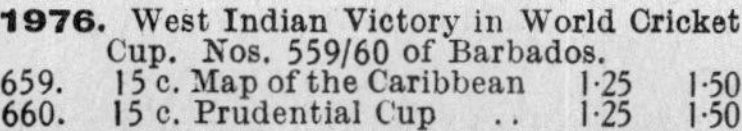

1976. West Indian Victory in World Cricket Cup. Nos. 559/60 of Barbados.

659. 15 c. Map of the Caribbean 1·25 1·50
660. 15 c. Prudential Cup .. 1·25 1·50

158. Flame in Archway.

1976. Deepavali Festival. Multicoloured.

661. 8 c. Type **158** 10 10
662. 15 c. Flame in hand .. 10 10
663. 35 c. Flame in bowl .. 15 20
664. 40 c. Goddess Latchmi .. 15 25

159. "Festival Emblem and Musical instrument".

1977. Second World Black and African Festival of Arts and Culture, Nigeria.

666. **159.** 10 c. red, black and gold 10 10
667. 25 c. blue, black & gold 20 10
668. 50 c. blue, black & gold 25 25
669. $1 green, black & gold 60 75

160. 1 c. and 5 c. Coins.

1977. New Coinage.

671. **160.** 8 c. multicoloured .. 15 10
672. – 15 c. brown, grey & black 20 10
673. – 35 c. green, grey & black 35 30
674. – 40 c. red, grey and black 40 35
675. – $1 multicoloured .. 80 90
676. – $2 multicoloured .. 1·40 2·00

DESIGNS: 15 c. 10 and 25 c. coins. 35 c., 50 c. and $1 coins. 40 c. $5 and $10 coins. $1, $50 and $100 coins. $2, Reverse of $1 coin.

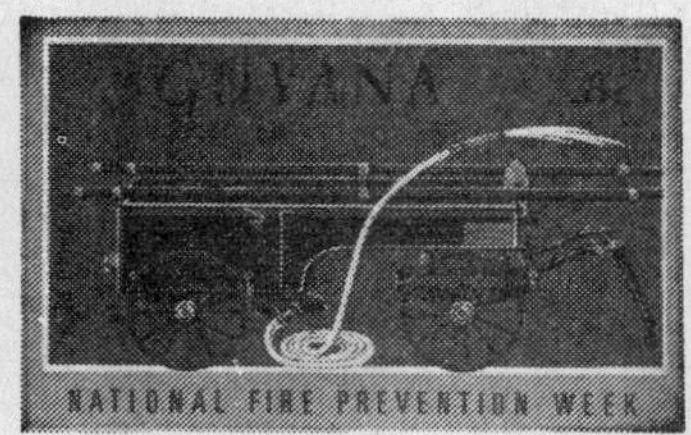

161. Hand Pump, circa 1850.

1977. Nat. Fire Prevention Week. Mult.

677. 8 c. Type **161** 15 10
678. 15 c. Steam engine, circa 1860 .. .. .. 30 10
679. 35 c. Fire engine, circa 1930 .. .. .. 50 40
680. 40 c. Fire engine, 1977 .. 60 55

162. Cuffy Monument.

1977. Cuffy Monument. Multicoloured.

681. 8 c. Type **162** 10 10
682. 15 c. Cuffy Monument (different view) 10 10
683. 35 c. Type **162** 15 20
684. 40 c. As 15 c. 15 30

163. American Manatee.

1978. Wildlife Conservation. Multicoloured.

685. 8 c. Type **163** 35 10
686. 15 c. Giant sea turtle .. 50 15
687. 35 c. Harpy Eagle (vert.) .. 1·50 1·25
688. 40 c. Iguana (vert.) .. 1·50 1·25

164. L.F.S. Burnham (Prime Minister) and Parliament Buildings, Georgetown.

1978. 25th Anniv. of Prime Minister's Entry into Parliament.

689. **164.** 8 c. black, violet & grey 10 10
690. – 15 c. black, blue & grey 10 10
691. – 35 c. black, red and grey 15 20
692. – 40 c. black, orge. & grey 15 20

DESIGNS: 15 c. Burnham, graduate and children ("Free Education"). 35 c. Burnham and industrial works (Nationalization of Bauxite industry). 40 c. Burnham and village scene ("The Co-operative Village").

165. Dr. George Giglioli (scientist & physician).

166. "Prepona pheridamus".

1978. National Science Research Council. Multicoloured.

694. 10 c. Type **165** 10 10
695. 30 c. Institute of Applied Science and Technology 15 15
696. 50 c. Emblem of National Science Research Council 25 25
697. 60 c. Emblem of Commonwealth Science Council (commemorating the 10th meeting) (horiz.) .. 25 25

1978. Butterflies. Multicoloured.

698 5 c. Type **166** 50 10
699 10 c. "Archonias bellona" 50 10
700 15 c. "Eryphanis polyxena" 60 10
701 20 c. "Helicopis cupido" 60 10
702 25 c. "Nessaea batesi" .. 70 10
702a 30 c. "Nymphidium mantus" 70 60
703 35 c. "Anaea galanthis" 80 10
704 40 c. "Morpho rhetenor" (male) 80 10
705 50 c. "Hamadryas amphinome" 80 10
705a 60 c. "Papilio androgeus" 80 60
706 $1 "Agrias claudina" .. 2·25 15
707 $2 "Morpho rhetenor" (female) .. .. 3·25 35
708 $5 "Morpho deidamia" .. 5·00 90
708a $10 "Elbella patrobas" .. 6·50 3·50

Nos. 706/8 are vertical, 25 × 39 mm.

168. Amerindian Stone-chip Grater in Preparation.

1978. National/International Heritage Year. Multicoloured.

709. 10 c. Type **168** 10 10
710. 30 c. Cassiri jar and decorated Amerindian jar .. 15 10
711. 50 c. Old Dutch fort, Kyk-over-al 20 15
712. 60 c. Fort Island 20 20

169. Dish Aerial by Night.

1979. Satellite Earth Station. Multicoloured.

713. 10 c. Type **169** 10 10
714. 30 c. Dish aerial by day .. 20 15
715. 50 c. Satellite with solar veins 30 15
716. $3 Cylinder satellite .. 1·50 90

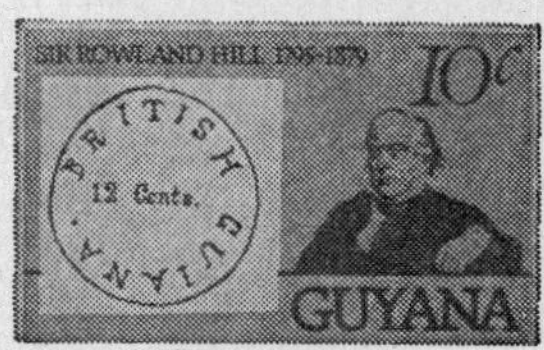

170. Sir Rowland Hill and British Guiana 1850 12 c. "Cottonreel" Stamp.

1979. Death Centenary of Sir Rowland Hill. Multicoloured.

717. 10 c. Type **170** 10 10
718. 30 c. British Guiana 1856 1 c. black on magenta stamp (vert.) 20 15
719. 50 c. British Guiana 1898 1 c. Mount Roraima stamp 30 25
720. $3 Printing press used for early British Guiana stamps (vert.) .. .. 1·00 1·50

171. "Me and my Sister".

1979. International Year of the Child. Children's Paintings. Multicoloured.

721. 10 c. Type **171** 10 10
722. 30 c. "Fun with the Fowls" (horiz.) .. 15 15
723. 50 c. "Two boys catching Ducks" (horiz.) .. 20 20
724. $3 "Mango Season" (horiz.) .. .. .. 65 1·25

172. "An 8 Hour Day".

1979. 60th Anniv. of Guyana Labour Union. Multicoloured

725. 10 c. Type **172** 10 10
726. "Abolition of Night Baking" (horiz.) 10 10
727. 50 c. "Introduction of the Workmen's Compensation Ordinance" 15 15
728. $3 H.N. Critchlow (founder) 55 90

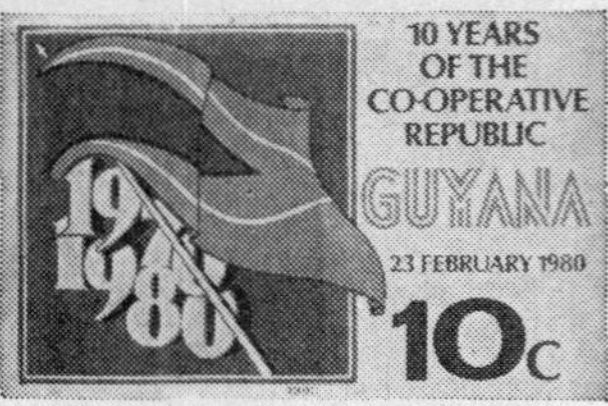

173. Guyana Flag.

1980. 10th Anniv. of Republic.

729. 173. 10 c. multicoloured .. 10 10
730. – 35 c. black and orange .. 20 10
731. – 60 c. multicoloured .. 35 20
732. – $3 multicoloured .. 70 90

DESIGNS: 35 c. Demerara River Bridge. 60 c. Kaieteur Falls. $3, "Makanaima, the Great Ancestral Spirit of the Amerindians".

174. Snoek.

1980. "London 1980" International Stamp Exhibition. Fishes. Multicoloured.

733. 35 c. Type **174** 25 25
734. 35 c. Haimara 25 25
735. 35 c. Electric Eel 25 25
736. 35 c. Golden Rivulus .. 25 25
737. 35 c. Pencil Fish 25 25
738. 35 c. Four-eyed Fish .. 25 25
739. 35 c. Pirai or Carib Fish 25 25
740. 35 c. Smoking Hassar .. 25 25
741. 35 c. Devil Ray 25 25
742. 35 c. Flying Patwa .. 25 25
743. 35 c. Arapaima Pirariucii 25 25
744. 35 c. Lukanani 25 25

175. Children's Convalescent Home (Community Service).

1980. 75th Anniv. of Rotary International. Multicoloured.

745. 10 c. Type **175** 10 10
746. 30 c. Georgetown Rotary Club and Rotary International emblems .. 10 10
747. 50 c. District 404 emblem (vert.) 20 20
748. $3 Rotary anniversary emblem (vert.) 80 80

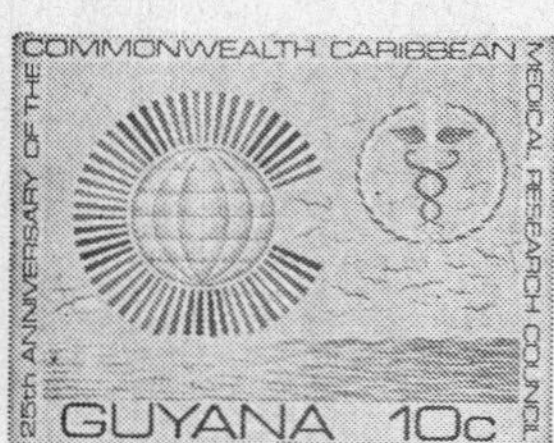

176. "C" encircling Globe, Caduceus Emblem and Sea.

1980. 25th Anniv. of Commonwealth Caribbean Medical Research Council. Mult.

749. 10 c. Type **176** 10 10
750. 60 c. Researcher with microscope, Caduceus emblem, stethoscope and beach scene 40 20
751. $3 Caduceus emblem, "C" encircling researcher and island silhouettes .. 1·10 1·00

177. "Virola surinamensis".

1980. Christmas. Trees and leaves. Mult.

752. 10 c. Type **177** 10 10
753. 30 c. "Hymenaea courbaril" 20 10
754. 50 c. "Mora excelsa" .. 30 15
755. $3 "Peltogyne venosa" 1·25 1·10

178. Brazilian Tree Porcupine.

1981. Wildlife. Multicoloured.

756 30 c. Type **178** 40 40
757 30 c. Red howler 40 40
758 30 c. Common squirrel-monkey 40 40
759 30 c. Two-toed sloth .. 40 40
760 30 c. Brazilian tapir .. 40 40
761 30 c. Collared peccary .. 40 40
852 30 c. Six-banded armadillo 40 40
763 30 c. Tamandua 40 40
764 30 c. Giant anteater .. 40 40
765 30 c. Murine opossum .. 40 40
766 30 c. Brown four-eyed opossum 40 40
767 30 c. Brazilian agouti .. 40 40

1981. Liberation of Southern Africa Conference. No. 635 surch. **1981 CONFERENCE. $1.05.**

768. $1·05 on 10 c. Type **152** .. 40 50

1981. Royal Wedding (1st issue). Nos. 554 and 556 surch. **ROYAL WEDDING 1981.**

769. $3·60 on $5 "Odontadenia grandiflora .. .. 1·25 1·00
770. $7·20 in $1 "Chelonanthus uliginoides .. .. 1·75 2·00

See also Nos. 841/3 and 930/6.

181. Map of Guyana.

1981.

771 181 10 c. on 3 c. black, blue and red 40 10
943 30 c. on 2 c. black, blue and grey 40 15
773 50 c. on 2 c. black, blue and grey 55 25
774 60 c. on 2 c. black, blue and grey 70 30
775 75 c. on 3 c. black, blue and red 70 45

See also Nos. 940/76.

1981. No. 544 surch.

775c. 720 c. on 3 c. mult. .. 50·00 15·00

1981. Various stamps optd. **1981.**

776 105 25 c. black, gold & lilac 10 10
777 – 30 c. black, gold & grn 15 15
778 – 35 c. mult (No. 645) .. 15 15
865 – $1 mult (No. 554) .. 40 35

See also Nos. 791/3 and 809 etc.

1981. Nos. 545 and 555 surch.

780. 75 c. on 5 c. Annatto Tree 50 30
781. 210 c. on $5 "Odontadenia grandiflora" 80 70
781a. 220 c. on 5 c. Annatto Tree .. .. 55·00 8·00

1981. Nos. D8/11 surch. **ESSEQUIBO IS OURS.**

782. D2. 10 c. on 2 c. black .. 25 10
783. 15 c. on 12 c. red .. 25 15
784. 20 c. on 1 c. green .. 20 20
785. 45 c. on 2 c. black .. 75 25
786. 55 c. on 4 c. blue .. 30 30
787. 60 c. on 4 c. blue .. 50 25
788. 65 c. on 2 c. black .. 40 40
789. 70 c. on 4 c. blue .. 1·00 1·25
790. 80 c. on 4 c. blue .. 35 40

1981. Nos. 454, 457 and 555 optd. **1981.**

791 15 c. Harpy eagle .. 3·25 10
792 40 c. Great kiskadee .. 3·25 40
866 $2 "Norantea guianensis" 90 95

1981. Nos. 545, 554, 556, 716, 843, F7 and F9 surch.

794. 50 c. on 5 c. Annatto tree (postage) 30 20
795. 120 c. on $1 "Chelonanthus uliginoides 75 50
796. 140 c. on $1 "Chelonanthus uliginoides" 70 50
797. 150 c. on $2 "Norantea guianensis" (F9) .. 75 50
798. 360 c. on $2 "Norantea guianensis" (F9) .. 3·00 1·50
799. 720 c. on 60 c. Soldier's Cap (F7) .. .. 3·00 2·75
800. 220 c. on $3 Cylinder satellite .. .. 1·75 75
801. 250 c. on $5 "Odontadenia grandiflora .. .. 1·25 80
802. 280 c. on $5 "Odontadenia grandiflora .. .. 1·50 1·25
803. 375 c. on $5 "Odontadenia grandiflora" .. .. 1·75 1·40
804. $1·10 on $2 "Norantea guianensis" (843) (air) .. 17·00 15·00

No. 804 has the Royal Wedding optd. cancelled by three bars.

1981. No. 448. surch.

805. 15 c. on 1 c. Type **87** (postage) 10 10
806. 100 c. on 1 c. Type **87** (air) 35 35
807. 110 c. on 1 c. Type **87** .. 40 40

1981. No. 700 optd. **ESSEQUIBO IS OURS.**

808. 15 c. "Eryphanis polyxena 30 10

1981. Various stamps optd. **1981.**

864 – 15 c. mult (No. 548a) 2·25 10
810 – 15 c. mult (No. 659) 3·00 20
811 – 15 c. mult (No. 660) 3·00 20
811c – 40 c. mult (No. F5) .. — £200
812 – 50 c. mult (No. 623) 60 20
813 150 50 c. multicoloured .. 1·00 25
814 – 50 c. blue and orange (No. 632) .. .. 13·00 1·00
815 – 50 c. mult (No. 646) 1·50 25
816 159 50 c. blue, blk & gold 7·50 1·00
817 – 50 c. mult (No. F6) .. 2·00 30
818 – 60 c. mult (No. 731) 60 25
819 – 60 c. mult (No. 750) 60 25
820 – $1 mult (No. 624) .. 6·00 1·00
821 159 $1 green, black & gold 3·75 50
823 – $3 mult (No. 732) .. 2·50 95
824 – $5 mult (No. 556) .. 3·25 2·25

1981. Various stamps surch.

825 116 55 c. on 6 c. mult .. 4·00 80
826 111 70 c. on 6 c. mult .. 70 30
827 100 c. on 6 c. mult .. 80 35
828 – 100 c. on 8 c. multicolured (No. 505) .. 3·75 40
829 – 100 c. on $1.05 on 10 c. multi (No. 768) .. 23·00 3·50
830 116 110 c. on 6 c. mult .. 4·00 40
831 149 110 c. on 10 c. mult .. 2·00 40
832 151 110 c. on 10 c. green and yellow .. 3·75 70
834 – 125 c. on $2 multicoloured (No. 555) 8·50 1·00
835 116 180 c. on 6 c. mult .. 4·50 65
840 – 240 c. on $3 multicoloured (No. 728) 9·50 1·50
836 116 400 c. on 6 c. mult .. 4·50 1·75
837a 440 c. on 6 c. mult .. 3·50 1·75
838 – 550 c. on $10 multicoloured (No. O21) 4·50 2·00
839 – 625 c. on 40 c. multicoloured (No. F5) 9·50 3·00

1981. Royal Wedding (2nd issue). Nos. 544 and 555/6 surch **Royal Wedding 1981** (No. 843 **Air Mail** also).

841 60 c. on 3 c. Hanging heliconia (postage) .. 70 80
842 75 c. on $5 "Odontadenia grandiflora" 80 90
843 $1.10 on $2 "Norantea guianensis" (air) .. 1·25 1·40

1981. World Cup Football Championship, Spain (1982) (1st issue). No. 781a surch **Espana 82.**

844. 220 c. on 5 c. Annatto tree 1·25 90

See also Nos. 937/9.

1981. 150th Birth Anniv. of Heinrich von Stephan (founder of U.P.U.) No. 720 surch. **1831—1981 Von Stephan. 330.**

845. 330 c. on $3 Printing press used for early British Guiana stamps .. .. 1·50 1·25

1981. No. 452 surch.

847 12 c. on 12 c. on 6 c. Patua 20 25
848 15 c. on 10 c. on 6 c. Patua 15 10
849 15 c. on 30 c. on 6 c. Patua 15 10
850 15 c. on 50 c. on 6 c. Patua 15 10
851 15 c. on 60 c. on 6 c. Patua 15 10

Nos. 847/51 are further surcharges on previously unissued stamps.

214. Coromantyn Free Negro Armed Ranger, c. 1772. and Cuffy Monument.

1981. 16th Anniv. of Guyana Defence Force. Multicoloured.

853. 15 c. on 10 c. Type **214** .. 30 10
854. 50 c. Private, 27th Foot Regiment, c. 1825 .. 40 30
855. $1 on 30 c. Private, Col. Fourgeoud's Marines c. 1775 .. .. .. 60 50
856. $1.10 on $3 W.O. and N.C.O., Guyana Defence Force 1966 .. .. .. 1·50 75

The 15 c., $1 and $1.10 values are surcharged on previously unissued stamps.

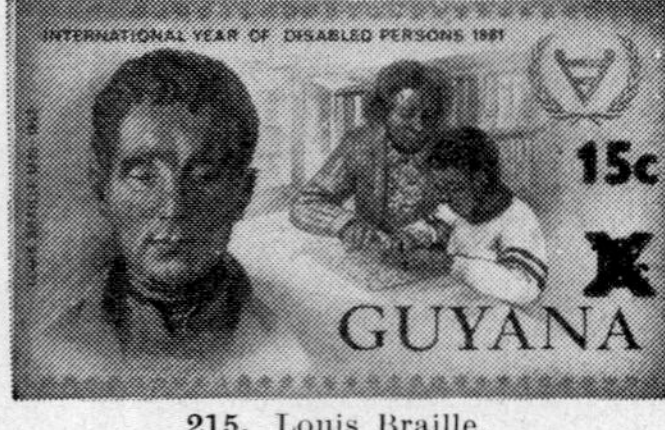

215. Louis Braille.

1981. International Year for Disabled Persons. Famous Disabled People. Multicoloured.

857. 15 c. on 10 c. Type **215** .. 30 10
858. 50 c. Helen Keller and Rajkumari Singh .. 75 55
859. $1 on 60 c. Beethoven and Sonny Thomas 80 60
860. $1.10 on $3 Renoir .. 90 70

The 15 c., $1 and $1.10 values are surcharged on previously unissued stamps.

1981. No. 452 surch (Nos. 862/3 optd **AIR** also).

861. 12 c. on 6 c. Patua (postage) 15 10
862. 50 c. on 6 c. Patua (air) .. 20 15
863. $1 on 6 c. Patua 50 30

1981. Nos. 601, 620, 644, O 13, 717, 720, 728, 749, 751 and 755 surch.

867 110 c. on 10 c. Type **154** 2·00 45
868 110 c. on 110 c. on 8 c. on 3 c. Hanging heliconia 2·25 65
869 110 c. on 110 c. on 8 c. on 6 c. Cannon-ball tree .. 2·25 75
869a 110 c. on 10 c. on 25 c. Marabunta .. .. 2·00 75
870 110 c. on 10 c. Type **170** 1·25 40
871 110 c. on 10 c. Type **176** 4·50 90
872 110 c. on $3 Printing press used for early British Guiana stamps .. 1·25 45
873 110 c. on $3 H. N. Critchlow .. .. 4·50 70
874 110 c. on $3 Caduceus emblem, "C" encircling researcher, and island silhouettes .. .. 1·40 45
875 110 c. on $3 "Peltogyne venosa" .. .. 3·00 80

1981. No. 698 surch. **Nov. 81 50 c.**

876. 50 c. on 5 c. Type **166** .. 2·00 20

222. Yellow Allamanda ("Allamanda cathartica").

1981. Flowers. Coil stamps.

877. 222. 15 c. on 2 c. lilac, blue and green 15 15
878. – 15 c. on 8 c. lilac, blue and mauve 15 15

DESIGN: 15 c. on 8 c. Mazaruni Pride ("Sipanea prolensis").

Nos. 877/8 are surcharges on previously unissued stamps.

1981. Air. Human Rights Day. No. 748 surch. **HUMAN RIGHTS DAY 1981 110 AIR.**

879. 110 c. on $3 Rotary anniversary emblem 1·75 1·50

1981. 35th Anniv. of U.N.I.C.E.F. No. 724 surch. **U.N.I.C.E.F. 1946-1981 125.**
880. 125 c. on $2 "Mango Season" 1·00 60

1981. "Cancun 81" International Conference. No. 698 surch **Cancun 81 50 c**.
880a. 50 c. on 5 c. Type **166**. 1·50 60

225. Tape Measure and Guyana Metrication Board Van.

1982. Metrication. Multicoloured.
881. 15 c. Type 225 15 15
882. 15 c. "Metric man" 15 15
883. 15 c. "Postal service goes metric" 15 15
884. 15 c. Weighing child on metric scales 15 15
885. 15 c. Canje Bridge 15 15
886. 15 c. Tap filling litre bucket 15 15

1982. Various stamps optd. **1982.**
887. – 20 c. multicoloured (No. 549) 2·00 20
888. **105.** 25 c. black, gold and lilac 60 25
889. – 25 c. mult. (No. 550a) 2·50 35
See also Nos. 914/7, 919/21, 923/4, 977/8, 992/8, 1001, 1004, 1006/8, 1015, 1017, 1059, 1117 and OP 3/4.

1982. No. 506 optd **POSTAGE** and Nos. 546 and 601 surch.
890 20 c. on 6 c. Cannon-ball tree 35 20
892 25 c. Type **116** 1·00 10
893 125 c. on 8 c. on 6 c. Cannon-ball tree 35 35

230. Guyana Soldier and Flag.

1982. Savings Campaign.
894. **230.** $1 multicoloured 30 30
No. 894 is a fiscal stamp overprinted for postal use.

1982. 125th Birth Anniv. of Lord Baden-Powell and 75th Anniv. of Boy Scout Movement. Nos. 543, 545 and 601 surch. as given in brackets.
895. 15 c. on 2 c. Type **132** (**BADEN-POWELL 1857-1982**) 10 10
896. 15 c. on 2 c. Type **132** (**Scout Movement 1907-1982**) 10 10
897. 15 c. on 2 c. Type **132** (**1907-1982**) 15 15
898. 15 c. on 2 c. Type **132** (**1857-1982**) 15 15
899. 15 c. on 2 c. Type **132** (**1982**) 10 10
900. 110 c. on 5 c. Annatto tree (**BADEN-POWELL 1857-1982**) 1·00 40
901. 110 c. on 5 c. Annatto tree (**Scout Movement 1907-1982**) 60 40
902. 110 c. on 5 c. Annatto tree (**1907-1982**) 1·25 80
903. 110 c. on 5 c. Annatto tree (**1857-1982**) 1·25 80
904. 110 c. on 5 c. Annatto tree (**1982**) 60 40
905. 125 c. on 8 c. on 6 c. Cannon-ball tree (**BADEN-POWELL 1857-1982**) 1·00 50
906. 125 c. on 8 c. on 6 c. Cannon-ball tree (**Scout Movement 1907-1982**) 1·00 50
907. 125 c. on 8 c. on 6 c. Cannon-ball tree (**1907-1982**) 1·50 90
908. 125 c. on 8 c. on 6 c. Cannon-ball tree (**1857-1982**) 1·50 90
909. 125 c. on 8 c. on 6 c. Cannon-ball tree (**1982**) 75 50

1982. 250th Birth. Anniv. of George Washington. Nos. 708, 718 and 720 optd. **GEORGE WASHINGTON 1732-1982** or surch. also.
910. 100 c. on $3 Printing press used for early British Guiana stamps 45 50
911. 400 c. on 30 c. British Guiana 1856 1 c. black on purple 1·60 1·90
912. $5 "Morpho deidamia" 4·50 2·25

1982. Savings Campaign. As T **230.** Mult.
913. 110 c. on $5 Guyana male and female soldiers with flag 50 35
No. 913 is a fiscal stamp surcharged for postal use.
See also No. 990.

1982. Easter. Optd. **1982** or surch. also.
914. **111.** 25 c. multicoloured 35 20
915. 30 c. multicoloured 30 15
916. 45 c. on 6 c. mult. 45 35
917. 75 c. on 40 c. mult. 75 35

1982. No. 703 surch.
918 20 c. on 35 c. "Anaea galanthis" 60 10

1982. No. F5 optd. **1982** and surch. in addition.
919. 180 c. on 40 c. Tiger Beard 3·25 60

1982. Nos. 555/6 optd. **1982.**
920. $2 "Norantea guianensis" 80 70
921. $5 "Odontadenia grandiflora" 1·40 1·60

1982. No. 542 surch.
922. 220 c. on 1 c. Pitcher Plant of Mt. Roraima 1·25 60

1982. Nos. 472 and 684 optd. **1982.**
923. **105.** 40 c. blk., gold & blue 35 20
924. – 40 c. multicoloured 50 40

1982. Nos. 469, 751 and 842/3 surch.
925. **105.** 80 c. on 6 c. black, gold and flesh 30 35
926. 85 c. on 6 c. black, gold and flesh 50 35
927. – 160 c. on $1.10 on $2 mult. (No. 843) 1·00 55
928. – 210 c. on $3 mult. (No. 751) 2·50 70

1982. Royal Wedding (3rd issue). Nos. 841/3 surch.
930 85 c. on 60 c. on 3 c. Hanging heliconia 1·25 35
931 130 c. on 60 c. on 3 c. Hanging heliconia 1·25 55
933 170 c. on $1.10 on $2 "Norantea guianensis" 7·00 4·00
934 210 c. on 75 c. on $5 "Odontadenia grandiflora" (B) 1·25 90
935 235 c. on 75 c. on $5 "Odontadenia grandiflora" 1·50 1·50
936 300 c. on $1.10 on $2 "Norantea guianensis" 6·00 1·50

1982. World Cup Football Championship, Spain (2nd issue). Nos. 544, 546 and 554 optd. **ESPANA 1982.** or surch. also.
937. $1 "Chelonanthus uliginoides" 75 60
938. 110 c. on 3 c. Hanging Heliconia (B.) 75 40
939. 250 c. on 6 c. Cannon-ball tree (B.) 1·00 90
See also No. 1218.

1982.
940 **181** 15 c. on 2 c. black, blue and grey 50 15
941 20 c. on 2 c. black, blue and grey 1·50 30
1029 25 c. on 2 c. black, blue and grey 50 10
989 40 c. on 2 c. black, blue and grey 35 15
945 45 c. on 2 c. black, blue and grey 1·75 45
948 75 c. on 2 c. black, blue and grey 2·00 25
949 80 c. on 2 c. black, blue and grey 1·25 20
950 85 c. on 2 c. black, blue and grey 75 25
951 100 c. on 3 c. black, blue and red 75 35
952 110 c. on 3 c. black, blue and red 80 30
953 120 c. on 3 c. black, blue and red 3·75 35
954 125 c. on 3 c. black, blue and red 1·50 35
955 130 c. on 3 c. black, blue and red 90 35
956 150 c. on 3 c. black, blue and red 3·50 40
957 160 c. on 3 c. black, blue and red 2·00 40
958 170 c. on 3 c. black, blue and red 1·40 45
959 175 c. on 3 c. black, blue and red 3·00 45
960 180 c. on 3 c. black, blue and red 2·00 50
961 200 c. on 3 c. black, blue and red 2·25 45
962 210 c. on 3 c. black, blue and red 4·50 50
963 220 c. on 3 c. black, blue and red 5·50 60
964 235 c. on 3 c. black, blue and red 4·75 60
965 240 c. on 3 c. black, blue and red 4·50 60
966 250 c. on 3 c. black, blue and red 2·25 60
967 300 c. on 3 c. black, blue and red 6·00 75
968 330 c. on 3 c. black, blue and red 2·75 90
969 375 c. on 3 c. black, blue and red 4·50 1·00
970 400 c. on 3 c. black, blue and red 6·50 1·10
971 440 c. on 3 c. black, blue and red 4·00 1·10
972 500 c. on 3 c. black, blue and red 3·50 1·40
973 550 c. on 3 c. black, blue and red 3·75 1·75
974 625 c. on 3 c. black, blue and red 2·75 2·00
975 1500 c. on 3 c. mult. 10·00 4·00
976 2000 c. on 3 c. mult. 11·00 5·50

1982. No. 548a optd. **1982.**
977. 15 c. Christmas Orchid 3·25 10

1982. No. O 26 optd. **POSTAGE.**
978. 110 c. on 6 c. Type **116** 2·50 35

1982. Air. 21st Birthday of Princess of Wales. Nos. 542, 545 and 555 surch.
979. 110 c. on 5 c. Annatto tree 60 50
980. 220 c. on 1 c. Pitcher Plant of Mt. Roraima 1·25 80
981. 330 c. on $2 "Norantea guianensis" 1·50 1·50

1982. Birth of Prince William of Wales. Surch. (a) On stamps of British Guiana.
982. 50 c. on 2 c. myrtle (No. 332) 40 45
983. $1·10 on 3 c. olive and brown (No. 333) 1·00 80

(b) On stamps of Guyana previously optd. **"GUYANA INDEPENDENCE 1966."**
984. 50 c. on 2 c. myrtle (No. 379) 5·00 2·50
985. $1·10 on 3 c. olive and brown (No. 395) 7·50 2·50
986. $1.25 on 6 c. green (No. 383) 70 80
987. $2.20 on 24 c. black and orange (No. 401) 1·50 1·50

1982. Savings Campaign. As No. 913 but showing inverted comma before "OURS" in opt.
990. 110 c. on $5 Guyana male and female soldiers with flag 5·50 50

1982. Italy's Victory in World Cup Football Championship. No. F7 surch. **ESPANA 1982. ITALY $2.35.**
991. $2.35 on 180 c. on 60 c. Soldier's Cap 2·25 75

1982. Wildlife Protection. Nos. 687 and 733/8 optd. **1982.**
992. 35 c. Harpy Eagle 2·00 40
993. 35 c. Type **174** 2·00 40
994. 35 c. Haimara 2·00 40
995. 35 c. Electric Eel 2·00 40
996. 35 c. Golden Rivulus 2·00 40
997. 35 c. Pencil Fish 2·00 40
998. 35 c. Four-eyed Fish 2·00 40

1982. Central American and Caribbean Games, Havana. Nos. 542/3 surch. **C.A. & CARIB GAMES 1982.**
999. 50 c. on 2 c. Type **132** 1·00 45
1000. 60 c. on 1 c. Pitcher Plant of Mt. Roraima 1·25 30

1982. No. 730 optd. **1982.**
1001. 35 c. black and orange 30 20

1982. Nos. 841 and 979 further surch.
1002. 130 c. on 60 c. on 3 c. Hanging Heliconia 60 50
1003. 170 c. on 110 c. on 5 c. Annatto tree 2·00 75

1982. No. 841 optd. **1982** and surch.
1004. 440 c. on 60 c. on 3 c. Hanging Heliconia 2·75 1·50

1982. Commonwealth Games, Brisbane, Australia. No. 546 surch. **Commonwealth GAMES AUSTRALIA 1982.**
1005. $1.25 on 6 c. Cannon-ball tree 1·50 40

1982. Nos. 552, 641 and 719 optd. **1982.**
1006. 50 c. multicoloured (No. 552) 2·00 25
1007. 50 c. blue, green & brown brown (No. 641) 1·50 25
1008. 50 c. mult. (No. 719) 60 25

1982. Various Official stamps additionally optd. **POSTAGE** for postal purposes.
1009. 15 c. Christmas Orchid (No. O 23) 4·50 10
1010. 50 c. "Guzamania lingulata" (No. O 14) 1·25 25
1011. 100 c. on $3 Cylinder satellite (No. O 19) 1·75 50

1982. International Food Day. No. 617 optd. **INT FOOD DAY 1982.**
1012. 50 c. Pawpaw and tangerine 14·00 1·25

1982. International Year of the Elderly. No. 747 optd. **INT YEAR OF THE ELDERLY.**
1013. 50 c. District 404 emblem 4·50 50

1982. Centenary of Robert Koch's Discovery of Tubercle Bacillus. No. 750 optd. **DR. R. KOCH CENTENARY TBC BACILLUS DISCOVERY**
1014. 60 c. Researcher with microscope, Caduceus emblem, stethoscope and beach scene 2·00 30

1982. International Decade for Women. No. 633 optd. **1982.**
1015. $1 brown and blue 3·25 80

1982. Birth Centenary of F. D. Roosevelt (American statesman). No. 706 optd. **F. D. ROOSEVELT 1882-1982.**
1016. $1 "Agrias claudina 1·50 45

1982. 1st Anniv. of G.A.C. Inaugural Flight Georgetown to Boa Vista, Brazil. No. 842 optd. with **1982** and surch. **GAC Inaug. Flight Georgetown-Boa Vista, Brasil.**
1017. 200 c. on 75 c. on $5 "Odontadenia grandiflora 15·00 3·00

1982. CARICOM Heads of Government Conference, Kingston, Jamaica. Nos. 881/6 surch. **CARICOM Heads of Gov't Conference July 1982.**
1018. 50 c. on 15 c. Type **225** 1·00 30
1019. 50 c. on 15 c. "Metric man" 1·00 30
1020. 50 c. on 15 c. "Postal service goes metric" 1·00 30
1021. 50 c. on 15 c. Weighing child on metric scales 1·00 30
1022. 50 c. on 15 c. Canje Bridge 1·00 30
1023. 50 c. on 15 c. Tap filling litre bucket 1·00 30

1982. Christmas. Nos. 895/9 optd. **CHRISTMAS 1982.**
1024. 15 c. on 2 c. Type **132** (surch. BADEN POWELL 1857-1982) 20 15
1025. 15 c. on 2 c. Type **132** (surch. "Scout Movement 1907-1982") 20 15
1026. 15 c. on 2 c. Type **132** (surch. "1907-1982") 30 25
1027. 15 c. on 2 c. Type **132** (surch. "1857-1982") 30 25
1028. 15 c. on 2 c. Type **132** (surch "1982") 2·50 2·50

1982. Nos. 543 and 546 surch. in figures (no "c" after face value).
1034 15 c. on 2 c. Type **132** 10 10
1035 20 c. on 6 c. Cannon-ball tree 10 10
See also No. 1086.

1982. No. 452 surch.
1032. 50 c. on 6 c. Patua 20 25
1033. 100 c. on 6 c. Patua 40 45

1983. Optd. **1983.**
1036. – 15 c. mult. (No. 655) 6·00 2·00
1037. – 15 c. brown, grey and black (No. 672) 50 10
1038. – 15 c. mult. (No. 682) 40 10
1039. **214.** 15 c. on 10 c. mult. 35 10
1040. **215.** 15 c. on 10 c. mult. 15 10
1041. – 50 c. mult. (No. 646) 3·00 25
1042. – 50 c. mult. (No. 696) 3·50 25
1043. – 50 c. mult. (No. 719) 1·50 25
See also Nos. 1060/1, 1069/70 and 1072/9.

1983. No. O 17 optd. **POSTAGE.**
1044. 15 c. Harpy Eagle 3·75 10

1983. National Heritage. Nos. 710/12 and 778 surch.
1045. 90 c. on 30 c. Cassiri and decorated Amerindian jars 2·40 1·60
1046. 90 c. on 35 c. Rock drawing of hunter and quarry 35 50
1047. 90 c. on 50 c. Fort Kyk-over-al 2·40 1·60
1048. 90 c. on 60 c. Fort Island 4·50 50

258. Guyana Flag (inscr. "60th BIRTHDAY ANNIVERSARY").

1983. 60th Birthday of President Burnham and 30 Years in Parliament. Mult.

1049. 25 c. Type **258** 15 20
1050. 25 c. As T **258**, but position of flag reversed and inscr. "30th ANNIVERSARY IN PARLIAMENT" .. 15 20
1051. $1.30 Youth display (41 × 25 mm.) 75 65
1052. $6 Presidential standard (43½ × 25 mm.) .. 2·50 2·75

1983. Surch. in words.

1053. **170.** 50 c. on 10 c. mult. (No. 717) .. 75 25
1054. – 50 c. on 100 c. on $3 mult. (No. 910) .. 1·00 25
1055. **152.** $1 on 10 c. mult. (No. 635) .. 6·00 45
1056. $1 on $1.05 on 10 c. mult. (No. 768) .. 3·00 45
1056a. – $1 on $1.10 on $2 mult. (No. 843) .. 2·50 2·00
1057. – $1 on 220 c. on 5 c. mult. (No. 844) .. 7·00 1·00
1058. – $1 on 330 c. on $2 mult. (No. 981) .. 75 45
1059. – $1 on $12 on $1.10 on $2 mult. (No. P3) .. 16·00 5·00

No. 1056a is surcharged on an unissued Royal Wedding surcharge, similar to No. 843. See also Nos. 1080/4.

1983. No. 859 optd. **1983.**

1060. $1 on 60 c. Beethoven and Sonny Thomas .. 2·50 45

1983. Conference of Foreign Ministers of Non-aligned Countries, New Delhi. No. 569 surch. and No. 570 optd. **1983.**

1061. **136.** 25 c. multicoloured .. 2·00 25
1062. 50 c. on 8 c. mult. .. 3·00 25

1983. No. 771 further surch.

1064. **181.** 20 c. on 10 c. on 3 c. black, blue & red .. 35 10

1983. Commonwealth Day. Nos. 383 and 401. surch. **Commonwealth Day 14 March 1983.**

1065. **60.** 25 c. on 6 c. green .. 1·50 20
1066. $1.20 on 6 c. green .. 75 50
1067. **63.** $1.30 on 24 c. black and orange 90 55
1068. $2.40 on 24 c. black and orange .. .. 1·50 1·25

1983. Easter. Nos. 482/3 optd. **1983.**

1069. **111.** 25 c. multicoloured .. 10 10
1070. 30 c. multicoloured .. 25 15

262.

1983. 25th Anniv. of International Maritime Organization. British Guiana fiscal stamp optd.

1071. **262.** $4.80 blue and green 4·50 5·50

1983. Optd. **1983.**

1072. **152.** 50 c. mult. (No. 637) 1·50 25
1073. **159.** 50 c. blue, black and yellow (No. 668) 5·00 25
1073a. – 50 c. mult. (No. 723)
1074. – 50 c. mult. (No. 854) 60 25
1075. – 50 c. mult. (No. 858) 30 25
1076. – $1 mult. (No. 628) .. 7·50 45
1077. – $1 mult. (No. 638) .. 6·50 45
1078. – $1 mult. (No. 675) .. 4·00 45
1079. – $1 on 30 c. mult. No. 855) .. .. 1·25 45
1079a. – $3 mult. (No. 720) .. 8·50 70
1079b. – $3 mult. (No. 724) ..
1079c. – $3 mult. (No. 748) ..

1983. Surch. **FIFTY CENTS.**

1080. **148.** 50 c. on 8 c. mult. (No. 615) .. 1·75 25
1081. **162.** 50 c. on 8 c. mult. (No. 681) .. 6·00 25
1082. **171.** 50 c. on 10 c. mult. (No. 721) .. 3·00 25
1083. – 50 c. on 10 c. on 25 c. mult. (No. O 13) .. 3·50 25
1084. – 50 c. on 330 c. on $3 mult. (No. 845) .. 3·00 25

1983. Surch, with c after new face value.

1085 **105** 15 c. on 6 c. blk, gold & pink (No. 469) .. 10 10
1086 – 20 c. on 6 c. multicoloured (No. 546) 10 10
1087 **111** 50 c. on 6 c. multicoloured (No. 481) 30 30
1099 – 50 c. on 6 c. multicoloured (No. 489) 30 30

1983. No. 639 surch.

1089. **153.** 110 c. on 10 c. yell., green and violet .. 1·25 50

1983. Nos. 551 and 556 surch.

1090. 250 c. on 40 c. Tiger Beard 4·50 1·25
1091. 400 c. on $5 " Odontadenia grandiflora " .. .. 4·50 1·90

1983. World Telecommunications and Health Day. Nos. 842 and 980 further surch.

1092. 25 c. on 220 c. on 1 c. Pitcher Plant of Mt. Roraima (surch **ITU 1983 25**) 20 20
1093. 25 c. on 220 c. on 1 c. Pitcher Plant of Mt. Roraima (surch **WHO 1983 25**) 20 20
1094. 25 c. on 220 c. on 1 c. Pitcher Plant of Mt. Roraima (surch **17 MAY '83 ITU/WHO 25** .. 20 20
1095. $4.50 on 75 c. on $5 " Odontadenia grandiflora " (surch **ITU/WHO 17 MAY 1983**) .. 11·00 3·00

1983. 30th Anniv. of President's Entry into Parliament, Nos. 690 and 692 surch, No. 1096 additionally optd **1983.**

1096. $1 on 15 c. black, blue and grey .. .. 4·50 50
1097. $1 on 40 c. black, orange and grey .. .. 6·50 50

1983. No. 611 optd **1983.**

1101. 25 c. Guides in camp .. 35·00 1·75

1983. No. 452 surch **$1.**

1102 $1 on 6 c. Patua 55 50

1983. 15th World Scout Jamboree, Alberta. Nos. 835/6 and O 25 optd. **CANADA 1983**, Nos. 1103 and 1105 additionally surch.

1103. – $1.30 on 100 c. on 8 c. multicoloured .. 3·00 1·00
1104. **116.** 180 c. on 6 c. mult. .. 3·00 2·00
1105. $3.90 on 400 c. on 6 c. multicoloured .. 3·50 3·50

1983. Nos. 659/60 surch.

1106. 60 c. on 15 c. Map of the Caribbean .. .. 7·00 35
1107. $1.50 on 15 c. Prudential Cup .. .. 8·00 80

1983. As Nos. 1049/50, but without commemorative inscr above flag.

1108. 25 c. As Type **258** .. 15 15
1109. 25 c. As No. 1050 .. 15 15

1983. Optd **1983.**

1110. **105.** 30 c. black, gold and green (No. 471) .. 40 20
1111. – 30 c. multicoloured (No. 695) .. 9·00 30
1112. – 30 c. multicoloured (No. 718) .. 4·00 20
1113. – 30 c. multicoloured (No. 722) .. 7·50 20
1114. – 30 c. multicoloured (No. 746) .. 4·00 20
1115. – 60 c. multicoloured (No. 697) .. 4·25 20
1116. – 60 c. multicoloured (No. 731) .. 5·00 20

1983. No. 553 optd **1982.**

1117. 60 c. Soldier's Cap .. 3·25 35

1983. Surch.

1118. **157.** 120 c. on 8 c. mult. (No. 654) .. 3·25 60
1119. **159.** 120 c. on 10 c. red, black and gold (No. 666) .. 3·50 60
1120. – 120 c. on 35 c. mult. (No. 622) .. 3·50 60
1121. – 120 c. on 35 c. orange, green and violet (No. 640) .. .. 3·50 60

1983. Nos. 716 and 729 surch.

1122. 120 c. on 10 c. Type **173** .. 3·25 60
1123. 120 c. on 375 c. on $3 Cylinder satellite .. 3·00 60

No. 1123 also carries an otherwise unissued surcharge in red, reading **INTERNATIONAL SCIENCE YEAR 1982 375.** As issued much of this is obliterated by two heavy bars.

1983. British Guiana No. D1a and Guyana. No. D8 surch **120 GUYANA.**

1124. D **1.** 120 c. on 1 c. green .. 3·25 60
1125. D **2.** 120 c. on 1 c. olive .. 3·25 60

See also Nos. 1399 and 1402.

1983. CARICOM Day. No. 823 additionally surch **CARICOM DAY 1983 60.**

1126. 60 c. on $3 " Makanaima the Great Ancestral Spirit of the Amerindians " 1·75 35

271. " Kurupukari ".

1983. Riverboats.

1127. **271.** 30 c. black and red .. 15 20
1128. – 60 c. black and violet 30 35
1129. – 120 c. black and yell. 1·00 60
1130. – 130 c. black 60 65
1131. – 150 c. black and green 75 80

DESIGNS: 60 c. " Makouria ". 120 c. " Powis ". 130 c. " Pomeroon ". 150 c. " Lukanani ".

1983. Unissued Royal Wedding **surch. similar to No. 843, additionally surch.**

1132. $2.30 on $1.10 on $2 " Norantea guianensis " 2·50 1·50
1133. $3.20 on $1.10 on $2 " Norantea guianensis " 3·00 1·75

1983. Bicentenary of Manned Flight and 20th Anniv. of Guyana Airways. Nos. 701/2a optd. as indicated in brackets.

1134. 20 c. multicoloured (**BW**) 10 10
1135. 20 c. multicoloured (**LM**) 10 10
1136. 20 c. multicoloured (**GY 1963 1983**) .. 10 10
1137. 20 c. multicoloured (**JW**) 10 10
1138. 20 c. multicoloured (**CU**) 10 10
1139. 20 c. multicoloured (**Mont Golfier 1783–1983**) 10 10
1140. 25 c. multicoloured (**BGI**) 50 25
1141. 25 c. multicoloured (**GEO**) 15 10
1142. 25 c. multicoloured (**MIA**) 50 25
1143. 25 c. multicoloured (**BVB**) 50 25
1144. 25 c. multicoloured (**PBM**) 50 25
1145. 25 c. multicoloured (**Mont Golfier 1783–1983**) 20 15
1146. 25 c. multicoloured (**POS**) 50 25
1147. 25 c. multicoloured (**JFK**) 50 25
1148. 30 c. multicoloured (**AHL**) 25 15
1149. 30 c. multicoloured (**BCG**) 25 15
1150. 30 c. multicoloured (**BMJ**) 25 15
1151. 30 c. multicoloured (**EKE**) 25 15
1152. 30 c. multicoloured (**GEO**) 25 15
1153. 30 c. multicoloured (**GFO**) 25 15
1154. 30 c. multicoloured (**IBM**) 25 15
1155. 30 c. multicoloured (**Mont Golfier 1783–1983**) 25 15
1156. 30 c. multicoloured (**KAI**) 25 15
1157. 30 c. multicoloured (**KAR**) 25 15
1158. 30 c. multicoloured (**KPG**) 25 15
1159. 30 c. multicoloured (**KRG**) 25 15
1160. 30 c. multicoloured (**KTO**) 25 15
1161. 30 c. multicoloured (**LTM**) 25 15
1162. 30 c. multicoloured (**MHA**) 25 15
1163. 30 c. multicoloured (**MWJ**) 25 15
1164. 30 c. multicoloured (**MYM**) 25 15
1165. 30 c. multicoloured (**NAI**) 25 15
1166. 30 c. multicoloured (**ORJ**) 25 15
1167. 30 c. multicoloured (**USI**) 25 15
1168. 30 c. multicoloured (**VEG**) 25 15

1983. No. 649 further surch.

1169. 240 c. on 35 c. on 60 c. Soldier's Cap .. .. 1·25 1·00

1983. F.A.O. Fisheries Project. Nos. 448 and 450 optd. **FAO 1983** and surch also.

1170. 30 c. on 1 c. Type **87** .. 15 15
1171. $2.60 on 3 c. Lukunani .. 1·50 1·75

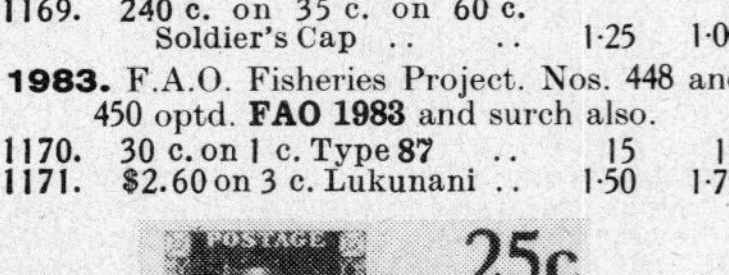

277. G.B. 1857 1d. with Georgetown " AO3 " Postmark.

1983. 125th Anniv. of Use of Great Britain Stamps in Guyana.

(a) Inscriptions in black.

1172. **277.** 25 c. brown and blk. 10 10
1173. – 30 c. red and black .. 10 15
1174. – 60 c. violet and blk. 25 30
1175. – 120 c. green and blk. 50 55

(b) Inscriptions in blue.

1176. **277.** 25 c. brown & black .. 10 10
1177. – 25 c. red and black .. 10 10
1178. – 25 c. violet & black .. 10 10
1179. – 25 c. green & black .. 10 10
1180. **277.** 30 c. brown & black .. 10 15
1181. – 30 c. red and black .. 10 15
1182. – 30 c. violet & black .. 10 15
1183. – 30 c. green & black .. 10 15
1184. **277.** 45 c. brown & black .. 20 25
1185. – 45 c. red and black .. 20 25
1186. – 45 c. violet & black .. 20 25
1187. – 45 c. green & black .. 20 25
1188. **277.** 120 c. brown & black 50 55
1189. – 130 c. red and black 55 60
1190. – 150 c. violet & black 65 70
1191. – 200 c. green and black 90 95

DESIGNS: Nos. 1173, 1177, 1181, 1185, 1189, G.B. 1857 4 d. red. Nos. 1174, 1178, 1182, 1186, 1190, G.B. 1856 6 d. lilac. Nos. 1175, 1179, 1183, 1187, 1191, G.B. 1856 1 s. green.

Each design incorporates the " AO3 " postmark except Nos. 1189/91 which show mythical postmarks of the Crowned-circle type inscribed " **DEMERARA** ", " **BERBICE** " or " **ESSEQUIBO** ".

1983. International Communications Year. No. 716 surch. **INT. COMMUNICATIONS YEAR 50.**

1192. 50 c. on 375 c. on $3 Cylinder satellite .. 3·50 30

No. 1192 also carries an otherwise unissued "375" surcharge. As issued much of this surcharge is obliterated by two groups of six thin horizontal lines.

1983. St. John's Ambulance Commemoration. Nos. 650 and 653 surch.

1193. **156.** 75 c. on 8 c. silver, black and mauve 2·50 30
1194. – $1.20 on 40 c. silver, black and blue .. 4·50 50

1983. International Food Day. No. 616 surch. **$1.20 Int. Food Day 1983.**

1195. $1.20 on 35 c. Five-fingers and awaras .. 1·00 50

1983. 65th Anniv. of I.L.O. and 25th Death Anniv. of H. N. Critchlow (founder of Guyana Labour Union). No. 840 further optd. **1918–1983 I.L.O.**

1196. 240 c. on $3 H. N. Critchlow .. .. 1·50 1·25

1983. Deepavali Festival. Nos. 661 and 663/4 surch. **25 c.**

1197. 25 c. on 8 c. Type **158** .. 20 10
1198. $1.50 on 35 c. Flame in bowl .. .. 1·25 60
1199. $1.50 on 40 c. Goddess Latchmi 80 60

1983. No. 732 optd. **1982** and No. 798 further optd. **1983.**

1200. $3 "Makanaima the Great Ancestral Spirit of the Amerindians" .. 1·50 1·00
1201. 360 c. on $2 "Norantea guianensis" .. .. 1·75 1·40

1983. Wildlife Protection. Nos. 686 and 688 surch. and No. 762 optd. **1983.**

1202. 30 c. Six-banded Armadillo .. 30 15
1203. 60 c. on 15 c. Giant sea turtle 45 30
1204. $1.20 on 40 c. Iguana .. 75 50

1983. Human Rights Day. No. 1079c optd. **Human Rights Day.**

1205. $3 Rotary anniversary emblem .. .. 1·40 1·25

1983. Olympic Games, Los Angeles (1984). Nos. 733/44 surch. **LOS ANGELES 1984.**

1206. 55 c. on 125 c. on 35 c. Type **174** 25 25
1207. 55 c. on 125 c. on 35 c. Haimara 25 25
1208. 55 c. on 125 c. on 35 c. Electric Eel 25 25
1209. 55 c. on 125 c. on 35 c. Golden Rivulus .. 25 25
1210. 55 c. on 125 c. on 35 c. Pencil Fish .. 25 25
1211. 55 c. on 125 c. on 35 c. Four-eyed Fish .. 25 25
1212. 55 c. on 125 c. on 35 c. Pirai or Carib Fish .. 25 25
1213. 55 c. on 125 c. on 35 c. Smoking Hassar .. 25 25
1214. 55 c. on 125 c. on 35 c. Devil Ray .. 25 25
1215. 55 c. on 125 c. on 35 c. Flying Patwa .. 25 25
1216. 55 c. on 125 c. on 35 c. Arapaima Pirariucii .. 25 25
1217. 55 c. on 125 c. on 35 c. Lukanani .. 25 25
1217a. 125 c. on 35 c. Type **174** 1·50
1217b. 125 c. on 35 c. Haimara 1·50
1217c. 125 c. on 35 c. Electric Eel 1·50
1217d. 125 c. on 35 c. Golden Rivulus 1·50
1217e. 125 c. on 35 c. Pencil Fish 1·50
1217f. 125 c. on 35 c. Four-eyed Fish 1·50
1217g. 125 c. on 35 c. Pirai or Carib Fish 1·50
1217h. 125 c. on 35 c. Smoking Hassar 1·50
1217i. 125 c. on 35 c. Devil Ray 1·50
1217j. 125 c. on 35 c. Flying Patwa 1·50
1217k. 125 c. on 35 c. Arapaima Pirariucii 1·50
1217l. 125 c. on 35 c. Lukanani 1·50

1983. No. F7 with unissued ("**ESPANA 1982**") surch. further optd. **1983.**

1218. 180 c. on 60 c. Soldier's Cap .. .. 1·00 65

1983. Commonwealth Heads of Government Meeting, New Delhi. No. 542 surch. **COMMONWEALTH HEADS OF GOV'T MEETING—INDIA 1983 150.**

1219. 150 c. on 1 c. Pitcher Plant of Mt. Roraima 1·00 60

1983. Christmas. No. 861 further surch. **CHRISTMAS 1983 20c.**

1220. 20 c. on 12 c. on 6 c. Patua 35 10

1984. Nos. 838 and F9 optd. **POSTAGE.**

1221. $2 "Norantea guianensis" .. .. 2·00 70
1221a. 550 c. on $10 "Elbella patrobas" .. .. 4·50 4·25

1984. Flowers. Unissued stamps as T **222** surch.

1222. 17 c. on 2 c. lilac, blue and green 25 25
1223. 17 c. on 8 c. lilac, blue and mauve 25 25

1984. Republic Day. No. 703 and 705a variously optd., 703 surch. also.

1224. 25 c. on 35 c. mult. (surch **ALL OUR HERITAGE 25**) 10 10
1225. 25 c. on 35 c. mult. (surch. **1984 25**) .. 10 10
1226. 25 c. on 35 c. mult. (surch. **REPUBLIC DAY 25**) 10 10
1227. 25 c. on 35 c. mult. (surch. **25**) 10 10
1228. 25 c. on 35 c. mult. (surch. **BERBICE 25**) 20 15
1229. 25 c. on 35 c. mult. (surch. **DEMERARA 25**) 20 15
1230. 25 c. on 35 c. mult. (surch. **ESSEQUIBO 25**) 20 15
1231. 25 c. on 35 c. mult. (surch. **1984 25**) .. 40 35
1232. 60 c. mult. (optd. **ALL OUR HERITAGE**) .. 25 30
1233. 60 c. mult. (optd. **REPUBLIC DAY**) .. 25 30
1234. 60 c. mult. (optd. **1984**) 25 30

1984. Guyana Olympic Committee Appeal. Nos. 841/3 handstamped **OLYMPIC GAMES 84 25 c. POSTAGE (+2.25 SURTAX)** and rings.

1235 25 c.+2.25 c. on 60 c. on 3 c. Hanging Heliconia 4·00 4·00
1236 25 c.+2.25 c. on 75 c. on $5 "Odontadenia grandiflora" 4·00 4·00
1237 25 c.+2.25 on $1.10 on $2 "Norantea guianensis" 4·00 4·00

1984. Nature Protection. Various stamps optd. **Protecting our Heritage** and some additionally surch.

1238. 20 c. on 15 c. mult. (No. 454) .. .. .. 2·50 10
1239. 20 c. on 15 c. mult. (No. 791) .. .. .. 2·50 10
1240a. 20 c. on 15 c. mult. (No. 1044) .. .. .. 5·50 1·00
1241. 25 c. mult. (No. 550a) .. 5·00 10
1242. 30 c. on 15 c. mult. (No. 548a) .. .. .. 6·50 20
1243. 40 c. mult. (No. 457) .. 3·00 20
1244. 50 c. mult. (No. 552) .. 60 25
1245. 50 c. mult. (No. F6) .. 60 25
1246. 60 c. mult. (No. 496) .. 5·50 30
1247. 90 c. on 40 c. mult. (No. 551) .. .. .. 4·00 40
1248. 180 c. on 40 c. mult. (No. 919) .. .. .. 4·00 70
1249. $2 mult. (No. 461) .. 32·00 1·25
1250. 225 c. on 10 c. mult. (No. 453) .. .. .. 8·00 90
1251. 260 c. on $1 mult. (No. 497) .. .. .. 5·50 1·00
1252. 320 c. on 40 c. mult. (No. 551) .. .. .. 3·25 1·25
1253. 350 c. on 40 c. mult. (No. 551) .. .. .. 6·50 1·50
1254. 380 c. on 50 c. mult. (No. 458) .. .. .. 3·25 1·75
1255. 450 c. on $5 mult. (No. 462) .. .. .. 3·50 1·90

1984. Easter. Nos. 483 and 916/17 optd. **1984** and No. 481 surch.

1256. **111.** 30 c. multicoloured .. 20 20
1257. 45 c. on 6 c. mult. .. 25 25
1258. 75 c. on 40 c. mult. .. 35 35
1259. 130 c. on 6 c. mult. .. 65 60

1984. Nos. 937/9 and 991 surch.

1260. 75 c. on $1 "Chelonanthus uliginoides" .. 6·00 35
1261. 75 c. on 110 c. on 3 c. Hanging Heliconia .. 7·00 35
1262. 225 c. on 250 c. on 6 c. Cannon-ball tree .. 2·00 1·25
1263. 230 c. on $2.35 on 180 c. on 60 c. Soldier's Cap 2·00 1·75

1984. Nos. 899/901, 904/6 and 909 surch.

1264. 20 c. on 15 c. on 2 c. Type **132** (No. 899) .. 75 15
1265. 75 c. on 110 c. on 5 c. Annatto tree (No. 904) 6·00 60
1266. 90 c. on 110 c. on 5 c. Annatto tree (No. 900) 4·00 75
1267. 90 c. on 110 c. on 5 c. Annatto tree (No. 901) 5·00 75
1268. 120 c. on 125 c. on 8 c. on 6 c. Cannon-ball tree (No. 905) .. .. 5·00 90
1269. 120 c. on 125 c. on 8 c. on 6 c. Cannon-ball tree (No. 906) .. .. 5·00 90
1270. 120 c. on 125 c. on 8 c. on 6 c. Cannon-ball tree (No. 909) .. .. 2·25 90

1984. World Telecommunications and Health Day. Nos. 802 and 980 surch.

1271. 25 c. on 220 c. on 1 c. Pitcher Plant of Mt. Roraima (surch. **ITU DAY 1984**) 20 20
1272. 25 c. on 220 c. on 1 c. Pitcher Plant of Mt. Roraima (surch. **WHO DAY 1984**) 20 20
1273. 25 c. on 220 c. on 1 c. Pitcher Plant of Mt. Roraima (surch. **ITU/WHO DAY 1984**) 20 20
1274. $4.50 on 280 c. on $5 "Odontadenia grandiflora" (surch. **ITU/WHO DAY 1984**) .. .. 1·75 1·75

1984. No. 1005 surch.

1275. 120 c. on $1.25 on 6 c. Cannon-ball tree .. 4·50 55

1984. World Forestry Conference. Nos. 752/5 surch or optd. **1984** ($3) and No. 875 surch.

1276. 55 c. on 30 c. "Hymenaea courbaril" .. .. 2·00 30
1277. 75 c. on 110 c. on $3 "Peltogyne venosa" .. 40 35
1278. 160 c. on 50 c. "Mora excelsa" 75 70
1279. 260 c. on 10 c. Type **177** 1·25 1·25
1280. $3 "Peltogyne venosa" .. 1·40 1·40

1984. No. 625 surch.

1281. 55 c. on 110 c. on 10 c. Type **150** 30 30
1282. 90 c. on 110 c. on 10 c. Type **150** 40 45

Nos. 1281/2 also carry an otherwise unissued 110 c. surch.

1984. U.P.U. Congress, Hamburg. Nos. 1188/91 optd **UPU Congress 1984 Hamburg**.

1283. 120 c. brown and black 50 55
1284. 130 c. red and black .. 55 60
1285. 150 c. violet and black .. 60 65
1286. 200 c. green and black .. 80 85

1984. Nos. 982/3 and 986/7 surch.

1287 45 c. on 50 c. on 2 c. green 20 25
1288 60 c. on $1.10 on 3 c. olive and brown 75 30
1289 120 c. on $1.25 on 6 c. grn 50 55
1290 200 c. on $2.20 on 24 c. black and orange .. 80 85

1984. Nos. 979/80 and 1003 surch. and No. 981 optd. **1984.**

1291. 75 c. on 110 c. on 5 c. Annatto tree 30 35
1292. 120 c. on 170 c. on 110 c. on 5 c. Annatto tree .. 50 55
1293. 200 c. on 220 c. on 1 c. Pitcher Plant of Mt. Roraima .. .. 4·50 85
1294. 330 c. on $2 "Norantea guianensis" .. .. 1·40 1·75

1984. CARICOM Day. No. 1200 additionally surch. **CARICOM DAY 1984 60.**

1295. 60 c. on $3 "Hakanaima the Great Ancestral Spirit of the Amerindians" 30 30

1984. No. 544 surch.

1296. 150 c. on 3 c. Hanging Heliconia 60 65

1984. CARICOM Heads of Government Conference. No. 544 surch. **60 CARICOM HEADS OF GOV'T CONFERENCE JULY 1984.**

1297. 60 c. on 3 c. Hanging Heliconia 30 30

301. Children and Thatched School.

1984. Centenary of Guyana Teachers' Association. Multicoloured.

1298. 25 c. Type **301** 10 15
1299. 25 c. Torch and graduates 10 15
1300. 25 c. Torch and target emblem 10 15
1301. 25 c. Teachers of 1884 and 1984 in front of school 10 15

1984. 50th Anniv. of International Chess Federation. No. 1048 optd. or surch. also.

1302. 25 c. on 90 c. on 60 c. Fort Island (surch. **INT. CHESS FED. 1924–1984**) 20 15
1303. 25 c. on 90 c. on 60 c. Fort Island (surch. **1984**) 50 15
1304. 75 c. on 90 c. on 60 c. Fort Island (surch. **INT. CHESS FED. 1924–1984**) 50 35
1305. 75 c. on 90 c. on 60 c. Fort Island (surch. **1984**) 75 35
1306. 90 c. on 60 c. Fort Island (optd. **INT. CHESS FED. 1924–1984**) .. 60 45
1307. 90 c. on 60 c. Fort Island (optd. **1984**) .. .. 1·00 45

1984. Olympic Games, Los Angeles. No. 1051 surch.

1308. 25 c. on $1.30 mult. (surch. **TRACK AND FIELD**) 20 25
1309. 25 c. on $1.30 mult. (surch. **BOXING**) .. 20 25
1310. 25 c. on $1.30 mult. (surch. **OLYMPIC GAMES 1984 LOS ANGELES**) 20 25
1311. 25 c. on $1.30 mult. (surch. **CYCLING**) .. 40 25
1312. 25 c. on $1.30 mult. (surch. **OLYMPIC GAMES 1984**) .. 2·50 50
1313. $1.20 on $1.30 mult. (surch. **TRACK AND FIELD**) .. .. 1·00 1·10
1314. $1.20 on $1.30 mult. (surch. **BOXING**) .. 1·00 1·10
1315. $1.20 on $1.30 mult. (surch. **OLYMPIC GAMES 1984 LOS ANGELES**) .. .. 1·00 1·10
1316. $1·20 on $1·30 mult. (surch. **CYCLING**) .. 1·50 1·10
1317. $1.20 on $1.30 mult. (surch. **OLYMPIC GAMES 1984**) .. 3·00 1·50

1984. 60th Anniv. of Girl Guide Movement in Guyana. Nos. 900/9 surch. **25 GIRL GUIDES 1924–1984.**

1318. 25 c. on 110 c. on 5 c. Annatto tree (No. 900) 10 15
1319. 25 c. on 110 c. on 5 c. Annatto tree (No. 901) 10 15
1320. 25 c. on 110 c. on 5 c. Annatto tree (No. 902) 10 15
1321. 25 c. on 110 c. on 5 c. Annatto tree (No. 903) 10 15
1322. 25 c. on 110 c. on 5 c. Annatto tree (No. 904) 75 40
1323. 25 c. on 125 c. on 8 c. on 6 c. Cannon-ball tree (No. 905) 10 15
1324. 25 c. on 125 c. on 8 c. on 6 c. Cannon-ball tree (No. 906) 10 15
1325. 25 c. on 125 c. on 8 c. on 6 c. Cannon-ball tree (No. 907) 10 15
1326. 25 c. on 125 c. on 8 c. on 6 c. Cannon-ball tree (No. 908) 10 15
1327. 25 c. on 125 c. on 8 c. on 6 c. Cannon-ball tree (No. 909) 75 40

1984. Various stamps surch.

1328 20 c. on 15 c. on 2 c. Type **132** (No. 1034) .. 30 10
1341 25 c. on 10 c. Cattleya (No. 547) .. 9·00 2·00
1343 25 c. on 15 c. Christmas orchid (No. 548a) .. 90·00
1342 25 c. on 15 c. Christmas orchid (No. 864) .. 2·00 15
1346 25 c. on 15 c. Christmas orchid (No. 977) .. 1·75 10
1347 25 c. on 15 c. Christmas orchid (No. 1009) .. 1·75 10
1348 25 c. on 15 c. Christmas orchid (No. O23) .. 1·75 10
1342a 25 c. on 35 c. on 60 c. Soldier's cap (No. 649) 70·00
1331 60 c. on 110 c. on 8 c. on 3 c. Hanging heliconia (No. 868) .. 27·00
1332 120 c. on 125 c. on 8 c. on 6 c. Cannon-ball tree (No. 893) .. .. 2·50 50
1333 120 c. on 125 c. on $2 "Norantea guianensis" (No. 834) .. .. 27·00
1334 120 c. on 125 c. on $2 "Norantea guianensis" (No. O 20) .. 1·25 50
1335 120 c. on 140 c. on $1 "Chelonanthus uliginoides" (No. 796) .. 3·50 50
1349 130 c. on 110 c. on $2 "Norantea guianensis" (No. 804) .. .. 70·00
1350 130 c. on 110 c. on $2 "Norantea guianensis" (No. O 22) .. .. 8·50 2·50
1336 200 c. on 220 c. on 1 c. Pitcher plant of Mt. Roraima (No. 922) .. 2·00 85
1337 320 c. on $1.10 on $2 "Norantea guianensis" (No. 804) .. .. 3·25 1·50
1338 350 c. on 375 c. on $5 "Odontadenia grandiflora" (No. 803) .. 2·25 1·60
1339 390 c. on 400 c. on $5 "Odontadenia grandiflora" (No. 1091) .. 3·00 2·00
1340 450 c. on $5 "Odontadenia grandiflora" (No. O 16) 3·25 2·50
1351a 600 c. on $7.20 on $1 "Chelonanthus uliginoides" (No. 770) .. 2·25 1·25

1984. Various stamps optd. **1984.**

1352. 20 c. "Paphinia cristata" (No. 549) .. .. 6·50 10
1358. 25 c. Marabunta (No. 550) .. .. .. 65·00
1359. 25 c. Marabunta (No. F4) 3·25 50
1359a. 25 c. Marabunta (No. F4a) .. .. .. 1·75 10
1354. 50 c. on 8 c. Type **136** (No. 1062) .. .. 5·00 25
1355. 60 c. on 1 c. Pitcher Plant of Mt. Roraima (No. 1000) 40 25
1356. $2 "Norantea "guianensis" (No. O 33) 1·50 1·00
1360. $3.60 on $5 "Odontadenia grandiflora" (No. 769) 2·25 1·50

1984. 40th Anniv. of International Civil Aviation Organization. Nos. 981, 1017 and 1148/68 optd. **ICAO.**

1361. 30 c. mult. (No. 1148) .. 10 15
1362. 30 c. mult. (No. 1149) .. 10 15
1363. 30 c. mult. (No. 1150) .. 10 15
1364. 30 c. mult. (No. 1151) .. 10 15
1365. 30 c. mult. (No. 1152) .. 10 15
1366. 30 c. mult. (No. 1153) .. 10 15
1367. 30 c. multicoloured (No. 1154) (optd. 'IMB/ICAO") 10 15
1368. 30 c. multicoloured (No. 1155) optd. "KCV/ICAO") 10 15
1369. 30 c. multicoloured (No. 1156) (optd "KAI/ICAO") 10 15
1370. 30 c. mult. (No. 1157) .. 10 15
1371. 30 c. mult. (No. 1158) .. 10 15
1372. 30 c. mult. (No. 1155) (optd. "1984") 10 15
1373. 30 c. multicoloured (No. 1155) (optd. "KPM/ICAO") 10 15
1374. 30 c. mult. (No. 1159) .. 10 15
1375. 30 c. mult. (No. 1160) .. 10 15
1376. 30 c. mult. (No. 1161) .. 10 15
1377. 30 c. multicoloured (No. 1155) (optd. "PMT/ICAO") 10 15
1378. 30 c. mult. (No. 1162) .. 10 15
1379. 30 c. mult. (No. 1163) .. 10 15
1380. 30 c. mult. (No. 1164) .. 10 15
1381. 30 c. mult. (No. 1165) .. 10 15
1382. 30 c. mult. (No. 1166) .. 10 15
1383. 30 c. mult. (No. 1167) .. 10 15
1384. 30 c. mult. (No. 1168) .. 10 15
1385. 200 c. on 330 c. on $2 mult. (No. 981) 65 70
1386. 200 c. on 75 c. on $5 mult. (No. 1017) .. .. 2·50 1·50

No. 1385 also carries an otherwise unissued surcharge **G.A.C. Inaug. Flight Georgetown—Toronto 200.**

1984. Wildlife Protection. Nos. 756/67 optd **1984.**

1387. 30 c. Type **178** 15 20
1388. 30 c. Red Howler .. 15 20
1389. 30 c. Common Squirrel-monkey 15 20
1390. 30 c. Two-toed Sloth .. 15 20
1391. 30 c. Brazilian Tapir .. 15 20
1392. 30 c. Collared Peccary .. 15 20
1393. 30 c. Six-banded Armadillo 15 20
1394. 30 c. Tamandua ("Ant Eater") 15 20
1395. 30 c. Giant Anteater .. 15 20
1396. 30 c. Brown Murine Opossum 15 20

1397. 30 c. Brown Four-eyed Opossum 15 20
1398. 30 c. Brazilian Agouti .. 15 20

1984. Nos. D10/11 surch. **120 GUYANA.**
1399. **D2.** 120 c. on 4 c. blue .. 4·00 45
1402. 120 c. on 12 c. red .. 4·00 45

1984. 175th Birth Anniv of Louis Braille (inventor of alphabet for the blind). No. 1040 surch. **$1.50.**
1403. $1.50 on 15 c. on 10 c. Type **215** .. .. 3·50 55

1984. International Food Day. No. 1012 surch.
1404. 150 c. on 50 c. Pawpaw and tangerine 50 55

The surcharge places a "1" alongside the original face value and obliterates the "1982" date on the previous overprint.

1984. Birth Centenary of H. N. Critchlow (founder of Guyana Labour Union). No. 873 surch. and No. 1196, both optd. **1984.**
1405. 240 c. on 110 c. on $3 H. N. Critchlow (No. 873) 1·00 85
1406. 240 c. on $3 H. N. Critchlow (No. 1196) .. 5·50 85

1984. Nos. 910/12 and 1184/7 surch.
1407. **277.** 25 c. on 45 c. brown and black 15 15
1408. – 25 c. on 45 c. red and black (No. 1185) .. 15 15
1409. – 25 c. on 45 c. violet and black (No. 1186) 15 15
1410. – 25 c. on 45 c. green and black (No. 1187) 15 15
1411. – 120 c. on 100 c. on $3 mult. (No. 910) .. 3·75 45
1412. – 120 c. on 400 c. on 30 c. mult. (No. 911) 55 45
1413. – 320 c. on $5 multi-coloured (No. 912) 5·50 1·25

1984. Deepavali Festival. Nos. 544/5 surch. **MAHA SABHA 1934–1984** and new value.
1414. 25 c. on 5 c. Annatto tree 10 10
1415. $1.50 on 3 c. Hanging Heliconia 50 55

1984. A.S.D.A. Philatelic Exhibition, New York. Nos. 1188/91 optd. **Philatelic Exhibition New York 1984.**
1416. **277.** 120 c. brn. and black 40 45
1417. – 130 c. red and black 45 50
1418. – 150 c. violet & black 50 55
1419. – 200 c. green & black 70 75

1984. Olympic Games, Los Angeles (2nd issue). Design as No. 1051, but with Olympic rings and inscr **"OLYMPIC GAMES 1984. LOS ANGELES".**
1420. $1.20, Youth display (41 × 25 mm) .. .. 1·50 45

1984. Nos. 847, 861 and 1032/3 surch.
1421. 20 c. on 12 c. on 12 c. on 6 c. mult. (No. 847) .. 35 10
1422. 20 c. on 12 c. on 6 c. mult. (No. 861) .. .. 60·00
1423. 25 c. on 50 c. on 6 c. mult. (No. 1032) 10 10
1424. 60 c. on $1 on 6 c. mult. (No. 1033) 20 25

318. Pair of Swallow-tailed Kites on Tree.

1984. Christmas. Swallow-tailed Kites. Mult.
1425. 60 c. Type **318** .. .. 1·00 1·00
1426. 60 c. Swallow-tailed Kite on branch .. .. 1·00 1·00
1427. 60 c. Kite in flight with wings raised .. .. 1·00 1·00
1428. 60 c. Kite in flight with wings lowered .. 1·00 1·00
1429. 60 c. Kite gliding .. 1·00 1·00

Nos. 1425/9 were printed together se-tenant with the backgrounds forming a composite design. Each stamp is inscribed "CHRISTMAS 1982".

319. St. George's Cathedral, Georgetown.

1985. Georgetown Buildings. Each black and stone.
1430. 25 c. Type **319** 10 10
1431. 60 c. Demerara Mutual Life Assurance Building 20 25
1432. 120 c. As No. 1431 .. 40 45
1433. 120 c. Town Hall .. 40 45
1434. 120 c. Victoria Law Courts 40 45
1435. 200 c. As No. 1433 .. 70 75
1436. 300 c. As No. 1434 .. 1·00 1·10

Nos. 1432/4 were printed together, se-tenant forming a composite design.

1985. International Youth Year. No. 1420 optd. **International Youth Year 1985.**
1437. $1.20, Youth display .. 1·25 45

Examples of No. 1420 used for this overprint all show the second line of the original inscription as "LOS ANGELLES".

1985. Republic Day. Nos. 1049/50 and 1052 optd. or surch. **Republic Day 1970–1985.**
1438. 25 c. Type **238** 10 10
1439. 25 c. Flag (inscr. "30th ANNIVERSARY IN PARLIAMENT") .. 10 10
1440. 120 c. on $6 Presidential standard 40 45
1441. 130 c. on $6 Presidential standard 45 50

322. Young Ocelot on Branch.

1985. Wildlife Protection. Multicoloured.
1442. 25 c. Type **322** olive background .. .. 1·00 10
1443. 60 c. Young ocelot (different) (brown background) 20 25
1444. 120 c. As No. 1443 .. 15 20
1445. 120 c. Type **322** .. 15 20
1446. 120 c. Young ocelot different) (brown background) .. 15 20
1447. 130 c. As No. 1446 .. 45 50
1448. 320 c. Scarlet macaw (28 × 46 mm.) .. 2·75 1·25
1449. 330 c. Young ocelot reaching for branch (28 × 46 mm.) .. .. 1·25 1·25

1985. No. 940, Revenue stamp as T **181**, Nos. 912, 1016 and unissued Official value (No. O 24 optd. **OPS**) surch.
1450. 30 c. on 50 c. mult. (as No. 719) 20 10
1451. 55 c. on 2 c. black, blue and grey 30 20
1452. 55 c. on 15 c. on 2 c. black, blue and grey 30 20
1453. 90 c. on $1 mult. (No. 1016) 1·25 30
1454. 225 c. on $5 mult. (No. 912) 1·75 70
1455. 230 c. on $5 mult. (No. 912) 1·50 75
1456. 260 c. on $5 mult. (No. 912) 1·50 80

1985. International Youth Year Save the Children Fund Campaign. Nos. 880, 1073a, 1079b and 1082 optd. **International Youth Year 1985** or surch. also.
1457. 50 c. "Two Boys catching Ducks" (No. 1073a) 1·50 20
1458. 50 c. on 10 c. Type **171** (No. 1082) .. .. 3·25 20
1459. 120 c. on 125 c. on $3 "Mango Season" (No. 880) .. .. .. 1·50 45
1460. $3 "Mango Season" (No. 1079b) .. .. 1·50 1·10

1985. 125th Anniv. of British Guiana Post Office (1st issue). No. 699 surch. with names of post offices and postal agencies open in 1860.
1461. 25 c. on 10 c. mult. (**Airy Hall**) 15 10
1462. 25 c. on 10 c. mult. (**Belfield Arab Coast**) .. 15 10
1463. 25 c. on 10 c. mult. (**Belfield E. C. Dem.**) .. 15 10
1464. 25 c. on 10 c. mult. (**Belladrum**) 15 10
1465. 25 c. on 10 c. mult. (**Beterver-wagting**) .. 15 10
1466. 25 c. on 10 c. mult. (**Blairmont Ferry**) .. 15 10
1467. 25 c. on 10 c. mult. (**Boeraserie**) 15 10
1468. 25 c. on 10 c. mult. (**Brahm**) 15 10
1469. 25 c. on 10 c. mult. (**Bushlot**) 15 10
1470. 25 c. on 10 c. mult. (**De Kinderen**) 15 10
1471. 25 c. on 10 c. mult. (**Fort Wellington**) 15 10
1472. 25 c. on 10 c. mult. (**Georgetown**) 15 10
1473. 25 c. on 10 c. mult. (**Hague**) 15 10
1474. 25 c. on 10 c. mult. (**Leguan**) 15 10
1475. 25 c. on 10 c. mult. (**Mahaica**) 15 10
1476. 25 c. on 10 c. mult. (**Mahaicony**) 15 10
1477. 25 c. on 10 c. mult. (**New Amsterdam**) 15 10
1478. 25 c. on 10 c. mult. (**Plaisance**) 15 10
1479. 25 c. on 10 c. mult. (**No. 6 Police Station**) .. 15 10
1480. 25 c. on 10 c. mult. (**Queenstown**) 15 10
1481. 25 c. on 10 c. mult. (**Vergenoegen**) 15 10
1482. 25 c. on 10 c. mult. (**Vigilance**) 15 10
1483. 25 c. on 10 c. mult. (**Vreed-en-Hoop**) .. 15 10
1484. 25 c. on 10 c. mult. (**Wakenaam**) 15 10
1485. 25 c. on 10 c. mult. (**Windsor Castle**) .. 15 10

See also Nos. 1694/1717 and 2140/64.

1985. I.T.U./W.H.O. Day. Nos. 1148/68 optd. **1985** or with single capital letter.
1486. 30 c. mult. (1148) .. 10 15
1487. 30 c. mult. (1149) .. 10 15
1488. 30 c. mult. (1150) .. 10 15
1489. 30 c. mult. (1151) .. 10 15
1490. 30 c. mult. (1152) .. 10 15
1491. 30 c. mult. (1153) .. 10 15
1492. 30 c. mult. (1154) (**I**) .. 10 15
1493. 30 c. mult. (1155) (**T**) .. 10 15
1494. 30 c. mult. (1156) (**U**) .. 10 15
1495. 30 c. mult. (1157) .. 10 15
1496. 30 c. mult. (1158) .. 10 15
1497. 30 c. mult. (1155) (**W**) .. 10 15
1498. 30 c. mult. (1155) (**H**) .. 10 15
1499. 30 c. mult. (1155) (**O**) .. 10 15
1500. 30 c. mult. (1159) .. 10 15
1501. 30 c. mult. (1160) .. 10 15
1502. 30 c. mult. (1161) (**D**) .. 10 15
1503. 30 c. mult. (1155) (**A**) .. 10 15
1504. 30 c. mult. (1162) (**Y**) .. 10 15
1505. 30 c. mult. (1163) .. 10 15
1506. 30 c. mult. (1164) .. 10 15
1507. 30 c. mult. (1165) .. 10 15
1508. 30 c. mult. (1166) .. 10 15
1509. 30 c. mult. (1167) .. 10 15
1510. 30 c. mult. (1168) .. 10 15

1985. No. 861 surch.
1511. 20 c. on 12 c. on 6 c. Patua 10 10

1985. 10th Anniv. of Caribbean Agricultural Research Development Institute. No. 544 surch. **CARDI 1975–85 60.**
1512. 60 c. on 3 c. Hanging Heliconia 30 25

1985. No. 839 surch.
1513. 600 c. on 625 c. on 40 c. Tiger Beard .. .. 5·50 2·25

1985. 80th Anniv. of Rotary International. Nos. 707 and 879 surch. **ROTARY INTERNATIONAL 1905–1985.**
1514. 120 c. on 110 c. on $3 Rotary anniversary emblem .. .. 5·50 45
1515. 300 c. on $2 "Morpho rhetenor" .. .. 1·75 1·10

1985. CARICOM Day. No. 1200 surch. **CARICOM DAY 1985 60.**
1516. 60 c. on $3 "Makanaima the Great Ancestral Spirit of the Amerindians" .. 30 30

1985. 135th Anniv. of First British Guiana Stamps. No. 870 surch. **135th Anniversary Cotton Reel 1980-1985 120.**
1517. 120 c. on 110 c. on 10 c. Type **170** 50 55

"REICHENBACHIA" ISSUES. Due to the proliferation of these designs the catalogue uses the book plate numbers as description for each design. The following index gives the species on each plate.

Series 1

Plate No. 1 (Series 1) "Odontoglossum crispum"
Plate No. 2 (Series 1) "Cattleya percivaliana"
Plate No. 3 (Series 1) "Cypripedium sanderianum"
Plate No. 4 (Series 1) "Odontoglossum rossi"
Plate No. 5 (Series 1) "Cattleya dowiana aurea"
Plate No. 6 (Series 1) "Coelogyne cristata maxima"
Plate No. 7 (Series 1) "Odontoglossum insleayi splendens"
Plate No. 8 (Series 1) "Laelia euspatha"
Plate No. 9 (Series 1) "Dendrobium wardianum"
Plate No. 10 (Series 1) "Laelia autumnalis xanthotropis"
Plate No. 11 (Series 1) "Phalaenopsis grandiflora aurea"
Plate No. 12 (Series 1) "Cattleya lawrenceana"
Plate No. 13 (Series 1) "Masdevallia shuttleworthii" and "M. xanthocorys"
Plate No. 14 (Series 1) "Aeranthus sesquipedalis"
Plate No. 15 (Series 1) "Cattleya mendelii Duke of Marlborough"
Plate No. 16 (Series 1) "Zygopetalum intermedium"
Plate No. 17 (Series 1) "Phaius humblotii"
Plate No. 18 (Series 1) "Chysis bractescens"
Plate No. 19 (Series 1) "Masdevallia backhousiana"
Plate No. 20 (Series 1) "Cattleya citrina"
Plate No. 21 (Series 1) "Oncidium jonesianum" and "Oncidium jonesianum phaeanthum"
Plate No. 22 (Series 1) "Saccolabium giganteum"
Plate No. 23 (Series 1) "Cypripedium io"
Plate No. 24 (Series 1) "Odontoglossum blandum"
Plate No. 25 (Series 1) "Maxillaria sanderiana"
Plate No. 26 (Series 1) "Odontoglossum Edward II"
Plate No. 27 (Series 1) "Vanda teres"
Plate No. 28 (Series 1) "Odontoglossum hallii xanthoglossum"
Plate No. 29 (Series 1) "Odontoglossum crispum hrubyanum"
Plate No. 30 (Series 1) "Oncidium concolor"
Plate No. 31 (Series 1) "Trichopilia suavis alba"
Plate No. 32 (Series 1) "Cattleya superba splendens"
Plate No. 33 (Series 1) "Odontoglossum luteo-purpureum"
Plate No. 34 (Series 1) "Cypripedium niveum"
Plate No. 35 (Series 1) "Stanhopea shuttleworthii"
Plate No. 36 (Series 1) "Laelia anceps percivaliana"
Plate No. 37 (Series 1) "Odontoglossum hebraicum"
Plate No. 38 (Series 1) "Cypripedium oenanthum superbum"
Plate No. 39 (Series 1) "Dendrobium superbiens"
Plate No. 40 (Series 1) "Laelia harpophylla"
Plate No. 41 (Series 1) "Lycaste skinneri" and "alba"
Plate No. 42 (Series 1) "Phalaenopsis stuartiana"
Plate No. 43 (Series 1) "Cattleya trianaei ernesti"
Plate No. 44 (Series 1) "Sobralia xantholeuca"
Plate No. 45 (Series 1) "Odontoglossum crispum kinlesideanum"
Plate No. 46 (Series 1) "Cattleya trianaei schroederiana"
Plate No. 47 (Series 1) "Epidendrum vitellinum"
Plate No. 48 (Series 1) "Laelia anceps stella" and "barkeriana"
Plate No. 49 (Series 1) "Odontoglossum harryanum"
Plate No. 50 (Series 1) "Dendrobium leechianum"
Plate No. 51 (Series 1) "Phalaenopsis speciosa"
Plate No. 52 (Series 1) "Laelia elegans schilleriana"
Plate No. 53 (Series 1) "Zygopetalum wendlandi"
Plate No. 54 (Series 1) "Cypripedium selligerum majus"
Plate No. 55 (Series 1) "Angraecum articulatum"
Plate No. 56 (Series 1) "Laelia anceps sanderiana"
Plate No. 57 (Series 1) "Vanda coerulea"
Plate No. 58 (Series 1) "Dendrobium nobile sanderianum"
Plate No. 59 (Series 1) "Laelia gouldiana"
Plate No. 60 (Series 1) "Odontoglossum grande"

Plate No. 61 (Series 1) "Cypripedium rothschildianum"
Plate No. 62 (Series 1) "Vanda sanderiana"
Plate No. 63 (Series 1) "Dendrobium aureum"
Plate No. 64 (Series 1) "Oncidium macranthum"
Plate No. 65 (Series 1) "Cypripedium tautzianum"
Plate No. 66 (Series 1) "Cymbidium mastersi"
Plate No. 67 (Series 1) "Angraecum caudatum"
Plate No. 68 (Series 1) "Laelia albida"
Plate No. 69 (Series 1) "Odontoglossum roezlii"
Plate No. 70 (Series 1) "Oncidium ampliatum majus"
Plate No. 71 (Series 1) "Renanthera lowii"
Plate No. 72 (Series 1) "Cattleya warscewiczii"
Plate No. 73 (Series 1) "Oncidium lanceanum"
Plate No. 74 (Series 1) "Vanda hookeriana"
Plate No. 75 (Series 1) "Cattleya labiata gaskelliana"
Plate No. 76 (Series 1) "Epidendrum prismatocarpum"
Plate No. 77 (Series 1) "Cattleya guttata leopoldi"
Plate No. 78 (Series 1) "Oncidium splendidum"
Plate No. 79 (Series 1) "Odontoglossum hebraicum aspersum"
Plate No. 80 (Series 1) "Cattleya dowiana var chrysotoxa"
Plate No. 81 (Series 1) "Cattleya trianae alba"
Plate No. 82 (Series 1) "Odontoglossum humeanum"
Plate No. 83 (Series 1) "Cypripedium argus"
Plate No. 84 (Series 1) "Odontoglossum luteopurpureum prionopetalum"
Plate No. 85 (Series 1) "Cattleya rochellensis"
Plate No. 86 (Series 1) "Odontoglossum triumphans" (inscr "ONTOGLOSSUM" in error)
Plate No. 87 (Series 1) "Phalaenopsis casta"
Plate No. 88 (Series 1) "Oncidium tigrinum"
Plate No. 89 (Series 1) "Cypripedium lemoinierianum"
Plate No. 90 (Series 1) "Catasetum bungerothii"
Plate No. 91 (Series 1) "Cattleya ballantiniana"
Plate No. 92 (Series 1) "Dendrobium brymerianum"
Plate No. 93 (Series 1) "Cattleya eldorado crocata"
Plate No. 94 (Series 1) "Odontoglossum sanderianum"
Plate No. 95 (Series 1) "Cattleya labiata warneri"
Plate No. 96 (Series 1) "Odontoglossum schroder-ianum"

Series 2

Plate No. 1 (Series 2) "Cypripedium morganiae burfordiense"
Plate No. 2 (Series 2) "Cattleya bowringiana"
Plate No. 3 (Series 2) "Dendrobium formosum"
Plate No. 4 (Series 2) "Phaius tuberculosus"
Plate No. 5 (Series 2) "Odontoglossum crispum mundyanum"
Plate No. 6 (Series 2) "Laelia praestans"
Plate No. 7 (Series 2) "Dendrobium phalaenopsis var statterianum"
Plate No. 8 (Series 2) "Cypripedium boxalli atratum"
Plate No. 9 (Series 2) "Odontoglossum wattianum"
Plate No. 10 (Series 2) "Cypripedium lathamianum inversum"
Plate No. 11 (Series 2) "Paphinia rugosa" and "Zygopetalum xanthinum"
Plate No. 12 (Series 2) "Dendrobium melanodiscus"
Plate No. 13 (Series 2) "Laelia anceps schroderiana"
Plate No. 14 (Series 2) "Phaius hybridus cooksonii"
Plate No. 15 (Series 2) "Disa grandiflora"
Plate No. 16 (Series 2) "Selenipedium hybridum grande"
Plate No. 17 (Series 2) "Cattleya schroederae alba"
Plate No. 18 (Series 2) "Lycaste skinnerii armeniaca"
Plate No. 19 (Series 2) "Odontoglossum excellens"
Plate No. 20 (Series 2) "Laelio-cattleya elegans var blenheimensis"
Plate No. 21 (Series 2) "Odontoglossum coradinei"
Plate No. 22 (Series 2) "Odontoglossum wilckeanum var rothschildianum"
Plate No. 23 (Series 2) "Cypripedium lawrenceanum hyeanum"
Plate No. 24 (Series 2) "Cattleya intermedia punctatissima"
Plate No. 25 (Series 2) "Laelia purpurata"
Plate No. 26 (Series 2) "Masdevallia harryana splendens"
Plate No. 27 (Series 2) "Selenipedium hybridum nitidissimum"
Plate No. 28 (Series 2) "Cattleya mendelii var measuresiana"
Plate No. 29 (Series 2) "Odontoglossum vexill-arium" ("miltonia vexillaria")
Plate No. 30 (Series 2) "Saccolabium coeleste"
Plate No. 31 (Series 2) "Cypripedium hybridum youngianum"
Plate No. 32 (Series 2) "Miltonia (hybrida) bleuana"
Plate No. 33 (Series 2) "Laelia grandis"
Plate No. 34 (Series 2) "Cattleya labiata var lueddemanniana"
Plate No. 35 (Series 2) "Odontoglossum coronarium"
Plate No. 36 (Series 2) "Cattleya granulosa var. schofieldiana"
Plate No. 37 (Series 2) "Odontoglossum (hybridum) leroyanum"
Plate No. 38 (Series 2) "Cypripedium (hybridum) laucheanum" and "eyermanianum"
Plate No. 39 (Series 2) "Cychnoches chlorochilon"
Plate No. 40 (Series 2) "Cattleya O'Brieniana"
Plate No. 41 (Series 2) "Odontoglossum ramosissimum"
Plate No. 42 (Series 2) "Dendrobium phalaenopsis var"
Plate No. 43 (Series 2) "Cypripedium (hybridum) pollettianum" and "maynardii"
Plate No. 44 (Series 2) "Odontoglossum naevium"
Plate No. 45 (Series 2) "Cypripedium (hybridium) castleanum"
Plate No. 47 (Series 2) "Cattleya amethystoglossa"
Plate No. 48 (Series 2) "Cattleya (hybrida) arnoldiana"
Plate No. 49 (Series 2) "Cattleya labiata"
Plate No. 50 (Series 2) "Dendrobium (hybridum) venus" and "cassiope"
Plate No. 51 (Series 2) "Selenipedium (hybridum) weidlichianum"
Plate No. 52 (Series 2) "Cattleya mossiae var. reineckiana"
Plate No. 53 (Series 2) "Cymbidium lowianum"
Plate No. 54 (Series 2) "Oncidium loxense"
Plate No. 56 (Series 2) "Coelogyne sanderae"
Plate No. 58 (Series 2) "Coelogyne pandurata"
Plate No. 59 (Series 2) "Schomburgkia sanderiana"
Plate No. 60 (Series 2) "Oncidium superbiens"
Plate No. 61 (Series 2) "Dendrobium johnsoniae"
Plate No. 62 (Series 2) "Laelia hybrida behrensiana"
Plate No. 63 (Series 2) Hybrid "Calanthes Victoria Regina", "Bella" and "Burfordiense"
Plate No. 64 (Series 2) "Cattleya mendelii Quorndon House var"
Plate No. 65 (Series 2) "Arachnanthe clarkei"
Plate No. 66 (Series 2) "Zygopetalum burtii"
Plate No. 67 (Series 2) "Cattleya (hybrida) parthenia"
Plate No. 68 (Series 2) "Phalaenopsis sanderiana" and "intermedia portei"
Plate No. 69 (Series 2) "Phaius blumei var. assamicus"
Plate No. 70 (Series 2) "Angraecum humblotii"
Plate No. 71 (Series 2) "Odontoglossum pescatorei"
Plate No. 72 (Series 2) "Cattleya rex"
Plate No. 73 (Series 2) "Zygopetalum crinitum"
Plate No. 74 (Series 2) "Cattleya lueddemanniana alba"
Plate No. 75 (Series 2) "Cymbidium (hybridum) winnianum"
Plate No. 76 (Series 2) Hybrid "Masdevallias courtauldiana", "geleniana" and "measuresiana"
Plate No. 77 (Series 2) "Cypripedium" (hybridum) calypso
Plate No. 78 (Series 2) "Masdevallia chimaera var. mooreana"
Plate No. 79 (Series 2) "Miltonia phalaenopsis"
Plate No. 80 (Series 2) "Lissochilus giganteus"
Plate No. 82 (Series 2) "Thunia brymeriana"
Plate No. 83 (Series 2) "Miltonia moreliana"
Plate No. 84 (Series 2) "Oncidium kramerianum"
Plate No. 85 (Series 2) "Cattleya Victoria Regina"
Plate No. 86 (Series 2) "Zygopetalum klabochorum"
Plate No. 87 (Series 2) "Laelia autumnalis alba"
Plate No. 88 (Series 2) "Spathoglottis kimballiana"
Plate No. 89 (Series 2) "Laelio-cattleya" ("The Hon. Mrs. Astor")
Plate No. 90 (Series 2) "Phaius hybridus amabilis" and "marthiae"
Plate No. 91 (Series 2) "Zygopetalum rostratum"
Plate No. 92 (Series 2) "Coelogyne swaniana"
Plate No. 93 (Series 2) "Laelio-cattleya" (hybrida) "phoebe"
Plate No. 94 (Series 2) "Epidendrum atro-purpureum var randianum"
Plate No. 95 (Series 2) "Dendrobium imperatrix"
Plate No. 96 (Series 2) "Vanda parishii var marriottiana"

331. "Cattleya lawrenceana" Plate No. 12 (Series 1).

1985. Centenary of Publication of Sanders's "Reichenbachia" (1st issue). Orchids. Mult.

1518	25 c. Type **331**	40	30
1519	60 c. Plate No. 2 (Series 1)	50	35
1520	60 c. Plate No. 7 (Series 1)	50	35
1521	60 c. Plate No. 10 (Series 1)	50	35
1522	60 c. Plate No. 19 (Series 1)	50	35
1523	60 c. Plate No. 31 (Series 1)	50	35
1524	120 c. Plate No. 27 (Series 1)	75	55
1525	130 c. Plate No. 3 (Series 1)	75	55
1759	130 c. Plate No. 6 (Series 1)	35	20
1760	130 c. Plate No. 13 (Series 1)	35	20
1528	130 c. Plate No. 18 (Series 1)	1·50	55
1761	130 c. Plate No. 20 (Series 1)	35	20
1762	130 c. Plate No. 25 (Series 1)	35	20
1531	130 c. Plate No. 29 (Series 1)	1·25	55
1532	130 c. Plate No. 30 (Series 1)	1·25	55
1533	200 c. Plate No. 4 (Series 1)	1·25	85

See also Nos. 1551/66, 1571/1806, 1597, 1620/1863, 1663/73, 1679/83, 1731/8, 1747/54, 1809/19, 1822, 1868/9, 1872/81, 1884/7, 1907, 1912/15, 1916/24, 1925/9, 2066/73, 2171/8, 2180/2, 2190/3, 2216/16, 2219/20, 2225/7, 2235/42, 2314/18, 2322/5, 2328, 2314/18, 2322/5, 2329/31, 2468/71 2498/2511 and 2605/8.

332. Arms of Guyana.

1985.

1534. **332.**	25 c. multicoloured ..	15	15

1985. 85th Birthday of Queen Elizabeth the Queen Mother (1st issue). Nos. 1528 and 1531/2 optd. **QUEEN MOTHER 1900-1985.**

1536.	130 c. Plate No. 18 (Series 1)	45	50
1537.	130 c. Plate No. 29 (Series 1)	45	50
1538.	130 c. Plate No. 30 (Series 1)	45	50

1985. International Youth Year. Nos. 900/4 surch. **International Youth Year 1985 25.**

1540.	25 c. on 110 c. on 5 c. multicoloured (900) ..	10	10
1541.	25 c. on 110 c. on 5 c. multicoloured (901) ..	10	10
1542.	25 c. on 110 c. on 5 c. multicoloured (902) ..	25	10
1543.	25 c. on 110 c. on 5 c. multicoloured (903) ..	25	10
1544.	25 c. on 100 c. on 5 c. multicoloured (904) ..	80	15

1985. 75th Anniv. of Girl Guide Movement. No. 612 surch. **1910-1985 225.**

1545.	225 c. on 350 c. on 225 c. on 40 c. Guide in camp	5·00	90

No. 1545 also carries two otherwise unissued surcharges at top right.

1985. Birth Bicentenary of John J. Audubon (ornithologist). No. 992 surch. **J. J. Audubon 1785-1985 240.**

1546.	240 c. on 35 c. Harpy Eagle	6·00	1·75

337. Leaders of the 1763 Rebellion.

1985. 150th Anniv (1984) of Abolition of Slavery (1st issue).

1547. **337.**	25 c. black and grey	50	10
1548. –	60 c. black & mauve	25	25
1549. –	130 c. black and blue	50	50
1550. –	150 c. black and lilac	60	55

DESIGNS: 60 c. Damon and Parliament Buildings, Georgetown. 130 c. Quamina and Demerara, 1823. 150 c. "Den Arendt" (slave ship), 1627.

For these designs in changed colours see Nos. 2552/5.

1985. Centenary of Publication of Sanders' "Reichenbachia" (2nd issue). As T **331** showing orchids. Multicoloured.

1551	25 c. Plate No. 52 (Series 1)	40	25
1763	55 c. Plate No. 9 (Series 1)	25	10
1764	55 c. Plate No. 22 (Series 1)	25	10
1765	55 c. Plate No. 49 (Series 1)	25	10
1766	55 c. Plate No. 64. (Series 1)	25	10
1556	60 c. Plate No. 44 (Series 1)	50	35
1557	60 c. Plate No. 47 (Series 1)	50	35
1558	120 c. Plate No. 36 (Series 1)	75	55
1559	130 c. Plate No. 16 (Series 1)	75	55
1560	130 c. Plate No. 38 (Series 1)	75	55
1561	150 c. Plate No. 32 (Series 1)	75	55
1562	150 c. Plate No. 34 (Series 1)	75	55
1563	150 c. Plate No. 35 (Series 1)	75	55
1564	150 c. Plate No. 41 (Series 1)	75	55
1565	150 c. Plate No. 48 (Series 1)	75	55
1566	150 c. Plate No. 62 (Series 1)	75	55

1985. Signing of Guyana—Libya Friendship Treaty. No. 621 surch. **Guyana/Libya Friendship 1985.**

1567. **149.**	150 c. on 10 c. mult.	7·50	2·75

1985. Namibia Day. No. 636 surch. with Fleur-de-lis and new value.

1568.	150 c. on 35 c. Unveiling of Monument	1·75	55

1985. World Cup Football Championship, Mexico (1986) (1st issue). No. F2 surch. **Mexico 1986.**

1569.	275 c. on 3 c. Hanging Heliconia	1·75	95

See also No. 1727.

1985. Centenary of Publication of Sanders' "Reichenbachia" (3rd issue). As T **331** showing orchids. Multicoloured.

1571	25 c. Plate No. 8 (Series 1)	30	30
1572	25 c. Plate No. 23 (Series 1)	30	30
1573	25 c. Plate No. 51 (Series 1)	30	30
1574	25 c. Plate No. 61 (Series 1)	30	30
1575	25 c. Plate No. 63 (Series 1)	30	30
1576	25 c. Plate No. 70 (Series 1)	30	30
1577	25 c. Plate No. 72 (Series 1)	30	30
1578	120 c. Plate No. 1 (Series 1) (horiz.) ..	75	55
1579	120 c. Plate No. 11 (Series 1) (horiz.) ..	75	55
1580	120 c. Plate No. 28 (Series 1) (horiz.) ..	75	55
1767	150 c. Plate No. 40 (Series 1) (horiz.) ..	35	20
1768	150 c. Plate No. 42 (Series 1) (horiz.) ..	35	20
1769	150 c. Plate No. 45 (Series 1) (horiz.) ..	35	20
1584	200 c. Plate No. 14 (Series 1)	1·00	80
1585	200 c. Plate No. 21 (Series 1) (horiz.) ..	1·00	80
1770	200 c. Plate No. 43 (Series 1) (horiz.) ..	45	30

1985. 30th Anniv. of Commonwealth Caribbean Medical Research Council. Nos. 819, 871, 874, 928 and 1014 optd. **1955–1985** or surch. also.

1587. – 60 c. mult. (No. 819) 20 25
1588. – 60 c. multicoloured (No. 1014) 20 25
1589. **176.** 120 c. on 110 c. on 10 c. multicoloured (No. 871) 40 45
1590. – 120 c. on 110 c. on $3 mult. (No. 874) .. 40 45
1592. – 120 c. on 210 c. on $3 mult. (No. 928) .. 40 45

1985. 20th Anniv. of Guyana Defence Force. No. 856 surch. **1965–1985.**

1593. 25 c. on $1.10 on $3 W.O. and N.C.O., Guyana Defence Force, 1966 .. 20 10
1594. 225 c. on $1.10 on $3 W.O. and N.C.O., Guyana Defence Force, 1966 .. .. 1·10 75

1985. Fire Prevention. Nos. 678 and 680 optd. **1985** and surch.

1595. 25 c. on 40 c. Fire engine, 1977 .. .. .. 3·00 10
1596. 320 c. on 15 c. Steam engine, circa 1860 .. 7·00 2·25

1985. Centenary of Publication of Sanders' "Reichenbachia" (4th issue). As T **331.** Multicoloured.

1597. 60 c. Plate No. 55 (Series 1) 60 30

1985. Columbus Day. Unissued value as T **331** surch. **CRISTOBAL COLON 1492–1992.** Multicoloured.

1598. 350 c. on 120 c. Plate No. 65 (Series 1) .. .. 2·00 1·60

1985. 20th Death Anniv. of Sir Winston Churchill. No. 707 optd. **SIR WINSTON CHURCHILL 1965–1985.**

1599. $2 "Morpho rhetenor" (female) .. .. 1·75 85

1985. 35th Anniv. of International Commission on Irrigation and Drainage. No. 625 with unissued surcharge further surch. **1950–1985.**

1600. **150.** 25 c. on 110 c. on 10 c. multicoloured 10 10
1601. 200 c. on 110 c. on 10 c. multicoloured 65 70

1985. 40th Anniv. of U.N.O. Nos. 714/16, 800 and O 19 optd. **United Nations 1945–1985.**

1602. 30 c. mult. (No. 714) .. 1·00 10
1603. 50 c. mult. (No. 715) .. 1·00 20
1604. 100 c. on $3 mult. (No. O 19) .. .. .. 1·00 40
1605. 225 c. on 220 c. on $3 mult. (No. 800) .. 4·00 75
1606. $3 mult. (No. 716) .. 2·00 1·10

1985. Nos. 551/3, O 14/15, O 18, O 21, O P1/2 and F 7 optd. **POSTAGE.**

1607. 30 c. on $2 "Norantea guianensis" (No. O 18) 20 10
1608. 40 c. Tiger Beard (No. 551) .. .. .. 15·00 20
1609. 50 c. "Guzmania lingulata" (No. 552) .. 35 20
1610. 50 c. "Guzmania lingulata" (No. O 14) 30 20
1611. 60 c. Soldier's Cap (No. 553) .. .. 1·75 25
1612. 60 c. Soldier's Cap (No. O 15) .. .. 1·25 25
1613. 60 c. Soldier's Cap (No. F 7) 40 25
1614. $10 "Elbella patrobas" (No. O 21) .. .. 7·00 5·50
1615. $15 on $1 "Chelonanthus uliginoides" (No. O P1) 8·00 8·00
1616. $20 on $1 "Chelonanthus uliginoides" (No. O P2) 9·00 9·50

1985. Deepavali Festival. Nos. 542/3 surch. **Deepavali 1985.**

1617. 25 c. on 2 c. Type **132** .. 10 10
1618. 150 c. on 1 c. Pitcher plant of Mt. Roraima 50 55

1985. Centenary of Publication of Sanders' "Reichenbachia" (5th issue). As T **331** showing orchids. Multicoloured.

1620 25 c. Plate No. 59 (Series 1) 30 20
1771 30 c. Plate No. 53 (Series 1) 10 10
1622 60 c. Plate No. 57 (Series 1) (horiz.) 50 35
1623 60 c. Plate No. 73 (Series 1) (horiz.) 50 35
1624 60 c. Plate No. 75 (Series 1) (horiz.) 50 35
1772 75 c. Plate No. 55 (Series 1) 20 15
1773 100 c. Plate No. 65 (Series 1) 25 15
1627 120 c. Plate No. 37 (Series 1) 75 55
1628 120 c. Plate No. 46 (Series 1) 75 55
1629 120 c. Plate No. 56 (Series 1) 75 55
1630 120 c. Plate No. 58 (Series 1) 75 55
1631 120 c. Plate No. 67 (Series 1) 75 55
1632 130 c. Plate No. 66 (Series 1) 80 65
1633 150 c. Plate No. 26 (Series 1) 90 75
1634 200 c. Plate No. 33 (Series 1) (horiz.) .. 1·00 85
1770 225 c. Plate No. 24 (Series 1) 35 35

351. Clive Lloyd (cricketer).

1985. Clive Lloyd's Testimonial Year. Multicoloured.

1636. 25 c. Type **351** 50 20
1637. 25 c. Clive Lloyd, bat and wicket 50 20
1638. 25 c. Cricket equipment 50 20
1639. 60 c. As No. 1638 (25 × 33 mm.) 75 30
1640. $1.30 As No. 1637 (25 × 33 mm.) .. .. 1·25 60
1641. $2.25 Type **351** (25 × 33 mm.) .. .. 2·00 90
1642. $3.50 Clive Lloyd with the Prudential Cup .. 2·50 1·50

1985. Wildlife Protection. Nos. 756/67 optd. **1985.**

1643. 30 c. Type **178** 30 30
1644. 30 c. Red howler 30 30
1645. 30 c. Common squirrel-monkey 30 30
1646. 30 c. Two-toed sloth .. 30 30
1647. 30 c. Brazilian tapir .. 30 30
1648. 30 c. Collared peccary .. 30 30
1649. 30 c. Six-banded armadillo 30 30
1650. 30 c. Tamandua 30 30
1651. 30 c. Giant anteater .. 30 30
1652. 30 c. Murine opossum .. 30 30
1653. 30 c. Brown four-eyed opossum 30 30
1654. 30 c. Brazilian agouti .. 30 30

1985. No. 847 surch.

1655. 20 c. on 12 c. on 12 c. on 6 c. Patua (No. 847) .. 30 15

1986. Centenary of the Appearance of "Reichenbachia". Volume I. Nos. 1802 and 1806 optd. **REICHENBACHIA 1886–1986.**

1657. 150 c. Plate No. 42 (Series 1) 60 60
1658. 200 c. Plate No. 43 (Series 1) 75 75

1986. Republic Day. Nos. 1108/9 and 1052 optd. **Republic Day 1986.** or surch. also.

1659. 25 c. As Type **258** .. 10 10
1660. 25 c. As No. 1050 .. 10 10
1661. 120 c. on $6 Presidential standard 40 45
1662. 225 c. on $6 Presidential standard 70 75

1986. Centenary of Publication of Sanders'. "Reichenbachia" (6th issue). As T **331.** Multicoloured.

1663. 40 c. Plate No. 77 (Series 1) 35 20
1664. 45 c. Plate No. 54 (Series 1) 35 25
1665. 50 c. Plate No. 92 (Series 1) 35 25
1666. 60 c. Plate No. 95 (Series 1) 40 30
1667. 75 c. Plate No. 5 (Series 1) 45 35
1668. 90 c. Plate No. 84 (Series 1) 55 40
1669. 150 c. Plate No. 78 (Series 1) 75 60
1670. 200 c. Plate No. 79 (Series 1) 90 80
1671. 300 c. Plate No. 83 (Series 1) .. .. 1·50 1·25
1672. 320 c. Plate No. 50 (Series 1) .. .. 1·60 1·40
1673. 360 c. Plate No. 85 (Series 1) .. .. 1·75 1·50

1986. Easter. No. 481 optd. **1986** and surch. also.

1674. **111.** 25 c. on 6 c. mult. .. 25 10
1675. 50 c. on 6 c. mult. .. 40 20
1676. 100 c. on 6 c. mult. .. 65 40
1677. 200 c. on 6 c. mult. .. 1·25 70

1986. 60th Anniv. of St. John's Ambulance in Guyana. No. 652 surch. **1926 1986.**

1678. 150 c. on 35 c. silver, black and green .. 1·50 55

1986. Centenary of Publication of Sanders' "Reichenbachia" (7th issue). As T **331.** Multicoloured.

1679. 25 c. Plate No. 71 (Series 1) (horiz.) .. 40 20
1680. 120 c. Plate No. 69 (Series 1) (horiz.) .. 1·00 55
1681. 150 c. Plate No. 87 (Series 1) (horiz.) .. 1·25 65
1682. 225 c. Plate No. 60 (Series 1) .. .. 1·50 90
1683. 350 c Plate No. 94 (Series 1) (horiz.) .. 2·00 1·50

1986. 60th Birthday of Queen Elizabeth II. No. 1768 optd. **1926 1986 QUEEN ELIZABETH.**

1684. 130 c. Plate No. 13 (Series 1) 60 50

1986. Wildlife Protection. Nos. 685, 739/44 and 993/8 surch. **Protect the 60.**

1686. 60 c. on 35 c. Type **174** .. 25 25
1687. 60 c. on 35 c. Haimara .. 25 25
1688. 60 c. on 35 c. Electric eel 25 25
1689. 60 c. on 35 c. Golden rivulus 25 25
1690. 60 c. on 35 c. Pencil fish 25 25
1691. 60 c. on 35 c. Four-eyed fish 25 25
1691a. 60 c. on 35 c. Pirai or Carib fish 25 25
1691b. 60 c. on 35 c. Smoking Hassar 25 25
1691c. 60 c. on 35 c. Devil Ray 25 25
1691d. 60 c. on 35 c. Flying Patwa 25 25
1691e. 60 c. on 35 c. Arapaima Pirariucii 25 25
1691f. 60 c. on 35 c. Lukanani 25 25
1692. $6 on 8 c. Type **163** .. 1·75 1·75

1986. No. 799 surch.

1693. 600 c. on 720 c. on 60 c. Soldier's cap .. .. 1·50 75

1986. 125th Anniv. of British Guiana Post Office (2nd issue). No. 702a surch. with names of postal agencies opened between 1860 and 1880.

1694. 25 c. on 30 c. mult. (surch. **Abary**) 15 15
1695. 25 c. on 30 c. mult. (surch. **Anna Regina**) 15 15
1696. 25 c. on 30 c. mult. (surch. **Aurora**) 15 15
1697. 25 c. on 30 c. mult. (surch. **Bartica Grove**) 15 15
1698. 25 c. on 30 c. mult. (surch. **Bel Air**) 15 15
1699. 25 c. on 30 c. mult. (surch. **Belle Plaine**) .. 15 15
1700. 25 c. on 30 c. mult. (surch. **Clonbrook**) 15 15
1701. 25 c. on 30 c. mult. (surch. **T.P.O. Dem. Railway**) 15 15
1702. 25 c. on 30 c. mult. (surch. **Enmore**) 15 15
1703. 25 c. on 30 c. mult. (surch. **Fredericksburg**) 15 15
1704. 25 c. on 30 c. mult. (surch. **Good Success**) 15 15
1705. 25 c. on 30 c. mult. (surch. **1986**) .. 15 15
1706. 25 c. on 30 c. mult. (surch. **Mariabba**) 15 15
1707. 25 c. on 30 c. mult. (surch. **Massaruni**) 15 15
1708. 25 c. on 30 c. mult. (surch. **Nigg**) .. 15 15
1709. 25 c. on 30 c. mult. (surch. **No. 50**) 15 15
1710. 25 c. on 30 c. mult. (surch. **No. 63 Benab**) 15 15
1711. 25 c. on 30 c. mult. (surch. **Philadelphia**) .. 15 15
1712. 25 c. on 30 c. mult. (surch. **Sisters**) 15 15
1713. 25 c. on 30 c. mult. (surch. **Skeldon**) 15 15
1714. 25 c. on 30 c. mult. (surch. **Suddie**) 15 15
1715. 25 c. on 30 c. mult. (surch. **Taymouth Manor**) 15 15
1716. 25 c. on 30 c. mult. surch. **Wales**) .. 15 15
1717. 25 c. on 30 c. mult. (surch. **Whim**) .. 15 15

1986. 20th Anniv. of Independence. (a) No. 332 of British Guiana surch **GUYANA INDEPENDENCE 1966–1986,** Nos. 398 and 491 surch. **1986** and No. 656 surch. with Fleur-de-lis and value.

1718. 25 c. on 2 c. green (No. 332) 15 10
1719. 25 c. on 35 c. mult. (No. 656) 15 10
1720. 60 c. on 2 c. green (No. 332) 20 10
1721. 120 c. on 6 c. green (No. 398) 35 20
1722. 130 c. on 24 c. black and orange (No. 401) .. 45 20

(b) Nos. 1188/91 surch. **INDEPENDENCE 1966–1986.**

1723. **277.** 25 c. on 120 c. brown, black and blue (No. 1188) 15 10
1724. – 25 c. on 130 c. red, black and blue (No. 1189) 15 10
1725. – 25 c. on 150 c. violet and blue (No. 1190) 15 10
1726. – 225 c. on 200 c. green, black and blue (No. 1191) 50 50

1986. World Cup Football Championship, Mexico (2nd issue). No. 544 surch. **MEXICO 1986 225.**

1727. 225 c. on 3 c. Hanging heliconia .. .. 1·50 45

1986. CARICOM Day. No. 705a optd. **CARICOM DAY 1986.**

1728. 60 c. "Papilio androgeus" 40 15

1986. CARICOM Heads of Government Conference, Georgetown. Nos. 544 and 601 surch. **CARICOM HEADS OF GOV'T CONFERENCE JULY 1986** and value.

1729. 25 c. on 8 c. on 6 c. Cannon-ball Tree .. 20 10
1730. 60 c. on 3 c. Hanging Heliconia 40 25

1986. Centenary of Publication of Sanders' "Reichenbachia" (8th issue). As T **331.** Multicoloured.

1731. 30 c. Plate No. 86 (Series 1) 25 15
1732. 55 c. Plate No. 17 (Series 1) 40 20
1733. 60 c. Plate No. 93 (Series 1) 40 20
1734. 100 c. Plate No. 68 (Series 1) 55 20
1735. 130 c. Plate No. 91 (Series 1) 60 30
1736. 250 c. Plate No. 74 (Series 1) 90 60
1737. 260 c. Plate No. 39 (Series 1) 90 60
1738. 375 c. Plate No. 90 (Series 1) .. .. 1·25 85

1986. International Peace Year. Nos. 542 and 546 surch. **INT. YEAR OF PEACE** and value.

1739. 25 c. on 1 c. Pitcher Plant of Mt. Roraima 10 10
1740. 60 c. on 6 c. Cannon-ball tree 10 10
1741. 120 c. on 6 c. Cannon-ball tree 15 20
1742. 130 c. on 6 c. Cannon-ball tree 15 20
1743. 150 c. on 6 c. Cannon-ball tree 20 25

363. Halley's Comet and British Guiana 1907 2 c. Stamp.

1986. Appearance of Halley's Comet.

1744. **363.** 320 c. red, black and lilac 60 60
1745. – 320 c. multicoloured 60 60

DESIGN: No. 1745, Guyana 1985 320 c. Macaw stamp.

1986. Centenary of Publication of Sanders' "Reichenbachia" (9th issue). As T **331**. Multicoloured.
1747. 40 c. Plate No. 96 (Series 1) 25 15
1748. 45 c. Plate No. 81 (Series 1) 25 15
1749. 90 c. Plate No. 89 (Series 1) 45 20
1750. 100 c. Plate No. 88 (Series 1) 45 20
1751. 150 c. Plate No. 76 (Series 1) 60 35
1752. 180 c. Plate No. 15 (Series 1) 70 40
1753. 320 c. Plate No. 82 (Series 1) 85 55
1754. 330 c. Plate No. 80 (Series 1) .. .. 1·00 70

1986. No. 489 surch. **20.**
1755. 20 c. on 6 c. Patua .. 30 15

1986. 50th Anniv. of Guyana United Sadr Islamic Association. Nos. 469/70 optd. **GUSIA 1936–1986**, No. 1757 surch. also.
1756. **105.** 25 c. black, gold and lilac 20 10
1757. $1.50 on 6 c. black, gold and flesh .. 65 40

1986. Regional Pharmacy Conference. No. 545 surch. **REGIONAL PHARMACY CONFERENCE 1986 130.**
1758. 130 c. on 5 c. Annatto tree 70 30

1986. Centenary of Publication of Sanders' "Reichenbachia" (10th issue) Multicoloured. As T **331**.
1809. 30 c. Plate No. 30 (Series 2) 25 15
1810. 45 c. Plate No. 21 (Series 2) (horiz.) .. 30 15
1811. 75 c. Plate No. 8 (Series 2) 55 15
1812. 80 c. Plate No. 42 (Series 2) (horiz.) .. 55 15
1813. 90 c. Plate No. 4 (Series 2) 65 25
1814. 130 c. Plate No. 38 (Series 2) 70 35
1815. 160 c. Plate No. 5 (Series 2) (horiz.) .. 85 40
1816. 200 c. Plate No. 9 (Series 2) .. .. 1·00 50
1817. 320 c. Plate No. 12 (Series 2) .. .. 1·75 70
1818. 350 c. Plate No. 29 (Series 2) (horiz.) .. 2·00 70
1819. 360 c. Plate No. 34 (Series 2) .. .. 2·00 70

1986. 20th Anniv. of Independence (2nd issue). As T **332** but additionally inscr. "1966–1986" at foot.
1820. 25 c. multicoloured .. 15 15

1986. Centenary of Publication of Sanders' "Reichenbachia" (11th issue). Design as No. 1735, but with different face value. Multicoloured.
1822. 40 c. Plate No. 91 (Series 1) 70 15

1986. Nos. 1361/84 surch.
1823. 120 c. on 30 c. mult. (No. 1361) 30 30
1824. 120 c. on 30 c. mult. (No. 1362) 30 30
1825. 120 c. on 30 c. mult. (No. 1363) 30 30
1826. 120 c. on 30 c. mult. (No. 1364) 30 30
1827. 120 c. on 30 c. mult. (No. 1365) 30 30
1828. 120 c. on 30 c. mult. (No. 1366) 30 30
1829. 120 c. on 30 c. mult. (No. 1367) 30 30
1830. 120 c. on 30 c. mult. (No. 1368) 30 30
1831. 120 c. on 30 c. mult. (No. 1369) 30 30
1832. 120 c. on 30 c. mult. (No. 1370) 30 30
1833. 120 c. on 30 c. mult. (No. 1371) 30 30
1834. 120 c. on 30 c. mult. (No. 1372) 30 30
1835. 120 c. on 30 c. mult. (No. 1373) 30 30
1836. 120 c. on 30 c. mult. (No. 1374) 30 30
1837. 120 c. on 30 c. mult. (No. 1375) 30 30
1838. 120 c. on 30 c. mult. (No. 1376) 30 30
1839. 120 c. on 30 c. mult. (No. 1377) 30 30
1840. 120 c. on 30 c. mult. (No. 1378) 30 30
1841. 120 c. on 30 c. mult. (No. 1379) 30 30
1842. 120 c. on 30 c. mult. (No. 1380) 30 30
1843. 120 c. on 30 c. mult. (No. 1381) 30 30
1844. 120 c. on 30 c. mult. (No. 1382) 30 30
1845. 120 c. on 30 c. mult. (No. 1383) 30 30
1846. 120 c. on 30 c. mult. (No. 1384) 30 30

1986. 12th World Orchid Conference, Tokyo. (1st issue). Unissued design as No. 1731, but with different face value, surch. **12th World Orchid Conference TOKYO JAPAN MARCH 1987 650.**
1847. 650 c. on 40 c. Plate No. 86 (Series 1) .. .. 2·10 1·75
No. 1847 is inscribed "ONTOGLOSSUM TRIUMPHANS" in error.
See also No. 2138.

1986. Columbus Day. Unissued design as No. 1863, but with different face value, surch. **1492–1992 CHRISTOPHER COLUMBUS 320.**
1864. 320 c. on 150 c. Plate No. 24 (Series 1) 75 45

1986. International Food Day. Nos. 1170/1 further surch. **1986** and value.
1866. 50 c. on 30 c. on 1 c. Type **87** 20 15
1867. 225 c. on $2.60 on 3 c. Lukunani 60 45

1986. Centenary of Publication of Sanders' "Reichenbachia" (12th issue). As T **331**, one as No. 1731 with different face value. Multicoloured.
1868. 40 c. Plate No. 86 (Series 1) 40 15
1869. 90 c. Plate No. 10 (Series 2) 70 30

1986. Air. 40th Annivs. of U.N.I.C.E.F. and U.N.E.S.C.O. No. 706 surch.
1870. 120 c. on $1 "Agrias claudina" (surch. **UNICEF 1946–1986 AIR 120**) 30 35
1871. 120 c. on $1 "Agrias claudina" (surch. **UNESCO 1946–1986 AIR 120**) 30 25

1986. Centenary of Publication of Sanders' "Reichenbachia" (13th issue). As T **331**. Multicoloured.
1872. 45 c. Plate No. 17 (Series 2) 30 15
1873. 50 c. Plate No. 33 (Series 2) 30 15
1874. 60 c. Plate No. 27 (Series 2) 45 15
1875. 75 c. Plate No. 56 (Series 2) 55 20
1876. 85 c. Plate No. 45 (Series 2) 55 20
1877. 90 c. Plate No. 13 (Series 2) 70 20
1878. 200 c. Plate No. 44 (Series 2) .. .. 1·00 45
1879. 300 c. Plate No. 50 (Series 2) .. .. 1·60 60
1880. 320 c. Plate No. 10 (Series 2) .. .. 1·75 70
1881. 390 c. Plate No. 6 (Series 2) .. .. 2·00 95

1986. Deepavali Festival. Nos. 543 and 601 surch. **Deepavali 1986** and values
1882. 25 c. on 2 c. Type **132** .. 15 10
1883. 200 c. on 8 c. on 6 c. Cannon-ball tree .. 55 40

1986. Centenary of Publication of Sanders' "Reichenbachia" (14th issue). As T **331**, two as Nos. 1732 and 1734 with different face values. Multicoloured.
1884. 40 c. Plate No. 68 (Series 1) 30 15
1885. 80 c. Plate No. 17 (Series 1) 60 25
1886. 200 c. Plate No. 2 (Series 2) .. .. 1·25 60
1887. 225 c. Plate No. 24 (Series 2) .. .. 1·50 70

1986. Christmas. No. 452 surch **CHRISTMAS 1986 20.**
1888 20 c. on 6 c. Patua .. 10 10

1986. Wildlife Protection. Nos. 756/67 optd. **1986.**
1894. 30 c. Type **178** 25 25
1895. 30 c. Red howler 25 25
1896. 30 c. Common squirrel-monkey 25 25
1897. 30 c. Two-toed sloth .. 25 25
1898. 30 c. Brazilian tapir .. 25 25
1899. 30 c. Collared peccary .. 25 25
1900. 30 c. Six-banded armadillo 25 25
1901. 30 c. Tamandua 25 25
1902. 30 c. Giant anteater .. 25 25
1903. 30 c. Murine opossum .. 25 25
1904. 30 c. Brown four-eyed opossum 25 25
1905. 30 c. Brazilian agouti .. 25 25

1986. No. 1642 surch. **$15.**
1906. $15 on $3.50 Clive Lloyd with Prudential Cup .. 7·00 6·00

1986. Centenary of Publication of Sanders' "Reichenbachia" (15th issue). Design as No. 1877, but with different face value. Multicoloured.
1907. 50 c. Plate No. 13 (Series 2) 55 15

375. Memorial.

1986. President Burnham Commemoration. Multicoloured.
1908. 25 c. Type **375** 10 10
1909. 120 c. Map of Guyana and flags 35 20
1910. 130 c. Parliament Buildings and mace .. 35 20
1911. $6 L.F. Burnham and Georgetown mayoral chain (vert.) .. .. 1·25 1·25

1986. Centenary of Publication of Sanders' "Reichenbachia" (16th issue). As Nos. 1554/5, 1874 and 1887 but with different face values. Multicoloured.
1912. 50 c. Plate No. 49 (Series 1) (22.12) .. 30 15
1913. 50 c. Plate No. 64 (Series 1) 30 15
1914. 85 c. Plate No. 24 (Series 2) 55 25
1915. 90 c. Plate No. 27 (Series 2) 55 25

1986. Centenary of Publication of Sanders' "Reichenbachia" (17th issue). As T **331**. Multicoloured.
1916. 25 c. Plate No. 20 (Series 2) 25 15
1917. 40 c. Plate No. 7 (Series 2) 25 15
1918. 85 c. Plate No. 15 (Series 2) 40 20
1919. 90 c. Plate No. 3 (Series 2) 40 20
1920. 120 c. Plate No. 14 (Series 2) 55 30
1921. 130 c. Plate No. 32 (Series 2) 55 30
1922. 150 c. Plate No. 22 (Series 2) 70 35
1923. 320 c. Plate No. 18 (Series 2) .. .. 1·00 55
1924. 330 c. Plate No. 28 (Series 2) .. .. 1·00 70

1987. Centenary of Publication of Sanders' "Reichenbachia" (18th issue). As Nos. 1853, 1876, 1886, 1918 and 1923 but with different face values Multicoloured.
1925 35 c. Plate No. 45 (Series 2) 30 15
1926 50 c. Plate No. 15 (Series 2) 30 15
1927 50 c. Plate No. 55 (Series 1) 30 15
1928 85 c. Plate No. 18 (Series 2) 55 25
1929 90 c. Plate No. 2 (Series 2) 55 25

1987. 10th Anniv. of Guyana Post Office Corporation (1st issue). Unissued designs as Nos. 1849 and 1863, but with different face values, surch or optd. **G P O C 1977–1987.**
1930 $2.25 Plate No. 53 (Series 1) 75 35
1931 $10 on 150 c. Plate No. 24 (Series 1) .. .. 2·25 2·50

1987. Various "Reichenbachia" issues surch.
2375 120 c. on 40 c. Plate No. 91 (Series 1) (No. 1822) 15 15
2380 120 c. on 40 c. Plate No. 90 (Series 1) 15 15
2387 120 c. on 50 c. Plate No. 9 (Series 1) 15 15
1994 120 c. on 50 c. Plate No. 49 (Series 1) (No. 1912) 30 30
1995 120 c. on 50 c. Plate No. 64 (Series 1) (No. 1913) 30 30
2388 120 c. on 50 c. Plate No. 22 (Series 1) 15 15
2389 120 c. on 50 c. Plate No. 3 (Series 2) 15 15
2390 120 c. on 50 c. Plate No. 6 (Series 2) 15 15
2391 120 c. on 50 c. Plate No. 20 (Series 2) 15 15
2392 120 c. on 50 c. Plate No. 32 (Series 2) 15 15
2019 120 c. on 50 c. Plate No. 24 (Series 1) 30 30
2020 120 c. on 50 c. Plate No. 53 (Series 1) 30 30
2021 120 c. on 50 c. Plate No. 65 (Series 1) 30 30
1980 120 c. on 55 c. Plate No. 9 (Series 1) (No. 1763) .. 30 30
2003 120 c. on 55 c. Plate No. 49 (Series 1) (No. 1765) 30 30
1981 120 c. on 55 c. Plate No. 64 (Series 1) (No. 1766) 30 30
2006 120 c. on 55 c. Plate No. 22 (Series 1) (No. 1764) 30 30
2009 120 c. on 55 c. Plate No. 15 (Series 1) 30 30
2010 120 c. on 55 c. Plate No. 81 (Series 1) 30 30
2011 120 c. on 55 c. Plate No. 82 (Series 1) 30 30
2012 120 c. on 55 c. Plate No. 89 (Series 1) 30 30
2394 120 c. on 60 c. Plate No. 2 (Series 1) (No. 1519) .. 15 15
2027 120 c. on 60 c. Plate No. 10 (Series 1) (No. 1521) 30 30
2028 120 c. on 60 c. Plate No. 19 (Series 1) (No. 1522) 30 30
2029 120 c. on 60 c. Plate No. 31 (Series 1) (No. 1523) 30 30
2030 120 c. on 60 c. Plate No. 5 (Series 1) 30 30
2403 120 c. on 60 c. Plate No. 50 (Series 1) 15 15
2404 120 c. on 60 c. Plate No. 54 (Series 1) 15 15
2405 120 c. on 60 c. Plate No. 69 (Series 1) 15 15
2034 120 c. on 60 c. Plate No. 71 (Series 1) 30 30
2406 120 c. on 60 c. Plate No. 79 (Series 1) 15 15
2036 120 c. on 60 c. Plate No. 87 (Series 1) 30 30
2407 120 c. on 60 c. Plate No. 94 (Series 1) 15 15
2038 120 c. on 75 c. Plate No. 60 (Series 1) 30 30
2039 120 c. on 75 c. Plate No. 83 (Series 1) 30 30
2040 120 c. on 75 c. Plate No. 92 (Series 1) 30 30
2041 120 c. on 75 c. Plate No. 95 (Series 1) 30 30
1933 200 c. on 25 c. Plate No. 8 (Series 1) (No. 1571) .. 40 40
1934 200 c. on 25 c. Plate No. 51 (Series 1) (No. 1573) 40 40
1949 200 c. on 25 c. Plate No. 52 (Series 1) (No. 1551) 40 40
1951 200 c. on 25 c. Plate No. 72 (Series 1) (No. 1577) 40 40
1952 200 c. on 25 c. Plate No. 71 (Series 1) (No. 1679) 40 40
1953 200 c. on 30 c. Plate No. 86 (Series 1) (No. 1731) 40 40
1954 200 c. on 30 c. Plate No. 53 (Series 1) (No. 1770) 40 40
1932 200 c. on 40 c. Plate No. 90 (Series 1) 40 40
1937 200 c. on 40 c. Plate No. 68 (Series 1) (No. 1884) 40 40
1955 200 c. on 40 c. Plate No. 77 (Series 1) (No. 1663) 40 40
1956 200 c. on 40 c. Plate No. 86 (Series 1) (No. 1868) 40 40
1957 200 c. on 45 c. Plate No. 81 (Series 1) (No. 1748) 40 40
1958 200 c. on 45 c. Plate No. 77 (Series 1) 40 40
1959 200 c. on 45 c. Plate No. 78 (Series 1) 40 40
1960 200 c. on 45 c. Plate No. 85 (Series 1) 40 40
2044 200 c. on 45 c. Plate No. 84 (Series 1) 30 30
1939 200 c. on 50 c. Plate No. 92 (Series 1) (No. 1665) 40 40
1940 200 c. on 50 c. Plate No. 22 (Series 1) 40 40
1961 200 c. on 50 c. Plate No. 24 (Series 1) 40 40
1962 200 c. on 50 c. Plate No. 53 (Series 1) 40 40

1963 200 c. on 50 c. Plate No. 65 (Series 1) 40 40
2046 200 c. on 50 c. Plate No. 55 (Series 1) (No. 1927) 40 40
1941 200 c. on 55 c. Plate No. 22 (Series 1) (No. 1764) 40 40
1964 200 c. on 55 c. Plate No. 49 (Series 1) (No. 1765) 40 40
1965 200 c. on 55 c. Plate No. 17 (Series 1) (No. 1732) 40 40
2050 200 c. on 55 c. Plate No. 15 (Series 1) .. 40 40
2051 200 c. on 55 c. Plate No. 81 (Series 1) 40 40
2052 200 c. on 55 c. Plate No. 82 (Series 1) 40 40
2053 200 c. on 55 c. Plate No. 89 (Series 1) 40 40
1942 200 c. on 60 c. Plate No. 5 (Series 1) 40 40
1967 200 c. on 60 c. Plate No. 7 (Series 1) (No. 1520) .. 40 40
1968 200 c. on 60 c. Plate No. 10 (Series 1) (No. 1521) 40 40
1969 200 c. on 60 c. Plate No. 19 (Series 1) (No. 1522) 40 40
1970 200 c. on 60 c. Plate No. 31 (Series 1) (No. 1523) 40 40
1971 200 c. on 60 c. Plate No. 44 (Series 1) (No. 1556) 40 40
1972 200 c. on 60 c. Plate No. 47 (Series 1) (No. 1557) 40 40
1973 200 c. on 60 c. Plate No. 57 (Series 1) (No. 1622) 40 40
1974 200 c. on 60 c. Plate No. 73 (Series 1) (No. 1623) 40 40
1975 200 c. on 60 c. Plate No. 75 (Series 1) (No. 1624) 40 40
1976 200 c. on 60 c. Plate No. 71 (Series 1) 40 40
1977 200 c. on 60 c. Plate No. 87 (Series 1) 40 40
1943 200 c. on 75 c. Plate No. 5 (Series 1) (No. 1667) .. 40 40
1944 200 c. on 75 c. Plate No. 60 (Series 1) 40 40
1945 200 c. on 75 c. Plate No. 92 (Series 1) 40 40
1946 200 c. on 85 c. Plate No. 18 (Series 2) (No. 1928) 40 40
1947 200 c. on 375 c. Plate No. 90 (Series 1) (No. 1738) 40 40
1987 225 c. on 40 c. Plate No. 91 (Series 1) (No. 1822) 50 50
1988 225 c. on 40 c. Plate No. 90 (Series 1) 50 50
2055 225 c. on 40 c. Plate No. 86 (Series 1) 50 50
2056 225 c. on 40 c. Plate No. 68 (Series 1) (No. 1884) 50 50
1989 225 c. on 50 c. Plate No. 22 (Series 1) 50 50
1990 225 c. on 60 c. Plate No. 55 (Series 1) (No. 1597) 50 50
1991 225 c. on 60 c. Plate No. 93 (Series 1) (No. 1733) 50 50
2058 225 c. on 65 c. Plate No. 76 (Series 1) 50 50
2059 225 c. on 65 c. Plate No. 80 (Series 1) 50 50
2060 225 c. on 65 c. Plate No. 88 (Series 1) 50 50
2061 225 c. on 65 c. Plate No. 96 (Series 1) 50 50
1992 225 c. on 80 c. Plate No. 93 (Series 1) 50 50
1978 225 c. on 90 c. Plate No. 89 (Series 1) (No. 1749) 40 40
1993 225 c. on 150 c. Plate No. 42 (Series 1) (No. 1657) 50 50
2062 600 c. on 80 c. Plate No. 17 (Series 1) (No. 1885) 1·25 1·25
2063 600 c. on 80 c. Plate No. 39 (Series 1) .. .. 1·25 1·25
2064 600 c. on 80 c. Plate No. 74 (Series 1) .. .. 1·25 1·25
2065 600 c. on 80 c. Plate No. 93 (Series 1) .. .. 1·25 1·25

1987. Nos. 1518 and 1572 surch **TWO DOLLARS**.
1935 $2 on 25 c. Plate No. 12 (Series 1) (No. 1518) .. 40 40
1936 $2 on 25 c. Plate No. 23 (Series 1) (No. 1572) 40 40

1987. Various "Reichenbachia" issues surch **1987**.
1983 $10 on 25 c. Plate No. 53 (Series 1) .. .. 1·75 1·75
1984 $12 on 80 c. Plate No. 74 (Series 1) .. .. 2·00 2·00
1985 $15 on 80 c. Plate No. 39 (Series 1) .. .. 2·50 2·50
1986 $25 on 25 c. Plate No. 53 (Series 1) .. .. 4·00 4·00

1987. Centenary of Publication of Sanders' "Reichenbachia" (19th issue). Multicoloured.
2066 180 c. Plate 41 (Series 2) 75 40
2067 230 c. Plate 25 (Series 2) 85 50
2068 300 c. Plate 85 (Series 2) 1·10 65
2069 330 c. Plate 82 (Series 2) 1·25 70
2070 425 c. Plate 87 (Series 2) 1·50 85
2071 440 c. Plate 88 (Series 2) 1·50 85
2072 590 c. Plate 52 (Series 2) 1·75 1·25
2073 650 c. Plate 65 (Series 2) 2·25 1·50

1987. 10th Anniv of Guyana Post Office Corporation (2nd issue). Nos. 543, 545, 548a and 601 surch **Post Office Corp. 1977-1987**.
2074 25 c. on 2 c. Type **132** .. 15 10
2075 25 c. on 5 c. Annatto tree 15 10
2076 25 c. on 8 c on 6 c. Cannon-ball tree .. 15 10
2077 25 c. on 15 c. Christmas orchid 15 10
2078 60 c. on 15 c. Christmas orchid 35 10
2079 $1.20 on 2 c. Type **132** .. 50 40
2080 $1.30 on 15 c. Christmas orchid 50 40

1987. No. 1534 surch **1987 200**.
2081 **332** 200 c. on 25 c. mult .. 50 40

1987. Various "Reichenbachia" issues optd **1987**.
2112 120 c. Plate No. 1 (Series 1) (No. 1578) 30 30
2113 120 c. Plate No. 11 (Series 1) (No. 1579) 30 30
2114 120 c. Plate No. 28 (Series 1) (No. 1580) 30 30
2115 120 c. Plate No. 37 (Series 1) (No. 1627) 30 30
2116 120 c. Plate No. 46 (Series 1) (No. 1628) 30 30
2117 120 c. Plate No. 56 (Series 1) (No. 1629) 30 30
2118 120 c. Plate No. 58 (Series 1) (No. 1630) 30 30
2132 120 c. Plate No. 67 (Series 1) (No. 1631) 30 30
2084 130 c. Plate No. 3 (Series 1) (No. 1525) 30 30
2093 130 c. Plate No. 6 (Series 1) (No. 1767) 30 30
2094 130 c. Plate No. 20 (Series 1) (No. 1770) 30 30
2087 130 c. Plate No. 18 (Series 1) (No. 1536) 30 30
2088 130 c. Plate No. 29 (Series 1) (No. 1537) 30 30
2089 130 c. Plate No. 30 (Series 1) (No. 1538) 30 30
2090 130 c. Plate No. 16 (Series 1) (No. 1559) 30 30
2091 130 c. Plate No. 66 (Series 1) (No. 1632) 30 30
2092 130 c. Plate No. 13 (Series 1) (No. 1684) 30 30
2109 130 c. Plate No. 91 (Series 1) (No. 1735) 30 30
2111 130 c. Plate No. 25 (Series 1) (No. 1771) 30 30
2123 150 c. Plate No. 40 (Series 1) (No. 1801) 40 40
2124 150 c. Plate No. 45 (Series 1) (No. 1803) 40 40
2125 150 c. Plate No. 42 (Series 1) (No. 1657) 40 40
2137 150 c. Plate No. 26 (Series 1) (No. 1633) 40 40
2095 200 c. Plate No. 4 (Series 1) (No. 1533) 40 40
2096 200 c. Plate No. 14 (Series 1) (No. 1584) 40 40
2097 200 c. Plate No. 21 (Series 1) (No. 1585) 40 40
2098 200 c. Plate No. 33 (Series 1) (No. 1634) 40 40
2099 200 c. Plate No. 43 (Series 1) (No. 1658) 40 40
2100 200 c. Plate No. 79 (Series 1) (No. 1670) 40 40
2101 200 c. Plate No. 9 (Series 2) (No. 1816) 40 40
2102 200 c. Plate No. 2 (Series 2) (No. 1886) 40 40
2103 250 c. Plate No. 74 (Series 1) (No. 1736) 50 50
2104 260 c. Plate No. 39 (Series 1) (No. 1737) 50 50

1987. 12th World Orchid Conference, Tokyo (2nd issue). Nos. 1776 surch **12th World Orchid Conference. 650**.
2138 650 c. on 55 c. Plate No. 9 (Series 1) .. .. 1·50 1·25

1987. 125th Anniv of British Guiana Post Office (3rd issue). No. 699 surch with names of postal agencies opened by 1885.
2140 25 c. on 10 c. multi (surch **AGRICOLA**) .. 15 15
2141 25 c. on 10 c. mult (surch **BAGOTVILLE**) .. 15 15
2142 25 c. on 10 c. mult (surch **BOURDA**) 15 15
2143 25 c. on 10 c. mult (surch **BUXTON**) 15 15
2144 25 c. on 10 c. mult (surch **CABACABURI**) .. 15 15
2145 25 c. on 10 c. mult (surch **CARMICHAEL STREET**) .. 15 15
2146 25 c. on 10 c. mult (surch **COTTON TREE**) .. 15 15
2147 25 c. on 10 c. mult (surch **DUNOON**) 15 15
2148 25 c. on 10 c. mult (surch **FELLOWSHIP**) .. 15 15
2149 25 c. on 10 c. mult (surch **GROVE**) 15 15
2150 25 c. on 10 c. mult (surch **HACKNEY**) 15 15
2151 25 c. on 10 c. mult (surch **LEONORA**) 15 15
2152 25 c. on 10 c. multd (surch **1987**) 15 15
2153 25 c. on 10 c. mult (surch **MALLALI**) 15 15
2154 25 c. on 10 c. mult (surch **PROVIDENCE**) .. 15 15
2155 25 c. on 10 c. mult (surch **RELIANCE**) .. 15 15
2156 25 c. on 10 c. mult (surch **SPARTA**) 15 15
2157 25 c. on 10 c. mult (surch **STEWARTVILLE**) 15 15
2158 25 c. on 10 c. mult (surch **TARLOGY**) 15 15
2159 25 c. on 10 c. mult (surch **T.P.O. BERBICE RIV.**) 15 15
2160 25 c. on 10 c. mult (surch **T.P.O. DEM. RIV.**) 15 15
2161 25 c. on 10 c. mult (surch **T.P.O. ESSEO. RIV.**) 15 15
2162 25 c. on 10 c. mult (surch **T.P.O. MASSA-RUNI RIV.**) 15 15
2163 25 c. on 10 c. mult (surch **TUSCHEN (De VRIENDEN)**) .. 15 15
2164 25 c. on 10 c. multd (surch **ZORG**) 15 15

1987. 50th Anniv of First Georgetown–Port-of-Spain Flight by P.A.A. No. 708a optd **28 MARCH 1927 PAA GEO- POS**.
2165 $10 "Elbella patrobas" .. 2·00 2·50

1987. No. 704 surch with figures only.
2166 25 c. on 40 c. "Morpho rhetenor" (male) .. 30 10

1987. Easter. Nos. 481/2 and 484 optd **1987** or surch also.
2167 **111** 25 c. multicoloured .. 15 10
2168 120 c. on 6 c. mult .. 20 20
2169 320 c. on 6 c. mult .. 50 45
2170 500 c. on 40 c. mult .. 75 70

1987. Centenary of Publication of Sanders' "Reichenbachia" (20th issue). As T **331**. Mult.
2171 240 c. Plate No. 47 (Series 2) 80 45
2172 260 c. Plate No. 39 (Series 2) 90 55
2173 275 c. Plate No. 58 (Series 2) (horiz) 90 55
2174 390 c. Plate No. 37 (Series 2) (horiz) .. .. 1·10 70
2175 450 c. Plate No. 19 (Series 2) (horiz) .. .. 1·50 90
2176 460 c. Plate No. 54 (Series 2) (horiz) .. .. 1·50 90
2177 500 c. Plate No. 51 (Series 2) .. .. .. 1·75 1·10
2178 560 c. Plate No. 1 (Series 2) .. .. .. 2·00 1·50

1987. No. 706 optd **1987**.
2179 167 $1 multicoloured .. 40 15

1987. Centenary of Publication of Sanders' "Reichenbachia" (21st issue). As T **331**. Mult.
2180 500 c. Plate No. 86 (Series 2) .. .. .. 1·75 1·10
2181 520 c. Plate No. 89 (Series 2) .. .. .. 1·90 1·25
2182 $20 Plate No. 83 (Series 2) 6·00 6·50

1987. As T **332**, but within frame.
2183 25 c. multicoloured .. 15 15

1987. "Capex '87" International Stamp Exhibition, Toronto. Nos. 1744/5 optd **CAPEX '87**.
2185 **363** 320 c. red, blk & lilac 40 45
2186 – 320 c. multicoloured 40 45

1987. Commonwealth Heads of Government Meeting, Vancouver. Nos. 1066/8 further optd **1987**.
2187 $1.20 on 6 c. green .. 15 20
2188 $1.30 on 24 c. black & orge 15 20
2189 $2.40 on 24 c. black & orge 30 35

1987. Centenary of Publication of Sanders' "Reichenbachia" (22nd issue). As T **331**. Mult.
2190 400 c. Plate No. 80 (Series 2) .. .. .. 1·25 80
2191 480 c. Plate No. 77 (Series 2) .. .. .. 1·50 1·00
2192 600 c. Plate No. 94 (Series 2) .. .. .. 2·00 1·50
2193 $25 Plate No. 72 (Series 2) 6·50 7·00

396 Steam Locomotive "Alexandra"

1987. Guyana Railways.
2194 **396** $1.20 green 25 25
2195 – $1.20 green 25 25
2196 – $1.20 green 25 25
2197 – $1.20 green 25 25
2198 **396** $1.20 purple .. 25 25
2199 – $1.20 purple .. 25 25
2200 – $1.20 purple .. 25 25
2201 – $1.20 purple .. 25 25
2202 **396** $3.20 blue 60 60
2203 – $3.20 blue 60 60
2204 – $3.20 blue 60 60
2205 – $3.20 blue 60 60
2206 – $3.20 blue 60 60
2207 – $3.30 black 60 60
2208 **396** $3.30 black 60 60
2209 – $3.30 black 60 60
2210 – $3.30 black 60 60
2211 – $3.30 black 60 60
2212 – $10 multicoloured .. 1·50 1·50
2213 – $12 multicoloured .. 1·75 1·75

DESIGNS: As T **396** —Nos. 2195, 2199, 2203, 2207, Front view of diesel locomotive; Nos. 2196, 2200, 2204, 2210, Steam locomotive with searchlight; Nos. 2197, 2201, 2205, 2209, Side view of diesel locomotive. 82 × 55 mm—No. 2206, Molasses warehouses and early locomotive; No. 2211, Diesel locomotive and passenger train. 88 × 39 mm—No. 2212, Cattle train; No. 2213, Molasses train.

1987. 50th Anniv of First Flights from Georgetown to Massaruni and Mabaruma. No. 706 optd.
2214 $1 multicoloured (optd **FAIREY NICHOLL 8 AUG 1927 GEO-MAZ**) 15 15
2215 $1 multicoloured (optd **FAIREY NICHOLL 15 AUG 1927 GEO-MAB**) .. 15 15

1987. Centenary of Publication of Sanders' "Reichenbachia" (23rd issue). As T **331**. Mult.
2216 200 c. Plate No. 43 (Series 2) 75 45
2217 200 c. Plate No. 48 (Series 2) 75 45
2218 200 c. Plate No. 92 (Series 2) 75 45

1987. Centenary of Publication of Sanders' "Reichenbachia" (24th issue). No.2219 surch **600**. Multicoloured.
2219 600 c. on 900 c. Plate No. 74 (Series 2) .. .. 2·00 2·00
2220 900 c. Plate No. 74 (Series 2) .. .. .. 4·00 4·00

1987. Columbus Day.
2221 225 c. on 350 c. on 120 c. Plate No. 65 (Series 1) (No. 1598 further surch **225**) 30 35
2222 950 c. on 900 c. Plate No. 74 (Series 2) (No. 2220 surch **950 CRIST-OVAO COLOMBO 1492 – 1992**) .. .. 1·25 1·40
2223 950 c. on 900 c. Plate No. 74 (Series 2) (No. 2220 surch **950 CHRISTOPHE COLOMB 1492 – 1992**) 1·25 1·40

1987. Centenary of Publication of Sanders' "Reichenbachia" (25th issue). As T **331**. Multicoloured.
2225 325 c. Plate No. 68 (Series 2) (horiz) .. .. 1·25 70
2226 420 c. Plate No. 95 (Series 2) (horiz) .. .. 1·50 90
2227 575 c. Plate No. 60 (Series 2) .. .. .. 1·75 1·25

1987. Deepavali Festival. Nos. 544/5 surch **DEEPAVALI 1987 25** and new value.
2228 25 c. on 3 c. Hanging heliconia 10 10
2229 $3 on 5 c. Annatto tree .. 40 45

1987. Christmas. No. 489 surch **CHRISTMAS 1987 20**.
2230 20 c. on 6 c. Patua .. 10 10

1987. Royal Ruby Wedding. No. 1684 optd **1987**.
2233 130 c. Plate No. 13 (Series 1) 15 20

1987. Centenary of Publication of Sanders' "Reichenbachia" (26th issue). As T **331**. Multicoloured.

2235 255 c. Plate No. 61 (Series 2) . . . . 1·75 1·00
2236 290 c. Plate No. 53 (Series 2) . . . . 2·00 1·25
2237 375 c. Plate No. 96 (Series 2) . . . . 2·50 1·40
2238 680 c. Plate No. 64 (Series 2) . . . . 3·50 2·25
2239 720 c. Plate No. 49 (Series 2) . . . . 4·00 3·50
2240 750 c. Plate No. 66 (Series 2) . . . . 4·00 3·50
2241 800 c. Plate No. 79 (Series 2) . . . . 4·50 4·00
2242 850 c. Plate No. 76 (Series 2) . . . . 4·50 4·00

1987. Air. No. 1620 surch **AIR 75**.

2243 75 c. on 25 c. Plate No. 59 (Series 1) 30 15

1987. Wildlife Protection. Nos. 756/67 optd **1987**, Nos. 1432/4 surch **320** and Nos. 1631/3, 1752/3 and 1847 optd **PROTECT OUR HERITAGE '87**.

2244 30 c. Type **178** 15 15
2245 30 c. Red howler . . 15 15
2246 30 c. Common squirrel-monkey . . 15 15
2247 30 c. Two-toed sloth . . 15 15
2248 30 c. Brazilian tapir . . 15 15
2249 30 c. Collared peccary . . 15 15
2250 30 c. Six-banded armadillo 15 15
2251 30 c. Tamandua 15 15
2252 30 c. Giant anteater . . 15 15
2253 30 c. Murine opossum . . 15 15
2254 30 c. Brown four-eyed opossum 15 15
2255 30 c. Brazilian agouti . . 15 15
2256 120 c. Plate No. 67 (Series 1) 30 30
2257 130 c. Plate No. 66 (Series 1) 30 30
2258 150 c. Plate No. 26 (Series 1) 35 35
2259 180 c. Plate No. 15 (Series 1) 40 40
2260 320 c. Plate No. 82 (Series 1) 60 60
2261 320 c. on 120 c. Demerara Mutual Life Assurance Building 60 60
2262 320 c. on 120 c. Town Hall 60 60
2263 320 c. on 120 c. Victoria Law Courts 60 60
2264 650 c. on 40 c. Plate No. 86 (Series 1) . . . . 1·25 1·25

1987. Air. Various "Reichenbachia" issues optd **AIR**.

2265 60 c. Plate No. 55 (Series 1) No. 1597) 30 30
2463 75 c. Plate No. 55 (Series 1 (No. 1853) 15 15
2464 75 c. Plate No. 5 (Series 1) (No. 1667) 15 15
2466 75 c. Plate No. 83 (Series 1) 15 15
2467 75 c. Plate No. 95) (Series 1) 15 15

1988. World Scout Jamboree, Australia. Nos. 830, 837 and 1104 optd **AUSTRALIA 1987 Jamboree 1988** or surch also.

2266 **116** 440 c. on 6 c. mult (No. 837) 30 30
2267 $10 on 110 c. on 6 c. mult (No. 830) . . 60 60
2268 $10 on 180 c. on 6 c. mult (No. 1104) . . 60 60
2269 $10 on 440 c. on 6 c. mult (No. 837) . . 60 60

1988. 10th Anniv of International Fund for Agricultural Development. Nos. 448 and 450 surch **IFAD For a World Without Hunger**.

2270 25 c. on 1 c. Type **87** . . 10 10
2271 $5 on 3 c. Lukunani . . 20 25

1988. Republic Day. Nos. 545, 548a and 555 surch **Republic Day 1988**.

2272 25 c. on 5 c. Annatto tree 10 10
2273 120 c. on 15 c. Christmas orchid 15 10
2274 $10 on $2 "Noranthea guianensis" 55 50

1988. Centenary of Publication of Sanders' "Reichenbachia" (28th series). As T **331**. Multicoloured.

2276 $10 Plate No. 40 (Series 2) 1·75 1·75
2277 $12 Plate No. 91 (Series 2) 1·75 1·75

1988. 125th Anniv of British Guiana Post Office (4th issue). No. 702a surch with names of postal agencies opened between 1886 and 1900.

2278 25 c. on 30 c. mult (surch **Albouystown**) . . 15 15
2279 25 c. on 30 c. mult (surch **Anns Grove**) . . 15 15
2280 25 c. on 30 c. mult (surch **Amacura**) 15 15
2281 25 c. on 30 c. mult (surch **Arakaka**) 15 15
2282 25 c. on 30 c. mult (surch **Baramanni**) 15 15
2283 25 c. on 30 c. mult (surch **Cuyuni**) 15 15
2284 25 c. on 30 c. mult (surch Hope Placer) 15 15
2285 25 c. on 30 c. mult (surch **H M P S**) 15 15
2286 25 c. on 30 c. mult (surch **Kitty**) 15 15
2287 25 c. on 30 c. mult (surch **M'M'Zorg**) 15 15
2288 25 c. on 30 c. mult (surch **Maccaseema**) . . 15 15
2289 25 c. on 30 c. mult (surch **1988**) 15 15
2290 25 c. on 30 c. mult (surch **Morawhanna**) . . 15 15
2291 25 c. on 30 c. mult (surch **Naamryck**) 15 15
2292 25 c. on 30 c. mult (surch **Purini**) 15 15
2293 25 c. on 30 c. mult (surch **Potaro Landing**) . . 15 15
2294 25 c. on 30 c. mult (surch **Rockstone**) 15 15
2295 25 c. on 30 c. mult (surch **Rosignol**) 15 15
2296 25 c. on 30 c. mult (surch **Stanleytown**) . . 15 15
2297 25 c. on 30 c. mult (surch **Santa Rosa**) . . 15 15
2298 25 c. on 30 c. mult (surch **Tumatumari**) . . 15 15
2299 25 c. on 30 c. mult (surch **Weldaad**) 15 15
2300 25 c. on 30 c. mult (surch **Wismar**) 15 15
2301 25 c. on 30 c. mult (surch **TPO Berbice Railway**) 15 15

1988. Olympic Games, Seoul. Nos. 1206/17 further surch **120 Olympic Games 1988**.

2302 120 c. on 55 c. on 125 c. on 35 c. Type **174** . . 15 15
2303 120 c. on 55 c. on 125 c. on 35 c. Haimara . . 15 15
2304 120 c. on 55 c. on 125 c. on 35 c. Electric eel . . 15 15
2305 120 c. on 55 c. on 125 c. on 35 c. Golden rivulus . . 15 15
2306 120 c. on 55 c. on 125 c. on 35 c. Pencil fish . . 15 15
2307 120 c. on 55 c. on 125 c. on 35 c. Four-eyed fish . . 15 15
2308 120 c. on 55 c. on 125 c. on 35 c. Pirai or Carib fish 15 15
2309 120 c. on 55 c. on 125 c. on 35 c. Smoking hassar . . 15 15
2310 120 c. on 55 c. on 125 c. on 35 c. Devil ray . . 15 15
2311 120 c. on 55 c. on 125 c. on 35 c. Flying patwa . . 15 15
2312 120 c. on 55 c. on 125 c. on 35 c. Arapaima pirariucii 15 15
2313 120 c. on 55 c. on 125 c. on 35 c. Lukanani . . 15 15

1988. Centenary of Publication of Sanders' "Reichenbachia" (29th issue). As T **331**. Multicoloured.

2314 320 c. Plate No. 16 (Series 2) 55 40
2315 475 c. Plate No. 73 (Series 2) 80 50
2316 525 c. Plate No. 36 (Series 2) . . . . 1·00 65
2317 530 c. Plate No. 69 (Series 2) . . . . 1·00 65
2318 $15 Plate No. 67 (Series 2) 2·75 2·25

1988. CARICOM Day. Nos. 545/6 and 555 surch **Caricom Day 1988** and new value.

2319 25 c. on 5 c. Annatto tree 10 10
2320 $1.20 on 6 c. Cannon-ball tree 10 10
2321 $10 on $2 "Norantea guianensis" 45 50

1988. Centenary of Publication of Sanders' "Reichenbachia" (30th issue). As T **331**. Multicoloured.

2322 700 c. Plate No. 62 (Series 2) . . . . 1·00 65
2323 775 c. Plate No. 59 (Series 2) . . . . 1·25 70
2324 875 c. Plate No. 31 (Series 2) . . . . 1·50 85
2325 950 c. Plate No. 78 (Series 2) . . . . 1·75 90

1988. 40th Anniv of World Health Day. No. 705a optd.

2326 60 c. "Papilio androgeus" (optd **WHO 1948–1988**) 2·50 3·00
2327 60 c. "Papilio androgeus" (optd **1988**) 10 10

1988. Centenary of Publication of Sanders' "Reichenbachia" (31st issue). As T **331**. Multicoloured.

2328 350 c. Plate No. 74 (Series 2) 35 30

1988. Centenary of Publication of Sanders "Reichenbachia" (32nd issue). As T **331**, but additionally inscr "1985–1988". Mult.

2329 130 c. Plate No. 73 (Series 2) 40 25
2330 200 c. Plate No. 96 (Series 2) 50 30
2331 260 c. Plate No. 16 (Series 2) 70 35

1988. Conservation of Resources.

(a) Nos. 1444/6 optd

2333 120 c. Young Ocelot (No. 1444) (optd **CONSERVE TREES**) 10 10
2334 120 c. Young Ocelot (No. 1444) (optd **CONSERVE ELECTRICITY**) 10 10
2335 120 c. Young Ocelot (No. 1444) (optd **CONSERVE WATER**) . . 10 10
2336 120 c. Type **322** (optd **CONSERVE ELECTRICITY**) . . 10 10
2337 120 c. Type **322** (optd **CONSERVE WATER**) 10 10
2338 120 c. Type **322** (optd **CONSERVE TREES**) 10 10
2339 120 c. Young Ocelot (No. 1446) (optd **CONSERVE WATER**) . . 10 10
2340 120 c. Young Ocelot (No. 1446) (optd **CONSERVE TREES**) . . 10 10
2341 120 c. Young Ocelot (No. 1446) (optd **CONSERVE ELECTRICITY**) . . 10 10

(b) Nos. 1634, 1670, 1683 and 1863 optd **CONSERVE WATER** (optd)

2342 200 c. Plate No. 33 (Series 1) 10 10
2343 200 c. Plate No. 79 (Series 1) 10 10
2344 225 c. Plate No. 24 (Series 1) 10 10
2345 350 c. Plate No. 94 (Series 1) 15 20

1988. Road Safety Campaign. Nos. 2194/2201 optd.

2346 **396** $1.20 green (optd **BEWARE OF ANIMALS**) . . 20 20
2347 – $1.20 green (No. 2195) (optd **BEWARE OF CHILDREN**) 20 20
2348 – $1.20 green (No. 2196) (optd **DRIVE SAFELY**) . . 20 20
2349 – $1.20 green (No. 2197) (optd **DO NOT DRINK AND DRIVE**) . . 20 20
2350 **396** $1.20 purple (optd **BEWARE OF ANIMALS**) . . 20 20
2351 – $1.20 purple (No. 2199) (optd **BEWARE OF CHILDREN**) 20 20
2352 – $1.20 purple (No. 2200) (optd **DRIVE SAFELY**) . . 20 20
2353 – $1.20 purple (No. 2201) (optd **DO NOT DRINK AND DRIVE**) . . 20 20

1988. No. 706 optd **1988** or surch **120**.

2354 $1 "Agrias claudina" . . 15 15
2355 120 c. on $1 "Agrias claudina" 15 15

1988. Various "Reichenbachia" issues surch.

2356 120 c. on 25 c. Plate No. 61 (Series 1) (No. 1574) 15 15
2357 120 c. on 25 c. Plate No. 63 (Series 1) (No. 1575) 15 15
2358 120 c. on 25 c. Plate No. 70 (Series 1) (No. 1576) 15 15
2359 120 c. on 25 c. Plate No. 59 (Series 1) (No. 1620) 15 15
2360 120 c. on 25 c. Plate No. 71 (Series 1) (No. 1679) 15 15
2429 120 c. on 25 c. Plate No. 72 (Seires 1) (No. 1577) 15 15
2361 120 c. on 30 c. Plate No. 53 (Series 1) (No. 1621) 15 15
2362 120 c. on 30 c. Plate No. 86 (Series 1) (No. 1731) 15 15
2363 120 c. on 30 c. Plate No. 30 (Series 2) (No. 1809) 15 15
2365 120 c. on 30 c. Plate No. 7 (Series 2) 15 15
2366 120 c. on 30 c. Plate No. 14 (Series 2) 15 15
2368 120 c. on 30 c. Plate No. 22 (Series 2) 15 15
2369 120 c. on 30 c. Plate No. 28 (Series 2) 15 15
2371 120 c. on 35 c. Plate No. 45 (Series 2) (No. 1925) 15 15
2372 120 c. on 40 c. Plate No. 77 (Series 1) (No. 1663) 15 15
2374 120 c. on 40 c. Plate No. 96 (Series 1) (No. 1747) 15 15
2377 120 c. on 40 c. Plate No. 86 (Series 1) (No. 1868) 15 15
2378 120 c. on 40 c. Plate No. 68 (Series 1) (No. 1884) 15 15
2381 120 c. on 45 c. Plate No. 54 (Series 1) (No. 1664) 15 15
2382 120 c. on 45 c. Plate No. 81 (Series 1) (No. 1748) 15 15
2383 120 c. on 45 c. Plate No. 21 (Series 2) (No. 1810) 15 15
2384 120 c. on 50 c. Plate No. 92 (Series 1) (No. 1665) 15 15
2385 120 c. on 50 c. Plate No. 13 (Series 2) (No. 1907) 15 15
2386 120 c. on 50 c. Plate No. 15 (Series 2) (No. 1926) 15 15
2393 120 c. on 55 c. Plate No. 17 (Series 1) (No. 1732) 15 15
2395 120 c. on 60 c. Plate No. 57 (Series 1) (No. 1622) 15 15
2397 120 c. on 60 c. Plate No. 73 (Series 1) (No. 1623) 15 15
2398 120 c. on 60 c. Plate No. 75 (Series 1) (No. 1624) 15 15
2400 120 c. on 60 c. Plate No. 95 (Series 1) (No. 1666) 15 15
2401 120 c. on 60 c. Plate No. 93 (Series 1) (No. 1733) 15 15
2402 120 c. on 60 c. Plate No. 27 (seies 2) (No. 1874) . . 15 15
2408 120 c. on 70 c. Plate No. 8 (Series 2) 15 15
2409 120 c. on 70 c. Plate No. 9 (Series 2) 15 15
2411 120 c. on 70 c. Plate No. 12 (Series 2) 15 15
2413 120 c. on 70 c. Plate No. 17 (Series 2) 15 15
2414 120 c. on 80 c. Plate No. 39 (Series 1) 15 15
2415 120 c. on 80 c. Plate No. 74 (Series 1) 15 15
2416 120 c. on 80 c. Plate No. 93 (Series 1) 15 15
2417 120 c. on 85 c. Plate No. 45 (Series 2) (No. 1876) 15 15
2418 120 c. on 85 c. Plate No. 24 (Series 2) (No. 1914) 15 15
2419 120 c. on 85 c. Plate No. 15 (Series 2) (No. 1918) 15 15
2420 120 c. on 85 c. Plate No. 18 (Series 2) (No. 1928) 15 15
2421 120 c. on 90 c. Plate No. 84 (Series 1) (No. 1668) 15 15
2422 120 c. on 90 c. Plate No. 89 (Series 1) (No. 1749) 15 15
2423 120 c. on 90 c. Plate No. 10 (Series 2) (No. 1869) 15 15
2424 120 c. on 90 c. Plate No. 13 (Series 2) (No. 1877) 15 15
2425 120 c. on 90 c. Plate No. 27 (Series 2) (No. 1915) 15 15
2426 120 c. on 90 c. Plate No. 2 (Series 2) (No. 1929) . . 15 15
2427 200 c. on 80 c. Plate No. 42 (Series 2) (No. 1812) 15 15
2428 200 c. on 90 c. Plate No. 4 (Series 2) (No. 1813) 15 15
2430 240 c. on 140 c. Plate No. 30 (Series 2) 15 15
2431 240 c. on 140 c. Plate No. 34 (Series 2) 15 15
2432 240 c. on 425 c. Plate No. 87 (Series 2) (No. 2070) 15 15
2433 260 c. on 375 c. Plate No. 90 (Series 1) (No. 1378) 15 15

1988. Conservation of Resources. Various "Reichenbachia" issues optd **CONSERVE OUR RESOURCES**.

2434 100 c. Plate No. 65 (Series 1) (No. 1854) 15 15
2435 100 c. Plate No. 68 (Series 1) (No. 1734) 15 15
2436 100 c. Plate No. 88 (Series 1) (No. 1750) 15 15
2437 100 c. Plate No. 65 (Series 1) (No. 1854) 15 15
2438 120 c. Plate No. 27 (Series 1) (No. 1524) 15 15

2439 120 c. Plate No. 36 (Series 1) (No. 1558) 15 15
2440 120 c. Plate No. 37 (Series 1) (No. 1627) 15 15
2441 120 c. Plate No. 56 (Series 1) (No. 1629) 15 15
2442 120 c. Plate No. 58 (Series 1) (No. 1630) 15 15
2443 120 c. Plate No. 67 (Series 1) (No. 1631) 15 15
2444 120 c. Plate No. 69 (Series 1) (No. 1680) 15 15
2445 130 c. Plate No. 38 (Series 1) (No. 1560) 15 15
2446 130 c. Plate No. 66 (Series 1) (No. 1632) 15 15
2447 130 c. Plate No. 91 (Series 1) (No. 1735) 15 15
2448 130 c. Plate No. 13 (Series 1) (No. 1684) 15 15
2449 130 c. Plate No. 20 (Series 1) (No. 1770) 15 15
2450 150 c. Plate No. 26 (Series 1) (No. 1633) 15 15
2451 150 c. Plate No. 78 (Series 1) (No. 1669) 15 15
2452 150 c. Plate No. 87 (Series 1) (No. 1681) 15 15
2453 150 c. Plate No. 76 (Series 1) (No. 1751) 15 15
2454 250 c. Plate No. 74 (Series 1) (No. 1736) 15 15

1988. 125th Anniv of International Red Cross. Nos. 2202/5 and 2207/10 optd with cross.
2455 **396** $3.20 blue 15 20
2456 – $3.20 blue (No. 2203) 15 20
2457 – $3.20 blue (No. 2204) 15 20
2458 – $3.20 blue (No. 2205) 15 20
2459 – $3.30 black (No. 2207) 15 20
2460 **396** $3.30 black 20
2461 – $3.30 black (No. 2209) 15 20
2462 – $3.30 black (No. 2210) 15 20

1988. Centenary of Publication of Sanders' "Reichenbachia" (33rd issue). As T **331**. Multicoloured.
2468 270 c. Plate No. 90 (Series 2) 70 60
2469 360 c. Plate No. 84 (Series 2) .. .. 1·00 75
2470 550 c. Plate No. 70 (Series 2) (horiz) .. .. 1·75 1·10
2471 670 c. Plate No. 71 (Series 2) (horiz) .. .. 2·25 1·40

1988. 60th Anniv of Cricket in Guyana. Nos. 1584, 1670, 1681 and 1815 optd **1928–1988 CRICKET JUBILEE** or surch also.
2472 200 c. Plate No. 14 (Series 1) 30 30
2473 200 c. Plate No. 79 (Series 1) 30 30
2474 800 c. on 150 c. Plate No. 87 (Series 1) .. .. 1·25 1·25
2475 800 c. on 160 c. Plate No. 5 (Series 2) .. .. 1·25 1·25

1988. Olympic Games, Seoul. (a) Nos. 1628, 1634, 1671, 1681, 1683, 1814, 1818/19, 1880 and 2069 optd **OLYMPIC GAMES 1988** or surch also.
2476 120 c. Plate No. 46 (Series 1) 10 10
2477 130 c. Plate No. 38 (Series 2) 10 10
2478 150 c. Plate No. 87 (Series 1) 10 10
2479 200 c. Plate No. 33 (Series 1) 10 10
2480 300 c. Plate No. 83 (Series 1) 15 20
2481 300 c. on 360 c. Plate No. 34 (Series 2) 15 20
2482 320 c. Plate No. 10 (Series 2) 15 20
2483 330 c. Plate No. 82 (Series 2) 15 20
2484 350 c. Plate No. 94 (Series 1) 15 20
2485 350 c. Plate No. 29 (Series 2) 15 20

(b) Design as No. 1420, but incorrectly inscr "LOS ANGELLES" optd or surch **"OLYMPICS 1988"** (A) or **"KOREA 1988"** (B).
2486 $1.20 multicoloured (A) .. 10 10
2487 $1.20 multicoloured (B) .. 10 10
2488 130 c. on $1.20 mult (A) .. 10 10
2489 130 c. on $1.20 mult (B) .. 10 10
2490 150 c. on $1.20 mult (A) .. 10 10
2491 150 c. on $1.20 mult (B) .. 10 10
2492 200 c. on $1.20 mult (A) .. 10 10
2493 200 c. on $1.20 mult (B) .. 10 10
2494 350 c. on $1.20 mult (A) .. 15 20
2495 350 c. on $1.20 mult (B) .. 15 20

1988. Columbus Day. Nos. 1672/3 optd or surch **V CENTENARY OF THE LANDING OF CHRISTOPHER COLUMBUS IN THE AMERICAS**.
2496 320 c. Plate No. 50 (Series 1) 15 20
2497 $15 on 360 c. Plate No. 85 (Series 1) 65 70

1988. Centenary of Publication of Sanders' "Reichenbachia" (34th issue). As T **331**. Multicoloured.
2498 100 c. Plate No. 44 (Series 2) 70 55
2499 130 c. Plate No. 42 (Series 2) (horiz) 70 55
2500 140 c. Plate No. 4 (Series 2) 90 65
2501 160 c. Plate No. 50 (Series 2) 90 65
2502 175 c. Plate No. 51 (Series 2) .. .. 1·10 75
2503 200 c. Plate No. 11 (Series 2) .. .. 1·10 75
2504 200 c. Plate No. 23 (Series 2) .. .. 1·10 75
2505 200 c. Plate No. 26 (Series 2) .. .. 1·10 75
2506 200 c. Plate No. 75 (Series 2) .. .. 1·10 75
2507 200 c. Plate No. 93 (Series 2) .. .. 1·10 75
2508 250 c. Plate No. 79 (Series 2) .. .. 1·40 90
2509 280 c. Plate No. 62 (Series 2) .. .. 1·50 1·00
2510 285 c. Plate No. 63 (Series 2) .. .. 1·50 1·00
2511 380 c. Plate No. 35 (Series 2) .. .. 1·75 1·25

1988. Christmas (1st issue). Various "Reichenbachia" issues optd or surch.

(a) Optd or surch **SEASON'S GREETINGS**.
2519 120 c. on 100 c. Plate No. 6 (Series 1) 15 20
2520 120 c. on 100 c. Plate No. 13 (Series 1) 15 20
2521 120 c. on 100 c. Plate No. 20 (Series 1) 15 20
2522 120 c. on 100 c. Plate No. 25 (Series 1) 15 20
2523 120 c. on 100 c. Plate No. 40 (Series 1) (horiz) .. 15 20
2524 120 c. on 100 c. Plate No. 42 (Series 1) (horiz) .. 15 20
2525 120 c. on 100 c. Plate No. 43 (Series 1) (horiz) .. 15 20
2526 120 c. on 100 c. Plate No. 45 (Series 1) (horiz) .. 15 20
2512 150 c. Plate No. 32 (Series 1) (No. 1561) 20 25
2513 150 c. Plate No. 62 (Series 1) (No. 1566) 20 25
2514 225 c. Plate No. 60 (Series 1) (No. 1682) 30 35
2532 240 c. on 180 c. Plate No. 15 (Series 1) (No. 1752) 30 35
2515 260 c. Plate No. 39 (Series 1) (No. 1737) 35 40
2516 320 c. Plate No. 82 (Series 1) (No. 1753) 40 45
2517 330 c. Plate No. 80 (Series 1) (No. 1754) 45 50
2518 360 c. Plate No. 85 (Series 1) (No. 1673) 45 50

(b) Optd **SEASON'S GREETINGS 1988**.
2527 225 c. Plate No. 24 (Series 1) (No. 1863) 30 35
2528 225 c. Plate No. 60 (Series 1) (No. 1682) 30 35
2530 225 c. on 350 c. on 120 c. Plate No. 65 (Series 1) (No. 2221) 30 35

1988. Christmas (2nd issue). Nos. 489, 1188/91 and 1449 surch or optd **CHRISTMAS 1988**.
2533 – 20 c. on 6 c. mult (No. 452) 10 10
2534 **277** 120 c. brown, blk & bl 15 20
2535 – 120 c. on 130 c. red, black and blue (No. 1189) 15 20
2536 – 120 c. on 150 c. violet, black and blue (No. 1190) 15 20
2537 – 120 c. on 200 c. green, black and blue (No. 1191) 15 20
2538 – 500 c. on 330 c. mult (No. 1449) 60 70

1988. AIDS Information Campaign. Nos. 707/8a optd or surch with various slogans.
2539 120 c. on $5 "Morpho deidamia" (A) .. 30 30
2540 120 c. on $5 "Morpho deidamia" (B) .. 30 30
2541 120 c. on $5 "Morpho deidamia" (C) .. 30 30
2542 120 c. on $5 "Morpho deidamia" (D) .. 30 30
2543 120 c. on $5 "Morpho deidamia" (E) .. 30 30
2544 120 c. on $10 "Elbella patrobas" (A) .. 30 30
2545 120 c. on $10 "Elbella patrobas" (B) .. 30 30
2546 120 c. on $10 "Elbella patrobas" (C) .. 30 30
2547 120 c. on $10 "Elbella patrobas" (D) .. 30 30
2548 120 c. on $10 "Elbella patrobas" (E) .. 30 30
2549 $2 "Morpho rhetenor" (female) (E) .. 40 40
2550 $5 "Morpho deidamia" (E) 90 90
2551 $10 "Elbella patrobas" (E) .. .. .. 1·75 1·75

OVERPRINTS: (A) **Be compassionate towards AIDS victims.**; (B) **Get information on AIDS. it may save your life.**; (C) **Get the facts. Education helps to prevent AIDS.**; (D) **Say no to Drugs and limit the spread of AIDS.**; (E) **Protect yourself from AIDS. Better safe than sorry.**.

1988. 150th Anniv of Abolition of Slavery (1984) (2nd issue). Designs as Nos. 1547/50, but colours changed.
2552 **337** 25 c. black and brown 10 10
2553 – 60 c. black and lilac 10 10
2554 – 130 c. black and green 15 20
2555 – 150 c. black and blue 20 25

1989. Olympic Medal Winners, Seoul. Nos. 1672, 1923 and 2178 surch **SALUTING WINNERS OLYMPIC GAMES 1988**.
2556 550 c. on 560 c. Plate No. 1 (Series 2) 70 75
2557 900 c. on 320 c. Plate No. 18 (Series 2) .. .. 1·10 1·25
2558 1050 c. on 320 c. Plate No. 50 (Series 1) .. .. 1·40 1·50

1989. Republic Day. Nos. 2194/2201 and 2212 optd **REPUBLIC DAY 1989**.
2559 **396** $1.20 green 15 20
2560 – $1.20 green (No. 2195) 15 20
2561 – $1.20 green (No. 2196) 15 20
2562 – $1.20 green (No. 2197) 15 20
2563 **396** $1.20 purple 15 20
2564 – $1.20 purple (No. 2199) 15 20
2565 – $1.20 purple (No. 2200) 15 20
2566 – $1.20 purple (No. 2201) 15 20
2567 – $10 multicoloured .. 1·25 1·40

1989. Nos. 2202/5 and 2207/10 surch.
2568 **396** $5 on $3.20 blue .. 65 70
2569 – $5 on $3.20 blue (No. 2203) 65 70
2570 – $5 on $3.20 blue (No. 2204) 65 70
2571 – $5 on $3.20 blue (No. 2205) 65 70
2572 – $5 on $3.30 black (No. 2207) 65 70
2573 **396** $5 on $3.30 black 65 70
2574 – $5 on $3.30 black (No. 2209) 65 70
2575 – $5 on $3.30 black (No. 2210) 65 70

1989. Various "Reichenbachia" issues surch.
2576 120 c. on 140 c. Plate No. 25 (Series 2) 15 20
2577 120 c. on 140 c. Plate No. 52 (Series 2) 15 20
2578 120 c. on 140 c. Plate No. 65 (Series 2) 15 20
2580 120 c. on 140 c. Plate No. 38 (Series 2) 15 20
2581 120 c. on 140 c. Plate No. 41 (Series 2) 15 20
2579 120 c. on 175 c. Plate No. 54 (Series 2) 15 20
2582 170 c. on 175 c. Plate No. 58 (Series 2) 20 25
2583 250 c. on 280 c. Plate No. 66 (Series 2) 30 35
2584 250 c. on 280 c. Plate No. 67 (Series 2) 30 35
2585 300 c. on 290 c. Plate No. 53 (Series 2) (No. 2236) 40 45

1989. Nos. 1744/5 and 2185/6 surch **TEN DOLLARS $10.00** (Nos. 2586, 2588) or **TEN DOLLARS** (Nos. 2587, 2589).
2586 **363** $10 on 320 c. red, blk & lilac (No. 1744) .. 1·25 1·40
2587 – $10 on 320 c. mult (No. 1745) .. .. 1·25 1·40
2588 **363** $10 on 320 c. red, blk & lilac (No. 2185) .. 1·25 1·40
2589 – $10 on 320 c. mult .. 1·25 1·40

1989. Nos. O54/7, O59/63 and O65/9 optd **POSTAGE** or surch also.
2591 125 c. on 130 c. Plate No. 92 (Series 2) 10 10
2592 125 c. on 140 c. Plate No. 36 (Series 2) 10 10
2593 150 c. Plate No. 43 (Series 2) 10 10
2594 150 c. on 175 c. Plate No. 31 (Series 2) 10 10
2595 250 c. Plate No. 59 (Series 2) 10 10
2596 250 c. on 225 c. Plate No. 26 (Series 2) 10 10
2597 250 c. on 230 c. Plate No. 68 (Series 2) 10 10
2598 250 c. on 260 c. Plate No. 69 (Series 2) 10 10
2599 300 c. on 275 c. Plate No. 90 (Series 2) 10 15
2600 350 c. Plate No. 95 (Series 2) 15 20
2601 350 c. on 330 c. Plate No. 23 (Series 2) 15 20
2602 600 c. Plate No. 70 (Series 2) 25 30
2603 $12 Plate No. 71 (Series 2) 50 55
2604 $15 Plate No. 84 (Series 2) 60 55

1989. Centenary of Publication of Sanders' "Reichenbachia" (35th issue). As T **331**. Mult.
2605 200 c. Plate No. 49 (Series 2) 10 10
2606 200 c. Plate No. 53 (Series 2) 10 10
2607 200 c. Plate No. 60 (Series 2) 10 10
2608 200 c. Plate No. 64 (Series 2) 10 10

1989. No. 1442 surch **250**.
2609 **322** 250 c. on 25 c. mult .. 10 10

1989. 40th Anniv of Guyana Red Cross. No. 1872 surch **RED CROSS 1948 1988** and new value.
2610 375 c. on 45 c. Plate No. 17 (Series 2) 15 20
2611 425 c. on 45 c. Plate No. 17 (Series 2) 15 10

1989. World Health Day. Nos. 1875 and 2239 surch.
2612 250 c. on 75 c. Plate No. 56 (Series 2) surch **HEALTH FOR ALL** 10 10
2613 250 c. on 75 c. Plate No. 56 (Series 2) surch **ALL FOR HEALTH** .. 10 10
2614 675 c. on 720 c. Plate No. 49 (Series 2) surch **ALL FOR HEALTH** .. 30 35
2615 675 c. on 720 c. Plate No. 49 (Series 2) surch **HEALTH FOR ALL** 30 35

1989. Scouting Anniversaries. Nos. 1873, 1879, 2322, 2509 and unissued value as No. 1873 optd or surch also.
2616 250 c. on 50 c. Plate No. 33 (Series 2) (surch **BOY SCOUTS 1909 1989**) 10 10
2617 250 c. on 50 c. Plate No. 33 (Series 2) (surch **GIRL GUIDES 1924 1989**) 10 10
2618 250 c. on 100 c. Plate No. 33 (Series 2) (surch **BOY SCOUTS 1909 1989**) 10 10
2619 250 c. on 100 c. Plate No. 33 (Series 2) (surch **GIRL GUIDES 1924 1989**) 10 10
2620 300 c. Plate No. 50 (Series 2) (optd **BOY SCOUTS 1909 1989**) .. 10 15
2621 300 c. Plate No. 50 (Series 2) (optd **GIRL GUIDES 1924 1989**) .. 10 15
2622 $25 on 280 c. Plate No. 62 (Series 2) (surch **LADY BADEN POWELL 1889 - 1989**) .. .. 1·00 1·10
2623 $25 on 700 c. Plate No. 62 (Series 2) (surch **LADY BADEN POWELL 1889 - 1989**) .. .. 1·00 1·10

The events commemorated are the 80th anniversary of Boy Scout Movement in Guyana, 65th anniversary of Girl Guide Movement in Guyana and birth centenary of Lady Baden-Powell.

1989. 150 Years of Photography. No. 1881 surch **PHOTOGRAPHY 1839 - 1989** and new value.
2624 550 c. on 390 c. Plate No. 6 (Series 2) 20 25
2625 650 c. on 390 c. Plate No. 6 (Series 2) 25 30

1989. 70th Anniv of International Labour Organization. No. 1875 surch **I.L.O. 1919–1989 300**.
2627 300 c. on 75 c. Plate No. 56 (Series 2) 10 15

1989. Various stamps surch.

(a) With obliterating devices over original value
2628 80 c. on 6 c. Patua (No. 452) 10 10
2629 $1 on 2 c. Type **132** .. 10 10
2630 $2.05 on 3 c. Hanging heliconia (No. 544) .. 10 10
2631 $2.55 on 5 c. Annatto tree (No. 545) 10 15
2632 $3.25 on 6 c. Cannon-ball tree (No. 546) 15 20
2633 $5 on 6 c. Type **111** .. 20 25

2634 $6.40 on 10 c. "Archonias bellona" (699) 25 30

2648 $6.40 on $3.30 black (No. 2207) 25 30

2649 $6.40 on $3.30 black (T **396**) 25 30

2650 $6.40 on $3.30 black (No. 2209) 25 30

2651 $6.40 on $3.30 black (No. 2210) 25 30

2646 640 c. on 675 c. on 720 c. Plate No. 49 (Series 2) (No. 2614) 20 25

2647 640 c. on 675 c. on 720 c. Plate No. 49 (Series 2) (No. 2615) 25 30

2652 $7.65 on $3.20 blue (T **396**) 30 35

2653 $7.65 on $3.20 blue (No. 2203) 30 35

2654 $7.65 on $3.20 blue (No. 2204) 30 35

2655 $7.65 on $3.20 blue (No. 2205) 30 35

2635 $8.90 on 60 c. "Papilio androgeus" (No. 705a) 35 40

2643 $50 on $2 "Morpho rhetenor" (female) (No. 707) 2·00 2·10

2644 $100 on $2 "Morpho rhetenor" (female) (No. 707) 4·00 4·25

(b) Without obliterating devices

2636 80 c. on 6 c. Patua (No. 452) 10 10

2637 $6.40 on 10 c. "Archonias bellona" (No. 699) 25 30

2638 $7.65 on 40 c. "Morpho rhetenor" (male) (No. 704) 30 35

2639 $8.90 on 60 c. "Papilio androgeus" (No. 705a) 35 40

1989. CARICOM Day. No. 1878 surch **CARICOM DAY**.

2656 125 c. on 200 c. Plate No. 44 (Series 2) 10 10

454 "Stalachtis calliope"

1989. Butterflies. Multicoloured.

2657 80 c. Type **454** 10 10

2658 $2.25 "Morpho rhetenor" 10 10

2659 $5 "Agrias claudia" 20 25

2660 $6.40 "Marpesia marcella" 25 30

2661 $7.65 "Papilio zagreus" 30 35

2662 $8.90 "Chorinea faunus" 35 40

2663 $25 "Cepheuptychia cephus" 1·00 1·10

2664 $100 "Nessaea regina" 4·00 4·25

455 Kathryn Sullivan (first U.S woman to walk in space)

1989. 25 Years of Women in Space. Mult.

2665 $6.40 Type **455** 25 30

2666 $12.80 Svetlana Savitskaya (first Soviet woman to walk in space) 50 55

2667 $15.30 Judy Resnik and Christa McAuliffe and "Challenger" logo 60 65

2668 $100 Sally Ride (first U.S woman astronaut) 4·00 4·25

1989. Centenary of Ahmadiyya (Moslem organization). Nos. 543/5 surch **AHMADIYYA CENTENARY 1899-1989**.

2669 80 c. on 2 c. Type **132** 10 10

2670 $6.40 on 3 c. Hanging heliconia 25 30

2671 $8.90 on 5 c. Annatto tree 35 40

457 Head of Harpy Eagle

1990. Endangered Species. Harpy Eagle. Multicoloured.

2672 $2.25 Type **457** 10 10

2673 $5 Harpy eagle with monkey prey 20 25

2674 $8.90 Eagle on branch (facing right) 35 40

2675 $30 Eagle on branch (facing left) 1·25 1·40

458 Channel-billed Toucan

1990. Birds of Guyana. Multicoloured.

2676 $15 Type **458** 60 65

2677 $25 Blue and yellow macaw 1·00 1·10

2678 $50 Wattled jacana (horiz) 2·00 2·25

2679 $60 Hoatzin (horiz) 2·40 2·50

EXPRESS LETTER STAMPS

1986. Various stamps surch. **EXPRESS** and new values.

E1. $12 on 350 c. on 120 c. multicoloured (No. 1598) 2·50 2·50

E2. $15 on 40 c. multicoloured (No. 1868) 3·00 3·00

E3. $20 on $6.40 multicoloured 3·00 3·50

E4. $25 on 25 c. multicoloured (as No. 1621, but value changed) 4·00 4·00

No. E3 was previously a miniature sheet for Halley's Comet containing two 320 c. stamps. As surcharged the orginal values on both designs have been cancelled and replaced by a single $20 face value.

1987. No. E3 additionally optd with small Maltese cross above surch.

E5 $20 on $6.40 mult 3·25 3·25

1987. Centenary of Publication of Sanders' "Reichenbachia". As T **331** additionally inscr "EXPRESS". Multicoloured.

E6 $15 Plate No. 11 (Series 2) 2·25 2·25

E7 $20 Plate No. 93 (Series 2) 2·50 2·75

E8 $25 Plate No. 63 (Series 2) 3·00 3·50

E9 $45 Plate No. 35 (Series 2) 6·00 6·50

1987. Nos. 1744/5 imperf between, surch **EXPRESS FORTY DOLLARS**.

E10 $40 on $6.40 multicoloured 7·00 7·50

1987. No. E 2 additionally optd **1987**.

E11 $15 on 40 c. multicoloured 2·75 3·00

1988. Nos. 2206 and 2211 surch **SPECIAL DELIVERY** and new value.

E12 $40 on $3.20 blue 5·50 6·50

E13 $45 on $3.30 black 6·00 7·00

1989. Horiz imperf between pairs of Nos. 1744 and 2185 surch **EXPRESS FORTY DOLLARS**.

E14 $40 on $6.40 multicoloured (No. 1744) 1·60 1·75

E15 $40 on $6.40 multicoloured (No. 2185) 1·60 1·75

1989. Nos. 2206 and 2211 surch **SPECIAL DELIVERY**.

E16 $190 on $3.30 black 7·50 8·00

E17 $225 on $3.20 blue 8·50 9·00

OFFICIAL STAMPS

1981. Nos. 556, F4 and F6/7 optd. **OPS** or surch also.

O 13. 10 c. on 25 c. Marabunta 1·50 1·40

O 14. 50 c. "Guzmania lingulata" 1·60 50

O 15. 60 c. Soldier's Cap 1·25 30

O 16. $5 Odonadenia grandiflora" 1·10 1·75

1981. Nos. 454, 708a, 716, 804, 834 and F9 optd. **OPS.** or surch. also.

O17 15 c. Harpy eagle (post) 3·50 30

O18 30 c. on $2 "Norantea guianensis" (F9) 45 30

O19 100 c. on $3 Cylinder satellite 3·00 60

O20 125 c. on $2 "Norantea guianensis" 3·00 65

O21 $10 "Elbella patrobas" 5·00 5·50

O22 $1.10 on $2 "Norantea guianensis" (804) (air) 3·00 3·50

1981. Nos. 548a. 719, 828 and 830 optd. **OPS** or surch. also.

O 23. 15 c. Christmas Orchid 4·00 1·00

O 24. 50 c. British Guiana 1898 1 c. stamp 1·25 35

O 25. 100 c. on 8 c. Camp-fire cooking 3·75 50

O 26. 110 c. on 6 c. Type **116** 4·50 75

1982. Various stamps optd. **OPS.**

O 27. – 20 c. multicoloured (No. 701) 30 20

O 28. **136.** 40 c. multicoloured 75 25

O 29. – 40 c. red, grey and blk. (No. 674) 1·00 25

O 30. – $2 multicoloured (No. 676) 6·00 1·00

1982. Nos. 911 and 980. optd. or surch. **OPS.**

O 31. 250 c. on 400 c. on 30 c. multicoloured (post.) 80 80

O 32. 220 c. on 1 c. multicoloured (air) 3·00 1·00

1982. No. F9 optd. **OPS.**

O 33. $2 "Norantea guianensis 12·00 2·00

1982. No. 979. optd. **OPS.**

O 34. 110 c. on 5 c. Annatto tree 3·00 1·00

1984. No. 912 surch.**OPS.**

O 35. 150 c. on $5 mult. 70 70

O 36. 200 c. on $5 mult. 85 85

O 37. 225 c. on $5 mult. 1·00 1·00

O 38. 230 c. on $5 mult. 1·00 1·00

O 39. 260 c. on $5 mult. 1·25 1·25

O 40. 320 c. on $5 mult. 1·50 1·50

O 41. 350 c. on $5 mult. 1·60 1·60

O 42. 600 c. on $5 mult. 2·50 2·50

1984. Nos. O 34 and O 34 surch. and No. 981 optd. **OPS.**

O 43. 25 c. on 110 c. on 5 c. Annatto tree 15 15

O 44. 30 c. on 110 c. on 5 c. Annatto tree 20 20

O 45. 45 c. on 220 c. on 1 c. Pitcher Plant of Mt. Roraima 20 20

O 46. 55 c. on 110 c. on 5 c. Annatto tree 25 25

O 47. 60 c. on 220 c. on 2 c. Pitcher Plant of Mt. Roraima 25 25

O 48. 75 c. on 220 c. on 1 c. Pitcher Plant of Mt. Roraima 30 30

O 49. 90 c. on 220 c. on 1 c. Pitcher Plant of Mt. Roraima 40 40

O 50. 120 c. on 220 c. on 1 c. Pitcher Plant of Mt. Roraima 50 50

O 51. 130 c. on 220 c. on 1 c. Pitcher Plant of Mt. Roraima 55 55

O 52. 330 c. on $2 "Norantea guianensis" 1·10 1·60

1987. Centenary of Publication of Sanders' "Reichenbachia". As T **331** additionally inscr "OFFICIAL". Multicoloured.

O53 120 c. Plate No. 48 (Series 2) 25 25

O54 130 c. Plate No. 92 (Series 2) 25 25

O55 140 c. Plate No. 36 (Series 2) 25 25

O56 150 c. Plate No. 43 (Series 2) 25 25

O57 175 c. Plate No. 31 (Series 2) 30 30

O58 200 c. Plate No. 61 (Series 2) 35 35

O59 225 c. Plate No. 26 (Series 2) 35 35

O60 230 c. Plate No. 68 (Series 2) (horiz) 35 35

O61 250 c. Plate No. 59 (Series 2) 40 40

O62 260 c. Plate No. 69 (Series 2) 40 40

O63 275 c. Plate No. 90 (Series 2) 40 40

O64 320 c. Plate No. 75 (Series 2) 50 50

O65 330 c. Plate No. 23 (Series 2) 60 60

O66 350 c. Plate No. 95 (Series 2) (horiz) 60 60

O67 600 c. Plate No. 70 (Series 2) 95 95

O68 $12 Plate No. 71 (Series 2) (horiz) 1·75 1·75

O69 $15 Plate No. 84 (Series 2) 2·00 2·00

OFFICIAL PARCEL POST STAMPS.

1981. Nos. P1/2 optd. **OPS.**

OP 1. $15 on $1 "Chelonanthus uliginoides" 7·50 4·00

OP 2. $20 on $1 "Chelonanthus uliginoides" 9·50 5·50

1983. No. 843 surch **OPS Parcel Post $12.00** and additionally optd **1982**.

OP 3. $12 on $1.10 on $2 "Norantea guianensis" 50·00 15·00

1983. No. OP3 with additional **OPS** opt.

OP 4. $12 on $1.10 on $2 "Norantea guianensis" 22·00 6·50

1983. No. P4 optd **OPS.**

OP5 $12 on $1.10 on $2 "Norantea guianensis" 11·00 5·00

PARCEL POST STAMPS

1981. No. 554 surch. **PARCEL POST** and new value.

P1. $15 in $1 "Chelonanthus uliginoides" 8·50 5·50

P2. $20 on $1 "Chelonanthus uliginoides" 10·00 8·50

1983. No. 843 surch **PARCEL POST.**

P3 $12 on $1.10 on $2 "Norantea guianensis" 10·00 4·00

1983. Unissued Royal Wedding surch. similar to No. 843, further surch **Parcel Post $12.00**

P4. $12 on $1.10 on $2 "Norantea guianesis" 1·75 2·00

1985. No. 673 surch. **TWENTY FIVE DOLLARS PARCEL POST 25.00.**

P5. $25 on 35 c. green, grey and black 12·00 12·00

POSTAGE DUE STAMPS

D 2.

1967.

D 8. D2. 1 c. green 15 1·25

D 9. 2 c. black 15 1·25

D 10. 4 c. blue 15 1·25

D 11. 12 c. red 20 1·50

POSTAL FISCAL STAMPS.

1975. Nos. 543/5 and 550a/6 optd. **REVENUE ONLY.**

F 1. 2 c. Type **132** 30 30

F 2. 3 c. Hanging Heliconia 30 30

F 3. 5 c. Annatto tree 30 30

F 4. 25 c. Marabunta 60 30

F 4a. 25 c. Marabunta (No. 550) 15·00 13·00

F 5. 40 c. Tiger Beard 30 30

F 6. 50 c. "Guzmania lingulata" 35 40

F 7. 60 c. Soldier's Cap 50 50

F 8. $1 "Chelonanthus uliginoides" 85 1·00

F 9. $2 "Norantea guianensis" 1·75 2·50

F10. $5 "Odontadenis grandiflora" 5·50 7·50

Although intended for fiscal use Nos. F1/10 were allowed, by the postal authorities as "an act of grace", to do duty as postage stamps until 30 June 1976.

GWALIOR

A "convention" state of Central India.

12 pies = 1 anna; 16 annas = 1 rupee.

1885. Queen Victoria stamps of India optd. **GWALIOR** at foot and native opt. at top.

No.	Type	Description	Unused	Used
1.	23.	½ a. turquoise	48·00	11·00
2.	–	1 a. purple	45·00	17·00
6.	–	1½ a. brown	38·00	—
3.	–	2 a. blue	35·00	11·00
8.	–	4 a. green (No. 69)	42·00	—
9.	–	6 a. brown (No. 80)	42·00	—
10.	–	8 a. mauve	38·00	—
11.	–	1 r. grey (No. 101)	38·00	—

Stamps of India overprinted **GWALIOR** above native overprint unless otherwise stated.

1885. Queen Victoria.

No.	Type	Description	Unused	Used
16	23.	½ a. turquoise	15	10
17	–	9 p. red	26·00	45·00
18	–	1 a. purple	20	15
20	–	1½ a. brown	25	30
21	—	2 a. blue	35	10
23	–	2½ a. green	2·75	8·00
25	–	3 a. orange	30	15
14	–	4 a. green (No. 69)	12·00	9·00
27	–	4 a. green (No. 96)	60	30
29	–	6 a. brown (No. 80)	60	2·25
30	–	8 a. mauve	55	55
32	–	12 a. purple on red	1·00	55
33	–	1 r. grey (No. 101)	65	70
34	37.	1 r. green and red	2·25	2·75
35	38.	2 r. red and orange	5·00	3·00
36		3 r. brown and green	7·00	3·50
37		5 r. blue and violet	12·00	6·50

1899. Queen Victoria.

No.	Type	Description	Unused	Used
38.	40.	3 p. red	10	20
39.		3 p. grey	5·50	45·00
40.	23.	½ a. green	10	45
41.	–	1 a. red	15	35
42.	–	2 a. lilac	35	1·50
43.	–	2½ a. blue	65	1·50

1903. King Edward VII.

No.	Type	Description	Unused	Used
46	41.	3 p. grey	15	15
48	–	½ a. green (No. 122)	10	10
49	–	1 a. red (No. 123)	10	10
50f	–	2 a. lilac	45	15
52	–	2½ a. blue	45	4·00
53	–	3 a. orange	50	15
54	–	4 a. olive	1·10	40
56	–	6 a. bistre	2·50	70
57	–	8 a. mauve	1·60	1·10
59	–	12 a. purple on red	1·75	3·25
60	–	1 r. green and red	1·90	1·10
61	52.	2 r. red and orange	8·50	12·00
62		3 r. brown and green	22·00	32·00
63		5 r. blue and violet	16·00	23·00

1907. King Edward VII inscr. "INDIA POSTAGE AND REVENUE".

No.	Type	Description	Unused	Used
64		½ a. green (No. 149)	10	20
66		1 a. red (No. 150)	30	10

1912. King George V.

No.	Type	Description	Unused	Used
67	55.	3 p. grey	10	10
68	56.	½ a. green	15	10
102	79.	½ a. green	20	10
88	80.	9 p. green	1·25	20
69	57.	1 a. red	15	10
80		1 a. brown	15	10
103	81.	1 a. brown	10	10
90	82.	1½ a. mauve	20	10
81	58.	1½ a. brown (No. 165)	55	50
82		1½ a. red	10	15
70	59.	2 a. lilac	30	10
91	70.	2 a. lilac	20	15
104	59.	2 a. red	30	1·00
83	61.	2½ a. blue	75	1·40
84		2½ a. orange	20	30
71	62.	3 a. orange	40	15
92		3 a. blue	40	40
72	63.	4 a. olive	40	40
93	71.	4 a. green	70	80
73	64.	6 a. bistre	65	75
74	65.	8 a. mauve	60	30
75	66.	12 a. red	85	1·40
76	67.	1 r. brown and green	1·25	40
77		2 r. red and orange	4·50	2·25
78		5 r. blue and violet	16·00	6·50

1922. No. 192 (King George V) optd **GWALIOR** only.

No.	Type	Description	Unused	Used
79.	57.	9 p. on 1 a. red	10	35

1928. King George V. Opt. in larger type (19 mm. long).

No.	Type	Description	Unused	Used
96.	67.	1 r. brown and green	1·00	1·50
97.		2 r. red and orange	2·50	2·50
98.		5 r. blue and violet	10·00	18·00
99.		10 r. green and red	28·00	30·00
100.		15 r. blue and olive	45·00	48·00
101.		25 r. orange and blue	80·00	85·00

1938. King George VI.

No.	Type	Description	Unused	Used
105.	91.	3 p. slate	2·75	10
106.		½ a. brown	2·25	10
107.		9 p. green	28·00	2·50
108.		1 a. red	3·25	15
109.	–	3 a. green (No. 253)	4·00	2·50
110.	–	4 a. brown (No. 255)	22·00	1·25
111.	–	6 a. green (No. 256)	2·25	4·25
112.	93.	1 r. slate and brown	2·75	1·50
113.		2 r. purple and brown	10·00	6·00
114.		5 r. green and blue	40·00	25·00
115.		10 r. purple and red	38·00	35·00
116.		15 r. brown and green	£120	£130
117.		25 r. slate and purple	£110	£110

1942. King George VI.

No.	Type	Description	Unused	Used
118	100a.	3 p. slate	45	10
119.		½ a. mauve	45	10
120.		9 p. green	45	10
121.		1 a. red	30	10
122.	101.	1½ a. violet	2·00	20
123.		2 a. red	55	20
124.		3 a. violet	1·25	30
125.	102.	4 a. brown	75	20
126.		6 a. green	17·00	14·00
127.		8 a. violet	2·75	2·75
128.		12 a. purple	5·50	11·00

OFFICIAL STAMPS

Stamps of India overprinted with native inscription at top and bottom, unless otherwise stated.

1895. Queen Victoria.

No.	Type	Description	Unused	Used
O 1	23.	½ a. turquoise	10	10
O 3	–	1 a. purple	65	10
O 4	–	2 a. blue	70	20
O 7	–	4 a. green (No. 96)	1·00	45
O 9	–	8 a. mauve	80	70
O 10	37.	1 r. green and red	2·75	3·00

1901. Queen Victoria.

No.	Type	Description	Unused	Used
O 23	40.	3 p. red	20	30
O 24		3 p. grey	75	1·25
O 26	23.	½ a. green	15	10
O 27	–	1 a. red	1·50	10
O 28	–	2 a. lilac	55	1·50

1903. King Edward VII.

No.	Type	Description	Unused	Used
O 29a.	41.	3 p. grey	30	10
O 31.	–	½ a. green (No. 122)	90	10
O 32.	–	1 a. red (No. 123)	35	10
O 33a.	–	2 a. lilac	60	15
O 44.	–	4 a. olive	2·50	70
O 36.	–	8 a. mauve	2·75	70
O 38.	–	1 r. green and red	1·90	1·10

1907. King Edward VII inscr. "POSTAGE & REVENUE".

No.	Type	Description	Unused	Used
O 49.	–	½ a. green (No. 149)	60	10
O 48.	–	1 a. red (No. 150)	2·00	10

1913. King George V.

No.	Type	Description	Unused	Used
O61	55	3 p. grey	10	10
O62	56	½ a. green	10	15
O73	79	½ a. green	15	15
O63	80	9 p. green	10	15
O53a	57	1 a. red	20	10
O64		1 a. brown	10	10
O74	81	1 a. brown	15	15
O65	82	1½ a. mauve	40	15
O55	59	2 a. lilac	35	10
O66	70	2 a. lilac	15	15
O75	59	2 a. red	20	30
O77	63	4 a. olive	30	35
O67	71	4 a. green	40	30
O68	65	8 a. mauve	40	30
O58	67	1 r. brown and green	6·50	7·50

1922. No. O 97 (King George V. Official) optd. **GWALIOR** only.

No.	Type	Description	Unused	Used
O 59.	57.	9 p. on 1 a. red	10	15

1927. King George V. Optd. in larger type (21 mm. long).

No.	Type	Description	Unused	Used
O 69.	67.	1 r. brown and green	60	70
O 70.		2 r. red and orange	2·25	4·00
O 71.		5 r. blue and violet	10·00	50·00
O 72.		10 r. green and red	48·00	£100

1938. King George VI.

No.	Type	Description	Unused	Used
O 78.	91.	½ a. brown	5·50	25
O 79.		1 a. red	1·10	15
O 91.	93.	1 r. slate and brown	5·00	5·00
O 92.		2 r. purple and brown	14·00	24·00
O 93.		5 r. green and blue	38·00	85·00
O 94.		10 r. purple and red	90·00	£170

1940. King George VI. Optd at bottom only.

No.	Type	Description	Unused	Used
O 80	O 20.	3 p. slate	50	10
O 81		½ a. brown	3·50	25
O 82		½ a. purple	50	10
O 83		9 p. green	70	45
O 84		1 a. red	3·00	10
O 85		1 a. 3 p. yell.-brn.	9·00	1·60
O 86		1 a. 6 p. violet	80	30
O 87		2 a. orange	80	30
O 88		4 a. brown	90	1·00
O 89		8 a. violet	2·25	3·25

1942. No. O65 surch **1 A 1 A** and bar.

No.	Type	Description	Unused	Used
O90	82	1 a. on 1½ a. mauve	12·00	2·25

HELIGOLAND

An island off the N. coast of Germany, ceded to that country by Great Britain in 1890.

1867. 16 schillings = 1 mark.
1875. 100 pfennig = 1 mark.

Many of the Heligoland stamps found in old collections, and the majority of those offered at a small fraction of catalogue prices to-day, are reprints which have very little value.

½ SCHILLING ½ HELIGOLAND HELIGOLAND

1.

1867. Perf. (½, 1, 2 and 6 sch. also roul.).

No.	Type	Description	Unused	Used
5	1	½ sch. green and red	21·00	£1500
6b		½ sch. green and red	90·00	£150
7		¾ sch. red and green	24·00	£1100
8a		1 sch. red and green	£110	£180
9		1½ sch. green and red	55·00	£250
3		2 sch. red and green	8·00	50·00
4		6 sch. green and red	10·00	£250

HELIGOLAND 2 FARTHINGS 2 PFENNIG

2.

HELIGOLAND 2½ 20 PENCE PFENNIG

3.

HELIGOLAND

4.

HELIGOLAND

5.

1875.

No.	Type	Description	Unused	Used
10	2	1 pf. (¼d.) green and red	8·00	£500
11		2 pf. (½d.) red and green	8·00	£600
12a	3	3 pf. (⅝d.) grn., red & yell.	£160	£850
13	2	5 pf. (¾d.) green and red	8·00	18·00
14a		10 pf. (1½d.) red and green	7·50	20·00
15b	3	20 pf. (2½d.) green, red and yellow	11·00	28·00
16	2	25 pf. (3d.) green and red	10·00	26·00
17		50 pf. (6d.) red and green	16·00	32·00
18	4	1 m. (1s.) grn., red & blk.	£140	32·00
19	5	5 m. (5s.) grn., red & blk.	£110	£950

HONG KONG

A Br. colony at the mouth of the Canton R., consisting of the island of Hong Kong and peninsula of Kowloon. Under Japanese Occupation from 25th December 1941, until liberated by British forces on 16th September, 1945.

100 cents = 1 Hong Kong dollar.

HONGKONG TWO CENTS

1.

1862.

No.	Type	Description	Unused	Used
8a	1	2 c. brown	55·00	3·75
34		4 c. grey	3·50	20
10		6 c. lilac	£180	4·50
11a		8 c. yellow	£170	4·50
12a		12 c. blue	12·00	3·00
22		16 c. yellow	£475	42·00
4		18 c. lilac	£250	25·00
14		24 c. green	£190	5·00
15a		30 c. red	£275	8·50
36		30 c. mauve	85·00	2·25
16		48 c. red	£400	20·00
18		96 c. olive	£10000	£425
19		96 c. grey	£425	19·00

1877. Surch. in figures and words, thus **5 cents.**

No.	Type	Description	Unused	Used
23.	1.	5 c. on 8 c. yellow	£275	50·00
24.		5 c. on 18 c. lilac	£225	35·00
25.		10 c. on 12 c. blue	£275	42·00
26.		10 c. on 16 c. yellow	£1000	75·00
27.		10 c. on 24 c. green	£400	5000
20.		16 c. on 18 c. lilac	£850	£120
21.		28 c. on 30 c. mauve	£500	40·00

1880.

No.	Type	Description	Unused	Used
33	1	2 c. red	10·00	30
56		2 c. green	6·00	20
57		4 c. red	3·50	20
35		5 c. blue	4·50	30
58		5 c. yellow	5·00	2·75
30		10 c. mauve	£130	6·50
37		10 c. green	65·00	60
38		10 c. purple on red	4·50	20
59		10 c. blue	11·00	55
39a		30 c. green	16·00	9·00
61		30 c. brown	6·00	13·00
31		48 c. brown	£325	48·00

1885. Surch. in figures and words, thus **20 CENTS.**

No.	Type	Description	Unused	Used
54	1	10 c. on 30 c. green	£225	£350
40		20 c. on 30 c. red	38·00	2·00
45a		20 c. on 30 c. green	55·00	50·00
41		50 c. on 48 c. brown	£140	9·50
46		50 c. on 48 c. purple	£180	£120
42		$1 on 96 c. olive	£200	25·00
47		$1 on 96 c. purple on red	£300	£120
53		$1 on 96 c. black	£325	£550

1891. Surch in figures and words, thus **7 cents.**

No.	Type	Description	Unused	Used
43	1	7 c. on 10 c. green	42·00	5·50
44		14 c. on 30 c. mauve	75·00	42·00

弍 五十 壹員

(13.) (20 c.) (14.) (50 c.) (15.) ($1)

1891. T 1 surch. with figures and words and with Chinese surcharge also.

No.	Type	Description	Unused	Used
55	–	10 c. on 30 c. green	16·00	35·00
48a	13	20 c. on 30 c. green	11·00	1·50
49	14	50 c. on 48 c. purple	30·00	2·50
50	15	$1 on 96 c. purple on red	42·00	10·00
52		$1 on 96 c. black	48·00	15·00

The Chinese surch on No. 55 is larger than Type 13.

1891. 50th Anniv. of Colony. Optd. **1841 HONG KONG JUBILEE 1891.**

No.	Type	Description	Unused	Used
51	1	2 c. red	£150	60·00

HONG KONG TWO CENTS

20.

HONG KONG ONE CENT 1c

24.

1903.

No.	Type	Description	Unused	Used
62	20	1 c. purple and brown	60	15
91		1 c. brown	1·00	75
77		2 c. green	60	35
78a		4 c. purple on red	1·25	10
93		4 c. red	1·50	25
79a		5 c. green and orange	3·00	1·75
94		6 c. brown and purple	7·00	2·50
66		8 c. grey and violet	3·00	60
81		10 c. purple & blue on blue	4·00	40
95		10 c. blue	5·00	30
68		12 c. green & pur. on yell.	4·50	2·00
83a		20 c. grey and brown	5·00	90
96		20 c. purple and green	25·00	23·00
84		30 c. green and black	9·50	4·50
97		30 c. purple and yellow	29·00	11·00
85		50 c. green and purple	13·00	3·00
98		50 c. black on green	17·00	6·00
86		$1 purple and olive	38·00	6·50
87a		$2 grey and red	65·00	45·00
99		$2 red and black	£100	90·00
88		$3 grey and blue	70·00	90·00
89		$5 purple and green	£130	£150
76		$10 grey & orange on blue	£375	£275

1912.

No.	Type	Description	Unused	Used
117	24	1 c. brown	30	25
118		2 c. green	65	20
118b		2 c. grey	6·00	3·25
119		3 c. grey	1·50	40
120a		4 c. red	55	15
121		5 c. violet	1·25	15
103a		6 c. orange	2·00	80
104		8 c. grey	12·00	3·25
123		8 c. orange	80	70
124		10 c. blue	60	10
106		12 c. purple on yellow	1·00	35
125		20 c. purple and olive	1·50	10
126		25 c. purple	80	30
127		30 c. purple and orange	3·50	1·25
128		50 c. black on green	3·25	10
129		$1 purple & blue on blue	7·00	50
130		$2 red and black	35·00	1·75
131		$3 green and purple	80·00	20·00
132		$5 green and red on green	£120	21·00
116		$10 purple & black on red	£170	45·00

1935. Silver Jubilee. As T 13 of Antigua.

No.	Type	Description	Unused	Used
133.		3 c. blue and black	1·75	2·00
134.		5 c. green and blue	4·00	1·50
135.		10 c. brown and blue	4·00	1·00
136.		20 c. grey and purple	16·00	4·00

1937. Coronation. As T 2 of Aden.

No.	Type	Description	Unused	Used
137.		4 c. green	1·25	1·00
138.		15 c. red	2·75	2·00
139.		25 c. blue	3·75	1·50

HONGKONG FOUR CENTS

29. King George VI.

HONG KONG STREET SCENE 1841-1941 2c

30. Street Scene.

1938.

No.	Type	Description	Unused	Used
140	29	1 c. brown	40	40
141		2 c. grey	30	15
142		4 c. orange	60	70
143		5 c. green	35	10
144		8 c. brown	35	1·75
145a		10 c. violet	1·75	10
146		15 c. red	30	15
147		20 c. black	20	15
148		20 c. red	1·50	20
149		25 c. blue	4·50	45
150		25 c. olive	70	1·25
151a		30 c. olive	5·50	6·00
152		30 c. blue	1·25	10
153b		50 c. lilac	1·25	10
154		80 c. red	1·00	50
155		$1 purple and blue	4·50	1·50
156		$1 orange and green	2·75	10
157		$2 orange and green	48·00	9·00
158		$2 violet and red	3·00	40
159		$5 purple and red	35·00	38·00
160		$5 green and violet	25·00	3·50
161		$10 green and violet	£325	48·00
162		$10 violet and blue	50·00	15·00

1941. Cent. of British Occupation. Dated "1841 1941".

No.	Type	Description	Unused	Used
163.	30.	2 c. orange and brown	1·25	1·00
164.	–	4 c. purple and mauve	2·25	1·00
165.	–	5 c. black and green	80	30
166.	–	15 c. black and red	3·00	60
167.	–	25 c. brown and blue	4·00	1·00
168.	–	$1 blue and orange	8·50	4·00

DESIGNS—VERT. 25 c. Hong Kong Bank. HORIZ. 4 c. Liner and junk. 5 c. University. 15 c. Harbour. $1, China Clipper and seaplane.

For Japanese issues see "Japanese Occupation of Hong Kong".

36.

1946. Victory.
169. **36.** 30 c. blue and red .. 1·00 30
170. $1 brown and red .. 1·00 30

1948. Silver Wedding. As T **10/11** of Aden.
171. 10 c. violet 60 40
172. $10 red .. .. .. 65·00 25·00

1949. U.P.U. As T **20/23** of Antigua.
173. 10 c. violet .. .. 1·00 25
174. 20 c. red .. .. .. 4·00 50
175. 30 c. blue .. .. .. 3·75 75
176. 80 c. mauve .. .. 5·50 1·75

1953. Coronation. As T **13** of Aden.
177. 10 c. black and purple .. 1·50 15

1954. As T **29** but portrait of Queen Elizabeth, facing left.
178 5 c. orange 35 10
179 10 c. lilac 80 10
180a 15 c. green .. .. .. 1·50 20
181 20 c. brown .. .. 1·75 15
182a 25 c. red 70 15
183 30 c. grey .. .. .. 2·00 10
184 40 c. blue .. .. .. 1·25 10
185 50 c. purple .. .. 1·75 10
186 65 c. grey .. .. .. 13·00 6·00
187 $1 orange and green .. 3·75 10
188 $1.30 blue and red .. 16·00 90
189 $2 violet and red .. .. 6·00 30
190 $5 green and purple .. 28·00 1·00
191 $10 violet and blue .. 27·00 4·25

38. University Arms.

1961. Golden Jubilee of Hong Kong University.
192. **38.** $1 multicoloured .. 2·50 80

39. Statue of Queen Victoria.

1962. Stamp Centenary.
193. **39.** 10 c. black and mauve .. 20 10
194. 20 c. black and blue .. 60 55
195. 50 c. black and bistre .. 70 20

40. Queen Elizabeth II (after Annigoni).

1962.
196 **40.** 5 c. orange 10 20
223 10 c. violet 25 15
224 15 c. green 35 30
199 20 c. brown 60 20
226 25 c. mauve .. .. 50 1·00
201 30 c. blue .. .. 1·00 10
202 40 c. turquoise 60 15
203 50 c. red 40 10
230a 65 c. blue .. .. 2·00 3·75
231 $1 sepia .. .. 6·00 60
206 – $1.30 multicoloured .. 2·00 10
207 – $2 multicoloured .. 3·25 15
208 – $5 multicoloured .. 7·00 60
209 – $10 multicoloured .. 16·00 1·50
210 – $20 multicoloured .. 32·00 10·00
Nos. 206/10 are as T **40** but larger (26 × 40½ mm).

1963. Freedom from Hunger. As T **28** of Aden.
211. $1·30 green .. .. 13·00 3·75

1963. Cent of Red Cross. As T **33** of Antigua.
212. 10 c. red and black .. 2·50 15
213. $1·30 red and blue .. 6·50 2·50

1965. Cent of I.T.U. As T **36** of Antigua.
214. 10 c. purple and yellow .. 2·50 15
215. $1·30 olive and green .. 8·50 75

1965. I.C.Y. As T **37** of Antigua.
216. 10 c. purple and turquoise 2·00 10
217. $1·30 green and lavender 6·50 65

1966. Churchill Commem. As T **38** of Antigua.
218. 10 c. blue .. .. .. 1·75 10
219. 50 c. green .. .. .. 2·25 15
220. $1·30 brown .. .. 5·00 1·25
221. $2 violet .. .. .. 5·50 4·00

1966. Inauguration of W.H.O. Headquarters, Geneva. As T **41** of Antigua.
237. 10 c. black, green and blue 1·50 10
238. 50 c. black, purple & ochre 2·00 60

1966. 20th Anniv. of U.N.E.S.C.O. As T **54/6** of Antigua.
239. 10 c. multicoloured .. 2·00 10
240. 50 c. yellow, violet & olive 5·50 40
241. $2 black, purple & orange 18·00 6·50

42. Ram's Heads on Chinese Lanterns.

1967. Chinese New Year.
242. **42.** 10 c. red, olive & yellow 75 15
243. – $1·30 green, red & yellow 4·00 3·00
DESIGN: $1·30, Three rams ("Year of the Ram").

44. Cable Route Map.

1967. Completion of Malaysia–Hong Kong Link of SEACOM Telephone Cable.
244. **44.** $1·30 blue and red .. 1·75 1·25

45. Rhesus Macaques in Tree ("Year of the Monkey").

1968. Chinese New Year ("Year of the Monkey").
245. **45.** 10 c. gold, black & red 2·00 15
246. – $1·30 gold, black & red 4·00 4·00
DESIGN: $1·30, Family of rhesus macaques.

47. "Iberia" (liner) at Ocean Terminal.

1968. Sea Craft.
247. **47.** 10 c. multicoloured .. 70 10
248. – 20 c. blue, black & brown 1·25 45
249. – 40 c. orge., blk. & mauve 2·75 3·75
250. – 50 c. red, black & green 3·25 50
251. – $1 yellow, black and red 4·75 2·25
252. – $1.30 blue, black & pink 6·00 1·75
DESIGNS: 20 c. Pleasure Launch. 40 c. Car Ferry. 50 c. Passenger Ferry. $1, Sampan. $1.30, Junk.

53. "Bauhinia blakeana".

1968. Multicoloured.
253. 65 c. Type **53** .. .. 2·00 30
254. $1 Arms of Hong Kong .. 2·00 30

55. "Aladdin's Lamp" and Human Rights Emblem.

1968 Human Rights Year.
255. **55.** 10 c. orge, blk. & green 25 10
256. 50 c. yell., blk. & purple 45 1·00

56. Cockerel.

1969. Chinese New Year ("Year of the Cock"). Multicoloured.
257. 10 c. Type **56** .. .. 1·00 15
258. $1·30 Cockerel (different) (vert.) .. .. 7·50 4·50

58. Arms of Chinese University.

1969. Establishment of Chinese University of Hong Kong.
259. **58.** 40 c. violet, gold & blue 50 75

59. Earth Station and Satellite.

1969. Opening of Communications Satellite Tracking Station.
260. **59.** $1 multicoloured .. 2·00 1·75

60. Chow's Head. 62. "Expo 70". Emblem.

1970. Chinese New Year ("Year of the Dog"). Multicoloured.
261. 10 c. Type **60** .. .. 2·00 25
262. $1.30 Chow standing (horiz.) .. .. .. 11·00 3·75

1970. Expo 70. Multicoloured.
263. 15 c. Type **62** 15 40
264. 25 c. Expo 70 emblem and junks (horiz.) 15 50

64. Plaque in Tung Wah Hospital.

1970. Cent. of "Tung Wah Hospital".
265. **64.** 10 c. multicoloured .. 15 10
266. 50 c. multicoloured .. 20 30

65. Symbol.

1970. Asian Productivity Year.
267. **65.** 10 c. multicoloured .. 15 15

66. Pig.

1971. Chinese New Year ("Year of the Pig").
268. **66.** 10 c. multicoloured .. 1·25 25
269. $1·30 multicoloured .. 4·25 4·25

67. "60" and Scout Badge.

1971. Diamond Jubilee of Scouting in Hong Kong.
270. **67.** 10 c. blk., red & yellow 45 10
271. 50 c. blk., green & blue 70 50
272. $2 blk., mauve & viloet 1·90 3·00

68. Festival Emblem.

1971. Hong Kong Festival.
273. **68.** 10 c. orange & purple .. 45 10
274. – 50 c. multicoloured .. 70 50
275. – $1 multicoloured .. 1·90 3·00
DESIGNS—HORIZ. (39 × 23 mm.) 50 c. Coloured streamers. VERT. (23 × 39 mm.) $1, "Orchid".

69. Stylised Rats.

1972. Chinese New Year. ("Year of the Rat").
276. **69.** 10 c. red, black & gold .. 75 25
277. $1.30 red, blk. & gold 4·00 4·00

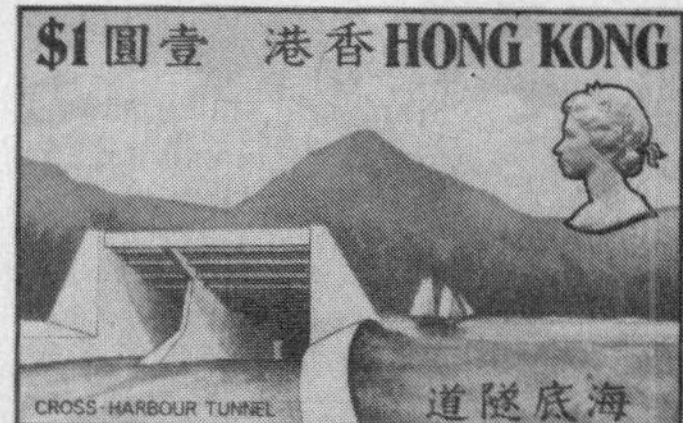

70. Tunnel Entrance.

1972. Opening of Cross Harbour Tunnel.
278. **70.** $1 multicoloured .. 1·75 1·50

1972. Royal Silver Wedding. As T **52** of Ascension, but with Phoenix and Dragon in background.
279. 10 c. multicoloured .. 10 10
280. 50 c. multicoloured .. 45 60

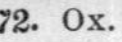
72. Ox. **73.** Queen Elizabeth II.

1973. Chinese New Year (" Year of the Ox ").
281. **72.** 10 c. orge., brn. & black 50 10
282. – $1.30 yell., orge. & blk. 2·25 4·00
DESIGN—HORIZ. $1.30, Ox.

1973.
311 **73.** 10 c. orange 55 20
284 15 c. green .. .. 4·75 2·75
313 20 c. violet 15 10
286 25 c. brown .. .. 4·75 3·00
315 30 c. blue 40 20
316 40 c. blue 50 70
317 50 c. red 85 30
318 60 c. lavender 80 75
290 65 c. brown .. .. 5·50 6·50
320 70 c. yellow .. .. 1·00 20
321 80 c. red .. .. 1·00 50
321b 90 c. brown .. .. 4·50 90
322a $1 green .. .. 1·50 50
323 – $1·30 yellow and violet 1·60 30
324 – $2 green and brown .. 1·75 80
324b – $5 pink and blue .. 2·00 75
324c – $10 pink and green .. 2·00 2·50
324d – $20 pink and black .. 4·00 5·00
Values of $1.30 and above are size 27 × 32 mm.

1973. Royal Wedding. As Type **47** of Anguilla. Multicoloured. Background colours given.
297. 50 c. brown 25 15
298. $2 mauve 65 80

75. Festival Symbols forming Chinese Character.

1973. Hong Kong Festival.
299. **75.** 10 c. red and green .. 15 10
300. 50 c. mauve & orange 40 35
301. – $1 green and mauve .. 90 1·60
DESIGNS—Festival symbols arranged to form a Chinese character: 10 c. "Hong". 50 c. "Kong". $1, "Festival".

76. Tiger.

1974. Chinese New Year (" Year of the Tiger ").
302. **76.** 10 c. multicoloured .. 1·50 15
303. – $1·30 multicoloured .. 5·50 7·00
DESIGN—VERT. $1·30, similar to Type **76.**

77. Chinese Mask.

1974. Arts Festival.
304. **77.** 10 c. multicoloured .. 40 10
305. – $1 multicoloured .. 1·50 2·75
306. – $2 multicoloured .. 1·75 3·75
DESIGNS: $1, $2, Chinese masks similar to Type **77.**

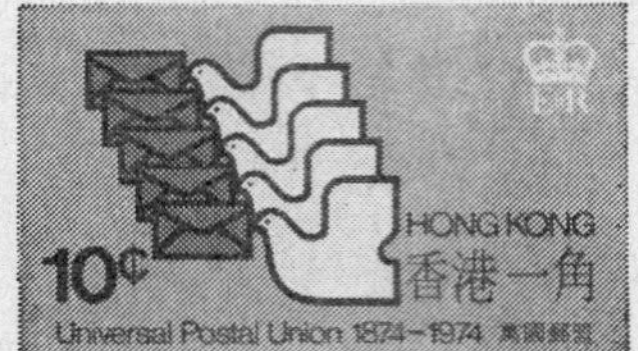

78. Pigeons with Letters.

1974. Centenary of U.P.U.
308. **78.** 10 c. bl., grn. & blk. .. 15 10
309. – 50 c. mauve, orge., blk. 30 25
310. – $2 multicoloured 60 2·25
DESIGNS: 50 c. Globe within letters. $2, Hands holding letters.

79. Stylised Rabbit.

1975. Chinese New Year (" Year of the Rabbit ").
325. **79.** 10 c. silver and red .. 30 15
326. – $1·30 gold and green .. 3·00 4·25
DESIGN: $1·30, Pair of rabbits.

80. Queen Elizabeth II, the Duke of Edinburgh and Hong Kong Arms.

1975. Royal Visit.
329. **80.** $1·30 multicoloured .. 1·25 1·75
330. $2 multicoloured .. 1·50 2·50

81. Mid-Autumn Festival.

1975. Hong Kong Festivals of 1975. **Mult.**
331. 50 c. Type **81** 50 20
332. $1 Dragon-boat Festival 1·25 2·00
333. $2 Tin Hau Festival .. 1·75 2·75

82. Hwamei.

1975. Birds. Multicoloured.
335. 50 c. Type **82** .. .. 1·25 30
336. $1·30 Chinese Bulbul .. 3·50 4·00
337. $2 Black-capped Kingfisher .. .. 4·00 5·00

83. Dragon.

1976. Chinese New Year (" Year of the Dragon ").
338. **83.** 20 c. mauve, pur. & gold 35 10
339. – $1·30 green, red & gold 1·40 2·50
DESIGN: $1·30, As Type **83** but dragon reversed.

84. " 60 " and Girl Guides Badge.

1976. Diamond Jubilee of Girl Guides. Mult.
354. 20 c. Type **84** 30 10
355. $1·30 Badge, stylised diamond and " 60 " .. .. 1·50 2·25

85. " Postal Services " in Chinese Characters.

1976. Opening of New G.P.O.
356. **85.** 20 c. green, grey & black 15 10
357. – $1·30 orge., grey & blk. 60 1·00
358. – $2 yellow, grey & black 80 1·75
DESIGNS: $1·30, Old G.P.O. $2, New G.P.O.

86. Tree Snake on Branch.

1977. Chinese New Year (" Year of the Snake "). Multicoloured.
359. 20 c. Type **86** 35 10
360. $1.30 Snake facing left .. 2·25 3·50

87. Presentation of the Orb.

1977. Silver Jubilee. Multicoloured.
361. 20 c. Type **87** .. 20 10
362. $1.30 The Queen's Visit, 1975 .. .. 70 1·10
363. $2 The Orb (vert.) .. 80 1·10

88. Tram Cars.

1977. Tourism. Multicoloured.
364. 20 c. Type **88** .. 40 10
365. 60 c. Star ferryboat .. 1·00 1·25
366. $1.30 The Peak railway .. 1·25 1·50
367. $2 Junk and sampan .. 1·25 2·25

89. Buttercup Orchid.

1977. Orchids. Multicoloured.
368. 20 c. Type **89** 75 10
369. $1.30 Lady's Slipper Orchid 1·75 1·50
370. $2 Susan Orchid .. .. 2·00 2·50

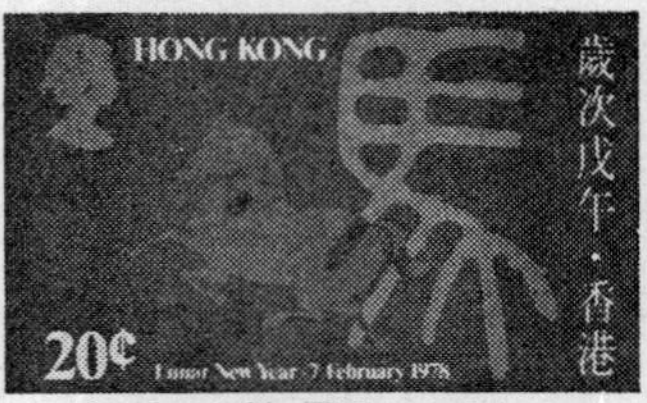

90. Horse.

1978. Chinese New Year (" Year of the Horse ").
371. **90.** 20 c. mauve, olive and bistre 30 10
372. $1.30 orange, brown and light brown .. .. 1·25 2·40

91. Queen Elizabeth II.

1978. 25th Anniversary of Coronation.
373. **91.** 20 c. mauve and blue 20 10
374. $1.30 blue and mauve 70 1·25

92. Girl and Boy holding Hands.

1978. Centenary of Po Leung Kuk (children's charity). Multicoloured.
375. 20 c. Type **92** .. 15 10
376. $1.30 Ring of children .. 60 1·00

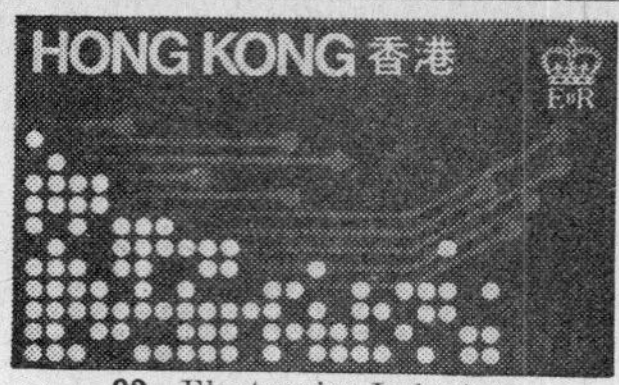

93. Electronics Industry.

1979. Hong Kong Industries.

377. **93.** 20 c. yell., olive & orge. .. 10 10
378. – $1.30 multicoloured .. 60 90
379. – $2 multicoloured .. 60 1·10

DESIGNS: $1.30, Toy industry. $2, Garment industry.

94. "Precis orithya".

1979. Butterflies. Multicoloured.

380 20 c. Type **94** 35 10
381 $1 "Graphium sarpedon" 70 70
382 $1.30 "Heliophorus epicles" 85 1·10
383 $2 "Danaus genutia" .. 1·10 2·50

95. Diagrammatic View of Railway Station.

1979. Mass Transit Railway. Multicoloured.

384. 20 c. Type **95** 15 10
385. $1.30 Diagrammatic view of car 50 50
386. $2 Plan showing route of railway 60 70

96. Tsui Shing Lau Pagoda.

1980. Rural Architecture.

387. **96.** 20 c. blk., mauve & yell. 10 10
388. – $1.30 multicoloured .. 60 85
389. – $2 multicoloured .. 75 1·60

DESIGNS—HORIZ. $1.30, Village House, Sai O. $2, Ching Chung Koon Temple.

97. Queen Elizabeth the Queen Mother.

1980. 80th Birthday of The Queen Mother.

390. **97.** $1.30 multicoloured .. 55 70

98. Botanical Gardens.

1980. Parks. Multicoloured.

391. 20 c. Type **98** 10 10
392. $1 Ocean Park 30 45
393. $1.30 Kowloon Park .. 40 75
394. $2 Country Parks .. 55 1·25

99. " Epinephelus akaara ".

1981. Fishes. Multicoloured.

395. 20 c. Type **99** 15 10
396. $1 " Nemipterus virgatus " 45 45
397. $1.30 " Choerodon azurio " 55 60
398. $2 " Scarus ghobban " .. 65 1·10

100. Wedding Bouquet from Hong Kong.

1981. Royal Wedding. Multicoloured.

399. 20 c. Type **100** 10 10
400. $1.30 Prince Charles in Hong Kong 35 35
401. $5 Prince Charles and Lady Diana Spencer .. .. 1·25 1·50

101. Surburban Development.

1981. Public Housing.

402. **101.** 20 c. multicoloured .. 10 10
403. – $1 multicoloured .. 25 30
404. – $1.30 multicoloured .. 35 40
405. – $2 multicoloured .. 50 60

DESIGNS: $1 to $2, Various suburban developments.

102. " Victoria from the Harbour, c. 1855 ".

1982. Hong Kong Port, Past and Present. Multicoloured.

407. 20 c. Type **102** 15 10
408. $1 " West Point, Hong Kong, 1847 " 45 45
409. $1.30 Fleet of junks .. 60 65
410. $2 Liner " Queen Elizabeth 2 " at Hong Kong .. 80 1·25

103. Large Indian Civet.

1982. Wild Animals.

411. **103.** 20 c. blk., pink & brn. 20 10
412. – $1 multicoloured .. 70 60
413. – $1.30 blk., grn. & orge. 80 90
414. – $5 black, brn.& yell. 1·40 2·50

DESIGNS: $1, Chinese pangolin. $1.30, Chinese porcupine. $5, Indian muntjac.

104. Queen Elizabeth II.

1982.

471 **104.** 10 c. bright red, red and yellow 40 20
416 20 c. blue, violet and lavender 45 15
417 30 c. light violet, violet and pink .. 60 20
474 40 c. red and blue .. 40 20
475 50 c. chestnut, brown and green 40 30
476 60 c. purple and grey 65 50
477 70 c. green, myrtle and yellow 70 35
478 80 c. bistre, brown & green 80 70
479 90 c. bottle green, green and turquoise 80 40
480 $1 deep orange, orange and red .. 85 40
481 $1.30 blue and mauve 1·25 45
482 $1.70 deep blue, blue and green .. .. 1·00 1·00
483 $2 blue and pink .. 1·50 1·00
484 – $5 red, pur. & yell. .. 2·00 2·50
485 – $10 brn. and light brn. 2·50 3·50
486 – $20 red and blue .. 3·00 5·00
487 – $50 red and grey .. 10·00 18·00

Nos. 484/7 are as Type **104** but larger, 26 × 30 mm.

106. Table Tennis.

1982. Sport for the Disabled. Multicoloured.

431. 30 c. Type **106** 20 10
432. $1 Racing 35 45
433. $1.30 Basketball 60 80
434. $5 Archery .. .. 1·40 2·50

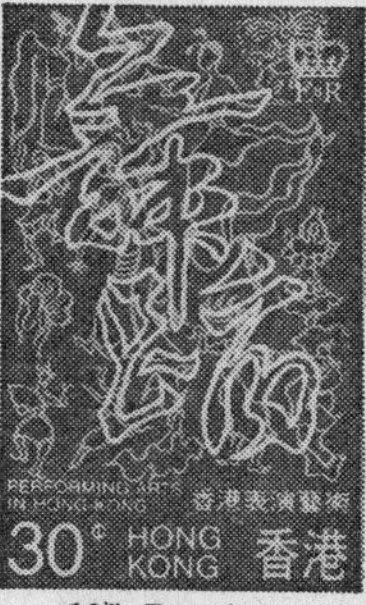

107. Dancing.

1983. Performing Arts.

435. **107.** 30 c. light blue & blue 20 10
436. $1.30 red and purple .. 60 80
437. $5 green & deep green 1·60 2·75

INDEX

Countries can be quickly located by referring to the index at the end of this volume.

108. Aerial View of Hong Kong.

1983. Commonwealth Day. Multicoloured.

438. 30 c. Type **108** 20 10
439. $1 "Liverpool Bay" (container ship) 45 65
440. $1.30 Hong Kong flag .. 55 80
441. $5 Queen Elizabeth II and Hong Kong .. .. 1·25 2·25

109. Victoria Harbour.

1983. Hong Kong by Night. Multicoloured.

442. 30 c. Type **109** 30 10
443. $1 Space Museum, Tsim Sha Tsui Cultural Centre 65 1·00
444. $1.30 Fireworks display .. 75 1·25
445. $5 " Jumbo ", floating restaurant .. .. .. 2·00 3·50

110. Old and new Observatory Buildings.

1983. Centenary of Hong Kong Observatory.

446. **110.** 40 c. orange, brown & black 30 10
447. – $1 mauve, deep mauve and black .. .. 65 1·00
448. – $1.30 blue, deep blue and black .. .. 75 1·25
449. – $5 yellow, green & black 2·00 3·50

DESIGNS: $1 Wind measuring equipment. $1.30 Thermometer. $5 Ancient and modern seismometers.

111. " DH 86 " Dorado (Hong Kong–Penang Service, 1936).

1984. Aviation in Hong Kong. Multicoloured.

450. 40 c. Type **111** 35 10
451. $1 Sikorsky " S-42B " (San Francisco-Hong Kong Service, 1937) .. .. 65 1·00
452. $1.30 Cathy-Pacific "Jumbo" jet leaving Kai Tak Airport .. .. .. 75 1·25
453. $5 Baldwin brothers' balloon, 1891 (vert.) .. 2·00 3·50

112. Map by Capt. E. Belcher.

1984. Maps of Hong Kong.

454. 40 c. Type **112** 35 15
455. $1 Bartholomew map of 1929 .. .. .. 55 1·00
456. $1.30 Early map of Hong Kong Waters .. .. 65 1·25
457. $5 Chinese style map of 1819 .. .. .. 1·75 3·50

113. Cockerel.

1984. Chinese Animal Lanterns. Mult.

458. 40 c. Type **113** 20 15
459. $1 Dog 35 55
460. $1.30 Butterfly 40 75
461. $5 Fish .. .. .. 1·40 3·00

114. Jockey on Horse and Nurse with Baby ("Health Care").

1984. Centenary of Royal Hong Kong Jockey Club. Designs showing aspects of Club's charity work. Multicoloured.

462. 40 c. Type **114** 20 15
463. $1 Disabled man playing handball ("Support for disabled") 40 70
464. $1.30 Ballerina ("The Arts") .. .. .. 45 1·00
465. $5 Humboldt penguins ("Ocean Park") .. .. 1·75 3·25

115. Hung Sing Temple.

1985. Historic Buildings. Multicoloured.

467. 40 c. Type **115** 25 20
468. $1 St. John's Cathedral .. 50 80
469. $1.30 The Old Supreme Court Building .. .. 55 1·00
470. $5 Wan Chai Post Office .. 1·75 3·50

116. Prow of Dragon Boat.

1985. 10th International Dragon Boat Festival. Designs showing different parts of dragon boat. Multicoloured.

488. 40 c. Type **116** 20 15
489. $1 Drummer and rowers .. 30 55
490. $1.30 Rowers 35 65
491. $5 Stern of boat .. .. 1·25 2·50

117. The Queen Mother with Prince Charles and Prince William, 1984.

1985. Life and Times of Queen Elizabeth the Queen Mother. Multicoloured.

493 40 c. At Glamis Castle, aged 7 .. .. .. 35 10
494 $1 Type **117** 65 50
495 $1.30 The Queen Mother 1970 (from photo by Cecil Beaton) 65 70
496 $5 With Prince Henry at his Christening (from photo by Lord Snowdon) 1·40 2·25

118. "Melastoma candidum".

1985. Native Flowers. Multicoloured.

497. 40 c. Type **118** 40 15
498. 50 c. Chinese Lily 40 25
499. 60 c. Grantham's Camellia 40 35
500. $1.30 "Narcissus tazetta" 70 75
501. $1.70 "Bauhinia blakeana" 80 1·25
502. $5 Chinese New Year Flower .. .. .. 1·75 3·25

119. Hong Kong Academy for Performing Arts.

1985. New Buildings. Multicoloured.

503. 50 c. Type **119** 35 15
504. $1.30 Exchange Square (vert.) 65 45
505. $1.70 Hong Kong Bank Headquarters (vert.) .. 85 75
506. $5 Hong Kong Coliseum .. 1·50 1·75

120. Halley's Comet in the Solar System.

1986. Appearance of Halley's Comet. Mult.

507. 50 c. Type **120** 20 15
508. $1.30 Edmond Halley and Comet 35 50
509. $1.70 Comet over Hong Kong 40 80
510. $5 Comet passing the Earth 1·25 2·75

1986. 60th Birthday of Queen Elizabeth II. As T **110** of Ascension. Multicoloured.

512. 50 c. At wedding of Miss Celia Bowes-Lyon, 1931 25 10
513. $1 Queen in Garter procession, Windsor Castle 1977 .. .. 40 30
514. $1.30 In Hong Kong, 1975 45 40
515. $1.70 At Royal Lodge, Windsor, 1980 (from photo by Norman Parkinson) .. 45 60
516. $5 At Crown Agents Head Office, London, 1983 .. 1·00 2·00

121. Train, Airliner and Map of World.

1986. "Expo '86" World Fair, Vancouver. Multicoloured.

517. 50 c. Type **121** 25 15
518. $1.30 Hong Kong Bank Headquarters and map of world 50 45
519. $1.70 Container ship and map of world 70 85
520. $5 Dish aerial and map of world .. .. .. 1·75 2·50

122. Hand-liner Sampan.

1986. Fishing Vessels. Designs showing fishing boat and outline of fish. Multicoloured.

521. 50 c. Type **122** 20 15
522. $1.30 Stern trawler .. 50 50
523. $1.70 Long liner junk .. 70 90
524. $5 Junk trawler .. .. 1·75 2·50

123. "The Second Puan Khequa" (attr Spoilum).

1986. 19th-century Hong Kong Portraits. Multicoloured.

525. 50 c. Type **123** 20 15
526. $1.30 "Chinese Lady" (19th-century copy) .. 50 45
527. $1.70 "Lamqua" (self-portrait) 60 70
528. $5 "Wife of Wo Hing Qua" (attr G. Chinnery) .. 1·75 2·00

124. Rabbit.

1987. Chinese New Year ("Year of the Rabbit"). Designs showing stylized rabbits.

529. **124.** 50 c. multicoloured .. 20 10
530. – $1.30 multicoloured .. 35 30
531. – $1.70 multicoloured .. 40 35
532. – $5 multicoloured .. 1·00 1·10

Nos. 530/1 have the "0" omitted from their face values.

125. "Village Square, Hong Kong Island, 1838" (Auguste Borget).

1987. 19th-century Hong Kong Scenes. Multicoloured.

534. 50 c. Type **125** 25 10
535. $1.30 "Boat Dwellers, Kowloon Bay, 1838" (August Borget) .. 45 35
536. $1.70 "Flagstaff House, 1846" (Murdoch Bruce) 55 60
537. $5 "Wellington Street late 19th-century" (C. Andrasi) .. .. .. 1·00 1·50

126. Queen Elizabeth II and Central Victoria.

127. Hong Kong Flag.

1987.

600 **126** 10 c. multicoloured .. 10 10
601 40 c. multicoloured .. 10 10
602 50 c. multicoloured .. 10 10
603 60 c. multicoloured .. 10 10
604 70 c. multicoloured .. 10 10
605 80 c. multicoloured .. 10 10
606 90 c. multicoloured .. 10 15
607 $1 multicoloured .. 15 20
607a $1.20 multicoloured .. 20 25
608 $1.30 multicoloured .. 20 25
609 $1.40 multicoloured .. 25 30
609a $1.70 multicoloured .. 25 30
610 $1.80 multicoloured .. 25 30
611 $2 multicoloured .. 30 35
611a $2.30 multicoloured .. 35 40
612 – $5 multicoloured .. 75 80
613 – $10 multicoloured .. 1·50 1·60
614 – $20 multicoloured .. 3·00 3·25
615 – $50 multicoloured .. 7·50 7·75

DESIGNS: 25 × 31 mm. Queen Elizabeth II and $5 Kowloon. $10 Victoria Harbour. $20 Legislative Council Building. $50 Government House.

With the exception of Nos. 607a and 611a which are undated, all the above exist with or without a date in the design.

1987.

533 **125** 10 c. multicoloured .. 10 10
554 – 50 c. brown, red & blk 10 10
554c – 80 c. mve, grn & blk 10 10
554d – 90 c. blue, brn & blk 10 10
554e – $1.30 green, bl & blk 20 25
554f – $2.30 brn, violet & blk 35 40

DESIGN: 50 c. to $2.30, Map of Hong Kong.

128. Alice Ho Miu Ling Nethersole Hospital, 1887.

1987. Hong Kong Medical Centenaries. Multicoloured.

555. 50 c. Type **128** .. 20 10
556. $1.30 Matron and nurses, Nethersole Hospital, 1891 .. .. .. 55 35
557. $1.70 Scanning equipment, Faculty of Medicine .. 45 50
558. $5 Nurse and patient Faculty of Medicine .. 1·10 1·40

129. Casual Dress with Fringed Hem, 220–589.

1987. Historical Chinese Costumes. Mult.

559. 50 c. Type **129** 15 10
560. $1.30 Two-piece dress and wrap, 581–960 .. .. 30 35
561. $1.70 Formal dress, Song Dynasty, 960–1279 .. 35 45
562. $5 Manchu empress costume, 1644–1911 .. 90 1·25

130. Dragon.

1988. Chinese New Year ("Year of the Dragon"). Designs showing dragons.

563. **130.** 50 c. multicoloured .. 35 15
564. – $1.30 multicoloured .. 45 50
565. – $1.70 multicoloured .. 60 75
566. – $5 multicoloured .. 1·40 2·25

131. White-breasted Kingfisher.

1988. Hong Kong Birds. Multicoloured.
568. 50 c. Type **131** 20 10
569. $1.30 Fukien niltava .. 40 35
570. $1.70 Black kite 45 50
571. $5 Pied kingfisher .. .. 1·00 1·40

132 Chinese Banyan

1988. Trees of Hong Kong. Multicoloured.
572 50 c. Type **132** 15 10
573 $1.30 Hong Kong orchid tree 25 25
574 $1.70 Cotton tree .. 30 30
575 $5 Schima 80 90

133 Lower Terminal, Peak Tramway

1988. Centenary of The Peak Tramway. Mult.
577 50 c. Type **133** 15 10
578 $1.30 Tram on incline .. 25 35
579 $1.70 Peak Tower Upper Terminal 30 45
580 $5 Tram .. .. 80 1·00

134 Hong Kong Catholic Cathedral

1988. Centenary of Hong Kong Catholic Cathedral.
582 **134** 60 c. multicoloured .. 20 20

135 Deaf Girl

1988. Community Chest Charity.
583 **135** 60 c.+10 c. black, red and blue 15 15
584 – $1.40+20 c. black, red and green .. 25 30
585 – $1.80+30 c. black, red and orange .. 30 35
586 – $5+$1 blk, red & brn 90 95
DESIGNS: $1.40, Elderly woman; $1.80, Blind boy using braille typewriter; $5 Mother and baby.

136 Snake

1989. Chinese New Year ("Year of the Snake"). Multicoloured.
587 60 c. Type **136** 10 15
588 $1.40 Snake and fish .. 20 25
589 $1.80 Snake on branch .. 25 30
590 $5 Coiled snake 75 80

137 Girl and Doll

1989. Cheung Chau Bun Festival. Mult.
592 60 c. Type **137** 15 15
593 $1.40 Girl in festival costume 30 30
594 $1.80 Paper effigy of god Taai Si Wong 45 45
595 $5 Floral gateway .. 1·00 1·10

138 "Twins" (wood carving, Cheung Yee)

1989. Modern Art. Multicoloured.
596 60 c. Type **138** 10 10
597 $1.40 "Figures" (acrylic on paper, Chan Luis) .. 20 25
598 $1.80 "Lotus" (copper sculpture, Van Lau) .. 30 35
599 $5 "Zen Painting" (ink and colour on paper, Lui Shou-kwan) 80 85

139 Lunar New Year Festivities

1989. Hong Kong People. Multicoloured.
616 60 c. Type **139** 10 10
617 $1.40 Shadow boxing and horse racing 20 25
618 $1.80 Foreign-exchange dealer and traditional builder 30 35
619 $5 Multi-racial society .. 80 85

140 University of Science and Technology

1989. Building for the Future.
620 **140** 60 c. black, yell & brn 10 10
621 – 70 c. black, pale pink and pink 10 15
622 – $1.30 blk, lt grn & grn 20 25
623 – $1.40 black, lt bl & bl 20 25
624 – $1.80 black, turq & bl 30 35
625 – $5 brown, orge & red 80 85
DESIGNS: 70 c. Cultural Centre; $1.30, Eastern Harbour motorway interchange; $1.40, New Bank of China Building; $1.80, Convention and Exhibition Centre; $5 Light Rail Transit train.

141 Prince and Princess of Wales and Hong Kong Skyline

1989. Royal Visit. Multicoloured.
626 60 c. Type **141** 10 10
627 $1.40 Princess of Wales .. 20 25
628 $1.80 Prince of Wales .. 30 35
629 $5 Prince and Princess of Wales in evening dress 80 85

143 Horse

1990. Chinese New Year ("Year of the Horse").
631 **143** 60 c. multicoloured .. 15 15
632 – $1.40 multicoloured .. 30 30
633 – $1.80 multicoloured .. 40 40
634 – $5 multicoloured .. 1·00 1·00
DESIGNS: $1.40 to $5, Different horse designs.

144 Chinese Lobster Dish

1990. International Cuisine. Designs showing various dishes. Multicoloured.
636 60 c. Type **144** 15 15
637 70 c. Indian 20 15
638 $1.30 Chinese vegetables .. 30 30
639 $1.40 Thai 30 30
640 $1.80 Japanese 40 40
641 $5 French .. .. 1·00 1·10

145 Air Pollution and Clean Air

1990. U.N. World Environment Day. Mult.
642 60 c. Type **145** 15 15
643 $1.40 Noise pollution and music 30 25
644 $1.80 Polluted and clean water 35 30
645 $5 Litter on ground and in bin .. .. .. 95 1·00

146 Street Lamp and Des Voeux Road, 1890

1990. Centenary of Electricity Supply.
647 **146** 60 c. blk, bisstre & brn 15 10
648 – $1.40 multicoloured .. 30 25
649 – $1.80 black, bistre & bl 35 30
650 – $5 multicoloured .. 1·00 1·00
DESIGNS: $1.40, Street lamp and "Jumbo" (floating restaurant), 1940; $1.80, Street lamp and pylon, 1960; $5 Street lamp and Hong Kong from harbour, 1980.

147 Christmas Tree and Skyscrapers

1990. Christmas. Multicoloured.
652 50 c. Type **147** 15 10
653 60 c. Dove with holly .. 15 15
654 $1.40 Firework display .. 30 30
655 $1.80 Father Christmas hat on skyscraper 35 40
656 $2 Children with Father Christmas 40 45
657 $5 Candy stick with bow and Hong Kong skyline 1·10 1·40

148 Ram

1991. Chinese New Year ("Year of the Ram").

658	148	60 c. multicoloured ..	15	10
659	–	$1.40 multicoloured ..	35	30
660	–	$1.80 multicoloured ..	40	40
661	–	$5 multicoloured ..	1·10	1·40

DESIGNS: $1.40 to $5, Different ram designs.

149 Letter "A", Clock, Teddy Bear and Building Bricks (Kindergarten)

1991. Education. Multicoloured.

663	80 c. Type **149**	15	15
664	$1.80 Globe, laboratory flask and mathematical symbols (Primary and Secondary)	35	35
665	$2.30 Machinery (Vocational)	55	60
666	$5 Mortar board, computer and books (Tertiary) ..	1·25	1·50

150 Rickshaw

1991. 100 Years of Public Transport. Mult.

667	80 c. Type **150**	15	15
668	90 c. Double-decker bus ..	15	15
669	$1.70 Harbour ferry ..	40	40
670	$1.80 Tram	40	45
671	$2.30 Mass Transit Railway train	60	70
672	$5 Jetfoil	1·25	1·40

151 Victorian Pillar Box and Cover of 1888

1991. 150th Anniv of Hong Kong Post Office. Multicoloured.

673	80 c. Type **151** ..	15	15
674	$1.70 Edwardian pillar box and cover	40	40
675	$1.80 King George V pillar box and cover of 1935 ..	40	45
676	$2.30 King George VI pillar box and cover of 1938 ..	55	60
677	$5 Queen Elizabeth II pillar box and cover of 1989	1·10	1·25

152 Bronze Buddha, Lantau Island

1991. Landmarks.

679	152	80 c. red and black ..	15	15
680	–	$1.70 green and black	35	40
681	–	$1.80 violet and black	35	40
682	–	$2.30 blue and black ..	50	60
683	–	$5 orange and black ..	1·00	1·25

DESIGNS: $1.70, Peak Pavilion; $1.80, Clock Tower; $2.30, Catholic Cathedral; $5 Wong Tai Sin Temple.

153 Monkey

1992. Chinese New Year ("Year of the Monkey").

686	153	80 c. multicoloured ..	10	15
687	–	$1.80 multicoloured ..	25	30
688	–	$2.30 multicoloured ..	35	40
689	–	$5 multicoloured ..	75	80

DESIGNS: $1.40 to $5, Different monkey designs.

1992. 40th Anniv of Queen Elizabeth II's Accession. As T **143** of Ascension. Mult.

691	80 c. Royal barge in Hong Kong harbour	10	15
692	$1.70 Queen watching dancing display ..	25	30
693	$1.80 Fireworks display ..	25	30
694	$2.30 Three portraits of Queen Elizabeth ..	35	40
695	$5 Queen Elizabeth II ..	75	80

154 Running

1992. Olympic Games, Barcelona. Mult.

696	80 c. Type **154**	10	15
697	$1.80 Swimming and javelin	25	30
698	$2.30 Cycling	35	40
699	$5 High jump	75	80

POSTAGE DUE STAMPS

D 1. Post Office Scales.

1923.

D 1b	D 1.	1 c. brown	15	70
D 2a		2 c. green	8·00	4·75
D 6a		2 c. grey	70	6·00
D 3		4 c. red	21·00	6·00
D 7a		4 c. orange	2·00	7·50
D 18		5 c. red (21 × 18 mm.)	1·00	4·00
D 4		6 c. yellow	22·00	13·00
D 8		6 c. red	8·00	6·00
D 9		8 c. brown	4·50	26·00
D 5		10 c. blue	19·00	7·50
D 15		10 c. violet	1·50	3·25
D 16		20 c. black	2·50	3·25
D 22		50 c. blue	3·00	9·50

1976. As Type **D 1** but smaller design (21 × 17 mm) with redrawn value.

D 25a.	D 1.	10 c. violet	20	1·00
D 26a.		20 c. grey	25	1·25
D 27a.		50 c. blue	50	1·75
D 28a.		$1 yellow	40	2·00

D 2.

1987.

D 31.	D 2.	10 c. green	10	10
D 32.		20 c. brown	10	10
D 33.		50 c. violet	10	10
D 34.		$1 orange	15	20
D 35.		$5 blue	75	80
D 36.		$10 red	1·50	1·60

JAPANESE OCCUPATION OF HONG KONG

100 sen = 1 yen.

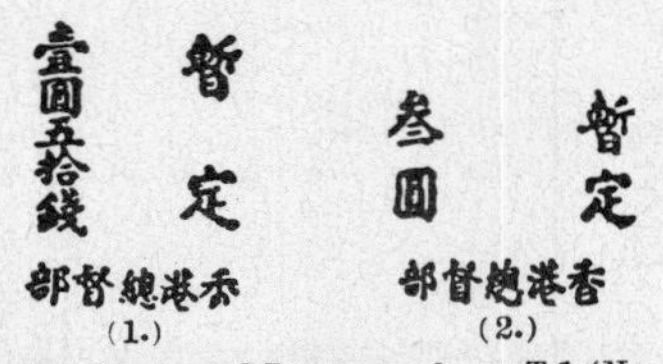

(1.) (2.)

1945. Stamps of Japan surch. as T **1** (No. 1) or **2**.

1.	126.	1.50 yen on 1 s. brown ..	18·00	16·00
2.	84.	3 yen on 2 s. red	11·00	14·00
3.	–	5 yen on 5 s. red (No. 396)	£400	70·00

HYDERABAD

A state in India. Now uses Indian stamps.

12 pies = 1 anna; 16 annas = 1 rupee.

1.

1869.

1.	1.	1 a. green	8·50	6·00

2.

3.

1870.

2.	2.	½ a. brown	4·00	4·00
3.		2 a. green	35·00	30·00

1871.

13	3	½ a. brown	30	10
13b		½ a. red	30	10
14		1 a. purple	1·75	2·25
14b		1 a. brown	30	10
14c		1 a. black	30	10
15		2 a. green	65	10
16a		3 a. brown	40	45
17b		4 a. grey	1·00	70
17c		4 a. green	2·00	1·00
18		8 a. brown	1·25	1·25
19		12 a. blue	2·25	2·50
19a		12 a. green	2·00	2·25

(4.)

1898. Surch. with T **4**.

20.	3.	¼ a. on ½ a. brown ..	50	75

5.

6.

1900.

21.	5.	¼ a. blue	3·00	1·90

1905.

22.	6.	¼ a. blue	1·25	30
32.		¼ a. grey	30	10
33.		¼ a. purple	30	10
23b.		½ a. red	1·50	25
34.		½ a. green	40	10
26.		1 a. red	1·00	10
27.		2 a. lilac	75	10
28.		3 a. orange	85	30
29.		4 a. green	85	20
30.		8 a. purple	1·10	30
31.		12 a. green	3·00	75

8. Symbol.

9.

1915.

35.	8.	½ a. green	60	10
58.		½ a. red	50	50
36.		1 a. red	75	10
37.	9.	1 r. yellow	9·00	11·00

(10.)

1930. Surch as T **10**.

38.	6.	4 p. on ¼ a. grey	38·00	11·00
39.		4 p. on ¼ a. purple	10	10
40.	8.	8 p. on ½ a. green	10	10

12. Symbols.

13. The Char Minar.

1931.

60.	**12.**	2 p. brown	1·00	1·10
41.		4 p. black	20	10
59.		6 p. red	2·50	2·00
42.		8 p. green	30	10
43.	**13.**	1 a. brown	20	10
44.	–	2 a. violet	1·00	10
45.	–	4 a. blue	90	15
46.	–	8 a. orange	2·00	1·10
47.	–	12 a. red	3·00	4·50
48.	–	1 r. yellow	3·00	2·50

In No. 59 "POSTAGE" is at foot.

DESIGNS—(Approx. 32½ × 21) HORIZ. 2 a. High Court of Justice. 4 a. Osman Sagar Reservoir. 12 a. Bidar College. VERT. 8 a. Entrance to Ajanta Caves. 1 r. Victory Tower, Daulatabad.

15. Unani General Hospital.

1937. Inscr. "H.E.H. THE NIZAM'S SILVER JUBILEE".

49.	**15.**	4 p. slate and violet	15	30
50.	–	8 p. slate and brown	20	40
51.	–	1 a. slate and yellow	30	30
52.	–	2 a. slate and green	50	1·10

DESIGNS: 8 p. Osmania General Hospital. 1 a. Osmania University. 2 a. Osmania Jubilee Hall.

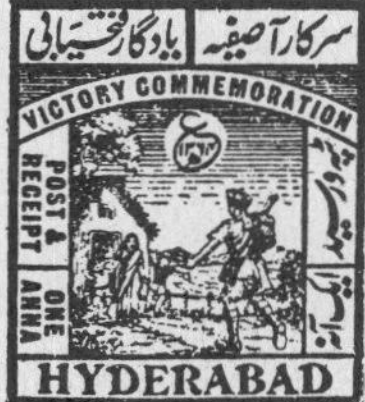

16. Family Reunion.

1945. Victory Commemoration.

53.	**16.**	1 a. blue	10	10

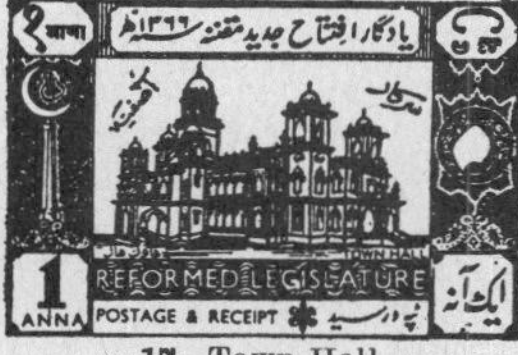

17. Town Hall.

1947. Reformed Legislature.

54.	**17.**	1 a. black	30	30

18. Power House, Hyderabad.

1947. Inser. as in T **18**.

55.	**18.**	1 a. 4 p. green	40	50
56.	–	3 a. blue	40	65
57.	–	6 a. brown	3·00	5·00

DESIGNS—HORIZ. 3 a. Kaktyai Arch, Warangal Fort. 6 a. Golkunda Fort.

OFFICIAL STAMPS

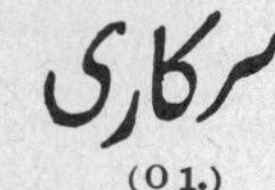

(O 1.)

1873. Optd. with Type O **1**.

O 2.	**2.**	½ a. brown	—	75·00
O 1.	**1.**	1 a. green	30·00	16·00
O 3.	**2.**	2 a. olive	—	95·00

1873. Optd. with Type **O 1**.

O 9	**3**	½ a. brown	2·25	1·00
O 11		1 a. brown	20·00	15·00
O 12		1 a. drab	1·25	85
O 19		1 a. black	24·00	10
O 13		2 a. green	2·25	2·25
O 20c		3 a. brown	2·00	70
O 15		4 a. grey	4·25	4·25
O 20d		4 a. green	—	3·25
O 16		8 a. brown	14·00	9·50
O 17		12 a. blue	16·00	
O 20f		12 a. green	—	42·00

1909. Optd. as Type O **1**, or similar smaller opt.

O30	**6**	¼ a. grey	45	20
O31		¼ a. lilac	50	10
O21a		½ a. red	40·00	15
O33		½ a. green	70	10
O40	**8**	½ a. green	80	10
O54		½ a. red	6·50	3·50
O34	**6**	1 a. red	75	10
O41e	**8**	1 a. red	60	10
O35	**6**	2 a. lilac	85	15
O36		3 a. orange	6·00	70
O37		4 a. green	1·40	10
O38		8 a. purple	2·25	20
O39		12 a. green	4·00	30

1930. Official stamps surch as T **10**.

O 42.	**6.**	4 p. on ¼ a. grey	£100	17·00
O 43.		4 p. on ¼ a. lilac	50	10
O 45.		8 p. on ½ a. green	35·00	45·00
O 44.	**8.**	8 p. on ½ a. green	45	10

1934. Optd as Type O **1** but smaller.

O 55.	**12.**	2 p. brown	5·50	4·00
O 46.		4 p. black	60	10
O 56.		6 p. red	7·00	7·50
O 47.		8 p. green	30	10
O 48.	**13.**	1 a. brown	30	10
O 49.	–	2 a. violet (No. 44)	2·00	10
O 50.	–	4 a. blue (No. 45)	1·00	10
O 51.	–	8 a. orange (No. 46)	5·00	50
O 52.	–	12 a. red (No. 47)	4·25	1·25
O 53.	–	1 r. yellow (No. 48)	6·00	2·00

IDAR

A State in Western India. Now uses Indian stamps.

12 pies = 1 anna; 16 annas = 1 rupee.

1. Maharaja Shri Himatsinhji. 2.

1939.

1b	**1.**	½ a. green	5·50	12·00

1944.

3.	**2.**	½ a. green	85	24·00
4.		1 a. violet	65	24·00
5.		2 a .blue	85	32·00
6.		4 a. red	2·40	40·00

INDIA

A peninsula in the S. of Asia. Formerly consisted of British India and numerous Native States, some of which issued stamps of their own. Divided in 1947 into the Dominion of India and the Dominion of Pakistan. Now a republic within the British Commonwealth.

1852. 12 pies = 1 anna; 16 annas = 1 rupee.
1957. 100 naye paise = 1 rupee.
1964. 100 paisa = 1 rupee.

1.

1852. "Scinde Dawk". Imperf.

S 1.	**1.**	½ a. white	£4250	£800
S 2.		½ a. blue	£10000	£3250
S 3.		½ a. red	—	£7000

3.

10.

9.

11.

1854. Imperf.

1.	**3.**	½ a. red	£800	
2.		½ a. blue	40·00	12·00
14.		1 a. red	35·00	35·00
31.	**10.**	2 a. green	85·00	22·00
23.	**9.**	4 a. blue and red	£1800	£225

1855. Perf.

75	**11**	½ a. blue	1·25	30
59		1 a. brown	2·25	30
41		2 a. pink	£160	12·00
63		2 a. orange	16·00	2·75
46		4 a. black	70·00	4·75
64		4 a. green	£180	18·00
73		8 a. red	15·00	3·75

12.

1860. Inscr. "EAST INDIA POSTAGE". Various Frames.

57	**12.**	8 p. mauve	5·50	7·00
77	–	9 p. lilac	6·50	6·50
71	–	4 a. green	9·50	55
81	–	6 a. brown	5·00	1·50
72	–	6 a. 8 p. grey	23·00	18·00
82	–	12 a. brown	6·00	13·00
79	–	1 r. grey	23·00	12·00

14.

23.

1866. Optd. **POSTAGE.**

66.	**14.**	6 a. purple	£500	£110

1882. Inscr. "INDIA POSTAGE". Various frames.

84.	**23.**	½ a. turquoise	2·00	10
86.	–	9 p. red	50	1·50
88.	–	1 a. purple	2·25	10
90.	–	1 a. 6 brown	50	70
91.	–	2 a. blue	2·75	20
94.	–	3 a. orange	5·00	45
96.	–	4 a. green	7·00	20
97.	–	4 a. 6 p. green	9·50	5·00
98.	–	8 a. mauve	12·00	2·00
100.	–	12 a. purple on red	4·50	2·00
101.	–	1 r. grey	11·00	4·25

1891. No. 97 surch. **2½ As.**

102.		2½ a. on 4½ a. green	1·50	60

40.

37.

38.

1892. As 1882 and some new designs.

111	**40.**	3 p. red	10	10
112		3 p. grey	10	40
113	**23.**	½ a. green	45	30
115	–	1 a. red	50	15
116	–	2 a. lilac	3·25	50
103	–	2½ a. green	1·00	40
118	–	2½ a. blue	3·00	3·75
106	**37.**	1 r. green and red	5·50	2·00
107	**38.**	2 r. red and orange	32·00	10·00
108		3 r. brown and green	25·00	10·00
109		5 r. blue and violet	30·00	22·00

1898. Surch. ¼.

110.	**23.**	"¼" on ½ a. turquoise	10	20

41.

52.

1902. As 1882 and 1892, but portrait of King Edward VII (inscribed "INDIA POSTAGE").

120	**41**	3 p. grey	30	10
121	–	½ a. green	35	10
123	–	1 a. red	45	10
125	–	2 a. lilac	1·50	10
126	–	2½ a. blue	3·25	15
127	–	3 a. orange	3·25	15
128	–	4 a. green	3·00	25
132	–	6 a. bistre	10·00	4·25
133	–	8 a. purple	7·50	1·00
135	–	12 a. purple on red	7·50	2·00
136	–	1 r. green and red	6·00	70
139	**52**	2 r. red and orange	23·00	3·25
140		3 r. brown and green	20·00	19·00
142		5 r. blue and violet	50·00	35·00
144		10 r. green and red	75·00	18·00
146		15 r. blue and brown	£130	42·00
147		25 r. orange and blue	£750	£800

1905. No. 122 surch. ¼.

148.		"¼" on ½ a. green	30	10

1906. As Nos. 122 and 123, but inscr. "INDIA POSTAGE & REVENUE".

149.		½ a. green	1·00	10
150.		1 a. red	60	10

55.

56.

57.

58.

59.

70.

60.

61.

62.

63.

71. 64. 65. 66.

67.

1911.

* Two types of 1½ a. brown. Type A as illustrated. Type B inscr. "1½ As. ONE AND A HALF ANNAS".

No.	Type	Description	Unused	Used
152	55.	3 p. grey	15	10
155	56.	½ a. green	30	10
161	57.	1 a. red	1·10	10
197		1 a. brown	30	10
163	58.	1½ a. brown (A)*	1·50	30
165		1½ a. brown (B)*	1·50	2·25
198		1½ a. red (B)*	80	30
166	59.	2 a. lilac	1·00	15
206	70.	2 a. lilac	90	10
170	60.	2½ a. blue	1·75	2·00
171	61.	2½ a. blue	1·00	20
207		2½ a. orange	75	10
173	62.	3 a. orange	2·50	20
209		3 a. blue	4·50	10
210	63.	4 a. olive	1·50	10
211	71.	4 a. green	5·00	10
176	64.	6 a. bistre	3·75	90
212	65.	8 a. mauve	4·00	10
213	66.	12 a. red	5·00	20
214	67.	1 r. brown and green	5·00	20
215		2 r. red and orange	7·50	45
216		5 r. blue and violet	20·00	1·25
217		10 r. green and red	35·00	2·25
218		15 r. blue and olive	24·00	24·00
219		25 r. orange and blue	90·00	24·00

See also Nos. 232, etc.

1921. Surch. **NINE PIES** and bar.

No.	Type	Description	Unused	Used
192.	57.	9 p. on 1 a. red	20	15

1922. Surch. ¼.

No.	Type	Description	Unused	Used
195.	56.	"¼" on ½ a. green	30	20

72. D.H. "Hercules".

1929. Air.

No.	Type	Description	Unused	Used
220.	72.	2 a. green	1·50	50
221.		3 a. blue	1·00	1·25
222.		4 a. olive	2·25	65
223.		6 a. bistre	2·25	90
224.		8 a. purple	2·50	1·00
225.		12 a. red	7·50	4·00

73. Purana Qila.

1931. Inscr. as in T **73.**

No.	Type	Description	Unused	Used
226.	73.	¼ a. green and orange	50	1·00
227.	–	½ a. violet and green	50	40
228.	–	1 a. mauve and brown	75	20
229.	–	2 a. green and blue	1·25	90
230.	–	3 a. brown and red	2·50	2·50
231.	–	1 r. violet and green	5·00	13·00

DESIGNS: ½ a. War Memorial Arch. 1 a. Council House. 2 a. Viceroy's House. 3 a. Secretariat. 1 r. Dominion Columns and Secretariat.

79. 80. 81. 82.

83.

1932.

No.	Type	Description	Unused	Used
232	79	½ a. green	35	10
233	80	9 p. green	30	10
234	81	1 a. brown	1·00	10
235	82	1¼ a. mauve	30	10
236	70	2 a. red	8·00	3·50
236a	59	2 a. red	3·75	50
237	62	3 a. red	80	10
238	83	3½ a. blue	1·25	10

84. Gateway of India, Bombay.

1935. Silver Jubilee.

No.	Type	Description	Unused	Used
240.	84.	½ a. black and green	30	10
241.	–	9 p. black and green	30	10
242.	–	1 a. black and brown	30	10
243.	–	1¼ a. black and violet	30	10
244.	–	2½ a. black and orange	45	45
245.	–	3½ a. black and blue	2·00	1·25
246.	–	8 a. black and purple	2·00	1·75

DESIGNS: 9 p. Victoria Memorial, Calcutta. 1 a. Rameswaram Temple, Madras. 1¼ a. Jain Temple, Calcutta. 2½ a. Taj Mahal, Agra. 3½ a. Golden Temple, Amritsar. 8 a. Pagoda in Mandalay.

91. King George VI.

DESIGNS—As Type **92**. 2½ a. Bullock cart. 3 a. Tonga. 3½ a. Camel. 4 a. Mail train. 6 a. Mail steamer. 8 a. Mail lorry. 12 a. Mail 'plane.

92. Dak Runner.

93. King George VI.

1937.

No.	Type	Description	Unused	Used
247.	91.	3 p. slate	40	10
248.		½ a. brown	40	10
249.		9 p. green	2·00	20
250.		1 a. red	15	10
251.	92.	2 a. red	1·25	20
252.	–	2½ a. violet	60	10
253.	–	3 a. green	2·75	20
254.	–	3½ a. blue	1·60	50
255.	–	4 a. brown	9·50	10
256.	–	6 a. blue	7·50	30
257.	–	8 a. violet	4·00	20
258.	–	12 a. red	16·00	50
259.	93.	1 r. slate and brown	1·00	10
260.		2 r. purple and brown	3·75	10
261.		5 r. green and blue	13·00	15
262.		10 r. purple and red	15·00	15
263.		15 r. brown and green	55·00	55·00
264.		25 r. slate and purple	60·00	11·00

100a. King George VI. 101.

102. King George VI.

1940.

No.	Type	Description	Unused	Used
265.	100a.	3 p. slate	25	10
266.		½ a. mauve	40	10
267.		9 p. green	40	10
268.		1 a. red	40	10
269.	101.	1 a. 3 p. yell.-brn.	50	10
269a.		1½ a. violet	40	10
270.		2 a. red	45	10
271.		3 a. violet	40	10
272.		3½ a. blue	70	10
273.	102.	4 a. brown	45	10
274.		6 a. green	65	10
275.		8 a. violet	1·00	10
276.		12 a. purple	2·50	15
277.	–	14 a. purple	4·50	30

No. 277 is as No. 258, but with large head.

105. "Victory" and King George VI.

1946. Victory Commem.

No.	Type	Description	Unused	Used
278.	105.	9 p. green	25	10
279.		1½ a. purple	25	10
280.		3½ a. blue	75	50
281.		12 a. red	1·25	55

1946. Surch. **3 PIES** and bars.

No.	Type	Description	Unused	Used
282.	101.	3 p. on 1 a. 3 p. yellow-brown	10	10

DOMINION OF INDIA

303. Douglas DC 4.

1947. Independence. Inscr. "Long Live India" and "15TH AUG 1947".

No.	Type	Description	Unused	Used
301.	–	1½ a. green	15	10
302.	–	3½ a. red, blue & green	25	30
303.	303.	12 a. blue	1·00	1·00

DESIGNS—VERT. 1½ a. Asokan Capital. HORIZ. 3½ a. Indian National Flag.

1948. Air. Inauguration of India–Britain Service. As T **303**, but showing Lockheed Constellation flying in opposite direction and inscr. "AIR INDIA INTERNATIONAL FIRST FLIGHT 8TH JUNE 1948".

No.	Type	Description	Unused	Used
304.	303.	12 a. black and blue	90	1·00

305. Mahatma Gandhi.

The 10 r. depicts a profile portrait of Mahatma Gandhi and is larger (22½ × 37 mm.).

1948. 1st Anniv. of Indian Independence.

No.	Type	Description	Unused	Used
305.	305.	1½ a. brown	1·00	30
306.	–	3½ a. violet	4·00	1·25
307.	–	12 a. green	5·00	60
308.	–	10 r. brown & red	55·00	40·00

307. Ajanta Panel.

308. Konarak Horse.

314. Bhuvanesvara.

315. Gol Gumbad, Bijapur.

319. Red Fort, Delhi.

322. Satrunjaya Temple, Palitana.

1949.

No.	Type	Description	Unused	Used
309.	307.	3 p. violet	15	10
310.	308.	6 p. brown	25	10
311.	–	9 p. green	40	10
312.	–	1 a. blue (A)	60	10
333.	–	1 a. blue (B)	2·75	10
313.	–	2 a. red	80	10
333a.	–	2½ a. lake	2·00	70
314.	–	3 a. salmon	1·50	10
315.	–	3½ a. blue	3·00	2·50
316.	314.	4 a. lake	5·00	10
333b.		4 a. blue	5·00	10
317.	315.	6 a. violet	2·00	10
318.	–	8 a. green	2·00	10
319.	–	12 a. blue	1·75	10
320.	–	1 r. violet and green	9·00	10
321.	319.	2 r. red and violet	8·00	15
322.	–	5 r. green and brown	22·00	50
323.	–	10 r. brown and blue	30·00	3·25
324.	322.	15 r. brown and red	12·00	12·00

1 anna: (A) Left arm of statue outstretched (B) Reversed—right arm outstretched.

DESIGNS—As Type **307**: 9 p. Trimurti. 1 a. Bodhisattva. 2 a. Nataraja. As Type **314**: 2½ a., 3½ a. Bodh Gaya Temple. 3 a. Sanchi Stupa, East Gate. As Type **315**: 8 a. Kandarya Mahadeva Temple. 12 a. Golden Temple, Amritsar. As Type **319**—VERT. 1 r. Victory Tower, Chittorgarh. 10 r. Qutb Minar, Delhi. HORIZ. 5 r. Taj Mahal, Agra.

323. Globe and Asokan Capital.

1949. 75th Anniv. of U.P.U.

No.	Type	Description	Unused	Used
325.	323.	9 p. green	75	75
326.		2 a. red	1·00	1·25
327.		3½ a. blue	1·75	2·25
328.		12 a. red	3·50	2·50

REPUBLIC OF INDIA

324. Rejoicing Crowds.

1950. Inauguration of Republic.

No.	Type	Description	Unused	Used
329.	324.	2 a. red	70	15
330.	–	3½ a. blue	1·50	2·75
331.	–	4 a. violet	1·50	40
332.	–	12 a. purple	3·00	2·25

DESIGNS—VERT. 3½ a. Quill, ink-well and verse. HORIZ. 4. a. Ear of corn and plough. 12 a. Spinning-wheel and cloth.

329. " Stegodon Ganesa ".

1951. Centenary of Geological Survey.
334. **329.** 2 a. black and red .. 1·00 15

330. Torch. 331. Kabir.

1951. 1st Asian Games, New Delhi.
335. **330.** 2 a. purple and orange 75 20
336. – 12 a. brown and blue 4·00 90

1952. Indian Saints and Poets.
337. **331.** 9 p. green 30 15
338. – 1 a. red (Tulsidas) .. 30 10
339. – 2 a. orange (Meera) .. 60 10
340. – 4 a. blue (Surdas) .. 1·25 15
341. – 4½ a. mauve (Ghalib) 30 10
342. – 12 a. brown (Tagore) 1·50 60

332. Locomotives in 1853 and 1953.

1953. Centenary of Indian Railways.
343. **332.** 2 a. black 40 10

333. Mount Everest.

1953. Conquest of Mount Everest.
344. **333.** 2 a. violet 40 10
345. 14 a. brown .. .. 3·00 25

334. Telegraph Poles of 1851 and 1951.

1953. Centenary of Indian Telegraphs.
346. **334.** 2 a. green 30 10
347. 12 a. blue .. .. 3·00 40

335. Postal Transport, 1854.

1954. Indian Stamp Centenary.
348. **335.** 1 a. purple 25 10
349. – 2 a. mauve 30 10
350. – 4 a. brown .. .. 1·75 15
351. – 14 a. blue .. .. 1·50 40
DESIGNS: 2 a., 14 a. Dove and Aeroplane. 4 a., Ship, cyclist, aeroplane and train.

338. U.N. Emblem and Lotus.

1954. U.N. Day.
352. **338.** 2 a. turquoise .. 30 10

339. Forest Research Institute.

1954. 4th World Forestry Congress, Dehra Dun.
353. **339.** 2 a. blue 15 10

340. Tractor. 344. Woman Spinning.

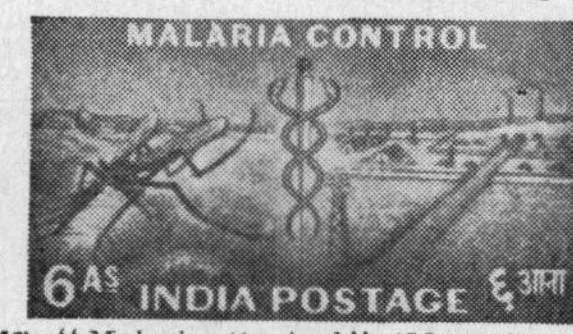

347. "Malaria Control" (Mosquito and Staff of Aesculapius).

1955. India's Five Year Plan.
354 **340.** 3 p. mauve 20 10
355 – 6 p. violet 20 10
356 – 9 p. brown 20 10
357 – 1 a. green 35 10
358 **344.** 2 a. blue 20 10
359 – 3 a. green 40 10
360 – 4 a. red 40 10
361 **347.** 6 a. brown 70 10
362 – 8 a. blue .. .. 4·25 10
363 – 10 a. turquoise .. 70 70
364 – 12 a. blue 50 10
365 – 14 a. green .. .. 1·50 20
413 – 1 r. myrtle .. .. 2·25 10
367 – 1 r. 2 a. grey .. .. 1·75 2·75
368 – 1 r. 8 a. purple .. 6·00 3·50
369 – 2 r. mauve .. .. 4·00 10
415 – 5 r. brown .. .. 9·00 30
371 – 10 r. orange .. .. 14·00 2·00
DESIGNS—As Type **340**: 6 p. Power loom. 9 p. Bullock-driven well. 1 a. Damodar Valley Dam. 4 a. Bullocks. 8 a. Chittarajan Locomotive Works. 12 a. Hindustan Aircraft Factory, Bangalore. 1 r. Telephone engineer. 2 r. Rare Earth Factory, Alwaye. 5 r. Sindri Fertiliser Factory. 10 r. Steel plant. As Type **344**: 3 a. Woman hand-weaving. As Type **347**: 10 a. Aeroplane over Marine Drive, Bombay. 14 a. Aeroplane over Kashmir landscape. 1 r. 2 a. Aeroplane over Cape Comorin. 1 r. 8 a. Aeroplane over Mt. Kangchenjunga.

358. Bodhi Tree.

1956. Buddha Jayanti.
372. **358.** 2 a. sepia 30 10
373. – 14 a. red .. .. 3·00 2·50
DESIGN—HORIZ. 14 a. Round parasol and Bodhi tree.

MORE DETAILED LISTS
are given in the Stanley Gibbons Catalogues referred to in the country headings.
For lists of current volumes see Introduction.

360. Lokmanya Bal Gangadhar Tilak. 361. Map of India.

1956. Birth Cent. of Tilak (journalist).
374. **360.** 2 a. brown 10 10

1957. Value in naye paise.
375 **361.** 1 n.p. green 10 10
376 2 n.p. brown 10 10
377 3 n.p. brown 10 10
402 5 n.p. green 10 10
379 6 n.p. grey 10 10
404 8 n.p. turquoise .. 30 10
405 10 n.p. myrtle .. 15 10
381 13 n.p. red 30 10
407 15 n.p. violet 30 10
408 20 n.p. blue 30 10
409 25 n.p. blue 30 10
410 50 n.p. orange .. 30 10
411 75 n.p. purple 40 10
385a 90 n.p. purple 70 40

362. The Rani of Jhansi.

363. Shrine.

1957. Centenary of Indian Mutiny.
386. **362.** 15 n.p. brown .. 15 10
387. **363.** 90 n.p. purple .. 1·50 40

364. Henri Dunant and Conference Emblem.

1957. 19th Int. Red Cross Conf., New Delhi.
388. **364.** 15 n.p. grey and red .. 10 10

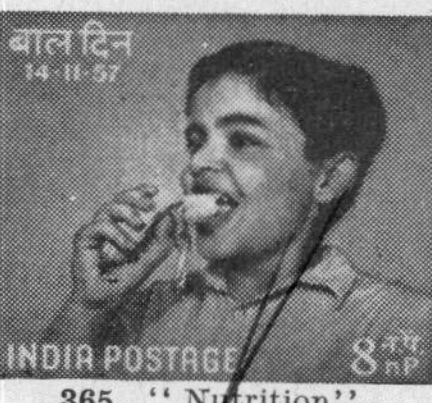

DESIGNS—HORIZ. 15 n.p. "Education". VERT. 90 n.p. "Recreation".

365. "Nutrition".

1957. Children's Day.
389. **365.** 8 n.p. purple 10 15
390. – 15 n.p. turquoise .. 10 10
391. – 90 n.p. brown .. 25 15

DESIGNS—VERT. No. 392, Bombay University. As Type **369**.—HORIZ. No. 394, Madras University.

369. Calcutta University.

1957. Centenary of Indian Universities.
392. – 10 n.p. violet (21½ × 38 mm.) 10 10
393. **369.** 10 n.p. grey 10 10
394. – 10 n.p. brown 15 10

371. J. N. Tata (founder) and Steel Plant.

1958. 50th Anniv. of Steel Industry.
395. **371.** 15 n.p. red 10 10

372. Dr. D. K. Karve.

1958. Birth Cent. of Karve (educationist).
396. **372.** 15 n.p. brown .. 10 10

373. "Wapiti" and "Hunter" Aircraft.

1958. Silver Jubilee of Indian Air Force.
397. **373.** 15 n.p. blue 40 10
398. 90 n.p. blue 85 90

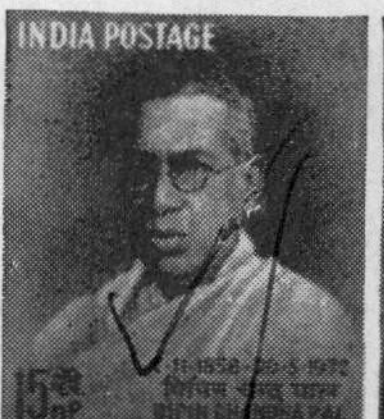

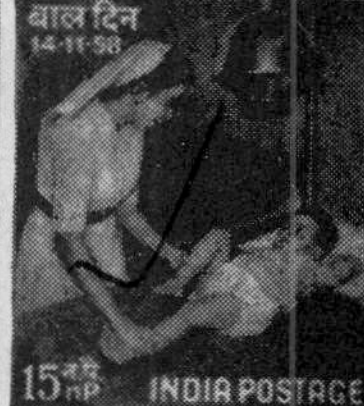

375. Bilpin Chandra Pal. 376. Nurse with Child Patient.

1958. Birth Centenary of Pal (patriot).
418. **375.** 15 n.p. green 10 10

1958. Children's Day.
419. **376.** 15 n.p. violet .. 10 10

377. Jagadish Chandra Bose.

1958. Birth Cent. of Bose (botanist).
420. **377.** 15 n.p. turquoise .. 10 10

378. Exhibition Gate.

1958. India 1958 Exn., New Delhi.
421. **378.** 15 n.p. purple .. 10 10

379. Sir Jamsetjee Jejeebhoy. 381. Boys awaiting admission to Children's Home.

380. " The Triumph of Labour " (after Chowdhury).

1959. Death Centenary of Sir Jamsetjee Jejeebhoy (philanthropist).
422. **379.** 15 n.p. brown 10 10

1959. 40th Anniv. of I.L.O.
423. **380.** 5 n.p. green 10 10

1959. Children's Day.
424. **381.** 15 n.p. green 10 10

382. " Agriculture ".

1959. 1st World Agriculture Fair, New Delhi.
425. **382.** 15 n.p. grey 10 10

383. Thiruvalluvar (philosopher).

1960. Thiruvalluvar Commem.
426. **383.** 15 n.p. purple .. 10 10

384. Yaksha pleading with the Cloud (from the " Meghaduta ").

385. Shakuntala writing a letter to Dushyanta (from the "Shakuntala").

1960. Kalidasa (poet) Commem.
427. **384.** 15 n.p. grey 15 10
428. **385.** 1 r. 3 n.p. yell. & brn. 70 20

386. S. Bharati (poet).

387. Dr. M. Visvesvaraya.

1960. Subramania Bahrati Commem.
429. **386.** 15 n.p. blue .. 10 10

1960. Birth Centenary of Dr. M. Visvesvaraya (engineer).
430. **387.** 15 n.p. brown and red 10 10

388. " Children's Health ".

1960. Children's Day.
431. **388.** 15 n.p. green 10 10

389. Children greeting U.N. Emblem.

1960. U.N.I.C.E.F. Day.
432. **389.** 15 n.p. brown & drab 10 10

390. Tyagaraja.

391. "First Aerial Post" Cancellation.

392. " Air India " Boeing 707 Jetliner and Humber-Sommer 'Plane.

1961. 114th Death Anniv of Tyagaraja (musician).
433. **390.** 15 n.p. blue 10 10

1961. 50th Anniv. of 1st Official Airmail Flight, Allahabad-Naini.
434. **391.** 5 n.p. olive 85 20
435. **392.** 15 n.p. green and grey 90 30
436. – 1 r. purple and grey .. 3·75 1·00

DESIGN—As Type **392**: 1 r. H. Pecquet flying Humber-Sommer 'plane, and " Aerial Post " cancellation.

394. Shivaji on Horseback.

1961. Chatrapati Shivaji (Maratha ruler) Commemoration.
437 **394** 15 n.p. brown and green 30 15

395. Motilal Nehru (politician).

396. Tagore (poet).

1961. Birth Cent. of Pandit Motilal Nehru.
438. **395.** 15 n.p. brn. & orge. .. 10 10

1961. Birth Cent. of Rabindranath Tagore.
439. **396.** 15 n.p. orge. and turq. 30 15

397. All India Radio Emblem and Transmitting Aerials.

1961. Silver Jubilee of All India Radio Broadcasting Service.
440. **397.** 15 n.p. blue 10 10

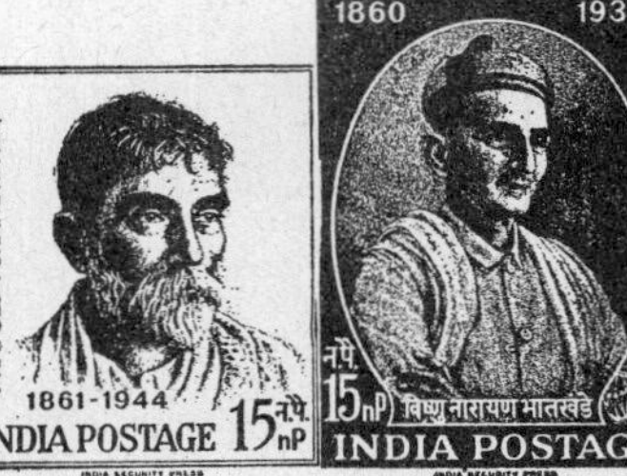

398. Ray.

399. Bhatkande.

1961. Birth Centenary of Prafulla Chandra Ray (social reformer).
441. **398.** 15 n.p. grey 10 10

1961. Birth Centenary (1960) of V. N. Bhatkande (composer).
442. **399.** 15 n.p. drab 10 10

400. Child at Lathe.

401. Fair Emblem and Main Gate.

1961. Children's Day.
443. **400.** 15 n.p. brown .. 10 10

1961. Indian Industries Fair, New Delhi.
444. **401.** 15 n.p. blue and red .. 10 10

402. Indian Forest.

403. Pitalkhora: Yaksha.

1961. Centenary of Scientific Forestry.
445. **402.** 15 n.p. green & brn... 10 10

1961. Cent. of Indian Archaeological Survey.
446. **403.** 15 n.p. brown .. 15 10
447. – 90 n.p. olive & brown 30 15

DESIGN—HORIZ. 90 n.p. Kalibangan seal.

405. M. M. Malaviya.

406. Gauhati Refinery.

1961. Birth Centenary of Malaviya (educationist).
448. **405.** 15 n.p. slate 10 10

1962. Inaug. of Gauhati Oil Refinery.
449. **406.** 15 n.p. blue 15 10

407. Bhikaiji Cama.

408. Village Panchayati at work and Parliament Building.

1962. Birth Centenary of Bhikaiji Cama (patriot).
450. **407.** 15 n.p. purple .. 10 10

1962. Inauguration of Panchayati System of Local Government.
451. **408.** 15 n.p. mauve .. 10 10

409. D. Saraswati (religious reformer).

410. G. S. Vidhyarthi (journalist).

1962. Dayanard Saraswati Commem.
452. **409.** 15 n.p. brown 10 10

1962. Ganesh Shankar Vidhyarthi Commem.
453. **410.** 15 n.p. brown .. 10 10

411. Malaria Eradication Emblem.

412. Dr. R. Prasad.

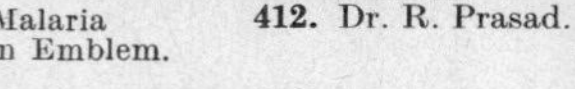

1962. Malaria Eradication.
454. **411.** 15 n.p. yellow and lake 10 10

1962. Retirement of President Dr. Rajendra Prasad.
455. **412.** 15 n.p. purple 15 10

413. Calcutta High Court.

1962. Centenary of Indian High Courts.
456. **413.** 15 n.p. green 15 15
457. – 15 n.p. brown (Madras) 15 15
458. – 15 n.p. slate (Bombay) 15 15

416. Ramabai Ranade.

1962. Birth Centenary of Ramabai Ranade (social reformer).
459. **416.** 15 n.p. orange .. 10 10

417. Indian Rhinoceros.

1962. Wild Life Week.
460. **417.** 15 n.p. brown and turq. 30 10
See also Nos. 472/6.

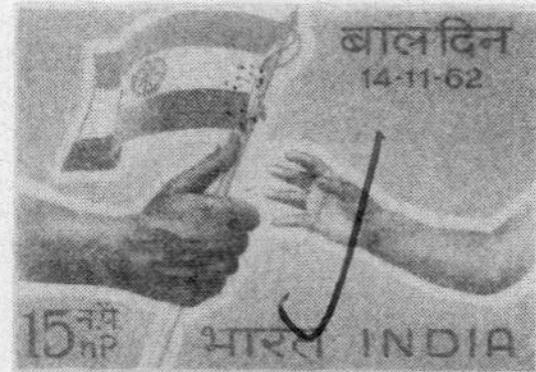
418. "Passing the Flag to Youth".

1962. Children's Day.
461. **418.** 15 n.p. red and green.. 10 10

419. Human Eye within Lotus Blossom.

1962. 19th Int. Ophthalmology Congress, New Delhi.
462. **419.** 15 n.p. brown 10 10

420. S. Ramanujan.

1962. 75th Birth Anniv of Srinivasa Ramanujan (mathematician).
463. **420.** 15 n.p. brown .. 20 15

421. S. Vivekananda.

424. Henri Dunant (founder) and Centenary Emblem.

427. D. Naoroji (parliamentarian).

423. Hands reaching for F.A.O. Emblem.

1963. Birth Cent. of Vivekananda (philosopher).
464. **421.** 15 n.p. brown and olive 15 15

1963. Surch.
465. **385.** 1 r. on 1 r. 3 n.p. yellow and brown 30 10

1963. Freedom from Hunger.
466. **423.** 15 n.p. blue 75 30

425. Artillery and Helicopter.

1963. Centenary of Red Cross.
467. **424.** 15 n.p. red and grey.. 1·75 30

1963. Defence Campaign.
468. **425.** 15 n.p. green 30 10
469. – 1 r. brown .. 55 45
DESIGN: 1 r. Sentry and parachutists.

1963. Dadabhoy Naoroji Commem.
470. **427.** 15 n.p. grey 10 10

428. Annie Besant (patriot and theosophist).

1963. Annie Besant Commem.
471 **428** 15 n.p. green 10 10
No. 471 is incorrectly dated "1837". Mrs Besant was born in 1847.

1963. Wild Life Preservation. Animal designs as T **417**.
472. 10 n.p. black and orange.. 60 1·50
473. 15 n.p. brown and green.. 1·00 50
474. 30 n.p. slate and ochre .. 3·25 1·50
475. 50 n.p. orange and green.. 2·75 60
476. 1 r. brown and blue .. 2·50 50
ANIMALS. As Type **417**: 10 n.p. Gaur. LARGER ($25\frac{1}{2} \times 35\frac{1}{2}$ mm.). 15 n.p. Lesser panda. 30 n.p. Indian elephant. ($35\frac{1}{2} \times 25\frac{1}{2}$ mm.): 50 n.p. Tiger 1 r. Lion.

434. "School Meals".

1963. Children's Day.
477. **434.** 15 n.p. bistre 10 10

435. Eleanor Roosevelt at Spinning-wheel.

1963. 15th Anniv. of Declaration of Human Rights.
478. **435.** 15 n.p. purple .. 10 10

436. Dipalakshmi (bronze).

1964. 26th Int. Orientalists Congress, New Delhi.
479. **436.** 15 n.p. blue 10 10

437. Gopabandhu Das (social reformer).

1964. Gopabandhu Das Commem.
480. **437.** 15 n.p. purple .. 10 10

438. Purandaradasa.

1964. 400th Death Anniv of Purandaradasa (composer).
481. **438.** 15 n.p. brown .. 10 10

439. S. C. Bose and I.N.A. Badge.

1964. 67th Birth Anniv. of Subhas Chandra Bose (nationalist). Inscr. "INA" on badge.
482. **439.** 15 n.p. olive 20 15
483. – 55 n.p. blk., orge & red 40 35
DESIGN: 55 n.p. Bose and Indian National Army.

441. Sarojini Naidu.

442. Kasturba Ghandi.

1964. 95th Birth Anniv. of Sarojini Naidu (poetess).
484. **441.** 15 n.p. green & purple 10 10

1964. 20th Death Anniv. of Kasturba Ghandi.
485. **442.** 15 n.p. brown.. .. 10 10

443. Dr. W. M. Haffkine (immunologist).

1964. Haffkine Commem.
486. **443.** 15 n.p. brown on buff 10 10

444. Jawaharlal Nehru (statesman).

1964. Nehru Mourning Issue.
487. **444.** 15 p. slate 10 10

445. Sir Asutosh Mookerjee.

1964. Birth Centenary of Sir Asutosh Mookerjee (education reformer).
488. **445.** 15 p. brown and olive 10 10

446. Sri Aurobindo.

1964. 92nd Birth Anniv of Sri Aurobindo (religious teacher).
489. **446.** 15 p. purple 10 10

447. Raja R. Roy (social reformer).

1964. Raja Rammohun Roy Commem.
490. **447.** 15 n.p. brown .. 10 10

448. I.S.O. Emblem and Globe.

1964. 6th Int. Organization for Standardisation General Assembly, Bombay.
491. **448.** 15 p. red 10 15

449 Jawaharlal Nehru (from 1 r. commemorative coin)

450. St. Thomas (after statue, Ortona Cathedral, Italy).

1964. Children's Day.
492. **449.** 15 p. slate 10 10

1964. St. Thomas Commem.
493. **450.** 15 p. purple 10 20
No. 493 was issued on the occasion of Pope Paul's visit to India.

MINIMUM PRICE

The minimum price quoted is 10p which represents a handling charge rather than a basis for valuing common stamps. For further notes about prices see introductory pages.

451. Globe.

1964. 22nd Int. Geological Congress.
494. **451.** 15 p. green 15 20

452. J. Tata (industrialist).

1965. Jamsetji Tata Commem.
495. **452.** 15 p. dull purple & orge. 10 20

453. Lala Lajpat Rai.

1965. Birth Centenary of Lala Lajpat Rai (social reformer).
496. **453.** 15 p. brown 10 10

454. Globe and Congress Emblem.

1965. 20th Int. Chamber of Commerce Congress, New Delhi.
497. **454.** 15 p. green and red .. 10 15

455. Freighter "Jalausha" and Visakhapatnam.

1965. National Maritime Day.
498. **455.** 15 p. blue 15 20

456. Abraham Lincoln.

1965. Death Centenary of Lincoln.
499. **456.** 15 p. brown and ochre 10 10

457. I.T.U. Emblem and Symbols.

1965. Centenary of I.T.U.
500. **457.** 15 p. purple .. 75 30

458. "Everlasting Flame".

1965. 1st Death Anniv. of Nehru.
501. **458.** 15 p. red and blue .. 10 10

459. I.C.Y. Emblem.

1965. Int. Co-operation Year.
502. **459.** 15 p. green and brown 60 40

460. Climbers on Summit.

467. Plucking Tea.

477. Atomic Reactor, Trombay.

1965. Indian Mount Everest Expedition.
503. **460.** 15 p. purple 10 10

1965.

504.	–	2 p. brown	10	30
505.	–	3 p. olive	10	70
505a.	–	4 p. brown	10	1·00
506.	–	5 p. red	10	10
507.	–	6 p. black	10	1·25
508.	–	8 p. brown	30	2·50
509.	–	10 p. blue	35	10
510.	**467.**	15 p. green	60	10
511.	–	20 p. purple	60	10
512.	–	30 p. sepia	15	10
513.	–	40 p. purple	15	10
514.	–	50 p. green	20	10
515.	–	60 p. grey	35	10
516.	–	70 p. blue	60	10
517.	–	1 r. brown and plum ..	60	10
518.	–	2 r. blue and violet ..	2·00	10
519.	–	5 r. violet and brown ..	2·50	25
520.	**477.**	10 r. black and green ..	12·00	80

DESIGNS—As Type **467**—VERT. 2 p. Bidri Vase. 3 p. Brass Lamp. 5 p. "Family Planning". 6 p. Konarak Elephant. 8 p. Spotted deer. 30 p. Indian Dolls. 50 p. Mangoes. 60 p. Somnath Temple. HORIZ. 4 p. Coffee Berries. 10 p. Electric Locomotive. 15 p. Plucking Tea. 20 p. Folland "Gnat" Fighter. 40 p. Calcutta G.P.O. 70 p. Hampi Chariot (sculpture). As Type **477**—VERT. 1 r. Medieval Sculpture. HORIZ. 2 r. Dal Lake, Kashmir. 5. r Bhakra Dam, Punjab.

479. G. B. Pant (statesman).

480. V. Patel.

1965. Govind Ballabh Pant Commem.
522. **479.** 15 p. brown and green 10 15

1965. 90th Birth Anniv. of Vallabhbhai Patel (statesman).
523. **480.** 15 p. brown 10 20

481. C. Das.

482. Vidyapati (poet).

1965. 95th Birth Anniv. of Chittaranjan Das (lawyer and patriot).
524. **481.** 15 p. brown 10 10

1965. Vidyapati Commem.
525. **482.** 15 p. brown 10 10

483. Sikandra, Agra.

1966. Pacific Area Travel Assn., Conf., New Delhi.
526. **483.** 15 p. slate 10 10

484. Soldier, Fighters and Warship.

1966. Indian Armed Forces.
527. **484.** 15 p. violet 30 15

485. Lal Bahadur Shastri (statesman).

486. Kambar (poet).

1966. Shastri Mourning Issue.
528. **485.** 15 p. black 10 10

1966. Kambar Commem.
529. **486.** 15 p. green 10 10

487. B. R. Ambedkar.

488. Kunwar Singh (patriot).

1966. 75th Birth Anniv of Dr. Bhim Rao Ambedkar (lawyer).
530. **487.** 15 p. purple 10 10

1966. Kunwar Singh Commem.
531. **488.** 15 p. brown 10 10

489. G. K. Gokhale.

1966. Birth Centenary of Gopal Krishna Gokhale (patriot).
532. **489.** 15 p. purple and yellow 10 10

490. Acharya Dvivedi (poet).

1966. Dvivedi Commem.
533. **490.** 15 p. drab 10 10

491. Maharaja Ranjit Singh (warrior).

1966. Maharaja Ranjit Singh Commem.
534. **491.** 15 p. purple 15 10

492. Homi Bhabha (scientist) and Nuclear Reactor.

1966. Dr. Homi Bhabha Commem.
535. **492.** 15 p. purple 15 30

493. A. K. Azad (scholar).

1966. Abul Kalam Azad Commem.
536. **493.** 15 p. blue 10 10

494. Swami Tirtha.

1966. 60th Death Anniv. of Swami Rama Tirtha (social reformer).
537. **494.** 15 p. blue 10 20

495. Infant and Dove Emblem.

1966. Children's Day.
538. **495.** 15 p. purple 20 15

496. Allahabad High Court.

1966. Cent. of Allahabad High Court.
539. **496.** 15 p. purple 15 30

497. Indian Family.

1966. Family Planning.
540. **497.** 15 p. brown 10 10

498. Hockey Game.

1966. India's Hockey Victory in 5th Asian Games.
541. **498.** 15 p. blue 70 30

499. " Jai Kisan ".

1967. 1st Death Anniv. of Shastri.
542. **499.** 15 p. green 10 15

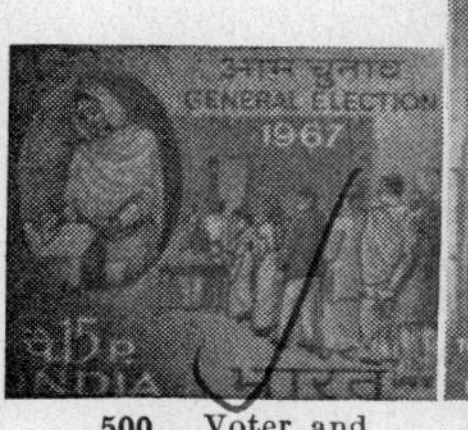

500. Voter and Polling Booth.
501. Gurudwara Shrine, Patna.

1967. Indian General Election.
543. **500.** 15 p. brown 10 10

1967. 300th Birth Anniv (1966) of Guru Gobind Singh (Sikh religious leader).
544. **501.** 15 p. violet 15 10

502. Taj Mahal, Agra.

1967. Int. Tourist Year.
545. **502.** 15 p. brown and orange 10 10

503. Nandalal Bose and " Garuda ".

1967. 1st Death Anniv. of Nandalal Bose (painter).
546. **503.** 15 p. brown 10 10

504. Survey Emblem and Activities.

1967. Bicentenary of Survey of India.
547. **504.** 15 p. lilac 10 15

505. Basaveswara.

1967. 800th Anniv. of Basaveswara (reformer and statesman).
548. **505.** 15 p. red 10 10

506. Narsinha Mehta (poet).
507. Maharana Pratap.

1967. Narsinha Mehta Commem.
549. **506.** 15 p. sepia 10 10

1967. Maharana Pratap (Rajput leader) Commemoration.
550. **507.** 15 p. brown 10 10

508. Narayana Guru.
509. Pres. Radhakrishnan.

1967. Narayana Guru (philosopher) Commem.
551 **508** 15 p. brown 10 10

1967. 75th Birth Anniv of Sarvepalli Radhakrishnan (former President).
552 **509** 15 p. red 20 10

510. Martyrs' Memorial, Patna.

1967. 25th Anniv. of "Quit India" Movement.
553. **510.** 15 p. lake 10 10

511. Route Map.

1967. Centenary of Indo-European Telegraph Service.
554. **511.** 15 p. black and blue 10 15

512. Wrestling.

1967. World Wrestling Championships, New Delhi.
555. **512.** 15 p. purple & brown 10 15

MORE DETAILED LISTS

are given in the Stanley Gibbons Catalogues referred to in the country headings. For lists of current volumes see Introduction.

513. Nehru leading Naga Tribesmen.
514. Rashbehari Basu (nationalist).

1967. 4th Anniv of Nagaland as a State of India.
556. **513.** 15 p. blue 10 10

1967. Rashbehari Basu Commem.
557. **514.** 15 p. purple 10 15

515. Bugle, Badge and Scout Salute.

1967. 60th Anniv of Scout Movement in India.
558 **515** 15 p. brown 40 20

516. Men Embracing Universe.

1968. Human Rights Year.
559. **516.** 15 p. green 20 15

517. Globe and Book of Tamil.

1968. Int. Conf.—Seminar of Tamil Studies, Madras.
560. **517.** 15 p. lilac 20 10

518. U.N. Emblem and Transport.

1968. United Nations Conference on Trade and Development, New Delhi.
561 **518** 15 p. blue 20 10

519. Quill and Bow Symbol.

1968. Centenary of Amrita Bazar Patrika (newspaper).
562. **519.** 15 p. sepia and yellow 10 10

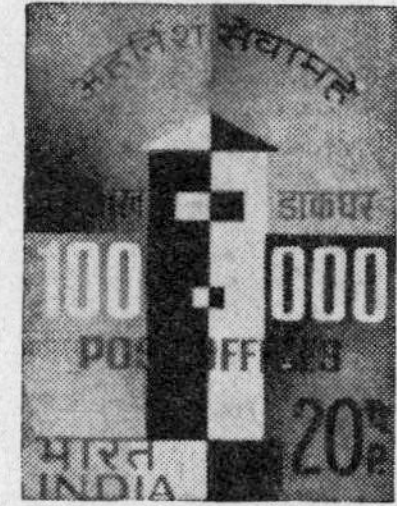

520. Maxim Gorky.
521. Emblem and Medal.

1968. Birth Cent. of Maxim Gorky.
563. **520.** 15 p. plum 10 15

1968. 1st Triennale Art Exhibition, New Delhi.
564 **521** 15 p. orange, bl & lt bl 20 15

522. Letter-box and "100,000".

1968 Opening of 100,000th Indian Post Office.
565. **522.** 20 p. red, blue & black 10 10

523. Stalks of Wheat, Agricultural Institute and Production Graph.

1968. Wheat Revolution.
566. **523.** 20 p. green and brown 15 15

524. " Self-Portrait ".

1968. 30th Death Anniv. of Gaganendranath Tagore.
567. **524.** 20 p. purple and ochre 20 10

525. Lakshminath Bezbaruah.

1968. Birth Centenary of Lakshminath Bezbaruah (writer).
568. **525.** 20 p. brown 15 10

526. Athlete's Legs and Olympic Rings.

1968. Olympic Games, Mexico.
569. **526.** 20 p. brown and grey .. 10 15
570. 1 r. sepia and olive .. 30 15

20 P.
भारत INDIA
BHAGAT SINGH
1907-1931

527. Bhagat Singh and Followers.

1968. 61st Birth Anniv of Bhagat Singh (patriot).
571 **527** 20 p. brown 20 15

INDEX

Countries can be quickly located by referring to the index at the end of this volume.

528. Azad Hind Flag, Swords and Chandra Bose (founder).

529. Sister Nivedita.

1968. 25th Anniv. of Azad Hind Government.
572. **528.** 20 p. blue 15 15

1968. Birth Cent of Sister Nivedita (social reformer).
573 **529** 20 p. green 20 20

530. Marie Curie and Radium Treatment.

1968. Birth Centenary of Marie Curie.
574. **530.** 20 p. lilac 60 30

531. Map of the World.

1968. 21st Int. Geographical Congress, New Delhi.
575. **531.** 20 p. blue 10 10

532. Cochin Synagogue.

1968. 400th Anniv. of Cochin Synagogue.
576. **532.** 20 p. blue and red .. 30 15

533. I.N.S. "Nilgiri".

1968. Navy Day.
577. **533.** 20 p. blue 50 30

534. Red-billed Blue Magpie.

1968. Birds.
578. **534.** 20 p. multicoloured .. 55 30
579. – 50 p. red, black & grn. 1·10 55
580. – 1 r. blue and brown .. 1·75 1·00
581. – 2 r. multicoloured .. 1·75 1·40

DESIGNS—HORIZ. 50 p. Brown-fronted pied woodpecker. 2 r. Yellow-backed sunbird. VERT. 1 r. Slaty-headed scimitar babbler.

538. Bankim Chandra Chatterjee.

539. Dr. Bhagavan Das.

1969. 130th Birth Anniv. of Chatterjee (writer).
582. **538.** 20 p. blue 10 15

1969. Birth Cent of Das (philosopher).
583. **539.** 20 p. brown 10 10

540. Dr. Martin Luther King.

1969. Martin Luther King Commem.
584. **540.** 20 p. brown 20 15

541. Mirza Ghalib and Letter Seal.

1969. Death Cent. of Mirza Ghalib (poet).
585. **541.** 20 p. sepia, red & flesh 10 15

542. Osmania University.

1969. 50th Anniv. of Osmania University.
586. **542.** 20 p. green 10 15

543. Rafi Ahmed Kidwai and Mail Plane.

1969. 20th Anniv. of Rafi Ahmed Kidwai (Author of "All-up" Airmail Scheme).
587. **543.** 20 p. blue 30 15

544. I.L.O. Badge and Emblem.

1969. 50th Anniv. of Int. Labour Organization.
588. **544.** 20 p. brown 10 15

545. Memorial, and Hands dropping Flowers.

1969. 50th Anniv of Jallianwala Bagh Massacre, Amritsar.
589. **545.** 20 p. red 10 15

546. K. Nageswara Rao Pantulu (journalist).

1969. Kasinadhuni Nageswara Rao Pantulu Commem.
590. **546.** 20 p. brown 10 15

547. Ardaseer Cursetjee Wadia, and Ships.

1969. Ardaseer Cursetjee Wadia (ship-builder) Commemoration.
591. **547.** 20 p. turquoise 10 15

548. Serampore College.

1969. 150th Anniv. of Serampore College.
592. **548.** 20 p. plum 10 15

549. Dr. Zakir Husain.

1969. Dr. Zakir Husain Commem.
593. **549.** 20 p. sepia 10 15

550. Laxmanrao Kirloskar.

1969. Birth Centenary of Laxmanrao Kirloskar (agriculturist).
594. **550.** 20 p. black 10 10

551. Gandhi and his wife.

1969. Birth Cent. of Mahatma Gandhi.
595. **551.** 20 p. brown 30 15
596. – 75 p. flesh and drab .. 85 70
597. – 1 r. blue .. .. 1·00 65
598. – 5 r. brown and orange 4·00 5·00

DESIGNS AND SIZES—VERT. 75 p. Gandhi's head and shoulders (28 × 38 mm.). 1 r. Gandhi walking (woodcut) (20 × 38 mm.). HORIZ. 5 r. Gandhi with charkha (36 × 26 mm.).

555. "Ayanta" (tanker) and I.M.C.O. Emblem.

1969. 10th Anniv. of Inter-Government Maritime Consulative Organization.
599. **555.** 20 p. blue 40 20

556. Outline of Parliament Building and Globe.

1969. Inter-Parliamentary Conf., New Delhi.
600. **556.** 20 p. blue 10 15

557. Astronaut walking beside Space Module on Moon.

558. Gurudwara Nankana Sahib (birthplace).

1969. 1st Man on the Moon.
601. **557.** 20 p. brown 10 15

1969. 500th Birth Anniv of Guru Nanak Dev (Sikh religious leader).
602. **558.** 20 p. violet 10 15

559. Tiger's Head and Hands holding Globe.

1969. Int. Union for the Conservation of Nature and Natural Resources Conf., New Delhi.
603. **559.** 20 p. brown and green 30 20

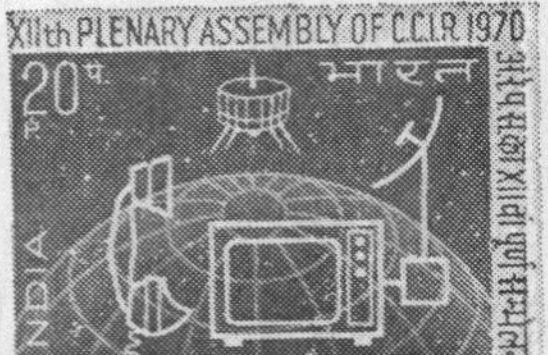

560. Sadhu Vaswani.

561. Thakkar Bapa.

1969. 90th Birth Anniv. of Sadhu Vaswani (educationist).
604. **560.** 20 p. grey 10 10

1969. Birth Centenary of Thakkar Bapa (humanitarian).
605. **561.** 20 p. brown 10 15

562. Satellite, Television, Telephone and Globe.

1970. 12th Plenary Assembly of Int. Radio Consultative Committee.
606. **562.** 20 p. blue 10 15

563 C. N. Annadurai.

564. M. N. Kishore and Printing Press.

1970. 1st Death Anniv of Conjeevaram Natrajan Annadurai (statesman).
607. **563.** 20 p. purple and blue 10 10

1970. 75th Death Anniv of Munshi Newal Kishore (publisher).
608. **564.** 20 p. lake 10 15

565. Nalanda College.

1970. Centenary of Nalanda College.
609. **565.** 20 p. brown 30 30

566. Swami Shraddhanand (social reformer).

1970. Swami Shraddhanand Commem.
610. **566.** 20 p. brown 30 20

567. Lenin.

1970. Birth Centenary of Lenin.
611. **567.** 20 p. brown and sepia 10 15

568. New U.P.U. H.Q. Building.

1970. New U.P.U. Headquarters Building, Berne.
612. **568.** 20 p. green, grey & black 10 15

569. Sher Shah Suri (15th Century ruler).

1970. Sher Shah Suri Commem.
613. **569.** 20 p. green 10 15

570. V. D. Savarkar (patriot) and Cellular Jail, Andaman Islands.

1970. Vinayak Damodar Savarkar Commem.
614. **570.** 20 p. brown 10 15

571. "UN" and Globe.

1970. 25th Anniv. of United Nations
615. **571.** 20 p. blue 20 15

572. Symbol and Workers.

1970. Asian Productivity Year.
616. **572.** 20 p. violet 15 15

573. Dr. Montessori and I.E.Y. Emblem.

1970. Birth Centenary of Dr. Maria Montessori (educationist).
617. **573.** 20 p. purple 30 20

574. J. N. Mukherjee (revolutionary) and Horse.

1970. Jatindra Nath Mukherjee Commem.
618. **574.** 20 p. brown 40 20

575. V.S. Srinivasa Sastri.

1970. Srinivasa Sastri (educationist) Commemoration.
619 **575** 20 p. yellow and purple 25 20

576. I. C. Vidyasagar.

1970. 150th Birth Anniv of Iswar Chandra Vidyasagar (educationist).
620 **576** 20 p. brown and purple 20 20

577. Maharishi Valmiki.

1970. Maharishi Valmiki (ancient author) Commemoration.
621 **577** 20 p. purple 15 15

578. Calcutta Port.

1970. Cent. of Calcutta Port Trust.
622. **578.** 20 p. blue 30 15

579. University Building.

1970. 50th Anniv. of Jamia Millia Islamia University.
623. **579.** 20 p. green 20 20

580. Jamnalal Bajaj.

1970. Jamnalal Bajaj (industrialist) Commemoration.
624. **580.** 20 p. grey 10 15

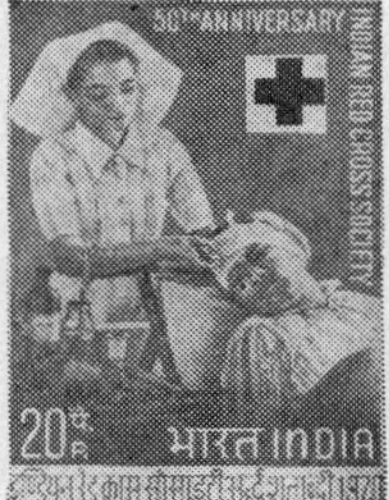

581. Nurse and Patient.

1970. 50th Anniv. of Indian Red Cross.
625. **581.** 20 p. red and blue .. 20 20

582. Sant Namdeo.

1970. 700th Birth Anniv of Sant Namdeo (mystic).
626. **582.** 20 p. orange 10 15

583. Beethoven.

1970. Birth Bicentenary of Beethoven.
627. **583.** 20 p. orange and black 80 30

584. Children examining Stamps.

1970. Indian National Philatelic Exhibition, New Dehli.
628. **584.** 20 p. orange and green 30 10
629. – 1 r. brown and ochre.. 1·25 80
DESIGN: 1 r. Gandhi commemorative through magnifier.

MINIMUM PRICE

The minimum price quoted is 10p which represents a handling charge rather than a basis for valuing common stamps. For further notes about prices see introductory pages.

585. Girl Guide.

1970. Diamond Jubilee of Girl Guide Movement in India.
630 585 20 p. purple 30 20

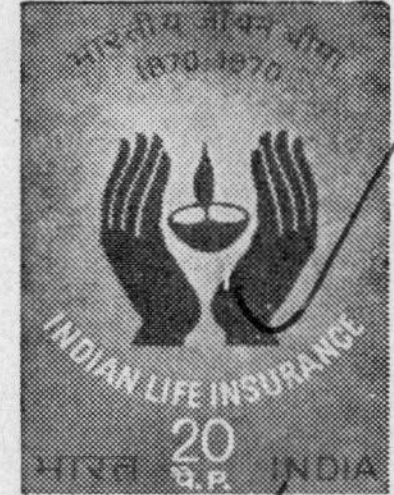

586. Hands and Lamp (emblem).

1971. Centenary of Indian Life Insurance.
631. **586.** 20 p. brown and red .. 15 20

587. Vidyapith Building.

1971. 50th Anniv of Kashi Vidyapith University.
632. **587.** 20 p. brown 15 20

588. Sant Ravidas.

1971. Sant Ravidas (15th-cent mystic) Commemoration.
633 **588** 20 p. red 15 20

589. C. F. Andrews.

1971. Birth Centenary of Charles Freer Andrews (missionary).
634 **589** 20 p. brown 35 20

590. Acharya Narendra Deo (scholar).

1971. 15th Death Anniv. of Acharya Narendra Deo.
635. **590.** 20 p. green 15 20

591. Crowd and "100".

1971. Centenary of Decennial Census.
636. **591.** 20 p. brown and blue 20 20

592. Sri Ramana Maharshi (mystic).

1971. 21st Death Anniv. of Ramana Maharshi.
637. **592.** 20 p. orange and brown 15 20

593. Raja Ravi Varma and "Damayanti and the Swan".

1971. 65th Death Anniv. of Ravi Varma (artist).
638. **593.** 20 p. green 15 20

594. Dadasaheb Phalke and Camera (cinematographer).

1971. Birth Centenary of Dadasaheb Phalke (cinematographer).
639 **594** 20 p. purple 40 20

595. "Abhisarika" (Tagore). **596.** Swami Virjanand (Vedic scholar).

1971. Birth Centenary of Abanindranath Tagore (painter).
640 **595** 20 p. grey, yell & brn .. 20 20

1971. Swami Virjanand Commemoration.
641. **596.** 20 p. brown 15 20

597. Cyrus the Great and Procession.

1971. 2500th Anniv. of Charter of Cyrus the Great.
642. **597.** 20 p. brown 35 30

598. Globe and Money Box.

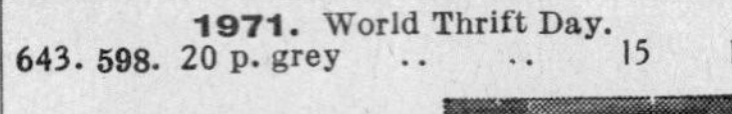
1971. World Thrift Day.
643. **598.** 20 p. grey 15 15

599. Ajanta Caves Paintings. **600** "Women at Work" (Geeta Gupta).

1971. 25th Anniv. of UNESCO.
644. **599.** 20 p. brown 65 30

1971. Children's Day.
645. **600.** 20 p. red .. 10 20

607. Refugees.

1971. Obligatory Tax. Refugee Relief.

(a) Optd. **REFUGEE RELIEF** in Hindi and English.
646. – 5 p. red (No. 506 .. 10 10

(b) Optd. **Refugee Relief.**
647. – 5 p. red (No. 506) .. 1·00 30

(c) Optd. **REFUGEE RELIEF.**
649. – 5 p. red (No. 506) .. 1·75 40

(d) Optd **Refugee relief**.
650c. – 5 p. red (No. 506) .. 3·25 1·00

(e) Optd. **Refugee Relief** in Hindi and English.
650d. – 5 p. red (No. 506) ..

(f) Type **607.**
651. **607.** 5 p. red 10 10

From 15 November 1971 until 31 March 1973 the Indian Government levied a 5 p. surcharge on all mail, except postcards and newspapers, for the relief of refugees from the former East Pakistan.

608. C. V. Raman (scientist) and Light Graph.

1971. 1st Death Anniv of Chandrasekhara Venkata Raman.
652 **608** 20 p. orange and brown 30 20

609. Visva Bharati Building and Rabindranath Tagore (founder).

1971. 50th Anniv of Visva Bharati University.
653 **609** 20 p. sepia and brown 15 25

610. Cricketers.

1971. Indian Cricket Victories.
654. **610.** 20 p. green, myrtle & sage 1·75 65

611. Map and Satellite.

1972. 1st Anniv of Arvi Satellite Earth Station.
655 **611** 20 p. purple 15 20

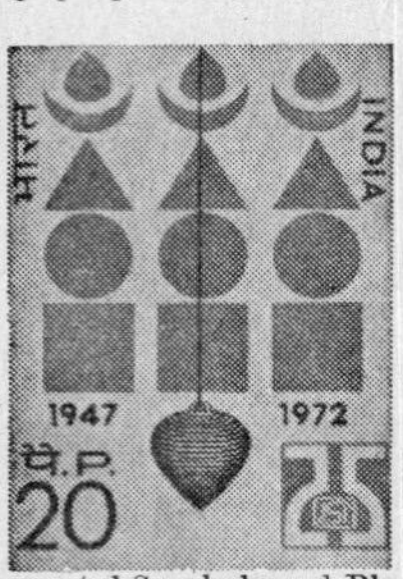
612. Elemental Symbols and Plumb-line.

1972. 25th Anniv of Indian Standards Institution.
656 **612** 20 p. grey and black .. 15 30

613. Signal-box Panel.

1972. 50th Anniv. of Int. Railways Union.
657. **613.** 20 p. multicoloured .. 40 40

614. Hockey-player.

1972. Olympic Games, Munich.
658. **614.** 20 p. violet 30 15
659. – 1 r. 45 green and lake 95 1·75
DESIGN: 1 r. 45, Various sports.

615. Symbol of Sri Aurobindo.

1972. Birth Centenary of Sri Aurobindo (religious teacher).
660. **615.** 20 p. yellow and blue 15 20

616. Celebrating Independence Day in front of Parliament.

1972. 25th Anniv. of Independence. (1st issue).
661. **616.** 20 p. multicoloured .. 15 20
See also Nos. 673/4.

617. Inter-Services Crest.

1972. Defence Services Commem.
662. **617.** 20 p. multicoloured .. 30 20

618. V. O. Chidambaran Pillai (trade union leader) and Ship.

1972. Birth Cent. of V. O. Chidambaram Pillai.
663. **618.** 20 p. blue and brown 30 30

619. Bhai Vir Singh.

1972. Birth Cent of Bhai Vir Singh (poet).
664 **619** 20 p. purple 30 30

620. T. Prakasam.

1972. Birth Centenary of Tanguturi Prakasam (lawyer).
665. **620.** 20 p. brown 15 30

621. Vemana.

1972. 300th Birth Anniv. of Vemana (poet).
666. **621.** 20 p. black 15 30

622. Bertrand Russell.

1972. Birth Centenary of Bertrand Russell (philosopher).
667. **622.** 1 r. 45 black .. .. 2·50 2·75

623. Symbol of "Asia '72".

1972. "Asia '72" (Third Asian International Trade Fair), New Delhi.
668. **623.** 20 p. black & orange .. 10 20
669. – 1 r. 45 orange and blk. 60 1·75
DESIGN: 1 r. 45, Hand of Buddha.

624. V. A. Sarabhai and Rocket.

1972. 1st Death Anniv. of Dr. Vikram A. Sarabhai (scientist).

670. **624.** 20 p. brown and green 15 30

625. Flag of U.S.S.R. and Kremlin Tower.

1972. 50th Anniv. of U.S.S.R.

671. **625.** 20 p. red and yellow 15 30

626. Exhibition Symbol.

1973. "Indipex '73" Stamp Exhibition (1st issue).

672. **626.** 1 r. 45 mve., gold & blk 45 1·25

627. "Democracy".

1973. 25th Anniv. of Independence. (2nd issue.) Multicoloured.

673. 20 p. Type **627** 15 15

674. 1 r. 45 "Gnat" fighters over India Gate.. .. 85 1·60

Size—Horiz. 1 r. 45, 38 × 20 mm.

628. Sri Ramakrishna Paramahamsa (religious leader).

1973. Sri Ramakrishna Paramahamsa Commemoration.

675. **628.** 20 p. brown 15 30

629. Postal Corps Emblem.

1973. 1st Anniv. of Army Postal Corps.

676. **629.** 20 p. blue and red .. 40 40

630. Flag and Map of Bangladesh.

1973. "Jai Bangla (Inauguration of 1st Bangladesh Parliament).

677. **630.** 20 p. multicoloured .. 15 30

631. Kumaran Asan.

1973. Birth Centenary of Kumaran Asan (writer and poet).

678. **631.** 20 p. brown 20 45

632. Flag and Flames.

1973. Homage to Martyrs for Independence.

679. **632.** 20 p. multicoloured .. 15 30

633. Dr. Bhim Rao Ambedkar (laywer).

1973. Ambedkar Commemoration.

680. **633.** 20 p. green and purple 15 50

634. "Radha-Kishangarh" (Nihal Chand).

1973. Indian Miniature Paintings. Mult.

681. 20 p. Type **634** 30 35

682. 50 p. "Dance Duet" (Aurangzeb's period) .. 60 1·50

683. 1 r. "Lovers on a Camel" (Nasir-ud-din) .. .. 1·50 2·50

684. 2 r. "Chained Elephant" (Zain-al-Abidin) .. 2·00 3·00

635. Mount Everest.

1973. 15th Anniv. of Indian Mountaineering Foundation.

685. **635.** 20 p. blue 30 40

336. Tail of Boeing "747".

1973. 25th Anniv. of Air-India's International Services.

686. **636.** 1 r. 45 blue and red .. 3·50 3·50

637. Cross, Church of St. Thomas' Mount, Madras.

1973. 19th Death Cent. of St. Thomas.

687. **637.** 20 p. grey and brown 15 35

638. Michael Madhusudan Dutt (poet—Death Centenary).

1973. Centenaries.

688. **638.** 20 p. green and brown 70 50

689. – 30 p. brown .. .. 70 1·50

690. – 50 p. brown .. .. 90 1·75

691. – 1 r. violet and red .. 90 1·50

Designs—Horiz. 30 p. Vishnu Digambar Paluskar (musician, birth centenary). 50 p. Dr. G. A. Hansen (centenary of discovery of leprosy bacillus). 1 r. Nicolaus Copernicus (astronomer, 5th birth centenary).

639. A. O. Hume.

1973. Allan Octavian Hume (founder of Indian National Congress) Commemoration.

692 **639** 20 p. grey 15 30

640. Gandhi and Nehru.

1973. Gandhi and Nehru Commemoration.

693. **640.** 20 p. multicoloured .. 15 20

641. R. C. Dutt.

1973. Romesh Chandra Dutt (writer) Commemoration.

694 **641** 20 p. brown 15 30

642. K. S. Ranjitsinhji.

1973. K. S. Ranjitsinhji (cricketer) Commemoration.

695 **642** 30 p. green .. .. 2·00 1·50

643. Vithalbhai Patel.

1973. Vithalbhai Patel (lawyer) Commem.

696 **643** 50 p. brown 15 40

644. Sowar of President's Bodyguard.

1973. Bicent. of President's Bodyguard.

697. **644.** 20 p. multicoloured .. 35 40

645. Interpol Emblem.

1973. 50th Anniv. of Interpol.

698. **645.** 20 p. brown .. 30 40

646. Syed Ahmad Khan (social reformer).

1973. Syed Ahmad Khan Commemoration.
699. **646.** 20 p. brown 10 40

647. "Children at Play" (Bela Raval).

1973. Children's Day.
700. **647.** 20 p. multicoloured .. 15 20

648. Indipex Emblem.
(Illustration reduced. Actual size 54 × 36 mm.)

1973. "Indipex '73" Philatelic Exhibition, New Delhi. (2nd issue). Multicoloured.
701. 20 p. Type **648** 20 30
702. 1 r. Ceremonial elephant and 1½ a. stamp of 1947 (vert.) .. 1·00 1·75
703. 2 r. Common Peafowl (vert.) 1·50 2·25

649. Emblem of National Cadet Corps.

1973. 25th Anniv of National Cadet Corps.
705 **649** 20 p. multicoloured .. 20 30

650. Rajagopalachari (statesman).

1973. Chakravanti Rajagopalachari Commemoration.
706 **650** 20 p. brown 15 40

651. "Sun" Mask.

1974. Indian Masks. Multicoloured.
707. 20 p. Type **651** 15 15
708. 50 p. "Moon" mask .. 30 55
709. 1 r. "Narasimha" .. 80 1·25
710. 2 r. "Ravana" (horiz.) .. 1·25 2·00

652. Chhatrapati.

1974. 300th Anniv. of Coronation of Chhatrapati Shri Shivaji Maharaj (patriot and ruler).
712. **652.** 25 p. multicoloured .. 30 30

653. Maithili Sharan Gupta (poet).

1974. Indian Personalities (1st series).
713. **653.** 25 p. brown 15 30
714. – 25 p. deep brown .. 15 30
715. – 25 p. brown 15 30
PORTRAITS: No. 714, Jainarain Vyas (politician and journalist). No. 715, Utkal Gourab Madhusudan Das (social reformer).

654. Kandukuri Veeresalingham (social reformer).

1974. Indian Personalities (2nd series).
716. **654.** 25 p. brown 25 40
717. – 50 p. purple .. .. 55 1·50
718. – 1 r. brown .. .. 70 1·50
PORTRAITS: 50 p. Tipu Sultan. 1 r. Max Mueller (Sanskrit scholar).

655. Kamala Nehru.

1974. Kamala Nehru Commemoration.
719. **655.** 25 p. multicoloured .. 35 40

656. W.P.Y. Emblem.

1974. World Population Year.
720. **656.** 25 p. purple and brown 15 20

657. Spotted Deer.

657a. Sitar.

1974.

(a) Values expressed with "p" or "Re"
721. – 15 p. brown .. .. 1·75 30
722. **657.** 25 p. brown 75 30
723. **657a.** 1 r. brown and black 2·50 30

(b) Values expressed as numerals only.
724 – 2 p. brown 30 70
725 – 5 p. red 20 10
729 – 10 p. blue 30 15
730 – 15 p. brown .. .. 1·25 10
731 – 20 p. green 10 10
732 – 25 p. brown .. .. 2·25 50
732b – 30 p. brown .. .. 1·25 30
733 – 50 p. violet .. .. 2·50 50
734 – 60 p. grey 50 60
735 **657a.** 1 r. brown and black .. 3·25 10
736 – 2 r. violet and brown .. 7·50 30
737 – 5 r. violet and brown .. 1·25 80
738c – 10 r. grey and green .. 1·10 1·10

DESIGNS—As Type **657**. VERT. 2 p. Bidri vase. 5 p. "Family Planning". 15 p. Tiger. 25 p. Gandhi. 30 p. Indian dolls. 60 p. Somnath Temple. HORIZ. 10 p. Electric Locomotive. 20 p. Handicrafts toy. 50 p. Demoiselle Crane in flight. As Type **657a**. 2 r. Himalayas. 5 r. Bhakra Dam, Punjab. 10 r. Atomic Reactor, Trombay.

For 30 p., 35 p., 50 p., 60 p., and 1 r. values as No. 732 see Nos. 968, 979, 1073, 1320 and 1436.

658. President V. Giri.

1974. Retirement of President Giri.
739. **658.** 25 p. multicoloured .. 10 15

659. U.P.U. Emblem.

1974. Centenary of U.P.U.
740. **659.** 25 p. vio., bl. & blk... 30 10
741. – 1 r. multicoloured .. 1·75 1·75
742. – 2 r. multicoloured .. 2·00 2·25
DESIGNS:—1 r. Birds and nest, "Madhubani" style. VERT. 2 r. Arrows around globe.

660. Lady Flute-player (sculpture).

1974. Centenary of Mathura Museum.
744. **660.** 25 p. chestnut & brown 40 20
745. – 25 p. chestnut & brown 40 20
DESIGN: No. 745, Vidyadhara with garland.

661. Nicholas Roerich (medallion by H. Dropsy).

1974. Birth Centenary of Professor Roerich (humanitarian).
746. **661.** 1 r. green & yellow .. 50 55

662. Pavapuri Temple.

1974. 2,500th Anniv. of Bhagwan Mahavira's Attainment of Nirvana.
747. **662.** 25 p. black 40 15

663. "Cat" (Rajesh Bhatia).

1974. Children's Day.
748. **663.** 25 p. multicoloured .. 40 30

664. "Indian Dancers" (Amita Shah).

1974. U.N.I.C.E.F. in India.
749. **664.** 25 p. multicoloured .. 35 30

665. Territorial Army Badge.

1974. 25th Anniv. of Indian Territorial Army.
750. **665.** 25 p. blk., yell. & green 50 30

666. Krishna as Gopal Bal with Cows (Rajasthan painting on cloth).

1974. 19th International Dairy Congress, New Delhi.
751. **666.** 25 p. purple and brown 40 20

667. Symbol and Child's Face.

1974. Help for Retarded Children.
752. **667.** 25 p. red and black .. 20 30

668. Marconi.

1974. Birth Centenary of Gugielmo Marconi (radio pioneer).
753. **668.** 2 r. blue .. .. 1·50 1·25

669. St. Francis Xavier's Shrine.

1974. St. Francis Xavier Celebration.
754. **669.** 25 p. multicoloured .. 15 30

670. Saraswati (Deity of Language and Learning).

1975. World Hindi Convention, Nagpur.
755. **670.** 25 p. grey and red .. 30 30

671. Parliament House, New Delhi.

1975. 25th Anniv. of Republic.
756. **671.** 25 p. blk., silver & blue 30 30

672. Table-tennis Bat.

1975. World Table-Tennis Championships, Calcutta.
757. **672.** 25 p. blk., red & green 55 15

673. " Equality, Development and Peace ".

1975. International Women's Year.
758. **673.** 25 p. multicoloured .. 90 45

674. Stylised Cannon.

1975. Bicent. of Indian Army Ordnance Corps.
759. **674.** 25 p. multicoloured .. 55 35

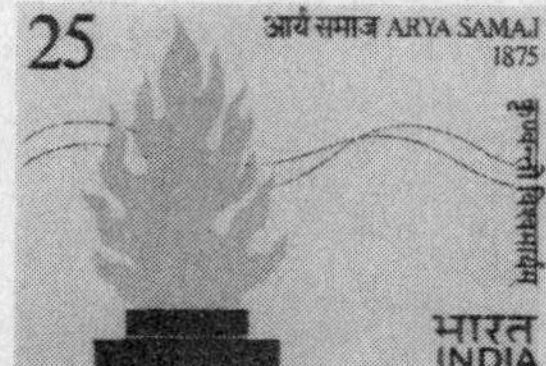

675. Arya Samaj Emblem.

1975. Cent. of Arya Samaj Movement.
760. **675.** 25 p. red and brown .. 30 30

676. Saraswati.

1975. World Telugu Language Conf., Hyderabad.
761. **676.** 25 p. black & green .. 45 30

677. Satellite " Aryabhata ".

1975. Launch of First Indian Satellite.
762. **677.** 25 p. light bl., bl. & pur. 40 40

678. Blue-winged Pitta.

1975. Indian Birds. Multicoloured.
763. 25 p. Type **678** 45 15
764. 50 p. Asian Black-headed Oriole .. .. 1·00 80
765. 1 r. Western Tragopan (vert.) .. .. 2·00 2·75
766. 2 r. Himalayan Monal Pheasant (vert.) .. .. 2·50 3·75

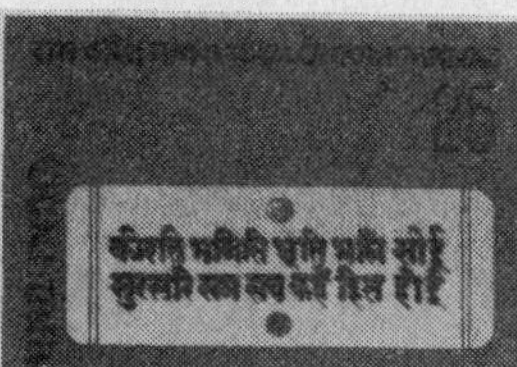

679. Page from "Ramcharitmanas" (manuscript).

1975. 4th Centenary of "Ramcharitmanas" (epic poem by Goswami Tulsidas).
767. **679.** 25 p. blk., yell. and red 40 15

680. Young Women within Y.W.C.A. Badge.

681. " The Creation ".

1975. Centenary of Indian Y.W.C.A.
768. **680.** 25 p. multicoloured .. 20 30

1975. 500th Birth Anniversary of Michelangelo. "Creation" Frescoes from Sistine Chapel.
769. **681.** 50 p. multicoloured .. 50 60
770. – 50 p. multicoloured .. 50 60
771. – 50 p. multicoloured .. 50 60
772. – 50 p. multicoloured .. 50 60

Nos. 770 and 772 are size 49 × 34 mm.
Nos. 769/70 and 771/2 form composite designs.

682. Commission Emblem.

1975. 25th Anniv. of Int. Commission of Irrigation and Drainage.
773. **682.** 25 p. multicoloured .. 40 20

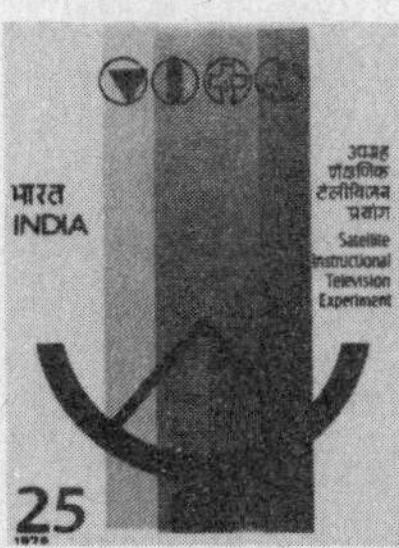

683. Stylised Ground Antenna.

1975. Inauguration of Satellite Instructional Television Experiment.
774 **683** 25 p. multicoloured .. 40 20

684. St. Arunagirinathar.

1975. 600th Birth Anniv. of St. Arunagirinathar.
775. **684.** 50 p. purple and black 1·00 1·00

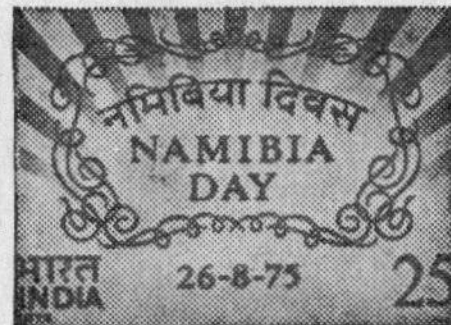

685. Commemorative Text.

1975. Namibia Day.
776. **685.** 25 p. black and red .. 40 40

686. Mir Anees (poet). **687.** Memorial Temple to Ahilyabai Holkar (ruler).

1975. Indian Celebrities.
777. **686.** 25 p. green 25 40
778. **687.** 25 p. brown 25 40

688. Bharata Natyam.

1975. Indian Dances. Multicoloured.
779. 25 p. Type **688** 55 20
780. 50 p. Orissi 85 80
781. 75 p. Kathak .. .. 1·00 1·00
782. 1 r. Kathakali .. .. 1·25 1·25
783. 1 r. 50 Kuchipudi .. .. 2·00 2·50
784. 2 r. Manipuri .. .. 2·25 3·25

689. Ameer Khusrau.

1975. 650th Death Anniv. of Ameer Khusrau (poet).
785. **689.** 50 p. brown and bistre 70 1·00

690. V. K. Krishna Menon.

1975. 1st Death Anniv. of V. K. Krishna Menon (statesman).
786. **690.** 25 p. green 40 40

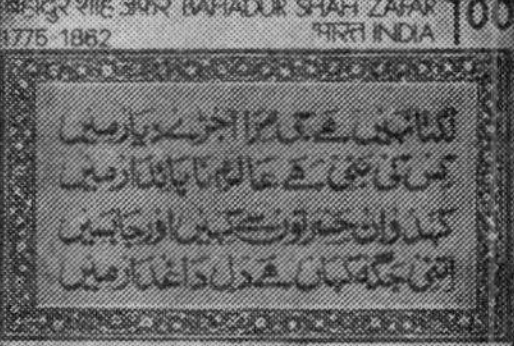

691. Text of Poem.

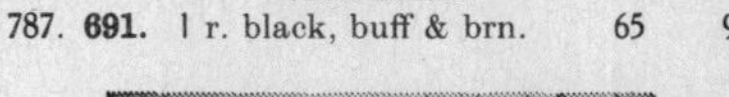

1975. Birth Bicentenary of Emperor Bahadur Shah Zafar.
787. **691.** 1 r. black, buff & brn. 65 90

692. Sansadiya Soudha, New Delhi.

1975. 21st Commonwealth Parliamentary Conference, New Delhi.
788. **692.** 2 r. green .. .. .. 1·75 2·50

693. V. Patel.

1975. Birth Centenary of Vallabhbhai Patel (statesman).
789. **693.** 25 p. green 15 30

694. N. C. Bardoloi.

1975. Birth Centenary of Nabin Chandra Bardoloi (politician).
790. **694.** 25 p. brown 20 40

695. "Cow" (Sanjay Nathubhai Patel).

1975. Children's Day.
791. **695.** 25 p. multicoloured .. 50 40

696. Original Printing Works, Nasik Road.

1975. 50th Anniv. of India Security Press.
792. **696.** 25 p. multicoloured .. 30 30

697. Gurdwara Sisganj (site of martyrdom).

1975. Tercentenary of the Martyrdom of Guru Tegh Bahadur (Sikh leader).
793 **697** 25 p. multicoloured .. 30 30

698. Theosophical Society Emblem.

1975. Centenary of Theosophical Society.
794. **698.** 25 p. multicoloured .. 40 40

699. Weather Cock.

1975. Centenary of Indian Meteorological Department.
795. **699.** 25 p. multicoloured .. 40 40

700. Early Mail Cart.

1975. "Inpex 75" Nat. Philatelic Exn., Calcutta.
796. **700.** 25 p. black and brown 50 30
797. – 2 r. brn., pur. and blk. 2·25 3·00
DESIGN: 2 r. Indian Bishop Mark, 1775.

701. L. N. Mishra.

1976. 1st Death Anniv of Lalit Narayan Mishra (politician).
798 **701** 25 p. brown 30 30

702. Tiger.

1976. Birth Cent. of Jim Corbett (naturalist).
799. **702.** 25 p. multicoloured .. 70 40

703. Painted Storks.

1976. Keoladeo Ghana Bird Sanctuary, Bharatpur.
800. **703.** 25 p. multicoloured .. 70 40

704. Vijayanta Tank.

1976. 200th Anniv. of 16th Light Cavalry Regiment.
801. **704.** 25 p. green and brown 80 30

705. Alexander Graham Bell.

1976. Alexander Graham Bell. Commem.
802. **705.** 25 p. brown and black 70 40

706. Muthuswami Dikshitar.

1976. Birth Bicentenary of Muthuswami Dikshitar (composer).
803. **706.** 25 p. violet 60 40

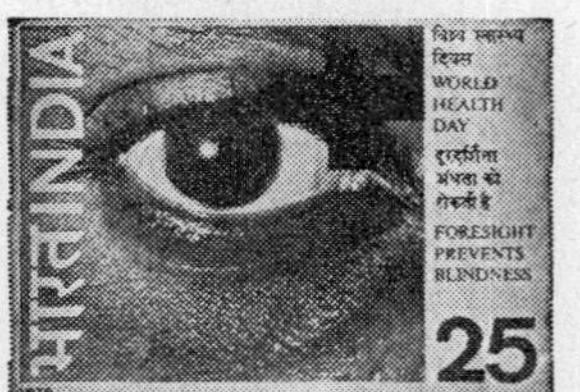
707. Eye and Red Cross.

1976. World Health Day. Prevention of Blindness.
804. **707.** 25 p. brown and red .. 50 40

708. "Industries".

1976. Industrial Development.
805. **708.** 25 p. multicoloured .. 30 30

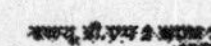

709. Diesel Locomotive, 1963.

1976. Locomotives. Multicoloured.
806. 25 p. Type **709** 55 10
807. 50 p. Steam locomotive, 1895 .. .. .. 1·25 55
808. 1 r. Steam locomotive, 1963 .. .. .. 2·25 1·25
809. 2 r. Steam locomotive, 1853 .. .. .. 3·00 2·50

710. Nehru.

1976.
810. **710.** 25 p. violet .. .. 3·50 60
811. – 25 p. brown .. .. 1·00 60
DESIGN: No. 811, Gandhi.
For these designs in a smaller format see Nos. 732, 968/9, 979/80, 1073/4 and 1320.

713. "Spirit of 76" (Willard).

1976. Bicent. of American Revolution.
812. **713.** 2 r. 80 multicoloured .. 1·25 1·25

714. K. Kamaraj (politician).

1976. Kumaraswumy Kamaraj Commem.
813 **714** 25 p. brown 15 15

715. "Shooting".

1976. Olympic Games, Montreal.
814. **715.** 25 p. violet and red .. 30 10
815. – 1 r. multicoloured .. 1·00 90
816. – 1 r. 50 mauve & black 1·50 2·00
817. – 2 r. 80 multicoloured .. 1·60 2·25
DESIGNS: 1 r. Shot-put. 1 r. 50, Hockey. 2 r. 80, Sprinting.

716. Subhadra Kumari Chauhan (poetess).

1976. S. K. Chauhan Commemoration.
818. **716.** 25 p. blue 15 30

717. Param Vir Chakra Medal.

1976. Param Vir Chakra Commemoration.
819. **717.** 25 p. multicoloured .. 15 30

718. University Building, Bombay.

1976. 60th Anniv of Shreemati Nathibai Damodar Thackersey Women's University.

820 **718** 25 p. violet 30 30

719. Bharatendu Harischandra (writer).

1976. Harishchandra Commemoration.

821. **719.** 25 p. brown 15 30

720. S. C. Chatterji. **721.** Planned Family.

1976. Birth Centenary of Sarat Churdra Chatterji (writer).

822 **720** 25 p. black 15 30

1976. Family Planning.

823. **721.** 25 p. multicoloured .. 15 30

722. Maharaja Agrasen and Coins.

1976. Maharaja Agrasen Commemoration.

824. **722.** 25 p. brown 10 30

723. Swamp Deer.

1976. Indian Wildlife. Multicoloured.

825.	25 p. Type 723	45	50
826.	50 p. Lion	1·25	1·75
827.	1 r. Leopard (horiz.) ..	1·75	2·00
828.	2 r. Caracal (horiz.) ..	2·00	3·00

HAVE YOU READ THE NOTES AT THE BEGINNING OF THIS CATALOGUE?

These often provide answers to the enquiries we receive.

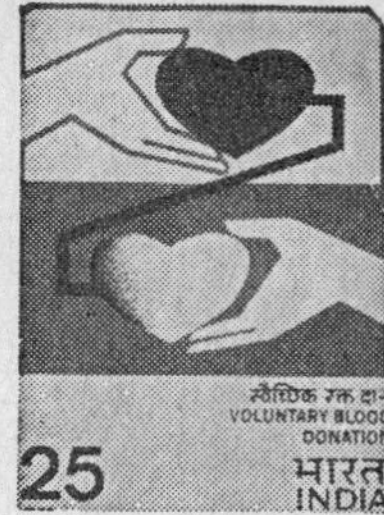

724. Hands holding Hearts.

1976. Voluntary Blood Donation.

829. **724.** 25 p. yell., red & blk. 30 40

725. Suryakant Tripathi ("Nirala").

1976. 80th Birth Anniv. of "Nirala" (poet and novelist).

830. **725.** 25 p. violet 15 30

726. "Loyal Mongoose" (H. D. Bhatia).

1976. Children's Day.

831. **726.** 25 p. multicoloured .. 40 40

727. Hiralal Shastri (social reformer).

1976. Shastri Commemoration.

832 **727** 25 p. brown 20 30

728. Dr. Hari Singh Gour.

1976. Dr. Hari Singh Gour (lawyer).

833. **728.** 25 p. purple 20 30

729. A300 B2 Airbus.

1976. Inauguration of Indian Airlines' Airbus Service.

834 **729** 2 r. multicoloured .. 2·25 2·25

730. Hybrid Coconut Palm.

1976. Diamond Jubilee of Coconut Research.

835. **730.** 25 p. multicoloured .. 20 30

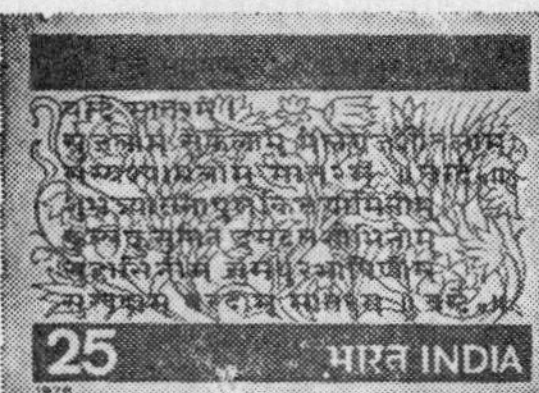

731. First Stanza of "Vande Mataram".

1976. Centenary of "Vande Mataram" (patriotic song by B. C. Chatterjee).

836 **731** 25 p. multicoloured .. 20 30

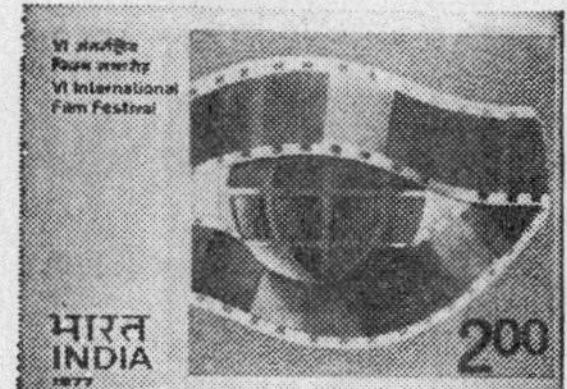

732. Globe and Film Strip.

1977. Sixth International Film Festival of India, New Delhi.

837. **732.** 2 r. multicoloured .. 1·50 2·00

733. Seismograph and Crack in Earth's Crust.

1977. Sixth World Conference on Earthquake Engineering, New Delhi.

838. **733.** 2 r. lilac .. .. 1·40 2·00

734. Tarun Ram Phookun.

1977. Tarun Ram Phookun (politican).

839. **734.** 25 p. grey 15 30

735. Paramansa Yogananda.

1977. Paramansa Yogananda (religious leader).

840. **735.** 25 p. orange 25 30

736. Asian Regional Red Cross Emblem.

1977. 1st Asian Regional Red Cross Conference, New Delhi.

841. **736.** 2 r. red, pink and blue 1·75 2·25

737. Fakhruddin Ali Ahmed.

1977. Death of President Ahmed.

842. **737.** 25 p. multicoloured .. 35 35

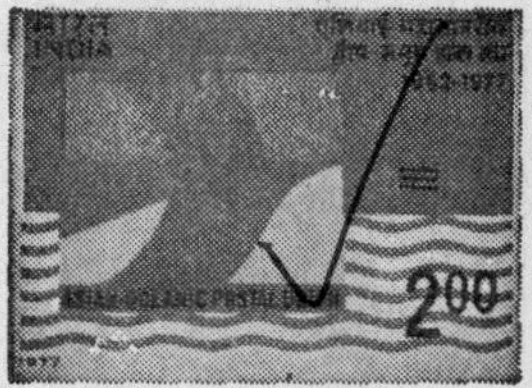

738. Emblem of Asian–Oceanic Postal Union.

1977. 15th Anniv. of Asian–Oceanic Postal Union.

843. **738.** 2 r. multicoloured .. 1·50 2·00

739. Narottam Morarjee and "Loyalty" (liner).

1977. Birth Cent of Morarjee (ship owner).

844 **739** 25 p. blue 40 40

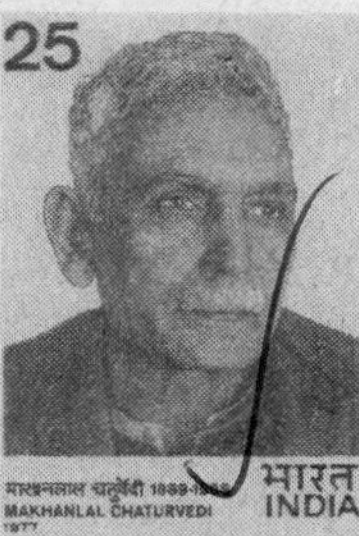

740. Makhanlal Chaturvedi (writer and poet).

1977. Chaturvedi Commemoration.

845. **740.** 25 p. brown 15 30

741. Mahaprabhu Vallabhacharya (philosopher).

1977. Vallabhacharya Commemoration.
846. **741.** 1 r. brown 30 40

742. Federation Emblem.

1977. 50th Anniv. of Federation of Indian Chambers of Commerce and Industry.
847. **742.** 25 p. purple, brown and yellow 15 40

744. "Environment Protection".

1977. World Environment Day.
848. **744.** 2 r. multicoloured .. 60 1·25

745. Rajya Sabha Chamber.

1977. 25th Anniv. of Rajya Sabha (Upper House of Parliament).
849. **745.** 25 p. multicoloured .. 15 30

746. Lotus.

1977. Indian Flowers. Multicoloured.
850. 25 p. Type **746** 25 15
851. 50 p. Rhododendron (vert.) 45 70
852. 1 r. Kadamba (vert.) .. 75 1·00
853. 2 r. Gloriosa Lily .. .. 1·00 2·00

747. Berliner Gramophone.

1977. Centenary of Sound Recording.
854. **747.** 2 r. brown and black 1·00 1·75

748. Coomaraswamy and Siva.

1977. Birth Centenary of Ananda Kentish Coomaraswamy (art historian).
855. **748.** 25 p. multicoloured .. 40 40

749. Ganga Ram and Hospital.

1977. 50th Death Anniv of Sir Ganga Ram (social reformer).
856 **749** 25 p. purple 20 30

750. Dr. Samuel Hahnemumann (founder of homeopathy).

1977. 32nd Int. Homeopathic Congress, New Delhi.
857. **750.** 2 r. black and green .. 2·50 2·50

751. Ram Manohar Lohia (politician).

1977. Ram Manohar Lohia Commemoration.
858. **751.** 25 p. brown 30 30

752. Early Punjabi Postman.

1977. "Inpex '77" Nat. Philatelic Exn., Bangalore.
859. **752.** 25 p. multicoloured .. 45 30
860. – 2 r. grey and red .. 1·75 2·50
DESIGN: 2 r. Unissued "Lion and Palm" stamp of 1853.

753. Scarlet "Scinde Dawks" of 1852.

1977. "Asiana '77" Int. Philatelic Exn., Bangalore.
861. **753.** 1 r. multicoloured .. 1·00 1·00
862. – 3 r. blue, orge. & black 2·00 2·50
DESIGN: 3 r. Foreign mail arriving at Ballard Pier, Bombay, 1927.

754. "Mother and Child" (Khajuraho sculpture).

1977. 15th Int. Congress on Pediatrics.
863. **754.** 2 r. blue and brown .. 2·25 2·75

755. Statue of Kittur Rani Channamma, Belgaum.

1977. Kittur Rani Channamma (ruler) Commemoration.
864 **755** 25 p. green 60 40

756. Symbolic Sun.

1977. Union Public Service Commission.
865. **756.** 25 p. multicoloured .. 35 30

757. Ear of Corn.

1977. "Agriexpo '77" Agricultural Exhibition, New Delhi.
866 **757** 25 p. green 40 40

758. "Cats" (Nikur Dilpbhai Mody).

1977. Children's Day. Multicoloured.
867. 25 p. Type **758** 50 30
868. 1 r. "Friends" (Bhavsar Ashish Ramanlal) .. 2·50 3·00

MORE DETAILED LISTS
are given in the Stanley Gibbons Catalogues referred to in the country headings.
For lists of current volumes see Introduction.

759. Jotirao Phooley (social reformer).

1977. Indian Personalities.
869. **759.** 25 p. olive 30 40
870. – 25 p. brown 30 40
DESIGN: No. 870, Senapti Bapat (patriot).

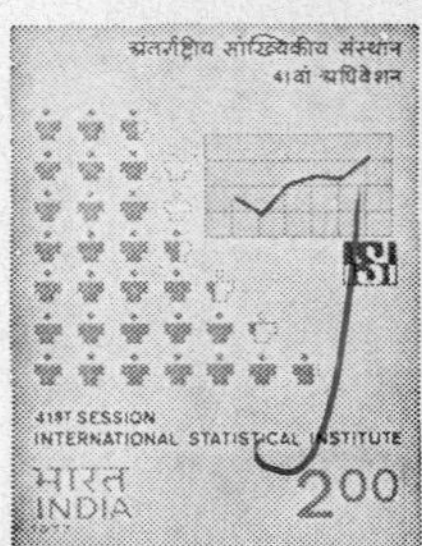

760. Diagram of Population Growth.

1977. 41st Session of International Statistical Institute, New Delhi.
871. **760.** 2 r. turquoise and red 85 1·40

761. Kamta Prasad Guru and Vyakarna (Hindi Grammar).

1977. Kamta Prasad Guru (writer) Commem.
872 **761** 25 p. brown 15 30

762. Kremlin Tower and Soviet Flag.

1977. 60th Anniv. of Russian Revolution.
873. **762.** 1 r. multicoloured .. 45 75

763. Climber crossing a Crevasse.

1978. Conquest of Kanchenjunga (1977). Multicoloured.
874. 25 p. Type **763** 10 10
875. 1 r. Indian flag near summit (horiz.) 45 80

764. "Shikara" on Lake Dal, Kashmir.

1978. 27th Pacific Area Travel Association Conf., New Delhi.
876. 764. 1 r. multicoloured .. 1·50 1·25

765. Children in Library.

1978. 3rd World Book Fair, New Delhi.
877. 765. 1 r. brown and slate .. 45 80

766. The Mother-Pondicherry.

1978. Birth Centenary of Mother-Pondicherry (philosopher).
878 766 25 p. brown and grey .. 15 30

767. Wheat and Globe.

1978. 5th International Wheat Genetics Symposium, New Delhi.
879. 767. 25 p. yellow and turq. 15 30

768. Nanalal Dalpatram Kavi (poet).

1978. Nanalal Dalpatram Kavi Commem.
880. 768. 25 p. brown 15 30

769. Surjya Sen (revolutionary).

1978. Surjya Sen Commemoration.
881. 769. 25 p. bistre and red .. 15 30

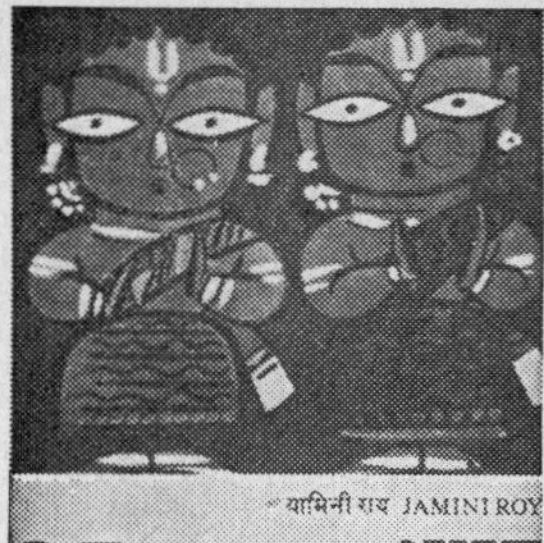
770. " Two Vaishnavas " (Jamini Roy).

1978. Modern Indian Paintings. Mult.
882. 25 p. Type 770 .. .. 20 30
883. 50 p. " The Mosque " (Sailoz Mookherjea) .. 40 1·25
884. 1 r. " Head " (Rabindranath Tagore) .. .. 70 1·50
885. 2 r. " Hill Women " (Amrita Sher Gil) .. .. 90 2·00

771. " Self Portrait " (Rubens).

1978. 400th Birth Anniv. of Peter Paul Rubens.
886. 771. 2 r. multicoloured .. 2·00 3·00

772. Charlie Chaplin.

1978. Charlie Chaplin Commemoration.
887. 772. 25 p. blue and gold .. 75 35

773. Deendayal Upadhyaya (politician).

1978. Deendayal Upadhyaya Commem.
888. 773. 25 p. brown & orange 15 30

774. Syama Prasad Mookerjee.

1978. Syama Prasad Mookerjee (politician) Commemoration.
889 774 25 p. brown 30 40

775. Airavat (mythological elephant). Jain Temple, Gujerat (Kachchh Museum).

1978. Treasures for Indian Museums. Mult.
890. 25 p. Type 775 .. .. 30 30
891. 50 p. Kalpadruma (magical tree), Besnagar (Indian Museum) .. .. 65 1·00
892. 1 r. Obverse and reverse of Kushan gold coin (National Museum) .. .. 1·25 1·50
893. 2 r. Dagger and knife of Emperor Jehangir, Mughal (Salar Jung Museum) .. 2·75 2·00

776. Krishna and Arjuna in Battle Chariot.

1978. Bhagawadgeeta (Divine Song of India) Commemoration.
894 776 25 p. gold and red .. 15 30

777. Bethune College.

1978. Centenary of Bethune College, Calcutta.
895. 777. 25 p. brown and green 15 30

778. E. V. Ramasami.

1978. E. V. Ramasami (social reformer) Commemoration.
896 778 25 p. black 15 15

779. Uday Shankar.

1978. Uday Shankar (dancer) Commem.
897. 779. 25 p. brown 15 30

780. Leo Tolstoy.

1978. 150th Birth Anniv. of Leo Tolstoy (writer).
898. 780. 1 r. multicoloured .. 30 30

781. Vallathol Narayana Menon.

1978. Birth Centenary of Vallathol Narayana Menon (poet).
899. 781. 25 p. purple and brown 15 30

782. " Two Friends " (Dinesh Sharma).

1978. Children's Day.
900. 782. 25 p. multicoloured .. 15 30

783. Machine Operator.

1978. National Small Industries Fair, New Delhi.
901 783 25 p. green 15 30

784. Sowars of Skinner's Horse.

1978. 175th Anniv. of Skinner's Horse (cavalry regiment).
902. 784. 25 p. multicoloured .. 40 50

785. Mohammad Ali Jauhar.

1978. Birth Centenary of Mohammad Ali Jauhar (patriot).
903. 785. 25 p. olive .. 15 30

786. Chakravarti Rajagopalachari.

1978. Birth Centenary of Chakravarti Rajagopalachari (first post-independence Governor-General).
904. 786. 25 p. brown 15 30

787. Wright Brothers and " Flyer ".

1978. 75th Anniv. of First Powered Flight.

905. **787.** 1 r. violet and yellow 45 30

788. Ravenshaw College.

1978. Cent of Ravenshaw College, Cuttack.

'906 788 25 p. red and green .. 15 30

789. Schubert.

1978. 150th Death Anniv. of Franz Schubert (composer).

907. **789.** 1 r. multicoloured .. 40 55

790. Uniforms of 1799, 1901 and 1979 with Badge.

1979. 4th Reunion of Punjab Regiment.

908 **790** 25 p. multicoloured 70 60

791. Bhai Parmanand.

1979. Bhai Parmanand (scholar) Commem.

909 **791** 25 p. violet 15 30

792. Gandhi with Young Boy.

1979. International Year of the Child.

910. **792.** 25 p. brown and red .. 40 30

911. – 1 r. brown and orge. 85 1·50

DESIGN: 1 r. India I.Y.C. emblem.

793. Albert Einstein.

1979. Birth Centenary of Albert Einstein (physicist).

912. **793.** 1 r. blue 30 50

794. Rajarshi Shahu Chhatrapati.

1979. Rajarshi Shahu Chhatrapati (ruler of Kolhapur State, and precursor of social reform in India) Commemoration.

913. **794.** 25 p. purple 15 30

795. Exhibition Logo.

1979. " India 80 " International Stamp Exhibition (1st issue).

914. **795.** 30 p. green and orange 15 30

See also Nos. 942/5 and 955/8.

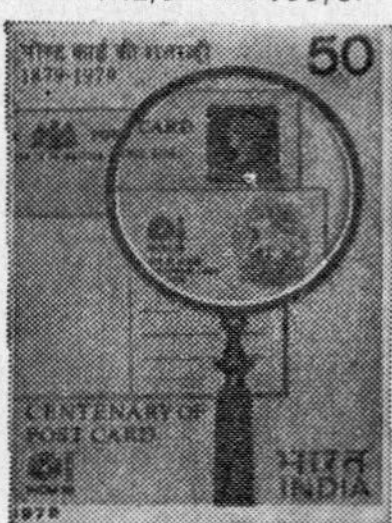

796. Postcards under Magnifying Glass.

1979. Centenary of Indian Postcards.

915. **796.** 50 p. multicoloured .. 15 40

797. Raja Mahendra Pratap.

1979. Raja Mahendra Pratap (patriot) Commemoration.

916 **797** 30 p. green 15 40

798. Flounder, Herring and Prawn.

1979.

920	–	2 p. violet	10	10
921	**798**	5 p. blue	10	10
922a	–	10 p. green	10	10
923	–	15 p. green	10	10
924a	–	20 p. red	10	10
925a	–	25 p. brown	30	10
925ba	–	25 p. green	10	10
926ab	–	30 p. green	10	10
927ab	–	35 p. red	20	10
928ba	–	50 p. violet	10	10
929b	–	1 r. brown	10	10
932a	–	2 r. lilac	10	15
933b	–	2 r.25 red and green	10	10
934	–	2 r.80 red and green	15	20
934b	–	3 r.25 orange & green	15	20
935b	–	5 r. red and green ..	60	40
936	–	10 r. red and green	75	55

DESIGNS—HORIZ. 2 p. Adult Education class. 10 p. Irrigation canal. 25 p. (925) Chick hatching from egg. 25 p. (925b) Village, wheat and tractor. 30 p. Harvesting maize. 50 p. Woman dairy farmer, cows and milk bottles. (36 × 19 mm.) 10 r. Forest on hillside. VERT. (17 × 20 mm.) 15 p. Farmer and agricultural symbols. 20 p. Mother feeding child. 35 p. "Family". (17 × 28 mm.) 1 r. Cotton plant. 2 r. Weaving. (20 × 38 mm.) 2 r. 25, Cashew. 2 r. 80, Apples. 3 r. 25, Oranges. 5 r. Rubber tapping.

For 75 p. in same design as No. 927 see No. 1214.

800. Jatindra Nath Das.

1979. 50th Death Anniv. of Jatindra Nath Das (revolutionary).

941. **800.** 30 p. brown 15 30

801. De Havilland " Puss Moth " Aeroplane.

1979. " Air India 80 " International Stamp Exhibition (2nd issue). Mail-carrying Aircraft. Multicoloured.

942.	30 p. Type **801**	25	25
943.	50 p. Indian Air Force " Chetak " helicopter ..	40	45
944.	1 r. Indian Airlines Boeing " 737 " airliner	55	75
945.	2 r. Air India Boeing " 747 " airliner	75	95

802. Early and Modern Lightbulbs.

1979. Centenary of Electric Lightbulb.

946. **802.** 1 r. purple 15 30

803. Gilgit Record.

1979. International Archives Week.

947 **803** 30 p. yellow and brown 15 40

804. Hirakud Dam, Orissa.

1979. 50th Anniv. and 13th Congress of International Commission on Large Dams.

948. **804.** 30 p. brown and turq. 15 30

805. Fair Emblem.

1979. India International Trade Fair.

949. **805.** 1 r. black and red .. 15 30

806. Child learning to Read.

1979. International Children's Book Fair, New Delhi.

950. **806.** 30 p. multicoloured .. 15 30

807. Dove with Olive Branch and I.A.E.A. Emblem.

1979. 23rd International Atomic Energy Agency Conference, New Delhi.

951. **807.** 1 r. multicoloured .. 20 45

808. " Hindustan Pushpak " Aircraft and " Rohini – 1 " Glider.

1979. Flying and Gliding.

952. **808.** 30 p. blk., brn. & blue 40 40

809. Gurdwara Baoli Sahib Temple, Goindwal, Amritsar District.

1979. 500th Birth Anniv of Guru Amar Das (Sikh leader).

953 **809** 30 p. multicoloured .. 60 50

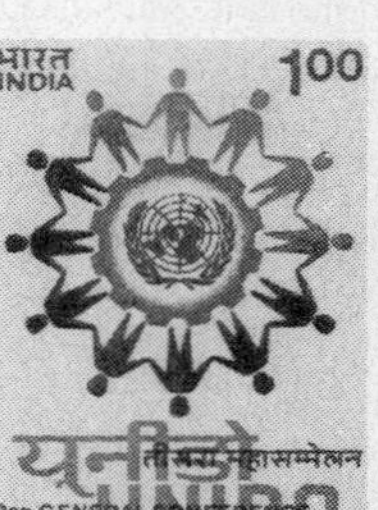

810. Ring of People encircling U.N. Emblem and Cog-wheel.

1980. Third United Nations Industrial Development Organization General Conference, New Delhi.

954. **810.** 1 r. multicoloured .. 15 30

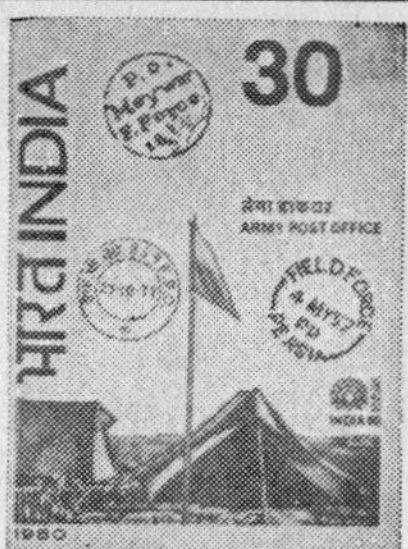

811. Army Post Office and Postmarks.

1980. "India 80" International Stamp Exhibition (3rd issue).

955. **811.** 30 p. green 30 30
956. – 50 p. brn. and deep brn. 50 75
957. – 1 r. red 60 80
958. – 2 r. brown .. .. 60 1·25

DESIGNS: 50 p. Money order transfer document, 1879. 1 r. Copper prepayment tickets, 1774. 2 r. Sir Rowland Hill and birthplace at Kidderminster.

812. Energy Symbols.

1980. Institution of Engineers Commem.

959. **812.** 30 p. gold and blue .. 15 30

813. Uniforms of 1780 and 1980, Crest and Ribbon.

1980. Bicentenary of Madras Sappers.

960. **813.** 30 p. multicoloured .. 40 40

814. Books.

1980. Fourth World Book Fair, New Delhi.

961. **814.** 30 p. blue 30 30

815. Bees and Honey-Comb.

1980. Second International Conference on Apiculture.

962. **815.** 1 r. bistre and brown 30 45

816. Welthy Fisher and Saksharta Nicketan (Literacy House), Lucknow.

1980. Welthy Fisher Commemoration.

963. **816.** 30 p. blue 30 30

817. Darul-Uloom, Deoband.

1980. Darul-Uloom Commemoration.

964. **817.** 30 p. green 15 30

818. Keshub Chunder Sen.

1980. Keshub Chunder Sen (religious and social reformer). Commemoration.

965. **818.** 30 p. brown 15 30

819. Chhatrapati Shivaji Maharaj.

1980. 300th Death Anniv. of Chhatrapati Shivaji Maharaj (Warrior).

966. **819.** 30 p. multicoloured .. 15 30

820. Table Tennis.

1980. Fifth Asian Table Tennis Championships, Calcutta.

967. **820.** 30 p. purple 20 30

1980. As Nos. 732 and 810. Size 17 × 20 mm.

968. 30 p. brown (Gandhi) .. 1·25 40
969. 30 p. violet (Nehru) .. 30 20

821. N. M. Joshi.

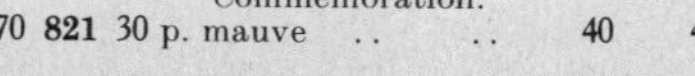

1980. Narayan Malhar Joshi (trade unionist) Commemoration.

970 **821** 30 p. mauve 40 40

822. Ulloor S. Parameswara Iyer.

1980. Ulloor S. Parameswara Iyer (poet). Commemoration.

971 **822** 30 p. purple 50 40

823. S. M. Zamin Ali.

1980. Syed Mohammed Zamin Ali (educationlist and poet) Commemoration.

972 **823** 30 p. green 15 40

824. Helen Keller.

1980. Birth Centenary of Helen Keller. (campaigner for the handicapped).

973. **824.** 30 p. black and orange 40 30

825. High-jumping.

1980. Olympic Games, Moscow. Multicoloured.

974. 1 r. Type **825** 40 40
975. 2 r. 80 Horse-riding .. 85 1·40

826. Prem Chand.

1980. Birth Cent of Prem Chand (novelist).

976 **826** 30 p. brown 15 30

827. Mother Teresa and Nobel Peace Prize Medallion.

1980. Award of 1979 Nobel Peace Prize to Mother Teresa.

977 **827** 30 p. violet 30 30

828. Lord Mountbatten.

1980. Lord Mountbatten Commemoration.

978. **828.** 2 r. 80 multicoloured 1·60 2·25

1980. As Nos. 968/9, but new face value.

979. 35 p. brown 40 30
980. 35 p. violet 30 20

DESIGNS: No. 979, Gandhi. No. 980, Nehru.

829. Scottish Church College, Calcutta.

1980. 150th Anniv. of Scottish Church College, Calcutta.

981. **829.** 35 p. lilac 15 30

830. Rajah Annamalai Chettiar. **831.** Gandhi marching to Dandi.

1980. Rajah Annamalai Chettiar (banker and educationist) Commemoration.

982 **830** 35 p. lilac 15 30

1980. 50th Anniv of "Dandi March" (Gandhi's defiance of Salt Tax Law) Commemoration.

983. **831.** 35 p. blk., blue & gold 15 45
984. – 35 p. blk., mauve & gold 15 45

DESIGN: No. 984, Gandhi picking up handful of salt at Dandi.

832. Jayaprakash Narayan.

1980. Jayaprakash Narayan (socialist) Commemoration.

985 **832** 35 p. brown 40 40

833. Great Indian Bustard.

1980. International Symposium on Bustards.

986. **833.** 2 r. 30 multicoloured .. 1·00 1·75

834. Arabic Commemorative Inscription.

1980. Moslem Year 1400 A.H. Commem.
~~987.~~ **834.** 35 p. multicoloured .. 15 30

835. "Girls Dancing" (Pampa Paul).

1980. Children's Day.
988. **835.** 35 p. multicoloured .. 40 40

836. Dhyan Chand.

1980. Dhyan Chand (hockey player). Commemoration.
989. **836.** 35 p. brown 70 50

837. Gold Mining.

1980. Cent of Kolar Gold Fields, Karnataka.
990 **837** 1 r. multicoloured .. 40 30

838. M. A. Ansari.

1980. Mukhtayar Ahmad Ansari (medical practitioner and politician) Commemoration.
991 **838** 35 p. green 30 30

839. India Government Mint, Bombay.

1980. 150th Anniv. of India Government Mint, Bombay.
992. **839.** 35 p. blk., blue & silver 15 30

840. Bride from Tamil Nadu.

1980. Indian Bridal Costumes. Multicoloured.
993. 1 r. Type **840** 40 55
994. 1 r. Rajasthan 40 55
995. 1 r. Kashmir 40 55
996. 1 r. Bengal 40 55

841. Mazharul Haque.

1981. Mazharul Haque (journalist) Commem.
997 **841** 35 p. blue 15 40

842. St. Stephen's College.

1981. Centenary of St. Stephen's College, Delhi.
998. **842.** 35 p. red 15 40

843. Gommateshwara

844. G. V. Mavalankar.

1981. Gommateshwara Statue at Shravanabelgola. Millennium.
999. **843.** 1 r. multicoloured .. 15 30

1981. 25th Death Anniv of Ganesh Vasudeo Mavalankar (parliamentarian).
1000 **844** 35 p. red 15 40

845. Flame of Martyrdom.

1981. " Homage to Martyrs ".
1001. **845.** 35 p. multicoloured .. 15 30

846. Heinrich von Stephan and U.P.U. Emblem.

1981. 150th Birth Anniv. of Heinrich von Stephan (founder of U.P.U.).
1002. **846.** 1 r. brown 15 50

847. Disabled Child being helped by Able-bodied Child.

1981. International Year for Disabled Persons.
1003. **847.** 1 r. black and blue .. 15 30

848. Bhil. **849.** Stylised Trees.

1981. Tribes of India. Multicoloured.
1004. 1 r. Type **848** 25 25
1005. 1 r. Dandami Maria .. 25 25
1006. 1 r. Toda.. .. .. 25 25
1007. 1 r. Khlamngam Naga .. 25 25

1981. Forests Conservation.
1008. **849.** 1 r. multicoloured .. 15 15

850. Nilmoni Phukan.

1981. Nilmoni Phukan (poet) Commemoration.
1009. **850.** 35 p. brown 15 20

851. Sanjay Gandhi.

1981. 1st Death Anniv. of Sanjay Gandhi (politician).
1010. **851.** 35 p. multicoloured .. 15 30

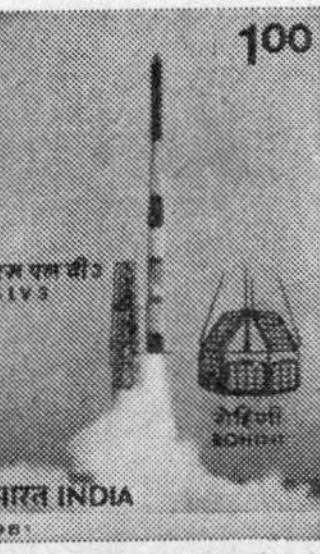

852. Launch of " SLV 3 " and Diagram of " Rohini ".

1981. Launch of " SLV 3 " Rocket with " Rohini " Satellite.
1011. **852.** 1 r. black, pink & blue 20 20

853. Games Logo.

1981. Asian Games, New Delhi (1st issue). Multicoloured.
1012. 1 r. Type **853** 65 35
1013. 1 r. Games emblem and stylised hockey players 65 35

See also Nos. 1026, 1033, 1057, 1059 and 1061/6.

854. Flame of the Forest.

1981. Flowering Trees. Multicoloured.
1014. 35 p. Type **854** 25 15
1015. 50 p. Crateva 35 40
1016. 1 r. Golden Shower .. 45 40
1017. 2 r. Bauhinia 65 75

855. W.F.D. Emblem and Wheat.

1981. World Food Day.
1018. **855.** 1 r. yellow and blue .. 20 20

856. "Stichopthalma camadeva".

1981. Butterflies. Multicoloured.
1019. 35 p. Type **856** 50 15
1020. 50 p. " Cethosia biblis " 80 40
1021. 1 r. " Cyrestis achates " 1·10 40
1022. 2 r. " Teinopalpus imperialis " (vert.) .. 1·25 1·50

857. Bellary Raghava.

1981. Bellary Raghava (actor) Commem.
1023. **857.** 35 p. green 30 20

858. Regimental Flag.

1981. 40th Anniv. of Mahar Regiment.
1024. **858.** 35 p. multicoloured .. 40 30

859. " Toyseller " (Kumari Ruchita Sharma).

1981. Children's Day. Child's Painting.
1025. 859. 35 p. multicoloured .. 30 20

860. Rajghat Stadium.

1981. Asian Games, New Delhi (2nd issue).
1026. 860. 1 r. multicoloured .. 65 30

861. Kashi Prasad Jayasawal and Yaudheya Coin.

1981. Birth Centenary of Kashi Prasad Jayasawal (lawyer and historian).
1027. 861. 35 p. blue 30 20

862. Indian and P.L.O. Flags, and People.

1981. Palestinian Solidarity.
1028. 862. 1 r. multicoloured .. 1·25 40

863. I.N.S. "Taragiri" (frigate).

1981. Indian Navy Day.
1029. 863. 35 p. multicoloured .. 1·00 65

864. Henry Heras and Indus Valley Seal.

1981. Henry Heras (historian) Commem.
1030. 864. 35 p. lilac 45 20

865. Map of South-East Asia showing Cable Route.

1981. Inauguration of I.O.C.O.M. (Indian Ocean Commonwealth Cable) Submarine Telephone Cable.
1031 865 1 r. multicoloured .. 1·00 35

866. Stylised Hockey-player and Championship Emblem.

1981. World Cup Hockey Championship, Bombay.
1032. 866. 1 r. multicoloured .. 50 30

867. Jawaharlal Nehru Stadium.

1981. Asian Games, New Delhi (3rd issue).
1033. 867. 1 r. multicoloured .. 30 15

868. Early and Modern Telephones.

1982. Centenary of Telephone Services.
1034. 868. 2 r. black, blue & grey 30 30

869. Map of World.

1982. International Soil Science Congress, New Delhi.
1035. 869. 1 r. multicoloured .. 30 15

870. Sir J. J. School of Art.

1982. 125th Anniv. of Sir J. J. School of Art, Bombay.
1036. 870. 35 p. multicoloured .. 20 20

871. " Three Musicians ".

1982. Birth Centenary (1981) of Picasso.
1037. 871. 2 r. 85 multicoloured 35 40

872. Deer (stone carving), 5th-century A.D.

1982. Festival of India. Ancient Sculpture. Multicoloured.
1038. 2 r. Type 872 .. .. 20 40
1039. 3 r. 05 Kaliya Mardana (bronze statue), 9th-century A.D. 35 60

873. Radio Telescope, Ooty.

1982. Festival of India. Science and Technology.
1040. 873. 3 r. 05 multicoloured 35 40

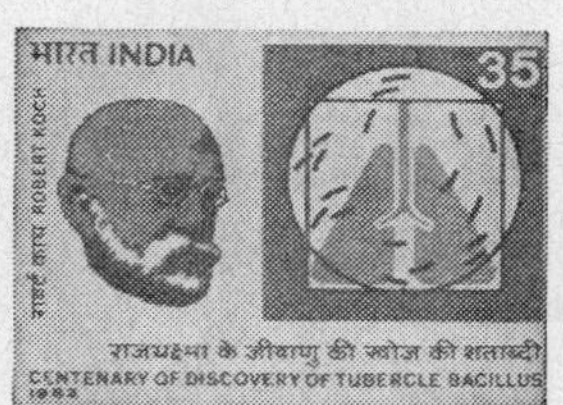

874. Robert Koch and Symbol of Disease.

1982. Centenary of Robert Koch's Discovery of Tubercle Bacillus.
1041. 874. 35 p. lilac 50 30

875. Durgabai Deshmukh.

1982. 1st Death Anniv. of Durgabai Deshmukh (social reformer).
1042. 875. 35 p. blue 30 40

876. Blue Poppy.

1982. Himalayan Flowers. Multicoloured.
1043 35 p. Type 876 .. .. 25 15
1044 1 r. Showy inula .. 50 20
1045 2 r. Cobra lily .. .. 75 1·00
1046 2 r. 85 Brahma kamal .. 1·00 1·50

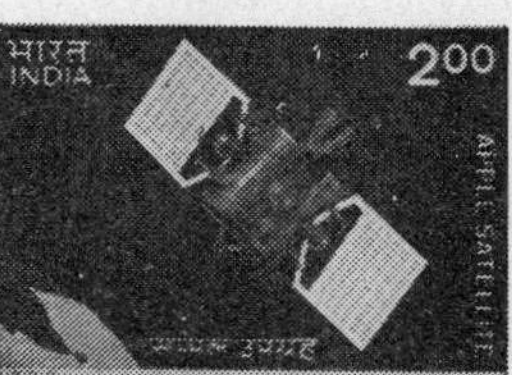

877. " Apple " Satellite.

1982. 1st Anniv. of "Apple" Satellite Launch.
1047. 877. 2 r. multicoloured .. 40 80

878. Bidhan Chandra Roy.

1982. Birth Centenary of Bidhan Chandra Roy (doctor and politician).
1048. 878. 50 p. brown 30 40

879. " Sagar Samrat " Oil Rig.

1982. 25th Anniv. of Oil and Natural Gas Commission.
1049. 879. 1 r. multicoloured .. 30 30

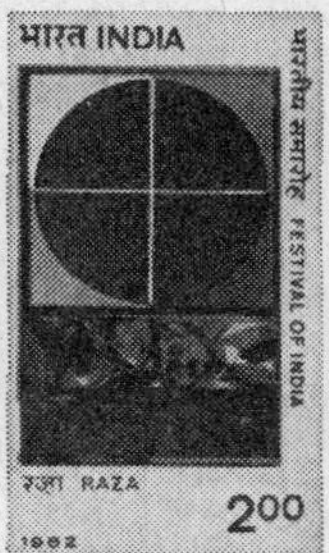

880. "Bindu" (S. H. Raza).

1982. Festival of India. Contemporary Paintings. Multicoloured.
1050 2 r. Type 880 .. .. 30 50
1051 3 r. 05 "Between the Spider and the Lamp" (M. F. Hussain) .. 45 1·25

881. Red Deer.

1982. Wildlife Conservation.
1052. 881. 2 r. 85 multicoloured 50 50

882. " Wapiti " and " Mig-25 " Aircraft.

1982. 50th Anniv. of Indian Air Force.
1053. 882. 1 r. multicoloured .. 1·00 40

883. J. Tata with " Puss Moth ".

1982. 50th Anniv. of Civil Aviation in India.
1054. 883. 3 r. 25 multicoloured 1·25 70

884. Police Patrol.

1982. Police Commemoration Day.

1055. 884. 50 p. green 40 20

885. Coins and Economic Symbols.

1982. Centenary of Post Office Savings Bank.

1056. 885. 50 p. brown and light brown 20 20

886. Wrestling Bout.

1982. Asian Games, New Delhi (4th issue).

1057. 886. 1 r. multicoloured .. 20 15

887. Troposcatter Communication Link.

1982. 1st Anniv. of Troposcatter Communication Link between India and U.S.S.R.

1058. 887. 3 r. 05 multicoloured 50 40

888. Krishna shooting Arrow at Fish.

1982. Asian Games, New Delhi (5th issue).

1059. 888. 1 r. multicoloured .. 20 20

889. "Mother and Child" (Deepak Sharma)

1982. Children's Day.

1060. 889. 50 p. multicoloured .. 20 20

890. Stylised Cyclists.

1982. Asian Games, New Delhi (6th issue). Multicoloured.

1061. 50 p. Type 890 .. .. 10 10
1062. 2 r. Javelin-throwing .. 25 30
1063. 2 r. 85 Discus-throwing 30 45
1064. 3 r. 25 Football 40 55

891. Yachting.

1982. Asian Games, New Delhi (7th issue). Multicoloured.

1065. 2 r. Type 891 .. .. 25 30
1066. 2 r. 25 Rowing 30 40

892. Chetwode Building.

1982. 50th Anniv of Indian Military Academy, Dehradun.

1067 892 50 p. multicoloured .. 20 30

893. Purushottamdas Tandon.

1982. Birth Cent of Purushottamdas Tandon (politician).

1068 893 50 p. brown 20 40

894. Darjeeling Himalayan Railway.

1982. Cent. of Darjeeling Himalayan Railway.

1069. 894. 2 r. 85 multicoloured 1·75 2·25

895. Vintage Rail Coach and Silhouette of Steam Engine.

1982. "Impex 82" Stamp Exhibition. Multicoloured.

1070. 50 p. Type 895 .. .. 30 50
1071. 2 r. 1854 ½ anna blue stamp and 1947 3½ anna Independence Commem. (33×44 mm.) .. 60 1·25

INDEX

Countries can be quickly located by referring to the index at the end of this volume.

896. Antarctic Camp.

1983. 1st Indian Antarctic Expedition.

1072. 896. 1 r. multicoloured .. 1·25 1·25

1983. As Nos. 968/9, but with new face value.

1073a 50 p. brown (Gandhi) .. 1·00 30
1074a 50 p. blue (Nehru) .. 40 10

897. Roosevelt with Stamp Collection.

1983. Birth Centenary of Franklin D. Roosevelt (American statesman).

1075. 897. 3 r. 25 brown .. 45 1·00

898. "Great White Cranes at Bharatpur" (Diane Pierce).

1983. International Crane Workshop, Bharatpur.

1076. 898. 2 r. 85 mult .. .. 1·10 1·60

899. Jat Regiment Uniforms Past and Present.

1983. Presentation of Colours to Battalions of the Jat Regiment.

1077. 899. 50 p. mult. 40 50

900. Non-aligned Summit Logo.

1983. 7th Non-aligned Summit Conference. New Delhi.

1078. 900. 1 r. lt. brown, brown and black 20 30
1079. – 2 r. multicoloured .. 30 95

DESIGN: 2 r. Nehru.

901. Shore Temple, Mahabalipuram.

1983. Commonwealth Day. Multicoloured.

1080. 1 r. Type 901 .. .. 15 30
1081. 2 r. Gomukh, Gantgotri Glacier 30 95

902. Acropolis and Olympic Emblems.

1983. International Olympic Committee Session, New Delhi.

1082. 902. 1 r. multicoloured .. 20 30

903. "St. Francis and Brother Falcon" (statue by Giovanni Collina).

1983. 800th Birth Anniv. of St. Francis of Assisi.

1083. 903. 1 r. brown 20 30

904. Karl Marx and "Das Kapital".

1983. Death Centenary of Karl Marx.

1084. 904. 1 r. brown 20 30

905. Darwin and Map of Voyage.

1983. Death Centenary of Charles Darwin.

1085. 905. 2 r. multicoloured .. 75 1·25

906. Swamp Deer.

1983. 50th Anniv. of Kanha National Park.

1086. 906. 1 r. multicoloured .. 30 40

907. Globe and Satellite.

1983. World Communications Year.

1087. 907. 1 r. multicoloured .. 30 40

908. Simon Bolivar.

1983. Birth Bicentenary of Simon Bolivar (South American statesman).

1088. **908.** 2 r. multicoloured .. 50 1·00

909. Meera Behn.

1983. India's Struggle for Freedom (1st series).

1089. 50 p. red and green .. 30 65
1090. 50 p. brown, green & red 30 65
1091. 50 p. multicoloured .. 30 45
1092. 50 p. brown, green & red 10 15
1093. 50 p. brn., grn. & orge... 10 15
1094. 50 p. grn., yell. & orge. 10 15

DESIGNS—VERT. No. 1089, Type **909.** 1090, Mahadev Desai 1092, Hemu Kalani (revolutionary). 1093, Acharya Vinoba Bhave (social reformer). 1094, Surendranath Banerjee (political reformer). HORIZ. (43 × 31 mm.). No. 1091, Quit India Resolution.

See also Nos. 1119/24, 1144/9, 1191/4, 1230/5, 1287/96 and 1345/9.

910. Ram Nath Chopra.

1983. Ram Nath Chopra (pharmacologist). Commemoration.

1095. **910.** 50 p. red 25 50

911. Nanda Devi Mountain.

1983. 25th Anniv. of Indian Mountaineering Federation.

1096. **911.** 2 r. multicoloured .. 50 70

912. Great Indian Hornbill.

1983. Centenary of Natural History Society, Bombay.

1097. **912.** 1 r. multicoloured .. 45 35

913. View of Garden.

1983. Rock Garden, Chandigarh.

1098. **913.** 1 r. multicoloured .. 30 30

914. Golden Langur.

1983. Indian Wildlife. Monkeys. Mult.

1099. 1 r. Type **914** 25 20
1100. 2 r. Lion-tailed Macaque 45 65

915. Ghats of Varanasi.

1983. Fifth General Assembly of World Tourism Organization.

1101. **915.** 2 r. multicoloured .. 30 30

916. Krishna Kanta Handique.

1983. Krishna Kanta Handique (scholar).

1102. **916.** 50 p. blue 20 30

918. Woman and Child (From "Festival" by Kashyap Premsawala).

1983. Children's Day.

1103. **918.** 50 p. multicoloured.. 20 30

920. "Udan Khatola", First Indian Hot Air Balloon.

1983. Bicentenary of Manned Flight.

1104. 1 r. Type **920** 20 20
1105. 2 r. Montgolfier balloon.. 30 35

921. Tiger.

1983. Ten Years of Project Tiger.

1106. **921.** 2 r. multicoloured .. 70 1·00

922. Commonwealth Logo.

1983. Commonwealth Heads of Government Meeting, New Delhi. Multicoloured.

1107. 1 r. Type **922** 10 15
1108. 2 r. Goanese couple, early 19th century 25 30

923. "Pratiksha".

1983. Birth Centenary of Nanda Lal Bose (artist).

1109. **923.** 1 r. multicoloured .. 20 20

925. Lancer.

1984. Bicentenary of 7th Light Calvary.

1110. **925.** 1 r. multicoloured .. 1·25 40

926. Troopers in Ceremonial Uniform and Tank.

1984. The Deccan Horse Calvary Regiment (1790–1984).

1111. **926.** 1 r. multicoloured .. 1·25 65

927. Society Building and Sir William Jones (founder).

1984. Bicentenary of Asiatic Society.

1112. **927.** 1 r. green and purple 30 40

928. Insurance Logo.

1984. Centenary of Postal Life Insurance.

1113. **928.** 1 r. multicoloured .. 30 30

929. "Sea Harrier" Aircraft.

1984. President's Review of the Fleet. Mult.

1114. 1 r. Type **929** 20 40
1115. 1 r. I.N.S. "Vikrant" (aircraft carrier) .. 20 40
1116. 1 r. I.N.S. "Vela" (submarine) 20 40
1117. 1 r. Destroyer 20 40

Nos. 1114/7 were printed in se-tenant blocks of four within the sheet, forming a composite design.

930. I.L.A. Logo and Hemispheres.

1984. 12th International Leprosy Congress.

1118. **930.** 1 r. multicoloured .. 30 30

1984. India's Struggle for Freedom (2nd series). As T **909.**

1119. 50 p. grn., lt. grn. & orge. 15 20
1120. 50 p. brn., grn. & orge... 15 20
1121. 50 p. multicoloured .. 15 20
1122. 50 p. multicoloured .. 15 20
1123. 50 p. multicoloured .. 15 20
1124. 50 p. multicoloured .. 15 20

DESIGNS: No. 1119, Vasudeo Balvant Phadke (revolutionary). 1120, Baba Kanshi Ram (revolutionary). 1121, Tatya Tope. 1122, Nana Sahib. 1123, Begum Hazarat Mahal. 1124, Mangal Pandey.

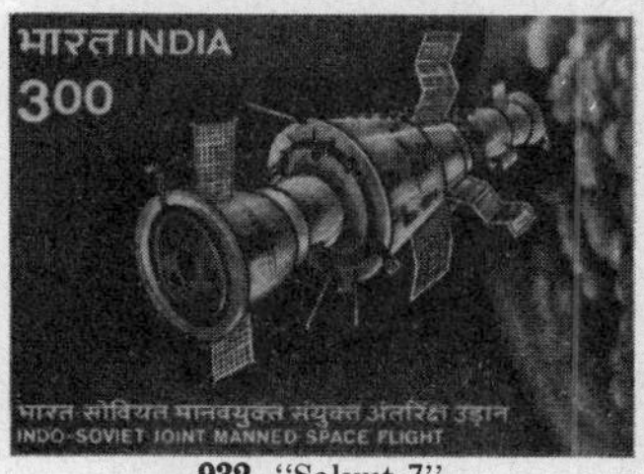

932. "Salyut 7".

1984. Indo-Soviet Manned Space Flight.

1125. **932.** 3 r. multicoloured .. 45 45

935. G. D. Birla.

1984. 90th Birth Anniv. of G. D. Birla (industrialist).

1126. **935.** 50 p. brown 20 50

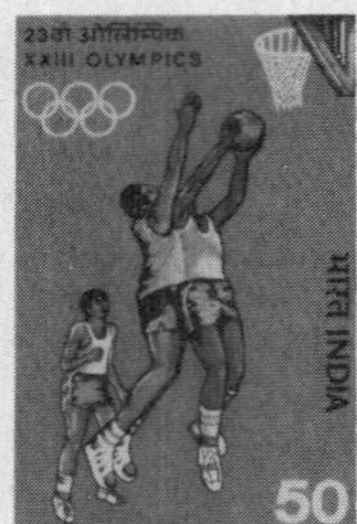

936. Basketball.

1984. Olympic Games, Los Angeles. Multicoloured.

1127.	50 p. Type **936**	15	15
1128.	1 r. High jumping ..	20	20
1129.	2 r. Gymnastics (horiz.)	40	60
1130.	2 r. 50 Weightlifting (horiz.)	50	80

937. Gwalior.

1984. Forts. Multicoloured.

1131.	50 p. Type **937**	35	25
1132.	1 r. Vellore (vert.) ..	40	25
1133.	1 r. 50 Simhagad (vert.)	60	75
1134.	2 r. Jodphur	80	1·25

938. B. V. Paradkar and Newspaper.

1984. B. V. Paradkar (journalist) Commemoration.

1135. **938.** 50 p. brown 20 30

939. Dr. D. N. Wadia and Institute of Himalayan Geology, Dehradun.

1984. Birth Centenary (1983) of Dr. D. N. Wadia (geologist).

1136. **939.** 1 r. multicoloured .. 30 30

940. "Herdsman and Cattle in Forest".

1984. Children's Day.

1137. **940.** 50 p. multicoloured 30 45

941. Indira Gandhi (Illustration reduced, actual size 51 × 51 mm.).

1984. Indira Gandhi (Prime Minister) Commemoration (1st issue).

1138. **941.** 50 p. black, violet and orange .. 50 50

See also Nos. 1151, 1167 and 1170.

942. Congress and Emblem.

1984. 12th World Mining Congress, New Delhi.

1139. **942.** 1 r. black and yellow 30 30

943. Dr. Rajendra Prasad at Desk.

1984. Birth Centenary of Dr. Rajendra Prasad (former President).

1140. **943.** 50 p. multicoloured 35 35

944. Mrinalini (rose)

1984. Roses. Multicoloured.

1141.	1 r. 50, Type **944** ..	60	60
1142.	2 r. Sugandha	80	80

945. "Fergusson College" (Gopal Deuskar).

1985. Centenary of Fergusson College, Pune.

1143. **945.** 1 r. multicoloured .. 30 30

1985. India's Struggle for Freedom (3rd series). As T **909**.

1144.	50 p. brn., grn. & orge. ..	25	30
1145.	50 p. brn., grn. & orge. ..	25	30
1146.	50 p. brn., grn. & orge. ..	25	30
1147.	50 p. brn., grn. & orge. ..	25	30
1148.	50 p. bl., grn. & orge. ..	25	30
1149.	50 p. blk., grn. & orge. ..	25	30

DESIGNS:—VERT. No. 1144, Narhar Vishnu Gadgil (politician). 1145, Jairamdas Doulatram (journalist). 1147, Kakasaheb Kalelkar (author). 1148, Master Tara Singh (politician). 1149, Ravishankar Maharaj (politician). HORIZ. No. 1146, Jatindra and Nellie Sengupta (politicians).

947. Gunner and Howitzer from Mountain Battery.

1985. 50th Anniv. of Regiment of Artillery.

1150. **947.** 1 r. multicoloured .. 1·50 1·00

948. Indira Gandhi making Speech.

1985. Indira Gandhi Commemoration (2nd issue).

1151. **948.** 2 r. multicoloured .. 90 1·25

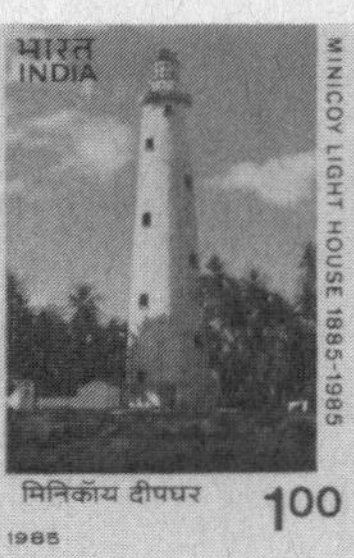

949. Minicoy Lighthouse.

1985. Centenary of Minicoy Lighthouse.

1152. **949.** 1 r. multicoloured .. 1·25 40

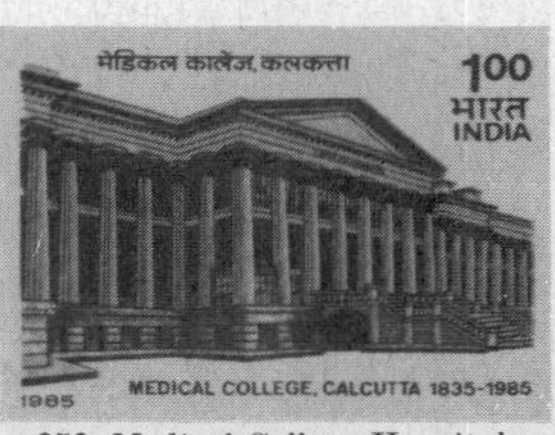

950. Medical College Hospital.

1985. 150th Anniv. of Medical College, Calcutta.

1153. **950.** 1 r. yellow, brown and purple .. 50 30

951. Medical College, Madras.

1985. 150th Anniv. of Medical College, Madras.

1154. **951.** 1 r. light brown and brown 60 30

952. Riflemen of 1835 and 1985, and Map of North-East India.

1985. 150th Anniv. of Assam Rifles.

1155. **952.** 1 r. multicoloured .. 1·25 75

953. Potato Plant.

1985. 50th Anniv. of Potato Research in India.

1156. **953.** 50 p. deep brown and brown 50 50

954. Baba Jassa Singh Ahluwalia.

1985. Death Bicentenary (1983) of Baba Jassa Singh Ahluwalia (Sikh leader).

1157. **954.** 50 p. purple 45 50

955. St. Xavier's College.

1985. 125th Anniv. of St. Xavier's College, Calcutta.

1158. **955.** 1 r. multicoloured .. 30 40

956. White-winged Wood Duck.

1985. Wildlife Conservation. White-winged Wood Duck.
1159. **956.** 2 r. multicoloured .. 2·25 2·00

957. "Mahara".

1985. Bougainvillea. Multicoloured.
1160. 50 p. Type **957** 30 30
1161. 1 r. "H. B. Singh" .. 40 40

958. Yaudheya Copper Coin, *c* 200 B.C.

1985. Festival of India (1st issue).
1162. **958.** 2 r. multicoloured .. 75 75

959. Statue of Didarganj Yakshi (deity).

1985. Festival of India (2nd issue).
1163. **959.** 1 r. multicoloured .. 30 30

962. Swami Haridas.

1985. Swami Haridas (philosopher) Commemoration.
1164. **962.** 1 r. multicoloured .. 60 50

963. Stylised Mountain Road.

1985. 25th Anniv. of Border Roads Organization.
1165. **963.** 2 r. red, violet and black 60 60

964. Nehru addressing General Assembly.

1985. 40th Anniv. of United Nations Organization.
1166. **964.** 2 r. multicoloured .. 40 40

965. Indira Gandhi with Crowd.

1985. Indira Gandhi Commemoration (3rd issue).
1167. **965.** 2 r. brown-black and black .. .. 80 1·00

966. Girl using Home Computer.

1985. Children's Day.
1168. **966.** 50 p. multicoloured 30 40

967. Halley's Comet.

1985. 19th General Assembly of International Astronomical Union, New Delhi.
1169. **967.** 1 r. multicoloured .. 40 50

968. Indira Gandhi.

1985. Indira Gandhi Commemoration (4th issue).
1170. **968.** 3 r. multicoloured .. 1·25 1·25

969. St. Stephen's Hospital.

1985. Centenary of St. Stephen's Hospital, Delhi.
1171. **969.** 1 r. black and brown 30 30

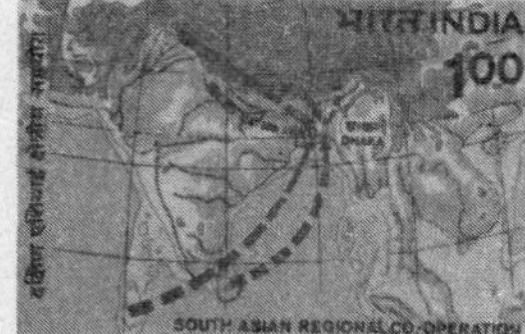

971. Map showing Member States.

1985. 1st Summit Meeting of South Asian Association for Regional Co-operation, Dhaka, Bangladesh. Multicoloured.
1172. 1 r. Type **971** 40 20
1173. 3 r. Flags of member nations (44 × 32 mm.) .. 1·25 1·40

972. Shyama Shastri.

1985. Shyama Shastri (composer) Commemoration.
1174. **972.** 1 r. multicoloured .. 75 40

975. Young Runners and Emblem.

1985. International Youth Year.
1175. **975.** 2 r. multicoloured .. 40 40

976. Handel and Bach. (Illustration reduced, actual size 55 × 35 mm.).

1985. 300th Birth Annivs. of George Frederick Handel and Johann Sebastian Bach (composers).
1176. **976.** 5 r. multicoloured .. 1·50 90

977. A. O. Hume (founder) and Early Congress Presidents.

1985. Centenary of Indian National Congress. Designs showing miniature portraits of Congress Presidents.
1177. **977.** 1 r. black, orange, green and grey .. 40 40
1178. – 1 r. black, orange and green 40 40
1179. – 1 r. black, orange and green 40 40
1180. – 1 r. black, orange, green and grey .. 40 40

Nos. 1178/80 each show sixteen miniature portraits. The individual stamps can be distinguished by the position of the face value and inscription which are at the top on Nos. 1177/8 and at the foot on Nos. 1179/80. No. 1180 shows a portrait of Prime Minister Rajiv Gandhi in a grey frame at bottom right.

978. Bombay and Duncan Dry Docks, Bombay.

1986. 250th Anniv. of Naval Dockyard, Bombay.
1181. **978.** 2 r. 50 multicoloured 1·50 1·50

979. Hawa Mahal and Jaipur 1904 2 a. Stamp.

1986. "INPEX 86" Philatelic Exhibition, Jaipur. Multicoloured.
1182. 50 p. Type **979** 50 30
1183. 2 r. Mobile camel post office, Thar Desert .. 90 1·10

980. I.N.S. "Vikrant" (aircraft carrier).

1986. Completion of 25 Years Service by I.N.S. "Vikrant".
1184. **980.** 2 r. multicoloured .. 1·75 1·75

981. Humber-Sommer Biplane and Later Mail Planes.

1986. 75th Anniversary of First Official Airmail Flight, Allahabad—Naini. Mult.

1185. 50 p. Type **981** 75 50
1186. 3 r. Modern Air India mail plane and Humber-Sommer biplane (37 × 24 mm) .. 2·00 2·50

982. Triennale Emblem.

1986. 6th Triennale Art Exhibition, New Delhi.

1187. **982.** 1 r. pur., yell. & blk. 60 40

983. Chaitanya Mahaprabhu.

1986. 500th Birth Anniv. of Chaitanya Mahaprabhu (religious leader).

1188. **983.** 2 r. multicoloured .. 1·50 1·75

984. Main Building, Mayo College.

1986. Mayo College (public school), Ajmer, Commemoration.

1189. **984.** 1 r. multicoloured .. 65 40

985. Two Footballers.

1986. World Cup Football Championship, Mexico.

1190. **985.** 5 r. multicoloured .. 2·00 2·00

1986. India's Struggle for Freedom (4th series). As T **909.**

1191. 50 p. brown, grn. & red 50 50
1192. 50 p. brown, grn. & red 50 50
1193. 50 p. black, grn. & orge. 50 50
1194. 50 p. brown, grn. & red 50 50

DESIGNS: No. 1191, Bhim Sen Sachar. 1192, Alluri Seetarama Raju. 1193, Sagarmal Gopa. 1194, Veer Surendra Sai.

987. Swami Sivananda.

1986. Swami Sivananda (spiritual leader) Birth Centenary.

1195. **987.** 2 r. multicoloured .. 1·75 1·25

988. Volleyball.

1986. Asian Games, Seoul, South Korea. Multicoloured.

1196. 1 r. 50 Type **988** .. .. 1·00 75
1197. 3 r. Hurdling .. .. 1·75 2·00

989. Madras G.P.O.

1986. Bicentenary of Madras G.P.O.

1198. **989.** 5 r. black and red .. 2·50 2·75

990. Parachutist.

1986. 225th Anniv. of 8th Battalion of Coast Sepoys (now 1st Battalion Parachute Regiment).

1199. **990.** 3 r. multicoloured .. 2·50 3·00

991. Early and Modern Policemen.

1986. 125th Anniv. of Indian Police. Designs showing early and modern police.

1200. **991.** 1 r. 50 multicoloured 1·50 2·00
1201. – 2 r. multicoloured .. 1·50 2·00

Nos. 1200/1 were printed together, se-tenant, forming a composite design.

992. Hand holding Flower and World Map.

1986. International Peace Year.

1202. **992.** 5 r. multicoloured .. 1·25 85

993. "Girl Rock Climber" (Sujasha Dasgupta).

1986. Children's Day.

1203. **993.** 50 p. multicoloured 1·00 75

994. Windmill.

1986. Science and Technology.

1211 – 35 p. red 10 10
1212 – 40 p. red 10 10
1213 – 60 p. green and red .. 10 10
1214 – 75 p. orange 10 10
1217 – 5 r. brown and orange 20 25
1218 – 20 r. brown and blue 80 85
1219 **994** 50 r. black, blue & red 2·00 2·10

DESIGNS—HORIZ. (20 × 17 mm). 35 p. Family planning. (37 × 20 mm). 60 p. Indian family (as T **994**) 20 r. Bio gas. VERT. (17 × 20 mm). 40 p. Television set, dish aerial and transmitter (as T **994**). 75 p. "Family" (as No. 927). 5 r. Solar energy.

995. Growth Monitoring.

1986. 40th Anniv. of U.N.I.C.E.F. Mult.

1221. 50 p. Type **995** 75 60
1222. 5 r. Immunization .. 2·25 2·50

996. Tansen.

1986. Tansen (musician and composer) Commemoration.

1223. **996.** 1 r. multicoloured .. 1·00 30

997. Indian Elephant.

1986. 50th Anniv. of Corbett National Park. Multicoloured.

1224. 1 r. Type **997** .. .. 1·75 70
1225. 2 r. Gharial .. .. 2·50 3·00

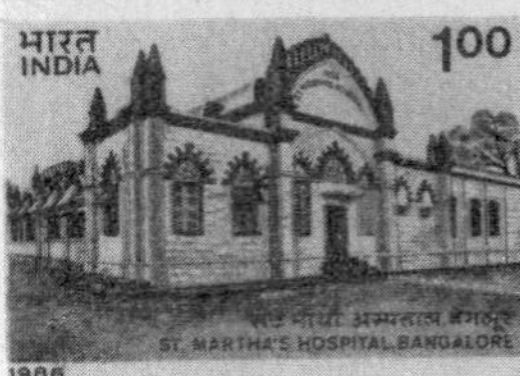

998. St. Martha's Hospital.

1986. Centenary of St. Martha's Hospital, Bangalore.

1226. **998.** 1 r. bl., orge. & blk. 1·00 70

999. Yacht "Trishna" and Route Map.

1987. Indian Army Round the World Yacht Voyage, 1985–7.

1227. **999.** 6 r. 50 multicoloured 2·50 1·75

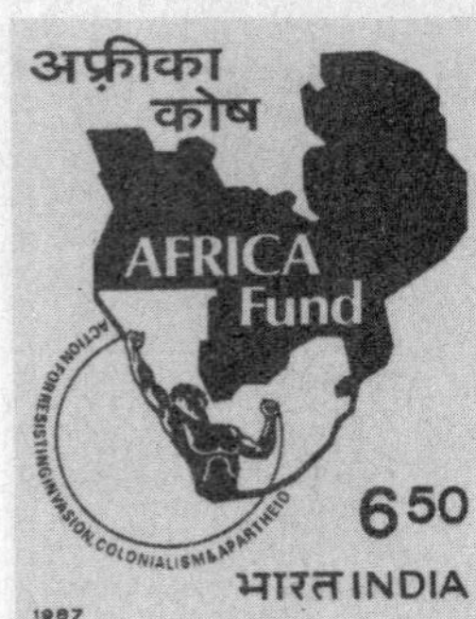

1000. Map of Southern Africa and Logo.

1987. Inauguration of AFRICA Fund.

1228. **1000.** 6 r. 50 black .. 2·50 2·25

1001. Emblem.

1987. 29th Congress of International Chamber of Commerce, New Delhi.

1229. **1001.** 5 r. violet, bl. & red 2·25 1·25

1987. India's Struggle for Freedom (5th series). As T **909.**

1230. 60 p. brown, grn. & orge. 20 20
1231. 60 p. violet, grn. & red 20 20
1232. 60 p. brown, grn. & red 20 20
1233. 60 p. blue, grn. & orge. 20 20
1234. 60 p. brown, grn. & red 20 20
1235. 60 p. brown, grn. & red 20 20
1236. 60 p. red, green & orge. 20 20

DESIGNS: No. 1230, Hakim Aimal Khan. No. 1231, Lala Har Dayal. No. 1232, M.N. Roy. No. 1233, Tripuraneni Ramaswamy Chowdary. No. 1234, Dr. Kailas Math Katyu. No. 1235, S. Satyamarti. No. 1236, Pandit Hriday Nath Kunzru.

MINIMUM PRICE

The minimum price quoted is 10p which represents a handling charge rather than a basis for valuing common stamps. For further notes about prices see introductory pages.

1002. Blast Furnace.

1987. Centenary of South Eastern Railway. Multicoloured.

1237. 1 r. Type **1002**. 40 15
1238. 1 r. 50 Metre-gauge tank locomotive, No. 691, 1887 (horiz.) 45 35
1239. 2 r. Electric train on viaduct, 1987 . . . . 55 50
1240. 4 r. Steam locomotive, c. 1900 (horiz.) . . 80 1·00

1003. Kalia Bhomora Bridge, Tezpur, Assam.

1987. Inauguration of Brahmaputra Bridge.

1241. **1003.** 2 r. multicoloured . . 30 30

1004. Madras Christian College.

1987. 150th Anniv. of Madras Christian College.

1242. **1004.** 1 r. 50 black and red 20 20

1005. Shree Shree Ma Anandamayee.

1987. Shree Shree Ma Anandamayee (Hindu spiritual leader) Commemoration.

1243. **1005.** 1 r. brown 20 15

1006. "Rabindranath Tagore" (self-portrait).

1987. Rabindranath Tagore (poet) Commem.

1244. **1006.** 2 r. multicoloured . . 30 30

1007. Garwhal Rifles Uniforms of 1887.

1987. Centenary of Garwhal Rifles Regiment.

1245. **1007.** 1 r. multicoloured . . 40 15

1008. J. Krishnamurti.

1987. J. Krishnamurti (philosopher) Commemoration.

1246. **1008.** 60 p. brown . . 40 55

1009. Regimental Uniforms of 1887.

1987. Centenary of 37th Dogra Regt (now 7th Battalion (1 Dogra), Mechanised Infantry Regt.

1247. **1009.** 1 r. multicoloured . . 40 15

1010. Hall of Nations, Pragati Maidan, New Delhi.

1987. "India-89" International Stamp Exhibition, New Delhi (1st issue). Multicoloured.

1248. 50 p. Exhibition logo . . 10 15
1249. 5 r. Type **1010** 45 50

See also Nos. 1264/7, 1333/4, 1341/2 and 1358/61.

1011. "Sadyah-Snata" Sculpture, Sanghol.

1987. Festival of India, U.S.S.R.

1251. **1011.** 6 r. 50 multicoloured 1·00 75

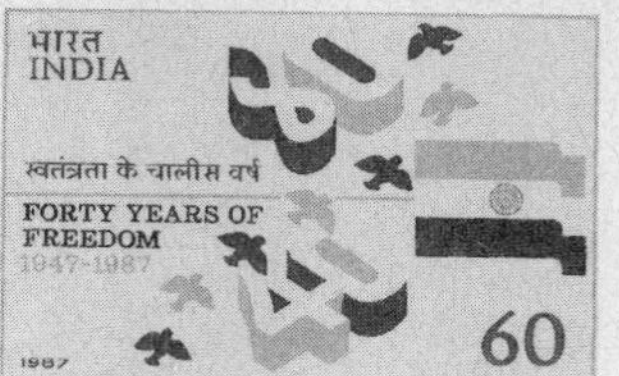

1012. Flag and Stylized Birds with "40" in English and Hindi. (Illustration reduced. Actual size 54 × 35 mm).

1987. 40th Anniv. of Independence.

1252. **1012.** 60 p. orge, grn. & bl. 15 15

1013. Sant Harchand Singh Longowal.

1987. Sant Harchand Singh Longowal (Sikh leader). Commemoration.

1253. **1013.** 1 r. multicoloured . . 30 15

1014. Guru Ghasidas.

1987. Guru Ghasidas (Hindu leader) Commemoration.

1254. **1014.** 60 p. red 15 15

1015. Thakur Anukul Chandra.

1987. Thakur Anukul Chandra (spiritual leader) Commemoration.

1255. **1015.** 1 r. multicoloured . . 40 15

1016. University of Allahabad.

1987. Centenary of Allahabad University.

1256. **1016.** 2 r. multicoloured . . 30 40

INDEX

Countries can be quickly located by referring to the index at the end of this volume.

1017. Pankha Offering.

1987. Phoolwalon Ki Sair Festival, Delhi.

1257. **1017.** 2 r. multicoloured . . 30 40

1018. Chhatrasal on Horseback.

1987. Chhatrasal (Bundela ruler) Commemoration.

1258. **1018.** 60 p. brown . . 30 20

1019. Family and Stylised Houses.

1987. International Year of Shelter for the Homeless.

1259. **1019.** 5 r. multicoloured . . 45 60

1020. Map of Asia and Logo.

1987. Asia Regional Conference of Rotary International.

1260. **1020.** 60 p. brn. & grn. . . 15 15
1261. – 6 r. 50 multicoloured 60 80

DESIGN: 6 r. 50, Oral polio vaccination.

1021. Blind Boy, Braille Books and Computer.

1987. Centenary of Service to Blind.

1262. **1021.** 1 r. multicoloured . . 15 15
1263. – 2 r. dp. bl. & bl. . . 35 30

DESIGN: 2 r. Eye donation.

1022. Iron Pillar, Delhi.

1987. "India-89" International Stamp Exhibition, New Delhi (2nd issue). Delhi Landmarks. Multicoloured.

1264	60 p. Type **1022** ..	10	15
1265	1 r. 50 India Gate ..	15	20
1266	5 r. Dewan-e-Khas, Red Fort	45	50
1267	6 r. 50 Old Fort	60	65

1023. Tyagmurti Goswami Ganeshdutt.

1987. Tyagmurti Goswami Ganeshdutt (spiritual leader and social reformer). Commemoration.

1269.	**1023.**	60 p. red	15	15

1024. "My Home" (Siddharth Deshprabha).

1987. Children's Day.

1270.	**1024.**	60 p. multicoloured	30	15

1025. Chinar.

1987. Indian Trees. Multicoloured.

1271.	**1025.**	60 p. multicoloured	15	15
1272.	–	1 r. 50 multicoloured	20	20
1273.	–	5 r. black, green and brown	55	65
1274.	–	6 r. 50 brown, red and green ..	70	80

DESIGNS:—HORIZ. 1 r. 50, Pipal. 6 r. 50, Banyan. VERT. 5 r. Sal.

1026. Logo (from sculpture "The Worker and the Woman Peasant" by V. Mukhina).

1987. Festival of U.S.S.R., India.

1275	**1026**	5 r. multicoloured ..	50	50

1027. White Tiger.

1987. Wildlife. Multicoloured.

1276.	1 r. type **1027**	30	15
1277.	5 r. Snow leopard (horiz.)	70	85

1028. Execution of Veer Narayan Singh.

1987. Veer Narayan Singh (patriot) Commemoration.

1278.	**1028.**	60 p. brown ..	15	15

1029. Rameshwari Nehru.

1987. Rameshwari Nehru (women's rights campaigner) Commemoration.

1279.	**1029.**	60 p. brown ..	15	15

1030. Father Kuriakose Elias Chavara.

1987. Father Kuriakose Elias Chavara (founder of Carmelites of Mary Immaculate) Commemoration.

1280.	**1030.**	60 p. brown ..	15	15

1031. Dr. Rajah Sir Muthiah Chettiar.

1987. Dr Rajah Sir Muthiah Chettiar (politician) Commemoration.

1281.	**1031.**	60 p. grey	15	15

1032. Golden Temple, Amritsar.

1987. 400th Anniv. of Golden Temple, Amritsar.

1282.	**1032.**	60 p. multicoloured	30	15

1033. Rukmini Devi and Dancer.

1987. Rukmini Devi (Bharatanatyam dance pioneer). Commemoration.

1283.	**1033.**	60 p. red	30	15

1034. Dr. Hiralal.

1987. Dr. Hiralal (historian) Commemoration.

1284.	**1034.**	60 p. blue	15	15

1035 Light Frequency Experiment and Bodhi Tree

1988. 75th Session of Indian Science Congress Association.

1285	**1035**	4 r. multicoloured ..	50	60

1036 Rural Patient

1988. 13th Asian Pacific Dental Congress.

1286	**1036**	4 r. multicoloured ..	50	50

1988. India's Struggle for Freedom (6th series). As T **909**.

1287	60 p. black, green & orge	15	15
1288	60 p. brown, green & orge	15	15
1289	60 p. red, green and orge	15	15
1290	60 p. purple, green & orge	15	15
1291	60 p. purple, green & red	15	15
1292	60 p. black, green & orge	15	15
1293	60 p. lilac, green and red	15	15
1294	60 p. dp green, grn & red	15	15
1295	60 p. brown, green & grn	15	15
1296	60 p mauve, green & orge	20	15

DESIGNS: No. 1287, Mohan Lal Sukhadia; No. 1288, Dr. S. K. Sinha; No. 1289, Chandra Shekhar Azad; No. 1290, G. B. Pant; No. 1291, Dr. Anugrah Narain Singh; No. 1292, Kuladhor Chaliha; No. 1293, Shivprasad Gupta; No. 1294, Sarat Chandra Bose; No. 1295, Baba Kharak Singh; 1296, Sheikh Mohammad Abdullah;

1037 U Tirot Singh

1988. U Tirot Singh (Khasis leader) Commem.

1297	**1037**	60 p. brown	15	15

1038 Early and Modern Regimental Uniforms

1988. Bicentenary of 4th Battalion of the Kumaon Regiment.

1298	**1038**	1 r. multicoloured ..	30	15

1039 Balgandharva

1988. Birth Cent of Balgandharva (actor).

1299	**1039**	60 p. brown	20	15

1040 Soldiers and Infantry Combat Vehicle

1988. Presentation of Colours to Mechanised Infantry Regiment.

1300	**1040**	1 r. multicoloured ..	35	15

1041 B. N. Rau

1988. B. N. Rau (constitutional lawyer) Commemoration.

1301	**1041**	60 p. black	15	15

1042 Mohindra Government College

1988. Mohindra Government College, Patiala.
1302 **1042** 1 r. mauve 15 15

1043 Dr. D. V. Gundappa

1988. Dr. D. V. Gundappa (scholar) Commem.
1303 **1043** 60 p. grey 15 15

1044 Rani Avantibai

1988. Rani Avantibai of Ramgarh Commem.
1304 **1044** 60 p. mauve .. 15 15

1045 "Malayala Manorama" Office, Kottayam

1988. Centenary of "Malayala Manorama" (newspaper).
1305 **1045** 1 r. black and blue .. 15 15

1046 Maharshi Dadhichi

1988. Maharshi Dadhichi (Hindu saint) Commemoraton.
1306 **1046** 60 p. red 15 15

1047 Mohammad Iqbal

1988. 50th Death Anniv of Mohammad Iqbal (poet)
1307 **1047** 60 p. gold and red .. 15 15

1048 Samarth Ramdas

1988. Samarth Ramdas (Hindu spiritual leader) Commemoration.
1308 **1048** 60 p. green .. 15 15

1049 Swati Tirunal Rama Varma

1988. 175th Birth Anniv of Swati Tirunal Rama Varma (composer).
1309 **1049** 60 p. mauve .. 20 15

1050 Bhaurao Patil and Class

1988. Bhaurao Patil (educationist) Commem.
1310 **1050** 60 p. brown 15 15

1051 "Rani Lakshmi Bai" (M. F. Husain)
(Illustration reduced, actual size 54 × 39 mm)

1988. Martyrs from 1st War of Independence.
1311 **1051** 60 p. multicoloured .. 15 15

1052 Broad Peak

1988. Himalayan Peaks.

1312	**1052**	1 r.50 lilac, violet and blue ..	25	25
1313	–	4 r. multicoloured	50	50
1314	–	5 r. multicoloured	60	60
1315	–	6 r.50 multicoloured	70	70

DESIGNS: 4 r. K 2 (Godwin Austen); 5 r. Kanchenjunga; 6 r.50, Nanda Devi.

1053 Child with Grandparents

1988. "Love and Care for Elders".
1316 **1053** 60 p. multicoloured .. 15 15

1054 Victoria Terminus, Bombay

1988. Centenary of Victoria Terminus Station, Bombay.
1317 **1054** 1 r. multicoloured .. 20 15

1055 Lawrence School, Lovedale

1988. 130th Anniv of Lawrence School, Lovedale.
1318 **1055** 1 r. brown and green 20 15

1056 Khejri Tree

1988. World Environment Day.
1319 **1056** 60 p. multicoloured .. 20 15

1988. As No. 732, but new face value.
1320 60 p. black (Gandhi) .. 10 10

1057 Rani Durgawati

1988. Rani Durgawati (Gondwana ruler) Commemoration.
1322 **1057** 60 p. red 15 15

1058 Acharya Shanti Dev

1988. Acharya Shanti Dev (Buddhist scholar) Commemoration.
1323 **1058** 60 p. brown .. 15 15

1059 Y. S. Parmar

1988. Dr. Yashwant Singh Parmar (former Chief Minister of Himachal Pradesh) Commemoration.
1324 **1059** 60 p. violet .. 15 15

1060 Arm pointing at Proclamation in Marathi
(Illustration reduced, actual size 53 × 38mm)

1988. 40th Anniv of Independence. Bal Gangadhar Tilak (patriot) Commem. Mult.
1325 60 p. Type **1060** 15 15
1326 60 p. Battle scene .. 15 15
Nos. 1325/6 were printed together, se-tenant, forming a composite design showing a painting by M. F. Husain.

1061 Durgadas Rathore

1988. 150th Birth Anniv of Durgadas Rathore (Regent of Marwar).
1327 **1061** 60 p. brown 15 15

1062 Gopinath Kaviraj

1988. Gopinath Kaviraj (scholar) Commem.
1328 **1062** 60 p. brown 15 15

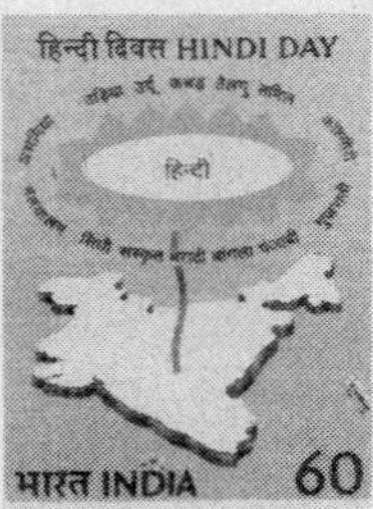

1063 Lotus and Outline Map of India

1988. Hindi Day.
1329 **1063** 60 p. red, green & brn 15 15

1064 Indian Olympic Association Logo

1988. "Sports-1988" and Olympic Games, Seoul.
1330 **1064** 60 p. purple .. 15 15
1331 – 5 r. multicoloured 40 45
DESIGN—HORIZ. 5 r. Various sports.

1065 Jerdon's Courser

1988. Wildlife Conservation. Jerdon's Courser.
1332 **1065** 1 r. multicoloured .. 50 20

1988. "India-89" International Stamp Exhibition, New Delhi (3rd issue). General Post Offices. As T **1022**. Multicoloured.
1333 4 r. Bangalore G.P.O. .. 40 35
1334 5 r. Bombay G.P.O. .. 50 45

1066 "Times of India" Front Page

1988. 150th Anniv of "The Times of India".
1335 **1066** 1 r.50 blk, gold & yell 15 15

1067 "Maulana Abul Kalam Azad" (K. Hebbar)

1988. Birth Centenary of Maulana Abul Kalam Azad (politician).
1336 **1067** 60 p. multicoloured .. 15 15

1068 Nehru
(Illustration reduced, actual size (54 × 39mm)

1988. Centenary (1989) of Jawaharlal Nehru (1st issue).
1337 **1068** 60 p. black, orange and green 20 15
1338 – 1 r. multicoloured 25 15
DESIGN—VERT. 1 r. "Jawaharlal Nehru" (Svetoslav Roerich).
See also NO. 1393.

1069 Birsa Munda

1988. Birsa Munda (Munda leader). Commem.
1339 **1069** 60 p. brown 15 15

1070 Bhakra Dam

1988. 25th Anniv of Dedication of Bhakra Dam.
1340 **1070** 60 p. red 35 40

1071 Dead Letter Office Cancellations of 1886

1988. "India-89" International Stamp Exhibition, New Delhi (4th issue). Postal Cancellations.
1341 **1071** 60 p. brn, blk & red 25 15
1342 – 6 r.50 brown & blk 1·00 1·00
DESIGN: 6 r.50, Travelling post office handstamp of 1864.

1072 K. M. Munshi

1988. Birth Centenary (1987) of K. M. Munshi (author and politician).
1343 **1072** 60 p. green .. 15 15

HAVE YOU READ THE NOTES AT THE BEGINNING OF THIS CATALOGUE?
These often provide answers to the enquiries we receive.

1073 Mannathu Padmanabhan

1989. Mannathu Padmanabhan (social reformer) Commemoration.
1344 **1073** 60 p. brown .. 15 15

1989. India's Struggle for Freedom (7th series). As T **909**.
1345 60 p. black, green & orge 20 20
1346 60 p. orange, green & lilac 20 20
1347 60 p. black, green & orge 20 20
1348 60 p. brown, green & orge 20 20
1349 60 p. brown, green & orge 20 20
DESIGNS:—No. 1345, Hare Krushna Mahtab; No. 1346, Balasaheb Gangadhar Kher; No. 1347, Raj kumari Amrit Kaur; No. 1348, Saifuddin Kitchlew; No. 1349, Asaf Ali.

1074 Lok Sabha Secretariat

1989. 60th Anniv of Lok Sabha Secretariat (formerly Legislative Assembly Department).
1355 **1074** 60 p. green 15 15

1075 Goddess Durga seated on Lion (5th-cent terracotta plaque)

1989. 125th Anniv of Lucknow Museum.
1356 **1075** 60 p. deep blue & blue 15 15

1076 Baldev Ramji Mirdha

1989. Birth Centenary of Baldev Ramji Mirdha (nationalist).
1357 **1076** 60 p. green 15 15

1077 Girl with Stamp Collection

1989. "India-89" International Stamp Exhibition, New Delhi (5th issue). Philately.
1358 **1077** 60 p. yell, red & bl 15 10
1359 – 1 r.50 grey, yellow and black .. 20 15
1360 – 5 r. red and blue .. 60 50
1361 – 6 r.50 blk, brn & bl 70 60
DESIGNS: 1 r.50, Dawk gharry, c. 1842; 5 r. Travancore 1888 2 ch. conch shell stamp; 6 r.50, Early Indian philatelic magazines.

1078 St. John Bosco and Boy

1989. St. John Bosco (founder of Salesian Brothers) Commemoration.
1362 **1078** 60 p. red 15 15

1079 Modern Tank and 19th-century Sowar

1989. 3rd Cavalry Regiment.
1363 **1079** 60 p. multicoloured .. 30 15

1080 Dargah Sharif, Ajmer

1989. Dargah Sharif (Sufi shrine), Ajmer.
1364 **1080** 1 r. multicoloured .. 20 20

1081 Task Force and Indian Naval Ensign

1989. President's Review of the Fleet.
1365 **1081** 6 r.50 multicoloured 1·25 1·00

1082 Shaheed Laxman Nayak and Barbed Wire Fence

1989. Shaheed Laxman Nayak Commem.
1366 **1082** 60 p. brn, grn & orge 15 15

1083 Rao Gopal Singh

1989. Rao Gopal Singh Commemoration.
1367 **1083** 60 p. brown 15 15

1084 Sydenham College

1989. 75th Anniv (1988) of Sydenham College, Bombay.
1368 **1084** 60 p. black 30 15

1085 Bishnu Ram Medhi

1989. Birth Centenary (1988) of Bishnu Ram Medhi (politician).
1369 **1085** 60 p. green, deep green and red .. 30 15

1086 Dr. N. S. Hardikar

1989. Birth Centenary of Dr. Narayana Subbarao Hardikar (nationalist).
1370 **1086** 60 p. brown .. 15 15

1087 "Advaita" in Devanagari Script

1989. Sankaracharya (philosopher) Commem.
1371 **1087** 60 p. multicoloured .. 20 20

1088 Gandhi Bhavan, Punjab University

1989. Punjab University, Chandigarh.
1372 **1088** 1 r. brown and blue 15 15

INDEX

Countries can be quickly located by referring to the index at the end of this volume.

1089 Scene from Film "Raja Harischandra"

1989. 75 Years of Indian Cinema.
1373 **1089** 60 p. black & yellow 20 15

1090 Cactus and Cogwheels

1989. Centenary of Kirloskar Brothers Ltd (engineering group).
1374 **1090** 1 r. multicoloured .. 15 15

1091 Early Class and Modern University Students

1989. Centenary of First D.A.V. College.
1375 **1091** 1 r. multicoloured .. 15 15

1092 Post Office, Dakshin Gangotri Base, Antarctica

1989. Opening of Post Office, Dakshin Gangotri Research Station, Antarctica.
1376 **1092** 1 r. multicoloured .. 30 15

1093 First Allahabad Bank Building

1989. 125th Anniv (1990) of Allahabad Bank.
1377 **1093** 60 p. purple and blue 15 15

1094 Nehru inspecting Central Reserve Police, Neemuch, 1954

1989. 50th Anniv of Central Reserve Police Force (formerly Crown Representative's Police).
1378 **1094** 60 p. brown 20 20

1095 Dairy Cow

1989. Centenary of Military Farms.
1379 **1095** 1 r. multicoloured .. 20 15

1096 Mustafa Kemal Ataturk

1989. 50th Death Anniv (1988) of Mustafa Kemal Ataturk (Turkish statesman).
1380 **1096** 5 r. multicoloured .. 40 45

1097 Dr. S. Radhakrishnan

1989. Birth Centenary (1988) of Dr. Sarvepalli Radhakrishnan (former President).
1381 **1097** 60 p. black .. 15 15

1098 Football Match

1989. Cent of Mohun Bagan Athletic Club.
1382 **1098** 1 r. multicoloured .. 20 15

1099 Dr. P. Subbarayan

1989. Birth Centenary of Dr. P. Subbarayan (politician).
1383 **1099** 60 p. brown .. 15 15

1100 Shyamji Krishna Varma

1989. Shyamji Krishna Varma (nationalist) Commemoration.
1384 **1100** 60 p. brn, grn & red 15 15

1101 Sayajirao Gaekwad III

1989. 50th Death Anniv of Maharaja Sayajirao Gaekwad III of Baroda.
1385 **1101** 60 p. grey 15 15

1102 Symbolic Bird with Letter

1989. "Use Pincode" Campaign.
1386 **1102** 60 p. multicoloured .. 15 15

1103 Namakkal Kavignar

1989. Namakkal Kavignar (writer) Commem.
1387 **1103** 60 p. black 15 15

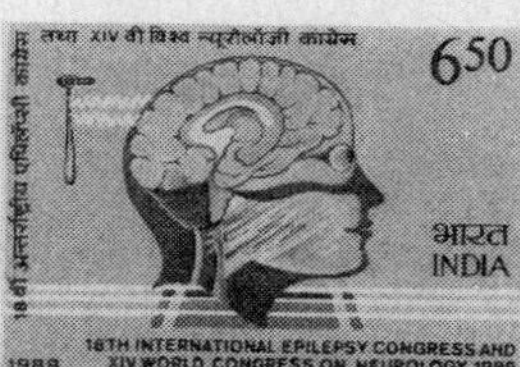
1104 Diagram of Human Brain

1989. 18th Int. Epilepsy Congress and 14th World Congress on Neurology, New Delhi.
1388 **1104** 6 r. 50 multicoloured 60 65

1105 Pandita Ramabai and Original Sharada Sadan Building

1989. Pandita Ramabai (women's education pioneer) Commemoration.
1389 **1105** 60 p. brown .. 15 15

1106 Releasing Homing Pigeons

1989. Orissa Police Pigeon Post.
1390 **1106** 1 r. red 20 15

1107 Acharya Narendra Deo

1989. Birth Centenary of Acharya Narendra Deo (scholar).
1391 **1107** 60 p. brn, grn & orge 15 15

1108 Acharya Kripalani

1989. Acharya Kripalani (politician) Commemoration.
1392 **1108** 60 p. black, grn & red 15 15

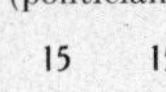

1109 Nehru
(illustration reduced to ⅔ size)

1989. Birth Centenary of Jawaharlal Nehru (2nd issue).
1393 **1109** 1 r. brown, deep brown and buff .. 20 15

1110 Meeting Logo

1989. 8th Asian Track and Field Meeting, New Delhi.
1394 **1110** 1 r. black, orge & grn 15 15

1111 Sir Gurunath Bewoor

1989. Sir Gurunath Bewoor (former Director-General, Posts and Telegraphs) Commem.
1395 **1111** 60 p. brown 15 15

1112 Balkrishna Sharma Navin

1989. Balkrishna Sharma Navin (politician and poet) Commemoration.
1396 **1112** 60 p. black 15 15

1113 Abstract Painting of Houses

1989. Cent of Bombay Art Society (1988).
1397 **1113** 1 r. multicoloured .. 15 15

1114 Likh Florican

1989. Wildlife Conservation. Likh Florican.
1398 **1114** 2 r. multicoloured .. 35 30

1115 Centenary Logo

1989. Centenary of Indian Oil Production.
1399 **1115** 60 p. brown 20 15

1116 Dr. M. G. Ramachandran

1990. Dr. M. G. Ramachandran (former Chief Minister of Tamil Nadu) Commemoration.
1400 **1116** 60 p. brown 15 15

1117 Volunteers working at Sukhna Lake, Chandigarh

1990. Save Sukhna Lake Campaign.
1401 **1117** 1 r. multicoloured .. 15 15

1118 Gallantry Medals

1990. Presentation of New Colours to Bombay Sappers.
1402 **1118** 60 p. multicoloured .. 20 20

1119 Conch Shell and Logo

1990. 23rd Annual General Meeting of Asian Development Bank, New Delhi.
1403 **1119** 2 r. black, orge & yell 15 15

1120 Penny Black and Envelope

1990. 150th Anniv of the Penny Black.
1404 **1120** 6r. multicoloured .. 50 40

1121 Ho Chi-Minh and Vietnamese House

1990. Birth Centenary of Ho Chi-Minh (Vietnamese leader).
1405 **1121** 2 r. brown and green 15 15

1122 Chaudhary Charan Singh

1990. 3rd Death Anniv of Chaudhary Charan Singh (former Prime Minister).
1406 **1122** 1 r. brown .. 10 10

1123 Armed Forces' Badge and Map of Sri Lanka

1124 Wheat

1990. Indian Peace-keeping Operations in Sri Lanka.
1407 **1123** 2 r. multicoloured .. 10 10

1990. 60th Anniv of Indian Council of Agricultural Research (1989).
1408 **1124** 2 r. blk, grn & dp grn 10 10

1125 Khudiram Bose

1990. Khudiram Bose (patriot) Commemoration.
1409 **1125** 1 r. orange, grn & red 10 10

1126 "Life in India" (Tanya Vorontsova)

1990. Indo-Soviet Friendship. Children's Paintings. Multicoloured.
1410 1 r. Type **1126** 10 20
1411 6 r. 50 "St. Basil's Cathedral and Kremlin, Moscow" (Sanjay Adhikari) 40 70

Stamps in similar designs were also issued by U.S.S.R.

1127 K. Kelappan

1990. K. Kelappan (social reformer) Commemoration.
1412 **1127** 1 r. brown 10 10

1128 Girl in Garden

1990. Year of the Girl Child.
1413 **1128** 1 r. multicoloured .. 10 10

1129 Hand guiding Child's Writing

1990. International Literacy Year.
1414 **1129** 1 r. multicoloured .. 10 10

1130 Woman using Water Pump

1990. Safe Drinking Water Campaign.
1415 **1130** 4 r. black, red & grn 30 30

1131 Sunder Lal Sharma

1990. 50th Death Anniv of Sunder Lal Sharma (patriot).
1416 **1131** 60 p. red .. 10 10

1132 Kabbadi

1990. 11th Asian Games, Peking. Mult.
1417 1 r. Type **1132** 15 15
1418 4 r. Athletics 40 40
1419 4 r. Cycling 40 40
1420 6 r. 50 Archery 70 70

1133 A. K. Gopalan

1990. Ayillyath Kuttiari Gopalan (social reformer) Commemoration.
1421 **1133** 1 r. brown .. 10 10

1134 Gurkha Soldier

1990. 50th Anniv of 3rd and 5th Battalions, 5th Gurkha Rifles.
1422 **1134** 2 r. black and brown 30 20

1135 Suryamall Mishran

1990. 75th Birth Anniv of Suryamall Mishran (poet).
1423 **1135** 2 r. brown and orange 10 10

1136 "Doll and Cat" (Subhash Kumar Nagarajan)

1990. Children's Day.
1424 **1136** 1 r. multicoloured .. 10 10

1137 Security Post and Border Guard on Camel

1990. 25th Anniv of Border Security Force.
1425 **1137** 5 r. blue, brown & blk 30 35

1138 Hearts and Flowers

1990. Greetings Stamps. Multicoloured.
1426 1 r. Type **1138** 15 10
1427 4 r. Ceremonial elephants (horiz) 35 40

1139 Bikaner

1990. Cities of India. Multicoloured.
1428 4 r. Type **1139** 35 35
1429 5 r. Hyderabad .. 45 45
1430 6 r. 50 Cuttack 60 60

1140 Bhakta Kanakadas and Udipi Temple

1141 Shaheed Minar Monument

1990. Bhakta Kanakadas (mystic and poet) Commemoration.
1431 **1140** 1 r. red 15 15

1990. 300th Anniv of Calcutta.
1432 **1141** 1 r. multicoloured .. 10 10
1433 – 6 r. black, brn & red 45 50
DESIGNS—HORIZ (44×36 mm). 6 r. 18th-century shipping on the Ganges.

1142 Dnyaneshwar (poet) and Manuscript

1990. 700th Anniv of Dnyaneshwari (spiritual epic).
1434 **1142** 2 r. multicoloured .. 10 15

1143 Madan Mohan Malaviya (founder) and University

1991. 75th Anniv of Banaras Hindu University.
1435 **1143** 1 r. red 10 10

1991. As No. 732 but new face value.
1436 1 r. brown (Gandhi) .. 10 10

1144 Road Users

1991. International Traffic Safety Conference, New Delhi.
1437 **1144** 6 r. 50 black, bl & red 40 45

1145 Exhibition Emblem

1991. 7th Triennale Art Exhibition, New Delhi.
1438 **1145** 6 r. 50 multicoloured 40 45

1146 Jagnnath Sunkersett and Central Railways Headquarters

1991. 98th Birth Anniv of Jagnnath Sunkersett (educationist and railway pioneer).
1439 **1146** 2 r. blue and red .. 10 15

1147 Tata Memorial Centre

1991. 50th Anniv of Tata Memorial Medical Centre.
1440 **1147** 2 r. brown and stone 10 15

1148 River Dolphin

1991. Endangered Marine Mammals.
1441 **1148** 4 r. brown, bl & grn 35 35
1442 – 6 r. 50 multicoloured 55 55
DESIGN: 6 r. 50, Sea Cow.

1149 Drugs

1991. International Conference on Drug Abuse, Calcutta.
1443 **1149** 5 r. violet and red .. 50 50

1150 Hand, Bomb Explosion and Dove

1991. World Peace.
1444 **1150** 6 r. 50 black, light brown and brown 55 60

1151 Remote Sensing Satellite "1A"

1991. Launch of Indian Remote Sensing Satellite "1A".
1445 **1151** 6 r. 50 brown & blue 25 30

1152 Babu Jagjivan Ram

1991. Babu Jagjivan Ram (politician) Commemoration.
1446 **1152** 1 r. brown 10 10

1153 Dr. B. R. Ambedkar and Demonstration

1991. Birth Centenary of Dr. Bhimrao Ramji Ambedkar (social reformer).
1447 **1153** 1 r. brown and blue 10 10

1154 Valar Dance

1991. Tribal Dances. Multicoloured.
1448 2 r. 50 Type **1154** .. 10 15
1449 4 r. Kayang 15 20
1450 5 r. Hozagiri 20 25
1451 6 r. 50 Velakali 25 30

1155 Ariyakudi Ramanuja Iyengar and Temples

1991. Ariyakudi Ramanuja Iyengar (singer and composer) Commemoration.
1452 **1155** 2 r. brown and green 10 15

1156 Karpoori Thakur

1991. Jan Nayak Karpoori Thakur (politician and social reformer) Commemoration.
1453 **1156** 1 r. brown 10 10

1157 Emperor Penguins

1991. 30th Anniv of Antarctic Treaty. Mult.
1454 5 r. Type **1157** 20 25
1455 6 r. 50 Antarctic map and pair of gentoo penguins 25 30
Nos. 1454/5 were printed together, se-tenant, forming a composite design.

1158 Rashtrapati Bhavan Building, New Delhi

1991. 60th Anniv of New Delhi. Multicoloured.
1456 5 r. Type **1158** 20 25
1457 6 r. 50 New Delhi monuments 25 30
Nos. 1456/7 were printed together, se-tenant, forming a composite design.

1159 Sri Ram Sharma Acharya

1991. Sri Ram Sharma Acharya (social refomer) Commemoration.
1458 **1159** 1 r. green and red .. 10 10

1160 "Shankar awarded Padma Vibhushan" (cartoon)

1991. Keshav Shankar Pillai (cartoonist) Commemoration.
1459 **1160** 4 r. brown 15 20
1460 – 6 r. 50 lilac 25 30
DESIGN—VERT. 6 r. 50, "The Big Show".

1161 Sriprakash and Kashi Vidyapith University

1991. 20th Death Anniv of Sriprakash (politician).
1461 **1161** 2 r. brown & lt brown 10 10

1162 Gopinath Bardoloi

1991. Birth Centenary (1990) of Gopinath Bardoloi (Assamese politician).
1462 **1162** 1 r. lilac 10 10

1163 Rajiv Gandhi

1991. Rajiv Gandhi (Congress Party leader) Commemoration.
1463 **1163** 1 r. multicoloured .. 10 10

1164 Muni Mishrimalji and Memorial

1991. Birth Centenary of Muni Mishrimalji (Jain religious leader).
1464 **1164** 1 r. brown 10 10

1165 Mahadevi Verma (poetess) and "Varsha"

1991. Hindu Writers.
1465 **1165** 2 r. black and blue .. 10 10
1466 – 2 r. black and blue .. 10 10
DESIGN: No. 1466, Jayshankar Prasad (poet and dramatist) and scene from "Kamayani".

1166 Parliament House and C.P.A. Emblem

1991. 37th Commonwealth Parliamentary Association Conference, New Delhi.
1467 **1166** 6 r. 50 blue & brown 25 30

1167 Frog

1991. Greetings Stamps.
1468 **1167** 1 r. green and red .. 10 10
1469 – 6 r. 50 red and green 25 30
DESIGN: 6 r. 50, Symbolic bird carrying flower.

1168 "Cymbidium aloifolium"

1991. Orchids. Multicoloured.
1470 1 r. Type **1168** 10 10
1471 2 r. 50 "Paphiopedilum venustum" 10 15
1472 3 r. "Aerides crispum" .. 10 15
1473 4 r. "Cymbidium bicolour" 15 20
1474 5 r. "Vanda spathulata" 20 25
1475 6 r. 50 "Cymbidium devonianum" 25 30

1169 Gurkha Soldier in Battle Dress

1991. 90th Anniv of 2nd Battalion, Third Gorkha Rifles.
1476 **1169** 4 r. multicoloured .. 15 20

1170 Couple on Horse (embroidery)

1991. 3rd Death Anniv of Kamaladevi Chattopadhyaya (founder of All India Handicrafts Board).
1477 **1170** 1 r. lake, red & yell 10 10
1478 – 6 r. 50 multicoloured 25 30
DESIGN: 6 r. 50, Traditional puppet.

1171 Chithiru Tirunal and Temple Sculpture

1991. Chithiru Tirunal Bala Rama Varma (former Maharaja of Travancore) Commem.
1479 **1171** 2 r. violet 10 15

1172 "Children in Traditional Costume" (Arpi Snehalbhai Shah)

1991. Children's Day.
1480 **1172** 1 r. multicoloured .. 10 10

1173 Mounted Sowar and Tanks

1991. 70th Anniv (1992) of the 18th Cavalry Regiment.
1481 **1173** 6 r. 50 multicoloured 25 30

1174 Kites

1991. India Tourism Year.
1482 **1174** 6 r. 50 multicoloured 25 30

1175 Sports on Bricks

1991. International Conference on Youth Tourism, New Delhi.
1483 **1175** 6 r. 50 multicoloured 25 30

1176 "Mozart at Piano" (unfinished painting, J. Lange)

1991. Death Bicentenary of Mozart.
1484 **1176** 6 r. 50 multicoloured 25 30

1177 Homeless Family

1991. South Asian Association for Regional Co-operation Year of Shelter.
1485 **1177** 4 r. brown and ochre 15 20

1178 People running on Heart

1991. "Run for Your Heart" Marathon, New Delhi.
1486 **1178** 1 r. black, grey & red 10 10

1179 "Sidhartha with an Injured Bird" (Asit Kumar Haldar)

1991. Birth Centenary (1990) of Asit Kumar Haldar (artist).
1487 **1179** 2 r. yellow, red & blk 10 10

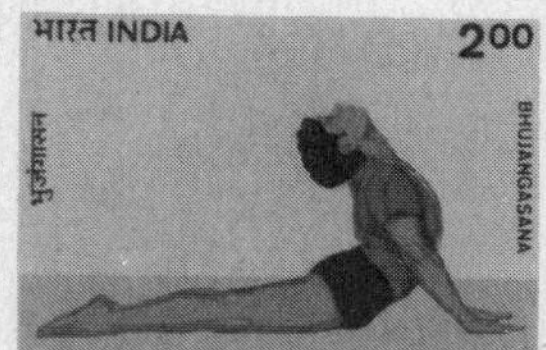

1180 Bhujangasana

1991. Yoga Exercises. Multicoloured.
1488 2 r. Type **1180** 10 10
1489 5 r. Dhanurasana .. 20 25
1490 6 r. 50 Ustrasana .. 25 30
1491 10 r. Utthita trikonasana 45 50

1181 Y.M.C.A. Logo

1992. Centenary (1991) of National Council of Y.M.C.A.
1492 **1181** 1 r. red and blue .. 10 10

1182 Madurai Temple Tower and Hooghly River Bridge

1992. 14th Congress of International Association for Bridge and Structural Engineering, New Delhi.
1493 **1182** 2 r. brown, red & bl 10 10
1494 – 2 r. brown, red & bl 10 10
DESIGN: No. 1494, Gate, Sanchi Stupa and Hall of Nations, New Delhi.

OFFICIAL STAMPS

1866. Optd. **Service.**
O 20 **11.** ½ a. blue .. .. 14·00 40
O 8 **12.** 8 p. mauve .. .. 17·00 32·00
O 23 **11.** 1 a. brown .. .. 14·00 45
O 27 2 a. orange .. .. 4·50 2·25
O 13 4 a. green .. .. £110 50·00
O 29 – 4 a. green (No. 69) .. 3·00 1·50
O 30 **11.** 8 a. red .. .. 3·25 1·50

1866. Fiscal stamp with head of Queen Victoria, surch. **SERVICE TWO ANNAS.**
O 15. 2 a. purple £350 £225

1866. Fiscal stamps optd. **SERVICE POSTAGE.**
O 19. ½ a. mauve on lilac .. £325 80·00
O 16. 2 a. purple £700 £375
O 17. 4 a. purple £2000 £900
O 18. 8 a. purple £3750 £2000

1874. Optd. **On H.M.S. (Queen Victoria).**
O 31. **11.** ½ a. blue .. .. 4·50 20
O 32. 1 a. brown .. .. 6·00 20
O 33a, 2 a. orange .. .. 18·00 4·50
O 34. – 4 a. green (No. 69) .. 4·75 2·50
O 35. **11.** 8 a. red .. .. 3·50 1·75

1883. Queen Victoria stamps of 1882 and 1892 optd. **On H.M.S.**
O 37a **40.** 3 p. red 20 10
O 39 **23.** ½ a. turquoise .. 20 10
O 49 ½ a. green 50 25
O 41 – 1 a. purple 30 10
O 50 – 1 a. red .. .. 1·25 10
O 42 – 2 a. blue .. .. 1·75 20
O 51 – 2 a. lilac .. .. 15·00 30
O 44a – 4 a. green .. .. 3·25 20
O 46 – 8 a. mauve .. .. 4·50 40
O 48 **37.** 1 r. green and red .. 3·50 40

1902. King Edward VII stamps optd. **On H.M.S.**
O 54 **41.** 3 p. grey 70 30
O 56 – ½ a. green (No. 122) .. 90 30
O 57 – 1 a. red (No. 123) .. 70 10
O 59 – 2 a. lilac .. .. 1·75 10
O 60 – 4 a. olive .. .. 3·00 15
O 62 – 6 a. bistre .. .. 1·50 15
O 63 – 8 a. mauve .. .. 6·00 70
O 65 – 1 r. green and red .. 4·00 30
O 68a **52.** 2 r. red and orange .. 7·00 80
O 69 5 r. blue and violet .. 14·00 1·50
O 70 10 r. green and red .. 16·00 8·50
O 71 15 r. blue and olive .. 55·00 28·00
O 72 25 r. orange and blue .. £140 60·00

1906. Nos. 149/50 optd. **On H.M.S.**
O 66. ½ a. green 30 10
O 67. 1 a. red 80 10

1912. King George V stamps optd. **SERVICE.**
O 73 **55.** 3 p. grey 15 10
O 76 **56.** ½ a. green 15 10
O 81 **57.** 1 a. red 50 10
O 111 1 a. brown 15 10
O 83 **59.** 2 a. lilac 45 10
O 112 **70.** 2 a. lilac 20 10
O 129 2 a. red 75 60
O 132 **63.** 4 a. olive 75 10
O 113 **71.** 4 a. green 25 10
O 87 **64.** 6 a. bistre .. .. 1·50 1·75
O 115 **65.** 8 a. mauve 60 10
O 116 **66.** 12 a. red 60 35
O 117 **67.** 1 r. brown and green .. 1·25 45
O 92 2 r. red and orange .. 3·00 2·00
O 93 5 r. blue and violet .. 11·00 9·50
O 94 10 r. green and red .. 27·00 28·00
O 95 15 r. blue and olive .. 70·00 85·00
O 96 25 r. orange and blue .. £170 £110

1921. No. O81 surch **NINE PIES.**
O97 **57** 9 p. on 1 a. red .. 30 30

1925. Nos. O 70/2 surch. in words.
O 99. **52.** 1 r. on 15 r. blue & olive 4·25 2·50
O 100. 1 r. on 25 r. orge. & bl. 17·00 42·00
O 101. 2 r. on 10 r. grn. & red 3·75 3·00

1925. Nos. O 94/6 surch in words.
O 102 **67** 1 r. on 15 r. bl & olive 17·00 45·00
O 103 1 r. on 25 r. orge & bl 5·00 7·00
O 104 2 r. on 10 r. grn & red £650

1926. No. O 62 surch. in words.
O 105. 1 a. on 6 a. bistre .. 30 30

1926. Surch. **SERVICE ONE ANNA** and two bars.
O 106. **58.** 1 a. on 1½ a. brown (A) 20 10
O 107. 1 a. on 1½ a. brown (B) 45 60
O 108. **61.** 1 a. on 2½ a. blue .. 60 1·25

1932. Optd. **SERVICE.**
O 126. **79.** ½ a. green 50 10
O 127. **80.** 9 p. green 20 10
O 127a. **81.** 1 a. brown 60 10
O 128. **82.** 1¼ a. mauve 20 10
O 130a. **59.** 2 a. red 75 10
O 131. **61.** 2½ a. orange 15 10

1937. King George VI stamps optd. **SERVICE.**
O 135. **91.** ½ a. brown .. .. 7·00 15
O 136. 9 p. green .. .. 7·00 10
O 137. 1 a. red .. .. 1·00 10
O 138. **93.** 1 r. slate and brown .. 50 20
O 139. 2 r. purple and brown 1·50 1·40
O 140. 5 r. green and blue .. 2·50 2·75
O 141. 10 r. purple and red .. 13·00 4·75

1939. King George V stamp surch. **SERVICE 1A.**
O 142. **82.** 1 a. on 1¼ a. mauve .. 4·50 20

O **20.** King George VI.

O **21.** Asokan Capital.

1939.
O 143. O **20.** 3 p. slate 20 10
O 144. ½ a. brown .. 75 10
O 144a. ½ a. purple .. 20 10
O 145. 9 p. green .. 30 10
O 146. 1 a. red 30 10
O 146a. 1 a. 3 p. brown .. 2·75 40
O 146b. 1½ a. violet .. 65 10
O 147. 2 a. orange .. 60 10
O 148. 2½ a. violet .. 60 15
O 149. 4 a. brown .. 60 10
O 150. 8 a. violet .. 90 20

1948. 1st Anniv of Independence. Optd **SERVICE.**
O 150a. **305.** 1½ a. brown .. 42·00 30·00
O 150b. 3½ a. violet .. £600 £350
O 150c. 12 a. green .. £1400 £1400
O 150d. – 10 r. brown and red (No. 308) .. £8500

1950.
O 151 O **21.** 3 p. violet 10 10
O 152 6 p. brown 10 10
O 153 9 p. green 20 10
O 154 1 a. blue 45 10
O 155 2 a. red 70 10
O 156 3 a. red .. .. 2·50 70
O 157 4 a. purple .. .. 7·00 10
O 158 4 a. blue 40 10
O 159 6 a. violet .. .. 2·00 40
O 160 8 a. brown .. .. 1·50 10
O 186 – 1 r. violet 15 10
O 187 – 2 r. red 25 10
O 188 – 5 r. green 50 55
O 189 – 10 r. brown .. 1·25 80
The rupee values are larger and with a different frame.

1957. Value in naye paise.
O 165 O **21.** 1 n.p. slate 10 10
O 166 2 n.p. violet .. 10 10
O 167 3 n.p. brown .. 10 10
O 168 5 n.p. green .. 10 10
O 169 6 n.p. turquoise .. 10 10
O 180 10 n.p. green .. 40 40
O 170 13 n.p. red 10 10
O 182 15 n.p. violet .. 10 10
O 172 20 n.p. red 10 10
O 184 25 n.p. blue .. 10 10
O 185 50 n.p. brown .. 15 10

O **23.**

O **25.**

1967.
O 200 O **23.** 2 p. violet 10 30
O 201 3 p. brown 10 40
O 202 5 p. green 10 10
O 203 6 p. blue 45 70
O 204 10 p. green 10 15
O 205 15 p. plum 10 20
O 206 20 p. red 10 20
O 207 25 p. red .. .. 3·00 2·75
O 208 30 p. blue 10 20
O 209 50 p. brown .. 10 20
O 197 1 r. purple 20 30

1971. Obligatory Tax. Refugee Relief. Nos. O 205/6 are optd. **REFUGEE RELIEF** in England and Hindi (No. O 205) or in English only (No. O 206).
O 210. O **23.** 5 p. green 20 20
O 211. 5 p. green 80 40
O 213. O **25.** 5 p. green 15 15
See note below Nos. 646/51.

O **26.**

1977. Various Designs redrawn, showing face-value in figures only and smaller Capital with Hindi motto beneath as Type **O 26.**

O 214	**O 26.**	2 p. violet	20	50
O 254		5 p. green	10	10
O 255		10 p. green ..	10	10
O 256		15 p. purple ..	10	10
O 257		20 p. red	10	10
O 258		25 p. red	10	10
O 259		30 p. blue	10	10
O 260		35 p. violet ..	10	10
O 261		40 p. violet ..	10	10
O 262		50 p. brown ..	10	10
O 263		60 p. brown ..	10	10
O 264		1 r. brown	10	10
O 225a		2 r. red	40	90
O 226a		5 r. green	60	1·50
O 227		10 r. red	1·25	2·75

The 2, 5 and 10 r. values are larger.

O 27.

O 28.

1981. Redrawn with face value figures in bottom corners.

O 265.	**O 27.**	2 r. red	10	15
O 266.		5 r. green	20	25
O 267.		10 r. brown ..	40	45

1982. As 1977 and 1981 issue but with simulated perforations. Imperf.

O 231	**O 28**	5 p. green	30	30
O 232		10 p. green ..	35	35
O 233		15 p. purple ..	35	35
O 234		20 p. red	40	40
O 235		25 p. red	90	65
O 236		35 p. violet ..	50	30
O 237		50 p. brown ..	90	60
O 238		1 r. brown ..	1·00	60
O 239		2 r. red	1·25	1·75
O 240		5 r. green	1·50	2·75
O 241		10 r. brown ..	2·00	3·25

INDIAN CUSTODIAN FORCES IN KOREA

Stamps used by the Indian Forces on custodian duties in Korea in 1953.

12 pies = 1 anna; 16 annas = 1 rupee.

भारतीय
संरक्षा कटक
कोरिया

(1.)

1953. Stamps of India (archaeological series), optd. with T **1.**

K 1.	**307.**	3 p. violet	70	3·00
K 2.	**308.**	6 p. brown	70	3·00
K 3.	–	9 p. green	70	3·00
K 4.	–	1 a. blue (B)	70	3·00
K 5.	–	2 a. red	90	3·00
K 6.	–	2½ a. lake	1·00	4·00
K 7.	–	3 a. salmon	1·25	4·00
K 8.	**314.**	4 a. blue	1·75	4·50
K 9.	**315.**	6 a. violet	6·50	8·50
K 10.	–	8 a. green	3·25	8·50
K 11.	–	12 a. blue	4·50	16·00
K 12.	–	1 r. violet and green ..	6·00	17·00

INDIAN EXPEDITIONARY FORCES

Stamps used by Indian Forces during, and after, the War of 1914–18.

12 pies = 1 anna; 16 annas = 1 rupee.

1914. Stamps of India (King George V) optd. **I.E.F.**

E 1.	**55.**	3 p. grey	15	25
E 2.	**56.**	½ a. green	20	20
E 3.	**57.**	1 a. red	30	20
E 5.	**59.**	2 a. lilac	50	30
E 6.	**61.**	2½ a. blue	70	1·00
E 7.	**62.**	3 a. orange	70	60
E 8.	**63.**	4 a. olive	60	60
E 9.	**65.**	8 a. mauve	1·00	1·00
E 12.	**66.**	12 a. red	2·25	5·00
E 13.	**67.**	1 r. brown and green ..	2·50	4·00

INDIAN FORCES IN INDO-CHINA

Stamps used by Indian Forces engaged in the International Commission in Indo-China.

1954. 12 pies = 1 anna; 16 annas = 1 rupee.
1957. 100 nay paise = 1 rupee.
1964. 100 paisa = 1 rupee.

अन्तर्राष्ट्रीय आयोग कम्बोज	अन्तर्राष्ट्रीय आयोग लाओस	अन्तर्राष्ट्रीय आयोग वियत नाम
(N 1)	(N 2)	(N 3.)

1954. Stamps of India (archaeological series) overprinted.

(a) Optd. with T **N 1**, for use in Cambodia.

N 1.	**307.**	3 p. violet	60	2·50
N 2.	–	1 a. blue (B)	90	75
N 3.	–	2 a. red	90	80
N 4.	–	8 a. green	2·00	3·50
N 5.	–	12 a. blue	2·25	4·00

(b) Optd. with T **N 2**, for use in Laos.

N 6.	**307.**	3 p. violet	60	2·50
N 7.	–	1 a. blue (B)	90	75
N 8.	–	2 a. red	90	80
N 9.	–	8 a. green	2·00	3·50
N 10.	–	12 a. blue	2·25	4·00

(c) Optd. with T **N 3**, for use in Viet-Nam.

N 11.	**307.**	3 p. violet	60	2·50
N 12.	–	1 a. blue (B)	90	75
N 13.	–	2 a. red	90	80
N 14.	–	8 a. green	2·00	3·50
N 15.	–	12 a. blue	2·25	4·00

1957. Map type of India overprinted.

(a) Optd. with T **N 1**, for use in Cambodia.

N 16.	**361.**	2 n.p. brown	40	30
N 17.		6 n.p. grey	35	30
N 18.		13 n.p. red	50	40
N 19.		50 n.p. orange ..	1·75	1·25
N 20.		75 n.p. purple ..	1·75	1·25

(b) Optd. with T **N 2**, for use in Laos.

N 21	**361.**	2 n.p. brown	40	30
N 39		3 n.p. brown	10	20
N 40		5 n.p. green	10	15
N 22		6 n.p. grey	35	30
N 23		13 n.p. red	50	40
N 24		50 n.p. orange ..	1·75	1·25
N 25		75 n.p. purple ..	1·75	1·25

(c) Optd. with T **N 3**, for use in Vietnam.

N 43	**361.**	1 n.p. turquoise ..	10	20
N 26		2 n.p. brown	40	30
N 45		3 n.p. brown	10	20
N 46		5 n.p. green	10	15
N 27		6 n.p. grey	35	30
N 28		13 n.p. red	50	40
N 29		50 n.p. orange ..	1·75	1·25
N 30		75 n.p. purple ..	1·75	1·25

1965. Children's Day stamp of India optd. **ICC** for use in Laos and Vietnam.

N 49.	**469.**	15 p. slate	20	2·00

1968. Nos. 504/6, 509/10, 515 and 517/18, of India optd. **ICC** in English and Indian, for use in Laos and Vietnam.

N 50.	–	2 p. brown	10	80
N 51.	–	3 p. olive	10	80
N 52.	–	5 p. red	10	40
N 53.	–	10 p. blue	75	40
N 54.	**467.**	15 p. green	50	75
N 55.	–	60 p. grey	35	75
N 56.	–	1 r. brown and plum	50	1·40
N 57.	–	2 r. blue and violet ..	1·00	4·25

INDIAN U.N. FORCE IN CONGO

Stamps used by Indian Forces attached to the United Nations Force in Congo.

100 naye paise = 1 rupee.

1962. Map type of India optd. **U.N. FORCE (INDIA) CONGO.**

U 1.	**361.**	1 n.p. turquoise ..	60	1·25
U 2.		2 n.p. brown	60	70
U 3.		5 n.p. green	60	45
U 4.		8 n.p. turquoise ..	65	30
U 5.		13 n.p. red	70	40
U 6.		50 n.p. orange ..	70	70

INDIAN U.N. FORCE IN GAZA (PALESTINE)

Stamps used by Indian Forces attached to the United Nations Force in Gaza.

100 paise = 1 rupee.

1965. Children's Day stamp of India optd. **UNEF.**

G 1.	**449.**	15 p. slate	40	2·00

INDORE (HOLKAR STATE)

A state in C. India. Now uses Indian stamps.

12 pies = 1 anna; 16 annas = 1 rupee.

1. Maharaja Tukoji Rao II Holkar XI.

1886.

2.	**1.**	½ a. mauve	1·25	1·10

2.

1889. No gum. Imperf.

4.	**2.**	½ a. black on pink	1·50	1·75

3. Maharaja Shivaji Rao Holkar XII.

5. Maharaja Tukoji Rao III Holkar XIII.

1889.

5.	**3.**	¼ a. orange	30	30
6a.		½ a. purple	30	15
7.		1 a. green	65	50
8.		2 a. red	1·60	1·00

1904.

9.	**5.**	¼ a. orange	30	10
10.		½ a. red	5·50	10
11.		1 a. green	1·60	10
12.		2 a. brown	5·00	30
13.		3 a. violet	6·50	2·00
14a.		4 a. blue	5·00	1·00

The ½ a. is inscr. "HOLKAR".

पांच आना.

(6.)

1905. No. 6a surch. as T **6.**

15.	**3.**	¼ a. on ½ a. purple ..	1·50	11·00

7. Maharaja Yeshwant Rao II Holkar XIV. 9.

1928.

16.	**7.**	¼ a. orange	30	10
17.		½ a. purple	30	10
18.		1 a. green	50	10
19.		1¼ a. green	50	15
20.		2 a. brown	2·50	80
21.		2 a. green	4·50	60
22.		3 a. violet	1·50	5·50
23.		3 a. blue	12·00	
24.		3½ a. violet	4·00	8·00
25.		4 a. blue	3·25	2·25
26.		4 a. yellow	13·00	1·50
27.		8 a. grey	5·50	5·00
28.		8 a. orange	10·00	9·00
29.		12 a. red	5·00	10·00
30.	–	1 r. black and blue	8·00	14·00
31.	–	2 r. black and red	30·00	30·00
32.	–	5 r. black and brown	42·00	42·00

The rupee values are larger (23 × 28 mm.).

1940. Surch. diagonally in words.

33.	–	¼ a. on 5 r. (No. 32)	2·50	30
34.	–	½ a. on 2 r. (No. 31)	4·00	75
35.	**7.**	1 a. on 1¼ a. green (No. 19)	4·75	35

1941.

36.	**9.**	¼ a. orange	1·50	10
37.		½ a. red	1·00	10
38.		1 a. green	4·25	10
39.		1¼ a. green	8·50	30
40.		2 a. blue	8·00	1·00
41.		4 a. yellow	9·00	7·00
42.	–	2 r. black and red	10·00	70·00
43.	–	5 r. black and orange	12·00	85·00

The rupee values are larger (23 × 28 mm.).

OFFICIAL STAMPS

1904. Optd. **SERVICE.**

S 1.	**5.**	¼ a. orange	10	30
S 2.		½ a. red	10	10
S 3.		1 a. green	10	15
S 4.		2 a. brown	30	20
S 5.		3 a. violet	1·75	1·25
S 6.		4 a. blue	2·25	1·40

IONIAN ISLANDS

A group of islands off the W. coast of Greece, placed under the protection of Gt. Britain in 1815 and ceded to Greece in 1864. Under Italian occupation in 1941 and occupied by Germany in 1943.

12 pence = 1 shilling.
20 shillings = 1 pound.

1.

1859. Imperf.

1.	**1.**	(½d.) orange	70·00	£500
2.		(1d.) blue	20·00	£180
3.		(2d.) red	15·00	£180

IRELAND

The Republic of Ireland (Eire) is an independent state comprising Ireland, except the six counties of N. Ireland. It was formerly part of the United Kingdom of Great Britain and Ireland.

1922. 12 pence = 1 shilling; 20 shillings = 1 pound.
1971. 100 (new) pence = 1 pound (Punt).

Rialtaṡ Sealaṫaċ na hÉireann 1922	Rialtaṡ Sealaḋaċ na hÉireann 1922.
(1.)	(2.)

(1.) "Provisional Government of Ireland, 1922". (2.)

King George V stamps of Gt. Britain overprinted.

1922. Optd. with T **1** (date in thin figures).

1	**105.**	½d. green	40	40
2	**104.**	1d. red	45	35
22		2½d. blue	85	2·50
5	**106.**	3d. violet	2·75	3·75
6		4d. green	2·50	6·50
7	**107.**	5d. brown	3·50	8·50
8	**108.**	9d. black	9·00	17·00
9		10d. blue	7·00	15·00
17	**109.**	2s. 6d. brown	30·00	60·00
19		5s. red	55·00	95·00
21		10s. blue	£120	£225

On Nos. 17, 19 and 21 the optd is in four lines instead of five.

1922. Optd. with T **2** (date in thick figures).

30.	**105.**	½d. green	1·60	80
31.	**104.**	1d. red	50	40
10.	**105.**	1½d. brown	1·75	75
12.	**106.**	2d. orange	1·50	60
35.	**104.**	2½d. blue	7·00	17·00
36.	**106.**	3d. violet	2·00	2·75
37.		4d. green	2·25	4·00
38.	**107.**	5d. brown	3·50	6·50
39.		6d. purple	6·50	2·50
40.	**108.**	9d. black	11·00	14·00
41.		9d. green	4·50	16·00
42.		10d. blue	25·00	45·00
43.		1s. brown	7·50	8·50

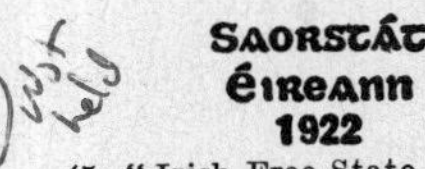

(5. "Irish Free State, 1922").

1922. Optd. with T **5.**

52	**105.**	½d. green	30	30
53	**104.**	1d. red	30	35
54	**105.**	1½d. brown	2·50	8·50
55	**106.**	2d. orange	1·00	2·00
56	**104.**	2½d. blue	3·00	6·50
57	**106.**	3d. violet	3·50	13·00
58		4d. green	2·50	4·50
59	**107.**	5d. brown	3·00	4·75
60		6d. purple	2·00	1·75
61	**108.**	9d. green	3·00	5·50
62		10d. blue	15·00	32·00
63		1s. brown	9·00	9·50
86	**109.**	2s. 6d. brown	38·00	40·00
87		5s. red	60·00	80·00
85		10s. blue	£110	£225

6. "Sword of Light".

7. Map of Ireland.

8. Arms of Ireland.

9. Celtic Cross.

1922.

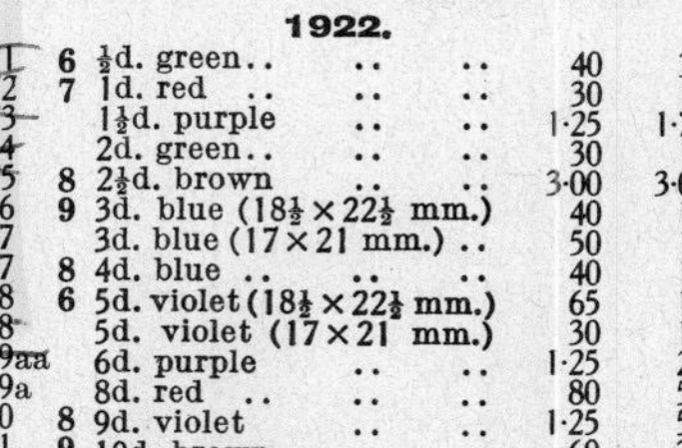

No.	Type	Description		
71	6	½d. green..	40	30
72	7	1d. red	30	10
73		1½d. purple	1·25	1·75
114		2d. green..	30	10
75	8	2½d. brown	3·00	3·00
116	9	3d. blue (18½ × 22½ mm.)	40	10
227		3d. blue (17 × 21 mm.) ..	50	15
117	8	4d. blue	40	10
118	6	5d. violet (18½ × 22½ mm.)	65	10
228		5d. violet (17 × 21 mm.)	30	15
119aa		6d. purple	1·25	20
119a		8d. red	80	50
120	8	9d. violet	1·25	50
121	9	10d. brown	60	35
121a		11d. red	1·25	1·50
82	6	1s. blue	28·00	4·50

12. Daniel O'Connell.

1929. Cent. of Catholic Emancipation.

No.	Type	Description		
89.	12.	2d. green	40	35
90.		3d. blue	4·00	8·50
91.		9d. violet	4·00	4·00

13. Shannon Barrage.

1930. Completion of Shannon Hydro-Electric Scheme.

No.	Type	Description		
92.	13.	2d. deep brown	60	30

14. Reaper.

15. The Cross of Cong.

1931. Bicent. of Royal Dublin Society.

No.	Type	Description		
93.	14.	2d. blue	45	20

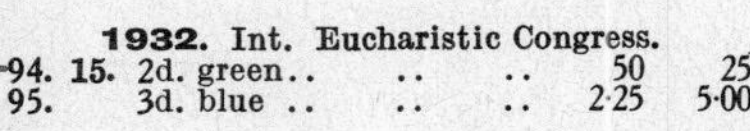

1932. Int. Eucharistic Congress.

No.	Type	Description		
94.	15.	2d. green..	50	25
95.		3d. blue	2·25	5·00

16. Adoration of the Cross.

17. Hurler.

1933. "Holy Year".

No.	Type	Description		
96.	16.	2d. green..	50	15
97.		3d. blue	2·25	2·00

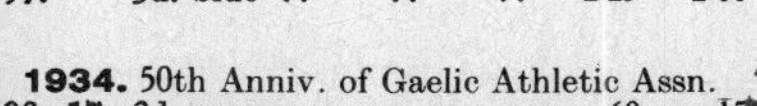

1934. 50th Anniv. of Gaelic Athletic Assn.

No.	Type	Description		
98.	17.	2d. green..	60	15

18. St. Patrick.

1937.

No.	Type	Description		
123a	18	2s. 6d. green	1·50	2·00
124ba		5s. purple	3·50	3·75
125ab		10s. blue	8·00	9·00

19. Ireland and New Constitution.

1937. Constitution Day.

No.	Type	Description		
105.	19.	2d. red	75	20
106.		3d. blue..	4·00	3·25

For similar stamps see No. 176/7.

20. Father Mathew.

1938. Centenary of Temperance Crusade.

No.	Type	Description		
107.	20.	2d. black	1·50	30
108.		3d. blue	10·00	6·00

21. George Washington, American Eagle and Irish Harp.

1939. 150th Anniv. of U.S. Constitution and Installation of First U.S. President.

No.	Type	Description		
109.	21.	2d. red	1·50	40
110.		3d. blue	4·50	3·75

24. Volunteer and G.P.O., Dublin.

1941. 25th Anniv. of Easter Rising (1916).
(a) Provisional issue. Optd. with two lines of Irish characters between the dates "1941" and "1916".

No.	Type	Description		
126.	7.	2d. orange	2·00	30
127.	9.	3d. blue	38·00	9·00

(b) Definitive Issue.

No.	Type	Description		
128.	24.	2½d. blue	70	20

25. Dr. Douglas Hyde.

26. Sir William Rowan Hamilton.

1943. 50th Anniv. of Gaelic League.

No.	Type	Description		
129.	25.	½d. green	40	30
130.		2½d. purple	60	10

1943. Centenary of Announcement of Discovery of Quaternions.

No.	Type	Description		
131.	26.	½d. green	40	40
132.		2½d. brown	1·00	10

27. Bro. Michael O'Clery.

28. Edmund Ignatius Rice.

1944. Death Tercentenary of O'Clery (Franciscan historian). (commemorating the "Annals of the Four Masters").

No.	Type	Description		
133.	27.	½d. green	10	10
134.		1s. brown	45	10

1944. Death Centenary of Edmund Rice (founder of Irish Christian Brothers).

No.	Type	Description		
135.	28.	2½d. slate	50	15

29. "Youth sowing Seeds of Freedom."

1945. Death Centenary of Thomas Davis (Founder of Young Ireland Movement).

No.	Type	Description		
136.	29.	2½d. blue	75	25
137.		6d. purple	7·00	3·75

30. "Country and Homestead".

1946. Birth Centenary of Michael Davitt and Charles Parnell.

No.	Type	Description		
138.	30.	2½d. red	75	15
139.		3d. blue	2·75	2·75

31. Angel Victor over Rock of Cashel.

1948. Air. Inscr. "VOX HIBERNIÆ".

No.	Type	Description		
140.	31.	1d. brown	2·25	3·00
141.	–	3d. blue..	4·50	2·25
142.	–	6d. purple	1·00	1·00
142a.	–	8d. lake..	5·50	4·50
143.	–	1s. green	1·75	1·00
143a.	31.	1s 3d. orange	5·50	1·25
143b.		1s. 5d. blue	3·50	1·00

DESIGNS: 3d., 8d. Angel Victor over Lough Derg. 6d. Over Croagh Patrick. 1s. Over Glendalough.

35. Theobald Wolfe Tone.

1948. 150th Anniv. of Insurrection.

No.	Type	Description		
144.	35.	2½d. purple	1·25	10
145.		3d. violet	3·75	3·25

For later issues see Volume 1.

POSTAGE DUE STAMPS

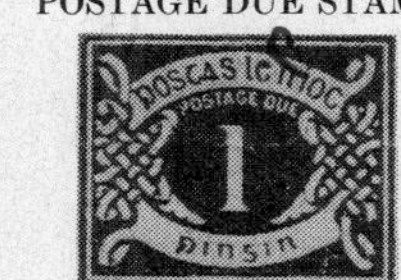

D 1.

1925.

No.	Type	Description		
D 1	D 1.	½d. green	10·00	16·00
D 6		1d. red	1·00	50
D 7		1½d. red	1·75	6·50
D 8		2d. green	2·25	50
D 9		3d. blue	1·75	1·00
D 10		5d. violet	3·00	3·00
D 11a		6d. plum	70	85
D 12		8d. orange	7·50	7·00
D 13		10d. purple.. ..	8·00	7·50
D 14		1s. green	7·50	7·00

ISLE OF MAN

An island in the Irish Sea to the north-west of England. Man became a possession of the English Crown during the Middle Ages, but retains its own Assembly.

Regional issues from 1958–71 are listed at end of GREAT BRITAIN.

Isle of Man had an independent postal administration from 1973.

100 pence = 1 pound.

4. Castletown.

5. Manx Cat.

1973. Multicoloured.

No.	Description		
12.	½p. Type 4	10	10
13.	1p. Port Erin	10	10
14.	1½p. Snaefell	10	10
15.	2p. Laxey	10	10
16.	2½p. Tynwald Hill.. ..	10	10
17.	3p. Douglas Promenade ..	10	10
18.	3½p. Port St. Mary ..	15	15
19.	4p. Fairy Bridge	15	15
20.	4½p. As 2½p.	20	20
21.	5p. Peel	20	20
22.	5½p. As 3p..	25	25
23.	6p. Cregneish	25	25
24.	7p. As 2p.	30	30
25.	7½p. Ramsey Bay	25	25
26.	8p. As 7½p..	35	35
27.	9p. Douglas Bay	30	35
28.	10p. Type 5	30	35
29.	11p. Monk's Bridge, Ballasalla	45	50
30.	13p. Derbyhaven	55	50
31.	20p. Manx Loaghtyn Ram	65	65
32.	50p. Manx Shearwater ..	1·60	1·60
33.	£1 Viking Longship ..	3·25	3·25

SIZES: Nos. 13/27 and 29/30 as Type 4. Nos. 31/3 as Type 5.

6. Viking landing on Man, A.D. 938.

1973. Inaug. of Postal Independence.

No.	Type	Description		
34.	6.	15p. multicoloured ..	80	80

7. "Sutherland".

1973. Cent. of Steam Railway. Multicoloured.

No.	Description		
35.	2½p. Type 7	20	20
36.	3p. "Caledonia"	20	20
37.	7½p. "Kissack"	1·40	1·50
38.	9p. "Pender"	1·50	1·50

8. Leonard Randles, First Winner, 1923.

1973. Golden Jubilee of Manx Grand Prix. Multicoloured.

39. 3p. Type **8** 30 20
40. 3½p. Alan Holmes, Double Winner, 1957 .. .. 30 20

9. Princess Anne and Capt. Mark Phillips.

1973. Royal Wedding.

41. **9.** 25p. multicoloured .. 1·00 90

10. Badge, Citation and Sir William Hillary (Founder).

1974. 150th Anniv. of Royal National Lifeboat Institution. Multicoloured.

42. 3p. Type **10** 10 10
43. 3½p. Wreck of "St. George", 1830 .. 15 15
44. 8p. R.N.L.B. "Manchester and Salford", 1868-87 .. 60 65
45. 10p. R.N.L.B. "Osman Gabriel" .. 60 65

11. Stanley Woods, 1935.

1974. Tourist Trophy Motor-cycle Races (1st issue). Multicoloured.

46. 3p. Type **11** 10 10
47. 3½p. Freddy Frith, 1937 .. 10 10
48. 8p. Max Deubel and Emil Horner, 1961 .. .. 45 45
49. 10p. Mike Hailwood, 1961 55 45

See also Nos 63/6.

12. Rushen Abbey and Arms.

1974. Historical Anniversaries. Multicoloured.

50. 3½p. Type **12** .. 10 10
51. 4½p. Magnus Haraldson rows King Edgar on the Dee .. 10 10
52. 8p. King Magnus and Norse fleet .. 40 40
53. 10p. Bridge at Avignon and bishop's mitre .. 50 50

COMMEMORATIONS: Nos. 50 and 53, William Russell, Bishop of Sodor and Man. 600th Death Anniv Nos. 51/2, Rule of King Magnus Haraldson. 1000th Anniv.

13. Churchill, and Bugler Dunne at Colenso, 1899.

1974. Birth Centenary of Sir Winston Churchill. Multicoloured.

54. 3½p. Type **13** 10 10
55. 4½p. Churchill and Government Buildings, Douglas 10 10
56. 8p. Churchill and Manx ack-ack crew 25 35
57. 20p. Churchill as Freeman of Douglas 65 55

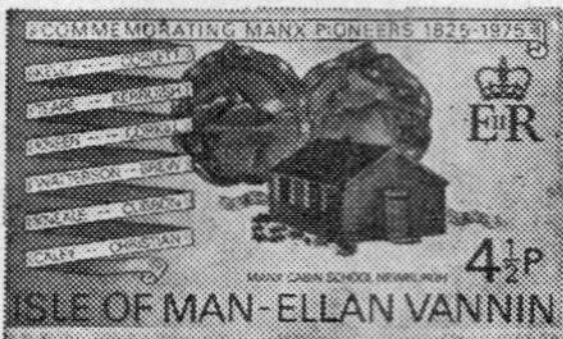

14. Cabin School and Names of Pioneers.

1975. Manx Pioneers in Cleveland, Ohio. Multicoloured.

59. 4½p. Type **14** 10 10
60. 5½p. Terminal Tower Building, J. Gill and R. Carran 15 10
61. 8p. Clague House Museum, & Robert & Margaret Clague 35 40
62. 10p. "S.S. William T. Graves" and Thomas Quayle .. 50 50

15. Tom Sheard, 1923.

1975. Tourist Trophy Motor-cycle Races (2nd issue). Multicoloured.

63. 5½p. Type **15** .. 10 15
64. 7p. Walter Handley, 1925 20 20
65. 10p. Geoff. Duke, 1955 .. 40 30
66. 12p. Peter Williams, 1973 40 45

16. Sir George Goldie and Birthplace.

1975. 50th Death Anniv. of Sir George Goldie. Multicoloured.

67. 5½p. Type **16** 10 15
68. 7p. Goldie and map of Africa (vert.) 20 20
69. 10p. Goldie as President of Geographical Society (vert.) 40 30
70. 12p. River scene on the Niger 40 45

17. Title Page of Manx Bible.

1975. Christmas and Bicentenary of Manx Bible. Multicoloured.

71. 5½p. Type **17** 15 15
72. 7p. Rev. Philip Moore and Ballaugh Old Church .. 20 20
73. 11p. Bishop Hildesley and Bishops Court .. 40 35
74. 13p. John Kelly saving Bible manuscript .. 45 40

18. William Christian listening to Patrick Henry.

1976. American Independence. Commemorating Col. William Christian. Mult.

75. 5½p. Type **18** 15 15
76. 7p. Conveying the Fincastle Resolutions 20 20
77. 13p. Patrick Henry and William Christian .. 35 35
78. 20p. Christian as an Indian fighter 50 50

19. First Horse Tram, 1876.

1976. Centenary of Douglas Horse-Trams. Multicoloured.

80. 5½p. Type **19** 10 15
81. 7p. "Toast-rack" tram, 1890 15 15
82. 11p. Horse-bus, 1895 .. 45 35
83. 13p. Royal tram, 1972 .. 50 45

20. Barrose Beaker. **21.** Diocesan Banner.

1976. Europa. Ceramic Art. Multicoloured.

84. 5p. Type **20** 20 25
85. 5p. Souvenir teapot .. 20 25
86. 5p. Laxey jug .. 20 25
87. 10p. Cronk Aust food vessel (horiz.) .. 40 45
88. 10p. Sansbury bowl (horiz.) 40 45
89. 10p. Knox urn (horiz.) .. 40 45

1976. Christmas and Centenary of Mothers' Union. Multicoloured.

90. 6p. Type **21** 15 15
91. 7p. Onchan banner .. 15 15
92. 11p. Castletown banner .. 40 35
93. 13p. Ramsey banner .. 40 45

22. Queen Elizabeth II.

1977. Silver Jubilee. Multicoloured.

94. 6p. Type **22** 20 20
95. 7p. Queen Elizabeth and Prince Philip (vert.) .. 20 20
96. 25p. Queen Elizabeth (different) 80 70

23. Carrick Bay from "Tom-the-Dipper". (Illustration reduced. Actual size 58×22 mm.)

1977. Europa. Multicoloured.

97. 6p. Type **23** 20 20
98. 10p. View from Ramsey 30 30

24. F. A. Applebee, 1912.

1977. Linked Anniversaries. Multicoloured.

99. 6p. Type **24** 15 15
100. 7p. St. John's Ambulance Brigade at Governor's Bridge, 1938 .. 15 20
101. 11p. Scouts operating the scoreboard 40 40
102. 13p. John Williams, 1976 40 40

ANNIVERSARIES: TT Races. 70th Anniv. Scouts Movement. 70th Anniv. St. John's Ambulance Brigade. Cent.

25. Old Summer House, Mount Morrison, Peel.

1977. Bicent. of First Visit of John Wesley. Multicoloured.

103. 6p. Type **25** 15 15
104. 7p. Wesley preaching in Castletown Square .. 20 20
105. 11p. Wesley preaching outside Bradden Church .. 35 35
106. 13p. New Methodist Church, Douglas 40 40

Nos. 104/5 are larger, 38 × 26 mm.

26. Short Type 184 Seaplane and H.M.S. "Ben-My-Chree", 1915.

1978. 60th Anniv. of Royal Air Force.

107. 6p. Type **26** 15 15
108. 7p. Bristol Scout and H.M.S. "Vindex", 1915 20 20
109. 11p. Boulton Paul "Defiant" over Douglas Bay, 1941 .. .. 40 35
110. 13p. "Jaguar" over Ramsey, 1977 .. 45 40

27. Watch Tower, Langness.

1978. Multicoloured.

111. ½p. Type **27** 20 10
112. 1p. Jurby Church (horiz.) 20 10
113. 6p. Government Buildings 30 25
114. 7p. Tynwald Hill (horiz.) 35 30
115. 8p. Milner's Tower .. 35 30
116. 9p. Laxey Wheel .. 35 35
117. 10p. Castle Rushen (horiz.) 35 35
118. 11p. St. Ninian's Church .. 40 40
119. 12p. Tower of Refuge (horiz.) 40 30
120. 13p. St. German's Cathedral (horiz.) 40 30
121. 14p. Point of Ayre Lighthouse (horiz.) 50 40
122. 15p. Corrin's Tower (horiz.) 50 30
123. 16p. Douglas Head Lighthouse (horiz.) 75 65
124. 20p. Fuchsia 60 50
125. 25p. Manx cat 75 65
126. 50p. Chough .. .. 1·25 1·25
127. £1 Viking warrior .. 2·50 2·50
128. £2 Queen Elizabeth II .. 4·75 3·75

Nos. 124/7 are larger, 25×31 mm. and No. 128, 38×48 mm.

28. Queen Elizabeth in Coronation Regalia.

1978. 25th Anniversary of Coronation.

132. 28. 25p. multicoloured .. 75 75

29. Wheel-headed Cross-slab.

1978. Europa. Celtic and Norse Crosses. Multicoloured.

133. 6p. Type **29** 15 15
134. 6p. Celtic wheel-cross .. 15 15
135. 6p. Keeil Chiggyrt Stone 15 15
136. 11p. Olaf Liotulfson Cross 25 30
137. 11p. Odd's and Thorleif's Crosses 25 30
138. 11p. Thor Cross 25 30

30. J. K. Ward and Ward Library, Peel.

1978. Anniversaries and Events. Mult.

139. 6p. Type **30** 15 15
140. 7p. Swimmer, cyclist and walker 20 20
141. 11p. American Bald Eagle, Manx arms and maple leaf (42 × 26 mm.) .. 35 35
142. 13p. Lumber camp, Three Rivers, Quebec .. 40 40

ANNIVERSARIES AND EVENTS: 6, 13p. James Kewley Ward (Manx pioneer in Canada) commemoration. 7p. Commonwealth Games, Edmonton. 11p. North American Manx Association. 50th Anniv.

31. Hunt the Wren.

1978. Christmas.

143. 31. 5p. multicoloured .. 30 25

32. P.M.C. Kermode and " Nassa kermodei ".

1979. Centenary of Natural History and Antiquarian Society. Multicoloured.

144 6p. Type **32** 15 15
145 7p. Peregrine falcon .. 20 20
146 11p. Fulmar 35 35
147 13p. "Epitriptus cowini" (fly) 40 40

33. Postman, 1859.

1979. Europa. Communications. Multicoloured.

148. 6p. Type **33** 20 20
149. 11p. Postman, 1979 .. 30 30

34. Viking Longship Emblem. 35. Viking Raid at Garwick.

1979. Millennium of Tynwald. Multicoloured.

150b 3p. Type **34** 10 10
151 4p. " Three Legs of Man " emblem 15 15
152 6p. Type **35** 15 15
153 7p. 10th-century meeting of Tynwald 20 20
154 11p. Tynwald Hill and St. John's Church .. 30 30
155 13p. Procession to Tynwald Hill 45 35

The 4p. value is as Type **34** and the remainder as Type **35**.

36. Queen and Court on Tynwald Hill.

1979. Royal Visit. Multicoloured.

156. 7p. Type **36** 30 20
157. 13p. Queen and Procession from St. John's Church to Tynwald Hill .. 40 40

37. " Odin's Raven ".

1979. Voyage of " Odin's Raven ".

158. 37. 15p. multicoloured .. 50 50

38. John Quilliam seized by the Press Gang.

1979. 150th Death Anniv. of Captain John Quilliam. Multicoloured.

159. 6p. Type **38** 15 15
160. 8p. Steering H.M.S. "Victory", Battle of Trafalgar .. 20 20
161. 13p. Captain John Quilliam and H.M.S. " Spencer " 50 40
162. 15p. Captain John Quilliam (member of the House of Keys) 55 45

39. Young Girl with Teddybear and Cat.

1979. Christmas. International Year of the Child. Multicoloured.

163. 5p. Type **39** 25 25
164. 7p. Father Christmas with young Children .. 35 35

40. Conglomerate Arch, Langness.

1980. 150th Anniversary of Royal Geographical Society. Multicoloured.

165. 7p. Type **40** 20 20
166. 8p. Braaid Circle 20 20
167. 12p. Cashtal-yn-Ard .. 30 30
168. 13p. Volcanic rocks at Scarlett 45 40
169. 15p. Sugar-loaf Rock .. 55 45

41. " Mona's Isle I ".

1980. 150th Anniv. of Isle of Man Steam Packet Company. Multicoloured.

170. 7p. Type **41** 20 20
171. 8p. "Douglas I" 20 20
172. 11½p. H.M.S. "Mona's Queen II" sinking U-Boat 30 30
173. 12p. H.M.S. "King Orry III" at surrender of German fleet, 1918 .. 30 30
174. 13p. "Ben-My-Chree IV" .. 35 35
175. 15p. "Lady of Mann II" .. 55 40

42. Stained Glass Window, T. E. Brown Room, Manx Museum.

1980. Europa. Personalities. Thomas Edward Brown (poet and scholar) Commemoration. Multicoloured.

177. 7p. Type **42** 20 20
178. 13½p. Clifton College, Bristol 40 40

43. King Olav V.

1980. Visit of King Olav of Norway, August 1979.

179. 43. 12p. multicoloured .. 50 50

44. Winter Wren and View of Calf of Man.

1980. Christmas and Wildlife Conservation Year. Multicoloured.

181. 6p. Type **44** 30 30
182. 8p. European Robin and view of Port Erin Marine Biological Station .. 45 45

45. William Kermode and Brig " Robert Quayle ", 1819.

1980. Kermode Family in Tasmania Commemoration. Multicoloured.

183. 7p. Type **45** 20 20
184. 9p. " Mona Vale ", Van Diemen's Land, 1834 .. 25 25
185. 13½p. Ross Bridge, Tasmania 40 35
186. 15p. " Mona Vale ", Tasmania 45 40
187. 17½p. Robert Quayle Kermode and Parliament Buildings, Tasmania 50 45

46. Peregrine Falcon.

1980. Multicoloured.

188. 1p. Type **46** 25 25
189. 5p. Loaghtyn ram .. 40 40

47. Luggers passing Red Pier, Douglas.

1981. Centenary of Royal National Mission to Deepsea Fishermen. Multicoloured.

190. 8p. Type **47** 25 25
191. 9p. Peel Lugger " Wanderer " rescuing survivors from " Lusitania " 30 30
192. 18p. Nickeys leaving Port St. Mary 55 45
193. 20p. Nobby entering Ramsey Harbour 55 50
194. 22p. Nickeys " Sunbeam " and " Zebra " at Port Erin 60 50

48. " Crosh Cuirn " Superstition.

1981. Europa. Folklore. Multicoloured.

195. 8p. Type **48** 25 25
196. 18p. " Bollan Cross " superstition 55 55

49. Lt. Mark Wilks (Royal Manx Fencibles) and Peel Castle.

1981. 150th Death Anniv. of Colonel Mark Wilks. Multicoloured.

197. 8p. Type **49** 25 25
198. 20p. Ensign Mark Wilks and Fort St. George, Madras 50 50
199. 22p. Governor Mark Wilks and Napoleon, St. Helena 70 55
200. 25p. Col. Mark Wilks (Speaker of the House of Keys) and estate, Kirby .. 80 80

50. Miss Emmeline Goulden (Mrs. Pankhurst) and Mrs. Sophia Jane Goulden.

1981. Centenary of Manx Women's Suffrage.

201. **50.** 9p. black, grey and stone 35 30

51. Prince Charles and Lady Diana Spencer.

1981. Royal Wedding.

202. **51.** 9p. black, blue and pale blue 25 25
203. 25p. black, blue & pink 75 75

52. Douglas War Memorial, Poppies and Commemorative Inscription.

1981. 60th Anniv. of The Royal British Legion. Multicoloured.

205. 8p. Type **52** 25 25
206. 10p. Major Robert Cain (war hero) 30 35
207. 18p. Festival of Remembrance, Royal Albert Hall 55 45
208. 20p. T.S.S. "Tynwald" at Dunkirk, May 1940 .. 60 50

53. Nativity Scene (stained glass window, St. George's Church).

1981. Christmas. Multicoloured.

209. 7p. Type **53** 20 20
210. 9p. Children from Special School performing nativity play (48 × 30 mm.) .. 25 25

54. Joseph and William Cunningham (founders of Isle of Man Boy Scout Movement) and Cunningham House Headquarters.

1982. 75th Anniv. of Boy Scout Movement and 125th Birth Anniv. of Lord Baden-Powell. Multicoloured.

211. 9p. Type **54** 30 30
212. 10p. Baden-Powell visiting Isle of Man, 1911 .. 30 30
213. 19½p. Baden-Powell and Scout emblem (40 × 31 mm.) 55 55
214. 24p. Scouts and Baden-Powell's last message .. 75 75
215. 29p. Scout salute, handshake, emblem and globe 95 95

55. "The Principals and Duties of Christianity" (Bishop T. Wilson) (first book printed in Manx, 1707). (Illustration reduced: Actual size 49 × 32 mm.)

1982. Europa. Historic Events. Mult.

216. 9p. Type **55** 25 25
217. 19½p. Landing at Derbyhaven (visit of Thomas, 2nd Earl of Derby, 1507) 50 50

56. Charlie Collier (first TT race (single cylinder) winner) and Tourist Trophy Race, 1907.

1982. 75th Anniv. of Tourist Trophy Motorcycle Racing. Multicoloured.

218. 9p. Type **56** 20 20
219. 10p. Freddie Dixon (Sidecar and Junior TT winner) and Junior TT race, 1927 25 25
220. 24p. Jimmie Simpson (TT winner and first to lap at 60, 70 and 80 mph) and Senior TT, 1932 .. 70 70
221. 26p. Mike Hailwood (winner of fourteen TT's) and Senior TT, 1961 .. 90 80
222. 29p. Jock Taylor (Sidecar TT winner, 1978, 1980 and 1981) and Sidecar TT (with Benga Johansson), 1980 .. .. .. 1·00 90

57. "Mona I".

1982. 150th Anniv. of Isle of Man Steam Packet Company Mail Contract. Mult.

223. 12p. Type **57** 40 40
224. 19½p. "Manx Maid II" .. 60 60

58. Three Wise Men bearing Gifts.

1982. Christmas. Multicoloured.

225. 8p. Type **58** 30 30
226. 11p. Christmas snow scene (vert.) 40 40

60. Opening of Salvation Army Citadel, and T. H. Carnell, J.P.

1983. Centenary of Salvation Army in Isle of Man. Multicoloured.

228. 10p. Type **60** 30 30
229. 12p. Early meeting place and Gen. William Booth 40 40
230. 19½p. Salvation Army band 60 60
231. 26p. Treating lepers and Lt.-Col. Thomas Bridson 90 90

61. Atlantic Puffins.

61a. "Queen Elizabeth II" (Ricardo Macarron).

1983. Sea Birds. Multicoloured.

232. 1p. Type **61** 15 15
233. 2p. Northern Gannets .. 15 15
234. 5p. Lesser Black-headed Gulls 30 30
235. 8p. Common Cormorants .. 30 30
236. 10p. Kittiwakes 35 35
237. 11p. Shags 35 35
238. 12p. Grey Herons 40 40
239. 13p. Herring-gulls 40 40
240. 14p. Razorbills 40 40
241. 15p. Great Black-backed Gulls 50 50
242. 16p. Common Shelducks .. 50 50
243. 18p. Oystercatchers .. 60 60
244. 20p. Arctic Terns 75 75
245. 25p. Common Guillemots 1·00 1·00
246. 50p. Redshanks .. .. 1·75 1·75
247. £1 Mute Swans .. .. 3·00 3·00
248. £5 Type **61a** .. .. 10·00 10·50

62. Design Drawings by Roger Casement for the Great Laxey Wheel. (Illustration reduced. Actual size 85 × 28 mm.)

1983. Europa. The Great Laxey Wheel.

249. **62.** 10p. blk., blue and buff 40 35
250. – 20½p. multicoloured .. 70 70

DESIGN: 20½p. Roger Casement and the Great Laxey Wheel.

63. Nick Keig (international yachtsman) and Trimaran "Three Legs of Man III".

1983. 150th Anniv. of King William's College. Multicoloured.

251. 10p. Type **63** 30 30
252. 12p. King William's College, Castletown 40 40
253. 28p. Sir William Bragg (winner of Nobel Prize for Physics) and spectrometer 90 90
254. 31p. General Sir George White, V.C., and action at Charasiah .. .. 1·10 1·10

64. New Post Office Headquarters, Douglas.

1983. World Communications Year and 10th Anniv. of Isle of Man Post Office Authority. Multicoloured.

255. 10p. Type **64** 40 30
256. 15p. As Type **64** but inscr. "POST OFFICE DECENNIUM 1983" .. 60 50

65. Shepherds.

1983. Christmas. Multicoloured.

257. 9p. Type **65** 50 50
258. 12p. Three Kings 50 50

66. "Manx King" (full-rigged ship).

1984. The Karren Fleet. Multicoloured.

259. 10p. Type **66** 35 35
260. 13p. "Hope" (barque) .. 45 45
261. 20½p. "Rio Grande" (brig) 70 70
262. 28p. "Lady Elizabeth" (barque) 85 85
263. 31p. "Sumatra" (barque) 95 95

67. C.E.P.T. 25th Anniversary Logo

1984. Europa.

265. **67.** 10p. orange, brown and pale orange 35 35
266. 20½p. blue, deep blue and pale blue .. 70 70

68. Railway Air Service "D.H.84"

1984. 50th Anniv. of First Official Airmail to the Isle of Man. 40th Anniv. of International Civil Aviation Organization. Multicoloured.

267. 11p. Type **68** 35 35
268. 13p. West Coast Air Services "D.H.86" 40 40
269. 26p. B.E.A. "DC-3" .. 85 85
270. 28p. B.E.A. Vickers "Viscount" 95 95
271. 31p. Telair "Islander" .. 1·10 1·10

69. Window from Glencrutchery House, Douglas.

1984. Christmas. Stained-glass Windows. Multicoloured.

272. 10p. Type **69** 50 50
273. 13p. Window from Lonan Old Church 50 50

70. William Cain's Birthplace, Ballasalla.

1984. William Cain (civic leader, Victoria) Commemoration. Multicoloured.

274. 11p. Type **70** 30 30
275. 22p. The "Anna" leaving Liverpool, 1852 .. .. 65 65
276. 28p. Early Australian railway 90 90
277. 30p. William Cain as Mayor of Melbourne, and Town Hall .. .. 1·00 1·00
278. 33p. Royal Exhibition Building, Melbourne .. 1·10 1·10

71. Queen Elizabeth II and Commonwealth Parliamentary Association Badge.

1984. Links with the Commonwealth. 30th Commonwealth Parliamentary Association Conference. Multicoloured.

279. 14p. Type **71** 45 45
280. 33p. Queen Elizabeth II and Manx emblem .. 1·00 1·00

72. Cunningham House Headquarters, and Mrs. Willie Cunningham and Mrs. Joseph Cunningham (former Commissioners).

1985. 75th Anniv. of Girl Guide Movement. Multicoloured.

281. 11p. Type **72** 45 45
282. 14p. Princess Margaret, Isle of Man standard and guides 70 70
283. 29p. Lady Olave Baden-Powell opening Guide Headquarters, 1955 .. 1·10 1·10
284. 31p. Guide uniforms from 1910 to 1985 .. .. 1·25 1·25
285. 34p. Guide handclasp, salute and early badge 1·50 1·50

73. Score of Manx National Anthem.

1985. Europa. European Music Year.

286. **73.** 12p. black, light brown and brown 45 45
287. – 12p. black, light brown and brown 45 45
288. – 22p. black, light blue and blue 95 95
289. – 22p. black, light blue and blue 95 95

Designs: No. 287, William H. Gill (lyricist). 288, Score of hymn "Crofton". 289, Dr. John Clague (composer).

74. Charles Rolls in 20 h.p. Rolls-Royce (1906 Tourist Trophy Race).

1985. Century of Motoring. Multicoloured.

290. 12p. Type **74** 40 40
291. 12p. W. Bentley in 3 litre Bentley (1922 Tourist Trophy Race) 40 40
292. 14p. F. Gerrard in E.R.A. (1950 British Empire Trophy Race) 55 55
293. 14p. Brian Lewis in Alfa Romeo (1934 Mannin Moar Race) 55 55
294. 31p. Jaguar "XJ-SC" ("Roads Open" car, 1984 Motor Cycle T.T. Races) 1·25 1·25
295. 31p. Tony Pond and Mike Nicholson in Vauxhall "Chevette" (1981 Rothmans International Rally) .. .. .. 1·25 1·25

75. Queen Alexandra and Victorian Sergeant with Wife.

1985. Centenary of Soldiers', Sailors' and Airmen's Families Association. Designs showing Association Presidents. Mult.

296. 12p. Type **75** 55 55
297. 15p. Queen Mary and Royal Air Force family 70 70
298. 29p. Earl Mountbatten and Royal Navy family .. 1·25 1·25
299. 34p. Prince Michael of Kent and Royal Marine with parents, 1982 .. 1·40 1·40

76. Kirk Maughold (birthplace).

1985. Birth Bicentenary of Lieutenant-General Sir Mark Cubbon (Indian administrator). Multicoloured.

300. 12p. Type **76** 45 45
301. 22p. Lieutenant-General Sir Mark Cubbon (vert.) 85 85
302. 45p. Memorial statue, Bangalore, India (vert.) 1·75 1·75

77. St. Peter's Church, Onchan.

1985. Christmas. Manx Churches. Mult.

303. 11p. Type **77** 45 45
304. 14p. Royal Chapel of St. John, Tynwald 55 55
305. 31p. Bride Parish Church 1·25 1·25

78. Swimming.

1986. Commonwealth Games, Edinburgh. Multicoloured.

306. 12p. Type **78** 50 50
307. 15p. Race walking .. 60 60
308. 31p. Rifle-shooting .. 1·40 1·40
309. 34p. Cycling .. .. 1·40 1·40

No. 309 also commemorates the 50th anniversary of Manx International Cycling Week.

79. Viking Necklace and Peel Castle.

1986. Centenary of Manx Museum. Mult.

310. 12p. Type **79** 45 45
311. 15p. Meayll Circle, Rushen 55 55
312. 22p. Skeleton of Great Deer and Manx Museum (vert.) 85 85
313. 26p. Viking longship model (vert.) 95 95
314. 29p. Open Air Museum, Cregneash .. .. 1·10 1·10

80. Viking Longship.

1986. Manx Heritage Year.

315. **80.** 2p. multicoloured .. 25 25
316. – 10p. black, green and grey 75 75

Design: 10p. Celtic cross logo.

81. "Usnea articulata" (lichen) and "Neotinea intacta" (orchid), The Ayres.

1986. Europa. Protection of Nature and the Environment. Multicoloured.

317. 12p. Type **81** 45 45
318. 12p. Hen harrier, Calf of Man 45 45
319. 22p. Manx stoat, Eary Cushlin 80 80
320. 22p. "Stenobothus stigmaticus" (grasshopper), St. Michael's Isle .. 80 80

82. Ellanbane (home of Myles Standish).

1986. "Ameripex '86" International Stamp Exhibition, Chicago. Captain Myles Standish of the "Mayflower". Multicoloured.

321. 12p. Type **82** 35 35
322. 15p. "Mayflower" crossing the Atlantic, 1620 .. 55 55
323. 31p. Pilgrim Fathers landing at Plymouth, 1620 .. 1·10 1·10
324. 34p. Captain Myles Standish .. .. .. 1·40 1·40

83. Prince Andrew in Naval Uniform and Miss Sarah Ferguson.

1986. Royal Wedding. Multicoloured.

326. 15 p. Type **83** 60 60
327. 40p. Engagement photograph .. .. 1·40 1·40

84. Prince Philip (from photo by Karsh).

1986. Royal Birthdays. Multicoloured.

328. 15p. Type **84** 60 60
329. 15p. Queen Elizabeth II (from photo by Karsh) 60 60
330. 34p. Queen Elizabeth and Prince Philip (from photo by Karsh) (48×35 mm.) .. .. 1·50 1·50

Nos. 328/30 also commemorate "Stockholmia '86" International Stamp Exhibition, Sweden and the 350th anniversary of the Swedish Post Office.

85. European Robins on Globe and "Peace and Goodwill" in Braille.

1986. Christmas and International Peace Year. Multicoloured.

331. 11p. Type **85** 50 50
332. 14p. Hands releasing peace dove 55 55
333. 31p. Clasped hands and "Peace" in sign language 1·25 1·25

86. North Quay.

1987. Victorian Douglas. Multicoloured.

334. 2p. Type **86** 10 10
335. 3p. Old Fishmarket .. 10 10
336. 10p. The Breakwater .. 35 35
337. 15p. Jubilee Clock 50 50
338. 31p. Loch Promenade .. 1·25 1·25
339. 34p. Beach .. .. .. 1·40 1·40

87. "Douglas Quay, 1899".

1987. Paintings by John Miller Nicholson. Multicoloured.

340.	12p. Type **87**	35	35
341.	26p. "Fishing Boats, Douglas, 1900"	80	80
342.	29p. "Peel Harbour, 1905"	95	95
343.	34p. "Fishing Boats and Castle, Peel, 1909" . .	1·25	1·25

88. Sea Terminal, Douglas.

1987. Europa. Architecture. Multicoloured.

344.	12p. Type **88**	45	45
345.	12p. Tower of Refuge, Douglas	45	45
346.	22p. Gaiety Theatre, Douglas	85	85
347.	22p. Villa Marina, Douglas	85	85

89. Supercharged "BMW" 500cc Motor Cycle, 1939.

1987. 80th Anniv. of Tourist Trophy Motor Cycle Races. Multicoloured.

348.	12p. Type **89**	40	40
349.	15p. Manx "Kneeler" Norton 350cc, 1953 . .	60	60
350.	29p. MV Agusta 500cc 4, 1956	1·00	1·00
351.	31p. Guzzi 500cc V8, 1957	1·10	1·10
352.	34p. Honda 250cc 6, 1967 . .	1·40	1·40

Nos. 348/52 also commemorate the Centenary of the St. John Ambulance Brigade.

90. Fuchsia and Wild Roses.

1987. Wild Flowers. Multicoloured.

354.	16p. Type **90**	50	50
355.	29p. Field scabious and ragwort	90	90
356.	31p. Wood anemone and celandine	1·00	1·00
357.	34p. Violets and primroses	1·25	1·25

91. Stirring the Christmas Pudding.

1987. Christmas. Victorian Scenes. Mult.

358.	12p. Type **91**	50	50
359.	15p. Bringing home the Christmas tree	65	65
360.	31p. Decorating the Christmas tree	1·10	1·10

92. Russell Brookes in Vauxhall "Opel" (Manx Rally winner, 1985). (Illustration reduced. Actual size 60 × 24 mm.).

1988. Motor Sport. Multicoloured.

361.	13p. Type **92**	60	60
362.	26p. Ari Vatanen in Ford "Escort" (Manx Rally winner, 1976)	90	90
363.	31p. Terry Smith in Repco "March 761" (Hill Climb winner, 1980)	1·00	1·00
364.	34p. Nigel Mansell in Williams/Honda (British Grand Prix winner, 1986 and 1987)	1·10	1·10

93. Horse Tram Terminus, Douglas Bay Tramway.

93a Queen Elizabeth II taking Salute at Trooping the Colour

1988. Manx Railways and Tramways. Mult.

365	1p. Type **93**	10	10
366	2p. Snaefell Mountain Railway	10	10
367	3p. Marine Drive Tramway	10	10
367c	4p. Douglas Cable Tramway	10	10
368	5p. Douglas Head Incline Railway	10	10
369	10p. Manx Electric Railway train at Maughold Head . .	20	25
370	13p. As 4p.	25	30
371	14p. Manx Northern Railway No. 4, "Caledonia", at Gob-y-Deigan . .	30	35
372	15p. Laxey Mine Railway Lewin locomotive "Ant"	30	35
373	16p. Port Erin Breakwater Tramway locomotive "Henry B. Loch"	30	35
374	17p. Ramsey Harbour Tramway	35	40
375	18p. Locomotive No. 7, "Tynwald", on Foxdale line	35	40
375a	18p. T.P.O. Special leaving Douglas, 3 July 1991	35	40
376	19p. Baldwin Reservoir Tramway steam locomotive "Injebreck" . .	40	45
377	20p. I.M.R. No. 13, "Kissack", near St. Johns	40	45
377a	21p. As 14p.	40	45
377b	23p. Double-decker horse tram, Douglas . .	45	50
378	25p. I.M.R. No. 12, "Hutchinson", leaving Douglas . .	50	55
379	50p. Groudle Glen Railway locomotive "Polar Bear"	1·00	1·10
380	£1 I.M.R. No. 11, "Maitland", pulling Royal Train, 1963 . .	2·00	2·10
380a	£2 Type **93a**	4·00	4·25

94. Laying Isle of Man–U.K. Submarine Cable.

1988. Europa. Transport and Communications. Multicoloured.

381.	13p. Type **94**	40	40
382.	13p. Cable ship	40	40
383.	22p. Earth station, Braddan	70	70
384.	22p. "INTELSAT 5" satellite	70	70

Nos. 381/2 and 383/4 were each printed together, se-tenant. Nos. 381/2 forming a composite design.

95 "Euterpe" (full-rigged ship) off Ramsey, 1863

1988. Manx Sailing Ships. Multicoloured.

385	16p. Type **95**	50	50
386	29p. "Vixen" (topsail schooner) leaving Peel for Australia, 1853 . .	85	85
387	31p. "Ramsey" (full-rigged ship) off Brisbane, 1870	90	90
388	34p. "Star of India" (formerly "Euterpe") (barque) off San Diego, 1976	1·10	1·10

Nos. 386/7 also commemorate the Bicent of Australian Settlement.

96 "Magellanica"

1988. 50th Anniv of British Fuchsia Society. Multicoloured.

390	13p. Type **96**	40	40
391	16p. "Pink Cloud" . .	50	50
392	22p. "Leonora"	70	70
393	29p. "Satellite"	1·00	1·00
394	31p. "Preston Guild" . .	1·10	1·10
395	34p. "Thalia" . .	1·25	1·25

97 Long-eared Owl

1988. Christmas. Manx Birds. Multicoloured.

396	12p. Type **97**	50	50
397	15p. European robin . .	65	65
398	31p. Grey partridge . .	1·10	1·10

98 Ginger Cat

1989. Manx Cats. Multicoloured.

399	16p. Type **98**	50	50
400	27p. Black and white cat	90	90
401	30p. Tortoiseshell and white cat	1·10	1·10
402	40p. Tortoiseshell cat . .	1·40	1·40

99 Tudric Pewter Clock, c. 1903

1989. 125th Birth Anniv of Archibald Knox (artist and designer). Multicoloured.

403	13p. Type **99**	35	35
404	16p. "Celtic Cross" watercolour	45	45
405	23p. Silver cup and cover, 1902–03	75	75
406	32p. Gold and silver brooches from Liberty's Cymric range (horiz) . .	1·10	1·10
407	35p. Silver jewel box, 1900 (horiz)	1·25	1·25

100 William Bligh and Old Church, Onchan

1989. Bicentenary of the Mutiny on the "Bounty". Multicoloured.

408	13p. Type **100**	25	30
409	16p. Bligh and loyal crew cast adrift	30	35
410	23p. Pitcairn Islands 1989 Settlement Bicentenary 90 c., No. 345	80	85
411	27p. Norfolk Island 1989 Bicentenary 39 c., No. 461	90	95
412	30p. Midshipman Peter Heywood and Tahiti . .	70	70
413	32p. H.M.S. "Bounty" anchored off Pitcairn Island	75	75
414	35p. Fletcher Christian and Pitcairn Island . .	80	80

101 Skipping and Hopscotch

1989. Europa. Children's Games. Mult.

416	13p. Type **101**	50	50
417	13p. Wheelbarrow, leapfrog and piggyback	50	50
418	23p. Building model house and blowing bubbles . .	75	75
419	23p. Girl with doll and doll's house	75	75

Nos. 416/17 and 418/19 were printed together, se-tenant, forming composite designs.

102 Atlantic Puffin

104 Mother with Baby, Jane Cookall Maternity Home

103 Red Cross Cadets learning Resuscitation

1989. Sea Birds. Multicoloured.

420 13p. Type **102** 40 40
421 13p. Black guillemot .. 40 40
422 13p. Common cormorant 40 40
423 13p. Kittiwake 40 40

1989. 125th Anniv of International Red Cross and Centenary of Noble's Hospital, Isle of Man.

424 **103** 14p. multicoloured .. 30 35
425 – 17p. grey and red .. 50 45
426 – 23p. multicoloured .. 75 75
427 – 30p. multicoloured .. 95 95
428 – 35p. multicoloured .. 1·10 1·10

DESIGNS: 17p. Anniversary logo; 23p. Signing Geneva Convention, 1864; 30p. Red Cross ambulance; 35p. Henri Dunant (founder).

1989. Christmas. 50th Anniv of Jane Crookall Maternity Home and 75th Anniv of St. Ninian's Church, Douglas. Multicoloured.

429 13p. Type **104** 35 35
430 16p. Mother with child .. 45 45
431 34p. Madonna and Child .. 90 90
432 37p. Baptism, St. Ninian's Church .. .. .. 1·10 1·10

105 "The Isle of Man Express going up a Gradient"

1990. Isle of Man Edwardian Postcards. Mult.

433 15p. Type **105** 30 35
434 19p. "A way we have in the Isle of Man" .. 50 45
435 32p. "Douglas–waiting for the male boat" .. 75 75
436 34p. "The last toast rack home, Douglas Parade" 95 95
437 37p. "The last Isle of Man boat" .. .. .. 1·10 1·10

106 Modern Postman

107 Penny Black

1990. Europa. Post Office Buildings. Mult.

438 15p. Type **106** 30 35
439 15p. Ramsey Post Office, 1990 (40 × 26 mm) .. 30 35
440 24p. Postman, 1890 .. 50 55
441 24p. Douglas Post Office, 1890 (40 × 26 mm) .. 50 55

1990. 150th Anniv of the Penny Black.

442 **107** 1p. black, buff & gold 10 10
443 – 19p. gold, black & buff 40 45
444 – 32p. multicoloured .. 65 70
445 – 34p. multicoloured .. 70 75
446 – 37p. multicoloured .. 75 80

DESIGNS: 19p. Wyon Medal, 1837; 32p. Wyon's stamp essay; 34p. Perkins Bacon engine-turned essay, 1839; 37p. Twopence Blue, 1840.

108 Queen Elizabeth the Queen Mother

1990. 90th Birthday of Queen Elizabeth the Queen Mother.

448 **108** 90p. multicoloured .. 2·25 2·25

109 Hurricane, Blenheim and Home Defence

1990. 50th Anniv of Battle of Britain. Mult.

449 15p. Type **109** 35 35
450 15p. Spitfire with rescue aircraft and launch .. 35 35
451 24p. Rearming fighters .. 70 70
452 24p. Ops room and scramble 70 70
453 29p. Civil Defence personnel 75 75
454 29p. Anti-aircraft battery 75 75

110 Churchill with Freedom of Douglas Casket

1990. 25th Death Anniv of Sir Winston Churchill. Multicoloured.

455 19p. Type **110** 55 55
456 32p. Churchill and London blitz 85 85
457 34p. Churchill and searchlights over Westminster 95 95
458 37p. Churchill with R.A.F. fighters .. .. 1·00 1·00

111 Boy on Toboggan and Girl posting Letter

1990. Christmas. Multicoloured.

459 14p. Type **111** 40 40
460 18p. Girl on toboggan and skaters 45 45
461 34p. Boy with snowman .. 95 95
462 37p. Children throwing snowballs .. .. 1·00 1·00

112 Henry Bloom Noble and Orphans (Marshall Wane)

1991. Manx Photography.

464 **112** 17p. brown, grey & blk 35 40
465 – 21p. brown and ochre 45 50
466 – 26p. brn, stone & blk 70 70
467 – 31p. brn, lt brn & blk 95 95
468 – 40p. multicoloured .. 1·10 1·10

DESIGNS: 21p. Douglas (Frederick Frith); 26p. Studio portrait of three children (Hilda Newby); 31p. Cashtal yn Ard (Christopher Killip); 40p. Peel Castle (Colleen Corlett).

113 Lifeboat "Sir William Hillary", Douglas

1991. Manx Lifeboats. Multicoloured.

469 17p. Type **113** 35 40
470 21p. "Osman Gabriel", Port Erin 50 50
471 26p. "James & Ann Ritchie", Ramsey .. 70 70
472 31p. "The Gough Ritchie", Port St. Mary 95 95
473 37p. "John Batstone", Peel 1·10 1·10

No. 469 is inscribed "HILARY" in error.

114 "Intelsat" Communications Satellite

1991. Europa. Europe in Space. Mult.

474 17p. Type **114** 50 50
475 17p. "Ariane" rocket launch and fishing boats in Douglas harbour .. 50 50
476 26p. Weather satellite and space station 75 75
477 26p. Ronaldsway Airport, Manx Radio transmitter and Space shuttle launch 75 75

Nos. 474/5 and 476/7 were each printed together, se-tenant, each pair forming a composite design.

115 Oliver Godfrey with Indian 500cc at Start, 1911

1991. 80th Anniv of Tourist Trophy Mountain Course. Multicoloured.

478 17p. Type **115** 40 40
479 21p. Freddie Dixon on Douglas "banking" sidecar, 1923 .. .. 50 50
480 26p. Bill Ivy on Yamaha 125cc, 1968 .. .. 70 70
481 31p. Giacomo Agostini on MV Agusta 500cc, 1972 95 95
482 37p. Joey Dunlop on RVF Honda 750cc, 1985 .. 1·10 1·10

116 Laxey Hand-cart, 1920

1991. Fire Engines. Multicoloured.

485 17p. Type **116** 35 40
486 21p. Horse-drawn steamer, Douglas, 1909 .. .. 40 45
487 30p. Merryweather "Hatfield" pump, 1936 .. 60 65
488 33p. Dennis "F8" pumping appliance, Peel, 1953 .. 65 70
489 37p. Volvo turntable ladder, Douglas, 1989 .. 75 80

117 Mute Swans, Douglas Harbour

1991. Swans. Multicoloured.

490 17p. Type **117** 35 40
491 17p. Black swans, Curraghs Wildlife Park 35 40
492 26p. Whooper swans, Bishop's Dub, Ballaugh 50 55
493 26p. Bewick's swans, Eairy Dam, Foxdale 50 55
494 37p. Coscaroba swans, Curraghs Wildlife Park 75 80
495 37p. Trumpeter swans, Curraghs Wildlife Park 75 80

The two designs of each value were printed together, se-tenant, forming a composite design.

118 The Three Kings

1991. Christmas. Paper Sculptures. Mult.

496 16p. Type **118** 30 35
497 20p. Mary with manger .. 40 45
498 26p. Shepherds with sheep 50 55
499 37p. Choir of angels .. 75 80

119 North African and Italian Campaigns, 1942–43

1992. 50th Anniv of Parachute Regiment. Multicoloured.

502 23p. Type **119** 45 50
503 23p. D-Day, 1944 .. .. 45 50
504 28p. Arnhem, 1944 .. .. 55 60
505 28p. Rhine crossing, 1945 55 60
506 39p. Operations in Near, Middle and Far East, 1945–68 .. .. .. 80 85
507 39p. Liberation of Falkland Islands, 1982 .. .. 80 85

120 Queen Elizabeth II at Coronation, 1953

1992. 40th Anniv of Accession. Multicoloured.

508	18p. Type **120**	35	40
509	23p. Queen visiting Isle of Man, 1979	45	50
510	28p. Queen in evening dress	55	60
511	33p. Queen visiting Isle of Man, 1989	70	75
512	39p. Queen arriving for film premiere, 1990	80	85

121 Brittle-stars

1992. Centenary of Port Erin Marine Laboratory. Multicoloured.

513	18p. Type **121**	35	40
514	23p. Phytoplankton	45	50
515	28p. Herring	55	60
516	33p. Great scallop	70	75
517	39p. Dahlia anemone and delesseria	80	85

122 The Pilgrim Fathers embarking at Delfshaven

1992. Europa. 500th Anniv of Discovery of America by Columbus. Multicoloured.

518	18p. Type **122**	35	40
519	18p. "Speedwell" leaving Delfshaven	35	40
520	28p. "Mayflower" setting sail for America	55	60
521	28p. "Speedwell" anchored at Dartmouth	55	60

The two designs for each value were printed together, se-tenant in horizontal pairs forming composite design.

123 Central Pacific Locomotive "Jupiter", 1869

1992. Construction of the Union Pacific Railroad, 1866–69. Multicoloured.

522	33p. Type **123**	70	75
523	33p. Union Pacific locomotive No. 119, 1869	70	75
524	39p. Union Pacific locomotive No. 844, 1992	80	85
525	39p. Union Pacific locomotive No. 3985, 1992	80	85

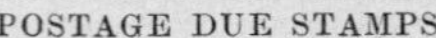

D 1.

D 2.

1973.

D 1.	D **1.**	½p. red, black and yell.	2·25	1·40
D 2.		1p. red, black and brn.	75	55
D 3.		2p. red, black and green	15	20
D 4.		3p. red, black and grey	25	25
D 5.		4p. red, black and pink	35	30
D 6.		5p. red, black and blue	40	35
D 7.		10p. red, blk. & violet	50	45
D 8.		20p. red, black and grn.	90	70

1975.

D 9.	D **2.**	½p. yellow, black & red	10	10
D 10.		1p. brown, black & red	10	10
D 11.		4p. lilac, black & red	10	10
D 12.		7p. blue, black & red	20	20
D 13.		9p. grey, black & red	25	25
D 14.		10p. mauve, blk. & red	30	30
D 15.		50p. orge., blk. & red	1·40	1·40
D 16.		£1 grn., blk. & red	2·00	2·00

D 3.

1982.

D 17.	D **3.**	1p. multicoloured	10	10
D 18.		2p. multicoloured	10	10
D 19.		5p. multicoloured	10	10
D 20.		10p. multicoloured	20	25
D 21.		20p. multicoloured	40	45
D 22.		50p. multicoloured	1·00	1·10
D 23.		£1 multicoloured	2·00	2·10
D 24.		£2 multicoloured	4·00	4·25

JAIPUR

A state of Rajasthan, India (q.v.). Now uses Indian stamps.

12 pies = 1 anna; 16 annas = 1 rupee.

1. Chariot of the Sun God, Surya. **3.**

1904.

5.	**1.**	½ a. blue	2·75	3·50
3.		1 a. red	2·75	7·50
4.		2 a. green	2·50	9·00

1904.

9	**3.**	¼ a. olive	20	20
25		½ a. blue	20	30
28		1 a. red	35	75
29		2 a. green	85	1·40
30		4 a. brown	1·25	2·75
14		8 a. violet	3·00	2·75
15		1 r. yellow	8·00	8·50

This set was issued engraved in 1904 and surface-printed in 1913.

4. Chariot of the Sun God, Surya.

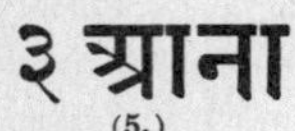

(**5.**)

1911. No gum.

17.	**4.**	¼ a. olive	30	40
18.		½ a. blue	30	40
20.		1 a. red	30	40
21.		2 a. green	2·00	5·50

1926. Surch. with T **5.**

32.	**3.**	3 a. on 8 a. violet	90	1·40
33.		3 a. on 1 r. yellow	1·00	2·00

6. Chariot of the Sun God, Surya.

7. Maharaja Sir Man Singh Bahadur.

1931. Investiture of H.H. the Maharaja. Centres in black.

40.	**6.**	¼ a. purple	45	45
58.	**7.**	¼ a. red	30	10
41.		½ a. violet	20	10
59.		¾ a. red	1·75	1·00
42.	–	1 a. blue	3·25	3·50
60.	**7.**	1 a. blue	2·25	45
43.	–	2 a. orange	3·25	3·50
61.	**7.**	2 a. orange	2·25	1·00
44.	–	2½ a. red	25·00	29·00
62.	**7.**	2½ a. red	55	40
45.	–	3 a. green	10·00	24·00
63.	**7.**	3 a. green	55	35
46.	–	4 a. green	11·00	26·00
64.	**7.**	4 a. green	5·50	30·00
47.	–	6 a. blue	6·00	26·00
65.	**7.**	6 a. blue	1·40	9·00
48.	–	8 a. brown	9·00	40·00
66.	**7.**	8 a. brown	6·50	35·00
49.	–	1 r. olive	22·00	75·00
67.	**7.**	1 r. bistre	13·00	50·00
50.	–	2 r. green	15·00	85·00
51.	–	5 r. purple	26·00	95·00

DESIGNS—VERT. 1 a. (No. 42), Elephant and banner. 2 a. (No. 43), Sowar in armour. 2½ a. (No. 44) Common Peafowl. 8 a. (No. 48), Sireh-Deorhi Gate. HORIZ. 3 a. (No. 45), Bullock carriage. 4 a. (No. 46), Elephant carriage. 6 a. (No. 47), Albert Museum. 1 r. (No. 49), Chandra Mahal. 2 r. Amber Palace. 5 r. Maharajas Sawai Jai Singh and Sir Man Singh.

1932. As T **7**, but inscr. "POSTAGE & REVENUE". Portrait in black.

52.	1 a. blue	30	20
53.	2 a. brown	45	40
54.	4 a. green	1·60	2·25
55.	8 a. brown	2·50	3·75
56.	1 r. bistre	12·00	40·00
57.	2 r. green	48·00	£150

1936. Nos. 57 and 51 surch. **One Rupee.**

68.	1 r. on 2 r. green	2·50	25·00
69.	1 r. on 5 r. purple	2·50	20·00

1938. No. 41 surch. in native characters.

70.	**7.**	¼ a. on ½ a. violet	3·25	6·00

13. Maharaja and Amber Palace.

1947. Silver Jubilee of Reign of H.H. the Maharaja of Jaipur. Inscr. as in T **13.**

71.	–	¼ a. brown and green	15	90
72.	**13.**	½ a. green and violet	15	90
73.	–	¾ a. black and red	15	1·25
74.	–	1 a. brown and blue	30	1·10
75.	–	2 a. violet and red	20	1·10
76.	–	3 a. green and black	30	1·75
77.	–	4 a. blue and brown	45	1·10
78.	–	8 a. red and brown	60	1·75
79.	–	1 r. purple and green	1·00	5·50

DESIGNS: ¼ a. Palace Gate. ¾ a. Map of Jaipur. 1 a. Observatory. 2 a. Wind Palace. 3 a. Coat of Arms. 4 a. Amber Fort Gate. 8 a. Chariot of the Sun. 1 r. Maharaja's portrait between State flags.

1947. No. 41 surch. **3 PIES** and bars.

80.	**7.**	3 p. on ½ a. violet	7·00	14·00

OFFICIAL STAMPS

1929. Optd. **SERVICE.** No gum (except for No. O 6).

O 1a.	**3.**	¼ a. bistre	40	40
O 2.		½ a. blue	30	10
O 3c.		1 a. red	35	20
O 5.		2 a. green	40	40
O 6.		4 a. brown (with gum)	2·00	1·75
O 7.		8 a. violet	18·00	42·00
O 8.		1 r. orange	35·00	£110

1931. Stamps of 1931–32 optd. **SERVICE.**

O 23	**7**	¼ a. red	30	10
O 13		½ a. violet	20	10
O 24		¾ a. orange	1·10	30
O 25		1 a. blue	4·25	30
O 14	–	1 a. blue (No. 42)	£170	1·50
O 18	–	1 a. blue (No. 52)	60	10
O 15	–	2 a. orange (No. 43)	2·00	2·25
O 19	–	2 a. brown (No. 53)	60	10
O 26	**7**	2 a. orange	3·75	50
O 27		2½ a. red	6·00	27·00
O 16	–	4 a. green (No. 46)	10·00	10·00
O 20	–	4 a. green (No. 54)	£150	3·50
O 28	**7**	4 a. green	3·25	1·50
O 21	–	8 a. brown (No. 55)	1·90	1·10
O 29	**7**	8 a. brown	2·75	2·50
O 22	–	1 r. bistre (No. 56)	7·50	8·50
O 30	**7**	1 r. bistre	£200	

1932. No. O 5 surch.

O 17.	**3.**	½ a. on 2 a. green	£100	40

1947. Official stamps surch.

O 33.	**7.**	3 p. on ½ a. violet	1·75	4·75
O 32.		9 p. on 1 a. blue	50	60

1949. No. O 14 surch. in native characters.

O 34.	**7.**	¾ a. on ½ a. violet	6·50	7·00

For later issues see **RAJASTHAN.**

JAMAICA

An island in the W. Indies. Part of the Br. Caribbean Federation from 3rd Jan. 1958, until 6th Aug. 1962 when Jamaica became an independent state within the Commonwealth.

1860. 12 pence = 1 shilling.
20 shillings = 1 pound.
1969. 100 cents = 1 dollar.

8.

11.

1860. Portrait as T **8**. Various frames.
7 **8** ½d. red .. .. .. 12·00 3·50
16a ½d. green 80 10
8 1d. blue .. .. .. 45·00 75
18a 1d. red .. .. .. 22·00 50
9 2d. red .. .. .. 48·00 70
20a 2d. grey .. .. .. 40·00 50
21a 3d. green .. .. .. 2·50 1·00
22a 4d. orange .. .. .. 2·00 35
52a 6d. lilac .. .. .. 7·00 11·00
23a 6d. yellow .. .. .. 4·00 3·50
24 1s. brown .. .. .. 5·00 4·50
25 2s. red .. .. .. 27·00 17·00
26 5s. lilac .. .. .. 48·00 48·00
See also Nos. 47a etc.

1889.
27. **11.** 1d. purple and mauve .. 2·25 10
28a. 2d. green.. .. .. 4·50 6·00
29. 2½d. purple and blue .. 4·50 40

1890. No. 22a surch. **TWO PENCE HALF-PENNY.**
30. **8.** 2½d. on 4d. orange .. 27·00 8·50

13. Llandovery Falls, Jamaica.

1900.
31. **13.** 1d. red .. .. .. 1·00 10
32. 1d. black and red .. .. 1·75 10

14. Arms of Jamaica **16.**

1903.
33. **14.** ½d. grey and green .. 1·50 10
34. 1d. grey and red .. 1·50 10
35. 2½d. grey and blue .. 2·00 30
42. 2½d. blue.. .. .. 2·50 1·25
36. 5d. grey and yellow .. 12·00 23·00
44. 6d. purple .. .. 11·00 12·00
45. 5s. grey and violet .. 40·00 30·00

1906.
38a. **16.** ½d. green.. .. .. 3·75 20
40. 1d. red .. .. .. 1·25 10

1908. Queen Victoria portraits as 1860.
47a. 3d. purple on yellow .. 2·00 1·40
48. 4d. brown .. .. 70·00 38·00
49. 4d. black on yellow .. 7·00 25·00
50. 4d. red on yellow .. 1·50 5·00
54. 1s. black on green .. 3·50 8·50
56. 2s. purple on blue .. 6·00 3·50

17.

1911.
57. **17.** 2d. grey .. .. .. 1·75 13·00

1912. As T **17**, but King George V.
89a ½d. green 20 10
58 1d. red 45 10
59 1½d. orange .. .. 1·00 15
60 2d. grey .. .. .. 90 1·75
61 2½d. blue 60 15
62 3d. purple on yellow .. 40 45
63 4d. black and red on yellow 50 1·50
64a 6d. purple and mauve .. 70 1·00
65a 1s. black on green .. 70 3·50
66 2s. purple and blue on blue 9·50 17·00
67 5s. green and red on yellow 35·00 55·00

1916. Optd **WAR STAMP** in one line.
76 **16.** ½d. green.. .. .. 10 15
77a – 3d. purple on yellow (62) 65 1·25

1916. Optd **WAR STAMP** in two lines.
73 **16.** ½d. green 10 20
74 – 1½d. orange (No. 59) .. 10 10
75 – 3d. purple on yellow (62) 15 30

23. Jamaica Exhibition, 1891. **24.** Arawak Woman preparing Cassava.

27. Return of War Contingent.

34.

1919.
91a **23.** ½d. green and olive .. 25 10
79 **24.** 1d. red and orange (A)* 1·75 90
92 1d. red and orange (B)* 1·50 10
93 – 1½d. green 30 15
94 – 2d. blue and green .. 3·00 30
82a **27.** 2½d. blue 70 90
96a – 3d. green and blue .. 40 15
97a – 4d. brown and green .. 40 15
98a – 6d. black and blue .. 6·50 60
99a – 1s. orange 60 15
100 – 2s. blue and brown .. 2·50 35
101 – 3s. violet and orange .. 6·50 9·50
102c – 5s. blue & bistre .. 22·00 22·00
103 **34.** 10s. green .. .. 48·00 60·00
* Two types of the 1d. (A) Without and (B) with "POSTAGE & REVENUE" at foot,
DESIGNS—41½ × 26 mm.: 1½d. War Contingent embarking. 6d. Port Royal, 1853. 27 × 22 mm.: 3d. Landing of Columbus. 22 × 29 mm.: 2d. King's House, Spanish Town. 22 × 28 mm.: 4d. Cathedral, Spanish Town. 25 × 30 mm.: 1s. Statue of Queen Victoria. 3s. Sir Charles Metcalfe Monument. 25 × 31 mm.: 2s Admiral Rodney Memorial. 5s. Jamaican scenery.

37.

1923. Child Welfare. Designs as T **37.**
104. **37.** ½d. + ½d. black and green 60 3·00
105. – 1d. + ½d. black and red 1·50 10·00
106. – 2½d. + ½d. black and blue 7·00 18·00

41.

43. Coco palms at Don Christopher's Cove.

1929. Various frames.
108 **41** 1d. red.. .. .. 40 10
109 1½d. brown 40 15
110 9d. red.. .. .. 2·50 1·00

1932.
111. **43.** 2d. black and green .. 4·25 1·25
112. – 2½d. green and blue .. 80 70
113. – 6d. grey and purple .. 3·75 1·25
DESIGNS—VERT. 2½d. Wag Water River, St. Andrew. HORIZ. 6d. Priestman's River. Portland.

1935. Silver Jubilee. As T **13** of Antigua.
114. 1d. blue and red 20 15
115. 1½d. blue and black .. 35 35
116. 6d. green and blue .. 3·00 5·00
117. 1s. grey and purple .. 3·00 5·00

1937. Coronation. As T **2** of Aden.
118. 1d. red 30 15
119. 1½d. grey 50 30
120. 2½d. blue .. .. .. 1·10 70

48. King George VI. **49.** Coco Palms at Don Christopher's Cove.

50. Bananas.

45. Priestman's River, Portland.

54. Bamboo Walk.

1938.
121 **48** ½d. green 20 10
121b ½d. orange 20 30
122 1d. red 10 10
122a 1d. green 30 10
123 1½d. brown 10 10
124 **49** 2d. black and green .. 10 30
125 – 2½d. green and blue .. 1·25 90
126 **50** 3d. blue and green .. 40 40
126a 3d. green and blue .. 1·25 85
126b 3d. green and red .. 80 20
127 – 4d. brown and green .. 15 10
128a **45** 6d. black & purple .. 60 10
129 – 9d. red 15 15
130 – 1s. green and brown .. 1·00 10
131 **54** 2s. blue and brown .. 7·00 60
132ba – 5s. blue and brown .. 4·00 2·75
133aa – 10s. green .. .. 8·50 5·00
133a – £1 brown and violet 24·00 26·00
DESIGNS—As Type **49**: 2½d. Wag Water River, St. Andrew. As Type **50**: 4d. Citrus grove. 9d. Kingston Harbour. 1s. Suger industry. £1, Tobacco growing and cigar making. As No. 102c, but with King's portrait added, 5s. As Type **34**: 10s. King George VI.

57. Courthouse, Falmouth.

59. Institute of Jamaica.

1945. New Constitution. Inscr. "NEW CONSTITUTION 1944".
134 **57** 1½d. brown 15 15
135a – 2d. green 15 30
136 **59** 3d. blue.. .. .. 15 20
137 – 4½d. black 15 25
138 – 2s. brown 25 40
139 – 5s. blue 50 70
140 **59** 10s. green .. .. 70 1·25
DESIGNS—As Type **57**—VERT. 2s. "Labour and Learning". HORIZ. 2d. Kings Charles II and George VI. As Type **59**—HORIZ. 4½d. House of Assembly. 5s. Scroll, flag and King George VI.

1946. Victory. As T **9** of Aden.
141 1½d. brown 55 10
142 3d. blue 55 45

1948. Silver Wedding. As T **10/11** of Aden.
143. 1½d. brown.. .. .. 30 10
144. £1 red .. .. .. 23·00 42·00

1949. U.P.U. As T **20/23** of Antigua.
145. 1½d. brown 25 15
146. 2d. green 45 90
147. 3d. blue 45 70
148. 6d. purple .. .. 55 1·25

1951. Inauguration of B.W.I. University College. As T **24/25** of Antigua.
149. 2d. black and brown .. 30 20
150. 6d. black and purple .. 35 20

69. Scout Badge and Map of Caribbean.

70. Scout Badge and Map of Jamaica.

1952. 1st Caribbean Scout Jamboree.
151 **69** 2d. blue, green & black 15 10
152 **70** 6d. green, red and black 15 30

1953. Coronation. As T **13** of Aden.
153. 2d. black and green .. 10 10

1953. Royal Visit. As T **49** but with portrait of Queen Elizabeth II and inscr "ROYAL VISIT 1953".
154. 2d. black and green .. 10 10

73. Man-o'-War at Port Royal.

1955. Tercentenary Issue.
155. **73** 2d. black and green .. 20 10
156. – 2½d. black and blue .. 15 35
157. – 3d. black and claret .. 15 30
158. – 6d. black and red .. 20 20
DESIGNS: 2½d. Old Montego Bay. 3d. Old Kingston. 6d. Proclamation of Abolition of Slavery, 1838.

74. Palms.

75. Mahoe.

76. Blue Mountain Peak.

77. Arms of Jamaica.

1956.

159	74	½d. black and red ..	10	10
160	–	1d. black and green ..	10	10
161	–	2d. black and red ..	10	10
162	–	2½d. black and blue ..	15	40
163	75	3d. green and brown ..	15	10
164	–	4d. green and blue ..	15	10
165	–	5d. red and green ..	20	1·00
166	–	6d. black and red ..	1·25	10
167	76	8d. blue and orange ..	15	10
168	–	1s. green and blue ..	30	10
169	–	1s. 6d. blue and purple	30	10
170	–	2s. blue and green ..	1·50	75
171	77	3s. black and blue ..	50	70
172	–	5s. black and red ..	1·00	1·25
173	–	10s. black and green ..	10·00	5·50
174	–	£1 black and purple ..	16·00	5·50

DESIGNS—As Type **74**: 1d. Sugar cane. 2d. Pineapples. 2½d. Bananas. As Type **75**: 4d. Breadfruit. 5d. Ackee. 6d. Streamertail. As Type **76**: 1s. Royal Botanic Gardens, Hope. 1s. 6d. Rafting on the Rio Grande. 2s. Fort Charles. As Type **77** but vert. 10s., £1, Arms without portrait.

1958. British Caribbean Federation. As T **28** of Antigua.

175.	2d. green	35	10
176.	5d. blue	60	1·25
177.	6d. red	60	30

81. "Britannia" flying over 1860 Packet-steamer.

83. 1s. Stamps of 1860 and 1956.

1960. Centenary of Jamaica Postage Stamps.

178.	81.	2d. blue and purple ..	35	10
179.	–	6d. red and olive ..	40	10
180.	83.	1s. brown, green & blue	40	15

DESIGN—As Type **81**: 6d. Postal mule-cart and motor-van.

1962. Independence. (a) Nos. 159/74 optd **INDEPENDENCE** and **1962.** (3d. to 2s.) or **1962 1962** (others).

205	74	½d. black and red ..	10	15
182	–	1d. black and green ..	10	10
183	–	2½d. black and blue ..	10	85
184	75	3d. green and brown ..	10	10
185	–	5d. red and olive ..	15	60
186	–	6d. black and red ..	75	10
187	76	8d. blue and orange ..	15	10
188	–	1s. green and blue ..	15	10
189	–	2s. blue and olive ..	80	80
190	77	3s. black and blue ..	90	1·50
191	–	10 s. black and green ..	2·00	4·00
192	–	£1 black and purple ..	2·75	5·50

86. Military Bugler and Map.

(b) As T **86** inscr. "INDEPENDENCE".

193.	86.	2d. multicoloured ..	15	10
194.		4d. multicoloured ..	15	10
195.	–	1s. 6d. black and red ..	65	85
196.	–	5s. multicoloured ..	1·25	2·00

DESIGNS: 1s. 6d. Gordon House and banner. 5s. Map, factories and fruit.

89. Kingston Seal, Weightlifting, Boxing, Football and Cycling.

1962. 9th Central American and Caribbean Games, Kingston.

197.	89.	1d. sepia and red ..	10	10
198.	–	6d. sepia and blue ..	10	10
199.	–	8d. sepia and bistre ..	10	10
200.	–	2s. multicoloured ..	25	40

DESIGNS: 6d. Diver, sailing, swimming and water polo. 8d. Javelin, discus, pole-vault, hurdles and relay-racing. 2s. Kingston Coat of Arms and athlete.

93. Farmer and Crops.

1963. Freedom from Hunger.

201.	93.	1d. multicoloured ..	15	10
202.		8d. multicoloured ..	50	20

1963. Cent of Red Cross. As T **33** of Antigua.

203.	2d. red and black	15	10
204.	1s. 6d. red and blue ..	40	65

95. Carole Joan Crawford ("Miss World 1963").

1964. "Miss World 1963" Commem.

214	95	3d. multicoloured ..	10	10
215		1s. multicoloured ..	10	10
216		1s. 6d. multicoloured ..	15	20

96. Lignum Vitae.

103. Gypsum Industry.

1964.

217	96	1d. blue, green & brown	10	10
218	–	1½d. multicoloured ..	15	10
219	–	2d. red, yell. and green	15	10
220	–	2½d. multicoloured ..	60	60
221	–	3d. yellow, black & grn.	15	10
222	–	4d. ochre and violet ..	35	10
223	–	6d. multicoloured ..	1·75	10
224	–	8d. multicoloured ..	1·25	60
225	103	9d. blue and bistre ..	45	10
226	–	1s. black and brown ..	20	10
227	–	1s. 6d. black, blue & buff	75	15
228	–	2s. brown, black & blue	1·25	15
229a	–	3s. blue and green ..	35	65
230	–	5s. black, ochre & blue	1·10	50
231	–	10s. multicoloured ..	1·25	1·00
232	–	£1 multicoloured ..	1·50	1·00

DESIGNS—As Type **96**—HORIZ. 1½d. Ackee (fruit). 2½d. Land shells. 3d. National flag over Jamaica. 4d. "Murex antillarum" (sea shell). 6d. "Papilio homerus" (butterfly). 8d. Streamertail. VERT. 2d. Blue Mahoe (tree). As Type **103**—HORIZ. 1s. National Stadium. 1s. 6d. Palisadoes International Airport 2s. Bauxite mining. 3s. Blue marlin (sport fishing). 5s. Exploration of Sunken City, Port Royal. £1 Queen Elizabeth II and National Flag. VERT. 10s. Arms of Jamaica.

114. Scout Badge and Alligator (reduced size Illustration. Actual size 61½ × 30½ mm.)

1964. 6th Inter-American Scout Conf., Kingston.

233.	–	3d. red, black and pink	10	10
234.	–	8d. blue, olive and black	10	20
235.	114.	1s. gold, blue & lt. blue	15	20

DESIGNS—VERT (25½ × 30 mm.): 3d. Scout belt. 8d. Globe, scout hat and scarf.

115. Gordon House, Kingston.

1964. 10th Commonwealth Parliamentary Conf. Kingston.

236.	115.	3d. black and green ..	10	10
237.	–	6d. black and red ..	10	10
238.	–	1s. 6d. black and blue ..	15	20

DESIGNS: 6d. Headquarters House, Kingston. 1s. 6d. House of Assembly, Spanish Town.

118. Eleanor Roosevelt.

1964. 16th Anniversary of Declaration of Human Rights.

239.	118.	1s. blk., red & grn. ..	10	10

119. Guides' Emblem on Map.

1965. Golden Jubilee of Jamaica Girl Guides' Assn. Inscr. "1915-1965".

240.	119.	3d. yellow, green & black	10	10
241.	–	1s. yellow, black & grn.	20	20

DESIGN — TRIANGULAR (61½ × 30½ mm.): 1s. Guide emblems.

121. Uniform Cap.

1965. Cent. of Salvation Army. Mult.

242.	3d. Type **121**	10	10
243.	1s. 6d. Flag-bearer and drummer..	25	25

123. Paul Bogle, William Gordon and Morant Bay Court House.

1965. Cent. of Morant Bay Rebellion.

244.	123.	3d. brown, blue & black	10	10
245.		1s. 6d. brn., grn. & blk.	10	10
246.		3s. brown, red & black	20	30

124. Abeng-blower "Telstar", Morse Key and I.T.U. Emblem.

1965. Centenary of I.T.U.

247.	124.	1s. blk, slate & red ..	40	15

1966. Royal Visit. Nos. 221, 223, 226/7 optd. **ROYAL VISIT MARCH 1966.**

248.	3d. yellow, black & green	15	10
249.	6d. multicoloured ..	70	10
250.	1s. black and brown ..	55	10
251.	1s. 6d. black, blue & buff	70	60

126. Sir Winston Churchill.

1966. Churchill Commem.

252.	126.	6d. black and green ..	35	20
253.		1s. brown and blue ..	65	70

127. Statue of Athlete and Flags.

1966. 8th British Empire and Commonwealth Games.

254.	127.	3d. multicoloured ..	10	10
255.	–	6d. multicoloured ..	10	10
256.	–	1s. multicoloured ..	10	10
257.	–	3s. gold and blue ..	20	35

DESIGNS: 6d. Racing cyclists. 1s. National Stadium, Kingston. 3s. Games Emblem.

131. Bolivar's Statue and Flags of Jamaica and Venezuela.

1966. 150th Anniv. "Jamaica Letter".

259.	131.	8d. multicoloured ..	10	10

INDEX

Countries can be quickly located by referring to the index at the end of this volume.

132. Jamaican Pavilion.

1967. World Fair, Montreal.
260 **132.** 6d. multicoloured .. 10 10
261. 1s. multicoloured .. 10 10

133. Sir Donald Sangster (Prime Minister).

1967. Sangster Memorial Issue.
262. **133.** 3d. multicoloured .. 10 10
263. 1s. 6d. multicoloured .. 10 10

134. Traffic Duty.

1967. Centenary of Constabulary Force.
264. **134.** 3d. multicoloured .. 10 10
265. – 1s. multicoloured .. 15 10
266. – 1s. 6d. multicoloured .. 20 20
DESIGNS: 1s. 6d. Badge and Constables of 1867 and 1967. ($56\frac{1}{2} \times 20\frac{1}{2}$ mm.): 1s. Personnel of the Force.

1968. M.C.C.'s West Indies Tour. As Nos. 445/7 of Guyana.
267. 6d. multicoloured 20 30
268. 6d. multicoloured 20 30
269. 6d. multicoloured 20 30

137. Sir Alexander and Lady Bustamante.

1968. Labour Day.
270. **137.** 3d. red and black .. 10 10
271. 1s. olive and black .. 10 10

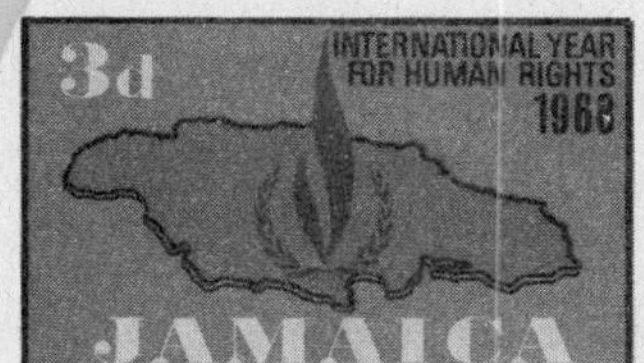

138. Human Rights Emblem over Map of Jamaica.

1968. Human Rights Year. Multicoloured.
272. 3d. Type **138** 10 10
273. 1s. Hands cupping Human Rights Emblem 10 10
274. 3s. Jamaican holding "Human Rights" .. 20 25

141. I.L.O. Emblem.

1969. 50th Anniversary of Labour Organization.
275. **141.** 6d. yellow and brown .. 10 10
276. 3s. green and brown .. 20 30

142. Nurse and Children being weighed and measured.

1969. 20th Anniv. of W.H.O. Multicoloured.
277. 6d. Type **142** 10 10
278. 1s. Malaria Eradication (horiz.) 10 10
279. 3s. Trainee nurse 20 30

1969. Decimal Currency. Nos. 217, 219, 221/3 and 225/32 surch. **C-DAY 8th, September 1969** in three lines, and value.
280. **95.** 1 c. on 1d. bl., grn. & brn. 10 10
281. – 2 c. on 2d. red, yell. & grn. 10 10
282. – 3 c. on 3d. yell., blk and green 10 10
283. – 4 c. on 4d. ochre & violet 45 10
284. – 5 c. on 6d. multicoloured 80 10
285. **103.** 8 c. on 9d. blue & bistre 10 10
286. – 10 c. on 1s. blk., & brn. 10 10
287. – 15 c. on 1s. 6d. black, blue and buff .. 30 60
288. – 20 c. on 2s. brn., blk. & bl. 1·00 55
289. – 30 c. on 3s. blue & green 1·50 2·00
290. – 50 c. on 5s. black, ochre and blue .. .. 1·25 2·00
291. – \$1 on 10s. multicoloured 1·50 3·25
292. – \$2 on £1 multicoloured 1·50 6·00

146. "The Adoration of the Kings" (detail, Foppa).

1969. Christmas. Paintings. Multicoloured.
293. 2 c. Type **146** 10 10
294. 5 c. "Madonna, Child and St. John" (Raphael) .. 10 10
295. 8 c. "The Adoration of the Kings" (detail, Dosso Dossi) 15 10

149. Half Penny, 1869.

1969. Centenary of 1st Jamaican Coins.
296b. **149.** 3 c. silver, blk. and mve. 10 10
297. – 15 c. silver, blk. & grn. 10 10
DESIGN: 15 c. One Penny, 1869.

151. George William Gordon. 156. "Christ Appearing to St. Peter" (Carracci).

1970. National Heroes. Multicoloured; background colours given.
298. **151.** 1 c. mauve 10 10
299. – 3 c. blue 10 10
300. – 5 c. grey 10 10
301. – 10 c. red 15 10
302. – 15 c. green 20 15
PORTRAITS: 3 c. Sir Alexander Bustamante. 5 c. Norman Manley. 10 c. Marcus Garvey. 15 c. Paul Bogle.

1970. Easter. Centres multicoloured; frame colours given.
303. **156.** 3 c. red 10 10
304. – 10 c. green 10 10
305. – 20 c. grey 20 25
DESIGNS: 10 c. "Christ Crucified" (Antonello). 20 c. Easter Lily.

1970. No. 219 surch.
306. 2 c. on 2d. red, yell. & grn. 15 20

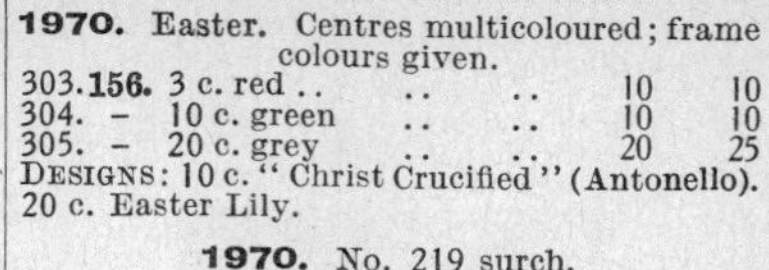

160. Lignum Vitae.

1970. Decimal currency. Designs as Nos. 217, 219, 221/223, 225/232, but with values inscribed as T **160** in new currency.
307. **160.** 1 c. blue, grn. and brn. 40 40
308. – 2 c. red, yellow and green (as 2d.) .. 15 10
309. – 3 c. yellow, black and green (as 3d.) .. 15 10
310. – 4 c. ochre & violet (as 4d.) 65 10
311. – 5 c. multicoloured (as 6d.) 2·25 10
312. **103.** 8 c. blue and yell. .. 20 10
313. – 10 c. blk. & brn. .. 20 10
314. – 15 c. black, blue and buff (as 1s. 6d.) .. 80 60
315. – 20 c. brown, black and blue (as 2s.) .. .. 1·00 1·00
316. – 30 c. blue & grn. (as 3s.) 1·25 1·25
317. – 50 c. black, ochre and blue (as 5s.) .. .. 1·25 2·50
318. – \$1 multicoloured (as 10s.) 1·25 2·50
319. – \$2 multicoloured (as £1) 1·50 2·75

161. Cable Ship "Dacia".

1970. Centenary of Telegraph Service.
320. **161.** 3 c. yell., blk. and red 15 10
321. – 10 c. black and green .. 20 10
322. – 50 c. multicoloured .. 50 1·00
DESIGNS: 10 c. Bright's Cable Gear aboard "Dacia". 50 c. Morse key and chart.

164. Bananas, Citrus, Sugar-Cane and Tobacco.

1970. 75th Anniversary of Jamaican Agricultural Society.
323. **164.** 2 c. multicoloured .. 10 30
324. 10 c. multicoloured .. 20 20

165. "The Projector" (1845).

1970. 125th Anniv. of Jamaican Railways.
325. 3 c. Type **165** 25 10
326. 15 c. Steam locomotive No. 54 (1944) 70 30
327. 50 c. Steam locomotive No. 102 (1967) .. .. 1·75 2·00

168. Church of St. Jago de la Vega.

1971. Centenary of Disestablishment of Church of England in Jamaica.
328. **168.** 3 c. multicoloured .. 10 10
329. 10 c. multicoloured .. 10 10
330. 20 c. multicoloured .. 15 25
331. – 30 c. multicoloured .. 20 45
DESIGNS: 30 c. Emblem of Church of England in Jamaica.

169. Henry Morgan and Ships.

1971. Pirates and Buccaneers. Multicoloured.
332. 3 c. Type **169** 30 10
333. 15 c. Mary Read, Anne Bonny and trial pamphlet 55 15
334. 30 c. Pirate schooner attacking merchantman 1·10 1·25

170. 1s. Stamp of 1919 with Frame Inverted.

1971. Tercentenary of Post Office.
335. – 3 c. black and brown .. 10 10
336. – 5 c. black and green .. 10 10
337. – 8 c. black and violet .. 15 10
338. – 10 c. brn., black and blue 15 10
339. – 20 c. multicoloured .. 25 35
340. **170.** 50 c. brn., black and grey 45 80
DESIGNS—HORIZ. 3 c. Dummer packet letter, 1705. 5 c. Pre-stamp inland letter, 1793. 8 c. Harbour St. P.O., Kingston, 1820. 10 c. Modern stamp and cancellation. 20 c. British stamps used in Jamaica, 1859.

171. Satellite and Dish Aerial.

1972. Opening of Jamaican Earth Satellite Station.
341. **171.** 3 c. multicoloured .. 15 10
342. 15 c. multicoloured .. 20 15
343. 50 c. multicoloured .. 55 1·25

172. Causeway, Kingston Harbour.

1972. Multicoloured.
344. 1 c. Pimento 10 10
345. 2 c. Red Ginger 10 10
346. 3 c. Bauxite Industry .. 10 10
347. 4 c. Type 172 .. .. 10 10
348. 5 c. Oil Refinery 10 10
349. 6 c. Senate Building, University of the West Indies 10 10
350. 8 c. National Stadium .. 10 10
351. 9 c. Devon House .. 10 10
352. 10 c. Air Jamaica Hostess and aircraft 10 10
353. 15 c. Old Iron Bridge, Spanish Town 55 10
354. 20 c. College of Arts, Science and Technology .. 30 15
355. 30 c. Dunn's River Falls .. 35 15
356. 50 c. River rafting .. 60 40
357. \$1 Jamaica House .. 75 65
358. \$2 Kings House .. .. 1·00 1·25
The 1, 2, 15 and 30 c. are vert. designs, size 35×27 mm., and the remainder are horiz. as Type **172**.

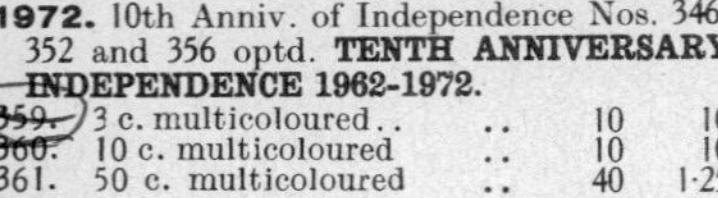

1972. 10th Anniv. of Independence Nos. 346, 352 and 356 optd. **TENTH ANNIVERSARY INDEPENDENCE 1962-1972.**

359. 3 c. multicoloured 10 10
360. 10 c. multicoloured .. 10 10
361. 50 c. multicoloured .. 40 1·25

175. Arms of Kingston.

1972. Centenary of Kingston as Capital.

362. 175. 5 c. multicoloured .. 10 10
363. 30 c. multicoloured .. 20 25
364. – 50 c. multicoloured .. 40 75

DESIGN—HORIZ. 50 c. design similar to Type 175.

176. Mongoose on Map.

1973. Centenary of Introduction of the Small Indian Mongoose.

365. 176. 8 c. green, yell. & black 10 10
366. – 40 c. dp. blue, blue & blk. 25 50
367. – 60 c. pink, salmon & blk. 50 1·00

DESIGNS: 40 c. Mongoose and rat. 60 c. Mongoose and chicken.

177. " Euphorbia punicea ".

1973. Flora. Multicoloured.

369. 1 c. Type 177 .. .. 10 10
370. 6 c. " Hylocereus triangularis " 15 10
371. 9 c. " Columnea argentea " 15 10
372. 15 c. " Portlandia grandiflora " 25 15
373. 30 c. " Samyda pubescens " 50 60
374. 50 c. "Cordia sebestena " 80 1·25

178. " Broughtonia sanguinea ".

1973. Orchids. Multicoloured.

375. 5 c. Type 178 .. .. 40 10
376. 10 c. " Arpophyllum jamaicense " (vert.) .. 50 10
377. 20 c. " Oncidium pulchellum " (vert.) .. 1·25 25
378. $1 " Brassia maculata " .. 2·75 2·75

179. " Mary ", 1808–15.

1974. Mail Packet Boats. Multicoloured.

380. 5 c. Type 179 .. .. 20 10
381. 10 c. " Queensbury ", 1814-27 25 10
382. 15 c. " Sheldrake ", 1829-34 45 40
383. 50 c. " Thames ", 1842 .. 1·75 2·25

180. "Journeys".

1974. National Dance Theatre Company. Mult.

385. 5 c. Type 180. .. .. 10 10
386. 10 c. "Jamaican Promenade" 10 10
387. 30 c. "Jamaican Promenade" (diff.) 25 30
388. 50 c. "Misa Criolla" .. 45 80

181. U.P.U. Emblem and Globe.

1974. Centenary of U.P.U.

390. 181. 5 c. multicoloured .. 10 10
391. 9 c. multicoloured .. 10 10
392. 50 c. multicoloured .. 35 80

182. Senate Building and Sir Hugh Wooding.

1975. 25th Anniversary. of University of West Indies. Multicoloured.

393. 5 c. Type 182 .. .. 10 10
394. 10 c. University Chapel and Princess Alice 10 10
395. 30 c. Type 182 .. .. 15 25
396. 50 c. As 10 c. 30 60

183. Commonwealth Symbol.

1975. Heads of Commonwealth Conf. Mult.

397. 5 c. Type 183 .. .. 10 10
398. 10 c. Jamaican coat of arms 10 10
399. 30 c. Dove of Peace .. 15 30
400. 50 c. Jamaican flag .. 30 80

184. "Eurytides marcellinus".

1975. Butterflies (1st series), showing the family "Papilionidae". Multicoloured.

401 10 c. Type 184 .. 55 20
402 20 c. "Papilo thoas" .. 1·10 1·10
403 25 c. "Papilo thersites" .. 1·25 1·60
404 30 c. "Papilo homerus" .. 1·40 2·00

See also Nos. 429/32 and 443/6.

185. Koo Koo or Actor Boy.

1975. Christmas. Belisario prints of " John Canoe " Festival (1st series). Multicoloured.

406. 8 c. Type 185 .. .. 10 10
407. 10 c. Red Set-girls .. 10 10
408. 20 c. French Set-girls .. 15 15
409. 50 c. Jaw-bone or House John Canoe 35 70

See also Nos. 421/3.

186. Bordone Map. 1528.

1976. 16th Century Maps of Jamaica.

411. 186. 10 c. brn., light brn. & red 20 10
412. – 20 c. multicoloured .. 35 25
413. – 30 c. multicoloured .. 60 75
414. – 50 c. multicoloured .. 85 1·25

DESIGNS: 20 c. Porcacchi map, 1576. 30 c. De Bry map. 1594. 50 c. Langenes map, 1598.

See also Nos. 425/8.

187. Olympic Rings.

1976. Olympic Games, Montreal.

415. 187. 10 c. multicoloured .. 10 10
416. 20 c. multicoloured .. 15 15
417. 25 c. multicoloured .. 15 20
418. 50 c. multicoloured .. 30 90

1976. West Indian Victory in World Cricket Cup. As Nos. 559/60 of Barbados.

419. 10 c. Map of the Caribbean 40 40
420. 25 c. Prudential Cup .. 85 1·25

1976. Christmas. Belisario Prints (2nd series). As T 185. Multicoloured.

421. 10 c. Queen of the set-girls 10 10
422. 20 c. Band of the Jaw-bone John-Canoe .. 15 10
423. 50 c. Koo Koo (actor-boy) 30 50

1977. 17th Cent. Maps of Jamaica. As T 186.

425. 9 c. multicoloured .. 30 10
426. 10 c. red, brown and buff 30 10
427. 25 c. blk., blue & pale blue 70 60
428. 40 c. black, blue & green.. 80 85

DESIGNS: 9 c. Hickeringill map, 1661. 10 c. Ogilby map, 1671. 25 c. Visscher map, 1680. 40 c. Thornton map, 1689.

1977. Butterflies (2nd series), showing the families "Nymphalidae" and "Pieridae". As T 184. Multicoloured.

429 10 c. "Eurema elathea" .. 35 10
430 20 c. "Dynamine egaea" .. 75 55
431 25 c. "Chlosyne pantoni" 1·00 1·25
432 40 c. "Hypolimnas missippus" .. .. 1·50 2·00

188. Map, Scout Emblem and Streamertail.

1977. Sixth Caribbean Scout Jamboree, Jamaica.

434. 188. 10 c. multicoloured .. 20 10
435. 20 c. multicoloured .. 40 15
436. 25 c. multicoloured .. 45 20
437. 50 c. multicoloured .. 75 1·10

189. Trumpeter.

1977. 50th Anniversary of Jamaica Military Band. Multicoloured

438. 9 c. Type 189 .. .. 15 10
439. 10 c. Clarinet players .. 15 10
440. 20 c. Two kettle drummers (vert.) 40 35
441. 25 c. Cellist and trumpeter (vert.) 55 65

1978. Butterflies (3rd series). As T 184. Multicoloured.

443 10 c. "Callophrys crethona" 25 10
444 20 c. "Siproeta stelenes" .. 50 20
445 25 c. "Urbanus proteus" .. 65 35
446 50 c. "Anaea troglodyta" 1·40 1·60

190. Half-figure with Canopy. 191. Norman Manley (statue).

1978. Arawak Artefacts (1st series).

448. 190. 10 c. brn., yell. & blk. 10 10
449. – 20 c. brn., mve. & blk. 10 10
450. – 50 c. brn., grn. & blk. 30 35

DESIGNS: 20 c. Standing figure. 50 c. Birdman.

See also Nos. 479/83.

1978. 24th Commonwealth Parliamentary Conference. Multicoloured.

452. 10 c. Type 191 .. .. 10 10
453. 20 c. Sir Alexander Bustamante (statue) .. 10 10
454. 25 c. City of Kingston Crest 15 15
455. 40 c. Gordon House Chamber House of Representatives 25 35

192. Band and Banner.

1978. Christmas. Centenary of Salvation Army. Multicoloured.

456. 10 c. Type 192 .. .. 20 10
457. 20 c. Trumpeter 25 10
458. 25 c. Banner 25 10
459. 50 c. William Booth (founder) 40 1·00

193. " Negro Aroused " (sculpture by Edna Manley).

1978. International Anti-Apartheid Year.

460. 193. 10 c. multicoloured .. 10 10

194. Tennis, Montego Bay.

1979. Multicoloured.

461. 1 c. Type **194** 30 30
462. 2 c. Golf, Tryall Hanover 40 40
463. 4 c. Horse riding, Negril Beach 15 20
464. 5 c. Old waterwheel, Tryall Hanover 15 10
465. 6 c. Fern Gully, Ocho Rios 15 10
466. 7 c. Dunn's River Falls, Ocho Rios 15 10
467. 8 c. Jamaican Tody .. 40 20
468. 10 c. Jamaican Mango .. 40 10
469. 12 c. Yellow Billed Amazon 40 20
470. 15 c. Streamertail 55 10
471. 35 c. White-chinned Thrush 55 10
472. 50 c. Jamaican Woodpecker 70 15
473. 65 c. Rafting, Martha Brae Trelawny 30 20
474. 75 c. Blue Marlin fleet, Port Antonio 30 20
475. $1 Scuba diving, Ocho Rios 30 30
476. $2 Sailing boats, Montego Bay 50 35
477. $5 Arms and map of Jamaica (37 × 27 mm.) .. 1·00 1·60

1979. 10th Anniversary of Air Jamaica. No. 352 optd. **10th ANNIVERSARY AIR JAMAICA, 1st APRIL 1979.**

478. 10 c. multicoloured .. 10 20

197. Grinding Stone, circa 400 B.C.

1979. Arawak Artefacts (2nd series). Multicoloured.

479. 5 c. Type **197** 10 10
480. 10 c. Stone implements, c. 500 B.C. (horiz.) .. 10 10
481. 20 c. Cooking pot, c. 300 A.D. (horiz.) 10 15
482. 25 c. Serving boat, c. 300 A.D. (horiz.) 10 20
483. 50 c. Storage jar fragment, c. 300 A.D. 25 35

198. 1962 1s. 6d. Independence Commemorative Stamp.

1979. Death Centenary of Sir Rowland Hill.

484. **198.** 10 c. blk., brn. and red 10 10
485. – 20 c. yellow and brown 15 15
486. – 25 c. mauve and blue .. 20 20
487. – 50 c. multicoloured .. 30 40

DESIGNS: 20 c. 1920 1s. with frame inverted. 25 c. 1860 6d. stamp. 50 c. 1968 3d. Human Rights Year commemorative.

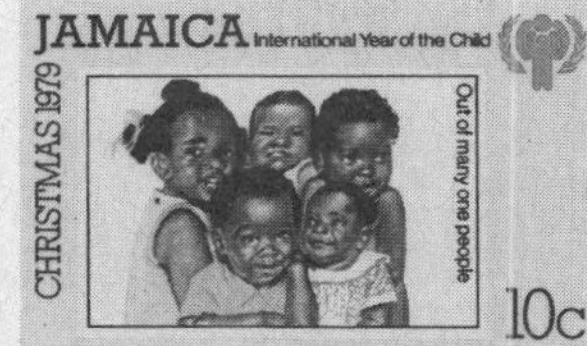

199. Group of Children.

1979. Christmas. International Year of the Child. Multicoloured.

489. 10 c. Type **199** 10 10
490. 20 c. Doll (vert.) 10 10
491. 25 c. "The Family" (painting by child) .. 15 15
492. 50 c. "House on the Hill" (painting by child) .. 25 40

200. Date Tree Hall, 1886 (original home of Institute).

1980. Centenary of Institute of Jamaica. Multicoloured.

493. 5 c. Type **200** .. 10 10
494. 15 c. Institute building 1980 15 10
495. 35 c. Microfilm reader (vert.) 20 20
496. 50 c. Hawksbill Turtle and Green Turtle 30 25
497. 75 c. Jamaican Owl (vert.) 75 50

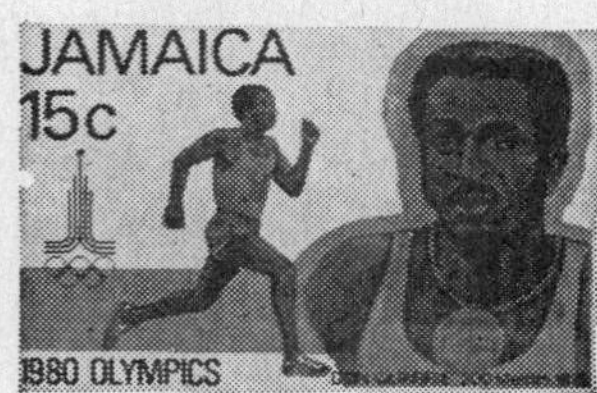

201. Don Quarrie (200 Metres, 1976).

1980. Olympic Games, Moscow. Jamaican Olympic Gold Medal Winners. Mult.

498. 15 c. Type **201** 15 10
499. 35 c. Arthur Wint (4 × 400 Metres Relay, 1952) .. 25 30
500. 35 c. Leslie Laing (4 × 400 Metres Relay, 1952) .. 25 30
501. 35 c. Herbert McKenley (4× 400 Metres Relay, 1952) 25 30
502. 35 c. George Rhoden (4 × 400 Metres Relay, 1952) .. 25 30

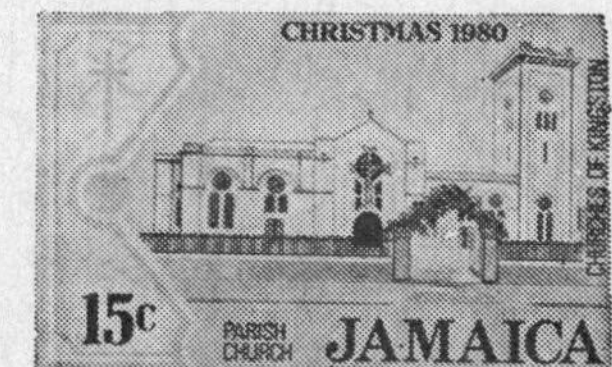

202. Parish Church.

1980. Christmas. Kingston Churches (1st series). Multicoloured.

503. 15 c. Type **202** 10 10
504. 20 c. Coke Memorial Church 10 10
505. 25 c. Church of the Redeemer 15 10
506. $5 Holy Trinity Cathedral 1·00 2·00

See also Nos. 537/9 and 570/2.

203. Blood Cup Sponge.

1981. Marine Line (1st series). Multicoloured.

508. 20 c. Type **203** 15 10
509. 45 c. Tube Sponge (horiz.) 25 30
510. 60 c. Black Coral 35 40
511. 75 c. Tyre Reef (horiz.) .. 40 55

See also Nos. 541/5.

204. Brown's Hutia (or Indian Coney).

1981. Brown's Hutia (or Indian Coney). Multicoloured.

512. 20 c. Hutia facing right .. 15 20
513. 20 c. Type **204** 15 20
514. 20 c. Hutia facing left and eating 15 20
515. 20 c. Hutia family .. 15 20

205. White Orchid.

1981. Royal Wedding. Multicoloured.

516. 20 c. Type **205** 20 10
517. 45 c. Royal Coach .. 35 20
518. 60 c. Prince Charles and Lady Diana Spencer .. 50 30
519. $5 St. James' Palace .. 1·00 1·50

206. Blind Man at work.

1981. International Year for Disabled Persons. Multicoloured.

521. 20 c. Type **206** 15 15
522. 45 c. Painting with the mouth 40 40
523. 60 c. Deaf student communicating with sign language 50 50
524. $1.50 Basketball players .. 1·25 1·25

207. W.F.D. Emblem on 1964 1½d. Definitive.

1981. World Food Day. Stamps on Stamps.

525. **207.** 20 c. multicoloured .. 30 15
526. – 45 c. blk., red and orge. 60 40
527. – $2 black, blue and grn. 1·75 1·40
528. – $4 blk, green and brn. 3·00 2·50

DESIGNS—VERT. (as T **207**) 45 c. 1922 1d. value. HORIZ. (40 × 26 mm.) $2 As 1938 3d. but with W.F.D. emblem replacing King's head. $4 As 1938 1s. but with W.F.D. emblem replacing King's head.

208. "Survival" (song title).

1981. Bob Marley (musician) Commemoration. Song Titles. Multicoloured.

529. 1 c. Type **208** 10 10
530. 2 c. "Exodus" 10 10
531. 3 c. "Is this Love" .. 10 10
532. 15 c. "Coming in from the Cold" 40 15
533. 20 c. "Positive Vibration" 50 20
534. 60 c. "War" .. .. 1·25 1·00
535. $3 "Could you be Loved" 6·50 5·00

No. 533 is incorrectly inscribed "OSITIVE VIBRATION".

209. Webb Memorial Baptist Church.

1981. Christmas. Churches (2nd series). Multicoloured.

537. 10 c. Type **209** 10 10
538. 45 c. Church of God in Jamaica 30 15
539. $5 Bryce United Church .. 2·25 2·50

210. Gorgonian Coral.

1982. Marine Life (2nd series. Multicoloured.

541. 20 c. Type **210** 25 10
542. 45 c. Hard Sponge and diver (horiz.) 45 25
543. 60 c. American Manatee (horiz.) 60 40
544. 75 c. Plume Worm (horiz.) 70 50
545. $3 Coral Banded Shrimp (horiz.) .. .. .. 2·00 1·60

211. Cub Scout.

1982. 75th Anniversary of Boy Scout Movement. Multicoloured.

546. 20 c. Type **211** 40 15
547. 45 c. Scout camp .. 75 35
548. 60 c. "Out of Many, One People" 95 45
549. $2 Lord Baden-Powell .. 1·75 1·50

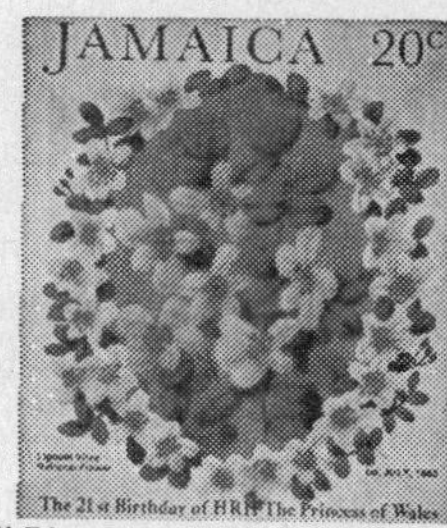

212. "Lignum vitae" (national flower).

1982. 21st Birthday of Princess of Wales.

551. 20 c. Type **212** 20 20
552. 45 c. Carriage ride .. 35 35
553. 60 c. Wedding 50 50
554. 75 c. "Saxifraga longifolia" 70 70
555. $2 Princess of Wales .. 1·25 1·50
556. $3 "Viola gracilis major" 1·50 2·00

1982. Birth of Prince William of Wales. Nos. 551/6 optd. **ROYAL BABY 26.6.82.**

558. 20 c. Type **212** 20 20
559. 45 c. Carriage ride .. 35 35
560. 60 c. Wedding 50 50
561. 75 c. "Saxifraga longifolia" 70 70
562. $2 Princess of Wales .. 1·25 1·50
563. $3 "Viola gracilis major" 1·50 2·00

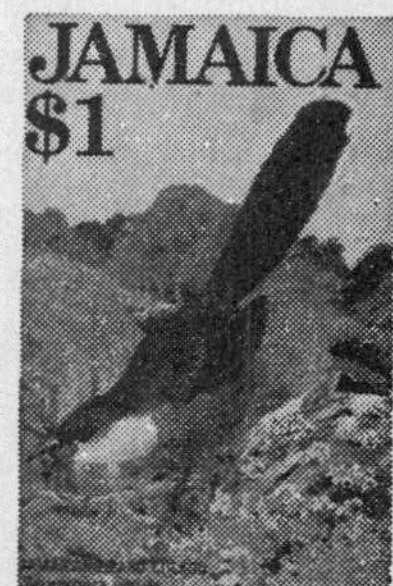

213. Prey Captured.

1982. Jamaican Birds (1st series). Jamaican Lizard Cuckoo. Multicoloured.

565. $1 Type **213** 80 80
566. $1 Searching for prey .. 80 80
567. $1 Calling prior to prey search 80 80
568. $1 Adult landing 80 80
569. $1 Adult flying in .. 80 80

See also Nos. 642/5 and 707/10.

1982. Christmas. Churches (3rd series). As T **209**. Multicoloured.

570.	20 c. United Pentecostal Church	15	10
571.	45 c. Disciples of Christ Church	30	25
572.	75 c. Open Bible Church ..	55	70

214. Queen Elizabeth II.

1983. Royal Visit. Multicoloured.

573.	$2 Type **214**	2·50	2·00
574.	$3 Coat of arms	3·50	2·75

215. Folk Dancing.

1983. Commonwealth Day. Multicoloured.

575.	20 c. Type **215**	15	15
576.	45 c. Bauxite mining ..	35	35
577.	75 c. World map showing position of Jamaica ..	45	45
578.	$2 Coat of arms and family	1·25	1·40

216. General Cargo Ship at Wharf.

1983. 25th Anniversary of International Maritime Organization. Multicoloured.

579.	15 c. Type **216**	65	20
580.	20 c. "Veendam" (cruise liner) at Kingston ..	90	25
581.	45 c. Container ship entering port	1·25	65
582.	$1 Tanker passing International Seabed Headquarters Building ..	2·25	2·50

217. Norman Manley and Sir Alexander Bustamante.

1983. 21st Anniversary of Independence.

583.	**217.**	15 c. multicoloured ..	15	15
584.		20 c. multicoloured ..	15	20
585.		45 c. multicoloured ..	30	40

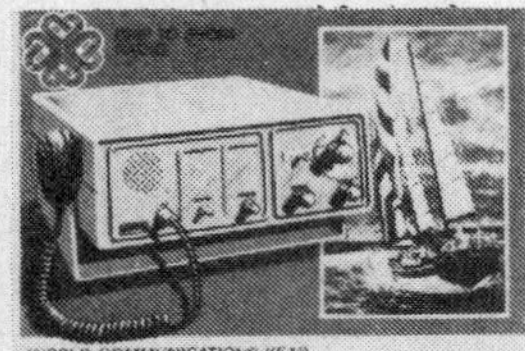

218. Ship-to-Shore Radio.

1983. World Communications Year. Mult.

586.	20 c. Type **218**	15	15
587.	45 c. Postal services ..	35	40
588.	75 c. Telephone communications	55	1·00
589.	$1 T.V. via satellite ..	75	1·50

219. "Racing at Caymanas" (Sidney McLaren).

1983. Christmas. Paintings. Multicoloured.

590.	15 c. Type **219**	10	10
591.	20 c. "Seated Figures" (Karl Parboosingh) ..	10	10
592.	75 c. "The Petitioner" (Henry Daley) (vert.) ..	30	25
593.	$2 "Banana Plantation" (John Dunkley) (vert.) ..	70	1·00

220. Sir Alexander Bustamante.

1984. Birth Centenary of Sir Alexander Bustamante. Multicoloured.

594.	20 c. Type **220**	30	40
595.	20 c. Blenheim Birthplace	30	40

221. "D.H. 60G Gipsy Moth" Seaplane.

1984. Seaplanes and Flying Boats. Multicoloured.

596.	25 c. Type **221**	55	15
597.	55 c. Consolidated "Commodore" flying boat ..	75	45
598.	$1.50 Sikorsky "S-38" flying boat	1·50	1·75
599.	$3 Sikorsky "S-40" flying boat	2·00	2·25

222. Cycling.

1984. Olympic Games, Los Angeles. Multicoloured.

600.	25 c. Type **222**	10	10
601.	55 c. Relay running ..	20	25
602.	$1.50 Start of race ..	60	1·00
603.	$3 Finish of race	1·10	1·75

1984. Nos. 465 and 469 surch.

605.	5 c. on 6 c. Fern Gully, Ocho Rios ..	10	15
606.	10 c. on 12 c. Yellow-billed Amazon	30	25

224. Head of Jamaican Boa Snake.

1984. Jamaican Boa Snake. Multicoloured.

607.	25 c. Type **224**	30	15
608.	55 c. Boa snake on branch over tree	50	45
609.	70 c. Snake with young ..	60	65
610.	$1 Snake on log	70	80

225. "Enterprise" (1845).

1984. Railway Locomotives (1st series). Multicoloured.

612.	25 c. Type **225**	50	15
613.	55 c. Tank locomotive (1880)	70	50
614.	$1.50 Kitson-Meyer tank locomotive (1904) ..	1·00	1·25
615.	$3 Super-heated locomotive (1916)	1·75	2·00

See also Nos. 634/7.

226. "Accompong Madonna" (Namba Roy).

1984. Christmas. Sculptures. Multicoloured.

616.	20 c. Type **226**	20	10
617.	25 c. "Head" (Alvin Marriott)	25	10
618.	55 c. "Moon" (Edna Manley)	50	40
619.	$1.50 "All Women are Five Women" (Mallica Reynolds (Kapo)) ..	1·00	1·50

227. Brown Pelicans flying.

1985. Birth Bicentenary of John J. Audubon (ornithologist). Brown Pelican. Mult.

620.	20 c. Type **227**	40	10
621.	55 c. Diving for fish ..	55	30
622.	$2 Young pelican taking food from adult ..	1·00	1·00
623.	$5 "Brown Pelican" (John J. Audubon)	1·50	2·25

228. The Queen Mother at Belfast University.

1985. Life and Times of Queen Elizabeth the Queen Mother. Multicoloured.

625.	25 c. With photograph album, 1963	10	10
626.	55 c. With Prince Charles at Garter Ceremony, Windsor Castle, 1983 ..	15	15
627.	$1.50 Type **228**	35	40
628.	$3 With Prince Henry at his christening (from photo by Lord Snowdon)	65	70

229. Maps and Emblems.

1985. International Youth Year and 5th Pan-American Scout Jamboree.

630.	**229.**	25 c. multicoloured ..	10	10
631.		55 c. multicoloured ..	15	15
632.		70 c. multicoloured ..	20	20
633.		$4 multicoloured ..	90	1·10

1985. Railway Locomotives (2nd series). As T **225**. Multicoloured.

634	25 c. Baldwin locomotive No. 16	45	10
635	55 c. Rogers locomotive ..	70	15
636	$1.50 Locomotive "The Projector"	1·00	75
637	$4 Diesel locomotive No. 102	1·75	1·75

230. "The Old Settlement" (Ralph Campbell).

1985. Christmas. Jamaican Paintings. Mult.

638.	20 c. Type **230**	10	10
639.	55 c. "The Vendor" (Albert Huie) (vert.)	15	15
640.	75 c. "Road Menders" (Gaston Tabois) ..	15	20
641.	$4 "Woman, must I not be about my Father's business?" (Carl Abrahams) (vert.) ..	90	95

1986. Jamaican Birds (2nd series). As T **213**. Multicoloured.

642.	25 c. Chestnut-bellied Cuckoo	40	10
643.	55 c. Jamaican Becard ..	55	30
644.	$1.50 White-eyed Thrush ..	70	1·00
645.	$5 Rufous-tailed Flycatcher	1·60	2·75

1986. 60th Birthday of Queen Elizabeth II. As T **110** of Ascension. Multicoloured.

646.	20 c. Princess Elizabeth and Princess Margaret, 1939	10	10
647.	25 c. With Prince Charles and Prince Andrew, 1962	10	10
648.	70 c. Queen visiting War Memorial, Montego Bay, 1983	15	25
649.	$3 On state visit to Luxembourg, 1976 ..	65	90
650.	$5 At Crown Agents Head Office, London, 1983 ..	1·25	1·75

231. Bustamante Children's Hospital.

1986. "Ameripex '86" International Stamp Exhibition, Chicago. Multicoloured.

651.	25 c. Type **231**	20	10
652.	55 c. Air Jamaica jet airliner and map of holiday resorts	25	15
653.	$3 Norman Manley Law School	1·00	90
654.	$5 Bauxite and agricultural exports	3·00	2·50

1986. Royal Wedding. As T **112** of Ascension. Multicoloured.

656.	20 c. Prince Andrew and Miss Sarah Ferguson, Ascot, 1985	15	10
657.	$5 Prince Andrew making speech, Fredericton, Canada, 1985	1·40	1·50

232. Richard "Shrimpy" Clarke.

1986. Jamaican Boxing Champions. Multicoloured.

658. 45 c. Type **232** 20 15
659. 70 c. Michael McCallum .. 30 20
660. $2 Trevor Berbick 70 55
661. $4 Richard "Shrimpy" Clarke, Michael McCallum and Trevor Berbick .. .. .. 1·25 1·25

1986. Nos. 472/3 surch.

662. 5 c. on 50 c. Jamaican woodpecker 20 25
663. 10 c. on 65 c. Rafting, Martha Brae Trelawny 25 25

234. "Heliconia wagneriana".

1986. Christmas. Flowers (1st series). Mult.

664. 20 c. Type **234** 10 10
665. 25 c. "Heliconia psittacorum" (horiz.) 10 10
666. 55 c. "Heliconia rostrata" 20 30
667. $5 "Strelitzia reginae" (horiz.) .. .. 1·60 2·75

See also Nos. 703/6 and 739/42.

235. Crown Cone.

1987. Sea Shells. Multicoloured.

668. 35 c. Type **235** 20 10
669. 75 c. Measled cowrie .. 30 20
670. $1 Trumpet triton .. 40 40
671. $5 Rooster tail conch .. 1·40 1·75

236. Norman Manley. **237.** Arms of Jamaica.

1987. Portraits.

672 **236** 1 c. red and pink .. 10 10
673 2 c. red and pink .. 10 10
674 3 c. green and stone 10 10
675 4 c. green & lt green 10 10
676 5 c. blue and grey 10 10
677 6 c. blue and grey .. 10 10
678 7 c. violet and mauve 10 10
679 8 c. mauve and pink 10 10
680 9 c. brown & lt brown 10 10
681 – 10 c. red and pink .. 10 10
682 – 20 c. orange and flesh 10 10
683 – 30 c. green & lt green 10 10
684 – 40 c. dp green & green 10 10
685 – 50 c. green and grey 10 10
686 – 60 c. blue & lt blue .. 10 10
687 – 70 c. violet & lt violet 10 10
688 – 80 c. violet and lilac 10 10
689 – 90 c. brown & lt brn 10 10
690 **237** $1 brown and cream 10 15
691 $2 orange and cream 15 20
692 $5 green and stone .. 35 40
693 $10 turquoise & blue 70 75
693c $25 violet & lavender 1·75 1·90
693d $50 mauve and lilac 3·50 3·75

DESIGN: 10 c. to 90 c. Sir Alexander Bustamante.

The 5 c. and 20 c. exist with or without imprint date at foot.

238. Jamaican Flag and Coast at Sunset.

1987. 25th Anniv. of Independence. Mult.

694. 55 c. Type **238** 40 30
695. 70 c. Jamaican flag and inscription (horiz.) .. 50 60

239. Marcus Garvey.

1987. Birth Centenary of Marcus Garvey (founder of Universal Negro Improvement Association). Each black, green and yellow.

696. 25 c. Type **239** 30 40
697. 25 c. Statue of Marcus Garvey 30 40

240. Salvation Army School for the Blind.

1987. Centenary of Salvation Army in Jamaica. Multicoloured.

698. 25 c. Type **240** 30 10
699. 55 c. Col. Mary Booth and Bramwell Booth Memorial Hall 45 20
700. $3 Welfare Service lorry, 1929 .. .. .. 1·25 1·25
701. $5 Col. Abram Davey and S.S. "Alene", 1887 .. 2·00 2·25

1987. Christmas. Flowers (2nd series). As T **234**. Multicoloured.

703. 20 c. Hibiscus hybrid .. 10 10
704. 25 c. "Hibiscus elatus" .. 10 10
705. $4 "Hibiscus cannabinus" 90 95
706. $5 "Hibiscus rosa-sinensis" 1·25 1·40

1988. Jamaican Birds (3rd series). As T **213**. Multicoloured.

707. 45 c. Chestnut-bellied cuckoo, black-billed parrot and Jamaican euphonia 50 50
708. 45 c. Jamaican white-eyed vireo, rufous-throated solitaire and yellow-crowned elaenia .. 50 50
709. $5 Snowy plover, little blue heron and great white heron .. .. 2·00 2·00
710. $5 Common stilt, snowy egret and black-crowned night heron .. .. 2·00 2·00

The two designs of each value were printed together, se-tenant, each pair forming a composite design.

243 Blue Whales

1988. Marine Mammals. Multicoloured.

711 20 c. Type **243** 40 15
712 25 c. Gervais's whales .. 40 15
713 55 c. Killer whales .. 60 20
714 $5 Common dolphins .. 2·50 2·00

1988. West Indian Cricket. As T **186** of Barbados, each showing portrait, cricket equipment and early belt buckle. Mult.

715 25 c. Jackie Hendriks .. 30 10
716 55 c. George Headley .. 55 20
717 $2 Michael Holding .. 1·25 85
718 $3 R. K. Nunes .. .. 1·50 1·25
719 $4 Allan Rae .. .. 1·75 1·50

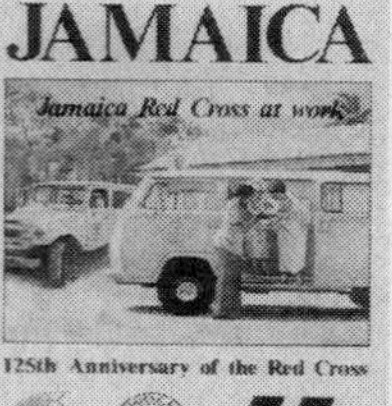

244 Jamaican Red Cross Workers with Ambulance

1988. 125th Anniv of International Red Cross. Multicoloured.

720 55 c. Type **244** 30 20
721 $5 Henri Dunant (founder) in field hospital .. 1·40 1·40

245 Boxing

1988. Olympic Games, Seoul. Multicoloured.

722 25 c. Type **245** 10 10
723 45 c. Cycling 10 10
724 $4 Athletics 85 90
725 $5 Hurdling .. .. 1·00 1·10

246 Bobsled Team Members and Logo

1988. Jamaican Olympic Bobsled Team. Mult.

727 25 c. Type **246** 10 30
728 25 c. Two-man bobsled .. 10 30
729 $5 Bobsled team members (different) and logo .. 1·00 1·50
730 $5 Four-man bobsled .. 1·00 1·50

1988. Hurricane Gilbert Relief Fund. Nos. 722/5 surch + **25 c HURRICANE GILBERT RELIEF FUND.**

731 25 c. + 25 c. Type **245** .. 10 15
732 45 c. + 45 c. Cycling .. 20 25
733 $4 + $4 Athletics .. .. 1·75 1·90
734 $5 + $5 Hurdling .. .. 2·10 2·25

248 Nurses and Firemen

1988. Year of the Worker. Multicoloured.

735 25 c. Type **248** 20 10
736 55 c. Woodcarver .. 25 20
737 $3 Textile workers .. 1·00 1·25
738 $5 Workers on fish farm .. 1·40 1·50

1988. Christmas Flowers (3rd series). As T **234**. Multicoloured.

739 25 c. "Euphorbia pulcherrima" 10 10
740 55 c. "Spathodea campanulata" (horiz) 15 15
741 $3 "Hylocereus triangularis" 75 80
742 $4 "Broughtonia sanguinea" (horiz) .. 85 90

249 Old York Castle School

1989. Bicent of Methodist Church in Jamaica.

743 **249** 25 c. black and blue .. 10 10
744 – 45 c. black and red .. 15 10
745 – $5 black and green .. 1·25 1·50

DESIGNS: 45 c. Revd. Thomas Coke and Parade Chapel, Kingston; $5 Father Hugh Sherlock and St. John's Church.

250 "Syntomidopsis variegata"

1989. Jamaican Moths (1st series). Mult.

746 25 c. Type **250** 30 10
747 55 c. "Himantoides perkinsae" 40 15
748 $3 "Arctia nigriplaga" .. 1·10 1·10
749 $5 "Sthenognatha toddi" 1·50 1·75

See also Nos. 758/61 and 790/3.

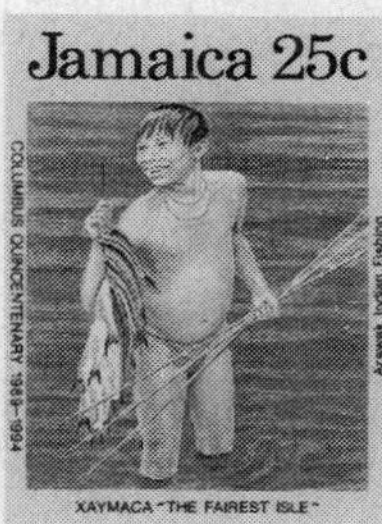

251 Arawak Fisherman with Catch

1989. 500th Anniv (1992) of Discovery of America by Columbus (1st issue). Mult.

750 25 c. Type **251** 20 10
751 70 c. Arawak man smoking 40 30
752 $5 King Ferdinand and Queen Isabella inspecting caravels .. 1·75 2·00
753 $10 Columbus with chart 3·00 3·25

See also Nos. 774/7 and 802/7.

252 Girl Guide

1990. 75th Anniv of Girl Guide Movement in Jamaica. Multicoloured.

No.	Description	Mint	Used
755	45 c. Type **252**	30	15
756	55 c. Guide leader ..	35	15
757	$5 Brownie, guide and ranger	2·00	2·25

1990. Jamaican Moths (2nd series). As T **250**. Multicoloured.

No.	Description	Mint	Used
758	25 c. "Eunomia rubripunctata"	20	10
759	55 c. "Perigonia jamaicensis"	30	15
760	$4 "Uraga haemorrhoa" ..	1·00	1·10
761	$5 "Empyreuma pugione"	1·10	1·25

1990. "EXPO 90" International Garden and Greenery Exhibition, Osaka. Nos. 758/61 optd **EXPO '90** and logo.

No.	Description	Mint	Used
762	25 c. "Eunomia rubripunctata"	20	10
763	55 c. "Perigonia jamaicensis"	30	15
764	$4 "Uraga haemorrhoa" ..	1·00	1·10
765	$5 "Empyreuma pugione"	1·10	1·25

254 Teaching English

1990. International Literacy Year. Mult.

No.	Description	Mint	Used
766	55 c. Type **254**	20	10
767	$5 Teaching maths ..	1·50	1·50

255 "To the Market"

1990. Christmas. Children's Paintings. Mult.

No.	Description	Mint	Used
768	20 c. Type **255**	10	10
769	25 c. "House and Garden"	10	10
770	55 c. "Jack and Jill" ..	15	15
771	70 c. "Market"	15	15
772	$1.50 "Lonely"	40	40
773	$5 "Market Woman" (vert)	1·25	1·25

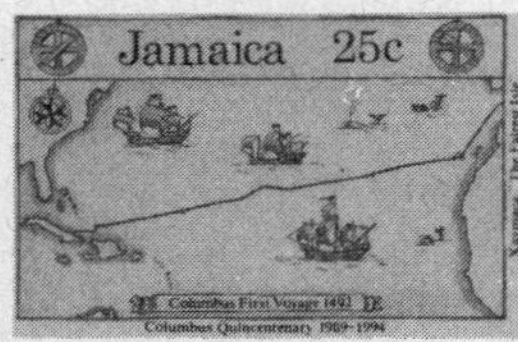

256 Map of First Voyage, 1492

1990. 500th Anniv (1992) of Discovery of America by Columbus (2nd issue). Mult.

No.	Description	Mint	Used
774	25 c. Type **256**	10	10
775	45 c. Map of second voyage, 1493	10	10
776	$5 Map of third voyage, 1498	1·00	1·10
777	$10 Map of fourth voyage, 1502	1·90	2·10

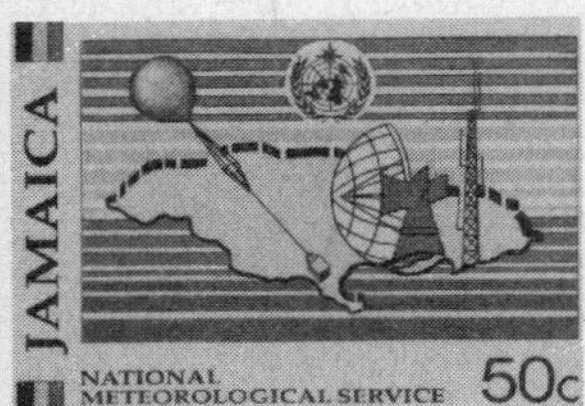

257 Weather Balloon, Dish Aerial and Map of Jamaica

1991. 11th World Meteorological Congress, Kingston.

No.	Type	Description	Mint	Used
780	**257**	50 c. multicoloured ..	10	10
781		$10 multicoloured ..	1·50	1·10

258 Bust of Mary Seacole

1991. International Council of Nurses Meeting of National Representatives. Multicoloured.

No.	Description	Mint	Used
782	50 c. Type **258**	15	10
783	$1.10 Mary Seacole House	20	20

259 Jamaican Iguana

1991. 50th Anniv of Natural History Society of Jamaica. Jamaican Iguana. Mult.

No.	Description	Mint	Used
785	$1.10 Type **259**	15	15
786	$1.10 Head of iguana looking right	15	15
787	$1.10 Iguana climbing ..	15	15
788	$1.10 Iguana on rock looking left	15	15
789	$1.10 Close-up of iguana's head	15	15

1991. Jamaican Moths (3rd series). As T **250**. Multicoloured.

No.	Description	Mint	Used
790	50 c. "Urania sloanus" ..	15	10
791	$1.10 "Phoenicoprocta jamaicensis"	20	15
792	$1.40 "Horama grotei" ..	25	30
793	$8 "Amplypterus gannascus"	90	95

1991. "Philanippon '91" International Stamp Exhibition, Tokyo. Nos. 790/3 optd **PHILA NIPPON 91** and emblem.

No.	Description	Mint	Used
794	50 c. "Urania sloanus" ..	15	10
795	$1.10 "Phoenicoprocta jamaicensis"	20	25
796	$1.40 "Horama grotei" ..	25	30
797	$8 "Amplypterus gannascus"	90	95

261 "Doctor Bird"

1991. Christmas. Children's Paintings. Mult.

No.	Description	Mint	Used
798	50 c. Type **261**	15	10
799	$1.10 "Road scene" ..	20	15
800	$5 "Children and house"	50	55
801	$10 "Cows grazing" ..	90	1·00

262 Indians threatening Ships

1991. 500th Anniv (1992) of Discovery of America by Columbus (3rd issue). Mult.

No.	Description	Mint	Used
802	50 c. Type **262**	10	10
803	$1.10 Spaniards setting dog on Indians	10	15
804	$1.40 Indian with gift of pineapple	10	15
805	$25 Columbus describes Jamaica with crumpled paper	1·75	1·90

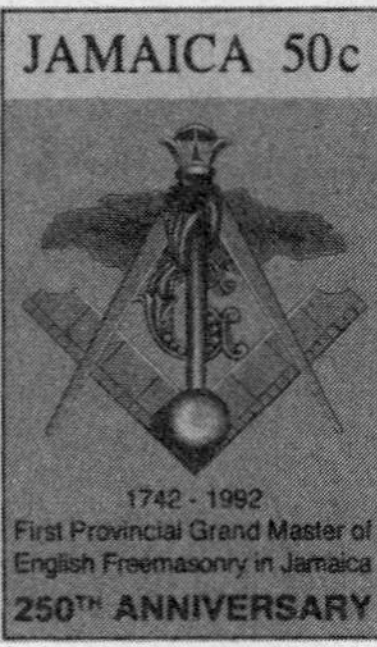

263 Compasses and Square Symbol

1992 250th Anniv of First Provisional Grand Master of English Freemasonry in Jamaica. Multicoloured.

No.	Description	Mint	Used
808	50 c. Type **263**	10	10
809	$1.10 Symbol in stained glass window	10	10
810	$1.40 Compasses and square on book ..	10	10
811	$25 Eye in triangle symbol	1·75	2·00

OFFICIAL STAMPS

1890. Optd. **OFFICIAL**

No.	Type	Description	Mint	Used
O 3.	**8.**	½d. green..	3·25	15
O 4.	**11.**	1d. red	3·25	40
O 5.		2d. grey	3·75	1·00

JAMMU AND KASHMIR

A state in the extreme N. of India.

12 pies = 1 anna; 16 annas = 1 rupee.

1.

Gum. The stamps of Jammu and Kashmir were issued without gum.

1866. Imperf.

No.	Type	Description	Mint	Used
41	1	½a. black	18·00	32·00
26		½a. red	23·00	32·00
44		½a. blue	18·00	
20		½a. green	65·00	
48		½a. yellow	95·00	
15		1 a. black	£150	
27		1 a. red	25·00	
5		1 a. blue	£225	65·00
20		1 a. green	65·00	
24		1 a. yellow	£375	
16		4 a. black	£110	
10		4 a. red	40·00	50·00
19		4 a. blue	£100	
22		4 a. green	75·00	
25		4 a. yellow	£350	

Prices for the circular stamps (Nos. 5/48) are for cut-square examples. Cut-to-shape examples are worth from 10% to 20% of these prices, according to condition.

½ a. ½ a.

1 a. **4.** ½ a.

1867.

No.	Type	Description	Mint	Used
69a	**4.**	½ a. black	95·00	£120
58		½ a. blue	80·00	60·00
60		½ a. red	3·00	2·50
64		½ a. orange	85·00	80·00
68		½ a. green	£900	£700
69b		1 a. black	£650	£550
55		1 a. blue	£120	85·00
61		1 a. red	5·00	5·00
65		1 a. orange	£350	£275
69		1 a. green	£1500	£1000

The characters denoting the value are in the upper part of the inner circle.

8. (¼a.)

12. (¼a.)

1867. Imperf.

No.	Type	Description	Mint	Used
90.	**8.**	¼ a. black	70	70
91.		½ a. blue	1·00	70
93.		1 a. blue	£2500	£1000
95.		1 a. orange	6·00	5·00
97.		2 a. yellow	7·00	6·00
99.		4 a. green	16·00	14·00
101.		8 a. red	17·00	16·00

1878. Imperf. or perf.

139 **12.** ⅛ a. yellow 20 30
125 ¼ a. red .. .. 1·25 1·50
131 ¼ a. orange .. .. 6·00 5·00
130a ¼ a. blue £550 £400
142 ¼ a. brown 30 20
105 ½ a. violet .. .. 13·00 12·00
147 ½ a. red 50 30
132 ½ a. orange .. .. 18·00 12·00
143 ½ a. blue .. .. 4·00
127 1 a. red .. .. 1·25 1·50
106 1 a. mauve .. .. 18·00 18·00
133 1 a. orange .. .. 13·00 7·00
148 1 a. grey 35 35
150 1 a. green 35 35
108 2 a. violet .. .. 19·00 19·00
110 2 a. blue .. .. 28·00 28·00
128 2 a. red .. .. 1·90 2·25
134 2 a. orange .. .. 14·00 7·00
152 2 a. red on yellow .. 55 55
153 2 a. red on green .. 80 1·00
129 4 a. red .. .. 4·00 4·50
135 4 a. orange .. .. 20·00
155 4 a. green .. .. 1·75 2·25
130 8 a. red .. .. 4·50 5·00
136 8 a. orange .. .. 35·00
159 8 a. blue .. .. 4·00 5·00
161a 8 a. lilac .. .. 10·00 12·00

OFFICIAL STAMPS

1878. Imperf. or perf.

O 6. **12.** ¼ a. black 30 30
O 7. ½ a. black 15 20
O 8. 1 a. black 20 20
O 9. 2 a. black 30 30
O 10. 4 a. black 35 50
O 11. 8 a. black 50 60

JASDAN

A State of India. Now uses Indian stamps.

12 pie = 1 anna; 16 annas = 1 rupee.

1. Sun.

1942.

4 1 1 a. green .. .. .. 5·50 45·00

JERSEY

Island in the English Channel off N.W. coast off France. Occupied by German forces from June 1940 to May 1945 with separate stamp issues.

The general issue of 1948 for Channel Islands and the regional issues of 1958 are listed at end of GREAT BRITAIN.

Jersey had its own postal administration from 1969.

1941. 12 pence = 1 shilling.
20 shillings = 1 pound.
1971. 100 (new) pence = 1 pound sterling.

(a) War Occupation Issues.

1.

2. Old Jersey Farm.

1941.

1. **1.** ½d. green .. .. .. 3·75 2·50
2. 1d. red .. .. .. 4·00 2·75

1943.

3. **2.** ½d. green .. .. .. 7·00 5·50
4. – 1d. red .. .. .. 1·50 50
5. – 1½d. brown .. .. .. 3·00 3·00
6. – 2d. yellow .. .. .. 3·00 2·25
7a.– 2½d. blue .. .. .. 1·00 1·50
8. – 3d. violet .. .. .. 1·00 2·75

DESIGNS: 1d. Portelet Bay. 1½d., Corbiere Lighthouse. 2d. Elizabeth Castle. 2½d., Mont Orgueil Castle. 3d. Gathering vraic (seaweed).

(b) Independent Postal Administration.

10. Elizabeth Castle.

1969. Multicoloured.

15. ½d. Type **10** 10 60
16. 1d. La Hougue Bie (Prehistoric Tomb) 15 20
17. 2d. Portelet Bay 10 15
18. 3d. Corbiere Lighthouse .. 20 15
19. 4d. Mont Orgueil Castle by night 15 10
20. 5d. Arms and Royal Mace .. 15 10
21. 6d. Jersey Cow 30 40
22. 9d. Chart of the English Channel 55 90
23. 1s. Mont Orgueil Castle by day 90 90
24. 1s. 6d. Chart of the English Channel .. .. 1·75 1·75
25. 1s. 9d. Queen Elizabeth II (after Cecil Beaton) 1·75 1·75
26. 2s. 6d. Jersey Airport .. 3·75 2·50
27. 5s. Legislative Chamber .. 15·00 7·50
28. 10s. The Royal Court .. 30·00 22·00
29. £1 Queen Elizabeth II (after Cecil Beaton) .. .. 2·00 1·50

The 1s. 9d. and £1 are vert.

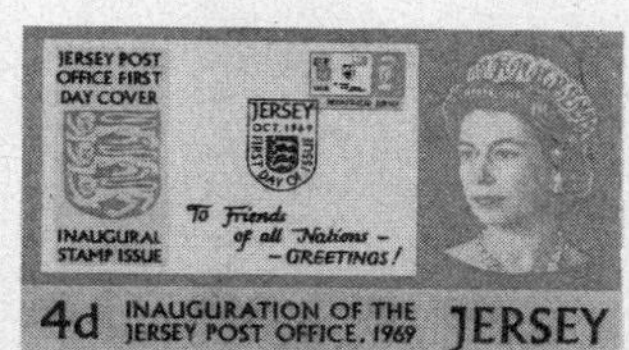

24. First Day Cover.

1969. Inauguration of Post Office.

30. **24.** 4d. multicoloured .. 25 30
31. 5d. multicoloured .. 50 60
32. 1s. 6d. multicoloured .. 2·50 4·00
33. 1s. 9d. multicoloured .. 2·50 4·00

25. Lord Coutanche, former Bailiff of Jersey.

1970. 25th Anniv. of Liberation. Mult.

34. 4d. Type **25** 25 25
35. 5d. Sir Winston Churchill .. 35 25
36. 1s. 6d. "Liberation" (Edmund Blampied) .. 3·00 2·00
37. 1s. 9d. S.S. "Vega" .. 3·00 2·00

Nos. 36/7 are horiz.

29. "A Tribute to Enid Blyton".

1970. "Battle of Flowers" Parade. Mult.

38. 4d. Type **29** 25 35
39. 5d. "Rags to riches" (Cinderella and pumpkin) 40 45
40. 1s. 6d. "Gourmet's delight" (lobster and cornucopia) 13·00 3·50
41. 1s. 9d. "We're the greatest" (ostriches) .. .. .. 13·00 3·50

33. Jersey Airport.

1970. Decimal currency. Nos. 15, etc., but with new colours, new design (6p.) and decimal values, as T **33.**

42. ½p. mult. (as No. 15) .. 10 10
43. 1p. mult. (as No. 18) .. 10 10
44. 1½p. mult. (as No. 21) .. 10 10
45. 2p. mult. (as No. 19) .. 10 10
46. 2½p. mult. (as No. 20) .. 10 10
47. 3p. mult. (as No. 16) .. 10 10
48. 3½p. mult. (as No. 17) .. 15 15
49. 4p. mult. (as No. 22) .. 15 15
49a. 4½p. mult. (as No. 20) .. 20 20
50. 5p. mult. (as No. 23) .. 10 15
50a. 5½p. mult. (as No. 21) .. 40 25
51. 6p. multicoloured (Martello Tower, Archirondel, 23 × 22 mm.) 25 30
52. 7½p. mult (as No. 24) .. 30 40
52a. 8p. mult. (as No. 19) .. 25 25
53. 9p. mult. (as No. 25) .. 30 30
54. 10p. mult. (as No. 26) .. 30 55
55. 20p. mult. (as No. 27) .. 60 75
56. 50p. mult. (as No. 28) .. 1·25 1·25

34. White-eared Pheasant.

1971. Wildlife Preservation Trust (1st series). Multicoloured.

57. 2p. Type **24** 75 25
58. 2½p. Thick-billed Parrot (vert.) 75 25
59. 7½p. Western Black-and-White Colobus (vert.) .. 11·50 4·25
60. 9p. Ring-tailed Lemur .. 11·50 4·25

See also Nos. 73/6, 217/21, 324/9 and 447/51.

35. Poppy Emblem and Field.

1971. 50th Anniversary of Royal British Legion. Multicoloured.

61. 2p. Royal British Legion Badge 40 35
62. 2½p. Type **35** 40 35
63. 7½p. Jack Counter and Victoria Cross .. .. 3·50 3·00
64. 9p. Crossed Tricolour and Union Jack .. .. 3·50 3·00

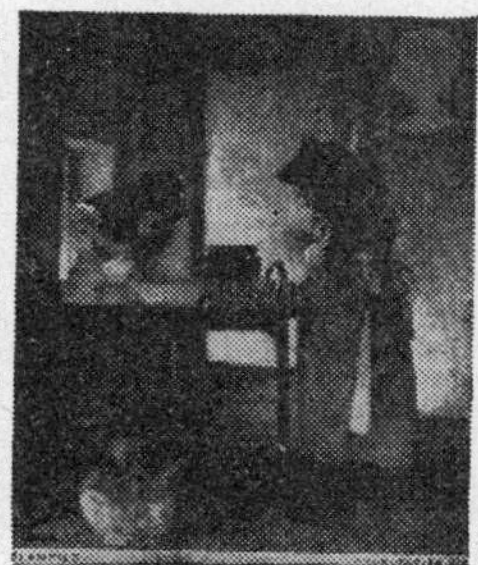

36. "Tante Elizabeth" (E. Blampied).

1971. Paintings (1st series). Multicoloured.

65. 2p. Type **36** 15 15
66. 2½p. "English Fleet in the Channel" (P. Monamy) (horiz.) 20 20
67. 7½p. "The Boyhood of Raleigh" (Millais) (horiz.) 4·25 3·25
68. 9p. "The Blind Beggar" (W. W. Ouless) .. .. 4·25 3·25

See also Nos. 115/118.

37. Jersey Fern.

38. Artillery Shako.

1972. Wild Flowers of Jersey. Multicoloured.

69. 3p. Type **37** 25 15
70. 5p. Jersey Thrift 60 50
71. 7½p. Jersey Orchid .. 3·25 3·00
72. 9p. Jersey Viper's Bugloss 3·25 3·00

1972. Wildlife Preservation Trust (2nd series). As T **34.** Multicoloured.

73. 2½p. Cheetah 75 20
74. 3p. Rothschild's Mynah (vert.) 40 35
75. 7½p. Spectacled Bear .. 2·00 2·50
76. 9p. Tuatara .. .. 2·40 2·50

1972. Royal Jersey Militia. Multicoloured.

77. 2½p. Type **38** 15 20
78. 3p. Shako (2nd North Regt.) 20 20
79. 7½p. Shako (5th South-West Regt.) .. .. .. 1·10 1·10
80. 9p. Helmet (3rd Jersey Light Infantry) .. .. .. 1·25 1·25

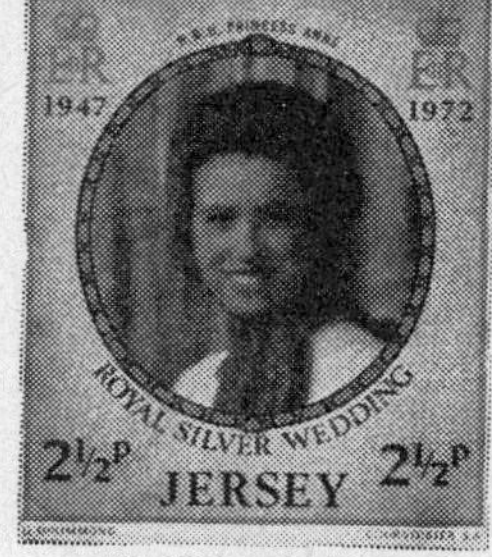

39. Princess Anne.

1972. Royal Silver Wedding. Multicoloured.

81. 2½p. Type **39** 10 10
82. 3p. Queen Elizabeth and Prince Philip (horiz.) .. 10 10
83. 7½p. Prince Charles .. 40 40
84. 20p. The Royal Family (horiz.) 50 50

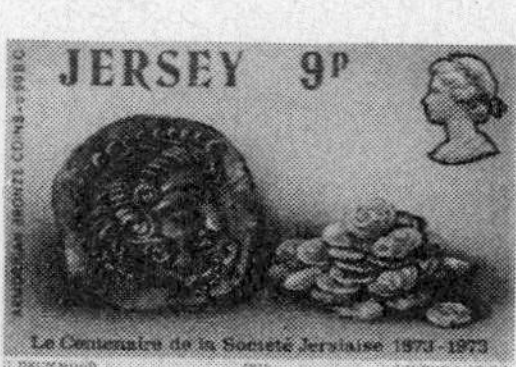

40. Armorican Bronze Coins.

1973. Centenary of La Societe Jersiaise. Multicoloured.

85. 2½p. Silver cups 10 10
86. 3p. Gold torque (vert.) .. 10 10
87. 7½p. Royal Seal of Charles II (vert.) 50 40
88. 9p. Type **40** 50 50

41. Balloon and Letter.

1973. Jersey Aviation History (1st series). Multicoloured.

89. 3p. Type **41** 10 10
90. 5p. Seaplane "Astra" .. 15 15
91. 7½p. Supermarine "Sea Eagle" 50 60
92. 9p. De Havilland "Express" .. 50 60

See also Nos. 340/3.

42. "North Western".

1973. Centenary of Jersey Eastern Railway. Early Locomotives. Multicoloured.

93. 2½p. Type **42** 10 10
94. 3p. "Calvados" 10 10
95. 7½p. "Carteret" 50 40
96. 9p. "Caesarea" 50 50

43. Princess Anne and Capt. Mark Phillips.

1973. Royal Wedding.

97. **43.** 3p. multicoloured .. 10 10
98. 20p. multicoloured .. 90 90

44. Spider Crab.

1973. Marine Life. Multicoloured.

99. 2½p. Type **44** 10 10
100. 3p. Conger-eel 10 10
101. 7½p. Lobster 35 35
102. 20p. Ormer 55 55

45. Freesias.

1974. Spring Flowers. Multicoloured.

103. 3p. Type **45** 10 10
104. 5½p. Anemones 10 10
105. 8p. Carnations and Gladioli 40 40
106. 10p. Daffodils and Iris .. 50 50

46. First Letter Box and Contemporary Cover.

1974. Centenary of U.P.U. Multicoloured.

107. 2½p. Type **46** 10 10
108. 3p. Postmen, 1862 and 1969 10 10
109. 5½p. Letter-box and letter, 1974 .. .. .. 25 30
110. 20p. R.M.S. "Aquila" (1874) and aeroplane (1974) 70 60

47. John Wesley.

1974. Anniversaries.

111. **47.** 3p. black and brown .. 10 10
112. – 3½p. violet and blue .. 10 10
113. – 8p. black and lilac .. 30 35
114. – 20p. black and stone .. 70 65

PORTRAITS AND EVENTS: 3p. (Methodism in Jersey.) Bicent. 3½p. Sir William Hillary, founder (R.N.L.I.) 150th anniv. 8p. Canon Wace (poet and historian), 800th death anniv. 20p. Sir Winston Churchill. (Birth Cent.).

48. Royal Yacht.

1974. Marine Paintings by Peter Monamy (2nd series). Multicoloured.

115. 3½p. Type **48** 10 10
116. 5½p. French two-decker .. 15 15
117. 8p. Dutch vessel (horiz.) .. 25 30
118. 25p. Battle of Cap La Hague, 1692 (55×27 mm.) 65 60

49. Potato Digger.

1975. 19th Century Farming. Multicoloured.

119. 3p. Type **49** 10 10
120. 3½p. Cider Crusher .. 10 15
121. 8p. Six-horse plough .. 35 35
122. 10p. Hay cart 55 50

50. H.M. Queen Elizabeth, the Queen Mother (photograph by Cecil Beaton).

1975. Royal Visit.

123 **50** 20p. multicoloured .. 75 75

51. Shell.

1975. Jersey Tourism. Multicoloured.

124. 5p. Type **51** 10 10
125. 8p. Parasol 15 15
126. 10p. Deckchair 35 35
127. 12p. Sandcastle with flags of Jersey and the U.K. 50 50

52. Common Tern.

1975. Sea Birds. Multicoloured.

129. 4p. Type **52** 15 15
130. 5p. British storm petrel .. 15 15
131. 8p. Brent geese 30 35
132. 25p. Shag 60 55

53. Siskin "3–A".

1975. 50th Anniv. of Royal Air Force Association, Jersey Branch. Multicoloured.

133. 4p. Type **53** 10 10
134. 5p. "Southampton" flying-boat 15 15
135. 10p. Mk. 1 "Spitfire" .. 30 30
136. 25p. Folland "Gnat" .. 60 60

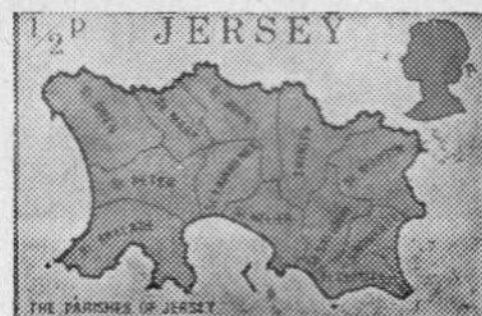

54. Map of Jersey Parishes.

55. Parish Arms and Island Scene.

1976. Multicoloured.
(a) Parish Arms and Views.

137. ½p. Type **54** 10 10
138. 1p. Zoological Park .. 10 10
139. 5p. St. Mary's Church .. 15 15
140. 6p. Seymour Tower .. 15 15
141. 7p. La Corbiere Lighthouse 20 20
142. 8p. St. Saviour's Church 20 20
143. 9p. Elizabeth Castle .. 25 25
144. 10p. Gorey Harbour .. 25 25
145. 11p. Jersey Airport .. 30 25
146. 12p. Grosnez Castle .. 30 30
147. 13p. Bonne Nuit Harbour 35 35
148. 14p. Le Hocq Tower .. 35 40
149. 15p. Morel Farm 40 45

(b) Emblems.

150. 20p. Type **55** 50 50
151. 30p. Flag and map .. 75 75
152. 40p. Postal H.Q. and badge 1·00 1·00
153. 50p. Parliament, Royal Court and arms .. 1·25 1·25
154. £1 Lieutenant-Governor's flag and Government House 2·50 2·50
155. £2 Queen Elizabeth II (vert.) .. .. .. 4·00 4·25

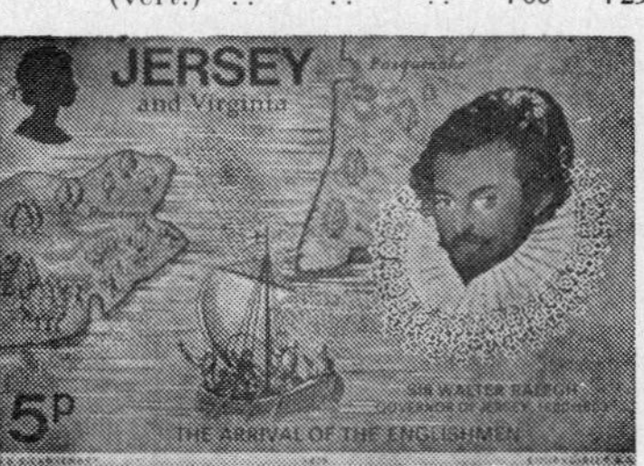

56. Sir Walter Raleigh and map of Virginia.

1976. Bicentenary of American Independence. Multicoloured.

160. 5p. Type **56** 10 10
161. 7p. Sir George Carteret and map of New Jersey .. 15 15
162. 11p. Philippe Dauvergne and Long Island Landing 40 35
163. 13p. John Copley and sketch 45 50

57. Dr. Grandin and Map of China.

1976. Birth Centenary of Dr. Lilian Grandin (medical missionary).

164. **57.** 5p. multicoloured .. 10 10
165. – 7p. yell., brn. and blk. 15 15
166. – 11p. multicoloured .. 50 35
167. – 13p. multicoloured .. 50 50

DESIGNS 7p. Sampan on the Yangtze. 11p. Overland trek. 13p. Dr. Grandin at work.

58. Coronation, 1953 (photographed by Cecil Beaton).

1977. Silver Jubilee. Multicoloured.

168. 5p. Type **58** 15 15
169. 7p. Visit to Jersey, 1957 .. 30 20
170. 25p. Queen Elizabeth II (photo by Peter Grugeon) 80 80

59. Coins of 1871 and 1877.

1977. Centenary of Currency Reform. Mult.

171. 5p. Type **59** 10 10
172. 7p. Obverse and reverse of 1949 Liberation penny 15 15
173. 11p. Obverse and reverse of 1966 crown 40 35
174. 13p. Obverse and reverse of 1972 Silver Wedding £2 45 50

60. Sir William Weston and "Santa Anna", 1530.

1977. Centenary of St. John Ambulance. Multicoloured.

175. 5p. Type **60** 10 10
176. 7p. Sir William Drogo and ambulance, 1877 .. 15 15
177. 11p. Duke of Connaught and ambulance, 1917 40 35
178. 13p. Duke of Gloucester and stretcher-team, 1977 45 50

61. Arrival of Queen Victoria, 1846.

1977. 125th Anniv. of Victoria College. Mult.

179. 7p. Type **61** 20 20
180. 10½p. Victoria College, 1852 25 20
181. 11p. Sir Galahad Statue, 1924 (vert.) 30 35
182. 13p. College Hall (vert.) .. 35 35

62. Harry Vardon Statuette and Map of Course.

1978. Cent. Royal Jersey Golf Club. Mult.

183. 6p. Type **62** 15 15
184. 8p. Vardon grip and swing 20 20
185. 11p. Vardon putt 35 35
186. 13p. "The Complete Golfer" and British and U.S.A. Open Golf Trophies 40 40

63. Mont Orgueil Castle.

1978. Europa. Castles from Paintings by Thomas Phillips. Multicoloured.

187. 6p. Type **63** 20 20
188. 8p. St. Aubin's Fort .. 40 40
189. 10½p. Elizabeth Castle .. 50 50

64. "Gaspe Basin" (P. J. Ouless).

1978. Links with Canada. Multicoloured.

190. 6p. Type **64** 15 15
191. 8p. Map of Gaspe Peninsula 20 20
192. 10½p. "Century" (brigantine) 25 25
193. 11p. Early map of Jersey 30 30
194. 13 p. St. Aubin's Bay town and harbour 35 35

65. Queen Elizabeth and Prince Philip.

1978. 25th Anniversary of Coronation.

195. 65. 8p. silver, black and red 30 30
196. – 25p. silver, black & blue 70 70

Design: 25p. Hallmarks of 1953 and 1977.

66. Mail Cutter, 1778–1827.

1978. Bicent. of England–Jersey Government Mail Packet Service.

197. 66. 6p. black, brown & yell. 15 15
198. – 8p. black, grn. & yell. 20 20
199. – 10½p. blk., ultram. & bl. 30 30
200. – 11p. black, purple & lilac 35 35
201. – 13p. black, red and pink 45 45

Designs—ships. 8p. "Flamer", 1831–7. 10½p. "Diana", 1877–90. 11p. "Ibex", 1891–1925. 13p. "Caesarea", 1960–75.

67. Jersey Calf.

1979. 9th International Conference of World Jersey Cattle Bureau. Multicoloured.

202. 6p. Type **67** 20 20
203. 25p. "Ansom Designette" (calf presented to the Queen, 1978) (45×30 mm.). 80 80

68. Jersey Pillar Box, c. 1860.

1979. Europa. Multicoloured.

204. 8p. Type **68** 20 25
205. 8p. Clearing modern post box 20 25
206. 10½p. Telephone switch-board, c. 1900 .. .. 25 30
207. 10½p. Modern SPC. tele-phone system 25 30

69. Percival "Mew Gull".

1979. 25th International Air Rally. Mult.

208. 6p. Type **69** 15 15
209. 8p. De Havilland "Chip-munk" 20 20
210. 10½p. Druine "Turbulent" 30 30
211. 11p. De Havilland "Tiger Moth" 45 35
212. 13p. North American "Harvard" Mk. 4 .. 50 40

70. "My First Sermon".

1979. International Year of the Child, and 150th Birth Anniversary of Sir John Millais (painter). Paintings. Multicoloured.

213. 8p. Type **70** 25 25
214. 10½p. "Orphans" 30 30
215. 11p. "The Princes in the Tower" 40 40
216. 25p. "Christ in the House of his Parents" (50×32 mm.) 65 65

1979. Wildlife Preservation Trust (3rd series). As T **34.** Multicoloured.

217. 6p. Pink pigeon (vert.) .. 15 15
218. 8p. Orang-utan (vert.) .. 20 20
219. 11½p. Waldrapp ibis .. 40 35
220. 13p. Gorilla (vert.) .. 45 40
221. 15p. Rodriguez flying fox (vert.) 60 45

71. Plan of Mont Orgueil.

1980. Jersey Fortresses. Drawings by Thomas Phillips. Multicoloured.

222. 8p. Type **71** .. 25 25
223. 11½p. Plan of La Tour de St. Aubin .. 30 30
224. 13p. Plan of Elizabeth Castle 45 35
225. 25p. Map of Jersey (38×27 mm.) .. 80 70

72. Sir Walter Raleigh and Paul Ivy (engineer) discussing Elizabeth Castle.

1980. Europa. Links with Britain. Multicoloured.

226. 9p. } Type **72** 20 20
227. 9p. } .. 20 20
228. 13½p. Charles II presenting deeds of Smith's island, Virginia to Sir George Carteret 40 35
229. 13½p. Lady Carteret, maid and Jean Chevalier .. 40 35

Nos. 226/7 and Nos. 228/9 were issued together, se-tenant, forming composite designs.

73. Planting.

1980. Centenary of Jersey Royal Potato. Multicoloured.

230. 7p. Type **73** 15 15
231. 15p. Digging 45 35
232. 17½p. Weighbridge .. 65 60

74. Three Lap Event.

1980. 60th Anniv. of Jersey Motor Cycle and Light Car Club. Multicoloured.

233. 7p. Type **74** 25 25
234. 9p. Jersey International Road Race 25 25
235. 13½p. Scrambling 40 40
236. 15p. Sand racing (saloon cars) 45 45
237. 17½p. National Hill Climb 50 50

75. "Eye of the Wind".

1980. "Operation Drake" and 150th Anniv. of Royal Geographical Society. (14p.). Multicoloured.

238. 7p. Type **75** 20 20
239. 9p. Inflatable raft .. 25 25
240. 13½p. Shooting rapids .. 45 35
241. 14p. "Discovery" .. 45 35
242. 15p. Aerial walkway .. 45 35
243. 17½p. Goodyear airship "Europa" 45 45

76. Detail of "The Death of Major Peirson".

1981. Bicentenary of Battle of Jersey. Details of J. S. Copley's painting.

244. **76.** 7p. multicoloured .. 25 25
245. – 10p. multicoloured .. 30 30
246. – 15p. multicoloured .. 50 50
247. – 17½p. multicoloured .. 55 55

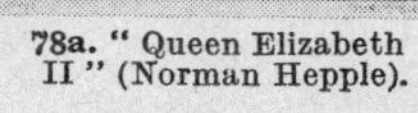

77. De Bagot.

78a. "Queen Elizabeth II" (Norman Hepple).

1981. Crests of Jersey Families.

249 **77** ½p. blk, silver & grn 10 10
250 – 1p. multicoloured .. 10 10
251 – 2p. multicoloured .. 10 10
252 – 3p. multicoloured .. 10 10
253a – 4p. silver, blk & mve 10 10
254 – 5p. multicoloured .. 15 15
255 – 6p. multicoloured .. 20 20
256 – 7p. multicoloured .. 20 20
257 – 8p. multicoloured .. 25 25
258 – 9p. multicoloured .. 30 30
259b – 10p. multicoloured .. 20 25
260 – 11p. multicoloured .. 35 35
261a – 12p. multicoloured .. 20 25
262a – 13p. multicoloured .. 25 30
263a – 14p. multicoloured .. 25 30
264a – 15p. multicoloured .. 25 30
265 – 16p. multicoloured .. 30 35
266 – 17p. multicoloured .. 50 50
266a – 18p. multicoloured .. 55 55
266b – 19p. multicoloured .. 60 60
267 – 20p. blk, silver & yell 60 60
268 – 25p. black and blue 45 50
268a **77** 26p. blk, silver & red 45 50
269a – 30p. multicoloured .. 50 55
270a – 40p. multicoloured .. 1·00 1·00
271a – 50p. multicoloured .. 1·25 1·25
272 – 75p. multicoloured .. 2·00 1·75
273 – £1 multicoloured .. 3·00 3·00
274 **78a** £5 multicoloured .. 10·00 10·50

Designs—vert. (as T **77**). 1p. De Carteret. 2p. La Cloche. 3p. Dumaresq. 4p. Payn. 5p. Jancrin. 6p. Poingdestre. 7p. Pipon. 8p. Marett. 9p. Le Breton. 10p. Le Maistre. 11p. Bisson. 12p. Robin. 13p. Herault. 14p. Messervy. 15p. Fiott. 16p. Malet. 17p. Mabon. 18p. De St. Martin. 19p. Hamptonne. 20p. Badier. 25p. L'Arbalestier. 30p. Journeaux. 40p. Lempriere. 50p. D'Auvergne. 75p. Remon. horiz. (38×22 mm.). £1, Jersey crest and map of The Channel.

79. Knight of Hambye slaying Dragon.

1981. Europa. Folklore. Multicoloured.

275. 10p. Type **79** 25 25
276. 10p. Servant slaying Knight of Hambye and awaiting execution .. 25 25
277. 18p. St. Brelade celebrating Easter on island 50 50
278. 18p. Island revealing itself as a Blue Whale. 50 50

Legends: 10p. (both) Slaying of the Dragon of Lawrence by the Knight of Hambye. 18p. (both) Voyages of St. Brelade.

80. The Harbour by Gaslight.

1981. 150th Anniv. of Gas in Jersey. Mult.

279. 7p. Type **80** 25 25
280. 10p. The Quay 30 30
281. 18p. Royal Square .. 55 45
282. 22p. Market Place .. 65 55
283. 25p. Central Market .. 75 65

81. Prince Charles and Lady Diana Spencer.

1981. Royal Wedding.

284. **81.** 10p. multicoloured .. 55 25
285. 25p. multicoloured .. 1·25 1·25

82. Christmas Tree in Royal Square.

1981. Christmas. Multicoloured.
286. 7p. Type **82** 25 25
287. 10p. East Window, Parish Church, St. Helier .. 40 40
288. 18p. Boxing Day meet of Jersey Drag Hunt .. 60 60

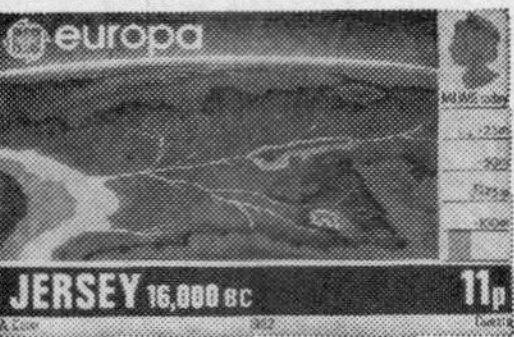

83. Jersey, 16,000 B.C.

1982. Europa. Formation of Jersey. Mult.
289. 11p. Type **83** 30 30
290. 11p. In 10,000 B.C. (vert.) 30 30
291. 19½p. In 7,000 B.C. (vert.) 60 60
292. 19½p. In 4,000 B.C. .. 60 60

84. Rollo, Duke of Normandy, William the Conqueror and " Clameur de Haro " (traditional procedure for obtaining justice).

1982. Links with France. Multicoloured.
293. 8p. Type **84** 30 30
294. 8p. John of England and Philippe Auguste of France, and Siege of Rouen 30 30
295. 11p. Jean Martell (brandy merchant), early still and view of Cognac 40 40
296. 11p. Victor Hugo, " Le Rocher des Proscrits " (rock where he used to meditate) and Marine Terrace 40 40
297. 19½p. Pierre Teilhard de Chardin (philosopher) and " Maison Saint Louis " (science institute) .. 70 70
298. 19½p. Père Charles Rey (scientist), anemotachymeter and The Observatory, St. Louis .. 70 70

85. Sir William Smith, Founder of Boys' Brigade.

1982. Youth Organizations. Mult.
299. 8p. Type **85** 25 25
300. 11p. Boy's Brigade "Old Boys" band, Liberation Parade, 1945 (vert.) .. 35 35
301. 24p. William Smith and Lord Baden-Powell at Royal Albert Hall, 1903 75 75
302. 26p. Lord and Lady Baden-Powell, St. Helier, 1924 (vert.) .. 90 90
303. 29p. Scouts at "Westward Ho" campsite, St. Ouen's Bay .. .. 1·10 1·10

Nos. 299/301 commemorate the centenary of the Boys' Brigade and Nos. 302/3 the 75th anniversary of the Boy Scout Movement.

86. H.M.S. "Tamar" and H.M.S. "Dolphin" at Port Egmont.

1983. Jersey Adventurers (1st series). Mult.
304. 8p. Type **86** 25 25
305. 11p. H.M.S. "Dolphin" and H.M.S. "Swallow" off Magellan Strait 35 35
306. 19½p. Discovering Pitcairn Island 60 60
307. 24p. Carteret taking possession of English Cove, New Ireland .. 85 85
308. 26p. H.M.S. "Swallow" sinking a pirate, Macassar Strait 90 90
309. 29p. H.M.S. "Endymion" leading convoy from West Indies .. .. 1·00 1·00
See also Nos. 417/21 and 573/8.

87. 1969 5s. Legislative Chamber Definitive.

1983. Europa. Multicoloured.
310. 11 p. Type **87** 50 50
311. 11 p. Royal Mace (23 × 32 mm) 50 50
312. 19½p. 1969 10s. Royal Court definitive showing green border error .. 85 85
313. 19½p. Bailiff's Seal (23 × 32 mm) 85 85

88. Charles Le Geyt and Battle of Minden (1759).

1983. World Communications Year and 250th Birth Anniv. of Charles Le Geyt (1st Jersey postmaster). Multicoloured.
314. 8p. Type **88** 25 25
315. 11p. London to Weymouth mail coach 35 35
316. 24p. P.O. Mail Packet " Chesterfield " attacked by French privateer .. 75 75
317. 26p. Mary Godfray and the Hue Street Post Office .. 90 90
318. 29p. Mail steamer leaving St. Helier harbour .. 1·10 1·10

89. Assembly Emblem.

1983. 13th General Assembly of the A.I.P.L.F. (Association Internationale des Parlementaires de Langue Francaise) Jersey.
319. **89.** 19½p. multicoloured .. 90 90

90. " Cardinal Newman ".

1983. 50th Death Anniv. of Walter Ouless (artist). Multicoloured.
320. 8p. Type **90** 25 25
321. 11p. " Incident in the French Revolution " 45 45
322. 20½p. " Thomas Hardy " .. 85 85
323. 31p. " David with the head of Goliath " (38 × 32 mm) 1·25 1·25

91. Golden Lion Tamarin.

1984. Wildlife Preservation Trust (4th series). Multicoloured.
324. 9p. Type **91** 30 30
325. 12p. Snow leopard .. 40 40
326. 20½p. Jamaican boa .. 65 65
327. 26p. Round island gecko .. 80 80
328. 28p. Coscoroba swan .. 90 90
329. 31p. St. Lucia amazon .. 1·00 1·00

92. C.E.P.T. 25th Anniversary Logo.

1984. Europa.
330. **92.** 9p. light bl., bl. & black 30 30
331. 12p. light grn., grn. & blk. 40 40
332. 20½p. lilac, pur. & black 70 70

94. "Sarah Bloomshoft" at Demie de Pas Light, 1906.

1984. Centenary of Jersey R.N.L.I. Lifeboat Station. Multicoloured.
334. 9p. Type **94** 30 30
335. 9p. "Hearts of Oak" and "Maurice Georges", 1949 30 30
336. 12p. "Elizabeth Rippon" and "Hanna", 1949 .. 40 40
337. 12p. "Elizabeth Rippon" and "Santa Maria", 1951 40 40
338. 20½p. "Elizabeth Rippon" and "Bacchus", 1973 .. 65 65
339. 20½p. "Thomas James King" and "Cythara", 1983 .. .. .. 65 65

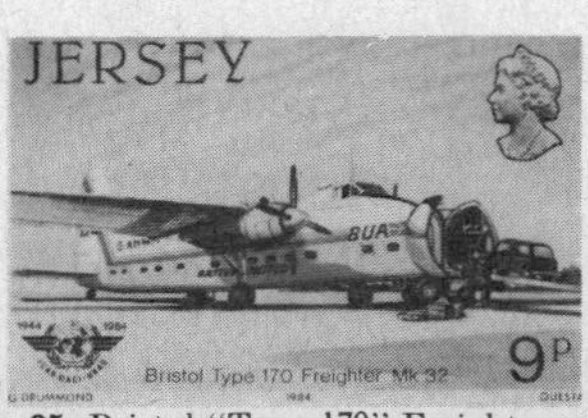

95. Bristol "Type 170" Freighter.

1984. Jersey Aviation History (2nd series). Multicoloured.
340. 9p. Type **95** 30 30
341. 12p. Airspeed "A.S.57 Ambassador 2" 40 40
342. 26p. De Havilland "D.H.114 Heron 1B" .. 90 90
343. 31p. De Havilland "D.H.89A Dragon Rapide" .. .. 1·10 1·10

96. "Robinson Crusoe leaves the Wreck".

1984. Links with Australia. Paintings by John Alexander Gilfillan. Multicoloured.
344. 9p. Type **96** 30 30
345. 12p. "Edinburgh Castle" .. 40 40
346. 20½p. "Maori Village" .. 75 75
347. 26p. "Australian Landscape" 90 90
348. 28p. "Waterhouse's Corner, Adelaide" .. .. 1·00 1·00
349. 31p. "Captain Cook at Botany Bay" .. .. 1·10 1·10

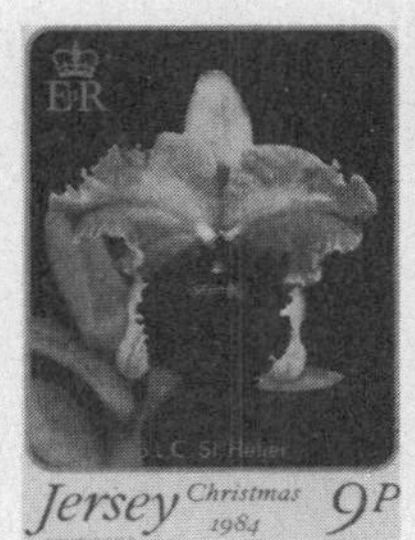

97. "B.L.C. St. Helier" Orchid.

1984. Christmas. Jersey Orchids (1st series). Multicoloured.
350. 9p. Type **97** 45 45
351. 12p. "Oda Mt Bingham" .. 75 75
See also Nos. 433/7.

98. "Hebe off Corbiere, 1874".

1984. Death Centenary of Philip John Ouless (artist). Multicoloured.
352. 9p Type **98** 30 30
353. 12p. "The Gaspe engaging the Diomede" 40 40
354. 22p. "The Paddle-steamer London entering Naples, 1856" 80 80
355. 31p. "The Rambler entering Cape Town, 1840" .. 1·10 1·10
356. 34p. "St. Aubin's Bay from Mount Bingham, 1871" 1·25 1·25

99. John Ireland (composer) and Faldouet Dolmen.

1985. Europa. European Music Year. Mult.
357. 10p. Type **99** 40 45
358. 13p. Ivy St. Helier (actress) and His Majesty's Theatre, London .. 55 60
359. 22p. Claude Debussy (composer) and Elizabeth Castle 90 95

100. Girls Brigade.

1985. International Youth Year. Mult.

360. 10p. Type **100** 30 30
361. 13p. Girl Guides (75th anniversary) 50 50
362. 29p. Prince Charles and Jersey Youth Service Activities Base .. .. 1·00 1·00
363. 31p. Sea Cadet Corps .. 1·00 1·00
364. 34p. Air Training Corps .. 1·10 1·10

101. "Duke of Normandy" at Cheapside.

1985. The Jersey Western Railway. Mult.

365. 10p. Type **101** 40 40
366. 13p. Saddletank at First Tower 50 50
367. 22p. "La Moye" at Millbrook 90 90
368. 29p. "St. Heliers" at St. Aubin .. .. .. 1·00 1·00
369. 34p. "St. Aubyns" at Corbiere .. .. .. 1·10 1·10

102. Memorial Window to Revd. James Hemery (former Dean) and St. Helier Parish Church.

1985. 300th Anniversary of Huguenot Immigration. Multicoloured.

370. 10p. Type **102** 20 30
371. 10p. Judge Francis Jeune, Baron St. Helier, and Houses of Parliament .. 20 30
372. 13p. Silverware by Pierre Amiraux 25 45
373. 13p. Francis Voisin (merchant) and Russian port 25 45
374. 22p. Robert Brohier, Schweppes carbonation plant and bottles .. 45 75
375. 22p. George Ingouville, V.C., R.N., and attack on Viborg 45 75

103. Howard Davis Hall, Victoria College.

1985. Thomas Benjamin Davis (philanthropist) Commemoration. Mult.

376. 10p. Type **103** 40 40
377. 13p. Racing schooner "Westward" 60 60
378. 31p. Howard Davis Park, St. Helier .. .. 1·10 1·10
379. 34p. Howard Davis Experimental Farm, Trinity .. 1·25 1·25

104. "Amaryllis belladonna" (Pandora Sellars).

1986. Jersey Lilies. Multicoloured.

380. 13p. Type **104** 50 50
381. 34p. "A Jersey Lily" (Lily Langtry) (Sir John Millais) (30 × 48 mm) .. 1·25 1·25

105. King Harold, William of Normandy and Halley's Comet, 1066 (from Bayeux Tapestry).

1986. Appearance of Halley's Comet. Multicoloured.

383. 10 p. Type **105** 40 40
384. 22p. Lady Carteret, Edmond Halley, map and Comet 85 85
385. 31p. Aspects of communications in 1910 and 1986 on TV screen .. .. 1·25 1·25

106. Dwarf Pansy.

1986. Europa. Environmental Conservation. Multicoloured.

386. 10p. Type **106** 35 35
387. 14p. Sea Stock 65 65
388. 22p. Sand Crocus 95 95

107. Queen Elizabeth II (from photo by Karsh).

1986. 60th Birthday of Queen Elizabeth II.

389. **107.** £1 multicoloured .. 2·75 2·75

108. Le Rat Cottage.

1986. 50th Anniv. of National Trust for Jersey. Multicoloured.

390. 10p. Type **108** 30 30
391. 14p. The Elms (Trust headquarters) 45 45
392. 22p. Morel Farm 80 80
393. 29p. Quetivel Mill .. .. 1·00 1·10
394. 31p. La Vallette .. .. 1·10 1·25

109. Prince Andrew and Miss Sarah Ferguson.

1986. Royal Wedding.

395. **109.** 14p. multicoloured .. 50 50
396. 40p. multicoloured .. 1·50 1·50

110. "Gathering Vraic".

1986. Birth Centenary of Edmund Blampied (artist).

397. **110.** 10p. multicoloured .. 30 30
398. – 14p. blk., bl. & grey .. 50 50
399. – 29p. multicoloured .. 1·00 1·00
400. – 31p. blk., orge. & grey 1·25 1·10
401. – 34p. multicoloured .. 1·40 1·25

DESIGNS: 14p. "Driving Home in the Rain". 29p. "The Miller". 31p. "The Joy Ride". 34p. "Tante Elizabeth".

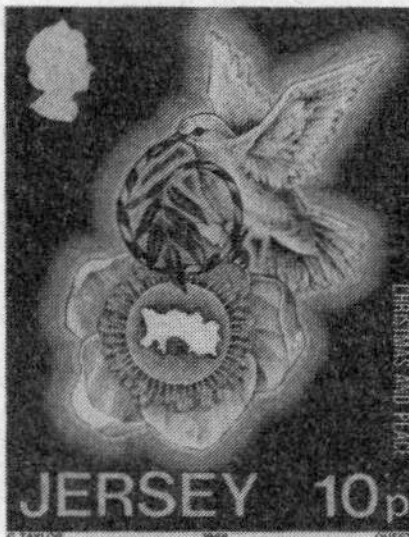

111. Island Map on Jersey Lily, and Dove holding Olive Branch.

1986. Christmas International Peace Year. Multicoloured.

402 10p. Type **111** 40 40
403 14p. Mistletoe wreath encircling European robin and dove .. 60 60
404 34p. Christmas cracker releasing dove .. .. 1·25 1·25

112. "Westward" under Full Sail.

1987. Racing Schooner "Westward". Mult.

405. 10p. Type **112** 40 40
406. 14p. T. B. Davis at the helm 60 60
407. 31p. "Westward" overhauling "Britannia" .. 1·10 1·10
408. 34p. "Westward" fitting-out at St. Helier .. 1·25 1·25

113. De Havilland "DH86" "Belcroute Bay".

1987. 50th Anniv. of Jersey Airport. Multicoloured.

409. 10p. Type **113** 30 30
410. 14p. Boeing "757" and Douglas "DC 9" .. 40 40
411. 22p. Britten Norman "Trislander" and "2A Islander" 70 70
412. 29p. Short "SD330" and Vickers "Viscount 800" 1·00 1·00
413. 31p. BAC "1–11" and HPR 7 "Dart Herald" .. 1·25 1·25

114. St. Mary and St. Peter's Roman Catholic Church.

1987. Europa. Modern Architecture. Mult.

414. 11p. Type **114** 35 35
415. 15p. Villa Devereux, St. Brelade 65 65
416. 22p. Fort Regent Leisure Centre, St. Helier (57 × 29 mm.) 90 90

115. H.M.S. "Racehorse" (bomb-ketch) trapped in Arctic.

1987. Jersey Adventurers (2nd series). Philippe D'Auvergne. Multicoloured.

417. 11p. Type **115** 40 40
418. 15p. H.M.S. "Alarm" on fire, Rhode Island .. 50 50
419. 29p. H.M.S. "Arethusa" wrecked off Ushant .. 90 90
420. 31p. H.M.S. "Rattlesnake" stranded on Isle de Trinidad .. .. 1·00 1·00
421. 34p. Mont Orgueil Castle and fishing boats .. 1·10 1·10

See also Nos. 501/6 and 539/44.

116. Grant of Lands to Normandy, 911 and 933.

1987. 900th Death Anniv. of William the Conqueror. Multicoloured.

422. 11p. Type **116** 40 40
423. 15p. Edward the Confessor and Duke Robert I of Normandy landing on Jersey, 1030 .. .. 45 45
424. 22p. King William's coronation, 1066, and fatal fall, 1087 .. .. 70 70
425. 29p. Death of William Rufus, 1100, and Battle of Tinchebrai, 1106 .. 85 85
426. 31p. Civil war between Matilda and Stephen, 1135–41 .. .. 95 95
427. 34p. Henry inherits Normandy, 1151; John asserts ducal rights in Jersey, 1213 .. .. 1·10 1·10

117. "Grosnez Castle".

1987. Christmas. Paintings by John Le Capelain. Multicoloured.

428.	11p. Type **117**	40	40
429.	15p. "St. Aubin's Bay"	60	60
430.	22p. "Mont Orgueil Castle"	80	80
431.	31p. "Town Fort and Harbour, St. Helier"	1·00	1·00
432.	34p. "The Hermitage"	1·10	1·10

118. "Cymbidium pontac".

1988. Jersey Orchids (2nd series). Mult.

433.	11p. Type **118**	40	40
434.	15p. "Odontioda" "Eric Young" (vert.)	50	50
435.	29p. "Lycaste auburn" "Seaford" and "Ditchling"	90	90
436.	31p. "Odontoglossum" "St. Brelade" (vert.)	1·00	1·00
437.	34p. "Cymbidium mavourneen" "Jester"	1·10	1·10

119. Labrador Retriever.

1988. Centenary of Jersey Dog Club. Mult.

438.	11p. Type **119**	40	40
439.	15p. Wire-haired dachshund	60	60
440.	22p. Pekingese	80	80
441.	31p. Cavalier King Charles spaniel	1·00	1·00
442.	34p. Dalmatian	1·10	1·10

120. D.H. "Dash 7" Aircraft, London Landmarks and Jersey Control Tower.

1988. Europa. Transport and Communications. Multicoloured.

443.	16p. Type **120**	50	50
444.	16p. Weather radar and Jersey airport landing system (vert.)	50	50
445.	22p. Hydrofoil, St. Malo and Elizabeth Castle, St. Helier	90	90
446.	22p. Port control tower and Jersey Radio maritime communication centre, La Moye (vert.)	90	90

121 Rodriguez Fody

1988. Wildlife Preservation Trust (5th series). Multicoloured.

447	12p. Type **121**	50	50
448	16p. Volcano rabbit (horiz)	60	60
449	29p. White-faced marmoset	1·00	1·00
450	31p. Ploughshare tortoise (horiz)	1·10	1·10
451	34p. Mauritius kestrel	1·25	1·25

122 Rain Forest Leaf Frog, Costa Rica

1988. Operation Raleigh. Multicoloured.

452	12p. Type **122**	45	45
453	16p. Archaeological survey, Peru	55	55
454	22p. Climbing glacier, Chile	70	70
455	29p. Red Cross Centre, Solomon Islands	80	80
456	31p. Underwater exploration, Australia	85	85
457	34p. "Zebu" (brigantine) returning to St. Helier	1·10	1·10

123 St. Clement Parish Church

1988. Christmas. Jersey Parish Churches (1st series). Multicoloured.

458	12p. Type **123**	35	35
459	16p. St. Ouen	60	60
460	31p. St. Brelade	1·00	1·00
461	34p. St. Lawrence	1·10	1·10

See also Nos. 535/8.

124 Talbot "Type 4 CT Tourer", 1912

1989. Vintage Cars. Multicoloured.

462	12p. Type **124**	45	35
463	16p. De Dion "Bouton Type 1-D", 1920	55	40
464	23p. Austin 7 "Chummy", 1926	80	55
465	30p. Ford "Model T", 1926	95	80
466	32p. Bentley 8 litre, 1930	1·10	1·00
467	35p. Cadillac "452A-V16 Fleetwood Sports Phaeton", 1931	1·25	1·10

125 Belcroute Bay

1989. Jersey Scenes. As T **125** and Queen's portrait as T **107**. Multicoloured.

468	1p. Type **125**	10	10
469	2p. High Street, St. Aubin	10	10
470	4p. Royal Jersey Golf Course	10	10
471	5p. Portelet Bay	10	10
472	10p. Les Charrieres D'Anneport	20	25
473	13p. St. Helier Marina	25	30
474	14p. Sand yacht racing, St. Ouen's Bay	30	35
475	15p. Rozel Harbour	30	35
476	16p. St. Aubin's Harbour	30	35
477	17p. Jersey Airport	35	40
478	18p. Corbiere Lighthouse	35	40
479	19p. Val de la Mare	40	45
480	20p. Elizabeth Castle	40	45
481	21p. Greve de Lecq	40	45
482	22p. Samares Manor	45	50
483	23p. Bonne Nuit Harbour	45	50
484	24p. Grosnez Castle	50	55
485	25p. Augres Manor	50	55
486	26p. Central Market	50	55
487	27p. St. Brelade's Bay	55	60
488	30p. St. Ouen's Manor	60	65
489	40p. La Hougue Bie	80	85
490	50p. Mont Orgueil Castle	1·00	1·10
491	75p. Royal Square, St. Helier	1·50	1·60
491b	£2 Type **107**	4·00	4·25

126 Agile Frog

1989. Endangered Jersey Fauna. Mult.

492	13p. Type **126**	40	35
493	13p. "Heteropterus morpheus" (butterfly) (vert)	40	35
494	17p. Barn owl (vert)	65	50
495	17p. Green lizard	65	50

127 Toddlers' Toys

1989. Europa. Children's Toys and Games. Designs showing clay plaques. Mult.

496	17p. Type **127**	50	50
497	17p. Playground games	50	50
498	23p. Party games	90	90
499	23p. Teenage sports	90	90

128 Queen Elizabeth II and Royal Yacht "Britannia" in Elizabeth Harbour

1989. Royal Visit.

500	**128**	£1 multicoloured	2·00	2·10

129 Philippe D' Auvergne presented to Louis XVI, 1786

1989. Bicentenary of the French Revolution. Philippe D' Auvergne. Multicoloured.

501	13p. Type **129**	35	35
502	17p. Storming the Bastille, 1789	55	45
503	23p. Marie de Bouillon and revolutionaries, 1790	65	55
504	30p. Auvergne's headquarters at Mont Orgueil, 1795	1·10	1·00
505	32p. Landing arms for Chouan rebels, 1796	1·10	1·00
506	35p. The last Chouan revolt, 1799	1·25	1·10

See also Nos. 539/44.

130 "St. Helier" off Elizabeth Castle

1989. Centenary of Great Western Railway Steamer Service to Channel Islands. Mult.

507	13p. Type **130**	50	50
508	17p. "Caesarea II" off Corbiere Lighthouse	60	60
509	27p. "Reindeer" in St. Helier harbour	1·00	95
510	32p. "Ibex" racing "Frederica" off Portelet	1·10	1·10
511	35p. "Lynx" off Noirmont	1·25	1·10

131 "Gorey Harbour"

1989. 150th Birth Anniv of Sarah Louisa Kilpack (artist). Multicoloured.

512	13p. Type **131**	50	45
513	17p. "La Corbiere"	60	55
514	23p. "Greve de Lecq"	1·00	95
515	32p. "Bouley Bay"	1·10	1·10
516	35p. "Mont Orgueil"	1·25	1·10

132 Head Post Office, Broad Street, 1969

1990. Europa. Post Office Buildings. Mult.

517	18p. Type **132**	45	45
518	18p. Postal Headquarters, Mont Millais, 1990	45	45
519	24p. Hue Street Post Office, 1815 (horiz)	65	65
520	24p. Head Post Office, Halkett Place, 1890 (horiz)	65	65

133 "Battle of Flowers" Parade

1990. Festival of Tourism. Multicoloured.

521	18p. Type **133**	50	50
522	24p. Sports	65	65
523	29p. Mont Orgueil Castle and German Underground Hospital Museum	80	80
524	32p. Salon Culinaire	85	85

134 Early Printing Press and Jersey Newspaper Mastheads

1990. International Literacy Year. Jersey News Media. Multicoloured.

526	14p. Type **134**	45	45
527	18p. Modern press, and offices of "Jersey Evening Post" in 1890 and 1990	50	50
528	34p. Radio Jersey broadcaster	90	90
529	37p. Channel Television studio cameraman ..	95	95

135 BAe Hawk

1990. 50th Anniv of Battle of Britain. Mult.

530	14p. Type **135**	45	45
531	18p. Supermarine Spitfire	50	50
532	24p. Hawker Hurricane ..	65	65
533	34p. Vickers Wellington ..	85	85
534	37p. Avro Lancaster ..	90	90

1990. Christmas. Jersey Parish Churches (2nd series). As T **123**. Multicoloured.

535	14p. St. Helier	40	40
536	18p. Grouville	45	45
537	34p. St. Saviour	95	95
538	37p. St. John	1·00	1·00

1991. 175th Death Anniv of Philippe D'Auvergne. As T **129**. Multicoloured.

539	15p. Prince's Tower, La Hougue Bie	40	40
540	20p. Auvergne's arrest in Paris	55	55
541	26p. Auvergne plotting against Napoleon ..	65	65
542	31p. Execution of George Cadoudal	90	90
543	37p. H.M. Cutter "Surly" attacking enemy convoy	1·00	1·00
544	44p. Auvergne's last days in London	1·25	1·25

136 "Landsat 5" and Thematic Mapper Image over Jersey

1991. Europa. Europe in Space. Mult.

545	20p. Type **136**	40	45
546	20p. "ERS-1" earth resources remote sensing satellite	40	45
547	26p. "Meteosat" weather satellite	50	55
548	26p. "Olympus" direct broadcasting satellite ..	50	55

137 1941 1d. Stamp (50th anniv of first Jersey postage stamp)

1991. Anniversaries. Multicoloured.

549	15p. Type **137**	40	40
550	20p. Steam train (centenary of Jersey Eastern Railway extension to Gorey Pier)	50	50
551	26p. Jersey cow and Herd Book (125th anniv of Jersey Herd Book) ..	60	60
552	31p. Stone-laying ceremony (from painting by P. J. Ouless) (150th anniv of Victoria Harbour) ..	70	70
553	53p. Marie Bartlett and hospital (250th anniv of Marie Bartlett's hospital bequest)	1·40	1·40

138 "Melitaea cinxia"

1991. Butterflies and Moths. Multicoloured.

554	15p. Type **138**	30	35
555	20p. "Euplagia quadripunctaria" ..	40	45
556	37p. "Deilephilia porcellus"	75	80
557	57p. "Inachis io"	1·10	1·25

139 Drilling for Water, Ethiopia

1991. Overseas Aid. Multicoloured.

558	15p. Type **139**	30	35
559	20p. Building construction, Rwanda	40	45
560	26p. Village polytechnic, Kenya	50	55
561	31p. Treating leprosy, Tanzania	60	65
562	37p. Ploughing, Zambia ..	75	80
563	44p. Immunisation clinic, Lesotho	90	95

140 "This is the Place for Me"

1991. Christmas. Illustrations by Edmund Blampied for J.M. Barrie's "Peter Pan". Multicoloured.

564	15p. Type **140**	30	35
565	20p. "The Island Come True"	40	45
566	37p. "The Never Bird" ..	75	80
567	53p. "The Great White Father"	1·10	1·25

141 Pied Wagtail

1992. Winter Birds. Multicoloured.

568	16p. Type **141**	30	35
569	22p. Firecrest	45	50
570	28p. Snipe	55	60
571	39p. Lapwing	80	85
572	57p. Fieldfare	1·10	1·25

142 Shipping at Shanghai, 1860

1992. Jersey Adventurers (3rd series). 150th Birth Anniv of William Mesny. Mult.

573	16p. Type **142**	30	35
574	16p. Mesny's junk running Taiping blockade, 1862	30	35
575	22p. General Mesny outside river gate, 1874 ..	45	50
576	22p. Mesny in Burma, 1877	45	50
577	33p. Mesny and Governor Chang, 1882	65	70
578	33p. Mesny in mandarin's saden chair, 1886 ..	65	70

143 "Tickler" (brig)

1992. Jersey Ship Building. Multicoloured.

579	16p. Type **143**	30	35
580	22p. "Hebe" (snow) ..	45	50
581	50p. "Gemini" (barque) ..	1·00	1·10
582	57p. "Percy Douglas" (full-rigged ship)	1·10	1·25

144 John Bertram (ship owner) and Columbus

1992. Europa. 500th Anniv of Discovery of America by Columbus. Multicoloured.

584	22p. Type **144**	45	50
585	28p. Sir George Carteret (founder of New Jersey)	55	60
586	39p. Sir Walter Ralegh (founder of Virginia) ..	80	85

145 "Snow Leopards" (Allison Griffiths)

1992. Batik Designs. Multicoloured.

587	16p. Type **145**	30	35
588	22p. "Three Elements" (Nataly Miorin) ..	45	50
589	39p. "Three Men in a Tub" (Amanda Crocker) ..	80	85
590	57p. "Cockatoos" (Michelle Millard)	1·10	1·25

POSTAGE DUE STAMPS

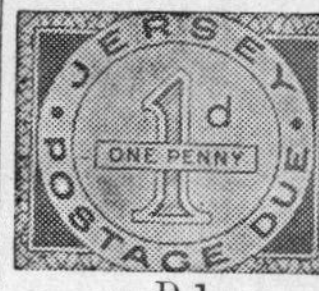

D 1.

D **3.** Arms of St. Clement and Dovecote at Samares.

1969.

D 1.	D **1.**	1d. violet	2·50	1·90
D 2.		2d. sepia	3·50	2·00
D 3.		3d. mauve	5·00	3·25
D 4.	–	1s. green	13·00	8·50
D 5.	–	2s. 6d. grey	25·00	22·00
D 6.	–	5s. red	35·00	40·00

DESIGNS: 1s., 2s. 6d. and 5s. Map.

1971. Decimal Currency. Design as Nos. D 4/6, but values in new currency.

D 7.	½p. black	10	10
D 8.	1p. blue	10	10
D 9.	2p. brown	10	10
D 10.	3p. purple	10	10
D 11.	4p. red	10	10
D 12.	5p. green	15	15
D 13.	6p. orange	15	15
D 14.	7p. yellow	15	15
D 15.	8p. blue	25	25
D 16.	10p. green	35	35
D 17.	11p. brown	35	40
D 18.	14p. violet	40	45
D 19.	25p. green	80	90
D 20.	50p. purple	1·40	1·50

1978. Parish Arms and Views.

D 21.	D **3.**	1p. black and green ..	10	10
D 22.	–	2p. black and yellow	10	10
D 23.	–	3p. black and brown	10	10
D 24.	–	4p. black and red ..	15	15
D 25.	–	5p. black and blue ..	15	20
D 26.	–	10p. black and olive ..	25	30
D 27.	–	12p. black and blue ..	30	35
D 28.	–	14p. black and orange	30	40
D 29.	–	15p. black and mauve	35	40
D 30.	–	20p. black and green	45	50
D 31.	–	50p. black and brown	1·25	1·40
D 32.	–	£1 black and blue ..	2·50	2·50

DESIGNS: 2p. Arms of St. Lawrence and Handois Reservoir. 3p. Arms of St. John and Sorel Point. 4p. Arms of St. Ouen and Pinnacle Rock. 5p. Arms of St. Peter and Quetivel Mill. 10p. Arms of St. Martin and St. Catherine's Breakwater. 12p. Arms of St. Helier and Harbour. 14p. Arms of St. Saviour and Highlands College. 15p. Arms of St. Brelade and Beauport Bay. 20p. Arms of Grouville and La Hougue Bie. 50p. Arms of St. Mary and Perry Farm. £1, Arms of Trinity and Bouley Bay.

D **4.** St. Brelade.

1982. Jersey Harbours.

D 33.	D **4.**	1p. green	10	10
D 34.	–	2p. yellow	10	10
D 35.	–	3p. brown	10	10
D 36.	–	4p. red	10	10
D 37.	–	5p. blue	10	10
D 38.	–	6p. green	10	15
D 39.	–	7p. mauve	15	20
D 40.	–	8p. red	15	20
D 41.	–	9p. green	20	45
D 42.	–	10p. blue	20	25
D 43.	–	20p. green	40	45
D 44.	–	30p. purple	60	65
D 45.	–	40p. orange	80	85
D 46.	–	£1 violet	2·00	2·10

DESIGNS: 2p. St. Aubin. 3p. Rozel. 4p. Greve de Lecq. 5p. Bouley Bay. 6p. St. Catherine. 7p. Gorey. 8p. Bonne Nuit. 9p. La Roque. 10p. St. Helier. 20p. Ronez. 30p. La Collette. 40p. Elizabeth Castle. £1, Upper Harbour Marina.

JHALAWAR

A State of Rajasthan, India. Now uses Indian stamps.
4 paisa = 1 anna.

1. Apsara.

1887. Imperf.
1. **1.** 1 paisa green .. .. 1·25 4·25
2. – ¼ a. green .. .. 60 1·25
The ¼ a. is larger and has a different frame.

JIND

A "convention" state of the Punjab, India, which now uses Indian stamps.
12 pies = 1 anna; 16 annas = 1 rupee.

J 1. (½ a.) J 6. (¼ a.)

1874. Imperf.
J 8 **J 1.** ½ a. blue .. .. 30 1·50
J 9 1 a. purple .. .. 1·25 3·50
J 3 2 a. bistre .. .. 1·00 2·50
J 11 4 a. green .. .. 1·00 5·00
J 12 8 a. purple .. .. 7·00 10·00

1882. Various designs and sizes. Imperf or perf.
J15 **J 6** ¼ a. brown 30 70
J17 ½ a. bistre 50 50
J20 1 a. brown .. .. 1·00 2·00
J22 2 a. blue .. .. 90 1·00
J23 4 a. green 80 90
J25 8 a. red .. .. 3·00 3·00

Stamps of India (Queen Victoria) overprinted.

1885. Optd. **JHIND STATE** vert. (curved).
1 **23** ½ a. turquoise .. .. 50 1·10
2 – 1 a. purple .. .. 9·50 13·00
3 – 2 a. blue .. .. 4·00 6·50
4 – 4 a. green (No. 71) .. 26·00 38·00
5 – 8 a. mauve £200
6 – 1 r. grey (No.101) .. £180

1885. Optd. **JEEND STATE.**
7 **23** ½ a. turquiose .. .. 42·00
8 – 1 a. purple .. .. 42·00
9 – 23 a. blue .. .. 55·00
10 – 4 a. green (No. 71) .. 70·00
11 – 8 a. mauve .. .. 75·00
12 – 1 r. grey (No. 101) .. 80·00

1886. Optd. **JHIND STATE** horiz.
17 **23** ½ a. turquiose 10 10
18 – 1 a. purple 20 15
20 – 1½ a. brown 50 90
21 – 2 a. blue 40 40
23 – 3 a. orange 40 45
15 – 4 a. green (No. 71) .. 22·00
24 – 4 a. green (No. 96) .. 1·10 1·00
27 – 6 a. brown .. .. 50 2·75
28 – 8 a. mauve .. .. 1·25 4·75
30 – 12 a. purple on red .. 1·60 6·00
31 – 1 r. grey (No. 101) .. 6·00 22·00
32 **37** 1 r. green and red .. 5·00 18·00
33 **38** 2 r. red and orange .. £140 £300
34 3 r. brown and green .. £225 £350
35 5 r. blue and violet .. £275 £400

1900. Optd. **JHIND STATE** horiz.
36. **40.** 3 p. red 20 85
37. 3 p. grey .. .. 10 1·00
38. **23.** ½ a. green .. .. 70 1·75
40. – 1 a. red .. .. 15 2·25

Stamps of India optd. **JHIND STATE.**

1903. King Edward VII.
41 **41.** 3 p. grey 10 10
43 – ½ a. green (No. 122) .. 10 50
44 – 1 a. red (No. 123) .. 40 50
46 – 2 a. lilac 35 55
47 – 2½ a. blue .. .. 30 2·75
48 – 3 a. orange 30 35
50 – 4 a. olive .. .. 1·00 2·75
51 – 6 a. bistre .. .. 1·40 4·75
52 – 8 a. mauve .. .. 1·50 4·75
54 – 12 a. purple on red .. 1·50 4·75
55 – 1 r. green and red .. 1·75 4·75

1907. King Edward VII (inscr. "INDIA POSTAGE and REVENUE").
56. ½ a. green (No. 149) .. 10 15
57. 1 a. red (No. 150) .. 15 40

1913. King George V.
58. **55.** 3 p. grey .. .. 10 1·00
59. **56.** ½ a. green 10 60
60. **57.** 1 a. red 10 35
61. **59.** 2 a. lilac .. .. 15 1·75
62. **62.** 3 a. orange .. .. 1·50 6·00
63. **64.** 6 a. bistre .. .. 3·25 13·00

1914. Stamps of India (King George V) optd. **JIND STATE** in two lines.
64. **55.** 3 p. grey 15 20
65. **56.** ½ a. green 30 15
66. **57.** 1 a. red 15 15
80. 1 a. brown 50 50
67. **58.** 1½ a. brown (A. No. 163) 35 1·60
68. 1½ a. brown (B. No. 165) 30 1·50
81. 1½ a. red (B.) .. .. 20 1·40
69. **59.** 2 a. lilac 30 45
70. **61.** 2½ a. blue .. .. 30 2·25
82. 2½ a. orange .. .. 30 3·25
71. **62.** 3 a. orange .. .. 30 1·25
83. 3 a. blue .. .. 50 3·25
72. **63.** 4 a. olive .. .. 30 1·75
73. **64.** 6 a. brown .. .. 45 3·50
74. **65.** 8 a. mauve .. .. 70 2·25
75. **66.** 12 a. red .. .. 55 3·50
76. **67.** 1 r. brown and green .. 2·50 4·75
77. 2 r. red and orange .. 4·00 25·00
78. 5 r. blue and violet .. 24·00 85·00

1922. No. 192 of India optd. **JIND.**
79. **57.** 9 p. on 1 a. red .. .. 1·50 8·50

Stamps of India optd. **JIND STATE** in one line.

1927. King George V.
84. **55.** 3 p. grey 10 10
85. **56.** ½ a. green 10 20
86. **80.** 9 p. green 15 40
87. **57.** 1 a. brown 10 10
88. **82.** 1¼ a. mauve 15 30
89. **58.** 1½ a. red .. .. 30 1·00
90. **70.** 2 a. lilac 30 25
91. **61.** 2½ a. orange .. .. 30 3·00
92. **62.** 3 a. blue .. .. 35 2·50
93. **83.** 3½ a. blue .. .. 35 4·25
94. **71.** 4 a. green 40 80
95. **64.** 6 a. bistre .. .. 40 5·50
96. **65.** 8 a. mauve .. .. 60 1·90
97. **66.** 12 a. red .. .. 85 6·00
98. **67.** 1 r. brown and green .. 80 1·90
99. 2 r. red and orange .. 8·00 32·00
100. 5 r. blue and violet .. 9·00 18·00
101. 10 r. green and red .. 12·00 18·00
102. 15 r. blue and olive .. 50·00 £160
103. 25 r. orange and blue .. 75·00 £200

1934. King George V.
104. **79.** ½ a. green 15 15
105. **81.** 1 a. brown 20 15
106. **59.** 2 a. orange 30 40
107. **62.** 3 a. red 40 40
108. **63.** 4 a. olive 45 65

1937. King George VI.
109. **91.** 3 p. slate .. .. 1·75 75
110. ½ a. brown .. .. 40 1·25
111. 9 p. green .. .. 50 1·50
112. 1 a. red 30 35
113. **92.** 2 a. red .. .. 1·00 5·50
114. – 2½ a. violet .. .. 70 5·50
115. – 3 a. green .. .. 1·75 5·50
116. – 3½ a. blue .. .. 75 6·00
117. – 4 a. brown .. .. 2·50 6·00
118. – 6 a. green .. .. 1·00 7·50
119. – 8 a. violet .. .. 2·00 8·50
120. – 12 a. red .. .. 1·60 9·50
121. **93.** 1 r. slate and brown .. 10·00 12·00
122. 2 r. purple and brown .. 15·00 38·00
123. 5 r. green and blue .. 20·00 38·00
124. 10 r. purple and red .. 55·00 50·00
125. 15 r. brown and green .. £180 £425
126. 25 r. slate and purple .. £250 £475

1941. Stamps of India (King George VI) optd. **JIND**

(a) On issue of 1937.
127. **91.** 3 p. slate .. .. 6·50 7·50
128. ½ a. brown .. .. 1·00 30
129. 9 p. green .. .. 5·50 7·00
130. 1 a. red .. .. 1·00 2·00
131. **93.** 1 r. slate and brown .. 6·00 11·00
132. 2 r. purple and brown .. 11·00 14·00
133. 5 r. green and blue .. 30·00 40·00
134. 10 r. purple and red .. 50·00 50·00
135. 15 r. brown and green .. £120 £110
136. 25 r. slate and purple .. £165 £300

(b) On issue of 1940.
137. **100a.** 3 p. slate 40 50
138. ½ a. mauve 40 50
139. 9 p. green 40 80
140. 1 a. red 50 45
141. **101.** 1 a. 3 yellow-brown .. 85 1·75
142. 1½ a. violet .. .. 2·75 1·75
143. 2 a. red .. .. 1·00 1·25
144. 3 a. violet .. .. 4·00 1·75
145. 3½ a. blue .. .. 2·00 3·25
146. **102.** 4 a. brown .. .. 2·00 1·75
147. 6 a. green .. .. 2·50 4·50
148. 8 a. violet .. .. 2·00 4·50
149. 12 a. purple .. .. 6·00 8·00

OFFICIAL STAMPS

Postage stamps of Jind optd. **SERVICE.**

1885. Nos. 1/3 (Queen Victoria).
O 1. **23.** ½ a. green 30 30
O 2. – 1 a. purple 20 10
O 3. – 2 a. blue .. .. 20·00 24·00

1886. Nos. 17/32 and No. 38 (Q.V.).
O 12. **23.** ½ a. turquoise 40 10
O 22. – ½ a. green (No. 38) .. 30 15
O 14. – 1 a. purple .. .. 3·00 15
O 16. – 2 a. blue 45 30
O 17. – 4 a. green (No. 24) .. 40 35
O 19. – 8 a. mauve .. .. 1·50 2·00
O 21. **37.** 1 r. green and red .. 6·00 16·00

1903. Nos. 42/55 (King Edward VII).
O 24. **41.** 3 p. grey 10 10
O 25. – ½ a. green (No. 43) .. 1·40 10
O 26. – 1 a. red (No. 44) .. 60 10
O 28. – 2 a. lilac 20 10
O 29. – 4 a. olive 40 45
O 31. – 8 a. mauve .. .. 2·25 1·50
O 32. – 1 r. green and red .. 2·50 2·25

1907. Nos. 56/7 (King Edward VII).
O 33. ½ a. green 15 10
O 34. 1 a. red 20 10

1914. Official stamps of India, Nos. O 75/96 (King George V), optd. **JIND STATE.**
O 35. **55.** 3 p. grey 10 10
O 36. **56.** ½ a. green 10 10
O 37. **57.** 1 a. red 10 10
O 46. 1 a. brown 10 10
O 39. **59.** 2 a. lilac 15 10
O 40. **63.** 4 a. olive 20 15
O 41. **64.** 6 a. bistre .. .. 40 2·25
O 42. **65.** 8 a. mauve 30 85
O 43. **67.** 1 r. brown and green .. 90 1·50
O 44. 2 r. red and orange .. 5·50 25·00
O 45. 5 r. blue and violet .. 16·00 55·00

Stamps of India optd. **JIND STATE SERVICE.**

1927. King George V.
O 47. **55.** 3 p. grey 10 15
O 48. **56.** ½ a. green 10 50
O 49. **80.** 9 p. green 30 15
O 50. **57.** 1 a. brown 10 10
O 51. **82.** 1¼ a. mauve 15 15
O 52. **70.** 2 a. lilac 15 15
O 64. **59.** 2 a. orange 15 15
O 53. **61.** 2½ a. orange .. .. 30 4·00
O 54. **71.** 4 a. green 20 20
O 55. **64.** 6 a. bistre .. .. 40 5·00
O 56. **65.** 8 a. mauve .. .. 35 1·25
O 57. **66.** 12 a. red .. .. 50 4·00
O 58. **67.** 1 r. brown and green .. 1·00 2·00
O 59. 2 r. red and orange .. 12·00 11·00
O 60. 5 r. blue and purple .. 10·00 60·00
O 61. 10 r. green and red .. 19·00 35·00

1934. King George V.
O 62. **79.** ½ a. green 15 10
O 63. **81.** 1 a. brown 15 10
O 65. **63.** 4 a. olive .. .. 1·75 30

1937. King George VI.
O 66. **91.** ½ a. brown .. .. 40·00 30
O 67. 9 p. green .. .. 70 2·25
O 68. 1 a. red 45 30
O 69. **93.** 1 r. slate and brown .. 18·00 25·00
O 70. 2 r. purple and brown .. 32·00 75·00
O 71. 5 r. green and blue .. 70·00 £130
O 72. 10 r. purple and red .. £120 £300

1939. Official stamps of India optd. **JIND.**
O 73. **020.** 3 p. slate 45 20
O 74. ½ a. brown .. .. 2·00 60
O 75. ½ a. purple 45 30
O 76. 9 p. green .. .. 1·75 2·50
O 77. 1 a. red .. .. 1·75 15
O 78. 1½ a. violet .. .. 2·75 40
O 79. 2 a. orange 65 30
O 80. 2½ a. violet .. .. 75 2·75
O 81. 4 a. brown .. .. 1·10 75
O 82. 8 a. violet .. .. 1·40 1·60

1943. Stamps of India (King George VI) optd. **JIND SERVICE.**
O 83. **93.** 1 r. slate and brown .. 16·00 24·00
O 84. 2 r. purple and brown 27·00 60·00
O 85. 5 r. green and blue .. 65·00 £130
O 86. 10 r. purple and red .. £120 £200

JOHORE

A State of the Federation of Malaya incorporated in Malaysia in 1963.
100 cents = 1 dollar (Straits or Malayan).
Queen Victoria stamps of Straits Settlements overprinted.

1876. Optd. with Crescent and star.
1. **1.** 2 cents brown £6500 £3000

1882. Optd. **JOHORE.**
8 **1** 2 c. red .. .. 35·00 48·00

1884. Optd. **JOHOR.**
10 **1** 2 c. red .. .. .. 4·25 4·25

1891. Surch. **JOHOR Two CENTS.**
17 **1** 2 c. on 24 c. green .. 22·00 35·00

21. Sultan Aboubakar. 24. Sultan Ibrahim

1891.
21 **21** 1 c. purple 30 50
22 2 c. purple and yellow .. 50 1·50
23 3 c. purple and red .. 55 50
24 4 c. purple and black .. 2·75 5·00
25 5 c. purple and green .. 8·00 20·00
26 6 c. purple and blue .. 10·00 20·00
27 $1 green and red .. 40·00 85·00

1892. Surch. **3 CENTS** and bar.
28 **21** 3 c. on 4 c. purple & black 75 50
29 3 c. on 5 c. purple & green 80 2·00
30 3 c. on 6 c. purple & blue .. 1·00 2·00
31 3 c. on $1 green and red .. 9·50 32·00

1896. Sultan's Coronation. Optd. **KEMAHKOTAAN**
32 **21** 1 c. purple 45 85
33 2 c. purple and yellow .. 45 1·00
34 3 c. purple and red .. 55 1·00
35 4 c. purple and black .. 80 2·25
36 5 c. purple and green .. 5·50 7·50
37 6 c. purple and blue .. 3·00 6·00
38 $1 green and red .. .. 29·00 60·00

1896.
39 **24** 1 c. green 70 45
40 2 c. green and blue .. 40 20
41 3 c. green and purple .. 1·25 40
42 4 c. green and red .. 50 35
43 4 c. yellow and red .. 75 50
44 5 c. green and brown .. 75 1·25
45 6 c. green and yellow .. 80 1·60
46 10 c. green and black .. 7·00 35·00
47 25 c. green and mauve .. 9·00 30·00
48 50 c. green and red .. 12·00 32·00
49 $1 purple and green .. 20·00 50·00
50 $2 purple and red .. 20·00 48·00
51 $3 purple and blue .. 28·00 75·00
52 $4 purple and brown .. 28·00 65·00
53 $5 purple and yellow .. 60·00 90·00

1903. Surch. in figures and words.
54 **24** 3 c. on 4 c. yellow and red 50 1·10
55 10 c. on 4 c. grn & red (A) 2·50 4·50
59 10 c. on 4 c. grn & red (B) 9·00 28·00
58 10 c. on 4 c. yell & red (B) 22·00 35·00
56 50 c. on $3 purple & blue 18·00 55·00
60 50 c. on $5 purple & yell 50·00 £110
57 $1 on $2 purple and red 48·00 80·00
10 c. on 4 c. Type A, "cents" in small letters. Type B, "CENTS" in capitals.

3. Sultan Sir Ibrahim.

1904.
78 **33** 1 c. purple and green .. 15 15
89 2 c. purple and orange .. 40 80
63 3 c. purple and black .. 70 40
91 4 c. purple and red .. 55 20
109 5 c. purple and green .. 30 30
66 8 c. purple and blue .. 2·50 4·00
84 10 c. purple and black .. 15·00 2·50
116 25 c. purple and green .. 1·40 1·00
119 50 c. purple and red .. 2·25 1·25
120 $1 green and mauve .. 2·00 85
121 $2 green and red .. 4·75 3·50
122 $3 green and blue .. 27·00 60·00
73 $4 green and brown .. 24·00 80·00
124 $5 green and orange .. 35·00 48·00
75 $10 green and black .. 48·00 £110
76 $50 green and blue .. £130 £190
77 $100 green and red .. £250 £400
128 $500 blue and red .. £1600

1912. Surch. **3 CENTS** and bars.
88 **33** 3 c. on 8 c. purple & blue 1·75 3·00

1918.
103 **33** 1 c. purple and black .. 30 20
89 2 c. purple and green .. 40 80
104 2 c. purple and sepia .. 75 1·40
105 2 c. green 30 30
106 3 c. green .. .. 1·50 3·00
107 3 c. purple and sepia .. 95 1·50
110 6 c. purple and red .. 40 40
93 10 c. purple and blue .. 1·50 1·40
112 10 c. purple and yellow 25 25
113 12 c. purple and blue .. 1·00 1·25
114 12 c. blue .. .. 20·00 10·00
115 21 c. purple and orange .. 2·50 3·00
117 30 c. purple and orange .. 2·25 2·75
118 40 c. purple and brown .. 2·75 3·25

37. Sultan Sir Ibrahim and Sultana. 38. Sultan Sir Ibrahim.

1935.
129 **37** 8 c. violet and grey .. 1·00 40

1940.
130 **38** 8 c. black and blue .. 5·50 15

1948. Silver Wedding. As T 10/11 of Aden.
131. 10 c. violet 20 15
132. $5 green .. .. 24·00 30·00

39. Sultan Sir Ibrahim.

1949.

133 39 1 c. black 10 10
134 2 c. orange 10 10
135 3 c. green 35 40
136 4 c. brown 10 10
136a 5 c. purple 30 20
137 6 c. grey 20 10
138 8 c. red 55 90
138a 8 c. green .. .. 75 1·25
139 10 c. mauve 20 10
139a 12 c. red .. .. 1·25 2·25
140 15 c. blue .. .. 1·00 10
141 20 c. black and green .. 45 1·00
141a. 20 c. blue 80 10
142 25 c. purple and orange 30 10
142a 30 c. red and purple .. 1·25 2·00
142b 35 c. red and purple .. 1·25 1·00
143 40 c. red and purple .. 1·75 4·75
144 50 c. black and blue .. 50 10
145 $1 blue and purple .. 2·00 75
146 $2 green and red .. 10·00 3·50
147 $5 green and brown .. 26·00 8·50

1949. U.P.U. As T **20/23** of Antigua.

148. 10 c. purple 20 15
149. 15 c. blue .. .. 50 1·00
150. 25 c. orange .. .. 65 1·50
151. 50 c. black .. .. 1·10 1·75

1953. Coronation. As T **13** of Aden.

152. 10 c. black and purple 30 10

40. Sultan Sir Ibrahim.

1955. Diamond Jubilee of Sultan.

153 40 10 c. red 10 10

41. Sultan Sir Ismail and Johore Coat of Arms.

1960. Coronation of Sultan.

154 41 10 c. multicoloured .. 15 15

1960. As Nos. 92/102 of Kedah but with inset portrait of Sultan Sir Ismail.

155. 1 c. black 10 20
156. 2 c. red 10 15
157. 4 c. sepia 10 10
158. 5 c. lake 10 10
159. 8 c. green .. .. 1·25 1·50
160. 10 c. purple 15 10
161. 20 c. blue 15 10
162. 50 c. black and blue .. 20 10
163. $1 blue and purple .. 1·25 1·25
164. $2 green and red .. 3·75 6·00
165. $5 brown and green .. 15·00 16·00

42. "Vanda hookeriana".

1965. Inset portrait of Sultan Ismail. Multicoloured.

166 1 c. Type **42** 10 30
167 2 c. "Arundina graminifolia" 10 35
168 5 c. "Paphiopedilum niveum" 10 10
169 6 c. "Spathoglottis plicata" 20 10
170 10 c. "Arachnis flosaeris" 20 10
171 15 c. "Rhyncostylis retusa" .. 70 10
172 20 c. "Phalaenopsis violacea" .. .. 1·00 30

The higher values used in Johore were Nos. 20/7 of Malaysia (National Issues).

44. "Delias ninus".

1971. Butterflies. Inset portrait of Sultan Ismail. Multicoloured.

175 1 c. Type **44** 15 40
176 2 c. "Danaus melanippus" 40 40
177 5 c. "Parthenos sylvia" .. 55 10
178 6 c. "Papilio demoleus" .. 55 40
179 10 c. "Hebomoia glaucippe" 55 10
180 15 c. "Precis orithya" .. 55 10
181 20 c. "Valeria valeria" .. 80 15

The higher values in use with this issue were Nos. 64/71 of Malaysia (National Issues).

45. "Rafflesia hasseltii" (inset portrait of Sultan Ismail).

1979. Flowers. Multicoloured.

188. 1 c. Type **45** 10 10
189. 2 c. "Pterocarpus indicus" 10 10
190. 5 c. "Lagerstroemia speciosa" 10 10
191. 10 c. "Durio zibethinus" 10 10
192. 15 c. "Hibiscus rosa-sinensis" 15 10
193. 20 c. "Rhododendron scortechinii" 15 10
194. 25 c. "Phaeomeria speciosa" 15 10

46. Coconuts. (Inset portrait of Sultan Mahmood).

1986. Agricultural Products of Malaysia. Multicoloured.

202. 1 c. Coffee 10 10
203. 2 c. Type **46** 10 10
204. 5 c. Cocoa 10 10
205. 10 c. Black pepper .. 10 10
206. 15 c. Rubber 10 10
207. 20 c. Oil palm 10 10
208. 30 c. Rice 10 15

POSTAGE DUE STAMPS

D 1.

1938.

D 1. D 1. 1 c. red .. .. 7·00 24·00
D 2. 4 c. green .. .. 22·00 35·00
D 3. 8 c. orange .. .. 26·00 80·00
D 4. 10 c. brown .. .. 26·00 40·00
D 5. 12 c. purple .. .. 30·00 90·00

KEDAH

A state of the Federation of Malaya, incorporated in Malaysia in 1963.

100 cents = 1 dollar (Straits or Malayan).

1. Sheaf of Rice. **2.** Malay ploughing.

1912.

1 1 1 c. black and green .. 25 25
26 1 c. brown 40 20
52 1 c. black 15 10
27 2 c. green 25 20
2 3 c. black and red .. 2·25 30
19 3 c. purple 65 70
53 3 c. green .. .. 1·50 65
3 4 c. red and grey .. 8·50 25
20 4 c. red .. .. 1·50 20
54 4 c. violet 90 10
4 5 c. green and brown .. 2·00 3·00
55 5 c. yellow .. .. 1·50 10
56 6 c. red 70 65
5 8 c. black and blue .. 1·00 2·00
57 8 c. black .. .. 8·00 10
30 2 10 c. blue and sepia .. 90 75
58 12 c. black and blue .. 2·00 4·00
31 20 c. black and green .. 1·50 2·00
32 21 c. purple .. .. 2·00 10·00
33 25 c. blue and purple .. 2·25 5·50
34 30 c. black and red .. 2·50 3·75
59 35 c. purple .. .. 4·50 22·00
9 40 c. black and purple .. 3·40 14·00
36 50 c. brown and blue .. 1·75 6·00
37 – $1 black & red on yellow 6·50 7·50
12 – $2 green and brown .. 11·00 50·00
39 – $3 black and blue on blue 30·00 50·00
40 – $5 black and red .. 45·00 90·00

DESIGN—As Type **2**: $1 to $5, Council Chamber.

1919. Surch. in words.

24. 50 c. on $2 green and brown 40·00 48·00
25. $1 on $3 blk. & blue on blue 20·00 65·00

1922. Optd. **MALAYA-BORNEO EXHIBITION.**

45. **1.** 1 c. brown .. .. 2·25 13·00
41. 2 c. green .. .. 3·50 16·00
46. 3 c. purple .. .. 3·00 27·00
47. 4 c. red .. .. 3·00 25·00
48. **2.** 10 c. blue and sepia .. 4·50 32·00
42. 21 c. purple .. .. 17·00 70·00
43. 25 c. blue and purple .. 18·00 70·00
44. 50 c. brown and blue .. 18·00 8·50

6. Sultan Abdul Hamid Halimshah.

1937.

60. **6.** 10 c. blue and brown .. 1·60 30
61. 12 c. black and violet .. 15·00 12·00
62. 25 c. blue and purple .. 4·75 4·50
63. 30 c. green and red .. 7·00 9·50
64. 40 c. black and purple .. 1·75 11·00
65. 50 c. brown and blue .. 2·75 4·50
66. $1 black and green .. 2·50 9·00
67. $2 green and brown .. 80·00 70·00
68. $5 black and red .. 29·00 55·00

1948. Silver Wedding. As T **10/11** of Aden.

70. 10 c. violet 20 20
71. $5 red .. .. .. 22·00 32·00

1949. U.P.U. As T **20/23** of Antigua.

72. 10 c. purple 25 20
73. 15 c. blue .. .. 50 1·25
74. 25 c. orange .. .. 65 1·25
75. 50 c. black .. .. 1·25 2·25

7. Sheaf of Rice. **8.** Sultan Tunku Badlishah.

1950.

76 7 1 c. black 10 30
77 2 c. orange 10 15
78 3 c. green 20 85
79 4 c. brown 15 10
79ab 5 c. purple 35 30
80 6 c. grey 10 15
81 8 c. red .. .. 30 1·75
81a 8 c. green .. .. 75 1·75
82 10 c. mauve 15 10
82a 12 c. red .. .. 85 2·50
83 15 c. blue 40 35
84 20 c. black and green .. 40 2·50
84a 20 c. blue 85 10
85 8 25 c. purple and orange .. 30 25
85a 30 c. red and purple .. 1·25 1·25
85b 35 c. red and purple .. 85 1·50
86 40 c. red and purple .. 1·00 6·00
87 50 c. black and blue .. 50 10
88 $1 blue and purple .. 2·25 1·50
89 $2 green and red .. 17·00 22·00
90 $5 green and brown .. 28·00 32·00

1953. Coronation. As T **13** of Aden.

91 10 c. black and purple .. 30 10

15. Fishing Craft. **20.** Sultan Abdul Halim Mu' Adzam Shah.

1957. Inset portrait of Sultan Tunku Badlishah.

92. – 1 c. black 10 35
93. – 2 c. red 10 40
94. – 4 c. sepia 10 10
95. – 5 c. lake 10 20
96. – 8 c. green .. .. 2·00 3·75
97. – 10 c. sepia 15 10
98. **15.** 20 c. blue 30 45
99. – 50 c. black and blue .. 40 1·00
100. – $1 blue and purple .. 2·75 5·00
101. – $2 green and red .. 11·00 12·00
102. – $5 brown and green .. 16·00 22·00

DESIGNS—HORIZ. 1 c. Copra. 2 c. Pineapples. 4 c. Ricefield. 5 c. Masjid Alwi Mosque, Kangar. 8 c. East Coast Railway. $1, Govt. Offices. $2, Bersilat (form of wrestling). $5, Weaving. VERT. 10 c. Tiger. 50 c. Aborigines with blowpipe.

1959. Installation of Sultan.

103. **20.** 10 c. yellow, brown & blue 10 10

21. Sultan Abdul Halim Mu' Adzam Shah.

1959. As Nos. 92/102 but with inset portrait of Sultan Tuanku Abdul as in T **21.**

104. 1 c. black 10 30
105. 2 c. red 10 30
106. 4 c. sepia 10 10
107. 5 c. lake 10 10
108. 8 c. green .. .. 2·75 1·25
109. 10 c. sepia 30 10
109a. 10 c. purple .. .. 1·50 10
110. 20 c. blue 20 10
111a. 50 c. black and blue .. 30 10
112. $1 blue and purple .. 1·50 2·25
113. $2 green and red .. 5·00 8·50
114a. $5 brown and green .. 11·00 10·00

22. "Vanda hookeriana".

1965. Flowers. Multicoloured.

115. 1 c. Type **22** 10 30
116. 2 c. "Arundina graminifolia" 10 30
117. 5 c. "Paphiopedilum niveum" 10 10
118. 6 c. "Spethoglottis plicata" 15 15
119. 10 c. "Arachnis flos-aeris" 20 10
120. 15 c. "Rhyncostylis retusa" 70 10
121. 20 c. "Phalaenopsis violacea" .. .. 1·00 40

The higher values used in Kedah were Nos. 20/7 of Malaysia.

23. "Danaus melanippus".

1971. Butterflies. Multicoloured.

124	1 c. "Delias ninus"	15	40
125	2 c. Type **23**	35	40
126	5 c. "Parthenos sylvia"	45	10
127	6 c. "Papilio demoleus"	45	40
128	10 c. "Hebomia glaucippe"	45	10
129	15 c. "Precis orithya"	60	10
130	20 c. "Valeria valeria"	95	35

The higher values in use with this issue were Nos. 64/71 of Malaysia.

24. "Pterocarpus indicus".

1979. Flowers. Multicoloured.

135	1 c. "Rafflesia hasseltii"	10	10
136	2 c. Type **24**	10	10
137	5 c. "Lagerstroemia speciosa"	10	10
138	10 c. "Durio zibethinus"	10	10
139	15 c. "Hibiscus rosa-sinensis"	15	10
140	20 c. "Rhododendron scortechinii"	15	10
141	25 c. "Etlingera elatior" (inscr "Phaeomeria speciosa")	15	10

25. Sultan Abdul Halim Mu'Adzam Shah.

1983. Silver Jubilee of Sultan's Installation Multicoloured.

142.	20 c. Type **25**	45	25
143.	40 c. Paddy fields (horiz.)	65	40
144.	60 c. Paddy fields and Mount Jerai (horiz.)	90	1·10

26. Cocoa.

1986. Agro-based products of Malaysia. Multicoloured.

152.	1 c. Coffee	10	10
153.	2 c. Coconuts	10	10
154.	5 c. Type **26**	10	10
155.	10 c. Black pepper	10	10
156.	15 c. Rubber	10	10
157.	20 c. Oil palm	10	10
158.	30 c. Rice	10	15

KELANTAN

A state in the Federation of Malaya, incorporated in Malaysia in 1963.

100 cents = 1 dollar (Straits or Malayan).

1.

3. Sultan Ismail.

1911.

1a	1	1 c. green	1·00	30
15	–	1 c. black	40	50
16		2 c. brown	2·75	3·50
16a		2 c. green	90	40
2		3 c. red	1·50	15
16b		3 c. brown	2·50	1·50
17		4 c. black and red	50	10
18		5 c. green & red on yell	50	10
19		6 c. purple	2·50	2·50
19a		6 c. red	4·00	5·50
5		8 c. blue	5·00	1·00
20		10 c. black and mauve	2·00	10
21		30 c. purple and red	4·00	5·50
8		50 c. black and orange	5·50	2·50
9		$1 green	40·00	48·00
13		$1 green and brown	27·00	2·00
10		$2 green and red	1·00	4·00
11		$5 green and blue	4·00	7·50
12		$25 green and orange	38·00	75·00

1922. Optd. **MALAYA BORNEO EXHIBITION.**

37.	1.	1 c. green	2·50	26·00
30.		4 c. black and red	2·75	32·00
31.		5 c. green & red on yellow	4·50	32·00
38.		10 c. black and mauve	4·75	48·00
32.		30 c. purple and red	4·50	55·00
33.		50 c. black and orange	7·50	60·00
34.		$1 green and brown	20·00	80·00
35.		$2 green and red	45·00	£150
36.		$5 green and blue	£130	£300

1928.

40.	3.	1 c. olive and yellow	30	40
41.		2 c. green	1·00	10
42.		4 c. red	3·50	45
43.		5 c. brown	3·75	10
44.		6 c. red	6·00	1·25
45.		8 c. olive	3·75	10
46.		10 c. purple	13·00	2·75
47.		12 c. blue	1·75	3·00
48.		25 c. red and purple	3·75	3·50
49.		30 c. violet and red	25·00	16·00
50.		40 c. orange and green	6·00	17·00
51.		50 c. olive and orange	38·00	9·00
39.		$1 blue	7·50	55·00
52.		$1 violet and green	22·00	12·00
53.		$2 red	£150	£200
54.		$5 red	£250	£400

All except No. 39 are larger than T **3.**

1948. Silver Wedding. As T **10/11** of Aden.

55.	10 c. violet	40	90
56.	$5 red	23·00	48·00

1949. U.P.U. As T **20/23** of Antigua.

57.	10 c. purple	25	30
58.	15 c. blue	50	90
59.	25 c. orange	60	2·25
60.	50 c. black	1·25	2·25

5. Sultan Tenkgu Ibrahim.

1951.

61	5.	1 c. black	10	30
62b		2 c. orange	15	30
63		3 c. green	1·25	90
64		4 c. brown	10	15
65a		5 c. purple	30	40
66		6 c. grey	10	20
67		8 c. red	30	3·00
68		8 c. green	75	1·75
69		10 c. mauve	15	10
70		12 c. red	75	2·25
71		15 c. blue	1·25	60
72		20 c. black and green	45	4·50
73		20 c. blue	80	25
74		25 c. purple and orange	40	55
75		30 c. red and purple	1·25	1·75
76		35 c. red and purple	90	1·50
77		40 c. red and purple	1·50	7·00
78		50 c. black and blue	50	40
79		$1 blue and purple	2·75	2·50
80		$2 green and red	12·00	20·00
81		$5 green and brown	38·00	38·00

1953. Coronation. As T **13** of Aden.

82	10 c. black and purple	30	15

1957. As Nos. 92/102 of Kedah but inset portrait of Sultan Tengku Ibrahim.

83	1 c. black	10	30
84	2 c. red	30	40
85	4 c. sepia	10	10
86	5 c. lake	10	10
87	8 c. green	80	1·75
88	10 c. sepia	15	10
89	10 c. purple	3·25	3·25
90	20 c. blue	30	30
91	50 c. black and blue	30	35
92	$1 blue and purple	2·00	1·50
93	$2 green and red	5·00	6·00
94	$5 brown and green	10·00	12·00

6. Sultan Yahya Petra and Crest of Kelantan.

1961. Coronation of the Sultan.

95.	6.	10 c. multicoloured	30	30

7. Sultan Yahya Petra.

1961. As Nos. 83, etc., but with inset portrait of Sultan Yahya Petra as in T **7.**

96.	1 c. black	10	45
97.	2 c. red	10	55
98.	4 c. sepia	10	10
99.	5 c. lake	10	10
100.	8 c. green	2·75	3·00
101.	10 c. purple	20	10
102.	20 c. blue	40	30

8. Vanda hookeriana".

1965. As Nos. 115/21 of Kedah but with inset portrait of Sultan Yahya Petra as in T **8.**

103.	8.	1 c. multicoloured	10	20
104.	–	2 c. multicoloured	10	20
105.	–	5 c. multicoloured	15	10
106.	–	6 c. multicoloured	45	40
107.	–	10 c. multicoloured	20	10
108.	–	15 c. multicoloured	1·00	20
109.	–	20 c. multicoloured	1·50	85

The higher values used in Kelantan were Nos. 20/7 of Malaysia (National Issues).

9. "Parthenos sylvia".

1971. Butterflies. As Nos. 124/30 of Kedah, but with portrait of Sultan Yahya Petra as in T **9.**

112.	–	1 c. multicoloured	15	65
113.	–	2 c. multicoloured	35	65
114.	9.	5 c. multicoloured	60	15
115.	–	6 c. multicoloured	60	50
116.	–	10 c. multicoloured	60	10
117.	–	15 c. multicoloured	85	10
118.	–	20 c. multicoloured	1·00	50

The higher values in use with this series were Nos. 64/71 of Malaysia (National Issues).

10. "Lagerstroemia speciosa".

1979. Flowers. As Nos. 135/41 of Kedah but with portrait of Sutan Yahya Petra as in T **10.**

123	1 c. "Rafflesia hasseltii"	10	30
124	2 c. "Pterocarpus indicus"	10	30
125	5 c. Type **10**	10	10
126	10 c. "Durio zibethinus"	10	10
127	15 c. "Hibiscus rosa-sinensis"	15	10
128	20 c. "Rhododendron scortechinii"	15	10
129	25 c. "Etlingera elatior" (inscr "Phaeomeria speciosa")	15	20

11. Sultan Tengku Ismail Petra.

1980. Coronation of Sultan Tengku Ismail Petra.

130.	11.	10 c. multicoloured	20	20
131.		15 c. multicoloured	20	15
132.		50 c. multicoloured	70	1·25

12. Black Pepper.

1986. Agro-based products of Malaysia. Multicoloured.

140.	1 c. Coffee	10	10
141.	2 c. Coconuts	10	10
142.	5 c. Cocoa	10	10
143.	10 c. Type **12**	10	10
144.	15 c. Rubber	10	10
145.	20 c. Oil palm	10	10
146.	30 c. Rice	10	15

KENYA

Formerly part of Kenya, Uganda and Tanganyika (q.v.). Became Independent in 1963 and a Republic in 1964.

100 cents = 1 shilling.

1. Cattle Ranching.

3. National Assembly.

1963. Independence.

No.	Type	Description	Unused	Used
1.	1.	5 c. multicoloured ..	10	30
2.	–	10 c. brown	10	10
3.	–	15 c. mauve	45	10
4.	–	20 c. black and green ..	15	10
5.	–	30 c. black and yellow ..	15	10
6.	–	40 c. brown and blue ..	15	20
7.	–	50 c. red, black & green	15	10
8.	–	65 c. turquoise & yellow	55	65
9.	3.	1 s. multicoloured ..	20	10
10.	–	1 s. 30 brn., blk. and grn.	1·75	10
11.	–	2 s. multicoloured ..	50	30
12.	–	5 s. brown, blue & green	1·25	40
13.	–	10 s. brown and blue ..	6·50	1·75
14.	–	20 s. black and red ..	5·50	4·50

DESIGNS—As Type **1**: 10 c. Wood-carving. 15 c. Heavy industry. 20 c. Timber industry. 30 c. Jomo Kenyatta facing Mt. Kenya. 40 c. Fishing industry. 50 c. Kenya flag. 65 c. Pyrethrum industry. As Type **3**: 1 s. 30, Tourism (Treetops hotel). 2 s. Coffee industry. 5 s. Tea industry. 10 s. Mombasa Port. 20 s. Royal College, Nairobi.

4. Cockerel.

1964. Inaug. of Republic. Multicoloured.

No.	Description	Unused	Used
15.	15 c. Type **4**	20	15
16.	30 c. Pres. Kenyatta ..	25	10
17.	50 c. African Lion ..	35	10
18.	1 s. 30 Hartlaub's Turaco	2·50	50
19.	2 s. 50 Nandi Flame ..	2·00	3·75

5. Thomson's Gazelle.

7. Greater Kudu.

1966.

No.	Type	Description	Unused	Used
20.	5.	5 c. orange, black & sepia	15	20
21.	–	10 c. black and green ..	10	10
22.	–	15 c. black and orange ..	10	10
23.	–	20 c. ochre, blk. & blue	10	15
24.	–	30 c. indigo, blue & blk.	10	10
25.	–	40 c. black and brown ..	40	30
26.	–	50 c. black and orange ..	40	10
27.	–	65 c. black and green ..	1·25	2·00
28.	–	70 c. black and red ..	2·25	1·25
29.	7.	1 s. brown, black & blue	20	10
30.	–	1 s. 30 blue, grn. & blk.	2·50	20
31.	–	1 s. 50 blk., brn. and grn.	2·00	2·00
32.	–	2 s. 50 yell., blk. & brn.	2·50	1·25
33.	–	5 s. yell., blk. and green	1·00	70
34.	–	10 s. ochre, blk. and brn.	2·50	2·00
35.	–	20 s. multicoloured ..	8·50	7·50

DESIGNS—As Type **5**: 10 c. Sable antelope. 15 c. Aardvark ("Ant Bear"). 20 c. Lesser bushbaby. 30 c. Warthog. 40 c. Common Zebra. 50 c. African buffalo. 65 c. Black rhinoceros. 70 c. Ostrich. As Type **7**: 1 s. 30, African elephant. 1 s. 50, Bat-eared fox. 2 s. 50, Cheetah. 5 s. Savanna monkey ("Vervet Monkey") 10 s. Giant ground pangolin. 20 s. Lion.

8. Rose Dawn.

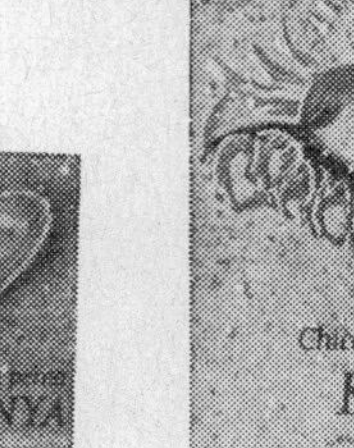

9. Rock Shell.

1971. Seashells. Multicoloured.

No.	Description	Unused	Used
36	5 c. Type **8**	10	30
37	10 c. Bishop's Cap	10	10
38	15 c. Strawberry Shell ..	15	10
39	20 c. Black Prince	15	10
40	30 c. Mermaid's Ear ..	20	10
41	40 c. Top Shell	20	10
42	50 c. Violet Shell	30	10
43	50 c. Violet Shell	8·50	1·25
44	60 c. Cameo..	30	45
45	70 c. Pearly Nautilus ..	45	1·50
46	70 c. Pearly Nautilus ..	8·50	4·50
47a	1 s. Type **9**	20	10
48	1 s. 50 Triton	60	10
49	2 s. 50 Neptune's Trumpet	80	10
50a	5 s. Turban Shell ..	1·00	10
51	10 s. Cloth of Gold	3·25	15
52a	20 s. Spider Shell	3·75	35

INSCRIPTIONS: No.42, "Janthina globosa". No.43, "Janthina janthina". No.45, "Nautilus pompileus". No.46, "Nautilus pompilius".

Nos.47/52 are larger, as Type **9**.

1975. Nos. 48/9 and 52 surch.

No.	Description	Unused	Used
53.	2 s. on 1 s. 50 Triton ..	3·50	2·50
54.	3 s. on 2 s. 50 Neptune's Trumpet..	9·50	15·00
55.	40 s. on 20 s. Spider Shell..	6·00	11·00

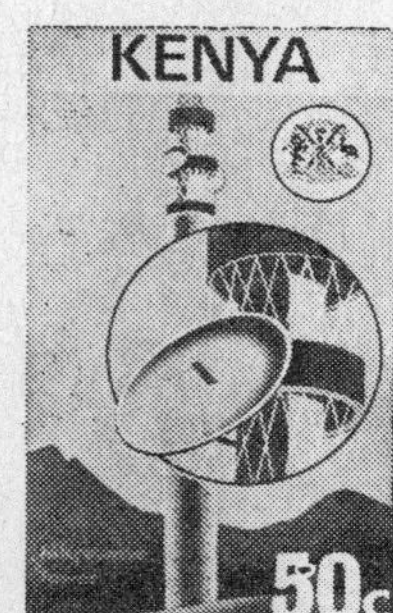

11. Microwave Tower.

1976. Telecommunications Development. Multicoloured.

No.	Description	Unused	Used
56.	50 c. Type **11**	10	10
57.	1 s. Cordless switchboard (horiz.)	10	10
58.	2 s. Telephones	20	30
59.	3 s. Message Switching Centre (horiz.)	25	45

12. Akii Bua, Ugandan Hurdler.

1976. Olympic Games, Montreal. Mult.

No.	Description	Unused	Used
61.	50 c. Type **12**	10	10
62.	1 s. Filbert Bayi, Tanzanian runner	15	10
63.	2 s. Steve Muchoki, Kenyan boxer	45	35
64.	3 s. Olympic flame and East African flags	60	50

13. Diesel Train Tanzania-Zambia Railway.

1976. Railway Transport. Multicoloured.

No.	Description	Unused	Used
66.	50 c. Type **13**	35	10
67.	1 s. Nile Bridge, Uganda ..	60	15
68.	2 s. Nakuru Station, Kenya	2·25	1·25
69.	3 s. Class "A" steam locomotive, 1896	2·50	1·75

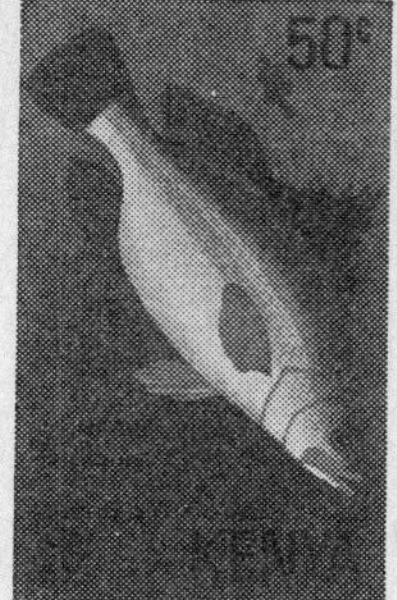

14. Nile Perch.

1977. Game Fish of East Africa. Mult.

No.	Description	Unused	Used
71.	50 c. Type **14**	20	10
72.	1 s. Tilapia	30	10
73.	3 s. Sailfish	1·60	90
74.	5 s. Black Marlin	1·90	1·25

15. Maasai Manyatta (Village), Kenya.

1977. Second World Black and African Festival of Arts and Culture, Nigeria. Multicoloured.

No.	Description	Unused	Used
76.	50 c. Type **15**	15	10
77.	1 s. "Heatbeat of Africa" (Ugandan dancers) ..	25	10
78.	2 s. Makonde sculpture, Tanzania	1·25	1·25
79.	3 s. "Early man and technology" (skinning hippopotamus)	1·50	1·75

16. Rally car and Villagers.

1977. 25th Anniv of Safari Rally. Mult.

No.	Description	Unused	Used
81.	50 c. Type **16**	20	10
82.	1s. Pres. Kenyatta starting rally	30	10
83.	2s. Car fording river ..	70	1·00
84.	5 s. Car and elephants ..	1·25	1·75

17. Canon Kivebulaya.

1977. Centenary of Ugandan Church. Multicoloured.

No.	Description	Unused	Used
86.	50 c. Type **17**	10	10
87.	1 s. Modern Namirembe Cathedral	10	10
88.	2 s. The first Cathedral..	30	45
89.	5 s. Early congregation, Kigezi	50	85

18. Sagana Royal Lodge, Nyeri, 1952.

1977. Silver Jubilee. Multicoloured.

No.	Description	Unused	Used
91.	2 s. Type **18**	30	30
92.	5 s. Treetops Hotel (vert.)	65	65
93.	10 s. Queen Elizabeth and Pres. Kenyatta ..	90	1·25
94.	15 s. Royal visit, 1972 ..	1·25	1·75

19. Pancake Tortoise.

1977. Endangered Species. Multicoloured.

No.	Description	Unused	Used
96.	50 c. Type **19**	30	10
97.	1 s. Nile Crocodile ..	40	10
98.	2 s. Hunter's Hartebeest..	1·40	75
99.	3 s. Red Colobus monkey	1·75	1·00
100.	5 s. Dugong	2·00	1·50

20. Kenya-Ethiopia Border Point.

1977. Nairobi–Addis Ababa Highway. Mult.

No.	Description	Unused	Used
102.	50 c. Type **20**	15	10
103.	1 s. Archer's Post ..	20	10
104.	2 s. Thika Flyover ..	75	60
105.	5 s. Marsabit Game Lodge	1·75	1·50

21. Gypsum.

20. Amethyst.

1977. Multicoloured.

No.	Description	Unused	Used
107.	10 c. Type **21**	75	20
108.	20 c. Trona	1·00	20
109.	30 c. Kyanite	1·10	20
110.	40 c. Amazonite	1·10	10
111.	50 c. Galena	1·10	10
112.	70 c. Silicified wood ..	1·40	30
113.	80 c. Fluorite	1·40	30
114.	1 s. Type **22**	1·40	10
115.	1 s. 50 Agate	1·75	20
116.	2 s. Tourmaline	1·75	20
117.	3 s. Aquamarine	1·75	45
118.	5 s. Rhodolite garnet ..	1·75	80
119.	10 s. Sapphire	2·00	1·75
120.	20 s. Ruby	5·00	2·75
121.	40 s. Green grossular garnet	11·00	12·00

23. Joe Kadenge (Kenya) and Forwards.

1978. World Cup Football championship, Argentina. Multicoloured.

No.	Description	Unused	Used
122.	50 c. Type **23**	10	10
123.	1 s. Mohamed Chuma (Tanzania) and cup presentation	10	10
124.	2 s. Omari Kidevu (Zanzibar) and goalmouth scene	40	60
125.	3 s. Polly Ouma (Uganda) and three forwards ..	50	85

24. Boxing.

1978. Commonwealth Games, Edmonton. Multicoloured.

No.	Description	Unused	Used
127.	50 c. Type **24**	15	10
128.	1 s. Welcoming the Olympic Games Team, 1968	20	10
129.	3 c. Javelin throwing	60	80
130.	5 s. Pres. Kenyatta admiring boxer's trophy	75	1·25

25. " Overloading is Dangerous ".

1978. Road Safety. Multicoloured.

No.	Description	Unused	Used
131.	50 c. Type **25**	35	10
132.	1 s. " Speed does not pay "	50	20
133.	1 s. 50 " Ignoring Traffic Signs may cause death "	65	40
134.	2 s. " Slow down at School Crossing "	90	80
135.	3 s. " Never cross a continuous line "	1·10	1·25
136.	5 s. " Approach Railway Level Crossing with extreme caution "	1·75	2·00

26. Pres. Kenyatta at Mass Rally, 1963.

1978. Kenyatta Day. Multicoloured.

No.	Description	Unused	Used
137.	50 c. " Harambee Water Project ".	15	10
138.	1 s. Handing over of Independence Instruments, 1963	25	10
139.	2 s. Type **26**	45	30
140.	3 s. " Harambee, 15 Great Years "	70	55
141.	5 s. " Struggle for Independence, 1952 "	90	80

27. Freedom Fighters, Namibia.

1978. International Anti-Apartheid Year.

No.	Type	Description	Unused	Used
142.	**27.**	50 c. multicoloured	20	10
143.	–	1 s. black and blue	25	10
144.	–	2 s. multicoloured	60	30
145.	–	3 s. multicoloured	80	55
146.	–	5 s. multicoloured	90	80

DESIGNS: 1 s. International seminar on Apartheid. 2 s. Steve Biko's tombstone. 3 s. Nelson Mandela. 5 s. Bishop Lamont.

28. Children Playing.

1979. International Year of the Child. Multicoloured.

No.	Description	Unused	Used
147.	50 c. Type **28**	15	10
148.	2 s. Boy fishing	40	40
149.	3 s. Children singing and dancing	60	60
150.	5 s. Children with camels	85	85

29. " The Lion and the Jewel ".

1979. Kenya National Theatre. Multicoloured.

No.	Description	Unused	Used
151.	50 c. Type **29**	15	10
152.	1 s. " Utisi "	20	10
153.	2 s. Theatre programmes	35	30
154.	3 s. Kenya National Theatre	50	45
155.	5 s. " Genesis "	90	75

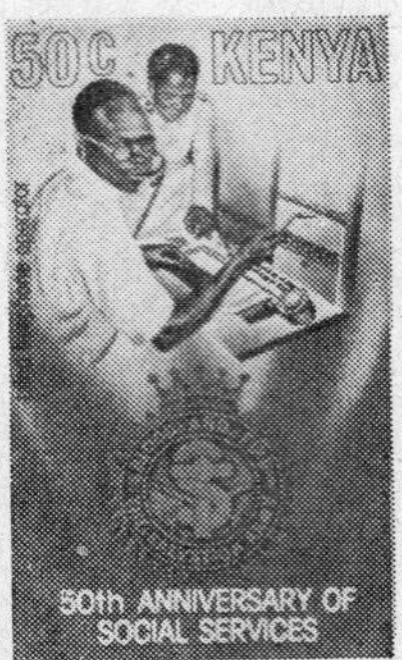

30. Blind Telephone Operator.

1979. 50th Anniv. of Salvation Army Social Services.

No.	Description	Unused	Used
156.	50 c. Type **30**	30	10
157.	1 s. Care for the aged	30	10
158.	3 s. Village polytechnic (horiz.)	85	70
159.	5 s. Vocational training (horiz.)	1·10	1·10

31. " Father of the Nation " (Kenyatta's funeral procession).

1979. 1st Death Anniv. of President Kenyatta. Multicoloured.

No.	Description	Unused	Used
160.	50 c. Type **31**	10	10
162.	1 s. " First president of Kenya " (Kenyatta receiving independence)	15	10
163.	3 s. " Kenyatta the politician " (speaking at rally)	35	45
164.	5 s. " A true son of Kenya " (Kenyatta as a boy carpenter)	60	85

32. British East Africa Company 1890 1a. Stamp.

1979. Death Centenary of Sir Rowland Hill.

No.	Type	Description	Unused	Used
164.	**32.**	50 c. multicoloured	15	10
165.	–	1 s. multicoloured	15	10
166.	–	2 s. black, red & brown	30	40
167.	–	5 s. multicoloured	60	1·00

DESIGNS: 1 s. Kenya, Uganda and Tanganyika 1935 1 s. Stamp. 2 s. Penny Black. 5 s. 1964 2 s. 50, Inauguration of Republic commemorative.

33. Roads, Globe and Conference emblem.

1980. I.R.F. African Highway Conference, Nairobi. Multicoloured.

No.	Description	Unused	Used
168.	50 c. Type **33**	10	10
169.	1 s. New weighbridge, Athi River	15	10
170.	3 s. New Nyali Bridge, Mombasa	40	75
171.	5 s. Highway to Jomo Kenyatta Int. Airport	70	1·25

34. Mobile Unit in action in Masailand.

1980. Flying Doctor Service. Multicoloured.

No.	Description	Unused	Used
172.	50 c. Type **34**	10	10
173.	1 s. Donkey transport to Turkana airstrip (vert.)	15	10
174.	3 s. Surgical team in action at outstation (vert.)	50	90
175.	5 s. Emergency airlift from North Eastern Province	80	1·40

35. Statue of Sir Rowland Hill.

1980. " London 1980 " International Stamp Exhibition.

No.	Type	Description	Unused	Used
177.	**35.**	25 s. multicoloured	1·50	2·50

36. Pope John Paul II.

1980. Papal Visit. Multicoloured.

No.	Description	Unused	Used
179.	50 c. Type **36**	30	10
180.	1 s. Pope, arms and cathedral (vert.)	40	10
181.	5 s. Pope, flags and dove (vert.)	85	70
182.	10 s. Pope, President Moi and map of Africa	1·40	1·40

37. " Taeniura lymma ".

1980. Marine Life. Multicoloured.

No.	Description	Unused	Used
183.	50 c. Type **37**	20	10
184.	2 s. " Amphiprion allardi "	65	50
185.	3 s. " Chromodoris quadricolor "	80	80
186.	5 s. " Eretmochelys imbricata "	1·25	1·25

38. National Archives.

1980. Historic Buildings. Multicoloured.

No.	Description	Unused	Used
187.	50 c. Type **38**	10	10
188.	1 s. Provincial Commissioner's Office, Nairobi	15	10
189.	1 s. 50 Nairobi House	20	20
190.	2 s. Norfolk Hotel	25	50
191.	3 s. McMillan Library	35	65
192.	5 s. Kipande House	55	1·00

39. " Disabled enjoys Affection ".

1981. International Year for Disabled Persons. Multicoloured.

No.	Description	Unused	Used
193.	50 c. Type **39**	15	10
194.	1 s. President Moi presenting flag to Disabled Olympic Games team captain	20	10
195.	3 s. Blind people climbing Mount Kenya, 1975	55	55
196.	5 s. Disabled artist at work	85	1·00

40. Longonot Complex.

1981. Satellite Communications. Multicoloured.

No.	Description	Unused	Used
197.	50 c. Type **40**	15	10
198.	2 s. " Intelsat V "	50	35
199.	3 s. " Longonot I "	60	55
200.	5 s. " Longonot II "	85	85

41. Kenyatta Conference Centre.

1981. O.A.U. (Organization of African Unity) Summit Conference, Nairobi.

No.	Type	Description	Unused	Used
201.	**41.**	50 c. multicoloured	15	10
202.	–	1 s. black, yellow & blue	20	10
203.	–	3 s. multicoloured	40	40
204.	–	5 s. multicoloured	65	65
205.	–	10 s. multicoloured	1·00	1·00

DESIGNS: 1 s. " Panaftel " earth stations. 3 s. Parliament Building. 5 s. Jomo Kenyatta International Airport. 10 s. O.A.U. flag.

42. St. Paul's Cathedral.

1981. Royal Wedding. Multicoloured.

No.	Description	Unused	Used
207.	50 c. Prince Charles and President Daniel Arap Moi	15	10
208.	3 s. Type **42**	25	20
209.	5 s. Royal Yacht " Britannia "	40	35
210.	10 s. Prince Charles on safari in Kenya	55	70

MINIMUM PRICE

The minimum price quoted is 10p which represents a handling charge rather than a basis for valuing common stamps. For further notes about prices see introductory pages.

43. Giraffe.

1981. Rare Animals. Multicoloured.

212. 50 c. Type 43 .. .. 15 10
213. 2 s. Bongo 35 20
214. 5 s. Roan Antelope .. 70 55
215. 10 s. Agile Mangabey .. 1·25 1·10

44. " Technical Development ".

1981. World Food Day. Multicoloured.

216. 50 c. Type 44 .. .. 10 10
217. 1 s. " Mwea rice projects " 15 10
218. 2 s. " Irrigation schemes " 30 25
219. 5 s. " Breeding livestock " 60 70

45. Kamba.

1981. Ceremonial Costumes (1st series). Multicoloured.

220. 50 c. Type 45 .. .. 25 10
221. 1 s. Turkana 30 10
222. 2 s. Giriama 65 25
223. 3 s. Masai 90 40
224. 5 s. Luo .. .. .. 1·25 85

See also Nos. 329/33, 413/17 and 515/19.

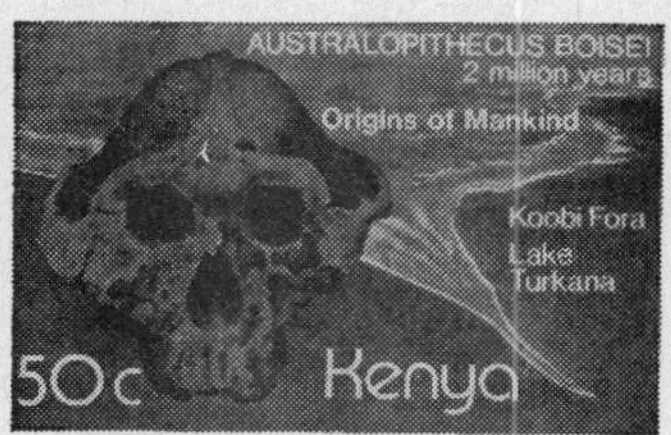

46. " Australopithecus boisei ".

1982. " Origins of Mankind ". Skulls. Multicoloured.

225. 50 c. Type 46 .. .. 65 10
226. 2 s. " Homo erectus " .. 1·50 55
227. 3 s. " Homo habilis " .. 1·90 1·25
228. 5 s. " Proconsul africanus " 2·75 2·50

47. Tree-planting.

1982. 75th Anniv. of Boy Scout Movement (Nos. 229, 231, 233 and 235) and 60th Anniv. of Girl Guide Movement (Nos. 230, 232, 234 and 236). Multicoloured.

229. 70 c. Type 47 .. .. 40 30
230. 70 c. Paying homage .. 40 30
231. 3 s. 50 " Be Prepared " .. 90 30
232. 3 s. 50 " International Friendship " 90 70
233. 5 s. Helping disabled .. 1·10 1·25
234. 5 s. Community service .. 1·10 1·25
235. 6 s. 50 Paxtu Cottage (Lord Baden-Powell's home) .. 1·50 1·75
236. 6 s. 60 Lady Baden-Powell 1·50 1·75

48. Footballer displaying Shooting Skill.

1982. World Cup Football Championship, Spain. Footballers silhouetted against Map of World. Multicoloured.

238. 70 c. Type 48 .. .. 75 30
239. 3 s. 50 Heading .. .. 1·40 1·25
240. 5 s. Goalkeeping .. .. 2·00 2·00
241. 10 s. Dribbling .. .. 3·00 3·25

49. Cattle Judging.

1982. 80th Anniv. of Agricultural Society of Kenya. Multicoloured.

243. 70 c. Type 49 .. .. 50 10
244. 2 s. 50 Farm machinery .. 1·25 1·00
245. 3 s. 50 Musical ride .. 1·50 1·50
246. 6 s. 50 Agricultural Society emblem .. .. 2·00 2·25

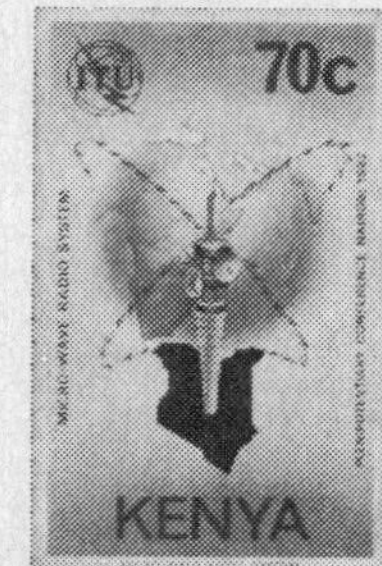

50. Micro-wave Radio System.

1982. I.T.U. Plenipotentiary Conference, Nairobi. Multicoloured.

247. 70 c. Type 50 .. .. 40 10
248. 3 s. 50 Sea-to-shore service link .. .. .. 1·00 1·25
249. 5 s. Rural telecommunications system .. .. 1·50 2·00
250. 6 s. 50 I.T.U. emblem .. 1·90 2·50

1982. No. 113 surch.

251. 70 c. on 80 c. Fluorite .. 50 50

52. Container Cranes.

1983. 5th Anniv. of Kenya Ports Authority. Multicoloured.

252. 70 c. Type 52 .. .. 50 10
253. 2 s. Port by night .. 1·25 1·00
254. 3 s. 50 Container Cranes (different) .. 1·75 1·75
255. 5 s. Map of Mombasa Port 2·00 2·50

53. Shada Zambarau.

54. Waridi Kikuba.

1983. Flowers. Multicoloured.

257. 10 c. Type 53 .. .. 30 15
258. 20 c. Kilua Kingulima .. 45 15
259. 30 c. Mwalika Mwiya .. 45 15
260. 40 c. Ziyungi Buluu .. 45 15
261. 50 c. Kilua Habashia .. 45 15
262. 70 c. Chanuo Kato .. 50 15
262a. 80 c. As 40 c. .. .. 1·50 30
262b. 1s. Waridi Kikuba .. 1·50 30
263. 1 s. Type 54 .. .. 45 15
264. 1 s. 50 Mshormoro Mtambazi 65 30
265. 2 s. Papatuo Boti 65 30
266. 2 s. 50 Tumba Mboni .. 1·00 30
266a. 3 s. Mkuku Mrembo .. 2·25 1·00
267. 3 s. 50 Mtongo Mbeja .. 1·00 70
267a. 4 s. Mnukia Muuma .. 2·25 2·00
268. 5 s. Nyungu Chepuo .. 1·00 60
268a. 7 s. Mlua Miba .. .. 2·75 3·00
269. 10 s. Muafunili .. .. 1·50 1·75
270. 20 s. Mbake Nyanza .. 2·25 2·50
271. 40 s. Njuga Pagwa .. 4·00 6·00

The 1 s. 50 to 40 s. are in the same format as T 54.

55. Coffee Plucking.

1983. Commonwealth Day. Multicoloured.

272. 70 c. Type 55 .. .. 10 10
273. 2 s. President Daniel Arap Moi 15 20
274. 5 s. Satellite View of Earth (horiz.) 45 45
275. 10 s. Masai dance (horiz.) 90 1·00

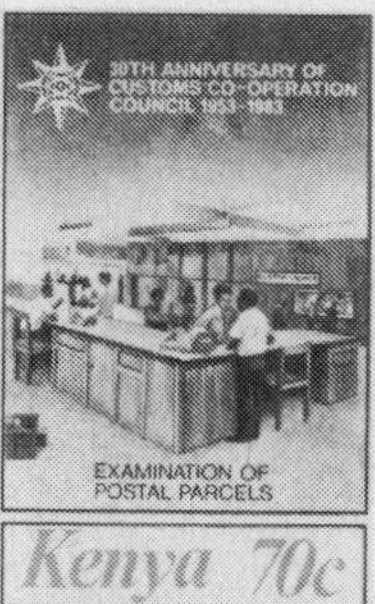

56. Examining Parcels.

1983. 30th Anniv. of Customs Co-operation Council. Multicoloured.

276. 70 c. Type 56 .. .. 15 10
277. 2 s. 50 Customs Headquarters, Mombasa .. 35 25
278. 3 s. 50 Customs Council Headquarters, Brussels 45 35
279. 10 s. Customs patrol boat .. 1·40 1·40

57. Communications via Satellite.

1983. World Communications Year. Multicoloured.

280. 70 c. Type 57 .. .. 45 10
281. 2 s. 50 " Telephone and Postal service " .. 1·00 1·00
282. 3 s. 50 Communications by sea and air (horiz.) .. 1·40 1·60
283. 5 s. Road and rail communications (horiz.) .. .. 1·75 2·00

58. Ships in Kilindini Harbour.

1983. 25th Anniv. of Intergovernmental Maritime Organization. Multicoloured.

284. 70 c. Type 58 .. .. 65 10
285. 2 s. 50 Life-saving devices 1·25 1·00
286. 3 s. 50 Mombasa container terminal .. .. 1·75 1·40
287. 10 s. Marine park .. 2·50 2·75

59. President Moi signing Visitors' Book.

1983. 29th Commonwealth Parliamentary Conference. Multicoloured.

288. 70 c. Type 59 .. .. 20 10
289. 2 s. 50 Parliament building, Nairobi (vert.) 45 35
290. 5 s. State opening of Parliament (vert.) .. 85 60

60. Kenyan and British Flags.

1983. Royal Visit. Multicoloured.

292. 70 c. Type 60 .. .. 40 10
293. 3 s. 50 Sagana State Lodge 1·25 45
294. 5 s. Treetops Hotel .. 1·75 80
295. 10 s. Queen Elizabeth II & President Moi .. .. 2·75 2·50

61. President Moi.

1983. 20th Anniv. of Independence. Mult.

297. 70 c. Type 61 .. .. 10 10
298. 2 s. President Moi planting tree 20 20
299. 3 s. 50 Kenyan flag & emblem 35 35
300. 5 s. School milk scheme .. 50 50
301. 10 s. People of Kenya .. 1·00 1·10

62. White-backed Night Heron.

1984. Rare Birds of Kenya. Multicoloured.

303. 70 c. Type **62** 90 20
304. 2 s. 50 Quail plover 1·50 1·40
305. 3 s. 50 Taita olive thrush 1·75 1·60
306. 5 s. Mufumbiri shrike 2·00 2·00
307. 10 s. White-winged apalis 2·75 2·50

63. Radar Tower.

1984. 40th Anniv. of International Civil Aviation Organization. Multicoloured.

308. 70 c. Type **63** 10 10
309. 2 s. 50 Kenya School of Aviation (horiz.) 30 30
310. 3 s. 50 Aircraft taking off from Moi airport (horiz.) 40 45
311. 5 s. Air traffic control centre 55 60

64. Running.

1984. Olympic Games, Los Angeles.

312. **64.** 70 c. black, green & deep green 20 10
313. – 2 s. 50 blk., pur. & vio. 45 25
314. – 5 s. black bl. & dp. bl. 90 55
315. – 10 s. blk., yell. & brn. 1·75 1·25

Designs: 2 s. 50 Hurdling. 5 s. Boxing. 10 s. Hockey.

65. Conference and Kenya Library Association Logos.

1984. 50th Conference of the International Federation of Library Associations. Mult.

317. 70 c. Type **65** 10 10
318. 3 s. 50 Mobile library 40 50
319. 5 s. Adult library 55 70
320. 10 s. Children's library 1·00 1·50

66. Doves and Cross.

1984. 4th World Conference on Religion and Peace. As T **66**, each design showing a different central symbol. Multicoloured.

321 70 c. Type **66** 30 10
322 2 s. 50 Arabic inscription 80 1·00
323 3 s. 50 Peace emblem 1·10 1·25
324 6 s. 50 Star and Crescent 1·60 2·00

67. Export Year Logo.

1984. Kenya Export Year. Multicoloured.

325. 70 c. Type **67** 30 10
326. 3 s. 50 Forklift truck with air cargo (horiz.) 1·25 1·25
327. 5 s. Loading ship's cargo 1·75 1·75
328. 10 s. Kenyan products (horiz.) 2·50 3·25

1984. Ceremonial Costumes (2nd series). As T **45**. Multicoloured.

329. 70 c. Luhya 40 15
330. 2 s. Kikuyu 1·00 90
331. 3 s. 50 Pokomo 1·40 1·25
332. 5 s. Nandi 1·75 1·75
333. 10 s. Rendile 2·50 3·25

68. Knight and Nyayo National Stadium.

1984. 60th Anniv. of World Chess Federation. Multicoloured.

334. 70 c. Type **68** 70 20
335. 2 s. 50 Rook and Fort Jesus 1·25 1·00
336. 3 s. 50 Bishop and National Monument 1·75 1·40
337. 5 s. Queen and Parliament Building 2·00 2·00
338. 10 s. King and Nyayo Fountain 2·75 3·25

69. Cooking with Wood-burning Stove and Charcoal Fire.

1985. Energy Conservation. Multicoloured.

339. 70 c. Type **69** 15 10
340. 2 s. Solar energy panel on roof 35 40
341. 3 s. 50 Production of gas from cow dung 55 75
342. 10 s. Ploughing with oxen 1·25 2·25

70. Crippled Girl Guide making Table-mat.

1985. 75th Anniv. of Girl Guide Movement. Multicoloured.

344. 1 s. Type **70** 40 15
345. 3 s. Girl Guides doing community service 1·00 75
346. 5 s. Lady Olave Baden-Powell (founder) 1·60 1·40
347. 7 s. Girl Guides gardening 2·00 2·25

71. Stylised Figures and Globe.

1985. World Red Cross Day.

348. **71.** 1 s. black and red 40 15
349. – 4 s. multicoloured 1·40 1·25
350. – 5 s. multicoloured 1·60 1·40
351. – 7 s. multicoloured 2·25 2·25

Designs: 4 s. First Aid team. 5 s. Hearts containing crosses ("Blood Donation"). 7 s. Cornucopia ("Famine Relief").

72. Man with Malaria.

1985. 7th International Congress of Protozoology, Nairobi. Multicoloured.

352 1 s. Type **72** 45 15
353 3 s. Child with Leishmaniasis 1·60 1·10
354 5 s. Cow with Trypanosomiasis 2·00 1·40
355 7 s. Dog with Babesiosis 2·50 2·25

73. Repairing Water Pipes.

1985. United Nations Women's Decade Conference. Multicoloured.

356. 1 s. Type **73** 10 10
357. 3 s. Traditional food preparation 40 35
358. 5 s. Basket-weaving 60 55
359. 7 s. Dressmaking 75 70

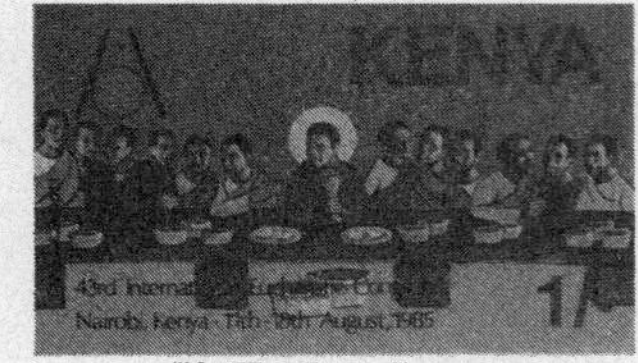

74. The Last Supper.

1985. 43rd International Eucharistic Congress, Nairobi. Multicoloured.

360. 1 s. Type **74** 35 10
361. 3 s. Village family ("The Eucharist and the Christian Family") 1·00 65
362. 5 s. Congress altar, Uhuru Park 1·25 95
363. 7 s. St. Peter Claver's Church, Nairobi 1·75 1·75

75. Black Rhinoceros.

1985. Endangered Animals. Multicoloured.

365. 1 s. Type **75** 60 20
366. 3 s. Cheetah 1·50 1·25
367. 5 s. De Brazza's Monkey 2·00 1·75
368. 10 s. Grevy's Zebra 3·00 3·50

76. "Borassus aethiopum".

1986. Indigenous Trees. Multicoloured.

370 1 s. Type **76** 40 15
371. 3 s. "Acacia xanthophloea" 1·25 1·25
372. 5 s. "Ficus natalensis" 1·90 2·00
373. 7 s. "Spathodea nilotica" 2·40 3·00

77. Dove and U.N. Logo (from poster).

1986. International Peace Year. Mult.

375. 1 s. Type **77** 15 10
376. 3 s. U.N. General Assembly (horiz.) 45 40
377. 7 s. Nuclear explosion 1·00 85
378. 10 s. Quotation from Wall of Isaiah, U.N. Building, New York (horiz.) 1·40 1·25

78. Dribbling the Ball.

1986. World Cup Football Championship, Mexico. Multicoloured.

379. 1 s. Type **78** 40 15
380. 3 s. Scoring from a penalty 1·00 55
381. 5 s. Tackling 1·75 1·25
382. 7 s. Cup winners 2·25 2·00
383. 10 s. Heading the ball 2·75 2·75

79. Rural Post Office and Telephone.

1986. "Expo '86" World Fair, Vancouver. Multicoloured.

385. 1 s. Type **79** 40 15
386. 3 s. Container depot, Embakasi 1·25 85
387. 5 s. Aircraft landing at game park airstrip 1·75 1·25
388. 7 s. Container ship 2·00 2·00
389. 10 s. Transporting produce to market 2·50 2·75

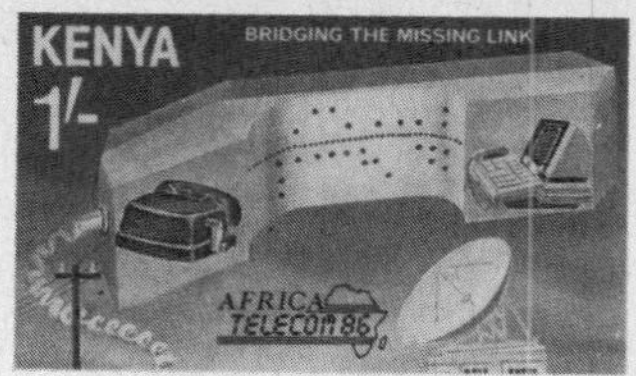

80. Telephone, Computer and Dish Aerial.

1986. African Telecommunications. Mult.

390.	1 s. Type **80**	25	10
391.	3 s. Telephones of 1876, 1936 and 1986	60	40
392.	5 s. Dish aerial, satellite, telephones and map of Africa	85	85
393.	7 s. Kenyan manufacture of telecommunications equipment	1·10	1·25

81. Mashua.

1986. Dhows of Kenya. Multicoloured.

394.	1 s. Type **81**	45	20
395.	3 s. Mtepe	1·25	1·00
396.	5 s. Dau La Mwao	1·75	1·50
397.	10 s. Jahazi	2·50	3·00

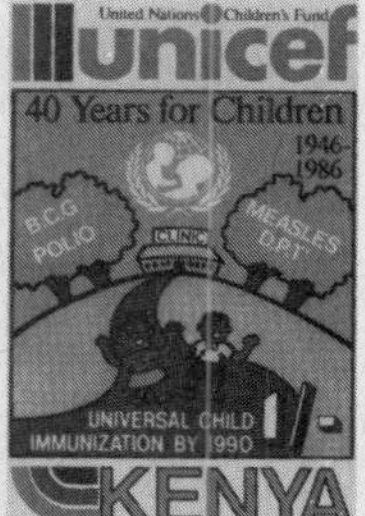

82. Nativity. **83.** Immunization.

1986. Christmas. Multicoloured.

399.	1 s. Type **82**	20	10
400.	3 s. Shepherd and sheep	60	45
401.	5 s. Angel and slogan "LOVE PEACE UNITY" (horiz.)	1·00	75
402.	7 s. The Magi riding camels (horiz.)	1·25	1·40

1987. 40th Anniv. of U.N.I.C.E.F. Multicoloured.

403.	1 s. Type **83**	20	10
404.	3 s. Food and nutrition	45	35
405.	4 s. Oral rehydration therapy	60	45
406.	5 s. Family planning	75	60
407.	10 s. Female literacy	1·25	1·25

84. Akamba Woodcarvers.

1987. Tourism. Multicoloured.

408.	1 s. Type **84**	30	10
409.	3 s. Tourists on beach	85	70
410.	5 s. Tourist and guide at view point	1·25	1·25
411.	7 s. Pride of lions	1·75	2·00

1987. Ceremonial Costumes (3rd series). As T **45**. Multicoloured.

413.	1 s. Embu	10	10
414.	3 s. Kisii	25	30
415.	5 s. Samburu	40	60
416.	7 s. Taita	60	80
417.	10 s. Boran	80	1·10

85. Telecommunications by Satellite.

1987. 10th Anniv. of Kenya Posts and Telecommunications Corporation. Mult.

418.	1 s. Type **85**	10	15
419.	3 s. Rural post office, Kajiado	20	35
420.	4 s. Awarding trophy, Welfare Sports	30	45
421.	5 s. Village and telephone box	35	50
422.	7 s. Speedpost labels and outline map of Kenya	50	70

86. Volleyball.

1987. 4th All-Africa Games, Nairobi. Mult.

424.	1 s. Type **86**	10	10
425.	3 s. Cycling	20	30
426.	4 s. Boxing	30	40
427.	5 s. Swimming	35	45
428.	7 s. Steeplechasing	50	75

87. "Aloe volkensii".

1987. Medicinal Herbs. Multicoloured.

430.	1 s. Type **87**	15	10
431.	3 s. "Cassia didymobotrya"	40	40
432.	5 s. "Erythrina abyssinica"	65	65
433.	7 s. "Adenium obesum"	85	1·00
434.	10 s. Herbalist's clinic	1·25	1·50

88. "Epamera sidus". **89.** "Papilio rex".

1988. Butterflies. Multicoloured.

434a	10 c. "Cyrestis camillus"	10	10
435	20 c. Type **88**	10	10
436	40 c. "Vanessa cardui"	10	10
437	50 c. "Colotis evippe"	10	10
438	70 c. "Precis westermanni"	10	10
439	80 c. "Colias electo"	10	10
440	1 s. "Eronia leda"	10	10
440a	1 s. 50 "Papilio dardanus"	10	10
441	2 s. Type **89**	10	10
442	2 s. 50 "Colotis phisadia"	10	15
443	3 s. "Papilio desmondi"	10	15
444	3 s. 50 "Papilio demodocus"	15	20
445	4 s. "Papilio phorcas"	15	20
446	5 s. "Charaxes druceanus"	20	25
447	7 s. "Cymothoe teita"	30	35
448	10 s. "Charaxes zoolina"	40	45
449	20 s. "Papilio dardanus"	80	85
450	40 s. "Charaxes cithaeron"	1·60	1·75

The 40 c. to 1 s. are the same format as T **88**.

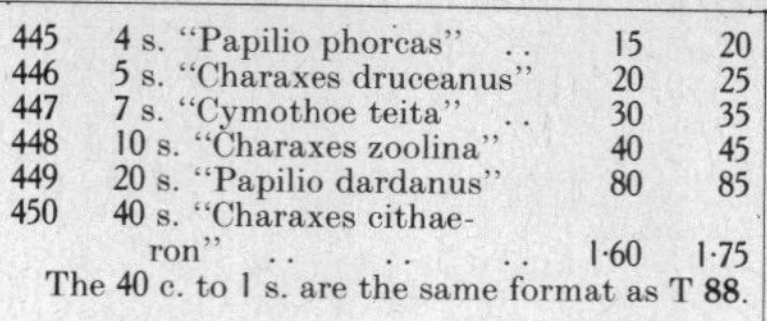

90 Samburu Lodge and Crocodiles

1988. Kenyan Game Lodges. Multicoloured.

451	1 s. Type **90**	20	10
452	3 s. Naro Moru River Lodge and rock climbing	55	35
453	4 s. Mara Serena Lodge and zebra with foal	65	50
454	5 s. Voi Safari Lodge and buffalo	70	60
455	7 s. Kilimanjaro Buffalo Lodge and giraffes	85	75
456	10 s. Meru Mulika Lodge and rhinoceroses	1·10	90

91 Athletes and Stadium, Commonwealth Games, Brisbane, 1982

1988. "Expo '88" World Fair, Brisbane, and Bicent of Australian Settlement. Mult.

457	1 s. Type **91**	15	10
458	3 s. Flying Doctor Service aircraft	40	35
459	4 s. H.M.S. "Sirius" (frigate), 1788	45	40
460	5 s. Ostrich and emu	55	50
461	7 s. Queen Elizabeth II, Pres. Arap Moi of Kenya and Prime Minister Hawke of Australia	70	80

92 W.H.O. Logo and Slogan

1988. 40th Anniv of W.H.O.

463	**92**	1 s. blue, gold & dp blue	20	10
464	–	3 s. multicoloured	50	40
465	–	5 s. multicoloured	70	60
466	–	7 s. multicoloured	1·00	90

DESIGNS: 3 s. Mother with young son and nutritious food; 5 s. Giving oral vaccine to baby; 7 s. Village women drawing clean water from pump.

93 Handball

1988. Olympic Games, Seoul. Multicoloured.

467	1 s. Type **93**	10	10
468	3 s. Judo	25	25
469	5 s. Weightlifting	35	35
470	7 s. Javelin	50	50
471	10 s. Relay racing	65	65

94 Calabashes

1988. Kenyan Material Culture. Mult.

473	1 s. Type **94**	10	10
474	3 s. Milk gourds	20	25
475	5 s. Cooking pots (horiz)	30	35
476	7 s. Winnowing trays (horiz)	45	50
477	10 s. Reed baskets (horiz)	60	65

95 Pres. Arap Moi taking Oath, 1978

1988. 10th Anniv of "Nyayo" Era. Mult.

479	1 s. Type **95**	20	10
480	3 s. Building soil conservation barrier	50	40
481	3 s. 50 Passengers boarding bus	50	40
482	4 s. Metalwork shop	60	60
483	5 s. Moi University, Eldoret	70	70
484	7 s. Aerial view of hospital	90	1·00
485	10 s. Pres. Arap Moi and Mrs. Thatcher at Kapsabet Telephone Exchange	1·75	1·90

96 Kenya Flag

1988. 25th Anniv of Independence. Mult.

486	1 s. Type **96**	15	10
487	3 s. Coffee picking	35	35
488	5 s. Proposed Kenya Posts and Telecommunications Headquarters building	60	60
489	7 s. Kenya Airways "Harambee Star" "A310-300" Airbus	80	80
490	10 s. New diesel locomotive No. 9401	1·10	1·25

97 Gedi Ruins, Malindi

1989. Historic Monuments. Multicoloured.

491	1 s. 20 Type **97**	15	10
492	3 s. 40 Vasco Da Gama Pillar, Malindi (vert)	30	30
493	4 s. 40 Ishiakani Monument, Kiunga	40	40
494	5 s. 50 Fort Jesus, Mombasa	50	50
495	7 s. 50 She Burnan Omwe, Lamu (vert)	65	70

98 125th Anniversary and Kenya Red Cross Logos

1989. 125th Anniv of International Red Cross. Multicoloured.

496	1 s. 20 Type **98**	15	10
497	3 s. 40 Red Cross workers with car crash victim ..	30	30
498	4 s. 40 Disaster relief team distributing blankets ..	40	40
499	5 s. 50 Henri Dunant (founder)	50	50
500	7 s. 70 Blood donor ..	65	70

99 Female Giraffe and Calf

1989. Reticulated Giraffe. Multicoloured.

501	1 s. 20 Type **99**	30	15
502	3 s. 40 Giraffe drinking ..	65	65
503	4 s. 40 Two giraffes ..	80	80
504	5 s. 50 Giraffe feeding ..	1·00	1·25

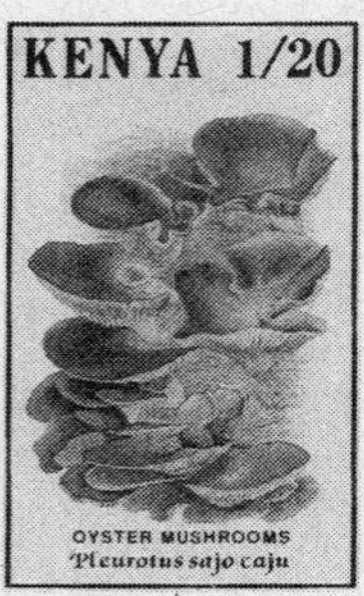

100 "Pleurotus sajor-ceju"

1989. Mushrooms. Multicoloured.

506	1 s. 20 Type **100**	30	15
507	3 s. 40 "Agaricus bisporus"	50	40
508	4 s. 40 "Agaricus bisporus" (different)	70	65
509	5 s. 50 "Termitomyces schimperi"	90	90
510	7 s. 70 "Lentinus edodes"	1·40	1·50

101 Independence Monuments

1989. Birth Centenary of Jawaharlal Nehru (Indian statesman). Multicoloured.

511	1 s. 20 Type **101**	30	15
512	3 s. 40 Nehru with graduates and open book	60	50
513	5 s. 50 Jawaharlal Nehru	80	70
514	7 s. 70 Industrial complex and cogwheels	1·25	1·25

1989. Ceremonial Costumes (4th series). As T **45**. Multicoloured.

515	1 s. 20 Kipsigis	25	15
516	3 s. 40 Rabai	55	50
517	5 s. 50 Duruma	75	70
518	7 s. 70 Kuria	1·10	1·25
519	10 s. Bajuni	1·50	1·60

102 EMS Speedpost Letters and Parcel

1990. 10th Anniv of Pan African Postal Union. Multicoloured.

520	1 s. 20 Type **102**	15	10
521	3 s. 40 Mail runner	30	30
522	5 s. 50 Mandera Post Office	50	50
523	7 s. 70 EMS Speedpost letters and globe (vert)	70	80
524	10 s. P.A.P.U. logo (vert)	80	90

103 "Stamp King" with Tweezers and Magnifying Glass

1990. "Stamp World London 90" International Stamp Exhibition.

525	**103**	1 s. 50 multicoloured ..	15	10
526	–	4 s. 50 multicoloured ..	40	35
527	–	6 s. 50 black, red & bl	45	60
528	–	9 s. multicoloured ..	70	1·00

DESIGNS: 4 s. 50, Penny Black and Kenya Stamp Bureau postmark; 6 s. 50, Early British cancellations; 9 s. Ronald Ngala Street Post Office, Nairobi.

104 Moi Golden Cup

1990. World Cup Football Championship, Italy. Trophies. Multicoloured.

530	1 s. 50 Type **104**	20	10
531	4 s. 50 East and Central Africa Challenge Cup ..	50	50
532	6 s. 50 East and Central Africa Club Championship Cup	70	70
533	9 s. World Cup	1·00	1·25

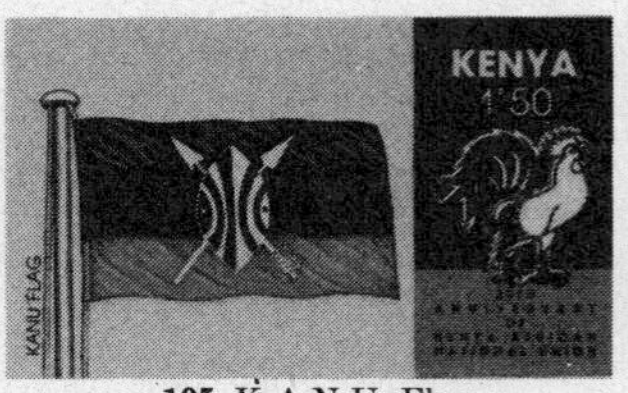

105 K.A.N.U. Flag

1990. 50th Anniv of Kenya African National Union. Multicoloured.

534	1 s. 50 Type **105**	15	10
535	2 s. 50 Nyayo Monument	15	15
536	4 s. 50 Party Headquarters	35	35
537	5 s. Jomo Kenyatta (Party founder)	40	40
538	6 s. 50 President Arap Moi	50	60
539	9 s. President Moi addressing rally ..	70	80
540	10 s. Queue of voters ..	80	1·00

106 Desktop Computer

1990. 125th Anniv of I. T. U. Multicoloured.

541	1 s. 50 Type **106**	15	10
542	4 s. 50 Telephone switchboard assembly, Gilgil ..	35	35
543	6 s. 50 "125 YEARS" ..	45	65
544	9 s. Urban and rural telecommunications ..	70	1·00

1990. 90th Birthday of Queen Elizabeth the Queen Mother. As T **134** of Ascension.

545	10 s. multicoloured ..	80	80
546	40 s. black and green ..	2·75	2·75

DESIGNS—21 × 36 mm. 10 s. Queen Mother at British Museum, 1988. 29 × 37 mm. 40 s. Queen Elizabeth at hospital garden party, 1947.

109 Kenya 1988 2 s. Definitive

1990. Cent of Postage Stamps in Kenya. Mult.

547	1 s. 50 Type **109**	15	10
548	4 s. 50 East Africa and Uganda 1903 1 a. ..	35	35
549	6 s. 50 British East Africa Co 1890 ½a. optd on G.B. 1d.	50	50
550	9 s. Kenya and Uganda 1922 20 c.	75	75
551	20 s. Kenya, Uganda, Tanzania 1971 2 s. 50 railway commemorative	1·25	1·50

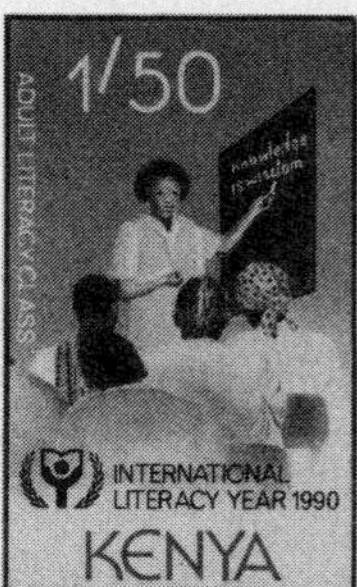

110 Adult Literacy Class

1990. International Literacy Year. Mult.

552	1 s. 50 Type **110**	15	10
553	4 s. 50 Teaching by radio	35	35
554	6 s. 50 Technical training	35	60
555	9 s. International Literacy Year logo	85	90

111 National Flag

1991. Olympic Games, Barcelona (1992). Mult.

556	2 s. Type **111**	10	10
557	6 s. Basketball	35	35
558	7 s. Hockey	45	45
559	8 s. 50 Table tennis ..	55	55
560	11 s. Boxing	65	65

1992. 40th Anniv of Queen Elizabeth II's Accession. As T **143** of Ascension. Mult.

561	3 s. Queen and Prince Philip with Pres. Moi	10	10
562	8 s. Storks in tree ..	30	35
563	11 s. Treetops Hotel ..	45	50
564	14 s. Three portraits of Queen Elizabeth ..	60	65
565	40 s. Queen Elizabeth II ..	1·60	1·75

113 Symbolic Man and Pointing Finger

1992. AIDS Day. Multicoloured.

566	2 s. Type **113**	10	10
567	6 s. Victim and drugs ..	25	25
568	8 s. 50 Male and female symbols	30	35
569	11 s. Symbolic figure and hypodermic syringe ..	45	50

POSTAGE DUE STAMPS

D **3**.

1967.

D 13	D **3**.	5 c. red	15	1·75
D 41		10 c. green	10	10
D 42		20 c. blue	10	10
D 44		30 c. brown ..	10	10
D 45		40 c. purple ..	10	10
D 46		80 c. red	10	10
D 47		1 s. orange ..	10	10
D 48		2 s. violet	10	10

OFFICIAL STAMPS

Intended for use on official correspondence of the Kenya Government only, but there is no evidence that they were so used.

1964. Stamps of 1963 optd. **OFFICIAL.**

O 21.	**46.**	5 c. multicoloured ..	10
O 22.	–	10 c. brown ..	10
O 23.	–	15 c. mauve ..	40
O 24.	–	20 c. black and green ..	20
O 25.	–	30 c. black and yellow	30
O 26.	–	50 c. red, black & green	1·50

KENYA, UGANDA AND TANGANYIKA

Kenya, a Br. Crown colony and Protectorate including British East Africa. From 1935 it had a common postal service with Tanganyika and Uganda. Tanganyika became independent and had its own stamps in 1961, Uganda in 1962 and Kenya in December 1963, when the stamps of Kenya, Tanganyika and Uganda (except for the Postage Due Stamps) were withdrawn. For earlier issues see under Br. East Africa, Tanganyika and Uganda.

1903–19. 16 annas = 100 cents = 1 rupee.
1922. 100 cents = 1s sterling.

1.

2.

1903.

17 1 ½ a. green .. .. 3·50 80
2 1 a. grey and red .. 1·75 30
19a 2 a. purple .. .. 2·50 1·00
21 2½ a. blue .. .. 7·50 16·00
22 3 a. purple and green .. 3·75 15·00
23 4 a. green and black .. 7·50 12·00
24 5 a. grey and brown .. 7·50 14·00
25 8 a. grey and blue .. 7·00 8·00
9 2 1 r. green .. .. 13·00 35·00
27 2 r. purple .. .. 30·00 45·00
28 3 r. green and black .. 45·00 80·00
29 4 r. grey and green .. 48·00 £100
30 5 r. grey and red .. 50·00 80·00
31 10 r. grey and blue .. £120 £150
15 20 r. grey and stone .. £450 £600
16 50 r. grey and brown .. £1100 £1400

1907.

34. 1. 1 c. brown 20 15
35. 3 c. green .. .. 3·00 25
36. 6 c. red .. .. 2·75 10
37. 10 c. lilac and olive .. 9·00 8·50
38. 12 c. purple .. .. 4·25 2·75
39. 15 c. blue .. .. 9·50 8·50
40. 25 c. green and black .. 3·75 6·50
41. 50 c. green and brown .. 6·50 12·00
42. 75 c. grey and blue .. 4·50 20·00

1912. As T **1/2**, but portraits of King George V.

44 1 c. black 20 55
45 3 c. green .. .. 2·00 25
46 6 c. red 50 15
47 10 c. orange .. .. 2·00 20
48 12 c. grey .. .. 2·75 50
49 15 c. blue .. .. 2·75 55
50 25 c. black & red on yellow 45 90
51 50 c. black and lilac .. 1·50 1·00
52a 75 c. black and green .. 90 8·50
53 1 r. black and green .. 1·75 3·25
54 2 r. red and black on blue 20·00 28·00
55 3 r. violet and green .. 20·00 42·00
56 4 r. red & green on yellow 42·00 80·00
57 5 r. blue and purple .. 42·00 85·00
58 10 r. red & green on green 75·00 £120
59 20 r. black & purple on red £250 £250
60 20 r. purple & blue on blue £225 £225
61 50 r. red and green .. £600 £600
62 100 r. purple & blk on red £2750 £1800
63 500 p. green & red on green £12000

1919. No. 46 surch **4 cents.**

64 4 c. on 6 c. red 20 15

6. 7.

1922.

76 6. 1 c. brown 60 70
77. 5 c. violet .. .. 2·00 30
78. 5 c. green .. .. 2·00 10
79. 10 c. green .. .. 1·25 10
80. 10 c. black .. .. 1·75 10
81a. 12 c. black .. .. 1·50 19·00
82. 15 c. red 80 10
83. 20 c. orange .. .. 2·50 10
84. 30 c. blue .. .. 1·25 20
85. 50 c. grey .. .. 1·75 10
86. 75 c. olive .. .. 2·25 7·50
87. 7. 1 s. green .. .. 2·75 2·00
88. 2 s. purple .. .. 7·50 7·00
89. 2 s. 50 brown .. 18·00 60·00
90. 3 s. grey .. .. 15·00 6·00
91. 4 s. grey .. .. 18·00 60·00
92. 5 s. red .. .. 22·00 18·00
93. 7 s. 50 orange .. 60·00 £130
94. 10 s. blue .. .. 48·00 48·00
95. £1 black and orange .. £140 £190
96. £2 green and purple .. £700
97. £3 purple and yellow .. £850
98. £4 black and mauve .. £1400
99. £5 black and blue .. £1800
100. £10 black and green .. £7500
101. £20 red and green .. £12000
102. £25 black and red .. £13000
103. £50 black and brown .. £17000
104. £75 purple and grey .. £32000
105. £100 red and black .. £35000

8. South African Crowned Cranes.

DESIGNS—VERT. 10 c. £1, Lion. 30 c. 5 s. Jinja Railway Bridge, Ripon Falls. HORIZ. 15 c. 2 s. Kilimanjaro. 65 c. Mt. Kenya. 1 s., 3 s. Lake Naivasha.

9. Dhow on Lake Victoria.

1935. King George V.

110 8. 1 c. black and brown .. 15 50
111 9. 5 c. black and green .. 40 15
112 – 10 c. black and yellow .. 2·25 15
113 – 15 c. black and red .. 75 10
114 8. 20 c. black and orange .. 85 10
115 – 30 c. black and blue .. 80 80
116 9. 50 c. purple and black .. 75 10
117 – 65 c. black and brown .. 90 2·00
118 – 1 s. black and green .. 75 35
119 – 2 s. red and purple .. 4·25 3·50
120 – 3 s. blue and black .. 5·00 13·00
121 – 5 s. black and red .. 15·00 23·00
122 8. 10 s. purple and blue .. 40·00 48·00
123 – £1 black and red .. £120 £130

1935. Silver Jubilee. As T **13** of Antigua.

124 20 c. blue and olive .. 35 10
125 30 c. brown and blue .. 2·00 1·50
126 65 c. green and blue .. 1·75 2·00
127 1 s. grey and purple .. 2·00 1·40

1937. Coronation. As T **2** of Aden.

128 5 c. green 25 10
129 20 c. orange 55 15
130 30 c. blue 85 85

15. Dhow on Lake Victoria.

1938. As 1935 (except 10 c.), but with portrait of King George VI as in T **15**.

131a 8. 1 c. black and brown 10 35
132 15. 5 c. black and green 55 10
133 5 c. brown and orange 35 1·50
134 – 10 c. brn. & orge. .. 40 10
135 – 10 c. black and green 20 20
136 – 10 c. brown and grey 35 20
137 – 15 c. black and red .. 2·50 15
138 – 15 c. black and green 60 1·25
139b 8. 20 c. black and orange 1·75 10
140 15. 25 c. black and red .. 1·25 80
141b – 30 c. black and blue .. 40 10
142 – 30 c. pur. & brn. .. 55 10
143 8. 40 c. black and blue .. 1·25 1·50
144e 15. 50 c. purple and black 2·50 30
145 – 1 s. black and brown 1·50 10
146b – 2 s. red and purple .. 5·50 10
147b – 3 s. blue and black .. 10·00 90
148b – 5 s. black and red .. 10·00 30
149b 8. 10 s. purple and blue 15·00 2·50
150ab – £1 black and red .. 10·00 11·00

DESIGN—HORIZ. 10 c. Lake Naivasha.

1941. Stamps of South Africa surch **KENYA TANGANYIKA UGANDA** and value. Alternate stamps inscr in English or Afrikaans.

151. 7. 5 c. on 1d. blk. and red 60 1·50
152. 22a. 10 c. on 3d. blue .. 1·00 2·75
153. 8. 20 c. on 6d. grn. & red 60 1·75
154. – 70 c. on 1s. (No. 120).. 4·50 4·00

Prices for Nos. 151/4 are for unused or used pairs.

1946. Victory. As T **9** of Aden.

155. 20 c. orange 10 10
156. 30 c. blue 10 10

1948. Silver Wedding. As T **10/11** of Aden.

157. 20 c. orange 15 10
158. £1 red .. .. 30·00 35·00

1949. U.P.U. As T **20/23** of Antigua.

159. 20 c. orange 15 10
160. 30 c. blue 40 25
161. 50 c. grey 40 10
162. 1 s. brown 75 40

1952. Visit of Queen Elizabeth II (as Princess) and Duke of Edinburgh. As Nos. 135 and 145 but inscr. "ROYAL VISIT 1952".

163. 10 c. black and green .. 10 30
164. 1 s. black and brown .. 20 1·75

1953. Coronation. As T **13** of Aden.

165 20 c. black and orange .. 15 10

1954. Royal Visit. As No. 171 but inscr. "ROYAL VISIT 1954".

166. 18. 30 c. black and blue .. 10 15

18. Owen Falls Dam. 21. Queen Elizabeth II.

20. Royal Lodge, Sagana.

DESIGNS (Size as Type **18**)—VERT 10 c., 50 c. Giraffe. 20 c., 40 c. 1 s. Lion. HORIZ. 1 c., 1 s. 30, 5 s. Elephants. 65 c., 2 s. Kilimanjaro.

1954.

167 18. 5 c. black and brown .. 10 10
168 – 10 c. red 40 10
169a – 15 c. black and blue .. 45 10
170 – 20 c. black and orange 30 10
171 18. 30 c. black and blue .. 35 10
172 – 40 c. brown .. .. 2·50 40
173 – 50 c. purple 20 10
174 – 65 c. green and lake .. 2·50 50
175 – 1 s. black and red .. 30 10
176 – 1 s. 30 orange and lilac 4·00 10
177 – 2 s. black and green .. 1·50 20
178 – 5 s. black and orange 4·25 60
179 20. 10 s. black and blue .. 10·00 1·50
180 21. £1 red and black .. 15·00 6·50

25. Map of E. Africa showing Lakes.

1958. Cent. of Discovery of Lakes Tanganyika and Victoria by Burton and Speke.

181. 25. 40 c. blue and green .. 20 15
182. 1 s. 30c. green & purple 30 70

26. Sisal.

29. Queen Elizabeth II.

28. Mt. Kenya and Giant Plants.

1960.

183. 26. 5 c. blue 10 10
184. – 10 c. green 10 10
185. – 15 c. purple 15 10
186. – 20 c. mauve 10 10
187. – 25 c. green .. .. 2·00 55
188. – 30 c. red 10 10
189. – 40 c. blue 15 10
190. – 50 c. violet 15 10
191. – 65 c. olive 30 45
192. 28. 1 s. violet and purple 40 10
193. – 1 s. 30 brown and red 1·00 10
194. – 2 s. indigo and blue .. 1·00 15
195. – 2 s. 50 olive & turq. .. 2·00 1·50
196. – 5 s. red and purple .. 3·25 45
197. – 10 s. myrtle and green 4·25 2·50
198. 29. 20 s. blue and lake .. 11·00 9·00

DESIGNS—As Type **26**: 10 c. Cotton. 15 c. Coffee. 20 c. Blue Wildebeest. 25 c. Ostrich. 30 c. Thomson's Gazelle. 40 c. Manta Ray. 50 c. Common Zebra. 65 c. Cheetah. As Type **28**: 1 s. 30, Murchison Falls and Hippopotamus. 2 s. Mt. Kilimanjaro and Giraffe. 2 s. 50, Candelabra tree and Black Rhinoceros. 5 s. Crater Lake and Mountains of the Moon. 10 s. Ngorongoro Crater and African Buffalo.

30. Land Tillage.

1963. Freedom from Hunger.

199. 30. 15 c. blue and olive .. 10 10
200. – 30 c. brown and yellow 20 10
201. 30. 50 c. blue and orange 30 10
202. – 1 s. 30 brown and blue 55 90

DESIGN: 30 c., 1 s. 30, African with corncob.

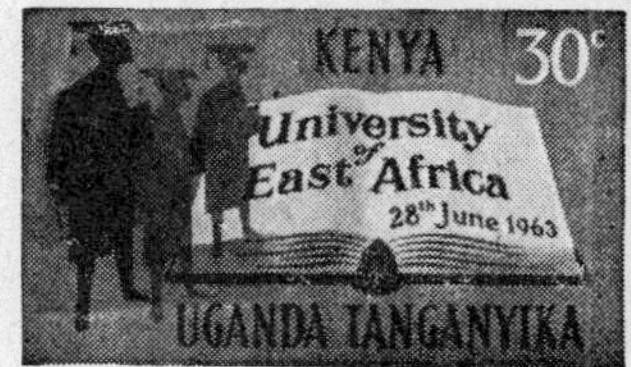

31. Scholars and Open Book.

1963. Founding of East African University.

203. 31. 30 c. multicoloured .. 10 10
204. 1 s. 30 multicoloured .. 10 10

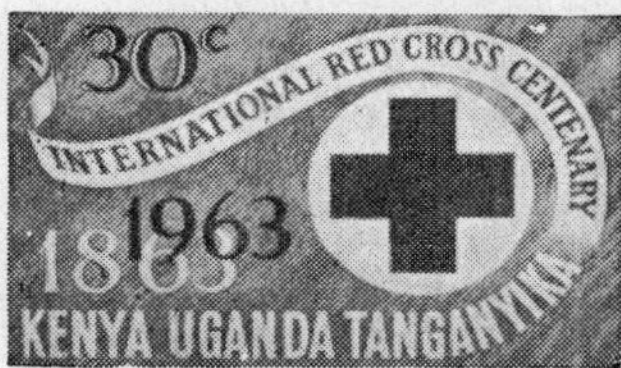

32. Red Cross Emblem.

1963. Centenary of Red Cross.

205. 32. 30 c. red and blue .. 75 10
206. – 50 c. red and brown .. 1·00 35

35. East African "Flags".

1964. Olympic Games, Tokyo.

207. – 30 c. yellow and purple 10 10
208. – 50 c. purple & yellow 10 10
209. 35. 1 s. 30 yell., grn. & blue 15 10
210. 2 s. 50 mve., vio. & bl. 25 60

DESIGNS—VERT. 30 c., 50 c. Chrysanthemum Emblem.

36. Rally Badge.

DESIGN. Nos. 213/14, Cars en route.

1965. 13th East African Safari Rally.

211. **36.** 30 c. blk., yell. & turq. 10 10
212. 50 c. blk., yell. & brn. 10 10
213. – 1 s. 30 green, ochre & blue 20 10
214. – 2 s. 50 grn., red & blue 30 45

38. I.T.U. Emblem and Symbols.

1965. Centenary of I.T.U. "I.T.U." and symbols in gold.

215. **38.** 30 c. brown & mauve 10 10
216. 50 c. brown & grey .. 15 10
217. 1 s. 30 brown & blue .. 30 10
218. 2 s. 50 brown & turq. 55 80

39. I.C.Y. Emblem.

1965. Int. Co-operation Year.

219. **39.** 30 c. green and gold .. 10 10
220. 50 c. black and gold .. 15 10
221. 1 s. 30 blue and gold .. 30 10
222. 2 s. 50 red and gold .. 75 1·75

40. Game Park Lodge, Tanzania.

1966. Tourism. Multicoloured.

223. 30 c. Type **40** 15 10
224. 50 c. Murchison Falls, Uganda 40 10
225. 1 s. 30 Lesser Flamingoes, Lake Nakuru, Kenya .. 1·50 20
226. 2 s. 50 Deep Sea Fishing, Tanzania .. .. 1·50 1·40

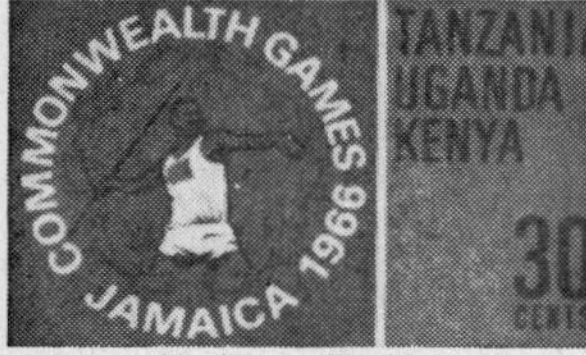

41. Games Emblem.

1966. 8th British Empire and Commonwealth Games, Jamaica.

227. **41.** 30 c. multicoloured .. 10 10
228. 50 c. multicoloured .. 10 10
229. 1 s. 30 multicoloured .. 15 10
230. 2 s. 50 multicoloured .. 30 55

42. U.N.E.S.C.O. Emblem.

1966. 20th Anniv. of U.N.E.S.C.O.

231. **42.** 30 c. blk., grn. & red .. 25 10
232. 50 c. blk., grn. & brn... 30 10
233. 1 s. 30 blk., grn. & grey 75 15
234. 2 s. 50 blk., grn. & yell. 1·40 1·25

43. D. H. "Dragon Rapide".

1967. 21st Anniv. of East African Airways. Multicoloured.

235. 30 c. Type **43** 30 10
236. 50 c. "Super VC-10" .. 40 10
237. 1 s. 30 "Comet" .. 85 15
238. 2 s. 50 "F-27 Friendship" 1·25 1·60

44. Pillar Tomb.

1967. Archaeological Relics.

239. **44.** 30 c. ochre, blk. & pur. 15 10
240. – 50 c. red, blk. & brn. .. 40 10
241. – 1 s. 30 blk., yell. & grn. 75 10
242. – 2 s. 50 blk., ochre & red 1·10 1·25

DESIGNS: 50 c. Rock painting. 1 s. 30, Clay head. 2 s. 50, Proconsul skull.

48. Unified Symbols of Kenya, Tanzania, and Uganda. (Illustration reduced. Actual size 58×21 mm.)

1967. Foundation of East African Community.

243. **48.** 5 s. gold, blk. & grey .. 40 1·00

49. Mountaineering.

1968. Mountains of East Africa. Mult.

244. 30 c. Type **49** 10 10
245. 50 c. Mount Kenya .. 15 10
246. 1 s. 30 Mount Kilimanjaro 30 10
247. 2 s. 50 Ruwenzori Mountains 55 1·00

50. Family and Rural Hospital.

1968. World Health Organization.

248. **50.** 30 c. grn., lilac & brn. 10 10
249. – 50 c. slate, lilac & black 10 10
250. – 1 s. 30 brown, lilac and light brown .. 15 10
251. – 2 s. 50 grey, black & lilac 25 60

DESIGNS: 50 c. Family and Nurse. 1 s. 30, Family and Microscope. 2 s. 50, Family and Hypodermic Syringe.

51. Olympic Stadium, Mexico City.

1968. Olympic Games, Mexico.

252. **51.** 30 c. green and black 10 10
253. – 50 c. green and black 10 10
254. – 1 s. 30 red, black & grey 15 10
255. – 2 s. 50 sepia and brown 25 60

DESIGNS—HORIZ. 50 c. High-diving Boards. 1 s. 30, Running Tracks. VERT. 2 s. 50, Boxing Ring.

52. "M.V. Umoja".

1969. Water Transport.

256. **52.** 30 c. blue and grey .. 15 10
257. – 50 c. multicoloured .. 20 10
258. – 1 s. 30 green and blue 45 15
259. – 2 s. 50 orange and blue 1·00 1·50

DESIGNS: 50 c. "S.S. Harambee". 1 s. 30, "M.V. Victoria". 2 s. 50, "St. Michael".

53. I.L.O. Emblem and Agriculture.

1969. 50th Anniv. of Int. Labour Organization.

260. **53.** 30 c. blk., grn. & yell. 10 10
261. – 50 c. multicoloured .. 10 10
262. – 1 s. 30 black, brown and orange 10 10
263. – 2 s. 50 blk., bl. & turq. 20 30

DESIGNS—I.L.O. Emblem and 50 c. Building-work. 1 s. 30, Factory-workers, 2 s. 50, Shipping.

54. Pope Paul VI and Ruwenzori Mountains. **55.** Euphorbia Tree shaped as Africa, and Emblem.

1969. Visit of Pope Paul VI to Uganda.

264. **54.** 30 c. black, gold & blue 15 10
265. 70 c. black, gold & red 20 10
266. 1 s. 50 blk., gold & bl. 30 20
267. 2 s. 50 black, gold & violet 45 75

1969. 5th Anniv. of African Development Bank.

268. **55.** 30 c. green and gold .. 10 10
269. 70 c. grn., gold & vio. 15 10
270. 1 s. 50 grn., gold & bl. 20 10
271. 2 s. 50 green, gold & brown 25 25

56. Marimba.

1970. Musical Instruments.

272. **56.** 30 c. buff and brown .. 15 10
273. – 70 c. green, brn. & yell. 20 10
274. – 1 s. 50 brown & yellow 40 10
275. – 2 s. 50 orange, yellow and brown 60 60

DESIGN: 70 c. Amadinda, 1 s. 50, Nzomari. 2 s. 50, Adeudeu.

57. Satellite Earth Station.

1970. Inaug. of Satellite Earth Station.

276. **57.** 30 c. multicoloured .. 10 10
277. – 70 c. multicoloured .. 15 10
278. – 1 s. 50 blk., vio. & orge. 20 10
279. – 2 s. 50 multicoloured .. 45 60

DESIGNS: 70 c. Transmitter—Daytime. 1 s. 50, Transmitter—Night. 2 s. 50, Earth and satellite.

58. Athlete.

1970. 9th Commonwealth Games.

280. **58.** 30 c. brown and black 10 10
281. 70 c. green, brown and black 10 10
282. 1 s. 50 lilac, brown and black 10 10
283. 2 s. 50 blue, brown and black 20 40

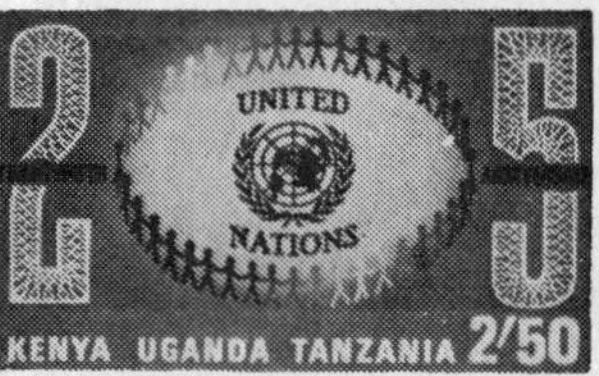

59. "25" and U.N. Emblem.

1970. 25th Anniv. of United Nations.

284. **59.** 30 c. multicoloured .. 10 10
285. 70 c. multicoloured .. 10 10
286. 1 s. 50 multicoloured .. 20 10
287. 2 s. 50 multicoloured .. 45 80

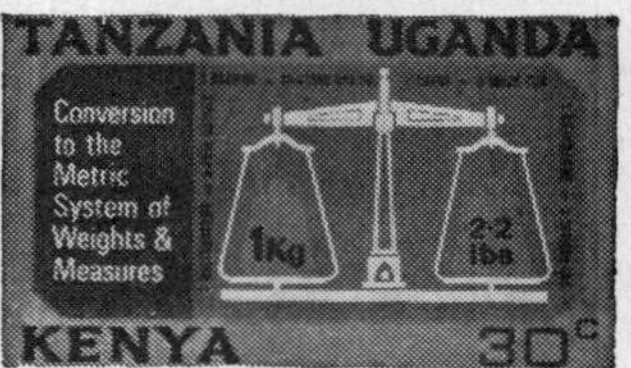

60. Balance and Weight Equivalents.

1970. Conversion to Metric System. **Mult.**

288. 30 c. Type **60** 10 10
289. 70 c. Fahrenheit and Centigrade Thermometers .. 10 10
290. 1 s. 50 Petrol Pump and Liquid Capacities .. 15 10
291. 2 s. 50 Surveyors and Land Measures 35 65

61. Class "11" Locomotive.

1971. Railway Transport. Multicoloured.

292. 30 c. Type **61** 35 10
293. 70 c. Class "90" Locomotive 55 10
294. 1 s. 50 Class "59" Locomotive .. .. .. 1·25 50
295. 2 s. 50 Class "30" Locomotive .. .. .. 2·25 2·75

62. Syringe and Cow.

1971. O.A.U. Rinderpest Campaign.

297. **62.** 30 c. blk., brn. and grn. 10 10
298. – 70 c. blk., blue & brn. 10 10
299. **62.** 1 s. 50 blk., pur. & brn. 15 10
300. – 2 s. 50 blk., red & brn. 25 50

DESIGN: 70 c., 2 s. 50, As Type **62** but with bull facing right.

63. Livingstone meets Stanley.

1971. Centenary of Livingstone and Stanley meeting at Ujiji.

301. **63.** 5 s. multicoloured .. 30 75

64. Pres. Nyerere and Supporters.

1971. 10th Anniv. of Tanzanian Independence. Multicoloured.

302. 30 c. Type **64** 10 10
303. 70 c. Ujama village .. 10 10
304. 1 s. 50 Dar-es-Salaam University .. 20 20
305. 2 s. 50 Kilimanjaro airport 55 1·40

65. Flags and Trade Fair Emblem.

1972. All-Africa Trade Fair.

306. **65.** 30 c. multicoloured .. 10 10
307. 70 c. multicoloured .. 10 10
308. 1 s. 50 multicoloured .. 10 10
309. 2 s. 50 multicoloured .. 25 55

66. Child with Cup.

1972. 25th Anniv. of U.N.I.C.E.F. Mult.

310. 30 c. Type **66** 10 10
311. 70 c. Children with ball .. 10 10
312. 1 s. 50 Child at blackboard 10 10
313. 2 s. 50 Child and tractor .. 25 50

67. Hurdling.

1972. Olympic Games, Munich. Mult.

314. 40 c. Type **67** 10 10
315. 70 c. Running 10 10
316. 1 s. 50 Boxing 20 10
317. 2 s. 50 Hockey .. .. 30 1·00

68. Ugandan Kobs.

1972. 10th Anniv. of Ugandan Independence. Multicoloured.

319. 40 c. Type **68** 20 10
320. 70 c. Conference Centre .. 20 10
321. 1 s. 50 Makerere University 45 20
322. 2 s. 50 Coat of Arms .. 85 1·25

69. Community Flag.

1972. 5th Anniv. of East African Community.

324. **69.** 5 s. multicoloured .. 75 1·25

70. Run-of-the-wind Anemometer.

1972. Cent. of IMO/WMO. Multicoloured.

325. 40 c. Type **70** 10 10
326. 70 c. Weather balloon (vert.) 15 10
327. 1 s. 50 Meterological rocket 25 15
328. 2 s. 50 Satellite Receiving aerial .. .. .. 55 1·25

71. " Learning by Serving ".

1973. 24th World Scouting Conference, Nairobi.

329. **71.** 40 c. multicoloured .. 15 10
330. – 70 c. red, violet & blk. 20 10
331. – 1 s. 50 blue, vio. & blk. 45 30
332. – 2 s. 50 multicoloured .. 1·00 1·75

Designs: 70 c. Baden-Powell's grave, Nyeri. 1 s. 50, World Scout emblem. 2 s. 50, Lord Baden-Powell.

72. Kenyatta Conference Centre.

1973. I.M.F./World Bank Conference.

333. **72.** 40 c. grn., grey & blk. 10 10
334. – 70 c. brn., grey & black 10 10
335. – 1 s. 50 multicoloured .. 25 35
336. – 2 s. 50 orange, grey & black 35 90

Designs: Nos. 334/6 show different arrangements of Bank emblems and the Conference Centre, the 1 s. 50 being vertical.

73. Police Dog-handler.

1973. 50th Anniversary of Interpol.

338. **73.** 40 c. yell., blue & black 40 10
339. – 70 c. grn., yell. & blk. 70 15
340. – 1 s. 50 vio., yell. & blk. 1·25 90
341. – 2 s. 50 grn., orge. & blk. 3·50 4·50
342. – 2 s. 50 grn., orge. & blk. 3·50 4·50

Designs: 70 c. East African policemen. 1 s. 50, Interpol emblem. 2 s. 50 (2), Interpol H.Q. No. 341 is inscribed "St. Clans" and No. 342 "St. Cloud".

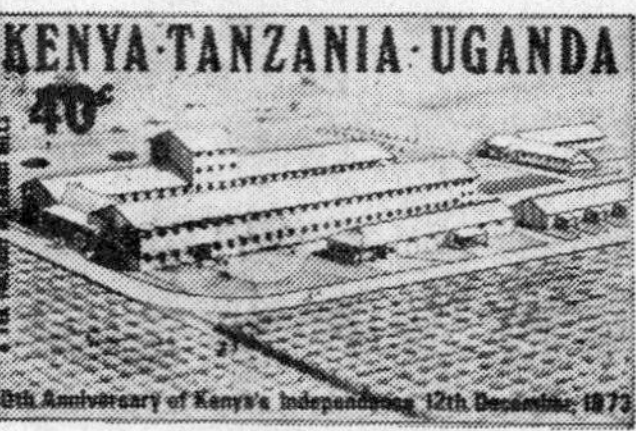

74. Tea Factory.

1973. 10th Anniv. of Kenya's Independence. Multicoloured.

343. 40 c. Type **74** 10 10
344. 70 c. Kenyatta Hospital .. 10 10
345. 1 s. 50 Nairobi Airport .. 20 15
346. 2 s. 50 Kindaruma hydro-electric scheme .. .. 50 1·25

75. Party H.Q.

1973. 10th Anniv. of Zanzibar's Revolution. Multicoloured.

347. 40 c. Type **75** 10 10
348. 70 c. Housing scheme .. 10 10
349. 1 s. 50 Colour T.V. .. 30 20
350. 2 s. 50 Amaan Stadium .. 65 1·50

76. " Symbol of Union ".

1974. 10th Anniv. of Tanganyika-Zanzibar Union. Multicoloured.

351. 40 c. Type **76** 10 10
352. 70 c. Handclasp and map 20 10
353. 1 s. 50 "Communications" 45 25
354. 2 s. 50 Flags of Tanu, Tanzania & Afro-Shirazi Party .. .. .. 95 1·25

77. East African Family (" Stability of the Home ").

1974. 17th Social Welfare Conf., Nairobi.

355. **77.** 40 c. yell., brn. & blk. 10 10
356. – 70 c. multicoloured .. 10 10
357. – 1 s. 50 yell., grn. & blk. 20 30
358. – 2 s. 50 red, vio. & blk. 45 1·50

Designs: 70 c. Dawn and Drummer (U.N. Second Development Plan). 1 s. 50, Agricultural scene (Rural Development Plan). 2 s. 50, Transport and Telephone ("Communications").

MORE DETAILED LISTS are given in the Stanley Gibbons Catalogues referred to in the country headings. For lists of current volumes see Introduction.

78. New Postal H.Q., Kampala.

1974. Centenary of U.P.U. Multicoloured.

359. 40 c. Type **78** 10 10
360. 70 c. Mail-train and post-van 15 10
361. 1 s. 50 U.P.U. Building, Berne 15 15
362. 2 s. 50 Loading mail into "VC-10" 30 80

79. Family-planning Clinic.

1974. World Population Year.

363. **79.** 40 c. multicoloured .. 10 10
364. – 70 c. mauve and red .. 10 10
365. – 1 s. 50 multicoloured .. 15 15
366. – 2 s. 50 blue, emerald and green 30 90

Designs: 70 c. "Tug of War". 1 s. 50, Population "scales". 2 s. 50, W.P.Y. emblem.

80. Seronera Wild-life Lodge, Tanzania.

1975. East African Game Lodges. Mult.

367. 40 c. Type **80** 15 10
368. 70 c. Mweya Safari Lodge, Uganda 20 10
369. 1 s. 50 "Ark"—Aberdare Forest Lodge, Kenya .. 35 30
370. 2 s. 50 Paraa Safari Lodge, Uganda .. .. .. 80 2·00

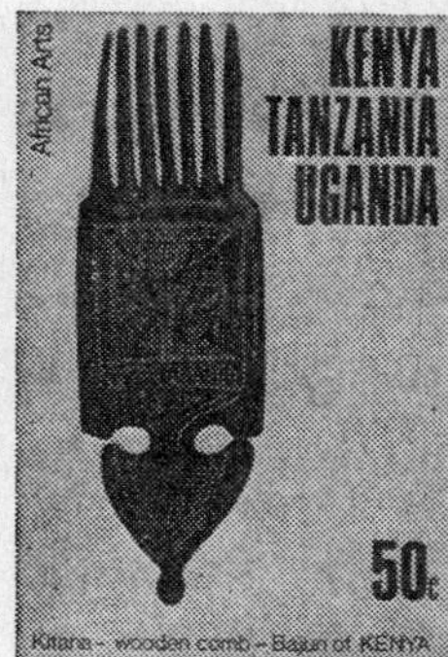

81. Kitana (wooden comb), Bajun of Kenya.

1975. African Arts. Multicoloured.

371. 50 c. Type **81** 10 10
372. 1 s. Earring, Chaga of Tanzania 15 10
373. 2 s. Okoco (armlet), Acholi of Uganda 30 35
374. 3 s. Kitete, Kamba gourd, Kenya 70 85

82. International Airport, Entebbe.

1975. O.A.U. Summit Conference, Kampala, Multicoloured.

375. 50 c. Type **82** 10 10
376. 1 s. Map of Africa and flag (vert.) 10 10
377. 2 s. Nile Hotel, Kampala 25 65
378. 3 s. Martyrs' Shrine Namugongo (vert.) .. .. 35 1·25

83. Ahmed (" Presidential " Elephant).

1975. Rare Animals. Multicoloured.

379. 50 c. Type **83** 40 10
380. 1 s. Albino buffalo .. 40 10
381. 2 s. Ahmed in grounds of National Museum .. 1·25 1·50
382. 3 s. Abbott's Duiker .. 1·25 2·25

84. Maasai Manyatta Village, Kenya.

1975. 2nd World Black and African Festival of Arts and Culture, Nigeria (1977). Mult.

383. 50 c. Type **84** 15 10
384. 1 s. "Heartbeat of Africa" (Ugandan Dancers) .. 15 10
385. 2 s. Makonde sculpture, Tanzania .. 45 65
386. 3 s. "Early Man and Technology" (Skinning animal) .. .. .. 75 1·10

85. Fokker " Friendship " at Nairobi Airport.

1975. 30th Anniv. of East African Airways. Multicoloured.

387. 50 c. Type **85** 55 20
388. 1 s. "DC9" at Kilimanjaro Airport 65 20
389. 2 s. Super "VC 10" at Entebbe Airport .. 2·00 2·00
390. 3 s. East African Airways Crest .. .. 2·50 2·50

Further commenorative sets were released during 1976–78 using common designs, but each inscribed for one republic only. See Kenya, Tanzania and Uganda.

Co-operation between the postal services of the three member countries virtually ceased after 30 June 1977. The postal services of Kenya, Tanzania and Uganda then operated independently.

OFFICIAL STAMPS

For use on official correspondence of the Tanganyika Government only.

1959. Stamps of 1954 optd. **OFFICIAL.**

O 1. **18.** 5 c. black and brown 10 10
O 2. – 10 c. red 10 10
O 3. – 15 c. black and blue 10 10
O 4. – 20 c. blk. & orge. .. 10 10
O 5. **18.** 30 c. black and blue 10 10
O 6. – 50 c. purple 10 10
O 7. – 1 s. black and red .. 15 10
O 8. – 1 s. 30 orge. & lilac .. 65 30
O 9. – 2 s. black and green 85 50
O 10. – 5 s. black and orange 2·00 1·25
O 11. **20.** 10 s. black and blue 2·00 2·50
O 12. **21.** £1 red and black .. 6·00 10·00

1960. Stamps of 1960 optd. **OFFICIAL.**

O 13. **26.** 5 c. blue 10 15
O 14. – 10 c. green 10 10
O 15. – 15 c. purple 10 15
O 16. – 20 c. mauve 10 10
O 17. – 30 c. red 10 10
O 18. – 50 c. violet 30 15
O 19. **28.** 1 s. violet and purple 30 10
O 20. – 5 s. red and purple .. 4·00 65

POSTAGE DUE STAMPS

D 1. D 2.

1923.

D1. **D1.** 5 c. violet .. .. 1·00 25
D2. 10 c. red .. .. 1·25 15
D3. 20 c. green .. .. 1·25 2·50
D4. 30 c. brown .. .. 7·50 7·50
D5. 40 c. blue .. .. 4·75 11·00
D6. 1 s. green .. .. 32·00 48·00

1935.

D 7. **D2.** 5 c. violet .. .. 1·25 40
D 8. 10 c. red 30 10
D 9. 20 c. green 40 15
D 10. 30 c. brown 60 50
D 11. 40 c. blue .. .. 1·50 3·00
D 12. 1 s. grey .. .. 10·00 17·00

KING EDWARD VII LAND

Stamps issued in connection with the Shackleton Antarctic Expedition in 1908. The expedition landed at Cape Royds in Victoria Land, instead of King Edward VII Land the intended destination.

1908. Stamp of New Zealand optd. **KING EDWARD VII LAND.**

A1 **40** 1d. red .. .. .. £400 35·00

KIRIBATI

The group of islands in the Pacific, formerly known as the Gilbert Islands achieved independence on 12th July, 1979, and was renamed Kiribati.

100 cents = $1 (Australian).

15. National Flag.

1979. Independence. Multicoloured.

84. 10 c. Type **15** 10 20
85. 45 c. Houses of Parliament and Maneaba ni Maungatabu (Houses of Assembly) 30 50

16. M.V. " Teraaka " (training ship).

1979. Multicoloured.

86 1 c. Type **16** 10 10
87 3 c. M.V. "Tautunu" (inter-island freighter) .. 10 10
88 5 c. Hibiscus 10 10
89 7 c. Catholic Cathedral, Tarawa 10 10
90 10 c. Maneaba, Bikenibeu 10 10
91 12 c. Betio Harbour .. 15 15
92 15 c. Eastern reef heron .. 35 20
93 20 c. Flamboyant tree .. 20 20
129 25 c. Moorish idol (fish) .. 25 30
95 30 c. Frangipani 25 25
96 35 c. G.I.P.C. Chapel, Tangintebu 25 25
97 50 c. "Hypolimnas bolina" (butterfly) 75 55
98 $1 "Tabakea" (Tarawa Lagoon ferry) 70 75
99 $2 Evening scene .. .. 80 1·00
135 $5 National flag .. .. 2·50 5·50

17. Gilbert and Ellice Islands 1911 ½d. Stamp.

1979. Death Centenary of Sir Rowland Hill. Multicoloured.

100. 10 c. Type **17** 10 10
101. 20 c. Gilbert & Ellice Islands 1956 2s. 6d. definitive .. 15 20
102. 25 c. G.B. Edward VII 2s. 6d. 15 20
103. 45 c. Gilbert and Ellice Islands 1924 10s. .. 25 35

18. Boy with Clam Shell.

1979. Int. Year of the Child. Multicoloured.

105. 10 c. Type **18** 10 10
106. 20 c. Child climbing coconut palm (horiz.) 10 10
107. 45 c. Girl reading .. 15 20
108. $1 Child in traditional costume 30 50

19. Downrange Station, Christmas Island.

1980. Satellite Tracking. Multicoloured.

109. 25 c. Type **19** 10 10
110. 45 c. Map showing satellite trajectory 15 15
111. $1 Rocket launch, Tanegashima, Japan (vert.) 30 35

20. T.S. " Teraaka ".

1980. " London 1980 " International Stamp Exhibition. Multicoloured.

112. 12 c. Type **20** 10 10
113. 25 c. Loading Air Tungaru aeroplane, Bonriki Airport 10 10
114. 30 c. Radio operator .. 15 10
115. $1 Bairiki Post Office .. 30 35

21. " Achaea janata ".

1980. Moths. Multicoloured.

117. 12 c. Type **21** 15 10
118. 25 c. " Ethmia nigroapicella " 20 15
119. 30 c. " Utetheisa pulchelloides " 20 15
120. 50 c. " Anua coronata " .. 25 25

22. Captain Cook Hotel.

1980. Development. Multicoloured.

136. 10 c. Type **22** 10 10
137. 20 c. Sports stadium .. 10 10
138. 25 c. International Airport, Bonriki 15 10
139. 35 c. National Library and Archives 15 10
140. $1 Otintai Hotel .. 30 40

23. " Acalypha godseffiana ".

1981. Flowers. Multicoloured.

141. 12 c. Type **23** 10 10
142. 30 c. " Hibiscus schizopetalus " 15 15
143. 35 c. " Calotropis gigantea " 15 15
144. 50 c. " Euphorbia pulcherrima " 20 20

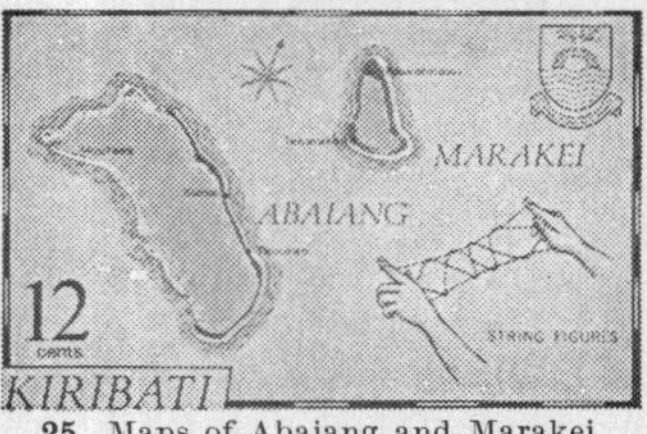

25. Maps of Abaiang and Marakei, and String Figures.

1981. Islands (1st series). Multicoloured.

145. 12 c. Type **25** 15 10
146. 30 c. Maps of Little Makin and Butaritari, and village house 25 10
147. 35 c. Map of Maiana, and Coral Road 30 15
148. $1 Map of Christmas Island, and Captain Cook's H.M.S. "Resolution" 90 75

See also Nos. 201/4, 215/18, 237/40, 256/60 and 270/3.

26. " Katherine ".

27. Prince Charles and Lady Diana Spencer. (Illustration reduced. Actual size 80 × 25 mm).

1981. Royal Wedding. Royal Yachts. Multicoloured.

149. 12 c. Type **26** 15 15
150. 12 c. Type **27** 30 30
151. 50 c. " Osborne " 45 45
157. 50 c. Type **27** 75 75
153. $2 " Britannia " .. .. 75 1·00
154. $2 Type **27** .. .. 2·00 3·00

28. Tuna Bait Breeding Centre, Bonriki Fish Farm.

1981. Tuna Fishing Industry. Multicoloured.

158. 12 c. Type **28** 15 10
159. 30 c. Tuna fishing .. 25 20
160. 35 c. Cold storage, Betio .. 25 25
161. 50 c. Government Tuna Fishing Vessel " Nei Manganibuka " .. 50 50

29. Pomarine Skua.

1982. Birds. Multicoloured.

163. 1 c. Type **29** 15 15
164. 2 c. Mallard 15 15
165. 4 c. White-winged petrel .. 20 20
166. 5 c. Blue-faced booby .. 20 20
167. 7 c. Friendly quail dove .. 20 20
168. 8 c. Common shoveller .. 20 20
169. 12 c. Polynesian reed warbler 20 20
170. 15 c. American golden plover 25 25
171. 20 c. Eastern reef heron .. 30 30
171a. 25 c. Brown noddy .. 1·50 1·00
172. 30 c. Brown booby .. 30 30
173. 35 c. Audubon's shearwater 30 35
174. 40 c. White-throated storm petrel (vert.) .. 35 40
175. 50 c. Bristle-thighed curlew (vert.) 40 45
175a. 55 c. White tern (vert.) .. 4·00 4·00
176. $1 Kuhl's lory (vert.) .. 85 90
177. $2 Long-tailed koel (vert.) .. .. .. 1·60 1·75
178. $5 Great frigate bird (vert.) .. .. .. 4·25 4·50

30. De Havilland " DH114 (Heron) ".

1982. Air. Inauguration of Tungaru Airline. Multicoloured.

179. 12 c. Type **30** 10 10
180. 30 c. Britten-Norman " Trislander " 20 20
181. 35 c. Casa " 212 (Aviocar) " 25 25
182. 50 c. Boeing " 727 " .. 35 35

31. Mary of Teck, Princess of Wales, 1893.

1982. 21st Birthday of Princess of Wales. Multicoloured.

183. 12 c. Type **31** 10 10
184. 50 c. Coat of arms of Mary of Teck 30 30
185. $1 Diana, Princess of Wales 50 50

1982. Birth of Prince William of Wales. Nos. 183/5 optd. **ROYAL BABY.**

186. 12 c. Type **31** 15 15
187. 50 c. Coat of arms of Mary of Teck 35 35
188. $1 Diana, Princess of Wales 55 55

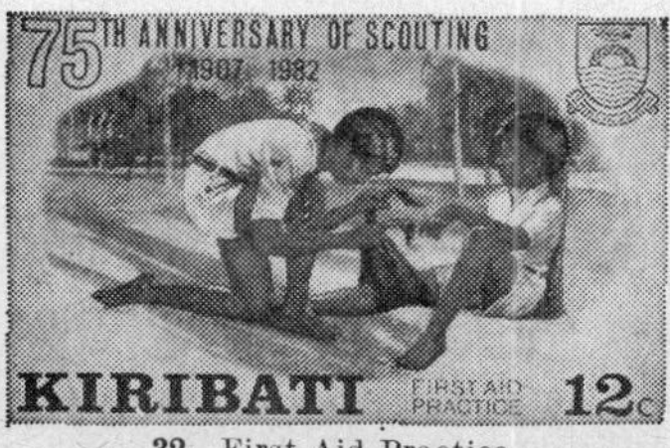

32. First Aid Practice.

1982. 75th Anniv. of Boy Scout Movement. Multicoloured.

189. 12 c. Type **32** 15 15
190. 25 c. Boat Repairs 30 30
191. 30 c. On parade 35 35
192. 40 c. Gilbert Islands 1977 8 c. Scouting stamp and " 75 " 60 60

33. Queen and Duke of Edinburgh with Local Dancer.

1982. Royal Visit. Multicoloured.

193. 12 c. Type **33** 15 15
194. 25 c. Queen, Duke of Edinburgh and outrigger canoe 20 20
195. 35 c. New Philatelic Bureau building 30 30

34. "Obaia, The Feathered" (Kiribati legend).

1983. Commonwealth Day. Multicoloured.

197. 12 c. Type **34** 15 10
198. 30 c. Robert Louis Stevenson Hotel, Abemama .. 20 20
199. 50 c. Container ship off Betio 25 25
200. $1 Map of Kiribati .. 45 65

1983. Island Maps (2nd series). As T **25**. Multicoloured.

201. 12 c. Beru, Nikunau & canoe 20 20
202. 25 c. Abemama, Aranuka, Kuria and fish 30 30
203. 35 c. Nonouti & reef fishing (vert.) 40 40
204. 50 c. Tarawa and House of Assembly (vert.) .. 60 55

35. Collecting Coconuts.

1983. Copra Industry. Multicoloured.

205. 12 c. Type **35** 25 20
206. 25 c. Selecting coconuts for copra 45 35
207. 30 c. Removing husks .. 50 40
208. 35 c. Drying copra .. 55 45
209. 50 c. Loading copra at Betio 65 55

36. War Memorials.

1983. 40th Anniv. of Battle of Tarawa. Multicoloured.

210. 12 c. Type **36** 20 20
211. 30 c. Maps of Tarawa and Pacific Ocean 45 40
212. 35 c. Gun emplacement .. 50 45
213. 50 c. Modern and war-time landscapes 75 65
214. $1 Aircraft carrier U.S.S. " Tarawa " .. .. 1·25 1·10

1983. Island Maps (3rd series). As T **25**. Multicoloured.

215. 12 c. Teraina and Captain Fenning's ship " Betsey " 1798 .. .. .. 40 15
216. 30 c. Nikumaroro & Hawksbill Turtle 70 35
217. 35 c. Kanton & local postmark 80 40
218. 50 c. Banaba & Flying Fish 1·10 55

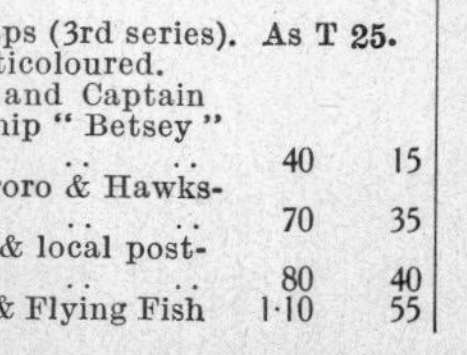

37. Tug " Riki ".

1984. Kiribati Shipping Corporation. Mult.

219. 12 c. Type **37** 25 15
220. 35 c. Ferry " Nei Nimanoa " 45 35
221. 50 c. Ferry " Nei Tebaa " 75 60
222. $1 Cargo ship " Nei Momi " 1·25 1·10

38. Water and Sewage Schemes.

1984. "Ausipex" International Stamp Exhibition, Melbourne. Multicoloured.

224. 12 c. Type **38** 25 15
225. 30 c. "Nouamake", (game fishing boat) 50 30
226. 35 c. Overseas training schemes 60 40
227. 50 c. International communications link .. 75 55

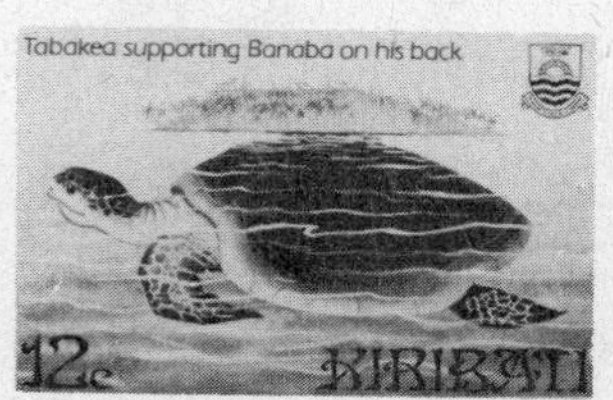

39. "Tabakea supporting Banaba".

1984. Kiribati Legends (1st series). Mult.

228. 12 c. Type **39** 20 20
229. 30 c. "Nakaa, Judge of the Dead" 35 35
230. 35 c. "Naareau and Dragonfly" 45 45
231. 50 c. "Whistling Ghosts" 55 55

See also Nos. 245/8.

40. Tang.

1985. Reef Fishes. Multicoloured.

232. 12 c. Type **40** 60 25
233. 25 c. White-barred Triggerfish .. .. .. 1·00 55
234. 35 c. Surgeon Fish .. 1·25 70
235. 80 c. Squirrel Fish .. 2·00 1·75

1985. Island Maps (4th series). As T **25**. Multicoloured.

237. 12 c. Tabuaeran and Great frigate bird .. 55 15
238. 35 c. Rawaki and germinating coconuts .. 85 40
239. 50 c. Arorae and xanthid crab .. .. .. 1·10 55
240. $1 Tamana and fish hook 1·75 1·00

41. Youths playing Football on Beach.

1985. International Youth Year. Mult.

241. 15 c. Type **41** 60 35
242. 35 c. Logos of I.Y.Y. and Kiribati Youth Year .. 1·00 90
243. 40 c. Girl preparing food (vert.) .. .. .. 1·10 1·00
244. 55 c. Map illustrating Kiribati's youth exchange links .. .. 1·40 1·40

1985. Kiribati Legends (2nd series). As T **39**. Multicoloured.

245. 15 c. "Nang Kineia and the Tickling Ghosts" .. 50 30
246. 35 c. "Auriaria and Tituabine" 85 75
247. 40 c. "The first coming of Babai at Arorae" .. 1·00 1·00
248. 55 c. "Riiki and the Milky Way" .. .. .. 1·25 1·50

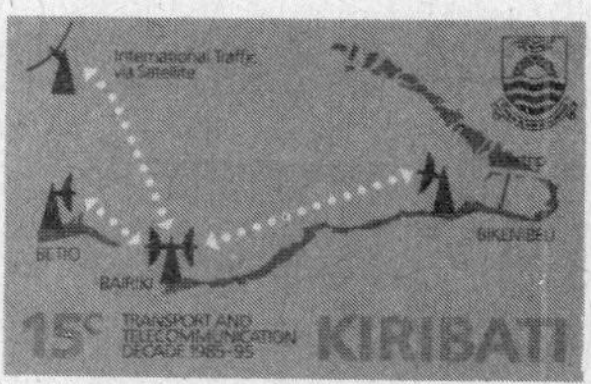

42. Map showing Telecommunications Satellite Link.

1985. Transport and Telecommunications Decade (1st issue). Multicoloured.

249. 15 c. Type **42** 70 55
250. 40 c. M.V. "Moanaraoi" (Tarawa–Suva service) 1·40 1·50

See also Nos. 268/9, 293/4 and 314/15.

1986. 60th Birthday of Queen Elizabeth II. As T **110** of Ascension. Multicoloured.

251. 15 c. Princess Elizabeth in Girl Guide uniform, Windsor Castle, 1938 .. 15 15
252. 35 c. At Trooping the Colour, 1980 .. .. 30 35
253. 40 c. With Duke of Edinburgh in Kiribati, 1982 .. .. .. 35 40
254. 55 c. At banquet, Austrian Embassy, London, 1966 50 60
255. $1 At Crown Agents Head Office, London, 1983 .. 90 1·25

1986. Island Maps (5th series). As T **25**. Multicoloured.

256. 15 c. Manra and Coconut Crab 70 35
257. 30 c. Birnie and McKean Islands and cowrie shells 1·25 80
258. 35 c. Orana and red-footed booby .. .. 1·40 1·00
259. 40 c. Malden Island and whaling ship, 1844 .. 1·50 1·50
260. 55 c. Vostok, Flint and Caroline Islands and "Vostok", 1820 .. .. 1·75 2·00

43. "Lepidodactylus lugubris".

1986. Geckos. Multicoloured.

261. 15 c. Type **43** 75 35
262. 35 c. "Gehyra mutilata" .. 1·25 90
263. 40 c. "Hemidactylus frenatus" .. .. 1·40 1·25
264. 55 c. "Gehyra oceanica" .. 1·90 2·00

See also Nos. 274/7.

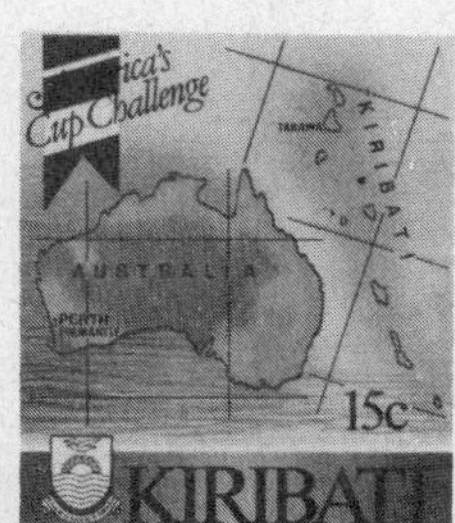

44. Maps of Australia and Kiribati.

1986. America's Cup Yachting Championship. Multicoloured.
265. 15 c. Type **44** 20 30
266. 55 c. America's Cup and map of course 50 75
267. $1·50 "Australia II" (1983 winner) .. .. .. 1·25 1·50

45. Freighter "Moamoa".

1987. Transport and Telecommunications Decade (2nd issue). Multicoloured.
268. 30 c. Type **45** .. .. 1·00 1·00
269. 55 c. Telephone switch-board and automatic exchange .. .. 1·75 1·75

1987. Island Maps (6th series). As T **25**. Multicoloured.
270. 15 c. Starbuck and red-tailed tropic bird .. 40 25
271. 30 c. Enderbury and white tern 60 45
272. 55 c. Tabiteuea and pandanus tree 85 70
273. $1 Onotoa and okai (house) 1·50 1·50

1987. Skinks. As T **43**. Multicoloured.
274. 15 c. "Emoia nigra" .. 30 25
275. 35 c. "Cryptoblepharus sp." 55 45
276. 40 c. "Emoia cyanura" .. 60 50
277. $1 "Lipinia noctua" .. 1·40 1·40

1987. Royal Ruby Wedding. Nos. 251/5 optd. **40TH WEDDING ANNIVERSARY.**
279. 15 c. Princess Elizabeth in Girl Guide uniform, Windsor Castle, 1938 .. 15 15
280. 35 c. At Trooping the Colour, 1980 .. .. 30 35
281. 40 c. With Duke of Edinburgh in Kiribati, 1982 .. .. .. 35 45
282. 55 c. At banquet, Austrian Embassy, London, 1966 50 60
283. $1 At Crown Agents Head Office, London, 1983 .. 90 1·25

46 Henri Dunant (founder)

1988. 125th Anniv of International Red Cross. Multicoloured.
284 15 c. Type **46** 25 20
285 35 c. Red Cross workers in Independence parade, 1979 .. .. .. 45 45
286 40 c. Red Cross workers with patient 55 55
287 55 c. Gilbert & Ellice Islands 1970 British Red Cross Cent 10 c. stamp 65 70

47 Causeway built by Australia

1988. Bicentenary of Australian Settlement and "Sydpex '88" National Stamp Exhibition, Sydney. Multicoloured.
288 15 c. Type **47** 25 20
289 35 c. Capt. Cook and Pacific map 60 50
290 $1 Obverse of Australian $10 Bicent banknote .. 1·25 1·25
291 $1 Reverse of $10 Bicentenary banknote 2·50 2·50

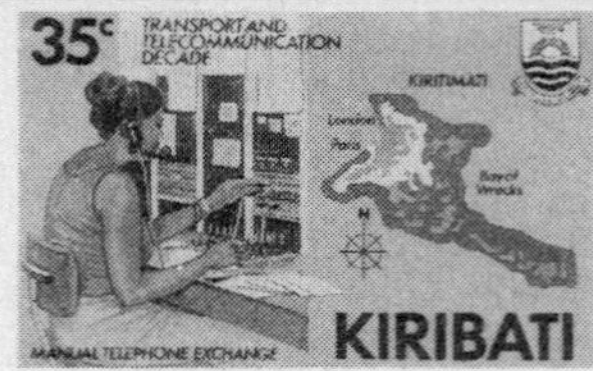

48 Manual Telephone Exchange and Map of Kiritimati

1988. Transport and Communications Decade (3rd issue). Multicoloured.
293 35 c. Type **48** 50 50
294 45 c. Betio–Bairiki Causeway 60 60

49 "Hound" (brigantine), 1835

1989. Nautical History (1st series). Mult.
295 15 c. Type **49** 55 30
296 30 c. "Phantom" (brig), 1854 .. .. .. 80 60
297 40 c. H.M.S."Alacrity" (schooner), 1873 .. 90 80
298 $1 "Charles W. Morgan" (whaling ship), 1851 .. 2·00 2·00
See also Nos. 343/7.

50 Eastern Reef Heron

1989. Birds with Young. Multicoloured.
299 15 c. Type **50** 35 35
300 15 c. Eastern reef heron chicks in nest 35 35
301 $1 White-tailed tropic bird 1·50 1·75
302 $1 Young white-tailed tropic bird .. .. 1·50 1·75
Nos. 299/300 and 301/2 were each printed together, se-tenant, each pair forming a composite design.

51 House of Assembly

1989. 10th Anniv of Independence. Mult.
303 15 c. Type **51** 25 25
304 $1 Constitution .. .. 1·25 1·25

1989. 20th Anniv of First Manned Landing on Moon. As T **126** of Ascension. Multicoloured.
305 20 c. "Apollo 10" on launch gantry 30 30
306 50 c. Crew of "Apollo 10" (30 × 30 mm) 70 70
307 60 c. "Apollo 10" emblem (30 × 30 mm) 80 80
308 75 c. "Apollo 10" splashdown, Hawaii .. 95 95

1989. "Philexfrance 89" International Stamp Exhibition, Paris, and "World Stamp Expo '89", Washington. As T **127** of Ascension showing Statue of Liberty. Multicoloured.
311 35 c. Examining fragment of Statue 45 55
312 35 c. Workman drilling Statue 45 55
313 35 c. Surveyor with drawing 45 55

52 Telecommunications Centre

1989. Transport and Communications Decade (4th issue). Multicoloured.
314 30 c. Type **52** 75 75
315 75 c. "Mataburo" (inter-island freighter) .. 1·50 1·50

1989. "Melbourne Stampshow '89". Nos. 301/2 optd with Exhibition emblem showing tram.
316 $1 White-tailed tropic bird 1·50 1·75
317 $1 Young white-tailed tropic bird .. .. 1·50 1·75

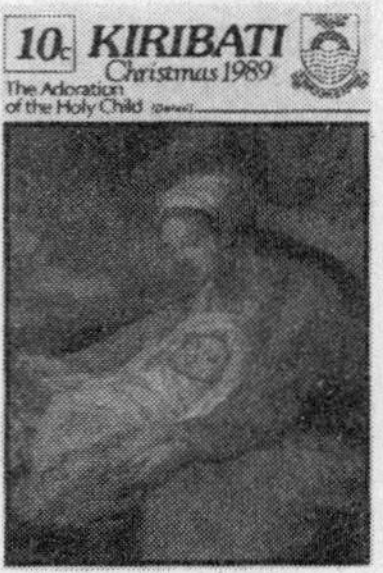

54 Virgin and Child (detail, "The Adoration of the Holy Child" (Denys Calvert))

1989. Christmas. Paintings. Multicoloured.
318 10 c. Type **54** 20 15
319 15 c. "The Adoration of the Holy Child" (Denys Calvert) 30 25
320 55 c. "The Holy Family and St. Elizabeth" (Rubens) 85 70
321 $1 "Madonna with Child and Maria Magdalena" (School of Correggio) .. 1·75 2·00

55 Gilbert and Ellice Islands 1912 1d. and G.B. Twopence Blue Stamps.

1990. 150th Anniv of the Penny Black and "Stamp World London 90" International Stamp Exhibition. Multicoloured.
322 15 c. Type **55** 30 20
323 50 c. Gilbert and Ellice Islands 1911 ½d. and G.B. Penny Black .. 75 65
324 60 c. Kiribati 1982 1 c. bird and G.B. 1870 ½d. .. 85 85
325 $1 Gilbert Islands 1976 1 c. ship and G.B. 1841 1d. brown .. .. .. 1·40 1·60

56 Blue-barred Orange Parrotfish

1990. Fishes. Mulricoloured.
326 1 c. Type **56** 10 10
327 5 c. Honycomb rock cod .. 10 10
328 10 c. Blue-fin jack 10 15
329 15 c. Paddle tail snapper .. 15 20
330 20 c. Variegated emperor .. 20 25
356 23 c. Bennett's pufferfish .. 20 25
331 25 c. Rainbow runner .. 25 30
332 30 c. Black-saddled coral trout 25 30
333 35 c. Great barracuda .. 30 35
334 40 c. Convict surgeonfish .. 35 40
335 50 c. Violet squirrelfish .. 45 50
336 60 c. Freckled hawkfish .. 55 60
337 75 c. Pennant coralfish .. 70 75
338 $1 Yellow and blue sea perch 90 95
339 $2 Pacific sailfish .. 1·90 2·00
340 $5 Whitetip reef shark .. 4·50 4·75

1990. 90th Birthday of Queen Elizabeth the Queen Mother. As T **134** of Ascension.
341 75 c. multicoloured .. 1·00 75
342 $2 black and green .. 2·25 2·50
DESIGNS—21 × 36 mm. 75 c. Queen Elizabeth the Queen Mother. 29 × 37 mm. $2 King George VI and Queen Elizabeth with air raid victim, London, 1940.

1990. Nautical History (2nd series). As T **49**. Multicoloured.
343 15 c. "Herald" (whaling ship), 1851 .. .. 25 20
344 50 c. "Belle" (barque), 1849 60 60
345 60 c. "Supply" (schooner), 1851 .. .. .. 70 70
346 75 c. "Triton" (whaling ship), 1848 .. .. 90 90

57 Manta Ray

1991. Endangered Fishes. Multicoloured.
348 15 c. Type **57** 30 20
349 20 c. Manta ray (different) 30 25
350 30 c. Whale shark .. 50 60
351 35 c. Whale shark (different) 50 60

1991. 65th Birthday of Queen Elizabeth II and 70th Birthday of Prince Philip. As T **139** of Ascension. Multicoloured.
366 65 c. Queen Elizabeth II .. 1·00 1·00
367 70 c. Prince Philip in R.A.F. uniform .. 1·00 1·00

59 Aerial View of Hospital

1991. "Philanippon '91" International Stamp Exhibition, Tokyo, and Opening of Tungaru Central Hospital. Multicoloured.
368 23 c. Type **59** 30 30
369 50 c. Traditional dancers 60 60
370 60 c. Hospital entrance .. 70 70
371 75 c. Foundation stone and plaques 95 95

60 Mother and Child

1991. Christmas. Multicoloured.
373 23 c. Type **60** 30 30
374 50 c. The Holy Family in Pacific setting .. 65 65
375 60 c. The Holy Family in traditional setting .. 75 75
376 75 c. Adoration of the Shepherds .. .. 1·00 1·00

1992. 40th Anniv of Quenn Elizabeth II's Accession. As T **143** of Ascension. Mult.
377 23 c. Kiribati village .. 20 25
378 30 c. Lagoon at sunset .. 30 35
379 50 c. Tarawa waterfront .. 45 50
380 60 c. Three portraits of Queen Elizabeth .. 55 60
381 75 c. Queen Elizabeth II .. 70 75

1992. "EXPO '92" Worlds Fair, Seville. Nos. 356, 336/7 and 339 optd **EXPO '92 SEVILLA**.

382	23 c. Bennett's pufferfish	20	25
383	60 c. Freckled hawkfish ..	55	60
384	75 c. Pennant coralfish ..	70	75
385	$2 Pacific sailfish ..	1·90	2·00

OFFICIAL STAMPS

1981. Nos. 86/135 optd **O.K.G.S.**

O 1	1 c. Type **16**	10	10
O 2	3 c. M.V. "Tautunu" (inter-island frighter) ..	10	10
O 3	5 c. Hibiscus	10	10
O 4	7 c. Catholic Cathedral, Tarawa	10	10
O 5	10 c. Maneaba, Bikenbeu	10	10
O 6	12 c. Betio Harbour ..	15	15
O 7	15 c. Eastern reef heron ..	15	20
O 8	20 c. Flamboyant tree ..	20	25
O 9	25 c. Moorish idol (fish) ..	25	30
O10	30 c. Frangipani	30	35
O11	35 c. G.I.P.C. Chapel, Tangintebu	35	40
O12	50 c. "Hypolimnas bolina" (butterfly)	50	55
O13	$1 "Tabakea" (Tarawa Lagoon ferry)	1·00	1·00
O14	$2 Evening scene ..	2·00	2·25
O15	$5 National flag	3·75	3·75

1983. Nos. 169, 172/3, 175 and 177 optd. **O.K.G.S.**

O 25.	12 c. Polynesian reed warbler	30	30
O 26.	30 c. Brown booby ..	50	50
O 27.	35 c. Audubon's shearwater	60	60
O 28.	50 c. Bristle-thighed curlew	80	80
O 29.	$2 Long-tailed koel ..	2·75	2·75

POSTAGE DUE STAMPS

D 1. Kiribati Coat of Arms.

1981.

D 1.	D 1.	1 c. black and mauve ..	10	10
D 2.		2 c. black and blue ..	10	10
D 3.		5 c. black and green ..	10	10
D 4.		10 c. black and brown	10	10
D 5.		20 c. black and blue ..	10	15
D 6.		30 c. black and brown	20	25
D 7.		40 c. black and purple	35	40
D 8.		50 c. black and green ..	45	50
D 9.		$1 black and red ..	90	95

KISHANGARH

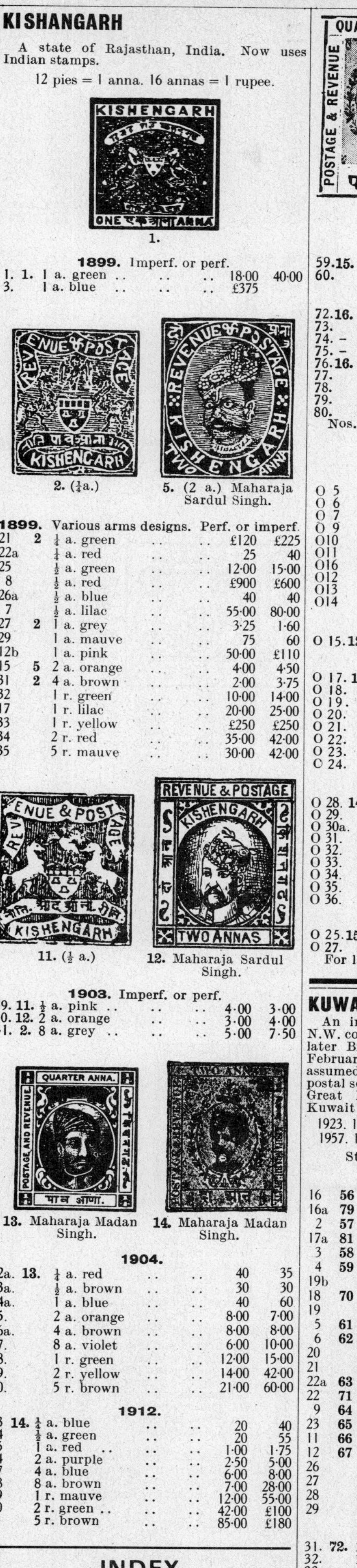

A state of Rajasthan, India. Now uses Indian stamps.

12 pies = 1 anna. 16 annas = 1 rupee.

1.

1899. Imperf. or perf.

1.	1.	1 a. green	18·00	40·00
3.		1 a. blue	£375	

2. (¼ a.)

5. (2 a.) Maharaja Sardul Singh.

1899. Various arms designs. Perf. or imperf.

21	2	¼ a. green	£120	£225
22a		¼ a. red	25	40
25		½ a. green	12·00	15·00
8		½ a. red	£900	£600
26a		½ a. blue	40	40
7		½ a. lilac	55·00	80·00
27	2	1 a. grey	3·25	1·60
29		1 a. mauve	75	60
12b		1 a. pink	50·00	£110
15	5	2 a. orange	4·00	4·50
31	2	4 a. brown	2·00	3·75
32		1 r. green	10·00	14·00
17		1 r. lilac	20·00	25·00
33		1 r. yellow	£250	£250
34		2 r. red	35·00	42·00
35		5 r. mauve	30·00	42·00

11. (½ a.)

12. Maharaja Sardul Singh.

1903. Imperf. or perf.

39.	11.	½ a. pink	4·00	3·00
40.	12.	2 a. orange	3·00	4·00
41.	2.	8 a. grey	5·00	7·50

13. Maharaja Madan Singh.

14. Maharaja Madan Singh.

1904.

42a.	13.	¼ a. red	40	35
43a.		½ a. brown	30	30
44a.		1 a. blue	40	60
45.		2 a. orange	8·00	7·00
46a.		4 a. brown	8·00	8·00
47.		8 a. violet	6·00	10·00
48.		1 r. green	12·00	15·00
49.		2 r. yellow	14·00	42·00
50.		5 r. brown	21·00	60·00

1912.

63	14.	¼ a. blue	20	40
64		½ a. green	20	55
65		1 a. red	1·00	1·75
54		2 a. purple	2·50	5·00
67		4 a. blue	6·00	8·00
68		8 a. brown	7·00	28·00
69		1 r. mauve	12·00	55·00
70		2 r. green	42·00	£100
71		5 r. brown	85·00	£180

INDEX

Countries can be quickly located by referring to the index at the end of this volume.

15.

16. Maharaja Yagyanarain Singhji.

1913.

59.	15.	¼ a. blue	20	30
60.		2 a. purple	7·00	16·00

1928.

72.	16.	¼ a. blue	35	1·40
73.		½ a. green	50	60
74.	–	1 a. red	60	1·00
75.	–	2 a. purple	3·00	6·50
76.	16.	4 a. brown	1·25	1·75
77.		8 a. violet	3·50	15·00
78.		1 r. green	7·50	30·00
79.		2 r yellow	22·00	65·00
80.		5 r. red	25·00	80·00

Nos. 74/5 are larger.

OFFICIAL STAMPS

1918. Optd. **ON K S D.**

O 5	2.	¼ a. green	—	85·00
O 6		¼ a. pink	1·50	60
O 7		½ a. blue	—	28·00
O 9		1 a. mauve	14·00	1·50
O10	5.	2 a. orange	—	90·00
O11	2.	4 a. brown	23·00	16·00
O16		8 a. grey	30·00	22·00
O12		1 r. green	80·00	75·00
O13		2 r. brown	—	£600
O14		5 r. mauve	—	£750

1918. Optd. **ON K S D.**

O 15.	12.	2 a. orange	25·00	7·00

1918. Optd. **ON K S D.**

O 17.	13.	¼ a. red	—	£100
O 18.		½ a. brown	65	35
O 19.		1 a. blue	7·00	4·00
O 20.		2 a. orange	—	£450
O 21.		4 a. brown	27·00	18·00
O 22.		8 a. violet	£140	£110
O 23.		1 r. green	£275	£250
O 24.		5 r. brown		

1918. Optd. **ON K S D.**

O 28.	14.	¼ a. blue	50	50
O 29.		½ a. green	75	75
O 30a.		1 a. red	1·00	1·00
O 31.		2 a. purple	5·50	4·00
O 32.		4 a. blue	20·00	15·00
O 33.		8 a. brown	65·00	40·00
O 34.		1 r. mauve	£180	£180
O 35.		2 r. green		
O 36.		5 r. brown	£750	

1918. Optd. **ON K S D.**

O 25.	15.	¼ a. blue	6·00	
O 27.		2 a. purple	£160	£170

For later issues see **RAJASTHAN.**

KUWAIT

An independent Arab Shaikhdom on the N.W. coast of the Persian Gulf with Indian and later British postal administration. On 1st February, 1959, the Kuwait Government assumed responsibility for running its own postal service. In special treaty relations with Great Britain until 19 June 1961 when Kuwait became completely independent.

1923. 12 pies = 1 anna; 16 annas = 1 rupee.
1957. 100 naye paise = 1 rupee.

Stamps of India optd. **KUWAIT.**

1923. King George V.

16	**56**	½ a. green	1·00	1·25
16a	**79**	½ a. green	4·50	60
2	**57**	1 a. brown	1·25	1·25
17a	**81**	1 a. brown	4·50	40
3	**58**	1½ a. brown (No. 163) ..	1·00	4·00
4	**59**	2 a. lilac	1·25	50
19b		2 a. red	2·75	1·60
18	**70**	2 a. lilac	1·25	40
19		2 a. red	23·00	60·00
5	**61**	2½ a. blue	1·75	7·50
6	**62**	3 a. orange	3·75	15·00
20		3 a. blue	2·75	1·25
21		3 a. red	5·50	4·00
22a	**63**	4 a. green	5·00	8·00
22	**71**	4 a. green	25·00	60·00
9	**64**	6 a. bistre	8·50	13·00
23	**65**	8 a. mauve	9·00	13·00
11	**66**	12 a. red	14·00	25·00
12	**67**	1 r. brown and green ..	14·00	11·00
26		2 r. red and orange ..	10·00	50·00
27		5 r. blue and violet ..	70·00	£180
28		10 r. green and red ..	£160	£350
29		15 r. blue and olive ..	£450	£700

1933. Air.

31.	**72.**	2 a. green	11·00	20·00
32.		3 a. blue	1·25	2·00
33.		4 a. olive	£100	£200
34.		6 a. bistre	1·25	4·00

1939. King George VI.

36.	**91.**	½ a. brown	6·00	75
38.		1 a. red	6·00	75
39.	**92.**	2 a. red	6·00	1·50
41.	–	3 a. green	4·75	1·25
43.	–	4 a. brown	21·00	8·00
44.	–	6 a. green	20·00	6·00
45.	–	8 a. violet	25·00	24·00
46.	–	12 a. red	32·00	24·00
47.	**93.**	1 r. slate and brown ..	3·75	1·90
48.		2 r. purple and brown ..	3·75	7·50
49.		5 r. green and blue ..	12·00	15·00
50.		10 r. purple and red ..	85·00	6000
51.		15 r. brown and green ..	£100	£140

1942. King George VI stamps of 1940.

52.	**100a.**	3 p. slate	70	1·25
53.		½ a. purple	70	1·00
54.		9 p. green	70	4·25
55.		1 a. red	70	70
56.	**101.**	1½ a. violet	70	3·00
57.		2 a. red	80	1·00
58.		3 a. violet	70	1·50
59.		3½ a. blue	2·50	2·00
60.	**102.**	4 a. brown	70	1·00
60a.		6 a. green	11·00	8·50
61.		8 a. violet	2·00	80
62.		12 a. purple	4·00	1·50
63.	–	14 a. purple (No. 277) ..	6·00	11·00

From 1948 onwards, for stamps with similar surcharges, but without name of country, see British Postal Agencies in Eastern Arabia.

Stamps of Great Britain surch. **KUWAIT** and new values in Indian currency.

1948. King George VI.

64.	**128.**	½ a. on ½d. pale green ..	10	30
84.		½ a. on ½d. orange ..	15	1·00
65.		1 a. on 1d. pale red ..	10	40
85.		1 a. on 1d. blue ..	15	50
66.		1½ a. on 1½d. pale brown	10	30
86.		1½ a. on 1½d. green ..	15	2·00
67.		2 a. on 2d. pale orange	10	30
87.		2 a. on 2d. brown ..	15	35
68.		2½ a. on 2½d. light blue	10	40
88.		2½ a. on 2½d. red ..	25	70
69.		3 a. on 3d. pale violet ..	10	10
89.	**129.**	4 a. on 4d. blue	20	25
70.		6 a. on 6d. purple ..	15	10
71.	**130.**	1 r. on 1s. brown ..	25	40
72.	**131.**	2 r. on 2s. 6d. green ..	70	2·00
73.		5 r. on 5s. red	1·50	4·00
73a.	–	10 r. on 10s. bright blue (No. 478a)	30·00	6·00

1948. Silver Wedding.

74.	**137.**	2½ a. on 2½d. blue ..	30	15
75.	**138.**	15 r. on £1 blue ..	30·00	27·00

1948. Olympic Games.

76.	**139.**	2½ a. on 2½d. blue ..	55	80
77.	**140.**	3 a. on 3d. violet ..	55	90
78.		6 a. on 5d. purple ..	80	1·25
79.	–	1 r. on 1s. brown ..	85	1·25

1949. U.P.U.

80.	**143.**	2½ a. on 2½d. blue ..	40	40
81.	**144.**	3 a. on 3d. violet ..	65	55
82.	–	6 a. on 6d. purple ..	80	55
83.	–	1 r. on 1s. brown ..	1·25	50

1951. Pictorial high values.

90.	**147.**	2 r. on 2s. 6d. green ..	11·00	4·25
91.	–	5 r. on 5s. red (No. 510)	14·00	5·00
92.	–	10 r. on 10s. blue No. 511)	26·00	5·50

1952. Queen Elizabeth II.

110	**154.**	½ a. on ½d. orange ..	10	10
94		1 a. on 1d. blue ..	15	10
95		1½ a. on 1½d. green ..	15	10
113		2 a. on 2d. brown ..	15	10
97	**155.**	2½ a. on 2½d. red ..	15	10
98		3 a. on 3d. lilac ..	40	10
99		4 a. on 4d. blue ..	1·25	45
100	**157.**	6 a. on 6d. purple ..	85	10
101	**160.**	12 a. on 1s. 3d. green ..	4·50	1·75
119		1 r. on 1s. 6d. blue ..	1·75	10

1953. Coronation.

103.	**161.**	2½ a. on 2½d. red ..	2·25	75
104.		4 a. on 4d. blue ..	3·00	80
105.	**163.**	12 a. on 1s. 3d. green ..	4·00	2·00
106.	–	1 r. on 1s. 6d. blue ..	4·00	80

1955. Pictorials.

107.	**166.**	2 r. on 2s. 6d. brown ..	5·00	1·00
108.	–	5 r. on 5s. red	7·00	3·25
109.	–	10 r. on 10s. blue ..	8·00	4·00

1957. Queen Elizabeth II.

120.	**157.**	1 n.p. on 5d. brown ..	10	40
121.	**154.**	3 n.p. on ½d. orange ..	30	65
122.		6 n.p. on 1d. blue ..	30	65
123.		9 n.p. on 1½d. green ..	30	40
124.		12 n.p. on 2d. pale brn.	30	50
125.	**155.**	15 n.p. on 2½d. red ..	30	10
126.		20 n.p. on 3d. lilac ..	30	10
127.		25 n.p. on 4d. blue ..	1·25	2·25
128.	**157.**	40 n.p. on 6d. purple ..	65	10
129.	**158.**	50 n.p. on 9d. olive ..	4·25	2·75
130.	**160.**	75 n.p. on 1s. 3d. green	4·25	3·25

For stamps issued by Kuwait government see volume 2.

OFFICIAL STAMPS

1923. Stamps of India (King George V) optd. **KUWAIT SERVICE.**

O 1	**56**	½ a. green	35	11·00
O 2	**57**	1 a. brown	40	6·00
O 3	**58**	1½ a. brown (No. 163)	1·00	16·00
O 4	**59**	2 a. lilac	3·00	14·00
O 17	**70**	2 a. lilac	45·00	£100
O 5	**61**	2½ a. blue	2·50	27·00
O 6	**62**	3 a. orange	3·25	40·00
O 19		3 a. blue	1·60	22·00
O 8	**63**	4 a. green	3·00	38·00
O 20	**71**	4 a. green	4·25	55·00
O 9	**65**	8 a. mauve	4·50	38·00
O 22	**66**	12 a. red	17·00	95·00
O 10	**67**	1 r. brown and green	10·00	65·00
O 11		2 r. red and orange ..	16·00	95·00
O 12		5 r. blue and violet ..	48·00	£225
O 13		10 r. green and red ..	90·00	£350
O 14		15 r. blue and olive ..	£150	£475

LABUAN

An island off the N. coast of Borneo, ceded to Great Britain in 1846, and a Crown Colony from 1902. Incorporated with Straits Settlements in 1906, it used Straits stamps till it became part of N. Borneo in 1946.

100 cents = 1 dollar.

1.

6 Cents (10.)   Two Cents (11.)

1879.
5 1 2 c. green .. 9·50 13·00
39 2 c. red .. 1·00 3·50
6 6 c. orange .. 60·00 70·00
40 6 c. green .. 5·00 4·50
7 8 c. red .. 65·00 75·00
41 8 c. violet .. 2·25 4·50
43 10 c. brown .. 3·75 7·00
9 12 c. red .. £160 £180
45 12 c. blue .. 3·25 6·00
4 16 c. blue .. 40·00 55·00
46 16 c. grey .. 3·25 6·00
21 40 c. orange .. 8·50 22·00

1880. Surch. in figures.
12 1. 6 on 16 c. blue .. £950 £550
11 8 on 12 c. red .. £550 £450

1881. Surch. **EIGHT CENTS.**
14. 1. 8 c. on 12 c. red .. £150 £180

1881. Surch. **Eight Cents.**
15. 1. 8 c. on 12 c. red .. 65·00 75·00

1883. Manuscript surch. **one Dollar A.S.H.**
22. 1. $1 on 16 c. blue .. £1900

1885. Surch. **2 CENTS** horiz.
23. 1. 2 c. on 8 c. red .. 65·00
24. 2 c. on 16 c. blue .. £650 £650

1885. Surch. **2 Cents** horiz.
25. 1. 2 c. on 16 c. blue .. 85·00 £100

1885. Surch. with large **2 Cents** diag.
26. 1. 2 c. on 8 c. red .. 38·00 50·00

1891. Surch. as **T 10.**
35. 1. 6 c. on 8 c. violet .. 4·50 4·50
37. 6 c. on 16 c. blue .. £1300 £1200
38. 6 c. on 40 c. orange .. £4000 £2500

1892. Surch. as **T 11.**
49. 1. 2 c. on 40 c. orange .. £100 75·00
50. 6 c. on 16 c. grey .. £180 £110

Most issues from 1894 exist cancelled-to-order with black bars. Our prices are for stamps postally used, cancelled-to-order examples being worth considerably less.

1894. Types of North Borneo (different colours) optd. **LABUAN.**
62 24 1 c. black and mauve .. 1·50 3·50
63 25 2 c. black and blue .. 2·50 4·00
64 26 3 c. black and yellow .. 2·75 6·00
65a 27 5 c. black and green .. 15·00 7·00
67 28 6 c. black and red .. 2·50 5·50
68 29 8 c. black and pink .. 9·00 15·00
70 30 12 c. black and orange .. 16·00 30·00
71 31 18 c. black and olive .. 22·00 32·00
73 32 24 c. blue and mauve .. 13·00 28·00
80 10 25 c. green .. 15·00 15·00
81 – 50 c. mauve (as No. 82) 15·00 16·00
82 – $1 blue (as No. 83) .. 30·00 22·00

1895. No. 83 of North Borneo surch. **LABUAN** and value in cents.
75. 4 c. on $1 red .. 1·00 1·25
76. 10 c. on $1 red .. 1·25 1·40
77. 20 c. on $1 red .. 11·00 6·00
78. 30 c. on $1 red .. 15·00 16·00
79. 40 c. on $1 red .. 10·00 10·00

1896. Jubilee of Cession of Labuan to Gt. Britain. Nos. 62 to 68 optd. **1846 JUBILEE 1896.**
83f 24 1 c. black and mauve .. 15·00 11·00
84 25 2 c. black and blue .. 16·00 12·00
85 26 3 c. black and yellow .. 18·00 20·00
86 27 5 c. black and green .. 30·00 16·00
87 28 6 c. black and red .. 14·00 17·00
88a 29 8 c. black and pink .. 19·00 11·00

1897. Stamps of North Borneo. Nos. 92 to 106 (different colours) optd. **LABUAN.**

Opt. at top of stamp.
89 1 c. black and brown .. 2·25 3·25
90 2 c. black and blue .. 5·50 3·00
91b 3 c. black and yellow .. 6·50 5·00
92a 5 c. black and green .. 20·00 24·00
93b 6 c. black and red .. 3·50 14·00
94a 8 c. black and pink .. 13·00 9·00
95a 12 c. black and orange .. 18·00 30·00

Overprint at foot of stamp.
98a. – 12 c. black and orange (as No. 106) .. 26·00 30·00

Opt. at foot. Inscr. "POSTAL REVENUE".
96b – 18 c. black and olive (as No. 108) .. 15·00 25·00

Opt. at foot. Inscr. "POSTAGE AND REVENUE".
99a. – 18 c. black and olive (as No. 110) .. 60·00 60·00

Opt. at top. Inscr. "POSTAGE AND REVENUE".
101b. – 18 c. black and olive (as No. 110) .. 22·00 32·00

Opt. at top. "POSTAGE AND REVENUE" omitted.
97. – 24 c. blue and lilac (as No. 109) .. 12·00 28·00

Opt. at top. Inscr. "POSTAGE AND REVENUE".
100. – 24 c. blue and mauve (No. 111) .. 15·00 38·00

1899. Stamps of Labuan surch **4 CENTS.**
102 4 c. on 5 c. blk & grn (92a) 18·00 26·00
103 4 c. on 6 c. blk & red (93b) 15·00 19·00
104a 4 c. on 8 c. black and pink (94a) .. 14·00 25·00
105 4 c. on 12 c. black and orange (98a) .. 20·00 27·00
106 4 c. on 18 c. black and olive (101b) .. 15·00 17·00
107 4 c. on 24 c. blue and mauve (100) .. 15·00 20·00
108 4 c. on 25 c. green (80) .. 5·50 7·50
109 4 c. on 50 c. purple (81) .. 5·50 7·50
110 4 c. on $1 blue (82) .. 5·50 7·50

1900. Stamps of North Borneo, as Nos. 95 to 107, optd **LABUAN.**
111 2 c. black and green .. 3·50 2·50
112 4 c. black and brown .. 4·25 13·00
113 4 c. black and red .. 7·00 2·75
114 5 c. black and blue .. 17·00 18·00
115 10 c. brown and grey .. 28·00 42·00
116 16 c. green and brown .. 38·00 45·00

18.

1902.
116d. 18. 1 c. black and purple 2·00 3·25
117. 2 c. black and green 2·00 2·50
117b. 3 c. black and brown 2·00 3·00
118. 4 c. black and red 2·00 2·50
119. 8 c. black and orange 1·50 3·75
120. 10 c. brown and blue 2·00 4·50
121. 12 c. black and yellow 2·50 5·00
122. 16 c. green and brown 2·00 6·50
123. 18 c. black and brown 2·00 6·00
124. 25 c. green and blue 2·00 7·50
125. 50 c. purple and lilac 8·50 17·00
126. $1 red and orange 3·00 19·00

1904. Surch **4 cents.**
127 – 4 c. on 5 c. black and green (92a) .. 18·00 26·00
128 – 4 c. on 6 c. black and red (93b) .. 12·00 25·00
129 – 4 c. on 8 c. black and pink (94a) .. 16·00 27·00
130 – 4 c. on 12 c. black and orange (98a) .. 19·00 27·00
131 – 4 c. on 18 c. black and olive (101b) .. 15·00 25·00
132 – 4 c. on 24 c. blue and mauve (100) .. 13·00 25·00
133 10 4 c. on 25 c. green (80) .. 8·50 18·00
134 4 c. on 50 c. purple (81) 8·50 18·00
135 4 c. on $1 blue (82) .. 8·50 18·00

POSTAGE DUE STAMPS

1901. Optd. **POSTAGE DUE.**
D 1. 2 c. black and green (111) 8·50 12·00
D 2. 3 c. black & yellow (91) .. 13·00 50·00
D 3. 4 c. black and red (113) .. 15·00 50·00
D 4. 5 c. black and blue (114) .. 20·00 50·00
D 5. 6 c. black and red (93b) .. 11·00 50·00
D 6. 8 c. black and pink (94a) 25·00 50·00
D 7. 12 c. black & orange (98a) 42·00 50·00
D 8. 18 c. black & olive (101b) 13·00 50·00
D 9. 24 c. blue & mauve (100) 22·00 50·00

LAGOS

A Br. Colony on the S. coast of Nigeria, united with Southern Nigeria in 1906 to form the Colony and Protectorate of Southern Nigeria. Now uses stamps of Nigeria.

12 pence = 1 shilling.
20 shillings = 1 pound.

1.

3.

1874.
21 1. ½d. green .. 50 20
17 1d. mauve .. 15·00 10·00
22 1d. red .. 60 25
11 2d. blue .. 35·00 11·00
23 2d. grey .. 35·00 5·00
19 3d. brown .. 10·00 5·00
5 4d. red .. 60·00 40·00
24 4d. lilac .. 65·00 8·50
25 6d. green .. 5·00 20·00
26 1s. orange .. 5·00 13·00
27 2s. 6d. black .. £275 £250
28 5s. blue .. £550 £400
29 10s. brown .. £1200 £800

1887.
30. 1. 2d. mauve and blue .. 1·25 1·00
31. 2½d. blue .. 1·25 1·75
32. 3d. mauve and brown .. 2·50 3·25
33. 4d. mauve and black .. 2·00 1·75
34. 5d. mauve and green .. 2·00 11·00
35. 6d. mauve .. 4·50 3·00
35a. 6d. mauve and red .. 4·50 12·00
36. 7½d. mauve and red .. 2·00 22·00
37. 10d. mauve and yellow .. 2·75 13·00
38. 1s. green and black .. 3·00 14·00
39. 2s. 6d. green and red .. 22·00 50·00
40. 5s. green and blue .. 32·00 90·00
41. 10s. green and brown .. 60·00 £130

1893. Surch. **HALF PENNY** and bars.
42. 1. ½d. on 4d. mauve & black 2·25 2·50

1904.
54a 3 ½d. green .. 3·25 1·75
55a 1d. purple & black on red 50 10
56 2d. purple and blue .. 1·75 75
47 2½d. purple & blue on bl 1·00 1·50
58 3d. purple and brown .. 2·75 90
59 6d. purple and mauve .. 3·25 1·25
60 1s. green and black .. 3·25 4·50
61 2s. 6d. green and red .. 10·00 23·00
62 5s. green and blue .. 16·00 60·00
63 10s. green and brown .. 48·00 £110

LAS BELA

A state of Baluchistan. Now part of Pakistan.

12 pies = 1 anna. 16 annas = 1 rupee.

1.

The 1 a. has the English inscriptions in a circle with the native inscription across the centre.

1897.
1. 1. ½ a. black on white .. 9·00 6·00
2 ½ a. black on blue .. 7·50 4·50
3. ½ a. black on grey .. 6·50 4·00
12. ½ a. black on green .. 7·00 6·00
8. – 1 a. black on orange .. 10·00 11·00

LEEWARD ISLANDS

A group of islands in the Br. W. Indies, including Antigua, Barbuda, British Virgin Islands, Dominica (till end of 1939), Montserrat, Nevis, and St. Christopher (St. Kitts). Stamps of Leeward Islands were used concurrent with the issues for the respective islands until they were withdrawn on the 1st July, 1956.

1890. 12 pence = 1 shilling;
20 shillings = 1 pound.
1951. 100 cents = 1 West Indian dollar.

1.

(3.)

1890.
1. 1. ½d. mauve and green .. 1·00 40
2. 1d. mauve and red .. 1·25 10
3. 2½d. mauve and blue .. 2·75 15
4. 4d. mauve and orange .. 2·75 7·00
5. 6d. mauve and brown .. 5·00 6·50
6. 7d. mauve and grey .. 1·75 9·00
7. 1s. green and red .. 11·00 27·00
8. 5s. green and blue .. £130 £225

1897. Diamond Jubilee. Optd. with **T 3.**
9. 1. ½d. mauve and green .. 2·50 8·00
10. 1d. mauve and red .. 3·25 8·50
11. 2½d. mauve and blue .. 3·50 8·50
12. 4d. mauve and orange .. 24·00 55·00
13. 6d. mauve and brown .. 40·00 75·00
14. 7d. mauve and grey .. 45·00 75·00
15. 1s. green and red .. £120 £190
16. 5s. green and blue .. £650 £950

1902. Surch. in words.
17. 1. 1d. on 4d. mauve & orange 80 3·75
18. 1d. on 6d. mauve & brown 90 4·50
19. 1d. on 7d. mauve and grey 90 3·25

1902. As **T 1,** but portrait of King Edward VII.
20. ½d. purple and green .. 1·00 40
21. 1d. purple and red .. 2·25 10
22. 2d. purple and brown .. 2·25 4·00
23. 2½d. purple and blue .. 1·25 1·25
24. 3d. purple and black .. 1·00 5·00
25. 6d. purple and brown .. 1·00 6·00
26. 1s. green and red .. 1·75 12·00
27. 2s. 6d. green and black .. 20·00 45·00
28. 5s. green and blue .. 32·00 50·00

1907. As last. Colours changed.
36. ¼d. brown .. 75 35
37. ½d. green .. 85 65
38. 1d. red .. 1·50 35
39. 2d. grey .. 1·00 6·50
40. 2½d. blue .. 1·40 2·50
41. 3d. purple and yellow .. 1·00 4·25
42. 6d. purple .. 3·00 5·50
43. 1s. black on green .. 2·75 14·00
44. 2s. 6d. black & red on blue 28·00 42·00
45. 5s. green and red on yellow 28·00 48·00

10. King George V.

14. King George VI.

1912.
46 10. ¼d. brown .. 40 20
59 ½d. green .. 30 20
60 1d. red .. 30 10
61 1d. violet .. 30 20
63 1½d. red .. 50 45
64 1½d. brown .. 30 10
65 2d. grey .. 50 25
67 2½d. blue .. 75 30
66 2½d. yellow .. 3·75 27·00
69 3d. purple on yellow .. 40 3·75
68 3d. blue .. 2·00 16·00
70 4d. black & red on yellow 1·25 11·00
71 5d. purple and green .. 50 4·25
53 6d. purple .. 1·00 6·00
54 1s. black on green .. 1·00 4·50
55 2s. purple & blue on blue 3·00 20·00
75 2s. 6d. black & red on blue 6·50 22·00
76 3s. green and violet .. 8·00 22·00
77 4s. black and red .. 8·00 32·00
57b 5s. green & red on yellow 10·00 40·00

Larger type, as **T 15** of Malta.
79. 10s. green and red on green 48·00 70·00
80. £1 purple and black on red £225 £250

1935. Silver Jubilee. As **T 13** of Antigua.
88. 1d. blue and red .. 60 40
89. 1½d. blue and grey .. 75 60
90. 2½d. brown and blue .. 1·00 2·50
91. 1s. grey and purple .. 4·75 9·00

1937. Coronation. As **T 2** of Aden.
92. 1d. red .. 30 15
93. 1½d. brown .. 30 25
94. 2½d. blue .. 30 35

1938.
95 14 ¼d. brown .. 10 15
96 ½d. green .. 15 15
97 ½d. grey .. 30 10
99 1d. red .. 60 30
100 1d. green .. 55 10
101 1½d. brown .. 20 15
102 1½d. orange and black .. 50 10
103 2d. grey .. 15 10
104 2d. red .. 1·40 15
105a 2½d. blue .. 40 20
106 2½d. black and purple .. 55 10
107a 3d. orange .. 30 40
108 3d. blue .. 65 10
109b 6d. purple .. 1·25 1·00
110b 1s. black on green .. 1·25 35
111ab 2s. purple & blue on blue 5·00 90
112a 5s. green & red on yellow 18·00 11·00
113b 10s. green & red on green 80·00 38·00
114b £1 purple and black on red 24·00 20·00

Nos. 113b/4b are as Type **15** of Bermuda but with portrait of King George VI.

1946. Victory. As **T 9** of Aden.
115. 1½d. brown .. 15 10
116. 3d. orange .. 15 10

1949. Silver Wedding. As **10/11** of Aden.
117. 2½d. blue .. 10 10
118. 5s. green .. 3·75 2·50

1949. U.P.U. As **T 20/23** of Antigua.
119. 2½d. black .. 15 10
120. 3d. blue .. 40 40
121. 6d. mauve .. 40 30
122. 1s. turquoise .. 45 30

1951. Inauguration of B.W.I. University College. As **T 24/25** of Antigua.
123. 3 c. orange and black .. 15 15
124. 12 c. red and violet .. 30 15

1953. Coronation. As **T 13** of Aden.
125. 3 c. black and green .. 10 25

1954. As **T 14** but portrait of Queen Elizabeth II facing left.
126. ½ c. brown .. 10 10
127. 1 c. grey .. 10 10
128. 2 c. green .. 10 10
129. 3 c. yellow and black .. 10 10
130. 4 c. red .. 10 10
131. 5 c. black and purple .. 30 10
132. 6 c. yellow .. 30 10
133. 8 c. blue .. 70 10
134. 12 c. purple .. 70 10
135. 24 c. black and green .. 70 10
136. 48 c. purple and blue .. 4·50 2·75
137. 60 c. brown and green .. 4·50 2·00
138. $1.20 green and red .. 3·75 2·75

Larger type as **T 15** of Malta.
139. $2.40 green and red .. 4·00 5·00
140. $4.80 purple and black 4·50 6·50

LESOTHO

Formerly Basutoland, attained independence on 4th October, 1966, and changed its name to Lesotho.

100 cents = 1 rand.

33. Moshoeshoe I and Moshoeshoe II.

1966. Independence.

106	33	2½ c. brown, black & red	10	10
107		5 c. brown, black & blue	10	10
108		10 c. brown, black & grn.	15	10
109		20 c. brown, black & pur.	20	10

1966. Nos. 69 etc. of Basutoland optd. **LESOTHO.**

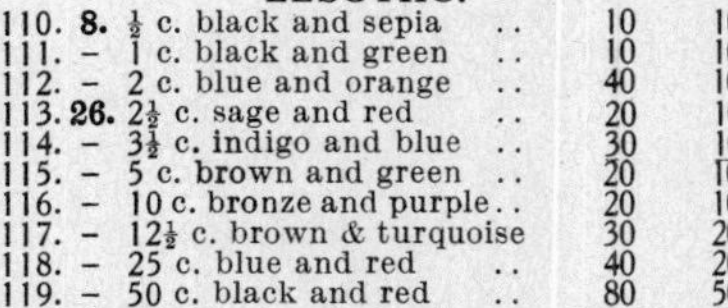

110.	8.	½ c. black and sepia ..	10	10
111.	–	1 c. black and green ..	10	10
112.	–	2 c. blue and orange ..	40	10
113.	26.	2½ c. sage and red ..	20	10
114.	–	3½ c. indigo and blue ..	30	10
115.	–	5 c. brown and green ..	20	10
116.	–	10 c. bronze and purple ..	20	10
117.	–	12½ c. brown & turquoise	30	20
118.	–	25 c. blue and red ..	40	20
119.	–	50 c. black and red ..	80	50
120.	9.	1 r. black and purple ..	1·00	75

35. "Education, Culture and Science".

1966. 20th Anniv. of U.N.E.S.C.O.

121	35	2½ c. yellow and green ..	10	10
122		5 c. green and olive ..	15	10
123		12½ c. blue and red ..	35	10
124		25 c. orange and blue ..	60	25

36. Maize.

1967.

125	36	½ c. green and violet ..	10	10
126	–	1 c. sepia and red ..	10	10
127	–	2 c. yellow and green ..	10	10
128	–	2½ c. black and ochre ..	10	10
151	–	3 c. choc., green & brown	15	15
129	–	3½ c. blue and yellow ..	10	10
130	–	5 c. bistre and blue ..	10	10
131	–	10 c. brown and grey ..	10	10
132	–	12½ c. black and orange ..	20	10
133	–	25 c. black and blue ..	35	20
134	–	50 c. black, blue & turq.	4·50	45
135	–	1 r. multicoloured ..	1·25	75
136	–	2 r. black, gold & purple	1·50	1·75

DESIGNS—HORIZ. 1 c. Cattle. 2 c. Aloes. 2½ c. Basotho Hat. 3 c. Sorghum. 3½ c. Merino Sheep ("Wool"). 5 c. Basotho Pony. 10 c. Wheat. 12½ c. Angora Goat ("Mohair"). 25 c. Maletsunyane Falls. 50 c. Diamonds. 1 r. Arms of Lesotho. VERT. 2 r. Moshoeshoe II.

See also Nos. 191/203.

46. Students and University.

1967. 1st Conferment of University Degrees.

137.	46.	1 c. sepia, blue & orange	10	10
138.		2½ c. sepia, ultram. & blue	10	10
139.		12½ c. sepia, blue and red	10	10
140.		25 c. sepia, blue & violet	15	10

47. Statue of Moshoeshoe I.

1967. 1st Anniv. of Independence.

141.	47.	2½ c. black and green ..	10	10
142.	–	12½ c. multicoloured ..	25	10
143.	–	25 c. black, green & ochre	35	15

DESIGNS: 12½ c. National Flag. 25 c. Crocodile (national emblem).

50. Lord Baden-Powell and Scout Saluting.

1967. 60th Anniv. of Scout Movement.

144.	50.	15 c. multicoloured ..	15	10

51. W.H.O. Emblem and World Map.

1968. 20th Anniv. of World Health Organization.

145.	51.	2½ c. blue, gold and red ..	15	10
146.	–	25 c. multicoloured ..	35	10

DESIGN: 25 c. Nurse and Child.

55. Running Hunters.

1968. Rock Paintings.

160.	55.	3 c. brn., turq. and grn.	15	10
161.	–	3½ c. yellow, olive & sepia	20	10
162.	–	5 c. red, ochre & brown	25	10
163.	–	10 c. yellow, red & purple	35	10
164.	–	15 c. buff, yellow & brown	65	25
165.	–	20 c. green, yell. & brown	75	35
166.	–	25 c. yell., brown & black	90	50

DESIGNS—HORIZ. 3½ c. Baboons. 10 c. Archers. 20 c. Eland. 25 c. Hunting Scene. VERT. 5 c. Javelin thrower. 15 c. Blue Cranes.

62. Queen Elizabeth II Hospital.

1969. Cent. of Maseru (capital). Mult.

167.		2½ c. Type **62**	10	10
168.		10 c. Lesotho Radio Station	10	10
169.		12½ c. Leabua Jonathan Airport	10	10
170.		25 c. Royal Palace ..	15	15

66. Rally Car passing Basuto Tribesman.

1969. "Roof of Africa" Car Rally.

171.	66.	2½ c. yell., mve. & plum	10	10
172.	–	12½ c. blue, yell. & grey	15	10
173.	–	15 c. blue, blk. & mauve	15	10
174.	–	20 c. blk., red & yellow	15	10

DESIGNS: 12½ c. Rally car on mountain road. 15 c. Chequered flags and "Roof of Africa" Plateau. 20 c. Map of rally route and Independence Trophy.

71. Gryponyx and Footprints.

1970. Prehistoric Footprints (1st series).

175.	–	3 c. brown and sepia ..	25	20
176.	71.	5 c. pur., pink & sepia	35	30
177.	–	10 c. yell., blk. & sepia	50	35
178.	–	15 c. yell., blk. & sepia	75	1·00
179.	–	25 c. blue and black ..	1·75	2·00

DESIGNS: 3 c. Dinosaur footprints at Moyeni. 10 c. Plateosauravus and footprints. 15 c. Tritylodon and footprints. 25 c. Massospondylus and footprints.

No. 175 is larger, 60 × 23 mm.

See also Nos. 596/8.

75. Moshoeshoe I, as a Young Man.

1970. Death Cent. of Chief Moshoeshoe I.

180.	75.	2½ c. green and mauve	10	10
181.	–	25 c. blue and brown ..	15	10

DESIGN: 25 c. Moshoeshoe I as an old man.

77. U.N. Emblem and "25".

1970. 25th Anniv. of U.N.

182.	77.	2½ c. pink, blue & purple	10	10
183.	–	10 c. multicoloured ..	10	10
184.	–	12½ c. red, blue and drab	10	10
185.	–	25 c. multicoloured ..	10	10

DESIGNS: 10 c. U.N. Building. 12½ c. "People of the World". 25 c. Symbolic Dove.

78. Gift Shop, Maseru.

1970. Tourism. Multicoloured.

186.		2½ c. Type **78**	10	10
187.		5 c. Trout Fishing ..	20	10
188.		10 c. Pony Trekking ..	25	10
189.		12½ c. Skiing, Maluti Mountains	45	10
190.		20 c. Holiday Inn, Maseru	45	50

79. Maize.

1971. As Nos. 147/58 but in new format omitting portrait, as in T **79**. New designs for 4 c., 2 r.

191.	79.	½ c. green and violet ..	10	10
192.	–	1 c. brown and red ..	10	10
193.	–	2 c. yellow and green ..	10	10
194.	–	2½ c. blk., grn. & yell.	10	10
195.	–	3 c. brn., grn. & yellow	10	10
196.	–	3½ c. blue and yellow ..	10	10
196a.	–	4 c. multicoloured ..	20	10
197.	–	5 c. brown and blue ..	15	10
198.	–	10 c. brown and grey ..	15	10
199.	–	12½ c. brown and orange	25	30
200.	–	25 c. slate and blue ..	60	40
201.	–	50 c. black, blue & green	4·50	2·25
202.	–	1 r. multicoloured ..	2·75	2·25
203.	–	2 r. brown and blue ..	2·75	3·00

DESIGNS—HORIZ. 4 c. National flag. VERT. 2 r. Statue of Moshoeshoe I.

80. Lammergeier.

1971. Birds. Multicoloured.

204.		2½ c. Type **80**	1·25	10
205.		5 c. Bald Ibis	2·00	90
206.		10 c. Rufous rockjumper ..	2·75	1·25
207.		12½ c. Blue bustard ..	3·25	1·40
208.		15 c. Painted snipe ..	4·00	2·50
209.		20 c. Golden-breasted bunting	4·00	2·50
210.		25 c. Ground woodpecker	4·25	2·75

81. Lionel Collett Dam.

1971. Soil Conservation. Multicoloured.

211.		4 c. Type **81**	10	10
212.		10 c. Contour ridges ..	10	10
213.		15 c. Earth dams ..	25	10
214.		25 c. Beaver dams ..	35	35

82. Diamond Mining.

1971. Development. Multicoloured.

215.		4 c. Type **82**	40	10
216.		10 c. Pottery	25	10
217.		15 c. Weaving	35	25
218.		20 c. Construction ..	45	30

83. Mail Cart.

1972. Centenary of Post Office.

219.	83.	5 c. brown and pink ..	15	10
220.	–	10 c. multicoloured ..	15	10
221.	–	15 c. blue, black and brown	30	15
222.	–	20 c. multicoloured ..	45	70

DESIGNS—HORIZ. 10 c. Postal Bus. 20 c. Maseru Post Office. VERT. 15 c., 4d. Cape of Good Hope stamp of 1876.

84. Sprinting.

1972. Olympic Games, Munich. Mult.

223.		4 c. Type **84**	10	10
224.		10 c. Shot putting ..	15	10
225.		15 c. Hurdling	20	10
226.		25 c. Long-jumping ..	30	20

85. "Adoration of the Shepherds" (Matthias Stomer).

1972. Christmas.

227. 85. 4 c. multicoloured .. 10 10
228. 10 c. multicoloured .. 10 10
229. 25 c. multicoloured .. 15 20

86. W.H.O. Emblem.

1973. 25th Anniv. of W.H.O.

230. 86. 20 c. yellow and blue .. 20 15

1973. O.A.U. 10th Anniv. Nos. 194 and 196a/8 optd. **O.A.U. 10th Anniversary Freedom in Unity.**

231. 2½ c. black, green & brown 10 10
232. 4 c. multicoloured .. 10 10
233. 5 c. brown and blue .. 10 10
234. 10 c. brown and blue .. 15 15

88. Basotho Hat and W.F.P. Emblem.

1973. 10th Anniv. of World Food Programme. Multicoloured.

235. 4 c. Type 88 .. .. 10 10
236. 15 c. School feeding .. 20 15
237. 20 c. Infant feeding .. 20 20
238. 25 c. "Food for work" .. 25 25

89. "Aeropetes tulbaghia".

1973. Butterflies. Multicoloured.

239 4 c. Type 89 .. .. 30 10
240 5 c. "Papilio demodocus" 40 25
241 10 c. "Vanessa cardui" .. 40 50
242 15 c. "Precis hierta" .. 1·10 1·00
243 20 c. "Precis oenone" .. 1·10 1·00
244 25 c. "Danaus chrysippus" 1·60 1·75
245 30 c. "Colotis evenina" .. 1·90 2·00

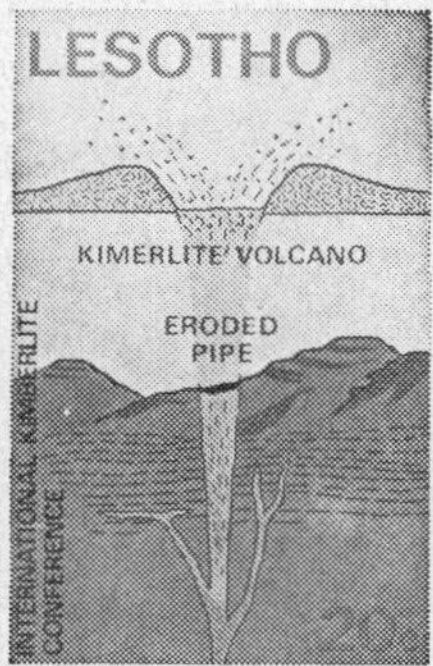

90. Kimberlite Volcano.

1973. Int., Kimberlite Conference. Mult.

246. 10 c. Map of diamond-mines (horiz.) 90 50
247. 15 c. Kimberlite-diamond rock (horiz.) .. .. 1·10 1·00
248. 20 c. Type 90 .. .. 1·40 1·50
249. 30 c. Diamond prospecting 2·25 3·00

91. "Health".

1974. Youth and Development. Mult.

250. 4 c. Type 91 .. .. 10 10
251. 10 c. "Education" .. 10 10
252. 20 c. "Agriculture" .. 15 10
253. 25 c. "Industry" .. 25 20
254. 30 c. "Service" .. 30 25

92. Open Book and Wreath.

1974. 10th Anniv. of U.B.L.S. Multicoloured

255. 10 c. Type 92 .. .. 10 10
256. 15 c. Flags, mortar-board and scroll 10 10
257. 20 c. Map of Africa .. 15 10
258. 25 c. King Moshoeshoe II capping a graduate .. 15 15

93. Senqunyane River Bridge, Marakabei.

1974. Rivers and Bridges. Multicoloured.

259. 4 c. Type 93 .. .. 10 10
260. 5 c. Tsoelike River and bridge 10 10
261. 10 c. Makhaleng River Bridge 20 10
262. 15 c. Seaka Bridge, Orange/Senqu River 35 35
263. 20 c. Masianokeng Bridge, Phuthiatsana River .. 40 40
264. 25 c. Mahobong Bridge, Hlotse River 45 45

94. U.P.U. Emblem

1974. Centenary of U.P.U.

265. 94. 4 c. green and black .. 10 10
266. – 10 c. orge., yell. & blk. 10 10
267. – 15 c. multicoloured .. 15 15
268. – 20 c. multicoloured .. 15 20

DESIGNS: 10 c. Map of air-mail routes. 15 c. Post Office H.Q., Maseru. 20 c. Horseman taking rural mail.

95. Siege of Thaba-Bosiu.

1974. 150th Anniv of Siege of Thaba-Bosiu. Multicoloured.

269 4 c. Type 95 .. .. 10 10
270 5 c. The wreath-laying .. 10 10
271 10 c. Moshoeshoe I (vert) 25 10
272 20 c. Makoanyane, the warrior (vert) 65 30

96. Mamokhorong.

1974. Basotho Musical Instruments. Mult.

273. 4 c. Type 96 .. .. 10 10
274. 10 c. Lesiba 10 10
275. 15 c. Setolotolo 15 20
276. 20 c. Meropa 15 20

97. Horseman in Rock Archway.

1975. Sehlabathebe National Park. Mult.

278. 4 c. Type 97 .. .. 15 10
279. 5 c. Mountain view through arch 15 10
280. 15 c. Antelope by stream .. 35 30
281. 20 c. Mountains and lake .. 40 35
282. 25 c. Tourists by waterfall 50 50

98. Morena Moshoeshoe I.

1975. Leaders of Lesotho.

283. 98. 3 c. black and blue .. 10 10
284. – 4 c. black and mauve .. 10 10
285. – 5 c. black and pink .. 10 10
286. – 6 c. black and brown .. 10 10
287. – 10 c. black and red .. 10 10
288. – 15 c. black and red .. 20 20
289. – 20 c. black and green .. 25 30
290. – 25 c. black and blue .. 25 40

DESIGNS: 4 c. King Moshoeshoe II. 5 c. Morena Letsie I. 6 c. Morena Lerotholi. 10 c. Morena Letsie II. 15 c. Morena Griffith. 20 c. Morena Seeiso Griffith Lerotholi. 25 c. Mofumahali Mantsebo Seeiso, O.B.E.

The 25 c. also commemorates International Women's Year.

99. Mokhibo Dance.

1975. Traditional Dances. Multicoloured.

291. 4 c. Type 99 .. .. 10 10
292. 10 c. Ndlamo 10 10
293. 15 c. Baleseli 25 30
294. 20 c. Mohobelo 30 35

100. Enrolment.

1976. 25th Anniv. of Lesotho Red Cross. Multicoloured.

296. 4 c. Type 100 .. .. 35 10
297. 10 c. Medical aid 50 10
298. 15 c. Rural service .. 95 45
299. 25 c. Relief supplies .. 1·25 55

101. Tapestry.

1976. Multicoloured.

300. 2 c. Type 101 .. .. 10 10
301. 3 c. Mosotho horseman .. 20 10
302. 4 c. Map of Lesotho .. 35 10
303. 5 c. Lesotho brown diamond 55 10
304. 10 c. Lesotho Bank .. 30 10
305. 15 c. Lesotho and O.A.U. flags 65 20
306. 25 c. Sehlabathebe National Park 80 35
307. 40 c. Pottery 80 50
308. 50 c. Pre-historic rock art 1·50 90
309. 1 r. King Moshoeshoe II (vert.) .. .. .. 1·40 1·75

102. Football.

1976. Olympic Games, Montreal. Mult.

310. 4 c. Type 102 .. .. 10 10
311. 10 c. Weightlifting .. 10 10
312. 15 c. Boxing 15 10
313. 25 c. Throwing the discus 30 25

103. "Rising Sun".

1976. 10th Anniv. of Independence. Mult.

314. 4 c. Type 103 .. .. 10 10
315. 10 c. Open gates 10 10
316. 15 c. Broken chains .. 30 10
317. 25 c. Aeroplane over hotel 40 25

104. Telephones, 1876 and 1976.

1976. Centenary of Telephone. Multicoloured.

318. 4 c. Type 104 .. .. 10 10
319. 10 c. Early handset and telephone-user, 1976 .. 10 10
320. 15 c. Wall telephone and telephone exchange .. 15 15
321. 25 c. Stick telephone and Alexander Graham Bell 30 40

105. "Aloe striatula".

1977. Aloes and Succulents. Multicoloured.
322. 3 c. Type **105** 20 10
323. 4 c. " Aloe aristata " .. 25 10
324. 5 c. " Kniphofia caulescens " 30 10
325. 10 c. " Euphorbia pulvinata " 45 10
326. 15 c. " Aloe saponaria " .. 80 40
327. 20 c. " Caralluma lutea " 1·10 65
328. 25 c. " Aloe polyphylla " 1·60 90
See also Nos. 347/54.

106. Large-toothed Rock Hyrax.

1977. Animals. Multicoloured.
329. 4 c. Type **106** 20 10
330. 5 c. Cape porcupine .. 25 10
331. 10 c. Zorilla (polecat) .. 40 10
332. 15 c. Klipspringer 90 70
333. 25 c. Chacma baboon .. 1·40 1·10

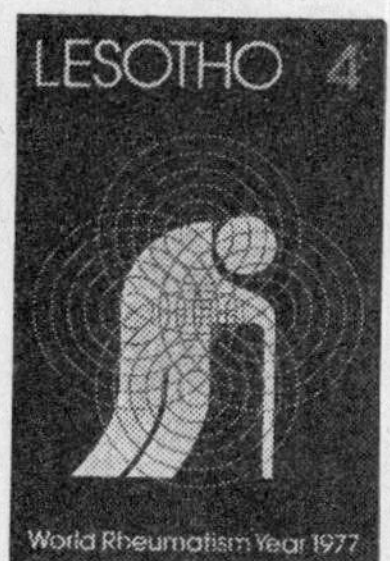

107. " Rheumatic Man ".

1977. World Rheumatism Year.
334. **107.** 4 c. yellow and red .. 10 10
335. – 10 c. blue and dark blue 10 10
336. – 15 c. yellow and blue .. 25 10
337. – 25 c. red and black .. 40 45
Designs: Each show the " Rheumatic Man " as Type **107**. 10 c. Surrounded by " pain ". 15 c. Surrounded by " chain ". 25 c. Supporting globe.

108. " Barbus holubi ".

1977. Fish. Multicoloured.
338. 4 c. Type **108** 15 10
339. 10 c. " Labeo capensis " .. 30 10
340. 15 c. " Salmo gairdneri " 60 35
341. 25 c. " Oreodaimon quathlambae " 85 60

1977. No. 198 surch.
342. 3 c. on 10 c. brown & blue 1·25 80

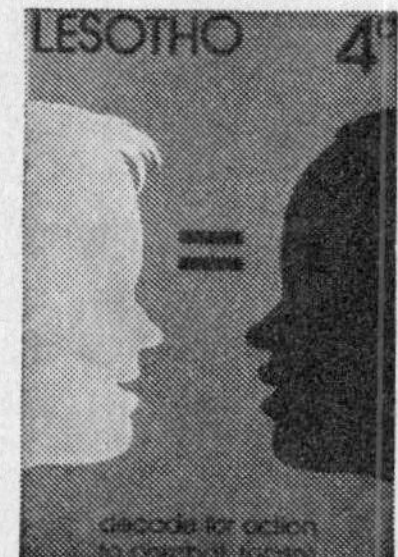

110. Black and White Heads.

1977. Decade for Action to Combat Racism.
343. **110.** 4 c. black and mauve .. 10 10
344. – 10 c. black and blue .. 10 10
345. – 15 c. black and orange .. 15 15
346. – 25 c. black and green .. 25 25
Designs: 10 c. Jigsaw pieces. 15 c. Cogwheels. 25 c. Handshake.

1978. Flowers. As T **105**. Multicoloured.
347. 2 c. " Papaver aculeatum " 10 25
348. 3 c. " Diascia integerrima " 10 15
349. 4 c. " Helichrysum trilineatum " 10 10
350. 5 c. " Zaluzianskya maritima " 10 10
351. 10 c. " Gladiolus natalensis " 20 20
352. 15 c. " Chironia krebsii " 30 30
353. 25 c. " Wahlenbergia undulata " 50 90
354. 40 c. " Brunsvigia radulosa " .. .. 85 1·75

111. Edward Jenner vaccinating Child.

1978. Global Eradication of Smallpox. Mult.
355. 5 c. Type **111** 10 10
356. 25 c. Head of child and W.H.O. emblem .. 30 25

112. Tsoloane Falls.

1978. Waterfalls. Multicoloured.
357. 4 c. Type **112** 15 10
358. 10 c. Qiloane Falls .. 25 10
359. 15 c. Tsoelikana Falls .. 45 25
360. 25 c. Maletsunyane Falls .. 75 60

113. Wright " Flyer ", 1903.

1978. 75th Anniv. of First Powered Flight. Multicoloured.
361. 5 c. Type **113** 10 10
362. 25 c. Wilbur and Orville Wright and " Flyer " .. 30 20

114. " Orthetrum farinosum ".

115. Oudehout Branch in Flower.

1978. Insects. Multicoloured.
363 4 c. Type **114** 10 10
364 10 c. "Phymateus viripides" 20 10
365 15 c. "Belonogaster lateris" 30 20
366 25 c. "Sphodromantis gastrica" 50 45

1979. Trees. Multicoloured.
367. 4 c. Type **115** 15 10
368. 10 c. Wild Olive 20 10
369. 15 c. Blinkblaar 35 60
370. 25 c. Cape Holly .. .. 70 1·25

116. Mampharoane.

1979. Reptiles. Multicoloured.
371. 4 s. Type **116** 10 10
372. 10 s. Qoaane 20 10
373. 15 s. Leupa 30 35
374. 25 s. Masumu 60 65

117. Basutoland 1933 1d. Stamp.

1979. Death Centenary of Sir Rowland Hill.
375. **117.** 4 s. multicoloured .. 10 10
376. – 15 s. multicoloured .. 30 20
377. – 25 s. black, orge. & bistre 40 30
Designs: 15 s. Basutoland 1962 ½ c. new currency definitive. 25 s. Penny Black.

118. Detail of painting " Children's Games " by Brueghel.

1979. International Year of the Child.
379. **118.** 4 s. multicoloured .. 10 10
380. – 10 s. multicoloured .. 10 10
381. – 15 s. multicoloured .. 15 15
Designs: 10, 15 s. Different details taken from Brueghel's " Children's Games ".

119. Beer Strainer, Broom and Mat.

1980. Grasswork. Multicoloured.
383. 4 s. Type **119** 10 10
384. 10 s. Winnowing Basket .. 10 10
385. 15 s. Basotho Hat .. 20 15
386. 25 s. Grain storage .. 35 25

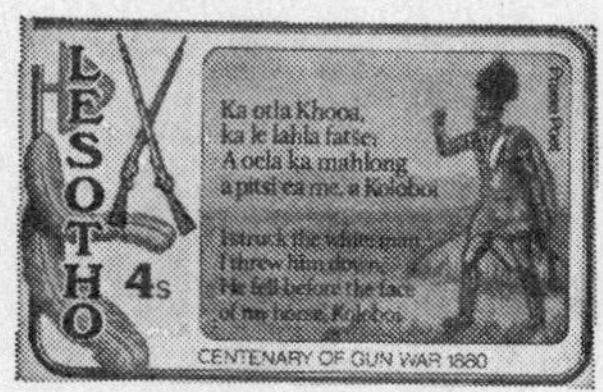

120. Praise Poet.

1980. Centenary of Gun War. Multicoloured.
387. 4 s. Type **120** 15 10
388. 5 s. Lerotholi, Commander of Basotho Army .. 15 10
389. 10 s. Ambush at Qalabane .. 20 10
390. 15 s. Snider and Martini-Henry rifles 40 25
391. 25 s. Map showing main areas of action 50 35

121. Olympic Flame, Flags and Kremlin.

1980. Olympic Games, Moscow. Mult.
392. 25 s. Type **121** 25 25
393. 25 s. Doves, flame and flags 25 25
394. 25 s. Football 25 25
395. 25 s. Running 25 25
396. 25 s. Opening ceremony .. 25 25

1980. Nos. 203 and 300/9 surch.
402 2 s. on 2 c. Type **101** .. 10 10
403 3 s. on 3 c. Mosotho horseman 10 10
410 5 s. on 5 c. Lesotho brown diamond 10 10
404 6 s. on 4 c. Map of Lesotho 10 10
411 10 s. on 10 c. Lesotho Bank 10 10
412 25 s. on 25 c. Sehlabathebe National Park 25 30
406 40 s. on 40 c. Pottery .. 45 50
407 50 s. on 50 c. Pre-historic rock art 50 55
408 75 s. on 15 c. Lesotho and O.A.U. flags 70 75
409 1 m. on 1 r. King Moshoeshoe II .. .. .. 95 1·00
417 2 m. on 2 r. Statue of King Moshoeshoe I .. .. 1·90 2·00

123. Beer Mug.

1980. Pottery. Multicoloured.
418. 4 s. Type **123** 10 10
419. 10 s. Beer brewing pot .. 10 10
420. 15 s. Water pot 15 15
421. 25 s. Pot shapes 25 30

124. Queen Elizabeth, the Queen Mother with Prince Charles.

1980. 80th Birthday of The Queen Mother. Multicoloured.
423. 5 s. Type **124** 25 25
424. 10 s. The Queen Mother .. 30 30
425. 1 m. 1947 Basutoland Royal Visit stamp (54 × 43 mm.) 1·25 1·25

125. Lesotho Evangical Church, Morija.

1980. Christmas. Multicoloured.
426. 4 s. Type **125** 10 10
427. 15 s. St. Agnes' Anglican Church, Teyateyaneng .. 10 10
428. 25 s. Our Lady's Victory Cathedral, Maseru .. 15 10
429. 75 s. University Chapel, Roma 45 50

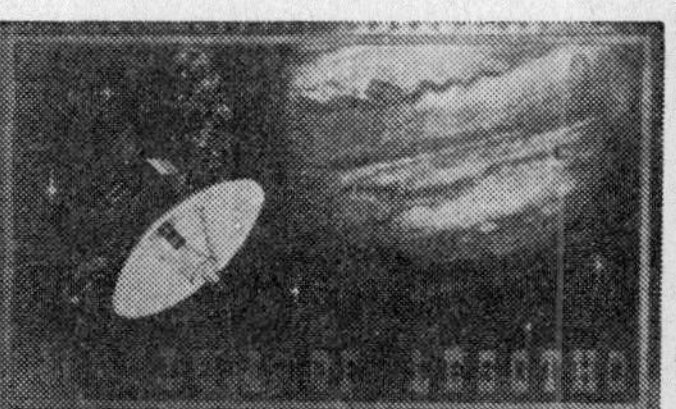
126. " Voyager " Satellite and Jupiter.

1981. Space Exploration. Multicoloured.
431. 25 c. Type **126** 40 30
432. 25 c. " Voyager " and Saturn 40 30
433. 25 c. " Voyager " passing Saturn 40 30
434. 25 c. " Space Shuttle " releasing satellite .. 40 30
435. 25 c. " Space Shuttle " launching into space .. 40 30

127. Greater Kestrel.

1981. Birds. Multicoloured.

437 1 s. Type **127** 15 10
438 2 s. Speckled Pigeon (horiz.) 15 10
439 3 s. South African Crowned Crane 15 10
503 5 s. Bokmakierie Shrike .. 10 10
504 6 s. Cape Robin Chat .. 10 10
505 7 s. Yellow Canary .. 10 10
506 10 s. Red-billed Pintail (horiz.) 15 10
507 25 s. Malachite Kingfisher 35 30
508 40 s. Yellow-tufted Malachite Sunbird (horiz.) .. 55 35
509 60 s. Cape Longclaw (horiz.) 80 70
510 75 s. Hoopoe (horiz.) .. 1·25 85
448 1 m. Red Bishop (horiz.) .. 2·50 1·00
449 2 m. Egyptian Goose (horiz.) 3·50 3·00
450 5 m. Lilac-breasted Roller (horiz.) .. .. .. 6·00 7·00

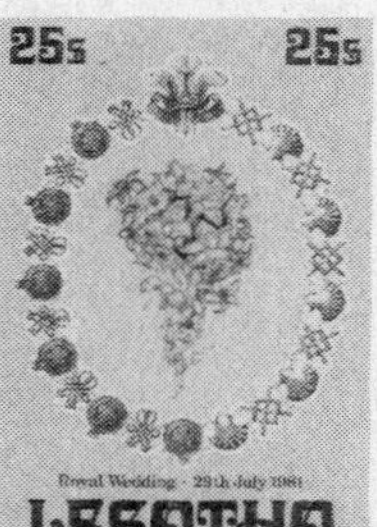

128. Wedding Bouquet from Lesotho.

1981. Royal Wedding. Multicoloured.

451. 25 s. Type **128** 30 40
452. 50 s. Prince Charles riding 55 75
453. 75 s. Prince Charles and Lady Diana Spencer .. 75 1·00

130. " Santa planning his Annual Visit ".

1981. Christmas. Paintings by Norman Rockwell.

455. 6 s. Type **130** 20 10
456. 10 s. " Santa reading his Mail " 30 10
457. 15 s. " The Little Spooners " 35 15
458. 20 s. " Raleigh Rockwell Travels " 45 20
459. 25 s. " Ride 'em Cowboy " 55 25
460. 60 s. " The Discovery " 1·00 75

131. Duke of Edinburgh, Award Scheme Emblem and Flags.

1981. 25th Anniv. of Duke of Edinburgh Award Scheme. Multicoloured.

462. 6 s. Type **131** 10 10
463. 7 s. Tree planting 10 10
464. 25 s. Gardening 30 30
465. 40 s. Mountain climbing .. 50 50
466. 75 s. Award Scheme emblem 85 85

132. African Wild Cat.

1981. Wildlife. Multicoloured.

468. 6 s. Type **132** 15 10
469. 20 s. Chacma Baboon (44×31 mm.) 30 30
470. 25 s. Cape Eland 35 35
471. 40 s. Porcupine 60 60
472. 50 s. Oribi (44×31 mm.) .. 75 75

133. Scout Bugler.

1982. 75th Anniv. of Boy Scout Movement. Multicoloured.

474. 6 s. Type **133** 45 25
475. 30 s. Scouts hiking .. 70 50
476. 40 s. Scout sketching .. 75 60
477. 50 s. Scout with flag .. 80 65
478. 75 s. Scouts saluting .. 90 80

134. Jules Rimet Trophy with Footballers and Flags of 1930 Finalists (Argentina and Uruguay).

1982. World Cup Football Championship, Spain. Each showing Trophy with Players and Flags from Past Finals. Multicoloured.

480. 15 s. Type **134** 20 20
481. 15 s. Czechoslovakia and Italy, 1934 .. .. 20 20
482. 15 s. Hungary and Italy, 1938 .. .. .. 20 20
483. 15 s. Brazil and Uruguay, 1950 .. .. .. 20 20
484. 15 s. Hungary and W. Germany, 1954 .. 20 20
485. 15 s. Sweden and Brazil, 1958 .. .. .. 20 20
486. 15 s. Czechoslovakia and Brazil, 1962 .. .. 20 20
487. 15 s. W. Germany and England, 1966 .. .. 20 20
488. 15 s. Italy and Brazil, 1970 20 20
489. 15 s. Holland and W. Germany, 1974 .. .. 20 20
490. 15 s. Holland and Argentina, 1978 .. .. 20 20
491. 15 s. Map of World on footballs 20 20

Nos. 480/8 show the Jules Rimet Trophy and Nos. 489/91 the World Cup Trophy.

135. Portrait of George Washington.

1982. 250th Anniv. of George Washington. Multicoloured.

493. 6 s. Type **135** 10 10
494. 7 s. Washington with step-children and dog .. 10 10
495. 10 s. Washington with Indian chief 15 10
496. 25 s. Washington with troops 35 35
497. 40 s. Washington arriving in New York 50 50
498. 1 m. Washington on parade 1·25 1·25

136. Lady Diana Spencer in Tetbury, May 1981.

1982. 21st Birthday of Princess of Wales. Multicoloured.

514. 30 s. Lesotho coat of arms 30 30
515. 50 s. Type **136** 45 50
516. 75 s. Wedding picture at Buckingham Palace .. 70 70
517. 1 m. Formal portrait .. 1·00 1·25

137. Mosotho reading Sesotho Bible.

1982. Centenary of Sesotho Bible. Mult.

518. 6 s. Type **137** 10 10
519. 15 s. Sesotho bible and Virgin Mary holding infant Jesus 20 20
520. 1 m. Sesotho bible and Cathedral (horiz.) (62×42 mm.) 70 80

138. Birthday Greetings.

1982. Birth of Prince William of Wales. Multicoloured.

521. 6 s. Type **138** 15 15
522. 60 s. Princess Diana and Prince William .. 80 80

139. "A Partridge in a Pear Tree".

1982. Christmas. "The Twelve Days of Christmas". Walt Disney cartoon Characters. Multicoloured.

523. 2 s. Type **139** 10 10
524. 2 s. "Two turtle doves" .. 10 10
525. 3 s. "Three French hens" .. 10 10
526. 3 s. "Four calling birds" .. 10 10
527. 4 s. "Five golden rings" .. 10 10
528. 4 s. "Six geese a-laying" .. 10 10
529. 75 s. "Seven swans a-swimming" .. .. 1·25 1·25
530. 75 s. "Eight maids a-milking" .. .. 1·25 1·25

140. " Lepista caffrorum ".

1983. Fungi. Multicoloured.

532. 10 s. Type **140** 15 10
533. 30 s. " Broomeia congregata " 40 40
534. 50 s. " Afroboletus luteolus " 85 85
535. 75 s. " Lentinus tuber-regium " .. .. 1·40 1·40

141. Ba-Leseli Dance.

1983. Commonwealth Day. Multicoloured.

536. 5 s. Type **141** 10 10
537. 30 s. Tapestry weaving .. 35 40
538. 60 s. Queen Elizabeth II (vert.) 70 85
539. 75 s. King Moshoeshoe II (vert.) .. .. .. 90 1·10

142. " Dancers in a Trance " (rock painting from Ntloana Tsoana).

1983. Rock Paintings. Multicoloured.

540. 6 s. Type **142** 15 10
541. 25 s. " Baboons ", Sehonghong 40 35
542. 60 s. " Hunters attacking Mountain Reedbuck ", Makhetha 90 95
543. 75 s. " Eland ", Lehaha la Likhomo .. .. 1·25 1·40

143. Montgolfier Balloon, 1783.

1983. Bicentenary of Manned Flight. Mult.

545. 7 s. Type **143** 15 10
546. 30 s. Wright brothers and " Flyer " 45 40
547. 60 s. First airmail flight .. 80 75
548. 1 m. " Concorde " .. 2·50 1·50

144. Rev. Eugene Casalis.

1983. 150th Anniv. of Arrival of the French Missionaries. Multicoloured.

550. 6 s. Type **144** 10 10
551. 25 s. The founding of Morija 30 40
552. 40 s. Baptism of Libe .. 50 70
553. 75 s. Map of Lesotho .. 90 1·25

145. Mickey Mouse and Pluto greeted by Friends.

1983. Christmas. Walt Disney Characters in scenes from " Old Christmas " (Washington Irving's sketchbook). Multicoloured.

554.	1 s. Type **145**	10	10
555.	2 s. Donald Duck and Pluto	10	10
556.	3 s. Donald Duck with Huey, Dewey and Louie	10	10
557.	4 s. Goofy, Donald Duck and Mickey Mouse ..	10	10
558.	5 s. Goofy holding turkey, Donald Duck and Mickey Mouse	10	10
559.	6 s. Goofy and Mickey Mouse	10	10
560.	7 s. Donald and Daisy Duck	1·50	70
561.	1 m. Goofy and Clarabell ..	2·00	1·25

146. "Danaus chrysippus".

1984. Butterflies. Multicoloured.

563	1 s. Type **146**	15	10
564	2 s. "Aeropetes tulbaghia"	15	10
565	3 s. "Colotis evenina" ..	20	10
566	4 s. "Precis oenone" ..	20	10
567	5 s. "Precis hierta" ..	20	10
568	6 s. "Catopsilia florella" ..	20	10
569	7 s. "Phalanta phalantha"	20	10
570	10 s. "Acraea stenobea" ..	30	10
571	15 s. "Cynthia cardui" ..	50	10
572	20 s. "Colotis subfasciatus"	60	10
573	30 s. "Charaxes jasius" ..	65	20
574	50 s. "Eurema brigitta" ..	85	30
575	60 s. "Pieris helice" ..	95	35
576	75 s. "Colotis regina" ..	1·25	40
577	1 m. "Hypolimnas misippus"	1·50	70
578	5 m. "Papilio demodocus"	4·50	4·00

147. " Thou shalt not have Strange Gods before Me ".

1984. Easter. The Ten Commandments. Multicoloured.

579.	20 s. Type **147**	30	25
580.	20 s. " Thou shalt not take the name of the Lord thy God in vain "	30	25
581.	20 s. " Remember thou keep holy the Lord's Day "	30	25
582.	20 s. " Honour thy father and mother "	30	25
583.	20 s. " Thou shalt not kill "	30	25
584.	20 s. " Thou shalt not commit adultery " ..	30	25
585.	20 s. " Thou shalt not steal "	30	25
586.	20 s. " Thou shalt not bear false witness against thy neighbour "	30	25
587.	20 s. " Thou shalt not covet thy neighbour's wife " ..	30	25
588.	20 s. " Thou shalt not covet thy neighbour's goods "	30	25

148. Torch Bearer.

1984. Olympic Games, Los Angeles. Mult.

590.	10 s. Type **148**	10	10
591.	30 s. Horse-riding	30	35
592.	50 s. Swimming	50	55
593.	75 s. Basketball	70	75
594.	1 m. Running	95	1·10

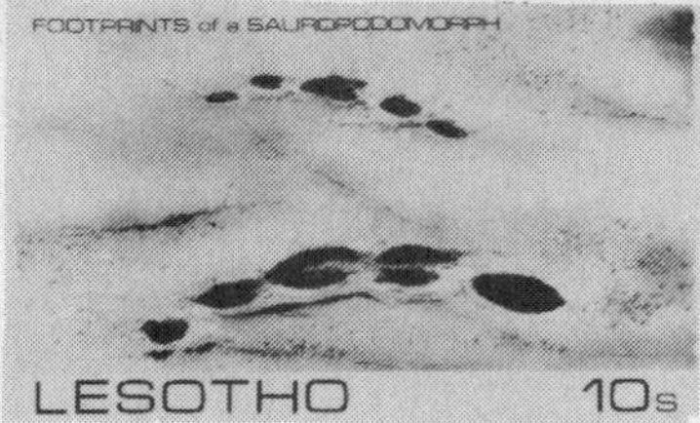

149. Sauropodomorph Footprints.

1984. Prehistoric Footprints (2nd series). Multicoloured.

596.	10 s. Type **149**	55	20
597.	30 s. Lesothosaurus footprints	1·50	75
598.	50 s. Footprint of carnivorous dinosaur ..	1·75	1·25

150. Wells Fargo Coach, 1852.

1984. "Ausipex" International Stamp Exhibition, Melbourne. Bicentenary of First Mail Coach Run. Multicoloured.

599.	6 s. Type **150**	10	10
600.	7 s. Basotho mail cart, circa 1900	10	10
601.	10 s. Bath mail coach, 1784	10	10
602.	30 s. Cobb coach, 1853 ..	30	35
603.	50 s. Exhibition logo and Royal Exhibition buildings, Melbourne (82 × 25 mm.)	50	55

151. "The Orient Express" (1900). (Illustration reduced, actual size 46 mm × 28 mm.).

1984. Railways of the World. Multicoloured.

605.	6 s. Type **151**	40	10
606.	15 s. German State Railways Class "05" No. 05001 (1935) ..	45	20
607.	30 s. Caledonian Railway "Cardean" (1906) ..	70	35
608.	60 s. Santa Fe "Super Chief" (1940)	1·25	65
609.	1 m. L.N.E.R. "Flying Scotsman" (1934) ..	1·75	1·00

152. Eland Calf.

1984. Baby Animals. Multicoloured.

611.	15 s. Type **152**	35	20
612.	20 s. Young Chacma Baboons	40	25
613.	30 s. Oribi calf	55	30
614.	75 s. Young Natal Red Hares	1·25	75
615.	1 m. Black-backed Jackal pups (46 × 27 mm.) ..	1·50	1·25

153. Crown of Lesotho.

1985. Silver Jubilee of King Moshoeshoe II. Multicoloured.

616.	6 s. Type **153**	10	10
617.	30 s. King Moshoeshoe in 1960	20	25
618.	75 s. King Moshoeshoe in traditional dress, 1985 ..	50	55
619.	1 m. King Moshoeshoe in uniform, 1985	70	75

154. Christ condemned to Death.

1985. Easter. The Stations of the Cross. Multicoloured.

620.	20 s. Type **154**	15	15
621.	20 s. Christ carrying the Cross	15	15
622.	20 s. Falling for the first time	15	15
623.	20 s. Christ meets Mary ..	15	15
624.	20 s. Simon of Cyrene helping to carry the Cross	15	15
625.	20 s. Veronica wiping the face of Christ ..	15	15
626.	20 s. Christ falling a second time	15	15
627.	20 s. Consoling the women of Jerusalem ..	15	15
628.	20 s. Falling for the third time	15	15
629.	20 s. Christ being stripped	15	15
630.	20 s. Christ nailed to the Cross	15	15
631.	20 s. Dying on the Cross ..	15	15
632.	20 s. Christ taken down from the Cross ..	15	15
633.	20 s. Christ being laid in the sepulchre	15	15

155. Duchess of York with Princess Elizabeth, 1931.

1985. Life and Times of Queen Elizabeth the Queen Mother. Multicoloured.

635.	10 s. Type **155**	15	10
636.	30 s. The Queen Mother in 1975	50	50
637.	60 s. Queen Mother with Queen Elizabeth and Princess Margaret, 1980	80	80
638.	2 m. Four generations of Royal Family at Prince Henry's christening, 1984	3·00	3·00

156. B.M.W. "732i".

1985. Century of Motoring. Multicoloured.

640.	6 s. Type **156**	25	15
641.	10 s. Ford "Crown Victoria"	35	15
642.	30 s. Mercedes-Benz "500SE"	75	50
643.	90 s. Cadillac "Eldorado Biarritz	2·00	2·00
644.	2 m. Rolls-Royce "Silver Spirit"	3·00	3·25

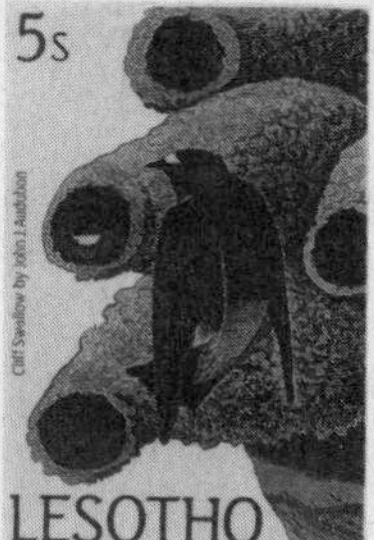

157. American Cliff Swallow.

1985. Birth Bicentenary of John J. Audubon (ornithologist). Designs showing original paintings. Multicoloured.

646.	5 s. Type **157**	30	15
647.	6 s. Great crested grebe (horiz.)	30	15
648.	10 s. Vesper sparrow (horiz.)	45	15
649.	30 s. Greenshank (horiz.) ..	1·00	55
650.	60 s. Stilt sandpiper (horiz.)	1·75	1·75
651.	2 m. Glossy ibis (horiz.) ..	3·25	3·50

158. Two Youths Rock-climbing.

1985. International Youth Year and 75th Anniv. of Girl Guide Movement. Mult.

652.	10 s. Type **158**	20	10
653.	30 s. Young technician in hospital laboratory ..	50	40
654.	75 s. Three guides on parade	1·00	90
655.	2 m. Guide saluting ..	2·40	2·40

159. U.N. (New York) 1951 1 c. Definitive and U.N. Flag.

1985. 40th Anniv. of U.N.O.

657.	**159.**	10 s. multicoloured ..	25	10
658.	–	30 s. multicoloured ..	60	35
659.	–	50 s. multicoloured ..	95	65
660.	–	2 m. black and green	5·00	3·25

DESIGNS—VERT. 30 s. Ha Sofonia Earth Satellite Station. 2 m. Maimonides (physician, philosopher and scholar). HORIZ. 50 s. Lesotho Airways aircraft at Maseru Airport.

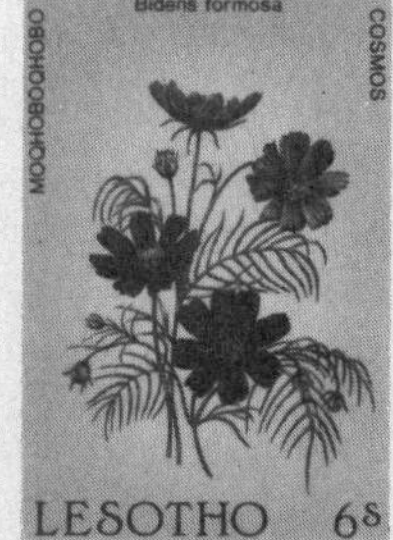

160. Cosmos.

1985. Wild Flowers. Multicoloured.

661.	6 s. Type **160**	40	15
662.	10 s. Small agapanthus ..	55	15
663.	30 s. Pink witchweed ..	1·10	50
664.	60 s. Small iris	1·75	1·25
665.	90 s. Wild geranium or Cranesbill	2·40	2·00
666.	1 m. Large spotted orchid	3·75	3·75

1985. 150th Birth Anniv. of Mark Twain. Walt Disney cartoon characters illustrating various Mark Twain quotations. As T **118** of Anguilla. Multicoloured.

667. 6 s. Mrs Jumbo and baby Dumbo 30 15
668. 50 s. Uncle Scrooge and Goofy reading newspaper .. .. .. 1·00 60
669. 90 s. Winnie the Pooh, Tigger, Piglet and Owl 1·50 1·10
670. 1 m. 50 Goofy at ship's wheel .. .. .. 2·25 1·75

1985. Birth Bicentenaries of Grimm Brothers (folklorists). Walt Disney cartoon characters in scenes from "The Wishing Table". As T **119** of Anguilla. Multicoloured.

672. 10 s. The tailor (Donald Duck) 35 15
673. 60 s. The second son (Dewey) with magic donkey and gold coins .. 1·25 75
674. 75 s. The eldest son (Huey) with wishing table laden with food .. .. 1·50 90
675. 1 m. The innkeeper stealing the third son's (Louie) magic cudgel .. 2·00 1·50

161. Male Lammergeier on Watch.

1986. Flora and Fauna of Lesotho. Multicoloured.

677. 7 s. Type **161** 60 15
678. 9 s. Prickly pear 60 15
679. 12 s. Stapelia 60 15
680. 15 s. Pair of lammergeiers 1·50 35
681. 35 s. Pig's ears .. .. 1·10 50
682. 50 s. Male lammergeier in flight .. .. 2·50 1·60
683. 1 m. Adult and juvenile lammergeiers .. .. 3·50 3·50
684. 2 m. Columnar cereus .. 3·75 4·00

162. Two Players chasing Ball.

1986. World Cup Football Championship, Mexico. Multicoloured.

686. 35 s. Type **162** 90 40
687. 50 s. Goalkeeper saving goal .. .. .. 1·25 90
688. 1 m. Three players chasing ball .. .. .. 2·50 2·25
689. 2 m. Two players competing for ball .. .. 4·00 4·00

1986. Appearance of Halley's Comet. As T **123** of Anguilla. Multicoloured.

691. 9 s. Galileo and 200 inch Hale telescope, Mount Palomar Observatory, California 40 15
692. 15 s. Halley's Comet and "Pioneer Venus 2" spacecraft 60 15
693. 70 s. Halley's Comet of 684 A.D. (from "Nuremberg Chronicle", 1493) .. 1·40 1·00
694. 3 m. Comet and landing of William the Conqueror, 1066 .. .. .. 3·50 4·00

163. International Year of the Child Gold Coin.

1986. First Anniv. of New Currency (1980). Multicoloured.

696. 30 s. Type **163** .. .. 6·50 5·50
697. 30 s. Five maloti banknote 6·50 5·50
698. 30 s. Fifty lisente coin .. 6·50 5·50
699. 30 s. Ten maloti banknote 6·50 5·50
700. 30 s. One sente coin .. 6·50 5·50

These stamps were prepared in 1980, but were not issued at that time.

1986. 60th Birthday of Queen Elizabeth II. As T **125** of Anguilla.

701. 90 s. black & yellow .. 60 60
702. 1 m. multicoloured .. 65 65
703. 2 m. multicoloured .. 1·40 1·40

DESIGNS. 90 s. Princess Elizabeth in Pantomime. 1 m. Queen at Windsor Horse Show, 1971. 2 m. At Royal Festival Hall, 1971.

1986. Centenary of Statue of Liberty. Immigrants to the U.S.A. As T **211** of Dominica. Multicoloured.

705. 15 s. Bela Bartok (composer) 55 20
706. 35 s. Felix Adler (philosopher) 65 30
707. 1 m. Victor Herbert (composer) .. .. 2·25 1·50
708. 3 m. David Niven (actor) 3·25 3·50

1986. "Ameripex" International Stamp Exhibition, Chicago. Walt Disney cartoon characters delivering mail. As T **212** of Dominica. Multicoloured.

710. 15 s. Mickey Mouse and Goofy as Japanese mail runners 30 20
711. 35 s. Mickey Mouse and Pluto with mail sledge .. 55 30
712. 1 m. Goofy as postman riding Harley-Davidson motorcycle .. .. 1·25 1·25
713. 2 m. Donald Duck operating railway mailbag apparatus .. .. 2·00 2·00

1986. Various stamps surch.

(a)

715 9 s. on 10 s. Red-billed pintail (horiz) (506) .. 1·25 1·25
722 9 s. on 30 s. "Charaxes jasius" (573) .. 15 10
723 9 s. on 60 s. "Pontia helice" (575) .. 4·00 4·00
716 15 s. on 1 s. Type **127** .. 4·00 3·00
724 15 s. on 1 s. Type **146** .. 2·75 2·75
717 15 s. on 2s. Speckled pigeon (horiz) (438) .. 4·00 4·50
725 15 s. on 2 s. "Aeropetes tulbaghia" (564) .. 20 20
726 15 s. on 3 s. "Colotis evenina" (565) .. 20 20
718 15 s. on 5 s. "Precis hierta" (567) 20 20
719 15 s. on 60 s. Cape longclaw (horiz) (509) .. 20 10
721 35 s. on 75 s. Hoopoe (510) 16·00 16·00
728 35 s. on 75 s. "Colotis regina" (576) 35 35

(b) On Nos. 503, 507, 566 and 569

729 9 s. on 5 s. Bokmakierie shrike 15 20
731 35 s. on 25 s. Malachite kingfisher 60 60
732 20 s. on 4 s. "Precis oenone" 10 10
733 40 s. on 7 s. "Phalanta phalantha" 15 20

(c) No. 722 further surch

734 3 s. on 9 s. on 30 s. "Charaxes jasius" .. 15 15
735 7 s. on 9 s. on 30 s. "Charaxes jasius" .. 25 25

1986. Royal Wedding. As T **213** of Antigua. Multicoloured.

736. 50 s. Prince Andrew and Miss Sarah Ferguson .. 40 40
737. 1 m. Prince Andrew .. 70 70
738. 3 m. Prince Andrew piloting helicopter .. 2·00 2·00

171. Basotho Pony and Rider.

1986. 20th Anniv. of Independence. Mult.

740. 9 s. Type **171** 25 10
741. 15 s. Basotho woman spinning mohair .. 30 15
742. 35 s. Crossing river rowing boat 45 30
743. 3 m. Thaba Tseka Post Office .. .. .. 2·40 2·50

1986. Christmas. Walt Disney cartoon characters. As T **220** of Antigua. Mult.

745. 15 s. Chip'n' Dale pulling Christmas cracker .. 20 15
746. 35 s. Mickey and Minnie Mouse 45 30
747. 1 m. Pluto pulling Christmas taffy .. .. 1·00 90
748. 2 m. Aunt Matilda baking 1·75 1·75

172. Rally Car. **173.** Lawn Tennis.

1987. Roof of Africa Motor Rally. Mult.

750. 9 s. Type **172** 10 10
751. 15 s. Motorcyclist 15 10
752. 35 s. Motorcyclist (different) 30 25
753. 4 m. Rally car (different) 2·50 2·50

1987. Olympic Games, Seoul (1988) (1st issue). Multicoloured.

754. 9 s. Type **173** 15 10
755. 15 s. Judo 15 10
756. 20 s. Athletics 20 15
757. 35 s. Boxing 30 30
758. 1 m. Diving 85 95
759. 3 m. Ten-pin bowling .. 2·25 2·50

See also Nos. 838/41.

174. Isaac Newton and Reflecting Telescope.

1987. Great Scientific Discoveries. Mult.

761. 5 s. Type **174** 10 10
762. 9 s. Alexander Graham Bell and first telephone 10 10
763. 75 s. Robert Goddard and liquid fuel rocket .. 40 45
764. 4 m. Chuck Yeager and "X-1" rocket plane .. 2·25 2·40

175. Grey Rhebuck.

1987. Flora and Fauna. Multicoloured.

766. 5 s. Type **175** 30 15
767. 9 s. Cape clawless otter .. 30 15
768. 15 s. Cape grey mongoose 40 20
769. 20 s. Free State daisy (vert.) 45 20
770. 35 s. River bells (vert.) .. 60 30
771. 1 m. Turkey flower (vert.) 1·50 1·50
772. 2 m Sweet briar (vert.) .. 2·25 2·50
773. 3 m. Mountain reedbuck .. 2·75 3·00

176. Scouts hiking.

1987. World Scout Jamboree, Australia. Multicoloured.

775. 9 s. Type **176** 30 15
776. 15 s. Scouts playing football 35 15
777. Kangaroos 45 30
778. 75 s. Scout saluting .. 90 55
779. 4 m. Australian scout windsurfing .. .. 3·00 3·00

177. Spotted Trunkfish and Columbus's Fleet.

1987. 500th Anniv. (1992) of Discovery of America by Columbus. Multicoloured.

781. 9 s. Type **177** 10 10
782. 15 s. Green turtle and ships 10 10
783. Columbus watching common dolphins from ship .. 20 25
784. 5 m. White-tailed tropic bird and fleet at sea .. 2·75 3·00

No. 782 is inscribed "Caribbean" in error.

178. "Madonna and Child" (detail).

1987. Christmas. Paintings by Raphael. Multicoloured.

786. 9 s. Type **178** 20 10
787. 15 s, "Marriage of the Virgin" 30 15
788. 35 s. "Coronation of the Virgin" (detail) 55 30
789. 90 s. "Madonna of the Chair" .. .. .. 1·25 1·25

179. Lesser Pied Kingfisher.

1988. Birds. Multicoloured.

791. 2 s. Type **179** 15 15
792. 3 s. Three-banded plover .. 15 15
793. 5 s. Spur-winged goose .. 15 15
794. 10 s. Clapper lark 15 15
795. 12 s. Red-eyed bulbul .. 30 15
796. 16 s. Cape weaver 30 15
797. 20 s. Paradise sparrow ("Red-headed Finch") .. 30 15
798. 30 s. Mountain chat .. 30 15
799. 40 s. Stonechat 30 20
800. 55 s. Pied barbet 35 25
801. 60 s. Cape glossy starling 40 30
802. 75 s. Cape sparrow .. 55 40
803. 1 m. Cattle egret 65 50
804. 3 m. Giant kingfisher .. 1·75 2·00
805. 10 m. Helmet guineafowl .. 5·50 6·00

1988. Royal Ruby Wedding. Nos. 701/3 optd. **40TH WEDDING ANNIVERSARY H.M. QUEEN ELIZABETH II H.R.H. THE DUKE OF EDINBURGH.**

806	90 s. black and yellow ..	35	40
807	1 m. multicoloured ..	40	45
808	2 m. multicoloured ..	80	85

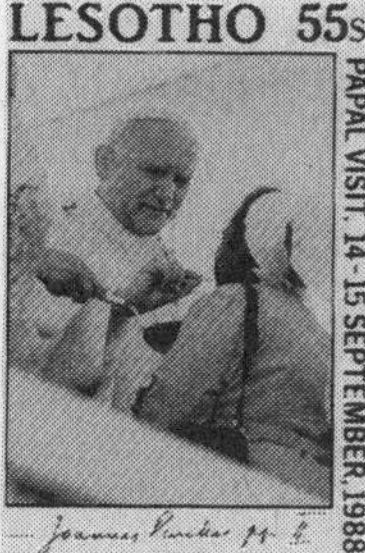

181 Mickey Mouse and Goofy outside Presidential Palace, Helsinki

1988. "Finlandia '88" International Stamp Exhibition, Helsinki. Designs showing Walt Disney cartoon characters in Finland. Mult.

810	1 s. Type **181**	10	10
811	2 s. Goofy and Mickey Mouse in sauna ..	10	10
812	3 s. Goofy and Mickey Mouse fishing in lake ..	10	10
813	4 s. Mickey and Minnie Mouse and Finlandia Hall, Helsinki	10	10
814	5 s. Mickey Mouse photographing Goofy at Sibelius Monument, Helsinki	10	10
815	10 s. Mickey Mouse and Goofy pony trekking ..	10	10
816	3 m. Goofy, Mickey and Minnie Mouse at Helsinki Olympic Stadium	1·25	1·40
817	5 m. Mickey Mouse and Goofy meeting Santa at Arctic Circle	2·00	2·10

182 Pope John Paul II giving Communion

1988. Visit of Pope John Paul II. Mult.

819	55 s. Type **182**	20	25
820	2 m. Pope leading procession	80	85
821	3 m. Pope at airport ..	1·25	1·40
822	4 m. Pope John Paul II ..	1·60	1·75

183 Large-toothed Rock Hyrax

1988. Small Mammals of Lesotho. Mult.

824	16 s. Type **183**	10	10
825	40 s. Ratel and honey guide (bird) ..	15	20
826	75 s. Small-spotted genet	30	35
827	3 m. Yellow mongoose ..	1·25	1·40

184 "Birth of Venus" (detail) (Botticelli)

1988. Famous Paintings. Multicoloured.

829	15 s. Type **184**	10	10
830	25 s. "View of Toledo" (El Greco)	10	15
831	40 s. "Maids of Honour" (detail) (Velasquez) ..	15	20
832	50 s. "The Fifer" (Manet)	20	25
833	55 s. "Starry Night" (detail) (Van Gogh) ..	20	25
834	75 s. "Prima Ballerina" (Degas)	30	35
835	2 m. "Bridge over Water Lilies" (Monet) ..	80	85
836	3 m. "Guernica" (detail) (Picasso)	1·25	1·40

185 Wrestling

1988. Olympic Games, Seoul (2nd series). Multicoloured.

838	12 s. Type **185**	10	10
839	16 s. Show jumping (vert)	10	10
840	55 s. Shooting	20	25
841	3 m. 50 As 16 s. (vert) ..	1·40	1·50

186 Yannick Noah and Eiffel Tower, Paris

1988. 75th Anniv of International Tennis Federation. Multicoloured.

843	12 s. Type **186** ..	10	10
844	20 s. Rod Laver and Sydney Harbour Bridge and Opera House ..	10	10
845	30 s. Ivan Lendl and Prague	10	15
846	65 s. Jimmy Connors and Tokyo (vert) ..	25	30
847	1 m. Arthur Ashe and Barcelona (vert) ..	40	45
848	1 m. 55 Althea Gibson and New York (vert) ..	60	65
849	2 m. Chris Evert and Vienna (vert) ..	80	85
850	2 m. 40 Boris Becker and Houses of Parliament, London (vert) ..	1·00	1·10
851	3 m. Martina Navratilova and Golden Gate Bridge, San Francisco ..	1·25	1·40

No. 844 is inscribed "SIDNEY" in error.

1988. Christmas. 500th Birth Anniv of Titian (artist). As T **238** of Antigua, but inscr "CHRISTMAS 1988". Multicoloured.

853	12 s. "The Averoldi Polyptych" (detail) ..	10	10
854	20 s. "Christ and the Adulteress" (detail) ..	10	10
855	35 s. "Christ and the Adulteress" (different detail)	15	20
856	45 s. "Angel of the Annunciation" ..	20	25
857	65 s. "Saint Dominic" ..	25	30
858	1 m. "The Vendramin Family" (detail) ..	40	45
859	2 m. "Mary Magdalen" ..	80	85
860	3 m. "The Tribute Money"	1·25	1·40

187 Pilatus "PC-6 Turbo Porter"

1989. 125th Anniv of International Red Cross. Aircraft. Multicoloured.

862	12 s. Type **187**	10	10
863	20 s. Unloading medical supplies from Cessna "Caravan"	10	10
864	55 s. De Havilland "DHC-6 Otter"	20	25
865	3 m. Douglas "DC-3" ..	1·25	1·40

1989. Japanese Art. Paintings by Hiroshige. As T **250** of Antigua. Multicoloured.

867	12 s. "Dawn Mist at Mishima"	10	10
868	16 s. "Night Snow at Kambara"	10	10
869	20 s. "Wayside Inn at Mariko Station" ..	10	10
870	35 s. "Shower at Shono" ..	15	20
871	55 s. "Snowfall on the Kisokaido near Oi" ..	20	25
872	1 m. "Autumn Moon at Seba"	40	45
873	3 m. 20 "Evening Moon at Ryogoku Bridge" ..	1·25	1·40
874	5 m. "Cherry Blossoms at Arashiyama" ..	2·00	2·10

188 Mickey Mouse as General

1989. "Philexfrance 89" International Stamp Exhibition, Paris. Designs showing Walt Disney cartoon characters in French military uniforms of the Revolutionary period. Mult.

876	1 s. Type **188**	10	10
877	2 s. Ludwig von Drake as infantryman	10	10
878	3 s. Goofy as grenadier ..	10	10
879	4 s. Horace Horsecollar as cavalryman	10	10
880	5 s. Pete as hussar ..	10	10
881	10 s. Donald Duck as marine	10	10
882	3 m. Gyro Gearloose as National Guard ..	1·25	1·40
883	5 m. Scrooge McDuck as admiral	2·00	2·10

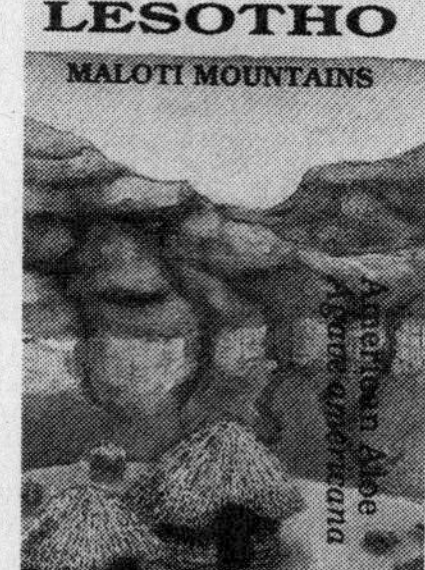

189 "Paxillus involutus"

1989. Fungi. Multicoloured.

900	12 s. Type **189**	10	10
901	16 s. "Ganoderma applanatum"	10	10
902	55 s. "Suillus granulatus"	20	25
903	5 m. "Stereum hirsutum"	2·00	2·25

INDEX

Countries can be quickly located by referring to the index at the end of this volume.

190 Sesotho Huts

1989. Maloti Mountains. Multicoloured.

905	1 m. Type **190**	40	45
906	1 m. American aloe and mountains	40	45
907	1 m. River valley with waterfall	40	45
908	1 m. Sesotho tribesman on ledge	40	45

Nos. 890/3 were printed together, se-tenant, forming a composite design.

191 Marsh Sandpiper

1989. Migrant Birds. Multicoloured.

910	12 s. Type **191**	10	10
911	65 s. Little stint	25	30
912	1 m. Ringed plover ..	40	45
913	4 m. Curlew sandpiper ..	1·60	1·75

192 Launch of "Apollo 11"

1989. 20th Anniv of First Manned Landing on Moon. Multicoloured.

915	12 s. Type **192**	10	10
916	16 s. Lunar module "Eagle" landing on Moon (horiz)	10	10
917	40 s. Neil Armstrong leaving "Eagle" ..	15	20
918	55 s. Edwin Aldrin on Moon (horiz)	20	25
919	1 m. Aldrin performing scientific experiment (horiz)	40	45
920	2 m. "Eagle" leaving Moon (horiz)	80	85
921	3 m. Command module "Columbia" in Moon orbit (horiz)	1·25	1·40
922	4 m. Command module on parachutes	1·60	1·75

193 English Penny Post Paid Mark, 1680

1989. "World Stamp Expo '89" International Stamp Exhibition, Washington. Stamps and Postmarks.

924	**193**	75 s. red, black & stone	30	35
925	–	75 s. black, grey & red	30	35
926	–	75 s. violet, blk & brn	30	35
927	–	75 s. brown, black and light brown ..	30	35

928 – 75 s. black and yellow 30 35
929 – 75 s. multicoloured .. 30 35
930 – 75 s. black and lilac .. 30 35
931 – 75 s. black, red & brn 30 35
932 – 75 s. red, black & yell 30 35

DESIGNS: No. 925, German postal seal and feather, 1807; 926, British Post Offices in Crete 1898 20 pa. stamp; 927, Bermuda 1848 Perot 1d. provisional; 928, U.S.A. Pony Express cancellation, 1860; 929, Finland 1856 5 k. stamp; 930, Fiji 1870 "Fiji Times" 1d. stamp, 1870; 931, Sweden newspaper wrapper handstamp, 1823; 932, Bhor 1879 ½a. stamp.

1989. Christmas. Paintings by Velasquez. As T **259** of Antigua. Multicoloured.

934 12 s. "The Immaculate Conception" 10 10
935 20 s. "St. Anthony Abbot and St. Paul the Hermit" 10 10
936 35 s. "St. Thomas the Apostle" 15 20
937 55 s. "Christ in the House of Martha and Mary" .. 20 25
938 1 m. "St. John writing The Apocalypse on Patmos" 40 45
939 3 m. "The Virgin presenting the Chasuble to St. Ildephonsus" .. .. 1·25 1·40
940 4 m. "The Adoration of the Magi" .. .. .. 1·60 1·75

194 Scene from 1966 World Cup Final, England

1989. World Cup Football Championship, Italy. Scenes from past finals. Multicoloured.

942 12 s. Type **194** 10 10
943 16 s. 1970 final, Mexico .. 10 10
944 55 s. 1974 final, West Germany 20 25
945 5 m. 1982 final, Spain .. 2·00 2·10

1990. No. 795 and 798/9 surch.

947 16 s. on 12 s. Red-eyed bulbul 25 15
948e 16 s. on 30 s. Mountain chat 10 10
948f 16 s. on 40 s. Stonechat .. 10 10

197 "Byblia anvatara"

1990. Butterflies. Multicoloured.

949 12 s. Type **197** 10 10
950 16 s. "Cynthia cardui" .. 10 10
951 55 s. "Precis oenone" .. 20 25
952 65 s. "Pseudacraea boisduvali" 25 30
953 1 m. "Precis orithya" .. 40 45
954 2 m. "Precis sohpia" .. 80 85
955 3 m. "Danaus chrysippus" 1·25 1·40
956 4 m. "Druryia antimachus" 1·60 1·75

198 "Satyrium princeps"

1990. "EXPO 90" International Garden and Greenery Exhibition, Osaka. Local Orchids. Multicoloured.

958 12 s. Type **198** 10 10
959 16 s. "Huttonaea pulchra" 10 10
960 55 s. "Herschelia graminifolia" 20 25
961 1 m. "Ansellia gigantea" 40 45
962 1 m. 55 "Polystachya pubescens" 60 65
963 2 m. 40 "Penthea filicornis" .. .. .. 1·00 1·10
964 3 m. "Disperis capensis" 1·25 1·40
965 4 m. "Disa uniflora" .. 1·60 1·75

1990. 90th Birthday of Queen Elizabeth the Queen Mother. As T **99** of Grenada Grenadines.

967 1 m. 50 black and mauve 60 65
968 1 m. 50 black and mauve 60 65
969 1 m. 50 black and mauve 60 65

DESIGNS: No. 967, Lady Elizabeth Bowes-Lyon and friend in fancy dress; 968, Lady Elizabeth Bowes-Lyon in evening dress; 969, Lady Elizabeth Bowes-Lyon wearing hat.

199 King Moshoeshoe II and Prince Mohato wearing Seana-Marena Blankets

1990. Traditional Blankets. Multicoloured.

971 12 s. Type **199** 10 10
972 16 s. Prince Mohato wearing Seana-Marena blanket 10 10
973 1 m. Pope John Paul II wearing Seana-Marena blanket 40 45
974 3 m. Basotho horsemen wearing Matlama blankets .. .. 1·25 1·40

200 Filling Truck at No. 1 Quarry

1990. Lesotho Highlands Water Project. Multicoloured.

976 16 s. Type **200** 10 10
977 20 s. Tanker lorry on Pitseng–Malibamatso road 10 10
978 55 s. Piers for Malibamatso Bridge 20 25
979 2 m. Excavating Mphosong section of Pitseng–Malibamatso road .. 80 85

201 Mother breastfeeding Baby

1990. U.N.I.C.E.F. Child Survival Campaign. Multicoloured.

981 12 s. Type **201** .. 10 10
982 55 s. Baby receiving oral rehydration therapy .. 20 25
983 1 m. Weight monitoring .. 40 45

1990. Olympic Games, Barcelona (1992). As T **268** of Antigua. Multicoloured.

984 16 s. Men's triple jump .. 10 10
985 55 s. Men's 200 metres race 20 25
986 1 m. Men's 5000 metres race 40 45
987 4 m. Show jumping .. 1·60 1·75

202 "Virgin and Child" (detail, Rubens)

1990. Christmas. Paintings by Rubens. Mult.

989 12 s. Type **202** 10 10
990 16 s. "Adoration of the Magi" (detail) 10 10
991 55 s. "Head of One of the Three Kings" 20 25
992 80 s. "Adoration of the Magi" (different detail) 35 40
993 1 m. "Virgin and Child" (different detail) .. 40 45
994 2 m. "Adoration of the Magi" (different detail) 80 85
995 3 m. "Virgin and Child" (different detail) .. 1·25 1·40
996 4 m. "Adoration of the Magi" (different detail) 1·60 1·75

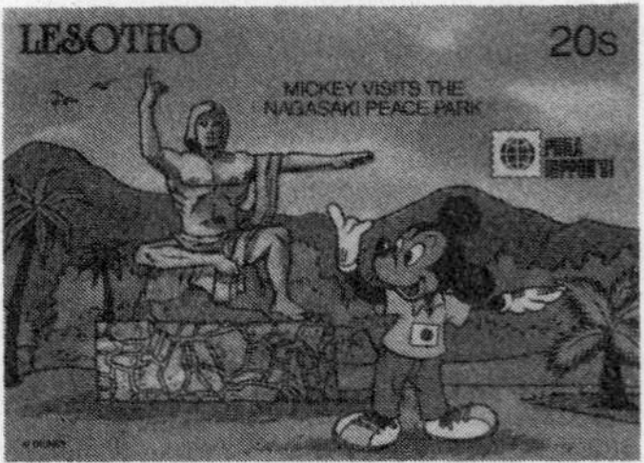

204 Mickey Mouse at Nagasaki Peace Park

1991. "Philanippon '91" International Stamp Exhibition, Tokyo. Walt Disney cartoon characters in Japan. Multicoloured.

998 20 s. Type **204** 10 10
999 30 s. Mickey Mouse on Kamakura Beach .. 10 15
1000 40 s. Mickey and Donald Duck with Bunraku puppet 15 20
1001 50 s. Mickey and Donald eating soba 20 25
1002 75 s. Mickey and Minnie Mouse at tea house .. 30 35
1003 1 m. Mickey running after bullet train 40 45
1004 3 m. Mickey Mouse with deer at Todaiji Temple, Nara .. .. .. 1·25 1·40
1005 4 m. Mickey and Minnie outside Imperial Palace 1·60 1·75

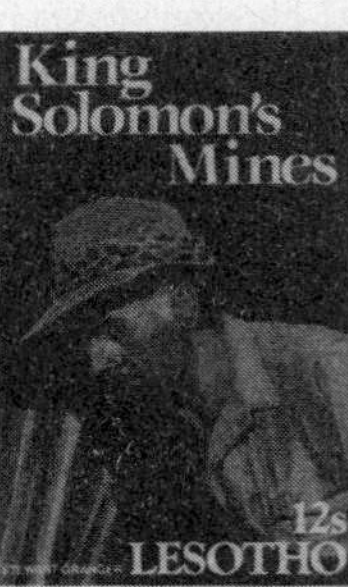

205 Stewart Granger ("King Solomon's Mines")

1991. Famous Films with African Themes. Multicoloured.

1007 12 s. Type **205** 10 10
1008 16 s. Johnny Weissmuller ("Tarzan the Ape Man") 10 10
1009 30 s. Clark Gable and Grace Kelly ("Mogambo") 10 15
1010 55 s. Sigourney Weaver and gorilla ("Gorillas in the Mist") 20 25
1011 70 s. Humphrey Bogart and Katharine Hepburn ("The African Queen") 30 35
1012 1 m. John Wayne and capture of rhinoceros ("Hatari!") 40 45
1013 2 m. Meryl Streep and aircraft ("Out of Africa") 80 85
1014 4 m. Arsenio Hall and Eddie Murphy ("Coming to America") 1·60 1·75

206 "Satyrus aello"

1991. Butterflies. Multicoloured.

1016 2 s. Type **206** 10 10
1017 3 s. "Erebia medusa" .. 10 10
1018 5 s. "Melanargia galathea" 10 10
1019 10 s. "Erebia aethiops" .. 10 10
1020 20 s. "Coenonympha pamphilus" 10 10
1021 25 s. "Pyrameis atalanta" .. 10 10
1022 30 s. "Charaxes jasius" .. 10 15
1023 40 s. "Colias palaeno" .. 15 20
1024 50 s. "Colias cliopatra" .. 20 25
1025 60 s. "Colias philodice" 25 30
1026 70 s. "Rhumni gonepterix" 30 35
1027 1 m. "Colias caesonia" .. 40 45
1028 2 m. "Pyrameis cardui" .. 80 85
1029 3 m. "Danaus chrysippus" 1·25 1·50
1030 10 m. "Apatura iris" .. 4·00 4·25

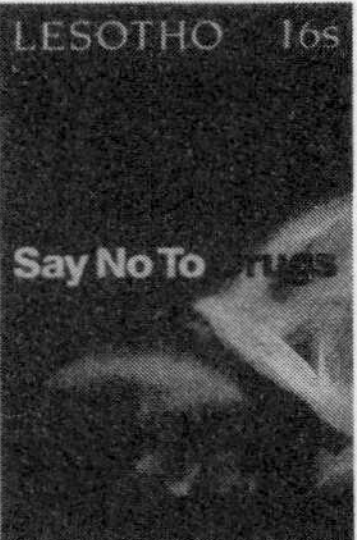

207 Victim of Drug Abuse

1991. "No To Drugs" Campaign.

1031 **207** 16 s. multicoloured .. 10 10

208 Wattled Cranes

1991. Southern Africa Development Coordination Conference Tourism Promotion. Multicoloured.

1032 12 s. Type **208** 10 10
1033 16 s. Butterfly on flowers 10 10
1034 25 s. Zebra and tourist bus at Mukurub (rock formation), Namibia .. 10 10

209 De Gaulle in 1939

1991. Birth Centenary of Charles de Gaulle (French statesman).

1036	**209**	20 s. black and brown	10	10
1037	–	40 s. black and purple	15	20
1038	–	50 s. black and green	20	25
1039	–	60 s. black and blue ..	25	30
1040	–	4 m. black and red ..	1·60	1·75

DESIGNS: 40 s. General De Gaulle as Free French leader; 50 s. De Gaulle as provisional President of France 1944–46; 60 s. Charles de Gaulle in 1958; 4 m. Pres. De Gaulle.

1991. 10th Wedding Anniv of Prince and Princess of Wales. As T **280** of Antigua. Multicoloured.

1041	50 s. Prince and Princess of Wales	20	25
1042	70 s. Prince Charles at polo and Princess Diana holding Prince Henry	30	35
1043	1 m. Prince Charles with Prince Henry and Princess Diana in evening dress	40	45
1044	3 m. Prince William and Prince Henry in school uniform	1·25	1·50

211 "St. Anne with Mary and the Child Jesus"

1991. Christmas. Drawings by Albrecht Durer.

1046	**211**	20 s. black and mauve	10	10
1047	–	30 s. black and blue ..	10	10
1048	–	50 s. black and green	20	25
1049	–	60 s. black and red ..	25	30
1050	–	70 s. black and yellow	30	35
1051	–	1 m. black and orange	40	45
1052	–	2 m. black and purple	80	85
1053	–	4 m. black and blue ..	1·60	1·75

DESIGNS: 30 s. "Mary on Grass Bench"; 50 s. "Mary with Crown of Stars"; 60 s. "Mary with Child beside Tree"; 70 s. "Mary with Child beside Wall"; 1 m. "Mary in Halo on Crescent Moon"; 2 m. "Mary breastfeeding Child"; 4 m. "Mary with Infant in Swaddling Clothes".

212 Mickey Mouse and Pluto pinning the Tail on the Donkey

1991. Children's Games. Walt Disney cartoon characters. Multicoloured.

1055	20 s. Type **212**	10	10
1056	30 s. Mickey playing mancala	10	10
1057	40 s. Mickey rolling hoop	15	20
1058	50 s. Minnie Mouse hula-hooping	20	25
1059	70 s. Mickey and Pluto throwing a frisbee ..	30	35
1060	1 m. Donald Duck with a diabolo	40	45
1061	2 m. Donald's nephews playing marbles	80	85
1062	3 m. Donald with Rubik's cube	1·25	1·50

213 Lanner Falcon

1992. Birds. Multicoloured.

1064	30 s. Type **213**	10	10
1065	30 s. Bateleur	10	10
1066	30 s. Paradise sparrow (inscr "Red-headed finch")	10	10
1067	30 s. Lesser striped swallow	10	10
1068	30 s. Alpine swift ..	10	10
1069	30 s. Didric cuckoo ..	10	10
1070	30 s. Yellow-tufted malachite sunbird (inscr "Crimson-breasted shirke")	10	10
1071	30 s. Burchell's gonolek ..	10	10
1072	30 s. Pin-tailed whydah ..	10	10
1073	30 s. Lilac-breasted roller	10	10
1074	30 s. Black korhaan ..	10	10
1075	30 s. Black-collared barbet	10	10
1076	30 s. Secretary bird ..	10	10
1077	30 s. Red-billed quelea ..	10	10
1078	30 s. Red bishop ..	10	10
1079	30 s. Ring-necked dove ..	10	10
1080	30 s. Yellow canary ..	10	10
1081	30 s. Cape longclaw ..	10	10
1082	30 s. Cordon-bleu (inscr "Blue waxbill") ..	10	10
1083	30 s. Golden bishop ..	10	10

Nos. 1064/83 were printed together, se-tenant, forming a composite design.

1992. 40th Anniv of Queen Elizabeth II's Accession. As T **292** of Antigua. Mult.

1084	20 s. Huts on mountain ..	10	10
1085	30 s. View from mountains	10	10
1086	1 m. Cacti and mountain	40	45
1087	4 m. Thaba-Bosiu ..	1·60	1·75

POSTAGE DUE STAMPS

1966. Nos. D 9/10 of Basutoland optd. **LESOTHO.**

D 11.	D 2.	1 c. red	20	60
D 12.		5 c. violet	20	90

D 1.

D 2.

1967.

D 13.	D 1.	1 c. blue	15	1·50
D 14.		2 c. red	15	2·00
D 15.		5 c. green	20	2·25

1986.

D 19	D 2	2 s. green	10	10
D 20		5 s. blue	10	10
D 21		35 s. violet	10	10

APPENDIX

The following stamps have either been issued in excess of postal needs, or have not been available to the public in reasonable quantities at face value.

1981–83.

15th Anniv. of Independence. Classic Stamps of the World. 10 m. × 40, each embossed on gold foil.

MAFEKING

A town in Bechuanaland. Special stamps issued by British garrison during Boer War.

12 pence = 1 shilling.
20 shillings = 1 pound.

1900. Stamps of Cape of Good Hope surch. **MAFEKING BESIEGED** and value.

1.	**6.**	1d. on ½d. green	£150	48·00
2.	**17.**	1d. on ½d. green	£180	55·00
3.		3d. on 1d. red	£150	48·00
4.	**6.**	6d. on 3d. mauve	£6500	£250
5.		1s. on 4d. olive	£3500	£325

1900. Stamps of Bechuanaland Prot. (Queen Victoria) surch. **MAFEKING BESIEGED** and value.

6.	**71.**	1d. on ½d. red (No. 59) ..	£150	48·00
7.	**57.**	3d. on 1d. lilac (No. 61)	£850	65·00
8.	**73.**	6d. on 2d. green and red (No. 62)	£1000	65·00
9.	**75.**	6d. on 3d. purple on yell. (No. 63)	£3000	£250
14.	**79.**	1s. on 6d. purple on red (No. 65)	£2570	80·00

1900. Stamps of Br. Bechuanaland surch. **MAFEKING BESIEGED** and value.

10.	**3.**	6d. on 3d. lilac and black (No. 12)	£400	60·00
11.	**76.**	1s. on 4d. green & brown (No. 35)	£1200	65·00
15.	**79.**	1s. on 6d. purple on red (No. 36)	£6000	£600
16.	**82.**	2s. on 1s. green (No. 37)	£5500	£300

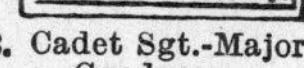

3. Cadet Sgt.-Major Goodyear.

4. General Baden-Powell.

1900.

17.	**3.**	1d. blue on blue ..	£800	£250
19.	**4.**	3d. blue on blue ..	£1100	£400

MALACCA

A British Settlement on the Malay Peninsula which became a state of the Federation of Malaya, incorporated in Malaysia in 1963.

100 cents = 1 dollar (Malayan).

1948. Silver Wedding. As T **10/11** of Aden.

1.	10 c. violet	25	30
2.	$5 brown	24·00	35·00

1949. As T **58** of Straits Settlements.

3.	1 c. black	10	60
4.	2 c. orange	20	45
5.	3 c. green	20	1·50
6.	4 c. brown	15	10
6a.	5 c. purple	45	85
7.	6 c. grey	20	50
8.	8 c. red	30	2·50
8a.	8 c. green	85	3·25
9.	10 c. mauve	15	10
9a.	12 c. red	95	1·75
10.	15 c. blue	30	60
11.	20 c. black and green ..	30	3·25
11a.	20 c. blue	1·25	1·40
12.	25 c. purple and orange ..	30	50
12a.	35 c. red and purple ..	1·00	1·50
13.	40 c. red and purple ..	1·25	8·50
14.	50 c. black and blue ..	50	75
15.	$1 blue and purple ..	4·00	8·50
16.	$2 green and red ..	11·00	16·00
17.	$5 green and brown ..	28·00	32·00

1949. U.P.U. As T **20/23** of Antigua.

18.	10 c. purple	15	45
19.	15 c. blue	45	1·75
20.	25 c. orange	45	2·50
21.	50 c. black	1·00	3·75

1953. Coronation. As T **13** of Aden.

22	10 c. black and purple ..	20	10

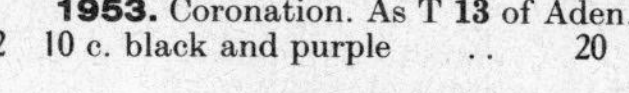

1. Queen Elizabeth II.

1954.

23.	**1.**	1 c. black	10	30
24.		2 c. orange	30	35
25.		4 c. brown	30	10
26.		5 c. mauve	30	60
27.		6 c. grey	10	15
28.		8 c. green	30	50
29.		10 c. purple	20	10
30.		12 c. red	20	85
31.		20 c. blue	20	15
32.		25 c. purple and orange ..	20	20
33.		30 c. red and purple ..	20	15
34.		35 c. red and purple ..	20	35
35.		50 c. black and blue ..	30	40
36.		$1 blue and purple ..	2·25	4·25
37.		$2 green and red ..	13·00	18·00
38.		$5 green and brown ..	14·00	19·00

1957. As Nos. 92/102 of Kedah but inset portrait of Queen Elizabeth II.

39.	1 c. black	10	40
40.	2 c. red	10	40
41.	4 c. sepia	10	10
42.	5 c. lake	10	10
43.	8 c. green	1·25	2·25
44.	10 c. sepia	15	10
45.	20 c. blue	30	40
46.	50 c. black and blue ..	30	50
47.	$1 blue and purple ..	2·00	2·50
48.	$2 green and red ..	6·50	12·00
49.	$5 brown and green ..	8·50	13·00

2. Copra.

1960. As Nos. 39/49 but with inset picture of Melaka tree and Pelandok (mouse-deer) as in T **2**.

50	1 c. black	10	30
51	2 c. red	10	30
52	4 c. sepia	10	10
53	5 c. lake	10	10
54	8 c. green	1·25	80
55	10 c. purple	15	10
56	20 c. blue	20	20
57	50 c. black and blue ..	30	30
58	$1 blue and purple ..	1·50	2·00
59	$2 green and red ..	3·00	4·50
60	$5 brown and green ..	7·50	5·50

3. "Vanda hookeriana".

1965. As Nos. 115/21 of Kedah but with Arms of Malacca inset and inscr. "MELAKA" as in T **3**.

61.	**3.**	1 c. multicoloured ..	10	50
62.	–	2 c. multicoloured ..	10	50
63.	–	5 c. multicoloured ..	10	10
64.	–	6 c. multicoloured ..	20	30
65.	–	10 c. multicoloured ..	15	10
66.	–	15 c. multicoloured ..	1·25	40
67.	–	20 c. multicoloured ..	1·75	65

The higher values used in Malacca were Nos. 20/7 of Malaysia.

4. "Papilio demoleus".

1971. Butterflies. As Nos. 124/30 of Kedah but with Arms of Malacca as in T **4**. Inscr. "melaka".

70.	–	1 c. multicoloured ..	15	50
71.	–	2 c. multicoloured ..	40	50
72.	–	5 c. multicoloured ..	55	10
73.	**4.**	6 c. multicoloured ..	55	40
74.	–	10 c. multicoloured ..	55	10
75.	–	15 c. multicoloured ..	80	10
76.	–	20 c. multicoloured ..	90	80

The higher values in use with this issue were Malaysia Nos. 64/71.

5. "Durio zibethinus".

1979. Flowers. As Nos. 135/41 of Kedah but with Arms of Malacca and inscr. "melaka" as in T **5**.

82	1 c. "Rafflesia hasseltii"	10	30
83	2 c. "Peterocarpus indicus"	10	30
84	5 c. "Lagerstroemia speciosa"	10	10
85	10 c. Type **5**	10	10
86	15 c. "Hibiscus rosa-sinesis"	15	10
87	20 c. "Rhododendron scortechinii"	15	10
88	25 c. "Etlingera elatior" (inscr "Phaeomeria speciosa"	15	30

6. Rubber.

1986. As Nos. 152/8 of Kedah but with Arms of Malacca and inscr. "MELAKA" as in T **6**.

96.	1 c. Coffee	10	10
97.	2 c. Coconuts	10	10
98.	5 c. Cocoa	10	10
99.	10 c. Black pepper ..	10	10
100.	15 c. Type **6**	10	10
101.	20 c. Oil palm	10	10
102.	30 c. Rice	10	15

MALAWI

Formerly Nyasaland, became an independent Republic within the Commonwealth on the 6th July, 1966.

1964. 12 pence = 1 shilling;
20 shillings = 1 pound
1970. 100 tambalas = 1 kwacha.

44. Dr. H. Banda (Prime Minister) and Independence Monument.

1964. Independence.

211.	**44.**	3d. olive and sepia ..	10	10
212.	–	6d. multicoloured ..	10	10
213.	–	1s. 3d. multicoloured ..	20	10
214.	–	2s. 6d. multicoloured ..	30	35

Designs (each with Dr. Hastings Banda): 6d. Rising Sun. 1s. 3d. National Flag. 2s. 6d. Coat of arms.

48. Tung Tree.

1964. As Nos. 199/210 of Nyasaland but inscr. "MALAWI" as in T **48**. The 9d., 1s. 6d. and £2 are new values and designs.

252	½d. violet	10	10
216	1d. black and green ..	10	10
217	2d. brown	10	10
218	3d. brown, green & bistre	15	10
219	4d. blue and yellow ..	25	15
256	6d. purple, green and blue	25	10
257	9d. brown, green & yellow	35	10
258	1s. brown, blue & yellow..	25	10
223	1s. 3d. bronze and brown..	50	40
259	1s. 6d. brown and green ..	30	10
224	2s. 6d. brown and blue ..	1·10	1·00
225	5s. multicoloured (I) ..	65	2·00
225a	5s. multicoloured (II) ..	3·25	90
226	10s. green, salmon & black	1·50	2·00
227	£1 brown and yellow ..	6·00	5·50
262	£2 multicoloured	25·00	24·00

Designs (New): 1s. 6d. Burley tobacco. £2, "Cyrestis camillus" (butterfly).

Two types of 5s. I, inscr "LAKE NYASA". II, inscr "LAKE MALAWI".

49. Christmas Star and Globe.

1964. Christmas.

228.	**49.**	3d. green and gold ..	10	10
229.		6d. mauve and gold ..	10	10
230.		1s. 3d. violet and gold ..	10	10
231.		2s. 6d. blue and gold ..	20	25

50. Coins.

1964. Malawi's 1st Coinage. Coins in black and silver.

232.	**50.**	3d. green..	10	10
233.		9d. mauve	10	10
234.		1s. 6d. purple	15	10
235.		3s. blue	25	20

1965. Nos. 223/4 surch.

236.	1s. 6d. on 1s. 3d. bronze & brown	10	10
237.	3s. on 2s. 6d. brown & blue	20	20

52. Chilembwe leading Rebels.

1965. 50th Anniversary of 1915 Rising.

238.	**52.**	3d. violet and green ..	10	10
239.		9d. olive and orange ..	10	10
240.		1s. 6d. brown and blue..	10	10
241.		3s. turquoise and blue ..	20	15

53. "Learning and Scholarship".

1965. Opening of Malawi University.

242.	**53.**	3d. black and green ..	10	10
243.		9d. black and mauve ..	10	10
244.		1s. 6d. black and violet..	10	10
245.		3s. black and blue ..	15	20

54. "Papilio ophidicephalus".

1966. Malawi Butterfiles. Multicoloured.

247	4d. Type **54**	60	10
248	9d. "Papilio desmondi" (magdae)	85	10
249	1s. 6d. "Epamera handmani"	1·25	30
250	3s. "Amauris crawshayi"	2·50	3·00

58. British Central Africa 6d. Stamp of 1891.

1966. 75th Anniv. of Postal Services.

263.	**58.**	4d. blue and green ..	10	10
264.		9d. blue and red ..	10	10
265.		1s. 6d. blue and lilac ..	15	10
266.		3s. grey and blue ..	25	30

59. President Banda.

1966. Republic Day.

268.	**59.**	4d. brown, silver & green	10	10
269.		9d. brown, silver & mauve	10	10
270.		1s. 6d. brown, silver & vio.	10	10
271.		3s. brown, silver and blue	15	10

60. Bethlehem.

1966. Christmas.

273.	**60.**	4d. green and gold ..	10	10
274.		9d. purple and gold ..	10	10
275.		1s. 6d. red and gold ..	15	10
276.		3s. blue and gold ..	40	50

61. "Ilala I".

1967. Lake Malawi Steamers.

277.	**61.**	4d. black, yellow & grn.	20	10
278.	–	9d. black, yellow & mve.	25	10
279.	–	1s. 6d. black, red & violet	40	15
280.	–	3s. black, red and blue..	1·00	1·25

Designs: 9d. "Dove". 1s. 6d. "Chauncy Maples I" (wrongly inscr. "Chauncey"). 3s. "Gwendolen".

62. "Turquoise-gold Chichlid".

1967. Lake Malawi Chichlids. Multicoloured.

281.	4d. Type **62**	15	10
282.	9d. "Red Finned Chichlid"	20	10
283.	1s. 6d. "Zebra Chichlid"	30	10
284.	3s. "Golden Chichlid" ..	1·00	1·00

63. Rising Sun and Gearwheel.

1967. Industrial Development.

285.	**63.**	4d. black and green ..	10	10
286.		9d. black and red ..	10	10
287.		1s. 6d. black and violet	10	10
288.		3s. black and blue ..	15	15

64. Mary and Joseph beside Crib.

1967. Christmas.

290.	**64.**	4d. blue and green ..	10	10
291.		9d. blue and red ..	10	10
292.		1s. 6d. blue and yellow	10	10
293.		3s. deep blue and blue	15	15

65. "Calotropis procera".

1968. Wild Flowers. Multicoloured.

295.	4d. Type **65**	15	10
296.	9d. "Borreria dibrachiata"	15	10
297.	1s. 6d. "Hibiscus rhodanthus"	15	10
298.	3s. "Bidens pinnatipartita"	20	20

66. Saddleback Steam Locomotive, "Thistle" No. 1.

1968. Malawi Locomotives.

300.	**66.**	4d. green, blue and red	25	10
301.	–	9d. red, blue and green	30	10
302.	–	1s. 6d. multicoloured ..	55	15
303.	–	3s. multicoloured ..	1·00	1·00

Designs: 9d. Class "G" steam locomotive. 1s. 6d. Diesel locomotive "Zambesi". 3s. Diesel railcar.

67. "The Nativity" (Piero della Francesca).

1968. Christmas. Multicoloured.

305.	4d. Type **67**	10	10
306.	9d. "The Adoration of the Shepherds" (Murillo) ..	10	10
307.	1s. 6d. "The Adoration of the Shepherds" (Reni) ..	10	10
308.	3s. "Nativity, with God the Father and Holy Ghost" (Pittoni) ..	15	10

69. Nyassa Lovebird.

70. Carmine Bee Eater.

1968. Birds (1st series). Multicoloured.

310.	1d. Scarlet-chested Sunbird (horiz.)	15	10
311.	2d. Violet Starling (horiz.)	15	10
312.	3d. White-browed Robin Chat (horiz.)	20	10
313.	4d. Red-billed Fire Finch (horiz.)	35	30
314.	6d. Type **69**	45	10
315.	9d. Yellow-rumped Bishop	50	60
316.	1s. Type **70**	60	15
317.	1s. 6d. Grey-headed Bush Shrike	5·00	6·00
318.	2s. Paradise Whydah ..	5·00	7·00
319.	3 s. African Paradise Flycatcher (vert.)	4·50	3·75
320.	5s. Bateleur (vert.) ..	5·50	4·00
321.	10s. Saddle-bill Stork (vert.)	5·50	7·50
322.	£1 Purple Heron (vert.) ..	12·00	17·00
323.	£2 Knysna Turaco ..	35·00	48·00

SIZES: 1d. to 9d. as Type **69**, 1s. 6d. to £2 as Type **70**.

See also Nos. 473/85.

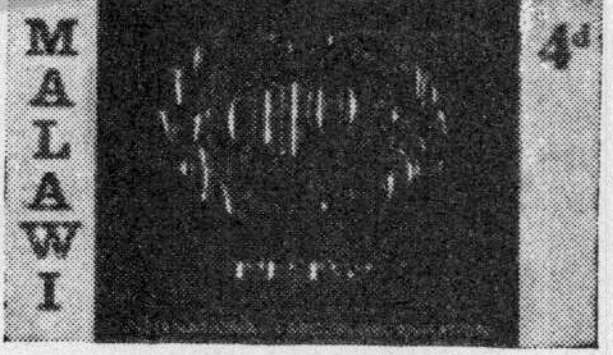

71. I.L.O. Emblem.

1969. 50th Anniv. of Int. Labour Organization.

324. **71.**	4d. gold and green ..	10	10
325.	9d. gold and brown ..	10	10
326.	1s. 6d. gold and brown	10	10
327.	3s. gold and blue ..	15	15

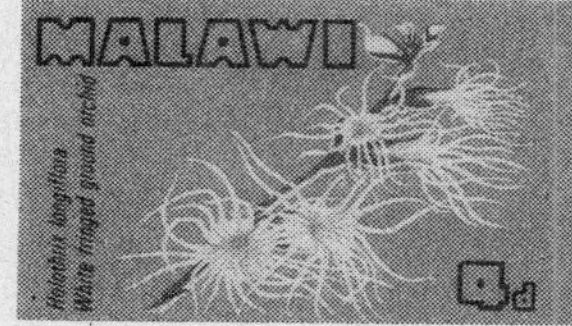

72. White-fringed Ground Orchid.

1969. Orchids of Malawi. Multicoloured.

329.	4d. Type **72** ..	15	10
330.	9d. Red Ground Orchid ..	20	10
331.	1s. 6d. Leopard Tree Orchid	30	10
332.	3s. Blue Ground Orchid ..	60	1·75

73. African Development Bank Emblem.

1969. 5th Anniv. of African Development Bank.

334. **73.**	4d. yellow, brn. & ochre	10	10
335.	9d. yellow, ochre & green	10	10
336.	1s. 6d. yell., ochre & brn.	10	10
337.	3s. yellow, ochre & blue	15	15

74. Dove over Bethlehem.

1969. Christmas.

339. **74.**	2d. black and yellow ..	10	10
340.	4d. black and turquoise	10	10
341.	9d. black and red ..	10	10
342.	1s. 6d. black and violet	10	10
343.	3s. black and blue ..	15	15

75. "Zonocerus elegans" (grasshopper).

1970. Insects of Malawi. Multicoloured.

345	4d. Type **75**	15	10
346	9d. "Mylabris dicincta" (beetle)	15	10
347	1s. 6d. "Henosepilachna elaterii" (ladybird) ..	20	10
348	3s. "Sphodromantis speculaburenda" (mantid)	35	45

1970. Rand Easter Show. No. 317 optd. **Rand Easter Show 1970.**

350.	1s. 6d. multicoloured ..	15	60

77. Runner.

1970. 9th Commonwealth Games, Edinburgh.

351. **77.**	4d. blue and green ..	10	10
352.	9d. blue and red ..	10	10
353.	1s. 6d. blue and yellow	10	10
354.	3s. deep blue and blue ..	15	15

1970. Decimal Currency. Nos. 316 and 318 surch.

356.	10 t. on 1 s. multicoloured	50	25
357.	20 t. on 2s. multicoloured	1·40	1·00

79. "Aegocera trimeni".

1970. Moths. Multicoloured.

358	4d. Type **79**	20	10
359	9d. "Faidherbia bauhiniae"	30	10
360	1s. 6d. "Parasa karschi" ..	50	10
361	3s. "Teracotona euprepia"	1·25	2·00

80. Mother and Child.

1970. Christmas.

363 **80.**	2d. black and yellow ..	10	10
364.	4d. black and green ..	10	10
365.	9d. black and red ..	10	10
366.	1s. 6d. black and purple	10	10
367.	3s. black and blue ..	15	15

1971. No. 319 surch. **30 t Special United Kingdom Delivery Service.**

369.	30 t. on 3s. multicoloured	20	1·75

No. 369 was issued for use on letters carried by an emergency airmail service from Malawi to Great Britain during the British postal strike. The fee of 30 t. was to cover the charge for delivery by a private service, and ordinary stamps to pay the normal airmail postage had to be affixed as well. These stamps were in use from 8th Feb. to 8th March.

82. Decimal Coinage and Cockerel.

1971. Decimal Coinage.

370. **82.**	3 t. multicoloured ..	10	10
371.	8 t. multicoloured ..	10	10
372.	15 t. multicoloured ..	15	10
373.	30 t. multicoloured ..	25	30

83. Greater Kudu.

EASTER 1971
MALAWI 3t

85. Christ on the Cross.

1971. Decimal Currency. Antelopes. Mult.

375.	1 t. Type **83**	10	10
376.	2 t. Nyala	15	10
377.	3 t. Mountain Reedbuck ..	20	10
378.	5 t. Puku	40	10
379.	8 t. Impala	45	10
380.	10 t. Eland	60	10
381.	15 t. Klipspringer	1·00	20
382.	20 t. Suni	1·50	50
383.	30 t. Roan Antelope ..	4·00	70
384.	50 t. Waterbuck	90	65
385.	1 k. Bushbuck	2·00	85
386.	2 k. Red Forest Duiker ..	3·50	1·50
387.	4 k. Common Duiker ..	19·00	17·00

Nos. 380/7 are larger, size 25 × 42 mm.

No. 387 is incorrectly inscr. "Gray Duiker".

1971. Easter. Multicoloured.

388. **85.**	3 t. black and green ..	10	10
389. –	3 t. black and green ..	10	10
390. **85.**	8 t. black and red ..	10	10
391. –	8 t. black and red ..	10	10
392. **85.**	15 t. black and violet ..	15	15
393. –	15 t. black and violet ..	15	15
394. **85.**	30 t. black and blue ..	25	25
395. –	30 t. black and blue ..	25	25

DESIGN: Nos. 389, 391, 393, 395, The Resurrection.

Both designs from "The Small Passion" (Durer).

87. "Holarrhena febrifuga".

1971. Flowering Shrubs and Trees. Mult.

397.	3 t. Type **87**	10	10
398.	8 t. "Brachystegia spiciformis"	15	10
399.	15 t. "Securidaca longepedunculata"	25	10
400.	30 t. "Pterocarpus rotundifolius"	40	50

88. Drum Major.

89. "Madonna and Child" (William Dyce).

1971. 50th Anniv. of Malawi Police Force.

402. **88.**	30 t. multicoloured ..	65	1·00

1971. Christmas. Multicoloured.

403.	3 t. Type **89**	10	10
404.	8 t. "The Holy Family" (M. Schongauer) ..	15	10
405.	15 t. "The Holy Family with St. John" (Raphael)	30	20
406.	30 t. "The Holy Family" (Bronzino)	65	80

90. Vickers "Viscount".

1972. Air. Malawi Aircraft. Multicoloured.

408.	3 t. Type **90**	25	10
409.	8 t. Hawker Siddeley "748"	40	10
410.	15 t. Britten-Norman "Islander"	65	30
411.	30 t. B.A.C. "One-Eleven"	1·10	1·75

91. Figures (Chencherere Hill).

1972. Rock Paintings.

413. **91.**	3 t. green and black ..	35	10
414. –	8 t. red, grey and black	45	10
415. –	15 t. multicoloured ..	70	30
416. –	30 t. multicoloured ..	1·00	1·00

DESIGNS: 8 t. Lizard and Cat (Chencherere Hill). 15 t. Schematics (Diwa Hill). 30 t. Sun Through Rain (Mikolongwe Hill).

92. Boxing.

1972. Olympic Games, Munich.

418. **92.**	3 t. multicoloured ..	10	10
419.	8 t. multicoloured ..	10	10
420.	15 t. multicoloured ..	15	10
421.	30 t. multicoloured ..	35	45

93. Arms of Malawi.

1972. Commonwealth Parliamentary Conf.

423.	93.	15 t. multicoloured ..	30	35

94. "Adoration of the Kings" (Orcagna).

1972. Christmas. Multicoloured.

424.	3 t. Type **94**	10	10
425.	8 t. "Madonna and Child Enthroned" (Florentine School) ..	10	10
426.	15 t. "Virgin and Child" (Crivelli) ..	20	10
427.	30 t. "Virgin and Child with St. Anne" (Flemish School)	45	70

95. "Charaxes bohemani".

1973. Butterflies. Multicoloured.

429	3 t. Type **95**	20	10
430	8 t. "Uranothauma crawshayi"	45	10
431	15 t. "Charaxes acuminatus" ..	65	30
432	30 t. "Amauris ansorgei" (inscr in error "EUPHAEDRA ZADDACHI")	3·00	6·00
433	30 t. "Amauris ansorgei" (inscr corrected) ..	3·00	6·00

96. Livingstone and Map.

1973. Death Centenary of David Livingstone. (1st issue).

435.	96.	3 t. multicoloured ..	10	10
436.		8 t. multicoloured ..	15	10
437.		15 t. multicoloured ..	30	10
438.		30 t. multicoloured ..	45	60

See also No. 450.

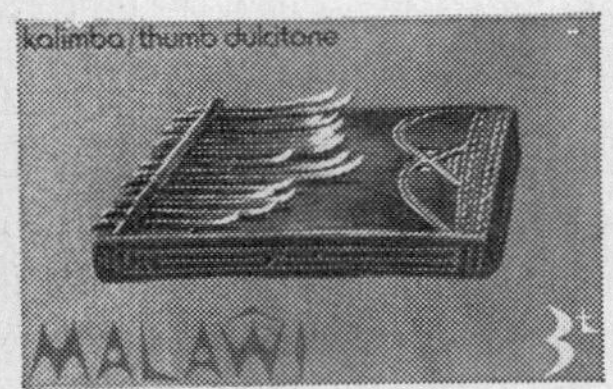

97. Thumb Dulcitone.

1973. Musical Instruments. Multicoloured.

440.	3 t. Type **97**	10	10
441.	8 t. Hand zither (vert.) ..	15	10
442.	15 t. Hand drum (vert.) ..	20	10
443.	30 t. One-stringed fiddle ..	40	60

98. The Magi.

1973. Christmas.

445.	98.	3 t. blue, lilac & ultram.	10	10
446.		8 t. red, lilac and brown	10	10
447.		15 t. mve., blue & deep mve.	15	10
448.		30 t. yell., lilac & brown	30	55

99. Stained-glass Window, Livingstonia Mission.

1973. Death Centenary of David Livingstone. (2nd issue).

450.	99.	50 t. multicoloured ..	45	1·00

100. Largemouth Black Bass.

1973. 35th Anniv. of Malawi Angling Society. Multicoloured.

452.	3 t. Type **100** ..	20	10
453.	8 t. Rainbow trout ..	25	10
454.	15 t. Lake salmon ..	45	20
455.	30 t. Tiger fish	75	75

101. U.P.U. Monument and Map of Africa.

1974. Centenary of U.P.U.

457.	101.	3 t. green and brown ..	10	10
458.		8 t. red and brown ..	10	10
459.		15 t. violet and brown ..	15	10
460.		30 t. blue and brown ..	30	70

102. Capital Hill, Lilongwe.

1974. 10th Anniv. of Independence.

462.	102.	3 t. multicoloured ..	10	10
463.		8 t. multicoloured ..	10	10
464.		15 t. multicoloured ..	10	10
465.		30 t. multicoloured ..	25	35

103. "Madonna of the Meadow" (Bellini).

1974. Christmas. Multicoloured.

467.	3 t. Type **103**	10	10
468.	8 t. "The Holy Family with Sts. John and Elizabeth" (Jordaens) ..	10	10
469.	15 t. "The Nativity" (Pieter de Grebber) ..	15	10
470.	30 t. "Adoration of the Shepherds" (Lorenzo di Credi)	30	50

104. Arms of Malawi. 105. African Snipe.

106. Spur-winged Goose.

1975.

472	104	1 t. blue	10	30
472a		5 t. red	20	30

1975. Birds (2nd series). Multicoloured.

(a) As Type **105**

473	1 t. Type **105**	30	70
474.	2 t. Double-handed sand grouse (horiz) ..	50	60
475	3 t. Blue quail (horiz) ..	1·50	40
476	5 t. Bare-throated francolin	3·00	35
477	8 t. Harlequin quail (horiz)	4·25	45

(b) As Type **106**

502	10 t. Type **106** ..	2·00	1·25
503	15 t. Barrow's bustard ..	2·00	1·75
480	20 t. Comb duck	1·00	1·25
481	30 t. Helmet guineafowl ..	1·25	70
482	50 t. African pygmy goose (horiz)	2·00	1·60
483	1 k. Garganey ..	3·00	4·00
504	2 k. White-faced whistling duck	9·50	9·50
485	4 k. African green pigeon	13·00	16·00

107. M.V. "Mpasa".

1975. Ships of Lake Malawi. Multicoloured.

486.	3 t. Type **107**	15	10
487.	8 t. M.V. "Ilala II" ..	25	10
488.	15 t. M.V. "Chauncy Maples II"	40	20
489.	30 t. M.V. "Nkwazi" ..	65	80

108. "Habenaria splendens".

1975. Malawi Orchids. Multicoloured.

491.	3 t. Type **108**	15	10
492.	10 t. "Eulophia cucullata"	25	10
493.	20 t. "Disa welwitschii"	40	20
494.	40 t. "Angraecum conchiferum"	70	85

109. Thick-tailed Bushbaby.

1975. Malawi Animals. Multicoloured.

496.	3 t. Type **109**	10	10
497.	10 t. Leopard ..	35	10
498.	20 t. Roan Antelope ..	55	30
499.	40 t. Common Zebra ..	1·00	1·75

1975. 10th African, Caribbean and Pacific Ministerial Conference. No. 482 optd. **10th ACP Ministerial Conference 1975.**

514.	50 t. African Pygmy Goose	75	1·10

111. "A Castle with the Adoration of the Magi".

1975. Christmas. Religious Medallions. Multicoloured.

515.	3 t. Type **111**	10	10
516.	10 t. "The Nativity" ..	15	10
517.	20 t. "Adoration of the Magi (different) ..	20	10
518.	40 t. "Angel appearing to Shepherds"	50	85

112. Alexander Graham Bell.

1976. Centenary of Telephone.

520.	112.	3 t. green and black ..	10	10
521.		10 t. purple and black	10	10
522.		20 t. violet and black ..	20	10
523.		40 t. blue and black ..	50	70

113. President Banda.

1976. 10th Anniv. of Republic. Mult.

525.	113.	3 t. green	10	10
526.		10 t. purple ..	10	10
527.		20 t. blue	20	10
528.		40 t. blue	50	70

114. Bagnall Diesel Shunter.

1976. Malawi Locomotives. Multicoloured.

530.	3 t. Type **114**	15	10
531.	10 t. "Shire" Class diesel locomotive	40	10
532.	20 t. Nippon Sharyo diesel locomotive	80	45
533.	40 t. Hunslet diesel locomotive	1·75	2·25

1976. Centenary of Blantyre Mission. Nos. 479 and 481 optd. **Blantyre Mission Centenary 1876–1976.**

535.	15 t. Barrow's bustard ..	55	70
536.	30 t. Helmet guineafowl ..	85	1·40

HAVE YOU READ THE NOTES AT THE BEGINNING OF THIS CATALOGUE?

These often provide answers to the enquiries we receive.

116. Child on Bed of Straw.

1976. Christmas.

537. 116. 3 t. multicoloured .. 10 10
538. 10 t. multicoloured .. 10 10
539. 20 t. multicoloured .. 20 10
540. 40 t. multicoloured .. 40 60

117. Man and Woman.

1977. Handicrafts showing wood-carvings. Multicoloured.

542. 4 t. Type **117** .. 10 10
543. 10 t. Elephant (horiz.) .. 15 10
544. 20 t. Rhinoceros (horiz.) .. 20 10
545. 40 t. Antelope .. 50 70

118. Chileka Airport.

1977. Transport. Multicoloured.

547. 4 t. Type **118** .. 15 10
548. 10 t. Blantyre-Lilongwe Road .. 25 10
549. 20 t. M.V. "Ilala II" .. 80 30
550. 40 t. Blantyre-Nacala rail line .. 1·50 1·40

119. "Pseudotropheus johanni".

1977. Fish of Lake Malawi. Multicoloured.

552. 4 t. Type **119** .. 15 10
553. 10 t. "Pseudotropheus livingstoni" .. 25 10
554. 20 t. "Pseudotropheus zebra" .. 85 25
555. 40 t. "Genyochromis mento" .. 95 95

120. "Madonna and Child with St. Catherine and the Blessed Stefano Maconi" (Bergognone).

1977. Christmas.

557. 120. 4 t. multicoloured .. 10 10
558. – 10 t. multicoloured .. 10 10
559. – 20 t. multicoloured .. 20 10
560. – 40 t. multicoloured .. 50 70

DESIGNS: 10 t. "Madonna and Child with the Eternal Father and Angels" (Bergognone). 20 t. Bottigella altarpiece (detail, Foppa). 40 t. "Madonna of the Fountain" (van Eyck).

121. "Entry of Christ into Jerusalem" (Giotto).

1978. Easter. Paintings by Giotto. Mult.

562. 4 t. Type **121** .. 10 10
563. 10 t. "The Crucifixion" .. 10 10
564. 20 t. "Descent from the Cross" .. 20 10
565. 40 t. "Jesus appears before Mary" .. 40 55

122. Nyala.

1978. Wildlife. Multicoloured.

567. 4 t. Type **122** .. 25 10
568. 10 t. Lion (horiz.) .. 60 15
569. 20 t. Common Zebra (horiz.) .. 85 60
570. 40 t. Mountain Reedbuck .. 1·40 2·00

123. Malamulo Seventh Day Adventist Church.

1978. Christmas. Multicoloured.

572. 4 t. Type **123** .. 10 10
573. 10 t. Likoma Cathedral .. 10 10
574. 20 t. St. Michael's and All Angels' Blantyre .. 20 10
575. 40 t. Zomba Catholic Cathedral .. 40 60

124. "Vanilla polylepis".

1979. Orchids. Multicoloured.

577. 1 t. Type **124** .. 30 10
578. 2 t. "Cirrhopetalum umbellatum" .. 30 10
579. 5 t. "Calanthe natalensis" .. 30 10
580. 7 t. "Ansellia gigantea" .. 30 10
581. 8 t. "Tridactyle bicaudata" .. 30 10
582. 10 t. "Acampe pachyglossa" .. 30 10
583. 15 t. "Eulophia quartiniana" .. 40 15
584. 20 t. "Cyrtorchis arcuata" .. 45 30
585. 30 t. "Eulophia tricristata" .. 65 30
586. 50 t. "Disa hamatopetala" .. 80 50
587. 75 t. "Cynorchis glandulosa" .. 1·00 1·00
588. 1 k. "Aerangis kotschyana" .. 1·40 80
589. 1 k. 50 "Polystachya dendrobiiflora" .. 1·50 1·40
590. 2 k. "Disa ornithantha" .. 1·75 1·60
591. 4 k. "Cyrtorchis praetermissa" .. 3·00 3·50

125. Tsamba.

1979. National Tree Planting Day. Mult.

592. 5 t. Type **125** .. 15 10
593. 10 t. Mulanje Cedar .. 20 10
594. 20 t. Mlombwa .. 30 20
595. 40 t. Mbawa .. 60 75

126. Train crossing Viaduct.

1979. Opening of Salima-Lilongwe Railway Line. Multicoloured.

597. 5 t. Type **126** .. 25 10
598. 10 t. Diesel railcar at station .. 40 10
599. 20 t. Train rounding bend .. 60 30
600. 40 t. Diesel train in cutting .. 85 1·25

127. Young Child.

1979. International Year of the Child. Designs showing young children. Multicoloured; background colours given.

602. 127. 5 t. green .. 10 10
603. – 10 t. red .. 10 10
604. – 20 t. mauve .. 20 10
605. – 40 t. blue .. 40 60

128. 1964 3d. Independence Commemorative Stamp.

1979. Death Centenary of Sir Rowland Hill. Designs showing Independence 1964 Commemorative Stamps. Multicoloured.

606. 5 t. Type **128** .. 10 10
607. 10 t. 6d. value .. 10 10
608. 20 t. 1s. 3d. value .. 20 10
609. 40 t. 2s. 6d. value .. 35 60

129. River Landscape.

1979. Christmas. Multicoloured.

611. 5 t. Type **129** .. 10 10
612. 10 t. Sunset .. 10 10
613. 20 t. Forest and hill .. 25 10
614. 40 t. Plain and mountains .. 50 50

130. Limbe Rotary Club Emblem.

1980. 75th Anniv. of Rotary International.

615. 130. 5 t. multicoloured .. 10 10
616. – 10 t. multicoloured .. 10 10
617. – 20 t. blue, gold and red 25 10
618. – 40 t. gold and blue .. 60 1·40

DESIGNS: 10 t. Blantyre Rotary Club Pennant. 20 t. Lilongwe Rotary Club Pennant. 40 t. Rotary International emblem.

131. Mangochi District Post Office.

1980. "London 1980" International Stamp Exhibition.

620. 131. 5 t. black and green .. 10 10
621. – 10 t. black and red .. 10 10
622. – 20 t. black and violet .. 15 10
623. – 1 k. black and blue .. 65 1·00

DESIGNS: 10 t. New Blantyre Sorting Office. 20 t. Mail transfer hut, Walala. 1 k. First Nyasaland Post Office, Chiromo.

132. Agate Nodule.

1980. Gemstones. Multicoloured.

625. 5 t. Type **132** .. 30 10
626. 10 t. Sunstone .. 45 10
627. 20 t. Smoky Quartz .. 70 15
628. 1 k. Kyanite crystal .. 2·25 2·00

133. Elephants.

1980. Christmas. Children's Paintings. Multicoloured.

629. 5 t. Type **133** .. 10 10
630. 10 t. Flowers .. 10 10
631. 20 t. "Shire" Class diesel train .. 20 10
632. 1 k. Malachite Kingfisher 70 1·10

134. Suni.

1981. Wildlife. Multicoloured.

633. 7 t. Type **134** .. 15 10
634. 10 t. Blue Duiker .. 20 10
635. 20 t. African Buffalo .. 30 15
636. 1 k. Lichtenstein's Hartebeest .. 1·25 1·60

135. " Kanjedza II " Standard " A " Earth Station.

1981. International Communications. Mult.

637.	7 t. Type **135**	10	10
638.	10 t. Blantyre International Gateway Exchange ..	15	10
639.	20 t. " Kanjedza I " standard " B " earth station	25	15
640.	1 k. " Satellite communications "	1·50	1·50

136. Maize.

1981. World Food Day. Agricultural Produce. Multicoloured.

642.	7 t. Type **136**	15	10
643.	10 t. Rice	20	10
644.	20 t. Finger-millet ..	30	20
645.	1 k. Wheat	1·00	1·40

137. " The Adoration of the Shepherds " (Murillo).

1981. Christmas. Paintings. Multicoloured.

646.	7 t. Type **137**	15	10
647.	10 t. " The Holy Family " (Lippi) (horiz.)	20	10
648.	20 t. " The Adoration of the Shepherds " (Louis le Nain) (horiz.)	35	15
649.	1 k. " The Virgin and Child " St. John the Baptist and an Angel " (Paolo Morando)	90	1·25

138. Impala Herd.

1982. National Parks. Wildlife. Mult.

650.	7 t. Type **138**	20	10
651.	10 t. Lions	35	10
652.	20 t. Greater Kudu ..	50	15
653.	1 k. Greater Flamingoes ..	2·25	2·25

139. Kamuzu Academy.

1982. Kamuzu Academy.

654. **139.**	7 t. multicoloured ..	10	10
655. –	20 t. multicoloured ..	20	10
656. –	30 t. multicoloured ..	30	30
657. –	1 k. multicoloured ..	75	1·60

DESIGNS: 20 t. to 1 k.. Various views of the Academy.

140. Attacker challenging Goalkeeper.

1982. World Cup Football Championship, Spain. Multicoloured.

658.	7 t. Type **140**	35	10
659.	20 t. FIFA World Cup trophy	70	40
660.	30 t. Football stadium ..	90	1·00

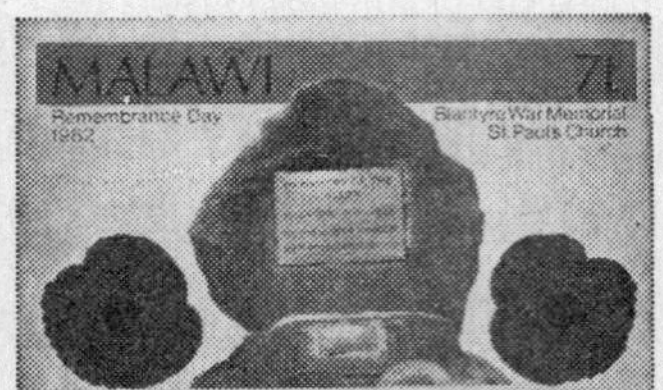

141. Blantyre War Memorial, St. Paul's Church.

1982. Remembrance Day. Multicoloured.

662.	7 t. Type **141**	10	10
663.	20 t. Zomba war memorial	15	10
664.	30 t. Chichiri war memorial	20	30
665.	1 k. Lilongwe war memorial	65	2·00

142. Kwacha International Conference Centre.

1983. Commonwealth Day. Multicoloured.

666.	7 t. Type **142**	10	10
667.	20 t. Tea-picking, Mulanje	20	10
668.	30 t. World map showing position of Malawi ..	30	30
669.	1 k. Pres. Dr. H. Kamuzu Banda	80	1·25

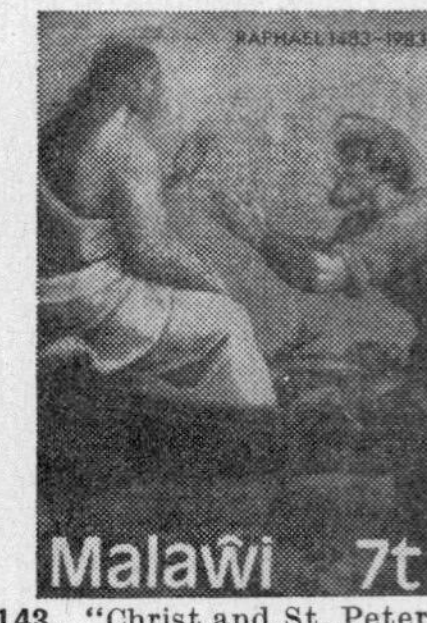

143. "Christ and St. Peter".

1983. 500th Birth Anniv. of Raphael. Details from the cartoon for "The Miraculous Draught of Fishes" Tapestry. Mult.

670.	7 t. Type **143**	25	10
671.	20 t. "Hauling in the Catch"	50	30
672.	30 t. "Fishing Village" (horiz.)	75	1·00

144. Pair by Lake.

1983. African Fish Eagle. Multicoloured.

674.	30 t. Type **144**	70	80
675.	30 t. Making gull-like call	70	80
676.	30 t. Diving on prey ..	70	80
677.	30 t. Carrying fish ..	70	80
678.	30 t. Feeding on catch ..	70	80

145. Kamuzu International Airport.

1983. Bicentenary of Manned Flight. Mult.

679.	7 t. Type **145**	10	10
680.	20 t. Kamuzu International Airport (different)	25	15
681.	30 t. BAC "One Eleven" ..	40	40
682.	1 k. Flying boat at Cape Maclear	1·10	2·00

146. " Clerodendrum myriciodes ".

1983. Christmas. Flowers. Multicoloured.

684.	7 t. Type **146**	35	10
685.	20 t. " Gloriosa superba "	75	15
686.	30 t. " Gladiolus laxiflorus "	1·00	40
687.	1 k. " Aframomum angustifolium "	2·00	2·50

147. " Melanochromis auratus ".

1984. Fishes. Multicoloured.

688.	1 t. Type **147**	10	15
689.	2 t. " Haplochromis compressiceps "	15	20
690.	5 t. " Labeotropheus fuelleborni "	20	20
691.	7 t. " Pseudotropheus lombardoi "	20	10
692.	8 t. Gold " Pseudotropheus " Zebra	20	10
693.	10 t. " Trematocranus jacobfreibergi "	20	10
694.	15 t. " Melanochromis crabro "	30	10
695.	20 t. Marbled " Pseudotropheus " Zebra ..	30	10
696.	30 t. " Labidochromis caeruleus "	40	10
697.	40 t. " Haplochromis venustus "	60	30
698.	50 t. " Aulonacara " of Thumbi	70	50
699.	75 t. " Melanochromis vermivorus "	90	65
700.	1 k. " Pseudotropheus " Zebra	1·25	1·00
701.	2 k. " Trematocranus spp. "	2·00	2·25
702.	4 k. " Aulonacara " of Mbenje	2·75	4·00

Nos. 688 and 691/7 exist with different imprint dates at foot.

148. Smith's Red Hare.

1984. Small Mammals. Multicoloured.

703.	7 t. Type **148**	30	10
704.	20 t. Gambian Sun Squirrel	70	15
705.	30 t. South African Hedgehog	1·00	50
706.	1 k. Large-spotted Genet	2·25	3·25

149. Running.

1984. Olympic Games, Los Angeles. Mult.

707.	7 t. Type **149**	10	10
708.	20 t. Boxing	25	15
709.	30 t. Cycling	35	25
710.	1 k. Long jumping ..	1·00	1·25

150. "Euphaedra neophron".

1984. Butterflies.

712. **150.**	7 t. multicoloured ..	60	10
713. –	20 t. yellow, brown and red	1·00	15
714. –	30 t. multicoloured ..	1·25	55
715. –	1 k. multicoloured ..	2·75	3·25

DESIGNS: 20 t. "Papilio dardanus". 30 t. "Antanartia schaeneia". 1 k. "Spindasis nyassae".

151. "Virgin and Child" (Duccio).

1984. Christmas. Religious Paintings. Multicoloured.

716.	7 t. Type **151**	30	10
717.	20 t. "Madonna and Child" (Raphael) ..	75	15
718.	30 t. "Virgin and Child" (ascr. to Lippi) ..	1·00	40
719.	1 k. "The Wilton Diptych"	2·25	2·25

152. "Leucopaxillus gracillimus".

1985. Fungi. Multicoloured.

720.	7 t. Type **152**	60	1
721.	20 t. "Limacella guttata"	1·25	2
722.	30 t. "Termitomyces eurrhizus"	1·50	4
723.	1 k. "Xerulina asprata" ..	2·50	3·2

153. Map showing Member States, and Lumberjack (Forestry).

1985. 5th Anniv. of Southern African Development Co-ordination Conference. Designs showing map and aspects of development.

724.	**153.** 7 t. black, green and light green	40	10
725.	– 15 t. black, red and pink	60	15
726.	– 20 t. black, violet and mauve	1·50	45
727.	– 1 k. black, blue and light blue	2·00	2·00

DESIGNS: 15 t. Radio mast (Communications). 20 t. Diesel locomotive (Transport). 1 k. Trawler and net (Fishing).

154. M.V. "Ufulu".

1985. Ships of Lake Malawi (2nd series). Multicoloured.

728.	7 t. Type **154**	55	10
729.	15 t. M.V. "Chauncy Maples II"	1·00	15
730.	20 t. M.V. "Mtendere" ..	1·25	30
731.	1 k. M.V. "Ilala II" ..	3·00	3·00

155. Stierling's Woodpecker. **156.** "The Virgin of Humility" (Jaime Serra).

1985. Birth Bicentenary of John J. Audubon (ornithologist). Multicoloured.

733.	7 t. Type **155**	55	10
734.	15 t. Lesser seedcracker ..	1·00	20
735.	20 t. East coast akelat ..	1·25	40
736.	1 k. Boehm's beeater ..	2·50	3·25

1985. Christmas. Nativity Paintings. Mult.

738.	7 t. Type **156**	20	10
739.	15 t. "The Adoration of the Magi" (Stefano da Zevio)	40	15
740.	20 t. "Madonna and Child" (Gerard van Honthorst)	45	20
741.	1 k. "Virgin of Zbraslav" (Master of Vissy Brod)	1·75	1·40

157. Halley's Comet and Path of "Giotto" Spacecraft.

1986. Appearance of Halley's Comet. Mult.

742.	8 t. Type **157**	10	10
743.	15 t. Halley's Comet above Earth	15	15
744.	20 t. Comet and dish aerial, Malawi	20	20
745.	1 k. "Giotto" spacecraft ..	85	1·00

158. Two Players competing for Ball.

1986. World Cup Football Championship, Mexico. Multicoloured.

746.	8 t. Type **158**	30	10
747.	15 t. Goalkeeper saving goal	45	15
748.	20 t. Two players competing for ball (different)	60	25
749.	1 k. Player kicking ball ..	2·25	1·40

159. President Banda. **160.** "Virgin and Child" (Botticelli).

1986. 20th Anniv. of Republic. Mult.

751.	8 t. Type **159**	30	30
752.	15 t. National flag ..	40	15
753.	20 t. Malawi coat of arms	45	25
754.	1 k. Kamuzu Airport and emblem of national airline	1·25	2·40

1986. Christmas. Multicoloured.

755.	8 t. Type **160**	20	10
756.	15 t. "Adoration of the Shepherds" (Guido Reni)	35	10
757.	20 t. "Madonna of the Veil" (Carlo Dolci) ..	45	20
758.	1 k. "Adoration of the Magi" (Jean Bourdichon)	2·00	1·10

161. Wattled Crane.

1987. Wattled Crane. Multicoloured.

763	8 t. Type **161**	40	10
764	15 t. Two cranes	65	15
765	20 t. Cranes at nest ..	80	10
766	75 t. Crane in lake ..	1·40	1·75

162. "Shamrock" No. 2 Locomotive, 1902.

1987. Steam Locomotives. Multicoloured.

767	10 t. Type **162**	50	10
768	25 t. "D" class, No. 8, 1914	70	15
769	30 t. "Thistle" No. 1, 1902	75	20
770	1 k. "Kitson" class, No. 6, 1903	1·75	1·25

163. Hippopotamus grazing. **164.** "Stathmostelma spectabile".

1987. Hippopotamus. Multicoloured.

771	10 t. Type **163**	30	10
772	25 t. Hippopotami in water	60	15
773	30 t. Female and calf in water	65	30
774	1 k. Hippopotami and egret	1·75	1·40

1987. Christmas. Wild Flowers. Mult.

776	10 t. Type **164**	25	10
777	25 t. "Pentanisia schweinfurthii"	50	15
778	30 t. "Chironia krebsii" ..	55	25
779	1 k. "Ochna macrocalyx"	1·75	1·10

165. Malawi and Staunton Knights.

1988. Chess. Local and Staunton chess pieces. Multicoloured.

780	15 t. Type **165**	50	15
781	35 t. Bishops	85	45
782	50 t. Rooks	1·25	80
783	2 k. Queens	3·00	3·25

166 High Jumping

1988. Olympic Games, Seoul. Multicoloured.

784	15 t. Type **166**	20	10
785	35 t. Javelin throwing ..	35	20
786	50 t. Tennis	45	30
787	2 k. Shot-putting ..	1·40	1·25

167 Eastern Forest Scrub Warbler **168** "Madonna in the Church" (Jan van Eyck)

1988. Birds. Multicoloured.

789	1 t. Type **167**	10	10
790	2 t. Yellow-throated woodland warbler ..	10	10
791	5 t. Moustached green tinkerbird	10	10
792	7 t. Waller's red-winged starling	10	10
793	8 t. Oriole-finch	10	10
794	10 t. Starred robin ..	10	10
795	15 t. Bar-tailed trogon ..	10	10
796	20 t. Green-backed twin-spot	10	10
797	30 t. African grey cuckoo shrike	10	15
798	40 t. Black-fronted bush shrike	15	20
799	50 t. White-tailed crested flycatcher	20	25
800	75 t. Green barbet ..	30	35
801	1 k. Lemon dove ("Cinnamon Dove") ..	40	45
802	2 k. Silvery-cheeked hornbill	80	85
803	4 k. Crowned eagle ..	1·60	1·75
804	10 k. Anchieta's sunbird ..	4·25	4·50

1988. 300th Anniv of Lloyd's of London. As T **123** of Ascension. Multicoloured.

805	15 t. Rebuilt Royal Exchange, 1844 ..	20	10
806	35 t. Opening ceremony, Nkula Falls Hydro-electric Power Station	45	20
807	50 t. Air Malawi "1-11" airliner (horiz)	60	30
808	2 k. "Seawise University" (formerly "Queen Elizabeth") on fire, Hong Kong, 1972 ..	1·90	1·90

1988. Christmas. Multicoloured.

809	15 t. Type **168**	20	10
810	35 t. "Virgin, Infant Jesus and St. Anna" (da Vinci)	35	20
811	50 t. "Virgin and Angels" (Cimabue)	45	40
812	2 k. "Virgin and Child" (Baldovinetti Apenio) ..	1·75	1·60

169 "Serranochromis robustus"

1989. 50th Anniv of Malawi Angling Society. Multicoloured.

813	15 t. Type **169**	35	10
812	35 t. Lake salmon ..	65	20
814	50 t. Yellow fish ..	85	55
815	2 k. Tiger fish	2·25	2·00

170 Independence Arch, Blantyre

1989. 25th Anniv of Independence. Mult.

817	15 t. Type **170**	20	10
818	35 t. Grain silos	35	20
819	50 t. Capital Hill, Lilongwe	50	45
820	2 k. Reserve Bank Headquarters	1·75	2·00

171 Blantyre Digital Telex Exchange

1989. 25th Anniv of African Development Bank. Multicoloured.

821	15 t. Type **171**	20	10
822	40 t. Dzalanyama steer ..	40	20
823	50 t. Mikolongwe heifer ..	50	45
824	2 k. Zebu bull	1·75	2·00

172 Rural House with Verandah

1989. 25th Anniv of Malawi–United Nations Co-operation. Multicoloured.

825	15 t. Type **172**	20	10
826	40 t. Rural house ..	40	20
827	50 t. Traditional hut and modern houses	50	45
828	2 k. Tea plantation ..	1·75	2·00

173 St. Michael and All Angels Church

1989. Christmas. Churches of Malawi. Mult.

829	15 t. Type **173**	20	10
830	40 t. Catholic Cathedral, Limbe	40	20
831	50 t. C.C.A.P. Church, Nkhoma	50	45
832	2 k. Cathedral, Likoma Island	1·75	2·00

174 Ford "Sedan", 1915

1990. Vintage Vehicles. Multicoloured.

833	15 t. Type **174**	20	10
834	40 t. Two-seater Ford, 1915	40	20
835	50 t. Ford pick-up, 1915 ..	50	40
836	1 k. Chevrolet bus, 1930 ..	1·50	1·60

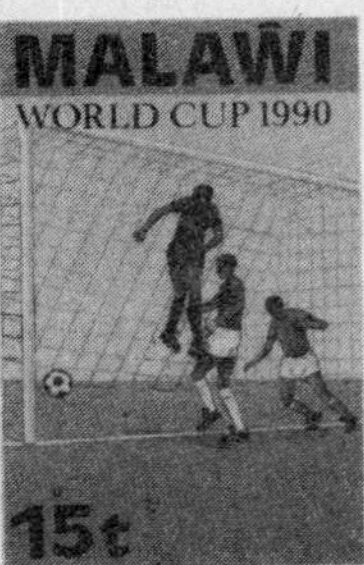

175 Player heading Ball into Net

1990. World Cup Football Championship, Italy. Multicoloured.

838	15 t. Type **175**	20	10
839	40 t. Player tackling	40	20
840	50 t. Player scoring goal ..	50	35
841	2 k. World Cup	1·50	1·60

176 Anniversary Emblem on Map

1990. 10th Anniv of Southern Africa Development Co-ordination Conference. Mult.

843	15 t. Type **176**	15	10
844	40 t. Chambo fish ..	25	20
845	50 t. Cedar plantation ..	35	30
846	2 k. Male nyala (antelope)	1·40	1·60

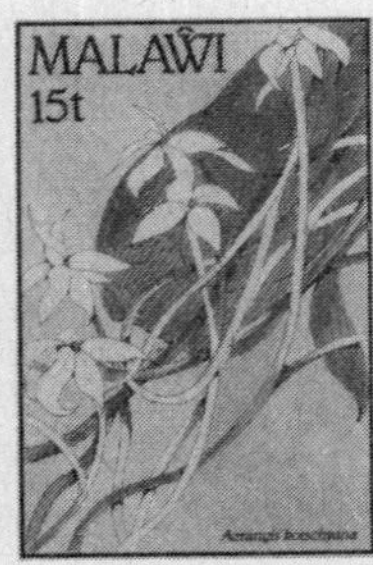

177 "Aerangis kotschyana"

1990. Orchids. Multicoloured.

848	15 t. Type **177**	20	10
849	40 t. "Angraecum eburneum"	35	20
850	50 t. "Aerangis luteo-alba rhodostica"	45	30
851	2 k. "Cyrtorchis arcuata whytei"	1·50	1·50

178 "The Virgin and the Child Jesus" (Raphael)

1990. Christmas. Paintings by Raphael. Mult.

853	15 t. Type **178**	15	10
854	40 t. "Transfiguration" (detail)	25	20
855	50 t. "St. Catherine of Alexandrie" (detail) ..	35	30
856	2 k. "Transfiguration" ..	1·40	1·50

179 Buffalo

1991. Wildlife. Multicoloured.

858	20 t. Type **179**	15	10
859	60 t. Cheetah	40	35
860	75 t. Greater kudu ..	50	40
861	2 k. Black rhinoceros ..	1·25	1·40

180 Chiromo Post Office, 1891

1991. Centenary of Postal Services. Mult.

863	20 t. Type **180**	15	10
864	60 t. Re-constructed mail exchange hut at Walala	40	35
865	75 t. Mangochi post office	50	40
866	2 k. Satellite Earth station	1·25	1·40

181 Red Locust

1991. Insects. Multicoloured.

868	20 t. Type **181**	15	10
869	60 t. Weevil	40	35
870	75 t. Cotton stainer bug ..	50	40
871	2 k. Pollen beetle ..	1·25	1·40

182 Child in a Manger

1991. Christmas. Multicoloured.

872	20 t. Type **182**	10	10
873	60 t. Adoration of the Kings and Shepherds ..	25	30
874	75 t. Nativity	30	35
875	2 k. Virgin and Child ..	80	85

POSTAGE DUE STAMPS

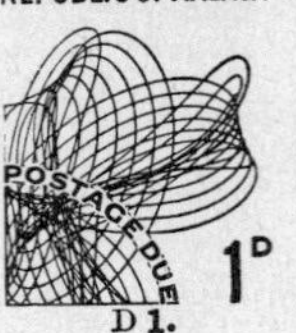

D 1.

1967.

D 6.	D 1.	1d. red	15	1·75
D 7.		2d. sepia	20	1·75
D 8.		4d. violet	25	2·00
D 9.		6d. blue	25	2·25
D 10.		8d. green	35	2·50
D 11.		1s. black	45	2·75

1971. Values in tambalas.

D 18	D 1	2 t. brown	10	10
D 19		4 t. mauve	10	10
D 20		6 t. blue	10	10
D 21		8 t. green	10	10
D 22		10 t. black	10	10

MALAYA (BRITISH MILITARY ADMINISTRATION)

The following stamps were for use throughout Malayan States and in Singapore during the period of the British Military Administration and were gradually replaced by individual issues for each state.

100 cents = 1 dollar.

1945. Straits Settlements stamps optd **BMA MALAYA**.

1a	58	1 c. black	10	10
2a		2 c. orange	10	10
4		3 c. green	10	10
5		5 c. brown	30	10
6a		6 c. grey	10	10
7		8 c. red	10	10
8a		10 c. purple	30	10
10		12 c. blue	1·75	2·75
12a		15 c. blue	30	10
13a		25 c. purple and red ..	70	15
14a		50 c. black on green ..	40	10
15		$1 black and red ..	1·50	10
16		$2 green and red ..	1·75	40
17		$5 green and red on green	48·00	48·00
18		$5 purple and orange ..	3·00	1·50

For stamps inscribed "MALAYA" at top and with Arabic characters at foot see under Kelantan, Negri Sembilan, Pahang, Perak, Selangor or Trengganu.

MALAYA (JAPANESE OCCUPATION OF)

Japanese forces invaded Malaya on 8 December 1941 and the conquest of the Malay penisula was completed by the capture of Singapore on 15 February.

The following stamps were used in Malaya until the defeat of Japan in 1945.

100 cents = 1 dollar.

(a) JOHORE

POSTAGE DUE STAMPS

(1)

大日本郵便

(2)

1942. Nos. D1/5 of Johore optd with T **1**.

JD1	D 1	1 c. red	45·00	—
JD2		4 c. green	55·00	—
JD3		8 c. orange	48·00	—
JD4		10 c. brown ..	15·00	—
JD5		12 c. purple	24·00	—

1943. Postage Due stamps of Johore opt with T **2**.

JD 6	D 1	1 c. red	1·75	8·00
JD 7		4 c. green	1·75	8·00
JD 8		8 c. orange ..	3·50	10·00
JD 9		10 c. brown ..	3·00	14·00
JD10		12 c. purple ..	4·00	18·00

(b) KEDAH

1942. Stamps of Kedah optd **DAI NIPPON 2602**.

J 1	1	1 c. black	1·75	3·50
J 2		2 c. green	23·00	30·00
J 3		4 c. violet	2·75	4·00
J 4		5 c. yellow	1·50	3·25
J 5		6 c. red	1·50	4·75
J 6		8 c. black	2·25	1·75
J 7	6	10 c. blue and brown ..	5·50	6·50
J 8		12 c. black and violet ..	10·00	17·00
J 9		25 c. blue and purple ..	4·00	8·00
J10		30 c. green and red ..	55·00	65·00
J11		40 c. black and purple	14·00	24·00
J12		50 c. brown and blue ..	16·00	27·00
J13		$1 black and green ..	£130	£15
J14		$2 green and brown ..	£120	£14
J15		$5 black and red ..	45·00	55·00

(c) KELANTAN

(5) Sunagawa Seal

(6) Handa Seal

1942. Stamps of Kelantan optd.

(a) With T **5**

J32	**4**	1 c. on 50 c. green & orge	65·00	65·00
J33		2 c. on 40 c. orange & grn	65·00	70·00
J18		4 c. on 30 c. violet & red	£750	£800
J34		5 c. on 12 c. blue	50·00	55·00
J20		6 c. on 25 c. orange & vio	£110	£130
J35		8 c. on 5 c. brown	50·00	55·00
J36		10 c. on 6 c. red	50·00	60·00
J23		12 c. on 8 c. green	45·00	65·00
J24		25 c. on 10 c. purple	£800	£850
J38		30 c. on 4 c. red	£800	£850
J26		40 c. on 2 c. green	48·00	60·00
J40		50 c. on 1 c. green & yell	£375	£400
J28		$1 on 4 c. black and red	48·00	60·00
J29		$2 on 5 c. grn & red on yellow	45·00	60·00
J30		$5 on 6 c. red	45·00	60·00

(b) With T **6**

J41	**4**	1 c. on 50 c. green & orge	75·00	85·00
J42		2 c. on 40 c. orge & grn	70·00	90·00
J43		8 c. on 5 c. brown	60·00	80·00
J44		10 c. on 6 c. red	75·00	90·00
J31		12 c. on 8 c. green	45·00	£110

(d) PENANG

(11) Okugawa Seal

(12) Ochiburi Seal

1942. Straits Settlements stamps optd.

(a) As T **11**

J56	**58**	1 c. black	6·50	8·00
J57		2 c. orange	18·00	16·00
J58		3 c. green	14·00	16·00
J59		5 c. brown	18·00	18·00
J60		8 c. grey	20·00	20·00
J61		10 c. purple	30·00	30·00
J62		12 c. blue	18·00	22·00
J63		15 c. blue	18·00	24·00
J64		40 c. red and purple	65·00	70·00
J65		50 c. black/green	95·00	£100
J66		$1 black & red on blue	£160	£170
J67		$2 green and red	£300	£325
J68		$5 green & red on green	£800	£900

(b) With T **12**

J69	**58**	1 c. black	32·00	42·00
J70		2 c. orange	32·00	42·00
J71		3 c. green	32·00	42·00
J72		5 c. brown	£425	£425
J73		8 c. grey	28·00	30·00
J74		10 c. purple	28·00	32·00
J75		12 c. blue	28·00	32·00
J76		15 c. blue	28·00	32·00

1942. Stamps of Straits Settlements optd **DAI NIPPON 2602 PENANG**.

J77	**58**	1 c. black	1·00	1·00
J78		2 c. orange	3·50	2·75
J79		3 c. green	1·40	1·75
J80		5 c. brown	1·00	2·00
J81		8 c. grey	2·25	1·40
J82		10 c. purple	1·50	2·00
J83		12 c. blue	2·00	4·50
J84		15 c. blue	1·75	3·75
J85		40 c. red and purple	2·50	5·50
J86		50 c. black and green	3·50	10·00
J87		$1 black & red on blue	6·00	15·00
J88		$2 green and red	22·00	45·00
J89		$5 green & red on green	£300	£400

(e) SELANGOR

1942. Agri-horticultural Exhibition. Stamps of Straits optd **SELANGOR EXHIBITION DAI NIPPON 2602 MALAYA**.

J90	**58**	2 c. orange	12·00	18·00
J91		8 c. grey	11·00	17·00

(f) SINGAPORE

(15) Seal of Post Office of Malayan Military Dept

1942. Stamps of Straits Settlements optd with T **15**.

J92	**58**	1 c. black	8·50	13·00
J93		2 c. orange	9·50	13·00
J94		3 c. green	42·00	60·00
J95		8 c. grey	15·00	17·00
J96		15 c. blue	13·00	15·00

(g) TRENGGANU

1942. Stamps of Trengganu optd with T **1**.

J 97	**4**	1 c. black	90·00	85·00
J 98		2 c. green	£130	£140
J 99a		2 c. on 5 c. purple on yellow (No. 59)	45·00	55·00
J100		3 c. brown	80·00	80·00
J101		4 c. red	£140	£130
J102		5 c. purple on yellow	7·50	12·00
J103		6 c. orange	6·50	16·00
J104		8 c. grey	8·00	12·00
J105		8 c. on 10 c. blue (No. 60)	12·00	20·00
J106		10 c. blue	8·00	16·00
J107		12 c. blue	7·00	15·00
J108		20 c. purple & orange	8·00	16·00
J109		25 c. green & purple	7·00	16·00
J110		30 c. purple & black	7·00	16·00
J111		35 c. red on yellow	11·00	17·00
J112		50 c. green and red	50·00	60·00
J113		$1 purple and blue on blue	£1100	£1100
J114		$3 green and red on green	42·00	65·00
J115	–	$5 green and red on yellow (No. 31)	£110	£160
J116	–	$25 purple and blue (No. 40)	£650	
J117		$50 green and yellow (No. 41)	£3500	
J118		$100 green and red (No. 42)	£750	

1942. Stamps of Trengganu optd **DAI NIPPON 2602 MALAYA**.

J119	**4**	1 c. black	6·00	8·00
J120		2 c. green	£130	£180
J121		2 c. on 5 c. purple on yellow (No. 59)	5·50	7·00
J122		3 c. brown	8·50	13·00
J123		4 c. red	6·50	9·50
J124		5 c. purple on yellow	4·75	7·50
J125		6 c. orange	4·25	9·50
J126		8 c. grey	55·00	16·00
J127		8 c. on 10 c. blue (No. 60)	4·00	9·00
J128		12 c. blue	4·25	10·00
J129		20 c. purple and orange	6·50	12·00
J130		25 c. green and purple	7·00	15·00
J131		30 c. purple and black	7·00	15·00
J132		$3 green & red on green	48·00	90·00

1942. Stamps of Trengganu optd with T **2**.

J133	**4**	1 c. black	5·50	14·00
J134		2 c. green	6·00	17·00
J135		2 c. on 5 c. purple on yellow (No. 59)	4·75	17·00
J136		5 c. purple on yellow	4·75	17·00
J137		6 c. orange	6·50	20·00
J138		8 c. grey	40·00	45·00
J139		8 c. on 10 c. bl (No. 60)	13·00	32·00
J140		10 c. blue	70·00	£110
J141		12 c. blue	8·50	28·00
J142		20 c. purple and orange	9·00	28·00
J143		25 c. green and purple	8·50	30·00
J144		30 c. purple and black	8·50	30·00
J145		35 c. red on yellow	8·50	30·00

1942. Postage Due stamps of Trengganu optd T **2**.

JD17	D **1**	1 c. red	45·00	70·00
JD18a		4 c. green	45·00	65·00
JD19		8 c. yellow	14·00	38·00
JD20		10 c. brown	14·00	38·00

GENERAL ISSUES

1942. Stamps of various states optd with T **1**.

(a) Straits Settlements

J146	**58**	1 c. black	3·00	3·25
J147		2 c. green	£900	£900
J148		2 c. orange	2·50	2·25
J149		3 c. green	2·50	2·25
J150		5 c. brown	16·00	18·00
J151		8 c. grey	2·75	2·25
J152		10 c. purple	28·00	30·00
J153		12 c. blue	65·00	80·00
J154		15 c. blue	3·50	2·75
J155		30 c. purple & orange	£750	£800
J156		40 c. red and purple	65·00	80·00
J157		50 c. black and green	40·00	40·00
J158		$1 black & red on blue	70·00	75·00
J159		$2 green and red	£120	£130
J160		$5 green & red on grn	£150	£160

There also exists a similar overprint with double-lined frame.

(b) Negri Sembilan

J161b	**6**	1 c. black	14·00	14·00
J162		2 c. orange	10·00	12·00
J163		3 c. green	14·00	18·00
J164b		5 c. brown	12·00	11·00
J165		6 c. grey	£120	£120
J166		8 c. red	25·00	35·00
J167a		10 c. purple	40·00	45·00
J168		12 c. blue	£550	£550
J169		15 c. blue	14·00	8·00
J170		25 c. purple and red	25·00	30·00
J171	**6**	30 c. purple & orange	£110	£120
J172		40 c. red and purple	£475	£475
J173		50 c. black on green	£140	£150
J174		$1 black & red on blue	85·00	95·00
J175		$5 green & red on grn	£325	£350

(c) Pahang

J176	**15**	1 c. black	24·00	28·00
J177		3 c. green	65·00	70·00
J178		5 c. brown	8·50	6·00
J179		8 c. grey	£110	£110
J180		8 c. red	16·00	10·00
J181		10 c. purple	32·00	38·00
J182		12 c. blue	£950	£1000
J183		15 c. blue	48·00	48·00
J184		25 c. purple and red	17·00	27·00
J185		30 c. purple & orange	12·00	23·00
J186		40 c. red and purple	15·00	25·00
J187		50 c. black on green	£160	£180
J188		$1 black & red on blue	75·00	85·00
J189		$5 green & red on grn	£550	£600

(d) Perak

J190	**51**	1 c. black	26·00	26·00
J191		2 c. orange	17·00	17·00
J192		3 c. green	22·00	25·00
J193		5 c. brown	5·50	5·50
J194		8 c. grey	26·00	26·00
J195		8 c. red	13·00	32·00
J196		10 c. purple	12·00	20·00
J197		12 c. blue	85·00	95·00
J198		15 c. blue	14·00	21·00
J199		25 c. purple and red	13·00	20·00
J200		30 c. purple & orange	17·00	32·00
J201		40 c. red and purple	£150	£160
J202		50 c. black on green	26·00	38·00
J203		$1 black & red on blue	£200	£225
J204		$2 green and red	£1200	£1200
J205		$5 green & red on grn	£425	

(e) Selangor

J206	**46**	1 c. black	9·00	12·00
J207		2 c. green	£400	£450
J209		2 c. orange	40·00	45·00
J210		3 c. green	13·00	14·00
J211		5 c. brown	4·50	4·50
J212		6 c. red	£150	£150
J213		8 c. grey	14·00	15·00
J214		10 c. purple	9·50	18·00
J215		12 c. blue	28·00	26·00
J216		15 c. blue	13·00	16·00
J217a		25 c. purple and red	55·00	65·00
J218		30 c. purple & orange	11·00	22·00
J219		40 c. red and purple	48·00	55·00
J220		50 c. black on green	32·00	35·00
J221	**48**	$1 blk & red on bl	30·00	40·00
J222		$2 green and red	35·00	50·00
J223		$5 green & red on grn	55·00	65·00

1942. Various stamps optd **DAI NIPPON 2602 MALAYA**.

(a) Stamps of Straits Settlements

J224	**58**	2 c. orange	50	50
J225		3 c. green	42·00	50·00
J226		8 c. grey	2·25	1·75
J227		15 c. blue	6·00	5·00

(b) Stamps of Negri Sembilan

J228	**6**	1 c. black	80	60
J229		2 c. orange	1·40	50
J230		3 c. green	90	45
J231		5 c. brown	45	55
J232		6 c. grey	1·25	1·00
J233		8 c. red	1·75	1·25
J234		10 c. purple	3·00	3·00
J235		15 c. blue	5·00	3·00
J236		25 c. purple and red	2·00	4·75
J237		30 c. purple and orange	3·25	3·00
J238		$1 black & red on blue	£100	£110

(c) Stamps of Pahang

J239	**15**	1 c. black	80	50
J240		5 c. brown	55	70
J241		8 c. red	22·00	2·50
J242		10 c. purple	8·50	5·00
J243		12 c. blue	1·00	2·75
J244		25 c. purple and red	3·75	6·50
J245		30 c. purple and orange	80	3·00

(d) Stamps of Perak

J246	**51**	2 c. orange	75	70
J247		3 c. green	50	60
J248		8 c. red	60	40
J249		10 c. purple	4·25	5·00
J250		15 c. blue	3·00	2·00
J251		50 c. black on green	1·75	2·75
J252		$1 black & red on blue	£275	£325
J253		$5 green & red on grn	28·00	45·00

(e) Stamps of Selangor

J254	**46**	3 c. green	40	60
J255		12 c. blue	1·10	4·00
J256		15 c. blue	2·75	2·00
J257		40 c. red and purple	2·00	2·50
J258	**48**	$2 green and red	10·00	18·00

1942. No. 108 of Perak surch **DAI NIPPON 2602 MALAYA 2 Cents**.

J259	**88**	2 c. on 5 c. brown	1·25	1·00

1942. Stamps of Perak optd **DAI NIPPON YUBIN** ("Japanese Postal Service") or surch also in figures and words.

J260	**51**	1 c. black	2·00	3·50
J261		2 c. on 5 c. brown	2·00	5·00
J262		8 c. red	2·75	1·25

1943. Various stamps optd vert or horiz with T **2** or surch in figures and words.

(a) Stamps of Straits Settlements

J263	**58**	8 c. grey	1·00	50
J264		12 c. blue	55	2·75
J265		40 c. red and purple	65	1·75

(b) Stamps of Negri Sembilan

J266	**6**	1 c. black	30	40
J267		2 c. on 5 c. brown	40	45
J268		6 c. on 5 c. brown	40	60
J269		25 c. purple and red	1·10	5·00

(c) Stamp of Pahang

J270	**7**	6 c. on 5 c brown	50	75

(d) Stamps of Perak

J272	**51**	1 c. black	80	60
J274		2 c. on 5 c. brown	45	45
J275		5 c. brown	45	40
J276		8 c. red	55	50
J277		10 c. purple	60	50
J278		30 c. purple & orange	1·25	2·50
J279		50 c. black on green	3·00	8·00
J280		$5 green & red on grn	40·00	60·00

(e) Stamps of Selangor

J288	**46**	1 c. black	35	50
J289		2 c. on 5 c. brown	30	50
J282		3 c. green	40	45
J290		3 c. on 5 c. brown	20	1·00
J291		5 c. brown	30	1·00
J293		6 c. on 5 c. brown	15	60
J283		12 c. blue	45	1·25
J284		15 c. blue	2·75	3·00
J285	**48**	$1 black & red on blue	3·00	8·50
J295	**46**	$1 on 10 c. purple	30	1·00
J296		$1.50 on 30 c. purple and orange	30	1·00
J286	**48**	$2 green and red	10·00	22·00
J287		$5 green & red on grn	22·00	50·00

25 Tapping Rubber

27 Japanese Shrine, Singapore

1943.

J297	**25**	1 c. green	15	35
J298	–	2 c. green	15	15
J299	**25**	3 c. grey	15	15
J300	–	4 c. red	15	15
J301	–	8 c. blue	15	15
J302	–	10 c. purple	15	15
J303	**27**	15 c. violet	35	65
J304	–	30 c. olive	35	35
J305	–	50 c. blue	75	75
J306	–	70 c. blue	11·00	10·00

DESIGNS—VERT. 2 c. Fruit. 4 c. Tin dredger. 8 c. War Memorial. 10 c. Huts. 30 c. Sago palms. 50 c. Straits of Johore. HORIZ. 70 c. Malay Mosque, Kuala Lumpur.

28 Ploughman

29 Rice-planting

1943. Savings Campaign.

J307	**28**	8 c. violet	7·00	2·75
J308		15 c. red	6·00	2·75

1944. "Re-birth of Malaya".

J309	**29**	8 c. red	8·00	2·75
J310		15 c. mauve	4·00	3·00

大日本

マライ郵便

50 セント

(30)

1944. Stamps intended for use on Red Cross letters. Surch with T **30**.

(a) On Straits Settlements

J311	**58**	50 c. on 50 c. black/grn	8·50	18·00
J312		$1 on $1 black & red/bl	13·00	24·00
J313		$1.50 on $2 grn on red	21·00	55·00

(b) On Johore

J314	**24**	50 c. on 50 c. pur & red	7·00	15·00
J315		$1.50 on $2 green & red	5·50	11·00

(c) On Selangor

J316	**48**	$1 on $2 black & red bl	4·00	11·00
J317		$1.50 on $2 green & red	6·00	14·00

POSTAGE DUE STAMPS

1942. Postage Due stamps of Malayan Postal Union optd with T 2.

JD21	D 1	1 c. violet	10·00	12·00
JD22		3 c. green	18·00	20·00
JD23		4 c. green	12·00	12·00
JD24		8 c. red	18·00	20·00
JD25		10 c. orange ..	14·00	17·00
JD26		12 c. blue	16·00	20·00
JD27		50 c. black	38·00	45·00

1942. Postage Due stamps of Malayan Postal Union optd **DAI NIPPON 2620 MALAYA.**

JD28	D 1	1 c. violet	1·00	3·25
JD29		3 c. green	4·50	7·50
JD30		4 c. green	4·50	7·50
JD31		8 c. red	5·50	8·50
JD32		10 c. orange ..	1·60	5·50
JD33		12 c. blue	1·60	8·50

1943. Postage Due stamps of Malayan Postal Union optd with T 2.

JD34	D 1	1 c. violet	30	1·50
JD35		3 c. green	30	1·75
JD36		4 c. green	23·00	28·00
JD37		5 c. red	50	2·25
JD38		9 c. orange	60	3·00
JD39		10 c. orange ..	60	3·00
JD40		12 c. blue	60	4·00
JD41		15 c. blue	60	4·00

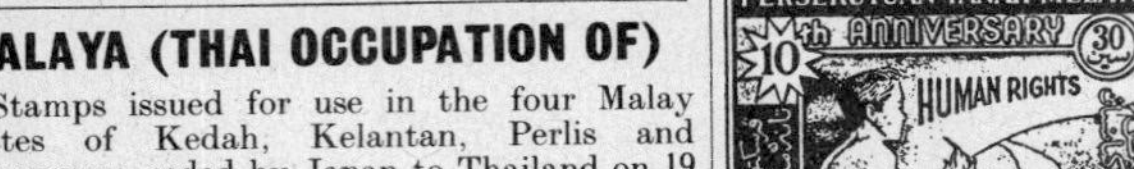

MALAYA (THAI OCCUPATION OF)

Stamps issued for use in the four Malay states of Kedah, Kelantan, Perlis and Trengganu, ceded by Japan to Thailand on 19 October 1943 and restored to British rule on the defeat of the Japanese.

100 cents = 1 dollar.

TM 1. War Memorial.

1943.

TM 1.	TM 1.	1 c. yellow ..	9·00	10·00
TM 2.		2 c. brown	3·25	6·00
TM 3.		3 c. green ..	5·50	11·00
TM 4.		4 c. purple	3·75	6·00
TM 5.		8 c. red ..	2·50	7·50
TM 6.		15 c. blue ..	6·50	12·00

MALAYAN FEDERATION

An independent country within the British Commonwealth, comprising all the Malay States (except Singapore) and the Settlements of Malacca and Penang. The component units retained their individual stamps. In 1963 the Federation became part of Malaysia (q.v.).

100 cents (sen) = 1 Malayan dollar.

1. Tapping Rubber.

1957.

1	1	6 c. blue, red and yellow	30	10
2	–	12 c. multicoloured ..	40	10
3	–	25 c. multicoloured ..	45	10
4	–	30 c. red and lake ..	40	10

DESIGNS—HORIZ. 12 c. Federation coat of arms. 25 c. Tin dredge. VERT. 30 c. Map of the Federation.

5. Prime Minister Tunku Abdul Rahman and Populace greeting Independence.

1957. Independence Day.

5.	5.	10 c. brown	10	10

DESIGN: 30 c. as Type 6 but vert.

6. United Nations Emblem.

1958. U.N. Economic Commission for Asia and Far East Conference, Kuala Lumpur.

6.	6.	12 c. red	30	40
7.	–	30 c. purple	40	20

DESIGN—VERT. 30 c. Portrait of the Yan di-Pertuan Agong (Tuanku Abdul Rahman).

8. Merdeka Stadium, Kuala Lumpur.

1958. 1st Anniv. of Independence.

8.	8.	10 c. multicoloured ..	15	10
9.	–	30 c. multicoloured ..	40	10

DESIGN—VERT. 10 c. "Human Rights".

11. Malayan with "Torch of Freedom".

1958. 10th Anniv. of Declaration of Human Rights.

10.	–	10 c. multicoloured ..	10	10
11.	11.	30 c. green	30	20

12. Mace and Malayan Peoples.

14.

1959. Inauguration of Parliament.

12.	12.	4 c. red	10	10
13.		10 c. violet	10	10
14.		25 c. green	35	20

1960. World Refugee Year

15.	–	12 c. purple	10	30
16.	14.	30 c. green	10	10

DESIGN: 12 c. As Type **14** but horiz.

15. Seedling Rubber Tree and Map.

16. The Yang di-Pertuan Agong (Tuanku Syed Putra).

1960. Natural Rubber Research Conf. and 15th Int. Rubber Study Group Meeting, Kuala Lumpur.

17.	15.	6 c. multicoloured ..	20	30
18.		30 c. multicoloured ..	50	15

No. 18 is inscr. "INTERNATIONAL RUBBER STUDY GROUP 15TH MEETING KUALA LUMPUR" at foot.

1961. Installation of Yang di-Pertuan Agong, Tuanku Syed Putra.

19.	16.	10 c. black and blue ..	10	10

17. Colombo Plan Emblem. 18. Malaria Eradication Emblem.

1961. Colombo Plan Conf., Kuala Lumpur.

20.	17.	12 c. black and mauve ..	35	1·50
21.		25 c. black and green ..	80	1·25
22.		30 c. black and blue ..	70	30

1962. Malaria Eradication.

23.	18.	25 c. brown	20	30
24.		30 c. lilac	20	10
25.		50 c. blue	40	15

19. Palmyra Palm Leaf.

1962. National Language Month.

26.	19.	10 c. brown and violet ..	15	10
27.		20 c. brown and green ..	25	25
28.		50 c. brown and mauve	45	60

20. "Shadows of the Future".

1962. Introduction of Free Primary Education.

29.	20.	10 c. purple	10	10
30.		25 c. ochre	30	30
31.		30 c. green	80	10

21. Harvester and Fisherman.

1963. Freedom from Hunger.

32.	21.	25 c. pink and green ..	85	80
33.		30 c. pink and lake ..	1·50	30
34.		50 c. pink and blue ..	1·50	1·10

22. Dam and Pylon.

1963. Cameron Highlands Hydro-Electric Scheme.

35.	22.	20 c. green and violet ..	35	10
36.		30 c. turquoise and blue	45	30

MALAYAN POSTAL UNION

In 1936 postage due stamps were issued in Type D 1 for use in Negri Sembilan, Pahang, Perak, Selangor and Straits Settlements but later their use was extended to the whole of the Federation and in Singapore, and from 1963 throughout Malaysia.

POSTAGE DUE STAMPS

D 1.

1936.

D 1	D 1.	1 c. purple	3·50	70
D 14		1 c. violet	30	60
D 15		2 c. slate	30	75
D 8		3 c. green	9·00	11·00
D 2		4 c. green	6·00	1·00
D 17		4 c. sepia	45	3·00
D 9		5 c. red	12·00	7·50
D 3		8 c. red	2·50	3·50
D 19		8 c. orange	1·75	3·25
D 11		9 c. orange	60·00	45·00
D 4		10 c. orange	2·00	25
D 5		12 c. blue	4·25	6·00
D 20		12 c. mauve	1·00	3·75
D 12		15 c. blue	80·00	35·00
D 21		20 c. blue	4·00	6·00
D 6		50 c. black	16·00	5·00

1965. Surch. **10 cents.**

D 29.	D 1.	10 c. on 8 c. orange ..	30	1·75

MALAYSIA

General issues for use throughout the new Federation comprising the old Malayan Federation (Johore ("JOHOR"), Kedah, Kelantan, Malacca ("MELAKA"), Negri Sembilan ("NEGERI SEMBILAN"), Pahang, Penang ("PULAU PINANG"), Perak, Perlis, Selangor and Trengganu), Sabah (North Borneo), Sarawak and Singapore, until the latter became an independent state on 9th August, 1965.

Stamps inscr. "MALAYSIA" and state name are listed under the various states, as above.

100 cents (sen) = 1 Malaysian dollar.

A. NATIONAL SERIES

General issues for use throughout the Federation.

1. Federation Map.

1963. Inauguration of Federation.

1.	1.	10 c. yellow and violet ..	15	10
2.		12 c. yellow and green ..	60	60
3.		50 c. yellow and brown ..	75	10

2. Bouquet of Orchids.

1963. 4th World Orchid Congress, Singapore

4.	2.	6 c. multicoloured ..	1·00	1·00
5.		25 c. multicoloured ..	1·25	2

4. Parliament House, Kuala Lumpur.

1963. 9th Commonwealth Parliamentary Conference, Kuala Lumpur.

7.	4.	20 c. mauve and gold ..	25	4
8.		30 c. green and gold ..	25	1

5. "Flame of Freedom" and Emblems of Goodwill, Health and Charity.

1964. Eleanor Roosevelt Commem.

9.	5.	25 c. blk., red & turquoise	15	10
10.		30 c. black, red and lilac	15	10
11.		50 c. black, red & yellow	15	10

6. Microwave Tower and I.T.U. Emblem.

1965. Centenary of I.T.U.

12.	6.	2 c. multicoloured ..	15	80
13.		25 c. multicoloured ..	60	40
14.		50 c. multicoloured ..	1·25	10

7. National Mosque.

1965. Opening of National Mosque, Kuala Lumpur.

15.	7.	6 c. red	10	10
16.		15 c. brown	10	10
17.		20 c. green	10	10

8. Air Terminal.

1965. Opening of Int. Airport, Kuala Lumpur.

18.	8.	15 c. black, green and blue	15	10
19.		30 c. black, green & mauve	25	20

9. Crested Wood Partridge.

17. Sepak Raga (ball-game) and Football.

1965. Birds. Multicoloured.

20.		25 c. Type 9	50	10
21.		30 c. Blue-backed Fairy Bluebird	60	10
22.		50 c. Black-naped Oriole ..	70	10
23.		75 c. Rhinoceros Hornbill ..	1·25	10
24.		$1 Zebra Dove	1·75	10
25.		$2 Great Argus Pheasant ..	4·00	30
26.		$5 Asiatic Paradise Fly-catcher	13·00	1·50
27.		$10 Blue-tailed Pitta ..	35·00	6·50

For the lower values see the individual sets listed under each of the states which form Malaysia.

1965. 3rd South East Asian Peninsular Games.

28.	17.	25 c. black and green ..	40	90
29.	–	30 c. black and purple ..	40	20
30.	–	50 c. black and blue ..	70	30

DESIGNS: 30 c. Running. 50 c. Diving.

20. National Monument.

1966. National Monument, Kuala Lumpur.

31.	20.	10 c. multicoloured ..	15	10
32.		20 c. multicoloured ..	25	15

21. The Yang di-Pertuan Agong (Tuanku Ismail Nasiruddin Shah).

1966. Installation of Yang di-Pertuan Agong, Tuanku Ismail Nasiruddin Shah.

33.	21.	15 c. black and yellow ..	10	10
34.		50 c. black and blue ..	20	15

22. School Building.

1966. 150th Anniv. of Penang Free School.

35.	22.	20 c. multicoloured ..	25	10
36.		50 c. multicoloured ..	60	10

23. "Agriculture".

1966. 1st Malaysia Plan. Multicoloured

37.		15 c. Type 23	20	10
38.		15 c. "Rural Health" ..	20	10
39.		15 c. "Communications" ..	75	15
40.		15 c. "Education" ..	20	10
41.		15 c. "Irrigation"	20	10

28. Cable Route Maps. (Reduced size illustration. Actual size 68 × 22 mm.).

1967. Completion of Malaysia-Hong Kong Link of SEACOM Telephone Cable.

42.	28.	30 c. multicoloured ..	80	25
43.		75 c. multicoloured ..	2·50	2·50

29. Hibiscus and Paramount Rulers.

1967. 10th Anniv. of Independence.

44.	29.	15 c. multicoloured ..	20	10
45.		50 c. multicoloured ..	50	35

30. Mace and Shield.

1967. Centenary of Sarawak Council.

46.	30.	15 c. multicoloured ..	10	10
47.		50 c. multicoloured ..	20	20

31. Straits Settlements 1867 8 c. Stamp and Malaysian 1965 25 c. Stamp.

1967. Stamp Cent.

48.	31.	25 c. multicoloured ..	1·00	1·50
49.	–	30 c. multicoloured ..	1·00	85
50.	–	50 c. multicoloured ..	1·40	1·25

DESIGN: 30 c. Straits Settlements 1867. 24 c. Stamp and Malaysian 1965 30 c. Stamp. 50 c. Straits Settlements 1867. 32 c. Stamp and Malaysian 1965 50 c. Stamp.

34. Tapping Rubber, and Molecular Unit.

1968. Natural Rubber Conf., Kuala Lumpur. Multicoloured.

51.		25 c. Type 34	25	10
52.		30 c. Tapping Rubber, and Export Consignment ..	40	20
53.		50 c. Tapping Rubber, and Aircraft Tyres	40	10

37. Mexican Sombrero and Blanket with Olympic Rings.

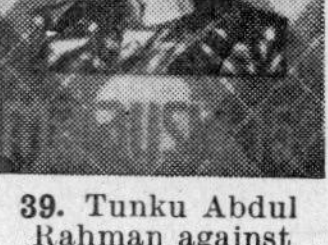

39. Tunku Abdul Rahman against background of Pandanus Weave.

1968. Olympic Games, Mexico. Mult.

54.		30 c. Type 37	20	10
55.		75 c. Olympic Rings and Mexican Embroidery ..	40	20

1969. Solidarity Week.

56.	39.	15 c. multicoloured ..	15	10
57.	–	20 c. multicoloured ..	20	40
58.	–	50 c. multicoloured ..	20	20

DESIGNS—VERT. 20 c. As Type 39 (different). HORIZ. 50 c. Tunku Abdul Rahman with pandanus pattern.

42. Peasant Girl with sheaves of Paddy.

1969. National Rice Year.

59.	42.	15 c. multicoloured ..	15	10
60.		75 c. multicoloured ..	45	55

43. Satellite tracking Aerial.

1970. Satellite Earth Station.

61.	43.	15 c. drab, black and blue	75	15
62.	–	30 c. multicoloured ..	75	1·40
63.	–	30 c. multicoloured ..	75	1·40

DESIGN—HORIZ. (40 × 27 mm): Nos. 62/3, "Intelstat III" in Orbit.

No. 62 has inscription and value in white and No. 63 has them in gold.

45. "Euploea leucostictus".

46. Emblem.

1970. Butterflies. Multicoloured.

64		25 c. Type 45	80	10
65		30 c. "Zeuxidia amethystus"	1·12	10
66		50 c. "Polyura athamas" ..	1·50	10
67		75 c. "Papilio memnon" ..	1·75	10
68		$1 "Appias nero" ..	1·75	10
69		$2 "Trogonoptera brookiana"	3·00	10
70		$5 "Narathlura centaurus"	4·50	1·25
71		$10 "Terinos terpander" ..	9·00	5·00

Lower values were issued for use in the individual States.

1970. 50th Anniv. of Int. Labour Organisation.

72.	46.	30 c. grey and blue ..	10	20
73.		75 c. pink and blue ..	20	30

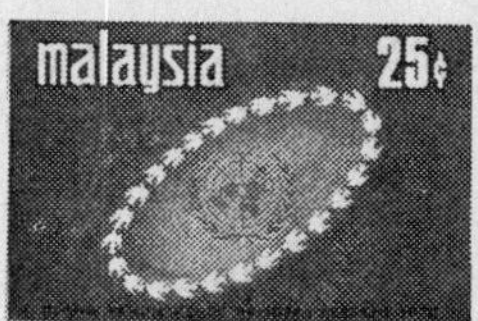

47. U.N. Emblem encircled by Doves.

1970. 25th Anniv. of United Nations.

74.	47.	25 c. gold, black & brown	35	40
75.	–	30 c. multicoloured ..	45	35
76.	–	50 c. black and green ..	75	75

DESIGNS: 30 c. Line of Doves and U.N. Emblem. 50 c. Doves looping U.N. Emblem.

50. The Yang di-Pertuan Agong (Tuanku Abdul Halim Shah).

1971. Installation of Yang di-Pertuan Agong. (Paramount Ruler of Malaysia).

77.	50.	10 c. blk., gold & yellow	20	30
78.		15 c. blk., gold & mauve	20	30
79.		50 c. blk., gold and blue	60	1·60

51. Bank Negara Complex.

1971. Opening of Bank Negara Building.

80.	51.	25 c. black and silver ..	70	90
81.		50 c. black and gold ..	70	1·10

52. Aerial view of Parliament Buildings. (Illustration reduced. Actual size 59 × 33 mm.)

1971. 17th Commonwealth Parliamentary Association Conference, Kuala Lumpur. Multicoloured.

82.		25 c. Type 52	90	50
83.		75 c. Ground view of Parliament Buildings (horiz. 73 × 23½ mm)	1·60	1·75

53. 54. 55.
Malaysian Carnival.
(Illustration reduced. Actual size $63\frac{1}{2} \times 32$ mm.)

1971. Visit ASEAN Year.
84. **53.** 30 c. multicoloured .. 1·25 35
85. **54.** 30 c. multicoloured .. 1·25 35
86. **55.** 30 c. multicoloured .. 1·25 35
ASEAN = Association of South East Asian Nations.
Nos. 84/6 form a composite design of a Malaysian Carnival, as Types **53/5**.

56. Trees, Elephant and Tiger.

1971. 25th Anniv. of U.N.I.C.E.F. Mult.
87. 15 c. Type **56** .. .. 1·25 25
88. 15 c. Cat and kittens .. 1·25 25
89. 15 c. Sun, flower and bird (vert. 22×29 mm.) .. 1·25 25
90. 15 c. Monkey, elephant and lion in jungle .. .. 1·25 25
91. 15 c. Spider and butterflies 1·25 25

57. Athletics.

1971. 6th S.E.A.P. Games, Kuala Lumpur. Multicoloured.
92. 25 c. Type **57** 35 40
93. 30 c. Sepak Raga players 50 50
94. 50 c. Hockey 80 95
S.E.A.P. = South East Asian Peninsular.

58. **59.** **60.**
Map and Tourist Attractions.
(Illustration reduced. Actual size 66×37 mm.).

1971. Pacific Area Tourist Association Conference.
95. **58.** 30 c. multicoloured .. 1·25 35
96. **59.** 30 c. multicoloured .. 1·25 35
97. **60.** 30 c. multicoloured .. 1·25 35
Nos. 95/7 form a composite design of a map showing tourist attractions, as Types **58/60**.

61. Kuala Lumpur City Hall.
(Illustration reduced. Actual size 54×33 mm.).

1972. City Status for Kuala Lumpur. Mult.
98. 25 c. Type **61** .. .. 1·00 1·25
99. 50 c. City Hall in Floodlights 1·50 1·25

62. SOCSO Emblem. **64.** Fireworks, National Flag and Flower.

63. W.H.O. Emblem.

1973. Social Security Organization.
100. **62.** 10 c. multicoloured .. 15 15
101. 15 c. multicoloured .. 25 10
102. 50 c. multicoloured .. 60 1·40

1973. 25th Anniv. of W.H.O.
103. **63.** 30 c. multicoloured .. 45 25
104. – 75 c. multicoloured .. 1·25 1·75
The 75 c. is similar to Type **63**, but vertical.

1973. 10th Anniv. of Malaysia.
105. **64.** 10 c. multicoloured .. 25 25
106. 15 c. multicoloured .. 30 15
107. 50 c. multicoloured .. 1·25 1·60

65. Emblems of Interpol and Royal Malaysian Police.

1973. 50th Anniv. of Interpol. Mult.
108. 25 c. Type **65** .. .. 1·00 50
109. 75 c. Emblems within "50" 1·75 2·00

66. Aeroplane and M.A.S. Emblem.

1973. Malaysian Airline System. Foundation.
110. **66.** 15 c. multicoloured .. 25 10
111. 30 c. multicoloured .. 45 60
112. 50 c. multicoloured .. 75 1·60

67. Kuala Lumpur.

1974. Establishment of Kuala Lumpur as Federal Territory.
113. **67.** 25 c. multicoloured .. 50 85
114. 50 c. multicoloured .. 1·00 1·75

68. Development Projects.

1974. 7th Annual Meeting of Asian Development Bank's Board of Governors, Kuala Lumpur.
115. **68.** 30 c. multicoloured .. 25 50
116. 75 c. multicoloured .. 80 1·75

69. Scout Badge and Map.

1974. Malaysian Scout Jamboree. Mult.
117. 10 c. Type **69** 30 20
118. 15 c. Scouts saluting and flags (46×24 mm.) .. 35 30
119. 50 c. Scout Badge .. 1·25 2·25

70. Coat of arms and Power Installations.

1974. 25th Anniv. of National Electricity Board. Multicoloured.
120. 30 c. Type **70** 30 50
121. 75 c. National Electricity Board Building (37×27 mm.) 1·00 2·00

71. U.P.U. and Post Office Emblems within "100".

1974. Centenary of U.P.U.
122. **71.** 25 c. green, yell. & red 20 35
123. 30 c. blue, yell. and red 25 35
124. 75 c. orange, yell. & red 65 1·75

72. Gravel Pump in Tin Mine.

1974. Fourth World Tin Conf. Kuala Lumpur. Multicoloured.
125. 15 c. Type **72** 70 15
126. 20 c. Open-cast mine .. 1·00 70
127. 50 c. Dredger within "ingot" .. .. .. 2·50 2·50

73. Hockey-players. World Cup and Federation Emblem.

1975. Third World Cup Hockey Championships.
128. **73.** 30 c. multicoloured .. 90 60
129. 75 c. multicoloured .. 2·10 2·25

74. Congress Emblem.

1975. 25th Anniv. of Malaysian Trade Union Congress.
130. **74.** 20 c. multicoloured .. 20 25
131. 25 c. multicoloured .. 30 30
132. 30 c. multicoloured .. 45 60

75. Emblem of M.K.P.W. (Malayan Women's Organization).

1975. International Women's Year.
133. **75.** 10 c. multicoloured .. 15 25
134. 15 c. multicoloured .. 30 25
135. 50 c. multicoloured .. 1·25 2·25

76. Ubudiah Mosque, Kuala Kangsar.

1975. Koran Reading Competition. Multicoloured.
136. 15 c. Type **76** .. .. 1·25 30
137. 15 c. Zahir Mosque, Alor Star .. .. 1·25 30
138. 15 c. National Mosque, Kuala Lumpur .. 1·25 30
139. 15 c. Sultan Abu Bakar Mosque, Johore Bahru 1·25 30
140. 15 c. Kuching State Mosque, Sarawak .. 1·25 30

77. Plantation and Emblem.

1975. 50th Anniv. of Malaysian Rubber Research Institute. Multicoloured.
141. 10 c. Type **77** 35 15
142. 30 c. Latex cup and emblem 1·00 70
143. 75 c. Natural rubber in test-tubes .. .. 1·60 2·25

77a. "Hebomoia glaucippe".

1976. Multicoloured.
144 10 c. Type **77a** .. .. 60 3·00
145 15 c. "Precis orithya" .. 65 3·00

78. Scrub Typhus. **79.** The Yang di Pertuan Agong (Tuanku Yahya Petra).

1976. 75th Anniv. of Institute of Medical Research. Multicoloured.
146. 20 c. Type **78** 25 15
147. 25 c. Malaria diagnosis .. 40 20
148. $1 Beri-beri .. .. 1·60 2·50

1976. Installation of Yang di-Pertuan Agong.
149. **79.** 10 c. blk., brn. & yell. 25 10
150. 15 c. blk., brn. & mauve 40 10
151. 50 c. blk., brn. & blue 2·25 2·50

80. State Council Complex.

1976. Opening of State Council Complex and Administrative Building, Sarawak.

152. **80.** 15 c. green and yellow .. 35 10
153. 20 c. green and mauve .. 45 40
154. 50 c. green and blue .. 1·00 1·40

81. E.P.F. Building.

1976. 25th Anniv. of Employees' Provident Fund. Multicoloured.

155. 10 c. Type **81** 15 10
156. 25 c. E.P.F. emblems (27 × 27 mm.) 25 35
157. 50 c. E.P.F. Building at night .. .. .. 60 1·00

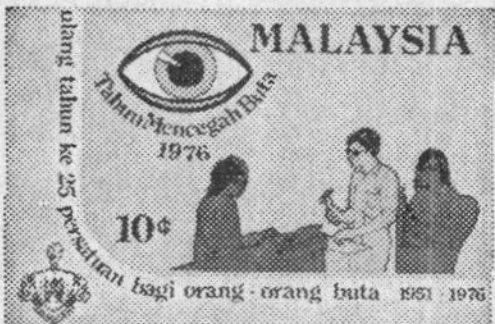

82. Blind People at Work.

1976. 25th Anniv. of Malayan Assn. for the Blind. Multicoloured.

158. 10 c. Type **82** .. 15 15
159. 75 c. Blind man and shadow 1·25 2·10

83. Independence Celebrations, 1957.

1977. 1st Death Anniv. of Tun Abdul Razak (Prime Minister).

160. 15 c. Type **83** .. .. 1·00 30
161. 15 c. "Education" .. 1·00 30
162. 15 c. Tun Razak and map ("Development") .. 1·00 30
163. 15 c. "Rukunegara" (National Philosophy) .. 1·00 30
164. 15 c. ASEAN meeting .. 1·00 30

84. F.E.L.D.A. Village Scheme.

1977. 21st Anniv. of Federal Land Development Authority (F.E.L.D.A.). Multicoloured.

165. 15 c. Type **84** 25 10
166. 30 c. Oil Palm settlement 60 80

85. Figure "10".

1977. 10th Anniv. of Association of South East Asian Nations (A.S.E.A.N.) Mult.

167. 10 c. Type **85** 10 10
168. 75 c. Flags of members .. 60 65

MORE DETAILED LISTS
are given in the Stanley Gibbons Catalogues referred to in the country headings.
For lists of current volumes see Introduction.

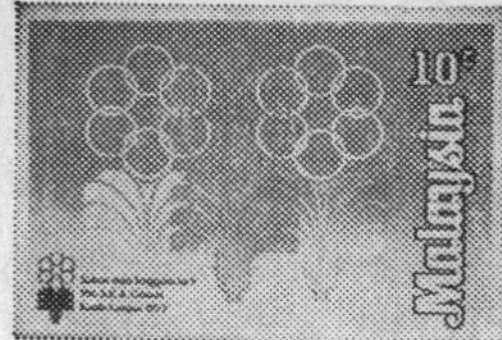

86. Games Logos.

1977. Ninth South East Asia Games, Kuala Lumpur. Multicoloured.

169. 10 c. Type **86** 15 15
170. 20 c. "Ball" 20 15
171. 75 c. Symbolic athletes .. 75 1·25

87. Islamic Development Bank Emblem.

1978. Islamic Development Bank Board of Governors' Meeting, Kuala Lumpur.

172. **87.** 30 c. multicoloured .. 15 15
173. 75 c. multicoloured .. 50 55

88. Mobile Post Office.

1978. Fourth Commonwealth Conference of Postal Administrations, Kuala Lumpur. Multicoloured.

174. 10 c. Type **88** 20 10
175. 25 c. G.P.O., Kuala Lumpur 65 75
176. 50 c. Rural delivery by motorcycle .. .. 95 1·10

89. Boy Scout Emblem.

1978. Fourth Malaysian Scout Jamboree, Sarawak. Multicoloured.

177. 15 c. Type **89** 40 10
178. $1 Bees and honeycomb .. 2·00 1·25

90. Dome of the Rock, Jerusalem.

1978. Palestinian Welfare.

179. **90.** 15 c. multicoloured .. 35 10
180. 30 c. multicoloured .. 60 40

91. Globe and Emblems.

1978. Global Eradication of Smallpox.

181. **91.** 15 c. black, red & blue 15 20
182. 30 c. black, red & green 20 10
183. 50 c. black, red & pink 35 45

92. "Seratus Tahun Getah Asli" and Tapping Knives Symbol.

1978. Centenary of Rubber Industry.

184. **92.** 10 c. gold and green .. 10 10
185. – 20 c. blue, brn. & green 10 10
186. – 75 c. gold and green .. 45 65

DESIGNS: 20 c. Rubber tree seedling and part of "maxi stump". 75 c. Graphic design of rubber tree, latex cup and globe arranged to form "100".

93. Sultan of Selangor's New Palace.

1978. Inaug. Shah Alam New Town, as State Capital of Selangor. Multicoloured.

187. 10 c. Type **93** 10 10
188. 30 c. Aerial view of Shah Alam 15 10
189. 75 c. Shah Alam 45 60

94. Tiger.

1979. Animals. Multicoloured.

190. 30 c. Type **94** 70 10
191. 40 c. Malayan Flying lemur 70 10
192. 50 c. Lesser Malay Chevrotain 80 10
193. 75 c. Leathery Pangolin .. 90 10
194. $1 Malayan Turtle .. 1·50 10
195. $2 Malayan Tapir .. .. 1·50 10
196. $5 Gaur .. .. .. 4·25 80
197. $10 Orang-utang (vert.) .. 7·00 3·25

96. View of Central Bank of Malaysia.

1979. 20th Anniv. of Central Bank of Malaysia. Multicoloured.

198. 10 c. Type **96** 10 10
199. 75 c. Central Bank (vert.) 40 45

97. I.Y.C. Emblem.

1979. International Year of the Child.

200. **97.** 10 c. gold, blue and salmon 30 10
201. – 15 c. multicoloured .. 40 10
202. – $1 multicoloured .. 1·75 2·00

DESIGNS: 15 c. Children holding hands in front of globe. $1, Children playing.

98. Dam and Power Station.

1979. Opening of Hydro-Electric Power Station, Temengor.

203. **98.** 15 c. multicoloured .. 15 15
204. – 25 c. multicoloured .. 25 45
205. – 50 c. multicoloured .. 45 75

DESIGNS: 25 c., 50 c. Different views of Dam.

99. Exhibition Emblem.

1979. 3rd World Telecommunications Exhibition, Geneva.

206. **99.** 10 c. orge., blue & silver 10 15
207. – 15 c. multicoloured .. 15 10
208. – 50 c. multicoloured .. 40 1·25

DESIGNS—(34 × 24 mm.). 15 c. Telephone receiver joining the one half of World to the other. (39 × 28 mm.). 50 c. Communications equipment.

100. Tuanku Haji Ahmad Shah.

1980. Installation of Tuanku Haji Ahmad Shah as Yang di-Pertuan Agong.

209. **100.** 10 c. blk., gold & yell... 10 10
210. 15 c. blk., gold & purple 15 10
211. 50 c. blk., gold and blue 40 90

101. Pahang and Sarawak Maps within Telephone Dials.

1980. Kuantan–Kuching Submarine Cable Project. Multicoloured.

212. 10 c. Type **101** 10 10
213. 15 c. Kuantan and Kuching views within telephone dials 15 10
214. 50 c. Pahang and Sarawak Maps within telephone receiver 35 60

102. Bangi Campus.

1980. 10th Anniv. of National University of Malaysia. Multicoloured.

215. 10 c. Type **102** .. 15 15
216. 15 c. Jalan Pantai Baru campus 20 10
217. 75 c. Great Hall .. .. 65 1·50

103. Mecca.

1980. Moslem Year 1400 A.H. Commemoration.

218. **103.** 15 c. multicoloured .. 10 10
219. 50 c. multicoloured .. 30 75

No. 219 is inscribed in Roman lettering.

INDEX
Countries can be quickly located by referring to the index at the end of this volume.

104. Disabled Child learning to Walk.

1981. International Year of Disabled Persons. Multicoloured.
220. 10 c. Type **104** 30 20
221. 15 c. Girl sewing 55 10
222. 75 c. Disabled athlete .. 1·50 1·75

105. Industrial Scene.

1981. Expo "81" Industrial Training Exposition, Kuala Lumpur and Seminar, Genting Highlands. Multicoloured.
223. 10 c. Type **105** 10 10
224. 15 c. Worker and bulldozer 15 10
225. 30 c. Workers at ship-building plant 25 30
226. 75 c. Agriculture and fishing produce, workers and machinery .. .. 65 1·25

106. "25".

1981. 25th Anniv. of Malaysian National Committee for World Energy Conferences. Multicoloured.
227. 10 c. Type **106** 15 15
228. 15 c. Drawings showing importance of energy sources in industry .. 20 10
229. 75 c. Symbols of various energy sources .. .. 85 1·75

107. Drawing showing development of Sabah from Village to Urbanised Area.

1981. Centenary of Sabah. Multicoloured.
230. 15 c. Type **107** 50 15
231. 80 c. Drawing showing traditional and modern methods of agriculture 2·00 3·00

108. "Samanea saman".

1981. Trees. Multicoloured.
232. 15 c. Type **108** 55 10
233. 50 c. "Dyera costulata" (vert.) .. .. 1·50 1·00
234. 80 c. "Dryobalanops aromatica" (vert.) .. 1·75 2·50

109. Jamboree Emblem.

1982. 5th Malaysian/7th Asia-Pacific Boy Scout Jamboree. Multicoloured.
235. 15 c. Type **109** 30 10
236. 50 c. Malaysian flag and scout emblem 70 80
237. 80 c. Malaysian and Asia-Pacific scout emblem .. 1·10 2·50

110. A.S.E.A.N. Building Emblem.

1982. 15th Anniv. of A.S.E.A.N. (Association of South East Asian Nations). Ministerial Meeting. Multicoloured.
238. 15 c. Type **110** 15 10
239. $1 Flags of members .. 60 1·25

111. Dome of the Rock, Jerusalem.

1982. "Freedom for Palestine".
240. **111.** 15 c. gold, green and blk. 75 15
241. $1 silver, green and blk. 2·75 2·25

112. Views of Kuala Lumpur in 1957 and 1982.

1982. 25th Anniv. of Independence. Mult.
242. 10 c. Type **112** 10 10
243. 15 c. Malaysian industries 15 15
244. 50 c. Soldiers on parade .. 40 55
245. 80 c. Independence ceremony 70 1·50

113. Shadow Play.

1982. Traditional Games. Multicoloured.
247. 10 c. Type **113** 30 20
248. 15 c. Cross Top 40 15
249. 75 c. Kite flying .. .. 1·50 2·25

114. Sabah Hats.

1982. Malaysian Handicrafts. Multicoloured.
250. 10 c. Type **114** 15 25
251. 15 c. Gold-threaded cloth 15 20
252. 75 c. Sarawak pottery .. 85 1·75

115. Gas Exploration Logo.

1983. Export of Liquefied Natural Gas from Bintulu Field, Sarawak. Multicoloured.
253. 15 c. Type **115** 45 10
254. 20 c. "Tenaga Satu" (liquid gas tanker) 70 40
255. $1 Gas drilling equipment 2·50 3·00

116. Flag of Malaysia.

1983. Commonwealth Day. Multicoloured.
256. 15 c. Type **116** 10 10
257. 20 c. The King of Malaysia 15 15
258. 40 c. Oil palm tree and refinery 25 30
259. $1 Satellite view of earth 60 1·50

117. "Tilapia nilotica".

1983. Freshwater Fishes. Multicoloured.
260. 20 c. Type **117** 30 30
261. 20 c. "Cyprinus carpio" .. 30 30
262. 40 c. "Puntius gonionotus" 50 60
263. 40 c. "Ctenopharyngodon idellus" 60 60

118. Lower Pergau River Bridge.

1983. Opening of the East-West Highway. Multicoloured.
264. 15 c. Type **118** 60 15
265. 20 c. Perak river reservoir bridge 70 35
266. $1 Map showing East-west highway .. .. .. 2·25 3·00

119. Northrop "RF-5E" Fighter.

1983. 50th Anniv. of Malaysian Armed Forces. Multicoloured.
267. 15 c. Type **119** 40 15
268. 20 c. Missile boat 65 30
269. 40 c. Battle of Pasir Panjang .. .. .. 1·00 90
270. 80 c. Trooping the Colour 1·50 2·25

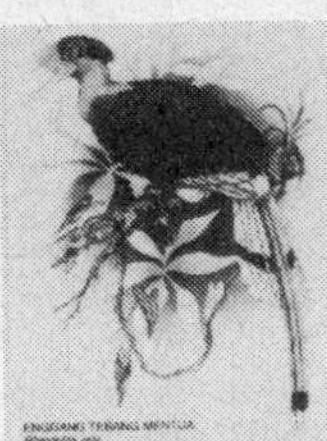

120. Helmeted Hornbill.

1983. Hornbills of Malaysia. Multicoloured.
280. 15 c. Type **120** 40 10
281. 20 c. Wrinkled hornbill .. 55 30
282. 50 c. Long-crested hornbill 85 90
283. $1 Rhinoceros hornbill .. 1·60 2·50

121. Bank Building, Ipoh.

1984. 25th Anniv. of Bank Negara. Mult.
284. 20 c. Type **121** 40 30
285. $1 Bank building, Alor Setar 1·40 2·25

122. Sky-scraper and Mosque, Kuala Lumpur.

1984. 10th Anniv. of Federal Territory. Multicoloured.
286. 20 c. Type **122** 50 20
287. 40 c. Aerial view .. 1·00 1·00
288. 80 c. Gardens and clock-tower (horiz.) .. .. 1·75 1·25

123. Map showing Industries. 124. Semananjung Keris.

1984. Formation of Labuan Federal Territory. Multicoloured.
289. 20 c. Type **123** 50 25
290. $1 Flag and map of Labuan 2·00 2·25

1984. Traditional Malay Weapons. Mult.
291. 40 c. Type **124** 70 70
292. 40 c. Pekakak keris .. 70 70
293. 40 c. Jawa keris 70 70
294. 40 c. Lada tumbuk .. 70 70

125. Map of World and Transmitter.

1984. 20th Anniv. of Asia-Pacific Broadcasting Union. Multicoloured.
295. 20 c. Type **125** 40 25
296. $1 Clasped hands within "20" .. .. .. 2·00 2·75

126. Facsimile service.

1984. Opening of New General Post Office, Kuala Lumpur. Multicoloured.
297. 15 c. Type **126** 30 20
298. 20 c. New G.P.O. building 40 30
299. $1 Mailbag conveyor .. 1·75 2·50

127. Yang di Pertuan Agong (Tuanku Mahmood).

1984. Installation of Yang di Pertuan Agong (Tuanku Mahmood).
300. **127.** 15 c. multicoloured .. 40 20
301. 20 c. multicoloured .. 40 20
302. – 40 c. multicoloured .. 75 85
303. – 80 c. multicoloured .. 1·40 2·00
DESIGN—HORIZ. 40 c., 80 c. Yang di Pertuan Agong and Federal Crest.

128. White Hibiscus.

1984. Hibiscus. Multicoloured.
304. 10 c. Type **128** 35 15
305. 20 c. Red Hibiscus 70 20
306. 40 c. Pink Hibiscus 1·25 1·00
307. $1 Orange Hibiscus 2·25 2·75

129. Parliament Building.

1985. 25th Anniv. of Federal Parliament. Multicoloured.
308. 20 c. Type **129** 30 15
309. $1 Parliament Building (different) (horiz.) 1·75 1·50

130. Banded Lingsang.

1985. Protected Animals of Malaysia. (1st series). Multicoloured.
310. 10 c. Type **130** 30 10
311. 40 c. Slow Loris (vert.) 80 80
312. $1 Spotted Giant Flying Squirrel (vert.) 1·75 2·50
See also Nos. 383/6.

131. Stylised Figures.

1985. International Youth Year. Mult.
313. 20 c. Type **131** 25 15
314. $1 Young workers 1·50 2·25

132. F.M.S.R. "No. 1" Steam Locomotive, 1885.

1985. Centenary of Malayan Railways.
315. **132.** 15 c. black, red and orange 50 15
316. – 20 c. multicoloured 60 20
317. – $1 multicoloured 1·50 2·25
DESIGNS: 20 c. Class "20" diesel locomotive, 1957. $1 Class "23" diesel locomotive, 1983.

133. Blue Proton "Saga 1.3s" Car.

1985. Production of Proton "Saga" (Malaysian national car). Multicoloured.
319. 20 c. Type **133** 30 15
320. 40 c. White Proton "Saga 1.3s" 45 40
321. $1 Red Proton "Saga 1.5s" 80 1·75

134. Penang Bridge.

1985. Opening of Penang Bridge. Mult.
322. 20 c. Type **134** 30 15
323 40 c. Penang Bridge and location map 55 35
324. $1 Symbolic bridge linking Penang to mainland (40 × 24 mm) 1·25 1·25

135. Offshore Oil Rig.

1985. Malaysian Petroleum Production. Multicoloured.
325. 15 c. Type **135** 15 10
326. 20 c. Malaysia's first oil refinery (horiz.) 20 20
327. $1 Map of Malaysian off-shore oil and gas fields (horiz.) 90 1·25

136. Sultan Azlan Shah and Perak Royal Crest.

1985. Installation of the Sultan of Perak.
328. **136.** 15 c. multicoloured 15 10
329. 20 c. multicoloured 20 20
330. $1 multicoloured 1·00 2·00

137. Crested Fireback Pheasant. **139.** Two Indonesian Dancers.

1986. Protected Birds of Malaysia (1st series). Multicoloured.
331. 20 c. Type **137** 70 70
332. 20 c. Malay peacock-pheasant 70 70
333. 40 c. Bulwer's pheasant (horiz.) 1·00 1·00
334. 40 c. Great argus pheasant (horiz.) 1·00 1·00
See also Nos. 394/7.

1986. Pacific Area Travel Association Conference, Malaysia. Multicoloured.
335. 20 c. Type **139** 15 20
336. 20 c. Dyak dancer and longhouse, Malaysia 15 20
337. 20 c. Dancers and church, Philippines 15 20
338. 40 c. Thai dancer and temple 15 40
339. 40 c. Chinese dancer, Singapore 30 40
340. 40 c. Indian dancer and Hindu temple stairway 30 40

140. Stylized Competitors.

1986. Malaysia Games. Multicoloured.
341. 20 c. Type **140** 55 20
342. 40 c. Games emblems (vert.) 1·00 1·00
343. $1 National and state flags (vert.) 2·50 2·75

141. Rambutan. **143.** MAS Logo and Map showing Routes.

142. Skull and Slogan "Drugs Can Kill".

1986. Fruits of Malaysia. Multicoloured.
344. 40 c. Type **141** 15 20
345. 50 c. Pineapple 20 25
346. 80 c. Durian 35 40
347. $1 Mangostene 40 45
348. $2 Starfruit 85 90
349. $5 Banana 2·10 2·25
350. $10 Mango 4·25 4·50
351. $20 Papaya 8·50 8·75

1986. 10th Anniv. of National Association for Prevention of Drug Addiction. Multicoloured.
352. 20 c. Type **142** 25 20
353. 40 c. Bird and slogan "Stay Free From Drugs" 40 40
354. $1 Addict and slogan "Drugs Can Destroy" (vert.) 1·00 1·60

1986. Inaugural Flight of Malaysian Airlines Kuala Lumpur–Los Angeles Service. Multicoloured.
355. 20 c. Type **143** 20 15
356. 40 c. Logo, stylized aircraft and route diagram 35 35
357. $1 Logo and stylized aircraft 80 1·10

144. Building Construction.

1986. 20th Anniv. of National Productivity Council and 25th Anniv. of Asian Productivity Organization. (40 c., $1). Multicoloured.
358. 20 c. Type **144** 45 20
359. 40 c. Planning and design (horiz.) 80 50
360. $1 Computer-controlled car assembly line (horiz.) 1·40 1·25

145. Old Seri Menanti Palace, Negri Sembilan.

1986. Historic Buildings of Malaysia (1st series). Multicoloured.
361. 15 c. Type **145** 15 15
362. 20 c. Old Kenangan Palace, Perak 20 15
363. 40 c. Old Town Hall, Malacca 35 35
364. $1 Astana, Kuching, Sarawak 75 1·10
See also Nos. 465/8.

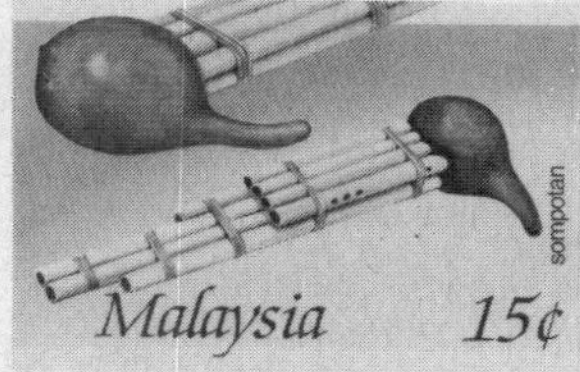

146. Sompotan (bamboo pipes).

1987. Malaysian Musical Instruments. Multicoloured.
365. 15 c. Type **146** 10 10
366. 20 c. Sapih (four-stringed chordophone) 15 15
367. 50 c. Serunai (pipes) (vert.) 30 30
368. 80 c. Rebab (three-stringed fiddle) (vert.) 45 45

147. Modern Housing Estate.

1987. International Year of Shelter for the Homeless. Multicoloured.
369. 20 c. Type **147** 15 15
370. $1 Stylised families and houses 60 65

148. Drug Addict and Family.

1987. International Conference on Drug Abuse, Vienna. Multicoloured.
371. 20 c. Type **148** 20 15
372. 20 c. Hands holding drugs and damaged internal organs 20 15
373. 40 c. Healthy boy and broken drug capsule 45 30
374. 40 c. Drugs and healthy internal organs 45 30
Nos. 371/2 and 373/4 were printed together, se-tenant, forming composite designs.

149. Spillway and Power Station.

1987. Opening of Sultan Mahmud Hydro-electric Scheme, Kenyir, Trengganu. Mult.
375. 20 c. Type **149** 20 10
376. $1 Dam, spillway and reservoir 80 50

150. Crossed Maces and Parliament Building, Kuala Lumpur.

1987. 33rd Commonwealth Parliamentary Conference. Multicoloured.

377.	20 c. Type **150**	10	10
378.	$1 Parliament building and crossed mace emblem ..	45	50

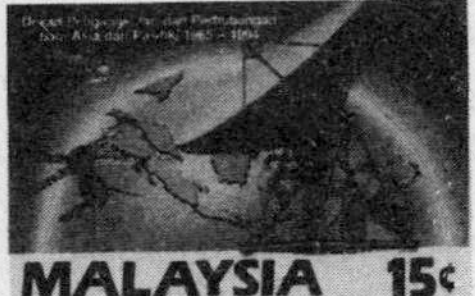

151. Dish Aerial, Satellite and Globe.

1987. Asia/Pacific Transport and Communications Decade. Multicoloured.

379.	15 c. Type **151**	15	10
380.	20 c. Diesel train and car	20	10
381.	40 c. Container ships and lorry	30	30
382.	$1 Malaysian Airlines jumbo jet, Kuala Lumpur Airport ..	65	90

152. Temminck's Golden Cat.

1987. Protected Animals of Malaysia (2nd series). Multicoloured.

383.	15 c. Type **152**	20	15
384.	20 c. Flatheaded cat ..	20	15
385.	40 c. Marbled cat	50	50
386.	$1 Clouded leopard ..	1·00	1·40

153. Flags of Member Nations and "20".

1987. 20th Anniv. of Association of South East Asian Nations. Multicoloured.

387.	20 c. Type **153**.	10	10
388.	$1 Flags of member nations and globe ..	45	70

154. Mosque and Portico.

1988. Opening of Sultan Salahuddin Abdul Aziz Shah Mosque. Multicoloured.

389.	15 c. Type **154**	10	10
390.	20 c. Dome, minarets and Sultan of Selangor ..	10	10
391.	$1 Interior and dome (vert.)	45	70

155. Aerial View.

1988. Sultan Ismail Hydro-electric Power Station, Paka, Trengganu. Multicoloured.

392.	20 c. Type **155**	10	10
393.	$1 Power station and pylons	45	50

156 Black-naped Blue Monarch

1988. Protected Birds of Malaysia (2nd series). Multicoloured.

394	20 c. Type **156**	10	10
395	20 c. Scarlet-backed flowerpecker	10	10
396	50 c. Yellow-backed sunbird	20	25
397	50 c. Black and red broadbill	20	25

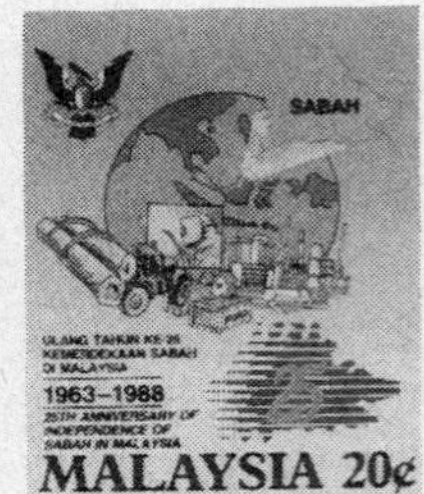

157 Outline Map and Products of Sabah

1988. 25th Anniv of Sabah and Sarawak as States of Malaysia. Multicoloured.

398	20 c. Type **157**	10	10
399	20 c. Outline map and products of Sarawak ..	10	10
400	$1 Flags of Malaysia, Sabah and Sarawak (30 × 40 mm)	40	45

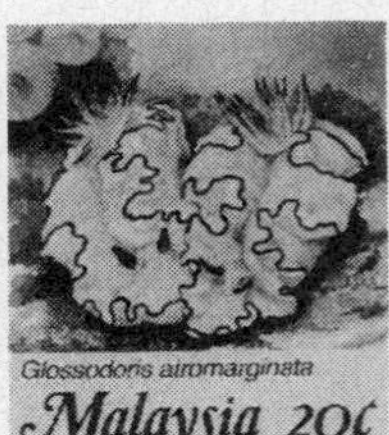

158 "Glossodoris atromarginata"

1988. Marine Life (1st series). Multicoloured.

401	20 c. Type **158**	15	15
402	20 c. "Phyllidia ocellata"	15	15
403	20 c. "Chromodoris annae"	15	15
404	20 c. "Flabellina macassarana"	15	15
405	20 c. "Fryeria ruppelli" ..	15	15

Nos. 401/5 were printed together, se-tenant, forming a composite background design.

See also Nos. 410/13 and 450/3.

159 Sultan's Palace, Malacca

1989. Declaration of Malacca as Historic City. Multicoloured

407	20 c. Type **159**	15	15
408	20 c. Independence Memorial Building ..	15	15
409	$1 Porta De Santiago Fortress (vert)	65	90

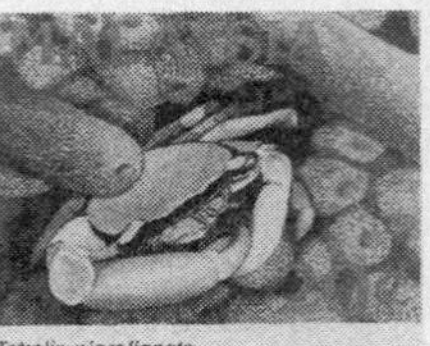

160 "Tetralia nigrolineata"

1989. Marine Life (2nd series). Crustaceans. Multicoloured.

410	20 c. Type **160**	15	15
411	20 c. "Neopetrolisthes maculatus" (crab) ..	15	15
412	40 c. "Periclimenes holthuisi" (shrimp) ..	20	25
413	40 c. "Synalpheus neomeris" (shrimp) ..	20	25

161 Map of Malaysia and Scout Badge

1989. 7th National Scout Jamboree. Mult.

414	10 c. Type **161**	10	10
415	20 c. Saluting national flag	15	15
416	80 c. Scouts around camp fire (horiz)	50	65

162 Cycling

1989. 15th South East Asian Games, Kuala Lumpur. Multicoloured.

417	10 c. Type **162**	15	15
418	20 c. Athletics	25	15
419	50 c. Swimming (vert) ..	50	50
420	$1 Torch bearer (vert) ..	85	1·00

163 Sultan Azlan Shah

1989. Installation of Sultan Azlan Shah as Yang di Pertuan Agong.

421	163	20 c. multicoloured ..	15	15
422		40 c. multicoloured ..	25	30
423		$1 multicoloured ..	60	75

164 Putra World Trade Centre and Pan-Pacific Hotel

1989. Commonwealth Heads of Government Meeting, Kuala Lumpur. Multicoloured.

424	20 c. Type **164**	15	10
425	50 c. Traditional dancers (vert)	35	45
426	$1 National flag and map showing Commonwealth countries	60	1·00

165 Clock Tower, Kuala Lumpur City Hall and Big Ben

1989. Inaugural Malaysia Airlines "747" Non-stop Flight to London. Each showing Malaysia Airlines Boeing "747-400". Mult.

427	20 c. Type **165** ..	15	15
428	20 c. Parliament Buildings, Kuala Lumpur, and Palace of Westminster	30	30
429	$1 World map showing route	70	80

166 Sloth and Map of Park

1989. 50th Anniv of National Park. Mult.

430	20 c. Type **166**	15	10
431	$1 Pair of crested argus pheasants	75	1·25

167 Outline Map of South-east Asia and Logo

1990. "Visit Malaysia Year". Multicoloured.

432	20 c. Type **167**	15	15
433	50 c. Traditional drums ..	35	50
434	$1 Scuba diving, windsurfing and yachting ..	65	1·00

Malaysia 15¢
SIMPUH AIR DILLENIA SUFFRUTICOSA 1990

168 "Dillenia suffruticosa"

1990. Wildflowers. Multicoloured.

435	15 c. Type **168**	15	1
436	20 c. "Mimosa pudica" ..	15	1
437	50 c. "Ipmoea carnea" ..	35	5
438	$1 "Nymphaea pubescens"	60	1·0

169 Monument and Rainbow

1990. Kuala Lumpur, Garden City of Lights. Multicoloured.

439 20 c. Type **169** 15 20
440 40 c. Mosque and sky-scrapers at night (horiz) 25 30
441 $1 Kuala Lumpur skyline (horiz) .. .. .. 60 1·00

170 Seri Negara Building

1990. 1st Summit Meeting of South–South Consultation and Co-operation Group, Kuala Lumpur. Multicoloured.

442 20 c. Type **170** 15 15
443 80 c. Summit logo .. 45 75

171 Alor Setar

1990. 250th Anniv of Alor Setar. Mult.

444 20 c. Type **171** 15 20
445 40 c. Musicians and monument (vert) .. 25 30
446 $1 Zahir Mosque (vert) .. 70 1·00

172 Sign Language Letters

1990. International Literacy Year. Mult.

447 20 c. Type **172** 10 10
448 40 c. People reading .. 25 30
449 $1 Symbolic person reading (vert) 65 80

173 Leatherback Turtle

1990. Marine Life (3rd series). Sea Turtles. Multicoloured.

450 15 c. Type **173** 15 10
451 20 c. Common green turtle 15 10
452 40 c. Olive Ridley turtle .. 30 30
453 $1 Hawksbill turtle .. 60 70

174 Safety Helmet, Dividers and Industrial Skyline

1991. 25th Anniv of MARA (Council of the Indigenous People). Multicoloured.

454 20 c. Type **174** 15 10
455 40 c. Documents and graph 25 25
456 $1 25th Anniversary logo 65 70

175 "Eustenogaster calyptodoma"

1991. Insects. Wasps. Multicoloured.

457 15 c. Type **175** 10 10
458 20 c. "Vespa affinis indonensis" 10 10
459 50 c. "Sceliphorn javanum" 20 25
460 $1 "Ampulex compressa" 40 45

176 Tunku Abdul Rahman Putra and Independence Rally

1991. Former Prime Ministers of Malaysia. Multicoloured.

462 $1 Type **176** 40 45
463 $1 Tun Abdul Razak Hussein and jungle village 40 45
464 $1 Tun Hussein Onn and standard-bearers .. 40 45

177 Maziah Palace, Terengganu

1991. Historic Buildings of Malaysia (2nd series). Multicoloured.

465 15 c. Type **177** 10 10
466 20 c. Grand Palace, Johore 10 10
467 40 c. Town Palace, Kuala Langat, Selangor .. 15 20
468 $1 Jahar Palace, Kelantan 40 45

178 Museum Building, Brass Lamp and Fabric

1991. Centenary of Sarawak Museum. Mult.

469 30 c. Type **178** 10 10
470 $1 Museum building, vase and fabric 40 45

B. FEDERAL TERRITORY ISSUES.

For use in the Federal Territory of Kuala Lumpur.

K 1. "Rafflesia hasseltii".

1979. Flowers. Multicoloured.

K1 1 c. Type **K 1** 10 10
K2 2 c. "Pterocarpus indicus" 10 10
K3 5 c. "Lagerstroemia speciosa" 10 10
K4 10 c. "Durio zibethinus" 10 10
K5 15 c. "Hibiscus rosa-sinensis" 15 10
K6 20 c. "Rhododendron scortechinii" 15 10
K7 25 c. "Etlingera elatior" (inscr "Phaeomeria speciosa") 15 10

K 2. Coffee.

1986. Agricultural Products of Malaysia. Multicoloured.

K 15. 1 c. Type **K 2** 10 10
K 16. 2 c. Coconuts 10 10
K 17. 5 c. Cocoa 10 10
K 18. 10 c. Black pepper .. 10 10
K 19. 15 c. Rubber 10 10
K 20. 20 c. Oil palm 10 10
K 21. 30 c. Rice 10 15

POSTAGE DUE STAMPS

Until 15th August, 1966, the postage due stamps of Malayan Postal Union were in use throughout Malaysia.

D 1.

D 2.

1966.

D 1 **D 1.** 1 c. red .. .. 15 1·00
D 17 2 c. blue .. .. 20 1·00
D 3 4 c. green .. .. 60 1·75
D 18 8 c. green .. .. 30 1·25
D 19 10 c. blue .. .. 40 1·40
D 6 12 c. violet .. . 45 2·00
D 20 20 c. brown .. .. 50 1·75
D 21 50 c. bistre .. 90 2·50

1986.

D 22. **D 2.** 5 c. mauve 10 10
D 23. 10 c. brown 10 10
D 24. 20 c. red 10 10
D 25. 50 c. green 20 25
D 26. $1 blue 40 45

MALDIVE ISLANDS

A group of islands W. of Ceylon. A republic from 1 Jan., 1953, but reverted to a sultanate in 1954. Became independent on 26 July, 1965, and left the British Commonwealth until re-admitted as an Associate Commonwealth Member on 9 July 1982.

1906. 100 cents = 1 rupee.
1951. 100 larees = 1 rupee.

1906. Nos. 268, 277/9 and 283/4 of Ceylon optd **MALDIVES.**

1 **44** 2 c. brown .. .. 11·00 23·00
2 **48** 3 c. green .. .. 15·00 23·00
3 4 c. orange and blue .. 32·00 65·00
4 – 5 c. purple .. .. 4·50 6·50
5 **48** 15 c. blue .. .. 50·00 90·00
6 25 c. brown .. .. 60·00 90·00

2. Minaret, Juma Mosque, Male.

5. Palm Tree and Boat.

1909.

7. **2.** 2 c. brown .. .. 2·25 70
11. 2 c. grey .. .. 1·50 1·50
8. 3 c. green 40 70
12. 3 c. brown .. .. 70 1·60
9. 5 c. purple 40 35
15. 6 c. red .. .. .. 1·25 2·25
10. 10 c. red .. .. 2·75 80
16. 10 c. green 55 55
17. 15 c. black .. .. 3·75 5·50
18. 25 c. brown .. .. 4·25 5·50
19. 50 c. purple .. .. 3·75 3·75
20. 1 r. blue .. .. .. 5·50 2·75

1950.

21. **5.** 2 l. olive 65 40
22. 3 l. blue .. .. .. 3·00 40
23. 5 l. green .. .. .. 3·25 50
24. 6 l. brown 35 20
25. 10 l. red 50 20
26. 15 l. orange 50 30
27. 25 l. purple 35 30
28. 50 l. violet 40 30
29. 1 r. brown .. .. 6·50 19·00

8. Native Products.

1952.

30. – 3 l. blue (Fish) 40 20
31. **8.** 5 l. green 30 30

9. Male Harbour.

10. Fort and Building.

1956.

32. **9.** 2 l. purple 10 10
33. 3 l. slate 10 10
34. 5 l. brown 10 10
35. 6 l. violet 10 10
36. 10 l. green 10 10
37. 15 l. brown 10 10
38. 25 l. red 10 10
39. 50 l. orange 10 10
40. **10.** 1 r. green 15 10
41. 5 r. blue 60 20
42. 10 r. mauve 85 40

11. Cycling.

1960. Olympic Games.

43. **11.** 2 l. purple and green .. 10 10
44. 3 l. slate and purple .. 10 10
45. 5 l. brown and blue .. 10 10
46. 10 l. green and brown .. 10 10
47. 15 l. sepia and blue .. 10 10
48. – 25 l. red and olive .. 10 10
49. – 50 l. orange and violet .. 10 10
50. – 1 r. green and purple .. 20 45

DESIGN—VERT. 25 l. to 1 r. Basketball.

13. Tomb of Sultan.

1960.

51. 13.	2 l. purple	10	10
52. –	3 l. green	10	10
53. –	5 l. brown	50	30
54. –	6 l. blue	10	10
55. –	10 l. red	10	10
56. –	15 l. sepia	10	10
57. –	25 l. violet	10	10
58. –	50 l. grey	10	10
59. –	1 r. orange	15	10
60. –	5 r. blue	1·75	60
61. –	10 r. green	4·50	1·25

DESIGNS: 3 l. Custom House. 5 l. Cowrie shells. 6 l. Old Royal Palace. 10 l. Road to Juma Mosque, Male. 15 l. Council House. 25 l. New Government Secretariat. 50 l. Prime Minister's Office. 1 r. Old Ruler's Tomb. 5 r. Old Ruler's Tomb (distant view). 10 r. Maldivian Port.

Higher values were also issued, intended mainly for fiscal use.

24. "Care of Refugees".

1960. World Refugee Year.

62. 24.	2 l. violet, orange & green	10	10
63.	3 l. brown, green and red	10	10
64.	5 l. green, sepia and red	10	10
65.	10 l. green, violet and red	10	10
66.	15 l. violet, green and red	10	10
67.	25 l. bl., brown and green	10	10
68.	50 l. olive, red and blue	10	10
69.	1 r. red, slate and violet	15	35

25. Coconuts.

26. Map of Male.

1961.

70. 25.	2 l. brown and green	10	10
71.	3 l. brown and blue	10	10
72.	5 l. brown and mauve	10	10
73.	10 l. brown and orange	10	10
74.	15 l. brown and black	10	10
75. 26.	25 l. multicoloured	10	10
76.	50 l. multicoloured	10	10
77.	1 r. multicoloured	20	30

27. 5 c. Stamp of 1906.

1961. 55th Anniv. of 1st Maldivian Stamp.

78. 27.	2 l. purple, blue & green	10	10
79.	3 l. purple, blue & green	10	10
80.	5 l. purple, blue & green	10	10
81.	6 l. purple, blue & green	10	10
82. –	10 l. green, red & purple	10	10
83. –	15 l. green, red & purple	10	10
84. –	20 l. green, red & purple	10	10
85. –	25 l. red, green & black	10	10
86. –	50 l. red, green & black	20	40
87. –	1 r. red, green & black	35	75

DESIGNS: 10 l. to 20 l. Post horn and 3 c. stamp of 1906. 25 l. to 1 r. Olive sprig and 2 c. stamp of 1906.

30. Malaria Eradication Emblem.

1962. Malaria Eradication.

88. 30.	2 l. brown	10	10
89.	3 l. green	10	10
90.	5 l. turquoise	10	10
91.	10 l. red	10	10
92. –	15 l. sepia	10	10
93. –	25 l. blue	10	10
94. –	50 l. myrtle	15	10
95. –	1 r. purple	35	25

Nos. 92/5 are as Type **30**, but have English inscriptions at the side.

31. Children of Europe and America.

1962. 15th Anniv. of U.N.I.C.E.F.

96. 31.	2 l. multicoloured	10	10
97.	6 l. multicoloured	10	10
98.	10 l. multicoloured	10	10
99.	15 l. multicoloured	10	10
100. –	25 l. multicoloured	10	10
101. –	50 l. multicoloured	10	10
102. –	1 r. multicoloured	10	20
103. –	5 r. multicoloured	45	1·75

DESIGN: Nos. 100/3, Children of Middle East and Far East.

33. Sultan Mohamed Farid Didi.

1962. 9th Anniv. of Enthronement of Sultan.

104. 33.	3 l. brown and green	10	10
105.	5 l. brown and blue	10	10
106.	10 l. brown and blue	10	10
107.	20 l. brown and olive	10	10
108.	50 l. brown and mauve	10	10
109.	1 r. brown and violet	15	25

34. Angel Fish.

1963. Tropical Fish. Multicoloured.

110	2 l. Type **34**	10	10
111	3 l. Type **34**	10	10
112	5 l. Type **34**	10	10
113	10 l. Moorish idol (fish)	10	10
114	25 l. As 10 l.	10	10
115	50 l. Soldier fish	10	10
116	1 r. Surgeon fish	30	30
117	5 r. Butterfly fish	2·75	4·25

39. Fishes in Net.

1963. Freedom from Hunger.

118. 39.	2 l. brown and green	30	60
119. –	5 l. brown and red	50	50
120. 39.	7 l. brown & turquoise	70	50
121. –	10 l. brown and blue	85	50
122. 39.	25 l. brown & red	3·00	2·75
123. –	50 l. brown and violet	4·75	5·50
124. 39.	1 r. brown and mauve	7·50	9·50

DESIGNS—VERT. 5 l., 10 l., 50 l. Handful of grain.

41. Centenary Emblem.

1963. Centenary of Red Cross.

125. 41.	2 l. red and purple	30	70
126.	15 l. red and green	50	65
127.	50 l. red and brown	1·25	1·50
128.	1 r. red and blue	2·00	1·75
129.	4 r. red and olive	6·50	17·00

42. Maldivian Scout Badge.

1964. World Scout Jamboree, Marathon (1963).

130. 42.	2 l. green and violet	10	10
131.	3 l. green and brown	10	10
132.	25 l. green and blue	10	10
133.	1 r. green and red	45	85

43. Mosque, Male.

1964. "Maldives Embrace Islam".

134. 43.	2 l. purple	10	10
135.	3 l. green	10	10
136.	10 l. red	10	10
137.	40 l. dull purple	15	10
138.	60 l. blue	20	10
139.	85 l. brown	20	15

44. Putting the Shot.

1964. Olympic Games, Tokyo.

140. 44.	2 l. purple and blue	10	10
141.	3 l. red and brown	10	10
142.	5 l. bronze and green	10	10
143.	10 l. violet and purple	15	10
144. –	15 l. sepia and brown	15	10
145. –	25 l. indigo and blue	25	10
146. –	50 l. bronze and olive	45	20
147. –	1 r. purple and grey	85	40

DESIGNS: 15 l. to 1 r. Running.

46. Telecommunications Satellite.

1965. Int. Quiet Sun Years.

148. 46.	5 l. blue	10	10
149.	10 l. brown	15	10
150.	25 l. green	25	10
151.	1 r. mauve	50	35

INDEPENDENT

47. Isis (wall carving, Abu Simbel).

1965. Nubian Monuments Preservation.

152. 47.	2 l. green and purple	10	10
153. –	3 l. lake and green	10	10
154. 47.	5 l. green and purple	10	10
155. –	10 l. blue and orange	10	10
156. 47.	15 l. brown and violet	10	10
157. –	25 l. purple and blue	15	10
158. 47.	50 l. green and sepia	25	15
159. –	1 r. ochre and green	50	30

DESIGNS: 3, 10, 25 l., 1 r. Rameses II on throne (wall carving, Abu Simbel).

48. Pres. Kennedy and Doves.

1965. 2nd Death Anniv. of Pres. Kennedy.

160. 48.	2 l. black and mauve	10	10
161.	5 l. brown and mauve	10	10
162.	25 l. blue and mauve	10	10
163. –	1 r. pur., yellow & green	25	25
164. –	2 r. bronze, yellow & grn.	40	40

DESIGN: 1 r., 2 r. Pres. Kennedy and hands holding olive-branch.

49. "XX" and U.N. Flag.

1965. 20th Anniv. of U.N.

165. 49.	3 l. blue and brown	10	10
166.	10 l. blue and violet	10	10
167	1 r. blue and green	35	35

50. I.C.Y. Emblem.

1965. Int. Co-operation Year.

168. 50.	5 l. brown and bistre	15	10
169.	15 l. brown and lilac	20	10
170.	50 l. brown and olive	45	30
171.	1 r. brown and red	1·25	1·50
172.	2 r. brown and blue	1·75	3·00

51. Seashells.

1966. Multicoloured.

174. 2 l. Type **51** 20 30
175. 3 l. Yellow flowers .. 20 30
176. 5 l. Seashells (different) .. 30 15
177. 7 l. Camellias 30 15
178. 10 l. Type **51** 40 15
179. 15 l. Crab Plover and seagull .. .. .. 1·50 30
180. 20 l. Yellow flowers .. 70 30
181. 30 l. Type **51** .. .. 1·25 35
182. 50 l. Crab Plover and seagull .. .. .. 2·50 55
183. 1 r. Type **51** .. .. 2·00 55
184. 1 r. Camellias .. .. 2·00 55
185. 1 r. 50 Yellow flowers .. 2·75 1·25
186. 2 r. Camellias .. .. 3·75 1·75
187. 5 r. Crab Plover and seagull .. .. .. 11·00 7·00
188. 10 r. Seashells (different) .. 14·00 11·00

The 3 l., 7 l., 20 l., 1 r. (No. 181), 1 r. 50, and 2 r. are DIAMOND ($43\frac{1}{2} \times 43\frac{1}{2}$ mm.).

52. Maldivian Flag.

1966. 1st Anniv. of Independence.

189. **52.** 10 l. green, red & turq. 10 10
190. 1 r. multicoloured .. 40 30

53. " Luna 9 " on Moon.

1966. Space Rendezvous and Moon Landing.

191. **53.** 10 l. brown, indigo & bl. 10 10
192. – 25 l. green and red .. 15 10
193. **53.** 50 l. brown and green .. 20 15
194. – 1 r. turquoise & brown 45 35
195. – 2 r. green and violet .. 75 65
196. – 5 r. pink and turquoise 1·75 1·60

DESIGNS: 25 l., 1 r., 5 r. " Gemini 6 " and " 7 " rendezvous in space. 2 r. " Gemini " spaceship as seen from the other spaceship.

54. U.N.E.S.C.O. Emblem and Owl on Book.

1966. 20th Anniv. of U.N.E.S.C.O. Mult.

198. 2 l. Type **54** 10 30
199. 3 l. U.N.E.S.C.O. emblem and globe and microscope 10 30
200. 5 l. U.N.E.S.C.O emblem and mask, violin and palette 15 15
201. 50 l. Type **54** 70 45
202. 1 r. Design as 3 l. .. .. 1·25 75
203. 5 r. Design as 5 l. .. .. 5·50 7·50

55. Sir Winston Churchill and Cortege.

1966. Churchill Commem. Flag in red and blue.

204. **55.** 2 l. brown 15 30
205. – 10 l. turquoise 40 10
206. **55.** 15 l. green 55 10
207. – 25 l. violet 95 10
208. – 1 r. brown .. .. 3·25 75
209. **55.** 2 r. 50 red .. .. 7·00 8·00

DESIGN: 10 l., 25 l., 1 r. Churchill and catafalque.

56. Footballers and Jules Rimet Cup.

1967. England's Victory in World Cup Football Championship. Multicoloured.

210 2 l. Type **56** 10 30
211 3 l. Player in red shirt kicking ball 10 30
212 5 l. Scoring goal 10 10
213 25 l. As 3 l. 20 10
214 50 l. Making a tackle .. 45 20
215 1 r. Type **56** .. .. 1·25 45
216 2 r. Emblem on Union Jack .. .. .. 2·00 2·50

57. Clown Butterfly Fish.

1967. Tropical Fishes. Multicoloured.

218. 2 l. Type **57** 10 30
219. 3 l. Striped Puffer .. 10 30
220. 5 l. Blue Spotted Boxfish 15 10
221. 6 l. Picasso Fish 15 20
222. 50 l. Blue Angelfish .. 1·50 30
223. 1 r. Blue Spotted Boxfish 3·00 75
224. 2 r. Blue Angelfish .. 5·00 5·00

58. Hawker Siddeley " HS748 " over Airport Building.

1967. Inauguration of Hulule Airport.

225. **58.** 2 l. violet and olive .. 10 30
226. – 5 l. green and lavender 10 10
227. **58.** 10 l. violet and green .. 10 10
228. – 15 l. green and ochre .. 15 10
229. **58.** 30 l. ultramarine & blue 40 10
230. – 50 l. brown and mauve 60 20
231. **58.** 5 r. blue & orange .. 2·75 3·50
232. – 10 r. brown and blue .. 4·75 5·75

DESIGN: 5 l., 15 l., 50 l. and 10 r. Airport building and aircraft.

59. "Man and Music" Pavilion.

1967. World Fair, Montreal. Multicoloured.

233. 2 l. Type **59** 10 10
234. 5 l. "Man and His Community" Pavilion .. 10 10
235. 10 l. Type **59** 10 10
236. 50 l. As 5 l. 25 20
237. 1 r. Type **59** 50 40
238. 2 r. As 5 l. 80 90

1968. Int. Tourist Year (1967). Nos. 225/32 optd. **International Tourist Year 1967.**

240. **58.** 2 l. violet and olive .. 10 30
241. – 5 l. green and lavender 10 15
242. **58.** 10 l. violet and green .. 10 15
243. – 15 l. green and ochre .. 10 15
244. **58.** 30 l. ultramarine & blue 20 20
245. – 50 l. brown and mauve 25 30
246. **58.** 5 r. blue and orange .. 2·25 3·00
247. – 10 r. brown and blue .. 3·75 5·00

MINIMUM PRICE

The minimum price quoted is 10p which represents a handling charge rather than a basis for valuing common stamps. For further notes about prices see introductory pages.

61. Cub signalling and Lord Baden-Powell.

1968. Maldivian Scouts and Cubs.

248 **61** 2 l. brown, green & yell 10 30
249 – 3 l. red, blue and lt blue 10 30
250 **61** 25 l. violet, lake & red 1·25 30
251 – 1 r. green, brown and light green .. .. 3·25 1·60

DESIGN: 3 l. and 1 r. Scouts and Lord Baden-Powell.

62. French Satellite " A 1 ".

1968. Space Martyrs.

252. **62.** 2 l. mauve and blue .. 10 30
253. – 3 l. violet and brown .. 10 30
254. – 7 l. brown and lake .. 10 30
255. – 10 l. blue, drab and black 10 15
256. – 25 l. green and violet .. 35 15
257. **62.** 50 l. blue and brown .. 65 30
258. – 1 r. purple and green .. 85 50
259. – 2 r. brown, blue & black 1·50 1·75
260. – 5 r. mauve, drab & blk. 2·75 3·00

DESIGNS: 3 l., 25 l. " Luna 10 ". 7 l., 1 r. " Orbiter " and " Mariner ". 10 l., 2 r. Astronauts White, Grissom and Chaffee. 5 r. Cosmonaut V. M. Komarov.

63. Putting the Shot.

1968. Olympic Games, Mexico. Mult.

262. 2 l. Type **63** 10 15
263. 6 l. Throwing the discus .. 10 15
264. 10 l. Type **63** 10 10
265. 25 l. As 6 l. 10 10
266. 1 r. Type **63** 35 35
267. 2 r. 50 As 6 l. 65 85

64. " Adriatic Seascape " (Bonington).

1968. Paintings. Multicoloured.

268. 50 l. Type **64** 40 20
269. 1 r. " Ulysses deriding Polyphemus " (Turner) 70 35
270. 2 r. "Sailing Boat at Argenteuil" (Monet) .. .. 1·25 1·25
271. 5 r. " Fishing Boat at Les Saintes-Maries " (Van Gogh) .. .. .. 3·00 3·50

65. " Graf Zeppelin " and Montgolfier's Balloon.

1968. Development of Civil Aviation.

272 **65** 2 l. brown, green & blue 15 40
273 – 3 l. blue, violet & brown 15 40
274 – 5 l. green, red and blue 15 15
275 – 7 l. blue, purple & orge 60 35
276 **65** 10 l. brown, blue & pur 30 15
277 – 50 l. red, green & olive 1·25 20
278 – 1 r. green, blue & red .. 2·00 50
279 – 2 r. purple, bistre & blue 12·00 9·00

DESIGNS: 3 l., 1 r. Boeing "707" and Douglas "DC-3". 5 l., 50 l. Wright Brothers' aircraft and Lilienthal's glider. 7 l., 2 r. Projected Boeing Supersonic "733" and "Concorde".

66. W.H.O. Building, Geneva.

1968. 20th Anniv. of World Health Organization.

280. **66.** 10 l. violet, turq. & blue 40 10
281. 25 l. green, brn. & yellow 80 10
282. 1 r. brown, emer. & grn. 2·25 75
283. 2 r. violet, pur. & mve. 3·75 4·25

1968. 1st Anniv. of Scout Jamboree, Idaho. Nos. 248/51 optd. **International Boy Scout Jamboree, Farragut Park, Idaho, U.S.A. August 1–9, 1967.**

284 **61** 2 l. brown, green & yell 10 30
285 – 3 l. red, blue and lt blue 10 30
286 **61** 25 l. violet, lake and red 1·00 30
287 – 1 r. green, brown and light green .. .. 3·50 1·60

68. Curlew and Redshank.

1968. Multicoloured.

288. 2 l. Type **68** 30 50
289. 10 l. Conches 80 20
290. 25 l. Shells .. .. 1·25 25
291. 50 l. Type **68** .. .. 3·75 90
292. 1 r. Conches .. .. 3·75 95
293. 2 r. Shells .. .. .. 4·25 4·00

69. Throwing the Discus.

1968. Olympic Games, Mexico. Multicoloured.

294. 10 l. Type **69** 10 10
295. 50 l. Running 10 10
296. 1 r. Cycling 35 35
297. 2 r. Basketball .. .. 75 1·00

70. Fishing Dhow.

1968. Republic Day.

298. **70.** 10 l. brown, blue & grn. 50 15
299. – 1 r. green, red and blue 1·75 60

DESIGN: 1 r. National flag, crest and map.

71. "The Thinker" (Rodin).

1969. U.N.E.S.C.O. "Human Rights". Designs showing sculptures by Rodin. Multicoloured.

No.	Description		
300.	6 l. Type **71**	30	15
301.	10 l. "Hands"	30	15
302.	1 r. 50 "Eve"	1·75	1·75
303.	2 r. 50 "Adam"	2·25	2·50

72. Module nearing Moon's Surface.

1969. 1st Man on the Moon. Multicoloured.

No.	Description		
305.	6 l. Type **72**	15	15
306.	10 l. Astronaut with hatchet	15	15
307.	1 r. 50 Astronaut and module	90	1·00
308.	2 r. 50 Astronaut using camera	1·50	1·75

1969. Gold Medal Winner, Olympic Games, Mexico (1968). Nos. 295/6 optd **Gold Medal Winner Mohamed Gammoudi 5000 m. run Tunisa REPUBLIC OF MALDIVES** or similar opt.

No.	Description		
310.	50 l. multicoloured	40	40
311.	1 r. multicoloured	60	60

The inscription on No. 310 honours P. Trentin (cycling, France).

74. Red-striped Butterfly Fish.

1970. Tropical Fishes. Multicoloured.

No.	Description		
312.	2 l. Type **74**	30	50
313.	5 l. Spotted Triggerfish	45	20
314.	25 l. Scorpion Fish	1·25	30
315.	50 l. Forceps Fish	1·75	75
316.	1 r. Imperial Angelfish	2·50	90
317.	2 r. Regal Angelfish	3·75	4·00

75. Columbia Dauman Victoria, 1899.

1970. "75 Years of the Automobile". Multicoloured.

No.	Description		
318.	2 l. Type **75**	10	20
319.	5 l. Duryea phaeton, 1902	15	20
320.	7 l. Packard S-24, 1906	20	20
321.	10 l. Autocar Runabout, 1907	25	20
322.	25 l. Type **75**	60	20
323.	50 l. As 5 l.	1·50	40
324.	1 r. As 7 l.	2·25	70
325.	2 r. As 10 l.	3·50	3·75

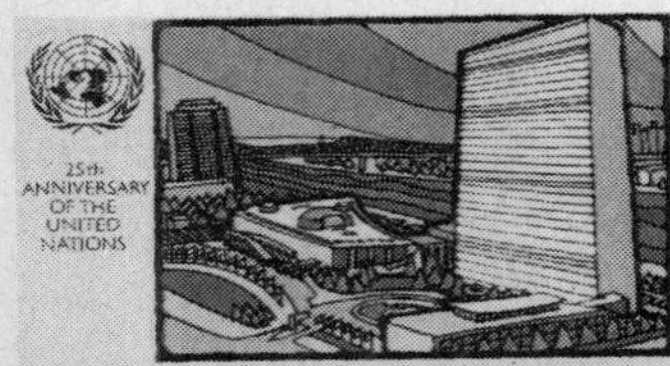

76. U.N. Headquarters, New York.

1970. 25th Anniv. of United Nations. Mult.

No.	Description		
327.	2 l. Type **76**	10	40
328.	10 l. Surgical operation (W.H.O.)	45	10
329.	25 l. Student, actress and musician (U.N.E.S.C.O.)	1·00	25
330.	50 l. Children at work and play (U.N.I.C.E.F.)	1·25	50
331.	1 r. Fish, corn and farm animals (F.A.O.)	1·50	80
332.	2 r. Miner hewing coal (I.L.O.)	3·00	3·25

77. Ship and Light Buoy.

1970. 10th Anniv. of I.M.C.O. Multicoloured.

No.	Description		
333.	50 l. Type **77**	45	40
334.	1 r. Ship and lighthouse	1·00	85

78. "Guitar-player and Masqueraders" (A. Watteau).

1970. Famous Paintings showing the Guitar. Multicoloured.

No.	Description		
335.	3 l. Type **78**	10	30
336.	7 l. "Spanish Guitarist" (Manet)	10	30
337.	50 l. "Costumed Player" (Watteau)	50	35
338.	1 r. "Mandoline-player" (Roberti)	85	55
339.	2 r. 50 "Guitar-player and Lady" (Watteau)	2·25	2·50
340.	5 r. "Mandoline-player" (Frans Hals)	4·00	4·25

79. Australian Pavilion.

1970. "EXPO 70" World Fair, Osaka, Japan. Multicoloured.

No.	Description		
342.	2 l. Type **79**	10	40
343.	3 l. West German Pavilion	10	40
344.	10 l. U.S. Pavilion	15	10
345.	25 l. British Pavilion	20	15
346.	50 l. Soviet Pavilion	35	35
347.	1 r. Japanese Pavilion	65	65

80. Learning the Alphabet.

1970. Int. Education Year. Multicolour.

No.	Description		
348.	5 l. Type **80**	10	15
349.	10 l. Training teachers	15	10
350.	25 l. Geography lesson	30	15
351.	50 l. School inspector	45	45
352.	1 r. Education by television	75	75

1970. "Philympia 1970" Stamp Exn., London. Nos. 306/8 optd. **Philympia London 1970.**

No.	Description		
353.	10 l. multicoloured	10	10
354.	1 r. 50 multicoloured	65	65
355.	2 r. 50 multicoloured	1·00	1·25

82. Footballers.

1970. World Cup Football Championships, Mexico.

No.	Description		
357. **82.**	3 l. multicoloured	10	30
358. –	6 l. multicoloured	10	30
359. –	7 l. multicoloured	10	20
360. –	25 l. multicoloured	50	15
361. –	1 r. multicoloured	1·75	80

DESIGNS: 6 l. to 1 r. Different designs showing footballers in action.

83. Little Boy and U.N.I.C.E.F. Flag.

1970. 25th Anniv. of U.N.I.C.E.F. Mult.

No.	Description		
362.	5 l. Type **83**	10	15
363.	10 l. Little girl with U.N.I.C.E.F. "balloon"	10	15
364.	1 r. Type **83**	80	55
365.	2 r. As 10 l.	1·75	1·90

84. Astronauts Lovell, Haise and Swigert.

1971. Safe Return of "Apollo 13". Multicoloured.

No.	Description		
366.	5 l. Type **84**	15	15
367.	20 l. "Explosion in Space"	15	15
368.	1 r. Splashdown	50	50

85. "Multiracial Flower".

1971. Racial Equality Year.

No.	Description		
369. **85.**	10 l. multicoloured	10	10
370.	25 l. multicoloured	20	10

86. "Mme. Charpentier and her Children" (Renoir).

1971. Famous Paintings showing "Mother and Child". Multicoloured.

No.	Description		
371.	5 l. Type **86**	10	10
372.	7 l. "Susanna van Collen and her Daughter" (Rembrandt)	15	10
373.	10 l. "Madonna nursing the Child" (Titian)	20	10
374.	20 l. "Baroness Belleli and her Children" (Degas)	40	15
375.	25 l. "The Cradle" (Morisot)	45	15
376.	1 r. "Helena Fourment and her Children" (Reubens)	1·50	75
377.	3 r. "On the Terrace" (Renoir)	3·50	3·75

87. Alan Shepard.

1971. Moon Flight of "Apollo 14". Mult.

No.	Description		
378	6 l. Type **87**	30	10
379	10 l. Staurt Roosa	35	10
380	1 r. 50 Edgar Mitchell	2·50	2·00
381	5 r. Mission insignia	5·75	5·50

88. "Ballerina" (Degas).

1971. Famous Paintings showing "Dancers". Multicoloured.

382. 5 l. Type **88** 15 10
383. 10 l. "Dancing Couple" (Renoir) 20 10
384. 2 r. "Spanish Dancer" (Manet) .. .. 2·50 2·25
385. 5 r. "Ballerinas" (Degas) 4·50 4·00
386. 10 r. "La Goulue at the Moulin Rouge" (Toulouse-Lautrec) .. .. 6·50 5·75

1972. Visit of Queen Elizabeth II and Prince Philip. Nos. 382/6 optd. **ROYAL VISIT 1972.**

387. **88.** 5 l. multicoloured .. 15 10
388. – 10 l. multicoloured .. 20 10
389. – 2 r. multicoloured .. 4·00 3·50
390. – 5 r. multicoloured .. 7·00 6·00
391. – 10 r. multicoloured .. 8·50 8·00

90. Book Year Emblem.

1972. Int. Book Year.

392. **90.** 25 l. multicoloured .. 15 10
393. 5 r. multicoloured .. 1·60 2·00

91. Scottish Costume.

1972. National Costumes of the World. Mult.

394. 10 l. Type **91** 20 10
395. 15 l. Netherlands 20 15
396. 25 l. Norway 40 15
397. 50 l. Hungary 70 45
398. 1 r. Austria .. .. 1·25 70
399. 2 r. Spain .. .. 2·50 2·25

92. Stegosaurus.

1972. Prehistoric Animals. Multicoloured.

400. 2 l. Type **92** 20 30
401. 7 l. Edaphosaurus 40 20
402. 25 l. Diplodocus 75 40
403. 50 l. Triceratops .. .. 1·00 60
404. 2 r. Pteranodon .. .. 3·50 4·00
405. 5 r. Tyrannosaurus .. .. 7·00 7·50

93. Cross-country Skiing.

1972. Winter Olympic Games, Sapporo, Japan. Multicoloured.

406 3 l. Type **93** 10 30
407 6 l. Bobsleighing 10 30
408 15 l. Speed skating 20 20
409 50 l. Ski jumping 85 45
410 1 r. Figure skating (pairs) 1·40 70
411 2 r. 50 Ice hockey .. 4·00 3·25

94. Scout Saluting.

1972. 13th Boy Scout Jamboree Asagiri, Japan (1971). Multicoloured.

412. 10 l. Type **94** 55 20
413. 15 l. Scout signalling .. 70 20
414. 50 l. Scout blowing bugle .. 2·50 1·00
415. 1 r. Scout playing drum .. 3·25 2·00

95. Cycling.

1972. Olympic Games, Munich. Mult.

416. 5 l. Type **95** 10 10
417. 10 l. Running 10 10
418. 25 l. Wrestling 15 10
419. 50 l. Hurdling 30 25
420. 2 r. Boxing .. .. 1·00 1·25
421. 5 r. Volleyball .. .. 2·10 2·50

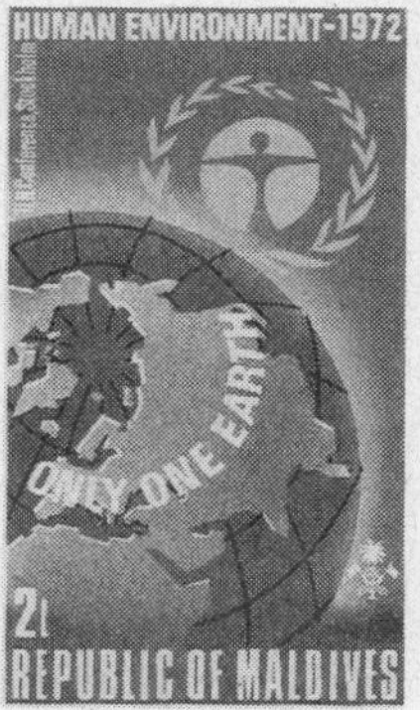

96. Globe and Conference Emblem.

1972. U.N. Environmental Conservation Conf., Stockholm.

423. **96.** 2 l. multicoloured .. 10 30
424. 3 l. multicoloured .. 10 30
425. 15 l. multicoloured .. 30 15
426. 50 l. multicoloured .. 75 40
427. 2 r. 50 multicoloured .. 3·25 3·75

97. "Flowers" (Van Gogh).

1973. Floral Paintings. Multicoloured.

428. 1 l. Type **97** 10 20
429. 2 l. "Flowers in Jug" (Renoir) 10 20
430. 3 l. "Chrysanthemums" (Renoir) 10 20
431. 50 l. "Mixed Bouquet" (Bosschaert) 30 15
432. 1 r. As 3 l. 55 40
433. 5 r. As 2 l. .. .. 2·75 3·00

1973. Gold-Medal Winners, Munich Olympic Games. Nos. 420/1 optd. as listed below.

435. 2 r. multicoloured .. 2·25 1·75
436. 5 r. multicoloured .. 3·25 2·75

OVERPRINTS: 2 r. **LEMECHEV MIDDLE-WEIGHT GOLD MEDALLIST.** 5 r. **JAPAN GOLD MEDAL WINNER.**

99. Animal Care.

1973. International Scouting Congress, Nairobi and Addis Ababa. Multicoloured.

438 1 l. Type **99** 10 20
439 2 l. Lifesaving 10 20
440 3 l. Agricultural training .. 10 20
441 4 l. Carpentry 10 20
442 5 l. Playing leapfrog .. 10 20
443 1 r. As 2 l. .. .. 2·25 75
444 2 r. As 4 l. .. .. 4·25 3·25
445 3 r. Type **99** .. .. 5·50 4·50

100. "Makaira herscheli".

1973. Fishes. Multicoloured.

447. 1 l. Type **100** 10 20
448. 2 l. "Katsuwonus pelamys" 10 20
449. 3 l. "Thunnus thynnus" .. 10 20
450. 5 l. "Coryphaena hippurus" 10 20
451. 60 l. "Lutjanus gibbus" .. 40 30
452. 75 l. "Lutjanus gibbus" 50 30
453. 1 r. 50 "Variola louti" .. 1·10 1·10
454. 2 r. 50 "Coryphaena hippurus" .. .. 1·60 1·40
455. 3 r. "Plectropoma maculatum" .. .. 1·75 2·00
456. 10 r. "Scomberomorus commerson" .. .. 4·75 6·00

Nos. 451/2 are smaller, size 29 × 22 mm.

101. Golden-fronted Leafbird.

1973. Fauna. Multicoloured.

458. 1 l. Type **101** 10 15
459. 2 l. Indian Flying Fox .. 10 15
460. 3 l. Land tortoise 10 15
461. 4 l. Butterfly ("Kallima inachus") 15 15
462. 50 l. As 3 l. 40 25
463. 2 r. Type **101** .. .. 3·00 2·75
464. 3 r. As 2 l. .. .. 3·00 2·75

102. "Lantana camara".

1973. Flowers of the Maldive Islands. Mult.

466. 1 l. Type **102** 10 10
467. 2 l. "Nerium oleander" .. 10 10
468. 3 l. "Rosa polyantha" .. 10 10
469. 4 l. "Hibiscus manihot" .. 10 10
470. 5 l. "Bougainvillea glabra" 10 10
471. 10 l. "Plumera alba" .. 10 10
472. 50 l. "Poinsettia pulcherrima" 55 20
473. 5 r. "Ononis natrix" .. 3·75 3·50

103. "Tiros" Weather Satellite.

1974. World Meteorological Organization. Multicoloured.

475. 1 l. Type **103** 10 10
476. 2 l. "Nimbus" satellite .. 10 10
477. 3 l. "Nomad" (weather ship) 10 10
478. 4 l. Scanner, A.P.T. Instant Weather Picture equipment .. 10 10
479. 5 l. Richard's wind-speed recorder 10 10
480. 2 r. Type **103** .. .. 2·00 1·50
481. 3 r. As 3 l. .. .. 2·25 1·75

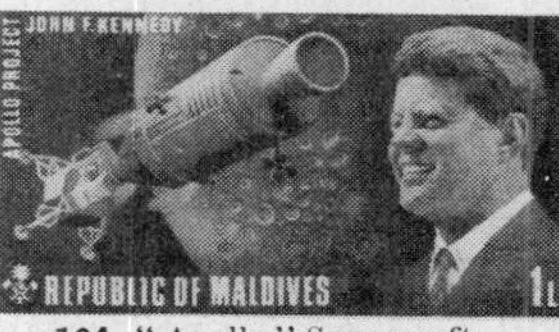

104. "Apollo" Spacecraft and Pres. Kennedy.

1974. American and Russian Space Exploration Projects. Multicoloured.

483. 1 l. Type **104** 10 15
484. 2 l. "Mercury" capsule and John Glenn 10 15
485. 3 l. "Vostok 1" and Yuri Gargarin 10 15
486. 4 l. "Vostok 6" and Valentina Tereshkova 10 15
487. 5 l. "Soyuz 11" and "Salyut" space-station 10 15
488. 2 r. "Skylab" space laboratory .. .. 2·50 2·25
489. 3 r. As 2 l. .. .. 3·00 2·75

105. Copernicus and "Skylab" Space Laboratory.

1974. 500th Birth Anniv. of Nicholas Copernicus (astronomer). Multicoloured.

491. 1 l. Type **105** 10 15
492. 2 l. Orbital space-station of the future 10 15
493. 3 l. Proposed "Space-shuttle" craft 10 15
494. 4 l. "Mariner 2" Venus probe 10 15
495. 5 l. "Mariner 4" Mars probe 10 15
496. 25 l. Type **105** 55 15
497. 1 r. 50 As 2 l. .. .. 2·50 2·25
498. 5 r. As 3 l. .. .. 6·00 6·00

106. "Maternity" (Picasso).

1974. Paintings by Picasso. Multicoloured.

500. 1 l. Type **106** 10 10
501. 2 l. "Harlequin and Friend" 10 10
502. 3 l. "Pierrot Sitting" .. 10 10
503. 20 l. "Three Musicians" .. 15 15
504. 75 l. "L'Aficionado" .. 30 30
505. 5 r. "Still Life" .. .. 2·50 2·50

107. U.P.U. Emblem, Steam and Diesel Locomotives.

1974. Cent. of Universal Postal Union. Multicoloured.

507. 1 l. Type **107**. 10 10
508. 2 l. Paddle-steamer and modern mailboat .. 10 10
509. 3 l. Airship and Boeing "747" airliner 10 10
510. 1 r. 50 Mailcoach and motor van 85 85
511. 2 r. 50 As 2 l. .. .. 1·60 1·60
512. 5 r. Type **107**. .. .. 3·50 3·50

108. Footballers.

1974 World Cup Football Championships, West Germany.

514. **108.** 1 l. multicoloured .. 15 10
515. – 2 l. multicoloured .. 15 10
516. – 3 l. multicoloured .. 15 10
517. – 4 l. multicoloured .. 15 10
518. – 75 l. multicoloured .. 90 50
519. – 4 r. multicoloured .. 3·00 2·25
520. – 5 r. multicoloured .. 3·50 2·50

DESIGNS: Nos. 515/20, show football scenes similar to Type **108**.

109. "Capricorn".

1974. Signs of the Zodiac. Multicoloured.

522. 1 l. Type **109** 10 15
523. 2 l. "Aquarius" 10 15
524. 3 l. "Pisces" 10 15
525. 4 l. "Aries" 10 15
526. 5 l. "Taurus" 10 15
527. 6 l. "Gemini" 10 15
528. 7 l. "Cancer" 10 15
529. 10 l. "Leo" 10 15
530. 15 l. "Virgo" 15 15
531. 20 l. "Libra" 15 15
532. 25 l. "Scorpio" 15 15
533. 5 r. "Sagittarius" .. 8·00 6·00

110. Churchill and Bomber Aircraft.

1974. Birth Cent. of Sir Winston Churchill. Multicoloured.

535 1 l. Type **110** 10 20
536 2 l. Churchill as pilot .. 10 20
537 3 l. Churchill as First Lord of the Admiralty .. 10 20
538 4 l. Churchill and H.M.S. "Indomitable" (aircraft carrier) 10 20
539 5 l. Churchill and fighter aircraft .. 10 20
540 60 l. Churchill and anti-aircraft battery .. 2·00 1·25
541 75 l. Churchill and tank in desert .. .. 2·25 1·25
542 5 r. Churchill and flying-boat .. .. 9·50 8·50

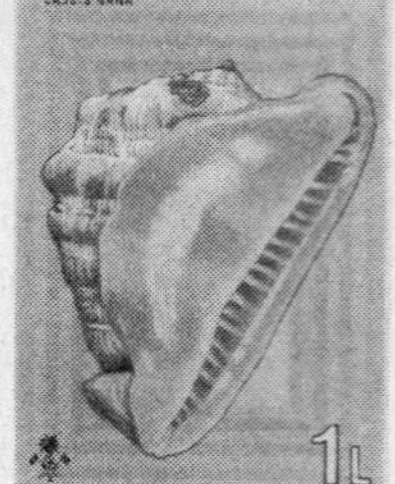

111. "Cassia nana".

1975. Seashells and Cowries. Multicoloured.

544. 1 l. Type **111** 10 15
545. 2 l. "Murex triremus" .. 10 15
546. 3 l. "Harpa major" .. 10 15
547. 4 l. "Lambis chiragra" .. 10 15
548. 5 l. "Conus pennaceus" .. 10 15
549. 60 l. "Cypraea diliculum" (22 × 30 mm.) .. 1·75 1·00
550. 75 l. "Clanculus pharaonis" (22 × 30 mm.) .. 2·25 1·10
551. 5 r. "Chicoreus ramosus" 7·00 6·50

112. Royal Throne.

1975. Historical Relics and Monuments. Multicoloured.

553. 1 l. Type **112** 10 10
554. 10 l. "Dullisa" (candle-sticks) 10 10
555. 25 l. Lamp-tree 15 10
556. 60 l. Royal umbrellas .. 30 20
557. 75 l. Eid-Miskith Mosque (horiz.) 35 25
558. 3 r. Tomb of Al-Hafiz Abu-al Barakath-al Barubari (horiz.) .. .. .. 1·60 2·00

113. Guavas.

1975. Exotic Fruits. Multicoloured.

559. 2 l. Type **113** 10 15
560. 4 l. Maldive mulberry .. 10 15
561. 5 l. Mountain apples .. 10 15
562. 10 l. Bananas 15 15
563. 20 l. Mangoes 30 15
564. 50 l. Papaya 65 30
565. 1 r. Pomegranates .. 1·50 45
566. 5 r. Coconut .. .. 7·00 7·00

114. "Phyllangia".

1975. Marine Life. Corals, Urchins and Sea Stars. Multicoloured.

568 1 l. Type **114** 10 10
569 2 l. "Madrepora oculata" 10 10
570 3 l. "Acropora gravida" .. 10 10
571 4 l. "Stylotella" 10 10
572 5 l. "Acrophora cervicornis" 10 10
573 60 l. "Strongylocentrotus purpuratus" 55 55
574 75 l. "Pisaster ochraceus" 65 65
575 5 r. "Marthasterias glacialis" .. .. 3·75 4·25

115. Clock Tower and Customs Building within "10".

1975. 10th Anniv. of Independence. Mult.

577. 4 l. Type **115** 10 10
578. 5 l. Government offices .. 10 10
579. 7 l. N.E. Waterfront, Male 10 10
580. 15 l. Mosque and Minaret 10 10
581. 10 r. Sultan Park and Museum .. .. 4·00 6·00

1975. "Nordjamb 75" World Scout Jamboree, Norway. Nos. 443/5 optd. **14th Boy Scout Jamboree July 29—August 7, 1975.**

582. – 1 r. multicoloured .. 30 30
583. – 2 r. multicoloured .. 50 50
584. **99.** 3 r. multicoloured .. 1·00 1·00

117. Madura Prau.

1975. Maldive Ships. Multicoloured.

586. 1 l. Type **117** 10 10
587. 2 l. Ganges patela 10 10
588. 3 l. Indian palla (vert.) .. 10 10
589. 4 l. "Odhi" (dhow) (vert.) 10 10
590. 5 l. Maldivian schooner .. 10 10
591. 25 l. "Cutty Sark" (British tea clipper) .. 35 20
592. 1 r. Maldivian baggala (vert.) 85 70
593. 5 r. "Maldive Courage" (freighter) .. .. 3·75 4·25

118. "Brahmophthalma wallichi" (moth).

1975. Butterflies and Moth. Multicoloured.

595 1 l. Type **118** 10 10
596 2 l. "Teinopalpus imperialis" 10 10
597 3 l. "Cethosia biblis" .. 10 10
598 4 l. "Idea jasonia" .. 10 10
599 5 l. "Apatura ilia" .. 10 10
600 25 l. "Kallima horsfieldi" 55 35
601 1 r. 50 "Hebomoia leucippe" .. .. 2·50 2·50
602 5 r. "Papilio memnon" .. 7·00 6·00

119. "The Dying Captive".

1975. 500th Birth Anniv of Michelangelo. Multicoloured.

604 1 l. Type **119** 10 10
605 2 l. Detail of "The Last Judgement" 10 10
606 3 l. "Apollo" 10 10
607 4 l. Detail of Sistine Chapel ceiling 10 10
608 5 l. "Bacchus" 10 10
609 1 r. Detail of "The Last Judgement" (different) 80 30
610 2 r. "David" .. .. 1·50 1·25
611 5 r. "Cumaean Sibyl" .. 3·50 3·50

120. Beaker and Vase.

1975. Maldivian Lacquerware. Multicoloured.

613. 2 l. Type **120** 10 10
614. 4 l. Boxes 10 10
615. 50 l. Jar with lid 40 20
616. 75 l. Bowls with covers .. 50 30
617. 1 r. Craftsman at work .. 65 40

121. Map of Maldives.

1975. Tourism. Multicoloured.

618. 4 l. Type **121** 10 10
619. 5 l. Motor launch and small craft 10 10
620. 7 l. Sailing-boats 10 10
621. 15 l. Underwater diving .. 10 10
622. 3 r. Hulule Airport .. 1·40 1·60
623. 10 r. Motor cruisers .. 4·00 5·00

122. Cross-country Skiing.

1976. Winter Olympic Games, Innsbruck. Multicoloured.

624. 1 l. Type **122** 10 10
625. 2 l. Speed-skating (pairs) .. 10 10
626. 3 l. Figure-skating (pairs) 10 10
627. 4 l. Four-man bobsleighing 10 10
628. 5 l. Ski-jumping 10 10
629. 25 l. Figure-skating (women's) 15 10
630. 1 r. 15 Skiing (slalom) .. 65 75
631. 4 r. Ice-hockey .. .. 2·25 2·50

123. "General Burgoyne" (Reynolds).

1976. Bicent. of American Revolution. Mult.

633. 1 l. Type **123** 10 10
634. 2 l. "John Hancock" (Copley) 10 10
635. 3 l. "Death of Gen. Montgomery" (Trumbull) (horiz.) 10 10
636. 4 l. "Paul Revere" (Copley) 10 10
637. 5 l. "Battle of Bunker Hill" (Trumbull) (horiz.) .. 10 10
638. 2 r. "The Crossing of the Delaware" (Sully) (horiz.) 1·75 1·50
639. 3 r. "Samuel Adams" (Copley) .. .. 2·25 2·00
640. 5 r. "Surrender of Cornwallis" (Trumbull) (horiz.) 2·75 2·50

124. Thomas Edison.

1976. Centenary of Telephone. Multicoloured.

642 1 l. Type **124** 10 10
643 2 l. Alexander Graham Bell 10 10
644 3 l. Telephone of 1919, 1937 and 1972 .. .. 10 10
645 10 l. Cable entrance into station 10 10
646 20 l. Equaliser circuit assembly 15 10
647 1 r. "Salernum" (cable ship) 70 55
648 10 r. "Intelsat IV-A" and Earth Station .. .. 4·25 5·50

1976. "Interphil 76" International Stamp Exhibition, Philadelphia. Nos. 638/40, optd. "**INTERPHIL**" and dates.

650. 2 r. multicoloured .. 1·25 1·50
651. 3 r. multicoloured .. 1·75 2·00
652. 5 r. multicoloured .. 2·25 2·50

126. Wrestling.

1976. Olympic Games, Montreal. Mult.

654 1 l. Type **126** 10 10
655 2 l. Putting the shot .. 10 10
656 3 l. Hurdling 10 10
657 4 l. Hockey 10 10
658 5 l. Running 10 10
659 6 l. Javelin-throwing .. 10 10
660 1 r. 50 Discus-throwing .. 1·25 1·50
661 5 r. Volleyball .. .. 3·50 4·00

127. " Dolichos lablab ".

1976. Vegetables. Multicoloured.

663. 2 l. Type **127** 10 10
664. 4 l. " Moringa pterygosperma " .. 10 10
665. 10 l. " Solanum melongena " 10 10
666. 20 l. " Moringa pterygosperma " .. 75 75
667. 50 l. " Cucumis sativus " 80 65
668. 75 l. " Trichosanthes anguina " 85 75
669. 1 r. " Momordica charantia " 95 85
670. 2 r. " Trichosanthes anguina " .. .. 3·00 3·50

128. " Viking " approaching Mars.

1977. " Viking " Space Mission.

671. **128.** 5 r. multicoloured .. 2·50 2·75

129. Coronation Ceremony.

1977. Silver Jubilee of Queen Elizabeth II. Multicoloured.

673 1 l. Type **129** 10 10
674 2 l. Queen and Prince Philip 10 10
675 3 l. Royal Couple with Princes Andrew and Edward 10 10
676 1 r. 15 Queen with Archbishops 25 35
677 3 r. State coach in procession 85 55
678 4 r. Royal couple with Prince Charles and Princess Anne .. .. 1·10 90

130. Beethoven and Organ.

1977. 150th Death Anniv. of Ludwig van Beethoven. Multicoloured.

680. 1 l. Type **130** 10 10
681. 2 l. Portrait and manuscript of " Moonlight Sonata " 10 10
682. 3 l. With Goethe at Teplitz 10 10
683. 4 l. Beethoven and string instruments 10 10
684. 5 l. Beethoven's home, Heiligenstadt .. 10 10
685. 25 l. Hands and gold medals 40 15
686. 2 r. Portrait and " Missa Solemnis " .. .. 2·00 1·60
687. 5 r. Composer's hearing-aids 3·75 3·00

131. Printed Circuit and I.T.U. Emblem.

1977. Inauguration of Satellite Earth Station. Multicoloured.

689. 10 l. Type **131** 10 10
690. 90 l. Central Telegraph Office .. 45 45
691. 10 r. Satellite Earth Station 5·00 6·00

132. " Miss Anne Ford " (Gainsborough).

1977. Artists' Birth Anniversaries. Mult.

693 1 l. Type **132** (250th anniv) 10 10
694 2 l. Group painting by Rubens (400th anniv) .. 10 10
695 3 l. "Girl with Dog" (Titian) (500th anniv) .. 10 10
696 4 l. "Mrs Thomas Graham" (Gainsborough) .. 10 10
697 5 l. "Artist with Isabella Brant" (Rubens) .. 10 10
698 95 l. Portrait by Titian .. 40 40
699 1 r. Portrait by Gainsborough 40 40
700 10 r. "Isabella Brant" (Rubens) .. .. 3·50 4·50

133. Lesser Frigate Birds.

1977. Birds of the Maldive Islands. Mult.

702. 1 l. Type **133** 10 10
703. 2 l. Crab Plover 10 10
704. 3 l. White-tailed Tropic Bird 10 10
705. 4 l. Wedge-tailed Shearwater 10 10
706. 5 l. Grey Heron 10 10
707. 20 l. White Tern 30 20
708. 95 l. Cattle Egret .. .. 1·25 95
709. 1 r. 25 Black-naped Tern 1·75 1·40
710. 5 r. Pheasant Coucal .. 6·50 6·50

134. Charles Lindbergh.

1977. 50th Anniv of Lindbergh's Transatlantic Flight and 75th Anniv of First Navigable Airships. Multicoloured.

712 1 l. Type **134** 10 10
713 2 l. Lindbergh and "Spirit of St. Louis" 10 10
714 3 l. "Mohawk" aircraft (horiz) 10 10
715 4 l. Julliot's airship "Lebaudy I" (horiz) .. 10 10
716 5 l. Airship "Graf Zeppelin" and portrait of Zeppelin 10 10
717 1 r. Airship "Los Angeles" (horiz) 60 30
718 3 r. Lindbergh and Henry Ford .. .. .. 1·40 1·50
719 10 r. Vickers rigid airship 3·50 4·00

135. Boat Building.

1977. Occupations. Multicoloured.

721. 6 l. Type **135** 30 15
722. 15 l. Fishing 35 15
723. 20 l. Cadjan weaving .. 40 15
724. 90 l. Mat-weaving .. .. 1·00 70
725. 2 r. Lace-making (vert.) .. 2·00 2·00

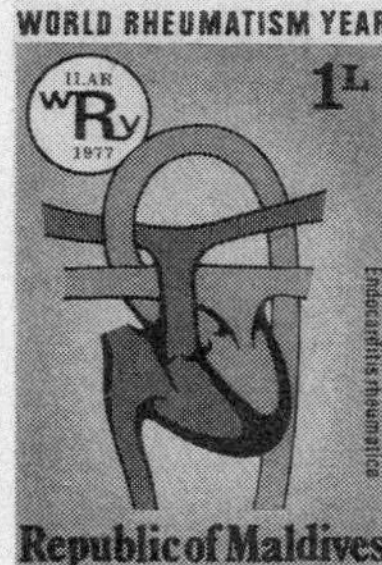

136. Rheumatic Heart.

1977. World Rheumatism Year. Multicoloured.

726. 1 l. Type **136** 10 10
727. 50 l. Rheumatic shoulder 20 10
728. 2 r. Rheumatic hands .. 85 1·00
729. 3 r. Rheumatic knees .. 1·10 1·25

137. Lilienthal's Glider.

1978. 75th Anniv. of First Powered Aircraft. Multicoloured.

730. 1 l. Type **137** 10 15
731. 2 l. Chanute's glider .. 10 15
732. 3 l. Wright Brothers' glider, 1900 .. .. 10 15
733. 4 l. A. V. Roe's triplane .. 10 15
734. 5 l. Wilbur Wright demonstrating aircraft for King Alfonso of Spain .. 10 15
735. 10 l. A. V. Roe's second biplane 15 15
736. 20 l. Wright Brothers and A. G. Bell at Washington 30 15
737. 95 l. Hadley's triplane .. 1·25 1·00
738. 5 r. " B.E.2s " at Upavon, Wiltshire, 1914 .. .. 4·75 5·00

138. Newgate Prison.

1978. World Eradication of Smallpox. Mult.

740. 15 l. Foundling Hospital, London (horiz.) 45 25
741. 50 l. Type **138** .. .. 1·00 45
742. 2 r. Edward Jenner (discoverer of smallpox vaccine) .. .. .. 3·00 2·25

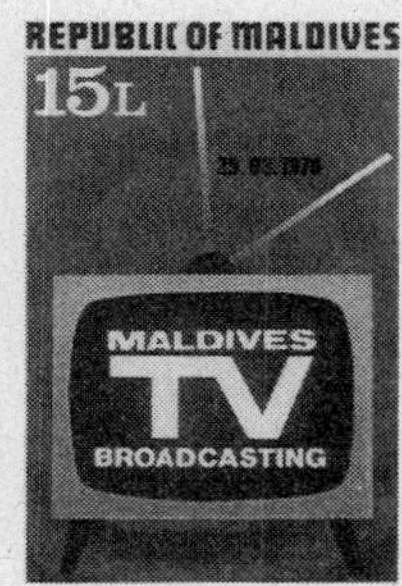

139. Television Set.

1978. Inauguration of Television in Maldive Islands. Multicoloured.

743 15 l. Type **139** 30 20
744 25 l. Television aerials .. 40 25
745 1 r. 50 Control desk (horiz) 1·60 1·60

140. Mas Odi.

1978. Maldive Ships. Multicoloured.

746. 1 l. Type **140** 10 10
747. 2 l. Battela 10 10
748. 3 l. Bandu Odi (vert.) .. 10 10
749. 5 l. "Maldive Trader" (freighter) 10 10
750. 1 r. "Fath-hul Baaree" (brigantine) (vert.) .. 35 30
751. 1 r. 25 Mas Dhoni 55 55
752. 3 r. Baggala .. .. 1·25 1·25
753. 4 r. As 1 r. 25 .. .. 1·60 1·60

141. Ampulla.

1978. 25th Anniv. of Coronation. Mult.

755. 1 l. Type **141** 10 10
756. 2 l. Sceptre with Dove .. 10 10
757. 3 l. Golden Orb 10 10
758. 1 r. 15 St. Edward's Crown 15 15
759. 2 r. Sceptre with Cross .. 30 25
760. 5 r. Queen Elizabeth II .. 80 70

142. Capt. Cook.

1978. 250th Birth Anniv. of Capt. James Cook and Bicentenary of Discovery of Hawaiian Islands. Multicoloured.

762. 1 l. Type **142** 10 15
763. 2 l. Kamehameha I .. 10 15
764. 3 l. H.M.S. "Endeavour" 10 15
765. 25 l. Route of third voyage 45 45
766. 75 l. H.M.S. "Discovery" H.M.S. "Resolution" and map of Hawaiian Islands (horiz.) .. .. 1·25 1·25
767. 1 r. 50 Cook meeting Hawaiian islanders (horiz.) 2·00 2·00
768. 10 r. Death of Capt. Cook (horiz.) .. .. 7·50 8·00

143. "Schizophrys aspera".

1978. Crustaceans. Multicoloured.

770 1 l. Type **143** 10 10
771 2 l. "Atergatis floridus" .. 10 10
772 3 l. "Perenon planissimum" 10 10
773 90 l. "Portunus granulatus" 50 40
774 1 r. "Carpilius maculatus" 50 40
775 2 r. "Huenia proteus" .. 1·00 1·25
776 25 r. "Etisus laevimanus" .. 9·00 12·00

144. "Four Apostles".

1978. 450th Death Anniv. of Albrecht Durer (artist).

778. **144.** 10 l. multicoloured .. 10 10
779. – 20 l. multicoloured .. 10 10
780. – 55 l. multicoloured .. 20 20
781. – 1 r. black, brown & buff 30 30
782. – 1 r. 80 multicoloured 50 60
783. – 3 r. multicoloured .. 1·00 1·25

DESIGNS—VERT. 20 l. "Self-portrait at 27". 55 l. "Madonna with Child with a Pear". 1 r. 80, "Hare". 3 r. "Great Piece of Turf". HORIZ. 1 r. "Rinhoceros".

145. T.V. Tower and Building.

1978. 10th Anniv. of Republic. Mult.

785. 1 l. Fishing boat 10 10
786. 5 l. Montessori School .. 10 10
787. 10 l. Type **145** 10 10
788. 25 l. Islet 15 15
789. 50 l. Boeing "737" aircraft 20 15
790. 95 l. Beach scene 30 30
791. 1 r. 25 Dhow at night .. 50 45
792. 3 r. President's residence .. 75 90
793. 5 r. Masjidh Afeefuddin Mosque .. .. .. 1·75 2·00

The 1, 5, 25 to 95, l., 1 r. 25 and 3, 5 r. are horiz. designs.

146. Human Rights Emblem.

1978. 30th Anniv. of Declaration of Human Rights.

795. **146.** 30 l. pink, lilac and green 15 15
796. 90 l. yellow, brown and green 40 50
797. 1 r. 80 pale blue, deep blue and green .. 70 85

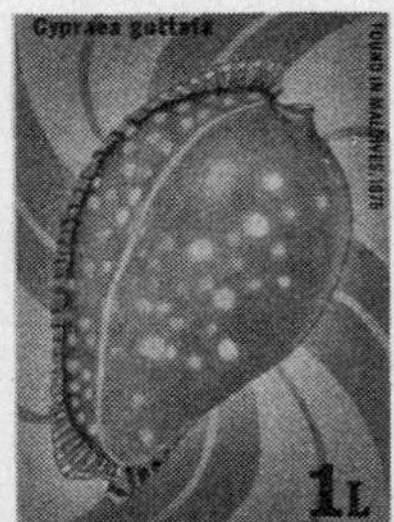

147. "Cypraea guttata".

1979. Shells. Multicoloured.

798. 1 l. Type **147** 10 10
799. 2 l. "Conus imperialis" .. 10 10
800. 3 l. "Turbo marmoratus" 10 10
801. 10 l. "Lambis truncata" 15 10
802. 1 r. "Cypraea leucodon" 70 40
803. 1 r. 80 "Conus figulinus" 1·25 1·25
804. 3 r. "Conus Gloria-maris" 1·90 2·00

148. Delivery by Bellman.

1979. Death Centenary of Sir Rowland Hill. Multicoloured.

806. 1 l. Type **148** 10 10
807. 2 l. Mail coach, 1840 (horiz.) 10 10
808. 3 l. First London letter box, 1855 .. .. .. 10 10
809. 1 r. 55 Penny Black .. 65 75
810. 5 r. First Maldive Islands stamp .. .. .. 2·00 2·25

149. Girl with Teddy Bear.

1979. International Year of the Child (1st issue). Multicoloured.

812 5 l. Type **149** 10 10
813 1 r. 25 Boy with sailing boat 40 50
814 2 r. Boy with toy rocket .. 45 55
815 3 r. Boy with toy airship 60 75

See also Nos. 838/46.

150. "White Feathers".

1979. 25th Death Anniv. of Henri Matisse (artist). Multicoloured.

817. 20 l. Type **150** 15 15
818. 25 l. "Joy of Life" .. 15 15
819. 30 l. "Eggplants" .. 15 15
820. 1 r. 50 "Harmony in Red" 55 55
821. 5 r. "Still-life" .. .. 1·50 1·75

151. Sari with Overdress.

1979. National Costumes. Multicoloured.

823. 50 l. Type **151** 25 25
824. 75 l. Sashed apron dress .. 40 40
825. 90 l. Serape 45 45
826. 95 l. Ankle-length dress 55 55

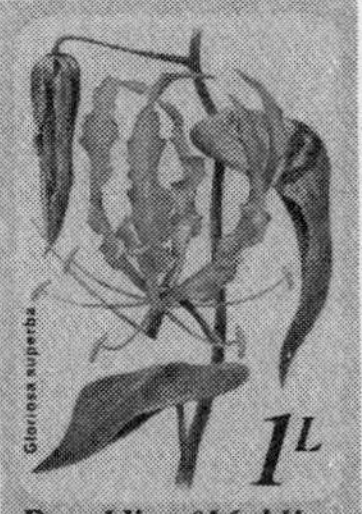

152. "Gloriosa superba".

1979. Flowers. Multicoloured.

827. 1 l. Type **152** 10 10
828. 3 l. "Hibiscus tiliaceus" 10 10
829. 50 l. "Barringtonia asiatica" 20 20
830. 1 r. "Abutilon indicum" 40 40
831. 5 r. "Guettarda speciosa" 1·75 2·00

153. Weaving.

1979. Handicraft Exhibition. Multicoloured.

833. 5 l. Type **153** 10 10
834. 10 l. Lacquerwork 10 10
835. 1 r. 30 Tortoiseshell jewellery 45 50
836. 2 r. Carved woodwork .. 70 80

154. Mickey Mouse attacked by Bird.

1979. International Year of the Child (2nd issue). Disney Characters. Multicoloured.

838 1 l. Goofy delivering parcel on motor-scooter (vert) 10 10
839 2 l. Type **154** 10 10
840 3 l. Goofy half-covered with letters 10 10
841 4 l. Pluto licking Minnie Mouse's envelopes .. 10 10
842 5 l. Mickey Mouse delivering letter letters on roller skates (vert) 10 10
843 10 l. Donald Duck placing letter in mail-box .. 10 10
844 15 l. Chip and Dale carrying letter 10 10
845 1 r. 50 Donald Duck on monocycle (vert) .. 75 75
846 5 r. Donald Duck with ostrich in crate (vert) .. 2·25 2·50

155. Post-Ramadan Dancing.

1980. National Day. Multicoloured.

848. 5 l. Type **155** 10 10
849. 15 l. Musicians and dancer, Eeduu Festival 10 10
850. 95 l. Sultan's Ceremonial Band 30 30
851. 2 r. Dancer and drummers, Circumcision Festival .. 55 70

156. Leatherback Turtle.

1980. Turtle Conservation Campaign. Mult.

853. 1 l. Type **156** 10 10
854. 2 l. Flatback Turtle .. 10 10
855. 5 l. Hawksbill Turtle .. 10 10
856. 10 l. Loggerhead Turtle .. 10 10
857. 75 l. Olive Ridley 30 30
858. 10 r. Atlantic Ridley .. 3·25 3·50

157. Paul Harris (founder).

1980. 75th Anniv. of Rotary International. Multicoloured.

860. 75 l. Type **157** 25 10
861. 90 l. Humanity 30 20
862. 1 r. Hunger 30 25
863. 10 r. Health .. .. 3·00 3·75

1980. "London 1980" International Stamp Exhibition. Nos. 809/10 optd. **LONDON 1980.**

865. 1 r. 55 Penny Black .. 1·00 75
866. 5 r. First Maldives Stamp 2·25 2·00

159. Swimming.

1980. Olympic Games, Moscow. Mult.

868 10 l. Type **159** 10 10
869 50 l. Running 20 15
870 3 r. Putting the shot .. 90 1·00
871 4 r. High jumping .. 1·10 1·25

160. White-tailed Tropic Bird.

1980. Birds. Multicoloured.

873. 75 l. Type **160** 25 15
874. 95 l. Sooty Tern 35 30
875. 1 r. Common Noddy .. 35 30
876. 1 r. 55 Curlew 50 40
877. 2 r. Wilson's Petrel .. 60 50
878. 4 r. Caspian Tern .. 1·10 1·00

161. Seal of Ibrahim II.

1980. Seals of the Sultans.

880. **161.** 1 l. rose and black .. 10 10
881. – 2 l. rose and black .. 10 10
882. – 5 l. rose and black .. 10 10
883. – 1 r. rose and black .. 30 30
884. – 2 r. rose and black .. 50 60

DESIGNS: 2 l. Mohammed Imadudeen II. 5 l. Bin Haji Ali. 1 r. Kuda Mohammed Rasgefaanu. 2 r. Ibrahim Iskander I.

162. Queen Elizabeth the Queen Mother.

1980. 80th Birthday of The Queen Mother.

886. **162.** 4 r. multicoloured .. 2·00 1·25

163. Munnaru.

1980. 1400th Anniv. of Hegira. Mult.

888. 5 l. Type **163** 10 10
889. 10 l. Hukuru Miskiiy mosque 10 10
890. 30 l. Medhuziyaaraiy .. 25 15
891. 55 l. Liyaa Filaa (wooden tablets) 30 25
892. 90 l. Ugenun (teaching the Koran) 50 45

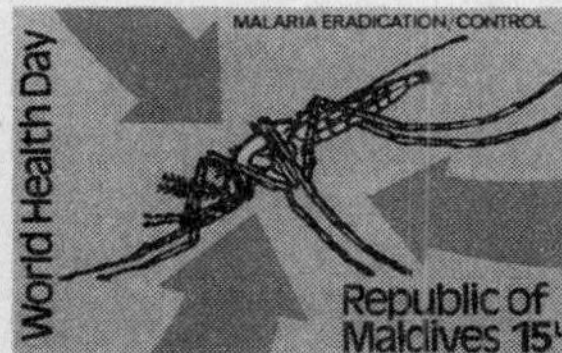

164. Malaria Eradication.

1980. World Health Day. Multicoloured.

894. 15 l. Type **164** 10 10
895. 25 l. Nutrition 15 10
896. 1 r. 50 Dental health .. 80 70
897. 5 r. Clinics .. .. 1·75 2·00

165. White Rabbit.

1980. Walt Disney's " Alice in Wonderland ". Multicoloured.

899. 1 l. Type **165** 10 10
900. 2 l. Alice falling down rabbit hole 10 10
901. 3 l. Alice and talking door-knob 10 10
902. 4 l. Alice with Tweedledum and Tweedledee .. 10 10
903. 5 l. Alice and caterpillar .. 10 10
904. 10 l. The Cheshire cat .. 10 10
905. 15 l. Alice helping the Queen's gardeners .. 10 10
906. 2 r. 50 Alice and the Queen of Hearts .. .. 1·25 1·25
907. 4 r. Alice on trial .. 1·75 1·75

166. Indian Ocean Ridley Turtle.

1980. Marine Animals. Multicoloured.

909. 90 l. Type **166** .. .. 1·00 50
910. 1 r. 25 Angel Flake Fish .. 1·25 85
911. 2 r. Spiny Lobster .. 1·75 1·40

167. Pendant Lamp.

1981. National Day. Multicoloured.

913. 10 l. Tomb of Ghaazee Muhammad Thakurufaan (horiz.) 10 10
914. 20 l. Type **167** 10 10
915. 30 l. Chair used by Muhammad Thakurufaan 15 10
916. 95 l. Muhammad Thakurufaan's palace (horiz.) .. 35 30
917. 10 r. Cushioned divan .. 2·75 3·25

168. Prince Charles and Lady Diana Spencer.

1981. British Royal Wedding. Multicoloured.

918. 1 r. Type **168** 25 25
919. 2 r. Buckingham Palace .. 40 40
920. 5 r. Prince Charles—polo player .. .. .. 75 1·25

169. First Majlis Chamber.

1981. 50th Anniv. of Citizens Majlis (grievance rights). Multicoloured.

922. 95 l. Type **169** 30 30
923. 1 r. Sultan Muhammed Shamsuddin III .. 35 35

170. " Self-portrait with a Palette ".

1981. Birth Centenary of Pablo Picasso. Multicoloured.

925. 5 l. Type **170** 10 10
926. 10 l. " Woman in Blue " .. 10 10
927. 25 l. " Boy with Pipe " .. 20 10
928. 30 l. " Card Player " .. 20 10
929. 90 l. " Sailor " 45 30
930. 3 r. " Self-portrait " .. 1·00 75
931. 5 r. " Harlequin " .. 1·50 1·25

171. Airmail Envelope.

1981. 75th Anniv. of Postal Service.

933. **171.** 25 l. multicoloured .. 15 10
934. 75 l. multicoloured .. 35 30
935. 5 r. multicoloured .. 1·25 1·40

172. Aircraft taking-off.

1981. Male International Airport. Mult.

936. 5 l. Type **172** 10 10
937. 20 l. Passengers leaving aircraft 20 15
938. 1 r. 80 Refuelling .. 75 75
939. 4 r. Plan of airport .. 1·40 1·40

173. Homer.

1981. International Year of Disabled People. Multicoloured.

941. 2 l. Type **173** 10 10
942. 5 l. Miguel Cervantes .. 10 10
943. 1 r. Beethoven .. .. 1·75 75
944. 5 r. Van Gogh .. .. 3·00 2·75

174. Preparation of Maldive Fish.

1981. Decade for Women. Multicoloured.

946. 20 l. Type **174** 10 10
947. 90 l. 16th century Maldive women 25 25
948. 1 r. Farming 30 30
949. 2 r. Coir rope-making .. 55 55

175. Collecting Bait.

1982. Fishermen's Day. Multicoloured.

950. 5 l. Type **175** 30 15
951. 15 l. Fishing boats .. 45 25
952. 90 l. Fisherman with catch 90 50
953. 1 r. 30 Sorting fish .. 1·25 65

176. Bread Fruit.

1981. World Food Day. Multicoloured.

955. 10 l. Type **176** 15 10
956. 25 l. Hen with chicks .. 40 15
957. 30 l. Maize 40 20
958. 75 l. Skipjack Tuna .. 85 40
959. 1 r. Pumpkin .. .. 1·00 50
960. 2 r. Coconuts .. .. 1·50 1·75

177. Pluto and Cat.

1982. 50th Anniversary of Pluto (Walt Disney Cartoon Character).

962. **177.** 4 r. multicoloured .. 2·50 2·00

178. Balmoral.

1982. 21st Birthday of Princess of Wales. Multicoloured.

964. 95 l. Type **178** 20 20
965. 3 r. Prince and Princess of Wales 55 55
966. 5 r. Princess on aircraft steps 85 85

COMMONWEALTH MEMBER

179. Scout saluting and Camp-site.

1983. 75th Anniv. of Boy Scout Movement. Multicoloured.

968.	1 r. 30, Type **179**	40	40
969.	1 r. 80, Lighting a fire	50	50
970.	4 r. Life-saving	1·10	1·10
971.	5 r. Map-reading	1·40	1·40

180. Footballer.

1982. World Cup Football Championship, Spain.

973. 180.	90 l. multicoloured	70	50
974. –	1 r. 50 multicoloured	1·10	70
975. –	3 r. multicoloured	1·75	1·25
976. –	5 r. multicoloured	2·25	2·00

DESIGNS: 1 r. 50 to 5 r. Various footballers.

1982. Birth of Prince William of Wales. Nos. 964/6 optd. **ROYAL BABY 21.6.82.**

978.	95 l. Type **178**	20	20
979.	3 r. Prince and Princess of Wales	55	55
980.	5 r. Princess on aircraft steps	85	85

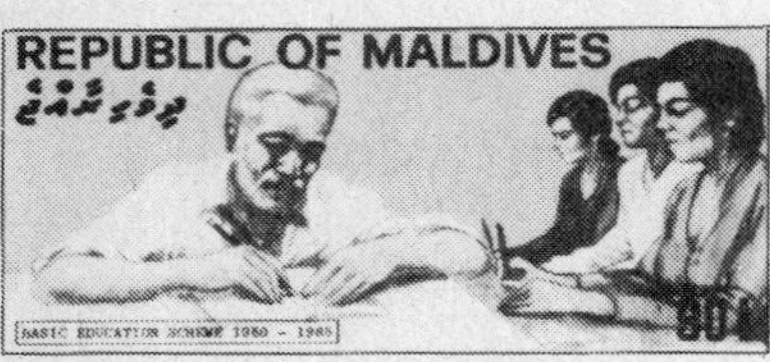

181. Basic Education Scheme.

1983. National Education. Multicoloured.

982.	90 l. Type **181**	15	20
983.	95 l. Primary education	15	20
984.	1 r. 30 Teacher training	20	25
985.	2 r. 50 Printing educational material	40	45

182. Koch isolates the Bacillus.

1983. Centenary of Robert Koch's Discovery of Tubercle Bacillus. Multicoloured.

987.	5 l. Type **182**	10	10
988.	15 l. Micro-organism and microscope	10	10
989.	95 l. Dr. Robert Koch in 1905	25	25
990.	3 r. Dr. Koch and plates from publication	65	65

183. Blohm and Voss " Ha 139 " Seaplane.

1983. Bicentenary of Manned Flight. Mult.

992.	90 l. Type **183**	1·25	50
993.	1 r. 45 Macchi-castoldi "MC.72"	1·75	1·25
994.	4 r. Boeing "F4B-3"	3·25	2·50
995.	5 r. " La France " airship	3·50	2·75

184. " Curved Dash " Oldsmobile, 1902.

1983. Classic Motor Cars. Multicoloured.

997.	5 l. Type **184**	10	15
998	30 l. Aston Martin " Tourer " 1932	35	15
999.	40 l. Lamborghini " Muira ", 1966	40	20
1000.	1 r. Mercedes-Benz " 300SL ", 1945	80	40
1001.	1 r. 40 Stutz " Bearcat ", 1913	1·25	90
1002.	5 r. Lotus " Elite ", 1913	3·00	3·00

185. Rough-toothed Dolphin.

1983. Marine Mammals. Multicoloured.

1004.	30 l. Type **185**	1·00	40
1005.	40 l. Indo-Pacific Hump-backed Dolphin	1·10	45
1006.	4 r. Finless Porpoise	4·00	2·50
1007.	6 r. Pygmy Sperm Whale	5·50	4·00

186. Dish Aerial.

1983. World Communications Year. Mult.

1009.	50 l. Type **186**	15	10
1010.	1 r. Land, sea and air communications	45	45
1011.	2 r. Ship-to-shore communications	55	55
1012.	10 r. Air traffic controller	1·90	2·50

187. "La Donna Gravida".

1983. 500th Birth Anniv of Raphael. Mult.

1014	90 l. Type **187**	20	25
1015	3 r. "Giovanna d'Aragona" (detail)	60	65
1016	4 r. "Woman with Unicorn"	80	85
1017	6 r. "La Muta"	1·25	1·40

188. Refugee Camp.

1983. Solidarity with the Palestinian People. Multicoloured.

1019.	4 r. Type **188**	1·50	1·50
1020.	5 r. Refugee holding dead child	1·60	1·60
1021.	6 r. Child carrying food	1·90	1·90

189. Education Facilities.

1983. National Development Programme. Multicoloured.

1022.	7 l. Type **189**	10	10
1023.	10 l. Health service and education	10	10
1024.	5 r. Growing more food	1·25	1·25
1025.	6 r. Fisheries development	1·50	1·50

190. Baseball.

1984. Olympic Games, Los Angeles. Mult.

1027.	50 l. Type **190**	15	15
1028.	1 r. 55 Backstroke	40	40
1029.	3 r. Judo	80	90
1030.	4 r. Shot putting	1·25	1·40

1984. U.P.U. Congress, Hamburg. Nos. 994/5 optd **19th UPU CONGRESS HAMBURG.**

1032.	4 r. Boeing " F4B-3 "	1·40	1·40
1033.	5 r. " La France " airship	1·60	1·60

1984. Surch.

(a) Nos. 964/6

1035.	1 r. 45 on 95 l. Type **178**	5·00	3·00
1036.	1 r. 45 on 3 r. Prince and Princess of Wales	5·00	3·00
1037.	1 r. 45 on 5 r. Princess on aircraft steps	5·00	3·00

(b) Nos. 978/80

1039.	1 r 45 on 95 l. Type **178**	5·00	3·00
1040.	1 r. 45 on 3 r. Prince and Princess of Wales	5·00	3·00
1041.	1 r 45. on 5 r. Princess on aircraft steps	5·00	3·00

193. Hands breaking Manacles.

1984. Namibia Day. Multicoloured.

1043.	6 r. Type **193**	1·50	1·60
1044.	8 r. Namibian family	2·00	2·10

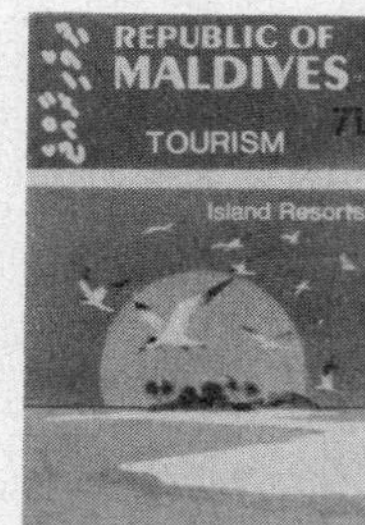

194. Island Resort and Sea Birds.

1984. Tourism. Multicoloured.

1046.	7 l. Type **194**	10	10
1047.	15 l. Dhow	10	10
1048.	20 l. Snorkelling	10	10
1049.	2 r. Wind-surfing	35	40
1050.	4 r. Aqualung diving	70	75
1051.	6 r. Night fishing	1·00	1·25
1052.	8 r. Game fishing	1·40	1·50
1053.	10 r Turtle on beach	1·60	1·75

195. Frangipani.

1984. "Ausipex" International Stamp Exhibition, Melbourne. Multicoloured.

1054.	5 r. Type **195**	1·75	1·75
1055.	10 r. Cooktown Orchid	3·75	3·75

196. Facade of Male Mosque.

1984. Opening of Islamic Centre. Multicoloured.

1057.	2 r. Type **196**	45	50
1058.	5 r. Male Mosque and minaret (vert.)	1·10	1·25

197. Air Maldives Boeing "737".

1984. 40th Anniv of I.C.A.O. Mult.

1059	7 l. Type **197**	15	15
1060	4 r. Airlanka Lockheed "L-1011 Tristar"	1·10	1·25
1061	6 r. Air Alitalia McDonnell Douglas "DC-30"	1·50	1·60
1062	8 r. L.T.U. Lockheed "L-1011 Tristar"	2·00	2·25

198. Daisy Duck.

1984. 50th Birthday of Donald Duck. Walt Disney Cartoon Characters. Multicoloured.

1064.	3 l. Type **198**	10	10
1065.	4 l. Huey, Dewey and Louie	10	10
1066.	5 l. Ludwig von Drake	10	10
1067.	10 l. Gyro Gearloose	10	10
1068.	15 l. Uncle Scrooge painting self-portrait	10	10
1069.	25 l. Donald Duck with camera	10	10
1070.	5 r. Donald Duck and Gus Goose	1·00	1·00
1071.	8 r. Gladstone Gander	1·60	1·60
1072.	10 r. Grandma Duck	2·00	2·00

199. "The Day" (detail).

200. "Edmond Iduranty" (Degas).

1984. 450th Death Anniversary of Correggio (artist). Multicoloured.
1075. 5 r. Type **199** .. .. 95 1·25
1076. 10 r. "The Night" (detail) .. .. 1·60 2·00

1984. 150th Birth Anniv. of Edgar Degas (artist). Multicoloured.
1078. 75 l. Type **200** 15 20
1079. 2 r. "James Tissot" .. 45 50
1080. 5 r. "Achille de Gas in Uniform" .. .. 1·10 1·25
1081. 10 r. "Lady with Chrysanthemums" .. .. 2·25 2·75

201. Pale-footed Shearwater.

1985. Birth Bicentenary of John J. Audubon (ornithologist) (1st issue). Designs showing original paintings. Multicoloured.
1083. 3 r. Type **201** .. .. 1·00 80
1084. 3 r. 50 Little grebe (horiz.) .. .. 1·10 90
1085. 4 r. Common cormorant 1·25 1·00
1086. 4 r. 50 White-faced storm petrel (horiz.) .. .. 1·50 1·10
See also Nos. 1192/9.

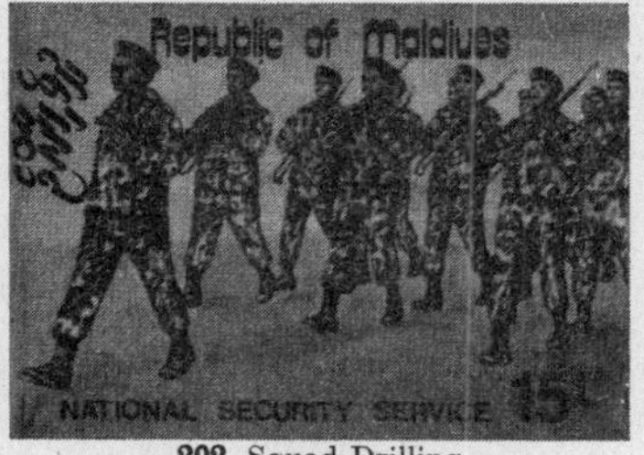

202. Squad Drilling.

1985. National Security Service. Mult.
1088. 15 l. Type **202** 15 10
1089. 20 l. Combat patrol .. 15 10
1090. 1 r. Fire fighting .. 35 25
1091. 2 r. Coastguard cutter .. 65 55
1092. 10 r. Independence Day Parade (vert.) .. 2·00 2·50

1985. Olympic Games Gold Medal Winners, Los Angeles. Nos. 1027/30 optd.
1094. 50 l. Type **190** (optd. **JAPAN**) 10 10
1095. 1 r. 55, Backstroke swimming (optd. **GOLD MEDALIST THERESA ANDREWS USA**) .. 30 35
1096. 3 r. Judo (optd. **GOLD MEDALIST FRANK WIENEKE USA**) .. 55 60
1097. 4 r. Shot-putting (optd. **GOLD MEDALIST CLAUDIA LOCH WEST GERMANY**) .. 80 85

204. Queen Elizabeth the Queen Mother, 1981.

1985. Life and Times of Queen Elizabeth the Queen Mother. Multicoloured.
1099. 3 r. Type **204** 55 60
1100. 5 r. Visiting the Middlesex Hospital (horiz.) .. 95 1·00
1101. 7 r. The Queen Mother .. 1·40 1·50
Stamps as Nos. 1099/1101, but with face values of 1 r., 4 r. and 10 r., exist from additional sheetlets with changed background colours.

1985. 300th Birth Anniversary of Johann Sebastian Bach (composer). As T **206** of Antigua. Multicoloured.
1103. 15 l. Lira da Braccio .. 10 10
1104. 2 r. Tenor oboe .. 50 45
1105. 4 r. Serpent 90 85
1106. 10 r. Table organ .. 1·90 2·25

205. Masodi (fishing boat).

1985. Maldives Ships and Boats. Mult.
1108 3 l. Type **205** 10 10
1109 5 l. Battela (dhow) .. 10 10
1110 10 l. Addu odi (dhow) .. 10 10
1111 2 r. 60 Modern dhoni (fishing boat) 30 35
1112 2 r. 70 Mas Dhoni (fishing boat) 30 35
1113 3 r. Baththeli dohni .. 35 40
1114 5 r. "Inter 1" (inter-island vessel) 55 60
1115 10 r. Dhoni-style yacht .. 1·10 1·25

206. Windsurfing.

1985. 10th Anniversary of World Tourism Organization. Multicoloured.
1116. 6 r. Type **206** .. .. 1·10 1·40
1117. 8 r. Scuba diving .. 1·50 1·75

207. United Nations Building, New York.

1985. 40th Anniversary of United Nations Organization and International Peace Year. Multicoloured.
1119. 15 l. Type **207** 10 10
1120. 2 r. Hands releasing peace dove 40 45
1121. 4 r. U.N. Security Council meeting (horiz.) 80 85
1122. 10 r. Lion and lamb .. 1·90 2·25

208. Maldivian Delegate voting in U.N. General Assembly.

1985. 20th Anniv. of United Nations Membership. Multicoloured.
1124. 20 l. Type **208** 10 10
1125. 15 r. U.N. and Maldivian flags, and U.N. Building, New York .. 2·75 3·25

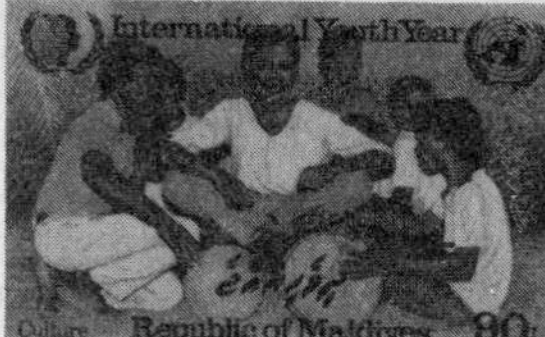

209. Youths playing Drums.

1985. International Youth Year. Mult.
1126. 90 l. Type **209** 15 20
1127. 6 r. Tug-of-war .. .. 1·10 1·40
1128. 10 r. Community service (vert.) .. .. .. 1·90 2·25

210. Quotation and Flags of Member Nations.

1985. 1st Summit Meeting of South Asian Association for Regional Co-operation, Dhaka, Bangladesh.
1130. **210.** 3 r. multicoloured .. 90 1·00

211. Frigate Tuna.

1985. Fishermen's Day. Species of Tuna. Multicoloured.
1131. 25 l. Type **211** 10 10
1132. 75 l. Little Tuna .. 15 15
1133. 3 r. Dogtooth Tuna .. 55 60
1134. 5 r. Yellowfin Tuna .. 95 1·00

1985. 150th Birth Anniv. of Mark Twain. Designs as T **118** of Anguilla, showing Walt Disney cartoon characters illustrating various Mark Twain quotations. Multicoloured.
1136. 2 l. Winnie the Pooh .. 10 10
1137. 3 l. Gepetto and Figaro the cat 10 10
1138. 4 l. Goofy and basket of broken eggs 10 10
1139. 20 l. Goofy as doctor scolding Donald Duck 10 10
1140. 4 r. Mowgli and King Louis 75 80
1141. 13 r. The wicked Queen and mirror .. .. 2·50 3·00

1985. Birth Bicentenaries of Grimm Brothers (folklorists). Designs as T **119** of Anguilla, showing Walt Disney cartoon characters in scenes from "Dr. Knowall". Multicoloured.
1143 1 l. Donald Duck as Crabb driving oxcart .. 10 10
1144 5 l. Donald Duck as Dr. Knowall 10 10
1145 10 l. Dr. Knowall in surgery 10 10
1146 15 l. Dr. Knowall with Uncle Scrooge as a lord 10 10
1147 3 r. Dr. and Mrs. Knowall in pony and trap .. 55 65
1148 15 r. Dr. Knowall and thief .. .. .. 2·75 3·25

1986. Appearance of Halley's Comet (1st issue). As T **123** of Anguilla. Multicoloured.
1150. 20 l. N.A.S.A. space telescope and Comet .. 40 15
1151. 1 r. 50 E.S.A. "Giotto" spacecraft and Comet 1·00 85
1152. 2 r. Japanese "Planet A" spacecraft and Comet 1·25 1·10
1153. 4 r. Edmond Halley and Stonehenge .. .. 2·50 2·25
1154. 5 r. Russian "Vega" spacecraft and Comet 2·75 2·50
See also Nos. 1206/10.

1986. Centenary of Statue of Liberty. Multicoloured. As T **211** of Dominica, showing the Statue of Liberty and immigrants to the U.S.A.
1156. 50 l. Walter Gropius (architect) 30 15
1157. 70 l. John Lennon (musician) .. .. 1·25 60
1158. 1 r. George Balanchine (choreographer) .. 1·25 60
1159. 10 r. Franz Werfel (writer) .. .. 3·25 3·50

1986. "Ameripex" International Stamp Exhibition, Chicago. As T **212** of Dominica, showing Walt Disney cartoon characters and U.S.A. stamps. Multicoloured.
1161. 3 l. Johnny Appleseed and 1966 Johnny Appleseed stamp .. 10 10
1162. 4 l. Paul Bunyan and 1958 Forest Conservation stamp 10 10
1163. 5 l. Casey and 1969 Professional Baseball Centenary stamp .. 10 10
1164. 10 l. Ichabod Crane and 1974 "Legend of Sleepy Hollow" stamp .. 10 10
1165. 15 l. John Henry and 1944 75th anniv. of completion of First Transcontinental Railroad stamp 10 10
1166. 20 l. Windwagon Smith and 1954 Kansas Territory Centenary stamp 10 10
1167. 13 r. Mike Fink and 1970 Great Northwest stamp .. .. .. 2·75 3·00
1168. 14 r. Casey Jones and 1950 Railroad Engineers stamp .. 3·00 3·25

1986. 60th Birthday of Queen Elizabeth II. As T **125** of Anguilla.
1170. 1 r. black and yellow .. 35 25
1171. 2 r. multicoloured .. 55 55
1172. 12 r. multicoloured .. 2·75 2·75
DESIGNS: 1 r. Royal Family at Girl Guides Rally, 1938; 2 r. Queen in Canada; 12 r. At Sandringham, 1970.

212. Player running with Ball.

1986. World Cup Football Championship, Mexico. Multicoloured.
1174. 15 l. Type **212** 20 15
1175. 2 r. Player gaining control of ball .. 1·00 80
1176. 4 r. Two players competing for ball .. 1·90 1·40
1177. 10 r. Player bouncing ball on knee .. .. 4·00 4·00

1986. Royal Wedding. As T **213** of Antigua. Multicoloured.
1179. 10 l. Prince Andrew and Miss Sarah Ferguson 10 10
1180. 2 r. Prince Andrew .. 60 60
1181. 12 r. Prince Andrew in naval uniform .. 2·75 3·00

213. Moorish Idol and Sea Fan.

1986. Marine Wildlife. Multicoloured.
1183. 50 l. Type **213** 50 30
1184. 90 l. Regal angelfish .. 70 45
1185. 1 r. Anemone fish .. 75 45
1186. 2 r. Tiger cowrie and stinging coral .. .. 1·25 1·00
1187. 3 r. Emperor angelfish and staghorn coral .. 1·50 1·25
1188. 4 r. Black-naped tern .. 2·25 2·00
1189. 5 r. Fiddler crab and staghorn coral .. 2·25 2·00
1190. 10 r. Hawksbill turtle .. 3·25 3·25

1986. Birth Bicentenary (1985) of John J. Audubon (ornithologist) (2nd issue). As T **201** showing original paintings. Multicoloured.
1192. 3 l. Little blue heron (horiz.) 10 10
1193. 4 l. White-tailed kite .. 10 10
1194. 5 l. Greater shearwater (horiz.) 10 10

1195. 10 l. Magnificent frigate bird 15 10
1196. 15 l. Black-necked grebe 25 20
1197. 20 l. Goosander 30 20
1198. 13 r. Peregrine falcon (horiz.) .. .. 4·50 4·50
1199. 14 r. Prairie chicken (horiz.) .. .. 4·50 4·50

1986. World Cup Football Championship Winners, Mexico. Nos. 1174/7 optd. **WINNERS Argentina 3 W. Germany 2.**

1201. 15 l. Type **212** 10 10
1202. 2 r. Player gaining control of ball .. 40 45
1203. 4 r. Two players competing for ball .. 75 80
1204. 10 f. Player bouncing ball on knee .. .. 1·90 2·25

1986. Appearance of Halley's Comet (2nd issue). Nos. 1150/4 optd. as **218** of Antigua.

1206. 20 l. N.A.S.A. space telescope and Comet .. 10 10
1207. 1 r. 50 E.S.A. "Giotto" spacecraft and Comet 30 35
1208. 2 r. Japanese "Planet A" spacecraft and Comet 40 45
1209. 4 r. Edmond Halley and Stonehenge 75 80
1210. 5 r. Russian "Vega" spacecraft and Comet 95 1·00

214. Servicing Aircraft.

1986. 40th Anniv. of U.N.E.S.C.O. Mult.

1212. 1 r. Type **214**. 20 25
1213. 2 r. Boat building .. 40 45
1214. 3 r. Children in classroom 55 60
1215. 5 r. Student in laboratory .. .. .. 95 1·00

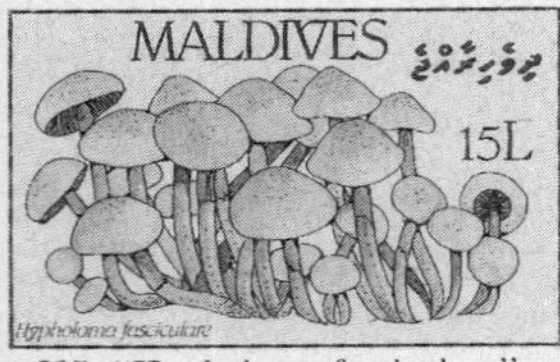

215. "Hypholoma fasciculare".

1986. Fungi of the Maldives. Multicoloured.

1217. 15 l. Type **215** 40 15
1218. 50 l. "Kuehneromyces mutabilis" (vert.) .. 65 30
1219. 1 r. "Amanita muscaria" (vert.) 85 40
1220. 2 r. "Agaricus campestris" .. .. 1·25 85
1221. 3 r. "Amanita pantherina" (vert.) .. 1·40 1·10
1222. 4 r. "Coprinus comatus" (vert.) .. .. .. 1·60 1·50
1223. 5 r. "Pholiota spectabilis" .. .. 1·75 2·00
1224. 10 r. "Pluteus cervinus" 3·00 3·25

216. Ixora.

1987. Flowers. Multicoloured.

1226. 10 l. Type **216** 10 10
1227. 20 l. Frangipani 10 10
1228. 50 l. Crinum 25 15
1229. 2 r. Pink rose 50 50
1230. 4 r. Flamboyant flower 80 80
1231. 10 r. Ground orchid .. 2·75 3·00

217. Guides studying Wild Flowers.

1987. 75th Anniv. (1985) of Girl Guide Movement. Multicoloured.

1233. 15 l. Type **217** 10 10
1234. 2 r. Guides with pet rabbits 40 40
1235. 4 r. Guide observing spoonbill 80 90
1236. 12 r. Lady Baden-Powell and Guide flag .. 2·50 3·00

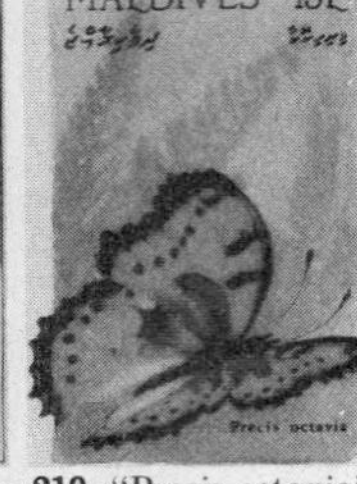

218. "Thespesia populnea". **219.** "Precis octavia".

1987. Trees and Plants. Multicoloured.

1238. 50 l. Type **218** 10 10
1239. 1 r. "Cocos nucifera" .. 15 20
1240. 2 r. "Calophyllum mophyllum" 30 35
1241. 3 r. "Xyanthosoma indica" (horiz.) .. 45 50
1242. 5 r. "Ipomoea batatas" (horiz.) 80 85
1243. 7 r. "Artocarpus altilis" 1·10 1·25

1987. America's Cup Yachting Championship. As T **222** of Antigua. Multicoloured.

1245. 15 l. "Intrepid", 1970 .. 10 10
1246. 1 r. "France II", 1974 .. 20 20
1247. 2 r. "Gretel", 1962 .. 40 50
1248. 12 r. "Volunteer", 1887 .. 2·00 2·50

1987. Butterflies. Multicoloured.

1250 15 l. Type **219** 35 30
1251 20 l. "Atrophaneura hector" 35 30
1252 50 l. "Teinopalpus imperialis" 60 40
1253 1 r. "Kallima horsfieldi" 80 45
1254 2 r. "Cethosia biblis" 1·25 1·00
1255 4 r. "Idea jasonia" .. 2·00 1·60
1256 7 r. "Papilio memnon" .. 2·75 2·75
1257 10 r. "Aeropetes tulbaghia" .. .. 3·50 3·75

220. Isaac Newton experimenting with Spectrum.

1988. Great Scientific Discoveries. Mult.

1259 1 r. 50 Type **220** 60 60
1260 3 r. Euclid composing "Principles of Geometry" (vert) .. 1·00 1·00
1261 4 r. Mendel formulating theory of Genetic Evolution (vert) .. 1·25 1·25
1262 5 r. Galileo and moons of Jupiter .. .. 1·50 1·50

221. Donald Duck and Weather Satellite. (Illustration reduced. Actual size 50 × 38 mm.).

1988. Space Exploration. Walt Disney cartoon characters. Multicoloured.

1264. 3 l. Type **221** 10 10
1265. 4 l. Minnie Mouse and navigation satellite .. 10 10
1266. 5 l. Mickey Mouse's nephews talking via communication satellite .. 10 10
1267. 10 l. Goofy in lunar rover (vert.) 10 10
1268. 20 l. Minnie Mouse delivering pizza to flying saucer (vert.) 10 10
1269. 13 r. Mickey Mouse directing spacecraft docking (vert.) .. 1·60 1·75
1270. 14 r. Mickey Mouse and "Voyager 2" .. .. 1·75 1·90

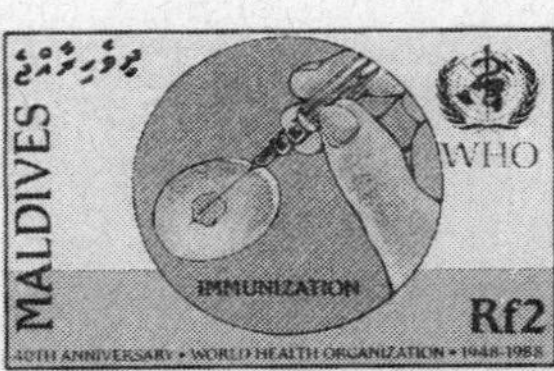

222 Syringe and Bacterium ("Immunization")

1988. 40th Anniv of W.H.O. Multicoloured.

1272 2 r. Type **222** 25 30
1273 4 r. Tap ("Clean Water") 50 55

223 Water Droplet and Atoll

1988. World Environment Day (1987). Mult.

1274 15 l. Type **223** 10 10
1275 75 l. Coral reef 20 20
1276 2 r. Audubon's shearwaters in flight .. 60 60

224 Globe, Carrier Pigeon and Letter

1988. Transport and Telecommunications Decade. Each showing central globe. Mult.

1278 2 r. Type **224** 40 40
1279 3 r. Dish aerial and girl using telephone .. 50 50
1280 5 r. Satellite, television, telephone and antenna tower 90 90
1281 10 r. Car, ship and airliner 1·75 2·00

1988. Royal Ruby Wedding. Nos. 1170/2 optd. **40TH WEDDING ANNIVERSARY H.M. QUEEN ELIZABETH II H.R.H. THE DUKE OF EDINBURGH.**

1282 1 r. black and yellow .. 20 20
1283 2 r. multicoloured .. 35 35
1284 12 r. multicoloured .. 1·90 2·40

226 Discus-throwing

1988. Olympic Games, Seoul. Multicoloured.

1286 15 l. Type **226** 10 10
1287 2 r. 100 metres race .. 35 35
1288 4 r. Gymnastics (horiz) .. 65 65
1289 12 r. Three-day equestrian event (horiz) .. .. 1·90 2·25

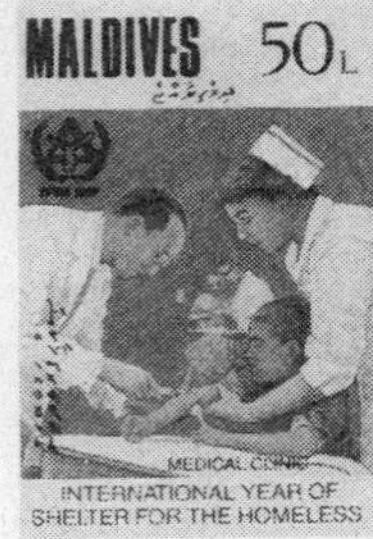

227 Immunization at Clinic

1988. International Year of Shelter for the Homeless. Multicoloured.

1291 50 l. Type **227** 20 20
1292 3 r. Prefab housing estate 80 80

228 Breadfruit

1988. 10th Anniv of International Fund for Agricultural Development. Multicoloured.

1294 7 r. Type **228** 85 90
1295 10 r. Mangos (vert) .. 1·25 1·40

1988. World Aids Day. Nos. 1272/3 optd **WORLD AIDS DAY** and emblem.

1297 2 r. Type **222** 20 25
1298 4 r. Tap ("Clean Water") 45 50

230 Pres. Kennedy and Launch of "Apollo" Spacecraft

1989. 25th Death Anniv of John F. Kennedy (American statesman). U.S. Space Achievements. Multicoloured.

1299 5 r. Type **230** 60 65
1300 5 r. Lunar module and astronaut on Moon .. 60 65
1301 5 r. Astronaut and buggy on Moon 60 65
1302 5 r. President Kennedy and spacecraft .. 60 65

1989. Olympic Medal Winners, Seoul. Nos. 1286/9 optd.

1304 15 l. Type **226** (optd **J. Schult DDR**) .. 10 10
1305 2 r. Athletics 100 metres (optd **C. LEWIS USA**) 20 25
1306 4 r. Gymnastics (horiz) (optd **MEN'S ALL AROUND V. ARTEMOV USSR**) .. 45 50
1307 12 r. Three-day equestrain event (horiz) (optd **TEAM SHOW JUMPING W. GERMANY**) .. 1·25 1·40

1989. 500th Birth Anniv of Titian (artist). As T **238** of Antigua showing paintings. Mult.

1309 15 l. "Benedetto Varchi" 10 10
1310 1 r. "Portrait of a Young Man" 10 15
1311 2 r. "King Francis I of France" 20 25
1312 5 r. "Pietro Aretino" .. 55 60
1313 15 r. "The Bravo" .. 1·60 1·75
1314 20 r. "The Concert" (detail) .. .. 2·25 2·40

1989. 10th Anniv of Asia–Pacific Telecommunity. Nos. 1279/80 optd **ASIA–PACIFIC TELECOMMUNITY 10 YEARS** and emblem. Multicoloured.

1316 3 r. Dish aerial and girl using telephone .. 35 40
1317 5 r. Satellite, television, telephone and antenna tower 55 60

1989. Japanese Art. Paintings by Hokusai. As T **250** of Antigua. Multicoloured.

1318 15 l. "Fuji from Hodogaya" 10 10
1319 50 l. "Fuji from Lake Kawaguchi" 10 10
1320 1 r. "Fuji from Owari" .. 10 15
1321 2 r. "Fuji from Tsukudajima in Edo" 20 25
1322 4 r. "Fuji from a Teahouse at Yoshida" 45 50
1323 6 r. "Fuji from Tagonoura" 65 70
1324 10 r. "Fuji from Mishima-goe" .. .. 1·10 1·25
1325 12 r. "Fuji from the Sumida River in Edo" 1·25 1·40

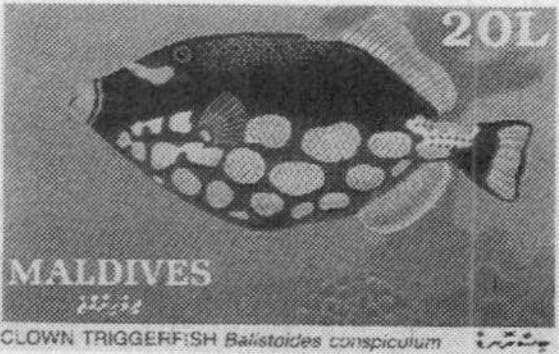

233 Clown Triggerfish

1989. Tropical Fishes. Multicoloured.

1327 20 l. Type **233** 10 10
1328 50 l. Bluestripe snapper .. 10 10
1329 1 r. Blue surgeonfish .. 10 15
1330 2 r. Oriental sweetlips .. 20 25
1331 3 r. Wrasse 35 40
1332 8 r. Threadfin butterfly-fish 90 95
1333 10 r. Bicolour parrotfish 1·10 1·25
1334 12 r. Sabre squirrelfish .. 1·25 1·40

234 Goofy, Mickey and Minnie Mouse with Takuri "Type 3", 1907

1989. "World Stamp Expo '89" International Stamp Exhibition, Washington (1st issue). Designs showing Walt Disney cartoon characters with Japanese cars. Mult.

1336 15 l. Type **234** 10 10
1337 50 l. Donald and Daisy Duck in Mitsubishi "Model A", 1917 .. 10 10
1338 1 r. Goofy in Datsun "Roadstar", 1935 .. 10 15
1339 2 r. Donald and Daisy Duck with Mazda, 1940 20 25
1340 4 r. Donald Duck with Nissan "Bluebird 310", 1959 .. .. .. 45 50
1341 6 r. Donald and Daisy Duck with Subaru "360", 1958 .. .. 65 70
1342 10 r. Mickey Mouse and Pluto in Honda "5800", 1966 .. .. .. 1·10 1·25
1343 12 r. Mickey Mouse and Goofy in Daihatsu "Fellow", 1966 .. 1·25 1·40

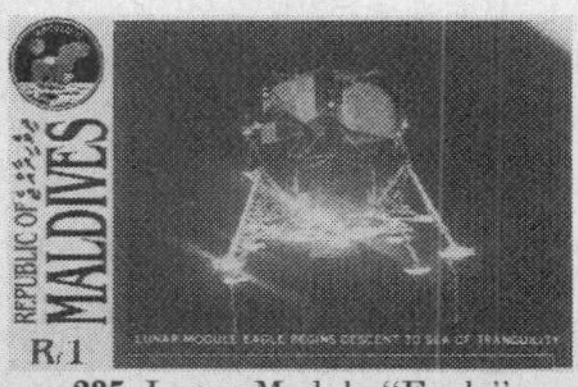

235 Lunar Module "Eagle"

1989. 20th Anniv of First Manned Landing on Moon. Multicoloured.

1346 1 r. Type **235** 10 15
1347 2 r. Astronaut Aldrin collecting dust samples 20 25
1348 6 r. Aldrin setting up seismometer 65 70
1349 10 r. Pres. Nixon congratulating "Apollo 11" astronauts .. 1·10 1·25

236 Jawaharlal Nehru with Mahatma Gandhi

1989. Anniversaries and Events. Mult.

1351 20 l. Type **236** (birth cent) 10 10
1352 50 l. Opium poppies and logo (anti-drugs campaign) (vert) .. 10 10
1353 1 r. William Shakespeare (425th birth anniv) .. 10 15
1354 2 r. Storming the Bastille (bicent of French Revolution) (vert) .. 20 25
1355 3 r. "Concorde" (20th anniv of first flight) .. 35 40
1356 8 r. George Washington (bicent of inauguration) 90 95
1357 10 r. William Bligh (bicent of mutiny on the "Bounty" .. 1·10 1·25
1358 12 r. Hamburg harbour (800th anniv) (vert) .. 1·25 1·40

237 Sir William van Horne, Locomotive and Map of Canadian Pacific Railway, 1894

1989. Railway Pioneers. Multicoloured.

1360 10 l. Type **237** 10 10
1361 25 l. Matthew Murray and Middleton Colliery rack locomotive, 1811 .. 10 10
1362 50 l. Louis Favre and locomotive entering tunnel, 1856 .. 10 10
1363 2 r. George Stephenson and "Locomotion", 1825 20 25
1364 6 r. Richard Trevithick and "Pen-y-darran" locomotive, 1804 65 70
1365 8 r. George Nagelmackers and "Orient Express" dining car, 1869 .. 90 95
1366 10 r. William Jessop and horse-drawn line, 1770 1·10 1·25
1367 12 r. Isambard Brunel and G.W.R. train, 1833 .. 1·25 1·40

238 Bodu Thakurufaanu Memorial Centre, Utheemu

1990. 25th Anniv of Independence. Mult.

1369 20 l. Type **238** 10 10
1370 25 l. Islamic Centre, Male 10 10
1371 50 l. National flag and logos of international organizations .. 10 10
1372 2 r. Presidential Palace, Male 20 25
1373 5 r. National Security Service 55 60

239 "Louis XVI in Coronation Robes" (Duplesis)

1990. Bicentenary of French Revolution and "Philexfrance '89" International Stamp Exhibition, Paris French. Paintings. Mult.

1375 15 l. Type **239** 10 10
1376 50 l. "Monsieur Lavoisier and his Wife" (David) 10 10
1377 1 r. "Madame Pastoret" (David) 10 15
1378 2 r. "Oath of Lafayette, 14 July 1790" (anon) .. 20 25
1379 4 r. "Madame Trudaine" (David) 45 50
1380 6 r. "Chenard celebrating the Liberation of Savoy" (Boilly) .. 65 70
1381 10 r. "An Officer swears Allegiance to the Constitution" (anon) 1·10 1·25
1382 12 r. "Self Portrait" (David) .. .. 1·25 1·40

1990. "Stamp World London 90" International Stamp Exhibition. As T **193** of Gambia, showing Walt Disney cartoon characters playing British sports. Multicoloured.

1384 15 l. Donald Duck, Mickey Mouse and Goofy playing rugby .. 10 10
1385 50 l. Donald Duck and Chip-n-Dale curling .. 10 10
1386 1 r. Goofy playing polo .. 10 15
1387 2 r. Mickey Mouse and nephews playing soccer 20 25
1388 4 r. Mickey Mouse playing cricket 45 50
1389 6 r. Minnie and Mickey Mouse at Ascot races .. 65 70
1390 10 r. Mickey Mouse and Goofy playing tennis 1·10 1·25
1391 12 r. Donald Duck and Mickey Mouse playing bowls .. .. .. 1·25 1·40

240 Silhouettes of Queen Elizabeth II and Queen Victoria

1990. 150th Anniv of the Penny Black.

1393 **240** 8 r. black and green 90 95
1394 – 12 r. black and blue .. 1·25 1·40

DESIGN: 12 r. As Type **240**, but with position of silhouettes reversed.

1990. 90th Birthday of Queen Elizabeth the Queen Mother. As T **103** of Grenada Grenadines.

1396 6 r. black, mauve & blue 65 70
1397 6 r. black, mauve & blue 65 70
1398 6 r. black, mauve & blue 65 70

DESIGNS: No. 1396, Lady Elizabeth Bowes-Lyon; 1397, Lady Elizabeth Bowes-Lyon wearing headband; 1398, Lady Elizabeth Bowes-Lyon leaving for her wedding.

241 Sultan's Tomb

1990. Islamic Heritage Year. Each black and blue.

1400 1 r. Type **242** 10 15
1401 1 r. Thakurufaan's Palace 10 15
1402 1 r. Male Mosque .. 10 15
1403 2 r. Veranda of Friday Mosque 20 25
1404 2 r. Interior of Friday Mosque 20 25
1405 2 r. Friday Mosque and Monument 20 25

1990. 50th Anniv of Second World War. As T **101** of Grenada Grenadines. Multicoloured.

1406 15 l. Defence of Wake Island, 1941 .. .. 10 10
1407 25 l. Stilwell's army in Burma, 1944 .. .. 10 10
1408 50 l. Normandy offensive, 1944 .. .. .. 10 10
1409 1 r. Capture of Saipan, 1944 .. .. .. 10 15
1410 2 r. 50 D-Day landings, 1944 .. .. .. 25 30
1411 3 r. 50 Allied landings in Norway, 1940 .. .. 40 45
1412 4 r. Lord Mountbatten, Head of Combined Operations, 1943 .. 45 50
1413 6 r. Japanese surrender, Tokyo Bay, 1945 .. 65 70
1414 10 r. Potsdam Conference, 1945 .. .. .. 1·10 1·25
1415 12 r. Allied invasion of Sicily, 1943 .. .. 1·25 1·40

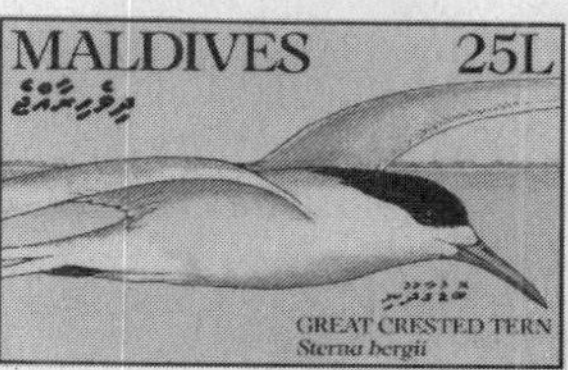

243 Great Crested Tern

1990. Birds. Multicoloured.

1417 25 l. Type **243** 10 10
1418 50 l. Koel 10 10
1419 1 r. White tern 10 15
1420 3 r. 50 Cinnamon bittern 40 45
1421 6 r. Sooty tern 65 70
1422 8 r. Audubon's shearwater 90 95
1423 12 r. Common noddy .. 1·25 1·40
1424 15 r. Lesser frigate bird 1·60 1·75

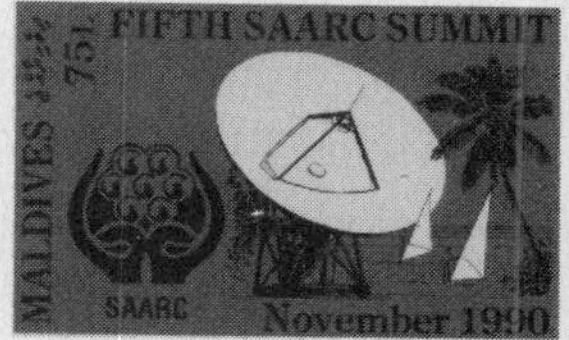

244 Emblem, Dish Aerial and Sailboards

1990. 5th South Asian Association for Regional Co-operation Summit.

1426 **244** 75 l. black and orange 10 10
1427 – 3 r. 50 multicoloured 40 45

DESIGN: 3 r. 50, Flags of member nations.

245 "Spathoglottis plicata"

1990. "EXPO '90" International Garden and Greenery Exhibition, Osaka. Flowers. Multicoloured.

1429 20 l. Type **245** 10 10
1430 75 l. "Hippeastrum puniceum" 10 10
1431 2 r. "Tecoma stans" (horiz) 20 25
1432 3 r. 50 "Catharanthus roseus" (horiz) .. 40 45
1433 10 r. "Ixora coccinea" (horiz) .. .. 1·10 1·25
1434 12 r. "Clitorea ternatea" (horiz) .. .. 1·25 1·40
1435 15 r. "Caesalpinia pulcherrima" .. .. .. 1·60 1·75

1990. International Literacy Year. As T **269** of Antigua, showing Walt Disney cartoon characters illustrating fables by Aesop. Multicoloured.

1437 15 l. "The Hare and the Tortoise" (horiz) .. 10 10
1438 50 l. "The Town Mouse and the Country Mouse" (horiz) .. 10 10
1439 1 r. "The Fox and the Crow" (horiz) 10 15
1440 3 r. 50 "The Travellers and the Bear" (horiz) 40 45
1441 4 r. "The Fox and the Lion" (horiz) 45 50
1442 6 r. "The Mice Meeting" (horiz) 65 70
1443 10 r. "The Fox and the Goat" (horiz) .. .. 1·10 1·25
1444 12 r. "The Dog in the Manger" (horiz) .. 1·25 1·40

247 East African Class "31" Locomotive

1990. Steam Railway Locomotives. Mult.

1446 20 l. Type **247** 10 10
1447 50 l. Sudan Railways Class "Mikado" .. 10 10
1448 1 r. South African Beyer-Garratt Class "GM" .. 10 15
1449 3 r. Rhodesia Railways Class "7" 35 40
1450 5 r. U.S.A. Central Pacific Class "229" 55 60
1451 8 r. U.S.A. Reading Class "415" 90 95
1452 10 r. Canada Porter narrow gauge .. .. 1·10 1·25
1453 12 r. U.S.A. Great Northern Class "515" .. 1·25 1·40

248 Rudd Gullit of Holland

1990. World Cup Football Championship, Italy. Multicoloured.

1455 1 r. Type **248** 10 15
1456 2 r. 50 Paul Gascoigne of England 25 30
1457 3 r. 50 Brazilian challenging Argentine player .. 40 45
1458 5 r. Brazilian taking control of ball .. 55 60
1459 7 r. Italian and Austrian jumping for header .. 75 80
1460 10 r. Russian being chased by Turkish player .. 1·10 1·25
1461 15 r. Andres Brehme of West Germany .. 1·60 1·75

249 Winged Euonymus

1991. Bonsai Trees and Shrubs. Mult.

1463 20 l. Type **249** 10 10
1464 50 l. Japanese black pine 10 10
1465 1 r. Japanese five needle pine 10 15
1466 3 r. 50 Flowering quince 40 45
1467 5 r. Chinese elm 55 60
1468 8 r. Japanese persimmon 90 95
1469 10 r. Japanese wisteria .. 1·10 1·25
1470 12 r. Satsuki azalea .. 1·25 1·40

250 "Summer" (Rubens)

1991. 350th Death Anniv of Rubens. Mult.

1472 20 l. Type **250** 10 10
1473 50 l. "Landscape with Rainbow" (detail) .. 10 10
1474 1 r. "Wreck of Aeneas" .. 10 15
1475 2 r. 50 "Chateau de Steen" (detail) .. 25 30
1476 3 r. 50 "Landscape with Herd of Cows" .. 40 45
1477 7 r. "Ruins on the Palantine" 75 80
1478 10 r. "Landscape with Peasants and Cows" .. 1·10 1·25
1479 12 r. "Wagon fording Stream" .. .. 1·25 1·40

251 Greek Messenger from Marathon, 490 BC (2480th Anniv)

1991. Anniversaries and Events (1990). Mult.

1481 50 l. Type **251** 10 10
1482 1 r. Anthony Fokker in early aircraft (birth centenary) 10 15
1483 3 r. 50 "Early Bird" satellite (25th anniv) .. 40 45
1484 7 r. Signing Reunification of Germany agreement (horiz) 75 80
1485 8 r. King John signing Magna Carta (775th anniv) 90 95
1486 10 r. Dwight D. Eisenhower (birth centenary) 1·10 1·25
1487 12 r. Sir Winston Churchill (25th death anniv) .. .. 1·25 1·40
1488 15 r. Pres. Reagan at Berlin Wall (German reunification) (horiz) .. 1·60 1·75

252 Arctic Iceberg and Maldives Dhoni

1991. Global Warming. Multicoloured.

1490 3 r. 50 Type **252** 40 45
1491 7 r. Antarctic iceberg and "Maldive Trader" (freighter) 75 80

253 S.A.A.R.C. Emblem and Medal

1991. Year of the Girl Child.

1492 **253** 7 r. multicoloured .. 75 80

254 Children on Beach

1991. Year of the Maldivian Child. Children's Paintings. Multicoloured.

1493 3 r. 50 Type **254** 40 45
1494 5 r. Children in a park .. 55 60
1495 10 r. Hungry child dreaming of food .. 1·10 1·25
1496 25 r. Scuba diver .. 2·75 3·00

1991. Death Centenary (1990) of Vincent van Gogh (artist). As T **195** of British Virgin Islands. Multicoloured.

1497 15 l. "Still Life: Japanese Vase with Roses and Anemones" (vert) .. 10 10
1498 20 l. "Still Life: Red Poppies and Daisies" (vert) 10 10
1499 2 r. "Vincent's Bedroom in Arles" 20 25
1500 3 r. 50 "The Mulberry Tree" 40 45
1501 7 r. "Blossoming Chestnut Branches" 75 80
1502 10 r. "Peasant Couple going to Work" .. 1·10 1·25
1503 12 r. "Still Life: Pink Roses" .. .. 1·25 1·50
1504 15 r. "Child with Orange" (vert) .. .. 1·60 1·75

1991. 65th Birthday of Queen Elizabeth II. As T **280** of Antigua. Multicoloured.

1506 2 r. Queen at Trooping the Colour, 1990 .. 20 25
1507 5 r. Queen with Queen Mother and Princess Margaret, 1973 .. 55 60
1508 8 r. Queen and Prince Philip in open carriage, 1986 .. .. .. 90 95
1509 12 r. Queen at Royal Estates Ball .. .. 1·25 1·50

1991. 10th Wedding Anniv of Prince and Princess of Wales. As T **280** of Antigua. Multicoloured.

1511 1 r. Prince and Princess skiing, 1986 .. 10 10
1512 3 r. 50 Separate photographs of Prince, Princess and sons .. 40 45
1513 7 r. Prince Henry in Christmas play and Prince William watching polo .. 75 80
1514 15 r. Princess Diana at Ipswich, 1990, and Prince Charles playing polo .. .. .. 1·60 1·75

256 Boy Painting

1991. Hummel Figurines. Multicoloured.

1516 10 l. Type **256** 10 10
1517 25 l. Boy reading at table 10 10
1518 50 l. Boy with school satchel 10 10
1519 2 r. Girl with basket .. 20 25
1520 3 r. 50 Boy reading .. 40 45
1521 8 r. Girl and young child reading 90 95
1522 10 r. School girls .. 1·10 1·25
1523 25 r. School boys .. 2·75 3·00

257 Class "C 57" Steam Locomotive

1991. "Philanippon '91" International Stamp Exhibition, Tokyo. Japanese Steam Locomotives. Multicoloured.

1525 15 l. Type **257** 10 10
1526 25 l. Class "6250" locomotive (horiz) .. 10 10
1527 1 r. Class "D 51" locomotive 10 10
1528 3 r. 50 Class "8620" locomotive (horiz) .. 40 45
1529 5 r. Class "10" locomotive (horiz) 55 60
1530 7 r. Class "C 61" locomotive 75 80
1531 10 r. Class "9600" locomotive (horiz) .. 1·10 1·25
1532 12 r. Class "D 52" locomotive (horiz) .. 1·25 1·50

MALTA

An island in the Mediterranean Sea, S. of Italy. After a period of self-government under various Constitutions, independence was attained on 21 September 1964. The island became a republic on 13 December 1974.

1860. 12 pence = 1 shilling;
20 shillings = 1 pound.
1972. 10 mils = 1 cent;
100 cents = M£1.

1.

5.

1860. Various frames

18.	**1.**	½d. yellow	19·00	35·00
20.		½d. green	1·25	35
22.	–	1d. red	1·75	35
23.	–	2d. grey	3·75	1·25
26.	–	2½d. blue	26·00	90
27.	–	4d. brown	8·50	3·00
28.	–	1s. violet	28·00	9·00
30.	**5.**	5s. red	£110	80·00

6. Harbour of Valletta.

7. Gozo Fishing Boat.

8. Ancient Maltese Galley. **9.** Emblematic figure of Malta.

10. Shipwreck of St. Paul.

12.

1899.

45a	**6.**	¼d. brown	75	10
79		4d. black..	10·00	2·50
32	**7.**	4½d. brown	11·00	8·50
58		4½d. orange	3·00	3·25
59	**8.**	5d. red	20·00	3·75
60		5d. green..	3·00	3·25
34	**9.**	2s. 6d. olive	32·00	12·00
35	**10.**	10s. black	75·00	60·00

1902. No. 26 surch. **ONE PENNY.**

36.		1d. on 2½d. blue ..	40	65

1903.

47a.	**12.**	½d. green..	1·50	10
48.		1d. black and red ..	4·50	10
49.		1d. red	80	10
50.		2d. purple and grey ..	4·50	45
51.		2d. grey	1·25	3·25
52.		2½d. purple and blue ..	9·00	40
53.		2½d. blue..	4·00	1·25
42.		3d. grey and purple ..	80	50
54.		4d. black and brown ..	8·00	5·00
55.		4d. black & red on yellow	3·50	3·00
44.		1s. grey and violet ..	13·00	6·00
62.		1s. black on green ..	6·00	2·00
63.		5s. green & red on yellow	60·00	65·00

13.

15.

17.

18.

1914.

69	13	¼d. brown	30	10
71a		½d. green	60	15
73		1d. red	60	10
75		2d. grey	4·50	2·50
77		2½d. blue	70	20
78		3d. purple on yellow ..	2·50	5·00
80		6d. purple	7·00	11·00
81		1s. black on green ..	8·00	17·00
86	15	2s. purple & blue on blue	50·00	28·00
88		5s. green & red on yellow	70·00	85·00
104	17	10s. black	£300	£475

1918. Optd. **WAR TAX.**

92.	**13.**	½d. green	20	15
93.	**12.**	3d. grey and purple ..	1·75	6·50

1921.

100	**18.**	2d. grey	2·50	80

1922. Optd. **SELF-GOVERNMENT.**

114.	**13.**	¼d. brown	10	20
106.		½d. green	20	40
116.		1d. red	20	15
117.	**18.**	2d. grey	80	45
118.	**13.**	2½d. blue	30	45
108.		3d. purple on yellow ..	1·25	9·50
109.		6d. purple	1·25	9·50
110.		1s. black on green ..	2·50	8·00
120.	**15.**	2s. purple & blue on blue	35·00	70·00
112.	**9.**	2s. 6d. olive	17·00	27·00
113.	**15.**	5s. green & red on yellow	50·00	75·00
105.	**10.**	10s. black	£170	£275
121.	**17.**	10s. black	£100	£150

1922. Surch. in words.

122	**18.**	¼d. on 2d. grey ..	15	25

22.

23.

1922.

123a	**22.**	¼d. brown	30	15
124		½d. green	55	10
125		1d. orange and purple..	1·25	15
126		1d. violet	90	35
127		1½d. red	1·00	10
128		2d. brown and blue ..	55	20
129		2½d. blue	1·00	4·50
130		3d. blue.. ..	1·75	50
131		3d. black on yellow ..	1·00	6·50
132		4d. yellow and blue ..	1·25	1·60
133		6d. green and violet ..	1·75	1·25
134	**23.**	1s. blue and brown ..	3·75	2·50
135		2s. brown and blue ..	5·50	8·50
136		2s. 6d. purple and black	7·00	8·50
137		5s. orange and blue ..	15·00	25·00
138		10s. grey and brown ..	45·00	80·00
140	**22.**	£1 black and red ..	£100	£190

1925. Surch. in words.

141.	**22.**	2½d. on 3d. blue ..	30	1·00

1926. Optd. **POSTAGE.**

143.	**22.**	¼d brown	15	80
144.		½d. green	15	15
145.		1d. violet	40	25
146.		1½d. red	45	25
147.		2d. brown and blue ..	30	20
148.		2½d. blue	55	40
149.		3d. black on yellow ..	30	50
150.		4d. yellow and blue ..	3·00	6·50
151.		6d. green and violet ..	1·50	1·40
152.	**23.**	1s. blue and brown ..	4·50	7·00
153.		2s. brown and blue ..	35·00	80·00
154.		2s. 6d. purple and black	9·00	22·00
155.		5s. orange and blue ..	8·00	25·00
156.		10s. grey and brown ..	6·00	14·00

26.

27. Valetta Harbour.

28. St. Publius.

DESIGNS—As Type **27:** 2s. Mdina (Notabile). 5s. Neolithic temple, Mnajdra. As Type **28:** 2s. 6d. Gozo boat. 3 s. Neptune. 10s. St. Paul.

1926. Inscr. "POSTAGE".

157.	**26.**	¼d. brown	20	15
158.		½d. green	30	15
159.		1d. red	40	40
160.		1½d. brown	60	10
161.		2d. grey	2·25	5·50
162.		2½d. blue	2·50	20
162a.		3d. violet	2·50	1·50
163.		4d. black and red ..	2·75	7·00
164.		4½d. violet and yellow..	2·50	2·50
165.		6d. violet and red ..	2·50	2·00
166.	**27.**	1s. black	3·00	2·25
167.	**28.**	1s. 6d. black and green	5·00	9·00
168.	–	2s. black and purple ..	5·50	13·00
169.	–	2s. 6d. black and red ..	10·00	27·00
170.	–	3s. black and blue ..	13·00	25·00
171.	–	5s. black and green ..	18·00	38·00
172.	–	10s. black and red ..	55·00	85·00

1928. Air. Optd. **AIR MAIL.**

173.	**26.**	6d. violet and red ..	1·75	1·25

1928. Optd. **POSTAGE AND REVENUE.**

174.	**26.**	¼d. brown	30	10
175.		½d. green	30	10
176.		1d. red	1·50	1·25
177.		1d. brown	2·50	10
178.		1½d. brown	1·00	30
179.		1½d. red..	2·75	10
180.		2d. grey..	3·25	8·00
181.		2½d. blue	1·25	10
182.		3d. violet	1·25	30
183.		4d. black and red ..	1·25	1·00
184.		4½d. violet and yellow..	2·25	1·50
185.		6d. violet and red ..	2·25	1·00
186.	**27.**	1s. black	2·25	2·00
187.	**28.**	1s. 6d. black and green	5·00	9·00
188.	–	2s. black and purple ..	17·00	30·00
189.	–	2s. 6d. black and red ..	13·00	23·00
190.	–	3s. black and blue ..	17·00	30·00
191.	–	5s. black and green ..	26·00	60·00
192.	–	10s. black and red ..	50·00	85·00

1930. As Nos. 157/72, but inscr. "POSTAGE & REVENUE".

193.		¼d. brown	30	10
194.		½d. green	30	10
195.		1d. brown	30	10
196.		1½d. red..	50	10
197.		2d. grey..	75	20
198.		2½d. blue	1·50	10
199.		3d. violet	1·50	20
200.		4d. black and red ..	1·25	2·25
201.		4½d. violet and yellow..	1·75	1·50
202.		6d. violet and red ..	1·25	75
203.		1s. black	4·00	8·00
204.		1s. 6d. black and green	5·00	12·00
205.		2s. black and purple ..	6·50	15·00
206.		2s. 6d. black and red ..	13·00	35·00
207.		3s. black and blue ..	20·00	45·00
208.		5s. black and green ..	25·00	55·00
209.		10s. black and red ..	60·00	95·00

1935. Silver Jubilee. As T **13** of Antigua.

210.		½d. black and green ..	30	35
211.		2½d. brown and blue ..	2·00	2·50
212.		6d. blue and olive ..	4·50	2·75
213.		1s. grey and purple ..	8·50	11·00

1937. Coronation. As T **2** of Aden.

214.		½d. green	10	10
215.		1½d. red..	35	15
216.		2½d. blue	50	35

37. Grand Harbour, Valletta.

38. H.M.S. "St. Angelo".

39. Verdala Palace.

1938. Various designs with medallion King George VI.

217.	**37.**	¼d. brown	10	10
218.	**38.**	½d. green	30	10
218a.		½d. brown	15	10
219.	**39.**	1d. brown	3·50	20
219a.		1d. green	20	10
220.	–	1½d. red	15	15
220b.	–	1½d. black	20	15
221.	–	2d. black	30	70
221a.	–	2d. red	15	10
222.	–	2½d. blue	15	30
222a.	–	2½d. violet	60	10
223.	–	3d. violet	20	60
223a.	–	3d. blue	30	10
224.	–	4½d. olive and brown	50	10
225.	–	6d. olive and red ..	30	15
226.	–	1s. black	50	30
227.	–	1s. 6d. black and olive	4·50	3·50
228.	–	2s. green and blue ..	3·25	2·75
229.	–	2s. 6d. black and red	6·00	4·50
230.	–	5s. black and green ..	6·00	5·50
231.	–	10s. black and red ..	13·00	14·00

DESIGNS—As Types **38/9:** VERT. 1½d. Hypogeum, Hal Saflieni. 3d. St. John's Co-Cathedral. 6d. Statue of Manoel de Vilhena. 1s. Maltese girl wearing faldetta. 5s. Palace Square, Valletta. 10s. St. Paul. HORIZ. 2d. Victoria and Citadel, Gozo. 2½d. De l'Isle Adam entering Mdina. 4½d. Ruins of Mnajdra. 1s. 6d. St. Publius. 2s. Mdina Cathedral. 2s. 6d. Statue of Neptune.

1946. Victory. As T **9** of Aden.

232.		1d. green	10	10
233.		3d. blue..	10	10

1948. Self-Government. As 1938 issue optd. **SELF-GOVERNMENT 1947.**

234		¼d. brown	10	20
235		½d. brown	15	10
236		1d. green	15	10
236a		1d. grey	10	10
237		1½d. black	30	10
237b		1½d. green	10	10
238		2d. red	30	10
238a		2d. yellow	10	10
239		2½d. violet	40	10
239a		2½d. red	25	65
240		3d. blue..	20	15
240a		3d. violet	35	15
241		4½d. olive and brown ..	1·25	1·50
241a		4½d. olive and blue ..	50	90
242		6d. olive and red ..	25	15
243		1s. black	90	40
244		1s. 6d. black and olive	2·50	45
245		2s. green and blue ..	4·00	1·50
246		2s. 6d. black and red ..	8·00	2·50
247		5s. black and green ..	13·00	5·50
248		10s. black and red ..	17·00	16·00

1949. Silver Wedding. As T **10/11** of Aden.

249.		1d. green	30	10
250.		£1 blue	40·00	35·00

1949. U.P.U. As T **20/23** of Antigua.

251.		2½d. violet	30	10
252.		3d. blue..	1·60	35
253.		6d. red	1·60	35
254.		1s. black	1·60	1·50

53. Queen Elizabeth II when Princess.

54. "Our Lady of Mount Carmel" (attrib. Palladino).

1950. Visits of Princess Elizabeth.

255.	**53.**	1d. green	10	10
256.		3d. blue..	20	10
257.		1s. black	40	45

1951. 7th Cent. of the Scapular.

258.	**54.**	1d. green	10	10
259.		3d. violet	15	10
260.		1s. black	30	40

1953. Coronation. As T **13** of Aden.

261		1½d. black and green ..	30	10

55. St. John's Co-Cathedral.

56. "Immaculate Conception" (Caruana) (altar-piece, Cospicua).

1954. Royal Visit.

262.	**55.**	3d. violet	15	10

1954. Centenary of Dogma of the Immaculate Conception.

263.	**56.**	1½d. green	10	10
264.		3d. blue..	10	10
265.		1s. grey	10	10

57. Monument of the Great Siege, 1565.

74. "Defence of Malta".

1956.

266. 57. ½d. violet 10 10
267. – ½d. orange 30 10
268. – 1d. black 40 10
269. – 1½d. green 30 10
270. – 2d. sepia 40 10
271. – 2½d. brown 30 30
272. – 3d. red 40 10
273. – 4½d. blue 50 20
274. – 6d. blue 30 10
275. – 8d. ochre .. .. 1·00 1·00
276. – 1s. violet 35 10
277. – 1s. 6d. turquoise .. 4·25 20
278. – 2s. olive.. .. .. 5·00 80
279. – 2s. 6d. brown .. .. 5·50 2·25
280. – 5s. green .. .. 9·00 2·75
281. – 10s. red.. .. .. 40·00 10·00
282. – £1 brown .. .. 40·00 25·00

DESIGNS—VERT. ½d. Wignacourt Aqueduct Horsetrough. 1d. Victory Church. 1½d. War Memorial. 2d. Mosta Dome. 3d. The King's Scroll. 4½d. Roosevelt's Scroll. 8d. Vedette. 1s. Mdina Gate. 1s. 6d. "Les Gavroches" (Statue). 2s. Monument of Christ the King. 2s. 6d. Monument of Grand Master Cottoner. 5s. Grand Master Perellos's Monument. 10s. St. Paul (statue). £1, Baptism of Christ (statue). HORIZ. 2½d. Auberge de Castile. 6d. Neolithic Temples at Tarxien.

1957. George Cross Commem. Cross in Silver.

283. 74. 1½d. green 15 10
284. – 3d. red 15 10
285. – 1s. brown 15 10

DESIGNS—HORIZ. 3d. Searchlights over Malta. VERT. 1s. Bombed buildings.

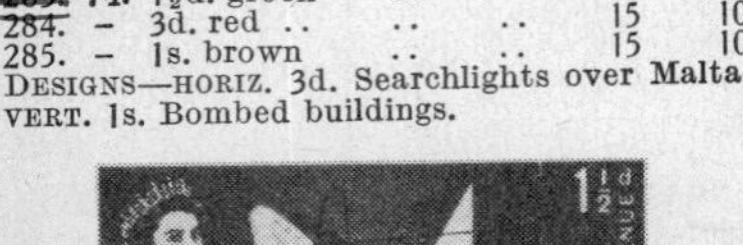

77. Design.

1958. Technical Education in Malta. Inscr. "TECHNICAL EDUCATION".

286. 77. 1½d. black and green .. 10 10
287. – 3d. black, red and grey 10 10
288. – 1s. grey, purple & black 15 10

DESIGNS—VERT. 3d. "Construction". HORIZ. 1s. Technical School, Paola.

81. Sea Raid on Grand Harbour, Valletta.

1958. George Cross Commem. Cross in first colour outlined in silver.

289. – 1½d. green and black .. 10 10
290. 81. 3d. red and black .. 10 10
291. – 1s. mauve and black .. 15 10

DESIGNS—HORIZ. 1½d. Bombed-out family. 1s. Searchlight crew.

83. Air Raid Casualties.

86. Shipwreck of St. Paul (after Palombi).

87. Statue of St. Paul, Rabat, Malta.

1959. George Cross Commem.

292. 83. 1½d. grn., black & gold 15 10
293. – 3d. mauve, black & gold 15 10
294. – 1s. grey, black and gold 55 55

DESIGNS—HORIZ. 3d. "For Gallantry". VERT. 1s. Maltese under bombardment.

1960. Shipwreck of St. Paul (19th Cent.). Inscr. as in T 86/7.

295. 86. 1½d. blue, gold & brown 15 10
296. – 3d. purple, gold and blue 15 10
297. – 6d. red, gold and grey.. 25 10
298. 87. 8d. black and gold .. 30 40
299. – 1s. purple and gold .. 25 10
300. – 2s. 6d. blue, green & gold 1·00 1·50

DESIGNS—As Type 86: 3d. Consecration of St. Publius, First Bishop of Malta. 6d. Departure of St. Paul (after Palombi). As Type 87: 1s. Angel with the "Acts of the Apostles". 2s. 6d. St. Paul with the "Second Epistle to the Corinthians".

92. Stamp of 1860.

1960. Centenary of Malta Stamp. Stamp in buff and blue.

301. 92. 1½d. green 20 10
302. 3d. red 25 10
303. 6d. blue.. .. .. 35 25

93. George Cross.

1961. George Cross Commem.

304. 93. 1½d. black, cream & bis. 15 10
305. – 3d. brown and blue .. 30 10
306. – 1s. green, lilac & violet 60 70

DESIGNS: 3d. and 1s. show George Cross as Type 93 over backgrounds with different patterns.

96. "Madonna Damascena".

100. Bruce, Zammit and Microscope.

1962. Great Siege Commem.

307. 96. 2d. blue 10 10
308. – 3d. red 10 10
309. – 6d. bronze 10 10
310. – 1s. purple 15 20

DESIGNS: 3d. Great Siege Monument. 6d. Grand Master La Valette. 1s. Assault on Fort St. Elmo.

1963. Freedom from Hunger. As T 28 of Aden.

311. 1s. 6d. sepia .. .. 4·50 2·75

1963. Cent of Red Cross. As T 33 of Antigua.

312. 2d. red on black 25 15
313. 1s. 6d. red and blue .. 3·75 3·75

1964. Anti-Brucellosis Congress.

316. 100. 2d. brown, black & green 10 10
317. – 1s. 6d. black and purple 55 20

DESIGN: 1s. 6d. Goat and laboratory equipment.

102. "Nicola Cotoner tending sick man" (M. Preti).

1964. 1st European Catholic Doctors' Congress, Valletta. Multicoloured

318. 2d. Type 102 .. .. 20 10
319. 6d. St. Luke and hospital.. 45 15
320. 1s. 6d. Sacra Infermeria, Valletta 85 85

106. Dove and British Crown.

110. Neolithic Era.

109. "The Nativity".

1964. Independence.

321. 106. 2d. olive, red and gold.. 30 10
322. – 3d. brown, red and gold 30 10
323. – 6d. slate, red and gold 90 15
324. 106. 1s. blue, red and gold.. 90 15
325. – 1s. 6d. blue, red & gold 2·50 1·50
326. – 2s. 6d. blue, red & gold 2·50 2·75

DESIGNS: 1d., 3d., 1s 6d. Dove and Pope's Tiara. 6d., 2s 6d. Dove and U.N. Emblem.

1964. Christmas.

327. 109. 2d. purple and gold .. 10 10
328. 4d. blue and gold .. 20 15
329. 8d. green and gold .. 45 45

1965. Multicoloured.

330. ½d. Type 110. .. .. 10 10
331. 1d. Punic Era 10 10
332. 1½d. Roman Era 10 10
333. 2d. Proto Christian Era .. 10 10
334. 2½d. Saracenic Era .. 30 10
335. 3d. Siculo Norman Era .. 10 10
336. 4d. Knights of Malta .. 30 10
337. 4½d. Maltese Navy .. 40 30
337b. 5d. Fortifications 30 20
338. 6d. French Occupation .. 20 10
339. 8d. British Rule 20 10
339c. 10d. Naval Arsenal .. 45 1·00
340. 1s. Maltese Corps of the British Army 30 10
341. 1s. 3d. International Eucharistic Congress, 1913 .. 1·50 1·40
342. 1s. 6d. Self-Government, 1921 .. .. .. 60 10
343. 2s. Gozo Civic Council .. 70 10
344. 2s. 6d. State of Malta .. 70 50
345. 3s. Independence 1964 .. 1·25 75
346. 5s. HAFMED (Allied Forces, Mediterranean) .. .. 4·50 1·00
347. 10s. The Maltese Islands (map) .. .. .. 3·50 3·00
348. £1 Patron Saints .. .. 3·50 5·00

Nos. 339/48 are larger, 41 × 29 mm. from perf. to perf. and include portrait of Queen Elizabeth II.

129. "Dante" (Raphael).

131. Turkish Fleet.

1965. 700th Birth Anniv. of Dante.

349. 129. 2d. blue 10 10
350. 6d. green 15 10
351. 2s. brown 50 70

1965. 400th Anniv. of Great Siege. Mult.

352. 2d. Turkish camp 25 10
353. 3d. Battle scene 25 10
354. 6d. Type 131 .. .. 50 10
355. 8d. Arrival of relief Force 75 75
356. 1s. Grand Master J. de La Valette's Arms 55 10
357. 1s. 6d. "Allegory of Victory" (from mural by M. Preti) 1·00 30
358. 2s. 6d. Victory Medal .. 1·50 2·00

SIZES—As Type 131: 1s. SQUARE (32½ × 32½ mm.): others.

HAVE YOU READ THE NOTES AT THE BEGINNING OF THIS CATALOGUE?

These often provide answers to the enquiries we receive.

137. "The Three Kings".

1965. Christmas.

359. 137. 1d. purple and red .. 10 10
360. 4d. purple and blue .. 30 25
361. 1s. 3d. slate and purple 30 30

138. Sir Winston Churchill.

1966. Churchill Commem.

362. 138. 2d. black, red and gold 15 10
363. – 3d. green, olive and gold 15 10
364. – 1s. purple, red and gold 20 10
365. – 1s. 6d. bl., ultram. & gold 35 40

DESIGN: 3d., 1s. 6d. Sir Winston Churchill and George Cross.

140. Grand Master La Valette.

1966. 400th Anniv. of Valletta. Mult.

366. 2d. Type 140. .. .. 10 10
367. 3d. Pope Pius V 10 10
368. 6d. Map of Valletta .. 10 10
369. 1s. F. Laparelli (architect) 10 10
370. 2s. 6d. G. Cassar (architect) 20 30

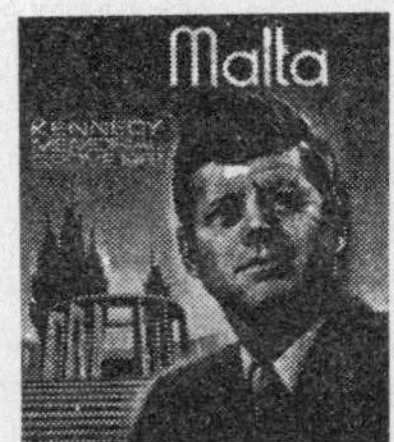

145. Pres. Kennedy and Memorial.

1966. Pres. Kennedy Commem.

371. 145. 3d. olive, gold and black 10 10
372. 1s. 6d. blue, gold & blk. 10 10

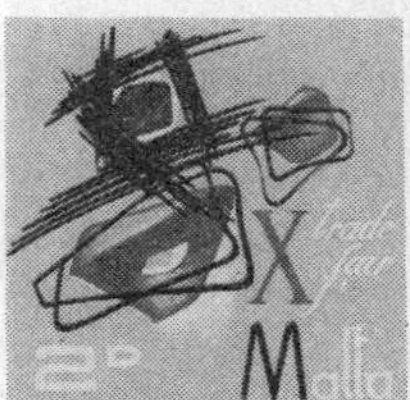

146. "Trade".

1966. 10th Malta Trade Fair.

373. 146. 2d. multicoloured .. 10 10
374. 8d. multicoloured .. 20 25
375. 2s. 6d. multicoloured .. 20 25

147. "The Child in the Manger".

148. George Cross.

1966. Christmas.
376. 147. 1d. multicoloured .. 10 10
377. 4d. multicoloured .. 10 10
378. 1s. 3d. multicoloured .. 10 10

1967. 25th Anniv. of George Cross Award to Malta.
379. 148. 2d. multicoloured .. 10 10
380. 4d. multicoloured .. 10 10
381. 3s. multicoloured .. 15 15

149. Crucifixion of St. Peter.

1967. 1,900th Anniv. of Martyrdom of Saints Peter and Paul.
382. 149. 2d. brown, orge. and black 10 10
383. – 8d. olive, gold and black 10 10
384. – 3s. blue and black .. 15 10
DESIGNS—As Type **149** 3s. Beheading of St. Paul. HORIZ. (47 × 25 mm.): 8d. Open Bible and Episcopal Emblems.

152. "St. Catherine of Siena".

1967. 300th Death Anniv. of Melchior Gafa (sculptor). Multicoloured.
385. 2d. Type **152** 10 10
386. 4d. "St. Thomas of Villanova" 10 10
387. 1s. 6d. "Baptism of Christ" (detail) 10 10
388. 2s. 6d. "St. John the Baptist" (from "Baptism of Christ") 10 10

156. Temple Ruins, Tarxien. **160.** "Angels".

1967. 15th Int. Historical Architecture Congress, Valletta. Multicoloured.
389. 2d. Type **156** 10 10
390. 6d. Facade of Palazzo Falzon, Notabile .. 10 10
391. 1s. Parish Church, Birkirkara 10 10
392. 3s. Portal, Auberge de Castille 15 15

1967. Christmas. Multicoloured.
393. 1d. Type **160** 10 10
394. 8d. "Crib" 10 10
395. 1s. 4d. "Angels" .. 10 10

163. Queen Elizabeth II and Arms of Malta.

1967. Royal Visit.
396. 163. 2d. multicoloured .. 10 10
397. – 4d. black, purple & gold 10 10
398. – 3s. multicoloured .. 15 15
DESIGNS—VERT. 4d. Queen in Robes of Order of St. Michael and St. George. HORIZ. 3s. Queen and outline of Malta.

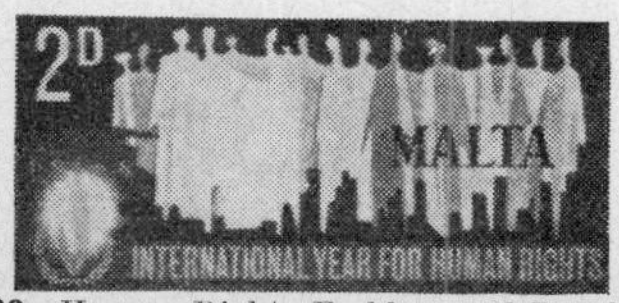

166. Human Rights Emblem and People.

1968. Human Rights Year. Multicoloured.
399. 2d. Type **166** 10 10
400 6d. Human Rights Emblem and People (different) .. 10 10
401. 2s. Type **166** (reversed) .. 10 10

169. Fair "Products".

1968. Malta Int. Trade Fair.
402. 169. 4d. multicoloured .. 10 10
403. 8d. multicoloured .. 10 10
404. 3s. multicoloured .. 15 10

170. Arms of the Order of St. John and La Valette.

1968. 4th Death Cent. of Grand Master La Valette. Multicoloured.
405. 1d. Type **170** 10 10
406. 8d. "La Valette" (A. de Favray) 10 10
407. 1s. 6d. La Valette's Tomb (28 × 23 mm.) 10 10
408. 2s. 6d. Angels and Scroll bearing Date of Death 15 20
The 8d., 2s. 6d. are vert.

174. Star of Bethlehem and Angel waking Shepherds.

1968. Christmas. Multicoloured.
409. 1d. Type **174**. .. 10 10
410. 8d. Mary and Joseph with Shepherd watching over Cradle 10 10
411. 1s. 4d. Three Wise Men and Star of Bethlehem .. 10 10

177. "Agriculture". **180.** Mahatma Gandhi.

1968. 6th Food and Agricultural Organization Regional Conf. for Europe. Multicoloured.
412. 4d. Type **177** 10 10
413. 1s. F.A.O. Emblem and Coin 10 10
414. 2s. 6d. "Agriculture" sowing Seeds .. 10 15

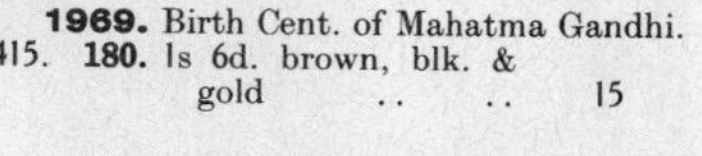

1969. Birth Cent. of Mahatma Gandhi.
415. 180. 1s 6d. brown, blk. & gold 15 10

181. ILO Emblem.

1969. 50th Anniv. of Int. Labour Organization.
416. 181. 2d. blue, gold and turq. 10 10
417. 6d. sepia, gold & brown 10 10

182. Robert Samut.

1969. Birth Centenary of Robert Samut (composer of Maltese National Anthem).
418. 182. 2d. multicoloured .. 10 10

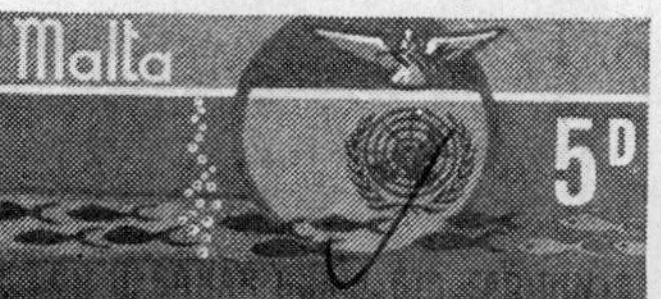

183. Dove of Peace, U.N. Emblem, and Sea-Bed.

1969. United Nations Resolution on Oceanic Resources.
419. 183. 5d. multicoloured .. 10 10

184. "Swallows" returning to Malta.

1969. Maltese Migrant's Convention.
420. 184. 10d. black, gold & olive 10 10

185. University Arms and Grand Master de Fonseca (founder).

1969. Bicent of University of Malta.
421. 185. 2s. multicoloured .. 10 20

187. Flag of Malta and Birds.

1969. 5th Anniv. of Independence.
422. – 2d. multicoloured 10 10
423. 187. 5d. black, red and gold 10 10
424. – 10d. black, blue & gold 10 10
425. – 1s. 6d. multicoloured .. 10 20
426. – 2s. 6d. blk., brn. & gold 15 25
DESIGN—SQUARE (31 × 31 mm.). 2d. 1919 War Monument. VERT. 10d. "Tourism". 1s. 6d. U.N. and Council of Europe Emblems. 2s. 6d. "Trade and Industry".

191. Peasants playing Tambourine and Bagpipes.

1969. Christmas. Children's Welfare Fund. Multicoloured.
427. 1d. + 1d. Type **191**. .. 10 10
428. 5d. + 1d. Angels playing trumpet and harp .. 10 10
429. 1s. 6d. + 3d. Choir boys singing 10 15

194. "The Beheading of St. John" (Caravaggio).

1970. 13th Council of Europe Art Exhibition. Multicoloured.
430. 1d. Type **194**. .. 10 10
431. 2d. "St. John the Baptist" (M. Preti) 10 10
432. 5d. Interior of St. John's Co-Cathedral, Valletta 10 10
433. 6d. "Allegory of the Order" (Neapolitan school) .. 10 10
434. 8d. "St. Jerome" (Caravaggio) 10 20
435. 10d. Articles from the Order of St. John in Malta .. 10 10
436. 1s. 6d. "The Blessed Gerard receiving Godfrey de Bouillon" (A. de Favray) 15 25
437. 2s. Cape and Stolone (16th-cent.) 20 35
SIZES—HORIZ. 1d., 8d. 56 × 30 mm. 2d., 6d. 45 × 32 mm. 10d., 2s. 63 × 21 mm. 1s. 6d. 45 × 34 mm. SQUARE. 5d. 39 × 39 mm.

202. Artist's Impression of Fujiyama.

1970. World Fair, Osaka.
438. 202. 2d. multicoloured .. 10 10
439. 5d. multicoloured .. 10 10
440. 3s. multicoloured .. 15 15

203. "Peace and Justice". **204.** Carol-Singers, Church and Star.

1970. 25th Anniv. of United Nations.
441. 203. 2d. multicoloured .. 10 10
442. 5d. multicoloured .. 10 10
443. 2s. 6d. multicoloured .. 15 15

1970. Christmas. Multicoloured.
444. 1d. + ½d. Type **204** .. 10 10
445. 10d. + 2d. Church, Star and Angels with Infant .. 10 15
446 1s. 6d. + 3d. Church, Star and Nativity Scene .. 15 25

207. Books and Quill.

1971. Literary Anniversaries. Multicoloured.
447. 1s. 6d. Type **207** (De Soldanis (historian) Death Bicent.) 10 10
448. 2s. Dun Karm (poet), books, pens and lamp (Birth Cent.) 10 15

209. Europa "Chain". **211.** "Centaurea spathulata".

210. "St. Joseph, Patron of the Universal Church" (G. Cali).

1971. Europa.

449.	209.	2d. orge., black & olive	10	10
450.		5d. orge., black and red	10	10
451.		1s. 6d. orge., blk. & slate	20	55

1971. Cent. of Proclamation of St. Joseph as Patron Saint of Catholic Church, and 50th Anniv. of Coronation of the Statue of "Our Lady of Victories". Multicoloured.

452.	2d. Type **210**	10	10
453.	5d. Statue of "Our Lady of Victories" and Galley	10	10
454.	10d. Type **210**	10	10
455.	1s. 6d. As 5d.	20	40

1971. National Plant and Bird of Malta. Multicoloured.

456.	2s. Type **211**	10	10
457.	5d. Blue rock thrush (horiz.)	10	10
458.	10d. As 5d.	20	15
459.	1s. 6d. Type **211**	20	80

212. Angel.

1971. Christmas. Multicoloured.

460.	1d.+½d. Type **212**	10	10
461.	10d.+2d. Mary and the Child Jesus	15	20
462.	1s. 6d.+3d. Joseph lying awake	20	30

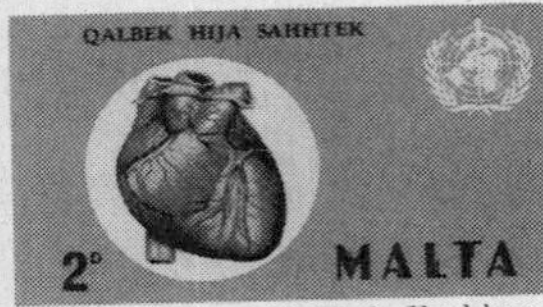

213. Heart and W.H.O. Emblem.

1972. World Health Day.

464.	213.	2d. multicoloured	10	10
465.		10d. multicoloured	15	10
466.		2s. 6d. multicoloured	40	80

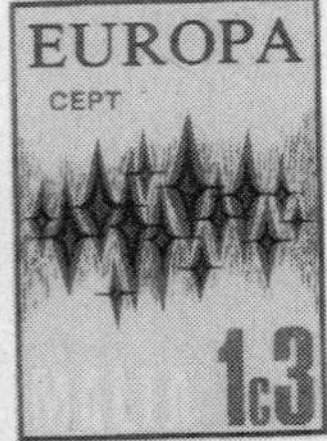

214. Maltese Cross. **216.** "Communications".

1972. Decimal Currency. Coins. Mult.

467.	2 m. Type **214**	10	10
468.	3 m. Bee on Honeycomb	10	10
469.	5 m. Earthen lampstand	10	10
470.	1 c. George Cross	10	10
471.	2 c. Classical head	10	10
472.	5 c. Ritual altar	10	10
473.	10 c. Grandmaster's galley	20	10
474.	50 c. Great Siege Monument	80	1·25

SIZES: 3 m., 2 c. As Type **214**. 5 m., 1 c., 5 c. 25×30 mm. 10 c., 50 c. 31×38 mm.

1972. Nos. 337a, 339 and 341 surch.

475.	1 c. 3 m. on 5 d. mult.	10	10
476.	3 c. on 8 d. multicoloured	15	10
477.	5 c. on 1 s. 3 d. multicoloured	15	20

1972. Europa.

478.	216.	1 c. 3 m. multicoloured	10	10
479.		3 c. multicoloured	10	10
480.		5 c. multicoloured	15	35
481.		7 c. 5 m. multicoloured	20	75

217. Angel.

1972. Christmas.

482.	217.	8 m.+2 m. brn., grey and gold	10	10
483.	–	3 c.+1 c. purple, violet and gold	15	35
484.	–	7 c. 5 m.+1 c. 5 m. indigo, blue & gold	20	45

DESIGNS: No. 483, Angel with tambourine. No. 484, Singing angel.

See also Nos. 507/9.

MINIMUM PRICE

The minimum price quoted is 10p which represents a handling charge rather than a basis for valuing common stamps. For further notes about prices see introductory pages.

218. Archaeology. **220.** Emblem, and Woman holding Corn.

219. Europa "Posthorn".

1973. Multicoloured.

486	2 m. Type **218**	10	10
487	4 m. History	10	10
488	5 m. Folklore	10	10
489	8 m. Industry	10	10
490	1 c. Fishing Industry	10	10
491	1 c. 3 Pottery	10	10
492	2 c. Agriculture	10	10
493	3 c. Sport	10	10
494	4 c. Yacht marina	15	10
495	5 c. Fiesta	15	10
496	7 c. 5 Regatta	25	10
497	10 c. Voluntary service	25	10
498	50 c. Education	75	1·00
499	£1 Religion	2·00	2·75
500	£2 Coat-of-arms (32×27 mm.)	14·00	16·00
500b	£2 National Emblem (32×27 mm.)	9·00	10·00

1973. Europa.

501.	219.	3 c. multicoloured	15	10
502.		5 c. multicoloured	15	35
503.		7 c. 5 m. multicoloured	25	60

1973. Anniversaries.

504.	220.	1 c. 3 m. multicoloured	10	10
505.	–	7 c. 5 m. multicoloured	25	40
506.	–	10 c. multicoloured	30	50

ANNIVERSARIES: 1 c. 3 m., World Food Programme. 10th anniv. 7 c. 5 m., W.H.O. 25th anniv. 10 c. Universal Declaration of Human Rights. 25th Anniv.

1973. Christmas. As T **217**. Multicoloured.

507.	8 m.+2 m. Angels and organ pipes	15	10
508.	3 c.+1 c. Madonna and Child	25	40
509.	7 c. 5 m.+1 c. 5 m. Buildings and Star	45	65

221. Girolamo Cassar (architect).

1973. Prominent Maltese.

511	221	1 c. 3 deep green, green and gold	10	10
512	–	3 c. green, blue & gold	10	10
513	–	5 c. brown, grn & gold	15	15
514	–	7 c. 5 bl, lt bl & gold	20	30
515	–	10 c. deep purple, purple and gold	20	40

DESIGNS: 3 c. Guiseppe Barth (ophthalmologist). 5 c. Nicolo' Isouard (composer). 7 c. 5, John Borg (botanist). 10 c. Antonio Sciortino (sculptor).

222. "Air Malta" Emblem.

1974. Air. Multicoloured.

516.	3 c. Type **222**	10	10
517.	4 c. Boeing "707"	15	10
518.	5 c. Type **222**	15	10
519.	7 c. 5 As 4 c.	20	10
520.	20 c. Type **222**	55	60
521.	25 c. As 4 c.	55	60
522.	35 c. Type **222**	1·00	1·40

223. Prehistoric Sculpture.

1974. Europa.

523	223	1 c. 3 blue, blk & gold	15	10
524	–	3 c. brown, blk & gold	20	15
525	–	5 c. purple, blk & gold	25	45
526	–	7 c. 5 green, blk & gold	35	80

DESIGNS—VERT. 3 c. Old Cathedral Door, Mdina. 7 c. 5 "Vetlina" (sculpture by A. Sciortino). HORIZ. 5 c. Silver monstrance.

224. Heinrich von Stephan (founder) and Land Transport.

1974. Centenary of U.P.U.

527.	224.	1 c. 3 grn., bl. & orge.	30	10
528.	–	5 c. brn., red & green	30	10
529.	–	7 c. 5 blue, vio. & grn.	35	20
530.	–	50 c. pur., red & orge.	1·00	1·25

DESIGNS: (each containing portrait as Type **224**). 5 c. "Washington" (paddle-steamer) and "Royal Viking Star" (liner). 7 c. 5 Balloon and Boeing "747". 50 c. U.P.U. Buildings, 1874 and 1974.

225. Decorative Star and Nativity Scene.

1974. Christmas. Multicoloured.

532.	8 m. + 2 m. Type **225**	10	10
533.	3 c + 1 c. "Shepherds"	15	20
534.	5 c. + 1 c. "Shepherds with gifts"	20	35
535.	7 c. 5 + 1 c. 5 "The Magi"	30	40

226. Swearing-in of Prime Minister.

1975. Inauguration of Republic.

536.	226.	1 c. 3 multicoloured	10	10
537.	–	5 c. red and black	20	10
538.	–	25 c. multicoloured	60	1·00

DESIGNS: 5 c. National flag. 25 c. Minister of Justice, President and Prime Minister.

227. Mother and Child ("Family Life").

1975. International Women's Year.

539.	227.	1 c. 3 violet and gold	15	10
540.	–	3 c. blue and gold	20	10
541.	227.	5 c. brown and gold	50	20
542.	–	20 c. brown and gold	2·25	3·00

DESIGN: 3 c., 20 c. Office Secretary ("Public Life").

228. "Allegory of Malta" (Francesco de Mura).

1975. Europa. Multicoloured.

543.	5 c. Type **228**	30	10
544.	15 c. "Judith and Holofernes" (Valentin de Boulogne)	50	65

The 15 c. is smaller: 47 × 23 mm.

229. Plan of Ggantija Temple.

1975. European Architectural Heritage Year.

545.	229.	1 c. 3 black and red	10	10
546.	–	3 c. purple, red & brn.	20	10
547.	–	5 c. brown and red	40	35
548.	–	25 c. grn., red & black	1·75	3·25

DESIGNS: 3 c. Mdina skyline. 5 c. View of Victoria, Gozo. 25 c. Silhouette of Fort St. Angelo.

230. Farm Animals. **231.** "The Right to Work".

1975. Christmas. Multicoloured.

549.	8 m. + 2 m. Type **230**	30	25
550.	3 c. + 1 c. Nativity scene (50 × 23 mm.)	60	75
551.	7 c. 5 + 1 c. 5 Approach of the Magi	1·50	1·75

1975. 1st Anniv of Republic.

552	231	1 c. 3 multicoloured	10	10
553	–	5 c. multicoloured	20	10
554	–	25 c. red. blue & black	70	1·10

DESIGNS: 5 c. "Safeguarding the Environment". 25 c. National Flag.

232. "Festa Tar-Rahal".

1976. Maltese Folklore. Multicoloured.

555.	1 c. 3 Type **232**	10	10
556.	5 c. "L-Imnarja" (horiz.)	15	10
557.	7 c. 5 "Il-Karnival" (horiz.)	45	70
558.	10 c. "Il-Gimgha L-Kbira"	70	1·40

233. Waterpolo.

1976. Olympic Games, Montreal. Mult.

559.	1 c. 7 Type **233**	10	10
560.	5 c. Sailing	20	10
561.	30 c. Athletics	65	1·50

234. Lace-making.

1976. Europa. Multicoloured.

562.	7 c. Type **234**	20	30
563.	15 c. Stone carving	25	40

235. Nicola Cotoner.

1976. 300th Anniv. of School of Anatomy and Surgery. Multicoloured.

564.	2 c. Type **235**	10	10
565.	5 c. Arm	10	10
566.	7 c. Giuseppe Zammit	15	10
567.	11 c. Sacra Infermeria	25	65

236. St. John the Baptist and St. Michael. **237.** Jean de la Valette's Armour.

1976. Christmas. Multicoloured.

568. 1 c.+5 m. Type **236** .. 15 20
569. 5 c.+1 c. Madonna and Child 50 70
570. 7 c.+1 c. 5 St. Christopher and St. Nicholas .. 65 1·00
571. 10 c.+2 c. Complete painting (32×27 mm.) .. 75 1·40

Nos. 568/71 show portions of " Madonna and Saints " by Domenico di Michelino.

1977. Suits of Armour. Multicoloured.

572. 2 c. Type **237** 10 10
573. 7 c. Aloph de Wignacourt's armour 20 10
574. 11 c. Jean Jacques de Verdelin's armour .. 25 50

1977. No. 336 surch.

575. 1 c. 7 on 4d. multicoloured 25 25

239. " Annunciation ".

1977. 4th Birth Cent. of Rubens. Flemish Tapestries. Multicoloured.

576. 2 c. Type **239** 10 10
577. 7 c. " Four Evangelists " 20 10
578. 11 c. " Nativity " 40 45
579. 20 c. " Adoration of the Magi " .. .. .. 65 1·00

See also Nos. 592/5, 615/18 and 638/9.

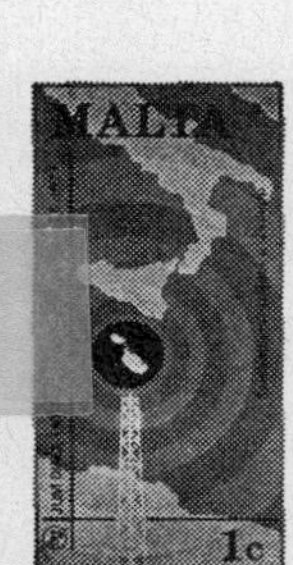

240. Map and Radio Aerial.

242. " Aid to Handicapped Workers " (detail from Workers' Monument).

241. Ta' L-Isperanza.

1977. World Telecommunications Day.

580. **240.** 1 c. black, grn. and red 10 10
581. 6 c. black, blue and red 15 10
582. – 8 c. black, brn. and red 15 10
583. – 17 c. blk., mauve & red 30 40

DESIGN—HORIZ. 8 and 17 c. Map, aerial and aeroplane tail-fin.

1977. Europa. Multicoloured.

584. 7 c. Type **241** 30 15
585. 20 c. Is-Salini 35 80

1977. Maltese Worker Commemoration.

586. **242.** 2 c. orange and brown 10 10
587. – 7 c. light brown & brown 15 10
588. – 20 c. multicoloured .. 40 60

DESIGNS—VERT. 7 c. " Stoneworker, modern industry and ship-building " (monument detail). HORIZ. 20 c. " Mother with Dead Son " and Service Medal.

243. The Shepherds.

1977. Christmas. Multicoloured.

589. 1 c.+5 m. Type **243** .. 10 20
590. 7 c.+1 c. The Nativity .. 15 30
591. 11 c.+1 c. 5 The Flight into Egypt 20 45

1978. Flemish Tapestries. (2nd series). As T **239**. Multicoloured.

592. 2 c. " The Entry into Jerusalem " 10 10
593. 7 c. " The Last Supper " (after Poussin) 20 10
594. 11 c. " The Raising of the Cross " (after Rubens) 25 25
595. 25 c. " The Resurrection " (after Rubens) 60 80

244. " Young Lady on Horseback and Trooper ".

1978. 450th Death Anniv of Albrecht Durer.

596 **244** 1 c. 7 black, red & blue 10 10
597 – 8 c. black, red and grey 15 10
598 – 17 c. black, red & grey 40 45

DESIGNS: 8 c. "The Bagpiper". 17 c. "The Virgin and Child with a Monkey".

245. Monument to Grand Master Nicola Cotoner (Foggini).

246. Goalkeeper.

1978. Europa. Monuments. Multicoloured.

599. 7 c. Type **245** 15 10
600. 25 c. Monument to Grand Master Ramon Perellos (Mazzuoli). 35 55

1978. World Cup Football Championship, Argentina. Multicoloured.

601. 2 c. Type **246** 10 10
602. 11 c. Players heading ball 15 10
603. 15 c. Tackling 25 35

247. Airliner over Megalithic Temple.

1978. Air. Multicoloured.

605. 5 c. Type **247** 15 10
606. 7 c. Air Malta Boeing " 720B " 15 10
607. 11 c. Boeing " 747 " taking off from Luqa Airport .. 25 10
608. 17 c. Type **247** 35 30
609. 20 c. As 7 c. 50 40
610. 75 c. As 11 c. .. .. 1·50 2·25

248. Folk Musicians and Village Church.

1978. Christmas. Multicoloured.

611. 1 c.+5 m. Type **248** .. 10 10
612. 5 c.+1 c. Choir of Angels 10 15
613. 7 c.+1 c. 5 Carol Singers 15 20
614. 11 c.+3 c. Folk musicians, church, angels and carol singers (58×22 mm.) .. 20 30

1979. Flemish Tapestries (3rd series) showing paintings by Rubens. As T **239**. Multicoloured.

615. 2 c. " The Triumph of the Catholic Church " .. 10 10
616. 7 c. " The Triumph of Charity " 15 10
617. 11 c. " The Triumph of Faith " 25 20
618. 25 c. " The Triumph of Truth " 70 55

249. Fishing Boat and Aircraft Carrier.

1979. End of Military Facilities Agreement. Multicoloured.

619. 2 c. Type **249** 10 10
620. 5 c. Raising the flag ceremony 10 10
621. 7 c. Departing soldier and olive sprig 15 10
622. 8 c. Type **249** 30 40
623. 17 c. As 5 c. 50 60
624. 20 c. As 7 c. 50 60

250. Speronara (fishing boat) and Tail of Air Malta Airliner.

251. Children on Globe.

1979. Europa. Communications. Mult.

625. 7 c. Type **250** 15 10
626. 25 c. Coastal watch tower and radio link towers .. 35 50

1979. International Year of the Child. Multicoloured.

627. 2 c. Type **251** 10 10
628. 7 c. Children flying kites (27×33 mm.) 15 10
629. 11 c. Children in circle (27×33 mm.) 20 35

252. Shells (" Gibbula nivosa ").

1979. Marine Life. Multicoloured.

630 2 c. Type **252** 10 10
631 5 c. Loggerhead turtle ("Garetta garetta") .. 20 10
632 7 c. Dolphin fish ("Coryphaena hippurus") 25 10
633 25 c. Noble pen shell ("Pinna nobilis") .. 90 1·25

253. " The Nativity " (detail).

1979. Christmas. Paintings by Giuseppe Cali. Multicoloured.

634. 1 c.+5 m. Type **253** .. 10 10
635. 5 c.+1 c. " The Flight into Egypt " (detail) .. 10 15
636. 7 c.+1 c. 5 m. " The Nativity " 15 20
637. 11 c.+3 c. " The Flight into Egypt " 25 50

1980. Flemish Tapestries (4th series). As T **239**. Multicoloured.

638. 2 c. " The Institution of Corpus Domini " (Rubens) 10 10
639. 8 c. " The Destruction of Idolatry " (Rubens) .. 20 20

254. Hal Saflieni Hypogeum, Paola.

255. Dun Gorg Preca.

1980. Restoration of Monuments. Multicoloured.

641. 2 c. 5 Type **254** 10 15
642. 6 c. Vilhena Palace, Mdina 25 20
643 8 c. Citadel of Victoria, Gozo (horiz.) 30 35
644. 12 c. Fort St. Elmo, Valletta (horiz.) 40 55

1980. Birth Centenary of Dun Gorg Preca (founder of Society of Christian Doctrine).

645. **255.** 2 c. 5 grey and black 10 10

256. Ruzar Briffa (poet).

1980. Europa.

646. **256.** 8 c. yell., brn. & grn... 20 10
647. – 30 c. grn., brn. & lake 55 70

DESIGN: 30 c. Nikiol Anton Vassalli (scholar and patriot).

257. " Annunciation ".

1980. Christmas. Paintings by A. Inglott. Multicoloured.

648. 2 c.+5 m. Type **257** .. 10 10
649. 6 c.+1 c. " Conception " .. 15 10
650. 8 c.+1 c. 5 " Nativity " .. 20 25
651. 12 c.+3 c. " Annunciation ", " Conception " and " Nativity " (47×38 mm.) .. 25 30

258. Chess Pieces.

1980. Chess Olympiad and F.I.D.E. (International Chess Federation) Congress. Multicoloured.

652. 2 c. 5 Type **258** 20 10
653. 8 c. Chess pieces (different) 50 15
654. 30 c. Chess pieces (vert.) .. 1·00 80

259. Barn Owl.

1981. Birds. Multicoloured.

655. 3 c. Type **259** 30 15
656. 8 c. Sardinian Warbler .. 50 20
657. 12 c. Woodchat Shrike .. 60 60
658. 23 c. British Storm Petrel 1·10 1·25

260. Traditional Horse Race.

1981. Europa. Folklore. Multicoloured.

659. 8 c. Type 260 . . . . 20 10
660. 30 c. Attempting to retrieve flag from end of "gostra" (greasy pole) 40 65

261. Stylised "25". 262. Disabled Artist at Work.

1981. 25th Maltese International Trade Fair.

661. 261. 4 c. multicoloured . . 15 15
662. 25 c. multicoloured . . 50 60

1981. International Year for Disabled Persons. Multicoloured.

663. 3 c. Type 262 . . . . 15 10
664. 35 c. Disabled child playing football 55 75

263. Wheat Ear in Conical Flask.

1981. World Food Day.

665. 263. 8 c. multicoloured . . 15 15
666. 23 c. multicoloured . . 60 50

264. Megalithic Building.

1981. History of Maltese Industry. Mult.

667. 5 m. Type 264 . . . . 10 10
668. 1 c. Cotton production . . 10 10
669. 2 c. Early ship-building . . 10 10
670. 3 c. Currency minting . . 10 10
671. 5 c. "Art" 20 25
672. 6 c. Fishing 20 25
673. 7 c. Agriculture 25 30
674. 8 c. Stone quarrying . . 30 35
675. 10 c. Grape pressing . . 35 40
676. 12 c. Modern ship-building 40 45
677. 15 c. Energy 50 55
678. 20 c. Telecommunications 70 75
679. 25 c. "Industry" 90 95
680. 50 c. Drilling for Water . . 1·75 1·90
681. £1 Sea transport . . . . 3·50 3·75
682. £3 Air transport . . . . 10·50 11·00

265. Children and Nativity Scene. 266. Shipbuilding.

1981. Christmas. Multicoloured.

683. 2 c.+1 c. Type 265 . . 15 10
684. 8 c.+2 c. Christmas eve procession (horiz.) . . 25 20
685. 20 c.+3 c. Preaching midnight sermon 50 60

1982. Shipbuilding Industry.

686. 266. 3 c. multicoloured . . 15 10
687. – 8 c. multicoloured . . 30 30
688. – 13 c. multicoloured . . 55 55
689. – 27 c. multicoloured . . 1·25 1·25

DESIGNS: 8 c. to 27 c. Differing shipyard scenes.

267. Elderly Man and Has-Serh (home for elderly).

1982. Care for Elderly. Multicoloured.

690. 8 c. Type 267 . . . . 40 20
691. 30 c. Elderly woman and Has-Zmien (hospital for elderly) . . . . . . 1·40 1·40

268. Redemption of Islands by Maltese, 1428.

1982. Europa. Historical Events. Mult.

692. 8 c. Type 268 . . . . 40 20
693. 30 c. Declaration of rights by Maltese, 1802 . . 1·00 1·40

269. Stylised Footballer.

1982. World Cup Football Championship, Spain.

694. 269. 3 c. multicoloured . . 20 10
695. – 12 c. multicoloured . . 60 55
696. – 15 c. multicoloured . . 70 65

DESIGNS: 12 c., 15 c. Various stylised footballers.

270. Angel appearing to Shepherds.

1982. Christmas. Multicoloured.

698. 2 c.+1 c. Type 270 . . 15 10
699. 8 c.+2 c. Nativity and Three Wise Men bearing gifts 40 40
700. 20 c.+3 c. Nativity scene (45×37 mm.) . . 85 85

271. "Ta Salvo Serafino" (oared brigantine), 1531.

1982. Maltese Ships (1st series). Mult.

701 3 c. Type 271 . . . . 40 10
702 8 c. "La Madonna del Rosario" (tartane), 1740 80 30
703 12 c. "San Paulo" (xebec), 1743 . . . . . . 1·25 55
704 20 c. "Ta Pietro Sablia" (xprunara), 1798 . . 1·60 90

See also Nos. 725/8, 772/5, 792/5 and 809/12.

272. "Manning Wardle", 1883.

1983. Centenary of Malta Railway. Mult.

705. 3 c. Type 272 . . . . 45 10
706. 13 c. "Black Hawthorn", 1884 . . . . . . 1·00 55
707. 27 c. "Beyer Peacock", 1895 . . . . . . 2·00 1·25

273. Peace Doves leaving Malta.

1983. Commonwealth Day. Multicoloured.

708. 8 c. Type 273 . . . . 30 30
709. 12 c. Tourist landmarks . . 40 40
710. 15 c. Holiday beach (vert.) 50 50
711. 23 c. Ship-building (vert.) 70 75

274. Ggantija Megalithic Temples, Gozo.

1983. Europa. Multicoloured.

712. 8 c. Type 274 . . . . 65 30
713. 30 c. Fort St. Angelo . . 1·75 1·40

275. Dish Aerials (World Communications Year).

1983. Anniversaries and Events. Mult.

714. 3 c. Type 275 . . . . 35 15
715. 7 c. Ships' prows and badge (25th anniv. of I.M.O. Convention) 60 40
716. 13 c. Container lorries and badge (30th anniv. of Customs Co-operation Council) 80 60
717. 20 c. Stadium and emblem (9th Mediterranean Games) 1·00 1·00

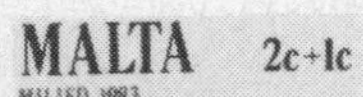

276. Monsignor Giuseppe de Piro. 277. Annunciation.

1983. 50th Death Anniv. of Monsignor Giuseppe de Piro.

718. 276. 3 c. multicoloured . . 10 10

1983. Christmas. Multicoloured.

719. 2 c.+1 c. Type 277 . . 30 15
720. 8 c.+2 c. The Nativity . . 75 40
721. 20 c.+3 c. Adoration of the Magi . . . . . . 1·40 85

278. Workers at Meeting.

1983. 40th Anniv. of General Workers' Union. Multicoloured.

722. 3 c. Type 278 . . . . 25 10
723. 8 c. Worker with family . . 50 30
724. 27 c. Union H.Q. Building 1·50 1·40

1983. Ships (2nd series). As T 271. Mult.

725. 2 c. "Strangier" (full-rigged ship), 1813 . . 20 15
726. 12 c. "Tigre" (topsail schooner), 1839 . . . . 90 60
727. 13 c. "La Speranza" (brig), 1844 . . . . . . 1·00 70
728. 20 c. "Wignacourt" (barque), 1844 . . . . 1·50 1·00

279. Boeing "737".

1984. Air. Multicoloured.

729. 7 c. Type 279 . . . . 25 30
730. 8 c. Boeing "720B" . . 30 35
731. 16 c. Vickers "Vanguard" 55 60
732. 23 c. Vickers "Viscount" 80 85
733. 27 c. Douglas "DC.3 Dakota" 95 1·00
734. 38 c. A.W. "Atlanta" . . 1·40 1·50
735. 75 c. Dornier "Wal" . . 2·75 3·00

280. Bridge.

1984. Europa. 25th Anniv. of C.E.P.T.

736. 280. 8 c. grn., blk. & yell. 35 35
737. 30 c. red, blk. & yell. 1·25 1·25

281. Early Policeman. 282. Running.

1984. 170th Anniv. of Malta Police Force. Multicoloured.

738. 3 c. Type 281 . . . . 55 15
739. 8 c. Mounted police . . 1·25 55
740. 11 c. Motorcycle policeman 1·50 1·25
741. 25 c. Policeman and firemen 2·50 2·50

1984. Olympic Games, Los Angeles Multicoloured.

742. 7 c. Type 282 . . . . 25 30
743. 12 c. Gymnastics 50 60
744. 23 c. Swimming . . . . 85 1·10

283. "The Visitation" (Pietru Caruana).

1984. Christmas. Paintings from Church of Our Lady of Porto Salvo, Valletta. Mult.

745. 2 c.+1 c. Type 283 . . 45 4
746. 8 c.+2 c. "The Epiphany" (Rafel Caruana) (horiz.) 85 8
747. 20 c.+3 c. "Jesus among the Doctors" (Rafel Caruana) (horiz.) . . 1·75 2·5

284. Dove on Map.

1984. 10th Anniv. of Republic. Mult.
748. 3 c. Type **284** 40 20
749. 8 c. Fort St. Angelo .. 75 50
750. 30 c. Hands .. .. 2·50 3·50

285. 1885 ½d. Green Stamp.

1985. Centenary of Malta Post Office. Mult.
751. 3 c. Type **285** 35 15
752. 8 c. 1885 1d. rose 55 40
753. 12 c. 1885 2½d. blue .. 75 95
754. 20 c. 1885 4d. brown .. 1·25 1·90

286. Boy, and Hands planting Vine.

1985. International Youth Year. Mult.
756 2 c. Type **286** 10 15
757 13 c. Young people and flowres (vert) 55 60
758 27 c. Girl holding flame in hand .. .. .. 1·25 1·40

287. Nicolo Baldacchino (tenor).

1985. Europa. European Music Year. Mult.
759. 8 c. Type **287** .. .. 1·50 30
760. 30 c. Francesco Azopardi (composer) .. .. 2·50 1·50

288. Guzeppi Bajada and Manwel Attard (victims).

1985. 66th Anniversary of 7 June 1919 Demonstrations. Multicoloured.
761. 3 c. Type **288** 35 15
762. 7 c. Karmnu Abela and Wenzu Dyer (victims) .. 75 35
763. 35 c. Model of projected Demonstration monument by Anton Agius (vert.) .. .. .. 2·25 1·75

289. Stylized Birds.

1985. 40th Anniversary of United Nations Organization. Multicoloured.
764. 4 c. Type **289** 20 15
765. 11 c. Arrow-headed ribbons 75 80
766. 31 c. Stylized figures .. 1·75 2·75

290. Giorgio Mitrovich (nationalist) (Death centenary).

1985. Celebrities' Anniversaries. Mult.
767. 8 c. Type **290** 70 35
768. 12 c. Pietru Caxaru (poet and administrator) (400th death anniv.) .. 1·40 90

291. The Three Wise Men.

1985. Christmas. Designs showing details of terracotta relief by Ganni Bonnici. Multicoloured.
769. 2 c.+1 c. Type **291** .. 55 60
770. 8 c.+2 c. Virgin and Child 1·25 1·50
771. 20 c.+3 c. Angels .. .. 2·25 2·75

1985. Maltese Ships (3rd series). Steamships. As T **271**. Multicoloured.
772. 3 c. "Scotia" (paddle-steamer), 1844 .. .. 55 20
773. 7 c. "Tagliaferro (screw steamer), 1822 .. .. 1·00 70
774. 15 c. "Gleneagles" (screw steamer), 1885 .. .. 1·50 1·75
775. 23 c. "L'Isle Adam" (screw steamer), 1886 .. .. 2·25 2·50

292. John XXIII Peace Laboratory and Statue of St. Francis of Assisi.

1986. International Peace Year. Mult.
776. 8 c. Type **292** .. .. 1·00 50
777. 11 c. Dove and hands holding olive branch (40 × 19 mm.). .. .. 1·50 1·50
778. 27 c. Map of Africa, dove and two heads .. .. 3·00 3·50

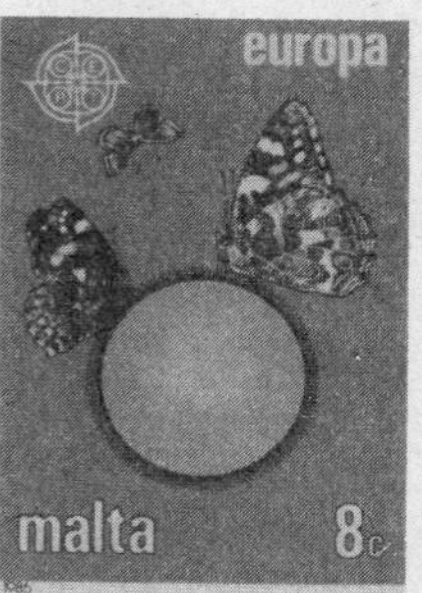

293. Symbolic Plant and "Cynthia cardui", "Vanessa atalanta" and "Polyommatus icarus".

1986. Europa. Environmental Conservation. Multicoloured.
779. 8 c. Type **293** .. .. 1·75 50
780. 35 c. Island, Neolithic frieze, sea and sun .. 3·25 4·00

294. Heading the Ball.

1986. World Cup Football Championship, Mexico. Multicoloured.
781. 3 c. Type **294** 60 20
782. 7 c. Saving a goal .. .. 1·25 65
783. 23 c. Controlling the ball .. 4·00 4·50

295. Father Diegu.

1986. Maltese Philanthropists. Multicoloured.
785. 2 c. Type **295** 40 30
786. 3 c. Adelaide Cini 50 30
787. 8 c. Alfonso Maria Galea .. 1·25 60
788. 27 c. Vincenzo Bugeja .. 3·25 4·00

296. "Nativity".

1986. Christmas. Multicoloured. Paintings by Giuseppe D'Arena.
789. 2 c.+1 c. Type **296** .. 50 60
790. 8 c.+2 c. "Nativity" (detail) (vert.) .. .. 1·50 1·75
791. 20 c+3 c. "Epiphany" .. 2·75 3·50

1986. Maltese Ships (4th series). As T **271**. Multicoloured.
792. 7 c. "San Paul" (freighter), 1921 .. .. .. 1·25 50
793. 10 c. "Knight of Malta" (cargo liner), 1930 .. 1·50 1·10
794. 12 c. "Valetta City" (freighter) 1948 .. .. 1·75 1·75
795. 20 c. "Saver" (freighter), 1959 .. .. .. 3·00 3·50

297. European Robin.

1987. 25th Anniv. of Malta Ornithological Society. Multicoloured.
796. 3 c. Type **297** 60 40
797. 8 c. Peregrine falcon (vert.) 1·50 75
798. 13 c. Hoopoe (vert.) .. 2·00 2·00
799. 23 c. Cory's shearwater .. 2·75 3·25

298. Aquasun Lido.

1987. Europa. Modern Architecture. Mult.
800. 8 c. Type **298** .. .. 1·25 65
801. 35 c. Church of St. Joseph, Manikata .. .. 3·50 4·25

299. 16th-century Pikeman.

1987. Maltese Uniforms (1st series). Mult.
802. 3 c. Type **299** 55 40
803. 7 c. 16th-century officer .. 1·00 70
804. 10 c. 18th-century standard bearer .. .. .. 1·50 40
805. 27 c. 18th-century General of the Galleys .. .. 3·25 3·75
See also Nos. 832/5, 851/4, 880/3 and 893/6.

300. Maltese Scenes, Wheat Ears and Sun.

1987. Anniversaries and Events. Mult.
806. 5 c. Type **300** (European Environment Year) .. 75 50
807. 8 c. Esperanto star as comet (Centenary of Esperanto) .. .. 1·00 60
808. 23 c. Family at house door (International Year of Shelter for the Homeless) .. .. 2·75 2·25

1987. Maltese Ships (5th series). As T **271**. Multicoloured.
809 2 c. "Medina" (freighter), 1969 .. .. .. 40 40
810 11 c. "Rabat" (container ship), 1974 .. .. 1·40 1·40
811 13 c. "Ghawdex" (passenger ferry), 1979 1·60 1·60
812 20 c. "Pinto" (car ferry), 1987 .. .. .. 2·25 2·50

301. "The Visitation".

1987. Christmas. Illuminated illustrations, score and text from 16th-century choral manuscript. Multicoloured.

813. 2 c.+1 c. Type **301** .. 40 40
814. 8 c.+2 c. "The Nativity" 1·25 1·50
815. 20 c.+3 c. "The Adoration of the Magi" .. .. 2·50 2·75

302. Dr. Arvid Pardo (U.N. representative).

1987. 20th Anniv. of United Nations Resolution on Peaceful Use of the Seabed. Multicoloured.

816. 8 c. Type **302** .. .. 1·00 65
817. 12 c. U.N. emblem and sea 1·75 2·00

303. Ven. Nazju Falzon (Catholic catechist).

1988. Maltese Personalities. Multicoloured.

819. 2 c. Type **303** 25 30
820. 3 c. Mgr. Sidor Formosa (philanthropist) 25 30
821. 4 c. Sir Luigi Preziosi (ophthalmologist) .. 30 30
822. 10 c. Fr. Anastasju Cuschieri (poet) 70 75
823. 25 c. Mgr. Pietru Pawl Saydon (Bible translator) .. .. .. 2·00 2·50

304. "St. John Bosco with Youth" (statue).

1988. Religious Anniversaries. Multicoloured.

824. 10 c. Type **304** (death centenary) 80 80
825. 12 c. "Assumption of Our Lady" (altarpiece by Perugino, Ta' Pinu, Gozo) (Marian Year) .. 1·00 1·00
826. 14 c. "Christ the King" (statue by Sciortino) (75th anniv. of International Eucharistic Congress, Valletta) .. 1·50 1·75

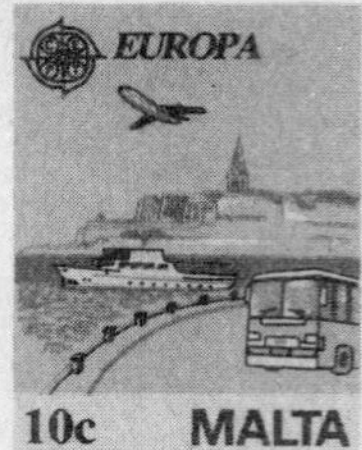

305. Bus, Ferry and Aircraft.

1988. Europa. Transport and Communications. Multicoloured.

827. 10 c. Type **305** .. .. 1·00 75
828. 35 c. Control panel, dish aerial and pylons .. 2·75 3·00

306 Globe and Red Cross Emblems

1988. Anniversaries and Events. Mult.

829 4 c. Type **306** (125th anniv of Int. Red Cross) .. 40 30
830 18 c. Divided globe (Campaign for North-South Interdependence and Solidarity) .. 1·75 1·75
831 19 c. Globe and symbol (40th anniv of W.H.O.) 1·75 1·75

1988. Maltese Uniforms (2nd series). As T **299**. Multicoloured.

832 3 c. Private, Maltese Light Infantry, 1800 .. .. 30 30
833 4 c. Gunner, Malta Coast Artillery, 1802 .. .. 35 35
834 10 c. Field Officer, 1st Maltese Provincial Battalion, 1805 .. 85 85
835 25 c. Subaltern, Royal Malta Regiment, 1809 .. 2·25 2·50

307 Athletics

309 Commonwealth Emblem

308 Shepherd with Flock

1988. Olympic Games, Seoul. Multicoloured.

836 4 c. Type **307** 30 30
837 10 c. Diving 70 70
838 35 c. Basketball .. .. 2·00 2·50

1988. Christmas. Multicoloured.

839 3 c.+1 c. Type **308** .. 25 30
840 10 c.+2 c. The Nativity .. 60 70
841 25 c.+3 c. Three Wise Men 1·50 1·75

1989. 25th Anniv of Independence. Mult.

842 2 c. Type **309** .. 25 25
843 3 c. Council of Europe flag 25 25
844 4 c. U.N. flag 30 30
845 10 c. Workers, hands gripping ring and national flag 75 75
846 12 c. Scales and allegorical figure of Justice .. 90 90
847 25 c. Prime Minister Borg Olivier with Independence constitution (42 × 28 mm) .. 1·90 2·40

310 New State Arms

1989.

848 **310** £1 multicoloured .. 3·50 3·75

311 Two Boys flying Kite

1989. Europa. Children's Games. Mult.

849 10 c. Type **311** .. .. 1·25 75
850 35 c. Two girls with dolls 3·25 3·50

1989. Maltese Uniforms (3rd series). As T **299**. Multicoloured.

851 3 c. Officer, Maltese Veterans, 1815 .. .. 35 35
852 4 c. Subaltern, Royal Malta Fencibles, 1839 .. 40 40
853 10 c. Private, Malta Militia, 1856 .. .. 1·00 1·00
854 25 c. Colonel, Royal Malta Fencible Artillery, 1875 2·25 2·75

312 Human Figures and Buildings

1989. Anniversaries and Commemorations. Designs showing logo and stylized human figures. Multicoloured.

855 3 c. Type **312** (20th anniv of U.N. Declaration on Social Progress and Development) 30 30
856 4 c. Workers and figure in wheelchair (Malta's Ratification of European Social Charter) .. 35 35
857 10 c. Family (40th anniv of Council of Europe) .. 80 80
858 14 c. Teacher and children (70th anniv of Malta Union of Teachers) .. 1·00 1·25
859 25 c. Symbolic knights (Knights of the Sovereign Military Order of Malta Assembly) .. 2·25 2·50

313 Angel and Cherub

1989. Christmas. Vault paintings by Mattia Preti from St. John's Co-Cathedral, Valletta.

860 3 c.+1 c. Type **313** .. 40 40
861 10 c.+2 c. Two angels .. 90 90
862 20 c.+3 c. Angel blowing trumpet .. .. 1·60 1·75

314 Presidents Bush and Gorbachev

1989. U.S.A.–U.S.S.R. Summit Meeting, Malta.

863 **314** 10 c. multicoloured .. 85 1·00

315 General Post Office, Auberge d'Italie, Valletta

1990. Europa. Post Office Buildings. Mult.

864 10 c. Type **315** 75 50
865 35 c. Branch Post Office, Zebbug (horiz) .. .. 2·25 2·75

316 Open Book and Letters from Different Alphabets (International Literacy Year)

1990. Anniversaries and Events. Mult.

866 3 c. Type **316** 25 25
867 4 c. Count Roger of Sicily and Norman soldiers (900th anniv of Sicilian rule) (horiz) .. 30 30
868 19 c. Communications satellite (25th anniv of I.T.U.) (horiz) .. 1·50 1·75
869 20 c. Football and map of Malta (Union of European Football Associations 20th Ordinary Congress, Malta) .. .. 1·50 1·75

317 Samuel Taylor Coleridge (poet) and Government House

1990. British Authors. Multicoloured.

870 4 c. Type **317** 25 30
871 10 c. Lord Byron (poet) and map of Valletta .. 50 60
872 12 c. Sir Walter Scott (novelist) and Great Siege 60 75
873 25 c. William Makepeace Thackeray (novelist) and Naval Arsenal .. .. 1·25 1·75

318 St. Paul

1990. Visit of Pope John Paul II. Bronze Bas-reliefs.

874 318 4 c. black, flesh & red 50 60
875 – 25 c. black, flesh & red 2·00 2·25
DESIGN: 25 c. Pope John Paul II.

319 Flags and Football

1990. World Cup Football Championship, Italy. Multicoloured.

876 5 c. Type **319** 35 30
877 10 c. Football in net .. 65 75
878 14 c. Scoreboard and football .. .. .. 1·00 1·10

1990. Maltese Uniforms (4th series). As T **299**. Multicoloured.

880 3 c. Captain, Royal Malta Militia, 1889 .. .. 30 30
881 4 c. Field officer, Royal Malta Artillery, 1905 .. 35 35
882 10 c. Labourer, Malta Labour Corps, 1915 .. 65 65
883 25 c. Lieutenant, King's Own Malta Regiment of Militia, 1918 .. .. 1·50 1·50

320 Innkeeper

1990. Christmas. Figures from Crib by Austin Galea, Marco Bartolo and Rosario Zammit. Multicoloured.

884 3 c.+1 c. Type **320** .. 30 30
885 10 c.+2 c. Nativity (41 ×28 mm) 70 80
886 25 c.+3 c. Shepherd with sheep .. .. .. 1·60 1·75

321 1899 10s. Stamp under Magnifying Glass

1991. 25th Anniv of Philatelic Society of Malta.

887 321 10 c. multicoloured .. 50 55

322 "Eurostar" Satellite and V.D.U. Screen

1991. Europa. Europe in Space. Mult.

888 10 c. Type **322** 60 70
889 35 c. "Ariane 4" rocket and projected HOTOL aero-spaceplane .. .. 2·00 2·10

323 St. Ignatius Loyola (founder of Jesuits) (500th birth anniv)

1991. Religious Commemorations. Mult.

890 3 c. Type **323** 20 20
891 4 c. Abbess Venerable Maria Adeodata Pisani (185th birth anniv) (vert) 25 25
892 30 c. St. John of the Cross (400th death anniv) .. 1·75 1·75

1991. Maltese Uniforms (5th series). As T **299**. Multicoloured.

893 3 c. Officer with colour, Royal Malta Fencibles, 1860 .. .. .. 25 25
894 10 c. Officer with colour, Royal Malta Regiment of Militia, 1903 .. .. 60 60
895 19 c. Officer with Queen's colour, King's Own Malta Regiment, 1968 .. 1·10 1·10
896 25 c. Officer with colour, Malta Armed Forces, 1991 .. .. .. 1·60 1·60

324 Interlocking Arrows

1991. 25th Anniv of Union Haddiema Maghqudin (public services union).

897 324 4 c. multicoloured .. 25 30

325 Honey Buzzard

1991. Endangered Species. Birds. Mult.

898 4 c. Type **325** 30 35
899 4 c. Marsh harrier .. 30 35
900 10 c. Eleonora's falcon .. 70 80
901 10 c. Lesser kestrel .. 70 80

326 Three Wise Men

1991. Christmas. Multicoloured.

902 3 c.+1 c. Type **326** .. 25 25
903 10 c.+2 c. Holy Family .. 65 65
904 25 c.+3 c. Two shepherds 1·25 1·25

327 Ta' Hagrat Neolithic Temple

1991. National Heritage of the Maltese Islands. Multicoloured.

905 1 c. Type **327** 10 10
906 2 c. Cottoner Gate .. 10 10
907 3 c. St. Michael's Bastion, Valletta 10 15
908 4 c. Spinola Palace, St. Julian's 15 20
909 5 c. Birkirkara Church .. 20 25
910 10 c. Mellieha Bay .. 35 40
911 12 c. Wied iz-Zurrieq .. 40 45
912 14 c. Mgarr harbour, Gozo 50 55
913 20 c. Yacht marina .. 70 75
914 50 c. Gozo Channel .. 1·75 1·90
915 £1 "Arab Horses" (sculpture by Antonio Sciortino) .. .. .. 3·50 3·75
916 £2 Independence Monument (Ganni Bonnici) (vert) .. .. .. 7·00 7·25

328 Aircraft Tailfins and Terminal

1992. Opening of International Air Terminal. Multicoloured.

917 4 c. Type **328** 15 20
918 10 c. National flags and terminal 35 40

329 Ships of Columbus

1992. Europa. 500th Anniv of Discovery of America by Columbus. Multicoloured.

919 10 c. Type **329** 35 40
920 35 c. Columbus and map of Americas .. .. 1·25 1·50

330 George Cross and Anti-aircraft Gun Crew

1992. 50th Anniv of Award of George Cross to Malta. Multicoloured.

921 4 c. Type **330** 15 20
922 10 c. George Cross and memorial bell 35 40
923 50 c. Tanker "Ohio" entering Grand Harbour 1·75 1·90

POSTAGE DUE STAMPS

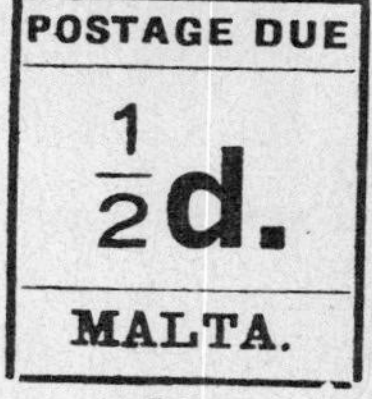

D 1.

D 2.

1925. Imperf.

D 1. D 1. ½d. black .. .. 1·25 3·75
D 2. 1d. black .. .. 2·00 2·50
D 3. 1½d. black .. .. 2·25 3·50
D 4. 2d. black .. .. 3·25 6·00
D 5. 2½d. black .. .. 2·75 2·75
D 6. 3d. black on grey .. 8·00 11·00
D 7. 4d. black on yellow .. 4·50 9·00
D 8. 6d. black on yellow .. 4·50 11·00
D 9. 1s. black on yellow .. 7·50 15·00
D 10. 1s. 6d. black on yellow 13·00 35·00

1925. Perf.

D 32 D 2 ½d. green .. .. 35 1·00
D 33 1d. violet 30 65
D 34 1½d. brown .. .. 35 1·50
D 14 2d. grey .. .. 11·00 1·50
D 35 2d. brown 85 70
D 36 2½d. orange .. 60 70
D 37 3d. blue 60 60
D 38 4d. green .. .. 1·00 80
D 39 6d. purple .. .. 75 1·00
D 40 1s. black .. .. 95 1·50
D 41 1s. 6d. red .. .. 2·25 4·25

D 3. Maltese Lace.

1973.

D 42. D 3. 2 m. brown and red .. 10 10
D 43. 3 m. orange and red .. 10 10
D 44. 5 m. pink and red .. 10 10
D 45. 1 c. blue and green .. 10 10
D 46. 2 c. grey and black .. 10 10
D 47. 3 c. light brn. and brn. 10 10
D 48. 5 c. dull blue and blue 15 20
D 49. 10 c. lilac and plum .. 30 35

MAURITIUS

An island in the Indian Ocean, E. of Madagascar. Attained Self-Government on 1 September 1967, and became independent on 12 March 1968.

1847. 12 pence = 1 shilling.
20 shillings = 1 pound.
1878. 100 cents = 1 rupee.

1. (" POST OFFICE "). 2. (" POST PAID ").

1847. Imperf.
1. 1. 1d. red £400000 £150000
2. 2d. blue £250000 £150000

1848. Imperf.
23. 2. 1d. red £850 £325
25. 2d. blue £900 £350

3. 5.

1854. Surch. **FOUR-PENCE.** Imperf.
26 3 4d. green £650 £350

1858. No value on stamps. Imperf.
27 3 (4d.) green £400 £200
28 (6d.) red 17·00 25·00
29 (9d.) purple £475 £200

1859. Imperf.
32 5 6d. blue £425 28·00
33 6d. black 15·00 20·00
34 1s. red £1800 45·00
35 1s. green £180 70·00

6. 8.

1859. Imperf.
39 6 2d. blue £850 £375

1859. Imperf.
42 8 1d. red £1100 £550
44 2d. blue £850 £300

9. 10.

1860.
56 9 1d. purple 30·00 6·50
57 1d. brown 45·00 5·00
60 2d. blue 48·00 4·50
61a 3d. red 30·00 8·00
62 4d. red 55·00 1·75
65 6d. green 75·00 3·75
50 6d. grey £120 70·00
63 6d. violet 90·00 23·00
51 9d. purple 65·00 30·00
66 9d. green £100 £100
67 10 10d. red £100 20·00
70 9 1s. yellow 95·00 12·00
53 1s. green £425 £120
69 1s. blue £120 18·00
71 5s. mauve £110 30·00

1862. Perf.
54 5 6d. black 14·00 24·00
55 1s. green £1400 £300

HALF PENNY (11.) HALF PENNY (13.)

1876. Surcharged with T 11.
76. 9. ½d. on 9d. purple 2·75 6·50
77. 10. ½d. on 10d. red 80 9·00

1877. Surch. with T 13.
79. 10. ½d. on 10d. red 2·00 20·00

One Penny (14.) 2 CENTS (16.)

1877. Surch. as T 14.
80. 9. 1d. on 4d. red 7·50 12·00
81. 1s. on 5s. mauve £170 85·00

1878. Surch. as T **16.**
83. 10. 2 c. red 5·00 4·25
84. 9. 4 c. on 1d. brown 7·00 3·75
85. 8 c. on 2d. blue 55·00 75
86. 13 c. on 3d. red 7·00 17·00
87. 17 c. on 4d. red 75·00 1·50
88. 25 c. on 6d. blue £110 4·75
89. 38 c. on 9d. purple 18·00 32·00
90. 50 c. on 1s. green 65·00 2·50
91. 2 r. 50 on 5s. mauve 12·00 9·00

18. 19.

1879. Various frames.
~~101~~ 18 1 c. violet 30 45
102 2 c. red 17·00 4·75
~~103~~ 2 c. green 90 30
104 19 4 c. orange 45·00 2·50
~~105~~ 4 c. red 1·00 20
106 – 8 c. blue 65 65
95 – 13 c. grey £110 £110
107 – 15 c. brown 1·00 35
108 – 15 c. blue 5·00 40
109 – 16 c. brown 2·00 45
96 – 17 c. red 32·00 3·50
110 – 25 c. olive 3·00 1·50
98 – 38 c. purple £130 £140
99 – 50 c. green 2·50 1·75
111 – 50 c. orange 26·00 7·50
100 – 2 r. 50 purple 23·00 40·00

1883. No. 96 surch **16 CENTS.**
112 16 c. on 17 c. red 70·00 38·00

1883. No. 96 surch **SIXTEEN CENTS.**
115 16 c. on 17 c. red 32·00 80

1885. No. 98 surch **2 CENTS** with bar.
116 2 c. on 38 c. purple 65·00 32·00

1887. No. 95 surch as above without bar.
117 2 c. on 13 c. grey 25·00 42·00

1891. Surch in words with or without bar.
~~123~~ 18 1 c. on 2 c. violet 30 35
124 – 1 c. on 16 c. brown (No. 109) 30 80
118 19 2 c. on 4 c. red 35 20
119 – 2 c. on 17 c. red (No. 96) 55·00 55·00
120 9 2 c. on 38 c. on 9 d. (89) 1·00 3·50
121 – 2 c. on 38 c. pur (No. 98) 2·00 2·50

36.

1895.
127 36 1 c. purple and blue 35 40
~~128~~ 2 c. purple and orange 2·00 10
~~129~~ 3 c. purple 50 30
~~130~~ 4 c. purple and green 3·25 30
131 – 6 c. green and red 3·00 2·00
132 – 18 c. green and blue 6·50 5·00

37.

1898. Diamond Jubilee.
133. 37. 36 c. orange and blue 9·00 12·00

1899. Surch in figures and words.
137 – 4 c. on 16 c. brown (No. 109) 70 3·25
134 36 6 c. on 18 c. (No. 132) 40 50
156 12 c. on 18 c. (No. 132) 80 5·00
163 37 12 c. on 36 c. (No. 133) 1·00 1·00
135 15 c. on 36 c. (No. 133) 1·00 80

40. Admiral Mahe de Labourdonnais, Governor of Mauritius 1735–46.

42.

1899. Birth Bicentenary of Labourdonnais.
136. 40. 15 c. blue 9·50 1·75

1900.
~~138~~ 36 1 c. grey and black 50 10
~~139~~ 2 c. purple 30 10
~~140~~ 3 c. green & red on yell. 1·00 30
141 4 c. purple & red on yell. 1·10 10
142 4 c. green and violet 60 85
~~167a~~ 4 c. black & red on blue 1·00 10
144 5 c. purple on buff 3·00 35·00
145 5 c. pur. & blk. on buff 1·60 1·75
~~168a~~ 6 c. purple & red on red 1·00 10
147 8 c. grn. & blk. on buff 80 3·00
148 12 c. black and red 1·50 70
149 15 c. green and orange 5·25 6·00
171 15 c. blk. & blue on blue 4·00 35
151a 25 c. grn. & red on grn. 2·00 6·50
174 50 c. green on yellow 1·00 2·25
175 42 1 r. grey and red 19·00 28·00
154 2 r. 50 grn. & blk. on bl. 11·00 40·00
155 5 r. purple & red on red 45·00 75·00

1902. Optd **Postage & Revenue.**
157 36 4 c. purple & red on yell 20 20
158 6 c. green and red 35 2·25
159 15 c. green and orange 45 30
160 – 25 c. olive (No. 110) 50 2·25
161 – 50 c. green (No. 99) 3·75 1·00
162 – 2 r. 50 purple (No. 100) 45·00 60·00

46. 47.

1910.
181 46 1 c. black 55 10
~~206~~ 2 c. brown 50 10
207 2 c. purple on yellow 30 20
~~183~~ 3 c. green 60 10
~~184~~ 4 c. green and red 80 10
210 4 c. green 90 10
~~211~~ 4 c. brown 60 60
~~186~~ 6 c. red 40 10
~~213~~ 6 c. mauve 90 10
187 8 c. orange 1·10 1·25
215 10 c. grey 2·00 3·25
216 10 c. red 2·00 80
217 12 c. red 80 40
218 12 c. grey 35 1·50
219a 15 c. blue 45 25
220 20 c. blue 2·00 50
221 20 c. purple 4·50 8·50

1910.
185. 47. 5 c. grey and red 50 1·50
188. 12 c. grey 30 50
190. 25 c. blk. & red on yell. 1·75 8·50
191. 50 c. purple and black 1·75 9·50
192. 1 r. black on green 3·75 6·00
193. 2 r. 50 blk. & red on blue 7·50 35·00
194. 5 r. green & red on yell. 24·00 55·00
195. 10 r. green & red on grn. 80·00 £140

48.

1913.
223 48 1 c. black 30 35
~~224~~ 2 c. brown 30 10
225 3 c. green 35 30
226 4 c. green and red 35 30
226b 4 c. green 1·25 45
~~227~~ 5 c. grey and red 40 10
228 6 c. brown 30 60
229 8 c. orange 30 5·50
~~230~~ 10 c. red 40 10
232b 12 c. grey 60 10
232 12 c. red 15 2·50
233 15 c. blue 45 20
234 20 c. purple 30 40
235 20 c. blue 7·00 80
236 25 c. blk. & red on yellow 20 15
237 50 c. purple and black 6·50 4·00
238 1 r. black on green 55 40
239 2 r. 50 blk. & red on bl. 13·00 6·00
240 5 r. grn. & red on yellow 17·00 45·00
204d 10 r. green & red on grn. 23·00 60·00

1924. As T **42** but Arms similar to T **46.**
222 50 r. purple and green £700 £1300

1925. Surch. with figures, words and **bar.**
242 46 3 c. on 4 c. green 2·50 3·25
243 10 c. on 12 c. red 15 10
244 15 c. on 20 c. blue 40 15

1935. Silver Jubilee. As T **13** of Antigua.
245 5 c. blue and grey 20 10
246 12 c. green and blue 1·75 10
247 20 c. brown and blue 2·75 20
248 1 r. grey and purple 24·00 26·00

1937. Coronation. As T **2** of Aden.
249 5 c. violet 30 10
250 12 c. red 30 40
251 20 c. blue 30 10

51.

1938.
~~252~~ 51 2 c. grey 15 10
~~253a~~ 3 c. purple and red 60 70
~~254a~~ 4 c. green 50 50
~~255a~~ 5 c. violet 70 10
~~256a~~ 10 c. red 1·00 10
~~257~~ 12 c. orange 60 10
~~258~~ 20 c. blue 1·00 10
259b 25 c. purple 1·50 10
~~260b~~ 1 r. brown 3·25 60
261a 2 r. 50 violet 12·00 6·00
262a 5 r. olive 24·00 17·00
263a 10 r. purple 8·00 13·00

1946. Victory. As T **9** of Aden.
264 5 c. violet 10 10
265 20 c. blue 10 10

52. 1d. " Post Office " Mauritius and King George VI.

1948. Cent. of First British Colonial Stamp.
266. 52. 5 c. orange and mauve 10 20
267. 12 c. orange and green 10 20
268. – 20 c. blue 10 10
269. – 1 r. blue and brown 15 20
DESIGN: 20 c., 1 r. As Type **52**, but showing 2d. " Post Office " Mauritius.

1948. Silver Wedding. As T **10/11** of Aden.
270 5 c. violet 10 10
271 10 r. mauve 8·00 12·00

1949. U.P.U. As Nos. **20/23** of Antigua.
272 12 c. red 60 60
273 20 c. blue 60 60
274 35 c. purple 60 40
275 1 r. brown 60 20

55. Aloe Plant.

60. Legend of Paul and Virginie.

67. Arms of Mauritius.

1950.
~~276~~ – 1 c. purple 10 40
~~277~~ – 2 c. red 15 10
~~278~~ 55. 3 c. green 60 1·25
~~279~~ – 4 c. green 20 30
~~280~~ – 5 c. blue 15 10
~~281~~ – 10 c. red 30 75
~~282~~ – 12 c. green 1·25 30
~~283~~ 60. 20 c. blue 40 15
284. – 25 c. red 65 40
~~285~~ – 35 c. violet 30 10
~~286~~ – 50 c. green 1·25 50
287. – 1 r. brown 2·00 10
288. – 2 r. 50 orange 7·50 5·50
289. – 5 r. brown 8·50 10·00
290. 67. 10 r. blue 12·00 14·00

DESIGNS—HORIZ. 1 c. Labourdonnais sugar factory. 2 c. Grand Port. 5 c. Rempart Mountain. 10 c. Transporting cane. 12 c. Mauritius dodo and map. 35 c. Government House, Reduit. 1 r. Timor deer. 2 r. 50, Port Louis; 5 r. Beach scene. VERT. 4 c. Tamarind Falls. 25 c. Labourdonnais statue. 50 c. Pieter Both Mountain.

1953. Coronation. As T **13** of Aden.
291 10 c. black and green .. 35 10

69. Historical Museum, Mahebourg.

1953. As 1950 but portrait of Queen Elizabeth II. Designs as for corresponding values except where stated.

No.	Type	Description	Unused	Used
293	–	2 c. red	10	10
294	–	3 c. green	30	40
295	–	4 c. purple (as 1 c.) ..	10	40
296	–	5 c. blue	10	10
297	–	10 c. green (as 4 c.) ..	10	10
298	69.	15 c. red	10	10
299	–	20 c. red (as 25 c.) ..	15	20
300a	–	25 c. blue (as 20 c.) ..	30	10
301	–	35 c. violet	20	10
302	–	50 c. green	45	35
315	–	60 c. green (as 12 c.) ..	1·50	10
303	–	1 r. sepia	30	10
316	–	2 r. 50 orange	2·75	5·00
305	–	5 r. brown	7·50	4·00
306	–	10 r. blue	10·00	60

70. Queen Elizabeth II and King George III (after Lawrence).

1961. 100th Anniv. of British Post Office in Mauritius.

No.	Type	Description	Unused	Used
307	70.	10 c. black and red ..	10	10
308		20 c. ultramarine & blue	15	25
309		35 c. black and yellow ..	20	25
310		1 r. purple and green ..	20	25

1963. Freedom from Hunger. As T **28** of Aden.
311 60 c. violet 40 10

1963. Cent of Red Cross. As T **33** of Antigua.
312 10 c. red and black .. 15 10
313 60 c. red and blue .. 60 20

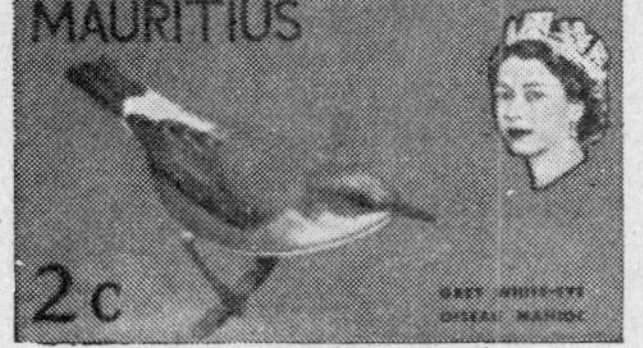

71. Bourbon White Eye.

1965. Birds. Multicoloured.

No.	Description	Unused	Used
317	2 c. Type **71** (yellow background)	10	15
318	3 c. Rodriguez fody (brown background)	10	15
319	4 c. Mauritius olive white eye	10	15
340	5 c. Mascarene paradise flycatcher	10	15
321	10 c. Mauritius fody ..	25	10
322	15 c. Mauritius parkeet (grey background) ..	70	20
323	20 c. Mauritius greybird (yellow background) ..	70	10
324	25 c. Mauritius kestrel ..	80	10
341	35 c. Pink pigeon ..	20	15
326	50 c. Reunion bulbul ..	35	35
327	60 c. Mauritius blue pigeon (extinct) (yellow background) ..	40	10
328	1 r. Mauritius dodo (extinct) (olive background) ..	75	10
329	2 r. 50 Rodriguez solitaire (extinct) ..	4·50	5·00
330	5 r. Mauritius red rail (extinct)	13·00	5·50
331	10 r. Broad-billed parrot (extinct)	18·00	8·00

For some values with background colours changed see Nos. 370/5.

1965. Centenary of I.T.U. As T **36** of Antigua.
332 10 c. orange and green .. 15 10
333 60 c. yellow and violet .. 40 20

1965. I.C.Y. As T **37** of Antigua.
334 10 c. purple and turquoise 15 10
335 60 c. green and violet .. 30 20

1966. Churchill Commem. As T **38** of Antigua.
336 2 c. blue 10 50
337 10 c. green 25 10
338 60 c. brown .. .. 1·10 15
339 1 r. violet .. .. 1·25 15

1966. 20th Anniv of U.N.E.S.C.O. As T **54/6** of Antigua.
342 5 c. multicoloured .. 15 20
343 10 c. yellow, violet & green 25 10
344 60 c. black, purple & orge 50 15

86. Red-tailed Tropic Bird.

1967. Self Government. Multicoloured.
345. 2 c. Type **86** 10 25
346. 10 c. Rodriguez brush warbler 10 10
347. 60 c. Rose-ringed parakeet (extinct) 15 10
348. 1 r. Grey-rumped swiftlet 25 10

1967. Self Government. Nos. 317/31 optd. **SELF GOVERNMENT 1967.**

No.	Type	Description	Unused	Used
349.	71.	2 c. multicoloured ..	10	50
350.	–	3 c. multicoloured ..	10	50
351.	–	4 c. multicoloured ..	10	50
352.	–	5 c. multicoloured ..	10	10
353.	–	10 c. multicoloured ..	10	10
354.	–	15 c. multicoloured ..	10	20
355.	–	20 c. multicoloured ..	15	10
356.	–	25 c. multicoloured ..	15	10
357.	–	35 c. multicoloured ..	20	10
358.	–	50 c. multicoloured ..	25	15
359.	–	60 c. multicoloured ..	25	10
360.	–	1 r. multicoloured ..	35	10
361.	–	2 r. 50 multicoloured ..	1·00	2·00
362.	–	5 r. multicoloured ..	2·50	3·25
363.	–	10 r. multicoloured ..	4·75	7·00

91. Flag of Mauritius.

1968. Independence. Multicoloured.
364. 2 c. Type **91** 10 35
365. 3 c. Arms and Mauritius dodo emblem 10 35
366. 15 c. Type **91** 10 10
367. 20 c. As 3 c. 10 10
368. 60 c. Type **91** 10 10
369. 1 r. As 3 c. 20 10

1968. As Nos. 317/8, 322/3 and 327/8 but background colours changed as below.

No.	Type	Description	Unused	Used
370	71	2 c. olive	20	1·00
371	–	3 c. blue	1·25	1·75
372	–	15 c. brown	55	20
373	–	20 c. buff	2·25	60
374	–	60 c. red	90	15
375	–	1 r. purple	1·75	1·00

93. Dominique rescues Paul and Virginie.

1968. Bicentenary of Bernardin de St. Pierre's Visit to Mauritius. Multicoloured.
376. 2 c. Type **93** 10 40
377. 15 c. Paul and Virginie Crossing the River .. 15 10
378. 50 c. Visit of Labourdonnais to Madame de la Tour .. 25 10
379. 60 c. Meeting of Paul and Virginie in Confidence .. 25 10
380. 1 r. Departure of Virginie for Europe 35 20
381. 2 r. 50 Bernardin de St. Pierre 95 2·25
Nos. 377, 379 and 381 are vert.

99. Batarde.

1969. Multicoloured.

No.	Description	Unused	Used
437	2 c. Type **99**	10	30
383	3 c. Red Reef Crab ..	10	50
384	4 c. Episcopal Mitre ..	90	1·25
440	5 c. Bourse	30	10
386	10 c. black, red and flesh (Starfish)	1·00	10
387	15 c. ochre, black & cobalt (Sea Urchin) ..	30	10
480	20 c. Fiddler Crab ..	30	30
389	25 c. red, black and green (Spiny Shrimp) ..	30	55
390	30 c. Single Harp Shells, and Double Harp Shell ..	1·50	75
483	35 c. Argonaute ..	60	15
484	40 c. Nudibranch ..	75	60
448	50 c. Violet and Orange Spider Shells	45	10
449	60 c. black, red and blue (Blue Marlin) ..	65	10
487	75 c. "Conus clytospira" ..	1·25	40
396	1 r. Dolphin	60	10
452	2 r. 50 Spiny Lobster ..	2·00	3·50
453	5 r. Sacre Chien Rouge ..	3·00	2·00
399	10 r. Croissant Queue Jaune	2·50	4·00

117. Gandhi as Law Student.

1969. Birth Centenary of Mahatma Gandhi. Multicoloured.
400. 2 c. Type **117** 10 10
401. 15 c. Gandhi as Stretcher-bearer during Zulu revolt 20 10
402. 50 c. Gandhi as Satyagrahi in South Africa .. 25 20
403. 60 c. Gandhi at No. 10 Downing Street, London 25 10
404. 1 r. Gandhi in Mauritius, 1901 .. .. .. 30 10
405. 2 r. 50 Gandhi, the "Apostle of Truth and Non Violence" .. .. 80 1·00

124. Frangourinier Cane-crusher (18th cent.).

1969. 150th Anniv. of Telfair's Improvements to the Sugar Industry. Multicoloured.
407. 2 c. Three-roller Vertical Mill 10 20
408. 15 c. Type **124** 10 10
409. 60 c. Beau Rivage Factory, 1867 .. .. .. 10 10
410. 1 r. Mon Desert-Alma Factory, 1969 .. .. 10 10
411. 2 r. 50 Dr. Charles Telfair (vert.) 25 50

1970. Expo 70. Nos. 394 and 396 optd. **EXPO '70' OSAKA.**
413. 60 c. black, red and blue .. 10 10
414. 1 r. multicoloured .. 10 10

129. Morne Plage, Mountain and Lufthansa Airliner.

1970. Inauguration of Lufthansa Flight, Mauritius-Frankfurt. Multicoloured.
415. 25 c. Type **129** 10 10
416. 50 c. Airliner and Map (vert.) 10 10

131. Lenin as a Student.

1970. Birth Centenary of Lenin.
417. **131.** 15 c. green and silver .. 10 10
418. – 75 c. brown .. 20 20
DESIGN: 75 c. Lenin as founder of U.S.S.R.

133. 2d. "Post Office" Mauritius and original Post Office.

1970. Port Louis, Old and New. Mult.
419. 5 c. Type **133** 10 10
420. 15 c. G.P.O. Building (built 1870) 10 10
421. 50 c. Mail Coach (c. 1870) 15 10
422. 75 c. Port Louis Harbour (1970) 20 10
423. 2 r. 50 Arrival of Pierre A. de Suffren (1783) .. 35 60

138. U.N. Emblem and Symbols.

1970. 25th Anniv. of U.N.
425. **138.** 10 c. multicoloured .. 10 10
426. 60 c. multicoloured .. 20 10

139. Rainbow over Waterfall.

1971. Tourism. Multicoloured.
427. 10 c. Type **139** 20 10
428. 15 c. Trois Mamelles Mountains 20 10
429. 60 c. Beach scene 35 10
430. 2 r. 50 Marine life .. .. 1·25 1·50
Nos. 427/30 have inscriptions on the reverse.

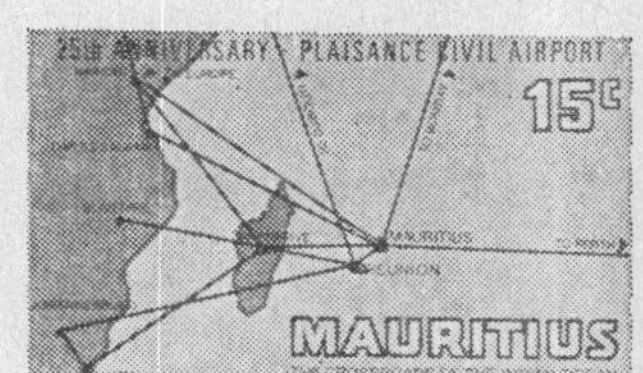

140. "Crossroads" of Indian Ocean.

1971. 25th Anniv. of Plaisance Airport. Multicoloured.
431. 15 c. Type **140** 10 10
432. 60 c. "Boeing 707" and Terminal Buildings .. 25 10
433. 1 r. Air Hostesses on gang-way 30 10
434. 2 r. 50 "Roland Garros" (plane), Choisy Airfield, 1937 .. .. .. 1·50 2·75

141. Princess Margaret Orthopaedic Centre.

1971. 3rd Commonwealth Medical Conference. Multicoloured.
435. 10 c. Type **141** 10 10
436. 75 c. Operating Theatre in National Hospital .. 20 20

142. Queen Elizabeth II and Prince Philip.

1972. Royal Visit. Multicoloured.
455. 15 c. Type **142** 15 10
456. 2 r. 50 Queen Elizabeth II (vert.) .. .. .. 2·00 2·00

143. Theatre Facade.

1972. 150th Anniv. of Port Louis Theatre. Multicoloured.
457. 10 c. Type **143** 10 10
458. 1 r. Theatre auditorium .. 30 10

144. Pirate Dhow.

1972. Pirates and Privateers. Multicoloured.
459. 15 c. Type **144** 45 10
460. 60 c. Treasure chest (vert.) 75 15
461. 1 r. Lememe and "L'Hirondelle" (vert.) 90 15
462. 2 r. 50 Robert Surcouf .. 3·50 5·50

145. Mauritius University.

1973. 5th Anniv. of Independence. Mult.
463. 15 c. Type **145** 10 10
464. 60 c. Tea Development .. 10 10
465. 1 r. Bank of Mauritius .. 10 10

146. Map and Hands.

1973. O.C.A.M. Conf. Multicoloured.
466. 10 c. O.C.A.M. emblem (horiz.) 10 10
467. 2 r. 50 Type **146** 40 45

O.C.A.M. = Organization Commune Africaine Malgache et Mauricienne.

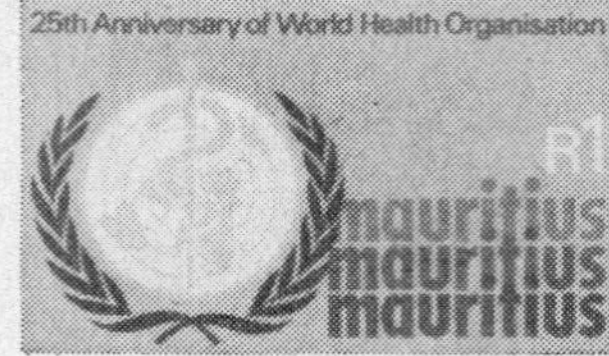

147. W.H.O. Emblem.

1973. 25th Anniv. of W.H.O.
468. **147.** 1 r. multicoloured .. 10 10

148. Meteorological Station, Vacoas.

1973. Centenary of I.M.O./W.M.O.
469. **148.** 75 c. multicoloured .. 20 30

149. Capture of the "Kent" 1800.

1973. Birth Bicentenary of Robert Surcouf (privateer).
470. **149.** 60 c. multicoloured .. 40 50

150. P. Commerson.

1974. Death Bicentenary (1973) of Philibert Commerson (naturalist).
471. **150.** 2 r. 50 multicoloured 30 40

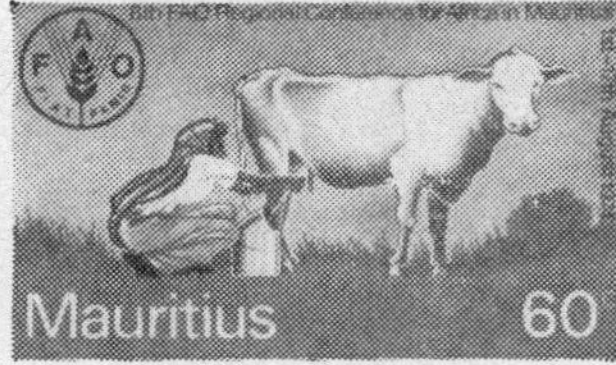

151. Cow being Milked.

1974. Eighth Regional Conf. for Africa, Mauritius.
472. **151.** 60 c. multicoloured .. 10 10

152. Mail Train.

1974. Centenary of U.P.U. Multicoloured.
473. 15 c. Type **152** 40 15
474. 1 r. New G.P.O., Port Louis 40 20

153. "Cottage Life" (F. Leroy).

1975. Aspects of Mauritian Life. Paintings. Multicoloured.
493. 15 c. Type **153** 10 10
494. 60 c. "Milk Seller" (A. Richard) (vert.) .. 30 10
495. 1 r. "Entrance of Port Louis Market" (Thuillier) 30 10
496. 2 r. 50 "Washerwomen" (Max Boulle) (vert.) .. 85 60

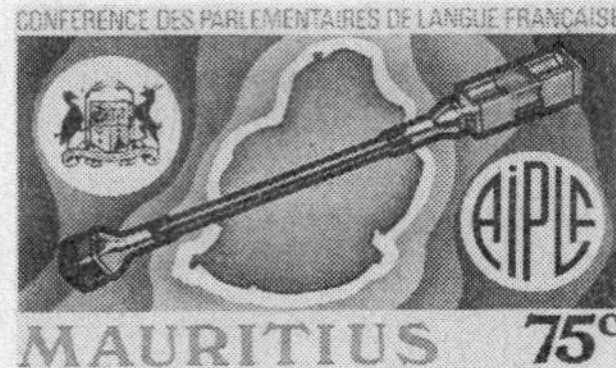

154. Mace across Map.

1975. French-speaking Parliamentary Assemblies Conf., Port Louis.
497. **154.** 75 c. multicoloured .. 30 45

155. Woman with Lamp ("The Light of the World").

1976. International Women's Year.
498. **155.** 2 r. 50 multicoloured .. 35 1·00

156. Parched Landscape.

1976. Drought in Africa. Multicoloured.
499. 50 c. Type **156** 15 15
500. 60 c. Map of Africa and carcass (vert.) 15 15

157. "Pierre Loti", 1953–70.

1976. Mail Carriers to Mauritius. Mult.
501. 10 c. Type **157** 15 10
502. 15 c. "Secunder", 1907 .. 20 10
503. 50 c. "Hindoostan", 1842 45 15
504. 60 c. "St. Geran", 1740 .. 50 15
505. 2 r. 50 "Maen", 1638 .. 2·00 4·00

158. "The Flame of Hindi carried across the Seas".

1976. Second World Hindi Convention. Multicoloured.
507. 10 c. Type **158** 10 10
508. 75 c. Type **158** 10 15
509. 1 r. 20 Hindi script .. 20 40

159. Conference Logo and Map of Mauritius.

1976. 22nd Commonwealth Parliamentary Conf. Multicoloured.
510. 1 r. Type **159** 25 10
511. 2 r. Conference logo .. 70 80

160. King Priest and Breastplate.

1976. Moenjodaro Excavations, Pakistan. Multicoloured.
512. 60 c. Type **160** 15 10
513. 1 r. House with well and goblet 30 10
514. 2 r. 50 Terracotta figurine and necklace 90 45

161. Sega Scene.

1977. 2nd World Black and African Festival of Arts and Culture, Nigeria.
515. **161.** 1 r. multicoloured .. 30 15

162. The Queen with Sceptre and Rod.

1977. Silver Jubilee. Multicoloured.
516. 50 c. The Queen at Mauritius Legislative Assembly 1972 20 10
517. 75 c. Type **162** 25 10
518. 5 r. Presentation of Sceptre and Rod 75 75

163. "Hugonia tomentosa".

1977. Indigenous Flowers. Multicoloured.
519. 20 c. Type **163** 10 10
520. 1 r. "Ochna mauritiana" (vert.) 20 10
521. 1 r. 50 "Dombeya acutangula" 30 20
522. 5 r. "Trochetia blackburniana" (vert.) .. 1·00 1·25

164. "Twin Otter".

1977. Air. Mauritius Inaugural Int. Flight. Multicoloured.
524. 25 c. Type **164** 15 10
525. 50 c. " Twin Otter " and Air Mauritius emblem .. 20 10
526. 75 c. Piper " Navajo " and Boeing " 747 " .. 30 10
527. 5 r. Boeing " 707 " .. 1·60 1·50

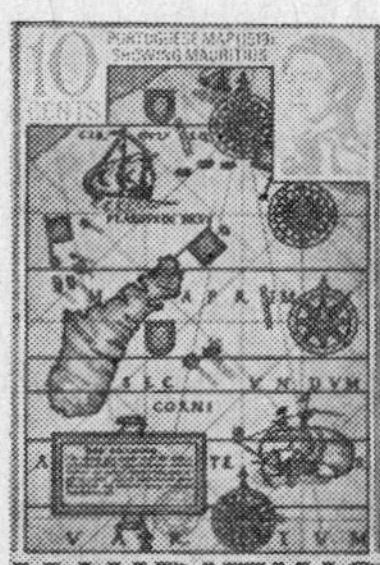

165. Portuguese Map of Mauritius, 1519.

1978.
529 **165.** 10 c. multicoloured .. 20 20
530 – 15 c. multicoloured .. 30 30
740 – 20 c. multicoloured .. 20 20
741 – 25 c. multicoloured .. 20 20
533 – 35 c. multicoloured .. 20 20
534 – 50 c. multicoloured .. 20 20
535 – 60 c. multicoloured .. 30 30
536 – 70 c. multicoloured .. 30 30
537 – 75 c. multicoloured .. 30 10
538 – 90 c. multicoloured .. 30 30
539 – 1 r. multicoloured .. 30 10
540 – 1 r. 20 multicoloured .. 35 35
541 – 1 r. 25 multicoloured .. 40 10
542 – 1 r. 50 multicoloured .. 35 15
752 – 2 r. multicoloured .. 35 20
544 – 3 r. multicoloured .. 50 30
545 – 5 r. multicoloured .. 60 50
546 – 10 r. multicoloured .. 90 90
547 – 15 r. multicoloured .. 1·00 1·10
548 – 25 r. grn., blk. & brn... 2·00 2·25

DESIGNS—HORIZ. 15 c. Scene of Dutch Occupation. 20 c. Map by Van Keulen, c. 1700. 50 c. Construction of Port Louis, c. 1736. 70 c. Map by Belin, 1763. 90 c. Battle of Grand Port, 1810. 1 r. Landing of the British, 1810. 1 r. 20, Government House c. 1840. 1 r. 50, Indian immigration to Mauritius, 1835. 2 r. Race Course (Champ de Mars), c. 1870. 3 r. Place d'Armes, c. 1880. 5 r. Royal Visit postcard, 1901. 10 r. Royal College of Curepipe, 1914. 25 r. First Mauritian Governor-General and First Prime Minister of Mauritius. VERT. 25 c. First settlement on Rodrigues, 1691. 35 c. Arrival of French settlers in Mauritius, 1715. 60 c. Pierre Poivre and the nutmeg tree. 75 c. First coin minted in Mauritius. 1 r. 25, Invitation and ball of Lady Gomm, 1847. 15 r. Unfurling of Mauritian flag.

166. Mauritius Dodo.

1978. 25th Anniv. of Coronation.
549. – 3 r. grey, black and blue 25 45
550. – 3 r. multicoloured .. 25 45
551. **166.** 3 r. grey, black and blue 25 45
DESIGNS: No. 549, Antelope of Bohun. No. 550, Queen Elizabeth II.

167. Problem of Infection, World War I.

1978. 50th Anniv. of Discovery of Penicillin.
552. **167.** 20 c. multicoloured .. 20 10
553. – 1 r. multicoloured .. 50 10
554. – 1 r. 50 black, brown and green 75 20
555. – 5 r. multicoloured .. 1·60 2·00
DESIGNS: 1 r. Microscope and first mould growth, 1928. 1 r. 50, Mould " penicillium notatum ". 5 r. Sir Alexander Fleming and nurse administering injection.

168. "Papilio manlius" (butterfly).

1978. World Wildlife. Multicoloured.
557. 20 c. Type **168** 20 10
558. 1 r. Geckos 20 10
559. 1 r. 50, Greater Mascarene flying fox 30 30
560. 5 r. Mauritius kestrel .. 2·25 2·75

169. Ornate Table.

1978. Bicentenary of Reconstruction of Chateau Le Reduit. Multicoloured.
562. 15 c. Type **169** 10 10
563. 75 c. Chateau Le Reduit .. 10 10
564. 3 r. Le Reduit gardens .. 30 45

170. Whitcomb Diesel Locomotive, "65 H.P." 1949.

1979. Railway Locomotives. Multicoloured.
565. 20 c. Type **170** 10 10
566. 1 r. " Sir William " 1922 .. 25 10
567. 1 r. 50 Kitson type 1930 .. 35 45
568. 2 r. Garratt type, 1927 .. 50 85

171. Father Laval and Crucifix.

1979. Beatification of Father Laval. Mult.
570. 20 c. Type **171** 10 10
571. 1 r. 50 Father Laval .. 10 10
572. 5 r. Father Laval's Tomb (horiz.) 35 50

172. Astronaut descending from Lunar Module.

1979. 10th Anniv. of Moon Landing. Multicoloured. Self-adhesive.
574. 20 c. Type **172** 15 15
575. 3 r. Astronaut performing experiment on moon .. 70 90
576. 5 r. Astronaut on Moon .. 2·00 3·25

173. Great Britain 1855 4d. Stamp and Sir Rowland Hill.

1979. Death Centenary of Sir Rowland Hill. Multicoloured.
577. 25 c. Type **173** 10 10
578. 2 r. 1954 60 c. definitive .. 45 40
579. 5 r. 1847 1d. "POST OFFICE" 90 1·00

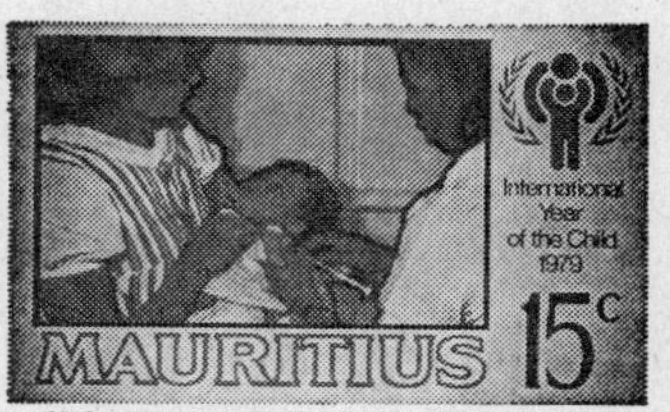

174. Young Child being Vaccinated.

1979. International Year of the Child.
581. **174.** 15 c. multicoloured .. 10 10
582. – 25 c. multicoloured .. 10 10
583. – 1 r. black, blue and bright blue 10 10
584. – 1 r. 50 multicoloured .. 20 20
585. – 3 r. multicoloured .. 35 50
DESIGNS—HORIZ. 25 c. Children playing. 1 r. 50, Girls in Chemistry laboratory. 3 r. Boy operating lathe. VERT. 1 r. I.Y.C. emblem.

175. The Lienard Obelisk.

1980. Pamplemousses Botanical Gardens. Multicoloured.
586. 20 c. Type **175** 10 10
587. 25 c. Poivre Avenue .. 10 10
588. 1 r. Varieties of Vacoas .. 20 10
589. 2 r. Giant water lilies .. 35 35
590. 5 r. Mon Plaisir (mansion) 60 1·00

176. " Emirne ".

1980. " London 1980 " International Stamp Exhibition. Mailships. Multicoloured.
592. 25 c. Type **176** 10 10
593. 1 r. " Boissevain " .. 20 10
594. 2 r. " La Boudeuse " .. 35 10
595. 5 r. " Sea Breeze " .. 55 55

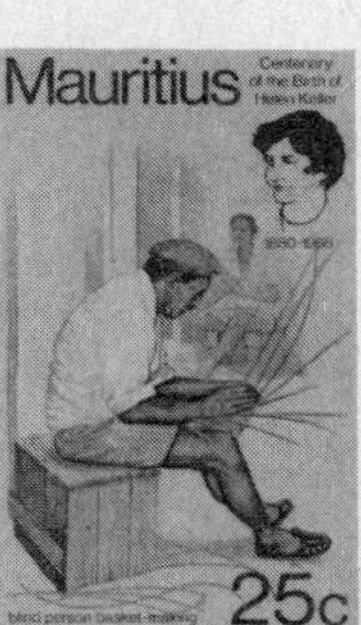

177. Blind Person Basket-making.

1980. Birth Centenary of Helen Keller (campaigner for the handicapped). Mult.
596 25 c. Type **177** 10 10
597. 1 r. Deaf child under instruction 30 10
598. 2 r. 50 Helen reading braille 50 25
599. 5 r. Helen at graduation, 1904 .. .. .. 90 70

178. Prime Minister Sir Seewoosagur Ramgoolam.

1980. 80th Birthday and 40th Year in Parliament of Prime Minister Sir Seewoosagur Ramgoolam.
600. **178.** 15 r. multicoloured .. 1·25 1·40

179. Headquarters, Mauritius Institute.

1980. Centenary of Mauritius Institute. Multicoloured.
501. 25 c. Type **179** 10 10
502. 2 r. Rare copy of Veda .. 25 10
503. 2 r. 50 Rare cone 30 15
504. 5 r. " Le Torrent " (painting, Harpignies) 45 50

180. " Hibiscus liliiflorus ".

1981. Flowers. Multicoloured.
605. 25 c. Type **180** 10 10
606. 2 r. " Erythrospermum monticolum " 35 40
607. 2 r. 50 " Chasalia boryana " 45 50
608. 5 r. " Hibiscus columnaris " 85 1·25

181. Beau-Bassin/Rose Hill.

1981. Mauritius. Coats of Arms. Mult.
609. 25 c. Type **181** 10 10
610. 1 r. 50 Curepipe 25 20
611. 2 r. Quatre-Bornes .. 30 25
612. 2 r. 50 Vacoas/Phoenix .. 35 30
613. 5 r. Port Louis 65 55

182. Prince Charles as Colonel-in-Chief, Royal Regiment of Wales.

1981. Royal Wedding. Multicoloured.
615. 25 c. Wedding bouquet from Mauritius .. 10 10
616. 2 r. 50 Type **182** .. 55 15
617. 10 r. Prince Charles and Lady Diana Spencer .. 1·40 90

183. Emmanuel Anquetil and Guy Rozemont.

1981. Famous Politicians and Physician.
618. **183.** 20 c. black and red .. 10 10
619. – 25 c. black and yellow .. 10 10
620. – 1 r. 25 black and green 25 15
621. – 1 r. 50 black and red .. 30 15
622. – 2 r. black and blue .. 40 20
623. – 2 r. 50 black and brown 45 25
624. – 5 r. black and blue .. 80 70
DESIGNS: 25 c. Remy Ollier and Sookdes Bissoondoyal. 1 r. 25, Maurice Cure and Barthelemy Ohsan. 1 r. 50, Sir Guy Forget and Renganaden Seeneevassen. 2 r. Sir Abdul Razak Mohamed and Jules Koeing. 2 r. 50, Abdoollatiff Mahomed Osman and Dazzi Rama (Pandit Sahadeo). 5 r. Sir Thomas Lewis (physician) and electrocardiogram.

184. Drummer and Piper.

1981. Religion and Culture. Multicoloured.
625. 20 c. Type **184** 10 10
626. 2 r. Swami Sivananda (vert.) 45 50
627. 5 r. Chinese Pagoda .. 75 1·75
The 20 c. value commemorates the World Tamil Culture Conference (1980).

185. " Skills ".

1981. 25th Anniv. of Duke of Edinburgh Award Scheme. Multicoloured.
628. 25 c. Type **185** 10 10
629. 1 r. 25 " Service " .. 10 10
630. 5 r. " Expeditions " .. 25 30
631. 10 r. Duke of Edinburgh .. 50 70

186. Kaaba (sacred shrine, Great Mosque of Mecca.)

1981. Moslem Year 1400 A.H. Commemoration. Multicoloured.
632. 25 c. Type **186** 10 10
633. 2 r. Mecca 40 50
634. 5 r. Mecca and Kaaba .. 85 1·60

187. Scout Emblem.

1982. 75th Anniv. of Boy Scout Movement and 70th Anniv. of Scouting in Mauritius.
635. **187.** 25 c. lilac and green .. 10 10
636. – 2 r. brown and ochre .. 30 30
637. – 5 r. green and olive .. 70 1·00
638. – 10 r. green and blue .. 1·25 2·00
DESIGNS: 2 r. Lord Baden-Powell and Baden-Powell House. 5 r. Grand Howl. 10 r. Ascent of Pieter Both.

188. Charles Darwin.

1982. 150th Anniv. of Charles Darwin's Voyage. Multicoloured.
639. 25 c. Type **188** 10 10
640. 2 r. Darwin's telescope .. 30 45
641. 2 r. 50 Darwin's elephant ride 35 55
642. 10 r. H.M.S. "Beagle" beached for repairs .. 1·40 2·50

189. Bride and Groom at Buckingham Palace.

1982. 21st Birthday of Princess of Wales. Multicoloured.
643. 25 c. Mauritius coat of arms 10 10
644. 2 r. 50 Princess Diana in Chesterfield, November, 1981 .. .. 45 35
645. 5 r. Type **189** 75 80
646. 10 r. Formal portrait .. 1·25 1·75

190. Prince and Princess of Wales with Prince William.

1982. Birth of Prince William of Wales.
647. **190.** 2 r. 50 multicoloured .. 55 30

191. Bois Fandamane Plant.

1982. Centenary of Robert Koch's Discovery of Tubercle Bacillus. Multicoloured.
648. 25 c. Type **191** 10 10
649. 1 r. 25 Central market, Port Louis 30 30
650. 2 r. Bois Banane plant .. 45 45
651. 5 r. Platte de Lezard plant 95 1·40
652. 10 r. Dr. Robert Koch .. 1·75 2·50

192. Arms and Flag of Mauritius.

1983. Commonwealth Day. Multicoloured.
653. 25 c. Type **192** 10 10
654. 2 r. 50 Satellite view of Mauritius .. 15 30
655. 5 r. Harvesting sugar cane 30 75
656. 10 r. Port Louis harbour .. 70 1·50

193. Early Wall-mounted Telephone. 194. Map of Namibia.

1983. World Communications Year. Mult.
657. 25 c. Type **193** 10 10
658. 1 r. 25 Early telegraph apparatus (horiz.) .. 40 15
659. 2 r. Earth satellite station 70 40
660. 10 r. First hot air balloon in Mauritius, 1784 (horiz.) 2·00 2·50

1983. Namibia Day. Multicoloured.
661. 25 c. Type **194** 20 10
662. 2 r. 50 Hand breaking chains 70 45
663. 5 r. Family and settlement 1·25 1·25
664. 10 r. Diamond mining .. 2·00 2·50

195. Fish Trap. 196. Swami Dayananda.

1983. Fishery Resources. Multicoloured.
665. 25 c. Type **195** 15 10
666. 1 r. Fishing boat (horiz.) .. 45 15
667. 5 r. Game fishing .. .. 1·25 1·25
668. 10 r. Octopus drying (horiz.) 1·25 2·50

1983. Death Centenary of Swami Dayananda. Multicoloured.
669. 25 c. Type **196** 10 10
670. 35 c. Last meeting with father 10 10
671. 2 r. Receiving religious instruction 30 35
672. 5 r. Swami demonstrating strength .. .. 70 1·25
673. 10 r. At a religious gathering .. .. .. 1·10 2·50

197. Adolf von Plevitz, 1837–93.

1983. 125th Anniv. of Adolf von Plevitz (reformer). Multicoloured.
674. 25 c. Type **197** 10 10
675. 1 r. 25 La Laura, Government school 30 30
676. 5 r. Von Plevitz addressing Commission of Enquiry, 1872 .. .. .. 90 1·25
677. 10 r. Von Plevitz with Indian farm workers .. 1·50 2·25

198. Courtship Chase.

1984. The Mauritius Kestrel. Multicoloured.
678. 25 c. Type **198** 45 10
679. 2 r. Kestrel in tree (vert.) .. 1·00 65
680. 2 r. 50 Young Kestrel .. 1·25 90
681. 10 r. Head (vert.) .. .. 2·75 4·00

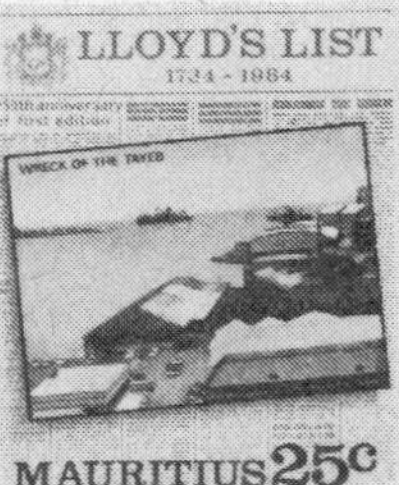

199. Wreck of S.S. " Tayeb ".

1984. 250th Anniv. of "Lloyd's List" (newspaper). Multicoloured.
682. 25 c. Type **199** 15 10
683. 1 r. S.S. " Taher " 55 15
684. 5 r. East Indiaman " Triton " 1·50 2·00
685. 10 r. M.S. " Astor " .. 2·00 3·00

200. Blue Latan Palm.

1984. Palm Trees. Multicoloured.
686. 25 c. Type **200** 10 10
687. 50 c. "Hyophorbe vaughanii" 20 15
688. 2 r. 50 "Tectiphiala ferox" 1·25 65
689. 5 r. Round Island Bottle-palm .. .. .. 2·00 2·25
690. 10 r. "Hyophorbe amaricaulis" .. .. .. 3·25 3·75

201. Slave Girl.

1984. 150th Anniv. of Abolition of Slavery and Introduction of Indian Immigrants.
691. **201.** 25 c. purple, lilac and brown 10 10
692. – 1 r. purple, lilac and brown 40 10
693. – 2 r. purple and lilac .. 75 50
694. – 10 r. purple and lilac 2·50 3·00
DESIGNS—VERT. 1 r. Slave market. HORIZ. 2 r. Indian immigrant family. 10 r. Arrival of Indian immigrants.

HAVE YOU READ THE NOTES AT THE BEGINNING OF THIS CATALOGUE?
These often provide answers to the enquiries we receive.

202. 75th Anniversary Production of "Faust" and Leoville L'Homme.

1984. Centenary of Alliance Francaise (cultural organization). Multicoloured.

695.	25 c. Type **202**	15	10
696.	1 r. 25 Prize-giving ceremony and Aunauth Beejadbur	40	40
697.	5 r. First headquarters and Hector Clarenc	1·25	1·60
698.	10 r. Lion Mountain and Labourdonnais	1·75	2·50

203. The Queen Mother on Clarence House Balcony, 1980.

1985. Life and Times of Queen Elizabeth the Queen Mother. Multicoloured.

699.	25 c. The Queen Mother in 1926	10	10
700.	2 r. With Princess Margaret at Trooping the Colour	30	30
701.	5 r. Type **203**	60	1·00
702.	10 r. With Prince Henry at his christening (from photo by Lord Snowdon)	1·10	1·75

204. High Jumping.

1985. 2nd Indian Ocean Islands Games. Multicoloured.

704.	25 c. Type **204**	15	10
705.	50 c. Javelin-throwing ..	25	15
706.	1 r. 25, Cycling	55	45
707.	10 r. Wind surfing	2·50	3·00

205. Adult and Fledgling Pink Pigeons.

1985. Pink Pigeon. Multicoloured.

708.	25 c. Type **205**	50	15
709.	2 r. Pink Pigeon displaying at nest	1·25	75
710.	2 r. 50, On nest	1·50	1·10
711.	5 r. Pair preening	2·25	2·75

206. Caverne Patates, Rodrigues.

1985. 10th Anniv. of World Tourism Organization. Multicoloured.

712.	25 c. Type **206**	20	10
713.	35 c. Coloured soils, Chamarel	20	10
714.	5 r. Serpent Island ..	1·75	2·00
715.	10 r. Coin de Mire Island ..	2·75	3·25

207. Old Town Hall, Port Louis.

1985. 250th Anniv. of Port Louis. Mult.

716.	25 c. Type **207**	10	10
717.	1 r. Al-Aqsa Mosque (180th anniv.)	25	10
718.	2 r. 50, Vase and trees (250th anniv. of settlement of Tamil-speaking Indians)	55	40
719.	10 r. Port Louis Harbour	1·50	2·50

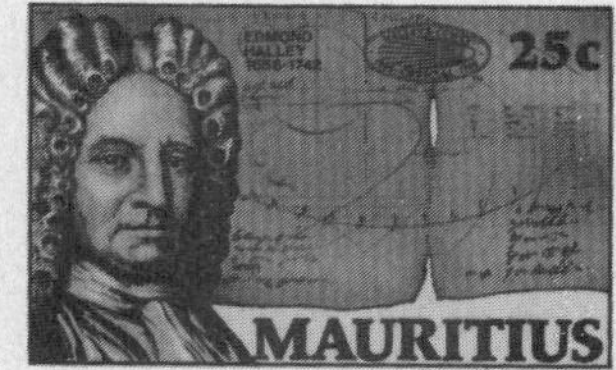

208. Edmond Halley and Diagram.

1986. Appearance of Halley's Comet. Mult.

720.	25 c. Type **208**	10	10
721.	1 r. 25 Halley's Comet (1682) and Newton's Reflector	30	20
722.	3 r. Halley's Comet passing Earth	65	50
723.	10 r. "Giotto" spacecraft ..	1·50	2·00

1986. 60th Birthday of Queen Elizabeth II. As T **110** of Ascension. Multicoloured.

724.	25 c. Princess Elizabeth wearing Badge of Grenadier Guards, 1942.	10	10
725.	75 c. Investiture of Prince of Wales, 1969	10	10
726.	2 r. With Prime Minister of Mauritius, 1972	20	25
727.	3 r. In Germany, 1978 ..	30	35
728.	15 r. At Crown Agents Head Office, London, 1983	1·50	1·75

209. Maize (World Food Day).

1986. International Events. Multicoloured.

729.	25 c. Type **209**	10	10
730.	1 r. African Regional Industrial Property Organization emblem (10th anniv.)	30	10
731.	1 r. 25 International Peace Year emblem	45	20
732.	10 r. Footballer and Mauritius Football Association emblem (World Cup Football Championship, Mexico)	2·25	2·25

210. "Cryptopus elatus".

1986. Orchids. Multicoloured.

733.	25 c. Type **210**	30	10
734.	2 r. "Jumellea recta" ..	90	40
735.	2 r. 50 "Angraecum mauritianum"	1·10	50
736.	10 r. "Bulbophyllum longiflorum"	2·25	2·50

211. Hesketh Bell Bridge.

1987. Mauritius Bridges. Multicoloured.

758.	25 c. Type **211**	15	10
759.	50 c. Sir Colville Deverell Bridge	20	10
760.	2 r. 50 Cavendish Bridge ..	70	45
761.	5 r. Tamarin Bridge ..	1·25	1·25
762.	10 r. Grand River North West Bridge	2·00	2·25

212. Supreme Court, Port Louis.

1987. Bicentenary of the Mauritius Bar. Multicoloured.

763.	25 c. Type **212**	10	10
764.	1 r. District Court, Flacq	20	10
765.	1 r. 25 Statue of Justice ..	30	20
766.	10 r. Barristers of 1787 and 1987	1·25	1·50

213. Mauritius Dodo Mascot.

1987. International Festival of the Sea. Multicoloured.

767.	25 c. Type **213**	10	10
768.	1 r. 50 Yacht regatta (horiz.)	50	30
769.	3 r. Water skiing (horiz.) ..	90	65
770.	5 r. "Svanen" (barquentine)	1·40	1·40

214. Toys.

1987. Industrialization. Multicoloured.

771.	20 c. Type **214**	10	10
772.	35 c. Spinning factory ..	10	10
773.	50 c. Rattan furniture ..	10	10
774.	2 r. 50 Spectacle factory ..	55	45
775.	10 r. Stone carving ..	1·60	1·75

215. Maison Ouvriere (Int. Year of Shelter for the Homeless).

1987. Art and Architecture.

776.	**215.**	25 c. multicoloured ..	10	10
777.	–	1 r. black and grey ..	10	10
778.	–	1 r. 25 multicoloured	15	15
779.	–	2 r. multicoloured ..	30	30
780.	–	5 r. multicoloured ..	75	80

DESIGNS: 1 r. "Paul and Virginie" (lithograph). 1 r. 25, Chateau de Rosnay; 2 r. "Vielle Ferme" (Boulle). 5 r. "Trois Mamelles".

216. University of Mauritius.

1988. 20th Anniv. of Independence. Mult.

781.	25 c. Type **216**	10	10
782.	75 c. Anniversary gymnastic display ..	15	10
783.	2 r. 50 Hurdlers and aerial view of Sir Maurice Rault Stadium	45	35
784.	5 r. Air. Mauritius aircraft at Sir Seewoosagur Ramgoolam International Airport ..	90	90
785.	10 r. Governor-General Sir Veerasamy Ringadoo and Prime Minister Anerood Jugnauth ..	1·60	1·75

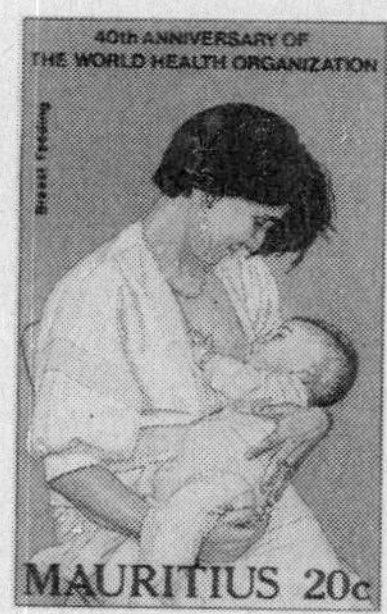

217 Breast Feeding

1988. 40th Anniv of W.H.O. Multicoloured.

786	20 c. Type **217**	10	10
787	2 r. Baby under vaccination umbrella and germ droplets	60	40
788	3 r. Nutritious food ..	70	60
789	10 r. W.H.O. logo ..	1·75	2·00

218 Modern Bank Building

1988. 150th Anniv of Mauritius Commercial Bank Ltd.

790	**218**	25 c. black, green & bl	10	10
791	–	1 r. black and red ..	15	10
792	–	1 r.25 multicoloured ..	20	20
793	–	25 r. multicoloured ..	3·75	4·00

DESIGNS: HORIZ—1 r. Mauritius Commercial Bank, 1897; 25 r. Fifteen dollar bank note of 1838. VERT—1 r.25, Bank arms.

219 Olympic Rings and Athlete

1988. Olympic Games, Seoul. Multicoloured.

794	25 c. Type **219**	10	10
795	35 c. Wrestling	10	10
796	1 r.50 Long distance running	40	30
797	10 r. Swimming	1·75	2·25

220 Nature Park

1989. Protection of the Environment. Mult.

799	15 c. Underwater view ..	10	10
806	30 c. Greenshank ..	10	10
800	40 c. Type **220**	10	10
808	50 c. Round Island (vert)	10	10
809	75 c. Bassin Blanc ..	10	10
810	1 r. Mangrove (vert) ..	10	10
801	1 r. 50 Whimbel ..	10	15
811	2 r. Le Morne	15	20
802	3 r. Marine life	20	25
803	4 r. Fern tree (vert) ..	30	35
812	5 r. Riviere du Poste estuary	35	40
804	6 r. Ecological scenery (vert)	40	45
813	10 r. "Phelsuma ornata" (gecko) on plant (vert)	70	75
814	15 r. Benares waves ..	1·10	1·25
805	25 r. Migratory birds and map (vert)	1·75	1·90

221 La Tour Sumeire, Port Louis

1989. Bicentenary of the French Revolution.

818	**221**	30 c. black, grn & yell	10	10
819	–	1 r. black, brown and light brown ..	20	10
820	–	8 r. multicoloured ..	1·25	1·25
821	–	15 r. multicoloured ..	2·00	2·00

DESIGNS: 1 r. Salle de Spectacle du Jardin; 8 r. Portrait of Comte de Malartic; 15 r. Bicentenary logo.

222 Cardinal Jean Margeot

1989. Visit of Pope John Paul II. Mult.

822	30 c. Type **222**	15	10
823	40 c. Pope John Paul II and Prime Minister Jugnauth, Vatican, 1988	20	15
824	3 r. Marie Magdeleine de la Croix and Chapelle des Filles de Marie, Port Louis, 1864 ..	40	40
825	6 r. St. Francis of Assise Church, Pamplemousses, 1756	1·00	1·00
826	10 r. Pope John Paul II ..	1·75	1·75

223 Nehru

1989. Birth Centenary of Jawaharlal Nehru (Indian statesman). Multicoloured.

827	40 c. Type **223**	15	10
828	1 r. 50 Nehru with daughter, Indira, and grandsons	30	30
829	3 r. Nehru and Gandhi ..	75	75
830	4 r. Nehru with Presidents Nasser and Tito ..	1·00	1·00
831	10 r. Nehru with children	2·25	2·50

224 Cane Cutting

1990. 350th Anniv of Introduction of Sugar Cane to Mauritius. Multicolored.

832	30 c. Type **224** ..	10	10
833	40 c. Sugar factory, 1867 ..	10	10
834	1 r. Mehanical loading of cane	15	10
835	25 r. Modern sugar factory	3·25	3·75

225 Industrial Estate

1990. 60th Birthday of Prime Minister Sir Anerood Jugnauth. Multicoloured.

836	35 c. Type **225**	10	10
837	40 c. Sir Anerood Jugnauth at desk	10	10
838	1 r. 50 Mauritius Stock Exchange symbol	15	15
839	4 r. Jugnauth with Sir Seewoosagur Ramgoolam (former Governor-General)	55	55
840	10 r. Jugnauth greeting Pope John Paul II ..	1·25	1·50

226 Desjardins (naturalist) (150th death anniv)

1990. Anniversaries. Multicoloured.

841	30 c. Type **226**	10	10
842	35 c. Logo on TV screen (25th anniv of Mauritius Broadcasting Corporation) (horiz) ..	10	10
843	6 r. Line Barracks (now Police Headquarters) (250th anniv)	70	70
844	8 r. Town Hall, Curepipe (centenary of municipality) (horiz)	90	90

227 Letters from Alphabets

1990. International Literacy Year. Mult.

845	30 c. Type **227**	10	10
846	1 r. Blind child reading Braille	15	10
847	3 r. Open book and globe	40	40
848	10 r. Book showing world map with quill pen ..	1·25	1·40

1991. 65th Birthday of Queen Elizabeth II and 70th Birthday of Prince Philip. As T **139** of Ascension. Multicoloured.

849	8 r. Queen Elizabeth II ..	90	90
850	8 r. Prince Philip in Grenadier Guards ceremonial uniform ..	90	90

228 City Hall, Port Louis (25th anniv of City status)

1991. Anniversaries and Events. Mult.

851	40 c. Type **228**	10	10
852	4 r. Colonel Draper (race course founder) (150th death anniv) (vert) ..	50	50
853	6 r. Joseph Barnard (engraver) and "POST PAID" 2d. stamp (175th birth anniv) (vert) ..	65	65
854	10 r. Spitfire "Mauritius II" (50th anniv of Second World War) ..	1·10	1·25

229 "Euploea euphon"

1991. "Philanippon '91" International Stamp Exhibition, Tokyo. Butterflies. Mult.

855	40 c. Type **229**	10	10
856	3 r. "Hypolimnas misippus" (female)	20	25
857	8 r. "Papilio manlius" ..	60	65
858	10 r. "Hypolimnas misippus" (male)	70	75

230 Green Turtle, Tromelin

1991. Indian Ocean Islands. Multicoloured.

859	40 c. Type **230**	10	10
860	1 r. Ibis, Agalega ..	10	10
861	2 r. Takamaka flowers, Chagos Archipelago ..	15	20
862	15 r. "Lambis violacea" sea shell, St. Brandon ..	1·10	1·25

231 Pres. Veerasamy Ringadoo and President's Residence

1992. Proclamation of Republic. Mult.

863	40 c. Type **231**	10	10
864	4 r. Prime Minister Anerood Jugnauth and Government House ..	30	35
865	8 r. Children and rainbow	60	65
866	10 r. Presidential flag ..	70	75

EXPRESS DELIVERY STAMPS

1903. No. 136 surch. **EXPRESS DELIVERY 15 c.**

E 1. **40.**	15 c. on 15 c. blue ..	4·00	14·00

1903. No. 136 surch. **EXPRESS DELIVERY (INLAND) 15 c.**

E 3. **40.**	15 c. on 15 c. blue ..	4·00	85

1904. T 18 without value in label. (a) Surch. **(FOREIGN) EXPRESS DELIVERY 18 CENTS.**

E5 **42**	18 c. green	1·50	10·00

(b) Surch. **EXPRESS DELIVERY. (INLAND) 15 c.**

E6 **42**	15 c. green	1·00	1·25

POSTAGE DUE STAMPS

D 1.

1933.

D 1	D 1.	2 c. black	35	50
D 2		4 c. violet	40	65
D 3		6 c. red	40	80
D 4		10 c. green	40	70
D 5		20 c. blue	50	90
D 6		50 c. purple	40	6·50
D 7		1 r. orange	65	9·00

1982. Nos. 530/1, 535, 540, 542 and 547 surch. **POSTAGE DUE** and value.

D 14.	10 c. on 15 c. Dutch Occupation, 1638–1710 ..	10	10
D 15.	20 c. on 20 c. Van Keulen's map, c. 1700	10	10
D 16.	50 c. on 60 c. Pierre Poivre, c. 1767 (vert.)	10	10
D 17.	1 r. on 1 r. 20 Government House, c. 1840 ..	10	10
D 18.	1 r. 50 on 1 r. 50 Indian immigration, 1835 ..	10	10
D 19.	5 r. on 15 r. Unfurling Mauritian flag, 1968 ..	30	35

MONTSERRAT

One of the Leeward Is., Br. W. Indies. Used general issues for Leeward Is. concurrently with Montserrat stamps until 1 July 1956, when Leeward Is. stamps were withdrawn.

1876. 12 pence = 1 shilling; 20 shillings = 1 pound.
1951. 100 cents = 1 West Indian dollar.

1876. Stamps of Antigua as T 1 optd **MONTSERRAT**.

1	1d. red	18·00	15·00
2	6d. green	55·00	40·00

3.

1880.

6. 3.	½d. green	1·00	5·50
9.	2½d. brown	£225	65·00
10.	2½d. blue	14·00	16·00
5.	4d. blue	£140	40·00
12.	4d. mauve	3·00	3·00

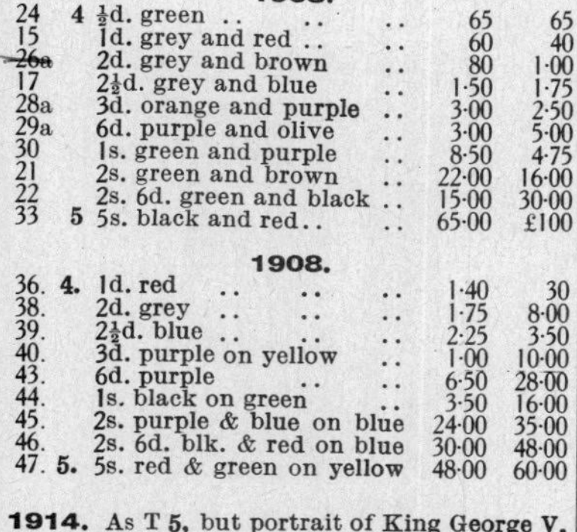

4. Device of the Colony. 5.

1903.

24 4	½d. green	65	65
15	1d. grey and red	60	40
26a	2d. grey and brown	80	1·00
17	2½d. grey and blue	1·50	1·75
28a	3d. orange and purple	3·00	2·50
29a	6d. purple and olive	3·00	5·00
30	1s. green and purple	8·50	4·75
21	2s. green and brown	22·00	16·00
22	2s. 6d. green and black	15·00	30·00
33 5	5s. black and red	65·00	£100

1908.

36. 4.	1d. red	1·40	30
38.	2d. grey	1·75	8·00
39.	2½d. blue	2·25	3·50
40.	3d. purple on yellow	1·00	10·00
43.	6d. purple	6·50	28·00
44.	1s. black on green	3·50	16·00
45.	2s. purple & blue on blue	24·00	35·00
46.	2s. 6d. blk. & red on blue	30·00	48·00
47. 5.	5s. red & green on yellow	48·00	60·00

1914. As T 5, but portrait of King George V.

48.	5s. red & green on yellow	48·00	75·00

8.

1916.

63. 8.	½d. brown	15	2·50
64.	½d. green	20	30
50.	1d. red	35	75
65.	1d. violet	25	30
67.	1½d. yellow	1·75	9·50
68.	1½d. red	20	1·50
69.	1½d. brown	70	50
70.	2d. grey	45	1·00
71a.	2½d. blue	60	90
72.	2½d. yellow	1·25	17·00
53.	3d. purple on yellow	75	5·00
73.	3d. blue	50	10·00
75.	4d. black & red on yellow	60	4·50
76.	5d. purple and olive	2·50	10·00
77.	6d. purple	11·00	5·50
78.	1s. black on green	3·00	7·00
79.	2s. pur. and blue on blue	3·50	10·00
80.	2s. 6d. blk. & red on blue	1·00	28·00
81.	3s. green and violet	12·00	17·00
82.	4s. black and red	13·00	20·00
83.	5s. green and red on yellow	18·00	26·00

1917. Optd. **WAR STAMP.**

60. 8.	½d. green	10	80
62.	1½d. black and orange	10	30

10. Plymouth.

1932. Tercentenary issue.

84. 10.	½d. green	75	3·00
85.	1d. red	75	2·50
86.	1½d. brown	1·25	1·75
87.	2d. grey	1·25	10·00
88.	2½d. blue	1·25	9·00
89.	3d. orange	1·50	9·00
90.	6d. violet	2·25	17·00
91.	1s. olive	8·00	25·00
92.	2s. 6d. purple	48·00	60·00
93.	5s. brown	£100	£130

1935. Silver Jubilee. As T 13 of Antigua.

94.	1d. blue and red	85	1·50
95.	1½d. blue and grey	75	2·25
96.	2½d. brown and blue	2·25	1·25
97.	1s. grey and purple	3·00	7·50

1937. Coronation. As T 2 of Aden.

98.	1d. red	20	40
99.	1½d. brown	30	25
100.	2½d. blue	30	60

DESIGNS: 1d., 1½d., 2½d. Sea Island cotton. 2d. 6d., 2s. 6d., 10s. Botanic Station.

11. Carr's Bay.

1938. King George VI.

101a. 11.	½d. green	10	10
102a. –	1d. red	20	10
103a. –	1½d. purple	20	30
104a. –	2d. orange	20	30
105a. –	2½d. blue	30	15
106a. 11.	3d. brown	30	20
107a. –	6d. violet	60	20
108a. 11.	1s. red	40	20
109. –	2s. 6d. blue	7·00	70
110a. 11.	5s. red	9·00	2·50
111. –	10s. blue	12·00	16·00
112. 11.	£1 black	12·00	22·00

1946. Victory. As T 9 of Aden.

113.	1½d. purple	10	10
114.	3d. brown	10	10

1949. Silver Wedding. As T 10/11 of Aden.

115.	2½d. blue	10	10
116.	5s. red	4·50	2·50

1949. U.P.U. As T 20/23 of Antigua.

117.	2½d. blue	15	20
118.	3d. brown	30	20
119.	6d. purple	30	20
120.	1s. purple	35	25

1951. Inauguration of B.W.I. University College. As T 24/25 of Antigua.

121.	3 c. black and purple	20	15
122.	12 c. black and violet	20	20

14. Government House.

1951.

123. 14.	1 c. black	10	45
124. –	2 c. green	15	40
125. –	3 c. brown	30	45
126. –	4 c. red	30	20
127. –	5 c. violet	30	40
128. –	6 c. brown	30	20
129. –	8 c. blue	35	20
130. –	12 c. blue and brown	35	30
131. –	24 c. red and green	45	30
132. –	60 c. black and red	2·50	1·75
133. –	$1·20 green and blue	5·50	2·75
134. –	$2·40 black and green	4·50	11·00
135. –	$4.80 black and purple	14·00	15·00

DESIGNS: 2 c., $1.20, Sea **Island cotton; cultivation.** 3 c. Map. **4 c., 24 c. Picking tomatoes.** 5 c., 12 c. St. **Anthony's Church.** 6 c., $4.80, Badge. 8 c., 60 c. **Sea Island cotton: ginning.** $2.40, **Government House (portrait on right).**

1953. Coronation. As T 13 of Aden.

136.	2 c. black and green	10	10

1953. As 1951 but portrait of Queen Elizabeth II.

136a.	½ c. violet (As 3 c.) (I)	15	10
136b.	½ c. violet (II)	30	10
137.	1 c. black	10	10
138.	2 c. green	10	10
139.	3 c. brown (I)	30	10
139a.	3 c. brown (II)	35	15
140.	4 c. red	30	15
141.	5 c. violet	30	30
142.	6 c. brown (I)	15	10
142a.	6 c. brown (II)	40	15
143.	8 c. blue	30	10
144.	12 c. blue & brown	75	10
145.	24 c. red and green	80	10
145a.	48 c. olive & pur. (As 2 c.)	8·50	2·00
146.	60 c. black and red	4·50	80
147.	$1.20 green and blue	7·50	3·75
148.	$2.40 black and green	5·00	8·00
149.	$4.80 black & purple (I)	6·00	10·00
149a.	$4.80 black & purple (II)	6·00	7·00

I. Inscr. "Presidency" II. Inscr. "Colony".

1958. British Caribbean Federation. As T 28 of Antigua.

150.	3 c. green	25	15
151.	6 c. blue	30	20
152.	12 c. red	40	10

1963. Freedom from Hunger. As T 28 of Aden.

153.	12 c. violet	30	15

1963. Cent of Red Cross. As T 33 of Antigua.

154.	4 c. red and black	10	10
155.	12 c. red and blue	25	25

1964. 400th Birth Anniv of Shakespeare. As T 34 of Antigua.

156.	12 c. blue	10	10

1965. Cent of I.T.U. As T 36 of Antigua.

158.	4 c. red and violet	15	10
159.	48 c. green and red	30	20

21. Pineapple.

1965. Multicoloured.

160	1 c. Type 21	10	10
161	2 c. Avocado	10	10
162	3 c. Soursop	10	10
163	4 c. Pepper	10	10
164	5 c. Mango	10	10
165	6 c. Tomato	10	10
166	8 c. Guava	10	10
167	10 c. Ochro	10	10
168	12 c. Lime	15	10
169	20 c. Orange	20	10
170	24 c. Banana	20	10
171	42 c. Onion	75	60
172	48 c. Cabbage	1·00	75
173	60 c. Pawpaw	1·75	90
174	$1.20 Pumpkin	2·00	1·75
175	$2.40 Sweet potato	5·00	2·50
176	$4.80 Egg plant	5·00	6·00

1965. I.C.Y. As T 37 of Antigua.

177.	2 c. purple and turquoise	10	10
178.	12 c. green and lavender	25	10

1966. Churchill Commem. As T 38 of Antigua.

179.	1 c. blue	10	10
180.	2 c. green	10	10
181.	24 c. brown	15	10
182.	42 c. violet	20	15

1966. Royal Visit. As T 39 of Antigua.

183.	14 c. black and blue	30	15
184.	24 c. black and mauve	50	15

1966. Inauguration of W.H.O. Headquarters, Geneva. As T 41 of Antigua.

185.	12 c. black, green and blue	10	10
186.	60 c. black, purple & ochre	25	20

1966. 20th Anniv of U.N.E.S.C.O. As T 54/6 of Antigua.

187.	4 c. multicoloured	10	10
188.	60 c. yellow, violet & olive	20	10
189.	$1.80 black, purple & orge.	70	70

25. Yachting.

1967. Int. Tourist Year. Multicoloured.

190.	5 c. Type 25	10	10
191.	15 c. Waterfall near Chance Mountain	15	10
192.	16 c. "Fishing, skin diving and swimming"	15	10
193.	24 c. Playing golf	30	10

No. 191 is vert.

1968. Nos. 168, 170, 172, 174/6 surch.

194.	15 c. on 12 c. Lime	20	15
195.	25 c. on 24 c. Banana	25	15
196.	50 c. on 48 c. Cabbage	45	15
197.	$1 on $1.20 Pumpkin	1·50	40
198.	$2.50 on $2.40 Sweet Potato	2·00	3·00
199.	$5 on $4.80 Egg plant	2·50	3·75

27. Sprinting.

1968. Olympic Games, Mexico.

200. 27.	15 c. mauve, grn. & gold	10	10
201. –	25 c. blue, orge. & gold	10	10
202. –	50 c. green, red & gold	10	10
203. –	$1 multicoloured	20	20

DESIGNS—HORIZ. 25 c. Weightlifting. 50 c. Gymnastics. VERT. $1, Sprinting and Aztec Pillars.

31. Alexander Hamilton.

1968. Human Rights Year. Multicoloured.

204.	5 c. Type 31	10	10
205.	15 c. Albert T. Marryshow	10	10
206.	25 c. William Wilberforce	10	10
207.	50 c. Dag Hammarskjold	10	10
208.	$1 Dr. Martin Luther King	25	30

32. "The Two Trinities" (Murillo).

34. Map showing "CARIFTA" Countries.

1968. Christmas.

209. 32.	5 c. multicoloured	10	10
210. –	15 c. multicoloured	10	10
211. 32.	25 c. multicoloured	10	10
212. –	50 c. multicoloured	15	20

DESIGN: 15 c., 50 c. "The Adoration of the Kings" (detail, Botticelli).

1969. 1st Anniv. of "CARIFTA". Mult.

223.	15 c. Type 34	10	10
224.	20 c. Type 34	10	10
225.	35 c. "Strength in Unity"	10	10
226.	50 c. As 35 c.	15	15

Nos. 225/6 are horiz.

36. Telephone Receiver and Map of Montserrat.

1969. Development Projects. Multicoloured.

227.	15 c. Type 36	10	10
228.	25 c. School symbols and map	10	10
229.	50 c. "HS 748" Aircraft and map	15	10
230.	$1 Electricity pylon and map	25	20

40. Dolphin.

1969. Game Fish. Multicoloured.

231.	5 c. Type 40	15	10
232.	15 c. Atlantic sailfish	30	10
233.	25 c. Blackfin tuna	35	10
234.	40 c. Spanish mackerel	55	20

41. King Caspar before the Virgin and Child (detail) (Norman 16th-cent. stained glass window).

1969. Christmas. Paintings multicoloured; frame colours given.

235. 41.	15 c. black, gold & violet	10	10
236.	25 c. black and red	10	10
237.	50 c. blk., blue & orge.	15	15

DESIGN—HORIZ. 50 c. "Nativity" (Leonard Limosin).

43. "Red Cross Sale".

1970. Cent. of British Red Cross. Mult.

238.	3 c. Type **43**	10	10
239.	4 c. School for deaf children	10	10
240.	15 c. Transport services for disabled	10	10
241.	20 c. Workshop	10	20

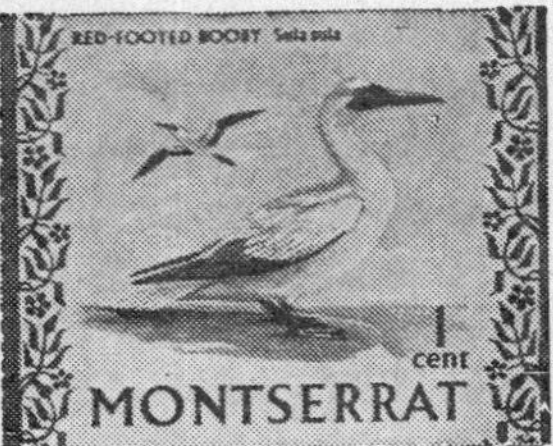

44. Red-Footed Booby.

1970. Bird. Multicoloured.

242	1 c. Type **44**	10	10
243	2 c. American kestrel	10	10
244	3 c. Magnificent frigate bird	15	15
245	4 c. Great egret	30	15
246	5 c. Brown pelican	50	10
247	10 c. Bananaquit	30	10
248	15 c. Smooth-billed ani	30	15
249	20 c. Red-billed tropic bird	35	15
250	25 c. Montserrat oriole	50	50
251	50 c. Green-throated carib	3·00	1·00
252	$1 Antillean crested hummingbird	3·00	1·00
253	$2.50 Little blue heron	3·00	4·00
254	$5 Purple-throated carib	7·50	9·00
254a	$10 Forest thrush	15·00	15·00

The 2, 3, 4, 5, 10, 50 c. and $2.50 are vert.

45. "Madonna and Child with Animals" (Brueghel the Elder, after Durer).

1970. Christmas. Multicoloured.

255.	5 c. Type **45**	10	10
256.	15 c. "The Adoration of the Shepherds" (Domenichino)	10	10
257.	20 c. Type **45**	10	10
258.	$1 As 15 c.	35	60

46. War Memorial.

1970. Tourism. Multicoloured.

259.	5 c. Type **46**	10	10
260.	15 c. Plymouth from Fort St. George	10	10
261.	25 c. Carr's Bay	15	10
262.	50 c. Golf Fairway	55	30

47. Girl Guide and Badge.

1970. Diamond Jubilee of Montserrat Girl Guides. Multicoloured.

264.	10 c. Type **47**	10	10
265.	15 c. Brownie and Badge	10	10
266.	25 c. As 15 c	15	10
267.	40 c. Type **47**	20	20

48. "Descent from the Cross" (Van Hemessen).

1971. Easter. Multicoloured.

268.	5 c. Type **48**	10	10
269.	15 c. "Noli me tangere" (Orcagna)	10	10
270.	20 c. Type **48**	10	10
271.	40 c. As 15 c.	15	15

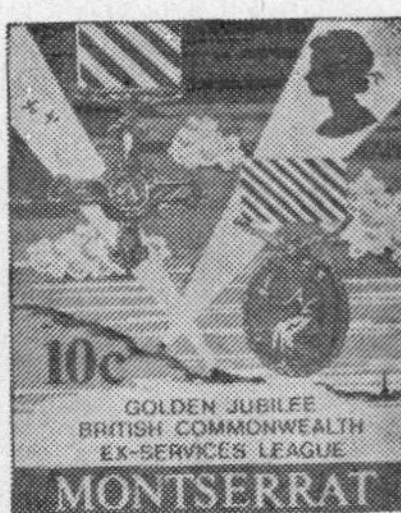

49. D.F.C. and D.F.M. in Searchlights.

1971. Golden Jubilee of Commonwealth Ex-Services League. Multicoloured.

272.	10 c. Type **49**	10	10
273.	20 c. M.C., M.M. and jungle patrol	15	10
274.	40 c. D.S.C., D.S.M. and submarine action	20	15
275.	$1 V.C. and soldier attacking bunker	50	70

50. "The Nativity with Saints" (Romanino).

1971. Christmas. Multicoloured.

276.	5 c. Type **50**	10	10
277.	15 c. "Choir of Angels" (Simon Marmion)	10	10
278.	20 c. Type **50**	10	10
279.	$1 As 15 c.	35	40

51. Piper "Apache".

1971. 14th Anniv of Inauguration of L.I.A.T. (Leeward Islands Air Transport). Mult.

280.	5 c. Type **51**	10	10
281.	10 c. Beech "Twin Bonanza"	15	15
282.	15 c. De Havilland "Heron"	30	15
283.	20 c. Britten Norman "Islander"	35	15
284.	40 c. De Havilland "Twin Otter"	65	45
285.	75 c. Hawker Siddeley "748"	2·00	2·25

52. "Chapel of Christ in Gethsemane", Coventry Cathedral.

1972. Easter. Multicoloured.

287.	5 c. Type **52**	10	10
288.	10 c. "The Agony in the Garden" (Bellini)	10	10
289.	20 c. Type **52**	10	10
290.	75 c. As 10 c.	35	50

53. Lizard.

1972. Reptiles. Multicoloured.

291.	15 c. Type **53**	15	10
292.	20 c. Mountain Chicken (frog)	20	10
293.	40 c. Iguana (horiz.)	35	20
294.	$1 Tortoise (horiz.)	2·00	2·00

54. "Madonna of the Chair" (Raphael).

1972. Christmas. Multicoloured.

303.	10 c. Type **54**	10	10
304.	35 c. "Virgin and Child with Cherub" (Fungai)	15	10
305.	50 c. "Madonna of the Magnificat" (Botticelli)	25	30
306.	$1 "Virgin and Child with St. John and an Angel" (Botticelli)	40	65

1972. Royal Silver Wedding. As T **52** of Ascension, but with Lime, Tomatoes and Pawpaw in background.

307.	35 c. pink	10	10
308.	$1 blue	20	20

56. "Passiflora herbertiana".

1973. Easter. Passion-flowers. Multicoloured.

309.	20 c. Type **56**	25	10
310.	35 c. "P. vitifolia"	35	10
311.	75 c. "P. amabilis"	1·40	1·40
312.	$1 "P. alata-cuerulea"	1·75	1·75

57. Montserrat Monastery, Spain.

1973. 480th Anniv. of Columbus's Discovery of Montserrat. Multicoloured.

313.	10 c. Type **57**	15	10
314.	35 c. Columbus sighting Montserrat	30	15
315.	60 c. Columbus's ship off Montserrat	1·50	1·50
316.	$1 Island badge and map of voyage	1·75	1·75

58. "Virgin and Child" (School of Gerard David).

1973. Christmas. Multicoloured.

318.	20 c. Type **58**	20	10
319.	35 c. "The Holy Family with St. John" (Jordaens)	25	10
320.	50 c. "Virgin and Child" (Bellini)	50	50
321.	90 c. "Virgin and Child with flowers" (Dolci)	80	1·00

1973. Royal Wedding. As T **47** of Anguilla. Multicoloured background colours given.

322.	35 c. green	10	10
323.	$1 blue	20	20

59. Steel Band.

1974. 25th Anniv. of University of West Indies. Multicoloured.

324.	20 c. Type **59**	15	10
325.	35 c. Masqueraders (vert.)	20	10
326.	60 c. Student weaving (vert.)	1·00	1·00
327.	$1 University Centre, Montserrat	1·10	1·25

60. Hands with Letters.

1974. Centenary of U.P.U.
329. 60. 1 c. multicoloured .. 10 10
330. – 2 c. red, orange & black 10 10
331. 60. 3 c. multicoloured .. 10 10
332. – 5 c. orge., red & blk. .. 10 10
333. 60. 50 c. multicoloured .. 20 20
334. – $1 blue, grn. & blk. .. 40 65
DESIGN: 2 c., 5 c., $1 Figures from U.P.U. Monument.

1974. Various stamps surch.
335. 2 c. on $1 (No. 252) .. 30 50
336. 5 c. on 50 c. (No. 333) .. 40 60
337. 10 c. on 60 c. (No. 326) .. 1·75 2·25
338. 20 c. on $1 mult. (No. 252) 30 40
339. 35 c. on $1 (No. 334) .. 75 1·25

62. Churchill and Houses of Parliament.

1974. Birth Centenary of Sir Winston Churchill. Multicoloured.
340. 35 c. Type 62 .. .. 15 10
341. 70 c. Churchill and Blenheim Palace 20 20

63. Carib "Carbet".

1975. Carib Artefacts.
343. 63. 5 c. brn., yell. & black.. 10 10
344. – 20 c. blk., brn. & yell... 10 10
345. – 35 c. blk., yell. & brn... 15 10
346. – 70 c. yell., brn. & blk... 25 40
DESIGNS: 20 c. "Caracoli". 35 c. Club or mace. 70 c. Canoe.
Nos. 343/46 also come self-adhesive from booklet panes.

64. One-Bitt Coin.

1975. Local Coinage, 1785-1801.
351. 64. 5 c. black, blue & silver 10 10
352. – 10 c. black, pink & silver 15 10
353. – 35 c. black, grn. & silver 20 15
354. – $2 black, red & silver.. 1·25 1·50
DESIGNS: 10 c. Eighth dollar. 35 c. Quarter dollar. $2, One dollar.

65. 1d. and 6d. Stamps of 1876.

1976. Centenary of 1st Montserrat Postage Stamp.
356. 65. 5 c. red, green & black.. 10 10
357. – 10 c. yellow, red & black 15 10
358. – 40 c. multicoloured .. 40 40
359. – 55 c. mauve, grn. & blk. 50 50
360. – 70 c. multicoloured .. 70 70
361. – $1.10 green, blue & black 1·00 1·00
DESIGNS: 10 c. G.P.O. and bisected 1d. stamp. 40 c. Bisects on cover. 55 c. G.B. 6d. used in Montserrat and local 6d. of 1876. 70 c. Stamps for 2½d. rate, 1876. $1.10, Packet boat "Antelope" and 6d. stamp.

66. "The Trinity".

1976. Easter. Paintings by Orcagna. Multicoloured.
363. 15 c. Type 66 .. .. 10 10
364. 40 c. "The Resurrection" 15 15
365. 55 c. "The Ascension" .. 15 15
366. $1.10 "Pentecost" .. 30 40

1976. Nos. 244, 246 and 247 surch.
368. 2 c. on 5 c. multicoloured 10 15
369. 30 c. on 10 c. multicoloured 30 20
370. 45 c. on 3 c. multicoloured 40 25

68. White Frangipani.

1976. Flowering Trees. Multicoloured.
371. 1 c. Type 68 .. .. 10 10
372. 2 c. Cannon-ball tree .. 10 10
373. 3 c. Lignum vitae .. 10 10
374. 5 c. Malay apple 15 10
375. 10 c. Jacaranda 20 10
376. 15 c. Orchid Tree .. 25 10
377. 20 c. Manjak 25 10
378. 25 c. Tamarind 25 10
379. 40 c. Flame of the Forest 35 20
380. 55 c. Pink Cassia .. 40 25
381. 70 c. Long John 50 30
382. $1 Saman 65 40
383. $2.50 Immortelle.. .. 1·25 1·50
384. $5 Yellow Poui .. .. 2·00 2·25
385. $10 Flamboyant .. .. 3·00 4·25

69. Mary and Joseph.

1976. Christmas. Multicoloured.
386. 15 c. Type 69 .. .. 10 10
387. 20 c. The Shepherds .. 10 10
388. 55 c. Mary and Jesus .. 15 15
389. $1.10 The Magi 30 50

70. Hudson River Review, 1976.

1976. Bicentenary of American Revolution. Multicoloured.
391. 15 c. Type 70 .. .. 30 15
392. 40 c. } "Raleigh" attack- 60 40
393. 75 c. } ing H.M.S. "Druid" 1777 .. .. 60 40
394. $1.25 Hudson River Review 1·10 60
Nos. 391 and 394 and 392/3 were issued in se-tenant pairs, each pair forming a composite design.

71. The Crowning.

1977. Silver Jubilee. Multicoloured.
396. 30 c. Royal Visit, 1966 .. 15 15
397. 45 c. Cannons firing a salute 20 20
398. $1 Type 71 .. .. 35 60

72. "Ipomoea Alba".

1977. Flowers of the Night. Multicoloured.
399. 15 c. Type 72 .. .. 15 10
400. 40 c. "Epiphyllum hookeri" (horiz.) 40 30
401. 55 c. "Cereus hexagonus" (horiz.) 55 45
402. $1.50 "Cestrum nocturnum" 1·50 1·25

73. Princess Anne laying Foundation Stone of Glendon Hospital.

1977. Development. Multicoloured.
404. 20 c. Type 73 .. .. 15 10
405. 40 c. "Statesman" (freighter) in Plymouth Port 25 15
406. 55 c. Glendon Hospital .. 30 20
407. $1.50 Jetty at Plymouth Port .. .. .. 80 1·00

1977. Royal Visit. Nos. 380/1 and 383 surch. **SILVER JUBILEE 1977 ROYAL VISIT TO THE CARIBBEAN** and new value.
409. $1 on 55 c. Pink Cassia .. 30 45
410. $1 on 70 c. Long John .. 30 45
411. $1 on $2.50 Immortelle .. 30 45

75. The Stable at Bethlehem.

1977. Christmas. Multicoloured.
412. 5 c. Type 75 .. .. 10 10
413. 40 c. The Three Kings .. 15 10
414. 55 c. Three Ships 20 10
415. $2 Three Angels 55 75

76. Four-eye Butterflyfish.

1978. Fish. Multicoloured.
417. 30 c. Type 76 .. .. 20 10
418. 40 c. French Angelfish .. 25 15
419. 55 c. Blue Tang 35 15
420. $1.50 Queen Triggerfish .. 80 90

77. St. Paul's Cathedral.

1978. 25th Anniv. of Coronation. Mult.
422. 40 c. Type 77 .. .. 10 10
423. 55 c. Chichester Cathedral 10 10
424. $1 Lincoln Cathedral .. 20 25
425. $2.50 Llandaff Cathedral 30 50

78. "Alpinia speciosa".

1978. Flowers. Multicoloured.
427. 40 c. Type 78 .. .. 20 10
428. 55 c. "Allamanda cathartica" 25 15
429. $1 "Petrea volubilis" .. 45 45
430. $2 "Hippeastrum puniceum" 70 80

79. Private, 21st (Royal North British Fusiliers), 1786.

1978. Military Uniforms (1st series). British Infantry Regiments. Multicoloured.
431. 30 c. Type 79 .. .. 15 15
432. 40 c. Corporal, 86th (Royal County Down), 1831 20 15
433. 55 c. Sergeant, 14th (Buckinghamshire), 1837 30 20
434. $1.50 Officer, 55th (Westmorland), 1784 .. .. 75 80
See also Nos. 441/4.

80. Cub Scouts.

1979. 50th Anniv. of Boy Scout Movement on Montserrat. Multicoloured.
436. 40 c. Type 80 .. .. 25 10
437. 55 c. Scouts with signalling equipment .. 35 20
438. $1.25 Camp fire (vert.) .. 60 55
439. $2 Oath ceremony (vert.) 1·00 1·00

1979. Military Uniforms (2nd series). As T **79**. Multicoloured.
441. 30 c. Private, 60th (Royal American), 1783 .. 15 15
442. 40 c. Private, 1st West India, 1819 .. .. 20 15
443. 55 c. Officer, 5th (Northumberland), 1819 .. 30 25
444. $2.50 Officer, 93rd (Sutherland Highlanders), 1830 1·00 1·10

81. Child reaching out to Adult.

1979. International Year of the Child.
446. **81.** $2 black, brown & flesh 50 55

82. Sir Rowland Hill with Penny Black and Montserrat 1876 1d. Stamp.

1979. Death Cent. of Sir Rowland Hill and Cent. of U.P.U. Membership. Multicoloured.
448. 40 c. Type **82** 20 10
449. 55 c. U.P.U. emblem and notice announcing Leeward Islands entry into Union 25 15
450. $1 1883 letter following U.P.U. membership .. 35 50
451. $2 Great Britain Post Office Regulations Notice and Sir Rowland Hill .. 60 80

83. Plume Worm.

1979. Marine Life. Multicoloured.
453. 40 c. Type **83** 20 15
454. 55 c. Sea Fans 30 20
455. $2 Sponge and coral .. 80 1·00

84. Tree Frog.

1980. Reptiles and Amphibians. Mult.
456. 40 c. Type **84** 20 15
457. 55 c. Tree Lizard 25 25
458. $1 Crapaud 45 50
459. $2 Wood Slave 80 90

85. " The Marquess of Salisbury " and 1838 Handstamps.

1980. "London 1980" International Stamp Exhibition. Multicoloured.
460. 40 c. Type **85** 20 15
461. 55 c. "H.S. 748" aircraft and 1976 55 c. definitive 25 25
462. $1.20 "La Plata" (liner) and 1903 5s. stamp .. 45 45
463. $1.20 "Lady Hawkins" (packet steamer) and 1932 Tercentenary 5s. commemorative .. 45 45
464. $1.20 "Avon" (paddle-steamer) and Penny Red stamp with "A 08" postmark 45 45
465. $1.20 "Aeronca" aeroplane and 1953 $1.20 definitive 45 45

1980. 75th Anniv. of Rotary International. No. 383 optd. **75th Anniversary of Rotary International.**
467. $2.50 Immortelle 70 85

87. Greek, French and U.S.A. Flags.

1980. Olympic Games, Moscow. Multicoloured.
468. 40 c. Type **87** 15 15
469. 55 c. Union, Swedish and Belgian flags 15 15
470. 70 c. French, Dutch and U.S.A. flags 20 20
471. $1 German, Union and Finnish flags 25 25
472. $1.50 Australian, Italian and Japanese flags .. 30 30
473. $2 Mexican, West German and Canadian flags .. 35 50
474. $2.50 " The Discus Thrower " (sculpture, Miron) .. 40 65

1980. Nos. 371, 373, 376 and 379 surch.
476. 5 c. on 3 c. Lignum vitae .. 10 10
477. 35 c. on 1 c. Type **68** .. 20 15
478. 35 c. on 3 c. Lignum vitae 20 15
479. 35 c. on 15 c. Orchid Tree 20 15
480. 55 c. on 40 c. Flame of the Forest 25 15
481. $5 on 40 c. Flame of the Forest .. .. .. 1·25 2·00

89. S.S. "Lady Nelson", 1928.

1980. Mail Packet Boats (1st series). Multicoloured.
482. 40 c. Type **89** 20 15
483. 55 c. R.M.S.P. "Chignecto", 1913 .. .. .. 30 25
484. $1 R.M.S.P. "Solent", 1878 50 50
485. $2 R.M.S.P. "Dee", 1841 .. 75 85
See also Nos 615/19.

90. "Heliconius charithonia".

1981. Butterflies. Multicoloured.
486. 50 c. Type **90** 60 40
487. 65 c. " Pyrgus oileus " .. 70 45
488. $1.50 " Poebis agarithe " 90 85
489. $2.50 " Danaus plexippus" 1·25 1·10

91. Spadefish.

1981. Fishes. Multicoloured.
555 5 c. Type **91** 15 10
556 10 c. Hogfish 15 10
492 15 c. Creole Wrasse .. 50 10
493 20 c. Yellow Damselfish .. 60 10
559 25 c. Sergeant Major .. 25 20
560 35 c. Clown Wrasse .. 35 30
496 45 c. Schoolmaster .. 50 25
497 55 c. Striped Parrotfish .. 95 30
498 65 c. Bigeye 50 30
499 75 c. French Grunt .. 60 40
500 $1 Rock Beauty 75 55
501 $2 Blue Chromis .. 1·75 1·10
502 $3 Fairy Basslet and Blueheads .. .. .. 1·90 1·75
503 $5 Cherubfish .. .. 2·75 2·75
504 $7. 50 Longspine Squirrelfish .. .. .. 5·50 4·75
570 $10 Longsnout Butterflyfish .. .. .. 5·50 6·00

92. Fort St. George.

1981. Montserrat National Trust. Mult.
506. 50 c. Type **92** 30 20
507. 65 c. Bird sanctuary, Fox's Bay 45 35
508. $1. 50 Museum 85 75
509. $2. 50 Bransby Point Battery, c. 1780 .. 1·40 1·40

1981. Royal Wedding, Royal Yachts. As T **26/27** of Kiribati. Multicoloured.
510 90 c. " Charlotte " .. 25 25
511 90 c. Prince Charles and Lady Diana Spencer .. 1·00 1·00
512 $3 " Portsmouth " .. 60 60
518 $3 As No. 511 .. .. 1·75 1·75
514 $4 " Britannia " 75 75
515 $4 As No. 511 .. .. 2·25 2·25

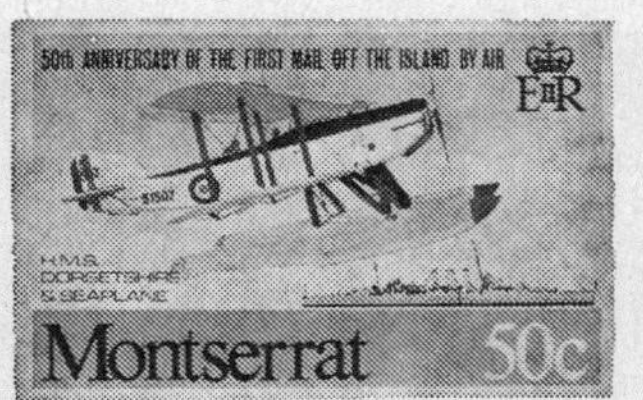

93. H.M.S. " Dorsetshire " and Seaplane.

1981. 50th Anniv. of Montserrat Airmail Service. Multicoloured.
519. 50 c. Type **93** 30 30
520. 65 c. Beechcraft " Twin Bonanza " aeroplane .. 45 50
521. $1. 50 De Haviland " Dragon Rapide " R.M. " Lord Shaftesbury " aeroplane 85 1·00
522. $2. 50 Hawker Siddeley Avro " 748 " aeroplane and Maps of Montserrat and Antigua .. .. 1·25 1·50

94. Methodist Church, Bethel.

1981. Christmas. Churches. Multicoloured.
523. 50 c. Type **94** 20 15
524. 65 c. St. George's Anglican Church, Harris .. 25 15
525. $1. 50 St. Peter's Anglican Church, St. Peter's .. 60 60
526. $2. 50 St. Patrick's R.C. Church, Plymouth .. 75 1·00

95. Rubiaceae (" Rondeletia buxifolia ").

1981. Plant Life. Multicoloured.
528. 50 c. Type **95** 30 30
529. 65 c. Boraginaceae (" Heliotropium ternatum ") (horiz.) 40 40
530. $1. 50 Simarubaceae ("Picramnia pentandra") 85 85
531. $2. 50 Ebenaceae (" Diospyrus revoluta ") (horiz.) 1·25 1·25

96. Plymouth.

1982. 350th Anniv. of Settlement of Montserrat by Sir Thomas Warner.
532. **96.** 40 c. green 30 30
533. 55 c. red 35 35
534. 65 c. brown 40 40
535. 75 c. grey 45 50
536. 85 c. blue 50 60
537. 95 c. orange 55 65
538. $1 violet 60 70
539. $1.50 olive .. .. 80 1·00
540. $2 claret .. .. 1·10 1·25
541. $2.50 brown .. .. 1·40 1·60

The design of Nos. 532/41 is based on the 1932 Tercentenary set.

97. Catherine of Aragon, Princess of Wales, 1501.

1982. 21st Birthday of Princess of Wales. Multicoloured.
542. 75 c. Type **97** 20 15
543. $1 Coat of Arms of Catherine of Aragon 30 20
544. $5 Diana, Princess of Wales 1·50 1·75

98. Local Scout.

1982. 75th Anniv. of Boy Scout Movement. Multicoloured.
545. $1.50 Type **98** 85 70
546. $2.20 Lord Baden-Powell 1·25 1·10

99. Annunciation.

1982. Christmas. Multicoloured.

547. 35 c. Type **99** 20 15
548. 75 c. Shepherds' Vision .. 40 35
549. $1.50 The Stable .. 85 85
550. $2.50 Flight into Egypt .. 1·00 1·10

100. " Lepthemis Vesiculosa ".

1983. Dragonflies. Multicoloured.

551. 50 c. Type **100** 25 20
552. 65 c. " Orthemis ferruginea" 30 25
553. $1.50 " Triacathagyna trifida" 70 75
554. $2.50 " Erythrodiplax umbrata " .. .. 1·25 1·25

101. Blue-headed Hummingbird.

1983. Hummingbirds. Multicoloured.

571. 35 c. Type **101** .. .. 1·25 35
572. 75 c. Green-throated Carib 1·50 55
573. $2 Antillean Crested Hummingbird .. .. 2·50 1·40
574. $3 Purple-throated Carib 3·00 1·75

102. Montserrat Emblem.

1983.

575. **102.** $12 blue and red .. 4·25 5·00
576. $30 red and blue .. 11·00 12·00

1983. Various stamps surch.

(a) Nos. 491, 494, 498/9, 501.

577. 40 c. on 25 c. Sergeant Major (No. 494) 20 20
578. 70 c. on 10 c. Hogfish (No. 491) 35 35
579. 90 c. on 65 c. Bigeye (No. 498) 50 55
580. $1.15 on 75 c. French Grunt (No. 499) .. 60 65
581. $1.50 on $2 Blue Chromis (No. 501) 80 85

(b) Nos. 512/15.

582. 70 c. on $3 " Portsmouth " 60 70
583. 70 c. on $3 Prince Charles and Lady Diana Spencer 60 70
584. $1.15 on $4 " Britannia " 1·00 1·10
585. $1.15 on $4, As No. 583 .. 1·00 1·10

INDEX

Countries can be quickly located by referring to the index at the end of this volume.

104. Montgolfier Balloon, 1783.

1983. Bicentenary of Manned Flight. Mult.

586. 35 c. Type **104** 15 15
587. 75 c. De Havilland "Twin Otter" (horiz.) 35 30
588. $1.50 Lockheed "Vega" (horiz.) 70 75
589. $2 "R 34" airship (horiz.) 1·00 1·25

Nos. 586/9 were re-issued optd. **"INAUGURAL FLIGHT Montserrat-Nevis-St. Kitts".**

105. Boys dressed as Clowns.

1983. Christmas. Carnival. Multicoloured.

591. 55 c. Type **105** 25 20
592. 90 c. Girls dressed as silver star bursts 40 35
593. $1.15 Flower girls .. 50 60
594. $2 Masqueraders .. .. 95 1·00

106. Statue of Discus Thrower.

1984. Olympic Games, Los Angeles. Mult.

595. 90 c. Type **106** 35 35
596. $1 Olympic torch 40 45
597. $1.15 Los Angeles Olympic stadium 45 50
598. $2.50 Olympic and American flags .. .. .. 80 1·00

107. Cattle Egret.

1984. Birds of Montserrat. Multicoloured.

600. 5 c. Type **107** 15 20
601. 10 c. Carib grackle .. 15 20
602. 15 c. Moorhen 15 20
603. 20 c. Brown booby .. 20 20
604. 25 c. Black-whiskered vireo 20 20
605. 40 c. Scaly-breasted thrasher 35 25
606. 55 c. Laughing gull .. 50 30
607. 70 c. Glossy ibis .. 60 45
608. 90 c. Green heron 75 50
609. $1 Belted kingfisher (vert.) 90 65
610. $1.15 Bananaquit (vert.) .. 1·10 1·25
611. $3 American kestrel (vert.) 2·25 3·25
612. $5 Forest thrush (vert.) .. 3·50 5·50
613. $7.50 Black-crowned night heron (vert.) .. .. 5·50 8·50
614. $10 Bridled quail dove (vert.) .. .. .. 7·00 11·00

1984. Mail Packet Boats (2nd series). As T **89**. Multicoloured.

615. 55 c. R.M.S.P. "Tagus", 1907 .. .. .. 50 40
616. 90 c. R.M.S.P. "Cobequid", 1913 .. 75 65
617. $1.15 S.S. "Lady Drake", 1942 .. .. .. 1·00 1·00
618. $2 M.V. "Factor", 1948 .. 1·75 2·00

108. Hermit Crab and Top Shell.

1984. Marine Life. Multicoloured.

620. 90 c. Type **108** 85 50
621. $1.15 Rough File Shell .. 1·10 70
622. $1.50 True Tulip Snail .. 1·50 90
623. $2.50 West Indian Fighting Conch .. .. .. 2·25 1·75

109. "Bull Man".

1984. Christmas. Carnival Costumes. Mult.

624. 55 c. Type **109** 30 25
625. $1.15 Masquerader Captain 90 70
626. $1.50 "Fantasy" Carnival Queen .. .. 1·00 85
627. $2.30 "Ebony and Ivory" Carnival Queen .. .. 1·60 1·40

110. Mango.

1985. National Emblems. Multicoloured.

628. $1.15 Type **110** .. .. 1·00 75
629. $1.50 Lobster Claw .. 1·50 95
630. $3 Montserrat Oriole .. 2·75 1·90

111. "Oncidium urophyllum".

1985. Orchids of Montserrat. Multicoloured.

631. 90 c. Type **111** 80 55
632. $1.15 "Epidendrum difforme" 90 70
633. $1.50 "Epidendrum ciliare" 1·00 85
634. $2.50 "Brassavola cucullata" .. .. 1·40 1·40

112. Queen Elizabeth the Queen Mother.

1985. Life and Times of Queen Elizabeth the Queen Mother. Various vertical portraits.

636. **112.** 55 c. multicoloured .. 30 35
637. – 55 c. multicoloured .. 30 35
638. – 90 c. multicoloured .. 40 55
639. – 90 c. multicoloured .. 40 55
640. – $1.15 multicoloured .. 50 65
641. – $1.15 multicoloured .. 50 65
642. – $1.50 multicoloured .. 65 70
643. – $1.50 multicoloured .. 65 70

Each value was issued in pairs showing a floral pattern across the bottom of the portraits which stops short of the left-hand edge on the first stamp and of the right-hand edge on the second.

113. Cotton Plants.

1985. Montserrat Sea Island Cotton Industry. Multicoloured.

645. 90 c. Type **113** 65 60
646. $1 Operator at carding machine 70 65
647. $1.15 Threading loom .. 85 85
648. $2.50 Weaving with hand loom .. .. .. 1·75 2·00

1985. Royal Visit. Nos. 514/15, 543, 587/8 and 640/1 optd. **CARIBBEAN ROYAL VISIT—1985** or surch. also.

650. 75 c. mult. (No. 587) .. 2·50 2·50
651. $1 multicoloured (No. 543) 4·00 3·00
652. $1.15 mult. (No. 640) .. 4·00 3·00
653. $1.15 mult. (No. 641) .. 4·00 3·50
654. $1.50 mult. (No. 588) .. 5·50 5·00
655. $1.60 on $4 multicoloured (No. 514) .. .. .. 3·50 3·50
656. $1.60 on $4 multicoloured (No. 515) .. .. .. 10·00 10·00

No. 656 shows a new face value only, "Caribbean Royal Visit—1985" being omitted from the surcharge.

115. Black-throated Blue Warbler.

1985. Leaders of the World. Birth Bicentenary of John J. Audubon (ornithologist). Designs showing original paintings. Multicoloured.

657. 15 c. Type **115** 15 15
658. 15 c. Palm Warbler .. 15 15
659. 30 c. Bobolink 20 20
660. 30 c. Lark Sparrow .. 20 20
661. 55 c. Chipping Sparrow .. 30 30
662. 55 c. Northern Oriole .. 30 30
663. $2.50 American Goldfinch 1·00 1·00
664. $2.50 Blue Grosbeak .. 1·00 1·00

116. Herald Angel appearing to Goatherds.

1985. Christmas. Designs showing Caribbean Nativity. Multicoloured.

665. 70 c. Type **116** 40 45
666. $1.15 Three Wise Men following Star 65 70
667. $1.50 Carol singing around War Memorial, Plymouth 80 85
668. $2.30 Praying to "Our Lady of Montserrat", Church of Our Lady, St. Patrick's Village .. 1·25 1·40

117. Lord Baden-Powell.

1986. 50th Anniv. of Montserrat Girl Guide Movement. Multicoloured.

669.	20 c. Type **117**	25	25
670.	20 c. Girl Guide saluting	25	25
671.	75 c. Lady Baden-Powell	65	65
672.	75 c. Guide assisting in old people's home	65	65
673.	90 c. Lord and Lady Baden-Powell	80	80
674.	90 c. Guides serving meal in old people's home	80	80
675.	$1.15 Girl Guides of 1936	1·00	1·00
676.	$1.15 Two guides saluting	1·00	1·00

1986. 60th Birthday of Queen Elizabeth II. As T **167** of British Virgin Islands. Multicoloured.

677.	10 c. Queen Elizabeth II	10	10
678.	$1.50 Princess Elizabeth in 1928	70	70
679.	$3 In Antigua, 1977	1·25	1·25
680.	$6 In Canberra, 1982 (vert.)	2·25	2·25

118. King Harold and Halley's Comet, 1066 (from Bayeux Tapestry).

1986. Appearance of Halley's Comet. Multicoloured.

682.	35 c. Type **118**	30	30
683.	50 c. Comet of 1301 (from Giotto's "Adoration of the Magi")	40	40
684.	70 c. Edmond Halley and comet of 1531	55	55
685.	$1 Comets of 1066 and 1910	70	70
686.	$1.15 Comet of 1910	80	80
687.	$1.50 E.S.A. "Giotto" spacecraft and comet	95	95
688.	$2.30 U.S. space telescope and comet	1·40	1·40
689.	$4 Computer reconstruction of 1910 comet	2·50	2·50

1986. Royal Wedding (1st issue). As T **168** of British Virgin Islands. Multicoloured.

691.	70 c. Prince Andrew	30	35
692.	70 c. Miss Sarah Ferguson	30	35
693.	$2 Prince Andrew wearing stetson (horiz.)	75	90
694.	$2 Miss Sarah Ferguson on skiing holiday (horiz.)	75	90

See also Nos. 705/8.

119. "Antelope" (1793).

1986. Mail Packet Sailing Ships. Mult.

696.	90 c. Type **119**	1·50	1·25
697.	$1.15 "Montagu" (1810)	1·75	1·50
698.	$1.50 "Little Catherine" (1813)	2·25	2·25
699.	$2.30 "Hinchingbrook" (1813)	2·75	3·00

120. Radio Montserrat Building, Dagenham.

1986. Communications. Multicoloured.

701.	70 c. Type **120**	1·00	70
702.	$1.15 Radio Gem dish aerial, Plymouth	1·00	1·25
703.	$1.50 Radio Antilles studio, O'Garro's	1·75	1·75
704.	$2.30 Cable and Wireless building, Plymouth	2·25	3·00

1986. Royal Wedding (2nd issue). Nos. 691/4 optd. **Congratulations to T.R.H. The Duke and Duchess of York.**

705.	70 c. Prince Andrew	50	50
706.	70 c. Miss Sarah Ferguson	50	50
707.	$2 Prince Andrew wearing stetson (horiz.)	1·25	1·25
708.	$2 Miss Sarah Ferguson on skiing holiday (horiz.)	1·25	1·25

122. Sailing and Windsurfing.

1986. Tourism. Multicoloured.

710.	70 c. Type **122**	1·00	70
711.	$1.15 Golf	2·50	1·50
712.	$1.50 Plymouth market	2·50	2·25
713.	$2.30 Air Recording Studios	2·75	3·25

123. Christmas Rose.

1986. Christmas. Flowering Shrubs. Mult.

714.	70 c. Type **123**	60	40
715.	$1.15 Candle flower	85	70
716.	$1.50 Christmas tree Kalanchoe	1·25	1·00
717.	$2.30 Snow on the mountain	1·75	2·00

124. Tiger Shark.

1987. Sharks. Multicoloured.

719.	40 c. Type **124**	75	55
720.	90 c. Lemon shark	1·50	90
721.	$1.15 White shark	1·75	1·50
722.	$3.50 Whale shark	3·50	3·75

1987. Nos. 601, 603, 607/8 and 611 surch.

724.	5 c. on 70 c. Glossy ibis	15	15
725.	$1 on 20 c. Brown booby	80	80
726.	$1.15 on 10 c. Carib grackle	90	90
727.	$1.50 on 90 c. Green heron	1·10	1·10
728.	$2.30 on $3 American kestrel (vert.)	1·75	2·00

127. "Phoebis trite".

1987. Butterflies. Multicoloured.

730	90 c. Type **127**	1·00	65
731	$1.15 "Biblis hyperia"	1·50	1·00
732	$1.50 "Polygorus leo"	1·75	1·50
733	$2.50 "Hypolimnas misippus"	2·25	2·75

128. "Oncidium variegatum".

1987. Christmas. Orchids. Multicoloured.

734.	90 c. Type **128**	60	45
735.	$1.15 "Vanilla planifolia" (horiz.)	85	55
736.	$1.50 "Gongora quinquenervis"	1·10	75
737.	$3.50 "Brassavola nodosa" (horiz.)	2·00	1·75

1987. Royal Ruby Wedding. Nos. 601, 604/5 and 608 surch. **40th Wedding Anniversary HM Queen Elizabeth II HRH Duke of Edinburgh. November 1987** and value.

739.	5 c. on 90 c. Green heron	15	15
740.	$1.15 on 10 c. Carib grackle	65	65
741.	$2.30 on 25 c. Black-whiskered vireo	1·40	1·40
742.	$5 on 40 c. Scaly-breasted thrasher	2·75	3·00

130. Free-tailed Bat.

1988. Bats. Multicoloured.

743.	55 c. Type **130**	35	35
744.	90 c. "Chiroderma improvisum" (fruit bat)	55	55
745.	$1.15 Fisherman Bat	75	75
746.	$2.30 "Brachyphylla cavernarum" (fruit bat)	1·40	1·40

131. Magnificent Frigate Bird.

1988. Easter. Birds. Multicoloured.

748.	90 c. Type **131**	60	45
749.	$1.15 Caribbean elaenia	80	65
750.	$1.50 Glossy ibis	1·00	1·00
751.	$3.50 Purple-throated carib	2·00	2·25

132 Discus throwing

1988. Olympic Games, Seoul. Multicoloured.

753	90 c. Type **132**	40	45
754	$1.15 High jumping	50	55
755	$3.50 Athletics	1·60	1·75

133 Golden Tulip

1988. Sea Shells. Multicoloured.

757	5 c. Type **133**	10	10
758	10 c. Little knobby scallop	10	10
759	15 c. Sozoni's cone	10	10
760	20 c. Globular coral shell	10	10
761	25 c. Sundial	10	15
762	40 c. King helmet	15	20
763	55 c. Channelled turban	25	30
764	70 c. True tulip shell	30	35
765	90 c. Music volute	40	45
766	$1 Flame auger	40	45
767	$1.15 Rooster tail conch	50	55
768	$1.50 Queen conch	65	70
769	$3 Teramachi's slit shell	1·25	1·40
770	$5 Florida crown conch	2·10	2·25
771	$7.50 Beau's murex	3·25	3·50
772	$10 Triton's trumpet	4·25	4·50

134 University Crest

1988. 40th Anniv of University of West Indies.

773	**134** $5 multicoloured	2·40	2·50

1988. Princess Alexandra's Visit. Nos. 763, 766 and 769/70 surch **HRH PRINCESS ALEXANDRA'S VISIT NOVEMBER 1988** and new value.

774	40 c. on 55 c. Channelled turban	35	35
775	90 c. on $1 Flame auger	55	55
776	$1.15 on $3 Teramachi's slit shell	70	70
777	$1.50 on $5 Florida crown conch	85	85

136 Spotted Sandpiper

1988. Christmas. Sea Birds. Multicoloured.

778	90 c. Type **136**	60	45
779	$1.15 Turnstone	70	55
780	$3.50 Red-footed booby	1·75	2·00

137 Handicapped Children in Classroom

1988. 125th Anniv of International Red Cross.
782 137 $3.50 multicoloured .. 1·50 1·60

138 Drum Major in Ceremonial Uniform

1989. 75th Anniv (1988) of Montserrat Defence Force. Uniforms. Multicoloured.
783 90 c. Type **138** 70 55
784 $1.15 Field training uniform 85 75
785 $1.50 Cadet in ceremonial uniform .. .. 1·25 1·25
786 $3.50 Gazetted Police Officer in ceremonial uniform .. .. 2·50 2·75

139 Amazon Lily

1989. Easter. Lilies. Multicoloured.
788 90 c. Type **139** 50 50
789 $1.15 Salmon blood lily (vert) 70 70
790 $1.50 Amaryllis (vert) .. 85 85
791 $3.50 Amaryllis (vert) .. 1·90 1·90

140 "Morning Prince" (schooner), 1942

1989. Shipbuilding in Montserrat. Mult.
793 90 c. Type **140** 40 45
794 $1.15 "Western Sun" (inter-island freighter) 55 60
795 $1.50 "Kim G" (inter-island freighter) under construction 70 75
796 $3.50 "Romaris" (inter-island ferry), c. 1942 .. 1·60 1·75

141 The Scarecrow

1989. 50th Anniv of "The Wizard of Oz" (film). Multicoloured.
797 90 c. Type **141** 40 45
798 $1.15 The Lion 55 60
799 $1.50 The Tin Man 70 75
800 $3.50 Dorothy .. .. 1·60 1·75

1989. Hurricane Hugo Relief Fund. Nos. 795/6 surch **Hurricane Hugo Relief Surcharge $2.50**.
802 $1.50+$2.50 "Kim G" (inter-island freighter under construction) .. 1·90 2·00
803 $3.50+$2.50 "Romaris" (inter-island ferry), c. 1942 .. 2·75 3·00

143 "Apollo 11" above Lunar Surface

1989. 20th Anniv of First Manned Landing on Moon. Multicoloured
804 90 c. Type **143** 35 40
805 $1.15 Astronaut alighting from lunar module "Eagle" 45 50
806 $1.50 "Eagle" and astronaut conducting experiment 60 65
807 $3.50 Opening "Apollo 11" hatch after splashdown 1·40 1·50

144 "Yamato" (Japanese battleship)

1990. World War II Capital Ships. Mult.
809 70 c. Type **144** 40 40
810 $1.15 U.S.S. "Arizona" at Pearl Harbour 60 60
811 $1.50 "Bismarck" (German battleship) in action .. 90 90
812 $3.50 H.M.S. "Hood" (battle cruiser) .. 1·75 1·75

145 The Empty Tomb

1990. Easter. Stained glass windows from St. Michael's Parish Church, Bray, Berkshire. Multicoloured.
814 $1.15 Type **145** .. 45 50
815 $1.50 The Ascension .. 60 65
816 $3.50 The Risen Christ with Disciples .. .. 1·40 1·50

1990. "Stamp World London 90" International Stamp Exhibition. Nos. 460/4 surch **Stamp World London 90** and value.
818 70 c. on 40 c. Type **85** .. 25 30
819 90 c. on 55 c. "H.S. 748" aircraft and 1976 55 c. definitive .. 35 40
820 $1 on $1.20 "La Plata" (liner) and 1903 5s. stamp 40 45
821 $1.15 on $1.20 "Lady Hawkins" (packet steamer) and 1932 Tercentenary 5s. commemorative .. 45 50
822 $1.50 on $1.20 "Avon" (paddle-steamer) and Penny Red stamp with "A 08" postmark 60 65

HAVE YOU READ THE NOTES AT THE BEGINNING OF THIS CATALOGUE?
These often provide answers to the enquiries we receive.

147 General Office, Montserrat, and 1884 ½d. Stamp

1990. 150th Anniv of the Penny Black. Mult.
823 90 c. Type **147** 35 40
824 $1.15 Sorting letters and Montserrat 1d. stamp of 1876 (vert) 45 50
825 $1.50 Posting letters and Penny Black (vert) .. 60 65
826 $3.50 Postman delivering letters and 1840 Two-pence Blue .. .. 1·40 1·50

148 Montserrat v. Antigua Match

1990. World Cup Football Championship, Italy. Multicoloured.
828 90 c. Type **148** 35 40
829 $1.15 U.S.A v. Trinidad match 45 50
830 $1.50 Montserrat team .. 60 65
831 $3.50 West Germany v. Wales match .. .. 1·40 1·50

149 Spinner Dolphin

1990. Dolphins. Multicoloured.
833 90 c. Type **149** 35 40
834 $1.15 Common dolphin .. 45 50
835 $1.50 Striped dolphin .. 60 65
836 $3.50 Atlantic spotted dolphin .. .. 1·40 1·50

150 Spotted Goatfish

1991. Tropical Fishes. Multicoloured.
838 90 c. Type **150** 40 45
839 $1.15 Cushion star .. 50 55
840 $1.50 Rock beauty .. 65 70
841 $3.50 French grunt .. 1·50 1·60

1991. Nos. 760/1, 768 and 771 surch.
843 5 c. on 20 c. Globular coral shell 10 10
844 5 c. on 25 c. Sundial .. 10 10
845 $1.15 on $1.50 Queen conch 50 55
846 $1.15 on $7.50 Beau's murex 50 55

152 Duck

1991. Domestic Birds. Multicoloured.
847 90 c. Type **152** 40 45
848 $1.15 Hen and chicks .. 50 55
849 $1.50 Rooster 65 70
850 $3.50 Helmeted guinea fowl 1·50 1·60

153 "Panaeolus antillarum"

1991. Fungi.
851 **153** 90 c. grey 40 45
852 – $1.15 red 50 55
853 – $1.50 brown 65 70
854 – $2 purple 85 90
855 – $3.50 blue .. .. 1·50 1·60
DESIGNS: $1.15, "Cantharellus cinnabarinus"; $1.50, "Gymnopilus chrysopellus"; $2, "Psilocybe cubensis"; $3.50, "Leptonia caeruleocapitata".

154 Red Water Lily

1991. Lilies. Multicoloured.
856 90 c. Type **154** 40 45
857 $1.15 Shell ginger .. 50 55
858 $1.50 Early day lily .. 65 70
859 $3.50 Anthurium .. .. 1·50 1·60

155 Tree Frog

1991. Frogs and Toad. Multicoloured.
860 $1.15 Type **155** 50 55
861 $2 Crapaud toad 85 90
862 $3.50 Mountain chicken (frog) .. .. .. 1·50 1·60

156 Black British Shorthair Cat

1991. Cats. Multicoloured.
864 90 c. Type **156** 40 45
865 $1.15 Seal point Siamese .. 50 55
866 $1.50 Silver tabby Persian 60 65
867 $2.50 Birman temple cat 1·00 1·10
868 $3.50 Egyptian mau .. 1·40 1·50

157 Navigational Instruments

1992. 500th Anniv of Discovery of America by Columbus. Multicoloured.

869 $1.50 Type **157** 65 70
870 $1.50 Columbus and coat of arms 65 70
871 $1.50 Landfall on the Bahamas 65 70
872 $1.50 Petitioning Queen Isabella 65 70
873 $1.50 Tropical birds 65 70
874 $1.50 Tropical fruits 65 70
875 $3 Ships of Columbus (81 × 26 mm) 1·25 1·50

OFFICIAL STAMPS

1976. Various stamps, some already surch. optd. **O.H.M.S.**

O 1. 5 c. multicoloured (No. 246) † 65
O 2. 10 c. multicoloured (No. 247) † 75
O 3. 30 c. on 10 c. multicoloured (No. 369) † 1·50
O 4. 45 c. on 3 c. multicoloured (No. 370) † 2·00
O 5. $5 multicoloured (No. 254) † £100
O 6. $10 multicoloured (No. 254a) † £550

These stamps were issued for use on mail from the Montserrat Philatelic Bureau. They were not sold to the public, either unused or used.

1976. Nos. 372, 374/82, 384/5 and 476 optd. **O.H.M.S.** or surch. also.

O 17 5 c. Malay Apple † 10
O 28 5 c. on 3 c. Lignum vitae † 10
O 18 10 c. Jacaranda † 10
O 19 15 c. Orchid Tree † 10
O 20 20 c. Manjak † 10
O 21 25 c. Tamarind † 15
O 33 30 c. on 15 c. Orchid Tree † 20
O 34 35 c. on 2 c. Cannon-ball Tree † 20
O 35 40 c. Flame of the Forest † 25
O 22 55 c. Pink Cassia † 35
O 23 70 c. Long John † 45
O 24 $1 Saman † 60
O 39 $2·50 on 40 c. Flame of the Forest † 1·75
O 25 $5 Yellow Poui † 2·75
O 26 $10 Flamboyant † 5·50

1981. Nos. 490/4, 496, 498, 500, 502/3 and 505 optd. **O.H.M.S.**

O 42. 5 c. Type **91** 10 10
O 43. 10 c. Hogfish 10 10
O 44. 15 c. Creole Wrasse 10 10
O 45. 20 c. Yellow Damselfish 15 15
O 46. 25 c. Sergeant Major 15 15
O 47. 45 c. Schoolmaster 25 20
O 48. 65 c. Bigeye 35 30
O 49. $1 Rock Beauty 65 65
O 50. $3 Fairy Basslet and Blueheads 1·75 1·75
O 51. $5 Cherubfish 3·00 3·00
O 52. $10 Longsnout Butterfly-fish 5·50 3·50

1983. Nos. 510/15 surch. and optd. **O.H.M.S.**

O 53. 45 c. on 90 c. " Charlotte " 25 30
O 54. 45 c. on 90 c. Prince Charles and Lady Diana Spencer 30 30
O 55. 75 c. on $3 " Portsmouth " 35 35
O 56. 75 c. on $3 Prince Charles and Lady Diana Spencer 45 45
O 57. $1 on $4 " Britannia " 50 50
O 58. $1 on $4 Prince Charles and Lady Diana Spencer 60 60

1983. Nos. 542/4 surch. and optd. **O.H.M.S.**

O 59. 70 c. on 75 c. Type **97** 60 40
O 60 $1 Coat of Arms of Catherine of Aragon 70 50
O 61. $1.50 on $5 Diana, Princess of Wales 1·00 80

1985. (12 Apr). Nos. 600/12 and 614 optd. **OHMS.**

O 62. 5 c. Type **107** 15 15
O 63. 10 c. Carib grackle 15 15
O 64. 15 c. Moorhen 15 15
O 65. 20 c. Brown booby 15 15
O 66. 25 c. Black-whiskered vireo 20 15
O 67. 40 c. Scaly-breasted thrasher 25 20
O 68. 55 c. Laughing gull 35 25
O 69. 70 c. Glossy ibis 45 35
O 70. 90 c. Green heron 55 40
O 71. $1 Belted kingfisher 70 45
O 72. $1.15 Bananaquit 80 60
O 73. $3 American kestrel 1·75 2·00
O 74. $5 Forest thrush 2·50 2·75
O 75. $10 Bridled quail dove 4·75 3·50

1989. Nos. 757/70 and 772 optd **O H M S.**

O 76 5 c. Type **133** 10 10
O 77 10 c. Little knobby scallop 10 10
O 78 15 c. Sozoni's cone 10 10
O 79 20 c. Globular coral shell 10 10
O 80 25 c. Sundial 10 15
O 81 40 c. King helmet 15 20
O 82 55 c. Channelled turban 25 30
O 83 70 c. True tulip shell 30 35
O 84 90 c. Music volute 40 45
O 85 $1 Flame auger 40 45
O 86 $1.15 Rooster tail conch 50 55
O 87 $1.50 Queen conch 65 70
O 88 $3 Teramachi's slit shell 1·25 1·40
O 89 $5 Florida crown counch 2·10 2·25
O 90 $10 Triton's trumpet 4·25 4·50

1989. Nos. 578 and 580/1 optd **OHMS.**

O91 70 c. on 10 c. Hogfish 30 35
O92 $1.15 on 75 c. French grunt 50 55
O93 $1.50 on $2 Blue chromis 65 70

MOROCCO AGENCIES

Stamps used at British postal agencies in Morocco, N. Africa, the last of which were closed on 30th April, 1957.

I. GIBRALTAR ISSUES OVERPRINTED.

For use at all British Post Offices in Morocco.

All British P.O.s in Morocco were under the control of the Gibraltar P.O. until 1907 when control was assumed by H.M. Postmaster-General.

1898. Stamps of Gibraltar (Queen) optd. **Morocco Agencies.**

9. **7.** 5 c. green 25 15
10 10 c. red 35 15
11 20 c. olive 1·50 70
3d 20 c. olive and brown 1·50 1·25
4 25 c. blue 1·50 60
5 40 c. brown 2·50 3·25
14 50 c. lilac 5·50 3·50
7 1 p. brown and blue 8·00 20·00
8 2 p. black and red 5·00 20·00

1903. Stamps of Gibraltar (King Edward VII) optd. **Morocco Agencies.**

24. **8.** 5 c. green 70 75
25. 10 c. purple and red 1·25 30
26. 20 c. green and red 1·50 18·00
26. 25 c. purple & blk. on bl. 90 15
28. 50 c. purple and violet 6·00 18·00
29. 1 p. black and red 22·00 60·00
30. 2 p. black and blue 15·00 32·00

II. BRITISH CURRENCY.

On sale at British P.Os throughout Morocco, including Tangier, until 1937.

PRICES. Our prices for used stamps with these overprints are for examples used in Morocco. These stamps could also be used in the United Kingdom, with official sanction, from the summer of 1950 onwards, and with U.K. postmarks are worth about 50 per cent less.

Stamps of Great Britain optd. **MOROCCO AGENCIES.**

1907. King Edward VII.

31 **83** ½d. green 75 5·50
32 1d. red 2·25 2·75
33 – 2d. green and red 2·50 4·50
34 – 4d. green and brown 15·00 3·25
35 – 4d. orange 3·75 3·50
36 – 6d. purple 4·75 7·50
37 – 1s. green and red 12·00 16·00
38 – 2s. 6d. purple 48·00 75·00

1914. King George V.

42 **105.** ½d. green 20 45
43 **104.** 1d. red 50 10
44 **105.** 1½d. brown 1·00 11·00
45 **106.** 2d. orange 1·00 35
58 **104.** 2½d. blue 2·00 5·00
46 **106.** 3d. violet 1·00 35
47 4d. green 1·00 70
60 **107.** 6d. purple 40 60
49 **108.** 1s. brown 5·00 75
53 **109.** 2s. 6d. brown 28·00 25·00
74 5s. red 22·00 55·00

1935. Silver Jubilee.

62. **123.** ½d. green 1·25 1·75
63. 1d. red 1·25 3·25
64. 1½d. brown 1·50 7·00
65. 2½d. blue 1·50 2·50

1935. King George V.

66. **119.** 1d. red 3·00 2·00
67. **118.** 1½d. brown 2·00 10·00
68. **120.** 2d. orange 35 60
69. **119.** 2½d. blue 1·75 4·25
70. **120.** 3d. violet 40 15
71. 4d. green 40 15
72. **122.** 1s. brown 80 90

1936. King Edward VIII.

75. **124.** 1d. red 10 30
76. 2½d. blue 10 15

In 1937 unoverprinted Great Britain stamps replaced overprinted **MOROCCO AGENCIES** issues as stocks became exhausted. In 1949 overprinted issues reappeared and were in use at Tetuan (Spanish Zone), the only remaining British P.O. apart from that at Tangier.

1949. King George VI.

77. **128.** ½d. green 1·25 1·25
94. ½d. orange 70 30
78. 1d. red 1·75 3·50
95. 1d. blue 70 30
79. 1½d. brown 2·00 2·75
96. 1½d. green 70 50
80. 2d. orange 2·00 3·50
97. 2d. brown 70 75
81. 2½d. blue 2·25 3·50
98. 2½d. red 70 40
82. 3d. violet 80 45
83. **129.** 4d. green 35 50
84. 5d. brown 2·00 5·50
85. 6d. purple 70 1·00
86. **130.** 7d. green 40 7·50
87. 8d. red 1·75 4·25
88. 9d. olive 40 6·00
89. 10d. blue 40 4·00
90. 11d. plum 70 3·75
91. 1s. brown 2·00 3·25
92. **131.** 2s. 6d. green 8·50 18·00
93. 5s. red 26·00 35·00

1951. Pictorials.

99. **147.** 2s. 6d. green 8·50 13·00
100. – 5s. red (No. 510) 10·00 16·00

1952. Queen Elizabeth II.

101. **154.** ½d. orange 10 10
102. 1d. blue 15 40
103. 1½d. green 15 10
104. 2d. brown 20 50
105. **155.** 2½d. red 25 10
106. 4d. blue 60 1·50
107. **156.** 5d. brown 65 60
108. 6d. purple 50 1·50
109. **158.** 8d. mauve 1·25 1·00
110. **159.** 1s. bistre 70 60

III. SPANISH CURRENCY.

Stamps surcharged in Spanish currency were sold at British P.Os throughout Morocco until the establishment of the French Zone and the Tangier International Zone, when their use was confined to the Spanish Zone.

Stamps of Great Britain optd. **MOROCCO AGENCIES** or surch. also in Spanish currency.

1907. King Edward VII.

112. **83.** 5 c. on ½d. green 45 15
113. 10 c. on 1d. red 85 10
114. – 15 c. on 1½d. purple and green 70 15
115. – 20 c. on 2d. green & red 60 15
116. **83.** 25 c. on 2½d. blue 85 15
117. – 40 c. on 4d. grn. & brn. 90 1·75
118. – 40 c. on 4d. orange 35 60
119. – 50 c. on 5d. pur. & blue 1·10 80
120. – 1 p. on 10d. pur. & red 6·00 5·50
121. – 3 p. on 2s. 6d. purple 17·00 23·00
122. – 6 p. on 5s. red 35·00 45·00
123. – 12 p. on 10s. blue 75·00 75·00

1912. King George V.

126 **101** 5 c. on ½d. green 90 10
127 **102** 10 c. on 1d. red 50 10

1914. King George V.

128 **105** 3 c. on ½d. green 20 2·50
129 **105** 5 c. on ½d. green 30 10
130 **104** 10 c. on 1d. red 30 10
131 **105** 15 c. on 1½d. brown 30 10
132 **106** 20 c. on 2d. orange 25 25
133 **104** 25 c. on 2½d. blue 50 25
148 **106** 40 c. on 4d. green 65 30
135 **108** 1 p. on 10d. blue 1·25 3·00
142 **109** 3 p. on 2s. 6d. brown 23·00 50·00
136 6 p. on 5s. red 27·00 48·00
138 12 p. on 10s. blue £100 £150

1935. Silver Jubilee.

149. **123.** 5 c. on ½d. green 1·00 45
150. 10 c. on 1d. red 2·75 2·25
151. 15 c. on 1½d. brown 1·40 7·50
152. 25 c. on 2½d. blue 5·50 2·25

1935. King George V.

153. **118.** 5 c. on ½d. green 65 5·50
154. **119.** 10 c. on 1d. red 2·25 2·75
155. **118.** 15 c. on 1½d. brown 2·50 3·25
156. **120.** 20 c. on 2d. orange 30 25
157. **119.** 25 c. on 2½d. blue 1·25 3·75
158. **120.** 40 c. on 4d. green 35 3·00
159. **122.** 1 p. on 10d. blue 50 30

1936. King Edward VIII.

160. **124.** 5 c. on ½d. green 10 10
161. 10 c. on 1d. red 50 50
162. 15 c. on 1½d. brown 10 10
163. 25 c. on 2½d. blue 10 10

1937. Coronation.

164. **126.** 15 c. on 1½d. brown 30 20

1937. King George VI.

165. **128.** 5 c. on ½d. green 45 15
182. 5 c. on ½d. orange 1·25 1·25
166. 10 c. on 1d. red 40 10
183. 10 c. on 1d. blue 2·00 1·00
167. 15 c. on 1½d. brown 45 25
184. 15 c. on 1½d. green 1·25 3·00
168. 25 c. on 2½d. blue 50 50
185. 25 c. on 2½d. red 1·25 1·50
169. **129.** 40 c. on 4d. green 6·50 6·00
186. 40 c. on 4d. blue 50 8·00
170. **130.** 70 c. on 7d. green 50 5·00
171. 1 p. on 10d. blue 30 3·50

1940. Stamp Cent.

172. **134.** 5 c. on ½d. green 25 1·00
173. 10 c. on 1d. red 1·00 1·50
174. 15 c. on 1½d. brown 25 1·25
175. 25 c. on 2½d. blue 25 50

1948. Silver Wedding.

176. **137.** 25 c. on 2½d. blue 30 15
177. **138.** 45 p. on £1 blue 15·00 22·00

1948. Olympic Games.

178. **139.** 25 c. on 2½d. blue 30 40
179. **140.** 30 c. on 3d. violet 30 40
180. – 60 c. on 6d. purple 30 40
181. – 1 p. 20 c. on 1s. brown 45 40

1954. Queen Elizabeth II.

189 **154** 5 c. on ½d. orange 15 30
188 10 c. on 1d. blue 30 40
190 **155** 40 c. on 4d. blue 70 1·50

IV. FRENCH CURRENCY.

Stamps surch. in French currency were sold at British P.Os in the French Zone.

Stamps of Great Britain surch. **MOROCCO AGENCIES** and value in French currency.

1917. King George V.

No.	Type	Description	Unused	Used
191	105.	3 c. on ½d. green	15	2·50
192		5 c. on ½d. green	10	10
203	104.	10 c. on 1d. red	30	25
194	105.	15 c. on 1½d. brown	80	15
195	104.	25 c. on 2½d. blue	30	15
196	106.	40 c. on 4d. green	70	25
207	107.	50 c. on 5d. brown	50	10
198	108.	75 c. on 9d. green	50	75
209		90 c. on 9d. green	2·25	3·00
210		1 f. on 10d. blue	70	10
211		1 f. 50 c. on 1s. brown	3·00	2·25
200	109.	3 f. on 2s. 6d. brown	7·50	2·00
226		6 f. on 5s. red	6·00	20·00

1935. Silver Jubilee.

No.	Type	Description	Unused	Used
212.	123.	5 c. on ½d. green	15	15
213.		10 c. on 1d. red	35	50
214.		15 c. on 1½d. brown	15	50
215.		25 c. on 2½d. blue	20	15

1935. King George V.

No.	Type	Description	Unused	Used
216.	118.	5 c. on ½d. green	45	1·25
217.	119.	10 c. on 1d. red	35	30
218.	118.	15 c. on 1½d. brown	1·25	1·50
219.	119.	25 c. on 2½d. blue	30	15
220.	120.	40 c. on 4d. green	30	15
221.	121.	50 c. on 5d. brown	30	15
222.	122.	90 c. on 9d. olive	35	55
223.		1 f. on 10d. blue	30	30
224.		1 f. 50 c. on 1s. brown	30	55

1936. King Edward VIII.

No.	Type	Description	Unused	Used
227.	124.	5 c. on ½d. green	10	15
228.		15 c. on 1½d. brown	10	15

1937. Coronation.

No.	Type	Description	Unused	Used
229.	126.	15 c. on 1½d. brown	30	30

1937. King George VI.

No.	Type	Description	Unused	Used
230.	128.	5 c. on ½d. green	30	70

V. TANGIER INTERNATIONAL ZONE.

This Zone was established in 1924 and the first specially overprinted stamps issued in 1927.

PRICES. Our note re U.K. usage (at beginning of Section II) also applies to **TANGIER** optd. stamps.

Stamps of Great Britain optd. **TANGIER.**

1927. King George V.

No.	Type	Description	Unused	Used
231.	105.	½d. green	50	10
232.	104.	1d. red	40	10
233.	105.	1½d. brown	2·00	2·00
234.	106.	2d. orange	3·25	10

1934. King George V.

No.	Type	Description	Unused	Used
235.	118.	½d. green	1·00	1·40
236.	119.	1d. red	65	70
237.	118.	1½d. brown	15	10

1935. Silver Jubilee.

No.	Type	Description	Unused	Used
238.	123.	½d. green	1·00	85
239.		1d. red	4·25	3·25
240.		1½d. brown	1·25	15

1936. King Edward VIII.

No.	Type	Description	Unused	Used
241.	124.	½d. green	10	10
242.		1d. red	10	10
243.		1½d. brown	10	10

1937. Coronation.

No.	Type	Description	Unused	Used
244.	126.	1½d. brown	40	15

1937. King George VI.

No.	Type	Description	Unused	Used
245.	128.	½d. green	40	15
280.		½d. orange	30	30
246.		1d. red	65	20
281.		1d. blue	50	60
247.		1½d. brown	60	10
282.		1½d. green	50	3·50
261.		2d. orange	2·00	2·00
283.		2d. brown	50	90
262.		2½d. blue	35	70
284.		2½d. red	55	45
263.		3d. violet	35	20
264.	129.	4d. green	2·00	4·25
285.		4d. blue	45	2·25
265.		5d. brown	75	4·50
266.		6d. purple	35	30
267.	130.	7d. green	55	5·00
268.		8d. red	1·00	4·50
269.		9d. olive	50	5·00
270.		10d. blue	50	5·50
271.		11d. plum	50	6·00
272.		1s. brown	50	75
273.	131.	2s. 6d. green	4·00	7·50
274.		5s. red	9·00	26·00
275.	–	10s. blue (No. 478a)	35·00	65·00

1940. Stamp Cent.

No.	Type	Description	Unused	Used
248.	134.	½d. green	20	1·50
249.		1d. red	35	30
250.		1½d. brown	80	30

1946. Victory.

No.	Type	Description	Unused	Used
253.	135.	2½d. blue	30	20
254.	–	3d. violet	30	20

1948. Silver Wedding.

No.	Type	Description	Unused	Used
255.	137.	2½d. blue	30	15
256.	138.	£1 blue	24·00	27·00

1948. Olympic Games.

No.	Type	Description	Unused	Used
257.	139.	2½d. blue	55	40
258.	140.	3d. violet	55	30
259.	–	6d. purple	55	40
260.	–	1s. brown	55	15

1949. U.P.U.

No.	Type	Description	Unused	Used
276.	143.	2½d. blue	40	50
277.	144.	3d. violet	40	50
278.	–	6d. purple	40	40
279.	–	1s. brown	40	1·00

1951. Pictorial stamps.

No.	Type	Description	Unused	Used
286.	147.	2s. 6d. green	3·25	2·25
287.	–	5s. red (No. 510)	8·50	8·50
288.	–	10s. blue (No. 511)	13·00	13·00

1952. Queen Elizabeth II.

No.	Type	Description	Unused	Used
313	154	½d. orange	10	10
290		1d. blue	15	20
291		1½d. green	10	20
292		2d. brown	20	20
293	155	2½d. red	10	20
294		3d. lilac	20	20
295		4d. blue	45	85
296	157	5d. brown	60	90
297		6d. purple	45	15
298		7d. green	80	1·60
299	158	8d. mauve	80	1·50
300		9d. olive	1·25	75
301		10d. blue	1·40	2·75
302		11d. plum	1·40	3·25
303	159	1s. bistre	50	30
304		1s. 3d. green	65	55
305		1s. 6d. blue	80	1·75

1953. Coronation.

No.	Type	Description	Unused	Used
306.	161.	2½d. red	50	30
307.	–	4d. blue	1·00	30
308.	163.	1s. 3d. green	1·25	1·25
309.	–	1s. 6d. blue	1·25	60

1955. Pictorials.

No.	Type	Description	Unused	Used
310.	166.	2s. 6d. brown	3·25	4·50
311.	–	5s. red	5·00	8·50
312.	–	10s. blue	18·00	20·00

1957. British Post Office in Tangier. Cent. Queen Elizabeth II stamps optd. **1857-1957 TANGIER.**

No.	Type	Description	Unused	Used
323.	154.	½d. orange	10	10
324.		1d. blue	10	10
325.		1½d. green	10	10
326.		2d. brown	10	10
327.	155.	2½d. red	15	15
328.		3d. lilac	15	10
329.		4d. blue	30	20
330.	157.	5d. brown	30	35
331.		6d. purple	30	15
332.		7d. green	30	30
333.	158.	8d. mauve	30	40
334.		9d. olive	30	30
335.		10d. blue	30	30
336.		11d. plum	30	30
337.	159.	1s. bistre	30	30
338.		1s. 3d. green	45	50
339.		1s. 6d. blue	50	55
340.	166.	2s. 6d. brown	2·00	2·25
341.	–	5s. red	2·75	2·25
342.	–	10s. blue	3·50	3·00

MORVI

A state of India, Bombay district. Now uses Indian stamps.

12 pies = 1 anna.

1. Maharaja Sir Lakhdirji Waghji. 3.

1931.

No.	Type	Description	Unused	Used
8	1.	3 p. red	75	2·50
9b		6 p. green	60	2·75
5		½ a. blue	1·75	4·50
6		1 a. brown	2·75	9·50
10		1 a. blue	1·25	5·50
7		2 a. brown	4·00	13·00
11		2 a. violet	10·00	18·00

1934.

No.	Type	Description	Unused	Used
16.	3.	3 p. red	40	1·25
17.		6 p. green	60	1·90
14.		1 a. brown	1·00	4·00
15.		2 a. violet	2·00	7·00

MUSCAT

Independent Sultanate in Eastern Arabia with Indian and, subsequently, British postal administration.

12 pies = 1 anna. 16 annas = 1 rupee.

١٣٦٣
آل بوسعيد

(2.)

1944. Bicentenary of Al-Busaid Dynasty. Stamps of India (King George VI) optd. as T **2.**

No.	Type	Description	Unused	Used
1.	100a.	3 p. slate	30	2·50
2.		½ a. mauve	30	2·50
3.		9 p. green	30	2·50
4.		1 a. red	30	2·50
5.	101.	1½ a. plum	30	2·50
6.		2 a. red	30	2·50
7.		3 a. violet	30	2·50
8.		3½ a. blue	30	2·50
9.	102.	4 a. brown	30	2·50
10.		6 a. green	45	2·50
11.		8 a. violet	40	3·00
12.		12 a. red	70	3·75
13.	–	14 a. purple (No. 277)	40	5·00
14.	93.	1 r. slate and brown	45	7·00
15.		2 r. purple and brown	50	12·00

OFFICIAL STAMPS

1944. Bicentenary of Al-Busaid Dynasty. Official stamps of India optd. as T **2.**

No.	Type	Description	Unused	Used
O 1.	O 20.	3 p. slate	50	4·50
O 2.		½ a. purple	50	4·50
O 3.		9 p. green	50	4·50
O 4.		1 a. red	50	4·50
O 5.		1½ a. violet	50	4·50
O 6.		2 a. orange	50	4·50
O 7.		2½ a. violet	50	4·50
O 8.		4 a. brown	50	5·00
O 9.		8 a. violet	50	5·50
O 10.	93.	1 r. slate and brown (No. O 138)	2·00	13·00

For later issues see **BRITISH POSTAL AGENCIES IN EASTERN ARABIA.**

NABHA

A "Convention" state in the Punjab, India.

Stamps of India optd. **NABHA STATE.**

12 pies = 1 anna; 16 annas = 1 rupee.

1885. Queen Victoria. Vert. optd.

No.	Type	Description	Unused	Used
1.	23.	½ a. turquoise	75	1·75
2.	–	1 a. purple	15·00	42·00
3.	–	2 a. blue	7·00	17·00
4.	–	4 a. green (No. 96)	40·00	75·00
5.	–	8 a. mauve	£225	
6.	–	1 r. grey (No. 79)	£180	

1885. Queen Victoria. Horiz. optd.

No.	Type	Description	Unused	Used
36	40.	3 p. red	10	15
14	23.	½ a. turquoise	10	10
15	–	9 p. red	35	1·60
17	–	1 a. purple	30	20
18	–	1½ a. brown	30	85
20	–	2 a. blue	30	50
22	–	3 a. orange	75	50
12	–	4 a. green (No. 69)	20·00	65·00
24	–	4 a. green (No. 96)	60	60
26	–	6 a. brown (No. 80)	80	1·75
27	–	8 a. mauve	65	1·40
28	–	12 a. purple on red	1·00	2·00
29	–	1 r. grey (No. 101)	5·50	18·00
30	37.	1 r. green and red	3·75	3·75
31	38.	2 r. red and orange	75·00	£120
32		3 r. brown and green	75·00	£120
33		5 r. blue and violet	85·00	£150

1903. King Edward VII.

No.	Type	Description	Unused	Used
37.		3 p. grey	10	15
38.		½ a. green (No. 122)	10	30
39.		1 a. red (No. 123)	15	30
40a.		2 a. lilac	50	20
40b.		2½ a. blue	18·00	50·00
41.		3 a. orange	30	30
42.		4 a. olive	60	1·75
43.		6 a. bistre	60	3·75
44.		8 a. mauve	1·50	4·50
45.		12 a. purple on red	1·10	6·00
46.		1 r. green and red	2·00	4·50

1907. As last, but inscr. "INDIA POSTAGE & REVENUE".

No.	Type	Description	Unused	Used
47.		½ a. green (No. 149)	30	60
48.		1 a. red (No. 150)	35	70

1913. King George V. Optd. in two lines.

No.	Type	Description	Unused	Used
49.	55.	3 p. grey	10	10
50.	56.	½ a. green	10	10
51.	57.	1 a. red	10	10
		1 a. brown	70	80
52.	59.	2 a. lilac	20	30
53.	62.	3 a. orange	30	30
54.	63.	4 a. olive	35	65
55.	64.	6 a. bistre	50	1·75
56.	65.	8 a. mauve	70	1·75
57.	66.	12 a. red	80	4·75
58.	67.	1 r. brown and green	2·00	2·50

1928. King George V. Optd. in one line.

No.	Type	Description	Unused	Used
60.	55.	3 p. grey	15	15
61.	56.	½ a. green	15	20
73.	79.	½ a. green	15	25
61a.	80.	9 p. green	40	1·10
62.	57.	1 a. brown	15	15
74.	81.	1 a. brown	15	30
63.	82.	1¼ a. mauve	20	1·25
64.	70.	2 a. lilac	55	35
65.	61.	2½ a. orange	30	2·25
66.	62.	3 a. blue	40	1·00
75.	63.	3 a. red	1·00	3·00
76.	63.	4 a. olive	90	1·25
67.	71.	4 a. green	1·25	1·00
71.	67.	2 r. red and orange	11·00	35·00
72.		5 r. blue and purple	42·00	90·00

1938. King George VI. Nos. 247/63.

No.	Type	Description	Unused	Used
77.	91.	3 p. slate	4·50	30
78.		½ a. brown	1·50	30
79.		9 p. green	14·00	3·00
80.		1 a. red	1·00	30
81.	92.	2 a. red	75	2·50
82.	–	2½ a. violet	85	3·25
83.	–	3 a. green	95	2·75
84.	–	3½ a. blue	1·00	6·50
85.	–	4 a. brown	1·75	3·00
86.	–	6 a. green	1·50	6·50
87.	–	8 a. violet	1·75	7·00
88.	–	12 a. red	2·25	8·50
89.	93.	1 r. slate and brown	9·00	12·00
90.		2 r. purple and brown	14·00	45·00
91.		5 r. green and blue	42·00	£100
92.		10 r. purple and red	80·00	£225
93.		15 r. brown and green	£180	£375
94.		25 r. slate and purple	£200	£425

1942. King George VI. Optd. **NABHA** only.

No.	Type	Description	Unused	Used
95.	91.	3 p. slate	24·00	1·50
105.	100a.	3 p. slate	60	40
96.	91.	½ a. brown	60·00	2·00
106.	100a.	½ a. mauve	1·90	40
97.	91.	9 p. green	10·00	6·00
107.	100a.	9 p. green	1·40	40
98.	91.	1 a. red	12·00	2·00
108.	100a.	1 a. red	70	1·50
109.	101.	1 a. 3 p. brown	70	70
110.		1½ a. violet	80	60
111.		2 a. red	70	1·40
112.		3 a. violet	1·40	2·50
113.		3½ a. blue	5·00	12·00
114.	102.	4 a. brown	1·50	75
115.		6 a. green	4·00	14·00
116.		8 a. violet	4·00	11·00
117.		12 a. purple	4·25	14·00

OFFICIAL STAMPS

Stamps of Nabha optd. **SERVICE.**

1885. Nos. 1 to 3 (Queen Victoria).

No.	Type	Description	Unused	Used
O 1.		½ a. turquoise	60	30
O 2.		1 a. purple	20	15
O 3.		2 a. blue	32·00	55·00

1885. Nos. 14 to 30 (Queen Victoria).

No.	Type	Description	Unused	Used
O 6		½ a. turquoise	10	10
O 7		1 a. purple	20	15
O 9		2 a. blue	35	30
O 12		3 a. orange	8·00	18·00
O 13		4 a. green (No. 4)	50	35
O 15		6 a. brown	9·00	9·00
O 17		8 a. mauve	60	70
O 18		12 a. purple on red	4·00	7·50
O 19		1 r. grey	21·00	85·00
O 20		1 r. green and red	18·00	32·00

1903. Nos. 37 to 46 (King Edward VII).

No.	Type	Description	Unused	Used
O 25.		3 p. grey	65	2·75
O 26.		½ a. green	30	10
O 27.		1 a. red	15	10
O 28.		2 a. lilac	40	40
O 30.		4 a. olive	1·10	45
O 32.		8 a. mauve	90	90
O 34.		1 r. green and red	1·50	2·00

1907. Nos. 47/8 (King Edward VII inscr. "INDIA POSTAGE & REVENUE").

No.	Type	Description	Unused	Used
O 35.		½ a. green	10	10
O 36.		1 a. red	15	20

1913. Nos. 54 and 58, (King George V).

No.	Type	Description	Unused	Used
O 37.	63.	4 a. olive	10·00	
O 38.	67.	1 r. brown and green	50·00	

1913. Official stamps of India (King George V), optd. **NABHA STATE.**

No.	Type	Description	Unused	Used
O 39.	55.	3 p. grey	20	2·50
O 40.	56.	½ a. green	15	10
O 41.	57.	1 a. red	15	10
O 42.	59.	2 a. lilac	25	15
O 43.	63.	4 a. olive	35	30
O 44.	65.	8 a. mauve	60	60
O 46.	67.	1 r. brown and green	1·75	1·75

1932. Stamps of India (King George V) optd. **NABHA STATE SERVICE.**

No.	Type	Description	Unused	Used
O 47.	55.	3 p. grey	10	15
O 50.	81.	1 a. brown	10	15
O 50a.	63.	4 a. olive	13·00	2·00
O 51.	65.	8 a. mauve	85	1·75

1938. Stamps of India (King George VI) optd. **NABHA STATE SERVICE.**

No.	Type	Description	Unused	Used
O 54.	91.	9 p. green	1·25	1·75
O 55.		1 a. red	3·75	30

1943. Stamps of India (King George VI) optd. **NABHA.**

No.	Type	Description	Unused	Used
O 56.	O 20.	3 p. slate	45	35
O 57.		½ a. brown	60	30
O 57a.		½ a. purple	80	30
O 58.		9 p. green	80	30
O 59.		1 a. red	40	20
O 61.		1½ a. violet	50	40
O 62.		2 a. orange	50	45
O 64.		4 a. brown	1·75	1·75
O 65.		8 a. violet	2·50	5·50

1943. Stamps of India (King George VI) optd. **NABHA SERVICE.**

No.	Type	Description	Unused	Used
O 66.	93.	1 r. slate and brown	7·50	21·00
O 67.		2 r. purple and brown	21·00	75·00
O 68.		5 r. green and blue	£170	£225

NAMIBIA

Formerly South West Africa which became independent on 21st March 1990.

100 cents - 1 rand.

141 Pres. Sam Nujoma, Map of Namibia and National Flag

1990. Independence. Multicoloured.

538	18 c. Type **141**	20	15
539	45 c. Hands releasing dove and map of Namibia (vert)	45	35
540	60 c. National flag and map of Africa	70	55

142 Fish River Canyon

1990. Namibia Landscapes. Multicoloured.

541	18 c. Type **142**	20	20
542	35 c. Quiver-tree forest, Keetmanshoop ..	35	35
543	45 c. Tsaris Mountains ..	40	40
544	60 c. Dolerite boulders, Keetmanshoop ..	50	50

143 Stores on Kaiser Street, c. 1899

1990. Centenary of Windhoek. Multicoloured.

545	18 c. Type **143**	15	15
546	35 c. Kaiser Street, 1990 ..	25	25
547	45 c. City Hall, 1914 ..	30	30
548	60 c. City Hall, 1990 ..	40	40

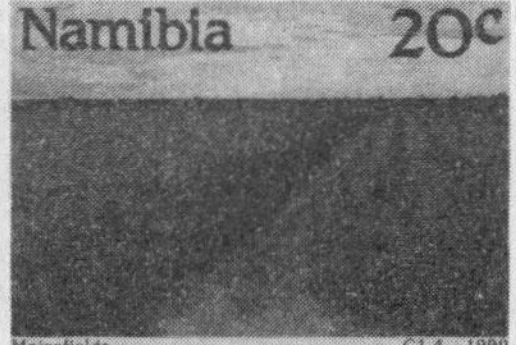

144 Maizefields

1990. Farming. Multicoloured.

549	20 c. Type **144**	15	15
550	35 c. Sanga bull	25	25
551	50 c. Damara ram ..	35	35
552	65 c. Irrigation in Okavango	45	45

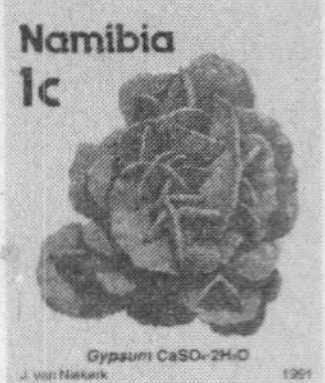

145 Gypsum

1991. Minerals. As Nos. 519/21 and 523/33 of South West Africa, some with values changed, and new design (5 r.) inscr "Namibia" as T **145**. Multicoloured.

553	1 c. Type **145**	10	10
554	2 c. Fluorite	10	10
555	5 c. Mimetite	10	10
556	10 c. Azurite	10	10
557	20 c. Dioptase	10	10
558	25 c. Type **139**	10	15
559	30 c. Tsumeb lead and copper complex ..	10	15
560	35 c. Rosh Pinah zinc mine	15	20
561	40 c. Diamonds	15	20
562	50 c. Uis tin mine ..	20	25
563	65 c. Boltwoodite ..	25	30
564	1 r. Rossing uranium mine	40	45
565	1 r. 50 Wulfenite	60	65
566	2 r. Gold	80	85
567	5 r. Willemite (vert as T **145**)	2·00	2·10

146 Radiosonde Weather Balloon

1991. Centenary of Weather Service. Mult.

568	20 c. Type **146**	20	20
569	35 c. Sunshine recorder ..	30	30
570	50 c. Measuring equipment	40	40
571	65 c. Meteorological station, Gobabeb ..	50	50

147 Herd of Zebras

1991. Endangered Species. Mountain Zebra. Multicoloured.

572	20 c. Type **147**	25	25
573	25 c. Mare and foal ..	30	30
574	45 c. Zebras and foal ..	50	50
575	60 c. Two zebras	65	65

148 Karas Mountains

1991. Mountains of Namibia. Multicoloured.

576	20 c. Type **148**	20	20
577	25 c. Gamsberg Mountains	25	25
578	45 c. Mount Brukkaros ..	45	45
579	60 c. Erongo Mountains ..	50	50

149 Bernabe de la Bat Camp

1991. Tourist Camps. Multicoloured.

580	20 c. Type **149**	20	20
581	25 c. Von Bach Dam Recreation Resort ..	25	25
582	45 c. Gross Barmen Hot Springs	40	40
583	60 c. Namutoni Rest Camp	50	50

150 Artist's Pallet

1992. 21st Anniv of Windhoek Conservatoire. Multicoloured.

584	20 c. Type **150**	10	10
585	25 c. French horn and cello	10	10
586	45 c. Theatrical masks ..	20	25
587	60 c. Ballet dancers ..	25	30

151 Blue Kurper

1992. Freshwater Angling. Multicoloured.

588	20 c. Type **151**	10	10
589	25 c. Largemouthed yellow fish	10	10
590	45 c. Carp	20	25
591	60 c. Sharptoothed catfish	25	30

NANDGAON (RAJNANDGAON)

A state of C. India. Now uses Indian stamps.

12 pies = 1 anna; 16 annas = 1 rupee.

1.

3 (2a.)

1892. Imperf.

1. **1.**	½ a. blue	1·60	75·00
2.	2 a. red	11·00	£150

1893. Imperf.

6. **3.**	½ a. green	2·75	5·00
8.	1 a. red	5·00	14·00
9.	2 a. red	5·50	14·00

NATAL

On the E. coast of S. Africa. Formerly a British Colony, later a province of the Union of S. Africa.

12 pence = 1 shilling.
20 shillings = 1 pound.

1.

1857. Embossed stamps. Various designs.

1. **1.**	1d. red	—	£1700
2.	1d. buff	—	£950
3.	1d. blue	—	£1100
4.	3d. red	—	£400
5. –	6d. green	—	£1100
6. –	9d. blue	—	£7000
7. –	1s. buff	—	£5500

The 3d., 6d., 9d. and 1s. are larger.
Beware of reprints.

6.

7.

1859.

19. **6.**	1d. red	75·00	20·00
12.	3d. blue	85·00	32·00
13.	6d. grey	£130	45·00
24.	6d. violet	38·00	25·00

1867.

25. **7.**	1s. green	£120	26·00

1869. Variously optd. **POSTAGE** or **Postage.**

50. **6.**	1d. red	65·00	25·00
82.	1d. yellow	70·00	65·00
53.	3d. blue	£100	38·00
83.	6d. violet	48·00	5·50
84. **7.**	1s. green	70·00	4·50

1870. Optd. **POSTAGE** in a curve.

59. **7.**	1s. green	45·00	10·00
108.	1s. orange	3·25	85

1870. Optd. **POSTAGE** twice, reading up and down.

60. **6.**	1d. red	55·00	13·00
61.	3d. blue	55·00	13·00
62.	6d violet	£100	25·00

1873. Optd. **POSTAGE** once, reading up.

63. **7.**	1s. brown	85·00	16·00

23.

28.

16.

1874. Queen Victoria. Various frames.

97a. **23.** ½d. green 50 20
99. – 1d. red 65 10
107. – 2d. olive .. .. .. 1·50 75
113. **28.** 2½d. blue .. .. .. 3·00 50
68. – 3d. blue .. .. .. 70·00 13·00
101. – 3d. grey .. .. .. 1·50 95
102. – 4d. brown .. .. 2·50 65
103. – 6d. lilac .. .. .. 3·00 70
73. **16.** 5s. red .. .. .. 60·00 28·00

1877. No. 99 surch. ½ **HALF.**

85. ½d. on 1d. red .. .. 18·00 60·00

POSTAGE — Half-penny (21.)

POSTAGE. — Half-Penny (29.)

1877. Surch. as T **21.**

91. **6.** ½d. on 1d. yellow .. .. 8·00 11·00
92. 1d. on 6d. violet .. .. 40·00 8·00
93. 1d. on 6d. red .. .. 65·00 87·00

1885. Surch. in words.

104. ½d. on 1d. red (No. 99) .. 16·00 11·00
105. 2d. on 3d. grey (No. 101) .. 18·00 5·50
109. 2½d. on 4d. brown (No. 102) 11·00 8·50

1895. No. 23 surch. with T **29.**

114. **6.** ½d. on 6d. violet .. 1·00 2·75

1895. No. 99 surch. **HALF.**

125. HALF on 1d. red 70 75

31.

32.

1902.

127 **31.** ½d. green 65 15
128 1d. red 80 15
129 1½d. green and black .. 90 90
130 2d. red and olive .. 80 25
131 2½d. blue .. .. .. 90 3·00
132 3d. purple and grey .. 80 30
152 4d. red and brown .. 1·75 1·00
134 5d. black and orange .. 1·25 2·25
135 6d. green and purple .. 1·25 1·10
136 1s. red and blue .. .. 3·50 1·10
137 2s. green and violet .. 42·00 9·00
138 2s. 6d. purple .. .. 32·00 12·00
139 4s. red and yellow .. 50·00 40·00
140 **32.** 5s. blue and red .. .. 16·00 7·50
141 10s. red and purple .. 48·00 23·00
142 £1 black and blue .. £110 42·00
143 £1 10s. green and violet .. £200 65·00
162 £1 10s. orange & purple .. £1100
144 £5 mauve and black .. £1300 £250
145 £10 green and orange .. £6000 £2250
145a £20 red and green .. £12000

1908. As T **31/2** but inscr. "**POSTAGE POSTAGE**".

165. **31.** 6d. purple .. .. 4·50 2·00
166. 1s. black on green .. 6·00 2·00
167. 2s. purple & blue on blue 15·00 3·00
168. 2s. 6d. blk. & red on blue 25·00 3·00
169. **32.** 5s. grn., & red on yellow 18·00 16·00
170. 10s. green & red on green 48·00 48·00
171. £1 purple & black on red £225 £150

OFFICIAL STAMPS

1904. Optd. **OFFICIAL.**

O 1. **31.** ½d. green .. .. .. 3·00 35
O 2. 1d. red .. .. .. 1·50 60
O 3. 2d. red and olive .. 11·00 7·50
O 4. 3d. purple and grey .. 7·00 4·00
O 5. 6d. green and purple .. 24·00 25·00
O 6. 1s. red and blue .. .. 60·00 £100

NAURU

An island in the W. Pacific Ocean, formerly a German possession and then administered by Australia under trusteeship. Became a Republic on the 31 January 1968.

1916. 12 pence = 1 shilling;
20 shillings = 1 pound.
1966. 100 cents = 1 Australian dollar.

1916. Stamps of Gt. Britain (King George V) optd. **NAURU.**

1. **105.** ½d. green .. .. 30 3·00
2. **104.** 1d. red .. .. .. 60 2·50
15. **105.** 1½d. brown .. .. 28·00 55·00
4. **106.** 2d. orange .. .. 1·75 8·00
6. **104.** 2½d. blue .. .. 2·75 5·00
7. **106.** 3d. violet .. .. 2·00 3·50
8. 4d. green .. .. 2·00 8·00
9. **107.** 5d. brown .. .. 2·25 8·50
10. 6d. purple .. .. 3·25 10·00
11. **108.** 9d. black .. .. 8·00 19·00
12. 1s. brown .. .. 7·00 19·00
25. **109.** 2s. 6d. brown .. .. 60·00 85·00
22. 5s. red £110 £150
23. 10s. blue £300 £400

4.

6.

1924.

26. **4.** ½d. brown .. .. .. 60 2·75
27. 1d. green .. .. .. 1·50 2·75
28. 1½d. red .. .. .. 90 1·50
29. 2d. orange .. .. 2·25 6·00
30b. 2½d. blue .. .. .. 1·25 3·50
31a. 3d. blue .. .. .. 1·50 5·50
32. 4d. green .. .. .. 3·50 6·00
33. 5d. brown .. .. 3·25 3·75
34. 6d. violet .. .. 3·00 3·50
35. 9d. brown .. .. 5·50 17·00
36. 1s. red .. .. .. 5·00 2·75
37. 2s. 6d. green .. .. 24·00 28·00
38. 5s. red .. .. .. 35·00 48·00
39. 10s. yellow .. .. 85·00 85·00

1935. Silver Jubilee. Optd. **HIS MAJESTY'S JUBILEE, 1910-1935.**

40. **4.** 1½d. red 60 80
41. 2d. orange .. .. .. 1·00 4·00
42. 2½d. blue .. .. .. 1·50 1·50
43. 1s. red .. .. .. 4·00 3·50

1937. Coronation.

44. **6.** 1½d. red 45 40
45. 2d. orange 45 75
46. 2½d. blue 45 30
47. 1s. purple 85 75

8. Anibare Bay.

18. "Iyo" ("calophyllum").

21. White Tern.

1954.

48. – ½d. violet 20 10
49. **8.** 1d. green 30 20
50. – 3½d. red .. .. .. 1·50 15
51. – 4d. blue .. .. .. 1·50 60
52. – 6d. orange 70 15
53. – 9d. red 50 15
54. – 1s. purple 30 15
55. – 2s. 6d. green .. .. 2·50 60
56. – 5s. mauve .. .. .. 8·00 2·00

DESIGNS—HORIZ. ½d. Nauruan netting fish. 3½d., Loading phosphate from cantilever. 4d. Great frigate bird. 6d. Canoe. 9d. "Domaneab" (Meeting House). 2s. 6d., Buada Lagoon. VERT. 1s. Palm trees. 5s. Map of Nauru.

1963.

57. – 2d. multicoloured .. 1·00 1·50
58. – 3d. multicoloured .. 75 35
59. **18.** 5d. multicoloured .. 75 75
60. – 8d. black and green .. 2·00 80
61. – 10d. black 50 30
62. **21.** 1s. 3d. blue, black & green 3·50 1·75
63. – 2s. 3d. blue .. .. 3·00 55
64. – 3s. 3d. multicoloured .. 4·50 2·50

DESIGNS—As Type **21**—VERT. 2d. Micronesian pigeon. As Type **18**—HORIZ. 3d. Poison nut (flower) 8d. Black lizard. 3s. 3d., Finsch's reed warbler. (26 × 29 mm.): 10d. Capparis (flower). (26 × 21 mm.): 2s. 3d., Coral pinnacles.

1965. 50th Anniv. of Gallipoli Landing. As T **184** of Australia, but slightly larger (22 × 34½ mm.).

65. 5d. sepia, black and green 15 10

24. Anibare Bay.

1966. Decimal currency. As earlier issues but with values in cents and dollars as in T **24.** Some colours changed.

66. **24.** 1 c. blue 15 10
67. – 2 c. purple (As No. 48) .. 15 20
68. – 3 c. green (As No. 50) .. 30 30
69. – 4 c. multicoloured (As T **18**) 25 10
70. – 5 c. blue (As No. 54) .. 25 30
71. – 7 c. black and brown (As No. 60) 25 10
72. – 8 c. green (As No. 61) .. 30 10
73. – 10 c. red (As No. 51) .. 40 10
74. – 15 c. blue, black and green (As T **21**) .. .. 80 1·00
75. – 25 c. brown (As No. 63) .. 45 40
76. – 30 c. mult. (As No. 58) .. 70 30
77. – 35 c. mult. (As No. 64) .. 1·25 35
78. – 50 c. mult. (As No. 57) .. 2·50 80
79. – $1 mauve (As No. 56) .. 2·00 1·00

The 25 c. is as No. 63 but larger, 27½ × 25 mm.

1968. Nos. 66/79 optd. **REPUBLIC OF NAURU.**

80. **24.** 1 c. blue 10 20
81. – 2 c. purple 10 10
82. – 3 c. green 15 10
83. – 4 c. multicoloured .. 15 10
84. – 5 c. blue 15 10
85. – 7 c. black and brown .. 25 10
86. – 8 c. green 25 10
87. – 10 c. red 30 15
88. – 15 c. blue, black and green 2·75 2·50
89. – 25 c. brown 30 15
90. – 30 c. multicoloured .. 55 15
91. – 35 c. multicoloured .. 1·25 30
92. – 50 c. multicoloured .. 2·00 50
93. – $1 purple .. .. .. 1·25 75

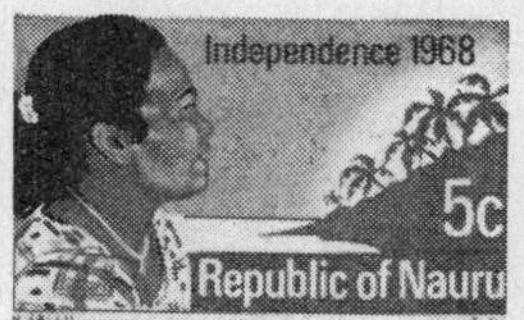

27. "Towards the Sunrise".

1968. Independence.

94. **27.** 5 c. multicoloured .. 10 10
95. – 10 c. black, green & blue 10 10

DESIGN: 10 c. Planting Seedling, and Map.

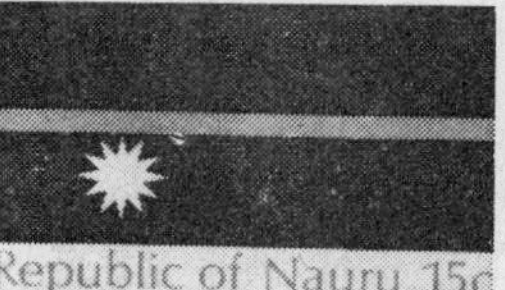

29. Flag of Independent Nauru.

1969.

96. **29.** 15 c. yellow, orange & blue 15 15

30. Island "C" and Stars.

1972. 25th Anniv. of South Pacific Commission.

97. **30.** 25 c. multicoloured .. 30 25

1973. 5th Anniv. of Independence. No. 96 optd. **Independence 1968-1973.**

98. **29.** 15 c. yellow, orge. & blue 20 30

INDEX

Countries can be quickly located by referring to the index at the end of this volume.

32. Denea.

33. Artefacts and Map.

1973. Multicoloured.

99. 1 c. Ekwenababae .. 40 20
100. 2 c. Kauwe ind 55 20
101. 3 c. Rimone 55 20
102. 4 c. Type **32** 55 30
103. 5 c. Erekogo 55 30
104. 7 c. Ikimago (fish) .. 30 20
105. 8 c. Catching flying-fish 30 20
106. 10 c. Itsibweb (ball game) 30 20
107. 15 c. Nauruan wrestling 35 20
108. 20 c. Great frigate birds 50 30
109. 25 c. Nauruan girl .. 50 30
110. 30 c. Catching common noddy birds 85 40
111. 50 c. Great frigate birds 1·75 75
112. $1 Type **33** .. .. 2·00 75

Nos. 104/106 and 110/111 are horiz. designs.

34. Co-op Store.

1973. 50th Anniv. of Nauru Co-operative Society. Multicoloured.

113. 5 c. Type **34** 20 30
114. 25 c. T. Detudamo (founder) 20 15
115. 50 c. N.C.S. trademark (vert.) 45 55

35. Phosphate Mining.

1974. 175th Anniv. of First Contact with the Outside World. Multicoloured.

116. 7 c. M.V. "Eigamoiya" (bulk carrier) .. .. 1·25 90
117. 10 c. Type **35** .. .. 1·00 25
118. 15 c. Fokker Friendship "Nauru Chief" .. .. 1·00 30
119. 25 c. Nauruan chief in early times .. .. 1·25 35
120. 35 c. Capt. Fearn and H.M.S. "Hunter" .. 5·50 2·50
121. 50 c. H.M.S. "Hunter" off Nauru .. .. .. 2·50 1·40

36. Map of Nauru.

37. Rev. P. A. Delaporte.

1974. Centenary of U.P.U. Multicoloured.

122. 5 c. Type **36** 20 20
123. 8 c. Nauru Post Office .. 20 20
124. 20 c. Nauruan postman .. 20 10
125. $1 U.P.U. Building and Nauruan flag 50 60

1974. Christmas and 75th Anniv. of Rev. Delaporte's Arrival.

127. **37.** 15 c. multicoloured .. 20 20
128. 20 c. multicoloured .. 30 30

38. Map of Nauru, Lump of Phosphate Rock and Albert Ellis.

1975. Phosphate Mining Anniversaries. Mult.

129.	5 c. Type **38**	30	30
130.	7 c. Coolies and mine ..	40	30
131.	15 c. Electric railway, barges and ship ..	1·00	90
132.	25 c. Modern ore extraction	1·25	1·00

ANNIVERSARIES. 5 c. 75th Anniversary of discovery. 7 c. 70th Anniversary of Mining Agreement. 15 c. 55th Anniversary of British Phosphate Commissioners. 25 c. 5th Anniversary of Nauru Phosphate Corporation.

39. Micronesian Outrigger.

1975. South Pacific Commission Conf., Nauru (1st issue). Multicoloured.

133.	20 c. Type **39**	75	40
134.	20 c. Polynesian double-hull	75	40
135.	20 c. Melanesian outrigger	75	40
136.	20 c. Polynesian outrigger	75	40

40. New Civic Centre.

1975. South Pacific Commission Conf., Nauru (2nd issue). Multicoloured.

137.	30 c. Type **40**	15	15
138.	50 c. Domaneab (meeting-house) ..	30	30

41. " Our Lady " (Yaren Church).

1975. Christmas. Stained-glass Windows. Multicoloured.

139.	5 c. Type **41**	15	10
140.	7 c. " Suffer little children . . ." (Orro Church) ..	15	10
141.	15 c. As 7 c.	30	20
142.	25 c. Type **41**	45	35

42. Flowers floating towards Nauru.

1976. 30th Anniv. of Islanders' Return from Truk. Multicoloured.

143.	10 c. Type **42**	10	10
144.	14 c. Nauru encircled by garland	15	10
145.	25 c. Finsch's reed warbler and maps	35	25
146.	40 c. Arrival of islanders ..	45	35

43. 3d. and 9d. Stamps of 1916.

1976. 60th Anniv. of Nauruan Stamps. Mult.

147.	10 c. Type **43**	15	15
148.	15 c. 6d. and 1s. stamps ..	20	15
149.	25 c. 2s.6d. stamp ..	30	25
150.	50 c. 5s. " Specimen " stamp	40	35

44. "Pandanus mei" and "Enna G" (cargo liner).

1976. South Pacific Forum, Nauru. **Mult.**

151.	10 c. Type **44**	15	10
152.	20 c. " Tournefortia argentea " and Nauruan aircraft ..	20	15
153.	30 c. " Thespesia populnea " and Nauru Tracking Station	25	15
154.	40 c. " Cordia Subcordata " and produce	35	25

45. Nauruan Choir.

1976. Christmas. Multicoloured.

155.	15 c. Type **45**	10	10
156.	15 c. Nauruan choir ..	10	10
157.	20 c. Angel in white dress	15	15
158.	20 c. Angel in red dress ..	15	15

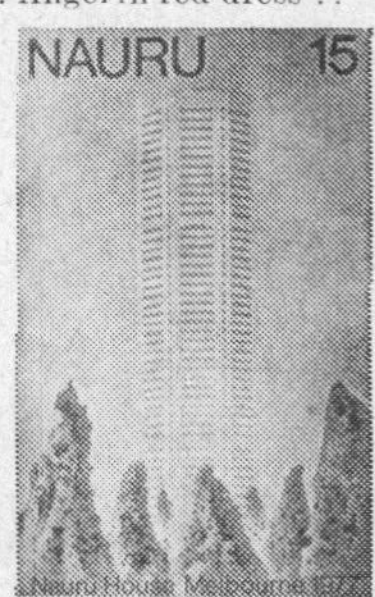

46. Nauru House and Coral Pinnacles.

1977. Opening of Nauru House, Melbourne. Multicoloured.

159.	15 c. Type **46**	15	15
160.	30 c. Nauru House and Melbourne skyline ..	25	25

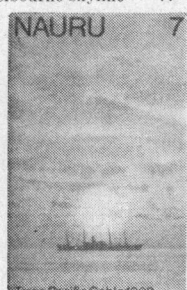

47. Cable Ship "Anglia".

1977. 75th Anniv. of First Trans-Pacific Cable and 20th Anniv. of First Artificial Earth Satellite.

161. **47.**	7 c. multicoloured ..	25	10
162. –	15 c. blue, grey & black	35	15
163. –	20 c. blue, grey & black	35	20
164. –	25 c. multicoloured ..	35	20

DESIGNS: 15 c. Tracking station, Nauru. 20 c. Stern of " Anglia ". 25 c. Dish aerial.

48. Father Kayser and First Catholic Church.

1977. Christmas. Multicoloured.

165.	15 c. Type **48**	10	10
166.	25 c. Congregational Church, Orro	15	15
167.	30 c. Catholic Church, Arubo	15	15

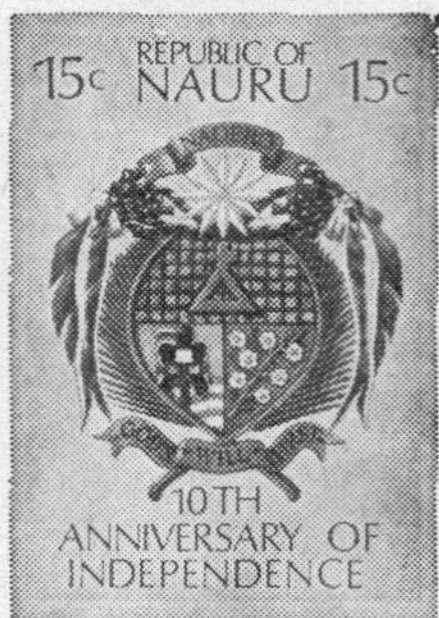

49. Arms of Nauru.

1978. 10th Anniv. of Independence.

168. **49.**	15 c. multicoloured ..	20	15
169.	60 c. multicoloured ..	35	30

1978. Nos. 159/60 surch.

170. **46.**	4 c. on 15 c. mult. ..	2·50	4·50
171.	5 c. on 15 c. mult. ..	2·50	4·50
172. –	8 c. on 30 c. mult. ..	2·50	4·50
173. –	10 c. on 30 c. mult. ..	2·50	4·50

51. Collecting Shellfish.

1978.

174. **51.**	1 c. multicoloured ..	20	20
175. –	2 c. Coral outcrop ..	20	20
176. –	3 c. White-capped Noddy	20	20
177. –	4 c. Girl with fish ..	25	20
178. –	5 c. Eastern Reef Heron	60	30
179. –	7 c. multicoloured ..	20	10
180. –	10 c. multicoloured ..	20	15
181. –	15 c. multicoloured ..	20	30
182. –	20 c. grey, black & blue	30	25
183. –	25 c. multicoloured ..	30	30
184. –	30 c. multicoloured ..	1·00	45
185. –	32 c. multicoloured ..	85	35
186. –	40 c. multicoloured ..	1·25	55
187. –	50 c. multicoloured ..	85	45
188. –	$1 multicoloured ..	70	55
189. –	$2 multicoloured ..	95	1·00
190. –	$5 grey, black and blue	1·75	2·25

DESIGNS: 7 c. Catching fish, Buada Lagoon. 10 c. Ijuw Lagoon. 15 c. Girl framed by coral. 20 c. Pinnacles, Anibare Bay reef. 25 c. Pinnacle at Meneng. 30 c. Head of Great Frigate-bird. 32 c. White-capped Noddy birds in coconut palm. 40 c. Wandering Tattler 50 c. Great Frigate Birds on perch. $1, Old coral pinnacles at Topside. $2, New pinnacles at Topside. $5, Blackened pinnacles at Topside.

52. A.P.U. Emblem.

1978. 14th General Assembly of Asian Parliamentarians' Union, Nauru.

191. **52.**	15 c. multicoloured ..	20	25
192. –	20 c. black, blue & gold	20	25

DESIGN: 20 c. As Type **52**, but with different background.

53. Virgin and Child.

1978. Christmas. Multicoloured.

193.	7 c. Type **53**	10	10
194.	15 c. Angel in sun-rise scene (horiz.)	10	10
195.	20 c. As 15 c.	15	15
196.	30 c. Type **53** ..	20	20

54. Baden-Powell and Cub Scout.

1978. 70th Anniv. of First Scout Troop. Multicoloured.

197.	20 c. Type **54**	20	15
198.	30 c. Scout	25	20
199.	50 c. Rover Scout ..	35	30

55. Wright " Flyer " over Nauru.

1979. Flight Anniversaries. Multicoloured.

200.	10 c. Type **55**	15	10
201.	15 c. " Southern Cross " Boeing " 727 " (nose) ..	25	15
202.	15. c. " Southern Cross" and Boeing " 727 " (front view) ..	25	15
203.	30 c. " Flyer " over Nauru airfield	35	20

ANNIVERSARIES: Nos. 200, 203, 75th anniv. of powered flight. Nos. 201/2, 50th anniv. of Kingsford Smith's Pacific flight.

56. Sir Rowland Hill and Marshall Islands 10 pf. stamp of 1901.

1979. Death Centenary of Sir Rowland Hill. Multicoloured.

204.	5 c. Type **56**	15	10
205.	15 c. Sir Rowland Hill and " Nauru " opt. on G.B. 10s. " Seahorse " stamp 1916–23 ..	25	20
206.	60 c. Sir Rowland Hill and Nauru 60 c. 10th Anniv. of Independence stamp, 1978	55	40

57. Dish Antenna, Transmitting Station and Radio Mast.

1979. 50th Anniv. of International Consultative Radio Committee. Multicoloured.

208.	7 c. Type **57**	15	10
209.	32 c. Telex operator ..	35	25
210.	40 c. Radio operator ..	40	25

58. Smiling Child.

1979. International Year of the Child.

211. **58.**	8 c. multicoloured ..	10	10
212. –	15 c. multicoloured ..	15	15
213. –	25 c. multicoloured ..	20	20
214. –	32 c. multicoloured ..	20	20
215. –	50 c. multicoloured ..	25	25

DESIGNS: 15 c. to 50 c. Smiling **Children.**

59. Ekwenababae (flower), Scroll inscribed " Peace on Earth " and Star.

1979. Christmas. Multicoloured.

216. 7 c. Type **59** 10 10
217. 15 c. " Thespia populnea " (flower), Scroll inscribed " Goodwill toward Men " and star 10 10
218. 20 c. Denea (flower), scroll inscribed " Peace on Earth " and star .. 10 10
219. 30 c. Erekogo (flower), inscribed " Goodwill toward Men " and star 20 20

60. Dassault " Falcon " over Melbourne.

1980. 10th Anniv. of "Air Nauru". Mult.

220. 15 c. Type **60** 30 15
221. 20 c. Fokker "F28 Fellowship " over Tarawa .. 35 15
222. 25 c. Boeing " 727 " over Hong Kong 35 15
223. 30 c. Boeing " 737 " over Auckland.. .. .. 35 15

61. Steam Locomotive.

1980. 10th Anniv. of Nauru Phosphate Corporate. Multicoloured.

224. 8 c. Type **61** 10 10
225. 32 c. Electric locomotive .. 20 20
226. 60 c. Diesel locomotive .. 35 35

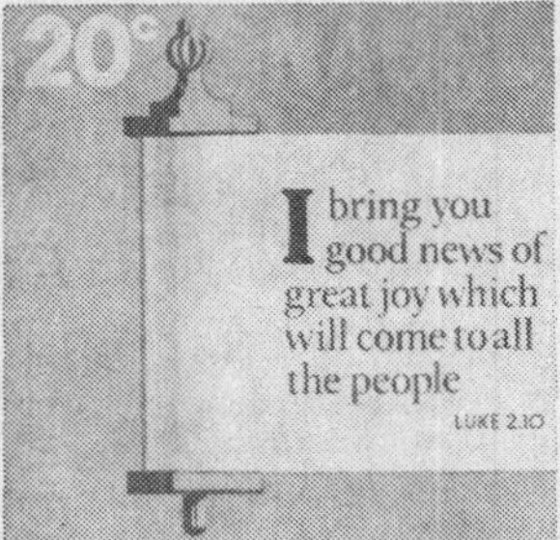

62. Verse 10 from Luke, Chapter 2 in English.

1980. Christmas. Verses from Luke, Chapter 2. Multicoloured.

228. 20 c. Type **62** 10 10
229. 20 c. Verse 10 in Nauruan 10 10
230. 30 c. Verse 14 in English.. 15 15
231. 30 c. Verse 14 in Nauruan 15 15

See also Nos. 248/51.

63. Nauruan, Australian, Union and New Zealand Flags on Aerial View of Nauru

1980. 20th Anniv. of U.N. Declaration on the Granting of Independence to Colonial Countries and Peoples. Multicoloured.

232. 25 c. Type **63** 15 15
233. 30 c. U.N. Trusteeship Council (72 × 23 mm.) .. 15 15
234. 50 c. Nauru independence ceremony, 1968.. .. 25 25

64. Timothy Detudamo.

1981. 30th Anniv. of Nauru Local Government Council, Head Chiefs. Multicoloured.

235. 20 c. Type **64** 15 15
236. 30 c. Raymond Gadabu .. 15 15
237. 50 c. Hammer DeRoburt 25 25

65. Casting Net by Hand.

1981. Fishing. Multicoloured.

238. 8 c. Type **65** 10 10
239. 20 c. Outrigger canoe .. 20 15
240. 32 c. Outboard motor boat 25 20
241. 40 c. Trawler 30 25

66. Bank of Nauru Emblem and Building.

1981. 5th Anniv. of Bank of Nauru.

243. **66.** $1 multicoloured .. 60 60

67. Inaugural Speech.

1981. U.N. Day. E.S.C.A.P. (United Nations Economic and Social Commission for Asia and the Pacific) Events. Multicoloured.

244. 15 c. Type **67** 15 15
245. 20 c. Presenting credentials 15 15
246. 25 c. Unveiling plaque .. 20 20
247. 30 c. Raising U.N. flag .. 25 25

1981. Christmas. Bible Verses. Designs as T **62**. Multicoloured.

248. 20 c. Matthew 1, 23 in English 15 15
249. 20 c. Matthew 1, 23 in Nauruan .. 15 15
250. 30 c. Luke 2, 11 in English 20 20
251. 30 c. Luke 2, 11 in Nauruan 20 20

68. Earth Satellite Station.

1981. 10th Anniv. of South Pacific Forum. Multicoloured.

252. 10 c. Type **68** 30 20
253. 20 c. "Enna G" (cargo liner) 35 25
254. 30 c. Airliner 35 30
255. 40 c. Local produce .. 45 40

MINIMUM PRICE

The minimum price quoted is 10p which represents a handling charge rather than a basis for valuing common stamps. For further notes about prices see introductory pages.

69. Nauru Scouts leaving for 1935 Frankston Scout Jamboree.

1982. 75th Anniv. of Boy Scout Movement. Multicoloured.

256 7 c. Type **69** 15 15
257 8 c. Two Nauru scouts on "Nauru Chief", 1935 (vert) 15 15
258 15 c. Nauru scouts making pottery, 1935 (vert) .. 20 20
259 20 c. Lord Huntingfield addressing Nauru scouts, Frankston Jamboree, 1935 .. .. 25 25
260 25 c. Nauru cub and scout, 1982 .. .. 30 30
261 40 c. Nauru cubs, scouts and scouters, 1982 .. 45 45

70. 100 kW Electricity Generating Plant under Construction (left side).

1982. Ocean Thermal Energy Conversion Multicoloured.

263. 25 c. Type **70** .. 50 30
264. 25 c. 100 kW Electricity Generating Plant under construction (right side) 50 30
265. 40 c. Completed plant (left) 70 40
266. 40 c. Completed plant (right) 70 40

Nos. 263/4 and 265/6 were each issued as horizontal se-tenant pairs, forming composite designs.

71. S.S. " Fido ".

1982. 75th Anniv. of Phosphate Shipments. Multicoloured.

267. 5 c. Type **71** 40 10
268. 10 c. Steam locomotive "Nellie" 75 20
269. 30 c. Modern "Clyde" class diesel locomotive .. 1·00 50
270. 60 c. M.V. "Eigamoiya" (bulk carrier) .. .. 1·40 80

72. Queen Elizabeth II on Horseback.

1982. Royal Visit. Multicoloured.

272. 20 c. Type **72** 40 30
273. 50 c. Prince Philip, Duke of Edinburgh 75 60
274. $1 Queen Elizabeth II and Prince Philip (horiz.) .. 1·40 1·25

73. Father Bernard Lahn.

1982. Christmas. Multicoloured.

275 10 c. Type **73** 35 30
276 30 c. Reverend Itubwa Amram 40 45
277 40 c. Pastor James Aingimen 45 60
278 50 c. Bishop Paul Mea .. 50 90

74. Speaker of the Nauruan Parliament.

1983. 15th Anniv. of Independence. Mult.

279. 15 c. Type **74** 15 15
280. 20 c. Family Court in session 20 20
281. 30 c. Law Courts building (horiz.) 25 25
282. 50 c. Parliamentary chamber (horiz.) .. 40 40

75. Nauru Satellite Earth Station.

1983. World Communications Year. Mult

283. 5 c. Type **75** 10 10
284. 10 c. Omni-directional range installation .. 15 15
285. 20 c. Emergency short-wave radio 20 25
286. 25 c. Radio Nauru control room 30 30
287. 40 c. Unloading air mail .. 45 45

76. Return of Exiles from Truk on M.V. " Trienza ", 1946.

1983. Angam Day. Multicoloured.

288. 15 c. Type **76** 20 25
289. 20 c. Mrs. Elsie Agio (exiled community leader) .. 20 25
290. 30 c. Child on scales .. 35 40
291. 40 c. Nauruan children .. 45 50

77. " The Holy Virgin, Holy Child and St. John " (School of Raphael).

1983. Christmas. Multicoloured.

292. 5 c. Type **77** 10 10
293. 15 c. "Madonna on the Throne, surrounded by Angels" (School of Sevilla) (horiz.) 15 15
294. 50 c. "The Mystical Betrothal of St. Catherine with Jesus" (School of Veronese) 40 40

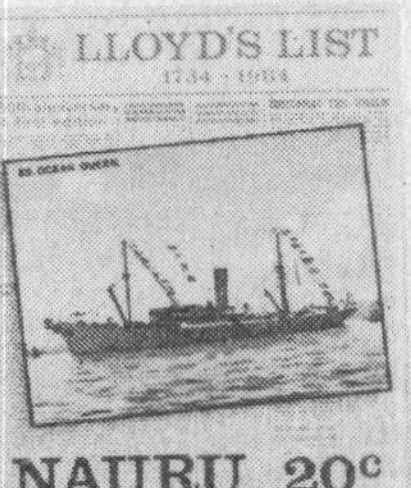

78. S.S. " Ocean Queen ".

1984. 250th Anniv. of "Lloyd's List" (newspaper). Multicoloured.
295. 20 c. Type **78** 45 30
296. 25 c. M.V. "Enna G" .. 50 35
297. 30 c. M.V. "Baron Minto" 55 40
298. 40 c. Sinking of M.V. "Triadic", 1940 .. .. 75 55

79. 1974 U.P.U. $1 Stamp.

1984. Universal Postal Union Congress. Hamburg.
299. **79.** $1 multicoloured .. 1·10 1·25

80. "Hypolimnas bolina" (female).

1984. Butterflies. Multicoloured
300 25 c. Type **80** 50 40
301 30 c. "Hypolimnas bolina" (male) 55 55
302 50 c. "Danaus plexippus" 70 85

81. Coastal Scene.

1984. Life in Nauru. Multicoloured.
303. 1 c. Type **81** 10 15
304. 3 c. Nauruan woman (vert.) 10 15
305. 5 c. Modern trawler .. 15 15
306. 10 c. Golfer on the links .. 30 20
307. 15 c. Excavating phosphate (vert.) 35 30
308. 20 c. Surveyor (vert.) .. 30 30
309. 25 c. Air Nauru airliner .. 35 35
310. 30 c. Elderly Nauruan (vert.) 35 35
311. 40 c. Loading hospital patient on to aircraft .. 40 40
312. 50 c. Skin-diver with fish (vert.) 55 55
313. $1 Tennis player (vert.) .. 1·25 1·25
314. $2 Anabar Lagoon .. 1·75 1·75

82. Buada Chapel.

1984. Christmas. Multicoloured.
315. 30 c. Type **82** 60 50
316. 40 c. Detudamo Memorial Church 80 65
317. 50 c. Candle-light service, Kayser College (horiz.) 90 70

83. Air Nauru Jet on Tarmac.

1985. 15th Anniv. of Air Nauru. Mult.
318. 20 c. Type **83** 55 35
319. 30 c. Stewardesses on aircraft steps (vert.) .. 70 60
320. 40 c. Fokker "F28" over Nauru 85 75
321. 50 c. Freight being loaded onto Boeing "727" (vert.) .. .. .. 1·00 85

84. Open Cut Mining.

1985. 15th Anniv. of Nauru Phosphate Corporation. Multicoloured.
322. 20 c. Type **84** 70 60
323. 25 c. Diesel locomotive hauling crushed ore .. 1·25 1·00
324. 30 c. Phosphate drying plant .. .. 1·25 1·00
325. 50 c. Early steam locomotive .. .. .. 2·00 1·75

85. Mother and Baby on Beach.

1985. Christmas. Multicoloured.
326. 50 c. Beach scene .. .. 1·25 1·25
327. 50 c. Type **85** .. .. 2·50 2·50
Nos. 326/7 were printed se-tenant forming a composite design.

86. Adult Common Noddy with Juvenile.

1985. Birth Bicentenary of John J. Audubon (ornithologist). Brown Noddy. Multicoloured.
328. 10 c. Type **86** 35 35
329. 20 c. Adult and immature birds in flight .. 50 70
330. 30 c. Adults in flight .. 65 85
331. 50 c. Common noddy (John J. Audubon) .. 80 1·10

87. Douglas Motor Cycle.

1986. Early Transport on Nauru. Mult.
332. 15 c. Type **87** 60 60
333. 20 c. Primitive lorry .. 75 75
334. 30 c. German 2 ft gauge locomotive (1910) .. 1·00 1·00
335. 40 c. "Baby" Austin car .. 1·25 1·25

88. Island and Bank of Nauru.

1986. 10th Anniv. of Bank of Nauru. Children's Paintings. Multicoloured.
336. 20 c. Type **88** 30 30
337. 25 c. Borrower with notes and coins 35 35
338. 30 c. Savers 40 40
339. 40 c. Customers at bank counter 55 55

89. "Plumeria rubra".

1986. Flowers. Multicoloured.
340. 20 c. Type **89** 55 70
341. 25 c. "Tristellateia australia" 65 85
342. 30 c. "Bougainvillea cultivar" .. .. 75 1·00
343. 40 c. "Delonix regia" .. 1·00 1·25

90. Carol Singers.

1986. Christmas. Multicoloured.
344. 20 c. Type **90** 45 30
345. $1 Carol singers and hospital patient .. 2·00 1·75

91. Young Girls Dancing.

1987. Nauruan Dancers. Multicoloured.
346. 20 c. Type **91** 55 55
347. 30 c. Stick dance 75 85
348. 50 c. Boy doing war dance (vert.) .. .. .. 1·25 1·50

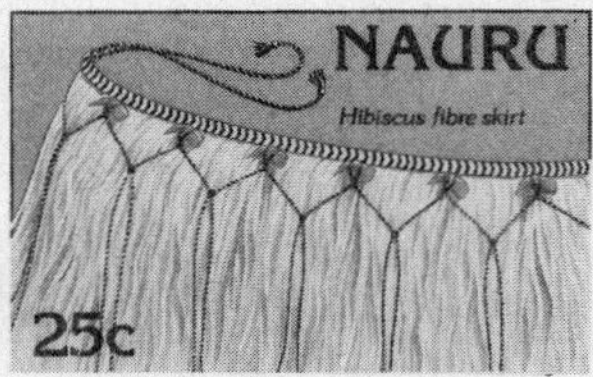

92. Hibiscus Fibre Skirt.

1987. Personal Artefacts. Multicoloured.
349. 25 c. Type **92** 75 75
350. 30 c. Headband and necklets 85 85
351. 45 c. Decorative necklets .. 1·10 1·10
352. 60 c. Pandanus leaf fan .. 1·60 1·60

93. U.P.U. Emblem and Air Mail Label.

1987. World Post Day.
353. **93.** 40 c. multicoloured .. 65 65

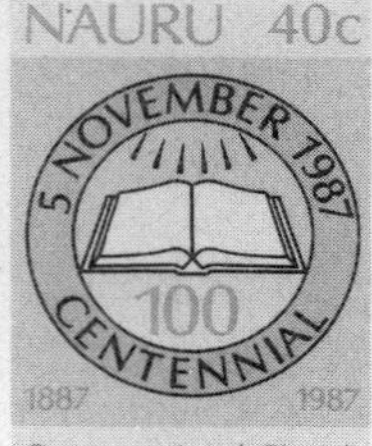

94. Open Bible.

1987. Centenary of Nauru Congregational Church.
355. **94.** 40 c. multicoloured .. 65 80

95. Nauruan Children's Party.

1987. Christmas. Multicoloured.
356. 20 c. Type **95** 75 35
357. $1 Nauruan Christmas dinner .. .. .. 2·75 2·75

96. Loading Phosphate on Ship.

1988. 20th Anniv. of Independence. Multicoloured.
358. 25 c. Type **96** 70 70
359. 40 c. Tomano flower (vert.) 1·25 1·25
360. 55 c. Frigate bird (vert.) .. 1·75 1·75
361. $1 Arms of Republic (35 × 35 mm.) .. .. 2·00 2·25

97 Map of German Marshall Is. and 1901 5 m. Yacht Definitive

1988. 80th Anniv of Nauru Post Office. Mult.
362 30 c. Type **97** 30 35
363 50 c. Letter and post office of 1908 .. .. .. 50 55
364 70 c. Nauru Post Office and airmail letter .. 65 [illegible]

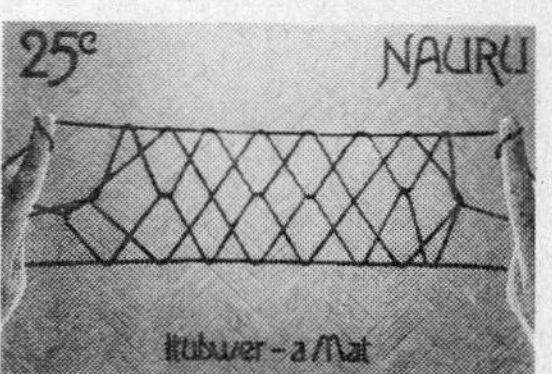

98 "Itubwer" (mat)

1988. String Figures. Multicoloured.
365 25 c. Type **98** 25 30
366 40 c. "Etegerer–the Pursuer" 40 45
367 55 c. "Holding up the Sky" 50 55
368 80 c. "Manujie's Sword" .. 75 80

99 U.P.U. Emblem and National Flag

1988. Cent of Nauru's Membership of U.P.U.

No.	Description	Unused	Used
369 99	$1 multicoloured	95	1·00

100 "Hark the Herald Angels"

1988. Christmas. Designs showing words and music from "Hark the Herald Angels Sing".

No.	Description	Unused	Used
370 100	20 c. black, red & yell	20	25
371 –	60 c. blk, red & mauve	55	60
372 –	$1 black, red and green	95	1·00

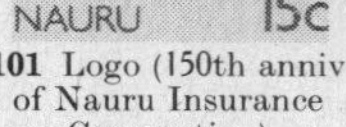

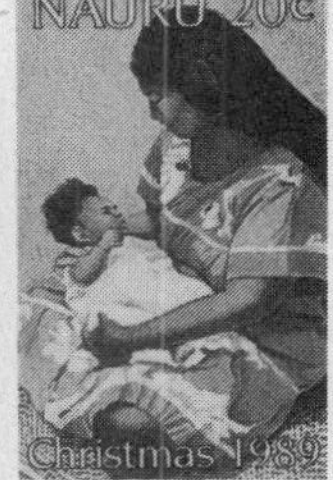

101 Logo (150th anniv of Nauru Insurance Corporation) 102 Mother and Baby

1989. Aniversaries and Events. Mult.

No.	Description	Unused	Used
373	15 c. Type **101**	15	30
374	50 c. Logos (World Telecommunications Day and 10th anniv of Asian-Pacific Telecommunity)	50	75
375	$1 Photograph of island scene (150 years of photography)	95	1·40
376	$2 Capitol and U.P.U. emblem (20th U.P.U. Congress, Washington)	1·90	2·50

1989. Christmas. Multicoloured.

No.	Description	Unused	Used
377	20 c. Type **102**	30	30
378	$1 Children opening presents	1·50	1·75

103 Eigigu working while Sisters play 104 Early Mining by Hand

1989. 20th Anniv of First Manned Landing on Moon. Legend of "Eigigu, the Girl in the Moon". Multicoloured.

No.	Description	Unused	Used
379	25 c. Type **103**	70	70
380	30 c. Eigigu climbing tree	80	80
381	50 c. Eigigu stealing toddy from blind woman	1·50	1·50
382	$1 Eigigu on Moon	2·75	2·75

1990. 20th Anniv of Nauru Phosphate Corporation. Multicoloured.

No.	Description	Unused	Used
383	50 c. Type **104**	65	65
384	$1 Modern mining by excavator	1·25	1·25

105 Sunday School Class 106 Eoiyepiang laying Baby on Mat

1990. Christmas. Multicoloured.

No.	Description	Unused	Used
385	25 c. Type **105**	40	40
386	25 c. Teacher telling Christmas story	40	40

Nos. 385/6 were printed together, se-tenant, forming a composite design.

1990. Legend of "Eoiyepiang, the Daughter of Thunder and Lightning". Multicoloured.

No.	Description	Unused	Used
387	25 c. Type **106**	20	25
388	30 c. Eoiyepiang making floral decoration	25	30
389	50 c. Eoiyepiang left on snow-covered mountain	45	50
390	$1 Eoiyepiang and warrior	85	90

107 Oleander

1991. Flowers. Multicoloured.

No.	Description	Unused	Used
391	15 c. Type **107**	15	20
392	20 c. Lily	20	25
393	25 c. Passion flower	20	25
394	30 c. Lily (different)	30	35
395	35 c. Caesalpinia	30	35
396	40 c. Clerodendron	35	40
397	45 c. "Baubina pinnata"	40	45
398	50 c. Hibiscus (vert)	45	40
399	75 c. Apocymaceae	70	75
400	$1 Bindweed (vert)	90	95
401	$2 Tristellateia (vert)	1·90	2·00
402	$3 Impala lily (vert)	2·75	3·00

109 Star and Symbol of Asian Development Bank

1992. 25th Annual Meeting of Asian Development Bank.

No.	Description	Unused	Used
404 109	$1.50 multicoloured	1·40	1·50

NAWANAGAR

A state of India, Bombay District. Now uses Indian stamps.

6 docra = 1 anna.

1. (1 docra). 2. (2 docra).

1877. Imperf. or perf.

No.	Description	Unused	Used
1. 1.	1 doc. blue	40	17·00

1880. Imperf.

No.	Description	Unused	Used
3a. 2.	1 doc. lilac	1·00	2·50
5.	2 doc. green	1·50	5·00
6a.	3 doc. yellow	3·00	7·00

4. (1 docra).

1893. Imperf. or perf.

No.	Description	Unused	Used
11 4.	1 doc. black	50	2·00
12	2 doc. green	50	2·25
13b	3 doc. yellow	60	3·50

NEGRI SEMBILAN

A state of the Federation of Malaya, incorporated in Malaysia in 1963.

100 cents = 1 dollar (Straits or Malayan).

1891. Stamp of Straits Settlements optd. **Negri Sembilan.**

No.	Description	Unused	Used
1. 5.	2 c. red	2·25	4·00

2. Tiger. 3.

1891.

No.	Description	Unused	Used
2. 2.	1 c. green	2·50	1·00
3.	2 c. red	3·25	3·75
4.	5 c. blue	22·00	26·00

1896.

No.	Description	Unused	Used
5. 3.	1 c. purple and green	4·00	2·50
6.	2 c. purple and brown	22·00	65·00
7.	3 c. purple and red	2·50	60
8.	5 c. purple and yellow	4·50	5·50
9.	8 c. purple and blue	22·00	13·00
10.	10 c. purple and orange	24·00	12·00
11.	15 c. green and violet	27·00	48·00
12.	20 c. green and olive	30·00	35·00
13.	25 c. green and red	55·00	70·00
14.	50 c. green and black	48·00	55·00

1898. Surch. in words and bar.

No.	Description	Unused	Used
15. 3.	1 c. on 15 c. grn. & violet	75·00	£150
16. 2.	4 c. on 1 c. green	1·00	9·00
17. 3.	4 c. on 3 c. purple and red	3·00	11·00
18. 2.	4 c. on 5 c. blue	1·00	8·50

1898. Surch. in words only.

No.	Description	Unused	Used
19. 3.	4 c. on 8 c. purple and blue	2·00	3·25

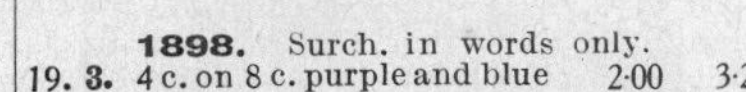

6. Arms of Negri Sembilan. 7.

1935.

No.	Description	Unused	Used
21. 6.	1 c. black	40	10
22.	2 c. green	70	20
23.	2 c. orange	60	24·00
24.	3 c. green	1·25	5·00
25.	4 c. orange	30	10
26.	5 c. brown	50	10
27.	6 c. red	4·50	1·75
28.	6 c. grey	2·25	45·00
29.	8 c. grey	1·75	10
30.	10 c. purple	30	10
31.	12 c. blue	1·00	25
32.	15 c. blue	3·25	30·00
33.	25 c. purple and red	75	70
34.	30 c. purple and orange	4·00	2·00
35.	40 c. red and purple	85	2·00
36.	50 c. black on green	3·50	1·25
37.	$1 black and red on blue	1·60	2·00
38.	$2 green and red	17·00	15·00
39.	$5 green and red on green	13·00	35·00

1948. Silver Wedding. As T **10/11** of Aden.

No.	Description	Unused	Used
40.	10 c. violet	15	15
41.	$5 green	17·00	28·00

1949.

No.	Description	Unused	Used
42 7.	1 c. black	10	10
43	2 c. orange	10	10
44	3 c. green	10	30
45	4 c. brown	10	10
46a	5 c. purple	30	30
47	6 c. grey	15	10
48	8 c. red	20	75
49	8 c. green	1·50	1·25
50	10 c. mauve	15	10
51	12 c. red	1·50	1·50
52	15 c. blue	1·00	10
53	20 c. black and green	25	75
54	20 c. blue	80	10
55	25 c. purple and orange	25	10
56	30 c. red and purple	1·25	1·50
57	35 c. red and purple	70	1·00
58	40 c. red and purple	65	2·50
59	50 c. black and blue	40	10
60	$1 blue and purple	2·00	65
61	$2 green and red	9·00	6·00
62	$5 green and brown	35·00	30·00

1949. U.P.U. As T **20/23** of Antigua.

No.	Description	Unused	Used
63.	10 c. purple	20	10
64.	15 c. blue	45	70
65.	25 c. orange	50	1·50
66.	50 c. black	80	2·50

1953. Coronation. As T **13** of Aden.

No.	Description	Unused	Used
67.	10 c. black and purple	20	10

1957. As Nos. 92/102 of Kedah but inset **Arms of Negri Sembilan.**

No.	Description	Unused	Used
68.	1 c. black	10	10
69.	2 c. red	10	10
70.	4 c. sepia	10	10
71.	5 c. lake	10	10
72.	8 c. green	85	80
73.	10 c. sepia	15	10
74.	10 c. purple	75	10
75.	20 c. blue	20	10
76a.	50 c. black and blue	20	10
77.	$1 blue and purple	1·25	55
78.	$2 green and red	3·75	7·00
79a.	$5 brown and green	10·00	11·00

8. Tuanku Munawir.

1961. Installation of Tuanku Munawir as Yang di- Pertuan Besar of Negri Sembilan.

No.	Description	Unused	Used
80. 8.	10 c. multicoloured	15	15

9. "Vanda hookeriana".

1965. As Nos. 115/21 of Kedah but with Arms of Negri Sembilan inset and inscr. "NEGERI SEMBILAN" as in T **6**.

No.	Description	Unused	Used
81. 9.	1 c. multicoloured	10	30
82. –	2 c. multicoloured	10	30
83. –	5 c. multicoloured	15	10
84. –	6 c. multicoloured	15	30
85. –	10 c. multicoloured	15	10
86. –	15 c. multicoloured	80	10
87. –	20 c. multicoloured	1·25	75

The higher values used in Negri Sembilan were Nos. 20/7 of Malaysia (National Issues).

10. Negri Sembilan Crest and Tuanku Ja'afar.

1968. Installation of Tuanku Ja'afar as Yang di-Pertuan Besar of Negri Sembilan.

No.	Description	Unused	Used
88. 10.	15 c. multicoloured	15	30
89.	50 c. multicoloured	30	1·10

11. "Hebomoia glaucippe".

1971. Butterflies. As Nos. 124/30 of Kedah but with Arms of Negri Sembilan inset as T **11** and inscr. "negeri sembilan".

91. –	1 c. multicoloured ..	15	40
92. –	2 c. multicoloured ..	40	40
93. –	5 c. multicoloured ..	50	10
94. –	6 c. multicoloured ..	50	30
95. **11.**	10 c. multicoloured ..	50	10
96. –	15 c. multicoloured ..	70	10
97. –	20 c. multicoloured ..	80	15

The higher values in use with this issue were Nos. 64/71 of Malaysia (National Issues).

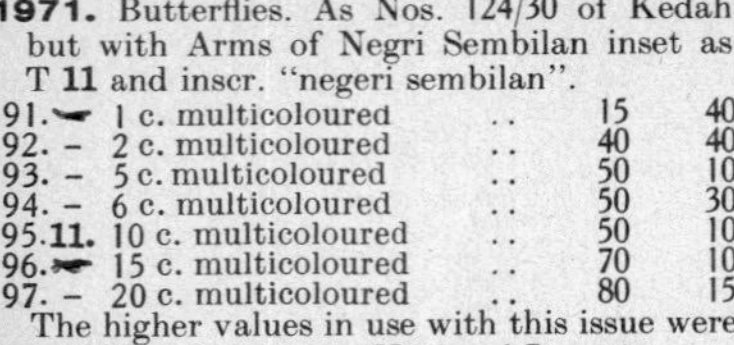

12. "Hibiscus rosa-sinensis".

1979. Flowers. As Nos. 135/41 of Kedah but with Arms of Negri Sembilan and inscr. "negeri sembilan" as in T **12**.

103	1 c. "Rafflesia hasseltii" ..	10	20
104	2 c. "Pterocarpus indicus"	10	20
105	5 c. "Lagerstroemia speciosa"	10	10
106	10 c. "Durio zibethinus" ..	10	10
107	15 c. Type **12**	15	10
108	20 c. "Rhododendron scortechionii"	15	10
109	25 c. "Etlingera elatior" (inscr "Phaeomeria speciosa")	15	10

13. Oil Palm.

1986. As Nos. 152/8 of Kedah but with Arms of Negri Sembilan and inscr. "NEGERI SEMBILAN" as in T **13**

117.	1 c. Coffee	10	10
118.	2 c. Coconuts	10	10
119.	5 c. Cocoa	10	10
120.	10 c. Black pepper ..	10	10
121.	15 c. Rubber	10	10
122.	20 c. Type **13**	10	10
123.	30 c. Rice	10	15

NEVIS

One of the Leeward Islands, Br. W. Indies. Used stamps of St. Kitts–Nevis from 1903 until June 1980 when Nevis, although remaining part of St. Kitts–Nevis, had a separate postal administration.

1861. 12 pence = 1 shilling.
20 shillings = 1 pound.
1980. 100 cents = 1 dollar.

1.

2.

(The design on the stamps refers to a medicinal spring on the island.)

1861. Various frames.

15	**1**	1d. red	15·00	12·00
6	**2**	4d. red	75·00	55·00
12		4d. orange	95·00	19·00
7	–	6d. grey	70·00	40·00
20	–	1s. green	55·00	80·00

5.

1879.

25	**5**	½d. green	2·50	4·50
23		1d. mauve	35·00	26·00
27a		1d. red	3·00	3·25
28		2½d. brown	90·00	45·00
29		2½d. blue	9·00	6·00
30		4d. blue	£275	45·00
31		4d. grey	3·75	2·50
32		6d. green	£350	£350
33		6d. brown	17·00	38·00
34		1s. violet	85·00	£150

1883. Half of No. 26 surch. **NEVIS ½d.**

36. **5.**	½d. on half 1d. mauve ..	£400	25·00

1980. Nos. 394/406 of St. Christopher, Nevis and Anguilla with "St. Christopher" and "Anguilla" obliterated.

37.	5 c. Radio and T.V. station	10	10
38.	10 c. Technical college ..	10	10
39.	12 c. T.V. assembly plant ..	40	40
40.	15 c. Sugar cane being harvested	10	10
41.	25 c. Crafthouse (craft centre)	15	10
42.	30 c. Cruise ship	20	15
43.	40 c. Lobster and sea crab ..	70	70
44.	45 c. Royal St. Kitts Hotel and golf course	70	70
45.	50 c. Pinney's Beach, Nevis	50	50
46.	55 c. New runway at Golden Rock	15	15
47.	$1 Picking cotton	45	45
48.	$5 The Brewery	75	75
49.	$10 Pineapples and peanuts	1·25	1·25

1980. 80th Birthday of Queen Elizabeth the Queen Mother. As T **10** of St. Kitts.

50.	$2 multicoloured	50	50

8. Nevis Lighter.

1980. Boats. Multicoloured.

51.	5 c. Type **8**	10	10
52.	30 c. Local fishing boat ..	15	10
53.	55 c. "Caona" (catamaran)	20	10
54.	$3 "Polynesia" (cruise schooner) (39 × 53 mm.) ..	65	55

9. Virgin and Child.

1980. Christmas. Multicoloured.

55.	5 c. Type **9**	10	10
56.	30 c. Angel	10	10
57.	$2·50 The Wise Men ..	30	30

10. Charlestown Pier.

11. New River Mill.

1981. Multicoloured.

58.	5 c. Type **10**	10	10
59.	10 c. The Court House and Library	10	10
60.	15 c. Type **11**	10	10
61.	20 c. The Nelson Museum	10	10
62.	25 c. St. James' Parish Church	15	15
63.	30 c. Nevis Lane	15	15
64.	40 c. Zetland Plantation ..	20	20
65.	45 c. Nisbet Plantation ..	20	25
66.	50 c. Pinney's Beach ..	25	25
67.	55 c. Eva Wilkin's Studio ..	25	30
68.	$1 Nevis at dawn	50	45
69.	$2.50 Ruins of Fort Charles	90	1·10
70.	$5 The Old Bath House ..	1·50	1·75
71.	$10 Beach at Nisbet's ..	2·75	3·50

1981. Royal Wedding. Royal Yachts. As T **26/27** of Kiribati. Multicoloured.

72	55 c. "Royal Caroline" ..	20	20
73	55 c. Prince Charles and Lady Diana Spencer ..	40	40
74	$2 "Royal Sovereign" ..	40	40
75	$2 As No. 73	80	80
76	$5 "Britannia"	80	80
77	$5 As No. 73	1·50	1·50

12. "Heliconius charithonia".

1982. Butterflies (1st series). Multicoloured.

81	5 c. Type **12**	10	10
82	30 c. "Siproeta stelenes" ..	15	10
83	55 c. "Marpesia petreus" ..	20	15
84	$2 "Phoebis agarithe" ..	60	70

See also Nos. 105/8.

13. Caroline of Brunswick, Princess of Wales, 1793.

1982. 21st Birthday of Princess of Wales. Multicoloured.

85.	30 c. Type **13**	25	20
86.	55 c. Coat of arms of Caroline of Brunswick ..	35	30
87.	$5 Diana, Princess of Wales	1·25	1·40

1982. Birth of Prince William of Wales. Nos. 85/7 optd. **ROYAL BABY.**

88.	30 c. As Type **13**	25	20
89.	55 c. Coat of arms of Caroline of Brunswick ..	35	30
90.	$5 Diana, Princess of Wales	1·25	1·40

14. Cyclist.

1982. 75th Anniv. of Boy Scout Movement. Multicoloured.

91.	5 c. Type **14**	20	10
92.	30 c. Athlete	50	10
93.	$2·50 Camp cook	1·25	80

15. Santa Claus.

1982. Christmas. Children's Paintings. **Mult.**

94.	15 c. Type **15**	10	10
95.	30 c. Carollers	10	10
96.	$1·50 Decorated house and local band (horiz.) ..	25	25
97.	$2·50 Adoration of the Shepherds (horiz.) ..	50	50

16. Tube Sponge.

1983. Corals (1st series). Multicoloured.

98.	15 c. Type **16**	10	10
99.	30 c. Stinging coral ..	15	10
100.	55 c. Flower coral ..	25	10
101.	$3 Sea Rod and Red Fire Sponge	70	80

See also Nos. 423/6.

17. H.M.S. "Boreas" off Nevis.

1983. Commonwealth Day. **Multicoloured.**

103.	55 c. Type **17**	20	10
104.	$2 Capt. Horatio Nelson and H.M.S. "Boreas" at anchor	65	75

1983. Butterflies (2nd series). As Type **12.** Multicoloured.

105	30 c. "Pyrgus oileus" ..	20	15
106	55 c. "Junonia evarete" (vert)	25	20
107	$1.10 "Urbanus proteus" (vert)	50	55
108	$2 "Hypolimnas misippus"	95	1·00

1983. Nos. 58 and 60/71 optd. **INDEPENDENCE 1983.**

109	5 c. Type **10**	10	10
110	15 c. Type **11**	10	10
111	20 c. Nelson Museum ..	10	10
112	25 c. St. James's Parish Church	10	15
113	30 c. Nevis Lane ..	15	15
114	40 c. Zetland Plantation	15	20
115	45 c. Nisbet Plantation	20	25
116	50 c. Pinney's Beach ..	20	25
117	55 c. Eva Wilkin's Studio	25	30
118	$1 Nevis at down ..	40	45
119	$2·50 Ruins of Fort Charles	90	1·10
120	$5 Old Bath House ..	1·50	1·75
121	$10 Beach at Nisbet's ..	2·75	3·00

19. Montgolfier Balloon, 1783.

1983. Bicentenary of Manned Flight. Mult.

122. 10 c. Type **19** 10 10
123. 45 c. Sikorsky "S-38" flying boat (horiz.) .. 15 10
124. 50 c. Beechcraft "Twin Bonanza" (horiz.) .. 15 10
125. $2·50 B. Ae. "Sea Harrier" (horiz.) 50 60

20. Mary Praying over Holy Child.

1983. Christmas. Multicoloured.

127. 5 c. Type **20** 10 10
128. 30 c. Shepherds with flock 10 10
129. 55 c. Three Angels .. 15 10
130. $3 Boy with girls 55 60

21. "County of Oxford" (1945).

1983. Leaders of the World. Railway Locomotives (1st series).

132. **21.** 55 c. multicoloured .. 20 25
133. – 55 c.multicoloured .. 20 25
134. – $1 red, blue and black 25 35
135. – $1 multicoloured .. 25 35
136. – $1 purple, blue & blk. 25 35
137. – $1 multicoloured .. 25 35
138. – $1 red, black & yellow 25 35
139. – $1 multicoloured .. 25 35
140. – $1 multicoloured .. 25 35
141. – $1 multicoloured .. 25 35
142. – $1 yellow, black & blue 25 35
143. – $1 multicoloured .. 25 35
144. – $1 yellow, black & pur. 25 35
145. – $1 multicoloured .. 25 35
146. – $1 multicoloured .. 25 35
147. – $1 multicoloured .. 25 35

DESIGNS: (The first in each pair shows technical drawings and the second the locomotive at work). Nos. 132/3 "County of Oxford", Great Britain (1945). 134/5 "Evening Star", Great Britain (1960). 136/7 "Stanier Class 5", Great Britain (1934). 138/9 "Pendennis Castle", Great Britain (1924). 140/1 "Winston Churchill", Great Britain (1946). 142/3 "Mallard", Great Britain (1935). 144/5 "Britannia", Great Britain (1951). 146/7 "King George V", Great Britain.

See also Nos. 219/26, 277/84, 297/308, 352/9 and 427/42.

22. Boer War.

1984. Leaders of the World. British Monarchs (1st series). Multicoloured.

148. 5 c. Type **22** 10 10
149. 5 c. Queen Victoria .. 10 10
150. 50 c. Queen Victoria at Osborne House .. 35 35
151. 50 c. Osborne House .. 35 35
152. 60 c. Battle of Dettingen .. 40 40
153. 60 c. George II 40 40
154. 75 c. George II at the Bank of England 40 40
155. 75 c. Bank of England .. 40 40
156. $1 Coat of Arms of George II 45 45
157. $1 George II (different) .. 45 45
158. $3 Coat of Arms of Queen Victoria .. .. .. 1·00 1·10
159. $3 Queen Victoria (different) 1·00 1·10

See also Nos. 231/6.

23. Golden Rock Inn.

1984. Tourism (1st series). Multicoloured.

160. 55 c Type **23** 35 20
161. 55 c. Rest Haven Inn .. 35 20
162. 55 c. Cliffdwellers Hotel .. 35 20
163. 55 c. Pinney's Beach Hotel 35 20

See also Nos 245/8.

24. Early Seal of Colony.

1984.

164. **24.** $15 red .. .. .. 4·50 5·50

25. Cadillac.

1984. Leaders of the World Automobiles (1st series). As T **25.** The first design in each pair shows technical drawings and the second paintings.

165. 1 c. yellow, black and mauve 10 10
166. 1 c. multicoloured 10 10
167. 5 c. blue, mauve and black 10 10
168. 5 c. multicoloured 10 10
169. 15 c. multicoloured .. 15 15
170. 15 c. multicoloured .. 15 15
171. 35 c. mauve, yellow and black 25 25
172. 35 c. multicoloured .. 25 25
173. 45 c. blue, mauve and black 30 30
174. 45 c. multicoloured .. 30 30
175. 55 c. multicoloured .. 35 35
176. 55 c. multicoloured .. 35 35
177. $2.50 mauve, black and yellow 80 65
178. $2.50 multicoloured .. 80 65
179. $3 blue, yellow and black 85 70
180. $3 multicoloured 85 70

DESIGNS: No. 165/6, Cadillac "V16 Fleetwood Convertible" (1932). 167/8, Packard "Twin Six Touring Car" (1916). 169/70, Daimler "2 Cylinder" (1886). 171/2, Porsche "911 S Targa" (1970). 173/4, Benz "Three Wheeler" (1885). 175/6, M.G. "TC" (1947). 177/8, Cobra "Roadster 289" (1966). 179/80, Aston Martin "DB6 Hardtop" (1966).

See also Nos. 203/10, 249/64, 326/37, 360/371 and 411/22.

26. Carpentry.

1984. 10th Anniv. of Culturama Celebrations. Multicoloured.

181. 30 c. Type **26** 10 10
182. 55 c. Grass mat and basket making 15 10
183. $1 Pottery firing .. 25 25
184. $3 Culturama Queen and dancers 55 55

27. Yellow Bell.

1984. Flowers. Multicoloured.

185. 5 c. Type **27** 10 10
186. 10 c. Plumbago 10 10
187. 15 c. Flamboyant 10 10
188. 20 c. Eyelash Orchid .. 10 10
189. 30 c. Bougainvillea .. 10 15
190. 40 c. Hibiscus 15 20
191. 50 c. Night-blooming Cereus 15 20
192. 55 c. Yellow Mahoe .. 20 25
193. 60 c. Spider-lily 20 25
194. 75 c. Scarlet Cordia .. 25 30
195. $1 Shell-ginger 35 40
196. $3 Blue Petrea .. .. 1·00 1·10
197. $5 Coral Hibiscus .. 1·75 2·00
198. $10 Passion Flower .. 3·25 3·50

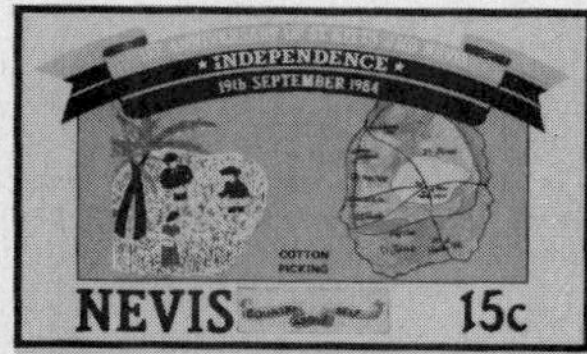

28. Cotton-picking and Map.

1984. 1st Anniv. of Independence of St. Kitts-Nevis. Multicoloured.

199. 15 c. Type **28** 15 10
200. 55 c. Alexander Hamilton's birthplace 20 10
201. $1.10 Local agricultural produce 35 40
202. $3 Nevis Peak and Pinneys Beach .. .. .. 75 1·00

1984. Leaders of the World. Automobiles (2nd series). As T **25.** The first in each pair shows technical drawings and the second paintings.

203. 5 c. black, blue and brown 10 10
204. 5 c. multicoloured 10 10
205. 30 c. black, turquoise and brown 15 15
206. 30 c. multicoloured .. 15 15
207. 50 c. black, drab & brown 20 20
208. 50 c. multicoloured .. 20 20
209. $3 black, brown and green 60 60
210. $3 multicoloured 60 60

DESIGNS: Nos. 203/4, Lagonda "Speed Model" touring car (1929). 205/6, Jaguar "E-Type" 4.2 litre (1967). 207/8, Volkswagen "Beetle" (1947). 209/10, Pierce Arrow "V12" (1932).

29. C. P. Mead.

1984. Leaders of the World. Cricketers (1st series). As T **29.** The first in each pair shows a head portrait and the second the cricketer in action. Multicoloured.

211. 5 c. Type **29** 10 10
212. 5 c. C. P. Mead 10 10
213. 25 c. J. B. Statham .. 30 30
214. 25 c. J. B. Statham .. 30 30
215. 55 c. Sir Learie Constantine 40 40
216. 55 c. Sir Learie Constantine 40 40
217. $2.50 Sir Leonard Hutton 1·25 1·25
218. $2.50 Sir Leonard Hutton 1·25 1·25

See also Nos 237/4.

1984. Leaders of the World. Railway Locomotives (2nd series). As T **21.** The first in each pair shows technical drawings and the second the locomotive at work.

219. 5 c. multicoloured 10 10
220. 5 c. multicoloured 10 10
221. 10 c. multicoloured .. 10 10
222. 10 c. multicoloured .. 10 10
223. 60 c. multicoloured .. 30 30
224. 60 c. multicoloured .. 30 30
225. $2 multicoloured 90 90
226. $2 multicoloured 90 90

DESIGNS: Nos. 219/20, Class "EF81", Japan (1968). 221/22, Class "5500", France (1927). 223/4, Class "240P", France (1940). 225/6, Shinkansen train, Japan (1964).

30. Fifer and Drummer from Honeybees Band.

1984. Christmas. Local Music. Multicoloured.

227. 15 c. Type **30** 15 10
228. 40 c. Guitar and "barhow" players from Canary Birds Band 25 10
229. 60 c. Shell All Stars steel band 30 10
230. $3 Organ and choir, St. John's Church, Fig Tree 1·25 1·00

1984. Leaders of the World. British Monarchs (2nd series). As T **22.** Multicoloured.

231. 5 c. King John and Magna Carta 10 10
232. 5 c. Barons and King John 10 10
233. 55 c. King John 25 25
234. 55 c. Newark Castle .. 25 25
235. $2 Coat of arms 75 75
236. $2 King John (different) .. 75 75

1984. Leaders of the World. Cricketers (2nd series). As T **29.** The first in each pair listed shows a head portrait and the second the cricketer in action. Multicoloured.

237. 5 c. J. D. Love 10 10
238. 5 c. J. D. Love 10 10
239. 15 c. S. J. Dennis 15 15
240. 15 c. S. J. Dennis 15 15
241. 55 c. B. W. Luckhurst .. 30 30
242. 55 c. B. W. Luckhurst .. 30 30
243. $2.50 B. L. D'Oliveira .. 1·00 1·00
244. $2.50 B. L. D'Oliveira .. 1·00 1·00

1984. Tourism (2nd series). As T **23.** Multicoloured.

245. $1.20 Croney's Old Manor Hotel 45 45
246. $1.20 Montpelier Plantation Inn 45 45
247. $1.20 Nisbet's Plantation Inn 45 45
248. $1.20 Zetland Plantation Inn 45 45

1985. Leaders of the World. Automobiles (3rd series). As T **25.** The first in each pair shows technical drawings and the second paintings.

249. 1 c. black, green and light green 10 10
250. 1 c. multicoloured 10 10
251. 5 c. black, blue and light blue 10 10
252. 5 c. multicoloured 10 10
253. 10 c. black, green and light green 10 10
254. 10 c. multicoloured .. 10 10
255. 50 c. black, green and brown 20 20
256. 50 c. multicoloured .. 20 20
257. 60 c. black, green and blue 20 20
258. 60 c. multicoloured .. 20 20
259. 75 c. black, red and orange 25 25
260. 75 c. multicoloured .. 25 25
261. $2.50 black, green and blue 40 40
262. $2.50 multicoloured .. 40 40
263. $3 black, green and light green 40 40
264. $3 multicoloured 40 40

DESIGNS: Nos. 249/50, Delahaye "Type 35 Cabriolet" (1935). 251/2, Ferrari "Testa Rossa" (1958). 253/4, Voisin "Aerodyne" (1934). 255/6, Buick "Riviera" (1963). 257/8, Cooper "Climax" (1960). 259/60, Ford "999" (1904). 261/2, MG "M-Type Midget" (1930). 263/4, Rolls Royce "Corniche" (1971).

31. Broad-winged Hawk.

1985. Local Hawks and Herons. Multicoloured.
265. 20 c. Type **31** 75 20
266. 40 c. Red-tailed hawk .. 1·00 30
267. 60 c. Little blue heron .. 1·25 40
268. $3 Great blue heron (white phase) .. .. .. 2·50 1·90

32. Eastern Bluebird.

1985. Leaders of the World. Birth Bicentenary of John J. Audubon (ornithologist) (1st issue). Multicoloured.
269. 5 c. Type **32** 15 10
270. 5 c. Common cardinal .. 15 10
271. 55 c. Belted kingfisher .. 65 65
272. 55 c. Mangrove cuckoo .. 65 65
273. 60 c. Yellow warbler .. 65 65
274. 60 c. Cerulean warbler .. 65 65
275. $2 Burrowing owl .. .. 1·75 1·75
276. $2 Long-eared owl .. 1·75 1·75
See also Nos. 285/92.

1985. Leaders of the World. Railway Locomotives (3rd series). As T **21**, the first in pair showing technical drawings and the second the locomotive at work.
277. 1 c. multicoloured 10 10
278. 1 c. multicoloured 10 10
279. 60 c. multicoloured .. 30 30
280. 60 c. multicoloured .. 30 30
281. 90 c. multicoloured .. 35 35
282. 90 c. multicoloured .. 35 35
283. $2 multicoloured 75 75
284. $2 multicoloured 75 75
DESIGNS: Nos. 277/8, Class "Wee Bogie", Great Britain (1882). 279/80, "Comet", Great Britain (1851). 281/2, Class "8H", Great Britain (1908). 283/4, Class "A", No. 23, Great Britain (1866).

1985. Leaders of the World. Birth Bicentenary of John J. Audubon (ornithologist) (2nd issue). As T **32**. Multicoloured.
285. 1 c. Painted bunting .. 10 10
286. 1 c. Golden-crowned kinglet 10 10
287. 40 c. Common flicker .. 40 40
288. 40 c. Western tanager .. 40 40
289. 60 c. Varied thrush .. 45 45
290. 60 c. Evening grosbeak .. 45 45
291. $2.50 Blackburnian warbler .. .. .. 1·00 1·00
292. $2.50 Northern oriole .. 1·00 1·00

33. Guides and Guide Headquarters.

1985. 75th Anniv. of Girl Guide Movement. Multicoloured.
293. 15 c. Type **33** 10 10
294. 60 c. Girl Guide uniforms of 1910 and 1985 (vert.) 30 30
295. $1 Lord and Lady Baden-Powell (vert.) 50 50
296. $3 Princess Margaret in Guide uniform (vert.) .. 1·25 1·50

1985. Leaders of the World. Railway Locomotives (4th series). As T **21**. The first in each pair shows technical drawings and the second the locomotive at work.
297. 5 c. multicoloured 10 10
298. 5 c. multicoloured 10 10
299. 30 c. multicoloured .. 15 15
300. 30 c. multicoloured .. 15 15
301. 60 c. multicoloured .. 30 30
302. 60 c. multicoloured .. 30 30
303. 75 c. multicoloured .. 35 35
304. 75 c. multicoloured .. 35 35
305. $1 multicoloured 35 35
306. $1 multicoloured 35 35
307. $2.50 multicoloured .. 80 80
308. $2.50 multicoloured .. 80 80
DESIGNS: Nos. 297/8, "Snowdon Ranger" (1878). 299/300, Large Belpaire Passenger Locomotive (1904). 301/2, Great Western Railway "County Class" (1904). 303/4, "Nord L'Outrance" (1877). 305/6, Q.R. "Class PB-15" (1899). 307/8, D.R.G. "Class 64" (1928).

34. The Queen Mother at Garter Ceremony.

1985. Leaders of the World. Life and Times of Queen Elizabeth the Queen Mother. Various vertical portraits.
309. **34.** 45 c. multicoloured .. 20 25
310. – 45 c. multicoloured .. 20 25
311. – 75 c. multicoloured .. 30 35
312. – 75 c. multicoloured .. 30 35
313. – $1.20 multicoloured .. 45 55
314. – $1.20 multicoloured .. 45 55
315. – $1.50 multicoloured .. 55 65
316. – $1.50 multicoloured .. 55 65
Each value was issued in pairs showing a floral pattern across the bottom of the portraits which stops short of the left-hand edge on the first stamp and of the right-hand edge on the second.

35. Isambard Kingdom Brunel.

1985. 150th Anniv. of Great Western Railway. Designs showing railway engineers and their achievements. Multicoloured.
318. 25 c. Type **35** 45 45
319. 25 c. Royal Albert Bridge, 1859 .. .. .. 45 45
320. 50 c. William Dean .. 55 55
321. 50 c. Locomotive "Lord of the Isles", 1895 .. .. 55 55
322. $1 Locomotive "Lode Star", 1907 .. .. 1·00 1·00
323. $1 G. J. Churchward .. 1·00 1·00
324. $2.50 Locomotive "Pendennis Castle", 1924 1·50 1·50
325. $2.50 C. B. Collett .. .. 1·50 1·50
Nos. 318/19, 320/1, 322/3 and 324/5 were printed together se-tenant, each pair forming a composite design.

1985. Leaders of the World. Automobiles (4th series). As T **25**. The first in each pair shows technical drawings and the second paintings.
326. 10 c. black, blue & red .. 10 10
327. 10 c. multicoloured .. 10 10
328. 35 c. black, turq, & blue .. 20 25
329. 35 c. multicoloured .. 20 25
330. 75 c. black, green & brown 35 40
331. 75 c. multicoloured .. 35 40
332. $1.15 black, brown & green 50 60
333. $1.15 multicoloured .. 50 60
334. $1.50 black, blue & red .. 60 70
335. $1.50 multicoloured .. 60 70
336. $2 black, lilac and violet .. 75 1·00
337. $2 multicoloured .. .. 75 1·00
DESIGNS: Nos. 326/7, Sunbeam "Coupe de L'Auto" (1912). 328/9, Cisitalia "Pininfarina Coupe" (1948). 330/1, Porsche "928 S" (1980). 332/3, MG "K3 Magnette" (1933). 334/5, Lincoln "Zephyr" (1937). 336/7, Pontiac 2 Door (1926).

1985. Royal Visit. Nos. 76/7, 83, 86, 92/3, 98/9 and 309/10 optd. **CARIBBEAN ROYAL VISIT—1985** or surch. also.
338. **16.** 15 c. multicoloured .. 1·00 1·00
339. – 30 c. mult. (No. 92) .. 2·00 1·50
340. – 30 c. mult. (No. 99) .. 1·00 1·00
341. – 40 c. on 55 c. multicoloured (No. 86) .. 2·00 1·75
342. **34.** 45 c. multicoloured .. 2·25 2·00
343. – 45 c. mult. (No. 310) .. 2·25 2·00
344. – 55 c. mult. (No. 83) .. 1·25 1·25
345. – $1.50 on $5 multicoloured (No. 76) .. 2·25 2·25
346. – $1.50 on $5 multicoloured (No. 77) .. 4·50 4·50
347. – $2.50 mult. (No. 93) .. 2·75 2·50

36. St. Pauls Anglican Church, Charlestown.

1985. Christmas. Churches of Nevis (1st series). Multicoloured.
348. 10 c. Type **36** 15 10
349. 40 c. St. Theresa Catholic Church, Charlestown .. 30 30
350. 60 c. Methodist Church, Gingerland 45 50
351. $3 St. Thomas Anglican Church, Lowland .. 2·00 2·25
See also Nos. 462/5.

1986. Leaders of the World. Railway Locomotives (5th series). As T **21**. The first in each pair shows technical drawings and the second the locomotive at work.
352. 30 c. multicoloured .. 25 25
353. 30 c. multicoloured .. 25 25
354. 75 c. multicoloured .. 50 50
355. 75 c. multicoloured .. 50 50
356. $1.50 multicoloured .. 80 80
357. $1.50 multicoloured .. 80 80
358. $2 multicoloured .. .. 1·10 1·10
359. $2 multicoloured .. .. 1·10 1·10
DESIGNS: Nos. 352/3, "Stourbridge Lion", U.S.A. (1829). 354/5, "EP-2 Bi-Polar", U.S.A. (1919). 356/7, turbine U.P. "Box 4" gas (1953). 358/9, N.Y., N.H. and H.R. "FL9", U.S.A. (1955).

1986. Leaders of the World. Automobiles (5th series). As T **25**, the first in each pair showing technical drawings and the second paintings. P $12\frac{1}{2}$.
360. 10 c. black, brown and green 10 10
361. 10 c. multicoloured .. 10 10
362. 60 c. black, orange and red 25 30
363. 60 c. multicoloured .. 25 30
364. 75 c. black, light brown and brown 30 35
365. 75 c. multicoloured .. 30 35
366. $1 black, light grey and grey 30 40
367. $1 multicoloured 30 40
368. $1.50 black, yellow and green 40 60
369. $1.50 multicoloured .. 40 60
370. $3 black, light blue and blue .. .. .. 70 1·10
371. $3 multicoloured .. .. 70 1·10
DESIGNS: Nos. 360/1, Adler "Trumpf" (1936). 362/3, Maserati "Tipo 250F" (1957). 364/5, Oldsmobile "Limited" (1910). 366/7, Jaguar "C-Type" (1951). 368/9, ERA "1.5L B Type" (1937). 370/1 Chevrolet "Corvette" (1953).

37. "Spitfire" Prototype "K.5054", 1936. (Illustration reduced. Actual size 55 × 38 mm.)

1986. 50th Anniv. of "Spitfire" (fighter aircraft). Multicoloured.
372. $1 Type **37** .. .. .. 1·00 85
373. $2.50 Mark "1A" in Battle of Britain, 1940 .. .. 1·75 2·00
374. $3 Mark "XII" over convoy, 1944 .. .. 2·00 2·25
375. $4 Mark "XXIV", 1948 .. 2·25 2·75

38. Head of Amerindian.

1986. 500th Anniv (1992) of Discovery of America by Columbus (1st issue). Mult.
377. 75 c. Type **38** 55 55
378. 75 c. Exchanging gifts for food from Amerindians 55 55
379. $1.75 Columbus's coat of arms .. .. .. 1·40 1·40
380. $1.75 Breadfruit plant .. 1·40 1·40
381. $2.50 Columbus's fleet .. 1·75 1·75
382. $2.50 Christopher Columbus .. .. 1·75 1·75
The two designs of each value were printed together, se-tenant, each pair forming a composite design showing charts of Columbus's route in the background.
See also Nos. 546/53.

1986. 60th Birthday of Queen Elizabeth II. As T **167** of British Virgin Islands. Mult.
384. 5 c. Queen Elizabeth in 1976 .. .. .. 10 10
385. 75 c. Queen Elizabeth in 1953 .. .. .. 25 25
386. $2 In Australia 60 60
387. $8 In Canberra, 1982 (vert.) 2·25 2·50

39. Brazilian Player.

1986. World Cup Football Championship, Mexico. Multicoloured.
389. 1 c. Official World Cup mascot (horiz.) 10 10
390. 2 c. Type **39** 10 10
391. 5 c. Danish player .. 10 10
392. 10 c. Brazilian player (different) 10 10
393. 20 c. Denmark v Spain .. 20 20
394. 30 c. Paraquay v Chile .. 30 30
395. 60 c. Italy v West Germany 55 55
396. 75 c. Danish team (56 × 36 mm.) 65 65
397. $1 Paraguayan team (56 × 36 mm.) 80 80
398. $1.75 Brazilian team (56 × 36 mm.) .. .. 1·40 1·40
399. $3 Italy v England .. 2·00 2·00
400. $6 Italian team (56 × 36 mm.) .. .. 3·50 3·50

40. Clothing Machinist.

1986. Local Industries. Multicoloured.
402. 15 c. Type **40** 20 15
403. 40 c. Carpentry/joinery workshop 45 30
404. $1.20 Agricultural produce market .. .. 1·25 1·25
405. $3 Fishing boats landing catch .. .. .. 2·50 2·75

1986. Royal Wedding. Multicoloured. As T **168** of British Virgin Islands.

406.	60 c. Prince Andrew in midshipman's uniform ..	25	25
407.	60 c. Miss Sarah Ferguson	25	25
408.	$2 Prince Andrew on safari in Africa (horiz.) ..	75	85
409.	$2 Prince Andrew at the races (horiz.)	75	85

1986. Automobiles (6th series). As T **25**, the first in each pair showing technical drawings and the second paintings.

411.	15 c. multicoloured ..	10	10
412.	15 c. multicoloured ..	10	10
413.	45 c. black, light blue and blue	25	25
414.	45 c. multicoloured ..	25	25
415.	60 c. multicoloured ..	30	30
416.	60 c. multicoloured ..	30	30
417.	$1 black, light green and green	40	40
418.	$1 multicoloured	40	40
419.	$1.75 black, lilac and deep lilac	60	60
420.	$1.75 multicoloured ..	60	60
421.	$3 multicoloured	1·10	1·10
422.	$3 multicoloured	1·10	1·10

DESIGNS: Nos. 411/12, Riley "Brooklands Nine" (1930). 413/14, Alfa Romeo "GTA" (1966). 415/16, Pierce Arrow "Type 66" (1913). 417/18, Willy-Knight "66 A" (1928). 419/20, Studebaker "Starliner" (1953). 421/2, Cunningham "V-8" (1919).

41. Gorgonia.

1986 Corals (2nd series). Multicoloured.

423	15 c. Type **41**	50	20
424	60 c. Fire coral	1·25	65
425	$2 Elkhorn coral	2·50	2·50
426	$3 Vase sponge and feather star	3·50	3·50

1986. Railway Locomotives (6th series). As T **21**, the first in each pair showing technical drawings and the second the locomotive at work.

427.	15 c. multicoloured ..	10	10
428.	15 c. multicoloured ..	10	10
429.	45 c. multicoloured ..	25	25
430.	45 c. multicoloured ..	25	25
431.	60 c. multicoloured ..	30	30
432.	60 c. multicoloured ..	30	30
433.	75 c. multicoloured ..	40	40
434.	75 c. multicoloured ..	40	40
435.	$1 multicoloured	45	50
436.	$1 multicoloured	45	50
437.	$1.50 multicoloured ..	60	70
438.	$1.50 multicoloured ..	60	70
439.	$2 multicoloured	70	80
440.	$2 multicoloured	70	80
441.	$3 multicoloured	90	1·10
442.	$3 multicoloured	90	1·10

DESIGNS: Nos. 427/8, Connor Single Class, Great Britain (1859). 429/30, Class "P2" "Cock o' the North", Great Britain (1934). 431/2, Class "7000", Japan (1926). 433/4, Palatinate Railway Class "P3", Germany (1897). 435/6, "Dorchester", Canada (1836). 436/7, "Centennial" Class diesel, U.S.A. (1969). 439/40, "Lafayette", U.S.A. (1837). 441/2, Class "C-16", U.S.A. (1882).

41a. Statue of Liberty and World Trade Centre, Manhattan.

1986. Centenary of Statue of Liberty. Multicoloured.

443.	15 c. Type **41a**	10	10
444.	25 c. Sailing ship passing statue	15	15
445.	40 c. Statue in scaffolding	20	25
446.	60 c. Statue (side view) and scaffolding	25	30
447.	75 c. Statue and regatta ..	35	40
448.	$1 Tall Ships parade passing statue (horiz.) ..	45	50
449.	$1.50 Head and arm of statue above scaffolding	70	75
450.	$2 Ships with souvenir flags (horiz.)	90	95
451.	$2.50 Statue and New York waterfront	1·10	1·25
452.	$3 Restoring statue ..	1·40	1·50

1986. Royal Wedding (2nd issue). Nos. 406/9 optd. **Congratulations to T.R.H. The Duke & Duchess of York.**

454.	60 c. Prince Andrew in midshipman's uniform ..	35	35
455.	60 c. Miss Sarah Ferguson	35	35
456.	$2 Prince Andrew on safari in Africa (horiz.) ..	1·10	1·10
457.	$2 Prince Andrew at the races (horiz.)	1·10	1·10

42. Dinghy sailing.

1986. Sports. Multicoloured.

458.	10 c. Type **42**	10	10
459.	25 c. Netball	30	15
460.	$2 Cricket	1·75	1·75
461.	$3 Basketball	2·00	2·00

43. St. George's Anglican Church, Gingerland.

1986. Christmas. Churches of Nevis (2nd series). Multicoloured.

462.	10 c. Type **43**	10	10
463.	40 c. Trinity Methodist Church, Fountain ..	20	25
464.	$1 Charlestown Methodist Church	45	55
465.	$5 Wesleyan Holiness Church, Brown Hill ..	2·25	2·75

44. Constitution Document, Quill and Inkwell.

1987. Bicentenary of U.S. Constitution and 230th Birth Anniv. of Alexander Hamilton (U.S. statesman). Multicoloured.

466.	15 c. Type **44**	10	10
467.	40 c. Alexander Hamilton and Hamilton House ..	20	25
468.	60 c. Alexander Hamilton	25	35
469.	$2 Washington and his Cabinet	90	1·25

1987. Victory of "Stars and Stripes" in America's Cup Yachting Championship. No. 54 optd. **America's Cup 1987 Winners 'Stars & Stripes'.**

471.	$3 Windjammer S.V. "Polynesia"	1·40	1·75

46. Fig Tree Church.

1987. Bicentenary of Marriage of Horatio Nelson and Frances Nisbet. Multicoloured.

472.	15 c. Type **46**	10	10
473.	60 c. Frances Nisbet ..	30	30
474.	$1 H.M.S. "Boreas" ..	65	65
475.	$3 Captain Horatio Nelson	1·90	2·00

47. Queen Angelfish. (Illustration reduced. Actual size 60 × 30 mm.).

1987. Coral Reef Fishes. Multicoloured.

477.	60 c. Type **47**	70	70
478.	60 c. Blue angelfish ..	70	70
479.	$1 Stoplight parrotfish (male)	90	90
480.	$1 Stoplight parrotfish (female)	90	90
481.	$1.50 Red hind	1·40	1·40
482.	$1.50 Rock hind	1·40	1·40
483.	$2.50 Coney (bicoloured phase)	2·25	2·25
484.	$2.50 Coney (red-brown phase)	2·25	2·25

Nos. 478, 480, 482 and 484 are inverted triangles.

48. "Panaeolus antillarum".

1987. Fungi. Multicoloured.

485.	15 c. Type **48**	30	20
486.	50 c. "Pycnoporus sanguineus"	75	50
487.	$2 "Gymnopilus chrysopellus"	2·25	2·00
488.	$3 "Cantharellus cinnabarinus"	2·75	2·75

49. Rag Doll.

1987. Christmas. Toys. Multicoloured.

489.	10 c. Type **49**	10	10
490.	40 c. Coconut boat ..	20	25
491.	$1.20 Sandbox cart ..	55	60
492.	$5 Two-wheeled cart ..	2·25	2·75

50. Hawk-wing Conch.

1988. Sea Shells and Pearls. Multicoloured.

493.	15 c. Type **50**	10	10
494.	40 c. Roostertail conch ..	15	20
495.	60 c. Emperor helmet ..	25	30
496.	$2 Queen conch	85	90
497.	$3 King helmet	1·25	1·40

51 Visiting Pensioners at Christmas

1988. 125th Anniv of International Red Cross. Multicoloured.

498	15 c. Type **51**	10	10
499	40 c. Teaching children first aid	15	20
500	60 c. Providing wheelchairs for the disabled ..	25	30
501	$5 Helping cyclone victim	2·10	2·50

52 Athlete on Starting Blocks

1988. Olympic Games, Seoul. Multicoloured.

502	10 c. Type **52**	10	10
503	$1.20 At start	50	55
504	$2 During race	85	90
505	$3 At finish	1·25	1·40

Nos. 502/5 were printed together, se-tenant, each strip forming a composite design showing an athlete from start to finish of race.

53 Outline Map and Arms of St. Kitts–Nevis

1988. 5th Anniv of Independence.

507 **53**	$5 multicoloured ..	2·10	2·25

1988. 300th Anniv of Lloyd's of London. As T **123** of Ascension. Multicoloured.

508	15 c. House of Commons passing Lloyd's Bill, 1871	10	10
509	60 c. "Cunard Countess" (liner) (horiz)	25	30
510	$2.50 Space shuttle deploying satellite (horiz) ..	1·00	1·10
511	$3 "Viking Princess" on fire, 1966	1·25	1·40

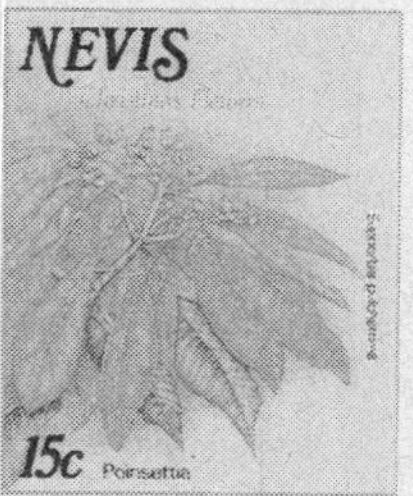

54 Poinsettia

1988. Christmas. Flowers. Multicoloured.

512	15 c. Type **54**	10	10
513	40 c. Tiger claws	15	20
514	60 c. Sorrel flower ..	25	30
515	$1 Christmas candle ..	40	45
516	$5 Snow bush	2·10	2·25

55 British Fleet off St. Kitts

1989. "Philexfrance 89" International Stamp Exhibition, Paris. Battle of Frigate Bay, 1782. Multicoloured.

517 50 c. Type **55** 20 25
518 $1.20 Battle off Nevis .. 50 55
519 $2 British and French fleets exchanging broadsides 85 90
520 $3 French map of Nevis, 1764 .. .. .. 1·25 1·40

Nos. 517/19 were printed together, se-tenant, forming a composite design.

56 Cicada

1989. "Sounds of the Night". Multicoloured.

521 10 c. Type **56** 10 10
522 40 c. Grasshopper .. 15 20
523 60 c. Cricket 25 30
524 $5 Tree frog .. .. 2·10 2·25

1989. 20th Anniv of First Manned Landing on Moon. As T **126** of Ascension. Multicoloured.

526 15 c. Vehicle Assembly Building, Kennedy Space Centre 10 10
527 40 c. Crew of "Apollo 12" (30 × 30 mm) .. 15 20
528 $2 "Apollo 12" emblem (30 × 30 mm) .. 85 90
529 $3 "Apollo 12" astronaut on Moon .. .. 1·25 1·40

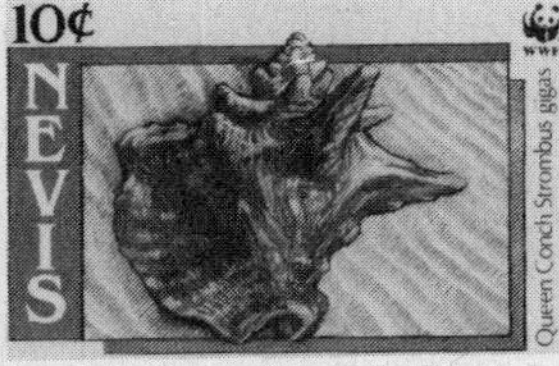

57 Queen Conch feeding

1990. Queen Conch. Multicoloured.

531 10 c. Type **57** 10 10
532 40 c. Queen Conch from front 15 20
533 60 c. Side view of shell .. 25 30
534 $1 Back and flare .. 40 45

58 Wyon Medal Portrait

1990. 150th Anniv of the Penny Black.

536 **58** 15 c. black and brown .. 10 10
537 – 40 c. black and green .. 15 20
538 – 60 c. black .. 25 30
539 – $4 black and blue .. 1·75 1·90

DESIGNS: 40 c. Engine-turned background; 60 c. Heath's engraving of portrait; $4 Essay with inscriptions.

59

1990. 500th Anniv of Regular European Postal Services.

541 **59** 15 c. brown 10 10
542 – 40 c. green 15 20
543 – 60 c. violet 25 30
544 – $4 blue .. .. 1·75 1·90

Nos. 541/4 commemorate the Thurn and Taxis postal service and the designs are loosely based on those of the initial 1852-58 series.

1990. 500th Anniv (1992) of Discovery of America by Columbus (2nd issue). New World Natural History—Crabs. As T **260** of Antigua. Multicoloured.

546 5 c. Sand fiddler .. 10 10
547 15 c. Great land crab .. 10 10
548 20 c. Blue crab .. 10 10
549 40 c. Stone crab 15 20
550 60 c. Mountain crab .. 25 30
551 $2 Sargassum crab .. 85 90
552 $3 Yellow box crab .. 1·25 1·40
553 $4 Spiny spider crab .. 1·75 1·90

1990. 90th Birthday of Queen Elizabeth the Queen Mother. As T **103** of Grenada Grenadines.

555 $2 black, mauve and buff 85 90
556 $2 black, mauve and buff 85 90
557 $2 black, mauve and buff 85 90

DESIGNS: No. 555, Duchess of York with corgi; 556, Queen Elizabeth in Coronation robes, 1937; 557, Duchess of York in garden.

61 MaKanaky, Cameroons

1990. World Cup Football Championship, Italy. Star Players. Multicoloured.

559 10 c. Type **61** 10 10
560 25 c. Chovanec, Czechoslovakia 10 15
561 $2.50 Robson, England .. 1·00 1·10
562 $5 Voller, West Germany 2·10 2·25

62 "Cattleya deckeri"

1990. Christmas. Native Orchids. Mult.

564 10 c. Type **62** 10 10
565 15 c. "Epidendrum ciliare" 10 10
566 20 c. "Epidendrum fragrans" 10 10
567 40 c. "Epidendrum ibaguense" 15 20
568 60 c. "Epidendrum latifolium" 25 30
569 $1.20 "Maxillaria conferta" 50 55
570 $2 "Epidendrum strobiliferum" 85 90
571 $3 "Brassavola cucullata" 1·25 1·40

1991. 350th Death Anniv of Rubens. As T **273** of Antigua, showing details from "The Feast of Achelous". Multicoloured.

573 10 c. Two jugs (vert) .. 10 10
574 40 c. Woman at table (vert) 15 20
575 60 c. Two servants with fruit (vert) 25 30
576 $4 Achelous (vert) .. 1·75 1·90

63 "Agraulis vanillae"

1991. Butterflies. Multicoloured.

578 5 c. Type **63** 10 10
579 10 c. "Historis odius" .. 10 10
580 15 c. "Marpesia corinna" .. 10 10
581 20 c. "Anartia amathea" 10 10
582 25 c. "Junonia evarete" .. 10 15
583 40c. "Heliconius charithonia" 15 20
584 50 c. "Marpesia petreus" 20 25
585 60 c. "Dione juno" .. 25 30
586 75 c. "Heliconius doris" .. 30 35
587 $1 "Hypolimnas misippus" 40 45
588 $3 "Danaus plexippus" .. 1·25 1·40
589 $5 "Heliconius sara" .. 2·10 2·25
590 $10 "Tithorea harmonia" 4·25 4·50
591 $20 "Dryas julia" .. 8·50 8·75

64 "Viking Mars Lander", 1976

1991. 500th Anniv of Discovery of America by Columbus (1992) (4th issue) Multicoloured.

592 15 c. Type **64** 10 10
593 40 c. "Apollo 11", 1969 15 20
594 60 c. "Skylab", 1973 .. 25 30
595 75 c. "Salyut 6", 1977 .. 30 35
596 $1 "Voyager 1", 1977 .. 40 45
597 $2 "Venera 7", 1970 .. 85 90
598 $4 "Gemini 4", 1965 .. 1·75 1·90
599 $5 "Luna 3", 1959 .. 2·10 2·25

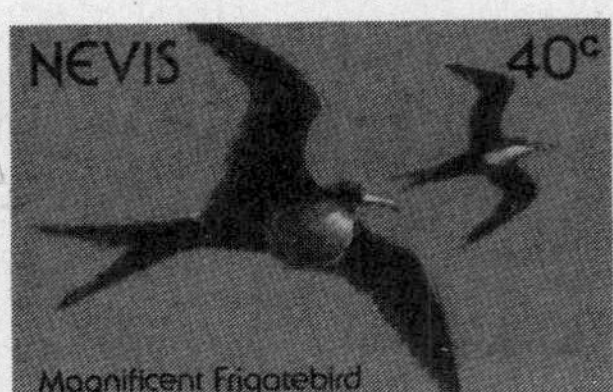

65 Magnificent Frigate Bird

1991. Island Birds. Multicoloured.

601 40 c. Type **65** 15 20
602 40 c. Roseate tern .. 15 20
603 40 c. Red-tailed hawk .. 15 20
604 40 c. Zenaida dove .. 15 20
605 40 c. Bananaquit 15 20
606 40 c. American kestrel .. 15 20
607 40 c. Grey kingbird .. 15 20
608 40 c. Prothonotary warbler 15 20
609 40 c. Blue-hooded euphonia 15 20
610 40 c. Antillean crested hummingbird .. 15 20
611 40 c. White-tailed tropic bird 15 20
612 40 c. Yellow-bellied sapsucker 15 20
613 40 c. Green-throated carib 15 20
614 40 c. Purple-throated carib 15 20
615 40 c. Black-bellied tree-duck 15 20
616 40 c. Ringed kingfisher .. 15 20
617 40 c. Burrowing owl .. 15 20
618 40 c. Ruddy turnstone .. 15 20
619 40 c. Great white heron .. 15 20
620 40 c. Yellow-crowned night-heron 15 20

Nos 601/20 were printed together, se-tenant, forming a composite design.

1991. 65th Birthday of Queen Elizabeth II. As T **280** of Antigua. Multicoloured.

622 15 c. Queen Elizabeth at polo match with Prince Charles 10 10
623 40 c. Queen and Prince Philip on Buckingham Palace balcony .. 15 20
624 $2 In carriage at Ascot, 1986 .. .. .. 85 90
625 $4 Queen Elizabeth II at Windsor polo match, 1989 .. .. .. 1·75 1·90

1991. 10th Wedding Anniv of Prince and Princess of Wales. As T **280** of Antigua. Multicoloured.

627 10 c. Prince Charles and Princess Diana .. 10 10
628 50 c. Prince of Wales and family 20 25
629 $1 Prince William and Prince Harry 40 45
630 $5 Prince and Princess of Wales .. .. .. 2·10 2·25

1991. "Philanippon '91" International Stamp Exhibition, Tokyo. Japanese Railway Locomotives. As T **257** of Maldives. Mult.

632 10 c. Class "C62" steam locomotive 10 10
633 15 c. Class "C56" steam locomotive (horiz) .. 10 10
634 40 c. Class "C-55" streamlined steam locomotive (horiz) 15 20
635 60 c. Class "1400" steam locomotive (horiz) .. 25 30
636 $1 Class "485 Bonnet" diesel rail car 40 45
637 $2 Class "C61" steam locomotive 85 90
638 $3 Class "485" express train (horiz) .. .. 1·25 1·40
639 $4 Class "7000" electric train (horiz) .. 1·75 1·90

1991. Christmas. Drawings by Albrecht Durer. As T **211** of Lesotho.

641 10 c. black and green .. 10 10
642 40 c. black and orange .. 15 20
643 60 c. black and blue .. 25 30
644 $3 black and mauve .. 1·25 1·50

DESIGNS: 10 c. "Mary being Crowned by an Angel"; 40 c. "Mary with the Pear"; 60 c. "Mary in a Halo"; $3 "Mary with Crown of Stars and Sceptre".

OFFICIAL STAMPS

1980. Nos. 40/49 optd. **OFFICIAL.**

O 1. 15 c. Sugar cane being harvested 10 10
O 2. 25 c. Crafthouse (craft centre) 10 10
O 3. 30 c. Cruise ship 10 10
O 4. 40 c. Lobster and sea crab 15 15
O 5. 45 c. Royal St. Kitts Hotel and golf course .. 20 25
O 6. 50 c. Pinneys Beach, Nevis 20 25
O 7. 55 c. New runway at Golden Rock 20 25
O 8. $1 Picking cotton .. 30 35
O 9. $5 The Brewery .. .. 1·00 1·00
O 10. $10 Pineapples and peanuts 2·25 2·25

1981. Nos. 60/71 optd. **OFFICIAL.**

O 11. 15 c. New River Mill .. 10 10
O 12. 20 c. Nelson Museum .. 10 10
O 13. 25 c. St. James' Parish Church 10 15
O 14. 30 c. Nevis Lane .. 15 15
O 15. 40 c. Zetland Plantation 15 20
O 16. 45 c. Nisbit Plantation .. 20 25
O 17. 50 c. Pinney's Beach .. 20 25
O 18. 55 c. Eva Wilkin's Studio 25 30
O 19. $1 Nevis at dawn .. 40 45
O 20. $2·50 Ruins of Fort Charles 85 90
O 21. $5 Old Bath House .. 1·25 1·75
O 22. $10 Beach at Nisbet's .. 2·25 2·75

1983. Nos. 72/7 optd. **OFFICIAL** and surch.

O 23. 45 c. on $2 "Royal Sovereign" 20 25
O 24. 45 c. on $2 Prince Charles & Lady Diana Spencer 20 25
O 25. 55 c. "Royal Caroline" 20 25
O 26. 55 c. Prince Charles and Lady Diana Spencer .. 25 25
O 27. $1·10 on $5 "Britannia" 45 50
O 28. $1·10 on $5 Prince Charles & Lady Diana Spencer 55 60

1985. Nos. 187/98 optd. **OFFICIAL.**

O29. 15 c. Flamboyant .. 10 10
O30. 20 c. Eyelash Orchid .. 10 10
O31. 30 c. Bougainvillea .. 10 15
O32. 40 c. Hibiscus 15 20
O33. 50 c. Night-blooming Cereus 20 25
O34. 55 c. Yellow Mahoe .. 25 30
O35. 60 c. Spider-lily 25 30
O36. 75 c. Scarlet Cordia .. 30 35
O37. $1 Shell-ginger 40 45
O38. $3 Blue Petrea .. .. 1·25 1·40
O39. $5 Coral Hibiscus .. 2·10 2·25
O40. $10 Passion flower .. 4·25 4·50

NEW BRUNSWICK

An eastern province of the Dominion of Canada, whose stamps are now used.

1851. 12 pence = 1 shilling.
20 shillings = 1 pound.
1860. 100 cents = 1 dollar.

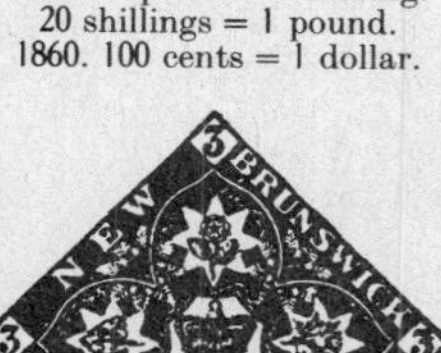

1. Royal Crown and Heraldic Flowers of the United Kingdom.

1851.

1	**1.**	3d. red	£1800	£300
4		6d. yellow	£4500	£700
6		1s. mauve	£14000	£4500

2. Locomotive.

3. Queen Victoria.

1860.

9.	**2.**	1 c. purple	19·00	19·00
10.	**3.**	2 c. orange	12·00	14·00
13.	–	5 c. brown	£2750	
14.	–	5 c. green	12·00	12·00
17.	–	10 c. red	35·00	24·00
18.	–	$12\frac{1}{2}$ c. blue	50·00	40·00
19.	–	17 c. black	32·00	27·00

DESIGNS—VERT. 5 c. brown, Charles Connell. 5 c. green. 10 c. Queen Victoria. 17 c. King Edward VII when Prince of Wales. HORIZ. $12\frac{1}{2}$ c. Steamship.

NEWFOUNDLAND

An island off the E. coast of Canada. A British Dominion merged since 1949 with Canada, whose stamps it now uses. Currency as Canada.

1857. 12 pence = 1 shilling.
20 shillings = 1 pound.
1866. 100 cents = 1 dollar.

1.

2.

3. Royal Crown and Heraldic flowers of the United Kingdom.

1857. Imperf.

1.	**1.**	1d. purple	75·00	£120
10.	**2.**	2d. red	£250	£300
11.	**3.**	3d. green	48·00	£120
12.	**2.**	4d. red	£1400	£500
13.	**1.**	5d. brown	60·00	£190
14.	**2.**	6d. red	£2500	£600
7.		$6\frac{1}{2}$d. red	£2250	£2750
8.		8d. red	£200	£250
9.		1s. red	£14000	£3750

The frame design of Type 2 differs from each value.

1861. Imperf.

21.	**1.**	1d. brown	£100	£180
22.	**2.**	2d. lake	£110	£350
23.		4d. lake	16·00	80·00
24a.	**1.**	5d. brown	28·00	£150
24b.	**2.**	6d. lake	15·00	£100
24c.		$6\frac{1}{2}$d. lake	55·00	£325
24d.		8d. lake	50·00	£350
24e.		1s. lake	23·00	£170

8. Prince Consort.

6. Codfish.

7. Common Seal on Ice-floe.

9. Queen Victoria.

10. Schooner.

11. Queen Victoria.

1866. Perf. (2 c. also roul.).

31	**6**	2 c. green	60·00	27·00
26	**7**	5 c. brown	£500	£150
32	**8**	10 c. black	£150	23·00
61	**9**	12 c. brown	32·00	42·00
29	**10**	13 c. orange	65·00	48·00
30	**11**	24 c. blue	32·00	32·00

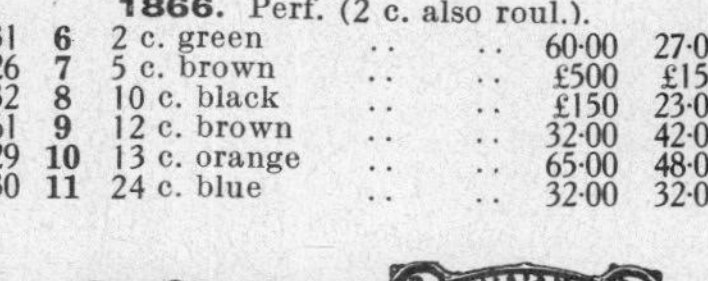

12. King Edward VII, when Prince of Wales.

14. Queen Victoria

1868. Perf. or roul.

34	**12.**	1 c. purple	40·00	45·00
36		3 c. orange	£300	£100
42		3 c. blue	£250	3·00
38	**7.**	5 c. black	£190	£100
43		5 c. blue	£170	2·75
39	**14.**	6 c. red	5·50	16·00

19. Newfoundland Dog.

15. King Edward VII, when Prince of Wales.

16. Codfish.

17.

18. Common Seal on Ice-floe.

20. Atlantic brigantine.

21. Queen Victoria.

1880.

49	**19**	$\frac{1}{2}$ c. red	5·50	6·00
59		$\frac{1}{2}$ c. black	3·75	3·50
44a	**15**	1 c. brown	12·00	7·00
50a		1 c. green	5·00	1·25
46	**16**	2 c. green	42·00	70·00
51		2 c. orange	9·50	3·00
47a	**17**	3 c. blue	42·00	1·00
52		3 c. brown	30·00	70
59a	**18**	5 c. blue	45·00	1·50
54	**20**	10 c. black	45·00	45·00

1890.

55	**21**	3 c. grey	17·00	75

This stamp on pink paper was stained by sea-water.

22. Queen Victoria.

23. John Cabot.

24. Cape Bonavista.

25. Reindeer hunting.

1897. 400th Anniv. of Discovery of Newfoundland and 60th Year of Queen Victoria's Reign. Dated "1497 1897"

66.	**22.**	1 c. green	80	2·25
67.	**23.**	2 c. red	80	1·50
68.	**24.**	3 c. blue	1·00	30
69.	**25.**	4 c. olive	6·50	1·50
70.	–	5 c. violet	5·50	1·50
71.	–	6 c. brown	4·75	1·50
72.	–	8 c. orange	11·00	6·50
73.	–	10 c. brown	18·00	1·75
74.	–	12 c. blue	25·00	1·75
75.	–	15 c. red	10·00	10·00
76.	–	24 c. violet	16·00	14·00
77.	–	30 c. blue	28·00	38·00
78.	–	35 c. red	48·00	48·00
79.	–	60 c. black	9·50	7·00

DESIGNS—As Type **24:** 5 c. Mining. 6 c. Logging. 8 c. Fishing. 10 c. Cabot's ship, the "Matthew". 15 c. Seals. 24 c. Salmon fishing. 35 c. Iceberg. As Type **23:** 12 c. Willow/red grouse. 30 c. Seal of the Colony. 60 c. Henry VII.

36. Prince Edward, later Duke of Windsor.

37. Queen Victoria.

1897. Royal portraits.

83	**36**	$\frac{1}{2}$ c. olive	80	60
84	**37**	1 c. red	1·75	2·25
85	–	1 c. green	3·25	10
86	–	2 c. orange	80	1·40
87	–	2 c. red	6·00	15
88	–	3 c. orange	5·00	10
89	–	4 c. violet	17·00	2·25
90	–	5 c. blue	23·00	2·75

DESIGNS: 2 c. King Edward VII when Prince of Wales. 3 c. Queen Alexandra when Princess of Wales. 4 c. Queen Mary when Duchess of York. 5 c. King George V when Duke of York.

1897. Surch **ONE CENT** and bar.

91	**21**	1 c. on 3 c. grey	30·00	15·00

45. Map of Newfoundland.

46. King James I.

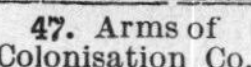

47. Arms of Colonisation Co.

49. "Endeavour" (immigrant ship), 1610.

1908.

94.	**45.**	2 c. lake	16·00	20

1910. Dated "1610 1910".

109	**46**	1 c. green	1·25	20
107	**47**	2 c. red	2·75	35
97	–	3 c. olive	2·00	11·00
98	**49**	4 c. violet	8·00	11·00
99	–	5 c. blue	5·50	4·00
111	–	6 c. purple	13·00	25·00
112	–	8 c. bistre	38·00	48·00
113	–	9 c. green	28·00	55·00
103	–	10 c. grey	40·00	70·00
115	–	12 c. brown	42·00	55·00
105	–	15 c. black	50·00	75·00

DESIGNS—HORIZ. 5 c. Cupids. 8 c. Mosquito. 9 c. Logging camp. 10 c. Paper mills. VERT. 3 c. John Guy. 6 c. Sir Francis Bacon. 12 c. King Edward VII. 15 c. King George V. (Cupids and Mosquito are places).

57. Queen Mary.

58. King George V.

67. Seal of Newfoundland.

1911. Coronation.

117a	**57**	1 c. green	2·00	20
118	**58**	2 c. red	1·75	20
119	–	3 c. brown	11·00	23·00
120	–	4 c. purple	14·00	22·00
121	–	5 c. blue	3·75	80
122	–	6 c. grey	10·00	22·00
123	–	8 c. blue	45·00	75·00
124	–	9 c. blue	9·00	28·00
125	–	10 c. green	16·00	29·00
126	–	12 c. plum	12·00	29·00
127	**67**	15 c. lake	13·00	38·00

PORTRAITS—VERT. As Types **57/8:** 3 c. Duke of Windsor when Prince of Wales. 4 c. King George VI when Prince Albert. 5 c. Princess Mary, the Princess Royal. 6 c. Duke of Gloucester when Prince Henry. 8 c. Duke of Kent when Prince George. 9 c. Prince John. 10 c. Queen Alexandra. 12 c. Duke of Connaught.

68. Caribou.

Each inscr. with the name of a different action: 1 c. Suvla Bay. 3 c. Gueudecourt. 4 c. Beaumont Hamel. 6 c. Monchy. 10 c. Steenbeck. 15c. Langemarck. 24 c. Cambrai. 36 c. Combles. The 2 c., 5 c., 8 c. and 12 c. are inscribed " Royal Naval Reserve. Ubique".

1919. Newfoundland Contingent. 1914-18.

130	**68.**	1 c. green	60	20
131		2 c. red	70	40
132		3 c. brown	1·00	20
133a		4 c. mauve	2·25	30
134		5 c. blue	1·50	60
135		6 c. grey	4·50	22·00
136		8 c. purple	4·25	29·00
137		10 c. green	3·50	1·75
138		12 c. orange	15·00	32·00
139		15 c. blue	14·00	38·00
140		24 c. brown	18·00	24·00
141		36 c. olive	7·50	16·00

1919. Air. Hawker Flight. No. 132a optd. **FIRST TRANS-ATLANTIC AIR POST April, 1919.**

142.	**68.**	3 c. brown	£14000	£8000

1919. Air. Alcock Flight. Surch. **Trans-Atlantic AIR POST 1919 ONE DOLLAR.**

143.	\$1 on 15 c. red (No. 75)	90·00	90·00

1920. Surch. in words between bars.

144.	2 c. on 30 c. blue (No. 77)	3·50	9·00
146.	3 c. on 15 c. red (No. 75)	6·50	9·00
147.	3 c. on 35 c. red (No. 78)	4·00	7·50

1921. Air. Optd. **AIR MAIL to Halifax N.S. 1921.**

148a	35 c. red (No. 78)	80·00	80·00

73. Twin Hills, Tors Cove.

75. Statue of Fighting Newfoundlander, St. John's.

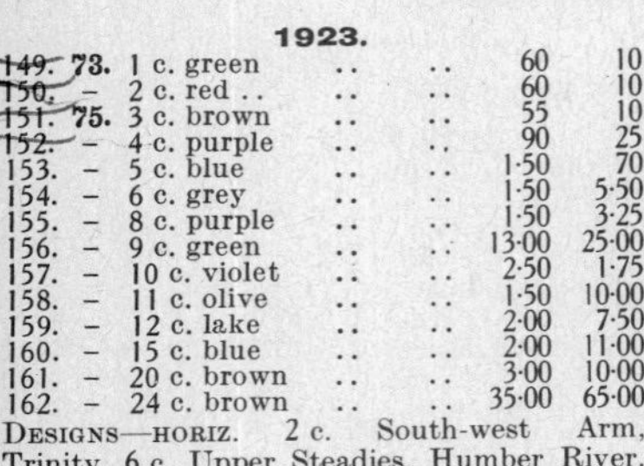

1923.

149.	73.	1 c. green	60	10
150.	–	2 c. red	60	10
151.	75.	3 c. brown	55	10
152.	–	4 c. purple	90	25
153.	–	5 c. blue	1·50	70
154.	–	6 c. grey	1·50	5·50
155.	–	8 c. purple	1·50	3·25
156.	–	9 c. green	13·00	25·00
157.	–	10 c. violet	2·50	1·75
158.	–	11 c. olive	1·50	10·00
159.	–	12 c. lake	2·00	7·50
160.	–	15 c. blue	2·00	11·00
161.	–	20 c. brown	3·00	10·00
162.	–	24 c. brown	35·00	65·00

DESIGNS—HORIZ. 2 c. South-west Arm, Trinity. 6 c. Upper Steadies, Humber River. 8 c. Quidi Vidi, near St. John's. 9 c. Reindeer crossing lake. 11 c. Shell Bird Island. 12 c. Mount Moriah, Bay of Islands. 20 c. Placentia. VERT. 4 c. Humber River. 5 c. Coast at Trinity. 10 c. Humber River Canon. 15 c. Humber River, near Little Rapids. 24 c. Topsail Falls.

1927. Air. Optd. **Air Mail DE PINEDO 1927.**

163.	60 c. black (No. 79)	£18000	£5000

88. Newfoundland and Labrador.

89. S.S. "Caribou".

90. King George V and Queen Mary.

91. Duke of Windsor when Prince of Wales.

1928. "Publicity" issue.

164	88	1 c. green	55	80
180	89	2 c. red	1·25	10
181	90	3 c. brown	80	10
182	91	4 c. mauve	1·50	20
183	–	5 c. grey	4·00	90
184	–	6 c. blue	2·00	6·50
170	–	8 c. brown	1·50	12·00
171	–	9 c. green	1·50	7·00
185	–	10 c. violet	2·00	1·50
173	–	12 c. lake	1·50	10·00
174	–	14 c. purple	3·00	5·00
175	–	15 c. blue	2·50	18·00
176	–	20 c. black	1·75	6·50
177	–	28 c. green	17·00	38·00
178	–	30 c. brown	4·50	10·00

DESIGNS—HORIZ. 5 c. Express train. 6 c. Hotel, St. John's. 8 c. Heart's Content. 10 c. War Memorial, St. John's. 15 c. Trans-Atlantic flight. 20 c. Colonial Building, St. John's. VERT. 9 c., 14 c. Cabot Tower, St. John's. 12 c., 28 c. G.P.O., St. John's. 30 c. Grand Falls, Labrador.

1929. Surch. in words.

188.	3 c. on 6 c. (No. 154)	55	2·40

1930. Air. No. 141 surch. **Trans-Atlantic AIR MAIL By B.M. "Columbia" September 1930 Fifty Cents.**

191.	68.	50 c. on 36 c. olive	£4250	£4000

103. Aeroplane and Dog-team.

104. Vickers-Vimy Biplane and early Sailing Packet.

105. Routes of historic Trans-Atlantic Flights.

1931. Air.

192	103	15 c. brown	3·00	7·00
193	104	50 c. green	18·00	26·00
194	105	$1 blue	32·00	70·00

107. Codfish.

108. King George V.

110. Duke of Windsor when Prince of Wales.

111. Reindeer.

112. Queen Elizabeth II when Princess.

121. Paper Mills.

1932.

209	107.	1 c. green	1·00	15
222		1 c. grey	30	10
210	108.	2 c. red	1·25	10
223		2 c. green	40	10
211	–	3 c. brown	80	10
212	110.	4 c. lilac	2·00	70
224		4 c. red	40	15
213	111.	5 c. purple	2·00	45
225c		5 c. violet	60	20
214	112.	6 c. blue	4·00	9·00
226	–	7 c. lake	85	2·50
282	121.	8 c. red	1·00	1·75
215	–	10 c. brown	55	25
216	–	14 c. black	80	1·50
217	–	15 c. purple	1·25	1·75
218	–	20 c. green	1·00	50
228	–	24 c. blue	60	1·75
219	–	25 c. grey	1·25	1·75
220	–	30 c. blue	15·00	22·00
289	–	48 c. brown	2·50	5·00

DESIGNS—VERT. 3 c. Queen Mary. 7 c. Queen Mother when Duchess of York. HORIZ. 10 c. Salmon. 14 c. Newfoundland dog. 15 c. Seal. 20 c. Trans-Atlantic beacon. 24 c. Bell Island. 25 c. Sealing fleet. 30 c., 48 c. Fishing fleet.

1932. Air. Surch. **TRANS-ATLANTIC WEST TO EAST Per Dornier DO-X May, 1932. One Dollar and Fifty Cents.**

221.	105.	$1·50 c. on $1 blue	£180	£225

1933. Optd. **L. & S. Post** ("Land and Sea") between bars.

229.	103.	15 c. brown	1·50	4·00

INDEX
Countries can be quickly located by referring to the index at the end of this volume.

124. Put to flight.

1933. Air.

230.	124.	5 c. brown	7·50	13·00
231.	–	10 c. yellow	4·00	14·00
232.	–	30 c. blue	20·00	32·00
233.	–	60 c. green	35·00	55·00
234.	–	75 c. brown	35·00	55·00

DESIGNS: 10 c. Land of Heart's Delight. 30 c. Spotting the herd. 60 c. News from home. 75 c. Labrador.

1933. Air. Balbo Trans-Atlantic Mass Formation Flight. No. 234 surch. **1933 GEN. BALBO FLIGHT, $4.50.**

235.	$4.50 on 75 c. brown	£275	£325

130. Sir Humphrey Gilbert.

131. Compton Castle, Devon.

1933. 350th Anniv. of Annexation. Dated "1583 1933"

236	130	1 c. black	50	60
237	131	2 c. green	65	35
238	–	3 c. brown	65	1·00
239	–	4 c. red	45	30
240	–	5 c. violet	75	70
241	–	7 c. blue	3·25	11·00
242	–	8 c. orange	5·00	7·50
243	–	9 c. blue	4·50	6·50
244	–	10 c. brown	3·75	4·00
245	–	14 c. black	7·00	26·00
246	–	15 c. red	7·00	14·00
247	–	20 c. green	7·00	12·00
248	–	24 c. purple	7·00	20·00
249	–	32 c. black	6·00	35·00

DESIGNS—VERT. 3 c. Gilbert Coat of Arms. 5 c. Anchor token. 14 c. Royal Arms. 15 c. Gilbert in the "Squirrel". 24 c. Queen Elizabeth I. 32 c. Gilbert's statue at Truro. HORIZ. 4 c. Eton College. 7 c. Gilbert commissioned by Elizabeth. 8 c. Fleet leaving Plymouth, 1583. 9 c. Arrival at St. John's. 10 c. Annexation, 5th August, 1583. 20 c. Map of Newfoundland.

1935. Silver Jubilee. As T **13** of Antigua.

250.	4 c. red	50	50
251.	5 c. violet	90	60
252.	7 c. blue	1·00	4·50
253.	24 c. olive	2·75	3·75

1937. Coronation. As T **2** of Aden.

254.	2 c. green	90	1·25
255.	4 c. red	1·10	50
256.	5 c. purple	1·60	2·00

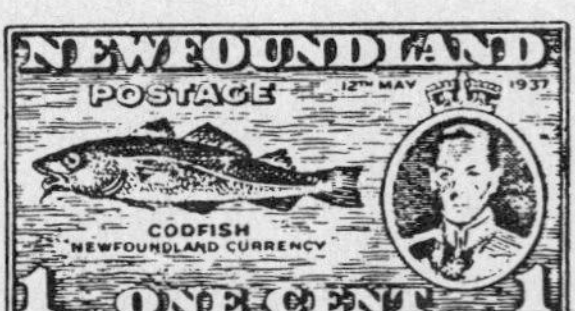

144. Codfish.

1937. Coronation

257.	144.	1 c. grey	70	15
258.	–	3 c. brown	1·40	70
259.	–	7 c. blue	1·00	60
260.	–	8 c. red	1·00	1·00
261.	–	10 c. black	2·75	3·25
262.	–	14 c. black	1·40	2·00
263.	–	15 c. red	6·00	4·00
264.	–	20 c. green	2·25	3·00
265.	–	24 c. blue	2·25	2·50
266.	–	25 c. black	2·75	1·75
267.	–	48 c. purple	6·00	4·00

DESIGNS: 3 c. Map of Newfoundland. 7 c. Reindeer. 8 c. Corner Brook Paper Mills. 10 c. Salmon. 14 c. Newfoundland Dog. 15 c. Harp Seal. 20 c. Cape Race. 24 c. Bell Island. 25 c. Sealing fleet. 48 c. The Banks Fishing Fleet.

155. King George VI.

DESIGNS: 3 c. Queen Mother. 4 c. Queen Elizabeth II, aged 12. 7 c. Queen Mary.

1938.

277.	155.	2 c. green	20	10
278.	–	3 c. red	30	10
279.	–	4 c. blue	1·00	10
271.	–	7 c. blue	65	2·00

159. King George VI and Queen Elizabeth.

1938. Royal Visit.

272.	159.	5 c. blue	75	30

1939. Surch. in figures and triangles.

273.	159.	2 c. on 5 c. blue	1·25	20
274.		4 c. on 5 c. blue	70	20

161. Grenfell on the "Strathcona" (after painting by Gribble).

1941. Sir Wilfred Grenfell's Labrador Mission.

275.	161.	5 c. blue	15	20

162. Memorial University College.

1942.

290.	162.	30 c. red	1·00	80

163. St. John's.

1943. Air.

291.	163.	7 c. blue	20	30

1946. Surch. **TWO CENTS.**

292.	162.	2 c. on 30 c. red	20	20

165. Queen Elizabeth II when Princess.

1947. 21st Birthday of Princess Elizabeth.

293.	165.	4 c. blue	15	20

166. Cabot off Cape Bonavista.

1947. 450th Anniv. of Cabot's Discovery of Newfoundland.

294.	166.	5 c. violet	15	35

POSTAGE DUE STAMPS

D 1.

1939.

D 1.	D 1.	1 c. green	1·75	6·00
D 2.		2 c. red	5·00	5·00
D 3.		3 c. blue	4·00	17·00
D 4.		4 c. orange	5·50	11·00
D 5.		5 c. brown	5·50	22·00
D 6.		10 c. purple	6·00	15·00

NEW GUINEA

Formerly a German Colony, part of the island of New Guinea. Occupied by Australian forces during the 1914–18 war and now joined with Papua and administered by the Australian Commonwealth under trusteeship. After the Japanese defeat in 1945 Australian stamps were used until 1952 when the combined issue appeared for Papua and New Guinea (q.v.). The stamps overprinted "N.W. PACIFIC ISLANDS" were also used in Nauru and other ex-German islands.

12 pence = 1 shilling.
20 shillings = 1 pound

1914. "Yacht" key-types of German New Guinea surch. **G.R.I.** and value in English currency.

No.	Description	Unused	Used
16 N	1d. on 3 pf. brown ..	40·00	50·00
17	1d. on 5 pf. green ..	14·00	20·00
18	2d. on 10 pf. red ..	18·00	25·00
19	2d. on 20 pf. blue ..	24·00	30·00
5	2½d. on 10 pf. red ..	65·00	£140
6	2½d. on 20 pf. blue ..	65·00	£140
22	3d. on 25 pf. black and red on yellow	75·00	95·00
23	3d. on 30 pf. black and orange on buff ..	70·00	90·00
24	4d. on 40 pf. black & red	85·00	£100
25	5d. on 50 pf. black and purple on buff ..	£120	£150
26	8d. on 80 pf. black and red on rose	£350	£450
12 O	1s. on 1 m. red	£1400	£1900
13	2s. on 2 m. blue	£1500	£2250
14	3s. on 3 m. black ..	£3000	£3750
15	5s. on 5 m. red and black	£5000	£6000

Nos. 3/4, surch. **1.**

No.	Description	Unused	Used
31. N.	"1" on 2d. on 10 pf. red ..	£9000	£9000
32.	"1" on 2 d. on 20 pf. blue	£9000	£6000

4.

1914. Registration labels with names of various town surch. **G.R.I. 3d.**

No.	Description	Unused	Used
33. 4.	3d. black and red ..	£110	£150

1914. "Yacht" key-types of German Marshall Islands surch. **G.R.I.** and value in English currency.

No.	Description	Unused	Used
50 N	1d. on 3 pf. brown ..	40·00	50·00
51	1d. on 5 pf. green ..	42·00	50·00
52	2d. on 10 pf. red ..	14·00	21·00
53	2d. on 20 pf. blue ..	15·00	24·00
64g	2½d. on 10 pf. red ..	£4250	
64h	2½d. on 20 pf. blue ..	£6500	
54	3d. on 25 pf. black and red on yellow ..	£250	£325
55	3d. on 30 pf. black and orange on buff ..	£275	£350
56	4d. on 40 pf. black & red	85·00	£110
57	5d. on 50 pf. black and purple on buff ..	£120	£160
58	8d. on 80 pf. black and red on rose	£450	£550
59 O	1s. on 1 m. red ..	£1600	£2250
60	2s. on 2 m. blue ..	£1000	£1500
61	3s. on 3 m. black ..	£2750	£3750
62	5s. on 5 m. red & black	£4750	£6000

1915. Nos. 52 and 53 surch. **1.**

No.	Description	Unused	Used
63. N.	"1" on 2d. on 10 pf. red ..	£140	£170
64.	"1" on 2d. on 20 pf. blue ..	£3000	£2000

1915. Stamps of Australia optd. **N.W. PACIFIC ISLANDS.**

No.	Description	Unused	Used
102 5a.	½d. green	50	3·25
103	1d. red	1·40	1·60
120	1d. violet	1·00	5·50
94 1.	2d. grey	4·50	11·00
121 5a.	2d. orange	2·75	4·50
122	2d. red	4·00	8·00
74 1.	2½d. blue	2·75	15·00
96	3d. olive	4·75	11·00
70 5a.	4d. orange	3·50	9·00
123	4d. violet	26·00	45·00
124	4d. blue	10·00	45·00
105	5d. brown	1·75	12·00
110 1.	6d. blue	4·50	14·00
89	9d. violet	13·00	15·00
90	1s. green	9·00	23·00
115	2s. brown	28·00	38·00
116	5s. grey and yellow ..	60·00	60·00
84	10s. grey and pink ..	£110	£160
99	£1 brown and blue ..	£300	£450

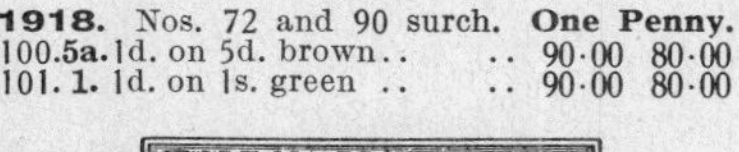

1918. Nos. 72 and 90 surch. **One Penny.**

No.	Description	Unused	Used
100. 5a.	1d. on 5d. brown	90·00	80·00
101. 1.	1d. on 1s. green	90·00	80·00

12. Native Village.

1925.

No.	Description	Unused	Used
125. 12.	½d. orange	1·75	3·75
126.	1d. green	1·75	3·75
126a.	1½d. red	1·75	2·25
127.	2d. red	1·75	4·50
128.	3d. blue	4·00	4·00
129.	4d. olive	11·00	15·00
130b.	6d. brown	4·50	40·00
131.	9d. purple	13·00	38·00
132.	1s. green	15·00	22·00
133.	2s. lake	30·00	40·00
134.	5s. brown	48·00	65·00
135.	10s. red	£110	£160
136.	£1 grey	£200	£250

1931. Air. Optd. with aeroplane and **AIR MAIL.**

No.	Description	Unused	Used
137. 12.	½d. orange	60	3·00
138.	1d. green	1·40	3·25
139.	1½d. red	1·00	4·50
140.	2d. red	1·00	7·00
141.	3d. blue	1·50	10·00
142.	4d. olive	1·25	7·50
143.	6d. brown	1·75	13·00
144.	9d. purple	3·00	16·00
145.	1s. green	3·00	16·00
146.	2s. lake	7·00	29·00
147.	5s. brown	20·00	55·00
148.	10 s. red	65·00	90·00
149.	£1 grey	£110	£150

14. Raggiana Bird of Paradise. (Dates either side of value).

1931. 10th Anniversary of Australian Administration. Dated "1921–1931".

No.	Description	Unused	Used
150 14.	1d. green	1·25	40
151	1½d. red	4·00	8·50
152	2d. red	2·50	2·00
153	3d. blue	3·00	4·00
154	4d. olive	5·00	11·00
155	5d. green	3·50	14·00
156	6d. brown	3·00	14·00
157	9d. violet	5·50	14·00
158	1s. grey	5·00	14·00
159	2s. lake	6·50	24·00
160	5s. brown	35·00	48·00
161	10s. red	75·00	£120
162	£1 grey	£140	£200

1931. Air. Optd. with aeroplane and **AIR MAIL.**

No.	Description	Unused	Used
163. 14.	½d. orange	55	1·25
164.	1d. green	1·50	2·75
165.	1½d. red	1·40	6·50
166.	2d. red	1·00	2·75
167.	3d. blue	3·00	3·25
168.	4d. olive	3·00	5·00
169.	5d. green	3·50	6·50
170.	6d. brown	6·00	21·00
171.	9d. violet	7·50	15·00
172.	1s. grey	6·50	15·00
173.	2s. lake	10·00	42·00
174.	5s. brown	32·00	60·00
175.	10s. red	60·00	£100
176.	£1 grey	£100	£170

1932. As T **14,** but without dates.

No.	Description	Unused	Used
177.	1d. green	50	20
178.	1½d. red	60	7·00
179.	2d. red	55	20
179a.	2½d. green	4·00	9·00
180.	3d. blue	90	80
180a.	3½d. red	10·00	9·00
181.	4d. olive	75	2·50
182.	5d. green	75	70
183.	6d. brown	1·00	3·00
184.	9d. violet	7·50	17·00
185.	1s. grey	4·00	10·00
186.	2s. lake	4·00	16·00
187.	5s. brown	27·00	45·00
188.	10s. red	60·00	80·00
189.	£1 grey	90·00	£100

1932. Air. T **14**, but without dates, optd. with aeroplane and **AIR MAIL**.

No.	Description	Unused	Used
190.	½d. orange	40	1·50
191.	1d. green	40	1·50
192.	1½d. mauve	60	4·50
193.	2d. red	60	30
193a.	2½d. green	3·50	2·25
194.	3d. blue	1·10	1·60
194a.	3½d. red	3·50	3·25
195.	4d. olive	2·50	6·50
196.	5d. green	4·50	7·50
197.	6d. brown	2·75	10·00
198.	9d. violet	5·50	9·00
199.	1s. grey	4·50	7·50
200.	2s. lake	5·50	28·00
201.	5s. brown	40·00	55·00
202.	10s. red	65·00	70·00
203.	£1 grey	75·00	55·00

16. Bulolo Goldfields.

1935. Air.

No.	Description	Unused	Used
204. 16.	£2 violet	£225	£150
205.	£5 green	£600	£500

1935. Silver Jubilee. Nos. 177 and 179 optd. **HIS MAJESTY'S JUBILEE 1910-1935.**

No.	Description	Unused	Used
206.	1d. green	45	35
207.	2d. red	55	35

18. King George VI.

1937. Coronation.

No.	Description	Unused	Used
208. 18.	2d. red	50	30
209.	3d. blue	60	30
210.	5d. green	50	35
211.	1s. purple	85	35

1939. Air. As T **16,** but inscr. "AIR MAIL POSTAGE".

No.	Description	Unused	Used
212.	½d. orange	80	3·75
213.	1d. green	2·00	2·50
214.	1½d. red	80	5·50
215.	2d. red	3·75	3·00
216.	3d. blue	4·00	9·50
217.	4d. olive	3·00	7·50
218.	5d. green	3·00	2·25
219.	6d. brown	6·00	9·50
220.	9d. violet	6·00	14·00
221.	1s. green	7·50	15·00
222.	2s. red	45·00	40·00
223.	5s. brown	85·00	85·00
224.	10s. pink	£225	£140
225.	£1 olive	£110	£120

OFFICIAL STAMPS

1915. Nos. 16 and 17 optd. **O.S.**

No.	Description	Unused	Used
O 1. N.	1d. on 3 pf. brown ..	25·00	60·00
O 2.	1d. on 5 pf. green ..	75·00	£130

1925. Optd. **O S.**

No.	Description	Unused	Used
O 3 12.	1d. green	80	4·25
O 4	1½d. red	5·50	17·00
O 5	2d. red	1·60	3·75
O 6	3d. blue	2·00	5·50
O 7	4d. olive	3·00	8·50
O 8a	6d. brown	7·00	40·00
O 9	9d. purple	3·75	40·00
O 10	1s. green	5·00	40·00
O 11	2s. lake	27·00	75·00

1931. Optd. **O S.**

No.	Description	Unused	Used
O 12. 14.	1d. green	1·50	11·00
O 13.	1½d. red	2·25	12·00
O 14.	2d. red	3·75	7·00
O 15.	3d. blue	2·25	6·00
O 16.	4d. olive	2·25	8·50
O 17.	5d. green	5·00	12·00
O 18.	6d. brown	8·00	17·00
O 19.	9d. violet	8·50	28·00
O 20.	1s. grey	12·00	28·00
O 21.	2s. lake	35·00	75·00
O 22.	5s. brown	£120	£180

1932. **T14**, but without dates, optd. **O S.**

No.	Description	Unused	Used
O 23.	1d. green	2·00	3·50
O 24.	1½d. red	2·75	12·00
O 25.	2d. red	2·75	2·75
O 26.	2½d. green	2·75	7·50
O 27.	3d. blue	5·50	14·00
O 28.	3½d. red	3·00	10·00
O 29.	4d. olive	4·50	14·00
O 30.	5d. green	4·50	14·00
O 31.	6d. brown	6·00	27·00
O 32.	9d. violet	10·00	40·00
O 33.	1s. grey	15·00	28·00
O 34.	2s. lake	35·00	85·00
O 35.	5s. brown	£120	£170

For later issues see **PAPUA AND NEW GUINEA.**

NEW HEBRIDES

A group of islands in the Pacific Ocean, E. of Australia, under joint administration of Gt. Britain and France. The Condominium ended in 1980, when the New Hebrides became independent as the Republic of Vanuatu.

1908. 12 pence = 1 shilling;
20 shillings = 1 pound.
1938. 100 gold centimes = 1 gold franc.
1977. 100 centimes = 1 franc (New Hebrides).

BRITISH ADMINISTRATION

1908. Stamps of Fiji optd **NEW HEBRIDES CONDOMINIUM**.

No.	Description	Unused	Used
1a 23	½d. green	40	6·00
2	1d. red	45	40
5	2d. purple and orange	60	70
12	2d. grey	60	3·00
6	2½d. purple & blue on bl	60	70
13	2½d. blue	65	3·75
7	5d. purple and green ..	80	2·00
8	6d. purple and red ..	70	1·25
15	6d. purple	85	5·00
3	1s. green and red ..	16·00	12·00
16	1s. black on green ..	85	7·00

3. Weapons and Idols.

1911.

No.	Description	Unused	Used
18. 3.	½d. green	85	1·60
19.	1d. red	2·50	2·00
20.	2d. grey	3·50	3·75
21.	2½d. blue	1·60	4·25
24.	5d. green	2·00	4·25
25.	6d. purple	1·50	4·75
26.	1s. black on green ..	1·50	7·50
27.	2s. purple on blue ..	13·00	18·00
28.	5s. green on yellow ..	26·00	48·00

1920. Surch. (a) On T **3.**

No.	Description	Unused	Used
40. 3.	1d. on ½d. green ..	2·50	17·00
30.	1d. on 5d. green ..	7·00	60·00
31.	1d. on 1s. black on green	1·00	11·00
32.	1d. on 2s. purple on blue	1·00	10·00
33.	1d. on 5s. green on yellow	1·00	10·00
41.	3d. on 1d. red	2·25	11·00
42.	5d. on 2½d. blue ..	4·75	18·00

(b) On No. F 16 French New Hebrides.

No.	Description	Unused	Used
34. 3.	2d. on 40 c. red on yellow	1·00	13·00

5.

1925.

No.	Description	Unused	Used
43. 5.	½d. (5 c.) black	60	5·00
44.	1d. (10c.) green	90	5·00
45.	2d. (20 c.) grey	1·75	2·25
46.	2½d. (25 c.) brown ..	1·00	4·75
47.	5d. (50 c.) blue	1·50	2·50
48.	6d. (60 c.) purple	2·75	7·50
49.	1s. (1 f. 25) black on green	3·00	12·00
50.	2s. (2 f. 50) purple on blue	6·00	18·00
51.	5s. (6 f. 25) green on yellow	6·00	21·00

6. Lopevi Islands and Copra Canoe.

1938.

No.	Description	Unused	Used
52. 6.	5 c. green	2·50	1·90
53.	10 c. orange	1·25	50
54.	15 c. violet	2·00	1·50
55.	20 c. red	1·60	80
56.	25 c. brown	1·60	1·00
57.	30 c. blue	1·60	1·00
58.	40 c. olive	4·25	2·00
59.	50 c. purple	1·60	50
60.	1 f. red on green	4·00	6·50
61.	2 f. blue on green	26·00	16·00
62.	5 f. red on yellow	65·00	48·00
63.	10 f. violet on blue ..	£170	70·00

1949. U.P.U. As T **20/23** of Antigua.

No.	Description	Unused	Used
64.	10 c. orange	30	15
65.	15 c. violet	30	15
66.	30 c. blue	30	15
67.	50 c. purple	40	20

7. Outrigger Sailing Canoes.

1953.

No.	Description	Unused	Used
68. 7.	5 c. green	40	10
69.	10 c. red	40	10
70.	15 c. yellow	40	10
71.	20 c. blue	40	10
72. –	25 c. olive	40	10
73. –	30 c. brown	40	10
74. –	40 c. sepia	40	10
75. –	50 c. violet	60	10
76. –	1 f. orange	5·50	70
77. –	2 f. purple	6·50	8·50
78. –	5 f. red	12·00	30·00

DESIGNS: 25 c. to 50 c. Native carving. 1 f. to 5 f. Two natives outside hut.

1953. Coronation. As T **13** of Aden.

No.	Description	Unused	Used
79.	10 c. black and red ..	30	25

10. Quiros Galleon and Map.

1956. 50th Anniv. of Condominium. Inscr. "1906 1956".

No.	Description	Unused	Used
80. **10.**	5 c. green	10	10
81.	10 c. red	10	10
82. –	20 c. blue	10	10
83. –	50 c. lilac	15	15

DESIGN: 20 c., 50 c. "Marianne", "Talking Drum" and "Britannia".

12. Port Vila: Iririki Islet.

1957.

No.	Description	Unused	Used
84. **12.**	5 c. green	40	10
85.	10 c. red	30	10
86.	15 c. yellow	50	20
87.	20 c. blue	40	10
88. –	25 c. olive	45	10
89. –	30 c. brown	45	10
90. –	40 c. sepia	45	10
91. –	50 c. violet	45	10
92. –	1 f. orange	1·00	80
93. –	2 f. mauve	6·00	4·00
94. –	5 f. black	15·00	6·00

DESIGNS: 25 c. to 50 c. River scene and spear fisherman. 1 f. to 5 f. Woman drinking from coconut.

1963. Freedom from Hunger. As T **28** of Aden.

No.	Description	Unused	Used
95.	60 c. green	50	15

1963. Cent of Red Cross. As T **33** of Antigua, but with British and French cyphers in place of Queen's portrait.

No.	Description	Unused	Used
96.	15 c. red and black ..	35	10
97.	45 c. red and blue	45	10

18. Copra.

1963.

No.	Description	Unused	Used
98. –	5 c. lake, brown and blue	35	30
99. –	10 c. brown, buff & green	15	10
100. **18.**	15 c. bistre, brown & violet	15	10
101. –	20 c. black, green and blue	45	10
102. –	25 c. violet, brown & red	50	70
103. –	30 c. brown, bistre & violet	75	10
104. –	40 c. red and blue ..	80	1·40
105. –	50 c. green, yellow and turquoise	60	10
129. –	60 c. red and blue ..	40	15
106. –	1 f. red, black and green	2·50	2·50
107. –	2 f. black, brown & olive	2·50	1·75
108. –	3 f. multicoloured ..	13·00	8·00
109. –	5 f. blue, indigo and black	18·00	15·00

DESIGNS: 5 c. Exporting manganese, Forari. 10 c. Cocoa beans. 20 c. Fishing from Palikulo Point. 25 c. Picasso fish. 30 c. Nautilus shell. 40 c., 60 c. Sting-fish. 50 c. Blue lined surgeon. 1 f. Cardinal honey-eater (bird). 2 f. Buff-bellied flycatcher. 3 f. Thicket warbler. 5 f. White-collared kingfisher.

1965. Centenary of I.T.U. As T **36** of Antigua, but with British and French cyphers in place of the Queen's portrait.

No.	Description	Unused	Used
110.	15 c. red and drab	20	10
111.	60 c. blue and red	35	20

1965. I.C.Y. As T **37** of Antigua, but with British and French cyphers in place of the Queen's portrait.

No.	Description	Unused	Used
112.	5 c. purple and turquoise ..	15	10
113.	55 c. green and lavender ..	20	20

1966. Churchill Commemoration. As T **38** of Antigua, but with British and French cyphers in place of Queen's portrait.

No.	Description	Unused	Used
114.	5 c. blue	20	10
115.	15 c. green	40	10
116.	25 c. brown	50	10
117.	30 c. violet	50	10

1966. World Cup Championship. As T **40** of Antigua, but with British and French cyphers in place of the Queen's portrait.

No.	Description	Unused	Used
118.	20 c. multicoloured ..	20	15
119.	40 c. multicoloured ..	30	15

1966. Ingauguration of W.H.O. Headquarters, Geneva. As T **41** of Antigua, but with British and French cyphers in place of the Queen's portrait.

No.	Description	Unused	Used
120.	25 c. black, green and blue	20	10
121.	60 c. black, purple and ochre	55	20

1966. 30th Anniv of U.N.E.S.C.O. As T **54/6** of Antigua, but with British and French cyphers in place of the Queen's portrait.

No.	Description	Unused	Used
122.	15 c. multicoloured ..	20	10
123.	30 c. yellow, violet and olive	65	10
124.	45 c. black, purple & orge.	70	15

36. The Coast Watchers.

1967. 25th Anniv. of Pacific War. Multi.

No.	Description	Unused	Used
125.	15 c. Type **36**	10	10
126.	25 c. Map of War Zone, U.S. Marine and Australian Soldier	10	15
127.	60 c. H.M.A.S. "Canberra"	15	15
128.	1 f. "Flying Fortress" ..	20	15

40. Globe and Hemispheres.

1968. Bicent. of Bougainville's World Voyage.

No.	Description	Unused	Used
130. **40.**	15 c. green, violet & red	10	10
131. –	25 c. olive, purple & blue	15	10
132. –	60 c. brown, purple & grn.	15	15

DESIGNS: 25 c. Ships "La Boudeuse" and "L'Etoile", and Map. 60 c. Bougainville, Ship's Figure-head and bougainvillea flowers.

43. "Concorde" and Vapour Trails.

1968. Anglo-French "Concorde" Project.

No.	Description	Unused	Used
133. **43.**	25 c. blue, red and blue	50	20
134. –	60 c. red, black and blue	60	25

DESIGN: 60 c. "Concorde" in flight.

45. Kauri Pine.

1969. Timber Industry.

No.	Description	Unused	Used
135. **45.**	20 c. multicoloured ..	10	10

46. Cyphers, Flags and Relay Runner receiving Baton.

1969. 3rd South Pacific Games, Port Moresby. Multicoloured.

No.	Description	Unused	Used
136.	25 c. Type **46**	10	10
137.	1 f. Similar to No. 136 ..	20	20

48. Diver on Platform.

1969. Pentecost Island Land Divers. Mult.

No.	Description	Unused	Used
138.	15 c. Type **48**	10	10
139.	25 c. Diver Jumping ..	10	10
140.	1 f. Diver at end of Fall ..	20	20

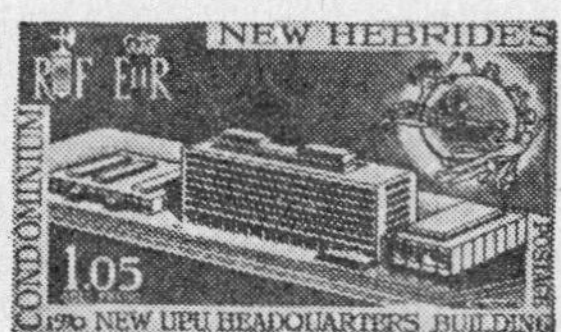

51. U.P.U. Emblem and Headquarters Building.

1970. New U.P.U. Headquarters Building.

No.	Description	Unused	Used
141. **51.**	1 f. 05 slate, orge. & pur.	15	15

52. General Charles de Gaulle.

1970. 30th Anniv. of New Hebrides' Declaration for the Free French Government.

No.	Description	Unused	Used
142. **52.**	65 c. multicoloured ..	35	15
143.	1 f. 10 multicoloured ..	45	15

1970. No. 101 surch.

No.	Description	Unused	Used
144.	35 c. on 20 c. black, green and blue	30	30

54. "The Virgin and Child" (Bellini).

1970. Christmas. Multicoloured.

No.	Description	Unused	Used
145.	15 c. Type **54**	10	10
146.	50 c. "The Virgin & Child" (Cima)	10	10

1971. Death of General Charles de Gaulle. Nos. 142/3 optd. **1890-1970 IN MEMORIAM 9-11-70.**

No.	Description	Unused	Used
147. **52.**	65 c. multicoloured ..	15	10
148.	1 f. 10 multicoloured ..	15	20

56. Football.

1971. 4th South Pacific Games, Papeete, French Polynesia.

No.	Description	Unused	Used
149.	20 c. Type **56**	10	10
150.	65 c. Basketball (vert.) ..	30	20

57. Kauri Pine, Cone and Arms of Royal Society.

1971. Royal Society's Expedition to New Hebrides.

No.	Description	Unused	Used
151. **57.**	65 c. multicoloured ..	20	10

58. "The Adoration of the Shepherds" (detail, Louis Le Nain).

1971. Christmas. Multicoloured.

No.	Description	Unused	Used
152.	25 c. Type **58**	10	10
153.	50 c. "The Adoration of the Shepherds" (detail, Tintoretto)	20	20

59. "Drover" Mk. III.

1972. Aircraft. Multicoloured.

No.	Description	Unused	Used
154.	20 c. Type **59**	35	15
155.	25 c. "Sandringham" flying-boat	45	15
156.	30 c. D.H. "Dragon Rapide"	45	15
157.	65 c. "Caravelle" ..	1·25	1·25

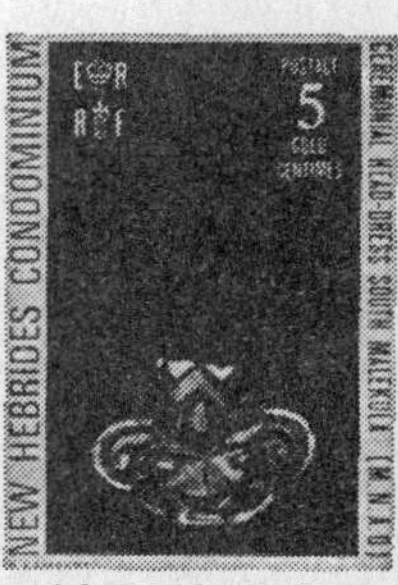

60. Ceremonial Headdress, South Malekula.

1972. Multicoloured.

No.	Description	Unused	Used
158.	5 c. Type **60**	10	10
159.	10 c. Baker's Pigeon ..	25	10
160.	15 c. Gong and carving (North Ambrym) ..	15	15
161.	20 c. Red-headed Parrot Finch	40	25
162.	25 c. "Cribraria fischeri" (shell)	40	25
163.	30 c. "Oliva rubrolabiata" (shell)	50	30
164.	35 c. Chestnut-bellied Kingfisher	65	40
165.	65 c. "Strombus plicatus" (shell)	75	60
166.	1 f. Gong (North Malekula) and carving (North Ambrym)	1·25	1·00
167.	2 f. Palm Lorikeet ..	4·00	4·50
168.	3 f. Ceremonial headdress (South Malekula (different))	3·75	6·00
169.	5 f. Green snail shell ..	7·50	13·00

61. " Adoration of the Kings " (Spranger).

1972. Christmas. Multicoloured.
170. 25 c. Type **61** 10 10
171. 70 c. " The Virgin and Child in a Landscape " (Provoost) 20 20

1972. Royal Silver Wedding. As T **52** of Ascension, but with Royal and French cyphers in background.
172. 35 c. deep violet 15 10
173. 65 c. green 20 10

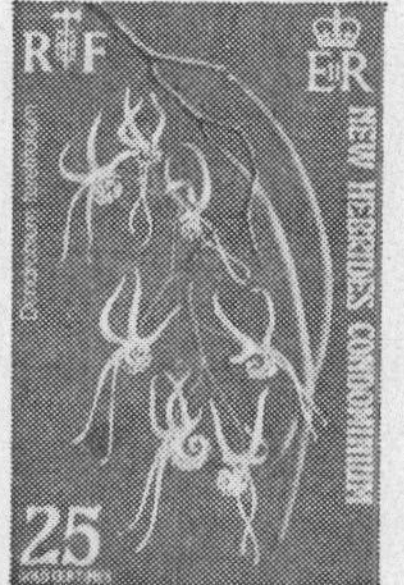

63. " Dendrobium teretifolium ".

1973. Orchids. Multicoloured.
174. 25 c. Type **63** 25 10
175. 30 c. " Ephemerantha comata " 30 10
176. 35 c. " Spathoglottis petri " 35 10
177. 65 c. " Dendrobium mohlianum " 60 55

64. New Wharf at Vila.

1973. Opening of New Wharf at Vila. Multicoloured.
178. 25 c. Type **64** 20 10
179. 70 c. As T **64** but horiz. format 40 30

65. Wild Horses.

1973. Tanna Island. Multicoloured.
180. 35 c. Type **65** 30 15
181. 70 c. Yasur Volcano .. 55 20

66. Mother and Child.

1973. Christmas. Multicoloured.
182. 35 c. Type **66** 10 10
183. 70 c. Lagoon scene .. 20 20

67. Pacific Pigeon.

1974. Wild Life. Multicoloured.
184 25 c. Type **67** 95 25
185 35 c. "Lyssa curvata" (moth) .. .. .. 1·25 60
186 70 c. Green sea turtle .. 1·50 70
187 1 f. 15 Grey-headed flying fox .. .. .. 1·75 1·50

1974. Royal Visit. Nos. 164 and 167 optd. **ROYAL VISIT 1974.**
188. 35 c. multicoloured .. 15 10
189. 2 f. multicoloured .. 30 40

69. Old Post Office.

1974. Inaug. of New Post Office. Mult.
190. 35 c. Type **69** 15 40
191. 70 c. New Post Office .. 15 45

70. Capt. Cook and Map.

1974. Bicent. of Discovery. Multicoloured.
192. 35 c. Type **70** .. .. 1·75 1·75
193. 35 c. William Wales and beach landing .. .. 1·75 1·75
194. 35 c. William Hodges and island scene .. .. 1·75 1·75
195. 1 f. 15 Capt. Cook, map and H.M.S. "Resolution" (59×34 mm.) .. .. 4·00 4·00

71. U.P.U. Emblem and Letters.

1974. Centenary of U.P.U.
196. **71.** 70 c. multicoloured .. 30 50

72. "Adoration of the Magi" (Velazquez).

1974. Christmas. Multicoloured.
197. 35 c. Type **72** 10 10
198. 70 c. " The Nativity " (Gerard van Honthorst) 20 20

73. Charolais Bull.

1975.
199. **73.** 10 f. brown, grn. & blue 11·00 18·00

74. Canoeing.

1975. World Scout Jamboree, Norway. Mult.
200. 25 c. Type **74** 30 10
201. 35 c. Preparing meal .. 30 10
202. 1 f. Map-reading 70 15
203. 5 f. Fishing .. .. 3·00 2·50

75. " Pitti Madonna " (Michelangelo).

1975. Christmas. Michelangelo's Sculptures. Multicoloured.
204. 35 c. Type **75** 10 10
205. 70 c. "Bruges Madonna" .. 15 10
206. 2 f. 50 "Taddei Madonna" 70 50

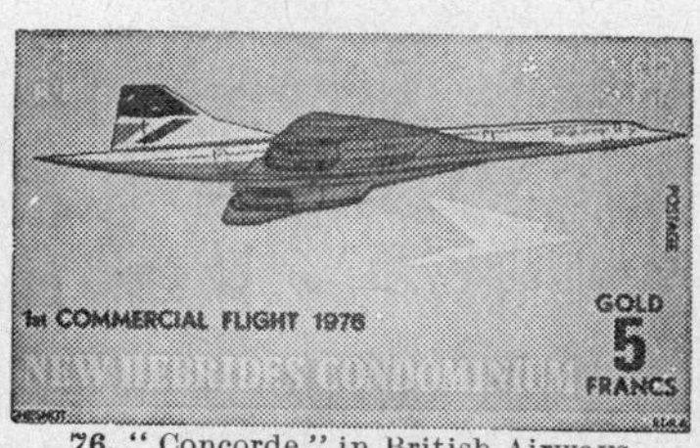

76. " Concorde " in British Airways Livery.

1976. 1st Commercial Flight of " Concorde ".
207. **76.** 5 f. multicoloured .. 15·00 6·00

77. Telephones of 1876 and 1976.

1976. Cent. of Telephone. Multicoloured.
208. 25 c. Type **77** 15 10
209. 70 c. Alexander Graham Bell 30 10
210. 1 f. 15 Satellite and Noumea Earth Station 50 50

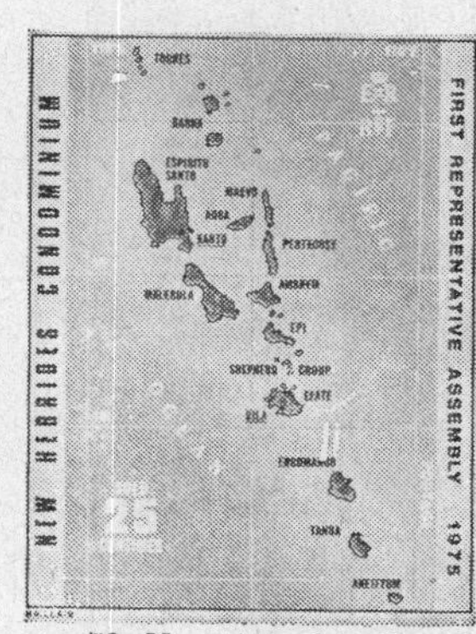

78. Map of the Islands.

1976. Constitutional Changes. Multicoloured.
211. 25 c. Type **78** 20 15
212. 1 f. View of Santo (horiz.) 45 60
213. 2 f. View of Vila (horiz.) .. 65 1·25
Nos. 212/13 are smaller, 36×26 mm.

79. " The Flight into Egypt " (Lusitano).

1976. Christmas. Multicoloured.
214. 35 c. Type **79** 10 10
215. 70 c. " Adoration of the Shepherds " 15 10
216. 2 f. 50 " Adoration of the Magi " 45 50
Nos. 215/16 show retables by the Master of Santos-o-Novo.

80. Royal Visit, 1974.

1977. Silver Jubilee. Multicoloured.
217. 35 c. Type **80** 15 10
218. 70 c. Imperial State Crown 20 10
219. 2 f. The Blessing 40 65

1977. Currency Change. Nos. 158/69 and 199 surch.

233	5 f. on 5 c. Type **60**	50	15
234	10 f. on 10 c. Baker's Pigeon	50	15
222	15 f. on 15 c. Gong and carving	60	60
223	20 f. on 20 c. Red-headed Parrot Finch	1·25	55
224	25 f. on 25 c. "Cribraria fischeri" (shell)	1·00	1·00
225	30 f. on 30 c. "Oliva rubrolabiata" (shell)	1·25	50
238	35 f. on 35 c. Chestnut-bellied Kingfisher	2·00	55
239	40 f. on 65 c. "Strombus plicatus" (shell)	1·50	55
228	50 f. on 1 f. Gong and carving	1·50	1·50
229	70 f. on 2 f. Palm Lorikeet	3·00	1·00
230	100 f. on 3 f. Ceremonial headdress	3·00	4·25
231	200 f. on 5 f. Green snail shell	7·00	14·00
241	500 f. on 10 f. Type **73**	18·00	17·00

89. Island of Erromango and Kauri Pine.

1977. Islands. Multicoloured.

242.	5 f. Type **89**	30	10
243.	10 f. Territory map and copra-making	40	30
244.	15 f. Espiritu Santo and cattle	30	30
245.	20 f. Efate and Vila P.O.	30	25
246.	25 f. Malekula and head-dresses	40	40
247.	30 f. Aobe, Maewo and pigs tusks	45	50
248.	35 f. Pentecost and land diver	50	65
249.	40 f. Tanna and volcano	70	60
250.	50 f. Shepherd Is. and canoe	70	40
251.	70 f. Banks Is. and dancers	1·75	1·40
252.	100 f. Ambrym and idols	1·75	90
253.	200 f. Aneityum and baskets	2·75	2·50
254.	500 f. Torres Is. and archer fishing	6·00	7·50

90. "Tempi Madonna" (Raphael).

1977. Christmas. Multicoloured.

255.	10 f. Type **90**	10	10
256.	15 f. "The Flight into Egypt" (Gerard David)	15	15
257.	30 f. "Virgin and Child" (Batoni)	20	40

91. "Concorde" over New York.

1978. "Concorde" Commemoration.

258.	10 f. Type **91**	65	65
259.	20 f. "Concorde" over London	85	85
260.	30 f. "Concorde" over Washington	1·10	1·10
261.	40 f. "Concorde" over Paris	1·40	1·40

92. White Horse of Hanover.

1978. 25th Anniv. of Coronation.

262. **92.**	40 f. brown, blue & silver	35	55
263. –	40 f. multicoloured	35	55
264. –	40 f. brown, blue & silver	35	55

DESIGNS: No. 263, Queen Elizabeth II. No. 264, Gallic Cock.

93. "Madonna and Child".

1978. Christmas. Paintings by Durer. Multicoloured.

265.	10 f. Type **93**	10	10
266.	15 f. "The Virgin and Child with St. Anne"	10	10
267.	30 f. "Madonna of the Siskin"	10	10
268.	40 f. "Madonna of the Pear"	15	15

1979. 1st Anniv. of Internal Self-Government. Surch. **11-1-79 FIRST ANNIVERSARY INTERNAL SELF-GOVERNMENT** and new value.

269. **78.**	10 f. on 25 f. mult. (blue background)	10	10
270.	40 f. on 25 f. mult. (grn. background)	20	20

95. 1938 5 c. Stamp and Sir Rowland Hill.

1979. Death Centenary of Sir Rowland Hill. Multicoloured.

271.	10 f. Type **95**	10	10
272.	20 f. 1969 25 c. Pentecost Island Land Divers Commemorative	15	10
273.	40 f. 1925 2d. (20 c.)	20	20

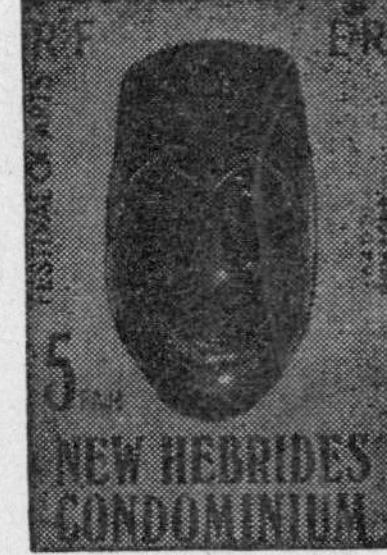

96. Chubwan Mask.

1979. Arts Festival. Multicoloured.

275.	5 f. Type **96**	10	10
276.	10 f. Nal-Nal clubs and spears	10	10
277.	20 f. Ritual puppet	15	10
278.	40 f. Neqatmalow head-dress	25	15

HAVE YOU READ THE NOTES AT THE BEGINNING OF THIS CATALOGUE?
These often provide answers to the enquiries we receive.

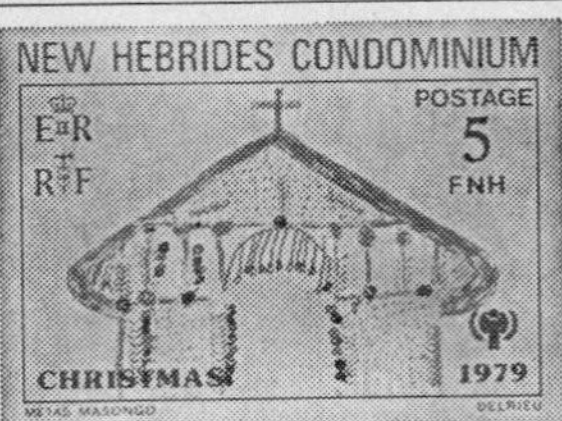

97. "Native Church" (Metas Masongo).

1979. Christmas and International Year of the Child. Children's Drawings. Mult.

279.	5 f. Type **97**	10	10
280.	10 f. "Priest and Candles" (Herve Rutu)	10	10
281.	20 f. "Cross and Bible" (Mark Deards) (vert.)	10	10
282.	40 f. "Green Candle and Santa Claus" (Dev Raj) (vert.)	15	15

98. White-bellied Honeyeater.

1980. Birds. Multicoloured.

283.	10 f. Type **98**	50	10
284.	20 f. Scarlet Robin	70	10
285.	30 f. Yellow-fronted White eye	90	35
286.	40 f. Fan-tailed Cuckoo	1·00	55

POSTAGE DUE STAMPS

1925. Optd. **POSTAGE DUE.**

D 1. **5.**	1d. (10 c.) green	38·00	1·00
D 2.	2d. (20 c.) grey	45·00	1·00
D 3.	3d. (30 c.) red	50·00	2·50
D 4.	5d. (50 c.) blue	55·00	4·50
D 5.	10d. (1 f.) red on blue	60·00	5·50

1938. Optd. **POSTAGE DUE.**

D 6. **6.**	5 c. green	14·00	20·00
D 7.	10 c. orange	14·00	20·00
D 8.	20 c. red	21·00	25·00
D 9.	40 c. olive	30·00	40·00
D 10.	1 f. red on green	45·00	55·00

1953. Nos 68/9, 71, 74 and 76 optd. **POSTAGE DUE.**

D 11. **7.**	5 c. green	5·00	6·50
D 12.	10 c. red	1·75	4·50
D 13.	20 c. blue	5·50	11·00
D 14. –	40 c. sepia (No. 74)	8·50	20·00
D 15. –	1 f. orange (No. 76)	6·00	20·00

1957. Optd. **POSTAGE DUE.**

D 16. **12.**	5 c. green	30	1·25
D 17.	10 c. red	30	1·25
D 18.	20 c. blue	1·25	1·75
D 19. –	40 c. sepia (No. 90)	2·50	3·50
D 20. –	1 f. orange (No. 92)	4·00	6·50

FRENCH ADMINISTRATION

1908. Stamps of New Caledonia optd. **NOUVELLES HEBRIDES.**

F 1. **15.**	5 c. green	1·00	1·60
F 2.	10 c. red	80	80
F 3. **16.**	25 c. blue on green	3·50	2·75
F 4.	50 c. red on orange	6·00	5·50
F 5. **17.**	1 f. blue on green	8·00	6·50

1910. Stamps of New Caledonia optd. **NOUVELLES HEBRIDES CONDOMINIUM.**

F 6. **15.**	5 c. green	1·25	1·50
F 7.	10 c. red	1·25	60
F 8. **16.**	25 c. blue on green	2·00	3·25
F 9.	50 c. red on orange	4·50	5·50
F 10. **17.**	1 f. blue on green	12·00	13·00

The following issues are as stamps of British Administration but inscr. "NOUVELLES HEBRIDES" except where otherwise stated.

1911.

F 11 **3.**	5 c. green	1·00	1·75
F 12	10 c. red	45	60
F 13	20 c. grey	1·00	1·50
F 25	25 c. blue	75	2·75
F 26	30 c. brown on yellow	1·50	5·00
F 16	40 c. red on yellow	1·40	2·75
F 17	50 c. olive	2·00	2·75
F 18	75 c. orange	6·50	11·00
F 19	1 f. red on blue	2·00	2·25
F 20	2 f. violet	8·00	13·00
F 21	5 f. red on green	11·00	18·00

1920. Surch in fgures.

F 34	05 c. on 40 c. red on yellow (No. F 16)	24·00	50·00
F 32a	5 c. on 50 c. red on orange (No. F 4)	£375	£375
F 33	5 c. on 50 c. red on orange (No. F 9)	2·00	4·00
F 38	10 c. on 5 c. green (No. F 11)	1·50	2·00
F 33a	10 c. on 25 c. blue on green (No. F 8)	30	1·25
F 35	20 c. on 30 c. brown on yellow (No. F 26)	8·00	32·00
F 39	30 c. on 10 c. red (No. F 12)	1·25	1·50
F 41	50 c. on 25 c. blue (No. F 25)	2·50	14·00

1921. Stamp of New Hebrides (British) surch. in figures.

F 37.	10 c. on 5d. green (No. 24)	14·00	23·00

1925.

F 42. **5.**	5 c. (½d.) black	60	5·00
F 43.	10 c. (1d.) green	50	4·00
F 44.	20 c. (2d.) grey	50	1·60
F 45.	25 c. (2½d.) brown	50	3·00
F 46.	30 c. (3d.) red	50	2·75
F 47.	40 c. (4d.) red on yellow	70	2·75
F 48.	50 c. (5d.) blue	80	2·50
F 49.	75 c. (7½d.) brown	1·00	5·00
F 50.	1 f. (10d.) red on blue	2·00	3·00
F 51.	2 f. (1s. 8d.) violet	4·00	14·00
F 52.	5 f. (4d.) red on green	5·50	18·00

1938.

F 53. **6.**	5 c. green	1·00	1·50
F 54.	10 c. orange	1·50	75
F 55.	15 c. violet	1·25	1·25
F 56.	20 c. red	1·25	1·00
F 57.	25 c. brown	2·75	1·40
F 58.	30 c. blue	2·75	1·40
F 59.	40 c. olive	1·25	2·75
F 60.	50 c. purple	1·25	1·00
F 61.	1 f. red on green	1·50	2·25
F 62.	2 f. blue on green	16·00	15·00
F 63.	5 f. red on yellow	28·00	25·00
F 64.	10 f. violet on blue	75·00	55·00

1941. Free French Issue. As last optd. **France Libre.**

F 65. **6.**	5 c. green	3·25	11·00
F 66.	10 c. orange	3·75	8·50
F 67.	15 c. violet	4·75	14·00
F 68.	20 c. red	8·50	14·00
F 69.	25 c. brown	11·00	15·00
F 70.	30 c. blue	11·00	15·00
F 71.	40 c. olive	11·00	16·00
F 72.	50 c. purple	11·00	14·00
F 73.	1 f. red on green	11·00	15·00
F 74.	2 f. blue on green	11·00	17·00
F 75.	5 f. red on yellow	11·00	17·00
F 76.	10 f. violet on blue	13·00	18·00

1949. 75th Anniv. of U.P.U. As Br. Administration but with inscriptions in French.

F 77.	10 c. orange	2·25	2·50
F 78.	15 c. violet	4·25	4·00
F 79.	30 c. blue	5·50	6·50
F 80.	50 c. purple	6·50	7·00

1953.

F 81. **7.**	5 c. green	30	30
F 82.	10 c. red	50	30
F 83.	15 c. yellow	50	40
F 84.	20 c. blue	60	40
F 85. –	25 c. olive	50	40
F 86. –	30 c. brown	50	40
F 87. –	40 c. sepia	50	50
F 88. –	50 c. violet	50	40
F 89. –	1 f. orange	11·00	3·50
F 90. –	2 f. purple	16·00	24·00
F 91. –	5 f. red	26·00	48·00

1956. 50th Anniv. of Condominium.

F 92. **10.**	5 c. green	1·00	70
F 93.	10 c. red	1·00	70
F 94. –	20 c. blue	1·00	80
F 95. –	50 c. violet	1·40	1·60

1957.

F 96. **12.**	5 c. green	65	40
F 97.	10 c. red	65	30
F 98.	15 c. yellow	1·00	40
F 99.	20 c. blue	1·00	40
F 100. –	25 c. olive	1·00	40
F 101 –	30 c. brown	1·10	50
F 102. –	40 c. sepia	1·10	50
F 103. –	50 c. violet	1·10	40
F 104. –	1 f. orange	7·00	2·50
F 105. –	2 f. mauve	18·00	22·00
F 106. –	5 f. black	28·00	32·00

F 7. Emblem and Globe.

1963. Freedom from Hunger.

F 107. **F 7.**	60 c. green & brown	13·00	9·00

F 8. Centenary Emblem.

1963. Centenary of Red Cross.

F 108 **F 8**	15 c. red, grey & orge	7·50	5·00
F 109	45 c. red, grey and bistre	13·50	16·00

1963.

F 110. – 5 c. lake, brown & blue .. 40 30
F 111. – 10 c. brown, buff & grn.* 80 80
F 112. – 10 c. brown, buff & grn. 30 15
F 113. 18. 15 c. bistre, brn. & vio. 4·50 40
F 114. – 20 c. black, grn. & blue* 2·25 2·75
F 115. – 20 c. black, green & blue 60 25
F 116. – 25 c. violet, brn. & red 60 60
F 117. – 30 c. brn., bistre & vio. 5·50 60
F 118. – 40 c. red and blue .. 3·50 5·00
F 119. – 50 c. green, yellow and turquoise .. .. 5·50 60
F 120. – 60 c. red and blue .. 1·50 80
F 121. – 1 f. red, black & green 2·00 2·50
F 122. – 2 f. black, brown & olive 18·00 7·00
F 123. – 3 f. multicoloured* 11·00 18·00
F 124. – 3 f. multicoloured .. 5·50 7·50
F 125. – 5 f. blue, indigo & black 18·00 22·00

The stamps indicated by an asterisk have "RF" wrongly placed on the left.

F 9. "Syncom" Communications Satellite, Telegraph Poles and Morse Key.

1965. Centenary of I.T.U.

F 126 F 9 15 c. blue, grn. & brn 6·00 5·00
F 127 60 c. red, grey & grn 16·00 17·00

1965. I.C.Y. As Nos. 112/13.

F 128. 5 c. purple and turquoise 3·00 2·25
F 129. 55 c. green and lavender 9·00 7·75

1966. Churchill Commem. As Nos. 114/17.

F 130. 5 c. multicoloured .. 1·00 55
F 131. 15 c. multicoloured .. 2·75 70
F 132. 25 c. multicoloured .. 3·25 3·25
F 133. 30 c. multicoloured .. 4·00 3·50

1966. World Cup Football Championships. As Nos. 118/19.

F 134. 20 c. multicoloured .. 2·50 2·25
F 135. 40 c. multicoloured .. 4·00 3·75

1966. Inauguration of W.H.O. Headquarters, Geneva. As Nos. 120/1.

F 136. 25 c. black, green & blue 3·00 1·50
F 137. 60 c. black, mauve & ochre 4·50 4·00

1966. 20th Anniv. of U.N.E.S.C.O. As Nos. 122/4.

F 138. 15 c. multicoloured .. 1·25 75
F 139. 30 c. yellow, violet & olive 2·25 2·00
F 140. 45 c. black, purple & orge. 2·50 2·50

1967. 25th Anniv. of Pacific War. As Nos. 125/8.

F 141. 15 c. multicoloured .. 40 30
F 142. 25 c. multicoloured .. 65 40
F 143. 60 c. multicoloured .. 95 1·00
F 144. 1 f. multicoloured .. 1·50 1·75

1968. Bicentenary of Bougainville's World Voyage. As Nos. 130/2.

F 145. 15 c. green, violet & red 20 20
F 146. 25 c. olive, purple & blue 40 40
F 147. 60 c. brn., pur. and grn. 90 90

1968. Anglo-French "Concorde" Project. As Nos. 133/4.

F 148. 25 c. blue, red and violet 2·00 1·50
F 149. 60 c. red, black and blue 3·50 3·00

1969. Timber Industry. As No. 135.

F 150. 20 c. multicoloured .. 20 30

1969. 3rd South Pacific Games, Port Moresby, Papua New Guinea. As Nos. 136/7.

F 151. 25 c. multicoloured .. 30 30
F 152. 1 f. multicoloured .. 1·50 1·75

1969. Land Divers of Pentecost Island. As Nos. 138/40.

F 153. 15 c. multicoloured .. 30 30
F 154. 25 c. multicoloured .. 40 40
F 155. 1 f. multicoloured .. 1·40 1·40

1970. Inaug. of New U.P.U. Headquarters Building, Berne. As No. 141.

F 156. 1 f. 05 slate, orge. & purple 50 70

1970. New Hebrides' Declaration for the Free French Government. As Nos. 142/3.

F 157. 65 c. multicoloured .. 55 55
F 158. 1 f. 10 multicoloured .. 1·10 1·10

1970. No. F 115 surch.

F 159. 35 c. on 20 c. black, green and blue .. 60 50

1970. Christmas. As Nos. 145/6.

F 160. 15 c. multicoloured .. 15 15
F 161. 50 c. multicoloured .. 25 40

1971. Death of General Charles de Gaulle. Nos. F 157/8 optd. **1890-1970 IN MEMORIAM 9-11-70.**

F 162. 65 c. multicoloured .. 75 55
F 163. 1 f. 10 multicoloured .. 1·50 1·25

1971. 4th South Pacific Games, Papeete, French Polynesia. As Nos. 149/50

F 164. 20 c. multicoloured .. 35 20
F 165. 65 c. multicoloured .. 95 80

1971. Royal Society Expedition to New Hebrides. As No. 151.

F 166. 65 c. multicoloured .. 50 50

1971. Christmas. As Nos. 152/3.

F 167. 25 c. multicoloured .. 15 20
F 168. 50 c. multicoloured .. 30 35

1972. Aircraft. As Nos. 154/7.

F 169. 20 c. multicoloured .. 1·00 60
F 170. 25 c. multicoloured .. 1·00 70
F 171. 30 c. multicoloured .. 1·10 75
F 172. 65 c. multicoloured .. 3·00 4·00

1972. As Nos. 158/69.

F 173. 5 c. multicoloured .. 40 10
F 174. 10 c. multicoloured .. 1·40 50
F 175. 15 c. multicoloured .. 50 15
F 176. 20 c. multicoloured .. 2·00 30
F 177. 25 c. multicoloured .. 1·50 30
F 178. 30 c. multicoloured .. 1·50 30
F 179. 35 c. multicoloured .. 2·75 40
F 180. 65 c. multicoloured .. 2·50 60
F 181. 1 f. multicoloured .. 2·50 1·75
F 182. 2 f. multicoloured .. 13·00 9·00
F 183. 3 f. multicoloured .. 9·00 12·00
F 184. 5 f. multicoloured .. 15·00 20·00

1972. Christmas. As Nos. 170/1.

F 185. 25 c. multicoloured .. 25 20
F 186. 70 c. multicoloured .. 50 45

1972. Royal Silver Wedding. As Nos. 172/3.

F 187. 35 c. multicoloured .. 75 50
F 188. 65 c. multicoloured .. 1·25 1·25

1973. Orchids. As Nos. 174/7.

F 189. 25 c. multicoloured .. 85 30
F 190. 30 c. multicoloured .. 90 50
F 191. 35 c. multicoloured .. 1·00 65
F 192. 65 c. multicoloured .. 2·75 3·25

1973. Opening of New Wharf at Villa. As Nos. 178/9.

F 193. 25 c. multicoloured .. 75 50
F 194. 70 c. multicoloured .. 1·50 1·75

1973. Tanna Island. As Nos. 180/1.

F 195. 35 c. multicoloured .. 2·00 1·00
F 196. 70 c. multicoloured .. 3·00 2·25

1973. Christmas. As Nos. 182/3.

F 197. 35 c. multicoloured .. 45 35
F 198. 70 c. multicoloured .. 1·00 75

1974. Wild Life. As Nos. 184/7.

F 199. 25 c. multicoloured .. 3·75 1·25
F 200. 35 c. multicoloured .. 5·50 1·50
F 201. 70 c. multicoloured .. 5·50 3·25
F 202. 1 f. 15 multicoloured 6·00 7·50

1974. Royal Visit of Queen Elizabeth II. Nos. F 179 and F 182 optd. **VISITE ROYALE 1974.**

F 203. 35 c. Chestnut-bellied Kingfisher .. 1·50 40
F 204. 2 f. Green palm Lorikeet 4·50 4·75

1974. Inauguration of New Post Office, Villa. As Nos. 190/1.

F 205. 35 c. multicoloured .. 50 65
F 206. 70 c. multicoloured .. 60 85

1974. Bicent. of Rediscovery of New Hebrides by Captain Cook. As Nos. 192/5.

F 207. 35 c. multicoloured .. 4·00 3·25
F 208. 35 c. multicoloured .. 4·00 3·25
F 209. 35 c. multicoloured .. 4·00 3·25
F 210. 1 f. 15 multicoloured .. 9·00 7·50

1974. Centenary of Universal Postal Union. As No. 196.

F 210a. 70 c. blue, red & black 1·00 1·00

1974. Christmas. As Nos. 197/8.

F 211. 35 c. multicoloured .. 25 20
F 212. 70 f. multicoloured .. 55 45

1975. Charolais Bull. As No. 199.

F 213. 10 f. brn., grn. and blue 35·00 32·00

1975. World Scout Jamboree, Norway. As Nos. 200/3.

F 214. 25 c. multicoloured .. 55 20
F 215. 35 c. multicoloured .. 75 30
F 216. 1 f. multicoloured .. 1·90 1·10
F 217. 5 f. multicoloured .. 10·00 9·00

1975. Christmas. As Nos. 204/6.

F 218. 35 c. multicoloured .. 25 15
F 219. 70 c. multicoloured .. 40 25
F 220. 2 f. 50 multicoloured .. 2·25 2·75

1976. 1st Commercial Flight of "Concorde". As No. 207, but Concorde in Air France livery.

F 221. 5 f. multicoloured .. 18·00 13·00

1976. Centenary of Telephone. As Nos. 208/10.

F 222. 25 c. multicoloured .. 45 35
F 223. 70 c. multicoloured .. 1·25 90
F 224. 1 f. 15 multicoloured .. 1·60 2·00

1976. Constitutional Changes. As Nos. 211/13.

F 225. 25 c. multicoloured .. 50 30
F 226. 1 f. multicoloured .. 1·50 1·00
F 227. 2 f. multicoloured .. 2·50 1·90

1976. Christmas. Paintings. As Nos. 214/16.

F 228. 35 c. multicoloured .. 25 15
F 229. 70 c. multicoloured .. 40 25
F 230. 2 f. 50 multicoloured .. 2·25 2·75

1977. Silver Jubilee. As Nos. 217/9.

F 231. 35 c. multicoloured .. 50 20
F 232. 70 c. multicoloured .. 75 50
F 233. 2 f. multicoloured .. 1·00 1·25

1977. Currency Change. Nos. F 173/84 and F 213, surch.

F 234 5 f. on 5 c. mult .. 40 40
F 235 10 f. on 10 c. mult .. 85 40
F 236 15 f. on 15 c. mult .. 70 60
F 237 20 f. on 20 c. mult .. 1·50 85
F 238 25 f. on 25 c. mult .. 1·50 1·00
F 239 30 f. on 30 c. mult .. 1·75 1·50
F 240 35 f. on 35 c. mult .. 2·50 1·50
F 241 40 f. on 65 c. mult .. 2·50 2·00
F 242 50 f. on 1 f. mult .. 2·50 2·00
F 243 70 f. on 2 f. mult .. 4·25 2·75
F 244 100 f. on 3 f. mult .. 4·50 4·50
F 245 200 f. on 5 f. mult .. 14·00 19·00
F 246 500 f. on 10 f. mult .. 26·00 35·00

1977. Islands. As Nos. 242/54.

F 256. 5 f. multicoloured .. 40 20
F 257. 10 f. multicoloured .. 60 20
F 258. 15 f. multicoloured .. 60 20
F 259. 20 f. multicoloured .. 65 30
F 260. 25 f. multicoloured .. 70 40
F 261. 30 f. multicoloured .. 70 45
F 262. 35 f. multicoloured .. 1·25 60
F 263. 40 f. multicoloured .. 1·25 75
F 264. 50 f. multicoloured .. 2·00 75
F 265. 70 f. multicoloured .. 3·25 1·50
F 266. 100 f. multicoloured .. 3·00 2·25
F 267. 200 f. multicoloured .. 4·75 7·00
F 268. 500 f. multicoloured .. 10·00 12·00

1977. Christmas. As Nos. 255/7.

F 269. 10 f. multicoloured .. 20 20
F 270. 15 f. multicoloured .. 35 35
F 271. 30 f. multicoloured .. 85 85

1978. "Concorde". As Nos. 258/61.

F 272. 10 f. multicoloured .. 2·00 1·00
F 273. 20 f. multicoloured .. 2·25 1·50
F 274. 30 f. multicoloured .. 2·75 2·00
F 275. 40 f. multicoloured .. 3·50 3·25

1978. Coronation. As Nos. 262/4.

F 276. 40 f. brn., blue & silver 50 85
F 277. 40 f. multicoloured .. 50 85
F 278. 40 f. brn., blue & silver 50 85

1978. Christmas. As Nos. 265/8.

F 279. 10 f. multicoloured .. 20 20
F 280. 15 f. multicoloured .. 25 30
F 281. 30 f. multicoloured .. 40 60
F 282. 40 f. multicoloured .. 50 70

1979. Internal Self-Government. Design as T37 surch. **PREMIER GOUVERNEMENT AUTONOME 11.1.78 - 11.1.79** and new value.

F 283. 10 f. on 25 f. mult. (blue background) .. 35 25
F 284. 40 f. on 25 f. mult. (green background) .. 90 1·00

1979. Death Centenary of Sir Rowland Hill. As Nos. 271/3.

F 285. 10 f. multicoloured .. 30 35
F 286. 20 f. multicoloured .. 45 55
F 287. 40 f. multicoloured .. 65 75

1979. Arts Festival. As Nos. 275/8

F 288. 5 f. multicoloured .. 20 10
F 289. 10 f. multicoloured .. 25 15
F 290. 20 f. multicoloured .. 45 40
F 291. 40 f. multicoloured .. 75 1·00

1979. Christmas and International Year of the Child. As Nos. 279/82.

F 292. 5 f. multicoloured .. 55 35
F 293. 10 f. multicoloured .. 75 35
F 294. 20 f. multicoloured .. 1·00 1·00
F 295. 40 f. multicoloured .. 1·90 2·00

1980. Birds. As Nos. 283/6.

F 296. 10 f. multicoloured .. 1·00 35
F 297. 20 f. multicoloured .. 1·25 80
F 298. 30 f. multicoloured .. 1·75 1·50
F 299. 40 f. multicoloured .. 2·00 2·00

POSTAGE DUE STAMPS

1925. Nos. F 32, etc., optd. **CHIFFRE TAXE.**

FD 53. 5. 10 c. (1d.) green .. 40·00 2·25
FD 54. 20 c. (2d.) grey .. 40·00 2·25
FD 55. 30 c. (3d.) red .. 40·00 2·25
FD 56. 50 c. (5d.) blue .. 40·00 2·25
FD 57. 1 f. (10d.) red on blue 40·00 2·25

1938. Optd. **CHIFFRE TAXE.**

FD 65. 6. 5 c. green .. .. 11·00 20·00
FD 66. 10 c. orange .. .. 14·00 20·00
FD 67. 20 c. red .. .. 18·00 26·00
FD 68. 40 c. olive .. .. 35·00 45·00
FD 69. 1 f. red on green .. 40·00 55·00

1941. Free French Issue. As last optd. **France Libre.**

FD 77. 6. 5 c green .. .. 8·00 18·00
FD 78. 10 c. orange .. .. 8·00 18·00
FD 79. 20 c. red .. .. 8·00 18·00
FD 80. 40 c. olive .. .. 8·00 18·00
FD 81. 1 f. red on green .. 12·00 18·00

1953. Optd. **TIMBRE-TAXE.**

FD 92. 7. 5 c. green .. .. 3·25 7·50
FD 93. 10 c. red .. .. 3·25 7·50
FD 94. 20 c. blue .. .. 8·50 13·00
FD 95. – 40 c. sepia (No. F 87) 13·00 25·00
FD 96. – 1 f. orange (No. F 89) 19·00 30·00

1957. Optd. **TIMBRE-TAXE.**

FD 107. 12. 5 c. green .. .. 1·75 4·00
FD 108. 10 c. red .. .. 1·75 4·00
FD 109. 20 c. blue .. .. 4·00 6·00
FD 110. – 40 c. sepia (No. F 102) 8·50 12·00
FD 111. – 1 f. orange (No. F 104) 10·00 15·00

For later issues see **VANUATU.**

NEW REPUBLIC

A Boer republic originally part of Zululand. It was incorporated with the S. African Republic in 1888 and annexed to Natal in 1903.

12 pence = 1 shilling.
20 shillings = 1 pound.

1.

1886. On yellow or blue paper.

1 1 1d. black .. .. — £2500
2 1d. violet .. .. 10·00 12·00
73 2d. violet .. .. 8·50 8·50
74 3d. violet .. .. 13·00 13·00
75 4d. violet .. .. 13·00 13·00
81 6d. violet .. .. 8·00 8·00
82 9d. violet .. .. 8·50 8·50
83 1s. violet .. .. 8·50 8·50
77 1s. 6d. violet .. .. 14·00 14·00
85 2s. violet .. .. 18·00 16·00
86 2s. 6d. violet .. .. 23·00 23·00
87 3s. violet .. .. 42·00 42·00
88 4s. violet .. .. 11·00 11·00
89 5s. violet .. .. 13·00 13·00
90 5s. 6d. violet .. .. 12·00 12·00
91 7s. 6d. violet .. .. 14·00 17·00
92 10s. violet .. .. 12·00 12·00
93 10s. 6d. violet .. .. 16·00 16·00
44 12s. violet £300
23 13s. violet £400
94 £1 violet .. .. 45·00 45·00
25 30s. violet .. .. 95·00

Some stamps are found with Arms embossed in the paper, and others with the Arms and without a date above "ZUID-AFRIKA".

NEW SOUTH WALES

A S.E. state of the Australian Commonwealth, whose stamps it now uses.

12 pence = 1 shilling.
20 shillings = 1 pound.

1. Seal of the Colony.

8.

1850 Imperf.

11 1 1d. red £2250 £275
25 2d. blue £1800 £130
42 3d. green £2500 £225

1851. Imperf.

47 8. 1d. red £900 £100
83 1d. orange .. .. .. £170 15·00
86 2d. blue .. .. .. £110 7·00
87 3d. green .. .. .. £200 25·00
76 6d. brown £1600 £250
79 8d. yellow £3500 £600

14.

15.

1854. Imperf.

104. 14. 1d. red .. .. .. £130 22·00
107. 2d. blue .. .. .. £130 8·00
111. 3d. green .. .. .. £700 80·00
114. 15. 5d. green £1000 £500
116. 6d. grey .. .. .. £400 32·00
122. 6d. brown .. .. .. £450 32·00
126. 8d. orange £3500 £800
128. 1s. red .. .. .. £750 65·00

For these stamps perforated, see No. 154, etc.

24.

1860. Perf.

173	**14.**	1d. red	30·00	12·00
134		2d. blue	90·00	10·00
226		3d. green..	5·00	80
243	**15.**	5d. green..	5·50	90
143		6d. brown	£275	45·00
[illegible]		6d. violet	55·00	4·50
218		8d. orange	90·00	17·00
168		1s. red	70·00	7·50
297c	**24.**	5s. purple	30·00	12·00

26.

28.

43.

1862. Queen Victoria. Various frames.

207	26	1d red..	5·00	20
210	28	2d. blue	6·50	20
230c	–	4d. brown	14·00	1·00
234	–	6d. lilac	30·00	1·00
310	–	10d. lilac	12·00	2·75
237	–	1s black	65·00	2·00

1871. As No. 206, surch. **NINEPENCE.**

236d	9d. on 10d. brown ..	8·00	3·75

1885.

244b	43	5s. green and lilac ..	£325	80·00
251b		10s. red and violet ..	£140	40·00
246a		£1 red and lilac ..	£2250	£1000

45. View of Sydney.

46. Emu.

52. Capt. Arthur Phillip, 1st Governor, and Lord Carrington, Governor in 1888.

1888. Inscr. " ONE HUNDRED YEARS ".

253	**45.**	1d. mauve	3·75	10
254	**46.**	2d. blue	3·25	10
335	–	4d brown	8·00	3·00
256	–	6d. red	20·00	2·50
297fa	–	6d. green	22·00	5·00
339	–	6d yellow	11·00	90
257	–	8d. purple	11·00	1·50
343	–	1s. brown	11·00	85
263	–	5s. violet	£150	27·00
346	**52.**	20s. blue	£160	60·00

DESIGNS—As Type **45.** 4d. Capt. Cook. 6d. Queen Victoria and Arms. 8d. Superb Lyrebird. 1s. Kangaroo. As Type **52.** 5s. Map of Australia.

55. Allegorical figure of Australia.

1890.

281.	**55.**	2½d. blue	2·00	40

1891. Types as 1862, but new value and colours, surch. in words.

282.	**26.**	½d. on 1d. grey	1·50	1·75
283.	–	7½d. on 6d. brown ..	3·50	2·00
284c.	–	12½d. on 1s. red	5·00	6·00

58.

59.

60.

61.

62. Superb Lyrebird.

63.

1892.

286	58	½d. grey	80	10
287a		½d. green	70	10
332	59	1d. red	75	10
315	60	2d. blue	1·50	10
296	61	2½d. violet	3·50	80
303		2½d blue	2·75	70
348	63	9d. brown and blue ..	6·00	90
345a	62	2s. 6d. green	27·00	12·00

58a. (Actual size 47×38 mm.)

1897. Charity. Inscr. " CONSUMPTIVES HOME ".

287c.	**58a.**	1d. (1s.) green & brown	40·00	40·00
287d.	–	2½d. (2s. 6d.) gold & blue	£150	£150

DESIGN—VERT. 2½d. Two female figures.

OFFICIAL STAMPS

1879-92. Various issues optd. **O.S.**

A. Issues of 1854 to 1871.

O20b	**26**	1d. red	4·00	1·40
O21c	**28**	2d. blue	5·00	1·00
O25c	**14**	3d. green	5·00	3·50
O27a	–	4d. brown (No. 230c)	12·00	3·00
O28	**15**	5d. green	12·00	8·00
O31b	–	6d. lilac (No. 234) ..	18·00	2·75
O32b	**15**	8d. orange	20·00	9·00
O11	–	9d. on 10d. (No. 309)..	£300	£160
O18a	–	10d. lilac (No. 206) ..	£130	80·00
O33	–	1s. black (No. 237d) ..	22·00	3·50
O18	**24**	5s. purple	£170	65·00

B. Fiscal stamps of 1885.

O37	**24**	10s. red and violet ..	£1200	£600
O38		£1 red and violet ..	£3500	£2750

C. Issue of 1888 (Nos. 253/346b).

O 39.	1d. mauve	1·75	10
O 40.	2d. blue..	2·00	10
O 41.	4d. brown	7·50	2·00
O 42.	6d. red	8·00	2·50
O 43.	8d. purple	14·00	6·50
O 44.	1s. brown	12·00	2·50
O 49.	5s. violet	£140	65·00
O 48.	20s. blue	£1100	£500

D. Issues of 1890 and 1892.

O 58.	**58.**	½d. grey	6·00	5·00
O 55.	**26.**	½d. on 1d. grey ..	45·00	40·00
O 54.	**55.**	2½d. blue	6·00	2·50
O 56.	–	7½d. on 6d. (No. 283)	32·00	27·00
O 57.	–	12½d. on 1s. (No. 2840)	55·00	50·00

POSTAGE DUE STAMPS

D 1.

1891.

D 1	**D 1.**	½d. green	2·50	2·00
D 2		1d. green	3·50	90
D 3		2d. green	5·50	80
D 4		3d. green	9·00	2·75
D 5		4d. green	7·50	80
D 6		6d. green	14·00	2·00
D 7		8d. green	60·00	6·00
D 8		5s. green	£120	30·00
D 9a		10s. green	£120	80·00
D 10b		20s. green	£180	£100

REGISTRATION STAMPS

13.

1856.

88.	**13.**	(6d.) red & bl. (Imp.) ..	£700	£150
92.		(6d.) orge & bl. (Imp.)	£700	£130
101.		(6d.) red & bl. (Perf.) ..	65·00	15·00
94.		(6d.) orge. & bl. (Perf.)	£325	40·00

NEW ZEALAND

A group of islands in the S. Pacific Ocean. A Commonwealth Dominion.

1855. 12 pence = 1 shilling;
20 shillings = 1 pound.
1967. 100 cents = dollar.

1.

3.

1855. Imperf.

35	1	1d. red	£350	£150
33		1d. orange..	£400	£120
38		2d. blue	£225	70·00
40		3d. lilac	£300	£100
43		6d. brown..	£500	65·00
45		1s. green	£700	£150

1862. Perf.

110	1	1d. orange	80·00	18·00
132		1d. brown	90·00	18·00
113		2d. blue	85·00	14·00
133		2d. orange	50·00	15·00
117		3d. lilac	65·00	17·00
119		4d. red	£1800	£250
120		4d. yellow	85·00	45·00
122		6d. brown	85·00	17·00
136		6d. blue	50·00	25·00
125		1s. green	£100	45·00

1873.

151.	8.	½d. red	5·00	30

5.

6.

7. 8.

9. 10.

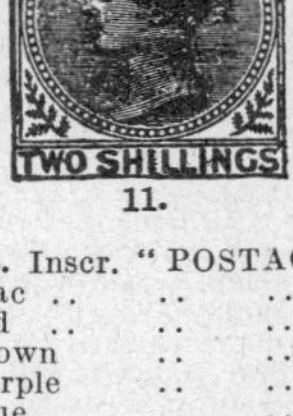

11.

1874. Inscr. " POSTAGE ".

180.	5.	1d. lilac	40·00	2·00
181.	6.	2d. red	40·00	1·40
154.	**7.**	3d. brown	95·00	50·00
182.	**8.**	4d. purple	£130	38·00
183.	9.	6d. blue	80·00	10·00
184.	**10.**	1s. green	£110	27·00
185.	**11.**	2s. red	£350	£275
186.		5s. grey	£375	£275

13.

16.

19.

F 4.

1882. Inscr. " POSTAGE & REVENUE ".

236	13	½d. black	2·50	15
218	10	1d. red	3·00	10
129	9	2d. mauve	7·00	20
239	16	2½d. blue	38·00	3·50
221	10	3d. yellow	35·00	7·00
222	6	4d. green	45·00	2·50
200	19	5d. black	40·00	9·00
224b	8	6d. brown	45·00	4·50
202	9	8d. blue..	65·00	38·00
245	7	1s. brown	70·00	5·50

1882.

F 90	F **4.**	2s. blue	25·00	4·00
F 99		2s. 6d. brown ..	27·00	4·50
F 100		3s. mauve	70·00	5·50
F 102		5s. green	70·00	7·50
F 87		10s. brown	£130	12·00
F 89		£1 red	£170	45·00

The above are revenue stamps authorised for use as postage stamps as there were no other postage stamps available in these denominations. Other values in this and similar types were mainly used for revenue purposes.

23. Mount Cook or Aorangi.

24. Lake Taupo and Mount Ruapehu.

26. Lake Wakatipu and Mount Earnslaw.

25. Pembroke Peak, Milford Sound.

28. Huia Birds.

29. White Terrace, Rotomahana.

30. Otira Gorge and Mount Ruapehu.

31. Brown Kiwi.

32. Maori War Canoe.

33. Pink Terrace, Rotomahana.

34. Kaka and Kea.

35. Milford Sound.

1898.

246	23.	½d. deep purple ..	3·75	35
302		½d. green	2·75	15
247	24.	1d. blue and brown ..	2·50	20
248	25.	2d. lake	20·00	20
249	26.	2½d. blue (A)*	6·00	18·00
320	–	2½d. blue (B)*	7·00	1·25
309	28.	3d. brown	16·00	35
252	29.	4d. red	12·00	14·00
311a	30.	5d. brown	16·00	2·50
254	31.	6d. green	48·00	22·00
265	–	6d. red	35·00	2·50
325	32.	8d. blue	25·00	4·50
326	33.	9d. purple	25·00	6·00
268a	34.	1s. orange	48·00	3·00
328	35.	2s. green	65·00	20·00
329	–	5s. red	£190	£150

Design—As Type **30**: 5s. Mount Cook.
*Type A of 2½d. is inscribed "WAKITIPU", Type B "WAKATIPU".

40. Commemorative of the New Zealand Contingent in the South African War.

1900.

274	29.	1d. red	9·50	10
275b	40.	1½d. brown	7·50	4·00
319	25.	2d. purple	5·50	50
322d	24.	4d. blue and brown ..	6·00	60

The 1d., 2d. and 4d. are smaller than the illustrations of their respective types.

INDEX

Countries can be quickly located by referring to the index at the end of this volume.

42.

1901.

303.	42.	1d. red	3·00	10

44. Maori Canoe "Te Arawa".

1906. Christchurch Exn. Inscr. "COMMEMORATIVE SERIES OF 1906".

370.	44.	½d. green	16·00	23·00
371.	–	1d. red	13·00	15·00
372.	–	3d. brown and blue ..	45·00	55·00
373.	–	6d. red and green ..	£140	£225

Designs: 1d. Maori art. 3d. Landing of Cook. 6d. Annexation of New Zealand.

50.

1907.

386	50	1d. red	30·00	50
383	28	3d. brown	48·00	7·00
376	31	6d. red	48·00	6·00
385	34	1s. orange	£120	24·00

These are smaller in size than the 1898 and 1901 issues. Type **50** also differs from Type **42** in the corner ornaments.

51. King Edward VII.

53. Dominion.

1909.

387	51	½d. green	3·00	10
405	53	1d. red	1·25	10
388	51	2d. mauve	14·00	5·00
389	–	3d. brown	18·00	30
390a	–	4d. orange	7·00	2·00
391a	–	5d. brown	11·00	80
392	–	6d. red	26·00	40
393	–	8d. blue	9·00	65
394		1s. orange	48·00	1·75

1913. Optd. **AUCKLAND EXHIBITION. 1913.**

412	51	½d. green	10·00	23·00
413	53	1d. red	15·00	26·00
414	51	3d. brown	£100	£160
415		6d. red	£100	£180

62. King George V.

1915.

446	62	½d. green	40	10
416a	–	1½d. grey	1·75	50
438	–	1½d. brown	1·50	10
417		2d. violet	6·50	17·00
439	–	2d. yellow	80	10
419a	–	2½d. blue	3·25	1·50
440	–	3d. brown	6·00	30
421		4d. yellow	4·25	30·00
422a	–	4d. violet	5·00	20
423a		4½d. green	12·00	2·50
424a	–	5d. blue	6·00	50
425a	–	6d. red	5·50	20
426a		7½d. brown	12·00	17·00
427a		8d. blue	15·00	30·00
428	–	8d. brown	15·00	55
429a		9d. green	13·00	60
430	–	1s. orange	13·00	30

1915. No. 446 optd **WAR STAMP** and stars.

452	62	½d. green	1·60	20

64. "Peace" and Lion.

65. "Peace" and Lion.

69. New Zealand.

1920. Victory. Inscr. "VICTORY" or dated "1914 1919" (6d.).

453.	64.	½d. green	2·00	1·40
454.	65.	1d. red	4·00	30
455.	–	1½d. orange	3·50	20
456.	–	3d. brown	13·00	11·00
457.	–	6d. violet	13·00	13·00
458.	–	1s. orange	24·00	42·00

Designs—horiz. (As Type **65**). 1½d. Maori Chief. (As Type **64**). 3d. Lion. 1s. King George V. vert. (As Type **64**). 6d. "Peace" and "Progress".

1922. Surch.

459.	64.	2d. on ½d. green ..	2·00	60

1923. Restoration of Penny Postage.

460.	69.	1d. red	1·50	30

70. Exhibition Buildings.

1925. Dunedin Exn.

463.	70.	½d. green on green ..	2·00	11·00
464.		1d. red on rose.. ..	2·50	5·00
465.		4d. mauve on mauve ..	38·00	60·00

71.

73. Nurse.

1926.

468.	71.	1d. red	40	10
469.	–	2s. blue	42·00	15·00
470.	–	3s. mauve	70·00	85·00

The 2s. and 3s. are larger (21 × 25 mm.).

1929. Anti-T.B. Fund.

544.	73.	1d. + 1d. red	11·00	14·00

1930. Inscr. "HELP PROMOTE HEALTH".

545.	73.	1d. + 1d. red	17·00	22·00

74. Smiling Boy.

F 6. "Arms" Type.

75. New Zealand Lake Scenery.

1931. Health stamps.

546.	74.	1d. + 1d. red	75·00	75·00
547.		2d. + 1d. blue	75·00	65·00

1931. Air.

548.	75.	3d. brown	18·00	11·00
549.		4d. purple	20·00	11·00
550.		7d. orange	22·00	7·50

1931. Air. Surch **FIVE PENCE**.

551	75	5d on 3d. green ..	9·00	6·50

1931. Various frames.

F 191	F 6	1s. 3d. yellow ..	3·50	70
F 192		1s. 3d. yellow & blk	1·00	30
F 193	–	2s. 6d. brown ..	5·00	30
F 194		4s. red	9·00	50
F 195	–	5s. green	12·00	60
F 196		6s. red	24·00	2·50
F 197		7s. blue	25·00	4·25
F 198		7s. 6d. grey ..	55·00	48·00
F 199		8s. violet	32·00	16·00
F 200		9s. orange	20·00	27·00
F 201		10s. red	20·00	2·25
F 156		12s. 6d. purple ..	£140	£140
F 202		15s. green	38·00	17·00
F 203		£1 pink	24·00	3·50
F 159		25s. blue	£225	£300
F 205		30s. brown	£190	95·00
F 161		35s. yellow	£2000	£2000
F 206		£2 violet	65·00	18·00
F 163		£2 10s. red	£180	£225
F 208		£3 green	80·00	45·00
F 165		£3 10s. red	£1200	£950
F 210		£4 blue	£100	55·00
F 167		£4 10s. grey ..	£1300	£1000
F 211		£5 blue	£130	45·00

77. Hygeia, Goddess of Health.

78. The Path to Health.

1932. Health stamp.

552.	77.	1d. + 1d. red	20·00	22·00

1933. Health stamp.

553.	78.	1d. + 1d. red	7·50	13·00

1934. Air. Optd. **TRANS-TASMAN AIR MAIL. "FAITH IN AUSTRALIA".**

554.	75.	7d. blue	35·00	38·00

80. Crusader.

1934. Health stamp.

555.	80.	1d. + 1d. red	5·50	7·00

81. Collared Grey Fantail.

83. Maori Woman.

85. Mt. Cook.

86. Maori Girl.

87. Mitre Peak.

89. Harvesting.

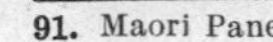

91. Maori Panel.

93. Capt. Cook at Poverty Bay.

1935.

577 81. ½d. green 80 10
578 1d. red 40 10
579 83. 1½d. brown .. .. 5·00 1·75
580 2d. orange 15 10
581b 85. 2½d. brown and grey 50 1·75
561 86. 3d brown .. .. 8·00 80
583c 87. 4d. black and brown 80 10
584c 5d. blue .. .. 2·25 65
585b 89. 6d. red 75 10
586b 8d. brown .. .. 1·00 20
631 91. 9d red and black .. 2·00 1·00
588 1s. green .. .. 1·75 20
589d 93. 2s. olive .. .. 12·00 1·25
590b 3s. chocolate and brown .. .. 6·00 1·50

Designs—vert. (Small as Type **81**). 1d Kiwi. 2d. Maori carved house. 1s. Tui. (Larger as Type **87**). 8d Tuatara lizard. horiz. (As Type **85**). 5d. Swordfish. 3s Mt. Egmont.

95. Bell Block Aerodrome.

1935. Air.

570. 95. 1d. red 30 30
571. 3d. violet .. .. 2·75 2·50
572. 6d. blue .. .. .. 6·00 1·75

96. King George V and Queen Mary.

1935. Silver Jubilee.

573. 96. ½d. green .. .. 1·00 60
574. 1d. red .. .. .. 1·40 40
575. 6d. orange .. .. 12·00 16·00

97. "The Key to Health". 99. N.Z. Soldier at Anzac Cove.

1935. Health stamp.

576. 97. 1d.+1d. red .. .. 1·50 2·25

1936. Charity. 21st Anniv. of Anzac Landing at Gallipoli.

591. 99. ½d+½d. green .. .. 30 1·10
592. 1d.+1d. red 30 90

100. Wool.

1936. Congress of British Empire Chambers of Commerce, Wellington, N.Z. Inscr. as in T 100.

593. 100. ½d. green 20 30
594. – 1d. red (Butter) .. 20 20
595. – 2½d. blue (Sheep) .. 1·00 5·00
596. – 4d. violet (Apples) .. 80 4·50
597. – 6d. brown (Exports) .. 1·25 3·50

105. Health Camp.

1936. Health stamp.

598. 105. 1d.+1d. red .. .. 1·00 3·25

106. King George VI and Queen Elizabeth.

1937. Coronation.

599. 106. 1d. red 30 10
600. 2½d. blue .. .. 1·50 1·60
601. 6d. orange .. .. 1·90 1·25

107. Rock Climbing. 108. King George VI.

1937. Health stamp.

602. 107. 1d.+1d. red .. .. 1·50 2·50

1938.

603. 108. ½d. green .. .. 5·50 10
604. ½d. orange 10 10
605. 1d. red .. .. .. 5·00 10
606. 1d. green 10 10
607. 1½d. brown .. .. 21·00 1·00
608. 1½d. red 10 10
680. 2d. orange 15 10
609. 3d. blue 10 10
681. 4d. purple 35 20
682. 5d. grey 50 40
683. 6d. red 40 10
684. 8d. violet 65 20
685. 9d. brown 70 20
686a. 1s. brown and red .. 50 30
687. 1s. 3d. brown and blue 70 40
688. 2s. orange and green .. 1·25 80
689. 3s. brown and grey .. 1·75 1·50

The shilling values are larger (22 × 25½ mm.) and "NEW ZEALAND" appears at the top.

109. Children Playing.

110. Beach Ball.

1938. Health stamp.

610. 109. 1d.+1d. red .. .. 2·50 1·60

1939. Health stamps. Surch.

611. 110. 1d. on ½d.+½d. green .. 1·50 3·25
612. 2d. on 1d.+1d. red .. 2·25 3·25

1939. Surch in bold figures.

F 212. F 6. 3/6 on 3s. 6d. green .. 20·00 5·00
F 214. 5/6 on 5s. 6d. lilac .. 22·00 11·00
F 215. 11/- on 11s. yellow .. 60·00 40·00
F 216. 22/- on 22s. red .. £180 £120
F 186. 35/- on 35s. orange .. £325 £200

112. "Endeavour", Chart of N.Z. and Captain Cook.

1940. Cent. of British Sovereignty. Inscr. "CENTENNIAL (OF NEW ZEALAND). 1840–1940".

613. ½d. green 30 10
614. 112. 1d. brown and red .. 2·50 10
615. 1½d. blue and mauve .. 30 20
616. 2d. green and brown .. 1·50 10
617. 2½d. green and blue .. 70 20
618. 3d. purple and red .. 2·50 25
619. 4d. brown and red .. 11·00 50
620. 5d. blue and brown .. 4·50 2·25
621. 6d. green and violet .. 11·00 35
622. – 7d. black and red .. 1·25 3·50
623. 8d. black and red .. 11·00 1·50
624. 9d. olive and orange .. 6·50 75
625. 1s. green .. .. 12·00 2·50

Designs—horiz. ½d. Arrival of the Maoris, 1350. 1½d. British Monarchs. 2d. Abel Tasman with "Heemskerk" and Chart. 3d. Landing of immigrants, 1840. 4d. Road, rail, ocean and air transport. 5d. H.M.S. "Britomart" at Akaroa, 1840. 6d. "Dunedin" and "frozen mutton" sea route to London. 7d., 8d. Maori Council. 9d, Gold mining methods, 1861 and 1940. vert. 2½d. Treaty of Waitangi. 1s. Giant Kauri tree.

1940. Health stamps.

626. 110. 1d.+½d. green .. 4·00 7·50
627. 2d.+1d. orange .. 4·00 7·50

1941. Surch.

628. 108. 1d. on ½d. green .. 30 10
629. 2d. on 1½d. brown .. 30 10

1941. Health stamps. Optd. **1941**.

632. 110. 1d.+½d. green .. 25 1·40
633. 2d.+1d. orange .. 25 1·40

125. Boy and Girl on Swing.

1942. Health stamps.

634. 125. 1d.+½d. green .. 15 35
635. 2d.+1d. orange .. 15 50

126. Princess Margaret.

1943. Health stamps.

636. 126. 1d.+½d. green .. 10 40
637. 2d.+1d. brown .. 10 10

Design: 2d. Queen Elizabeth II as Princess.

1944. Surch. TENPENCE between crosses.

662. 10d. on 1½d. blue and mauve (No. 615) .. 10 10

129. Queen Elizabeth II as Princess and Princess Margaret.

1944. Health stamps.

663. 129. 1d.+½d. green 10 15
664. 2d.+1d. blue 10 15

130. Peter Pan Statue, Kensington Gardens.

1945. Health stamps.

665. 130. 1d.+½d. green and buff 10 10
666. 2d.+1d. red and buff .. 10 10

131. Lake Matheson.

132. King George VI and Parliament House, Wellington.

133. St. Paul's Cathedral.

135. R.N.Z.A.F. Badge and Aeroplanes.

139. "St. George", (Wellington College War memorial window). 141. National Memorial Campanile.

1946. Peace Issue.

667. 131. ½d. green and brown .. 15 20
668. 132. 1d. green 10 10
669. 133. 1½d. red 10 10
670. 2d. purple 15 10
671. 135. 3d. blue and grey .. 20 15
672. 4d. green and orange .. 20 20
673. 5d. green and blue .. 20 15
674. 6d. brown and red .. 15 10
675. 139. 8d. black and red .. 15 10
676. 9d. blue and black .. 15 10
677. 141. 1s. grey 15 15

Designs—horiz. (As Type **132**). 2d. The Royal Family. (As Type **135**). 4d. Army (N.Z.) badge, tank and plough. 5d. Navy (anchor) badge, H.M.N.Z.S. "Achilles" (cruiser) and "Dominion Monarch" (liner). 6d. N.Z. Coat of Arms, foundry and farm. 9d. Southern Alps and Frans Josef Glacier, seen through chapel window.

142. Soldier helping Child over Stile.

1946. Health stamps.

678. 142. 1d.+½d. green & orange 10 10
679. 2d.+1d. brown & orge. 10 10

145. Statue of Eros.

1947. Health stamps.

690. 145. 1d.+½d. green 10 10
691. 2d.+1d. red 10 10

146. Port Chalmers, 1848.

1948. Centenary of Otago. Various designs inscr. "CENTENNIAL OF OTAGO".

692. 146. 1d. blue and green .. 10 10
693. — 2d. green and brown .. 10 10
694. — 3d. purple .. 10 15
695. — 6d. black and red .. 10 15

DESIGNS—HORIZ. 2d. Cromwell, Otago. 6d. Otago University. VERT.: 3d. First church, Dunedin.

150. Boy Sunbathing and Children Playing.

1948. Health stamps.

696. 150. 1d.+½d. blue and green 10 10
697. — 2d.+1d. purple and red 10 10

151. Nurse and Child.

153. Queen Elizabeth II and Prince Charles.

1949. Health stamps.

698. 151. 1d.+½d. green .. 10 10
699. — 2d.+1d. blue .. 10 10

1950. As Type F 6, but without value, surch. 1½d. POSTAGE.

700. — 1½d. red 10 10

1950. Health stamps.

701. 153. 1d.+½d. green .. 10 10
702. — 2d.+1d. purple .. 10 10

155. Cairn on Lyttleton Hills.

1950. Cent. of Canterbury, N.Z.

703. — 1d. green and blue .. 15 10
704. 155. 2d. red and orange .. 15 10
705. — 3d. blue .. 20 10
706. — 6d. brown and blue .. 20 25
707. — 1s. purple and blue .. 20 30

DESIGNS—VERT. 1d. Christchurch Cathedral. 3d. John Robert Godley. HORIZ. 6d. Canterbury University College. 1s. Aerial view of Timaru.

159. "Takapuna" class Yachts.

1951. Health stamps.

708. 159. 1½d.+½d. red & yellow 10 20
709. — 2d.+1d. green & yellow 10 10

160. Princess Anne.

161. Prince Charles.

1952. Health stamps.

710. 160. 1½d.+½d. red 10 10
711. 161. 2d.+1d. brown .. 10 10

1952. Surch. in figures.

712. 103. 1d. on ½d. orange .. 10 20
713. — 3d. on 1d. green .. 10 10

164. Queen Elizabeth II.

166. Westminster Abbey.

165. Coronation State Coach.

1953. Coronation.

714. — 2d. blue 20 15
715. 164. 3d. brown 20 10
716. 165. 4d. red .. .. 75 1·50
717. 166. 8d. grey 70 70
718. — 1s. 6d. purple & blue 1·25 80

DESIGNS—As Type 165: 2d. Queen Elizabeth II and Buckingham Palace. 1s. 6d. St. Edward's Crown and Royal Sceptre.

168. Girl Guides.

169. Boy Scouts.

1953. Health stamps.

719. 168. 1½d.+½d. blue 10 10
720. 169. 2d.+1d. green 10 20

170. Queen Elizabeth II.

171. Queen Elizabeth II and Duke of Edinburgh.

1953. Royal Visit.

721. 170. 3d. purple 10 10
722. 171. 4d. blue 10 25

172.

173. Queen Elizabeth II.  174.

1953. Small figures of value.

723. 172. ½d. slate 15 30
724. — 1d. orange 15 10
725. — 1½d. brown 20 10
726. — 2d. green 20 10
727. — 3d. red 20 10
728. — 4d. blue 40 30
729. — 6d. purple 70 90
730. — 8d. red 60 30
731. 173. 9d. brown and green .. 60 20
732. — 1s. black and red .. 65 10
733. — 1s. 6d. black and blue 1·75 30
733a — 1s. 9d. black & orange 5·50 75
733b. 174. 2s. 6d. brown .. .. 23·00 5·00
734. — 3s. green .. .. 11·00 30
735. — 5s. red .. .. 17·00 2·50
736. — 10s. blue .. .. 45·00 15·00

175. Young Climber and Mts. Aspiring and Everest.

176. Maori Mail-carrier.

177. Queen Elizabeth II.

179. Children's Health Camps Federation Emblem.

1954. Health stamps.

737. 175. 1½d.+½d. brn. & violet 10 10
738. — 2d.+1d. brn. and blue 10 10

1955. Centenary of New Zealand Stamp. Inscr. "1855–1955".

739. 176. 2d. brown and green .. 10 10
740. 177. 3d. red 10 10
741. — 4d. black and blue .. 15 25

DESIGN—HORIZ. (As Type 176). 4d. Douglas DC 3 Airliner.

1955. Health stamps.

742. 179. 1½d.+½d. brn. & chest. 10 25
743. — 2d.+1d. red and green 10 15
744. — 3d.+1d. brown and red 15 10

180.

183. Takahe.

181. "The Whalers of Foveaux Strait".

1955. As 1953 but larger figures of value and stars omitted from lower right corner.

745. 180. 1d. orange 50 10
746. — 1½d. brown 60 60
747. — 2d. green 40 10
748. — 3d. red .. .. 1·10 10
749. — 4d. blue .. .. 1·75 35
750. — 6d. purple .. .. 7·50 10
751. — 8d. brown .. .. 5·50 5·00

1956. Southland Centennial.

752. 181. 2d. green 10 10
753. — 3d. brown 10 10
754. 183. 8d. slate and red .. 40 60

DESIGN—As Type 181: 3d. Allegory of farming.

184. Children picking Apples.

187. Sir Truby King.

185. New Zealand Lamb and Map.

1956. Health stamps.

755. 184. 1½d.+½d. brown .. 10 20
756. — 2d.+1d. green .. 10 15
757. — 3d.+1d. red .. 15 10

1957. 75th Anniv. of First Export of N.Z. Lamb.

758. 185. 4d. blue 40 45
759. — 8d. red 60 65

DESIGN—HORIZ. 8d. Lamb sailing ship "Dunedin" and modern ship.

1957. 50th Anniv. of Plunket Society.

760. 187. 3d. red 10 10

188. Life-savers in Action.

1957. Health stamps.

761. 188. 2d.+1d. black & green 15 20
762. — 3d.+1d. blue and red 15 10

DESIGN: 3d. Children on seashore.

1958. Surch.

763 180 2d. on 1½d. brown .. 40 10
808 — 2½d. on 3d. red .. 10 10

192. Boys Brigade Bugler.

194. Seal of Nelson.

1958. Health stamps.

764. — 2d.+1d. green .. 15 10
765. 192. 3d.+1d. blue .. 15 10

DESIGN: 2d. Girls' Life Brigade cadet.

1958. 30th Anniv. of 1st Air Crossing of Tasman Sea. As T 120 of Australia.

766. — 6d. blue 30 30

1958. Centenary of City of Nelson.

767 194 3d. red 10 10

195. "Pania" Statue, Napier.

197. 'Brown Kiwi' Jamboree Badge.

196. Australian Gannets on Cape Kidnappers.

1958. Centenary of Hawke's Bay Province.

768 195 2d. green 10 10
769 196 3d. blue 15 10
770 — 8d. brown 45 75

DESIGN—As Type 195: 8d. Maori sheep-shearer.

1959. Pan-Pacific Scout Jamboree, Auckland.

771. 197. 3d. brown and red .. 10 10

198. Careening H.M.S. "Endeavour" at Ship Cove.

1959. Centenary of Marlborough Province. Inscr. as in T 198.

772. 198. 2d. green 15 10
773. — 3d. blue 15 10
774. — 8d. brown 60 60

DESIGNS: 3d. Shipping wool, Wairau bar, 1857. 8d. Salt industry, Grassmere.

201. Red Cross Flag.

1959. Red Cross Commem.

775. 201. 3d.+1d. red and blue .. 10 10

202. Grey Teal. 204. "The Explorer".

1959. Health stamps.

776. 202. 2d.+1d. yellow, olive and red 15 15
777. – 3d.+1d. black, pink and blue 15 15

DESIGN: 3d. New Zealand Stilt.

1960. Centenary of Westland Province.

778. 204. 2d. green 15 10
779. – 3d. salmon 15 10
780. – 8d. black .. .. 40 1·50

DESIGNS: 3d. "The Gold Digger". 8d. "The Pioneer Woman".

207. Manuka (Tea Tree). 215. Timber Industry.

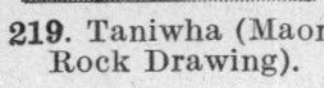

219. Taniwha (Maori Rock Drawing). 225. Sacred Kingfisher.

1960.

781	207.	½d. green and red ..	10	10
782	–	1d. multicoloured ..	10	10
783	–	2d. multicoloured ..	10	10
784	–	2½d. multicoloured ..	60	10
785	–	3d. multicoloured ..	30	10
786	–	4d. multicoloured ..	40	10
787	–	5d. multicoloured ..	60	10
788	–	6d. lilac, grn. & turq.	50	10
788d	–	7d. red, green & yellow	35	80
789	–	8d. multicoloured ..	40	10
790	–	9d. red and blue ..	30	10
791	215.	1s. brown and green ..	25	10
792b	–	1s. 3d. red, sepia & blue	80	10
793	–	1s. 6d. olive and brown	50	10
794	–	1s. 9d. brown	15·00	15
795	–	1s. 9d. multicoloured ..	6·50	50
796	219.	2s. black and buff ..	3·00	10
797	–	2s. 6d. yell. and brown	1·75	65
798	–	3s. sepia	48·00	65
799	–	3s. bistre, blue & grn.	7·50	1·50
800	–	5s. myrtle	5·50	80
801	–	10s. blue	9·00	1·25
802	–	£1 mauve	8·50	6·00

DESIGNS—As Type **207**: 1d. Karaka. 2d. Kowhai Ngutu-kaka (Kaka Beak). 2½d. Titoki (plant). 3d. Kowhai. 4d. Puarangi (Hibiscus). 5d. Matua tikumu (Mountain daisy). 6d. Pikiarero (Clematis). 7d. Koromiko. 8d. Rata. As Type **215**—HORIZ. 9d. National flag. 1s. 9d. Aerial top-dressing. VERT. 1s. 3d. Trout. 1s. 6d. Tiki. As Type **219**—HORIZ. 2s. 6d. Butter-making. 3s. Tongariro National Park and Chateau. 10s. Tasman Glacier. VERT. 5s. Sutherland Falls. £1, Pohutu Geyser.

1960. Health stamps.

803. 225. 2d.+1d. sepia and blue 30 30
804. – 3d.+1d. purple & orge. 30 35

DESIGN: 3d. New Zealand Pigeon.

227. "The Adoration of the Shepherds" (Rembrandt). 228. Great Egret.

1960. Christmas.

805. 227. 2d. red & brn. on cream 15 10

1961. Health stamps.

806. 228. 2d.+1d. black & pur. 20 20
807. – 3d.+1d. sepia & green 20 20

DESIGN: 3d. New Zealand Falcon.

232. "Adoration of the Magi" (Durer).

1961. Christmas.

809. 232. 2½d. multicoloured .. 10 10

233. Morse Key and Port Hills, Lyttleton.

1962. Telegraph Centenary.

810. 233. 3d. sepia and green .. 10 10
811. – 8d. black and red .. 35 55

DESIGN: 8d. Modern teleprinter.

236. Saddleback.

DESIGN: 2½d. Red-fronted Parakeet.

1962. Health stamps.

812. – 2½d.+1d. multicoloured 20 30
813. 236. 3d.+1d. multicoloured 20 30

237. "Madonna in Prayer" (Sassoferrato). 238. Prince Andrew.

1962. Christmas.

814. 237. 2½d. multicoloured .. 10 10

1963. Health stamps.

815. 238. 2½d.+1d. blue .. 10 20
816. – 3d.+1d. red 10 10

DESIGN: 3d. Prince Andrew (different).

240. "The Holy Family" (Titian).

1963. Christmas.

817. 240. 2½d. multicoloured .. 10 10

241. Steam Loco. "Pilgrim" and "DG" Diesel Electric Loco.

1963. Centenary of Railway. Inscr. as in T **241**. Multicoloured.

818. – 3d. Type **241** 30 10
819. – 1s. 9d. Diesel Express and Mt. Ruapehu .. .. 1·60 80

1963. Opening of COMPAC (Trans-Pacific Telephone Cable). As T **174** of Australia.

820. – 8d. multicoloured .. 50 90

244. Road Map and Car Steering-wheel.

1964. Road Safety Campaign.

821 244 3d. black, yellow & blue 10 10

245. Silver Gulls.

1964. Health stamps. Multicoloured.

822 – 2½d.+1d. Type **245** .. 20 15
823 – 3d.+1d. Little penguin .. 20 15

246. Rev. S. Marsden taking first Christian service at Rangihoua Bay, 1814.

1964. Christmas.

824. 246. 2½d. multicoloured .. 10 10

1964. Surch. **7D POSTAGE.**

825. F 6. 7d. on (—) red 30 80

248. Anzac Cove.

1965. 50th Anniv. of Gallipoli Landing.

826. 248. 4d. brown 10 10
827. – 5d. green and red .. 10 30

The 5d. also has a poppy in the design.

249. I.T.U. Emblem and Symbols.

1965. Centenary of I.T.U.

828 249. 9d. blue and brown .. 30 35

1965. Churchill Commem. As T **186** of Australia.

829. – 7d. black, grey and blue .. 15 50

251. Wellington Provincial Council Building.

1965. Cent. of Government in Wellington.

830. 251. 4d. multicoloured .. 10 10

252. Kaka.

1965. Health stamps. Multicoloured.

831. – 3d.+1d. Type **252** .. 25 15
832. – 4d.+1d. Collared Grey Fantail 25 15

254. I.C.Y. Emblem.

1965. Int. Co-operation Year.

833. 254. 4d. red and olive .. 15 10

255. "The Two Trinities", (Murillo).

1965. Christmas.

834. 255. 3d. multicoloured .. 10 10

256. Arms of New Zealand.

1965. 11th Commonwealth Parliamentary Conf. Multicoloured.

835. – 4d. Type **256** 25 20
836. 9d. Parliament House, Wellington, and Badge 45 75
837. 2s. Wellington from Mt. Victoria .. .. 80 2·25

259. "Progress" Arrowhead. 260. New Zealand Bell Bird.

1966. 4th National Scout Jamboree, Trentham.

838. 259. 4d. gold, and green .. 10 10

1966. Health stamps. Multicoloured.

839. 260 3d. + 1d. Type 260 .. 15 20
840. – 4d. + 1d. Weka Rail .. 15 20

262. "The Virgin with Child" (Maratta). **263.** Queen Victoria and Queen Elizabeth II.

1966. Christmas

842. 262. 3d. multicoloured 10 10

1967. Centenary of New Zealand Post Office Savings Bank.

843. 263. 4d. black, gold & purple 10 10
844. – 9d. multicoloured .. 10 15

DESIGN: 9d. Half-sovereign of 1867 and Commemorative Dollar coin.

265. Manuka (Tea Tree). **268.** Running with Ball.

1967. Decimal Currency. Designs as earlier issues, but with values inscr in decimal currency as T **265**.

845 265 ½ c. blue, green & red 10 10
846 – 1 c. mult (No. 782) .. 10 10
847 – 2 c. mult (No. 783) .. 10 10
848 – 2½ c. mult (No. 785) 10 10
849 – 3 c. mult (No. 786) .. 10 10
850 – 4 c. mult (No. 787) .. 30 10
851 – 5 c. lilac, olive & green (No. 788) .. 65 10
852 – 6 c. mult (No. 788c) 70 10
853 – 7 c. mult (No. 789) .. 85 15
854 – 8 c. red and blue (No. 790) 85 10
855 215 10 c. brown & green 60 10
856 – 15 c. green and brown (No. 793) .. 60 60
857 219 20 c. black and buff 2·00 10
858 – 25 c. yellow and brown (No. 797) .. 6·00 90
859 – 30 c. yellow, green and blue (No. 799) 4·25 25
860 – 50 c. green (No. 800) 4·00 75
861 – $1 blue (No. 801) .. 16·00 1·25
862 – $2 mauve (No. 802) 10·00 11·00
F 219 F 6 $4 violet .. .. 2·00 55
F 220 $6 green .. .. 3·00 1·50
F 221 $8 blue .. .. 4·00 3·50
F 222 $10 blue .. .. 5·00 3·50

For 15 c. in different colours, see No. 874.

1967. Health Stamps. Rugby Football.

867. 2½ c. + 1 c. multicoloured .. 10 10
868. 3 c. + 1 c. multicoloured .. 10 10

DESIGNS—VERT. 2½ c. Type **268**. HORIZ. 3 c. Positioning for Place-kick.

271. Brown Trout.

273. Forest and Timber.

1967.

870 – 7 c. multicoloured .. 1·25 75
871 271. 7½ c. multicoloured .. 30 70
872 – 8 c. multicoloured .. 75 70
873 273. 10c. multicoloured .. 50 10
874 – 15 c. grn., myrtle & red 1·00 50
875 – 18 c. multicoloured .. 1·40 55
876 – 20 c. multicoloured .. 1·40 20
877 – 25 c. multicoloured .. 6·00 2·00
878 – 28 c. multicoloured .. 60 10
879 – $2 black, ochre & blue 35·00 19·00

DESIGNS: 7 c. "Kaiti" (trawler) and catch. 8 c. Apples and orchard. 15 c. as No. 793. 18 c. Sheep and the "Woolmark". 20 c. Consignments of beef and herd of cattle. 25 c. Dairy farm, Mt. Egmont and butter consignment. 28 c. Fox Glacier, Westland National Park. $2 as No. 802.

No. 871a was originally issued to commemorate the introduction of the brown trout into New Zealand.

No. 874 is slightly larger than No. 856, measuring 21 × 25 mm. and the inscr. and numerals differ in size.

278. "The Adoration of the Shepherds" (Poussin). **279.** Mount Aspiring, Aurora Australis and Southern Cross.

1967. Christmas.

880. 278. 2½ c. multicoloured .. 10 10

1967. Cent. of Royal Society of New Zealand.

881. 279. 4 c. multicoloured .. 15 20
882. – 8 c. multicoloured .. 15 30

DESIGN: 8 c. Sir James Hector (founder).

281. Open Bible.

1968. Centenary of Maori Bible.

883. 281. 3 c. multicoloured .. 10 10

282. Soldiers and Tank.

1968. New Zealand Armed Forces. Mult.

884. 4 c. Type **282** 30 15
885. 10 c. Airmen, Canberra and "Kittyhawk" Aircraft .. 50 25
886. 28 c. Sailors and H.M.N.Z.S. "Achilles", 1939 and H.M.N.Z.S. "Waikato", 1968 .. .. 70 1·40

285. Boy Breasting Tape and Olympic Rings.

1968. Health stamps. Multicoloured.

887. 2½ c. + 1 c. Type **285** .. 10 10
888. 3 c. + 1 c. Girl swimming and Olympic Rings .. 10 10

287. Placing Votes in Ballot Box. **288.** Human Rights Emblem.

1968. 75th Anniversary of Universal Suffrage in New Zealand.

890. 287. 3 c. ochre, grn. & blue 10 10

1968. Human Rights Year.

891. 288. 10 c. red, yellow & grn. 10 30

289. "Adoration of the Holy Child" (G. van Honthorst).

1968. Christmas.

892. 289. 2½ c. multicoloured .. 10 10

290. ILO Emblem.

1969. 50th Anniv. of Int. Labour Organization.

893. 290. 7 c. black and red .. 15 30

291. Supreme Court Building, Auckland.

1969. Cent. of New Zealand Law Society.

894. 291. 3 c. multicoloured .. 10 10
895. – 10 c. multicoloured .. 35 45
896. – 18 c. multicoloured .. 45 70

DESIGNS—VERT. 10 c. Law Society's Coat of Arms. 18 c. "Justice" (from Memorial Window in University of Canterbury, Christchurch).

295. Student being conferred with degree.

1969. Cent. of Otago University. Mult.

897. 3 c. Otago University (vert.) 10 10
898. 10 c. Type **295** 20 25

296. Boys playing Cricket.

1969. Health stamps.

899. 296. 2½ c. + 1 c. multicoloured 40 40
900. – 3 c. + 1 c. multicoloured 40 40
901. – 4 c. + 1 c. brown & ultram. 40 1·25

DESIGNS—HORIZ. 3 c. Girls playing cricket. VERT. 4 c. Dr. Elizabeth Gunn (founder of 1st Children's Health Camp).

299. Oldest existing House in New Zealand, and Old Stone Mission Store, Kerikeri.

1969. Early European Settlement in New Zealand, and 150th Anniv. of Kerikeri. Multicoloured.

903. 4 c. Type **299** 20 25
904. 6 c. View of Bay of Islands 30 1·00

301. "The Nativity" (Federico Fiori (Barocci)).

1969. Christmas.

905. 301. 2½ c. multicoloured .. 10 10

302. Captain Cook, Transit of Venus and "Octant".

1969. Bicentenary of Captain Cook's landing in New Zealand.

906. 302. 4 c. black, red and blue 75 35
907. – 6 c. grn., brn. and blk. 1·00 2·75
908. – 18 c. brn., grn. & blk. 2·50 2·75
909. – 28 c. red, blk. and blue 4·00 4·75

DESIGNS: 6 c. Sir Joseph Banks (naturalist) and outline of H.M.S. "Endeavour". 18 c. Dr. Daniel Solander (botanist) and his plant. 28 c. Queen Elizabeth II and Cook's Chart, 1769.

306. Girl, Wheat Field and C.O.R.S.O. Emblem.

1969. 25th Anniversary of C.O.R.S.O. (Council of Organizations for Relief Services Overseas). Multicoloured.

911. 7 c. Type **306** .. 20 90
912. 8 c. Mother feeding her child, dairy herd and C.O.R.S.O. Emblem (horiz.) .. 20 90

308. "Cardigan Bay" (Champion trotter).

1970. Return of "Cardigan Bay" to New Zealand.

913. 308. 10 c. multicoloured .. 20 25

309. "Vanessa gonerilla".

310. Queen Elizabeth II and New Zealand Coat of Arms.

1970.

914 – ½ c. multicoloured .. 10 20
915 309 1 c. multicoloured .. 10 10
916 – 2 c. multicoloured .. 10 10
917 – 2½ c. multicoloured .. 40 10
918 – 3 c. multicoloured .. 15 10
919 – 4 c. multicoloured .. 15 10
920 – 5 c. multicoloured .. 45 10
921 – 6 c. black, green and red 45 20
922 – 7 c. multicoloured .. 55 40
923 – 7½ c. multicoloured .. 1·00 1·50
924 – 8 c. multicoloured .. 65 40

925 310 10 c. multicoloured .. 40 15
926 – 15 c. blk., flesh & brn. 1·50 50
927 – 18 c. grn., brn. & blk. 1·50 40
1020 – 20 c. black and brown 80 10
929 – 23 c. multicoloured .. 80 20
930b – 25 c. multicoloured .. 70 40
931 – 30 c. multicoloured .. 2·75 15
932 – 50 c. multicoloured .. 80 20
933 – $1 multicoloured .. 2·00 85
934 – $2 multicoloured .. 5·00 1·25

DESIGNS—As Type **309**. ½ c. "Lycaena salustius" (butterfly). 2 c. "Argyrophenga antipodum" (butterfly). 2½ c. "Nyctemera annulata" (moth). 3 c. "Detunda egregia" (moth). 4 c. "Charagia virescens" (moth). 5 c. Scarlet parrot fish. 6 c. Sea horses. 7 c. Leather jacket (fish). 7½ c. Garfish. 8 c. John Dory (fish). As Type **310**. HORIZ. 15 c. Maori fish hook. 20 c. Maori tattoo pattern. 23 c. Egmont National Park. 50 c. Abel Tasman National Park. $1 Geothermal power. $2 Agricultural technology. VERT. 18 c. Maori club. 25 c. Hauraki Gulf Maritime Park. 30 c. Mt. Cook National Park.

311. Geyser Restaurant.

1970. World Fair, Osaka. Multicoloured.
935. 7 c. Type **311** 40 65
936. 8 c. New Zealand Pavilion 40 65
937. 18 c. Bush Walk 60 65

312. U.N. H.Q. Building.
314. "The Virgin adoring the Child" (Correggio).

313. Soccer.

1970. 25th Anniv. of United Nations.
938. **312.** 3 c. multicoloured .. 10 10
939. – 10 c. red and yellow .. 20 20
DESIGN: 10 c. Tractor on horizon.

1970. Health Stamps. Multicoloured.
940. 2½ c.+1 c. Netball (vert.) 10 15
941. 3 c.+1 c. Type **313** .. 10 15

1970. Christmas.
943. **314.** 2½ c. multicoloured .. 10 10
944. – 3 c. multicoloured .. 10 10
945. – 10 c. blk., orge. & silver 30 75
DESIGNS—VERT. 3 c. Stained Glass Window, Invercargill Presbyterian Church "The Holy Family". HORIZ. 10 c. Tower of Roman Catholic Church, Seckburn.

316. Chatham Islands Lily.

1970. Chatham Islands. Multicoloured.
946. 1 c. Type **316** 10 15
947. 2 c. Shy Albatross .. 20 25

317. Country Women's Institutes Emblem.

1971. 50th Anniv. of Country Women's Institutes and Rotary International in New Zealand. Multicoloured.
948. 4 c. Type **317** 10 10
949. 10 c. Rotary emblem and map of New Zealand .. 10 20

318. "Rainbow II" (yacht).

1971. One-Ton Cup Racing Trophy. **Mult.**
950. 5 c. Type **318** 15 20
951. 8 c. One-Ton Cup 25 65

319. Civic Arms of Palmerston North.

1971. City Centenaries. Multicoloured.
952. 3 c. Type **319** 10 10
953. 4 c. Arms of Auckland .. 10 10
954. 5 c. Arms of Invercargill .. 15 40

320. Antarctica on Globe.

1971. 10th Anniv. of Antarctic Treaty.
955. **320.** 6 c. multicoloured .. 1·50 1·50

321. Child on Swing.

1971. 25th Anniv. of U.N.I.C.E.F.
956. **321.** 7 c. multicoloured .. 50 70

1971. No. 917 surch.
957. 4 c. on 2½ c. multicoloured 15 10

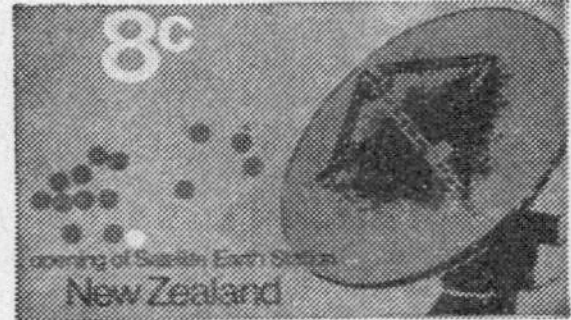

323. Satellite-tracking Aerial.

1971. Opening of Satellite Earth Station.
958. **323.** 8 c. blk., grey and red 60 1·00
959. – 10 c. blk., green & violet 65 1·00
DESIGN: 10 c. Satellite.

324. Girls playing Hockey.

1971. Health Stamps. Multicoloured.
960. 3 c.+1 c. Type **324** .. 35 40
961. 4 c.+1 c. Boys playing Hockey 35 40
962. 5 c.+1 c. Dental Health .. 90 1·60

325. "Madonna bending over the Crib." (Maratta).

1971. Christmas. Multicoloured.
964. 3 c. Type **325** 10 10
965. 4 c. "The Annunciation" (stained-glass window) 10 10
966. 10 c. "The Three Kings" 70 1·25
Nos. 965/6 are smaller, size 21½ × 38 mm.

326. "Tiffany" Rose.

1971. 1st World Rose Convention, **Hamilton** Roses. Multicoloured.
967. 2 c. Type **326** 15 30
968. 5 c. "Peace" 35 35
969. 8 c. "Chrysler Imperial" 60 1·10

327. Lord Rutherford and Alpha Particles.

1971. Birth Centenary of Lord Rutherford (scientist). Multicoloured.
970. 1 c. Type **327** 25 40
971. 7 c. Lord Rutherford and formula .. .. 85 1·40

328. Benz (1895).

1972. Int. Vintage Car Rally. Multicoloured.
972. 3 c. Type **328** 20 10
973. 4 c. Oldsmobile (1904) .. 25 10
974. 5 c. Ford "Model T" (1914) 35 10
975. 6 c. Cadillac Service car (1915) 55 45
976. 8 c. Chrysler (1924) .. 1·25 1·00
977. 10 c. Austin "7" (1923) .. 1·25 1·00

329. Coat of Arms of Wanganui.
330. Black Scree Cotula.

1972. Anniversaries.
978. **329.** 3 c. multicoloured .. 15 10
979. – 4 c. orge., brn. & blk. .. 15 10
980. – 5 c. multicoloured .. 25 10
981. – 8 c. multicoloured .. 1·50 1·50
982. – 10 c. multicoloured .. 1·50 1·50
DESIGNS AND EVENTS—VERT. 3 c. (Wanganui Council Govt. Cent.). 5 c. De Havilland DH 89 "Rapide Dominie" and Boeing "737" (National Airways Corp. 25th Anniv.). 8 c. French frigate and Maori palisade (landing by Marion du Fresne. Bicent.). HORIZ. 4 c. Postal Union symbol (Asian–Oceanic Postal Union. 10th Anniv.). 10 c. Stone cairn (New Zealand Methodist Church. 15th Anniv.).

1972. Alpine Plants. Multicoloured.
983. 4 c. Type **330** 30 10
984. 6 c. North Island Edelweiss 75 60
985. 8 c. Haast's Buttercup .. 1·25 1·25
986. 10 c. Brown Mountain Daisy 1·75 1·75

331. Boy playing Tennis.
332. "Madonna with Child" (Murillo).

1972. Health Stamps.
987. **331.** 3 c.+1 c. grey & brown 25 35
988. – 4 c.+1 c. brn., grey & yellow 25 35
DESIGN: No. 988, Girl playing tennis.

1972. Christmas. Multicoloured.
990. 3 c. Type **332** 10 10
991. 5 c. "The Last Supper" (stained-glass window, St. John's Church, Levin) 15 10
992. 10 c. Pohutukawa flower .. 55 1·00

333. Lake Waikaremoana.

1972. Lake Scenes. Multicoloured.
993. 6 c. Type **333** .. .. 1·00 1·25
994. 8 c. Lake Hayes .. .. 1·10 1·25
995. 18 c. Lake Wakatipu .. 2·00 2·25
996. 23 c. Lake Rotomahana .. 2·25 2·75

334. Old Pollen Street.

1973. Commemorations.
997. **334.** 3 c. multicoloured .. 15 10
998. – 4 c. multicoloured .. 15 10
999. – 5 c. multicoloured .. 15 15
1000. – 6 c. multicoloured .. 50 80
1001. – 8 c. grey, blue & gold 45 1·00
1002. – 10 c. multicoloured 50 1·60
DESIGNS AND EVENTS: 3 c. (Thames Borough. Cent.). 4 c. Coalmining and pasture (Westport Borough. Cent.). 5 c. Cloister (Canterbury University. Cent.) 6 c. Forest, birds and lake (Royal Forest and Bird Protection Society. 50th Anniv.) 8 c. Rowers (Success of N.Z. Rowers in 1972 Olympics). 10 c. Graph and people (E.C.A.F.E. 25th Anniv.).

335. Class "W" Locomotive.

1973. New Zealand Steam Locomotives. Multicoloured.
1003. 3 c. Type **335** 45 10
1004. 4 c. Class "X" 55 10
1005. 5 c. Class "Ab" 60 10
1006. 10 c. Class "Ja" .. .. 2·50 1·75

336. "Maori Woman and Child".
337. Prince Edward.

1973. Paintings by Frances Hodgkins. Multicoloured.
1027. 5 c. Type **336** 40 15
1028. 8 c. "Hilltop" 75 75
1029. 10 c. "Barn in Picardy" 1·00 1·25
1030. 18 c. "Self-portrait Still Life" .. .. 1·50 2·50

1973. Health Stamps.
1031. **337.** 3 c.+1 c. green & brn. 30 30
1032. 4 c.+1 c. red & brown 30 30

338. "Tempi Madonna" (Raphael). **339.** Mitre Peak.

1973. Christmas. Multicoloured.
1034. 3 c. Type **338** 10 10
1035. 5 c. "Three Kings" (Stained-glass window, St. Theresa's Church, Auckland) 10 10
1036. 10 c. Family entering church 25 50

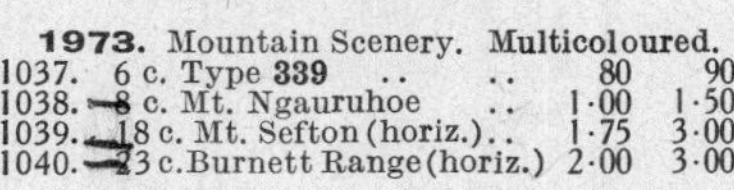

1973. Mountain Scenery. Multicoloured.
1037. 6 c. Type **339** .. 80 90
1038. 8 c. Mt. Ngauruhoe .. 1·00 1·50
1039. 18 c. Mt. Sefton (horiz.) .. 1·75 3·00
1040. 23 c. Burnett Range (horiz.) 2·00 3·00

340. Hurdling. **342.** "Spirit of Napier" Fountain.

1974. 10th British Commonwealth Games, Christchurch.
1041. **340.** 4 c. multicoloured .. 10 10
1042. – 5 c. black and violet .. 15 10
1043. – 10 c. multicoloured .. 20 15
1044. – 18 c. multicoloured .. 35 65
1045. – 23 c. multicoloured .. 50 85
DESIGNS: 5 c. Ball-player (4th Paraplegic Games, Dunedin). 10 c. Cycling. 18 c. Rifle-shooting. 23 c. Bowls.

1974. Cents. of Napier and U.P.U. Mult.
1047. 4 c. Type **342** .. 10 10
1048. 5 c. Clock Tower, Berne .. 10 15
1049. 8 c. U.P.U. Monument, Berne 35 90

343. Boeing Seaplane, 1919.

1974. History of New Zealand Airmail Transport. Multicoloured.
1050. 3 c. Type **343** 25 10
1051. 4 c. Lockheed "Electra", 1937 30 10
1052. 5 c. Bristol Freighter, 1958 35 10
1053. 23 c. Empire "S-30" Flying-boat, 1940 .. 1·50 1·50

344. Children, Cat and Dog.

1974. Health Stamps.
1054. **344.** 3 c.+1 c. multicoloured 20 30
1055. – 4 c.+1 c. multicoloured 25 30
1056. – 5 c.+1 c. multicoloured 1·00 1·25
Nos. 1055/56 are similar to Type **344** showing children with pets.

345. "The Adoration of the Magi" (Konrad Witz).

1974. Christmas. Multicoloured.
1058. 3 c. Type **345** 10 10
1059. 5 c. "The Angel window" (stained-glass window Old St. Pauls Church, Wellington) 10 10
1060. 10 c. Madonna Lily .. 30 50

346. Great Barrier Island.

1974. Off-shore Islands. Mult.
1061. 6 c. Type **346** 30 40
1062. 8 c. Stewart Island .. 40 80
1063. 18 c. White Island .. 70 1·50
1064. 23 c. The Brothers .. 1·00 2·00

347. Crippled Child.

1975. Anniversaries and Events. Mult.
1065. 3 c. Type **347** .. 10 10
1066. 5 c. Farming family .. 15 10
1067. 10 c. I.W.Y. symbols .. 20 55
1068. 18 c. Medical School Building, Otago University 35 80
COMMEMORATIONS: 3 c. New Zealand Crippled Children Society. 40th anniv. 5 c. Women's Division, Federated Farmers of New Zealand. 50th anniv. 10 c. International Women's Year. 18 c. Otago Medical School. Centenary.

348. Scow "Lake Erie".

1975. Historic Sailing Ships.
1069. **348.** 4 c. black and red .. 30 10
1070. – 5 c. black and blue .. 30 10
1071. – 8 c. black and yellow 45 35
1072. – 10 c. black and yellow 45 40
1073. – 18 c. black & brown .. 70 90
1074. – 23 c. black & lilac .. 80 1·25
SHIPS: 5 c. Schooner "Herald". 8 c. Brigantine "New Zealander". 10 c. Topsail schooner "Jessie Kelly". 18 c. Barque "Tory". 23 c. Full-rigged clipper "Ragitiki".

349. Lake Sumner Forest Park.

1975. Forest Park Scenes. Multicoloured.
1075. 6 c. Type **349** 50 70
1076. 8 c. North-west Nelson .. 60 1·00
1077. 18 c. Kaweka .. .. 1·25 1·75
1078. 23 c. Coromandel .. 1·50 2·00

350. Girl feeding Lamb.

1975. Health Stamps. Multicoloured.
1079. 3 c.+1 c. Type **350** .. 20 25
1080. 4 c.+1 c. Boy with hen chicks 20 25
1081. 5 c.+1 c. Boy with duck and duckling .. .. 60 1·10

351. "Virgin and Child" (Zanobi Machiavelli).

1975. Christmas. Multicoloured.
1083. 3 c. Type **351** 10 10
1084. 5 c. "Cross in Landscape" (stained-glass window, Greendale Church) .. 10 10
1085. 10 c. "I saw three ships..." (carol) 35 65
The 5 c. and 10 c. are horizontal.

352. "Sterling Silver". **353.** Queen Elizabeth II (photograph by W. Harrison).

353a. Maripi (knife). **353b.** "Paua".

1975.
(a) Garden Roses. Multicoloured.
1086 1 c. Type **352** 10 10
1087 2 c. "Lilli Marlene" .. 10 10
1088 3 c. "Queen Elizabeth" 60 10
1089 4 c. "Super Star" .. 10 10
1090 5 c. "Diamond Jubilee" 10 10
1091a 6 c. "Cresset" 40 30
1092a 7 c. "Michele Meilland" 40 10
1093a 8 c. "Josephine Bruce" 65 10
1094 9 c. "Iceberg" 15 15
(b) Type **353**.
1094ab. 10 c. multicoloured .. 30 10
(c) Maori Artefacts.
1095. **353a.** 11 c. brn., yell. & blk. 45 30
1096. – 12 c. brn., yell. & blk. 30 10
1097. – 13 c. brn., mve. & blk. 60 30
1098. – 14 c. brn., yell. & blk. 30 20
DESIGNS: 12 c. Putorino (flute). 13 c. Wahaika (club). 14 c. Kotiate (club).
(d) Seashells. Multicoloured.
1099. 20 c. Type **353b** .. 15 20
1100. 30 c. "Toheroa" .. 25 30
1101. 40 c. "Coarse Dosinia" 30 35
1102. 50 c. "Spiny Murex" .. 40 45
1103. $1 Scallop 70 85
1104. $2 Circular saw .. .. 1·00 1·75
(e) Building. Multicoloured.
1105. $5 "Beehive" (section of Parliamentary Buildings, Wellington) (22 × 26 mm.) .. .. 3·00 2·00

INDEX

Countries can be quickly located by referring to the index at the end of this volume.

354. Family and League of Mothers Badge.

1976. Anniversaries and Metrication. Mult.
1110. 6 c. Type **354** 10 10
1111. 7 c. Weight, temperature, linear measure and capacity 10 10
1112. 8 c. "William Bryon" (immigrant ship), mountain and New Plymouth 15 10
1113. 10 c. Two women shaking hands and Y.W.C.A. badge .. 15 40
1114. 25 c. Map of the world showing cable links .. 30 1·25
ANNIVERSARIES. 6 c. League of Mothers, 50th Anniversary. 7 c. Metrication. 8 c. Centenary of New Plymouth. 10 c. 50th Anniversary of New Zealand Y.W.C.A. 25 c. Link with International Telecommunications Network, Centenary.

355. Gig.

1976. Vintage Farm Transport. Multicoloured.
1115. 6 c. Type **355** 15 20
1116. 7 c. Thorneycroft lorry .. 20 10
1117. 8 c. Scandi wagon .. 50 20
1118. 9 c. Traction engine .. 30 40
1119. 10 c. Wool wagon .. 30 75
1120. 25 c. Cart .. .. 80 1·75

356. Purakaunui Falls.

1976. Waterfalls. Multicoloured.
1121. 10 c. Type **356** 40 10
1122. 14 c. Marakopa Falls .. 75 55
1123. 15 c. Bridal Veil Falls .. 80 60
1124. 16 c. Papakorito Falls .. 90 70

357. Boy and Pony.

1976. Health Stamps. Multicoloured.
1125. 7 c.+1 c. Type **357** .. 25 30
1126. 8 c.+1 c. Girl and calf .. 25 30
1127. 10 c.+1 c. Girls and bird 50 65

358. "Nativity" (Spanish carving).

1976. Christmas. Multicoloured.
1129. 7 c. Type **358** 15 10
1130. 11 c. "Resurrection" (stained-glass window, St. Joseph's Catholic Church, Grey Lynn) (horiz.) 25 30
1131. 18 c. Angels (horiz.) .. 40 60

359. Arms of Hamilton. **361.** Physical Education and Maori Culture.

1977. Anniversaries. Multicoloured.

1132. 8 c. Type **359** 15 10
1133. 8 c. Arms of Gisborne 15 10
1134. 8 c. Arms of Masterton .. 15 10
1135. 10 c. A.A. emblem .. 15 30
1136. 10 c. Arms of the Royal Australasian College of Surgeons .. 15 30

ANNIVERSARIES: No. 1132, Hamilton Cent. No. 1133, Gisborne Cent. No. 1134, Masterton Cent. No. 1135, Automobile Association in New Zealand. 75th Anniv. No. 1136, R.A.C.S. 50th Anniv.

1977. Education. Multicoloured.

1138. 8 c. Type **361** 30 60
1139. 8 c. Geography, science and woodwork .. 30 60
1140. 8 c. Teaching the deaf, kindergarten and wood-work 30 60
1141. 8 c. Tertiary and language classes 30 60
1142. 8 c. Home science, correspondence school and teacher training .. 30 60

1977. Nos. 918/19 surch.

1143 7 c. on 3 c. "Detunda egregia" (moth) .. 40 65
1144 8 c. on 4 c. "Charagia virescens" (moth) .. 40 65

363. Karitane Beach.

1977. Seascapes. Multicoloured.

1145. 10 c. Type **363** 20 10
1146. 16 c. Ocean Beach, Mount Maunganui 35 35
1147. 18 c. Piha Beach .. 40 40
1148. 30 c. Kaikoura Coast .. 50 50

364. Girl with Pigeon.

1977. Health Stamps. Multicoloured.

1149. 7 c.+2 c. Type **364** .. 20 35
1150. 8 c.+2 c. Boy with frog 25 35
1151. 10 c.+2 c. Girl with Butterfly 45 70

365. " The Holy Family " (Correggio).

1977. Christmas. Multicoloured.

1153. 7 c. Type **365** .. 15 10
1154. 16 c. " Madonna and Child " (stained-glass window, St. Michael's and All Angels, Dunedin) .. 25 20
1155. 23 c. " Partridge in a Pear Tree " 40 45

The 16 c. and 23 c. are vertical.

366. Merryweather Manual Pump, 1860.

1977. Fire Fighting Appliances. Mult.

1156. 10 c. Type **366** 15 10
1157. 11 c. 2-wheel hose reel and ladder, 1880 .. 15 10
1158. 12 c. Shand Mason steam fire engine, 1873 .. 20 15
1159. 23 c. Chemical fire engine, 1888 .. .. .. 30 30

367. Town Clock and Coat of Arms, Ashburton. **368.** Students and Ivey Hall, Lincoln College.

1978. Centenaries.

1160. **367.** 10 c. multicoloured .. 15 10
1161. – 10 c. multicoloured .. 15 10
1162. – 12 c. red, yell. & blk. 15 15
1163. – 20 c. multicoloured .. 20 30

DESIGNS—VERT. No. 1161, Mount Egmont (Centenary of Stratford). No. 1162, Early telephone (Centenary of telephone in New Zealand). HORIZ. No. 1163, Aerial view of the Bay of Islands (Centenary of the Bay of Islands County).

1978. Centenary of Land Resources and Lincoln College of Agriculture. Multicoloured.

1164. 10 c. Type **368** .. 15 10
1165. 12 c. Sheep grazing .. 20 25
1166. 15 c. Fertiliser ground spreading 20 30
1167. 16 c. Agricultural Field Days 20 30
1168. 20 c. Harvesting grain .. 25 40
1169. 30 c. Dairy farming .. 40 70

369. **370.** Maui Gas Drilling Platform.

1978. Coil Stamps.

1170. **369.** 1 c. purple 10 30
1171. 2 c. orange 10 30
1172. 5 c. brown 10 30
1173. 10 c. blue 30 45

1978. Resources of the Sea. Multicoloured.

1174. 12 c. Type **370** 20 15
1175. 15 c. Trawler 30 25
1176. 20 c. Map of 200 mile fishing limit 40 35
1177. 23 c. Humpback Whale and Bottle-nosed Dolphins 50 40
1178. 35 c. Kingfish, snapper, grouper and squid .. 75 75

371. First Health Charity Stamp. **372.** " The Holy Family " (El Greco).

1978. Health Stamps.

1179. **371.** 10 c.+2 c. black, red and gold .. 25 35
1180. – 12 c.+2 c. mult. .. 25 40

DESIGN: 10 c. Type **371** (50th anniv. of Health Stamps). 12 c. Heart Operation (National Heart Foundation).

1978. Christmas. Multicoloured.

1182. 7 c. Type **372** 10 10
1183. 16 c. All Saints' Church, Howick (horiz.) .. 25 30
1184. 23 c. Beach scene (horiz.) 30 45

373. Sir Julius Vogel.

1979. Statesmen. Designs each brown and drab.

1185. 10 c. Type **373** .. 30 55
1186. 10 c. Sir George Grey .. 30 55
1187. 10 c. Richard John Seddon 30 55

374. Riverlands Cottage, Blenheim.

1979. Architecture (1st series).

1188. **374.** 10 c. black, bright blue and blue 10 10
1189. – 12 c. black, pale green and green 15 20
1190. – 15 c. black and grey .. 20 25
1191. – 20 c. black, yellow-brown and brown .. 25 30

DESIGNS: 12 c. The Mission House, Waimate North. 15 c. " The Elms ", Tauranga. 20 c. Provincial Council Buildings, Christchurch.

See also Nos. 1217/20 and 1262/5.

375. Whangaroa Harbour.

1979. Small Harbours. Multicoloured.

1192. 15 c. Type **375** 20 10
1193. 20 c. Kawau Island .. 25 30
1194. 23 c. Akaroa Harbour (vert.) 30 35
1195. 35 c. Picton Harbour (vert.) 45 50

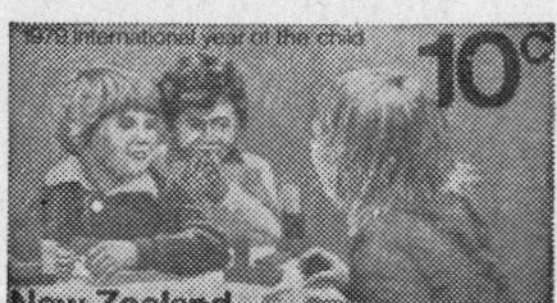

376. Children with Building Bricks.

1979. International Year of the Child.

1196. **376.** 10 c. multicoloured .. 15 10

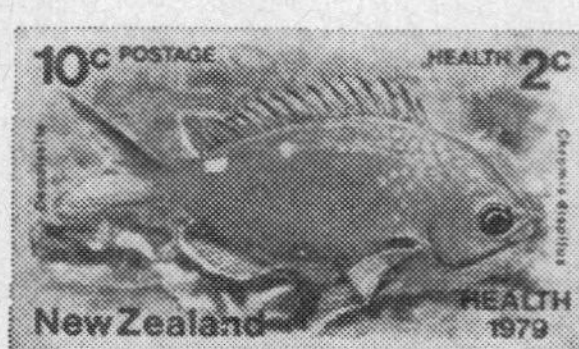

377. Demoiselle.

1979. Health Stamps. Marine Life. Multicoloured.

1197. 10 c.+2 c. Type **377** .. 40 50
1198. 10 c.+2 c. Sea Urchin .. 40 50
1199. 12 c.+2 c. Fish and Underwater cameraman (vert.) 40 50

1979. Nos. 1091/3 and 1094a surch.

1201. 4 c. on 8 c. " Josephine Bruce " 10 15
1202. 14 c on 10 c. Type **353** .. 40 20
1203. 17 c. on 6 c. " Cresset " 40 60
1203a. 20 c. on 7 c. " Michele Meilland " 35 10

379. " Madonna and Child ". (sculpture, Ghiberti).

1979. Christmas. Multicoloured.

1204. 10 c. Type **379** 15 10
1205. 25 c. Christ Church, Russell 30 40
1206. 35 c. Pohutukawa (tree) 40 55

380. Chamber, House of Representatives.

1979. 25th Commonwealth Parliamentary Conference, Wellington. Multicoloured.

1207. 14 c. Type **380** 15 10
1208. 20 c. Mace and Black Rod 20 20
1209. 30 c. " Beehive " wall hanging 30 45

381. 1855 1d. Stamp.

1980. Anniversaries and Events.

1210. **381.** 14 c. blk, red & yellow 20 20
1211. – 14 c. blk, blue & yell. 20 20
1212. – 14 c. blk., grn. & yell. 20 20
1213. – 17 c. multicoloured 20 25
1214. – 25 c. multicoloured 25 30
1215. – 30 c. multicoloured 25 35

DESIGNS: No. 1211, 1855 2d. stamp. No. 1212, 1855 1s. stamp (New Zealand stamps, 125th anniv.). No. 1213, Geyser, wood-carving and building (Rotorua (town) cent.). No. 1214, " Earina autumnalis " and " Thelymitra venosa " (International Orchid Conference, Auckland). No. 1215, Ploughing and Golden Plough Trophy (World Ploughing Championships, Christchurch).

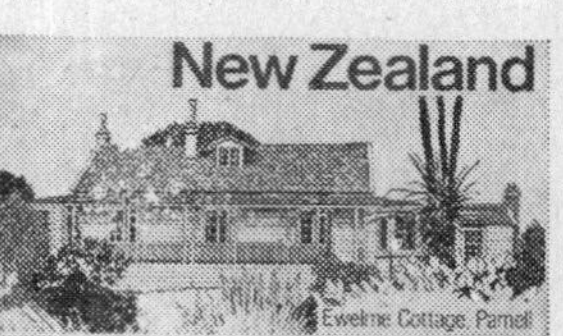

382. Ewelme Cottage, Parnell.

1980. Architecture (2nd series). Mult.

1217. 14 c. Type **382** 15 10
1218. 17 c. Broadgreen, Nelson 25 30
1219. 25 c. Courthouse, Oamaru 30 40
1220. 30 c. Government Buildings, Wellington .. 35 45

383. Auckland Harbour.

1980. Large Harbours. Multicoloured.

1221. 25 c. Type **383** 30 25
1222. 30 c. Wellington Harbour 35 30
1223. 35 c. Lyttelton Harbour 40 40
1224. 50 c. Port Chalmers .. 65 65

384. Surf-fishing.

1980. Health Stamps. Fishing. Mult.
1225. 14 c. + 2 c. Type **384** .. 45 55
1226. 14 c. + 2 c. Wharf-fishing 45 55
1227. 17 c. + 2 c. Spear-fishing 45 55

385. " Madonna and Child with Cherubim " (sculpture, Andrea della Robbia).

1980. Christmas. Multicoloured.
1229. 10 c. Type **385** 15 10
1230. 25 c. St. Mary's Church, New Plymouth .. 25 25
1231. 35 c. Picnic scene .. 40 45

386. Te Heu Heu (chief).

1980. Maori Personalities. Multicoloured.
1232. 15 c. Type **386** 10 10
1233. 25 c. Te Hau (chief) .. 15 10
1234. 35 c. Te Puea (princess) 20 10
1235. 45 c. Ngata (politician) 30 15
1236. 60 c. Te Ata-O-Tu (warrior) 35 20

387. Lt. Col. the Hon. W. H. A. Feilding and Borough of Feilding Crest (cent.).

1981. Commemorations.
1237. **387.** 20 c. multicoloured .. 20 20
1238. — 25 c. orange and black 25 25
DESIGN and COMMEMORATION: 25 c. I.Y.D. emblem and cupped hands (International Year of Disabled).

388. The Family at Play.

1981. " Family Life ". Multicoloured.
1239. 20 c. Type **388** 20 10
1240. 25 c. The family young and old 25 25
1241. 30 c. The family at home 30 30
1242. 35 c. The family at church 35 40

389. Kaiauai River.

1981. River Scenes. Multicoloured.
1243. 30 c. Type **389** 30 30
1244. 35 c. Mangahao 40 40
1245. 40 c. Shotover (horiz.) .. 45 45
1246. 60 c. Cleddau (horiz.) .. 75 75

390. St. Paul's Cathedral.

1981. Royal Wedding. Multicoloured.
1247. 20 c. Type **390** 20 30
1248. 20 c. Prince Charles and Lady Diana Spencer .. 20 30

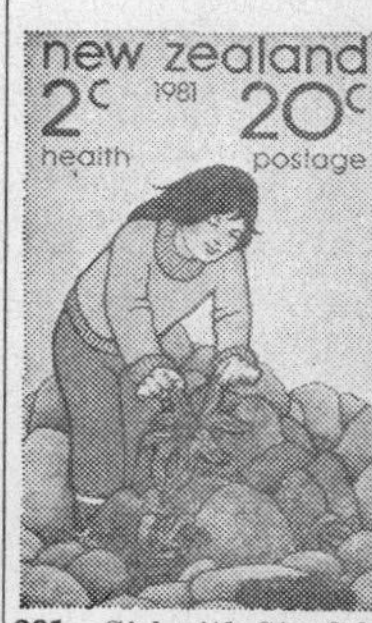

391. Girl with Starfish. **392.** " Madonna Suckling the Child " (painting, d'Oggiono).

1981. Health stamps. Children playing by the Sea. Multicoloured.
1249. 20 c.+2 c. Type **391** .. 25 40
1250. 20 c.+2 c. Boy fishing 25 40
1251. 25 c.+2 c. Children exploring rock pool .. 25 30
Nos. 1249/50 were printed together, se-tenant, forming a composite design.

1981. Christmas. Multicoloured.
1253. 14 c. Type **392** 15 10
1254. 30 c. St. John's Church, Wakefield 35 25
1255. 40 c. Golden Tainui (flower) 45 35

393. Tauranga Mission House. **394.** Map of New Zealand.

1981. Commemorations. Multicoloured.
1256. 20 c. Type **393** 25 10
1257. 20 c. Water tower, Hawera 25 10
1258. 25 c. Cat 35 35
1259. 30 c. "Dunedin" (refrigerated sailing ship) 35 40
1260. 35 c. Scientific research equipment 40 45
COMMEMORATIONS: No. 1256. Centenary of Tauranga (town). No. 1257. Centenary of Hawera (town). No. 1258. Centenary of S.P.C.A. (Society for the Prevention of Cruelty to Animals in New Zealand). No. 1259. Centenary of Frozen Meat Exports. No. 1260. International Year of Science.

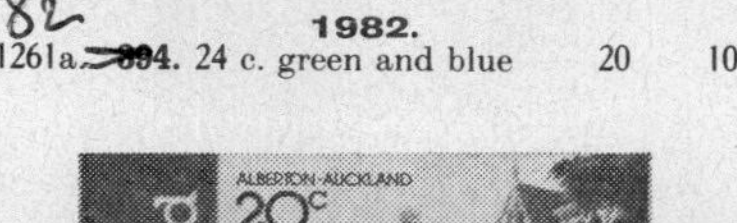

1982.
1261a. **394.** 24 c. green and blue 20 10

395. Alberton, Auckland.

1982. Architecture (3rd series). Multicoloured.
1262. 20 c. Type **395** 20 15
1263. 25 c. Caccia Birch, Palmerston North 25 25
1264. 30 c. Railway station, Dunedin .. 30 30
1265. 35 c. Post Office, Ophir .. 35 40

396. Kaiteriteri Beach, Nelson, (Summer).

1982. New Zealand Scenes. Multicoloured.
1266. 35 c. Type **396** 40 40
1267. 40 c. St. Omer Park, Queenstown, (Autumn) 45 45
1268. 45 c. Mt. Naguruhoe, Tongariro National Park, (Winter) 50 50
1269. 70 c. Wairarapa farm, (Spring) 75 75

397. Labrador.

1982. Health Stamps. Dogs. Multicoloured.
1270. 24 c.+2 c. Type **397** .. 65 70
1271. 24 c.+2 c. Border Collie 65 70
1272. 30 c.+2 c. Cocker Spaniel 65 70

398. " Madonna with Child and Two Angels " (painting by Piero di Cosimo).

1982. Christmas. Multicoloured.
1274. 18 c. Type **398** 20 10
1275. 35 c. Rangiatea Maori Church, Otaki .. 35 30
1276. 45 c. Surf life-saving .. 50 40

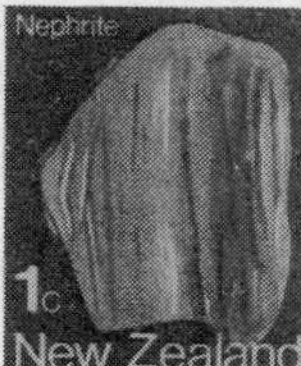

399. Nephrite. **399a.** Grapes.

399b. Kokako.

1982. (a) Minerals. Multicoloured.
1277. 1 c. Type **399** 10 10
1278. 2 c. Agate 10 10
1279. 3 c. Iron Pyrites .. 10 10
1280. 4 c. Amethyst .. 10 10
1281. 5 c. Carnelian .. 10 10
1282. 9 c. Native Sulphur 20 10

(b) Fruits. Multicoloured.
1283. 10 c. Type **399a** .. 55 10
1284. 20 c. Citrus Fruit .. 35 10
1285. 30 c. Nectarines .. 30 10
1286. 40 c. Apples .. 35 10
1287. 50 c. Kiwifruit .. 40 10

(c) Native Birds. Multicoloured.
1288. 30 c. Kakapo 50 25
1289. 40 c. Mountain duck .. 60 35
1290. 45 c. New Zealand falcon .. .. .. 1·00 35
1291. 60 c. New Zealand teal 1·00 40
1292. $1 Type **399b** .. .. 1·00 30
1293. $2 Chatham Island robin 1·40 50
1294. $3 Stitchbird .. .. 1·75 1·40
1295. $4 Saddleback .. .. 2·50 2·00
1296. $5 Takahe .. .. 3·25 3·50
1297. $10 Little spotted Kiwi 5·75 6·00

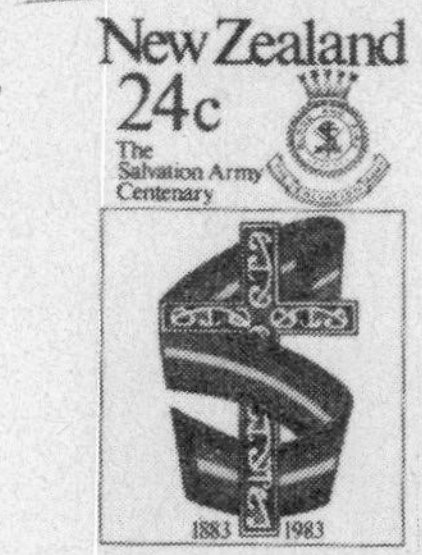

400. Salvation Army Centenary Logo.

1983. Commemorations. Multicoloured.
1303. 24 c. Type **400** 30 10
1304. 30 c. Old Arts building, University of Auckland 40 35
1305. 35 c. Stylised Kangaroo and Kiwi 45 35
1306. 40 c. Rainbow Trout .. 50 45
1307. 45 c. Satellite over Earth 55 50
COMMEMORATIONS: 24 c. Salvation Army Centenary. 30 c. Auckland University Centenary. 35 c. Closer Economic Relationship agreement with Australia. 40 c. Introduction of Rainbow Trout into New Zealand Centenary. 45 c. World Communications Year.

401. Queen Elizabeth II.

1983. Commonwealth Day. Multicoloured.
1308. 24 c. Type **401** 20 10
1309. 35 c. Maori rock drawing 30 40
1310. 40 c. Woolmark and wool-scouring symbols .. 35 45
1311. 45 c. Coat of arms .. 40 55

402. " Boats, Island Bay " (Rita Angus).

1983. Paintings by Rita Angus. Mult.
1312. 24 c. Type **402** 25 10
1313. 30 c. " Central Otago Landscape " .. 30 45
1314. 35 c. " Wanaka Landscape " 35 50
1315. 45 c. " Tree " 45 70

403. Mt. Egmont.

1983. Beautiful New Zealand. Mult.
1316. 35 c. Type **403** 30 35
1317. 40 c. Cooks Bay 35 40
1318. 45 c. Lake Matheson (horiz.) 40 45
1319. 70 c. Lake Alexandrina (horiz.) 65 70

404. Tabby.

1983. Health Stamps. Cats. Mult.

1320. 24 c.+2 c. Type **404** .. 30 25
1321. 24 c.+2 c. Siamese .. 30 25
1322. 30 c.+2 c. Persian .. 50 30

405. " The Family of the Holy Oak Tree ".

1983. Christmas. Multicoloured.

1324. 18 c. Type **405** 10 10
1325. 35 c. St. Patrick's Church, Greymouth 30 35
1326. 45 c. " The Glory of Christmas " 40 45

406. Geology.

1984. Antarctic Research. Multicoloured.

1327. 24 c. Type **406** 25 10
1328. 40 c. Biology 35 40
1329. 58 c. Glaciology 50 55
1330. 70 c. Meteorology .. 60 70

407. " Mountaineer ".

1984. New Zealand Ferry Boats. Mult.

1332. 24 c. Type **407** 30 10
1333. 40 c. " Waikana " 40 40
1334. 58 c. " Britannia " 55 55
1335. 70 c. " Wakatere " 65 65

408. Mount Hutt.

1984. Ski-slope Scene. Multicoloured.

1336. 35 c. Type **408** 40 40
1337. 40 c. Coronet Park .. 45 45
1338. 45 c. Turoa 50 50
1339. 70 c. Whakapapa .. 75 75

409. Hamilton's Frog.

1984. Amphibians and Reptiles. Multicoloured.

1340. 24 c. Type **409** 30 30
1341. 24 c. Great Barrier Skink 30 30
1342. 30 c. Harlequin Gecko .. 35 35
1343. 58 c. Otago Skink .. 70 70
1344. 70 c. Gold-striped Gecko 75 75

410. Clydesdales ploughing.

1984. Health Stamps Horses. Multicoloured.

1345. 24 c.+2 c. Type **410** .. 30 30
1346. 24 c.+2 c. Shetland ponies 30 30
1347. 30 c.+2 c. Thoroughbreds 45 35

411. "Adoration of the Shepherds."

1984. Christmas. Multicoloured.

1349. 18 c. Type **411** 20 10
1350. 35 c. "Old St. Paul's, Wellington" (vert.) .. 40 35
1351. 45 c. "The Joy of Christmas" 50 45

412. Mounted Riflemen, South Africa, 1901

1984. New Zealand Military History. Multicoloured.

1352. 24 c. Type **412** 30 10
1353. 40 c. Engineers, France, 1917 .. .. 45 45
1354. 58 c. Tanks of 2nd N.Z. Divisional Cavalry, North Africa, 1942 .. 60 60
1355. 70 c. Infantryman in jungle kit, and 25-pounder gun, Korea and South-East Asia, 1950–72 .. .. 70 75

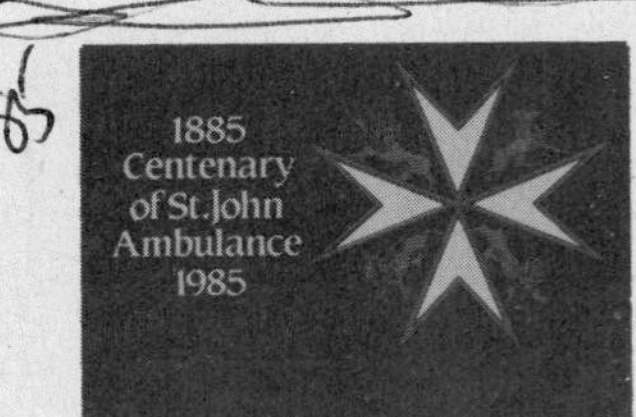

413. St. John Ambulance Badge.

1985. Centenary of St. John Ambulance in New Zealand.

1357. **413.** 24 c. black, gold and red 25 10
1358. 30 c. blk. silver & bl. 35 30
1359. 40 c. black and grey 40 45

The colours of the badge depicted are those for Bailiffs and Dames Grand Cross (24 c.), Knights and Dames of Grace (30 c.) and Serving Brothers and Sisters (40 c.).

414. Nelson Horse-drawn Tram, 1862.

1985. Vintage Trams. Multicoloured.

1360. 24 c. Type **414** 25 10
1361. 30 c. Graham's Town steam tram, 1871 .. 35 50
1362. 35 c. Dunedin cable car, 1881 .. .. 35 60
1363. 40 c. Auckland electric tram, 1902 .. .. 35 60
1364. 45 c. Wellington electric tram, 1904 .. .. 40 70
1365. 58 c. Christchurch electric tram, 1905 .. .. 50 1·10

415. Shotover Bridge.

1985. Bridges of New Zealand. Mult.

1366. 35 c. Type **415** 40 50
1367. 40 c. Alexandra Bridge .. 45 55
1368. 45 c. South Rangitikei railway Bridge (vert.) 50 65
1369. 70 c. Twin Bridges (vert.) 70 95

416. Queen Elizabeth II (from photo by Camera Press).

1985. Mult., background colours given.

1370. **416.** 25 c. red 50 10
1371. 35 c. blue 90 10

417. Princess of Wales and Prince William.

1985. Health Stamps. Designs showing photographs by Lord Snowdon. Mult.

1372. 25 c.+2 c. Type **417** 35 55
1373. 25 c.+2 c. Princess of Wales and Prince Henry 35 55
1374. 35 c.+2 c. Prince and Princess of Wales with Princes William and Henry 35 55

418. The Holy Family in the Stable.

1985. Christmas. Multicoloured.

1376. 18 c. Type **418** 20 10
1377. 40 c. The shepherds .. 40 75
1378. 50 c. The angels 45 90

HAVE YOU READ THE NOTES AT THE BEGINNING OF THIS CATALOGUE?
These often provide answers to the enquiries we receive.

419. H.M.N.Z.S. "Philomel" (1914–47).

1985. New Zealand Naval History. Mult.

1379. 25 c. Type **419** 60 15
1380. 45 c. H.M.N.Z.S. "Achilles" (1936–46) .. 95 1·25
1381. 60 c. H.M.N.Z.S. "Rotoiti" (1949–65) .. 1·25 1·50
1382. 75 c. H.M.N.Z.S. "Canterbury" (from 1971) .. .. .. 1·50 1·75

420. Police Computer Operator.

1986. Centenary of New Zealand Police. Designs showing historical aspects above modern police activities. Multicoloured.

1384 25 c. Type **420** 35 50
1385 25 c. Detective and mobile control room 35 50
1386 25 c. Policewoman and badge 35 50
1387 25 c. Forensic scientist, patrol car and policeman with child .. 35 50
1388 25 c. Police College, Porirua, "Lady Elizabeth II" (patrol boat) and dog handler .. 35 50

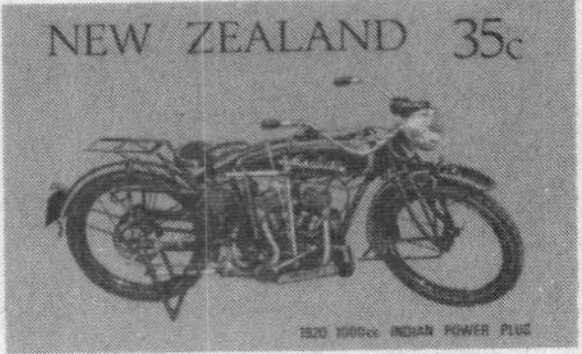

421. Indian "Power Plus" 1000 cc Motor Cycle (1920).

1986. Vintage Motor Cycles. Multicoloured.

1389. 35 c. Type **421** 40 30
1390. 45 c. Norton "CS1" 500 cc (1927) 50 45
1391. 60 c. B.S.A. "Sloper" 500 cc (1930) 65 65
1392. 75 c. Triumph "Model H" 550 cc (1915) .. 75 85

422. Tree of Life.

1986. International Peace Year. Mult.

1393. 25 c. Type **422** 30 30
1394. 25 c. Peace dove .. 30 30

423. Knights Point.

1986. Coastal Scenery. Multicoloured.

1395.	55 c. Type **423**	55	45
1396.	60 c. Becks Bay	55	45
1397.	65 c. Doubtless Bay ..	60	50
1398.	80 c. Wainui Bay ..	75	65

424. "Football" (Kylie Epapara).

1986. Health Stamps. Children's Paintings (1st series). Multicoloured.

1400.	30 c. + 3 c. Type **424** ..	30	40
1401.	30 c. + 3 c. "Children at Play" (Phillip Kata) ..	30	40
1402.	45 c. + 3 c. "Children Skipping" (Mia Flannery) (horiz.)	40	50

See also Nos. 1433/5.

425. "A Partridge in a Pear Tree".

1986. Christmas. "The Twelve Days of Christmas" (carol). Multicoloured.

1404.	25 c. Type **425**	20	10
1405.	55 c. "Two turtle doves"	45	45
1406.	65 c. "Three French hens"	50	50

426. Conductor and Orchestra.

1986. Music in New Zealand.

1407.	**426.**	30 c. multicoloured ..	25	10
1408.	–	60 c. blk, bl. & orge	45	50
1409.	–	80 c. multicoloured ..	70	75
1410.	–	$1 multicoloured ..	80	85

DESIGNS: 60 c. Cornet and brass band. 80 c. Piper and Highland pipe band. $1 Guitar and country music group.

427. Jetboating.

1987. Tourism. Multicoloured.

1411.	60 c. Type **427**	50	50
1412.	70 c. Sightseeing flights	60	60
1413.	80 c. Camping	70	75
1414.	85 c. Windsurfing ..	70	75
1415.	$1.05 Mountaineering ..	90	1·00
1416.	$1.30 River rafting ..	1·10	1·25

428. Southern Cross Cup.

1987. Yachting Events. Designs showing yachts. Multicoloured.

1417.	40 c. Type **428**	35	15
1418.	80 c. Admiral's Cup ..	70	80
1419.	$1.05 Kenwood Cup ..	85	1·25
1420.	$1.30 America's Cup ..	1·10	1·40

429. Hand writing Letter and Postal Transport.

1987. New Zealand Post Ltd Vesting day. Multicoloured.

1421.	40 c. Type **429**	75	80
1422.	40 c. Posting letter, train and mailbox	75	80

430. Avro "626" and Wigram Airfield, 1937.

1987. 50th Anniv. of Royal New Zealand Air Force. Multicoloured.

1423.	40 c. Type **430**	35	15
1424.	70 c. "P-40 Kittyhawk" over World War II Pacific airstrip ..	55	60
1425.	80 c. Short "Sunderland" flying boat and Pacific lagoon	60	70
1426.	85 c. A-4 "Skyhawk" and Mt. Ruapehu	65	75

431. Urewera National Park and Fern Leaf.

1987. Centenary of National Parks Movement. Multicoloured.

1428.	70 c. Type **431**	70	55
1429.	80 c. Mt. Cook and buttercup	75	60
1430.	85 c. Fiordland and pine-apple shrub	80	65
1431.	$1.30 Tongariro and tussock	1·40	95

432. "Kite Flying" (Lauren Baldwin).

1987. Health Stamps. Children's Paintings (2nd series). Multicoloured.

1433.	40 c. + 3 c. Type **432** ..	65	75
1434.	40 c. + 3 c. "Swimming" (Ineke Schoneveld) ..	65	75
1435.	60 c. + 3 c. "Horse Riding" (Aaron Tylee) (vert.)	85	1·00

433. "Hark the Herald Angels Sing".

1987. Christmas. Multicoloured.

1437	35 c. Type **433**	40	10
1438	70 c. "Away in a Manger"	80	55
1439	85 c. "We Three Kings of Orient Are"	1·00	65

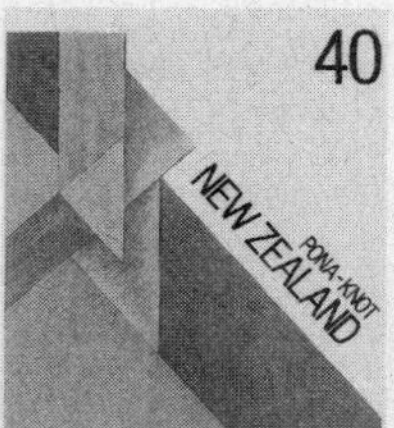

434. Knot ("Pona").

1987. Maori Fibre-work. Multicoloured.

1440.	40 c. Type **434**	35	10
1441.	60 c. Binding ("Herehere")	45	45
1442.	80 c. Plait ("Whiri") ..	60	65
1443.	85 c. Cloak weaving ("Korowai") with flax fibre ("Whitau") ..	65	70

435. "Geothermal".

1988. Centenary of Electricity. Each shows radiating concentric circles representing energy generation.

1444.	**435.**	40 c. multicoloured ..	30	35
1445.	–	60 c. black, red and brown	40	45
1446.	–	70 c. multicoloured ..	50	55
1447.	–	80 c. multicoloured ..	55	60

DESIGNS: 60 c. "Thermal". 70 c. "Gas". 80 c. "Hydro".

436. Queen Elizabeth II and 1882 Queen Victoria 1d. Stamp.

1988. Centenary of Royal Philatelic Society of New Zealand. Multicoloured.

1448.	40 c. Type **436**	35	40
1449.	40 c. As Type **436**, but 1882 Queen Victoria 2d.	35	40

437. "Mangopare".

1988. Maori Rafter Paintings. Multicoloured.

1451.	40 c. Type **437**	40	40
1452.	40 c. "Koru"	40	40
1453.	40 c. "Raupunga" ..	40	40
1454.	60 c. "Koiri"	55	65

438 "Good Luck"

1988. Greetings Stamps. Multicoloured.

1455	40 c. Type **438**	25	30
1456	40 c. "Keeping in touch"	25	30
1457	40 c. "Happy birthday"	25	30
1458	40 c. "Congratulations" (41 × 27 mm)	25	30
1459	40 c. "Get well soon" (41 × 27 mm)	25	30

439 Paradise Shelduck

1988. Native Birds. Multicoloured.

1459a	5 c. Spotless crake ..	10	10
1460	10 c. Banded dotterel ..	10	10
1461	20 c. Yellowhead ..	10	15
1462	30 c. Silvereye	20	25
1463	40 c. Brown kiwi ..	25	30
1463b	45 c. Rock wren ..	30	35
1464	50 c. Kingfisher ..	35	40
1465	60 c. Spotted shag ..	40	45
1466	70 c. Type **439**	45	50
1467	80 c. Fiordland crested penguin	55	60
1468	90 c. South Island robin	60	65

See also Nos. 1589/a.

440 Milford Track

1988. Scenic Walking Trails. Multicoloured.

1469	70 c. Type **440**	50	60
1470	80 c. Heaphy Track ..	55	70
1471	85 c. Copland Track ..	60	75
1472	$1.30 Routeburn Track ..	90	1·10

441 Kiwi and Koala at Campfire

1988. Bicent of Australian Settlement.

1474	**441**	40 c. multicoloured ..	45	35

A stamp in a similar design was also issued by Australia.

442 Swimming

1988. Health Stamps. Olympic Games, Seoul. Multicoloured.
1475 40 c.+3 c. Type **442** .. 35 45
1476 60 c.+3 c. Athletics .. 50 65
1477 70 c.+3 c. Canoeing .. 60 75
1478 80 c.+3 c. Show-jumping 70 85

443 "O Come All Ye Faithful"

1988. Christmas. Carols. Designs showing illuminated verses. Multicoloured.
1480 35 c. Type **443** 30 30
1481 70 c. "Hark the Herald Angels Sing" 55 65
1482 80 c. "Ding Dong Merrily on High" 60 70
1483 85 c. "The First Nowell" 65 80

444 "Lake Pukaki" (John Gully)

1988. New Zealand Heritage (1st issue). "The Land". Designs showing 19th-century paintings. Multicoloured.
1484 40 c. Type **444** 35 35
1485 60 c. "On the Grass Plain below Lake Arthur" (William Fox) .. 45 45
1486 70 c. "View of Auckland" (John Hoyte) 55 55
1487 80 c. "Mt. Egmont from the Southward" (Charles Heaphy) .. 60 60
1488 $1.05 "Anakiwa, Queen Charlotte Sound" (John Kinder) 80 80
1489 $1.30 "White Terraces, Lake Rotomahana", (Charles Barraud) .. 95 95

See also Nos. 1505/10, 1524/9, 1541/6, 1548/53 and 1562/7.

445 Brown Kiwi

1988.
1490 **445** $1 green .. .. 1·25 1·60
1490b $1 red 65 70

446 Humpback Whale and Calf

1988. Whales. Multicoloured.
1491 60 c. Type **446** 70 55
1492 70 c. Killer whales 85 65
1493 80 c. Southern right whale 90 70
1494 85 c. blue whale .. 95 75
1495 $1.05 Southern bottlenose whale and calf .. 1·25 90
1496 $1.30 Sperm whale .. 1·40 1·10

Although inscribed "ROSS DEPENDENCY" Nos. 1491/6 were available from post offices throughout New Zealand.

447 Clover

1989. Wild Flowers. Multicoloured.
1497 40 c. Type **447** 40 35
1498 60 c. Lotus 50 55
1499 70 c. Montbretia .. 60 65
1500 80 c. Wild ginger .. 70 75

448 Katherine Mansfield

1989. New Zealand Authors. Multicoloured.
1501 40 c. Type **448** 30 35
1502 60 c. James K. Baxter .. 40 50
1503 70 c. Bruce Mason .. 50 60
1504 80 c. Ngaio Marsh .. 55 70

449 Moriori Man and Map of Chatham Islands

1989. New Zealand Heritage (2nd issue). The People.
1505 **449** 40 c. multicoloured .. 45 35
1506 – 60 c. brown, grey and deep brown .. 60 70
1507 – 70 c. green, grey and deep green .. 65 75
1508 – 80 c. blue, grey and deep blue .. 75 85
1509 – $1.05 grey, light grey and black .. 1·00 1·10
1510 – $1.30 red, grey, & brn 1·25 1·40

DESIGNS: 60 c. Gold prospector; 70 c. Settler ploughing; 80 c. Whaling; $1.05, Missionary preaching to Maoris; $1.30, Maori village.

450 White Pine (Kahikatea)

1989. Native Trees. Multicoloured.
1511 80 c. Type **450** 75 80
1512 85 c. Red pine (Rimu) .. 80 85
1513 $1.05 Totara .. .. 1·00 1·10
1514 $1.30 Kauri .. .. 1·25 1·40

451 Duke and Duchess of York with Princess Beatrice

1989. Health Stamps. Multicoloured.
1516 40 c.+3 c. Type **451** .. 50 55
1517 40 c.+3 c. Duchess of York with Princess Beatrice 50 55
1518 80 c.+3 c. Princess Beatrice 75 75

452 One Tree Hill, Auckland, through Bedroom Window

1989. Christmas. Designs showing Star of Bethlehem. Multicoloured.
1520 35 c. Type **452** .. 35 30
1521 65 c. Shepherd and dog in mountain valley .. 65 70
1522 80 c. Star over harbour .. 85 90
1523 $1 Star over globe .. 1·25 1·40

453 Windsurfing

1989. New Zealand Heritage (3rd issue). The Sea. Multicoloured.
1524 40 c. Type **453** 40 35
1525 60 c. Fishes of many species 60 70
1526 65 c. Marlin and game fishing launch .. 65 75
1527 80 c. Rowing boat and yachts in harbour .. 80 85
1528 $1 Coastal scene .. 1·00 1·10
1529 $1.50 Container ship and tug .. .. .. 1·50 1·60

454 Games Logo

1989. 14th Commonwealth Games, Auckland. Multicoloured.
1530 40 c. Type **454** 40 35
1531 40 c. Goldie (games kiwi mascot) 40 35
1532 40 c. Gymnastics .. 40 35
1533 50 c. Weightlifting .. 50 55
1534 65 c. Swimming .. 65 70
1535 80 c. Cycling .. 80 90
1536 $1 Lawn bowling .. 1·00 1·25
1537 $1.80 Hurdling .. 1·75 1·90

MINIMUM PRICE

The minimum price quoted is 10p which represents a handling charge rather than a basis for valuing common stamps. For further notes about prices see introductory pages.

455 Short "S.30" Empire Flying Boat and Boeing "747"

1990. 50th Anniv of Air New Zealand.
1539 **455** 80 c. multicoloured .. 1·00 80

457 Maori Voyaging Canoe

1990. New Zealand Heritage (4th issue). The Ships. Multicoloured.
1541 40 c. Type **457** 55 35
1542 50 c. H.M.S. "Endeavour" (Cook), 1769 .. .. 70 50
1543 60 c. "Tory" (barque), 1839 .. .. .. 80 60
1544 80 c. "Crusader" (full-rigged immigrant ship), 1871 .. .. .. 1·10 85
1545 $1 "Edwin Fox" (full-rigged immigrant ship), 1873 .. .. .. 1·25 1·10
1546 $1.50 "Arawa" (steamer), 1884 .. .. .. 2·00 1·75

459 Grace Neill (social reformer) and Maternity Hospital, Wellington

1990. New Zealand Heritage (5th issue). Famous New Zealanders. Multicoloured.
1548 40 c. Type **459** 40 30
1549 50 c. Jean Batten (pilot) and Percival "Gull" aircraft 45 45
1550 60 c. Katherine Sheppard (suffragette) and 19th-century women .. 60 60
1551 80 c. Richard Pearse (inventor) and early flying machine .. 75 75
1552 $1 Lt.-Gen. Sir Bernard Freyberg and tank .. 95 95
1553 $1.50 Peter Buck (politician) and Maori pattern .. .. 1·25 1·40

460 Akaroa

1990. 150th Anniv of European Settlements. Multicoloured.
1554 80 c. Type **460** 75 75
1555 $1 Wanganui 95 95
1556 $1.50 Wellington .. 1·40 1·40
1557 $1.80 Takapuna Beach, Auckland .. .. 1·60 1·60

461 Jack Lovelock (athlete) and Race

1990. Health Stamps. Sportsmen. Mult.

1559 40 c.+5 c. Type **461** .. 50 50
1560 80 c.+5 c. George Nepia (rugby player) and match 75 75

462 Creation Legend of Rangi and Papa

1990. New Zealand Heritage (6th issue). The Maori. Multicoloured.

1562 40 c. Type **462** 40 30
1563 50 c. Pattern from Maori feather cloak 55 50
1564 60 c. Maori women's choir 60 60
1565 80 c. Maori facial tattoos 75 75
1566 $1 War canoe prow (detail) 90 95
1567 $1.50 Maori haka .. 1·40 1·50

464 Angel

1990. Christmas.

1569 **464** 40 c. purple, bl & brn 40 30
1570 – $1 purple, green & brn 80 80
1571 – $1.50 pur, red & brn 1·40 1·60
1572 – $1.80 pur, red & brn 1·60 1·75

DESIGNS: $1 to $1.80, Different angels.

465 Antarctic Petrel

1990. Antarctic Birds. Multicoloured.

1573 40 c. Type **465** 40 30
1574 50 c. Wilson's petrel .. 50 50
1575 60 c. Snow petrel .. 60 60
1576 80 c. Fulmar 75 75
1577 $1 Chinstrap penguin .. 85 85
1578 $1.50 Emperor penguin .. 1·40 1·50

Although inscribed "Ross Dependency" Nos. 1573/8 were available from post offices throughout New Zealand.

466 Coopworth Ewe and Lambs

1991. New Zealand Farming and Agriculture. Sheep Breeds. Multicoloured.

1579 40 c. Type **466** 40 30
1580 60 c. Perendale 55 55
1581 80 c. Corriedale 70 70
1582 $1 Drysdale 85 85
1583 $1.50 South Suffolk .. 1·25 1·25
1584 $1.80 Romney .. .. 1·50 1·60

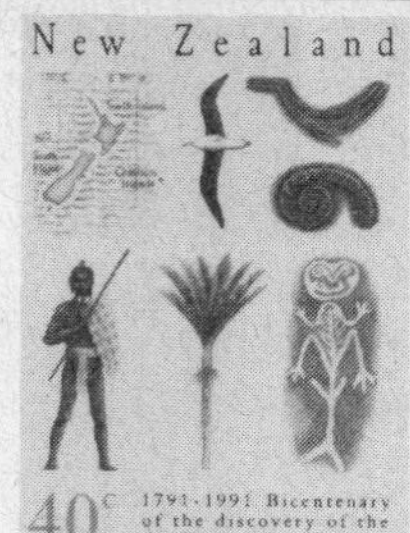

467 Moriori, Royal Albatross, Nikau Palm and Artefacts

1991. Bicentenary of Discovery of Chatham Islands. Multicoloured.

1585 40 c. Type **467** 40 40
1586 80 c. Carvings, H.M.S. "Chatham", Moriori house of 1870, and Tommy Solomon .. 70 70

468 Goal and Footballers

1991. Centenary of New Zealand Football Association. Multicoloured.

1587 80 c. Type **468** 75 75
1588 80 c. Five footballers and referee 75 75

Nos. 1587/8 were printed together, se-tenant, forming a composite design.

1991. As Nos. 1463 and 1463b but self-adhesive.

1589 40 c. Brown kiwi .. 25 30
1589a 45 c. Rock wren .. 30 35

469 Tuatara on Rocks

1991. Endangered Species. The Tuatara. Multicoloured.

1590 40 c. Type **469** 40 45
1591 40 c. Tuatara in crevice .. 40 45
1592 40 c. Tuatara with foliage 40 45
1593 40 c. Tuatara in dead leaves 40 45

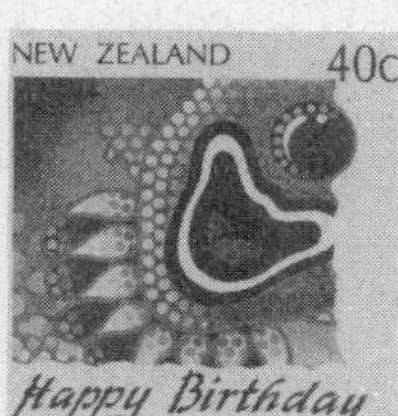

470 Clown

1991. "Happy Birthday". Multicoloured.

1594 40 c. Type **470** 25 30
1595 40 c. Balloons 25 30
1596 40 c. Party hat 25 30
1597 40 c. Birthday present (41 × 27 mm) 25 30
1598 40 c. Birthday cake (41 × 27 mm) 25 30
1599 45 c. Type **470** 30 35
1600 45 c. As No. 1595 .. 30 35
1601 45 c. As No. 1596 .. 30 35
1602 45 c. As No. 1597 .. 30 35
1603 45 c. As No. 1598 .. 30 35

INDEX

Countries can be quickly located by referring to the index at the end of this volume.

471 Cat at Window

1991. "Thinking of You". Multicoloured.

1604 40 c. Type **471** 25 30
1605 40 c. Cat playing with slippers 25 30
1606 40 c. Cat with alarm clock 25 30
1607 40 c. Cat in window (41 × 27 mm) 25 30
1608 40 c. Cat at door (41 × 27 mm) 25 30
1609 45 c. As Type **471** .. 30 35
1610 45 c. As No. 1605 .. 30 35
1611 45 c. As No. 1606 .. 30 35
1612 45 c. As No. 1607 .. 30 35
1613 45 c. As No. 1608 .. 30 35

472 Punakaiki Rocks

1991. Scenic Landmarks. Multicoloured.

1614 40 c. Type **472** 35 30
1615 50 c. Moeraki Boulders .. 50 45
1616 80 c. Organ Pipes .. 75 75
1617 $1 Castle Hill 85 85
1618 $1.50 Te Kaukau Point 1·40 1·50
1619 $1.80 Ahuriri River Clay Cliffs .. .. .. 1·60 1·75

473 Dolphins Underwater

1991. Health Stamps. Hector's Dolphin. Multicoloured.

1620 45 c.+5 c. Type **473** .. 45 50
1621 80 c.+5 c. Dolphins leaping 80 90

474 Children's Rugby

1991. World Cup Rugby Championship. Multicoloured.

1623 80 c. Type **474** 75 75
1624 $1 Women's rugby .. 85 85
1625 $1.50 Senior rugby .. 1·40 1·40
1626 $1.80 "All Blacks" (national team) .. 1·60 1·60

475 "Three Shepherds"

1991. Christmas. Multicoloured.

1628 45 c. Type **475** 45 45
1629 45 c. Two Kings on camels 45 45
1630 45 c. Mary and Baby Jesus 45 45
1631 45 c. King with gift .. 45 45
1632 65 c. Star of Bethleham .. 60 60
1633 $1 Crown 85 85
1634 $1.50 Angel .. .. 1·40 1·40

476 "Dodonidia helmsii"

1991. Butterflies. Multicoloured.

1635 $1 Type **476** 65 70
1636 $2 "Zizina otis oxleyi" 1·25 1·40
1637 $3 "Bassaris itea" .. 2·00 2·10

479 Yacht "Kiwi Magic", 1987

1992. New Zealand Challenge for America's Cup. Multicoloured.

1655 45 c. Type **479** 30 35
1656 80 c. Yacht "New Zealand", 1988 .. .. 55 60
1657 $1 Yacht "America", 1851 65 70
1658 $1.50 Yacht "New Zealand", 1992 .. .. 1·00 1·10

480 "Heemskerk"

1992. Great Voyages of Discovery. Mult.

1659 45 c. Type **480** 30 35
1660 80 c. "Zeehan" 55 60
1661 $1 "Santa Maria" .. 65 70
1662 $1.50 "Pinta" and "Nina" 1·00 1·10

Nos. 1659/60 commemorate the 350th anniv of Tasman's discovery of New Zealand and Nos. 1661/2 the 500th anniv of discovery of America by Columbus.

481 Sprinters

1992. Olympic Games, Barcelona (1st issue).

1663 **481** 45 c. multicoloured .. 30 35

See also Nos. 1670/3.

482 Weddell Seal and Pup

1992. Antarctic Seals. Multicoloured.
1664 45 c. Type **482** 30 35
1665 50 c. Crabeater seals swimming 35 40
1666 65 c. Leopard seal and penguins 45 50
1667 80 c. Ross seal 55 60
1668 $1 Southern elephant seal and harem 65 70
1669 $1.80 Hooker's sea lion and pup .. .. 1·25 1·50

Although inscribed "Ross Dependency" Nos. 1664/9 were available from post offices throughout New Zealand.

483 Cycling

1992. Olympic Games, Barcelona (2nd issue). Multicoloured.
1670 45 c. Type **483** 30 35
1671 80 c. Archery 55 60
1672 $1 Equestrian three-day eventing 65 70
1673 $1.50 Sailboarding .. 1·00 1·10

484 Ice Pinnacles, Franz Josef Glacier

1992. Glaciers. Multicoloured.
1675 45 c. Type **484** 30 35
1676 50 c. Tasman Glacier .. 35 40
1677 80 c. Snowball glacier, Marion Plateau .. 55 60
1678 $1 Brewster Glacier .. 65 70
1679 $1.50 Fox Glacier .. 1·00 1·10
1680 $1.80 Franz Josef Glacier 1·25 1·40

EXPRESS DELIVERY STAMPS

E 1.

1903.
E1 E 1 6d. red and violet .. 32·00 20·00

E 2. Express Mail Delivery Van.

1939.
E 6. E 2. 6d. violet .. .. 1·50 1·75

LIFE INSURANCE DEPARTMENT

L. 1.

1891.
L 13 L 1. ½d. purple .. .. 55·00 2·75
L 14 – 1d. blue .. .. 55·00 75
L 15 – 2d. brown .. .. 70·00 3·25
L 4 3d. brown .. .. £190 20·00
L 5 6d. green .. .. £275 60·00
L 6 1s. pink £650 £120

1905. Similar type but " V.R." omitted.
L 37 ½d. green .. .. 2·50 4·25
L 22 1d. blue .. .. £150 30·00
L 38 1d. red .. .. 1·50 1·50
L 26 1½d. black .. .. 35·00 6·00
L 27 1½d. brown .. .. 1·25 2·25
L 21 2d. brown .. .. £1200 80·00
L 28 2d. purple .. .. 40·00 19·00
L 29 2d. yellow .. .. 3·50 2·00
L 30 3d. orange .. .. 40·00 23·00
L 40 3d. brown .. .. 11·00 14·00
L 41 6d. red .. .. 7·50 20·00

L 3. Castlepoint Lighthouse.

1947. Lighthouses.
L 42. L 3. ½d. green and orange 80 60
L 43. – 1d. olive and blue.. 50 30
L 44. – 2d. blue and black.. 70 25
L 45. – 2½d. black and blue.. 9·00 12·00
L 46. – 3d. mauve and blue.. 2·25 35
L 47. – 4d. brown and orange 1·75 40
L 48. – 6d. brown and blue.. 1·75 1·25
L 49. – 1s. brown and blue.. 2·25 75

LIGHTHOUSES—HORIZ. 1d. Taiaroa. 2d. Cape Palliser. 6d. The Brothers Lighthouse. VERT. 2½d. Cape Campbell. 3d. Eddystone. 4d. Stephens Island. 1s. Cape Brett.

1967. Decimal currency. Stamps of 1947-65 surch.
L 50a. 1 c. on 1d. (No. L 43) 2·25 3·25
L 51. 2 c. on 2½d. (No. L 45) 5·50 8·00
L 52. 2½ c. on 3d. (N. L 46) 1·75 4·50
L 53. 3 c. on 4d. (No. L 47) 4·50 4·75
L 54. 5 c. on 6d. (No. L 48) 2·00 6·50
L 55a. 10 c. on 1s. (No. L 49) 1·25 4·00

L 13. Moeraki Point Lighthouse.

1969.
L 56 L 13. ½ c. yell., red & violet 2·00 2·00
L 57 – 2½ c. blue, grn. & buff 1·00 1·25
L 58 – 3 c. stone, yell. & brn. 75 75
L 59 – 4 c. grn., ochre & blue 1·00 1·00
L 60 – 8 c. multicoloured .. 45 2·25
L 61 – 10 c. multicoloured .. 45 2·25
L 62 – 15 c. multicoloured .. 60 1·75

DESIGNS—HORIZ. 2½ c. Puysegur Point Lighthouse. 4 c. Cape Egmont Lighthouse. VERT. 3 c. Baring Head Lighthouse. 8 c. East Cape. 10 c. Farewell Spit. 15 c. Dog Island Lighthouse.

1978. No. L57 surch.
L 63. 25 c. on 2½ c. blue, green and buff .. 75 1·75

5c N.Z.GOVERNMENT LIFE INSURANCE OFFICE
L 17.

1981.
L 64. L 17. 5 c. multicoloured .. 10 10
L 65. 10 c. multicoloured .. 10 10
L 66. 20 c. multicoloured .. 15 15
L 67. 30 c. multicoloured .. 25 25
L 68. 40 c. multicoloured .. 35 30
L 69. 50 c. multicoloured .. 45 35

OFFICIAL STAMPS

Optd. **OFFICIAL.**

1907. Pictorials.
O 59. **23.** ½d. green .. .. 7·00 50
O 61a. **25.** 2d. purple .. .. 7·00 1·00
O 63. **28.** 3d. brown .. .. 35·00 1·75
O 64. **31.** 6d red .. .. £110 15·00
O 65. **34.** 1s orange .. .. 85·00 15·00
O 66. **35.** 2s. green .. .. 70·00 48·00
O 67. – 5s red (No. 329) .. £150 £160

1907. " Universal " type.
O 60c. **42.** 1d. red .. 7·00 30

1908.
O 70 **50.** 1d. red .. .. 60·00 1·25
O 72 31 6d. red (No. 254) .. £110 35·00

1910. King Edward VII etc.
O 73 **51** ½d. green .. .. 3·75 30
O 78 **53.** 1d. red.. .. .. 3·00 10
O 74 **51** 3d. brown .. .. 14·00 80
O 75 6d. red.. .. .. 18·00 3·75
O 76 8d. blue .. .. 14·00 18·00
O 77 1s. orange .. .. 45·00 12·00

1913. Queen Victoria.
O 82. **F 4.** 2s. blue .. .. 40·00 27·00
O 83. 5s. green .. .. 70·00 75·00
O 84. £1 red £550 £450

1915. King George V.
O 96 **62** ½d. green 50 10
O 90 – 1½d. grey .. .. 3·25 40
O 91 – 1½d. brown .. .. 3·25 30
O 98 – 2d. yellow .. .. 1·50 20
O 100 3d. brown .. .. 3·00 70
O 101 4d. violet .. .. 12·00 2·00
O 102a 6d. red .. .. 3·75 60
O 103 8d. brown .. .. 70·00 85·00
O 104 9d. green .. .. 35·00 30·00
O 105 1s. orange .. .. 5·50 2·00

1927. King George V.
O 111. **71.** 1d. red .. .. 1·00 10
O 112. 2s. blue .. .. 70·00 70·00

1933. " Arms ".
O 113. **F 6.** 5 s. green .. £250 £250

Optd. **Official.**

1936. " Arms ".
O 133. **F 6.** 5s. green .. .. 27·00 5·00

1936. As 1935.
O 120 **81.** ½d. green .. .. 4·25 3·75
O 115 – 1d. red (No. 557) .. 1·00 30
O 122 **83.** 1½d. brown .. 8·00 4·00
O 123 – 2d. orange (No. 580) 1·25 10
O 124a **85.** 2½d. brown & grey 10·00 9·00
O 125 **86.** 3d. brown .. .. 40·00 2·00
O 126b **87.** 4d. black & brown 2·75 1·75
O 127b **89.** 6d. red .. .. 3·50 30
O 128a – 8d. brn. (No. 586b) 5·50 9·00
O 130 **91.** 9d. red and black 13·00 18·00
O 131 – 1s. green (No. 588) 14·00 85
O 132d **93.** 2s. olive .. .. 30·00 7·00

1938. King George VI.
O 134 **108.** ½d. green .. .. 8·50 1·00
O 135 – ½d. orange .. .. 1·25 1·00
O 136 – 1d. red .. .. 8·00 15
O 137 – 1d. green .. .. 1·25 10
O 138 – 1½d. brown .. .. 60·00 18·00
O 139 – 1½d. red .. .. 7·50 2·50
O 152 – 2d. orange 75 10
O 140 – 3d. blue .. .. 1·75 10
O 153 – 4d. purple .. .. 2·00 50
O 154 – 6d. red .. .. 6·50 40
O 155 8d. violet .. .. 8·00 6·00
O 156 9d. brown .. .. 9·00 6·50
O 157a – 1s. brn. & red (No. 686b).. 8·00 3·50
O 158 – 2s. orange and green (No. 688) .. 17·00 12·00

1940. Centenary stamps.
O 141. ½d. green 60 35
O 142. – 1d. brown and red.. 3·00 10
O 143. 1½d. blue and mauve 1·50 2·00
O 144. – 2d. green and brown.. 2·75 10
O 145. 2½d. green and blue.. 2·25 2·75
O 146. 3d. purple and red .. 6·50 80
O 147. 4d. brown and red .. 35·00 2·00
O 148. 6d. green and violet.. 19·00 2·00
O 149. 8d. black and red .. 20·00 14·00
O 150. 9d. olive and red .. 7·50 7·00
O 151. 1s. green .. .. 38·00 4·00

O 6. Queen Elizabeth II.

1954.
O 159. O 6. 1d. orange 45 15
O 160. 1½d. brown .. .. 55 2·50
O 161. – 2d. green 30 15
O 162. 2½d. olive .. .. 3·75 1·50
O 163. – 3d. red 40 10
O 164. 4d. blue 70 15
O 165. 9d. red .. .. 2·50 60
O 166. – 1s. purple 50 10
O 167. 3s. slate .. .. 35·00 45·00

1959. Surch.
O 169. O 6. 2½d. on 2d. green .. 35 1·00
O 168. 6d. on 1½d. brown .. 20 85

POSTAGE DUE STAMPS

D 1. D 2.

1899.
D 9. D 1. ½d. red and green .. 2·50 14·00
D 10. 1d. red and green .. 8·50 1·00
D 15. 2d. red and green .. 28·00 4·75
D 12. 3d. red and green .. 12·00 3·50
D 16. 4d. red and green .. 26·00 9·00
D 6. 5d. red and green .. 19·00 18·00
D 7. 6d. red and green .. 22·00 18·00
D 2. 8d. red and green .. 60·00 75·00
D 8. 10d. red and green .. 70·00 80·00
D 3. 1s. red and green .. 65·00 60·00
D 4. 2s. red and green .. £110 £130

1902.
D18 D 2 ½d. red and green .. 1·50 1·50
D30 – 1d. red and green .. 3·25 80
D22a 2d. red and green .. 4·75 1·00
D36 3d. red and green .. 15·00 38·00

D 3.

1939.
D 41. D 3. ½d. green .. .. 3·25 4·00
D 42. 1d. red .. .. 1·25 30
D 46. 2d. blue .. .. 1·00 80
D 47. 3d. brown .. .. 4·00 5·00

NIGER COAST PROTECTORATE

A district on the W. coast of Africa absorbed into S. Nigeria. Now uses stamps of Nigeria.

12 pence = 1 shilling.
20 shillings = 1 pound.

1892. Stamps of Gt. Britain (Queen Victoria) optd. **BRITISH PROTECTORATE OIL RIVERS.**
1. 71. ½d. red .. .. .. 5·50 4·50
2. 57. 1d. lilac .. .. .. 5·50 4·50
3. 73. 2d. green and red.. .. 13·00 8·00
4. 74. 2½d. purple and blue .. 6·50 2·00
5. 78. 5d. purple and blue .. 7·50 7·50
6. 82. 1s. green .. .. .. 45·00 55·00

1893. Half of No. 2 surch. ½d.
7. 57. ½d. on half of 1d. lilac .. £150 £140

1893. Nos. 1 to 6 surch. in words or figs.
20 **73.** ½d. on 2d. green and red £250 £225
21 **74.** ½d. on 2½d. pur. on blue £225 £200
37 **73.** 1s. on 2d. green and red £450 £400
40 5s. on 2d. green and red £7000 £8000
41 **78.** 10s. on 5d. purple & blue £6000 £8000
42 **82.** 20s. on 1s. green .. £65000

13. 14.

1893. Various frames with "OIL RIVERS" barred out and "NIGER COAST" above.
45.13. ½d. red .. .. .. 4·00 3·75
46. 1d. blue .. .. .. 3·75 3·25
47. 2d. green .. .. .. 14·00 13·00
48. 2½d. red .. .. .. 3·50 3·50
49. 5d. lilac .. .. .. 9·50 9·00
50. 1s. black .. .. .. 14·00 12·00

1894. Various frames.
66.14. ½d. green .. .. .. 1·50 1·00
67. 1d. red .. .. .. 2·00 1·00
68. 2d. red .. .. .. 1·50 1·00
69a. 2½d. blue .. .. .. 2·75 1·00
55. 5d. purple .. .. .. 4·50 5·50
71. 6d. brown .. .. .. 7·00 6·50
56a. 1s. black .. .. .. 10·00 7·00
73b. 2s. 6d. brown .. .. 20·00 55·00
74. 10s. violet .. .. .. 75·00 £140

1894. Surch with large figures.
58 "½" on half 1d. (No. 46) .. £550 £225
59 "1" on half 2d. (No. 3) .. £500 £300

1894. No. 67 bisected and surch.
64.14. ½d. on half of 1d. red .. £1200 £250

1894. Surch. **ONE HALFPENNY** and bars.
65.14. ½d. on 2½d. blue .. £275 £200

NIGERIA

A former Br. colony on the W. coast of Africa, comprising the territories of N. and S. Nigeria and Lagos. Now a Federation divided into the three self-governing Regions of Northern Nigeria, Western Nigeria and Eastern Nigeria and the Federal Territory of Lagos. Attained full independence within the Br. Commonwealth in 1960 and became a Federal Republic in 1963.

The Eastern Region (known as Biafra) (q.v) seceded in 1967, remaining independent until overrun by Federal Nigerian troops during Jan. 1970.

1914. 12 pence = 1 shilling.
20 shillings = 1 pound.
1973. 100 kobo = 1 naira.

1.

1914.
1 1. ½d. green 40 30
16 1d. red 40 15
26 1½d. orange .. .. 1·50 15
3 2d. grey .. .. .. 2·00 70
28 2d. brown 45 15
4 2½d. blue .. .. .. 1·00 80
5a 3d. purple on yellow .. 1·25 90
25d 3d. violet .. .. 5·50 1·50
29 3d. blue .. .. .. 2·25 2·00
20 4d. black & red on yellow 50 55
7 6d. purple .. .. 1·75 2·50
22 1s. black on green .. 65 70
9 2s. 6d. blk. & red on blue 5·00 3·00
10 5s. green & red on yellow 6·00 17·00
11d 10s. green & red on green 27·00 65·00
12 £1 purple & black on red £150 £180

1935. Silver Jubilee. As T **13** of Antigua.
30. 1½d. blue and grey .. 60 30
31. 2d. green and blue .. 1·50 30
32. 3d. brown and blue .. 2·25 4·00
33. 1s. grey and purple .. 2·75 11·00

3. Apapa Wharf.

Designs—vert. 1d. Cocoa. 1½d. Tin dredger. 2d. Timber industry. 3d. Fishing village. 4d. Cotton ginnery. 6d. Habe Minaret. 1s. Fulani cattle. horiz. 5s. Oil palms. 10s. Niger at Jebba. £1, Canoe pulling.

5. Victoria-Buea Road.

1936.
34 3 ½d. green 65 65
35 – 1d. red 30 35
36 – 1½d. brown 30 30
37 – 2d. black 30 55
38 – 3d. blue 50 75
39 – 4d. brown .. .. 1·25 2·00
40 – 6d. violet 40 60
41 – 1s. green .. .. .. 1·10 1·40
42 5 2s. 6d. black and blue 3·50 12·00
43 – 5s. black and green .. 6·00 17·00
44 – 10s. black and grey .. 42·00 60·00
45 – £1 black and orange .. 75·00 £120

1937. Coronation. As T **2** of Aden.
46. 1d. red 30 65
47. 1½d. brown 75 55
48. 3d. blue .. .. .. 1·25 1·75

15. King George VI.

Designs: 2s. 6d., 5s As Nos. 42 and 44 but with portrait of King George VI.

1938.
49 15 ½d. green 10 10
50a 1d. red 20 10
50b 1d. lilac 10 10
51 1½d. brown 10 10
52 2d. black 10 40
52aa 2d. red 10 40
52a 2½d. orange 10 35
53 3d. blue 10 10
53b 3d. black 10 15
54 4d. orange .. .. 45·00 2·50
54a 4d. blue 10 80
55 6d. violet 10 10
56a 1s. olive 10 10
57 1s. 3d. blue 30 10
58b 2s. 6d. black and blue .. 1·25 90
59c 5s. black and orange .. 3·25 1·00

1946. Victory. As T **9** of Aden.
60. 1½d. brown 15 10
61. 4d. blue 15 35

1948. Silver Wedding. As T **10/11** of Aden.
62. 1d. mauve 35 10
63. 5s. orange .. .. .. 5·00 7·00

1949. U.P.U. As T **20/23** of Antigua.
64. 1d. purple 15 10
65. 3d. blue 35 55
66. 6d. purple .. .. .. 50 1·00
67. 1s. olive .. .. .. 70 1·40

1953. Coronation. As T **13** of Aden.
68 1½d. black and green .. 30 10

18. Old Manilla Currency.

26. Victoria Harbour.

29. New and Old Lagos.

1953.
69 18 ½d. black and orange .. 15 20
70 – 1d. black and bronze .. 20 10
71 – 1½d. turquoise 35 30
72 – 2d. black and ochre .. 2·75 15
72cc – 2d. slate .. .. 2·50 10
73 – 3d. black and purple .. 55 10
74 – 4d. black and blue .. 1·50 10
75 – 6d. brown and black .. 20 10
76 – 1s. black and purple .. 40 10
77 26 2s. 6d. black green .. 3·50 20
78 – 5s. black and red .. 3·25 60
79 – 10s. black and brown .. 5·00 1·25
80 29 £1 black and violet .. 10·00 4·50

Designs—horiz. As Type **18**: 1d. Bornu horsemen. 1½d. "Groundnuts". 2d. "Tin". 3d. Jebba Bridge and R. Niger. 4d. "Cocoa". 1s. "Timber". As Type **26**: 5s. "Palm-oil". 10s. "Hides and skins". vert. as Type **18**: 6d. Ife bronze.

1956. Royal Visit. No. 72 optd. **ROYAL VISIT 1956.**
81. 2d. black and ochre 30 10

31. Victoria Harbour.

1958. Cent. of Victoria, S. Cameroons.
82. 31. 3d. black and purple .. 10 10

32. Lugard Hall.

1959. Attainment of Self-Government. Northern Region of Nigeria.
83. 32. 3d. black and purple .. 10 10
84. – 1s. black and green .. 35 35
Design: 1s. Kano Mosque.

35. Legislative Building.

1960. Independence Commem.
85. 35. 1d. black and red .. 10 10
86. – 3d. black and blue .. 10 10
87. – 6d. green and brown .. 15 10
88. – 1s. 3d. blue and yellow .. 20 10

Designs—As Type **35**: 3d. African paddling canoe. 6d. Federal Supreme Court. larger (40 × 24 mm.): 1s. 3d. Dove, torch and map.

39. Groundnuts.

48. Central Bank.

1961.
89. 39. ½d. green 10 40
90. – 1d. violet 40 10
91. – 1½d. red .. .. 40 1·25
92. – 2d. blue 20 10
93. – 3d. green 30 10
94. – 4d. blue 30 35
95. – 6d. yellow and black .. 40 10
96. – 1s. green .. .. 1·75 10
97. – 1s. 3d. orange .. 30 10
98. 48. 2s. 6d. black and yellow 75 15
99. – 5s. black and green .. 50 25
100. – 10s. black and blue .. 75 90
101. – £1 black and red .. 5·00 3·75

Designs—As Type **39**: 1d. Coal mining. 1½d. Adult education 2d, Pottery. 3d. Oyo carver. 4d. Weaving. 6d. Benin mask. 1s. Yellow-casqued Hornbill. 1s. 3d. Camel train. As Type **48**: 5s. Nigeria Museum. 10s. Kano Airport. £1, Lagos Railway Station.

52. Globe and Diesel Locomotive.

1961. Admission into U.P.U. Inscr. as in T **52.**
102. 52. 1d. orange and blue .. 10 10
103. – 3d. olive and black .. 10 10
104. – 1s. 3d. blue and red .. 15 10
105. – 2s. 6d. green and blue 25 35

Designs: Globe and mail-van (3d.); aircraft (1s. 3d); liner (2s. 6d.).

56. Coat of Arms.

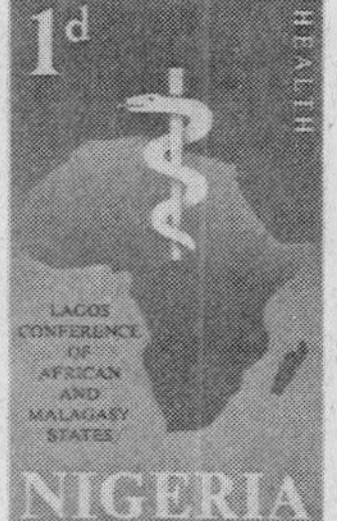

61. "Health".

1961. 1st Anniv. of Independence.
106. 56. 3d. multicoloured .. 10 10
107. – 4d. green and orange .. 10 10
108. – 6d. green 15 10
109. – 1s. 3d. grey and blue .. 20 10
110. – 2s. 6d. green and blue .. 25 20

Designs—horiz. 4d. Natural Resources Map. 6d. Nigerian Eagle. 1s. 3d. Eagles in flight. 2s. 6d. Nigerians and flag.

1962. Lagos Conf. of African and Malagasy States.
111. 61. 1d. bistre 10 10
112. – 3d. purple 10 10
113. – 6d. green 10 10
114. – 1s. brown 15 10
115. – 1s. 3d. blue 20 15

Designs: Map and emblems symbolising Culture (3d.); Commerce (6d.); Communications (1s.); Co-operation (1s. 3d.).

66. Malaria Eradication Emblem and Parasites.

1962. Malaria Eradication.
116. 66. 3d. green and red .. 10 10
117. – 6d. blue and purple .. 10 10
118. – 1s. 3d. mauve & blue 15 10
119. – 2s. 6d. blue and brown 25 20

Designs (embodying emblem): 6d. Insecticide-spraying. 1s. 3d. Aerial spraying. 2s. 6d. Mother, child and microscope.

70. National Monument.

1962. 2nd Anniv. of Independence.
120. 70. 3d. green and blue .. 10 10
121. – 5s. red, green and violet 80 30
Design—vert. 5s. Benin Bronze.

72. Fair Emblem. **76.** "Arrival of Delegates".

1962. Int. Trade Fair, Lagos.

122. **72.** 1d. red and olive .. 10 10
123. – 6d. black and red .. 10 10
124. – 1s. black and brown .. 10 10
125. – 2s. 6d. yellow and blue 20 20

DESIGNS—HORIZ. 6d. "Cogwheels of Industry". 1s. "Cornucopia of Industry". 2s. 6d. Oilwells and tanker.

1962. 8th Commonwealth Parliamentary Conference, Lagos.

126. **76.** 2½d. blue 10 15
127. – 4d. blue and rose .. 10 10
128. – 1s. 3d. sepia and yellow 15 20

DESIGNS—HORIZ. 4d. National Hall. VERT. 1s. 3d. Mace as Palm Tree.

80. Tractor and Maize.

81. Mercury Capsule and Kano Tracking Station.

1963. Freedom from Hunger.

129. – 3d. olive 30 15
130. **80.** 6d. mauve 70 15

DESIGN—VERT. 3d. Herdsman.

1963. "Peaceful Use of Outer Space".

131. **81.** 6d. blue and green .. 20 10
132. – 1s. 3d. black & turquoise 30 10

DESIGN: 1s. 3d. Satellite and Lagos Harbour.

83. Scouts Shaking Hands.
(Illustration reduced. Actual size 60 × 30 mm.).

1963. 11th World Scout Jamboree. Marathon.

133. **83.** 3d. red and bronze .. 15 15
134. – 1s. black and red .. 35 35

DESIGN: 1s. Campfire.

85. Emblem and First Aid Team.

1963. Centenary of Red Cross.

135. **85.** 3d. red and blue .. 45 10
136. – 6d. red and green .. 70 10
137. – 1s. 3d. red and sepia .. 1·25 45

DESIGNS: 6d. Emblem and "Hospital Services". 1s. 3d. Patient and emblem.

88. President Azikiwe and State House. **90.** "Freedom of Worship".

1963. Republic Day.

138. **88.** 3d. olive and green .. 10 10
139. 1s. 3d. brown and sepia 10 10
140. 2s. 6d. turquoise & blue 15 15

The buildings on the 1s. 3d. and the 2s. 6d. are the Federal Supreme Court and the Parliament Building respectively.

1963. 15th Anniversary of Declaration of Human Rights.

141. – 3d. red 10 10
142. **90.** 6d. green 10 10
143. – 1s. 3d. blue 15 10
144. – 2s. 6d. purple 30 30

DESIGNS—HORIZ. 3d. (Inscr. "1948-1963"), Charter and broken whip. VERT. 1s. 3d. "Freedom from Want". 2s. 6d. "Freedom of Speech".

93. Queen Nefertari. **98.** President Azikiwe.

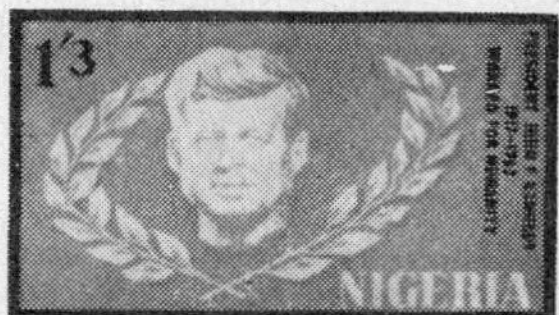

95. President Kennedy.

1964. Nubian Monuments Preservation.

145. **93.** 6d. olive and green .. 30 10
146. – 2s. 6d. brn., olive & grn. 1·25 1·40

DESIGN: 2s. 6d. Rameses II.

1964. Pres. Kennedy Memorial Issue.

147. **95.** 1s. 3d. lilac and black .. 30 15
148. – 2s. 6d. multicoloured .. 45 50
149. – 5s. multicoloured .. 70 1·25

DESIGNS: 2s. 6d. Kennedy and flags. 5s. Kennedy (U.S. Coin Head) and flags.

1964. 1st Anniv. of Republic.

150. **98.** 3d. brown 10 10
151. – 1s. 3d. green 20 10
152. – 2s. 6d. green 30 20

DESIGNS (25 × 42 mm.): 1s. 3d. Herbert Macaulay. 2s. 6d. King Jaja of Opobo.

101. Boxing Gloves.

1964. Olympic Games, Tokyo.

153. **101.** 3d. sepia and green .. 10 10
154. – 6d. green and blue .. 15 10
155. – 1s. 3d. sepia and olive .. 35 10
156. – 2s. 6d. sepia and brown 75 90

DESIGNS—HORIZ. 6d. High-jumping. VERT. 1s. 3d. Running. TRIANGULAR. 2s. 6d. Hurdling (size 60 × 30 mm.).

105. Scouts on Hill-top. **109.** "Telstar".

1965. 50th Anniv. of Nigerian Scout Movement.

157. **105.** 1d. brown 10 10
158. – 3d. red, black and green 15 10
159. – 6d. red, sepia and green 25 15
160. – 1s. 3d. brown, yellow and deep green .. 40 55

DESIGN: 3d. Scout badge on shield. 6d. Scout badges. 1s. 3d. Chief Scout and Nigerian Scout.

1965. International Quiet Sun Years.

161. **109.** 6d. violet and turquoise 10 10
162. – 1s. 3d. green and lilac .. 10 10

DESIGN: 1s. 3d. Solar Satellite.

111. Native Tom-tom and Modern Telephone.

1965. Centenary of I.T.U.

163. **111.** 3d. black, red & brown 15 10
164. – 1s. 3d. blk., grn. & blue 1·25 1·00
165. – 5s. multicoloured .. 3·75 4·50

DESIGNS—VERT. 1s. 3d. Microwave Aerial. HORIZ. 5s. Telecommunications satellite and part of globe.

114. I.C.Y. Emblem and Diesel Locomotive.

1965. Int. Co-operation Year.

166. **114.** 3d. green, red & orange 1·50 10
167. – 1s. black, blue & lemon 1·75 40
168. – 2s. 6d. grn., blue & yell. 5·50 4·00

DESIGNS: 1s. Students and Lagos Teaching Hospital. 2s. 6d. Kainji (Niger) Dam.

117. Carved Frieze.

1965. 2nd Anniv. of Republic.

169. **117.** 3d. black, red & yellow 10 10
170. – 1s. 3d. brown, green & bl. 55 20
171. – 5s. brown, sepia & green 1·60 2·00

DESIGNS—VERT. 1s. 3d. Stone Images at Ikom. 5s. Tada Bronze.

121. African Elephants.

1965. Multicoloured.

172. ½d. Lion and cubs (vert.) 40 60
173. 1d. Type **121** 20 15
174. 1½d. Splendid Sunbird 3·75 4·00
175. 2d. Village Weavers and Red-headed Malimbe .. 2·00 15
176. 3d. Cheetah 80 15
177a. 4d. Leopards 20 30
178. 6d. Saddle-bill Stork (vert.) 1·00 30
179. 9d. Grey Parrot .. .. 2·25 40
180. 1s. Blue-breasted Kingfisher .. .. 1·50 40
181. 1s. 3d. Crowned Crane .. 6·50 45
182. 2s. 6d. Kobs 75 30
183. 5s. Giraffes .. .. 1·50 1·25
184. 10s. Hippopotamus (vert.) 5·50 3·00
185. £1 African Buffalo .. 13·00 8·50

Nos. 180/5 are larger, 46 × 26½ mm. See also Nos. 220/30.

The 1d., 3d., 4d., 1s. 3d., 2s. 6d., 5s. and £1 exist optd. **F.G.N.** (Federal Government of Nigeria) twice in black. They were prepared in November 1968 as official stamps, but the scheme was abandoned. Some stamps held at a Head Post Office were sold in error and passed through the post. The Director of Posts then decided to put limited supplies on sale, but they had no postal validity.

1966. Commonwealth Prime Minister's Meeting, Lagos. Optd. **COMMONWEALTH P. M. MEETING 11. JAN. 1966.**

186. **48.** 2s. 6d. black & yellow 30 30

135. Y.W.C.A. Emblem and H.Q., Lagos.

1966. Diamond Jubilee of Nigerian Y.W.C.A.

187. **135.** 4d. multicoloured .. 10 10
188. 9d. multicoloured .. 10 30

137. Telephone Handset and Linesman.

1966. 3rd Anniv. of Republic.

189. – 4d. green 10 10
190. **137.** 1s. 6d. blk., brn. & violet 45 50
191. – 2s. 6d. multicoloured 1·25 2·00

DESIGNS—VERT. 4d. Dove and flag. HORIZ. 2s. 6d. Niger Bridge, Jebba.

139. "Education, Science and Culture".

1966. 20th Anniv. of U.N.E.S.C.O.

192. **139.** 4d. black, lake & orange 40 10
193. 1s. 6d. black, lake & turq. 1·50 2·00
194. 2s. 6d. black, lake & pink 2·50 4·00

140. Children Drinking.

1966. Nigerian Red Cross.

195. **140.** 4d. + 1d. blk., violet & red 30 25
196. – 1s. 6d. + 3d. multicoloured 1·00 3·50
197. – 2s. 6d. + 3d. multicoloured 1·25 4·00

DESIGNS—VERT. 1s. 6d. Tending patient. HORIZ. 2s. 6d. Tending casualties and Badge.

143. Surveying.

1967. Int. Hydrological Decade. Mult.

198. 4d. Type **143** 10 10
199. 2s. 6d. Water gauge on dam (vert.) 25 60

145. Globe and Weather Satellite.

1967. World Meteorological Day.

200. **145.** 4d. mauve and blue .. 10 10
201. – 1s. 6d. blk., yell. & blue 40 50

DESIGN: 1s. 6d. Passing storm and sun.

147. Eyo Masquerades.

1967. 4th Anniv. of Republic. Multicoloured.

202.	4d. Type **147**	20	10
203.	1s. 6d. Crowds watching acrobat	1·25	1·25
204.	2s. 6d. Stilt dancer (vert.)	1·50	2·25

150. Tending Sick Animal.

1967. Rinderpest Eradication Campaign.

205.**150.**	4d. multicoloured ..	10	10
206.	1s. 6d. multicoloured ..	45	65

151. Smallpox Vaccination.

1968. 20th Anniversary of World Health Organization.

207.**151.**	4d. mauve and black ..	10	10
208. –	1s. 6d. orge., lemon & blk.	45	40

DESIGN: 1s. 6d. African and Mosquito.

153. Chained Hands and Outline of Nigeria.

1968. Human Rights Year.

209.**153.**	4d. blue, black & yellow	10	10
210. –	1s. 6d. green, red & black	20	30

DESIGN—VERT. 1s. 6d. Nigerian Flag and Human Rights Emblem.

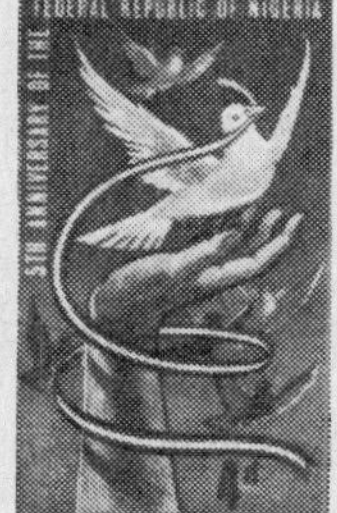

155. Hand grasping at Doves of Freedom.

1968. 5th Anniv. of Federal Republic.

211.**155.**	4d. multicoloured ..	10	10
212.	1s. 6d. multicoloured ..	20	20

156. Map of Nigeria and Olympic Rings.

1968. Olympic Games, Mexico.

213.**156.**	4d. black, green and red	10	10
214. –	1s. 6d. multicoloured ..	20	20

DESIGN: 1s. 6d. Nigerian Athletes, Flag and Olympic Rings.

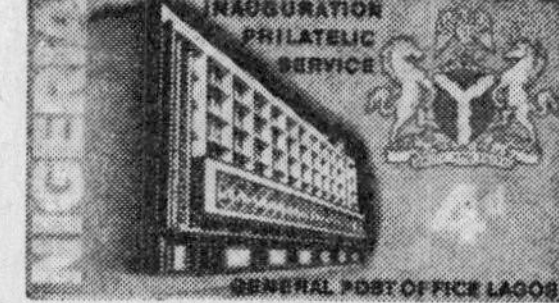

158. G.P.O., Lagos.

1969. Inauguration of Philatelic Service.

215.**158.**	4d. black and green ..	10	10
216.	1s. 6d. black and blue ..	20	20

159. Yakubu Gowon and Victoria Zakari.

1969. Wedding of General Gowon.

217.**159.**	4d. brown and green ..	10	10
218.	1s. 6d. black and green	20	20

1969. As Nos. 172/185, but inscr. "N.S.P. & M. Co. Ltd." (Nigerian Security Printing and Minting Co. Ltd.) at foot.

220.	1d. (As No. 173)	1·75	40
222.	2d. (As No. 175)	1·25	50
223.	3d. (As No. 176)	65	40
224.	4d. (As No. 177)	5·00	60
225.	6d. (As No. 178)	1·00	70
226.	9d. (As No. 179)	5·00	3·00
227.	1s. (As No. 180)	2·00	40
228.	1s. 3d. (As No. 181) ..	8·00	3·25
229.	2s. 6d. (As No. 182) ..	4·00	6·00
230.	5s. (As No. 183)	3·00	7·00

160. Bank Emblem and "5th Anniversary".

1969. 5th Anniv of African Development Bank.

233 **160**	4d. orange, black & bl	10	10
234 –	1s. 6d. yellow, black and purple	20	20

DESIGN: 1s. 6d. Bank emblem and rays.

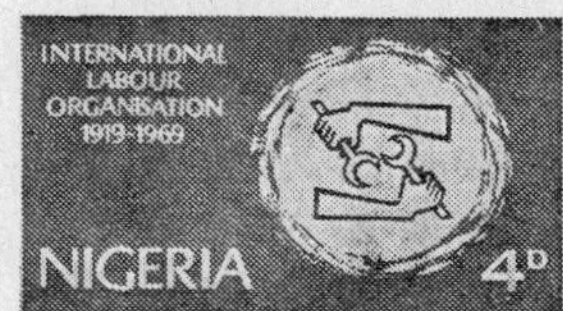

162. I.L.O. Emblem.

1969. 50th Anniversary of I.L.O.

235.**162.**	4d. black and violet ..	10	10
236. –	1s. 6d. green and black	20	25

DESIGN: 1s. 6d. World map and I.L.O. Emblem.

164. Olumo Rock.

1969. Int. Year of African Tourism.

237.**164.**	4d. multicoloured ..	10	10
238. –	1s. black and green ..	15	10
239. –	1s. 6d. multicoloured ..	30	20

DESIGNS—VERT. 1s. Traditional musicians. 1s. 6d. Assob Falls.

167. Symbolic Tree.

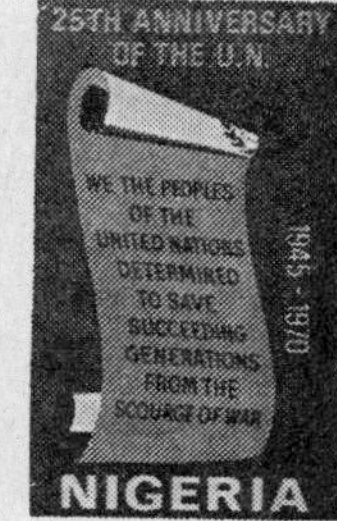

169. Scroll.

168. U.P.U. Headquarters Building.

1970. "Stamp of Destiny". End of Civil War.

240.**167.**	4d. gold, blue and black	10	10
241. –	1s. multicoloured ..	10	10
242. –	1s. 6d. green and black	10	10
243. –	2s. multicoloured ..	15	20

DESIGNS—VERT. 1s. Symbolic Wheel. 1s. 6d. United Nigerians supporting Map. HORIZ. 2s. Symbolic Torch.

1970. New U.P.U. Headquarters Building.

244.**168.**	4d. violet and yellow ..	10	10
245.	1s. 6d. blue and indigo	20	20

1970. 25th Anniv. of United Nations.

246.**169.**	4d. brn., buff and black	10	10
247. –	1s. 6d. blue, brown & gold	20	20

DESIGN: 1s. 6d. U.N. Building.

170. Oil Rig.

172. Ibibio Face Mask.

171. Children and Globe.

1970. 10th Anniv. of Independence.

248.	2d. Type **170**	10	10
249.	4d. University Graduate	15	10
250.	6d. Durbar Horsemen ..	15	10
251.	9d. Servicemen raising Flag	20	10
252.	1s. Footballer	20	10
253.	1s. 6d. Parliament Building	20	25
254.	2s. Kainji Dam	50	70
255.	2s. 6d. Agricultural Produce	50	75

1971. Racial Equality Year. Multicoloured.

256.	4d. Type **171**	10	10
257.	1s. Black and white men uprooting "Racism" (vert.)	10	10
258.	1s. 6d. "The World in Black and White" (vert.) ..	15	50
259.	2s. Black and white men united	15	75

1971. Antiquities of Nigeria.

260.**172.**	4d. black and blue ..	10	10
261. –	1s. 3d. brn. and ochre ..	15	30
262. –	1s. 9d. grn., brn. & yell.	20	80

DESIGN: 1s. 3d. Benin bronze. 1s. 9d. Ife bronze.

173. Children and Symbol.

174. Mast and Dish Aerial.

1971. 25th Anniv. of U.N.I.C.E.F.

263.**173.**	4d. multicoloured ..	10	10
264. –	1s. 3d. orge., red & brn.	15	40
265. –	1s. 9d. pale turquoise & deep turquoise ..	15	85

DESIGNS: Each with U.N.I.C.E.F. symbol. 1s. 3d. Mother and child. 1s. 9d. Mother carrying child.

1971. Opening of Nigerian Earth Satellite Station.

266.**174.**	4d. multicoloured ..	15	10
267. –	1s. 3d. grn., blue & blk.	30	50
268. –	1s. 9d. brn., orge. & blk.	40	1·00
269. –	3s. mauve, blk. & pur.	85	2·00

DESIGNS: Nos. 267/9, as Type **174**, but showing different views of the Satellite Station.

MORE DETAILED LISTS

are given in the Stanley Gibbons Catalogues referred to in the country headings.
For lists of current volumes see Introduction.

175. Trade Fair Emblem.

177. Nok Style Terracotta Head.

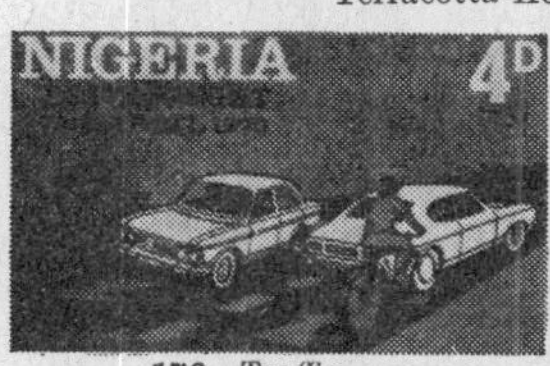

176. Traffic.

1972. All-Africa Trade Fair.

270.**175.**	4d. multicoloured ..	10	10
271. –	1s. 3d. lilac, yell. & gold	15	35
272. –	1s. 9d. yell., orge. & blk.	15	90

DESIGNS—HORIZ. 1s. 3d. Map of Africa with pointers to Nairobi. VERT. 1s. 9d. Africa on globe.

1972. Change to Driving on the Right.

273.**176.**	4d. orge., brn. & black	15	10
274. –	1s. 3d. multicoloured ..	70	70
275. –	1s. 9d. multicoloured ..	80	1·25
276. –	3s. multicoloured ..	2·00	3·00

DESIGNS: 1s. 3d. Roundabout. 1s. 9d. Highway. 3s. Road junction.

1972. All-Nigeria Arts Festival. Mult.

277.	4d. Type **177**	10	10
278.	1s. 3d. Bronze pot from Igbo-Ukwu	25	60
279.	1s. 9d. Bone harpoon (horiz.)	30	1·00

178. Hides and Skins.

1973.

290	**178**	1 k. multicoloured ..	10	10
281	–	2 k. multicoloured ..	35	10
291	–	3 k. multicoloured ..	15	10
282a	–	5 k. multicoloured ..	50	10
294	–	7 k. multicoloured ..	30	50
295	–	8 k. multicoloured ..	40	10
283	–	10 k. multicoloured ..	70	30
297	–	12 k. blk., grn. & bl.	20	60
298	–	15 k. multicoloured ..	20	40
299	–	18 k. multicoloured ..	50	30
300	–	20 k. multicoloured ..	65	30
301	–	25 k. multicoloured ..	85	45
302	–	30 k. blk., yell. & bl.	40	70
303	–	35 k. multicoloured ..	3·50	2·00
288a	–	50 k. multicoloured ..	1·50	90
305	–	1 n. multicoloured ..	1·25	1·10
306	–	2 n. multicoloured ..	3·50	3·75

DESIGNS—HORIZ. 2 k. Natural gas tanks. 3 k. Cement works. 5 k. Cattle-ranching. 7 k. Timber mill. 8 k. Oil refinery. 10 k. Cheetahs. Yankari Game Reserve. 12 k. New Civic building. 15 k. Sugar-cane harvesting. 20 k. Vaccine production. 25 k. Modern wharf. 35 k. Textile machinery. 1 n. Eko Bridge. 2 n. Teaching Hospital, Lagos. VERT. 18 k. Palm oil production. 30 k. Argungu Fishing Festival. 50 k. Pottery.

179. Athlete.

1973. Second All-African Games, Lagos.

307.**179.**	5 k. lilac, blue & blk.	15	10
308. –	12 k. multicoloured ..	25	50
309. –	18 k. multicoloured ..	60	1·00
310. –	25 k. multicoloured ..	70	1·50

DESIGNS—HORIZ. 12 k. Football. 18 k. Table-tennis. VERT. 25 k. National stadium.

180. All-Africa House, Addis Ababa.

1973. 10th Anniv. of O.A.U. Multicoloured.

311. 5 k. Type **180** 10 10
312. 18 k. O.A.U. flag (vert.) .. 30 40
313. 30 k. O.A.U. emblem and symbolic flight of ten stairs (vert.) 50 80

181. Dr. Hansen.

1973. Cent. of Discovery of Leprosy Bacillus.

314. **181.** 5 k.+2 k. brown, pink and black 20 50

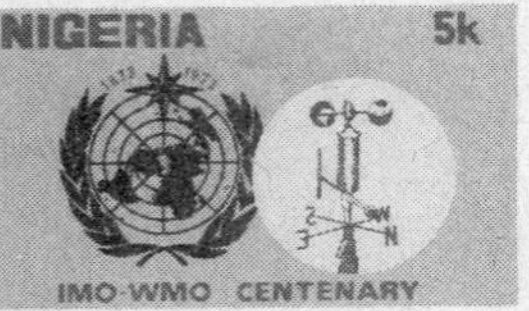

182. W.M.O. Emblem and Weather-vane.

1973. Centenary of I.M.O./W.M.O.

315. **182.** 5 k. multicoloured .. 15 10
316. 30 k. multicoloured .. 85 1·75

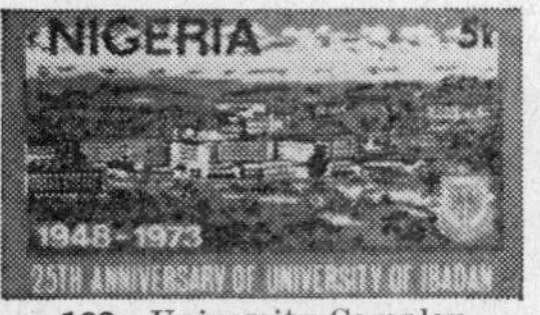

183. University Complex.

1973. 25th Anniv. of Ibadan University. Multicoloured.

317. 5 k. Type **183** 10 10
318. 12 k. Students' population growth (vert.) 25 30
319. 18 k. Tower and students .. 35 55
320. 30 k. Teaching Hospital .. 50 85

184. Lagos 1d. Stamp of 1874.

1974. Stamp Centenary.

321. – 5 k. grn., orge. & blk... 15 10
322. – 12 k. multicoloured .. 40 60
323. **184.** 18 k. grn., mve. & blk. 70 1·00
324. – 30 k. multicoloured .. 1·60 2·50

DESIGNS: 5 k. Graph of mail traffic growth. 12 k. Northern Nigeria £25 stamp of 1904. 30 k. Forms of mail transport.

185. U.P.U. Emblem on Globe.

1974. Centenary of U.P.U.

325. **185.** 5 k. bl., orge. & blk. .. 15 10
326. – 18 k. multicoloured .. 1·00 60
327. – 30 k. brn., grn. & blk... 1·50 1·75

DESIGNS: 18 k. World transport map. 30 k. U.P.U. emblem and letters.

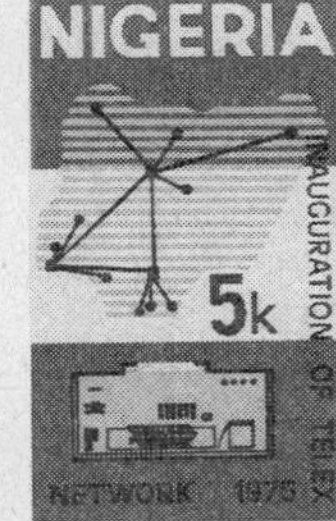

186. Starving and Well-fed Children. **187.** Telex Network and Teleprinter.

1974. Freedom from Hunger Campaign. Mult.

328. 5 k. Type **186** 10 10
329. 12 k. Poultry battery ("More Protein") 40 50
330. 30 k. Water-hoist ("Irrigation increases food production") 1·10 1·75

1975. Inauguration of Telex Network.

331. **187.** 5 k. blk., orge. and grn. 10 10
332. – 12 k. blk., yell. and brn. 20 20
333. – 18 k. multicoloured .. 50 30
334. – 30 k. multicoloured .. 50 50

DESIGNS: 12 k., 18 k. and 30 k. are as Type **187** but with the motifs arranged differently.

188. Queen Amina of Zaria. **190.** Alexander Graham Bell.

1975. International Women's Year.

335. **188.** 5 k. grn., yell. and blue 15 10
336. 18 k. pur., blue and mve. 50 65
337. 30 k. multicoloured .. 60 1·10

1976. Centenary of Telephone.

355. **190.** 5 k. multicoloured .. 10 10
356. – 18 k. multicoloured .. 40 55
357. – 25 k. blue, light blue and brown .. .. 70 1·00

DESIGNS—HORIZ. 18 k. Gong and modern telephone system. VERT. 25 k. Telephones, 1876 and 1976.

191. Child Writing.

1976. Universal Primary Education. Launching.

358. **191.** 5 k. yell., violet & mauve 10 10
359. – 18 k. multicoloured .. 45 60
360. – 25 k. multicoloured .. 70 85

DESIGNS—VERT. 18 k. Children entering school. 25 k. Children in class.

192. Festival Emblem.

1976. 2nd World Black and African Festival of Arts and Culture, Nigeria.

361. **192.** 5 k. gold and brown .. 15 10
362. – 10 k. brn., yell. & blk.. 35 40
363. – 12 k. multicoloured .. 40 55
364. – 18 k. yell., brn. and blk. 60 80
365. – 30 k. red and black .. 1·00 1·50

DESIGNS: 10 k. National Arts Theatre. 12 k. African hair-styles. 18 k. Musical instruments. 30 k. "Nigerian arts and crafts".

193. General Murtala Muhammed and Map of Nigeria.

1977. 1st Death Anniv. of General Muhammed (Head of State). Multicoloured.

366. 5 k. Type **193** 10 10
367. 18 k. The General in dress uniform (vert.) 20 35
368. 30 k. The General in battle dress (vert.) 30 70

194. Scouts Saluting.

1977. 1st All-African Scout Jamboree, Jos, Nigeria. Multicoloured.

369. 5 k. Type **194** 15 10
370. 18 k. Scouts cleaning street (horiz.) 70 70
371. 25 k. Scouts working on farm (horiz.) 85 95
372. 30 k. Jamboree emblem and map of Africa (horiz.) .. 1·10 1·40

195. Trade Fair Complex.

1977. First Lagos Int. Trade Fair.

373. **195.** 5 k. black, blue & green 10 10
374. – 18 k. blk., blue and pur. 20 25
375. – 30 k. multicoloured .. 30 45

DESIGNS: 18 k. Globe and Trade Fair emblem. 30 k. Weaving and basketry.

196. Map showing Nigerian Universities.

1978. Global Conference on Technical Co-operation between Developing Countries, Buenos Aires.

376. **196.** 5 k. multicoloured .. 10 10
377. – 12 k. multicoloured .. 15 15
378. – 18 k. multicoloured .. 25 25
379. – 30 k. yell., violet & black 45 60

DESIGNS: 12 k. Map of West African highways and telecommunications. 18 k. Technologists undergoing training. 30 k. World map.

197. Microwave Antenna.

1978. 10th World Telecommunications Day.

380. **197.** 30 k. multicoloured .. 50 60

198. Students on Operation "Feed the Nation".

1978. "Operation Feed the Nation" Campaign. Multicoloured.

381. 5 k. Type **198** 10 10
382. 18 k. Family backyard farm 20 20
383. 30 k. Plantain farm (vert.) 35 60

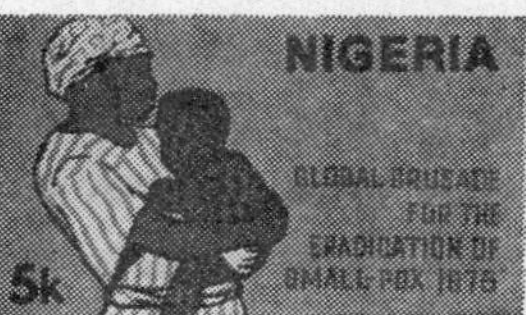

199. Mother with Infected Child.

1978. Global Eradication of Smallpox.

384. **199.** 5 k. black, brown & lilac 10 10
385. – 12 k. multicoloured .. 25 20
386. – 18 k. blk., brn. and yell. 40 30
387. – 30 k. black, silver & pink 60 50

DESIGNS—HORIZ. 12 k. Doctor and infected child. 18 k. Group of children being vaccinated. VERT. 30 k. Syringe.

200. Nok Terracotta Human Figure, Bwari (900 B.C. – 200 A.D.). **201.** Anti-Apartheid Emblem.

1978. Antiquities.

388. **200.** 5 k. black, blue and red 10 10
389. – 12 k. multicoloured .. 10 10
390. – 18 k. black, blue and red 15 15
391. – 30 k. multicoloured .. 20 20

DESIGNS—HORIZ. 12 k. Igbo-Ukwu bronze snail shell, Igbo Isaiah (9th-century A.D.). VERT. 18 k. Ife bronze statue of a king (12th – 15th century A.D.). 30 k. Benin bronze equestrian figure (about 1700 A.D.).

1978. International Anti-Apartheid Year.

392. **201.** 18 k. black, yell. and red 15 15

202. Wright Brothers and "Flyer".

1978. 75th Anniv. of Powered Flight.

393. **202.** 5 k. multicoloured .. 15 10
394. – 18 k. black, blue and light blue 50 20

DESIGN: 18 k. Nigerian Air Force formation.

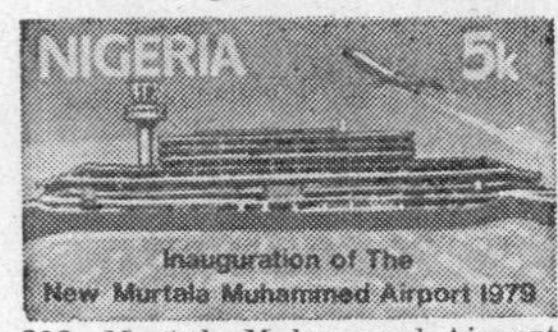

203. Murtala Muhammed Airport.

1979. Opening of Murtala Muhammed Airport.

395. **203.** 5 k. black, grey and blue 20 20

204. Child with Stamp Album.

1979. 10th Anniversary of National Philatelic Service.

396. **204.** 5 k. multicoloured .. 10 10

205. Mother and Child.

1979. International Year of the Child. Multicoloured.

397. 5 k. Type **205** .. 10 10
398. 18 k. Children studying .. 30 30
399. 25 k. Children playing (vert.) 45 50

206. Trainee Teacher making Audio Visual Aid Materials. **207.** Necom House.

1979. 50th Anniversary of International Bureau of Education. Multicoloured.

400. 10 k. Type **206** 10 10
401. 30 k. Adult education class 25 30

1979. 50th Anniversary of Consultative Committee of International Radio.

402. **207.** 10 k. multicoloured .. 15 20

208. Trainees of the Regional Air Survey School, Ile-Ife.

1979. 21st Anniversary of Economic Commission for Africa.

403. **208.** 10 k. multicoloured .. 20 20

209. Football, Cup and Map of Nigeria.

1980. African Cup of Nations Football Competition, Nigeria. Multicoloured.

404. 10 k. Type **209** 15 10
405. 30 k. Footballer (vert.) .. 50 50

210. Wrestling.

1980. Olympic Games, Moscow.

406. **210.** 10 k. multicoloured .. 10 10
407. – 20 k. black and green 10 10
408. – 30 k. blk., orge. & blue 15 15
409. – 45 k. multicoloured .. 20 20

DESIGNS: VERT. 20 k. Long jump. 45 k. Netball. HORIZ. 30 k. Swimming.

211. Figures supporting O.P.E.C. Emblem.

1980. 20th Anniv. of O.P.E.C. (Organization of Petroleum Exporting Countries).

410. **211.** 10 k. black, blue & yell. 15 10
411. – 45 k. black, blue & mve. 55 60

DESIGN—VERT. 45 k. O.P.E.C. emblem and globe.

212. Steam Locomotive.

1980. Nigerian Railway Corporation. Multicoloured.

412. 10 k. Type **212** 45 10
413. 20 k. Loading goods train 85 60
414. 30 k. Diesel goods train .. 95 70

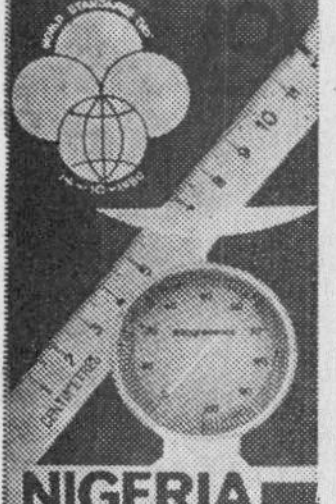

213. Metric Scales. 215. Disabled Woman Sweeping.

214. " Communication " Symbols and Map of West Africa.

1980. World Standards Day.

415. **213.** 10 k. red and black .. 10 10
416. – 30 k. multicoloured .. 35 40

DESIGN—HORIZ. 30 k. Quality control.

1980. 5th Anniversary of Economic Community of West African States.

417. **214.** 10 k. blk., orge. & olive 10 10
418. – 25 k. blk., green & red 10 10
419. – 30 k. blk., yell. & brn. 15 15
420. – 45 k. blk, turq. & blue 20 25

DESIGNS: 25 k. " Transport ". 30 k. " Agriculture ". 45 k. " Industry ".

1981. International Year for Disabled Persons.

421. **215.** 10 k. multicoloured .. 20 10
422. – 30 k. blk., brn. & blue 65 65

DESIGN: 30 k. Disabled man filming.

216. President launching " Green Revolution " (food production campaign).

1981. World Food Day.

423. **216.** 10 k. multicoloured .. 10 10
424. – 25 k. blk., yell. & green 20 50
425. – 30 k. multicoloured .. 25 55
426. – 45 k. blk., brn. & yell. 45 85

DESIGNS—VERT. 25 k. Food Crops. 30 k. Harvesting tomatoes. HORIZ. 45 k. Pig farming.

217. Rioting in Soweto.

1981. Anti-Apartheid Movement.

427. **217.** 30 k. multicoloured .. 35 45
428. – 45 k. blk., red & green 50 80

DESIGN—VERT. 45 k. " Police brutality ".

218. " Preservation of Wildlife ".

1982. 75th Anniversary of Boy Scout Movement. Multicoloured.

429. 30 k. Type **218** 75 55
430. 45 k. Lord Baden-Powell taking salute .. .. 1·00 95

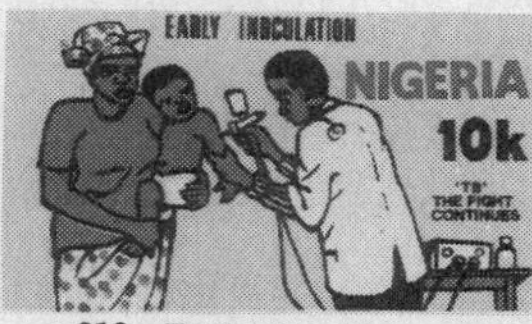

219. Early Inoculation.

1982. Centenary of Robert Koch's Discovery of Tubercle Bacillus.

431. **219.** 10 k. multicoloured .. 25 15
432. – 30 k. black, brown and green 65 55
433. – 45 k. black, brown and green 1·10 85

DESIGNS:—HORIZ. 30 k. Technician and microscope. VERT. 45 k. Patient being X-Rayed.

220. " Keep Your Environment Clean ".

1982. 10th Anniversary of U.N. Conference on Human Environment.

434. **220.** 10 k. multicoloured .. 15 10
435. – 20 k. orange, grey and black 40 40
436. – 30 k. multicoloured .. 55 60
437. – 45 k. multicoloured .. 80 85

DESIGNS: 20 k. " Check air pollution ". 30 k. " Preserve natural environment ". 45 k. " Reafforestation concerns all ".

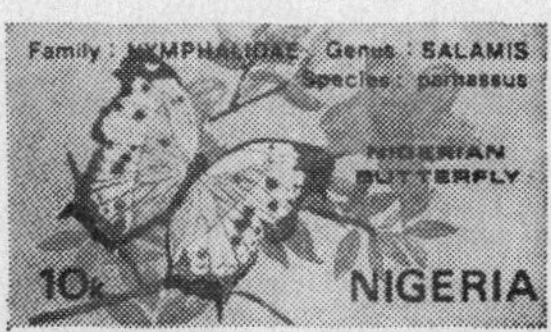

221. " Salamis parhassus ".

1982. Nigerian Butterflies. Multicoloured.

438 10 k. Type **221** 15 10
439 20 k. "Iterus zalmoxis" .. 40 40
440 30 k. "Cymothoe beckeri" 55 60
441 45 k. "Papilio hesperus" .. 80 85

222. Carving of " Male and Female Twins ".

1982. 25th Anniv. of National Museum. Multicoloured.

442. 10 k. Type **222** 25 10
443. 20 k. Royal Bronze Leopard (horiz.) 50 55
444. 30 k. Soapstone seated figure .. .. 80 1·25
445. 45 k. Wooden Helmet mask 1·25 1·75

223. Three Generations.

1983. Family Day. Multicoloured.

446. 10 k. Type **223** 15 10
447. 30 k. Parents with three children (vert.) 50 65

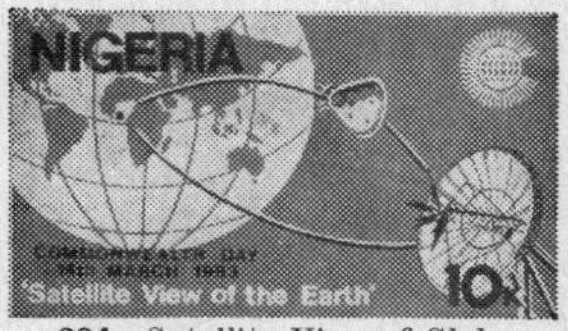

224. Satellite View of Globe.

1983. Commonwealth Day.

448. **224.** 10 k. brown & black 15 10
449. – 25 k. multicoloured 45 50
450. – 30 k. blk., pur. & grey 50 55
451. – 45 k. multicoloured 80 85

DESIGNS—HORIZ. 25 k. National Assembly Buildings. VERT. 30 k. Drilling for oil. 45 k. Athletics.

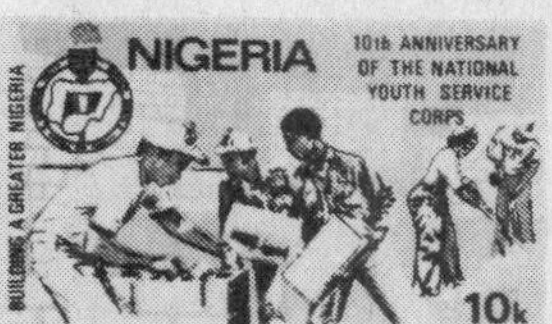

225. Corps Members on Building Project.

1983. 10th Anniv. of National Youth Service Corps. Multicoloured.

452. 10 k. Type **225** 15 10
453. 25 k. On the assault-course (vert.) 45 50
454. 30 k. Corps members on parade 50 60

226. Postman on Bicycle.

1983. World Communications Year. Multicoloured.

455. 10 k. Type **226** 15 10
456. 25 k. Newspaper kiosk (horiz.) 45 50
457. 30 k. Town crier blowing elephant tusk (horiz.) .. 50 55
458. 45 k. T.V. newsreader (horiz.) 80 85

227. Pink Shrimp.

1983. World Fishery Resources.

459. **227.** 10 k. red, blue & black 15 10
460. – 25 k. multicoloured .. 35 50
461. – 30 k. multicoloured .. 40 55
462. – 45 k. multicoloured .. 65 85

DESIGNS: 25 k. Long Necked Croaker. 30 k. Barracuda. 45 k. Fishing techniques.

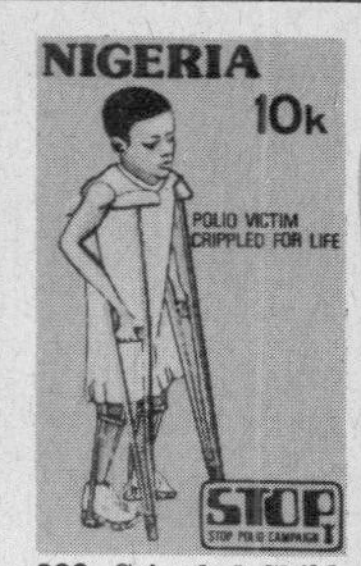

228. On Parade. 229. Crippled Child.

1983. Centenary of Boys' Brigade, and 75th Anniv. of Founding in Nigeria. Mult.

463. 10 k. Type **228** 40 10
464. 30 k. Members working on Cassava plantation (horiz.) .. .. .. 1·25 1·25
465. 45 k. Skill training (horiz.) 2·00 2·25

1984. Stop Polio Campaign.

466. **229.** 10 k. blue, blk. & brn. 20 15
467. – 25 k. orge., blk. & yell. 45 60
468. – 30 k. red, black & brn. 55 75

DESIGNS—HORIZ. 25 k. Child receiving vaccine. VERT. 30 k. Healthy child.

230. Waterbuck. 232. Boxing.

231. Obverse and Reverse of 1969 £1 Note.

1984. Nigerian Wildlife.

469. **230.** 10 k. green, brn. & blk. 20 10
470. – 25 k. multicoloured .. 50 50
471. – 30 k. brown, blk. & grn. 60 70
472. – 45 k. blue, orge. & blk. 80 95

DESIGNS—HORIZ. 25 k. Hartebeest. 30 k. African Buffalo. VERT. 45 k. Diademed Monkey.

1984. 25th Anniv. of Nigerian Central Bank.

473. **231.** 10 k. multicoloured .. 20 10
474. – 25 k. brown, black and green 45 50
475. – 30 k. red, black and green 55 60

DESIGNS: 25 k. Central Bank. 30 k. Obverse and reverse of 1959 £5 note.

1984. Olympic Games, Los Angeles. Mult.

476. 10 k. Type **232** 15 10
477. 25 k. Discus-throwing .. 35 50
478. 30 k. Weightlifting .. 40 60
479. 35 k. Cycling 60 90

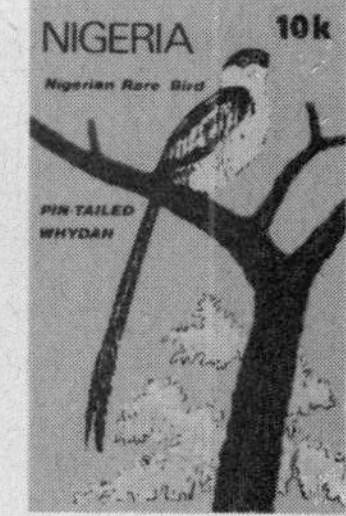

233. Irrigation Project, Lesotho. 234. Pin-tailed Whydah.

1984. 20th Anniv. of African Development.

480. **233.** 10 k. multicoloured .. 20 10
481. – 25 k. multicoloured .. 50 50
482. – 30 k. blk, yell. & bl. .. 60 60
483. – 45 k. blk., brn. & bl. 1·75 90

DESIGNS—HORIZ. 25 k. Bomi Hills Road, Liberia. 30 k. School building project, Seychelles. 45 k. Coal mining, Niger.

1984. Rare Birds. Multicoloured.

484. 10 k. Type **234** 65 10
485. 25 k. Spur-winged plover .. 1·50 60
486. 30 k. Red bishop .. .. 1·50 1·25
487. 45 k. Double-spurred francolin .. .. .. 1·75 1·75

235. Aircraft taking-off.

1984. 40th Anniversary of International Civil Aviation Organization. Multicoloured.

488.	10 k. Type **235**	50	10
489.	45 k. Aircraft circling globe	1·75	1·50

236. Office Workers and Clocks ("Punctuality").

1985. "War against Indiscipline". Mult.

490.	20 k. Type **236**	30	35
491.	50 k. Cross over hands passing banknotes ("Discourage Bribery")	70	75

237. Footballers receiving Flag from Major-General Buhari.

1985. International Youth Year. Mult.

492.	20 k. Type **237**	30	35
493.	50 k. Girls of different tribes with flag (vert.) ..	70	75
494.	55 k. Members of youth organizations with flags (vert.)	75	80

238. Globe and O.P.E.C. Emblem.

1985. 25th Anniversary of Organization of Petroleum Exporting Countries.

495. **238.**	20 k. blue and red ..	1·00	35
496. –	50 k. black and blue	1·75	75

DESIGN—HORIZ. 50 k. World map and O.P.E.C. emblem.

239. Rolling Mill.

1985. 25th Anniv. of Independence. Mult.

497.	20 k. Type **239**	40	10
498.	50 k. Map of Nigeria ..	60	35
499.	55 k. Remembrance Arcade	60	40
500.	60 k. Eleme, first Nigerian oil refinery	85	50

240. Waterfall.

241. Map of Nigeria and National Flag.

1985. World Tourism Day. Multicoloured.

502.	20 k. Type **240**	45	10
503.	50 k. Pottery, carved heads and map of Nigeria (horiz.)	55	40
504.	55 k. Calabash carvings and Nigerian flag ..	55	40
505.	60 k. Leather work ..	55	45

1985. 40th Anniv. of United Nations Organization and 25th Anniv. of Nigerian Membership.

506. **241.**	20 k. blk., grn. & bl.	15	10
507. –	50 k. black, bl. & red	30	30
508. –	55 k. black, bl. & red	30	30

DESIGNS—HORIZ. 50 k. United Nations Building, New York. 55 k. United Nations logo.

242. Rock Python.

1986. African Reptiles.

509. **242.**	10 k. multicoloured ..	35	10
510. –	20 k. blk., brn. & bl.	65	50
511. –	25 k. multicoloured ..	70	65
512. –	30 k. multicoloured ..	70	85

DESIGNS: 20 k. Long snouted crocodile. 25 k. Gopher tortoise. 30 k. Chameleon.

243. Social Worker with Children.

1986. Nigerian Life. Multicoloured.

513	1 k. Type **243**	10	10
514	2 k. Volkswagen motor assembly line (horiz) ..	10	10
515	5 k. Modern housing estate (horiz)	10	10
516	10 k. Harvesting oil palm fruit	10	10
517	15 k. Unloading freighter (horiz)	10	10
518	20 k. "Tecoma stans" (flower)	10	10
519	25 k. Hospital ward (horiz)	10	10
519a	30 k. Birom dancers ..	10	10
520	35 k. Telephonists operating switchboard (horiz)	10	10
521	40 k. Nkpokiti dancers ..	10	10
522	45 k. Hibiscus (horiz) ..	10	10
523	50 k. Post Office counter (horiz)	10	10
524	1 n. Stone quarry (horiz)	10	15
525	2 n. Students in laboratory (horiz) ..	25	30

244. Emblem and Globe.

1986. International Peace Year. Mult.

526.	10 k. Type **244**	10	10
527.	20 k. Hands of five races holding globe	10	10

245. "Goliathus goliathus" (beetle).

1986. Nigerian Insects. Multicoloured.

528	10 k. Type **245**	35	10
529	20 k. "Vespa vulgaris" (wasp)	45	40
530	25 k. "Acheta domestica" (cricket)	55	55
531	30 k. "Anthrenus verbasci" (beetle)	75	85

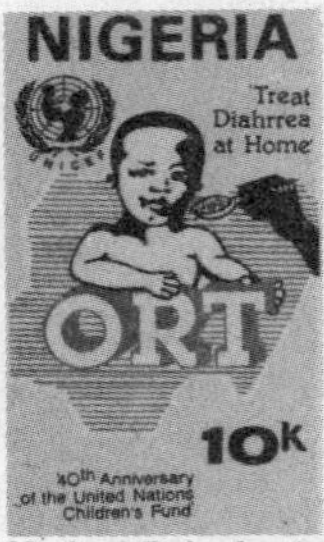
246. Oral Rehydration Therapy.

1986. 40th Anniv. of U.N.I.C.E.F.

533. **246.**	10 k. multicoloured ..	30	10
534. –	20 k. blk., brn. & yell.	50	30
535. –	25 k. multicoloured ..	55	40
536. –	30 k. multicoloured ..	70	55

DESIGNS: 20 k. Immunisation. 25 k. Breast feeding. 30 k. Mother and child.

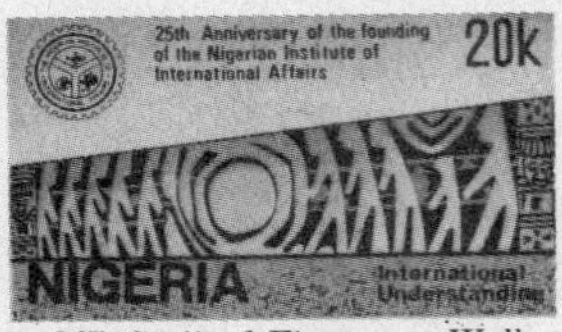
247. Stylized Figures on Wall ("International Understanding").

1986. 25th Anniv. of Nigerian Institute of International Affairs.

537. **247.**	20 k. blk., bl. & grn.	50	40
538. –	30 k. multicoloured ..	75	1·00

DESIGN—VERT. 30 k. "Knowledge" (bronze sculpture).

248. Freshwater Clam.

1987. Shells.

539. **248.**	10 k. multicoloured ..	35	10
540. –	20 k. black, brown and pink	60	60
541. –	25 k. multicoloured ..	60	60
542. –	30 k. multicoloured ..	75	90

DESIGNS: 20 k. Periwinkle; 25 k. Bloody cockle (inscr. "BLODDY COCKLE"). 30 k. Mangrove oyster.

249. "Clitoria ternatea". 250. Doka Hairstyle.

1987. Nigerian Flowers.

543. **249.**	10 k. multicoloured ..	10	10
544. –	20 k. brown, yellow and green	15	10
545. –	25 k. multicoloured ..	15	15
546. –	30 k. multicoloured ..	20	20

DESIGNS: 20 k. "Hibiscus tiliaceus". 25 k. "Acanthus montanus". 30 k. "Combretum racemosum".

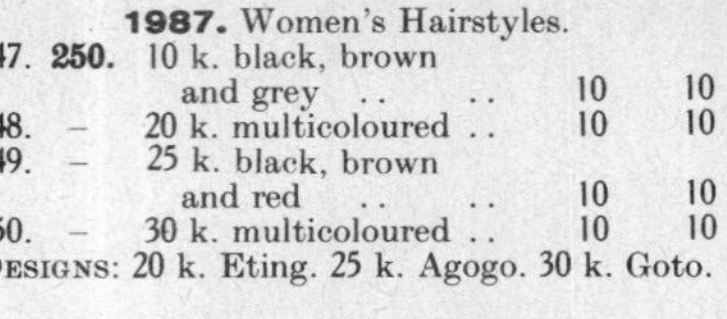

1987. Women's Hairstyles.

547. **250.**	10 k. black, brown and grey	10	10
548. –	20 k. multicoloured ..	10	10
549. –	25 k. black, brown and red	10	10
550. –	30 k. multicoloured ..	10	10

DESIGNS: 20 k. Eting. 25 k. Agogo. 30 k. Goto.

251. Family sheltering under Tree.

252. Red Cross Worker distributing Food.

1987. International Year of Shelter for the Homeless. Multicoloured.

551.	20 k. Type **251**	15	10
552.	30 k. Family and modern house	15	20

1988. 125th Anniv. of International Red Cross. Multicoloured.

553.	20 k. Type **252**	15	10
554.	30 k. Carrying patient to ambulance	15	40

253. Doctor vaccinating Baby.

1988. 40th Anniv. of W.H.O. Multicoloured.

555.	10 k. Type **253**	10	10
556.	20 k. W.H.O. logo and outline map of Nigeria ..	15	15
557.	30 k. Doctor and patients at mobile clinic	15	15

254 O.A.U. Logo

1988. 25th Anniv of Organization of African Unity.

558 **254**	10 k. brn, grn & orge	15	15
559 –	20 k. multicoloured ..	15	15

DESIGN: 20 k. Four Africans supporting map of Africa.

255 Pink Shrimp

1988. Shrimps.

560 **255**	10 k. multicoloured ..	15	10
561 –	20 k. black and green	20	10
562 –	25 k. black, red & brn	20	10
563 –	30 k. orange, brn & blk	25	10

DESIGNS: 20 k. Tiger shrimp; 25 k. Deepwater roseshrimp; 30 k. Estuarine prawn.

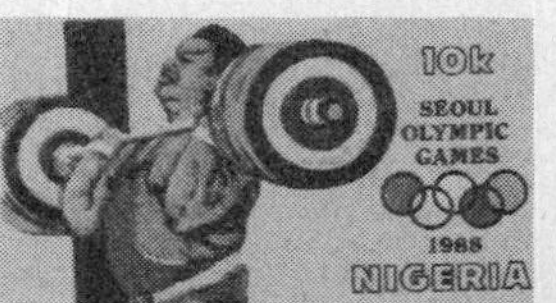
256 Weightlifting

1988. Olympic Games, Seoul. Multicoloured.

565	10 k. Type **256**	15	10
566	20 k. Boxing	20	10
567	30 k. Athletics (vert)	30	15

257 Banknote Production Line (Illustration reduced, actual size 74 x 22 mm)

1988. 25th Anniv of Nigerian Security Printing and Minting Co Ltd.

568	**257**	10 k. multicoloured	10	10
569	–	20 k. blk, silver & grn	10	10
570	–	25 k. multicoloured	10	10
571	–	30 k. multicoloured	15	15

DESIGNS: HORIZ (As T **257**)—20 k. Coin production line. VERT (37 × 44 mm)—25 k. Montage of products; 30 k. Anniversary logos.

258 Tambari

1989. Nigerian Musical Instruments.

572	**258**	10 k. multicoloured	10	10
573	–	20 k. multicoloured	10	10
574	–	25 k. brown, grn & blk	10	10
575	–	30 k. brown and black	15	15

DESIGNS: 20 k. Kundung; 25 k. Ibid; 30 k. Dundun.

259 Construction of Water Towers, Mali

1989. 25th Anniv of African Development Bank. Multicoloured.

576	10 k. Type **259**	10	10
577	20 k. Paddy field, Gambia	10	10
578	25 k. Bank Headquarters, Abidjan, Ivory Coast	10	10
579	30 k. Anniversary logo (vert)	15	15

260 Lighting Camp Fire

1989. 70th Anniv of Nigerian Girl Guides Association. Multicoloured.

580	10 k. Type **260**	15	10
581	20 k. Guide on rope bridge (vert)	15	20

261 Etubom Costume

262 Dove with Letter and Map of Africa

1989. Traditional Costumes. Multicoloured.

582	10 k. Type **261**	15	10
583	20 k. Fulfulde	20	10
584	25 k. Aso-Ofi	25	10
585	30 k. Fuska Kura	30	15

1990. 10th Anniv of Pan African Postal Union. Multicoloured.

586	10 k. Type **262**	15	10
587	20 k. Parcel and map of Africa	15	20

263 Oil Lamps

1990. Nigerian Pottery.

588	**263**	10 k. black, brn & vio	10	10
589	–	20 k. black, brn & vio	10	10
590	–	25 k. brown and violet	10	10
591	–	30 k. multicoloured	15	15

DESIGNS: 20 k. Water pots; 25 k. Musical pots; 30 k. Water jugs.

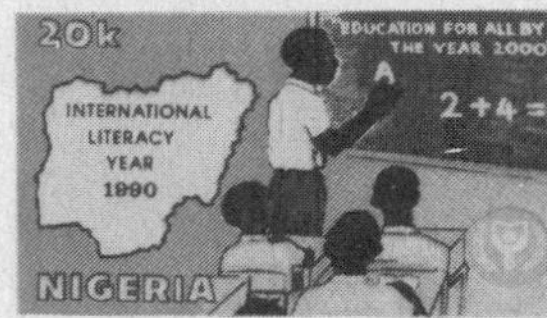

264 Teacher and Class

1990. International Literacy Year.

593	**264**	20 k. multicoloured	10	10
594	–	30 k. brown, bl & yell	15	15

DESIGN: 30 k. Globe and book.

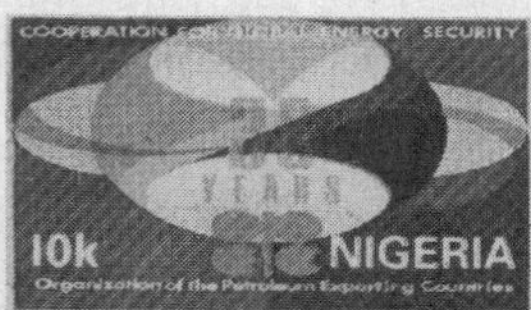

265 OPEC Logo

1990. 30th Anniv of the Organization of Petroleum Exporting Countries. Mult.

595	10 k. Type **265**	10	10
596	20 k. Logo and flags of member countries (vert)	10	10
597	25 k. World map and logo	15	15
598	30 k. Logo within inscription "Co-operation for Global Energy Security" (vert)	15	15

266 Grey Parrot

267 Eradication Treatment

1990. Wildlife. Multicoloured.

599	20 k. Type **266**	10	10
600	30 k. Roan antelope	10	10
601	1 n. 50 Grey-necked bald crow ("Rockfowl")	20	25
602	2 n. 50 Mountain gorilla	35	40

1991. National Guineaworm Eradication Day. Multicoloured.

604	10 k. Type **267**	10	10
605	20 k. Women collecting water from river (horiz)	10	10
606	30 k. Boiling pot of water	10	10

268 Hand Holding Torch (Progress)

1991. Organization of African Unity Heads of State and Governments Meeting, Abuja. Each showing outline map of Africa. Mult.

607	20 k. Type **268**	10	10
608	30 k. Cogwheel (Unity)	10	10
609	50 k. O.A.U flag (Freedom)	10	10

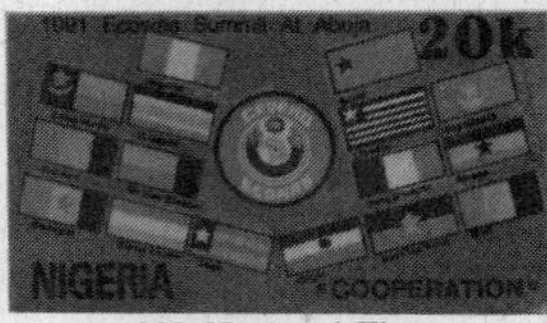

269 National Flags

1991. Economic Community of West African States Summit Meeting, Abuja. Multicoloured.

610	20 k. Type **269**	10	10
611	50 k. Map showing member states	10	10

270 Electric Catfish

1991. Nigerian Fishes. Multicoloured.

612	10 k. Type **270**	10	10
613	20 k. Niger perch	10	10
614	30 k. Talapia	10	10
615	50 k. African catfish	10	10

271 Telecom '91 Emblem

1991. "Telecom '91" 6th World Telecommunication Exhibition, Geneva.

617	**271**	20 k. black, green & vio	10	10
618	–	50 k. multicoloured	10	10

DESIGN—VERT. 50 k. Emblem and patchwork.

POSTAGE DUE STAMPS

D 1.

1959.

D 1.	D 1.	1d. orange	10	55
D 2.		2d. orange	15	70
D 3.		3d. orange	20	1·00
D 4.		6d. orange	20	3·00
D 5.		1s. black	45	4·25

1961.

D 6.	D 1.	1d. red	10	25
D 7.		2d. blue	10	30
D 8.		3d. green	15	50
D 9.		6d. yellow	30	70
D 10.		1s. blue	45	1·75

1973. As Type D 1.

D 11.	2 k. red	10	10
D 12.	3 k. blue	10	10
D 13.	5 k. yellow	10	10
D 14.	10 k. green	10	10

NIUAFO'OU

A remote island, part of the Kingdom of Tonga, with local autonomy.

100 seniti = 1 pa'anga.

1. Map of Niuafo'ou.

1983.

1.	1.	1 s. stone, black and red	10	10
2.		2 s. stone, black & green	10	10
3.		3 s. stone, black and blue	10	10
4.		3 s. stone, black & brown	10	10
5.		5 s. stone, black & purple	10	10
6.		6 s. stone, black and blue	10	10
7.		9 s. stone, black & green	10	10
8.		10 s. stone, black & blue	15	15
9.		13 s. stone, black & green	30	30
10.		15 s. stone, black & brn.	30	30
11.		20 s. stone, black & blue	35	35
12.		29 s. stone, black & pur.	50	50
13.		32 s. stone, black & grn.	60	60
14.		47 s. stone, black & red	75	75

1983. No. 820 of Tonga optd. **NIUAFO'OU KINGDOM OF TONGA,** or surch. also.

15.	1 p. on 2 p. green and black	1·75	2·00
16.	2 p. green	2·75	3·00

1983. Inauguration of Niuafo'ou Airport. As T 153 of Tonga.

17.	29 s. multicoloured	80	1·00
18.	1 p. multicoloured	2·50	3·25

1983. As T 1 but without value, surch.

19.	3 s. stone, black and blue	10	10
20.	5 s. stone, black and blue	10	10
21.	32 s. stone, black and blue	65	65
22.	2 p. stone, black and blue	3·00	3·25

4. Eruption of Niuafo'ou.

1983. 25th Anniv. of Re-settlement. Mult.

23.	5 s. Type **4**	30	20
24.	29 s. Lava flow	80	70
25.	32 s. Islanders move to safety	90	80
26.	1 p. 50 Evacuation by canoe	3·00	3·25

5. Purple Swamphen.

1983. Birds of Niuafo'ou.

27.	5.	1 s. black and mauve	20	20
28.	–	2 s. black and blue	20	20
29.	–	3 s. black and green	20	20
30.	–	5 s. black and yellow	20	20
31.	–	6 s. black and orange	20	20
32.	–	9 s. multicoloured	20	20
33.	–	10 s. multicoloured	30	30
34.	–	13 s. multicoloured	35	35
35.	–	15 s. multicoloured	35	35
36.	–	20 s. multicoloured	50	50
37.	–	29 s. multicoloured	80	80
38.	–	32 s. multicoloured	90	90
39.	–	47 s. multicoloured	1·40	1·40
40.	–	1 p. multicoloured	3·00	3·00
41.	–	2 p. multicoloured	4·50	4·50

DESIGNS—VERT. (22 × 29 mm.) 2 s. White-collared kingfisher. 3 s. Red-headed parrot finch. 5 s. Banded rail. 6 s. Polynesian scrub hen ("Niuafo'ou megapode"). 9 s. Green honeyeater. 10 s. Purple swamphen (different). (22 × 36 mm.) 29 s. Red-headed parrot finch (different). 32 s. White-collared kingfisher (different). (29 × 42 mm.) 1 p. As 10 s. HORIZ. (29 × 22 mm.) 13 s. Banded rail (different). 15 s. Polynesian scrub hen (different). (36 × 22 mm.) 20 s. As 13 s. 47 s. As 15 s. (42 × 29 mm.) 2 p. As 15 s.

6. Green Turtle.

1984. Wildlife and Nature Reserve. Mult.

42. 29 s. Type **6** 50 50
43. 32 s. Insular flying fox (vert.) 50 50
44. 47 s. Humpback whale .. 80 80
45. 1 p. 50 Polynesian scrub hen ("Niuafo'ou megapode") (vert.) .. .. .. 2·75 2·75

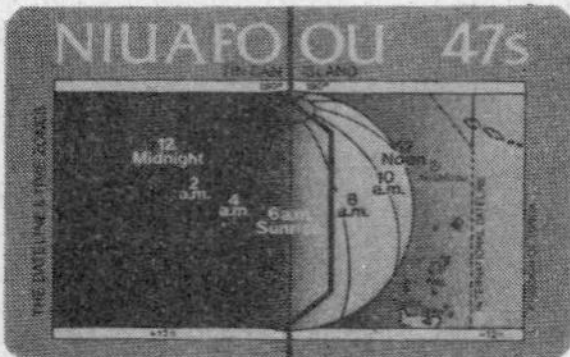

7. Diagram of Time Zones.

1984. Centenary of International Dateline. Multicoloured.

46. 47 s. Type **7** 40 50
47. 2 p. Location map showing Niuafo'ou .. .. .. 1·50 1·75

8. Australia 1913 £2 Kangaroo Definitive.

9. Dutch Brass Band entertaining Tongans.

1984. "Ausipex" International Stamp Exhibition, Melbourne. Multicoloured.

48. 32 s. Type **8** 40 45
49. $1.50 Niuafo'ou 1983 10 s. map definitive .. .. 1·50 2·00

1985. 400th Birth Anniv. of Jacob Le Maire (discoverer of Niuafo'ou).

51. **9.** 13 s. brown, yell. & orge. 20 20
52. – 32 s. brown, yell. & bl. 50 50
53. – 47 s. brown, yell. & grn. 65 65
54. – 1 p. 50 brown, pale yellow and yellow .. 2·00 2·00

Designs: No. 52, Tongans preparing kava. 53, Tongan canoes and outriggers. 54, "Eendracht" at anchor off Tafahi Island.

10. "Ysabel", 1902.

1985. Mail Ships. Multicoloured.

56. 9 s. Type **10** 15 15
57. 13 s. "Tofua I", 1908 .. 20 20
58. 47 s. "Mariposa", 1934 .. 55 55
59. 1 p. 50 "Matua", 1936 .. 1·60 1·60

11. Preparing to fire Rocket.

1985. Niuafo'ou Rocket Mails. Multicoloured.

60. 32 s. Type **11** 60 60
61. 42 s. Rocket in flight .. 80 80
62. 57 s. Ship's crew watching rocket's descent .. .. 1·00 1·00
63. 1 p. 50 Islanders reading mail .. .. 2·50 2·50

12. Halley's Comet, 684 A.D.

1986. Appearance of Halley's Comet. Multicoloured.

64. 42 s. Type **12** 80 80
65. 42 s. Halley's Comet, 1066, from Bayeux Tapestry .. 80 80
66. 42 s. Edmond Halley .. 80 80
67. 42 s. Halley's Comet, 1910 .. 80 80
68. 42 s. Halley's Comet, 1986 .. 80 80
69. 57 s. Type **12** .. .. 1·10 1·10
70 57 s. As No. 65 .. .. 1·10 1·10
71. 57 s. As No. 66 .. .. 1·10 1·10
72. 57 s. As No. 67 .. .. 1·10 1·10
73. 57 s. As No. 68 .. .. 1·10 1·10

Nos. 64/8 and 69/73 were printed together, se-tenant, forming composite designs.

1986. Nos. 32/9 surch.

74. 4 s. on 9 s. Green honey-eater 20 20
75. 4 s. on 10 s. Purple swamp-hen 20 20
76. 42 s. on 13 s. Banded rail .. 80 80
77. 42 s. on 15 s. Polynesian scrub hen 80 80
78. 57 s. on 29 s. Red-headed parrot finch .. .. 1·10 1·10
79. 57 s. on 32 s. White-collared kingfisher .. .. .. 1·10 1·10
80. 2 p. on 20 s. Banded rail .. 3·50 3·50
81. 2 p. 50 on 47 s. Polynesian scrub hen .. .. .. 3·50 3·50

1986. "Ameripex '86" International Stamp Exhibition, Chicago. 25th Anniv. of United States Peace Corps. As T **173** of Tonga. Multicoloured.

82. 57 s. Peace Corps surveyor and pipeline .. .. 1·00 1·00
83. 1 p. 50 Inspecting crops .. 2·00 2·00

14. Swimmers with Mail.

1986. Centenary of First Tonga Stamps. Designs showing Niuafo'ou mail transport. Multicoloured.

85. 42 s. Type **13** 80 80
86. 57 s. Collecting tin can mail 1·00 1·00
87. 1 p. Ship firing mail rocket 1·75 1·75
88. 2 p. 50 "Collecting the Mails" (detail) (C. Mayger) .. .. .. 3·25 3·25

15. Woman with Nourishing Foods ("Eat a balanced diet").

1987. Red Cross. Preventive Medicine. Mult.

90. 15 s. Type **15** 55 55
91. 42 s. Nurse with baby ("Give them post-natal care") .. .. .. 1·40 1·40
92. 1 p. Man with insecticide ("Insects spread disease") 2·25 2·25
93. 2 p. 50 Boxer ("Say no to alcohol, drugs, tobacco") 3·75 3·75

16. Hammerhead Shark.

1987. Sharks. Multicoloured.

94. 29 s. Type **16** 80 80
95. 32 s. Tiger shark 85 85
96. 47 s. Grey nurse shark .. 1·25 1·25
97. 1 p. Great white shark .. 2·25 2·25

17. Capt. E. C. Musick and Sikorsky "S-42" Flying Boat.

1987. Air. Pioneers of the South Pacific. Multicoloured.

99. 42 s. Type **17** 85 85
100. 57 s. Capt. J. W. Burgess and Shorts "S-30" flying boat .. .. .. 1·25 1·25
101. 1 p. 50. Sir Charles Kingsford Smith and Fokker "F.VIIb-3m" Southern Cross 2·00 2·00
102. 2 p. Amelia Earhart and Lockheed "Electra 10A" 2·50 2·50

18 Polynesian Scrub Hen and 1983 1 s. Map Definitive

1988. 5th Anniversaries of First Niuafo'ou Postage Stamp (42, 57 s.) or Niuafo'ou Airport Inauguration (1, 2 p.). Multicoloured.

103 42 s. Type **18** 65 65
104 57 s. As Type **18**, but with stamp at left 85 85
105 1 p. "Concorde" and 1983 Airport Inauguration 29 s. stamp .. .. 1·75 1·75
106 2 p. As 1 p., but with stamp at left .. .. 2·75 2·75

20 Audubon's Shearwaters and Blowholes, Houma, Tonga

1988. Islands of Polynesia. Multicoloured.

108 42 s. Type **20** 85 85
109 57 s. Kiwi at Akaroa Harbour, New Zealand 1·25 1·25
110 90 s. Red-tailed tropic birds at Rainmaker Mountain, Samoa .. 1·75 1·75
111 2 p.50 Laysan albatross at Kapoho Volcano, Hawaii 3·75 3·75

INDEX

Countries can be quickly located by referring to the index at the end of this volume.

22 Hatchet Fish

1989. Fishes of the Deep. Multicoloured.

113 32 s. Type **22** 50 50
114 42 s. Snipe eel 65 65
115 57 s. Viper fish 80 80
116 1 p. 50 Football fish .. 1·75 1·75

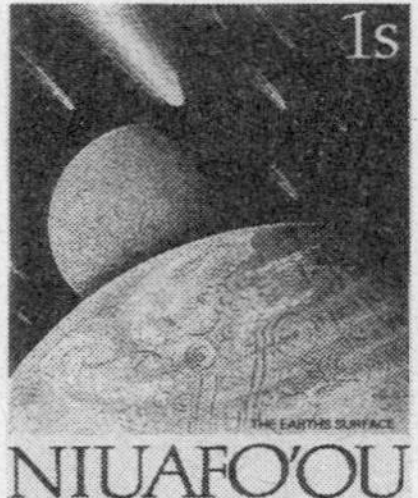

23 Formation of Earth's Surface

1989. The Evolution of the Earth. Mult.

(a) Size 27 × 35½ mm

117 1 s. Type **23** 10 10
118 2 s. Cross-section of Earth's crust 10 10
119 5 s. Volcano 10 10
120 10 s. Cross-section of Earth during cooling 10 10
121 15 s. Sea 15 20
122 20 s. Mountains 20 25
123 32 s. River gorge 30 35
124 42 s. Early plant life, Silurian era 40 45
125 50 s. Fossils and Cambrian lifeforms 45 50
126 57 s. Carboniferous forest and coal seams .. 50 55

(b) Size 25½ × 40 mm

127 1 p. Dragonfly and amphibians, Carboniferous era 90 95
128 1 p. 50 Dinosaurs, Jurassic era .. .. .. 1·40 1·50
129 2 p. Early bird and mammals, Jurassic era 1·90 2·00
130 5 p. Human family and domesticated dog, Pleistocene era .. 4·50 4·75

24 Astronaut on Moon and Newspaper Headline

1989. "World Stamp Expo '89" International Stamp Exhibition, Washington.

131 **24** 57 s. multicoloured .. 85 85

25 Lake Vai Lahi

1990. Niuafo'ou Crater Lake. Multicoloured.

133 42 s. Type **25** 55 55
134 42 s. Islands in centre of lake 55 55
135 42 s. South-west end of lake and islet 55 55
136 1 p. Type **25** .. .. 1·25 1·25
137 1 p. As No. 134 .. .. 1·25 1·25
138 1 p. As No. 135 .. .. 1·25 1·25

Nos. 133/8 were printed together in se-tenant strips of each value, forming a composite design.

26 Penny Black and Tin Can Mail Service

1990. 150th Anniv of the Penny Black. Mult.

139	42 s. Type **26**	70	70
140	57 s. U.S.A. 1847 10 c. stamp	85	85
141	75 s. Western Australia 1854 1d. stamp	1·00	1·00
142	2 p. 50 Mafeking Siege 1900 1d. stamp	3·50	3·50

27 Humpback Whale surfacing (illustration reduced, actual size 57 × 41 mm)

1990. Polynesian Whaling. Multicoloured.

143	15 s. Type **27**	45	45
144	42 s. Whale diving under canoe	80	80
145	57 s. Tail of Blue whale ..	1·00	1·00
146	2 p. Old man and pair of whales	2·75	2·75

1990. 40th Anniv of U.N. Development Programme. As T **203** of Tonga. Mult.

148	57 s. Agriculture and Fisheries	75	75
149	57 s. Education	75	75
150	2 p. 50 Healthcare ..	3·00	3·00
151	2 p. 50 Communications ..	3·00	3·00

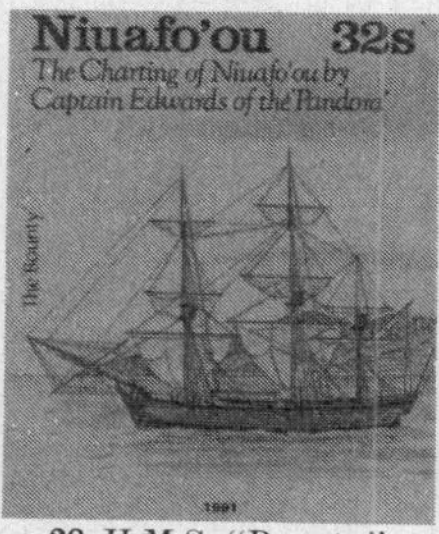

28 H.M.S. "Bounty"

1991. Bicentenary of Charting of Niuafo'ou. Multicoloured.

152	32 s. Type **28**	55	55
153	42 s. Chart of "Pandora's" course	70	70
154	57 s. H.M.S. "Pandora" ..	85	85

30 Longhorned Beetle Grub

1991. Longhorned Beetle. Multicoloured.

157	42 s. Type **30**	60	60
158	57 s. Adult beetle ..	80	80
159	1 p. 50 Grub burrowing ..	2·00	2·00
160	2 p. 50 Adult on tree trunk	3·00	3·00

31 Heina meeting the Eel

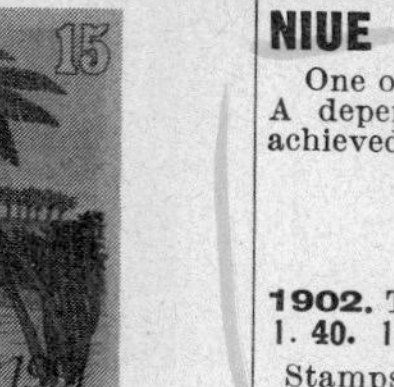

1991. The Legend of the Coconut Tree. Mult.

161	15 s. Type **31**	25	25
162	42 s. Heina crying over the eel's grave	60	60

1992. 50th Anniv of War in the Pacific. As T **215** of Tonga, each showing contemporary newspaper headline. Multicoloured.

165	42 c. American battleship ablaze, Pearl Harbor ..	60	60
166	42 c. Destroyed American aircraft, Hawaii ..	60	60
167	42 c. Newspaper and Japanese A6M Zero fighter	60	60
168	42 c. Pres. Roosevelt signing declaration of War	60	60
169	42 c. Japanese T 95 light tank and Gen. MacArthur	60	60
170	42 c. Douglas SBD Dauntless dive-bomber and Admiral Nimitz ..	60	60
171	42 c. Bren gun and Gen. Sir Thomas Blamey ..	60	60
172	42 c. Australian mortar crew, Kokoda	60	60
173	42 c. U.S.S. "Mississippi" in action and Maj. Gen. Julian C. Smith ..	60	60
174	42 c. U.S.S. "Enterprise" aircraft carrier	60	60
175	42 c. American marine and Maj. Gen. Curtis Lemay	60	60
176	42 c. B-29 bomber and Japanese surrender, Tokyo bay	60	60

Nos. 165/76 were printed together, se-tenant, forming a composite design.

NIUE

One of the Cook Is. group, in the S. Pacific. A dependency of New Zealand, the island achieved local self-government in 1974.

1902. 12 pence = 1 shilling.
20 shillings = 1 pound.
1967. 100 cents = 1 dollar.

1902. T **35** of New Zealand optd. **NIUE** only.

1. **40.**	1d. red	£375	£375

Stamps of New Zealand surch. **NIUE** and value in native language.

1902. Pictorials of 1898, etc.

8. **23.**	½d. green	65	80
9. **42.**	1d. red	50	65
2. **27.**	2½d. blue (No. 382) ..	1·25	2·75
13. **28.**	3d. brown	5·00	5·00
14. **31.**	6d. red	5·00	10·00
16. **34.**	1s. orange	24·00	25·00

1911. King Edward VII stamps.

17 **51**	½d. green	45	40
18	6d. red	2·00	7·00
19	1s. orange	6·50	35·00

1917. Dominion and King George V stamps.

21 **53**	1d. red	5·00	5·50
22 **60b**	3d. brown	48·00	75·00

1917. Stamps of New Zealand (King George V, etc.) optd. **NIUE** only.

23 **60b**	½d. green	50	85
24 **53**	1d. red	2·00	3·25
25 **60b**	1½d. grey	80	1·75
26	1½d. brown	70	2·25
28	2½d. blue	90	2·75
29	3d. brown	1·25	1·50
30	6d. red	4·24	15·00
31	1s. orange	4·75	15·00

1918. Stamps of New Zealand optd. **NIUE.**

33. **F 4.**	2s. blue	15·00	32·00
34.	2s. 6d. brown	17·00	38·00
35.	5s. green	20·00	48·00
36.	10s. red	70·00	90·00
37.	£1 red	£130	£150

1920. Pictorial types as Cook Islands (1920), but inscr. "NIUE".

38 **9**	½d. black and green ..	2·25	3·25
45 –	1d. black and red ..	75	75
40 –	1½d. black and red ..	2·50	3·50
46 –	2½d. black and blue ..	1·50	6·00
41 –	3d. black and blue ..	60	4·75
47 **7**	4d. black and violet ..	2·00	8·00
42 –	6d. brown and green ..	80	11·00
43 –	1s. black and brown ..	1·50	11·00

1927. Admiral type of New Zealand optd. **NIUE.**

49. **71.**	2s. blue	15·00	30·00

1931. No. 40 surch. **TWO PENCE.**

50.	2d. on 1½d. black and red	1·25	90

1931. Stamps of New Zealand (Arms types) optd. **NIUE.**

87 **F 6.**	2s. 6d. brown	3·75	4·50
84	5s. green	5·50	9·00
85	10s. red	45·00	60·00
86	£1 pink	38·00	45·00

1932. Pictorial stamps as Cook Islands (1932) but inscr. additionally "NIUE".

89 **20.**	½d. black and green ..	50	60
63 –	1d. black and red ..	50	30
64 **22.**	2d. black and brown ..	40	70
92 –	2½d. black and blue ..	60	85
93 –	4d. black and blue ..	60	90
67 –	6d. black and orange ..	70	65
61 –	1s. black and violet ..	2·00	5·00

1935. Silver Jubilee. Nos. 63, 65 and 94, colours changed optd. **SILVER JUBILEE OF KING GEORGE V. 1910-1935.**

69.	1d. red	60	1·50
70.	2½d. blue	3·25	2·50
71.	6d. green and orange ..	3·25	5·00

1937. Coronation. New Zealand stamps optd. **NIUE.**

72. **106.**	1d. red	30	10
73.	2½d. blue	40	20
74.	6d. orange	40	10

1938. As 1938 issue of Cook Islands, but inscr. "NIUE" "COOK ISLANDS".

95. **29.**	1s. black and violet ..	1·25	85
96. **30.**	2s. black and brown ..	4·00	2·75
97. –	3s. blue and green ..	8·50	6·00

1940. As T **32** of Cook islands, but inscr. "NIUE" "COOK ISLANDS".

78. **32.**	3d. on 1½d. black & purple	10	10

1946. Peace. New Zealand stamps optd. **NIUE.**

98. **132.**	1d. green	10	10
99. –	2d. purple (No. 670) ..	10	10
100. –	6d. brn. & red (No. 674)	10	10
101. **139.**	8d. black and red ..	10	10

17. Map of Niue.

18. H.M.S. "Resolution".

1950.

113 **17**	½d. orange and blue ..	10	10
114 **18**	1d. brown and green ..	2·00	55
115 –	2d. black and red ..	10	10
116 –	3d. blue and violet ..	10	10
117 –	4d. olive and purple ..	10	10
118 –	6d. green and orange ..	45	15
119 –	9d. orange and brown ..	10	15
120 –	1s. purple and black ..	10	10
121 –	2s. brown and green ..	75	2·00
122 –	3s. blue and black ..	3·50	3·75

DESIGNS—HORIZ. 2d. Alofi Landing. 3d. Native hut. 4d. Arch of Hikutavake. 6d. Alofi Bay. 1s. Cave, Makefu. VERT. 9d. Spearing fish. 2s. Bananas. 3s. Matapa Chasm.

1953. Coronation. As types of New Zealand but inscr. "NIUE".

123. **164.**	3d. brown	65	30
124. **168.**	6d. grey	95	30

26.

27. "Pua".

1967. Decimal Currency. (a) Nos. 113/22 surch.

125 **17**	½ c. on ½d.	10	10
126 **18**	1 c. on 1d.	80	15
127 –	2 c. on 2d.	10	10
128 –	2½ c. on 3d.	10	10
129 –	3 c. on 4d.	10	10
130 –	5 c. on 6d.	10	10
131 –	8 c. on 9d.	10	10
132 –	10 c. on 1s.	10	10
133 –	20 c. on 2s.	60	1·25
134 –	30 c. on 3s.	1·50	1·75

(b) Arms type of New Zealand without value, surch. as in T **26**.

135. **26.**	25 c. brown	65	65
136.	50 c. green	1·00	1·00
137.	$1 mauve	80	1·50
138.	$2 pink	1·40	2·50

1967. Christmas. As T **278** of New Zealand but inscr. "NIUE".

139.	2½ c. multicoloured ..	10	10

1969. Christmas. As No. 905 of New Zealand but inscr. "NIUE".

140.	2½ c. multicoloured ..	10	10

1969. Flowers. Multicoloured; frame colours given.

141. **27.**	½ c. green	10	10
142. –	1 c. red	10	10
143. –	2 c. olive	10	10
144. –	2½ c. brown	10	10
145. –	3 c. blue	10	10
146. –	5 c. red	10	10
147. –	8 c. violet	10	10
148. –	10 c. yellow	10	10
149. –	20 c. blue	1·00	1·25
150. –	30 c. green	1·75	1·75

DESIGNS: 1 c. "Golden Shower". 2 c. Flamboyant. 2½ c. Frangipani. 3 c. Niue Crocus. 5 c. Hibiscus. 8 c. "Passion Fruit". 10 c. "Kampui". 20 c. Queen Elizabeth II (after Anthony Buckley). 30 c. Tapeu Orchip.

37. Kalahimu.

1970. Indigenous Edible Crabs. Mult.

151.	3 c. Type **37**	10	10
152.	5 c. Kalavi	10	10
153.	30 c. Unga	30	25

1970. Christmas. As T **314** of New Zealand, but inscr. "NIUE".

154.	2½ c. multicoloured ..	10	10

38. Outrigger Canoe, and Aircraft over Jungle.

1970. Niue Airport Opening. Multicoloured.

155.	3 c. Type **38**	10	10
156.	5 c. Cargo liner, and aircraft over harbour ..	15	10
157.	8 c. Aircraft over Airport	15	20

39. Spotted Triller.

1971. Birds. Multicoloured.

158. 5 c. Type **39** 15 10
159. 10 c. Purple-capped Fruit Dove 70 15
160. 20 c. Blue Crowned Lory 80 20

1971. Christmas. As T **325** of New Zealand, but inscr. "Niue".

161. 3 c. multicoloured 10 10

40. Niuean Boy. 41. Octopus Lure.

1971. Niuean Portraits. Multicoloured.

162. 4 c. Type **40** 10 10
163. 6 c. Girl with garland .. 10 10
164. 9 c. Man 10 10
165. 14 c. Woman with garland 15 20

1972. South Pacific Arts Festival, Fiji. Multicoloured.

166. 3 c. Type **41** 10 10
167. 5 c. War weapons 15 10
168. 10 c. Sika throwing (horiz.) 20 10
169. 25 c. Vivi dance (horiz.) .. 30 20

42. Alofi Wharf.

1972. 25th Anniversary of South Pacific Commission. Multicoloured.

170. 4 c. Type **42** 10 10
171. 5 c. Medical Services .. 15 10
172. 6 c. Schoolchildren .. 15 10
173. 18 c. Dairy cattle .. 25 20

1972. Christmas. As T **332** of New Zealand, but inscr. "NIUE".

174. 3 c. multicoloured 10 10

43. Kokio.

1973. Fishes. Multicoloured.

175. 8 c. Type **43** 25 25
176. 10 c. Loi 30 30
177. 15 c. Malau 40 40
178. 20 c. Palu 45 45

44. "Large Flower Piece" (Jan Brueghel). 46. King Fataaiki.

45. Capt. Cook and Bowsprit.

1973. Christmas. Flower studies by the artists listed. Multicoloured.

179. 4 c. Type **44** 10 10
180. 5 c. Bollongier 10 10
181. 10 c. Ruysch 20 20

1974. Bicent. of Capt. Cook's Visit. Mult.

182. 2 c. Type **45** 30 20
183. 3 c. Niue landing place .. 30 25
184. 8 c. Map of Niue 50 40
185. 20 c. Ensign of 1774 and Administration Building 70 80

1974. Self-Government. Multicoloured.

186. 4 c. Type **46** 10 10
187. 8 c. Annexation Ceremony, 1900 .. .. .. 10 10
188. 10 c. Legislative Assembly Chambers (horiz.) .. 10 10
189. 20 c. Village meeting (horiz.) 15 15

47. Decorated Bicycles.

1974. Christmas. Multicoloured

190. 3 c. Type **47** 10 10
191. 10 c. Decorated motorcycle 10 10
192. 20 c. Motor transport to church 20 20

48. Children going to Church.

1975. Christmas. Multicoloured.

193. 4 c. Type **48** 10 10
194. 5 c. Child with balloons on bicycle 10 10
195. 10 c. Balloons and gifts on tree 20 20

49. Hotel Buildings.

1975. Opening of Tourist Hotel. Mult.

196. 8 c. Type **49** 10 10
197. 20 c. Ground-plan and buildings 20 20

50. Preparing Ground for Taro.

1976. Food Gathering. Multicoloured.

198. 1 c. Type **50** 10 10
199. 2 c. Planting Taro .. 10 10
200. 3 c. Banana gathering .. 10 10
201. 4 c. Harvesting taro .. 10 10
202. 5 c. Gathering shell fish .. 15 10
203. 10 c. Reef fishing 15 10
204. 20 c. Luku gathering .. 20 15
205. 50 c. Canoe fishing .. 40 60
206. $1 Coconut husking .. 60 80
207. $2 Uga gathering .. 1·00 1·40

See also Nos. 249/58 and 264/73.

51. Water.

1976. Utilities. Multicoloured.

208 10 c. Type **51** 10 10
209 15 c. Telecommunications 15 15
210 20 c. Power 15 15

52. Christmas Tree, Alofi.

1976. Christmas. Multicoloured.

211. 9 c. Type **52** 15 15
212. 15 c. Church Service, Avatele 15 15

53. Queen Elizabeth II and Westminster Abbey.

1977. Silver Jubilee. Multicoloured.

213. $1 Type **53** .. .. 1·50 75
214. $2 Coronation regalia .. 2·00 1·00

54. Child Care.

1977. Personal Services. Multicoloured.

216. 10 c. Type **54** 15 10
217. 15 c. School dental clinic 20 20
218. 20 c. Care of the aged .. 20 20

55. "The Annunciation".

1977. Christmas. Paintings by Rubens. Multicoloured.

219. 10 c. Type **55** 20 10
220. 12 c. "Adoration of the Magi" 20 10
221. 20 c. "Virgin in a Garland" 35 20
222. 35 c. "The Holy Family" 55 35

1977. Nos. 198/207, 214, 216 and 218 surch.

224. 12 c. on 1 c. Type **50** .. 25 25
225. 16 c. on 2 c. Planting taro 30 30
226. 20 c. on 3 c. Banana gathering 40 40
227. 35 c. on 4 c. Harvesting taro 45 45
228. 40 c. on 5 c. Gathering shell fish 50 50
229. 60 c. on 20 c. Luku gathering 70 65
230. 70 c. on $1 Coconut husking 75 70
231. 85 c. on $2 Uga gathering 80 70
232. $1.10 on 10 c. Type **22** .. 90 75
233. $2.60 on 20 c. Care of the aged .. .. .. 1·50 1·25
234. $3.20 on $2 Coronation regalia .. .. .. 1·75 1·50

57. "An Island View, in Atooi".

1978. Bicent. of Discovery of Hawaii. Paintings by John Webber. Multicoloured.

235. 12 c. Type **57** 75 30
236. 16 c. "A View of Karakaooa, in Owhyhee" 85 40
237. 20 c. "An Offering before Capt. Cook in the Sandwich Islands" .. 1·00 45
238. 30 c. "Tereoboo, King of Owhyhee, bringing presents to Capt. Cook" .. 1·25 50
239. 35 c. "A Canoe in the Sandwich Islands, the rowers masked" .. 1·25 55

58. "The Deposition of Christ". (Caravaggio).

1978. Easter. Paintings from the Vatican Galleries. Multicoloured.

241. 10 c. Type **58** 15 10
242. 20 c. "The Burial of Christ" (Bellini) .. 35 25

59. Flags of Niue and U.K.

1978. 25th Anniv. of Coronation. Mult.

245. $1.10 Type **59** .. .. 1·25 1·00
246. $1.10 Coronation portrait by Cecil Beaton .. 1·25 1·00
247. $1.10 Queen's personal flag for New Zealand .. 1·25 1·00

1978. Designs as Nos. 198/207 but margin colours changed and silver frame.

249. 12 c. Type **50** .. 20 20
250. 16 c. Planting taro .. 20 20
251. 30 c. Banana gathering .. 30 25
252. 35 c. Harvesting taro .. 30 30
253. 40 c. Gathering shell-fish 40 30
254. 60 c. Reef fishing .. 45 35
255. 75 c. Luku gathering .. 50 40
256. $1.10 Canoe fishing .. 1·10 80
257. $3.20 Coconut husking .. 1·25 1·25
258. $4.20 Uga gathering .. 1·40 1·40

60. "Festival of the Rosary".

1978. Christmas. 450th Death Anniv. of Durer. Multicoloured.

259. 20 c. Type **60** .. 40 20
260. 30 c. "The Nativity" .. 50 30
261. 35 c. "Adoration of the Magi" 60 35

1979. Air. Designs as Nos. 249/58 but gold frames and additionally inscr. "AIRMAIL".

264. 15 c. Planting taro .. 20 15
265. 20 c. Banana gathering .. 25 15
266. 23 c. Harvesting taro .. 30 15
267. 50 c. Canoe fishing .. 70 20
268. 90 c. Reef fishing 85 35
269. $1.35 Type **50** .. .. 1·25 1·50
270. $2.10 Gathering shell fish 2·00 2·25
271. $2.60 Luku gathering .. 2·00 2·50
272. $5.10 Coconut husking .. 2·25 3·50
273. $6.35 Uga gathering .. 2·50 4·50

61. "Pieta" (Gregorio Fernandez).

1979. Easter. Paintings. Multicoloured.

274. 30 c. Type **61** .. 30 25
275. 35 c. "Burial of Christ" (Pedro Roldan) .. 35 25

62. " The Nurse and Child " (Franz Hals).

1979. International Year of the Child. Details of Paintings. Multicoloured.

278. 16 c. Type **62** 30 15
279. 20 c. " Child of the Duke of Osuna " (Goya) .. 35 20
280. 30 c. " Daughter of Robert Strozzi " (Titian) .. 55 35
281. 35 c. " Children eating Fruit " (Murillo) .. 60 40

63. Penny Black Stamp.

1979. Death Centenary of Sir Rowland Hill. Multicoloured.

284. 20 c. Type **63** 20 15
285. 20 c. Sir Rowland Hill and original Bath mail coach 20 15
286. 30 c. Basel 1845 2½ r. stamp 30 20
287. 30 c. Sir Rowland Hill and Alpine village coach .. 30 20
288. 35 c. U.S.A. 1847 5 c. stamp 35 25
289. 35 c. Sir Rowland Hill and first Transatlantic U.S.A. mail vessel 35 25
290. 50 c. France 1849 20 c. stamp 50 35
291. 50 c. Sir Rowland Hill and French Post Office railway van, 1849 .. .. 50 35
292. 60 c. Bavaria 1849 1 k. stamp 55 40
293. 60 c. Sir Rowland Hill and Bavarian coach with mail 55 40

The two versions of each value were issued se-tenant within the sheet, forming composite designs.

64. Cook's Landing at Botany Bay.

1979. Death Bicentenary of Captain Cook. Multicoloured.

295. 20 c. Type **64** 55 30
296. 30 c. Cook's men during a landing on Erromanga .. 75 40
297. 35 c. H.M.S. "Resolution" and H.M.S. "Discovery" in Queen Charlotte's Sound 85 45
298. 75 c. Death of Captain Cook, Hawaii .. .. 1·50 70

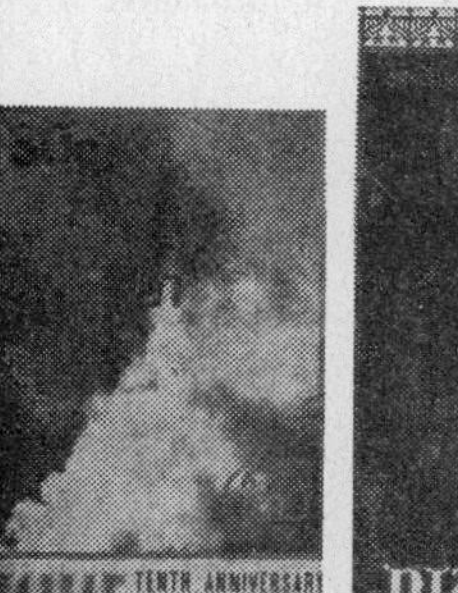

65. Launch of " Apollo 11 ".

66. " Virgin of Tortosa " (P. Serra).

1979. 10th Anniv. of Moon Landing. Mult.

300. 30 c. Type **65** 25 20
301. 35 c. Lunar module on Moon 30 25
302. 60 c. Helicopter, recovery ship and command module after splashdown .. 40 40

1979. Christmas. Paintings. Multicoloured.

304. 20 c. Type **66** 10 10
305. 25 c. " Virgin with Milk " (R. de Mur) 15 15
306. 30 c. " Virgin and Child " (S. di G. Sassetta) .. 20 20
307. 50 c. " Virgin and Child " (J. Huguet) 25 25

1980. Hurricane Relief. Surch. **HURRICANE RELIEF Plus 2c.**

(a) On Nos. 284/93 **(HURRICANE RELIEF** spread over each se-tenant pair).

310. **63.** 20 c.+2 c. multicoloured 20 25
311. – 20 c.+2 c. multicoloured (No. 285) 20 25
312. – 30 c.+2 c. multicoloured (No. 286) 30 35
313. – 30 c.+2 c. multicoloured (No. 287) 30 35
314. – 35 c.+2 c. multicoloured (No. 288) 35 40
315. – 35 c.+2 c. multicoloured (No. 289) 35 40
316. – 50 c.+2 c. multicoloured (No. 290) 50 55
317. – 50 c.+2 c. multicoloured (No. 291) 50 55
318. – 60 c.+2 c. multicoloured (No. 292) 60 65
319. – 60 c.+2 c. multicoloured (No. 293) 60 65

(b) On Nos. 295/8.

320. **64.** 20 c.+2 c. multicoloured 20 25
321. – 30 c.+2 c. multicoloured 30 35
322. – 35 c.+2 c. multicoloured 35 40
323. – 75 c.+2 c. multicoloured 75 80

(c) On Nos. 300/2.

324. **65.** 30 c.+2 c. multicoloured 30 35
325. – 35 c.+2 c. multicoloured 35 40
326. – 60 c.+2 c. multicoloured 60 65

(d) On Nos. 304/7.

327. **66.** 20 c.+2 c. multicoloured 20 25
328. – 25 c.+2 c. multicoloured 25 30
329. – 30 c.+2 c. multicoloured 30 35
330. – 50 c.+2 c. multicoloured 50 55

68. " Pieta " (Bellini).

1980. Easter. " Pieta ". Paintings. Mult.

331. 25 c. Type **68** 30 15
332. 30 c. Botticelli 35 20
333. 35 c. A. Van Dyck 35 20

69. Ceremonial Stool, New Guinea.

1980. South Pacific Festival of Arts, New Guinea. Multicoloured.

336. 20 c. Type **69** 20 20
337. 20 c. Ku-Tagwa plaque, New Guinea 20 20
338. 20 c. Suspension Hook, New Guinea 20 20
339. 20 c. Ancestral Board, New Guinea 20 20
340. 25 c. Platform Post, New Hebrides 25 25
341. 25 c. Canoe ornament, New Ireland 25 25
342. 25 c. Carved figure, Admiral Islands 25 25
343. 25 c. Female with child, Admiralty Islands .. 25 25
344. 30 c. The God A'a, Rurutu (Austral Islands) .. 25 30
345. 30 c. Statue of Tangaroa, Cook Islands 25 30
346. 30 c. Ivory Pendant, Tonga 25 30
347. 30 c. Tapa (Hiapo) cloth, Niue 25 30
348. 35 c. Feather box (Waka), New Zealand 30 35
349. 35 c. Hei-Tiki Amulet, New Zealand 30 35
350. 35 c. House Post, New Zealand 30 35
351. 35 c. Feather image of God Ku, Hawaii 30 35

1980. " Zeapex ' 80 " International Stamp Exhibition, Auckland. Nos. 284/93 optd. (A) **ZEAPEX '80 AUCKLAND** or (B) **NEW ZEALAND STAMP EXHIBITION** and emblem.

353. **63.** 20 c. multicoloured (A) 20 20
354. – 20 c. multicoloured (B) 20 20
355. – 30 c. multicoloured (A) 30 25
356. – 30 c. multicoloured (B) 30 25
357. – 35 c. multicoloured (A) 35 25
358. – 35 c. multicoloured (B) 35 25
359. – 50 c. multicoloured (A) 45 30
360. – 50 c. multicoloured (B) 45 30
361. – 60 c. multicoloured (A) 55 35
362. – 60 c. multicoloured (B) 55 35

72. Queen Elizabeth the Queen Mother.

1980. 80th Birthday of The Queen Mother.

364. **72.** $1.10 multicoloured .. 1·25 1·50

73. 100 Metre Dash.

1980. Olympic Games, Moscow.

366. 20 c. Type **73** 15 15
367. 20 c. Allen Wells, Great Britain (winner, 100 meter dash) 15 15
368. 25 c. } 400 metre freestyle (winner, Ines Diers, 15 20
369. 25 c. } D.D.R.) 15 20
370. 30 c. } Soling Class (winner, 20 20
371. 30 c. } Denmark) 20 20
372. 35 c. } Football (winner, 20 25
373. 35 c. } Czechoslovakia) .. 20 25

Nos. 366/7, 368/9, 370/1, and 372/3 were printed se-tenant in pairs, each pair forming a composite design. On the 25 c. and 35 c. stamps the face value is at right on the first design and at left on the second in each pair. For the 30 c. No. 370 has a yacht with a green sail at left and No. 371 on yacht with a red sail.

74. " The Virgin and Child "

1980. Christmas. Various Virgin and Child paintings by Andrea del Sarto.

375. **74.** 20 c. multicoloured .. 15 15
376. – 25 c. multicoloured .. 15 15
377. – 30 c. multicoloured .. 20 20
378. – 35 c. multicoloured .. 20 20

75. " Phalaenopsis sp ".

1981. Flowers (1st series). Multicoloured.

381. 2 c. Type **75** 10 10
382. 2 c. Moth Orchid 10 10
383. 5 c. " Euphorbia pulcherrima " 10 10
384. 5 c. Poinsettia 10 10
385. 10 c. " Thunbergia alata " 10 10
386. 10 c. Black-eyed Susan .. 10 10
387. 15 c. " Cocholspermum hibiscoides " 15 15
388. 15 c. Buttercup Tree .. 15 15
389. 20 c. " Begonia sp ". .. 20 20
390. 20 c. Begonia 20 20
391. 25 c. " Plumeria sp " .. 25 25
392. 25 c. Frangipani 25 25
393. 30 c. " Strelitzia reginae " 30 30
394. 30 c. Bird of Paradise .. 30 30
395. 35 c. " Hibiscus syriacus " 30 30
396. 35 c. Rose of Sharon .. 30 30
397. 40 c. " Nymphaea sp ". .. 35 35
398. 40 c. Water Lily 35 35
399. 50 c. " Tibouchina sp ". .. 45 45
400. 50 c. Princess Flower .. 45 45
401. 60 c. " Nelumbo sp ". .. 55 55
402. 60 c. Lotus 55 55
403. 80 c. " Hybrid hibiscus " 75 75
404. 80 c. Yellow Hibiscus .. 75 75
405. $1 Golden Shower Tree (cassia fistula) .. .. 1·00 1·00
406. $2 " Orchid var ". .. 2·50 2·50
407. $3 " Orchid sp ". .. 3·50 3·50
408. $4 " Euphorbia pulcherrima poinsettia " .. .. 3·00 3·25
409. $6 " Hybrid hibiscus " .. 4·50 4·75
410. $10 Scarlet hibiscus (" hibiscus rosa-sinensis ") 7·50 7·75

Nos. 405/10 are larger, 47×33 mm.

See also Nos. 527/36.

76. " Jesus Defiled " (El Greco).

1981. Easter. Details of Paintings. Mult.

425. 35 c. Type **76** 30 30
426. 50 c. " Pieta " (Fernando Gallego) 50 50
427. 60 c. " The Supper at Emmaus " (Jacopo de Pontormo) 55 55

77. Prince Charles.

1981. Royal Wedding. Multicoloured.

430. 75 c. Type **77** 90 80
431. 95 c. Lady Diana Spencer 1·00 90
432. $1.20 Prince Charles and Lady Diana Spencer .. 1·25 1·00

78. Footballer Silhouettes.

1981. World Cup Football Championship, Spain (1982).

434. **78.** 30 c. grn., gold and blue 20 20
435. – 30 c. grn., gold and blue 20 20
436. – 30 c. grn., gold and blue 20 20
437. – 35 c. blue, gold and orge. 25 25
438. – 35 c. blue, gold and orge. 25 25
439. – 35 c. blue, gold and orge. 25 25
440. – 40 c. orge., gold and grn. 25 25
441. – 40 c. orge, gold and grn. 25 25
442. – 40 c. orge., gold and grn. 25 25

DESIGNS: Various footballer silhouettes. No. 435, gold figure 3rd from left. No. 436, gold figure 4th from left. No. 437, gold figure 3rd from left. No. 438, gold figure 4th from left. No. 439, gold figure 2nd from left. No. 440, gold figure 3rd from left, displaying close control. No. 441, gold figure 2nd from left. No. 442, gold figure 3rd from left, heading.

1982. International Year for Disabled Persons Nos. 430/2. surch +**5c.**

444. 75 c.+5 c. Type **77** .. 2·25 1·50
445. 95 c.+5 c. Lady Diana Spencer .. .. 2·75 1·75
446. $1.20+5 c. Prince Charles and Lady Diana .. 3·75 2·00

80. "The Holy Family with Angels" (detail).

1981. Christmas. 375th Birth Anniv. of Rembrandt. Multicoloured.

448. 20 c. Type **80** 35 20
449. 35 c. " Presentation in the Temple " 50 30
450. 50 c. " Virgin and Child in Temple " 60 40
451. 60 c. " The Holy Family " 70 45

81. Prince of Wales.

1982. 21st Birthday of Princess of Wales. Multicoloured.

454. 50 c. Type **81** 55 55
455. $1.25 Prince and Princess of Wales .. .. 1·25 1·25
456. $2.50 Princess of Wales .. 2·00 2·00

1982. Birth of Prince William of Wales (1st issue). Nos. 430/2 optd.

458. 75 c. Type **77** .. .. 2·25 1·75
459. 75 c. Type **77** .. .. 2·25 1·75
460. 95 c. Lady Diana Spencer 3·25 2·25
461. 95 c. Lady Diana Spencer 3·25 2·25
462. $1.20 Prince Charles and Lady Diana Spencer .. 4·25 2·75
463. $1.20 Prince Charles and Lady Diana Spencer .. 4·25 2·75

OVERPRINTS: Nos. 458, 460 and 462 **COMMEMORATING THE ROYAL BIRTH 21 JUNE 1982.** 459, 461 and 463 **BIRTH OF PRINCE WILLIAM OF WALES 21 JUNE 1982.**

1982. Birth of Prince William of Wales (2nd issue). As Nos. 454/6, but with changed inscriptions. Multicoloured.

465. 50 c. Type **81** 55 55
466. $1.25 Prince and Princess of Wales .. .. 1·25 1·25
467. $2.50 Princess of Wales .. 2·00 2·00

83. Infant.

1982. Christmas. Paintings of Infants by Bronzion, Murillo and Boucher.

469. **83.** 40 c. multicoloured .. 55 35
470. – 52 c. multicoloured .. 65 45
471. – 83 c. multicoloured .. 1·10 80
472. – $1.05 multicoloured .. 1·25 95

85. Prime Minister Robert Rex.

1983. Commonwealth Day. Multicoloured.

475. 70 c. Type **85** .. 65 70
476. 70 c. H.M.S. "Resolution" and H.M.S. "Adventure" off Niue, 1774 .. .. .. 65 70
477. 70 c. Passion flower .. 65 70
478. 70 c. Limes 65 70

86. Scouts signalling.

1983. 75th Anniv. of Boy Scout Movement and 125th Birth Anniv. of Lord Baden-Powell. Multicoloured.

479. 40 c. Type **86** 35 40
480. 50 c. Planting sapling .. 45 50
481. 83 c. Map-reading .. 85 90

1983. 15th World Scout Jamboree, Alberta, Canada. Nos. 479/81 optd with **XV WORLD JAMBOREE CANADA**.

483. 40 c. Type **86** 35 40
484. 50 c. Planting sapling .. 45 50
485. 83 c. Map-reading 85 90

88. Black Right Whale.

1983. Protect the Whales. Multicoloured.

487. 12 c. Type **88** 55 45
488. 25 c. Fin Whale 75 60
489. 35 c. Sei Whale .. .. 1·00 90
490. 40 c. Blue Whale .. .. 1·25 1·00
491. 58 c. Bowhead Whale .. 1·40 1·10
492. 70 c. Sperm Whale .. 1·75 1·50
493. 83 c. Humpback Whale .. 2·00 1·75
494. $1·05 Minke Whale .. 2·50 2·00
495. $2·50 Grey Whale .. .. 3·75 3·50

89. Montgolfier Balloon, 1783.

1983. Bicentenary of Manned Flight. Mult.

496. 25 c. Type **89** 20 20
497. 40 c. Wright Brothers "Flyer", 1903 .. .. 35 35
498. 58 c. "Graf Zeppelin", 1928 50 50
499. 70 c. Boeing "247", 1933 .. 65 65
500. 83 c. "Apollo 8", 1968 80 80
501. $1.05 Space shuttle "Columbia", 1982 .. 95 95

90. " The Garagh Madonna ".

1983. Christmas. 500th Birth Anniv. of Raphael. Multicoloured.

503. 30 c. Type **90** 25 30
504. 40 c. " Madonna of the Granduca " 30 35
505. 58 c. " Madonna of the Goldfish " 45 50
506. 70 c. " The Holy Family of Francis I " 55 60
507. 83 c. " The Holy Family with Saints " 65 70

1983. Various stamps surch.

(a) Nos. 393/4, 399/404 and 407.

509. 52 c. on 30 c. " Strelitzia reginae " 40 45
510. 52 c. on 30 c. Bird of Paradise 40 45
511. 58 c. on 50 c. " Tibouchina sp. " 50 55
512. 58 c. on 50 c. Princess Flower 50 55
513. 70 c. on 60 c. " Nelumbo sp. " 55 60
514. 70 c. on 60 c. Lotus .. 55 60
515. 83 c. on 80 c. " Hybrid hibiscus " 70 75
516. 83 c. on 80 c. Yellow hibiscus 70 75
517. $3·70 on $3 " Orchid sp. " 3·00 3·25

(b) Nos. 431/2 and 455/6.

518. $1·10 on 95 c. Lady Diana Spencer .. .. 3·00 2·25
519. $1·10 on $1·25 Prince & Princess of Wales .. 2·25 2·00
520. $2·60 on $1·20 Prince Charles and Lady Diana 5·50 3·50
521. $2·60 on $2·50 Princess of Wales .. .. .. 3·50 3·25

91. Morse Key Transmitter.

1984. World Communications Year. Multicoloured.

523. 40 c. Type **91** 30 35
524. 52 c. Wall mounted phone 40 45
525. 83 c. Communications satellite 60 65

92. " Phalaenopsis sp. ".

1984. Flowers (2nd series). Multicoloured.

527. 12 c. Type **92** 10 10
528. 25 c. "Euphorbia pulcherrima" 15 20
529. 30 c. "Cochlospermum hibiscoides" 20 25
530. 35 c. "Begonia sp." .. 25 30
531. 40 c. "Plumeria sp." .. 25 30
532. 52 c. "Strelitzia reginae" .. 35 40
533. 58 c. "Hibiscus syriacus" 40 45
534. 70 c. "Tibouchina sp." .. 45 50
535. 83 c. "Nelumbo sp." .. 55 60
536. $1.05 Hybrid hibiscus .. 70 75
537. $1.75 "Cassia fistula" .. 1·10 1·25
538. $2.30 "Orchid var" .. 1·50 1·60
539. $3.90 "Orchid sp." .. 2·50 2·75
540. $5 "Euphorbia pulcherrima poinsettia" .. .. 3·25 3·50
541. $6.60 "Hybrid hibiscus" .. 4·25 4·50
542. $8.30 "Hibiscus rosa-sinensis" .. .. .. 5·50 5·75

Sizes: Nos. 537/542, 39 × 31 mm.

93. Discus Throwing.

1984. Olympic Games, Los Angeles. Multicoloured.

547. 30 c. Type **93** 25 30
548. 35 c. Sprinting (horiz.) .. 30 35
549. 40 c. Horse racing (horiz.) 35 40
550. 58 c. Boxing (horiz.) .. 50 55
551. 70 c. Javelin throwing .. 60 65

94. Koala.

1984. "Ausipex" International Stamp Exhibition, Melbourne.

a. Designs showing Koala Bears.

552. **94.** 25 c. mult. (postage) .. 40 30
553. – 35 c. multicoloured .. 45 35
554. – 40 c. multicoloured .. 50 40
555. – 58 c. multicoloured .. 70 55
556. – 70 c. multicoloured .. 85 65

b. Vert. designs showing Kangaroos.

557. – 83 c. multicoloured (air) 1·00 75
558. – $1.05 multicoloured .. 1·25 95
559. – $2.50 multicoloured .. 2·75 2·25

1984. Olympic Gold Medal Winners, Los Angeles. Nos. 547/51 optd.

561. 30 c. Type **93** 25 30
562. 35 c. Sprinting 30 35
563. 40 c. Horse racing 30 35
564. 58 c. Boxing 45 50
565. 70 c. Javelin throwing .. 55 60

OPTS: 30 c. **Discus Throw Rolf Denneberg Germany.** 35 c. **1,500 Meters Sebastian Coe Great Britain.** 40 c. **Equestrian Mark Todd New Zealand.** 58 c. **Boxing Tyrell Biggs United States.** 70 c. **Javelin Throw Arto Haerkoenen.**

96. Niue National Flag and Premier Sir Robert Rex.

1984. Self-Government. 10th Anniv. Multicoloured.

568. 40 c. Type **96** 30 35
569. 58 c. Map of Niue and Premier Rex 45 50
570. 70 c. Premier Rex receiving proclamation of self-government 55 60

1984. Birth of Prince Henry. Nos. 430 and 454 optd. **Prince Henry 15.9.84.**

573. $2 on 50 c. Type **81** .. 2·50 1·75
574. $2 on 75 c. Type **77** .. 2·50 1·75

98. "The Nativity" (A. Vaccaro).

1984. Christmas. Multicoloured.

575. 40 c. Type **98** 30 35
576. 58 c. "Virgin with Fly" (anon, 16th-century) .. 45 50
577. 70 c. "The Adoration of the Shepherds" (B. Murillo) 55 60
578. 80 c. "Flight into Egypt" (B. Murillo) 65 70

99. House Wren.

1985. John J. Audubon (ornithologist). Birth Bicentenary. Multicoloured.

581.	40 c. Type **99**	1·00	35
582.	70 c. Veery	1·40	60
583.	83 c. Grasshopper Sparrow	1·50	70
584.	$1.50 Henslow's Sparrow ..	2·00	85
585.	$2.50 Vesper Sparrow ..	2·75	2·00

100. The Queen Mother in Garter Robes.

1985. Life and Times of Queen Elizabeth the Queen Mother. Multicoloured.

587.	70 c. Type **100**	55	60
588.	$1.15 In open carriage with the Queen	90	95
589.	$1.50 With Prince Charles during 80th birthday celebrations	1·10	1·25

1985. South Pacific Mini Games, Rarotonga. Nos. 547/8 and 550/1 surch. **MINI SOUTH PACIFIC GAMES, RAROTONGA** and emblem.

591.	52 c. on 70 c. Javelin throwing..	40	45
592.	83 c. on 58 c. Boxing ..	65	70
593.	95 c. on 35 c. Sprinting ..	75	80
594.	$2 on 30 c. Type **93** ..	1·50	1·60

1985. Pacific Islands Conference, Rarotonga. Nos. 475/8 optd. **PACIFIC ISLANDS CONFERENCE, RAROTONGA** and emblem.

595.	70 c. Type **85**	55	60
596.	70 c. "Resolution" and "Adventure" off Niue, 1774	55	60
597.	70 c. Passion flower ..	55	60
598.	70 c. Limes..	55	60

No. 595 also shows an overprinted amendment to the caption which now reads **Premier Sir Robert Rex K.B.E.**

103. "R. Strozzi's Daughter" (Titian).

1985. International Youth Year. Mult.

599.	58 c. Type **103**	75	50
600.	70 c. "The Fifer" (E. Manet)	90	60
601.	$1.15 "Portrait of a Young Girl" (Renoir)	1·40	1·25
602.	$1.50 "Portrait of M. Berard" (Renoir) ..	1·75	1·50

104. "Virgin and Child".

1985. Christmas. Details of Paintings by Correggio. Multicoloured.

604.	58 c. Type **104**	60	50
605.	85 c. "Adoration of the Magi"	80	70
606.	$1.05 "Virgin with Child and St. John"	1·00	85
607.	$1.45 "Virgin and Child with St. Catherine" ..	1·50	1·25

105. "The Constellations" (detail).

1986. Appearance of Halley's Comet. Designs showing details from ceiling painting "The Constellations" by Giovanni De Vecchi. Nos. 611/13 show different spacecraft at top left. Multicoloured.

610.	60 c. Type **105**	50	50
611.	75 c. "Vega" spacecraft ..	65	65
612.	$1.10 "Planet A" spacecraft	90	90
613.	$1.50 "Giotto" spacecraft	1·25	1·25

106. Queen Elizabeth II and Prince Philip.

1986. 60th Birthday of Queen Elizabeth II. Multicoloured.

615.	$1·10 Type **106**	1·00	1·00
616.	$1·50 Queen and Prince Philip at Balmoral ..	1·25	1·25
617.	$2 Queen at Buckingham Palace	1·75	1·75

107. U.S.A. 1847 Franklin 5 c. Stamp and Washington Sculpture, Mt. Rushmore, U.S.A.

1986. "Ameripex '86" International Stamp Exhibition, Chicago. Multicoloured.

620.	$1 Type **107**	1·40	1·40
621.	$1 Flags of Niue and U.S.A. and Mt. Rushmore sculptures.. ..	1·40	1·40

Nos. 620/1 were printed together, se-tenant, forming a composite design.

108. "Statue under Construction, Paris, 1883" (Victor Dargaud).

1986. Centenary of Statue of Liberty. Multicoloured.

622.	$1 Type **108**	1·50	1·50
623.	$2.50 "Unveiling of Statue of Liberty" (Edmund Morand)	2·25	2·25

109. Prince Andrew, Miss Sarah Ferguson and Westminster Abbey. (Illustration reduced. Actual size 57 × 32 mm.).

1986. Royal Wedding.

625. **109.**	$2.50 multicoloured ..	2·75	2·75

110. Great Egret.

1986. "Stampex '86" Stamp Exhibition, Adelaide. Australian Birds. Multicoloured.

628.	40 c. Type **110**	1·25	75
629.	60 c. Painted finch (horiz.)	1·50	85
630.	75 c. Australian king parrot	1·75	1·10
631.	80 c. Variegated wren (horiz.)	2·00	1·40
632.	$1 Peregrine falcon ..	2·25	1·75
633.	$1.65 Azure kingfisher (horiz.)	3·00	2·25
634.	$2.20 Brilliant budgerigars	3·75	3·25
635.	$4.25 Emu (horiz.) ..	5·50	5·00

111. "Virgin and Child" (Perugino).

1986. Christmas from Vatican Museum. Multicoloured.

636.	80 c. Type **111**	1·00	1·00
637.	$1.15 "Virgin of St. N. dei Frari" (Titian)	1·25	1·25
638.	$1.80 "Virgin with Milk" (Lorenzo di Credi) ..	1·90	1·90
639.	$2.60 "Madonna of Foligno" (Rapheal) ..	2·75	2·75

1986. Visit of Pope John Paul II to South Pacific. Nos. 636/9 surch. **CHRISTMAS VISIT TO SOUTH PACIFIC OF POPE JOHN II, NOVEMBER 21–24 1986.**

642.	80 c. + 10 c. "Virgin and Child" (Perugino) ..	1·40	1·40
643.	$1.15 + 10 c. "Virgin of St. N. dei Frari" (Titian) ..	1·75	1·75
644.	$1.80 + 10 c. "Virgin with Milk" (Lorenzo di Credi)	2·75	2·75
645.	$2.60 + 10 c. "Madonna of Foligno" (Raphael) ..	3·25	3·25

113. Boris Becker, Olympic Rings and Commemorative Coin.

1987. Olympic Games, Seoul (1988). Tennis (1st issue). Designs showing Boris Becker in play.

649. **113.**	80 c. multicoloured ..	1·00	1·00
650.	$1.15 multicoloured ..	1·25	1·25
651.	$1.40 multicoloured ..	1·50	1·50
652.	$1.80 multicoloured ..	1·75	1·75

1987. Olympic Games, Seoul (1988). Tennis (2nd issue). As T **113**, but showing Steffi Graf.

653.	85 c. multicoloured ..	1·00	1·00
654.	$1.05 multicoloured ..	1·25	1·25
655.	$1.30 multicoloured ..	1·50	1·50
656.	$1.75 multicoloured ..	1·75	1·75

1987. Royal Ruby Wedding. Nos. 616/17 surch. **40TH WEDDING ANNIV. 4.85.**

657.	$4.85 on $1.50 Queen and Prince Philip at Balmoral	3·50	3·75
658.	$4.85 on $2 Queen at Buckingham Palace ..	3·50	3·75

115. "The Nativity".

1987. Christmas. Religious Paintings by Durer. Multicoloured.

659.	80 c. Type **115**	55	60
660.	$1.05 "Adoration of the Magi"	75	80
661.	$2.80 "Celebration of the Rosary"	2·00	2·10

Nos. 659/61 each include detail of an angel with lute as in T **115.**

116 Franz Beckenbauer in Action

1988. European Cup Football Championship, West Germany. Multicoloured.

664	20 c. Type **116**	30	30
665	40 c. German "All Star" team in action	45	45
666	60 c. Bayern Munich team with European Cup, 1974	55	55
667	80 c. World Cup match, England, 1966	75	75
668	$1.05 World Cup match, Mexico, 1970	1·00	1·00
669	$1.30 Beckenbauer with pennant, 1974	1·40	1·40
670	$1.80 Beckenbauer and European Cup, 1974 ..	1·75	1·75

1988. Steffi Graf's Tennis Victories. Nos. 653/6 optd.

671	85 c. mult (optd **Australia 24 Jan 88 French Open 4 June 88**) ..	60	65
672	$1.05 multicoloured (optd **Wimbledon 2 July 88 U S Open 10 Sept. 88**)	75	80
673	$1.30 multicoloured (optd **Women's Tennis Grand Slam: 10 September 88**) ..	90	95
674	$1.75 mult (optd **Seoul Olympic Games Gold Medal Winner**) ..	1·25	1·40

118 Angels

1988. Christmas. Details from "The Adoration of the Shepherds" by Rubens. Multicoloured.

675	60 c. Type **118**	60	60
676	80 c. Shepherds	80	80
677	$1.05 Virgin Mary ..	1·25	1·25
678	$1.30 Holy Child	1·50	1·50

119 Astronaut and "Apollo 11" Emblem

1989. 20th Anniv of First Manned Landing on Moon. Multicoloured.

680	$1.50 Type **119**	2·00	2·00
681	$1.50 Earth and Moon ..	2·00	2·00
682	$1.50 Astronaut and "Apollo 11" emblem ..	2·00	2·00

120 Priests

1989. Christmas. Details from "Presentation in the Temple" by Rembrandt. Mult.

684	70 c. Type **120**	75	75
685	80 c. Virgin and Christ Child in Simeon's arms	85	85
686	$1.05 Joseph	1·25	1·25
687	$1.30 Simeon and Christ Child	1·50	1·50

121 Fritz Walter

1990. World Cup Football Championship, Italy. German Footballers. Multicoloured.

689	80 c. Type **121**	1·40	1·40
690	$1.15 Franz Beckenbauer	1·75	1·75
691	$1.40 Uwe Seeler	2·00	2·00
692	$1.80 German team emblem and signatures of former captains ..	2·50	2·50

122 "Merchant Maarten Looten" (Rembrandt)

1990. 150th Anniv of the Penny Black. Rembrandt Paintings. Multicoloured.

693	80 c. Type **122**	90	90
694	$1.05 "Rembrandt's Son Titus with Pen in Hand"	1·25	1·25
695	$1.30 "The Shipbuilder and his Wife"	1·50	1·50
696	$1.80 "Bathsheba with King David's Letter"	2·00	2·00

123 Queen Elizabeth the Queen Mother

1990. 90th Birthday of Queen Elizabeth the Queen Mother.

698	**123** $1.25 multicoloured ..	2·00	2·00

124 "Adoration of the Magi" (Dirk Bouts)

1990. Christmas. Religious Paintings. Mult.

700	70 c. Type **124**	75	75
701	80 c. "Holy Family" (Fra. Bartolommeo)	90	90
702	$1.05 "Nativity" (Memling)	1·10	1·10
703	$1.30 "Adoration of the Kings" (Bruegel, the Elder)	1·40	1·40

1990. "Birdpex '90" Stamp Exhibition, Christchurch, New Zealand. No. 410 optd **Birdpex '90** and logo.

705	$10 Scarlet hibiscus ..	8·00	8·50

1991. 65th Birthday of Queen Elizabeth II. No. 409 optd **SIXTY FIFTH BIRTHDAY QUEEN ELIZABETH II**.

706	$6 "Hybrid hibiscus" ..	5·50	6·00

1991. 10th Wedding Anniv of Prince and Princess of Wales. Nos. 430/2 optd **TENTH ANNIVERSARY**.

707	75 c. Type **77**	70	70
708	95 c. Lady Diana Spencer	85	85
709	$1.20 Prince Charles and Lady Diana	1·25	1·25

129 "The Virgin and Child with Sts. Jerome and Dominic" (Lippi)

1991. Christmas. Religious Paintings. Mult.

710	20 c. Type **129**	10	15
711	50 c. "The Isenheim Altar-piece" (M. Grunewald)	35	40
712	$1 "The Nativity" (G. Pittoni)	60	70
713	$2 "Adoration of the Kings" (J. Brueghel the Elder)	1·25	1·40

130 Banded Rail

1992. Birds. Multicoloured.

718	20 c. Type **130**	10	10
719	50 c. Red-tailed tropic bird	35	40
720	70 c. Purple swamphen ..	45	50
721	$1 Pacific pigeon	65	70
722	$1.50 White-collared kingfisher	1·00	1·10
723	$2 Blue-crowned lory ..	1·25	1·40
724	$3 Purple-capped fruit dove	2·00	2·10
726	$5 Barn owl	3·25	3·40

131 Columbus before King Ferdinand and Queen Isabella

1992. 500th Anniv of Discovery of America by Columbus. Multicoloured.

731	$2 Type **131**	1·25	1·40
732	$3 Fleet of Columbus ..	2·00	2·10
733	$5 Claiming the New World for Spain ..	3·25	3·40

OFFICIAL STAMPS

1985. Nos. 409/10 and 527/42 optd. **O.H.M.S.**

O 1.	12 c. "Phalaenopsis" sp.	10	10
O 2.	25 c. "Euphorbia pulcherrima"	15	20
O 3.	30 c. "Cochlospermum hibiscoides"	20	25
O 4.	35 c. "Begonia" sp. ..	25	30
O 5.	40 c. "Plumeria" sp. ..	25	30
O 6.	52 c. "Strelitzia reginae"	35	40
O 7.	58 c. "Hibiscus syriacus"	40	45
O 8.	70 c. "Tibouchina" sp. ..	45	50
O 9.	83 c. "Nelumbo" sp. ..	55	60
O 10.	$1.05 Hybrid hibiscus ..	70	75
O 11.	$1.75 "Cassia fistula" ..	1·10	1·25
O 12.	$2.30 Orchid var. ..	1·50	1·60
O 13.	$3.90 Orchid sp. ..	2·50	2·75
O 14.	$4 "Euphorbia pulcherrima poinsettia ..	2·75	3·00
O 15.	$5 "Euphorbia pulcherrima poinsettia" ..	3·25	3·50
O 16.	$6 Hybrid hibiscus ..	4·00	4·25
O 17.	$6.60 "Hybrid hibiscus"	4·25	4·50
O 18.	$8.30 "Hibiscus rasasinensis"	5·50	5·75
O 19.	$10 Scarlet hibiscus ..	6·50	6·75

NORFOLK ISLAND

A small island East of New South Wales, administered by Australia until 1960 when local government was established.

1947. 12 pence = 1 shilling, 20 shillings = 1 pound.
1966. 100 cents = $1 Australian.

1. Ball Bay.

1947.

1.	**1.**	½d. orange..	35	40
2.		1d. violet	50	40
3.		1½d. green..	50	40
4.		2d. violet	55	30
5.		2½d. red	80	30
6.		3d. brown	70	45
6a.		3d. green	14·00	3·75
7.		4d. red	70	40
8.		5½d. blue	70	30
9.		6d. brown	70	30
10.		9d. pink	1·25	40
11.		1s. green	70	40
12.		2s. brown	4·00	1·25
12a.		2s. blue	24·00	5·00

12. "Hibiscus insularis".

2. Warder's Tower.

4. First Governor's Residence.

17. Queen Elizabeth II (after Annigoni) and Cereus.

22. Red-tailed Tropic Bird.

1953.

24.	**12.**	1d. green	15	10
25.	–	2d. red and myrtle ..	20	10
26.	–	3d. green	70	15
13.	**2.**	3½d. lake	3·00	90
27.	–	5d. purple	55	20
14	–	6½d. green	3·00	1·00
15.	**4.**	7½d. blue	4·00	3·00
28.	–	8d. red	80	50
16.	–	8½d. brown	7·00	3·50
29.	**17.**	9d. blue	80	45
17.	–	10d. violet	5·00	75
30.	–	10d. brown and violet ..	2·50	1·25
31.	–	1s. 1d. red	80	35
32.	–	2s. sepia	6·00	90
33.	–	2s. 5d. violet	1·00	40
34.	–	2s. 8d. brown & green ..	2·00	55
18.	–	5s. brown	38·00	8·00
35.	–	5s. sepia and green ..	6·00	75
36.	**22.**	10s. green	60·00	26·00

DESIGNS—VERT. 2d. "Lagunaria patersonii". 5d. Lantana. 8d. Red hibiscus. 8½d. Barracks entrance. 10d. Salt House. 1s. 1d. Fringed hibiscus. 2s. Solander's Petrel. 2s. 5d. Passion-flower. 2s. 8d. Rose-apple. HORIZ. 3d. White Tern. 6½d. Airfield. 5s. Bloody Bridge.

8. Norfolk Is. Seal and Pitcairners Landing.

1956. Centenary of Landing of Pitcairners on Norfolk Is.

19.	**8.**	3d. green	1·25	30
20.		2s. violet	1·75	50

1958. Surch.

21.	**4.**	7d. on 7½d. blue	1·00	45
22.	–	8d. on 8½d. brown (No. 16)	1·00	45

1959. 150th Anniv. of Australian P.O. No. 331 of Australia surch. **NORFOLK ISLAND 5D.** in red.
23. 143. 5d. on 4d. slate .. 35 15

1960. As Nos. 13 and 14/15 but colours changed and surch.
37. 2. 1s. 1d. on 3½d. blue .. 3·50 1·25
38. 2s. 5d. on 6½d. turquoise .. 3·50 1·25
39. 4. 2s. 8d. on 7½d. sepia .. 8·00 2·25

36. Queen Elizabeth II and Map.

1960. Introduction of Local Government.
40 36 2s. 8d. purple .. .. 15·00 6·00

1960. Christmas. As No. 338 of **Australia.**
41. 150. 5d. mauve 80 30

1961. Christmas. As No. 341 of **Australia.**
42. 153. 5d. blue 30 30

DESIGNS: 11d. "Trumpeter". 1s. "Po'ov". 1s. 3d. "Dreamfish". 1s. 6d. "Hapoeka" ("Promicrops lanceolatus"). 2s. 3d. "Ophie" ("carangidae").

27. Tweed Trousers ("Atypichthyslatus").

1962.
43. 27. 6d. sepia, yellow & green .. 1·00 25
44. – 11d. orange, brown & blue 2·50 80
45. – 1s. blue, pink and olive .. 1·00 25
46. – 1s. 3d. blue, brown & green 2·50 1·75
47. – 1s. 6d. sepia, violet & blue 3·00 80
48. – 2s. 3d. multicoloured .. 4·50 80

1962. Christmas. As No. 345 of **Australia.**
49. 157. 5d. blue 35 15

1963. Christmas. As No. 361 of **Australia.**
50. 173. 5d. red 30 15

33. Overlooking Kingston. 37. Norfolk Pine.

1964. Multicoloured.
51. 5d. Type **33** 50 15
52. 8d. Kingston .. .. 1·00 20
53. 9d. The Arches (Bumboras) 2·00 15
54. 10d. Slaughter Bay .. 3·00 25

1964. 50th Anniv. of Norfolk Island as Australian Territory.
55. 37. 5d. black, red & orange 20 10
56. 8d. black, red and green 30 10

1964. Christmas. As No. 372 of **Australia.**
57. 183. 5d. multicoloured .. 30 10

1965. 50th Anniv. of Gallipoli Landing. As T **184** of Australia, but slightly larger (22 × 34½ mm.).
58. 5d. brown, black and green 10 10

1965. Christmas. As No. 381 of **Australia.**
59. 190. 5d. multicoloured .. 10 10

38. "Hibiscus insularis".

1966. Decimal Currency. As earlier issue but with values in cents and dollars. Surch. in black on silver tablets obliterating old value as in T **38.**
60. 38. 1 c. on 1d. 20 10
61. – 2 c. on 2d. (No. 25) .. 20 10
62. – 3 c. on 3d. (No. 26) .. 50 10
63. – 4 c. on 5d. (No. 27) .. 25 10
64. – 5 c. on 8d. (No. 28) .. 30 10
65. – 10 c. on 10d. (No. 30) .. 40 15
66. – 15 c. on 1s. 1d. (No. 31) 45 15
67. – 20 c. on 2s (No. 32) .. 3·50 1·75
68. – 25 c. on 2s. 5d. (No. 33) 1·50 40
69. – 30 c. on 2s. 8d. (No. 34) 1·00 50
70. – 50 c. on 5s. (No. 35) .. 4·50 75
71. 22. $1 on 10s. .. .. 3·50 1·75

39. Headstone Bridge.

1966. Multicoloured.
72. 7 c. Type **39** 40 15
73. 9 c. Cemetery Road .. 40 15

41. St. Barnabas' Chapel (interior).

1966. Cent. of Melanesian Mission. Mult.
74. 4 c. Type **41** 10 10
75. 25 c. St. Barnabas' Chapel (exterior) 20 10

43. Star over Philip Island.

1966. Christmas.
76. 43. 4 c. multicoloured .. 10 10

44. H.M.S. "Resolution", 1774.

1967. Multicoloured.
77. 1 c. Type **44** 10 10
78. 2 c. "La Boussole" and "L'Astrolabe", 1788 .. 15 10
79. 3 c. H.M.S. "Supply" (brig), 1788 .. .. 15 10
80. 4 c. H.M.S. "Sirius" (frigate), 1790 .. 15 10
81. 5 c. "Norfolk" (cutter), 1798 20 10
82. 7 c. H.M.S. "Mermaid" (survey cutter), 1825 .. 20 10
83. 9 c. "Lady Franklin", 1853 20 10
84. 10 c. "Morayshire" (emigrant ship), 1856 .. 20 20
85. 15 c. "Southern Cross", 1866 45 30
86. 20 c. "Pitcairn", 1891 .. 60 40
87. 25 c. Norfolk Island whaleboat, 1895 .. .. 1·00 75
88. 30 c. "Iris" (cable ship), 1907 .. .. 2·00 1·50
89. 50 c. "Resolution", 1926 .. 3·00 2·00
90. $1 "Morinda", 1931 .. 5·50 2·50

1967. 50th Anniv. of Lions Int. As T **205** of Australia.
91. 4 c. black, green and yellow 10 10

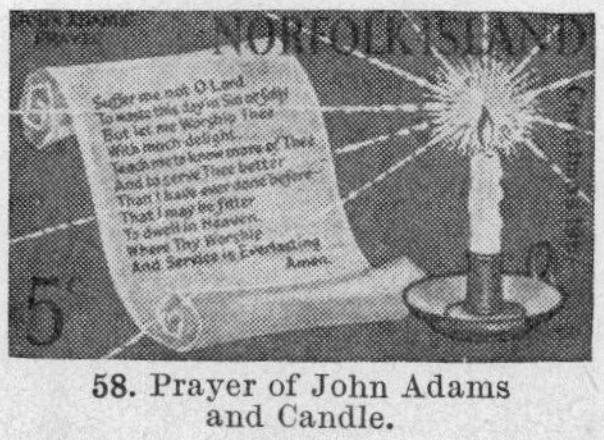

58. Prayer of John Adams and Candle.

1967. Christmas.
92. 58. 5 c. black olive and red 10 10

1968. As T **191** of Australia, but inscr NORFOLK ISLAND.
93. 3 c. black, brown and red .. 10 10
94. 4 c. black, brown and green 10 10
95. 5 c. black, brown and violet 10 10
95a. 6 c. black, brown and lake 30 35

59. "Skymaster" and "Lancastrian" Aircraft.

1968. 21st Anniv. of QANTAS Air Service, Sydney-Norfolk Island.
96. 59. 5 c. black, red and blue 10 10
97. 7 c. brown, red & turq. 10 10

60. Bethlehem Star and Flowers.

1968. Christmas.
98. 60. 5 c. multicoloured .. 10 10

61. Captain Cook, Quadrant and Chart of Pacific Ocean.

1969. Captain Cook Bicentenary (1st issue). Observation of the transit of Venus across the Sun, Tahiti.
99. 61. 10 c. multicoloured .. 10 10
See also Nos. 118/19, 129, 152/5, 200/2 and 213/14.

62. Van Diemen's Land, Norfolk Island and Sailing Cutter.

1969. 125th Anniv. of Annexation of Norfolk Island to Van Diemen's Land.
100. 62. 5 c. multicoloured .. 10 10
101. 30 c. multicoloured .. 20 10

63. "The Nativity" (carved mother-of-pearl plaque).

1969. Christmas.
102. 63. 5 c. multicoloured .. 10 10

64. New Zealand Grey Flyeater.

1970. Birds. Multicoloured.
103. 1 c. Scarlet robin 30 10
104. 2 c. Golden whistler .. 30 20
105. 3 c. Type **64** 30 10
106. 4 c. Long-tailed koel .. 60 10
107. 5 c. Red-fronted parakeet 1·50 45
108. 7 c. Long-tailed triller .. 45 10
109. 9 c. Island thrush 70 10
110. 10 c. Boobook owl .. 1·75 40
111. 15 c. Norfolk Island pigeon 1·50 65
112. 20 c. White-chested white-eye .. .. .. 4·50 2·50
113. 25 c. Norfolk Island parrots .. .. .. 2·50 40
114. 30 c. Collared grey fantail 4·50 1·75
115. 45 c. Norfolk Islands starling .. .. 3·50 80
116. 50 c. Crimson rosella .. 4·00 1·75
117. $1 Sacred kingfisher .. 9·00 8·00
Nos. 105/6, 109, 112, 114/5 and 117 are horiz; the remainder being vert.

65. Cook and Map of Australia.

1970. Captain Cook Bicentenary. (2nd issue). Discovery of Australia's East Coast. Mult.
118. 5 c. Type **65** 10 10
119. 20 c. H.M.S. "Endeavour" and Aborigine 20 10

66. First Christmas Service, 1788.

1970. Christmas.
120. 66. 5 c. multicoloured .. 10 10

67. Bishop Patteson, and Martyrdom of St. Stephen.

1971. Death Cent. of Bishop Patteson. Multicoloured.
121. 6 c. Type **67** 10 10
122. 6 c. Bible, Martyrdom of St. Stephen and knotted palm-frond 10 10
123. 10 c. Bishop Patteson and stained glass 10 10
124. 10 c. Cross and Bishop's Arms 10 10

68. Rose Window, St. Barnabas Chapel, Kingston.

1971. Christmas.
125. 68. 6 c. multicoloured .. 10 10

69. Map and Flag.

1972. 25th Anniv. of South Pacific Commission.
126. **69.** 7 c. multicoloured .. 15 10

70. " St. Mark " (Stained-glass Window) (All Saints, Norfolk Is.). **71.** Cross and Pines (Stained-glass Window All Saints Church).

1972. Christmas.
127. **70.** 7 c. multicoloured .. 10 10

1972. Cent. of First Pitcairner-built Church.
128. **71.** 12 c. multicoloured .. 10 10

72. H.M.S. "Resolution" in the Antarctic.

1973. Capt. Cook Bicentenary (3rd issue). Crossing of the Antarctic Circle.
129. **72.** 35 c. multicoloured .. 3·00 2·25

73. Child and Christmas Tree.

1973. Christmas. Multicoloured.
130. 7 c. Type **73** 20 10
131. 12 c. Type **73** 25 10
132. 35 c. Fir trees and star 70 80

74. Protestant Clergyman's Quarters.

1973. Historic Buildings. Multicoloured.
133. 1 c. Type **74** 10 10
134. 2 c. Royal Engineer's Office 10 10
135. 3 c. Double Quarters for Free Overseers 25 15
136. 4 c. Guard House 20 20
137. 5 c. Entrance to Pentagonal Gaol 25 15
138. 7 c. Pentagonal Gaol .. 35 35
139. 8 c. Prisoners' Barracks .. 1·00 35
140. 10 c. Officer's Quarters, New Military Barracks 50 45
141. 12 c. New Military Barracks 50 30
142. 14 c. Beach Stores .. 60 60
143. 15 c. The Magazine .. 1·50 50
144. 20 c. Entrance, Old Military Barracks 80 65
145. 25 c. Old Military Barracks 1·50 90
146. 30 c. Old Stores (Crankmill) 1·00 60
147. 50 c. Commissariat Stores 1·25 1·75
148. $1 Government House .. 2·25 3·75

75. Royal Couple and Map.

1974. Royal Visit.
149. **75.** 7 c. multicoloured .. 40 15
150. 25 c. multicoloured .. 1·25 75

76. Chichester's " Madame Elijah ".

1974. 1st Aircraft Landing on Norfolk Island.
151. **76.** 14 c. multicoloured .. 1·00 70

77. "Captain Cook" (Engraving by J. Basire).

1974. Capt. Cook Bicentenary (4th issue). Discovery of Norfolk Is. Multicoloured.
152. 7 c. Type **77** .. 1·50 75
153. 10 c. H.M.S. "Resolution" (H. Roberts) .. .. 2·50 1·75
154. 14 c. Norfolk Island Pine 2·75 2·00
155. 25 c. "Norfolk Island flax" (G. Raper) .. .. 3·25 2·75

78. Nativity Scene (Pear-shell pew carving).

1974. Christmas.
156. **78.** 7 c. multicoloured .. 15 10
157. 30 c. multicoloured .. 60 75

79. Norfolk Pine.

1974. Centenary of Universal Postal Union. Multicoloured. Imperf. Self-adhesive.
158. 10 c. Type **79** .. 35 40
159. 15 c. Offshore islands .. 40 45
160. 35 c. Crimson Rosella and Sacred Kingfisher .. 70 75
161. 40 c. Pacific map 75 90

INDEX

Countries can be quickly located by referring to the index at the end of this volume.

80. H.M.S. "Mermaid" (survey cutter).

1975. 150th Anniv. of Second Settlement. Multicoloured.
163. 10 c. Type **80** 45 45
164. 35 c. Kingston, 1835 (from painting by T. Seller) 80 80

81. Star on Norfolk Island Pine. **82.** Memorial Cross.

1975. Christmas.
165. **81.** 10 c. multicoloured .. 15 10
166. 15 c. multicoloured .. 20 10
167. 35 c. multicoloured .. 30 35

1975. Centenary of St. Barnabas Chapel. Multicoloured.
168. 30 c. Type **82** 20 15
169. 60 c. Laying foundation stone, and Chapel in 1975 40 40

83. Launching of " Resolution ".

1975. 50th Anniv. of Launching of "Resolution" (schooner). Multicoloured.
170. 25 c. Type **83** 25 30
171. 45 c. "Resolution" at sea 40 55

84. Whaleship " Charles W. Morgan ".

1976. Bicent. of American Revolution. Mult.
172. 18 c. Type **84** 30 15
173. 25 c. Thanksgiving Service 40 20
174. 40 c. " Flying Fortress " over Norfolk Island .. 75 45
175. 45 c. California Quail .. 1·00 55

85. Swallow-tailed Tern and Sun.

1976. Christmas.
176. **85.** 18 c. multicoloured .. 25 15
177. 25 c. multicoloured .. 40 20
178. 45 c. multicoloured .. 85 50

86. " Bassaris itea ".

1977. Butterflies and Moths. Multicoloured.
179 1 c. Type **86** 10 40
180 2 c. "Utetheisa pulchelloides" 10 40
181 3 c. "Agathia asterias" .. 10 20
182 4 c. "Cynthia kershawi" .. 10 25
183 5 c. "Leucania loreyimima" 15 30
184 10 c. "Hypolimnas bolina" 30 35
185 15 c. "Pyrrhorachis pyrrhogona" 30 30
186 16 c. "Austrocarea iocephala" 30 30
187 17 c. "Pseudocoremia christiani" 35 30
188 18 c. "Cleora idiocrossa" .. 35 30
189 19 c. "Simplicia caeneusalis" 35 30
190 20 c. "Austrocidaria ralstonae" 40 30
191 30 c. "Hippotion scrofa" .. 50 40
192 40 c. "Papilio ilioneus" .. 55 40
193 50 c. "Tiracola plagiata" 70 60
194 $1 "Precis villida" .. 1·00 75
195 $2 "Cepora perimale" .. 1·75 1·40

87. Queen's View, Kingston.

1977. Silver Jubilee.
196. **87.** 25 c. multicoloured .. 35 30

88. Hibiscus Flowers and Oil Lamp. **89.** Captain Cook (from a portrait by Nathaniel Dance).

1977. Christmas.
197. **88.** 18 c. multicoloured .. 15 10
198. 25 c. multicoloured .. 15 10
199. 45 c. multicoloured .. 30 35

1978. Capt. Cook Bicentenary (5th issue). Discovery of Hawaii. Multicoloured.
200. 18 c. Type **89** 30 20
201. 25 c. Discovery of northern Hawaiian islands .. 40 30
202. 80 c. British flag against island background .. 90 70

90. Guide Flag and Globe.

1978. 50th Anniv. of Girl Guides. Multicoloured. Imperf. Self-adhesive.
203. 18 c. Type **90** 30 15
204. 25 c. Trefoil and scarf badge 45 25
205. 35 c. Trefoil and Queen Elizabeth 60 35
206. 45 c. Trefoil and Lady Baden-Powell 75 45

91. St. Edward's Crown.

1978. 25th Anniv. of Coronation. Mult.

207. 25 c. Type **91** 15 15
208. 70 c. Coronation regalia .. 40 45

92. View of Duncombe Bay with Scout at Camp Fire.

1978. 50th Anniv. of Boy Scout Movement. Multicoloured. Imperf. Self-adhesive.

209. 20 c. Type **92** 35 30
210. 25 c. View from Kingston and emblem 55 40
211. 35 c. View of Anson Bay and Link Badge .. 85 75
212. 45 c. Sunset scene and Lord Baden-Powell .. .. 1·00 85

93. Chart showing Route of Arctic Voyage.

1978. Captain Cook Bicentenary (6th issue). Northern-most Voyage. Multicoloured.

213. 25 c. Type **93** 60 30
214. 90 c. "H.M.S. "Resolution" and H.M.S. "Discovery" in Pack Ice" (Webber) 1·50 80

94. Poinsettia and Bible.

1978. Christmas. Multicoloured.

215. 20 c. Type **94** 15 10
216. 30 c. Native Oak and bible 20 15
217. 55 c. Hibiscus and bible .. 30 30

95. Cook and Village of Staithes near Marton.

1978. 250th Birth Anniv. of Captain Cook. Multicoloured.

218. 20 c. Type **95** 35 25
219. 80 c. Cook and Whitby Harbour .. .. 1·40 1·25

96. H.M.S. "Resolution".

1979. Death Bicent. of Captain Cook. Mult.

220. 20 c. Type **96** 80 30
221. 20 c. Cook statue 80 30
222. 40 c. } " Death of Captain 90 50
223. 40 c. } Cook " 90 50

Nos. 220/1 were issued se-tenant, in horizontal pairs throughout the sheet, forming a composite design. A chart of Cook's last voyage is shown in the background. Nos. 222/3 were also issued se-tenant, the horizontal pair forming a composite design taken from an aquatint by John Clevely.

97. Assembly Building.

1979. First Norfolk Island Legislative Assembly.

224. **97.** $1 multicoloured .. 50 50

98. Tasmania 1853 1d. Stamp and Sir Rowland Hill.

1979. Death Centenary of Sir Rowland Hill.

225. **98.** 20 c. blue and brown .. 20 10
226. – 30 c. red and grey .. 25 15
227. – 55 c. violet and indigo .. 40 30

DESIGNS: 30 c. Great Britain 1841 1d. red. 55 c. 1947 " Ball Bay " 1d. stamp.

99. I.Y.C. Emblem and Map of Pacific showing Norfolk Island as Pine Tree.

1979. International Year of the Child.

229. **99.** 80 c. multicoloured .. 40 45

100. Emily Bay.

1979. Christmas.

230. **100.** 15 c. multicoloured .. 15 15
231. – 20 c. multicoloured .. 15 15
232. – 30 c. multicoloured .. 15 15

DESIGNS: 20, 30 c. Different scenes.

Nos. 230/2 were printed together, se-tenant, in horizontal strips of 3 throughout the sheet, forming a composite design.

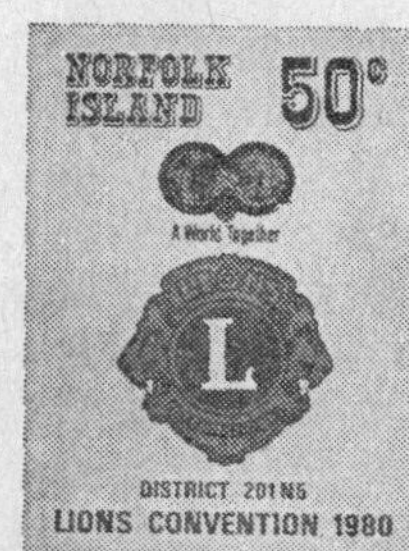

101. Lions International Emblem.

1980. Lions Convention.

234. **101.** 50 c. multicoloured .. 35 30

102. Rotary International Emblem.

1980. 75th Anniv. of Rotary International.

235. **102.** 50 c. multicoloured .. 35 30

103. D.H. 60 (Gypsy Moth) " Mme Elijah ".

1980. Aeroplanes. Multicoloured.

236. 1 c. Hawker Siddeley " H.S. 748 " 15 20
237. 2 c. Type **103** 15 20
238. 3 c. Curtis " P-40 Kittyhawk " 15 20
239. 4 c. Chance Vought " F4U-1 Corsair " .. 15 20
240. 5 c. Grumman " TBF-1c Avenger " 30 20
241. 15 c. Douglas " SBD-5 " Dauntless " 30 30
242. 20 c. Cessna " 172 " .. 25 30
243. 25 c. Lockheed " Hudson " 30 35
244. 30 c. Lockheed " PV-1 Ventura " 40 35
245. 40 c. Avro " York " .. 50 45
246. 50 c. Douglas " DC-3 " .. 65 55
247. 60 c. Avro " 691 Lancastrian " 75 65
248. 80 c. Douglas " DC-4 " .. 95 85
249. $1 Beechcraft " Super King Air " .. .. 1·25 90
250. $2 Fokker " F-27 Friendship " .. .. 2·50 90
251. $5 Lockheed " C-130 Hercules " .. .. 6·00 2·00

104. Queen Elizabeth the Queen Mother.

1980. 80th Birthday of The Queen Mother.

252. **104.** 22 c. multicoloured .. 30 20
253 60 c. multicoloured .. 65 40

105. Red-tailed Tropic Birds.

1980. Christmas. Birds. Multicoloured.

254. 15 c. Type **105** 35 25
255. 22 c. White Terns .. 35 25
256. 35 c. White-capped Noddys 35 25
257. 60 c. White Terns (different) 60 45

106. " Morayshire " and View of Norfolk Island.

1981. 125th Anniv. of Pitcairn Islanders' Migration to Norfolk Island. Multicoloured.

258. 5 c. Type **106** 15 15
259. 35 c. Islanders arriving ashore 55 30
260. 60 c. View of new settlement 85 45

MINIMUM PRICE

The minimum price quoted is 10p which represents a handling charge rather than a basis for valuing common stamps. For further notes about prices see introductory pages.

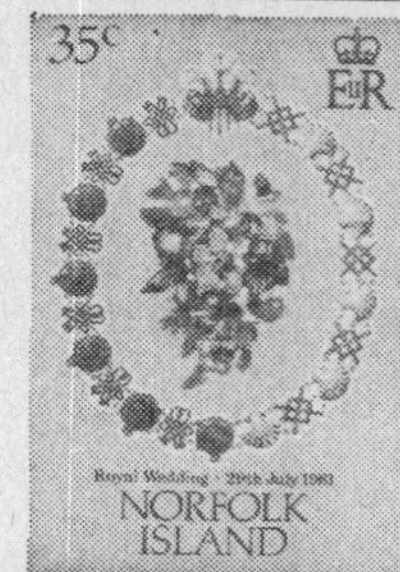

107. Wedding Bouquet from Norfolk Island.

1981. Royal Wedding. Multicoloured.

262. 35 c. Type **107** 20 15
263. 55 c. Prince Charles at horse trials 35 25
264. 60 c. Prince Charles and Lady Diana Spencer .. 35 35

108. Uniting Church of Australia.

1981. Christmas. Churches. Multicoloured.

265. 18 c. Type **108** 20 10
266. 24 c. Seventh Day Adventist Church 25 15
267. 30 c. Church of the Sacred Heart 30 20
268. $1 St. Barnabas Chapel .. 70 70

109. Pair of " White-breasted Silvereyes".

1981. White-breasted Silvereye. Mult.

269. 35 c. Type **109** 45 40
270. 35 c. (White-chested White eye.) Bird on nest .. 45 40
271. 35 c. Bird with egg .. 45 40
272. 35 c. Parents with chicks 45 40
273. 35 c. Fledgelings 45 40

110. Aerial view of Philip Island.

1982. Philip and Nepean Islands. Mult.

274. 24 c. Type **110** 30 25
275. 24 c. Close-up view of Philip Island landscape 30 25
276. 24 c. Gecko (" phyllodactylus guentheri "), Philip Island 30 25
277. 24 c. Sooty Tern, Philip Island 30 25
278. 24 c. Philip Island Hibiscus (" hibiscus insuarlis ") 30 25
279. 35 c. Aerial view of Nepean Island 40 35
280. 35 c. Close-up view of Nepean Island landscape 40 35
281. 35 c. Gecko (" phyllodactylus guentheri "), Nepean Is. 40 35
282. 35 c. Blue-faced Boobies .. Nepean Island 40 35
283. 35 c. " Carpobrotus glaucescens" (flower), Nepean Island 40 35

111. Sperm Whale.

1982. Whales.

284. **111.** 24 c. multicoloured .. 45 35
285. – 55 c. multicoloured .. 85 75
286. – 80 c. black, mve. & stone 1·10 1·00

DESIGNS: 55 c. Black Right Whale. 80 c. Humpback Whale.

112. "Dioret", Wrecked 20 April 1873.

1982. Shipwrecks. Multicoloured.

No.	Description		
287.	24 c. H.M.S. "Sirius", wrecked 19 March 1790	50	50
288.	27 c. Type **112**	50	50
289.	35 c. "Friendship", wrecked 17 May 1835 ..	70	70
290.	40 c. "Mary Hamilton", wrecked 6 May 1873 ..	80	80
291.	55 c. "Fairlie", wrecked 14 February 1840	95	95
292.	65 c. "Warrigal", wrecked 18 March 1918 ..	1·25	1·25

113. R.N.Z.A.F. "Hudson" dropping Christmas Supplies, 1942.

1982. Christmas. 40th Anniv. of First Supply-plane Landings on Norfolk Island (Christmas Day 1942). Multicoloured.

No.	Description		
293.	27 c. Type **113**	30	35
294.	40 c. R.N.Z.A.F. "Hudson" landing Christmas supplies 1942	45	65
295.	75 c. Christmas, 1942 ..	90	1·40

114. 50th (Queen's Own) Regiment.

1982. Military Uniforms. Multicoloured.

No.	Description		
296.	27 c. Type **114**	30	35
297.	40 c. 58th (Rutlandshire) Regiment	45	75
298.	55 c. 80th (Staffordshire Volunteers) Battalion Company	65	95
299.	65 c. 11th (North Devonshire) Regiment ..	80	1·25

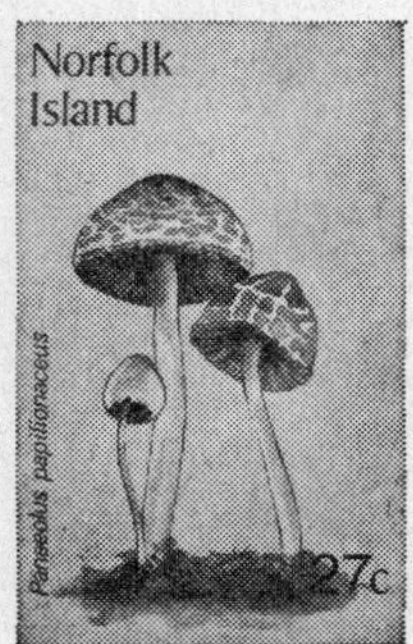

115. "Panaeolus papilionaceus"

1983. Fungi. Multicoloured.

No.	Description		
300.	27 c. Type **115**	45	35
301.	40 c. "Coprinus domesticus"	70	50
302.	55 c. "Marasmius niveus"	95	70
303.	65 c. "Cymatoderma elegans var. lamellatum" ..	1·25	85

116. Beechcraft "18".

1983. Bicentenary of Manned Flight. Mult.

No.	Description		
304.	10 c. Type **116**	15	15
305.	27 c. Fokker "F 28 Fellowship"	30	35
306.	45 c. French military "DC-4"	50	60
307.	75 c. Sikorsky helicopter..	90	95

117. St. Matthew.

1983. Christmas. 150th Birth Anniv. of Sir Edmond Burne-Jones.

No.	Description		
309.	5 c. Type **117**	10	10
310.	24 c. St. Mark	30	30
311.	30 c. Jesus Christ ..	40	40
312.	45 c. St. Luke	55	55
313.	85 c. St. John	1·10	1·10

DESIGNS: showing stained glass windows from St. Barnabas Chapel, Norfolk Island.

118. Cable Ship "Chantik".

1983. World Communications Year. ANZCAN Cable. Multicoloured.

No.	Description		
314.	30 c. Type **118**	40	40
315.	45 c. "Chantik" during in-shore operations ..	55	55
316.	75 c. Cable ship "Mercury"	95	95
317.	85 c. Diagram of cable route	1·10	1·10

119. Strand Morning Glory.

1984. Flowers. Multicoloured.

No.	Description		
318.	1 c. Popwood	20	20
319.	2 c. Type **119**	30	20
320.	3 c. Native Phreatia ..	35	20
321.	4 c. Philip Island Wisteria	35	20
322.	5 c. Norfolk Island Palm	35	20
323.	10 c. Evergreen	40	20
324.	15 c. Bastard Oak ..	50	30
325.	20 c. Devil's Guts.. ..	50	30
326.	25 c. White Oak	60	35
327.	30 c. Ti	70	40
328.	35 c. Philip Island Hibiscus	70	40
329.	40 c. Native Wisteria ..	80	45
330.	50 c. Native Jasmine ..	1·25	50
331.	$1 Norfolk Island Passion-fruit ..	1·25	1·00
332.	$3 Native Oberonia ..	3·00	2·75
333.	$5 Norfolk Island Pine ..	4·50	4·00

120. "Cheilodactylidae".

1984. Reef Fish. Multicoloured.

No.	Description		
334.	30 c. Type **120**	40	45
335.	45 c. "Pseudopeneus signatus"	60	65
336.	75 c. "Acanthuridae" ..	1·00	1·10
337.	85 c. "Chaeton ancinetus"	1·25	1·40

121. Owl with eggs.

1984. Boobook Owl. Multicoloured.

No.	Description		
338.	30 c. Type **121**	65	50
339.	30 c. Fledgling	65	50
340.	30 c. Young owl on stump	65	50
341.	30 c. Adult on branch ..	65	50
342.	30 c. Owl in flight	65	50

122. 1953 7½d. and 1974 Cook Bicent. 10 c. Stamp.

1984. "Ausipex" International Stamp Exhibition, Melbourne. Multicoloured.

No.	Description		
343.	30 c. Type **122**	30	35
344.	45 c. John Buffett commemorative postal stationery envelope ..	45	75
345.	75 c. Design from Presentation Pack for 1982 Military Uniforms issue ..	90	1·75

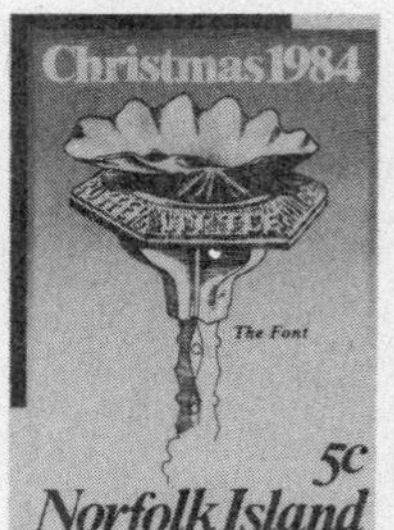

123. Font, Kingston Methodist Church.

1984. Christmas. Centenary of Methodist Church on Norfolk Island. Multicoloured.

No.	Description		
347.	5 c. Type **123**	10	10
348.	24 c. Church service in Old Barracks, Kingston, late 1800s	35	40
349.	30 c. The Revd. & Mrs. A.H. Phelps and sailing ship	40	45
350.	45 c. The Revd. A.H. Phelps and First Congregational Church, Chester, U.S.A.	60	65
351.	85 c. Interior of Kingston Methodist Church ..	1·25	1·40

124. The Revd. Nobbs teaching Pitcairn Islanders.

1984. Death Centenary of Revd. George Hunn Nobbs (leader of Pitcairn community). Multicoloured.

No.	Description		
352.	30 c. Type **124**	40	45
353.	45 c. The Revd. Nobbs with sick islander ..	60	65
354.	75 c. Baptising baby ..	1·00	1·10
355.	85 c. Presented to Queen Victoria, 1852	1·25	1·40

125. "Fanny Fisher".

1985. 19th-Century Whaling Ships (1st series). Multicoloured.

No.	Description		
356.	5 c. Type **125**	30	15
357.	33 c. "Costa Rica Packet"	85	55
358.	50 c. "Splendid"	1·25	1·00
359.	90 c. "Onward"	1·75	1·75

See also Nos. 360/3.

1985. 19th-Century Whaling Ships (2nd series). As T **125**. Multicoloured.

No.	Description		
360.	15 c. "Waterwitch" ..	50	50
361.	20 c. "Canton"	60	60
362.	60 c. "Aladdin"	1·25	1·25
363.	80 c. "California"	1·60	1·75

126. The Queen Mother (from photo by Norman Parkinson).

1985. Life and Times of Queen Elizabeth the Queen Mother. Multicoloured.

No.	Description		
364.	5 c. The Queen Mother (from photo by Dorothy Wilding)	10	10
365.	33 c. With Princess Anne at Trooping the Colour	35	40
366.	50 c. Type **126**	50	55
367.	90 c. With Prince Henry at his christening (from photo by Lord Snowdon)	95	1·00

127. "Swimming".

1985. International Youth Year. Children's Paintings. Multicoloured.

No.	Description		
369.	33 c. Type **127**	75	40
370.	50 c. "A Walk in the Country"	1·50	85

128. Prize-winning Cow and Owner.

1985. 125th Anniv. of Royal Norfolk Island Agricultural and Horticultural Show. Mult.

No.	Description		
371.	80 c. Type **128**	75	80
372.	90 c. Show exhibits ..	85	90

129. Shepherds with Flock.

1985. Christmas. Multicoloured.
374. 27 c. Type **129** 60 30
375. 33 c. Mary and Joseph with donkey 75 40
376. 50 c. The Three Wise Men 1·40 65
377. 90 c. The Nativity .. 1·75 1·25

130. Long-spined Sea Urchin.

1986. Marine Life. Multicoloured.
378. 5 c. Type **130** 10 10
379. 33 c. Blue Starfish .. 40 35
380. 55 c. Eagle Ray 60 75
381. 75 c. Moray Eel .. .. 85 1·00

131. "Giotto" Spacecraft.

1986. Appearance of Halley's Comet. Mult.
383. $1 Type **131** .. .. 1·50 1·75
384. $1 Halley's Comet .. 1·50 1·75
Nos. 383/4 were printed together, se-tenant, forming a composite design.

132. Isaac Robinson (U.S. Consul 1887–1908).

1986. "Ameripex '86" International Stamp Exhibition, Chicago. Multicoloured.
385. 33 c. Type **132** 60 35
386. 50 c. Ford "Model T" (first vehicle on island) (horiz.) 80 50
387. 80 c. Statue of Liberty .. 1·10 80
No. 387 also commemorates the Centenary of the Statue of Liberty.

133. Princess Elizabeth and Dog.

1986. 60th Birthday of Queen Elizabeth II. Multicoloured.
389. 5 c. Type **133** 10 10
390. 33 c. Queen Elizabeth II .. 50 35
391. 80 c. Opening Norfolk Island Golf Club .. 1·25 1·40
392. 90 c. With Duke of Edinburgh in carriage .. 1·50 1·60

134. Stylized Dove and Norfolk Island.

1986. Christmas.
393. **134.** 30 c. multicoloured .. 35 30
394. 40 c. multicoloured .. 50 45
395. $1 multicoloured .. 1·40 1·50

135. British Convicts, 1787.

1986. Bicentenary (1988) of Norfolk Island Settlement (1st issue). Governor Phillip's Commission. Multicoloured.
396. 36 c. Type **135** 75 35
397. 55 c. Judge passing sentence of transportation .. .. .. 1·25 65
398. 90 c. Governor Phillip meeting Home Secretary (inscr "Home Society") 1·90 1·25
399. 90 c. As No. 398, but correctly inscr "Home Secretary" (16.12) .. 1·90 1·25
400. $1 Captain Arthur Phillip 2·00 1·40
See also Nos. 401/4, 421/4, 433/5, 436/7 and 438/43.

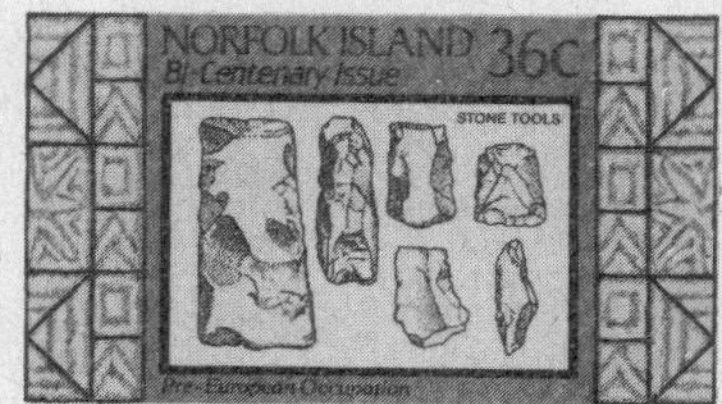

136. Stone Tools.

1986. Bicentenary (1988) of Norfolk Island Settlement (2nd issue). Pre-European Occupation. Multicoloured.
401. 36 c. Type **136** 65 45
402. 36 c. Bananas and taro .. 65 45
403. 36 c. Polynesian outrigger canoe 65 45
404. 36 c. Maori chief 65 45

137. Philip Island from Point Ross.

1987. Norfolk Island Scenes. Multicoloured.
405. 1 c. Cockpit Creek Bridge 20 30
406. 2 c. Cemetery Bay Beach 20 30
407. 3 c. Island guesthouse .. 20 30
408. 5 c. Type **137** 20 15
409. 15 c. Cattle in pasture .. 25 30
410. 30 c. Rock fishing 30 30
411. 37 c. Old Pitcairner-style house 50 50
412. 40 c. Shopping centre .. 35 35
413. 50 c. Emily Bay 45 45
414. 60 c. Bloody Bridge .. 65 75
415. 80 c. Pitcairner-style shop 85 95
416. 90 c. Government House .. 85 1·10
417. $1 Melanesian Memorial Chapel 90 95
418. $2 Convict settlement, Kingston .. .. 1·75 1·75
419. $3 Ball Bay .. .. 3·00 3·25
420. $5 Northern cliffs .. .. 4·75 5·50

1987. Bicentenary of Norfolk Island Settlement (1988) (3rd issue). The First Fleet. As T **135.** Multicoloured.
421. 5 c. Loading supplies, Deptford 40 40
422. 55 c. Fleet leaving Spithead .. .. .. 1·40 1·50
423. 55 c. H.M.S. "Sirius" leaving Spithead .. 1·40 1·50
424. $1 Female convicts below decks .. .. .. 2·25 2·25
Nos. 422/3 were printed together, se-tenant, forming a composite design.

138. Male Red-fronted Parakeet.

1987. Red-fronted Parakeet ("Green Parrot"). Multicoloured.
425. 5 c. Type **138** 60 60
426. 15 c. Adult with fledgeling and egg .. .. .. 1·00 1·00
427. 36 c. Young parakeets .. 1·75 1·75
428. 55 c. Female parakeet .. 2·00 2·00

139. Christmas Tree and Restored Garrison Barracks.

1987. Christmas. Multicoloured.
429. 30 c. Type **139** 30 30
430. 42 c. Children opening presents 45 55
431. 58 c. Father Christmas with children 60 65
432. 63 c. Children's party .. 70 80

1987. Bicentenary of Norfolk Island Settlement (1988) (4th issue). Visit of La Perouse (navigator). As T **135.** Mult.
433. 37 c. La Perouse with King Louis XVI 75 55
434. 90 c. "L'Astrolabe" and "La Boussole" off Norfolk Island .. .. 1·75 2·00
435. $1 "L'Astrolabe" wrecked in Solomon Islands .. 2·25 2·50

1988. Bicentenary of Norfolk Island Settlement (5th issue). Arrival of First Fleet at Sydney. As T **135.** Multicoloured.
436. 37 c. Ship's cutter approaching Port Jackson 90 65
437. $1 Landing at Sydney Cove .. .. .. 2·10 2·10

1988. Bicentenary of Norfolk Island Settlement (6th issue). Foundation of First Settlement. As T **135.** Multicoloured.
438. 5 c. Lt. Philip Gidley King 20 20
439. 37 c. Raising the flag, March 1788 .. .. 75 75
440. 55 c. King exploring .. 1·25 1·25
441. 70 c. Landing at Sydney Bay, Norfolk Island .. 1·50 1·50
442. 90 c. H.M.S. "Supply" (brig) 1·75 1·75
443. $1 Sydney Bay Settlement, 1788 .. .. .. 1·90 1·90

140 Airliner, Container Ship and Sydney Harbour Bridge

1988. "Sydpex '88" National Stamp Exhibition, Sydney. Multicoloured.
444 37 c. Type **140** 55 65
445 37 c. Exhibition label under magnifying glass (horiz) 55 65
446 37 c. Telephone and dish aerial 55 65

141 Flowers and Decorations

1988. Christmas. Multicoloured.
448 30 c. Type **141** 40 40
449 42 c. Flowers 60 70
450 58 c. Fishes and beach .. 75 85
451 63 c. Norfolk Island .. 85 1·00

142 Pier Store and Boat Shed

1988. Restored Buildings from the Convict Era. Multicoloured.
452 39 c. Type **142** 35 40
453 55 c. Royal Engineers Building 50 55
454 90 c. Old Military Barracks 85 90
455 $1 Commissariat Store and New Military Barracks 95 1·00

143 "Lamprima aenea"

1989. Endemic Insects. Multicoloured.
456 39 c. Type **143** 45 40
457 55 c. "Insulascirtus nythos" 60 70
458 90 c. "Caedicia araucariae" 1·00 1·10
459 $1 "Thrincophora aridela" 1·10 1·25

144 H.M.S. "Bounty" off Tasmania

1989. Bicentenary of the Mutiny on the "Bounty". Multicoloured.

460	5 c. Type **144**	30	30
461	39 c. Mutineers and Polynesian women, Pitcairn Island	1·25	1·25
462	55 c. Lake Windermere, Cumbria (Christian's home county)	1·75	1·75
463	$1.10 "Mutineers casting Bligh adrift" (Robert Dodd)	2·50	2·50

145 Norfolk Island Flag

1989. 10th Anniv of Internal Self-Government. Multicoloured.

465	41 c. Type **145**	60	55
466	55 c. Old ballot box	70	65
467	$1 Norfolk Island Act, 1979	1·40	1·40
468	$1.10 Island crest	1·50	1·60

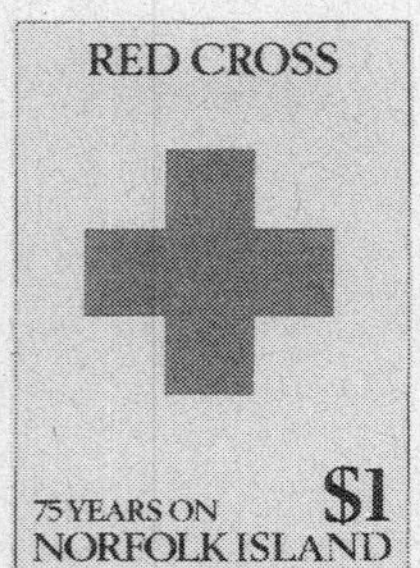

146 Red Cross

1989. 75th Anniv of Red Cross on Norfolk Island.

469	**146**	$1 red and blue	2·00	1·75

147 "Gethsemane"

1989. Christmas. Designs showing opening lines of hymns and local scenes. Multicoloured.

470	36 c. Type **147**	70	40
471	60 c. "In the Sweet Bye and Bye"	1·10	1·10
472	75 c. "Let the Lower Lights Be Burning"	1·40	1·40
473	80 c. "The Beautiful Stream"	1·50	1·75

148 John Royle (first announcer)

149 H.M.S. "Bounty" on fire, Pitcairn Island, 1790

1989. 50th Anniv of Radio Australia. Designs each showing Kingston buildings. Mult.

474	41 c. Type **148**	75	55
475	65 c. Radio waves linking Australia and Norfolk Island	1·25	1·25
476	$1.10 Anniversary kookaburra logo	2·00	2·00

1990. History of the Norfolk Islanders (1st series). Settlement on Pitcairn Island. Mult.

477	70 c. Type **149**	1·50	1·50
478	$1.10 Arms of Norfolk Island	1·75	1·75

See also Nos. 503/4 and 516/17.

150 H.M.S. "Sirius" striking Reef

1990. Bicentenary of Wreck of H.M.S. "Sirius". Multicoloured.

479	41 c. Type **150**	1·00	1·00
480	41 c. H.M.S. "Sirius" failing to clear bay	1·00	1·00
481	65 c. Divers at work on wreck	1·40	1·40
482	$1 Recovered artifacts and chart of site	2·00	2·00

Nos. 479/80 were printed together, se-tenant, forming a composite design.

151 Unloading Lighter, Kingston

152 "Ile de Lumiere" (freighter)

1990. Ships.

483	**151**	5 c. brown	10	10
484		10 c. brown	10	10
485	–	45 c. multicoloured	40	45
486	–	50 c. multicoloured	45	50
487	–	65 c. multicoloured	60	65
488	**152**	70 c. multicoloured	65	70
489	–	75 c. multicoloured	70	75
490	–	80 c. multicoloured	75	80
491	–	90 c. multicoloured	85	90
492	–	$1 multicoloured	90	95
493	–	$2 multicoloured	1·90	2·00
494	–	$5 multicoloured	4·50	4·75

DESIGNS—As T **152**. 45 c. "La Dunkerquoise" (French patrol vessel); 50 c. "Dmitri Mendeleev" (Soviet research vessel); 65 c. "Pacific Rover" (tanker); 75 c. "Norfolk Trader" (freighter); 80 c. "Roseville" (transport); 90 c. "Kalia" (container ship); $1 "Bounty" (replica); $2 H.M.A.S. "Success" (supply ship); $5 H.M.A.S. "Whyalla" (patrol vessel).

153 Santa on House Roof

154 William Charles Wentworth

1990. Christmas. Multicoloured.

499	38 c. Type **153**	50	45
500	43 c. Santa at Kingston Post Office	55	50
501	65 c. Santa over Sydney Bay, Kingston (horiz)	85	75
502	85 c. Santa on Officers' Quarters (horiz)	1·10	1·10

1990. History of the Norfolk Islanders (2nd series). The First Generation.

503	**154**	70 c. brn & cinnamon	85	85
504	–	$1.20 brn & cinnamon	1·40	1·40

DESIGN: $1.20, Thursday October Christian.

155 Adult Robin and Chicks in Nest

156 Map of Norfolk Island

1990. "Birdpex '90" Stamp Exhibition, Christchurch, New Zealand. Scarlet Robin. Multicoloured.

505	65 c. Type **155**	75	75
506	$1 Hen on branch	1·25	1·25
507	$1.20 Cock on branch	1·40	1·40

1991. Ham Radio Network. Multicoloured.

509	43 c. Type **156**	60	50
510	$1 Globe showing Norfolk Island	1·40	1·40
511	$1.20 Map of south-west Pacific	1·60	1·75

157 Display in "Sirius" Museum

1991. Norfolk Island Museums. Mult.

512	43 c. Type **157**	60	50
513	70 c. 19th-century sitting room, House Museum (horiz)	95	95
514	$1 Carronade, "Sirius" Museum (horiz)	1·40	1·40
515	$1.20 Reconstructed jug and beaker, Archaeological Museum	1·60	1·60

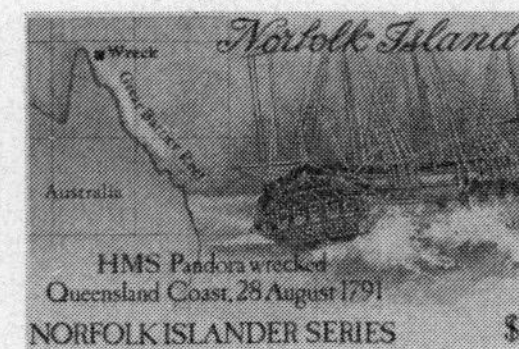

158 H.M.S. "Pandora" wrecked on Great Barrier Reef (1791)

1991. History of the Norfolk Islanders (3rd series). Search for the "Bounty". Mult.

516	$1 Type **158**	1·40	1·40
517	$1.20 H.M.S. "Pandora" leaving bay	1·60	1·60

159 Hibiscus and Island Scene

1991. Christmas.

518	**159**	38 c. multicoloured	50	40
519		43 c. multicoloured	60	55
520		65 c. multicoloured	80	80
521		85 c. multicoloured	1·00	1·10

160 Tank and Soldier in Jungle

1991. 50th Anniv of Outbreak of Pacific War. Multicoloured.

522	43 c. Type **160**	55	45
523	70 c. B17 Flying Fortress on jungle airstrip	90	90
524	$1 Warships	1·40	1·50

161 Coat of Arms

1992. 500th Anniv of Discovery of America by Columbus. Multicoloured.

525	45 c. Type **161**	40	45
526	$1.05 "Santa Maria"	95	1·00
527	$1.20 Columbus and globe	1·10	1·25

162 Deployment Map

1992. 50th Anniv of Battle of the Coral Sea. Multicoloured.

528	45 c. Type **162**	40	45
529	70 c. H.M.A.S. "Australia" (cruiser)	90	95
530	$1.05 U.S.S. "Yorktown" (aircraft carrier)	95	1·00

1992. 50th Anniv of Battle of Midway. As T **162**. Multicoloured.

531	45 c. Battle area	40	45
532	70 c. Catalina PBY 5 flying boat over task force	90	95
533	$1.05 Douglas SBD 5 Dauntless dive bomber and burning Japanese aircraft carrier	95	1·00

NORTH BORNEO

A territory in the N. of the Island of Borneo in the China Sea, formerly under the administration of the Br. N. Borneo Co. A Crown Colony since 1946. Joined Malaysia in 1963 and renamed Sabah in 1964.

100 cents = 1 dollar (Malayan).

1.

1883. "POSTAGE NORTH BORNEO" at top.

8	**1.**	½ c. mauve	45·00	£100
9		1 c. orange	£140	£200
10		2 c. brown	12·00	14·00
11		4 c. pink	12·00	35·00
12		8 c. green	14·00	35·00
13		10 c. blue	14·00	32·00

1883. Surch. **8 Cents.** vert.

2.	**1.**	8 c. on 2 c. brown	£800	£550

1883. Surch. **EIGHT CENTS.**

3.	**1.**	8 c. on 2 c. brown	£350	£150

Where there are three price columns, prices in the second column are for postally used stamps and those in the third column are for stamps cancelled with black bars.

4. 5.

1883.

4.	**4.**	50 c. violet ..	70·00	—	12·00
5.	**5.**	$1 red ..	50·00	—	8·00

1886. Optd. **and Revenue.**

14.	**1.**	½ c. mauve	50·00	£110
15.		10 c. blue	90·00	£140

1886. Surch. in words and figures.

18.	**1.**	3 c. on 4 c. pink ..	48·00	85·00
19.		5 c. on 8 c. green ..	60·00	85·00

9. 10.

1886. Inscr. "BRITISH NORTH BORNEO".

22.	**9.**	½ c. red	1·75	8·50
24.		1 c. orange ..	1·25	5·50
25.		2 c. brown ..	1·50	6·00
26.		4 c. pink	1·25	6·00
27.		8 c. green ..	2·75	11·00
28.		10 c. blue ..	4·50	18·00

1887.

45.	**10.**	25 c. blue ..	19·00	65·00	50
46.	–	50 c. violet ..	35·00	95·00	50
47.	–	$1 red ..	20·00	90·00	50
48.	–	$2 green ..	65·00	£130	1·10
49.	–	$5 purple ..	80·00	90·00	6·00
50.	–	$10 brown ..	£120	£160	9·00

The $5 and $10 are much larger than Type **5** and show the arms with supporters as in Type **3**.

14.

1888. Inscr. "POSTAGE & REVE[illegible]

36b	**14.**	½ c. red	30	2·50	[illegible]
37		1 c. orange ..	50	2·25	[illegible]
38b		2 c. brown ..	1·00	6·00	[illegible]
39		3 c. violet ..	1·25	8·50	[illegible]
40		4 c. pink ..	2·25	13·00	[illegible]
41		5 c. grey ..	2·00	9·00	[illegible]
42		6 c. deep red ..	4·50	11·00	[illegible]
43		8 c. green ..	7·00	12·00	[illegible]
44b		10 c. blue ..	4·25	12·00	[illegible]

1890. Surch. in words.

51.	**10.**	2 c. on 25 c. blue	40·00	[illegible]
52.		8 c. on 25 c. blue	60·00	8[illegible]

1891. Surch. in figures and words.

63.	**14.**	1 c. on 4 c. pink ..	12·00	14·00
64.		1 c. on 5 c. grey ..	6·00	6·00
54.	**9.**	6 c. on 8 c. green ..	£5000	£3500
55.	**14.**	6 c. on 8 c. green ..	7·00	8·50
56.	**9.**	6 c. on 10 c. blue ..	32·00	17·00
57.	**14.**	6 c. on 10 c. blue ..	70·00	24·00
65.	**10.**	8 c. on 25 c. blue ..	£110	£130

24. Dyak Chief.

25. Sambar Stag ("Cervus unicolor").

26. Sago Palm.

27. Great Argus Pheasant.

28. Arms of the Company.

29. Malay Prau.

30. Estuarine Crocodile.

31. Mt. Kinabalu.

32. Arms of the Company with Supporters.

1894.

[illegible]	**24.**	1 c. blk. & bis.	1·00	6·00	20
[illegible]	**25.**	2 c. blk. & red	3·25	4·00	30
[illegible]	**26.**	3 c. grn. & mve.	2·25	7·00	30
[illegible]	**27.**	5 c. blk. & red	6·00	10·00	40
[illegible]	**28.**	6 c. blk. & brn.	3·50	13·00	40
[illegible]	**29.**	8 c. blk. & lilac	2·50	8·00	50
[illegible]	**30.**	12 c. blk. & bl.	24·00	60·00	2·00
[illegible]	**31.**	18 c. blk. & grn.	15·00	40·00	2·00
[illegible]	**32.**	24 c. bl. & red ..	16·00	48·00	2·00

1894. As Nos. 47, etc., but inscr. "THE STATE OF NORTH BORNEO".

81	25 c. blue	8·00	26·00	70
82	50 c. violet	9·00	40·00	70
83	$1 red	10·00	22·00	90
84	$2 green	13·00	55·00	90
85b	$5 purple	65·00	£100	3·50
86	$10 brown	£130	£190	5·00

1895. No. 83 surch. in figures and words.

87.	4 cents on $1 red	2·50	1·50	30
88.	10 cents on $1 red	4·75	1·75	30
89.	20 cents on $1 red	15·00	9·50	30
90.	30 cents on $1 red	10·00	13·00	30
91.	40 cents on $1 red	15·00	23·00	30

37. Orang-utan.

41. Sun Bear.

43. Borneo Steam Train.

1897. As 1894. issue with insertion of native inscriptions.

92a	**24.**	1 c. blk. & bis.	3·75	2·00	20
94a	**25.**	2 c. black & red	6·00	2·75	20
95		2 c. blk & grn.	21·00	1·50	20
97	**26.**	3 c. grn. & mve.	4·50	3·00	30
98	**37.**	4 c. blk. & grn.	6·00	—	40
99		4 c. black & red	13·00	4·75	30
100	**27.**	5 c. blk. & orge	40·00	3·50	30
101a	**28.**	6 c. blk. & brn.	8·00	3·00	30
102b	**29.**	8 c. blk. & lilac	14·00	2·75	40
104	**41.**	10 c. brn. & grey	45·00	27·00	1·00
106b	**30.**	12 c. blk. & bl.	48·00	28·00	1·00
107	**43.**	16 c. grn. & brn.	75·00	70·00	2·50
108	**31.**	18 c. blk. & grn.	12·00	27·00	50
110		18 c. blk. & grn.*	42·00	12·00	75
109	**32.**	24 c. bl. & red*	8·50	48·00	1·00
111		24 c. bl. & red*	35·00	30·00	1·00

* No. 110 is inscribed "POSTAGE & REVENUE" at the sides instead of "POSTAL REVENUE" as in No. 108. No. 111 has the words "POSTAGE & REVENUE" at the sides below the Arms; these words were omitted in No. 109.

1899. Stamps of 1897 and Nos. 81/6 surch. **4 CENTS.**

112a	4 c. on 5 c. black & orange	10·00	10·00
113a	4 c. on 6 c. black & brown	10·00	26·00
114	4 c. on 8 c. black and lilac	12·00	10·00
115	4 c. on 12 c. black & blue	11·00	13·00
116	4 c. on 18 c. black and green (110) ..	9·50	13·00
117	4c. on 24 c. bl & red (111)	11·00	12·00
118	4 c. on 25 c. blue ..	5·00	8·50
119	4 c. on 50 c. violet ..	6·00	12·00
121	4 c. on $1 red ..	5·00	8·50
122	4 c. on $2 green ..	5·00	12·00
125	4 c. on $5 purple ..	5·50	11·00
126	4 c. on $10 brown ..	5·50	11·00

1901. Stamps of 1897 and Nos. 81/6 optd. **BRITISH PROTECTORATE.**

127a	1 c. blk. & bistre ..	1·50	1·60	10
128	2 c. black & green ..	2·25	1·75	10
129	3 c. grn. & mve. ..	1·10	2·50	10
130	4 c. black and red ..	4·50	1·50	10
131a	5 c. black & orange	4·75	2·25	15
132b	6 c. black & brown	2·50	6·00	20
133	8 c. black and lilac	2·75	3·00	20
134	10 c. brown & grey	11·00	4·50	30
135	12 c. black and blue	23·00	12·00	1·00
136	16 c. green & brown	50·00	20·00	1·50
137	18 c. blk. & grn. (110)	8·00	19·00	60
138	24 c. bl. & red (111)	14·00	26·00	1·00
139	25 c. blue	2·00	10·00	30
140	50 c. violet	2·75	11·00	40
142	$1 red	6·50	28·00	2·50
143	$2 green	25·00	75·00	3·50
144	$5 purple	£130	£300	4·00
145	$10 brown	£190	£375	7·00

1904. Stamps of 1897. and Nos. 81/6 surch. **4 cents.**

146.	4 c. on 5 c. black & orange	15·00	26·00	3·00
147.	4 c. on 6 c. black & brown	5·00	15·00	2·00
148.	4 c. on 8 c. black and lilac	11·00	23·00	2·25
149.	4 c. on 12 c. black and blue	17·00	30·00	2·50
150.	4 c. on 18 c. blk. & green (110)	14·00	28·00	3·00
151a.	4 c. on 24 c. bl. and red (111) ..	15·00	38·00	3·00
152.	4 c. on 25 c. blue ..	3·50	22·00	2·50
153.	4 c. on 50 c. violet ..	3·50	28·00	2·50
154.	4 c. on $1 red ..	4·25	40·00	3·00
155.	4 c. on $2 green ..	5·50	42·00	3·75
156.	4 c. on $5 purple ..	11·00	45·00	3·50
157.	4 c. on $10 brown ..	11·00	45·00	3·50

51. Malayan Tapir.

52. Traveller's-tree.

64.

(68.)

1909. The 18c. is surch. **20 CENTS.**

277	**51.**	1 c. black & brn	75	70	—
160	**52.**	2 c. black & grn.	75	30	10
278		2 c. blk. & red	35	50	—
161	–	3 c. black & red	2·00	90	10
279	–	3 c. black & grn.	2·00	1·25	—
280	–	4 c. black & red	45	10	—
281	–	5 c. black & brn.	3·00	2·00	—
282	–	6 c. black & grn.	2·50	40	—
283	–	8 c. black & red	1·50	10	—
284	–	10 c. black & bl.	1·75	40	—
285	–	12 c. black & bl.	5·50	40	—
174	–	16 c. blk. & brn.	14·00	5·00	40
175	–	18 c. blk. & grn.	55·00	27·00	50
177	–	20 c. on 18 c. black and grn.	4·00	35	10
176	–	24 c. blk. & mve.	16·00	2·25	30
178	**64.**	25 c. blk. & grn.	4·00	3·25	1·00
179		50 c. blk. & blue	5·50	3·25	1·25
180		$1 black & brn.	11·00	3·25	1·25
181		$2 black & lilac	27·00	11·00	3·00
182	–	$5 black & red	55·00	60·00	20·00
183	–	$10 blk. & orge.	£140	£170	40·00

DESIGNS—As Type **51**: 3 c. Railway at Jesselton. 4 c. Sultan of Sulu, his staff and W. C. Cowie first Chairman of the Company. 5 c. Asiatic elephant. 8 c. Ploughing with buffalo. 24 c. Dwarf Cassowary. As Type **52**: 6 c. Rhinoceros. 10 c. Wild boar. 12 c. Palm Cockatoo. 16 c. Rhinoceros Hornbill. 18 c. Wild bull. As Type **64** but Arms with supporters: $5, $10.

1916. Stamps of 1909 surch.

186.	2 c. on 3 c. black and red	9·50	7·50
187.	4 c. on 6 c. black and olive.	9·50	9·50
188.	10 c. on 12 c. black & blue	25·00	35·00

1916. Nos. 277 etc., optd with T **68**.

189.	1 c. black and brown ..	6·50	26·00
203.	2 c. black and green ..	26·00	38·00
191.	3 c. black and red ..	20·00	35·00
192.	4 c. black and red ..	5·50	23·00
193.	5 c. black and brown	18·00	50·00
206.	6 c. black and green	26·00	65·00
195.	8 c. black and red ..	17·00	50·00
208.	10 c. black and blue	30·00	60·00
197.	12 c. black and blue	60·00	70·00
198.	16 c. black and brown	60·00	70·00
199.	20 c. on 18 c. black & green	25·00	70·00
200.	24 c. black and mauve	60·00	70·00
201.	25 c. black and green ..	£250	£350

1918. Nos. 159, etc., surch. **RED CROSS TWO CENTS.**

214.	1 c. + 2 c. black and brown	2·25	7·00
215.	2 c. + 2 c. black and green	70	7·00
216.	3 c. + 2 c. black and red ..	4·50	12·00
218.	4 c. + 2 c. black and red ..	55	3·75
219.	5 c. + 2 c. black and brown	4·50	14·00
221.	6 c. + 2 c. black and olive	3·50	17·00
222.	8 c. + 2 c. black and red ..	4·00	7·00
223.	10 c. + 2 c. black and blue	6·50	22·00
224.	12 c. + 2 c. black and blue	10·00	30·00
225.	16 c. + 2 c. black & brn. ..	11·00	30·00
226.	24 c. + 2 c. black & mve, ..	12·00	30·00
229.	25 c. + 2 c. black and green	10·00	38·00
230.	50 c. + 2 c. black and blue	12·00	38·00
231.	$1 + 2 c. black and brown	38·00	48·00
232.	$2 + 2 c. black and lilac ..	55·00	90·00
233.	$5 + 2 c. black and red ..	£250	£400
234.	$10 + 2 c. black and orange	£250	£400

The premium of 2 c. on each value was for Red Cross Funds.

1918. Nos. 159, etc., surch. **FOUR CENTS** and a red cross.

235.	1 c. + 4 c. black and brown	50	3·50
236.	2 c. + 4 c. black and green	65	6·50
237.	3 c. + 4 c. black and red ..	80	3·25
238.	4 c. + 4 c. black and red ..	40	4·50
239.	5 c. + 4 c. black and brown	1·75	16·00
240.	6 c. + 4 c. black and olive	1·75	11·00
241.	8 c. + 4 c. black and red ..	1·10	9·00
242.	10 c. + 4 c. black and blue	2·00	12·00
243.	12 c. + 4 c. black and blue	6·00	12·00
244.	16 c. + 4 c. black & brn. ..	5·00	16·00
245.	24 c. + 4 c. black & mve. ..	5·00	20·00
246.	25 c. + 4 c. black and green	3·25	38·00
248.	50 c. + 4 c. black and blue	14·00	38·00
249.	$1 + 4 c. black and brown	14·00	50·00
250.	$2 + 4 c. black and lilac	40·00	75·00
251.	$5 + 4 c. black and red ..	£200	£400
252.	$10 + 4 c. black and orange	£200	£400

The premium of 4 c. on each value was for Red Cross Funds.

1922. Nos. 159, etc., optd. **MALAYA-BORNEO EXHIBITION 1922.**

253.	1 c. black and brown ..	5·50	40·00
255.	2 c. black and green ..	1·40	14·00
256.	3 c. black and red ..	5·00	30·00
257.	4 c. black and red ..	1·40	24·00
258.	5 c. black and brown ..	6·00	42·00
260.	6 c. black and green ..	2·75	38·00
261.	8 c. black and red ..	4·00	38·00
263.	10 c. black and blue ..	4·50	38·00
265.	12 c. black and blue ..	3·75	20·00
267.	16 c. black and brown ..	6·50	45·00
268.	20 c. on 18 c. black & green	7·00	45·00
270.	24 c. black and mauve ..	16·00	48·00
274.	25 c. black and green ..	3·75	45·00
275.	50 c. black and blue ..	6·00	35·00

1923. No. 280 surch. **THREE CENTS** and bars.

276.	–	3 c. on 4 c. black & red	1·00	4·00

DESIGNS—VERT. 6 c. Orang-utan. 10 c. Dyak warrior. $1, $2, $5, Arms. HORIZ. 25 c. Clouded leopard.

73. Head of a Murut.

76. Mount Kinabalu.

1931. 50th Anniv. of North Borneo Company.

295.	73.	3 c. black and green ..	80	50
296.	–	6 c. black and orange ..	12·00	3·00
297.	–	10 c. black and red ..	2·75	9·00
298.	76.	12 c. black and blue ..	3·75	7·00
299.	–	25 c. black and violet ..	28·00	27·00
300.	–	$1 black and green ..	15·00	55·00
301.	–	$2 black and brown ..	35·00	75·00
302.	–	$5 black and purple ..	£110	£200

81. Buffalo Transport.

DESIGNS—VERT 3c. Native. 4 c. Proboscis monkey. 6 c. Mounted Bajaus. 10 c. Orang-Utan. 15 c. Dyak. $1, $2, Arms. HORIZ. 8 c. Map of East Indies. 12 c. Murut with blow-pipe. 20 c. River scene. 25 c. Native boat. 50 c. Mt. Kinabalu. $5, Arms with supporters.

82. Palm Cockatoo.

1939.

303.	81.	1 c. green and brown ..	30	
304.	82.	2 c. purple and blue ..	1·50	
305.	–	3 c. blue and green ..	45	
306.	–	4 c. green and violet ..	65	
307.	–	6 c. blue and red ..	45	1
308.	–	8 c. red	4·00	
309.	–	10 c. violet and green ..	24·00	4
310.	–	12 c. green and blue ..	6·00	2
311.	–	15 c. green and brown	10·00	4·
312.	–	20 c. violet and blue ..	5·50	3·
313.	–	25 c. green and brown ..	6·50	4·5
314.	–	50 c. brown and violet ..	8·00	4·0
315.	–	$1 brown and red ..	38·00	15·0
316.	–	$2 violet and olive ..	70·00	60·0
317.	–	$5 blue	£225	£160

1941. Optd. **WAR TAX.**

318.	81.	1 c. green and brown ..	10	30
319.	82.	2 c. purple and blue ..	45	1·75

1945. British Military Administration. Stamps of 1939 optd. **BMA.**

320.	81.	1 c. green and brown ..	2·00	40
321.	82.	2 c. purple and blue ..	4·50	75
322.	–	3 c. blue and green ..	1·00	80
323.	–	4 c. green and violet ..	14·00	9·00
324.	–	6 c. blue and red ..	1·00	30
325.	–	8 c. red	1·25	45
326.	–	10 c. violet and green ..	1·75	30
327.	–	12 c. green and blue ..	2·25	80
328.	–	15 c. green and brown ..	1·00	1·00
329.	–	20 c. violet and blue ..	1·00	1·00
330.	–	25 c. green and brown ..	2·25	75
331.	–	50 c. brown and violet ..	2·00	1·00
332.	–	$1 brown and red ..	18·00	15·00
333.	–	$2 violet and olive ..	18·00	15·00
334.	–	$5 blue	8·00	8·00

1947. Stamps of 1939 optd. with Crown over **GR** monogram and bars obliterating "THE STATE OF" and "BRITISH PROTECTORATE".

335.	81.	1 c. green and brown ..	15	40
336.	82.	2 c. purple and blue ..	45	50
337.	–	3 c. blue and green ..	15	15
338.	–	4 c. green and violet ..	20	10
339.	–	6 c. blue and red ..	15	20
340.	–	8 c. red	20	15
341.	–	10 c. violet and green ..	40	15
342.	–	12 c. green and blue ..	70	85
343.	–	15 c. green and brown ..	1·00	30
344.	–	20 c. violet and blue ..	35	30
345.	–	25 c. green and brown ..	40	30
346.	–	50 c. brown and violet ..	75	55
347.	–	$1 brown and red ..	60	85
348.	–	$2 violet and olive ..	2·25	4·25
349.	–	$5 blue	8·50	7·00

1948. Silver Wedding. As T **10/11** of Antigua.

350.	8 c. red	30	40
351.	$10 mauve	11·00	24·00

1949. U.P.U. As T **20/23** of Antigua.

352.	8 c. red	30	30
353.	10 c. brown	60	30
354.	30 c. brown	70	80
355.	55 c. blue	75	90

100. Mt. Kinabalu.

DESIGNS—VERT. 4 c. Hemp-drying. 5 c. Cattle farm. 30 c. Sailing craft 50 c. Clock tower. $1. Horsemen. HORIZ. 2 c. Musician. 8 c. Map. 10 c. Log pond. 15 c. Malay prau, Sardakan. 20 c. Chieftain. $2, Murut with blowpipe. $5, Net fishing. $10, King George VI and arms.

102. Coconut Grove.

1950.

356.	100.	1 c. brown	15	30
357.	–	2 c. blue	15	15
358.	102.	3 c. green	15	10
359.	–	4 c. purple	15	10
360.	–	5 c. violet	15	10
361.	–	8 c. red	30	45
362.	–	10 c. purple	30	10
363.	–	15 c. blue	30	30
364.	–	20 c. brown	40	10
365.	–	30 c. buff	45	10
366.	–	50 c. red ("JESLETON") ..	45	1·75
366a.	–	50 c. red ("JESSELTON") ..	2·00	50
367.	–	$1 orange	1·25	55
368.	–	$2 green	2·00	6·00
369.	–	$5 green	9·50	11·00
370.	–	$10 blue	24·00	32·00

1953. Coronation. As T **13** of Aden.

371.	10 c. black and red	30	20

As 1950 but with portrait of **Queen** Elizabeth II.

c. brown	10	30
c. blue	30	15
c. green	30	1·50
c. purple	30	20
c. violet	40	10
8 c. red	30	15
10 c. purple	15	10
15 c. blue	25	10
20 c. brown	15	15
30 c. buff	40	15
50 c. red (No. 366a) ..	2·50	10
$1 orange	3·00	20
$2 green	7·00	40
$5 green	8·00	17·00
$10 blue	20·00	28·00

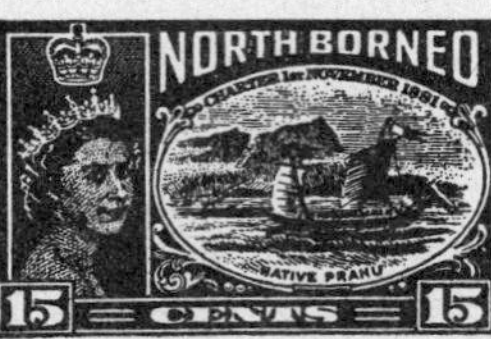

117. Malay Prau.

1956. 75th Anniv. of Foundation of British North Borneo Co. Inscr. "CHARTER 1ST NOVEMBER 1881".

387.	–	10 c. black and red ..	1·00	30
388.	117.	15 c. black and brown ..	25	30
389.	–	35 c. black and green ..	30	75
390.	–	$1 black and slate	65	1·25

DESIGNS—HORIZ. 10 c. Borneo Railway, 1902. 35 c. Mt. Kinabalu. VERT. $1, Arms of Chartered Company.

120. Sambar Stag.

1961.

391.	120.	1 c. green and red ..	10	10
392.	–	4 c. olive and orange ..	15	40
393.	–	5 c. sepia and violet ..	15	10
394.	–	6 c. black and turquoise	10	30
395.	–	10 c. green and red ..	15	10
396.	–	12 c. brown and myrtle	15	10
397.	–	20 c. turquoise and blue	2·25	10
398.	–	25 c. black and red ..	45	40
399.	–	30 c. sepia and olive ..	20	10
400.	–	35 c. slate and brown ..	45	10
401.	–	50 c. green and bistre ..	45	10
402.	–	75 c. blue and purple ..	3·00	75
403.	–	$1 brown and green ..	6·50	55
404.	–	$2 brown and slate ..	9·50	2·25
405.	–	$5 green and purple ..	22·00	11·00
406.	–	$10 red and blue ..	20·00	16·00

DESIGNS—HORIZ. 4 c. Sun Bear. 5 c. Clouded leopard. 6 c. Dusun woman with gong. 10 c. Map of Borneo. 12 c. Banteng. 20 c. Butterfly orchid. 25 c. Sumatran Rhinoceros. 30 c. Murut with blow-pipe. 35 c. Mt. Kinabalu. 50 c. Dunsun and buffalo transport. 75 c. Bajau horseman. VERT. $1, Orang-utan. $2, Rhinoceros Hornbill. $5, Crested Wood Partridge. $10, Arms of N. Borneo.

1963. Freedom from Hunger. As T **28** of Aden.

407.	12 c. blue	70	15

POSTAGE DUE STAMPS

Overprinted **POSTAGE DUE**

1895. Issue of 1894.

D 2	25.	2 c. blk. & red	9·00	15·00	60
D 3	26.	3 c. grn. & mve.	3·25	9·00	75
D 4	27.	5 c. blk. & red	20·00	20·00	1·50
D 5a	28.	6 c. blk. & brn.	7·00	28·00	1·50
D 7	29.	8 c. blk. & lilac	18·00	32·00	1·50
D 8b	30.	12 c. blk. & bl.	26·00	29·00	1·50
D 10	31.	18 c. blk. & grn	32·00	45·00	3·00
D 11b	32.	24 c. bl. & red	16·00	45·00	—

1897. Issue of 1897.

D 12	25.	2 c. blk. & red	3·50	6·50	50
D 15		2 c. blk. & grn.	15·00	22·00	60
D 16b	26.	3 c. grn. & mve.	4·25	12·00	40
D 18		4 c. blk. & red	14·00	15·00	50
D 19	27.	5 c. blk. & orge.	13·00	19·00	75
D 20a	28.	6 c. blk. & brn.	3·00	13·00	40
D 21a	29.	8 c. black and lilac ..	3·00	13·00	40
D 22	30.	12 c. black and blue ..	35·00	85·00	2·00
D 23	31.	18 c. black and green (No. 108) ..			
D 24		18 c. black and green (No. 110) ..	24·00	85·00	2·00
D 25	32.	24 c. blue and red (No. 109) ..	—	32·00	60
D 26a		24 c. blue and red (No. 111) ..	12·00	70·00	1·00

1902. Issue of 1901.

D 47	1 c. black & bistre	3·25	45·00	—
D 36	2 c. black and green	3·75	1·50	10
D 37	3 c. grn. & mve.	1·75	1·50	10
D 38	4 c. black and red ..	4·50	4·25	20
D 39	5 c. blk. & orge	5·00	3·00	20
D 40	6 c. blk. & brn.	6·50	6·00	25
D 41	8 c. black and lilac	13·00	4·00	40
D 42b	10 c. brn. & grey	29·00	12·00	1·00
D 43	12 c. black and blue	6·50	11·00	1·00
D 44	16 c. grn. & brn.	14·00	14·00	1·00
D 45	18 c. blk. & grn.	4·00	11·00	1·00
D 46	24 c. blue and red ..	6·50	17·00	1·00

1919. Issue of 1909.

D49	2 c. black and green ..	5·50	45·00
D57	2 c. black and red ..	40	1·75
D58	3 c. black and green ..	2·25	11·00
D51	4 c. black and red ..	70	1·00
D52	5 c. black and brown ..	4·00	10·00
D61	6 c. black and olive ..	2·75	2·00
D54	8 c. black and red ..	1·25	1·25
D55	10 c. black and blue ..	7·00	12·00
D56	12 c. black and blue ..	19·00	25·00
D56ba	16 c. black and brown ..	6·00	40·00

D 2. Crest of the Company.

1939.

D 66.	D 2.	2 c. brown	4·50	55·00
D 67.		4 c. red	5·50	60·00
D 68.		6 c. violet	12·00	75·00
D 69.		8 c. green	12·00	£120
D 70.		10 c. blue	25·00	£160

For later issues see **SABAH.**

JAPANESE OCCUPATION

1942. Stamps of North Borneo optd. as T **1** of Japanese Occupation of Brunei.

(a) Issue of 1939.

J 1.	81.	1 c. green and brown ..	85·00	£120
J 2.	82.	2 c. purple and blue ..	80·00	£110
J 3.	–	3 c. blue and green ..	75·00	£110
J 4.	–	4 c. green and violet ..	38·00	75·00
J 5.	–	6 c. blue and **red** ..	75·00	£110
J 6.	–	8 c. red	75·00	£110
J 7.	–	10 c. violet and green	75·00	£110
J 8.	–	12 c. green and blue ..	95·00	£170
J 9.	–	15 c. green and brown	95·00	£170
J 10.	–	20 c. violet and blue ..	£130	£190
J 11.	–	25 c. green and brown	£130	£190
J 12.	–	50 c. brown and violet	£180	£250
J 13.	–	$1 brown and red ..	£160	£300
J 14.	–	$2 violet and olive ..	£275	£400
J 15.	–	$5 blue	£325	£500

(b) War Tax issue of 1941.

J 16.	81.	1 c. green and brown ..	£225	£150
J 17.	82.	2 c purple and blue ..	£475	£200

2. Mt. Kinabalu.

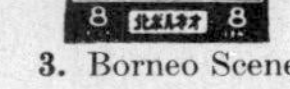

3. Borneo Scene.

1943.

J18	2	4 c. red	10·00	18·00
J19	3	8 c. blue	10·00	18·00

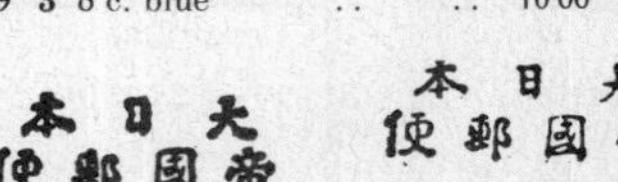

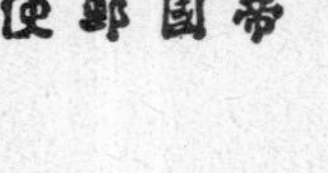

(4.)

(5.)

("Imperial Japanese Postal Service, North Borneo".)

1944. Stamps of North Borneo of 1939 optd as T **4**.

J 20.	81.	1 c. green and brown ..	2·25	5·00
J 21.	82.	2 c. purple and blue ..	3·25	5·00
J 22.	–	3 c. blue and green ..	2·00	3·50
J 23.	–	4 c. green and violet ..	2·50	4·75
J 24.	–	6 c. blue and red ..	2·25	3·50
J 25.	–	8 c. red	3·75	8·50
J 26.	–	10 c. violet and green ..	2·50	6·50
J 27.	–	12 c. green and blue ..	2·75	6·50
J 28.	–	15 c. green and brown	3·25	8·50
J 29.	–	20 c. violet and blue ..	9·50	20·00
J 30.	–	25 c. green and brown	9·50	20·00
J 31.	–	50 c. brown and violet	32·00	48·00
J 32.	–	$1 brown and red ..	48·00	75·00

1944. No. J7 optd with T **4**.

J32a	–	10 c. violet and green ..	£160	£325

1945. No. J1 surch with T **5**.

J33	81	$2 on 1 c. green & brown	£3250	£2500

大日本

五弗

帝國郵便

(6.)

1945. No. 315 of North Borneo surch with T **6**.

J34		$5 on $1 brown and red ..	£2750	£2250

1945. Stamps of Japan as bottom line in T 4.

J 35.	**126.**	1 s. brown	2·00	5·50
J 36.	**84.**	2 s. red	2·25	5·50
J 37.	–	3 s. green (No. 319) ..	1·50	5·50
J 38.	**129.**	4 s. green	2·00	5·50
J 39.	–	5 s. red (No. 396)	2·25	6·00
J 40.	–	6 s. orange (No. 322)	2·25	7·00
J 41.	–	8 s. violet (No. 324) ..	1·75	7·00
J 42.	–	10 s. red (No. 399) ..	2·25	7·00
J 43.	–	15 s. blue (No. 401) ..	2·25	7·00
J 44.	–	20 s. blue (No. 328) ..	65·00	80·00
J 45.	–	25 s. brown (No. 329)	55·00	85·00
J 46.	–	30 s. blue (No. 330) ..	£150	95·00
J 47.	**–**	**50 s. olive and brown (No. 331)**	50·00	60·00
J 48.	–	1 y. brown (No. 332)	48·00	65·00

NORTHERN NIGERIA

A Br. Protectorate on the W. coast of Africa in 1914 incorporated in Nigeria, whose stamps it now uses.

12 pence = 1 shilling.
20 shillings = 1 pound.

1.

5.

1900.

1.	1.	½d. mauve and green ..	1·00	5·50
2.		1d. mauve and red ..	1·60	2·25
3.		2d. mauve and yellow ..	3·00	17·00
4.		2½d. mauve and blue ..	6·00	17·00
5.		5d. mauve and brown ..	10·00	24·00
6.		6d. mauve and violet ..	13·00	17·00
7.		1s. green and black ..	13·00	35·00
8.		2s. 6d. green and blue ..	60·00	£150
9.		10s. green and brown ..	£160	£375

1902. As T **1**, but portrait of King Edward VII.

10	½d. purple and green ..	65	60
11	1d. purple and red ..	80	20
12	2d. purple and yellow ..	60	1·40
13	2½d. purple and blue ..	55	2·75
14	5d. purple and brown ..	1·50	4·50
15	6d. purple and violet ..	3·00	4·50
16	1s. green and black ..	2·50	3·50
17	2s. 6d. green and blue ..	8·00	20·00
18	10s. green and brown ..	45·00	48·00

1910. As last. New colours etc.

28	½d. green	60	30
29	1d. red	50	15
30	2d. grey	1·00	2·00
31	2½d. blue	60	2·75
32	3d. purple on yellow ..	1·00	30
34	5d. purple and green ..	2·00	3·75
35a	6d. purple	1·25	3·50
36	1s. black and green ..	90	55
37	2s. 6d. black & red on blue	7·50	15·00
38	5s. green and red on yellow	17·00	48·00
39	10s. green and red on green	42·00	45·00

1912.

40.	5.	½d. green	30	20
41.		1d. red	30	15
42.		2d. grey	1·25	2·25
43.		3d. purple on yellow ..	60	65
44.		4d. black & red on yellow	40	50
45.		5d. purple and olive ..	1·25	4·00
46.		6d. purple and violet ..	1·25	2·75
47.		9d. purple and red ..	1·00	5·50
48.		1s. black on green ..	1·50	50
49.		2s. 6d. black & red on blue	7·00	22·00
50.		5s. green & red on yellow	16·00	50·00
51.		10s. green & red on green	30·00	45·00
52.		£1 purple and black on red	£170	£140

NORTHERN RHODESIA

A Br. territory in C. Africa, N. of the Zambesi. From 1954 to 1963 part of the Central African Federation and using the stamps of Rhodesia and Nyasaland (q.v.). A new constitution was introduced on 3rd January, 1964, with internal self-government and independence came on 24th October, 1964, when the country was renamed Zambia (q.v.).

12 pence = 1 shilling.
20 shillings = 1 pound.

1.

1925. The shilling values are larger and the view is in first colour.

1.	1.	½d. green	40	10
2.		1d. brown	40	10
3.		1½d. red	40	20
4.		2d. orange	45	10
5.		3d. blue	75	30
6.		4d. violet	90	35
7.		6d. grey	90	30
8.		8d. purple	3·75	13·00
9.		10d. olive	3·75	12·00
10.		1s. orange and black ..	1·00	75
11.		2s. brown and blue ..	5·50	10·00
12.		2s. 6d. black and green ..	6·00	4·50
13.		3s. violet and blue ..	15·00	9·00
14.		5s. grey and violet ..	10·00	8·50
15.		7s. 6d. purple and black ..	85·00	£120
16.		10s. green and black ..	42·00	48·00
17.		20s. red and purple ..	£150	£160

1935. Silver Jubilee. As T **13** of Antigua.

18.	1d. blue and olive ..	50	20
19.	2d. green and blue ..	50	40
20.	3d. brown and blue ..	2·00	2·50
21.	6d. grey and purple ..	2·00	1·00

1937. Coronation. As T **2** of Aden.

22.	1½d. red	40	35
23.	2d. brown	70	35
24.	3d. blue	1·25	1·75

1938. As 1925, but with portrait of King George VI facing right and "POSTAGE & REVENUE" omitted.

25	½d. green	10	10
26	½d. brown	10	70
27	1d. brown	10	10
28	1d. green	60	60
29	1½d. red	24·00	25
30	1½d. orange	10	10
31	2d. brown	65·00	70
32	2d. red	20	10
33	2d. purple	45	30
34	3d. blue	20	10
35	3d. red	50	50
36	4d. violet	20	10
37	4½d. blue	40	2·25
38	6d. grey	20	10
39	9d. violet	40	2·00
40	1s. orange and black ..	50	10
41	2s. 6d. black and green ..	4·75	1·25
42	3s. violet and blue ..	9·00	4·00
43	5s. grey and violet ..	6·00	3·00
44	10s. green and black ..	5·00	8·50
45	20s. red and purple ..	24·00	38·00

1946. Victory. As T **9** of Aden.

46.	1½d. orange	10	10
47.	2d. red	10	10

1948. Silver Wedding As T10/11 of Aden.

48.	1½d. orange	30	10
49.	20s. red	38·00	38·00

1949. U.P.U. As T **20/23** of Antigua.

50.	2d. red	30	30
51.	3d. blue	85	1·00
52.	6d. grey	85	1·00
53.	1s. orange	85	1·00

5. Cecil Rhodes and Victoria Falls.

1953. Birth Centenary of Cecil Rhodes.

54.	5.	½d. brown	30	30
55.		1d. green	30	40
56.		2d. mauve	30	15
57.		4½d. blue	40	3·25
58.		1s. orange and black ..	45	2·00

6. Arms of the Rhodesia and Nyasaland.

1953. Rhodes Centenary Exhibition.

59.	6.	6d. violet	20	30

1953. Coronation. As T **13** of Antigua.

60	1½d. black and orange ..	15	10

1953. As 1938 but with portrait of Queen Elizabeth II facing left.

61.	½d. brown	65	10
62.	1d. green	65	10
63.	1½d. orange	60	10
64.	2d. purple	75	10
65.	3d. red	60	10
66.	4d. violet	1·25	50
67.	4½d. blue	60	75
68.	6d. grey	1·25	10
69.	9d. violet	60	60
70.	1s. orange and black ..	60	10
71.	2s. 6d. black and green ..	5·00	2·75
72.	5s. grey and purple ..	5·50	12·00
73.	10s. green and black ..	5·50	14·00
74.	20s. red and purple ..	16·00	23·00

9. Arms.

1963. Arms black, gold and blue; portrait and inscriptions black; background colours given.

75.	9.	½d. violet	20	35
76.		1d. blue	30	10
77.		2d. brown	20	10
78.		3d. yellow	15	10
79.		4d. green	20	10
80.		6d. green	20	10
81.		9d. bistre	20	20
82.		1s. purple	20	10
83.		1s. 3d. purple	70	10
84.	–	2s. orange	70	60
85.	–	2s. 6d. purple	80	80
86.	–	5s. mauve	3·00	3·50
87.	–	10s. mauve	3·00	4·50
88.	–	20s. blue	5·00	14·00

Nos. 84/88 are as Type **9** but larger 27 × 23 mm.).

POSTAGE DUE STAMPS

D 1.

D 2.

1929.

D1	D 1	1d. black	2·50	2·50
D2		2d. black	3·00	3·00
D3		3d. black	3·00	21·00
D4		4d. black	5·00	26·00

1963.

D 5.	D 2.	1d. orange	30	1·75
D 6.		2d. blue	30	2·00
D 7.		3d. lake	35	2·50
D 8.		4d. blue	50	3·50
D 9.		6d. purple	1·25	4·00
D 10.		1s. green	3·50	10·00

For later issues see **ZAMBIA**.

NOVA SCOTIA

An eastern province of the Dominion of Canada, whose stamps it now uses.

Currency: As Canada.

1.

2. Emblems of the United Kingdom.

1853. Imperf.

1	1.	1d. brown	£2000	£400
4	2.	3d. blue	£700	£130
5		6d. green	£4750	£400
8		1s. purple	£14000	£2500

3.

4.

1860. Perf.

10.	3.	1 c. black	3·00	12·00
20.		2 c. purple	3·25	14·00
13.		5 c. blue	£225	16·00
26.	4.	8½ c. green	17·00	40·00
27.		10 c. red	3·50	20·00
17.		12½ c. black	24·00	16·00

NYASALAND PROTECTORATE

A Br. Protectorate in C. Africa. Formerly known as Br. Central Africa. From 1954 to 1963 part of the Central African Federation and using the stamps of Rhodesia and Nyasaland (q.v.). From July, 1964, independent within the Commonwealth under its new name of Malawi.

12 pence = 1 shilling.
20 shillings = 1 pound.

1891. Stamps of Rhodesia optd. **B.C.A.**

1.	**1.**	1d. black	1·75	2·25
2.		2d. green and red ..	1·75	2·50
3.		4d. brown and black ..	1·50	3·75
5.		6d. blue	5·00	8·00
6.		8d. red and blue	12·00	28·00
7.		1s. brown	9·50	11·00
8.		2s. red	20·00	38·00
9.		2s. 6d. purple	42·00	60·00
10.		3s. brown and green ..	45·00	48·00
11.		4s. black and red ..	45·00	70·00
12.		5s. yellow	45·00	60·00
13.		10s. green	85·00	£110
14.	–	£1 blue	£425	£425
15.	–	£2 red	£650	
16.	–	£5 olive	£1200	
17.	–	£10 brown	£2500	

1892. Stamps of Rhodesia surch. **B.C.A.** and value in words.

18.	**1.**	3s. on 4s. black and red ..	£300	£300
19.		4s. on 5s. yellow	70·00	80·00

1895. Stamp of Rhodesia surch. **B.C.A. ONE PENNY** and bar.

20.	**1.**	1d. on 2d. green and red	6·00	25·00

5. Arms of the Protectorate. 7.

1895. The 2s. 6d. and higher values are larger.

32	5.	1d. black	3·00	4·50
33		2d. black and green ..	13·00	5·00
34		4d. black and orange ..	15·00	17·00
35		6d. black and blue ..	12·00	9·00
36		1s. black and red ..	17·00	10·00
37		2s. 6d. black and mauve ..	80·00	80·00
38		3s. black and yellow ..	60·00	32·00
39		5s. black and olive ..	80·00	90·00
29		£1 black and orange ..	£650	£350
40		£1 black and blue ..	£650	£350
30		£10 black and orange ..	£3000	£2750
31		£25 black and green ..	£5500	

1897. The 2s. 6d. and higher values are larger.

43.	7.	1d. black and blue ..	1·00	60
57d.		1d. purple and red ..	1·00	40
44.		2d. black and yellow ..	1·25	80
45.		4d. black and red ..	5·00	1·50
57e.		4d. purple and olive ..	4·00	5·00
46.		6d. black and green ..	25·00	4·25
58.		6d. purple and brown ..	3·50	3·00
47.		1s. black and purple ..	6·00	7·00
48.		2s. 6d. black and blue ..	35·00	38·00
49.		3s. black and green ..	£160	£200
50.		4s. black and red	50·00	70·00
50a.		10s. black and olive ..	80·00	90·00
51.		£1 black and purple ..	£200	£140
52.		£10 black and yellow ..	£2750	£1500

1897. No. 49 surch ONE PENNY.

No.	Description	Unused	Used
53 7	1d. on 3s. black and green	5·00	8·50

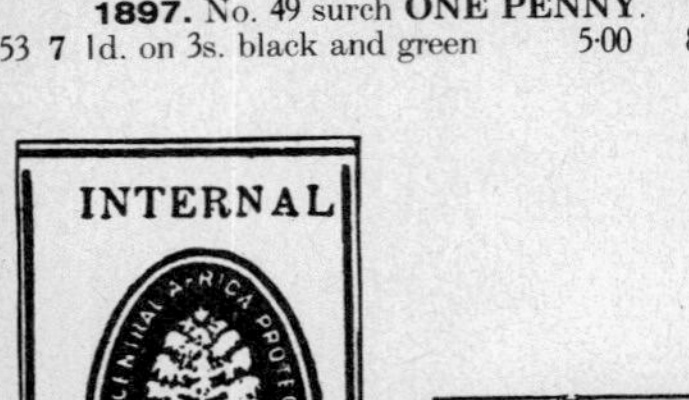

10. 11.

1898.

No.	Description	Unused	Used
56. 10.	1d. red and blue (Imperf.)	—	40·00
57.	1d. red and blue (Perf.)	£1300	14·00

1903. The 2s. 6d. and higher values are larger.

No.	Description	Unused	Used
68 11.	1d. grey and red..	1·50	90
60	2d. purple..	3·25	1·00
61	4d. green and black	2·50	5·00
62	6d. grey and brown	2·50	2·00
62a	1s. grey and blue..	2·50	6·50
63	2s. 6d. green	25·00	35·00
64	4s. purple..	48·00	70·00
65	10s. green and black	65·00	£110
66	£1 grey and red	£180	£150
67	£10 grey and blue	£3500	£3250

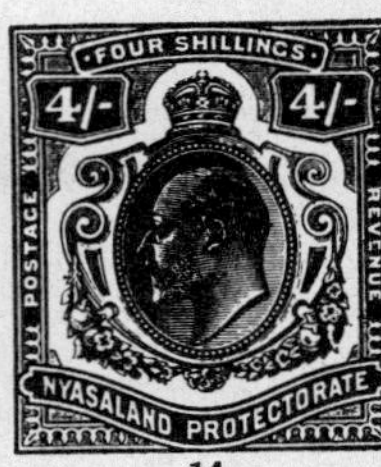

13. 14.

1908.

No.	Description	Unused	Used
73. 13.	½d. green..	65	60
74.	1d. red	1·00	20
75.	3d. purple on yellow	1·00	2·25
76.	4d. black & red on yellow	1·00	1·50
77.	6d. purple	3·75	6·00
72.	1s. black on green	1·40	5·50
78. 14.	2s. 6d. black & red on blue	32·00	55·00
79.	4s. red and black..	55·00	70·00
80.	10s. green & red on green	70·00	£110
81.	£1 purple & black on red	£375	£425
82.	£10 purple and blue	£7000	£4250

1913. As 1908, but portrait of King George V.

No.	Description	Unused	Used
100	½d. green..	60	20
101	1d. red	50	25
102	1½d. orange	3·25	15·00
103	2d. grey	55	20
89	2½d. blue	70	2·00
90	3d. purple on yellow	2·00	2·25
91	4d. black and red on yellow	2·00	2·00
107	6d. purple	3·00	3·25
93a	1s. black on green	2·00	1·50
109	2s. purple and blue on blue	9·00	10·00
94	2s. 6d. black & red on blue	9·50	10·00
111	4s. red and black..	10·00	12·00
112	5s. green & red on yellow	27·00	42·00
96	10s. green & red on green	48·00	70·00
98	£1 purple & black on red	£150	£140
99a	£10 purple and blue	£2750	£1500

17. King George V and Symbol of the Protectorate.

1934.

No.	Description	Unused	Used
114. 17.	½d. green..	75	45
115.	1d. brown	75	40
116.	1½d. red	75	1·25
117.	2d. grey	80	1·00
118.	3d. blue	1·50	1·25
119.	4d. mauve	2·25	1·75
120.	6d. violet	1·50	40
121.	9d. olive	2·50	8·50
122.	1s. black and orange	2·50	5·50

1935. Silver Jubilee. As T 13 of Antigua.

No.	Description	Unused	Used
123.	1d. blue and grey	65	45
124.	2d. green and blue	70	45
125.	3d. brown and blue	6·00	9·50
126.	1s. grey and purple	13·00	17·00

1937. Coronation. As T 2 of Aden.

No.	Description	Unused	Used
127.	½d. green	30	20
128.	1d. brown	55	20
129.	2d grey	55	40

1938. As T 17, but with head of King George VI and "POSTAGE REVENUE" omitted.

No.	Description	Unused	Used
130.	½d. green	30	20
130a.	½d. brown	10	40
131.	1d. brown	30	10
131a.	1d. green	10	10
132.	1½d. red	55	2·25
132a.	1½d. grey	10	1·00
133.	2d. grey	75	30
133a.	2d. red	10	20
134.	3d. blue	10	10
135.	4d. mauve	55	20
136.	6d. violet	85	20
137.	9d. olive	1·00	1·75
138.	1s. black and orange	1·25	30

1938. As T 14, but with head of King George VI facing right.

No.	Description	Unused	Used
139.	2s. purple and blue on blue	10·00	4·75
140.	2s. 6d. black & red on blue	10·00	4·50
141.	5s. green & red on yellow	38·00	14·00
142.	10s. green & red on green	38·00	18·00
143.	£1 purple & black on red	27·00	20·00

20. Lake Nyasa.

21. King's African Rifles.

DESIGNS — HORIZ. 1½d., 6d. Tea estate. 2d., 1s., 10s. Map of Nyasaland. 4d., 2s. 6d. Tobacco. 5s., 20s. Badge of Nyasaland. VERT. 1d. (No. 160), Leopard and sunrise. 3d., 2s. Fishing village.

1945.

No.	Description	Unused	Used
144. 20.	½d. black and brown	10	10
145. 21.	1d. black and green	10	40
160. –	1d. brown and green	20	10
146. –	1½d. black and grey	10	10
147. –	2d. black and red	10	10
148. –	3d. black and blue	10	20
149. –	4d. black and red	50	35
150. –	6d. black and violet	75	15
151. 20.	9d. black and olive	60	2·00
152. –	1s. blue and green	70	10
153. –	2s. green and purple	3·25	3·25
154. –	2s. 6d. green and blue	4·25	2·50
155. –	5s. purple and blue	4·25	3·50
156. –	10s. red and green	7·50	6·50
157. –	20s. red and black	13·00	14·00

1946. Victory. As T 9 of Aden.

No.	Description	Unused	Used
158.	1d. green..	10	10
159.	2d. red	10	10

1948. Silver Wedding. As T 10/11 of Aden.

No.	Description	Unused	Used
161.	1d. green..	15	10
162.	10s. mauve	11·00	15·00

1949. U.P.U. As T 20/23 of Antigua.

No.	Description	Unused	Used
163.	1d. green..	30	15
164.	3d. blue	1·00	50
165.	6d. purple	1·00	50
166.	1s. blue	1·00	50

28. Arms in 1891 and 1951.

1951. Diamond Jubilee of Protectorate.

No.	Description	Unused	Used
167. 28.	2d. black and red	50	30
168.	3d. black and blue	50	75
169.	6d. black and violet	50	90
170.	5s. black and blue	1·10	5·00

1953. Rhodes Centenary Exn. As T 6 of Northern Rhodesia.

No.	Description	Unused	Used
171.	6d. violet	10	15

1953. Coronation. As T 13 of Aden.

No.	Description	Unused	Used
172	2d. black and orange	20	10

29. Grading Cotton.

1953. As 1945 but with portrait of Queen Elizabeth II as in T 29. Designs as for corresponding values except where stated.

No.	Description	Unused	Used
173a 20	½d. black and brown	10	40
174 –	1d. brown and green (as No. 160)	30	10
175 –	1½d. black and grey	15	1·25
176a –	2d. black and orange	15	10
177 29	2½d. green and black	10	15
178 –	3d. black & red (as 4d.)	30	10
179 –	4½d. black & blue (as 3d.)	30	40
180a –	6d. black and violet	15	10
181 20	9d. black and olive	70	2·00
182 –	1s. blue and green	35	10
183 –	2s. green and red	2·00	2·75
184 –	2s. 6d. green and blue	2·75	4·00
185 –	5s. purple and blue	4·50	4·50
186 –	10s. red and green	4·00	7·00
187 –	20s. red and black	9·50	9·50

30.

1963. Revenue stamps optd. POSTAGE as in T 30 or surch. also.

No.	Description	Unused	Used
188. 30.	½d. on 1d. blue..	20	15
189.	1d. green	20	10
190.	2d. red	20	20
191.	3d. blue..	20	10
192.	6d. purple	20	10
193.	9d. on 1s. red	30	25
194.	1s. purple	35	10
195.	2s. 6d. black	40	1·50
196.	5s. brown	65	1·25
197.	10s. olive	1·25	3·50
198.	£1 violet	3·25	3·50

32. Mother and Child.

34. Tea Industry.

1964.

No.	Description	Unused	Used
199. 32.	½d. violet	10	10
200. –	1d. black and green	10	10
201. –	2d. brown	10	10
202. –	3d. brown, green & bistre	10	10
203. –	4d. blue and yellow	20	20
204. 34.	6d. purple, green & blue	30	10
205. –	1s. brown, blue & yellow	15	10
206. –	1s. 3d. bronze & brown	90	10
207. –	2s. 6d. brown and blue	90	50
208. –	5s. bl., grn., yell. & blk.	90	1·25
209. –	10s. green, salmon & blk.	1·50	3·00
210. –	£1 brown and yellow	5·50	4·00

DESIGNS—As Type 32. 1d. Chambo (fish). 2d. Zebu bull. 3d. Groundnuts. 4d. Fishing. As Type 34—HORIZ. 1s. Timber. 1s. 3d. Turkish tobacco industry. 2s. 6d. Cotton industry. 5s. Monkey Bay, Lake Nyasa. 10s. Forestry—Afzelia. VERT. £1, Nyala.

POSTAGE DUE STAMPS

1950. As Type D 1 of Gold Coast, but inscr. "NYASALAND".

No.	Description	Unused	Used
D 1.	1d. red	2·00	7·00
D 2.	2d. blue	5·00	13·00
D 3.	3d. green	7·50	4·75
D 4.	4d. purple	12·00	30·00
D 5.	6d. orange	20·00	55·00

For later issues see MALAWI.

ORANGE FREE STATE (ORANGE RIVER COLONY)

Br. possession. 1848-54. Independent 1854-99. Annexed by Great Britain, 1900. Later a province of the Union of S. Africa.

12 pence = 1 shilling.
20 shillings = 1 pound.

1.

38. King Edward VII, Springbok and Gnu.

1868.

No.	Description	Unused	Used
48 1	½d. brown	60	55
84	½d. yellow	60	35
2	1d. brown	2·25	35
68	1d. purple	60	30
50	2d. mauve	2·75	30
51	3d. blue	1·75	2·00
19	4d. blue	4·00	2·50
7	6d. red	3·25	2·00
9	1s. orange	10·00	1·50
87	1s. brown	6·50	1·50
20	5s. green	8·50	9·00

1877. Surch. in figures.

No.	Description	Unused	Used
75 1	½d. on 3d. blue	1·75	2·25
36	½d. on 5s. green	2·50	3·25
54	1d. on 3d. blue	1·10	60
57	1d. on 4d. blue	13·00	3·00
22	1d. on 5s. green	25·00	10·00
53	2d. on 3d. blue	10·00	2·00
67	"2½d." on 3d. blue	2·50	70
83	"2½" on 3d. blue	1·25	80
40	3d. on 4d. blue	25·00	16·00
12	"4" on 6d. red	80·00	25·00

1896. Surch. Halve Penny.

No.	Description	Unused	Used
77. 1.	½d. on 3d. blue	35	50

1900. Surch. V.R.I. and value in figures.

No.	Description	Unused	Used
112 1.	½d. on ½d. orange	20	20
113	1d. on 1d. purple	20	20
114	2d. on 2d. mauve	35	30
104	2½ on 3d blue (No. 83)	4·50	3·50
117	3d. on 3d. blue	30	30
118	4d. on 4d. blue	1·10	1·50
108	6d. on 6d. red..	35·00	35·00
120	6d. on 6d. blue	70	40
121	1s. on 1s. brown	70	40
122	5s. on 5s. green	4·00	5·50

1900. Stamps of Cape of Good Hope optd. ORANGE RIVER COLONY.

No.	Description	Unused	Used
133. 17.	½d. green..	20	10
134.	1d. red	25	10
135. 6.	2½d. blue..	30	35

1902. No. 120 surch. 4d and bar.

No.	Description	Unused	Used
136. 1.	4d. on 6d. blue	50	60

1902. Surch. E.R.I. and 6d.

No.	Description	Unused	Used
137. 1.	6d. on 6d. blue	1·75	4·00

1902. No. 20 surch. V.R.I. One Shilling and star.

No.	Description	Unused	Used
138. 1.	1s. on 5s. green..	3·50	5·00

1903.

No.	Description	Unused	Used
148 38.	½d. green..	3·25	30
140	1d. red	75	10
141	2d. brown	2·25	70
142	2½d. blue..	85	50
143	3d. mauve	3·25	90
150	4d. red and green	4·00	1·75
145	6d. red and mauve	4·75	70
146	1s. red and brown	13·00	1·75
147	5s. blue and brown	60·00	20·00

MILITARY FRANK STAMP

M 1

1899.

No.	Description	Unused	Used
M1 M 1	(-) black/yellow	10·00	40·00

POLICE FRANK STAMPS

PF 1

PF 2

1896.

No.	Description	Unused	Used
PF1 PF 1	(-) black		

1899.

No.	Description	Unused	Used
PF3 PF 2	(-) black on yellow	—	70·00

ORCHHA

A state of C. India. Now uses Indian stamps.

12 pies = 1 anna; 16 annas = 1 rupee.

1.

2.

1913. Imperf.

No.	Type	Description	Unused	Used
1.	1.	$\frac{1}{2}$ a. green	18·00	40·00
2.		1 a. red	19·00	

1914. Imperf.

No.	Type	Description	Unused	Used
3a.	2.	$\frac{1}{4}$ a. blue	35	2·00
4.		$\frac{1}{2}$ a. green	40	2·00
5.		1 a. red	1·75	3·25
6.		2 a. brown	4·50	11·00
7.		4 a. bistre	8·00	16·00

3. Maharaja Vir Singh Deo Bahadur.

5. H.H. the Maharaja of Orchha.

1935.

No.	Type	Description	Unused	Used
8a	3	$\frac{1}{4}$ a. purple and grey	20	40
9		$\frac{1}{2}$ a. grey and green	40	40
10		$\frac{3}{4}$ a. mauve and green	40	40
11	–	1 a. green and brown	40	40
12	3	$1\frac{1}{4}$ a. grey and mauve	40	40
13		$1\frac{1}{2}$ a. brown and red	40	40
14		2 a. blue and orange	40	40
15		$2\frac{1}{2}$ a. brown and orange	50	50
16		3 a. blue and mauve	50	50
17		4 a. purple and green	50	75
18		6 a. black and buff	50	80
19		8 a. brown and purple	60	80
20		12 a. green and purple	70	1·00
21		12 a. blue and purple	14·00	20·00
22		1 r. brown and green	70	1·25
24		2 r. brown and yellow	1·25	2·00
25		3 r. black and blue	1·25	2·25
26		4 r. black and brown	1·60	2·75
27		5 r. blue and purple	2·50	3·75
28	–	10 r. green and red	5·00	8·50
29	–	15 r. black and green	8·50	15·00
30	–	25 r. orange and blue	11·00	19·00

DESIGN: 1 a., 10 r. to 25 r. As Type **3**, but inscr. "POSTAGE & REVENUE". There are two different versions of the portrait for the 1 r. value.

1939.

No.	Type	Description	Unused	Used
31	5	$\frac{1}{4}$ a. brown	1·00	24·00
32		$\frac{1}{2}$ a. green	1·00	17·00
33		$\frac{3}{4}$ a. blue	1·00	30·00
34		1 a. red	1·00	7·50
35		$1\frac{1}{4}$ a. blue	1·00	30·00
36		$1\frac{1}{2}$ a. mauve	1·40	38·00
37		2 a. red	1·40	24·00
38		$2\frac{1}{2}$ a. green	1·40	
39		3 a. violet	2·00	35·00
40		4 a. slate	2·50	12·00
41		8 a. mauve	4·75	55·00
42	–	1 r. green	8·00	
43	–	2 r. violet	19·00	
44	–	5 r. orange	65·00	
45	–	10 r. green	£200	
46	–	15 r. c lilac	£1600	
47	–	25 r. purple	£1600	

The rupee values are larger (25 × 30 mm).

PAHANG

A state of the Federation of Malaya, incorporated in Malaysia in 1963.

100 cents = 1 dollar (Straits or Malayan).

1889. Nos. 52/3 and 63 of Straits Settlements optd. **PAHANG.**

No.	Type	Description	Unused	Used
4.		2 c. red	3·75	6·50
2.		8 c. orange	£1600	£1300
3.		10 c. grey	£250	£250

1891. No. 68 of Straits Settlements surch. **PAHANG Two CENTS.**

No.	Type	Description	Unused	Used
7.		2 c. on 24 c. green	55·00	75·00

9. Tiger.

10. Tiger.

1891.

No.	Type	Description	Unused	Used
11.	9.	1 c. green	3·50	2·50
12.		2 c. red	1·75	90
13.		5 c. blue	7·00	19·00

1895.

No.	Type	Description	Unused	Used
14.	10.	3 c. purple and red	2·25	1·00
15.		4 c. purple and red	9·00	4·00
16.		5 c. purple and yellow	16·00	12·00

1897. No. 13 divided, and each half surch.

No.	Type	Description	Unused	Used
18	9	2 c. on half of 5 c. blue	£750	£250
18d		3 c. on half of 5 c. blue	£750	£250

1898. Stamps of Perak optd. **Pahang.**

No.	Type	Description	Unused	Used
19	44	10 c. purple and orange	14·00	23·00
20		25 c. green and red	40·00	85·00
21		50 c. purple and black	£130	£140
22		50 c. green and black	95·00	£100
23	45	$1 green	£140	£150
24		$5 green and blue	£450	£550

1898. Stamp of Perak surch. **Pahang Four cents.**

No.	Type	Description	Unused	Used
25.	44.	4 c. on 8 c. purple & blue	2·50	5·50

1899. No. 15 surch. **Four cents.**

No.	Type	Description	Unused	Used
28.	10.	4 c. on 5 c. purple & yellow	6·50	29·00

15. Sultan Sir Abu Bakar. 16.

1935.

No.	Type	Description	Unused	Used
29.	15.	1 c. black	10	20
30.		2 c. green	50	15
31.		3 c. green	1·25	5·50
32.		4 c. orange	30	10
33.		5 c. brown	50	10
34.		6 c. red	4·50	2·25
35.		8 c. grey	50	10
36.		8 c. red	70	27·00
37.		10 c. purple	30	10
38.		12 c. blue	1·50	1·75
39.		15 c. blue	2·50	32·00
40.		25 c. purple and red	80	1·00
41.		30 c. purple and orange	55	80
42.		40 c. red and purple	75	1·40
43.		50 c. black on green	3·25	1·75
44.		$1 black and red on blue	2·25	4·75
45.		$2 green and red	18·00	26·00
46.		$5 green and red on green	8·00	48·00

1948. Silver Wedding. As T **10/11** of Aden.

No.	Type	Description	Unused	Used
47.		10 c. violet	15	40
48.		$5 green	20·00	40·00

1949. U.P.U. As T **20/23** of Antigua.

No.	Type	Description	Unused	Used
49.		10 c. purple	20	20
50.		15 c. blue	35	70
51.		25 c. orange	35	1·10
52.		50 c. black	70	2·00

1950.

No.	Type	Description	Unused	Used
53	16.	1 c. black	10	10
54		2 c. orange	10	10
55		3 c. green	20	25
56		4 c. brown	15	10
57a		5 c. purple	25	15
58		6 c. grey	15	10
59		8 c. red	20	1·00
60		8 c. green	85	75
61		10 c. mauve	15	10
62		12 c. red	85	1·25
63		15 c. blue	30	10
64		20 c. black and green	25	1·75
65		20 c. blue	75	10
66		25 c. purple and orange	20	10
67		30 c. red and purple	1·25	35
68		35 c. red and purple	60	25
69		40 c. red and purple	90	6·00
70		50 c. black and blue	40	10
71		$1 blue and purple	2·00	90
72		$2 green and red	9·50	16·00
73		$5 green and brown	38·00	35·00

1953. Coronation. As T **13** of Aden.

No.	Type	Description	Unused	Used
74.		10 c. black and purple	20	10

1957. As Nos. 92/102 of Kedah but inset portrait of Sultan Sir Abu Bakar.

No.	Type	Description	Unused	Used
75		1 c. black	10	10
76		2 c. red	10	10
77		4 c. sepia	10	10
78		5 c. lake	10	10
79		8 c. green	80	80
80		10 c. sepia	15	10
81		10 c. purple	65	10
82		20 c. blue	20	10
83		50 c. black and blue	20	10
84		$1 blue and purple	1·50	1·00
85		$2 green and red	3·00	5·50
86		$5 brown and green	6·00	8·50

INDEX

Countries can be quickly located by referring to the index at the end of this volume.

17. "Vanda hookeriana".

1965. As Nos. 115/21 of Kedah but with inset portrait of Sultan Sir Abu Bakar as in T **17.**

No.	Type	Description	Unused	Used
87.	17.	1 c. multicoloured	10	20
88.	–	2 c. multicoloured	10	15
89.	–	5 c. multicoloured	10	10
90.	–	6 c. multicoloured	15	10
91.	–	10 c. multicoloured	15	10
92.	–	15 c. multicoloured	80	10
93.	–	20 c. multicoloured	1·40	25

The higher values used in Pahang were Nos. 20/7 of Malaysia (National Issues).

18. "Precis orithya".

1971. Butterflies. As Nos. 124/30 of Kedah, but with portrait of Sultan Sir Abu Bakar as in T **18.**

No.	Type	Description	Unused	Used
96.	–	1 c. multicoloured	15	30
97.	–	2 c. multicoloured	40	30
98.	–	5 c. multicoloured	50	10
99.	–	6 c. multicoloured	50	20
100.	–	10 c. multicoloured	50	10
101.	18.	15 c. multicoloured	70	10
102.	–	20 c. multicoloured	85	20

The higher values in use with this issue were Nos. 64/71 of Malaysia (National Issues).

19. Sultan Haji Ahmad Shah.

1975. Installation of the Sultan.

No.	Type	Description	Unused	Used
103.	19.	10 c. green, lilac and gold	50	30
104.		15 c. black, yell. and grn.	60	10
105.		50 c. black, blue & green	1·75	2·25

1977. As Nos. 97/8, 100/102 but with **portrait of Sultan Haji Ahmad Shah.**

No.	Type	Description	Unused	Used
106.	–	2 c. multicoloured	25·00	25·00
107.	–	5 c. multicoloured	60	20
108.	–	10 c. multicoloured	80	10
109.	18.	15 c. multicoloured	80	20
110.	–	20 c. multicoloured	2·50	1·25

20. "Rhododendron scortechinii".

1979. Flowers. as Nos. 135/41 of Kedah but with portrait of Sultan Haji Ahmad Shah as in T **20.**

No.	Type	Description	Unused	Used
111		1 c. "Rafflesia hasseltii"	10	10
112		2 c. "Pterocarpus indicus"	10	10
113		5 c. "Lagerstroemia speciosa"	10	10
114		10 c. "Durio zibethinus"	10	10
115		15 c. "Hibiscus rosa-sinensis"	15	10
116		20 c. Type **20**	15	10
117		25 c. "Etlingera elatior" (inscr "Phaeomeria speciosa")	15	10

21. Rice.

1986. As Nos. 152/8 of Kedah but with portrait of Sultan Ahmad Shah as in T **21.**

No.	Type	Description	Unused	Used
125.		1 c. Coffee	10	10
126.		2 c. Coconuts	10	10
127.		5 c. Cocoa	10	10
128.		10 c. Black pepper	10	10
129.		15 c. Rubber	10	10
130.		20 c. Oil Palm	10	10
131.		30 c. Type **21**	10	15

PAKISTAN

A Dominion created in 1947 from territory with predominantly Moslem population of Eastern and Western India. Became an independent Islamic Republic within the British Commonwealth in 1956. The eastern provinces declared their independence in 1971 and are now known as Bangladesh.

On 30 January 1972 Pakistan left the Commonwealth but rejoined on 1 October 1989.

1947. 12 pies = 1 anna; 16 annas = 1 rupee.
1961. 100 paisa = 1 rupee.

1947. King George VI stamps of India optd. **PAKISTAN.**

1.	**100a.**	3 p. slate	10	10
2.		½ a. mauve	10	10
3.		9 p. green	10	10
4.		1 a. red	10	10
5.	**101.**	1½ a. violet	10	10
6.		2 a. red	10	10
7.		3 a. violet	10	10
8.		3½ a. blue	45	2·00
9.	**102.**	4 a. brown	10	10
10.		6 a. green	40	20
11.		8 a. violet	20	15
12.		12 a. purple	1·00	15
13.	–	14 a. purple (No. 277)	1·40	35
14.	**93.**	1 r. slate and brown	1·00	15
15.		2 r. purple and brown	1·50	40
16.		5 r. green and blue	2·75	1·25
17.		10 r. purple and red	4·00	90
18.		15 r. brown and green	40·00	60·00
19.		25 r. slate and purple	42·00	30·00

3. Constituent Assembly Building, Karachi.

1948. Independence.

20.	**3.**	1½ a. blue	20	30
21.	–	2½ a. green	20	10
22.	–	3 a. brown	20	10
23.	–	1 r. red	40	20

DESIGNS—HORIZ. 2½ a. Entrance to Karachi Airport. 3 a. Gateway to Lahore Fort. VERT. 1 r. Crescent and Stars in foliated frame.

7. Scales of Justice. **9.** Lloyd Barrage.

12. Salimullah Hostel, Dacca University.

13. Khyber Pass.

DESIGNS—VERT. As Type **7**: 1 a., 1½ a., 2 a. Star and Crescent. 6 a., 8 a., 12 a. Karachi Port Trust. HORIZ. As Type **12**: 3 a., 10 a. Karachi Airport.

1948. Designs with crescent moon pointing to right.

24	**7**	3 p. red	10	10
25		6 p. violet	30	10
26a		9 p. green	10	10
27	–	1 a. blue	10	10
28	–	1½ a. green	10	10
29	–	2 a. red	20	10
30	**9**	2½ a. green	90	2·50
31	–	3 a. green	60	20
32	**9**	3½ a. blue	55	2·00
33		4 a. brown	25	10
34	–	6 a. blue	30	50
35	–	8 a. black	30	30
36	–	10 a. red	60	2·50
37	–	12 a. red	1·75	30
38	**12**	1 r. blue	2·50	10
39		2 r. brown	17·00	30
40a		5 r. red	8·50	20
41b	**13**	10 r. mauve	11·00	30
42		15 r. green	13·00	8·50
210a		25 r. violet	2·00	2·50

1949. As 1948 but with crescent moon pointing to left.

44	–	1 a. blue	1·75	10
45	–	1½ a. green	1·75	10
46	–	2 a. red	1·75	10
47	–	3 a. green	1·75	65
48	–	6 a. blue	5·50	15
49	–	8 a. black	2·75	35
50	–	10 a. red	5·00	60
51	–	12 a. red	8·50	15

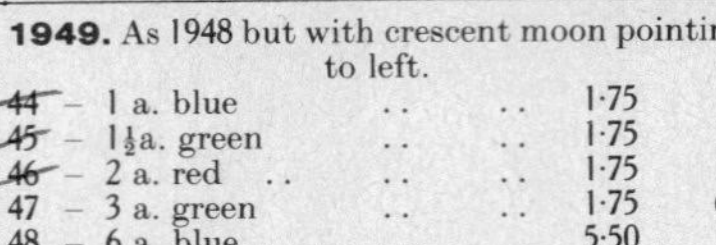

16.

1949. 1st Death Anniv of Mohammed Ali Jinnah.

52	**16**	1½ a. brown	1·25	55
53		3 a. green	1·25	55
54		10 a. black	2·75	4·25

DESIGN: 10 a. inscription reads "QUAID-I-AZAM MOHAMMAD ALI JINNAH", etc.

17. Pottery.

DESIGNS—VERT. 3a., 12a. Aeroplane and hour-glass. 4a., 6a. Saracenic leaf pattern. HORIZ. 8a., 10a. Archway and lamp.

1951. 4th Anniversary of Independence.

55.	**17.**	2½ a. red	70	35
56.	–	3 a. purple	40	10
57.	**17.**	3½ a. blue (A)	60	1·00
57a.		3½ a. blue (B)	2·00	60
58.	–	4 a. green	35	10
59.	–	6 a. orange	45	10
60.	–	8 a. sepia	3·50	10
61.	–	10 a. violet	80	10
62.	–	12 a. slate	80	10

(A) has Arabic fraction on left as in Type **17**; (B) has it on right. For similar 3½ a. see No. 88.

21. "Scinde Dawk" stamp and Ancient and Modern Transport.

1952. Cent. of "Scinde Dawk" Issue of India.

63.	**21.**	3 a. green on olive	75	50
64.		12 a. brown on salmon	1·00	15

22. Kaghan Valley.

DESIGNS — As Type **22**: HORIZ. 9 p. Mountains, Gilgit. 1 a. Badshahi Mosque, Lahore. VERT. 1½ a. Mausoleum of Emperor Jehangir, Lahore. As Type **24**: HORIZ. 1 r. Cotton plants, West Pakistan. 2 r. Jute fields and river, East Pakistan.

24. Tea Plantation, East Pakistan.

1954. 7th Anniv. of Independence.

65.	**22.**	6 p. violet	10	10
66.	–	9 p. blue	1·25	70
67.	–	1 a. red	10	10
68.	–	1½ a. red	10	10
69.	**24.**	14 a. myrtle	55	10
70.	–	1 r. green	8·00	10
71.	–	2 r. orange	2·00	10

29. View of K2.

1954. Conquest of K 2 (Mount Godwin-Austen).

72.	**29.**	2 a. violet	30	15

30. Karnaphuli Paper Mill, East Bengal.

DESIGNS: 6 a. Textile mill W. Pakistan. 8 a. Jute mill, E. Pakistan. 12 a. Main Sui gas plant.

1955. 8th Anniv. of Independence.

73.	**30.**	2½ a. red (A)	30	30
73a.		2½ a. red (B)	30	30
74.	–	6 a. blue	60	10
75.	–	8 a. violet	2·25	10
76.	–	12 a. red and orange	2·00	10

(A) has Arabic fraction on left as in Type **30**; (B) has it on right. For similar 2½ a. see No. 87.

1955. 10th Anniv. of U.N. Nos. 68 and 76 optd. **TENTH ANNIVERSARY, UNITED NATIONS 24.10.55.**

77.	1½ a red	1·75	5·00
78.	12 a. red and orange	75	4·50

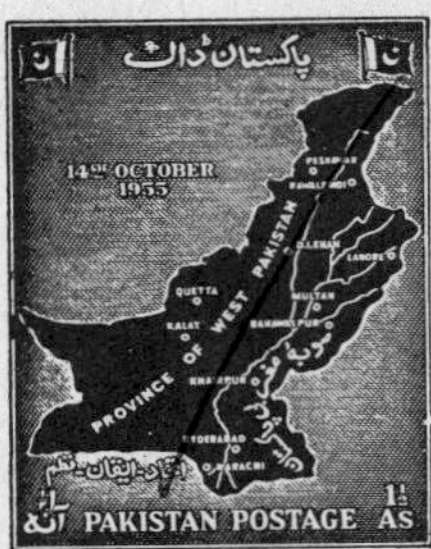

35. Map of W. Pakistan.

1955. West Pakistan Unity.

79.	**35.**	1½ a. green	15	10
80.		2 a. brown	15	10
81.		12 a. red	55	15

36. Constituent Assembly Building, Karachi.

1956. Republic Day.

82.	**36.**	2 a. green	35	10

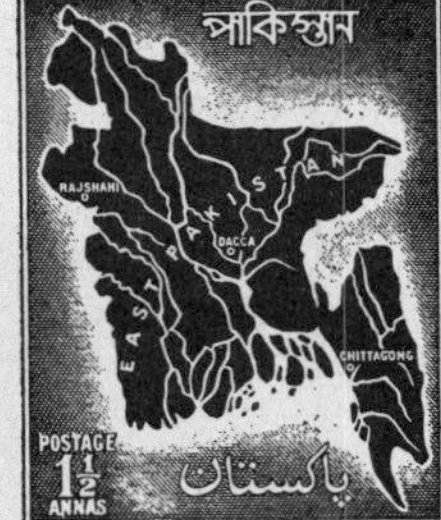

37. **38.** Map of East Pakistan.

1956. Independence. 9th Anniv.

83.	**37.**	2 a. red	20	10

1956. 1st Session of National Assembly of Pakistan at Dacca.

84.	**38.**	1½ a. green	15	60
85.		2 a. brown	15	10
86.		12 a. red	20	30

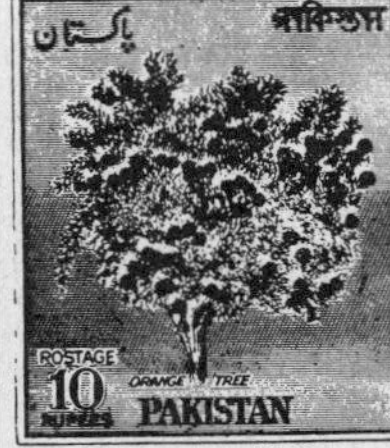

41. Orange Tree.

DESIGNS—2½ a. as Type **30** without value in Arabic at right. 3½ a. as Type **17** without value in Arabic at right.

1957. 1st Anniv. of Republic.

87	–	2½ a. red	20	10
88	–	3½ a. blue	30	10
89	**41.**	10 r. green and orange	80	20

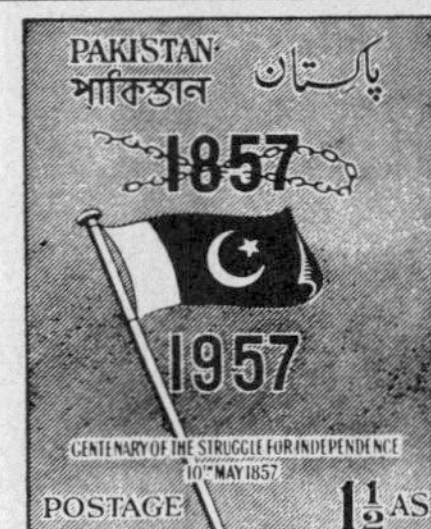

42. Pakistani Flag.

1957. Centenary of Struggle for Independence (Indian Mutiny).

90.	**42.**	1½ a. green	20	10
91.		12 a. blue	45	10

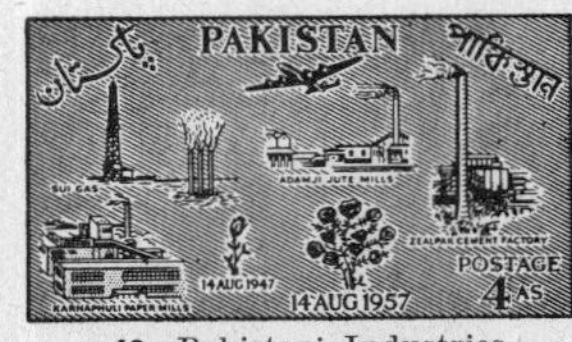

43. Pakistani Industries.

1957. 10th Anniv. of Independence.

92.	**43.**	1½ a. blue	15	10
93.		4 a. salmon	25	30
94.		12 a. mauve	30	40

1958. 2nd Anniv of Republic. As T **41**.

209	15 r. red and purple	80	1·00

DESIGNS: 15 r. Coconut tree.

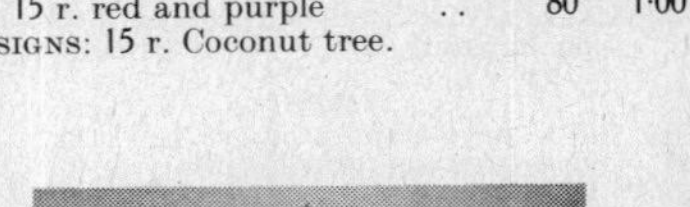

45.

1958. 20th Death Anniv. of Mohammed Iqbal (poet).

96.	**45.**	1½ a. olive and black	20	10
97.		2 a. brown and black	20	10
98.		14 a. turquoise and black	45	10

46. U.N. Charter and Globe.

1958. 10th Anniv. of Declaration of Human Rights.

99.	**46.**	1½ a. turquoise	10	10
100.		14 a. sepia	40	10

1958. Scout Jamboree. Optd. **PAKISTAN BOY SCOUT 2nd NATIONAL JAMBOREE CHITTAGONG Dec. 58-Jan. 59.**

101.	**22.**	6 p. violet	15	10
102.	–	8 a. violet (No. 75)	30	10

1959. Revolution Day. No. 74 optd. **REVOLUTION DAY Oct. 27, 1959.**

103.	–	6a. blue	30	10

49. "Centenary of an Idea".

1959. Red Cross Commem.

104.	**49.**	2 a. red and green	15	10
105.		10 a. red and blue	55	10

50. Armed Forces Badge.

1960. Armed Forces Day.
106. **50.** 2 a. red, blue and green 20 10
107. 14 a. red and blue .. 65 10

51. Map of Pakistan.

1960.
108. **51.** 6 p. purple 15 10
109. 2 a. red 30 10
110. 8 a. green 60 10
111. 1 r. blue 70 10

52. "Uprooted Tree".

1960. World Refugee Year.
112. **52.** 2 a. red 10 10
113. 10 a. green 20 10

53. Punjab Agricultural College.

1960. Golden Jubilee of Punjab Agricultural College, Lyallpur.
114. **53.** 2 a. blue and red 10 10
115. – 8 a. green and violet .. 10 10
DESIGN: 8 a. College Arms.

55. "Land Reforms, Rehabilitation and Reconstruction".

1960. Revolution Day.
116. **55.** 2 a. green, pink & brown 10 10
117. 14 a. green, yellow & blue 20 20

56. Caduceus.

1960. Centenary of King Edward Medical College, Lahore.
118. **56.** 2 a. yellow, black & blue 30 10
119. 14 a. green, black & red 70 10

57. "Economic Co-operation".

1960. Int. Chamber of Commerce C.A.F.E.A. Meeting, Karachi.
120. **57.** 14 a. brown 15 10

58. Zam-Zama Gun, Lahore. ("Kim's Gun" after Rudyard Kipling.)

1960. 3rd Pakistan Boy Scouts' National Jamboree, Lahore.
121. **58.** 2 a. red, yellow & green 30 10

1961. Surch. in "PAISA".
122. – 1 p. on 1½ a. red (No. 68) 15 10
123. **7.** 2 p. on 3 p. red .. 10 10
124. **51.** 3 p. on 6 p. purple .. 10 10
125. – 7 p. on 1 a. red (No. 67) 20 10
126. **51.** 13 p. on 2 a. red .. 20 10
127. **37.** 13 p. on 2 a. red .. 15 10
See also Nos. 262/4.

60. Khyber Pass.

61. Shalimar Gardens, Lahore.

62. Chota Sona Masjid (gateway).

1961.
170 **60** 1 p. violet 10 10
132 2 p. red 10 10
133 3 p. purple 30 10
173 5 p. blue 10 10
135 7 p. green 50 10
175 **61** 10 p. brown 10 10
176 13 p. violet 10 10
176a 15 p. purple 15 10
176b 20 p. green 30 10
177 25 p. blue .. .. 2·50 10
178 40 p. purple 15 10
179 50 p. turquoise 15 10
141 75 p. red 40 10
142 90 p. green 40 10
204 **62** 1 r. red 30 10
144 1 r. 25 violet 75 10
206 2 r. orange 55 15
207 5 r. green .. .. 3·50 40

1961. Lahore Stamp Exn. No. 110 optd. **LAHORE STAMP EXHIBITION 1961** and emblem.
145. **51.** 8 a. green 40 70

64. Warsak Dam and Power Station.

1961. Completion of Warsak Hydro-Electric Project.
146. **64.** 40 p. black and blue .. 40 10

65. Narcissus.

1961. Child Welfare Week.
147. **65.** 13 p. turquoise .. 15 10
148. 90 p. mauve .. 35 20

66. Ten Roses.

1961. Co-operative Day.
149. **66.** 13 p. red and green .. 30 10
150. 90 p. red and blue .. 70 20

67. Police Crest and "Traffic Control".

1961. Centenary of Police.
151. **67.** 13 p. silver, black & blue 40 10
152. 40 p. silver, black & red 85 20

68. Locomotive "Eagle" of 1861.

1961. Centenary of Railway.
153. **68.** 13 p. green, blk. & yell. 50 40
154. – 50 p. yell., black & green 75 40
DESIGN: 50 p. Diesel locomotive.

1962. Karachi–Dacca Flight. No. 87 surch. with 'plane and **FIRST JET FLIGHT KARACHI-DACCA 13 Paisa.**
155. 13 p. on 2½ a. red .. 50 30

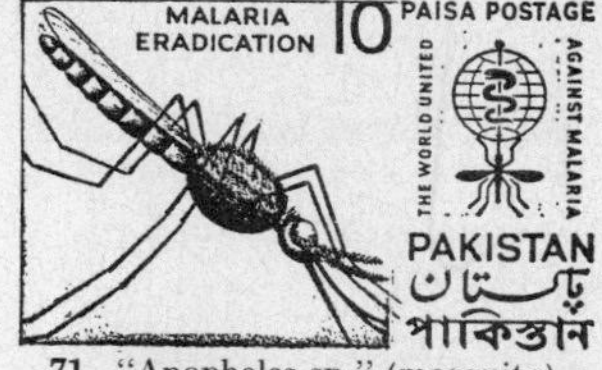

71. "Anopheles sp." (mosquito).

1962. Malaria Eradication.
156. **71.** 10 p. black, yellow & red 20 10
157. – 13 p. black, lemon & red 20 10
DESIGN: 13 p. Mosquito pierced by blade.

73. Pakistan Map and Jasmine.

1962. New Constitution.
158. **73.** 40 p. green, turq. & grey 45 10

74. Football.

1962. Sports.
159. **74.** 7 p. black and blue .. 10 10
160. – 13 p. black and green .. 10 10
161. – 25 p. black and purple .. 10 10
162. – 40 p. black and brown .. 1·40 80
DESIGNS: 13 p. Hockey. 25 p. Squash. 40 p. Cricket.

DESIGNS: 13 p. Sports equipment. 25 p. Camelskin lamp and brassware. 40 p. Wooden powder-bowl and basket-work. 50 p. Inlaid cigarette-box and brassware.

78. Marble Fruit Dish and Bahawalpuri Clay Flask.

1962. Small Industries.
163. **78.** 7 p. lake 10 10
164. – 13 p. green .. .. 1·75 50
165. – 25 p. violet 10 10
166. – 40 p. green 10 10
167. – 50 p. red 10 10

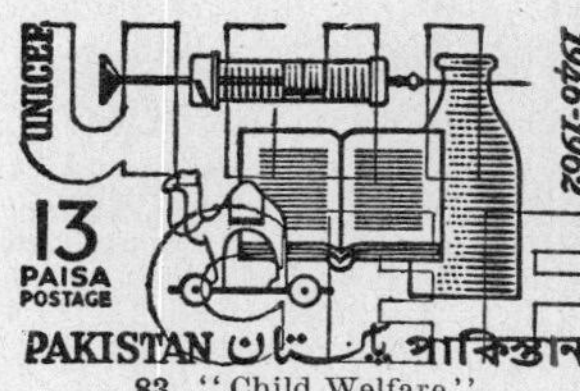

83. "Child Welfare".

1962. 16th Anniv. of U.N.I.C.E.F.
168. **83.** 13 p. blk., blue & purple 15 10
169. 40 p. blk., yell. & turq. 15 10

1963. Pakistan U.N. Force in West Irian. Optd. **U.N. FORCE W. IRIAN.**
182. **61.** 13 p. violet 10 10

85. "Dancing" Horse, Camel and Bull.

1963. Nat. Horse and Cattle Show.
183. **85.** 13 p. blue, sepia & pink 10 10

86. Wheat and Tractor.

1963. Freedom from Hunger.
184. **86.** 13 p. brown 50 10
185. – 50 p. bistre .. .. 1·50 40
DESIGN: 50 p. Lifting rice.

1963. 2nd Int. Stamp Exn., Dacca. Surch. **INTERNATIONAL DACCA STAMP EXHIBITION 1963 13 PAISA** and bars.
186. **51.** 13 p. on 2 a. red .. 30 10

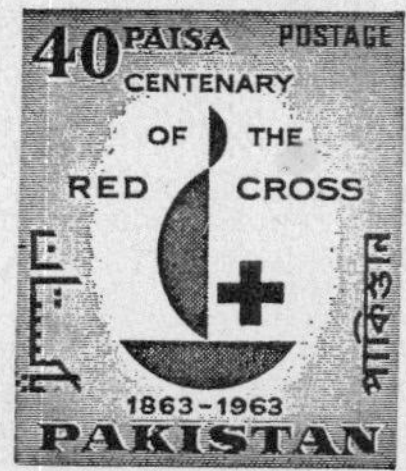

89. Centenary Emblem.

1963. Centenary of Red Cross.
187. **89.** 40 p. red and olive .. 85 15

90. Paharpur.

1963. Archaeological Series.
188. **90.** 7 p. blue 15 10
189. – 13 p. sepia 20 10
190. – 40 p. red 25 10
191. – 50 p. violet 30 10
DESIGNS—VERT. 13 p. Moenjodaro. HORIZ. 40 p. Taxila. 50 p. Mainamati.

1963. Pakistan Public Works Department Cent. Surch. **100 YEARS OF P.W.D. OCTOBER, 1963 13** and bars.
192. **60.** 13 p. on 3 p. purple .. 10 10

95. Ataturk's Mausoleum.

1963. 25th Death Anniv. of Kemal Ataturk.
193. **95.** 50 p. red 35 10

96. Globe and U.N.E.S.C.O. Emblem.

1963. 15th Anniv. of Declaration of Human Rights.
194. **96.** 50 p. brown, red & blue 30 10

97. Thermal Power Installations.

1963. Completion of Multan Thermal Power Station.
195. **97.** 13 p. blue 10 10

99. Temple of Thot, Queen Nefertari and Maids.

1964. Nubian Monuments Preservation.
211. **99.** 13 p. blue and red .. 20 10
212. – 50 p. purple and black 60 10
DESIGN: 50 p. Temple of Abu Simbel.

101. "Unisphere" and Pakistan Pavilion.

1964. New York World's Fair.
213. **101.** 13 p. blue 10 10
214. – 1 r. 25 blue and orange 30 20
DESIGN—VERT. 1 r. 25, Pakistan Pavilion on "Unisphere".

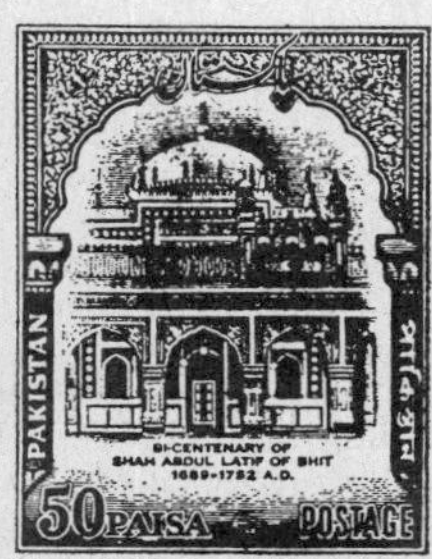

103. Shah Abdul Latif's Mausoleum.

1964. Death Bicentenary of Shah Abdul Latif of Bhit.
215. **103.** 50 p. blue and lake .. 40 10

104. Mausoleum of "Quaid-i-Azam".

1964. 16th Death Anniv. of Mohammed Ali Jinnah ("Quaid-i-Azam").
216. **104.** 15 p. green 15 10
217. – 50 p. bronze 50 10
DESIGN: 50 p. As Type **104**, but 26½ × 31½ mm.

106. Bengali and Urdu Alphabets.

1964. "Universal Children's Day".
218. **106.** 15 p. brown 10 10

107. University Building.

1964. 1st Convocation of the West Pakistan University of Engineering and Technology, Lahore.
219. **107.** 15 p. brown 10 10

108. "Help the Blind".

1965. Blind Welfare.
220. **108.** 15 p. blue and yellow .. 10 10

109. I.T.U. Emblem and Symbols.

1965. Centenary of I.T.U.
221. **109.** 15 p. purple .. .. 1·25 30

110. I.C.Y. Emblem.

1965. Int. Co-operation Year.
222. **110.** 15 p. black and blue .. 40 15
223. 50 p. green and yellow 85 40

111. "Co-operation".

1965. 1st Anniversary of Regional Development Co-operation Pact. Mult.
224. 15 p. Type **111** .. 15 10
225. 50 p. Globe and Flags of Turkey, Iran and Pakistan (54½ × 30½ mm.) .. 45 10

113. Soldier and Tanks.

1965. Pakistan Armed Forces. Multicoloured.
226. 7 p. Type **113** 35 15
227. 15 p. Naval Officer and "Taghril" (destroyer) .. 60 10
228. 50 p. Pilot and "F–104" Starfighters 95 15

116. Army, Navy and Air Force Crests.

1966. Armed Forces Day.
229. **116.** 15 p. bl., grn. & buff 10 10

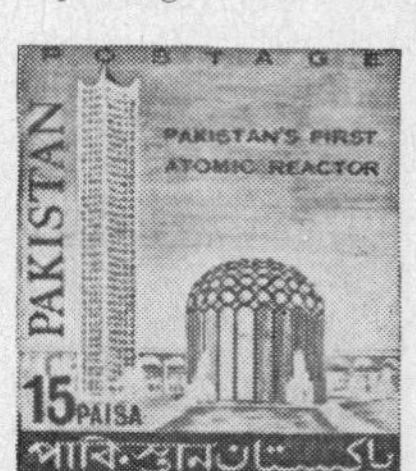

117. Atomic Reactor, Islamabad.

1966. Pakistan's 1st Atomic Reactor. Inauguration.
230. **117.** 15 p. black 10 10

118. Bank Crest.

1966. Silver Jubilee of Habib Bank.
231. **118.** 15 p. grn., orge. & sepia 10 10

119. Children.

1966. "Universal Children Day".
232. **119.** 15 p. black, red & yellow 10 10

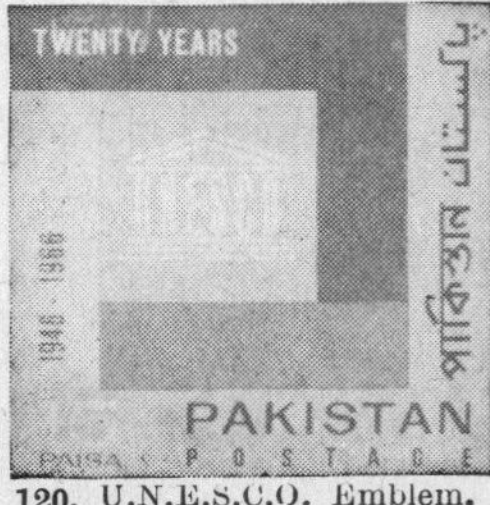

120. U.N.E.S.C.O. Emblem.

1966. 20th Anniversary of U.N.E.S.C.O.
233. **120.** 15 p. multicoloured .. 1·60 30

121. Flag, Secretariat Building and President Ayub.

1966. Islamabad (new capital).
234. **121.** 15 p. multicoloured .. 10 10
235. 50 p. multicoloured .. 30 10

122. Avicenna.

1966. Health and Tibbi Research Institute Foundation.
236. **122.** 15 p. green and salmon 15 10

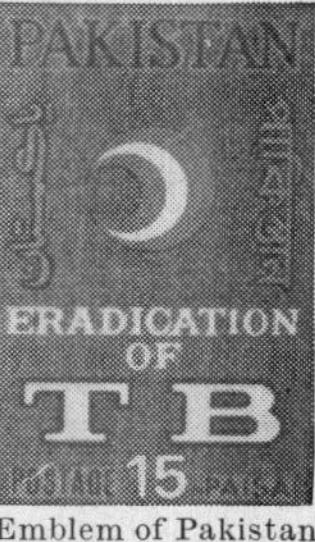

123. Mohammed Ali Jinnah. **125.** Emblem of Pakistan T.B. Association.

124. Tourist Year Emblem.

1966. 40th Birth Anniv. of Mohammed Ali Jinnah.
237. **123.** 15 p. black, orge. & blue 10 10
238. – 50 p. blk., pur. and blue 30 10
DESIGN: 50 p. Same portrait as 15 p. but different frame.

1967. Int. Tourist Year.
239. **124.** 15 p. black, blue & brn. 10 10

1967. T.B. Eradication Campaign.
240. **125.** 15 p. red, sepia & brown 10 10

126. Scout Salute and Badge.

1967. 4th National Scout Jamboree.
241. **126.** 15 p. brown and purple 15 10

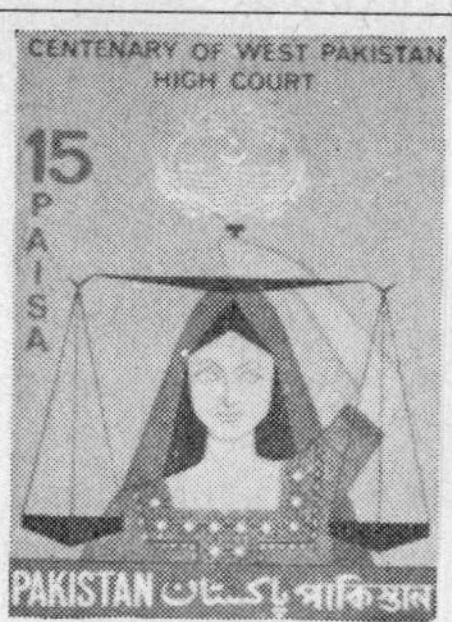

127. "Justice".

1967. Cent. of West Pakistan High Court.
242. **127.** 15 p. multicoloured .. 10 10

128. Dr. Mohammed Iqbal (philosopher).

1967. Iqbal Commem.
243. **128.** 15 p. sepia and red .. 10 10
244. 1 r. sepia and green .. 30 10

129. Hilal-i-Isteqlal Flag.

1967. Award of Hilal-i-Isteqlal (for Valour) to Lahore, Sialkot and Sargodha.
245. **129.** 15 p. multicoloured .. 10 10

130. "20th Anniversary".

1967. 20th Anniv. of Independence.
246. **130.** 15 p. red and green .. 10 10

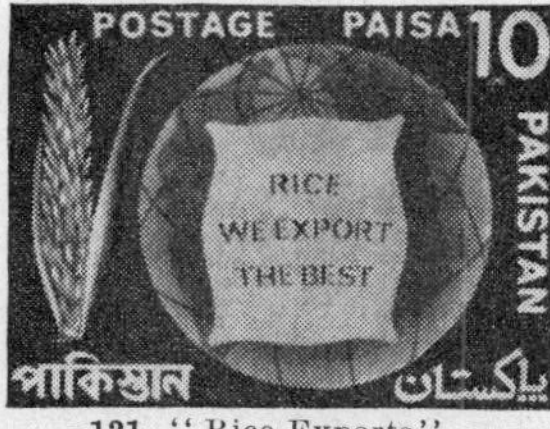

131. "Rice Exports".

1967. Pakistan Exports. Multicoloured.
247. 10 p. Type **131** .. 10 15
248. 15 p. Cotton plant, yarn and textiles .. 10 10
249. 50 p. Raw jute, bale and bags .. 20 15
Nos. 248/9 are vert. and larger 27 × 45 **mm.**

134. Clay Toys.

1967. Children's Day.
250. **134.** 15 p. multicoloured .. 10 10

135. Shah and Empress of Iran and Gulistan Palace, Teheran.

1967. Coronation of Shah Mohammed Riza Pahlavi and Empress Farah of Iran.
251. **135.** 50 p. purple, blue & ochre 30 10

136. "Each For All—All for Each".

1967. Co-operative Day.
252. **136.** 15 p. multicoloured .. 10 10

137. Mangla Dam.

1967. Indus Basin Project.
253. **137.** 15 p. multicoloured .. 10 10

138. Crab Pierced by Sword.

1967. The Fight Against Cancer.
254. **138.** 15 p. red and black .. 40 10

139. Human Rights Emblem.

1968. Human Rights Year.
255. **139.** 15 p. red and blue .. 10 15
256. 50 p. red, yellow & grey .. 10 15

140. Agricultural University, Mymensingh.

1968. East Pakistan Agricultural University. First Convocation.
257. **140.** 15 p. multicoloured .. 10 10

141. W.H.O. Emblem.

1968. 20th Anniversary of World Health Organization.
258. **141.** 15 p. green and red .. 10 15
259. 50 p. orange and blue .. 10 15

142. Kazi Nazrul Islam (poet, composer and patriot).

1968. Nazrul Islam Commem.
260. **142.** 15 p. sepia and yellow .. 15 15
261. 50 p. sepia and red .. 35 15

1968. Nos. 56, 74 and 61 surch.
262. 4 p. on 3 a. purple .. 20 45
263. 4 p. on 6 a. blue .. 40 55
264. 60 p. on 10 a. violet .. 30 35

144. Children running with Hoops.

1968. Universal Children's Day.
265. **144.** 15 p. multicoloured .. 10 10

145. National Assembly.

1968. "A Decade of Development".
266. **145.** 10 p. multicoloured .. 10 10
267. – 15 p. multicoloured .. 15 10
268. – 50 p. multicoloured .. 40 15
269. – 60 p. blue, pur. & red .. 40 15
DESIGNS: 15 p. Industry and Agriculture. 50 p. Army, Navy and Air Force. 60 p. Minaret and Atomic Reactor Plant.

149. Chittagong Steel Mill.

1969. Pakistan's 1st Steel Mill, Chittagong.
270. **149.** 15 p. grey, blue and olive 10 10

150. "Family".

1969. Family Planning.
271. **150.** 15 p. purple and blue .. 10 10

151. Olympic Gold Medal and Hockey Player.

1969. Olympic Hockey Champions.
272. **151.** 15 p. multicoloured .. 55 35
273. 1 r. multicoloured .. 1·50 60

152. Mirza Ghalib and Lines of Verse.

1969. Death Cent. of Mirza Ghalib (poet).
274. **152.** 15 p. multicoloured .. 15 15
275. 50 p. multicoloured .. 40 15
The lines of verse on No. 275 are different from those in Type **152.**

153. Dacca Railway Station.

1969. 1st Anniversary of New Dacca Railway Station.
276. **153.** 15 p. multicoloured .. 30 10

154. I.L.O. Emblem and "1919-1969".

1969. 50th Anniversary of I.L.O.
277. **154.** 15 p. buff and green .. 10 10
278. 50 p. brown and red .. 30 10

155. Mughal Miniature (Pakistan).

1969. 5th Anniversary of Regional Co-operation for Development. Multicoloured.
279. 20 p. Type **155** .. 15 10
280. 50 p. Safavi miniature (Iran) .. 15 10
281. 1 r. Ottoman miniature (Turkey) .. 20 10

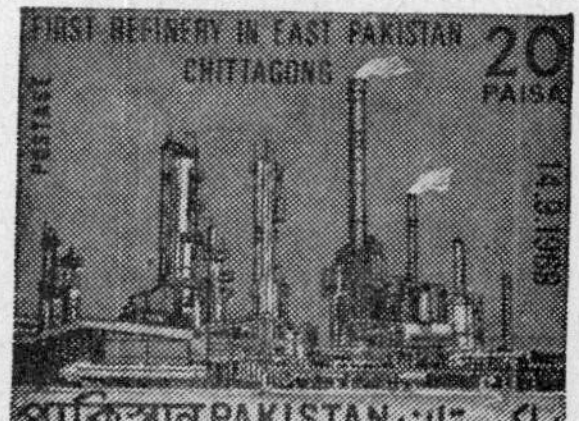

158. Eastern Refinery, Chittagong.

1969. 1st East Pakistan Oil Refinery.
282. **158.** 20 p. multicoloured .. 10 10

159. Children playing outside "School". (Reduced size Illustration—actual size 52 × 52 mm.).

1969. Universal Children's Day.
283. **159.** 20 p. multicoloured .. 10 10

160. Japanese Doll and P.I.A. Air Routes.

1969. Inauguration of P.I.A. Pearl Route, Dacca-Tokyo.
284. **160.** 20 p. multicoloured .. 20 10
285. 50 p. multicoloured .. 35 40

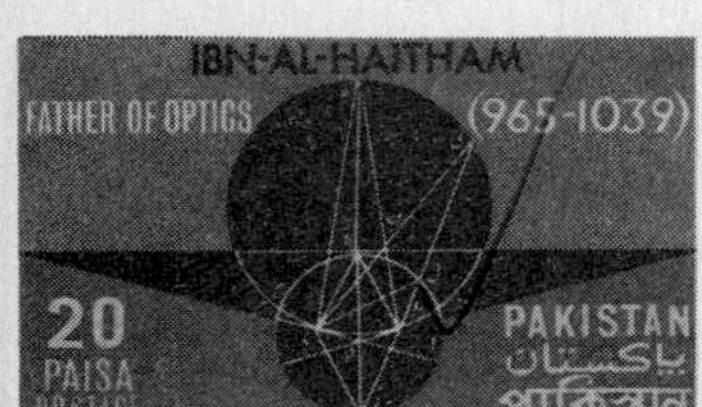

161. "Reflection of Light" Diagram.

1969. Millenary Commemorative of Ibn-al-Haitham (physicist).
286. **161.** 20 p. black, yell. & blue 10 10

162. Vickers "Vimy" and Karachi Airport.

1969. 50th Anniv. of 1st England–Australia Flight.
287. **162.** 50 p. multicoloured .. 40 35

163. Flags, Sun Tower and Expo Site Plan.

1970. World Fair, Osaka. Expo 70.
288. **163.** 50 p. multicoloured .. 15 30

164. New U.P.U. H.Q. Building.

1970. New U.P.U. Headquarters Building.
289. **164.** 20 p. multicoloured .. 10 10
290. 50 p. multicoloured .. 20 25

165. U.N. H.Q. Building.

1970. 25th Anniv. of United Nations. Mult.
291. 20 p. Type **165** 10 10
292. 50 p. U.N. Emblem .. 15 20

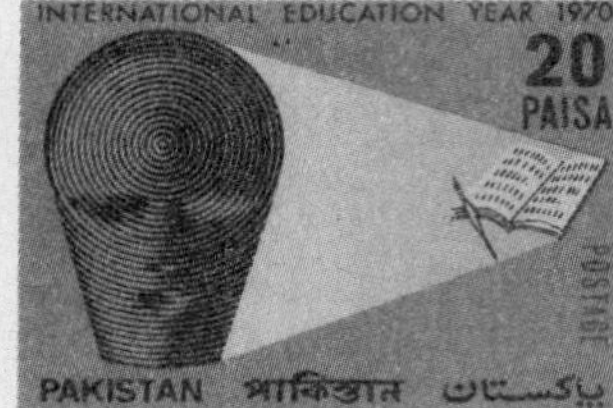

167. I.E.Y. Emblem, Book and Pen.

1970. Int. Education Year.
293. **167.** 20 p. multicoloured .. 10 10
294. 50 p. multicoloured .. 20 20

168. Saiful Malook Lake (Pakistan).

1970. 6th Anniv. of Regional Co-operation for Development. Multicoloured.
295. 20 p. Type **168** 15 10
296. 50 p. Seeyo-Se-Poi Bridge, Esfahan (Iran) 20 10
297. 1 r. View from Fethiye (Turkey) 20 15

171. Asian Productivity Symbol.

1970. Asian Productivity Year.
298. **171.** 50 p. multicoloured .. 10 15

172. Dr. Maria Montessori.

1970. Birth Centenary of Dr. Maria Montessori (educationalist).
299. **172.** 20 p. multicoloured .. 10 10
300. 50 p. multicoloured .. 10 20

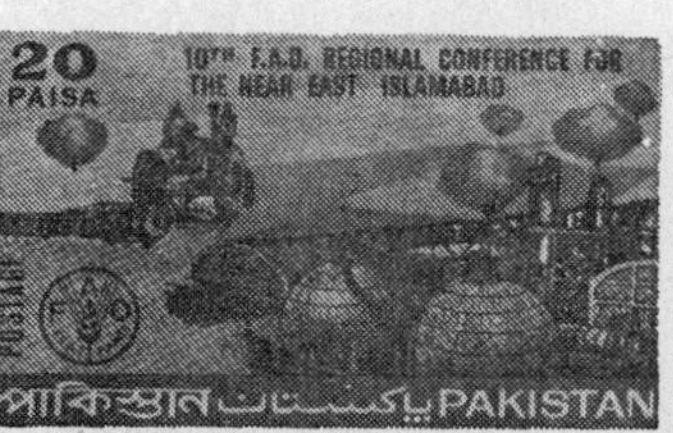

173. Tractor and Fertilizer Factory.

1970. Near East F.A.O. Regional Conference, Islamabad.
301. **173.** 20 p. green and brown 10 15

174. Children and Open Book. **175.** Pakistan Flag and Text.

1970. Universal Children's Day.
302. **174.** 20 p. multicoloured .. 10 10

1970. Elections for National Assembly.
303. **175.** 20 p. green and violet 10 10

1970. Elections for Provincial Assemblies. As No. 303, but inscr. "PROVINCIAL ASSEMBLIES".
304. **175.** 20 p. green and red .. 10 10

176. Conference Crest and burning Al-Aqsa Mosque.

1970. Conference of Islamic Foreign Ministers, Karachi.
305. **176.** 20 p. multicoloured .. 10 15

177. Coastal Embankments.

1971. East Pakistan Coastal Embankments Project.
306. **177.** 20 p. multicoloured .. 10 10

178. Emblem and United Peoples of the World.

1971. Racial Equality Year.
307. **178.** 20 p. multicoloured .. 10 10
308. 50 p. multicoloured .. 20 20

179. Maple Leaf Cement Factory, Daudkhel.

1971. 20th Anniversary of Colombo Plan.
309. **179.** 20 p. brn., blk. & violet 10 10

180. Chaharbagh School (Iran).

1971. 7th Anniversary of Regional Co-operation for Development. Multicoloured.
310. 10 p. Selimiye Mosque (Turkey) 10 15
311. 20 p. Badshahi Mosque, Lahore (horiz.) .. 20 25
312. 50 p. Type **180** 30 35

181. Electric Locomotive and Boy with Toy Train.

1971. Universal Children's Day.
313. **181.** 20 p. multicoloured .. 1·00 30

182. Horseman and Symbols.

1971. 2500th Anniv. of Persian Empire.
314. **182.** 10 p. multicoloured .. 25 30
315. 20 p. multicoloured .. 35 40
316. 50 p. multicoloured .. 45 50

183. Hockey-player and Trophy.

1971. World Cup Hockey Tournament, Barcelona.
317. **183.** 20 p. multicoloured .. 1·00 45

184. Great Bath, Moenjodaro.

1971. 25th Anniv. of U.N.E.S.C.O. and Campaign to save the Moenjodaro Excavations.
318. **184.** 20 p. multicoloured .. 15 20

185. U.N.I.C.E.F. Symbol.

1971. 25th Anniv. of U.N.I.C.E.F.
319. 185. 50 p. multicoloured .. 30 30

186. King Hussein and Jordanian Flag.

1971. 50th Anniv. of Hashemite Kingdom of Jordan.
320. 186. 20 p. multicoloured .. 15 15

187. Badge of Hockey Federation and Trophy.

1971. Hockey Championships Victory.
321. 187. 20 p. multicoloured .. 1·50 90

188. Reading Class.

1972. Int. Book Year.
322. 188. 20 p. multicoloured .. 20 20

189. View of Venice.

1972. U.N.E.S.C.O. Campaign to Save Venice.
323. 189. 20 p. multicoloured .. 30 30

190. E.C.A.F.E. Emblem and Discs.

1972. 25th Anniv. of E.C.A.F.E.
324. 190. 20 p. multicoloured .. 10 20

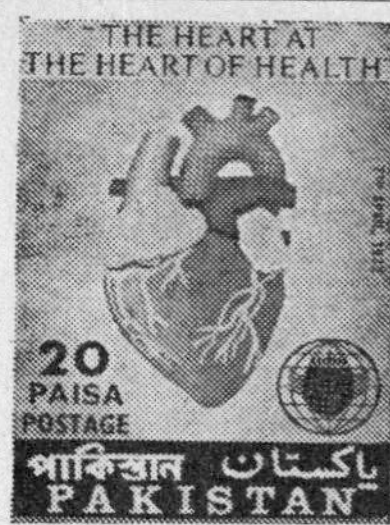

191. Human Heart.

1972. World Health Day.
325. 191. 20 p. multicoloured .. 20 20

192. " Only One Earth".

1972. U.N. Conf. on the Human Environment, Stockholm.
326. 192. 20 p. multicoloured .. 20 20

193. " Fisherman" (Cevat Dereli).

1972. 8th Anniversary of Co-operation for Regional Development. Multicoloured.
327. 10 p. Type 193 .. .. 10 20
328. 20 p. " Iranian Woman" (Behzad) 15 25
329. 50 p. " Will and Power" (A. R. Chughtai) .. 35 45

194. Mohammed Ali Jinnah and Tower.

1972. 25th Anniv. of Independence. Mult.
330. 10 p. Type 194 .. .. 10 10
331. 20 p. " Land Reform " .. 15 20
332. 20 p. " Labour Reform " .. 15 20
333. 20 p. " Education Policy " 15 20
334. 20 p. " Health Policy " .. 15 20
335. 60 p. National Assembly Building 25 25
The 60 p. is 46 × 28 mm.: Nos. 331/4 are 74 × 23½ mm.

195. Donating Blood.

1972. Nat. Blood Transfusion Service.
336. 195. 20 p. multicoloured .. 15 30

196. People and Squares.

1972. Centenary of Population Census.
337. 196. 20 p. multicoloured .. 15 20

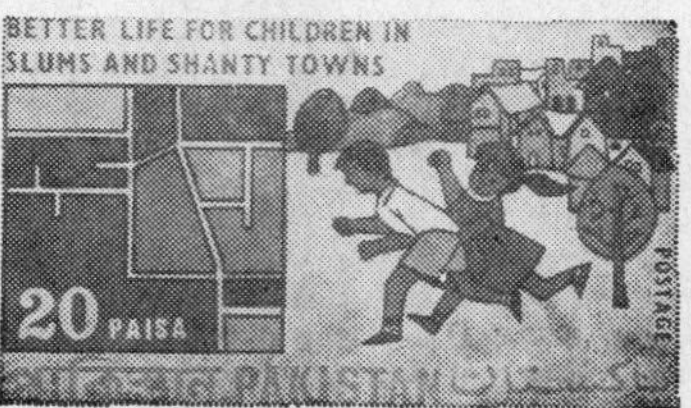

197. Children from Slums.

1972. Universal Children's Day.
338. 197. 20 p. multicoloured .. 15 30

198. People and Open Book.

1972. Education Week.
339. 198. 20 p. multicoloured .. 20 20

199. Nuclear Power Plant.

1972. Inauguration of Karachi Nuclear Power Plant.
340. 199. 20 p. multicoloured .. 15 30

200. Copernicus in Observatory.

1973. 500th Birth Anniversary of Nicholas Copernicus (astronomer).
341. 200. 20 p. multicoloured .. 20 30

201. Moenjodaro Excavations.

1973. 50th Anniversary of Moenjodaro Excavations.
342. 201. 20 p. multicoloured .. 20 30

202. Elements of Meteorology.

1973. Centenary of I.M.O./W.M.O.
343. 202. 10 p. multicoloured .. 20 30

203. Prisoners-of-war.

1973. Prisoners-of-war in India.
344. 203. 1 r. 25 multicoloured .. 1·50 1·50

204. National Assembly Building and Constitution Book.

1973. Constitution Week.
345. 204. 20 p. multicoloured .. 40 40

205. Badge and State Bank Building.

1973. 25th Anniv. of Pakistan State Bank.
346. 205. 20 p. multicoloured .. 15 20
347. 1 r. multicoloured .. 30 40

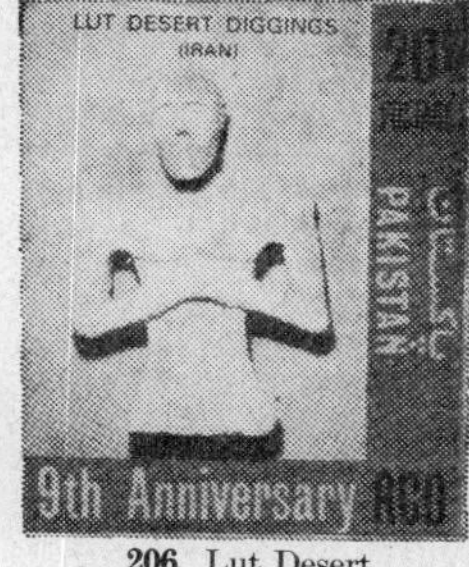

206. Lut Desert Excavations (Iran).

1973. 9th Anniversary of Regional Co-operation for Development. Multicoloured.
348. 20 p. Type 206 .. .. 30 20
349. 60 p. Main Street, Moenjodaro (Pakistan) 55 40
350. 1 r. 25 Mausoleum of Antiochus I (Turkey) .. 75 1·00

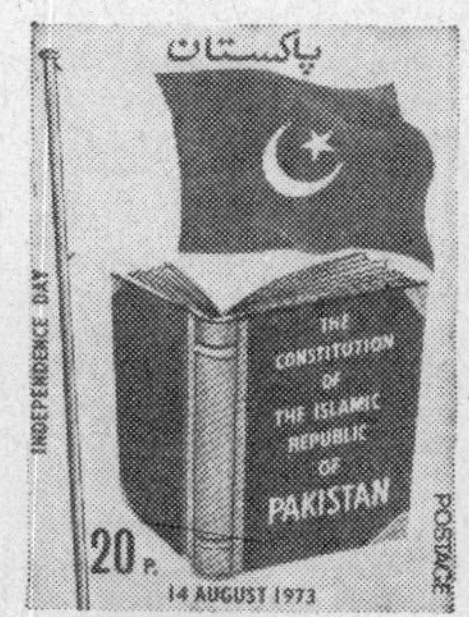

207. Constitution Book and Flag.

1973. Independence Day and Enforcement of the Constitution.
351. **207.** 20 p. multicoloured .. 15 20

208. Mohammed Ali Jinnah (Quaid-i-Azam).

1973. 25th Death Anniversary of Mohammed Ali Jinnah.
352. **208.** 20 p. grn., yell. & blk. 15 20

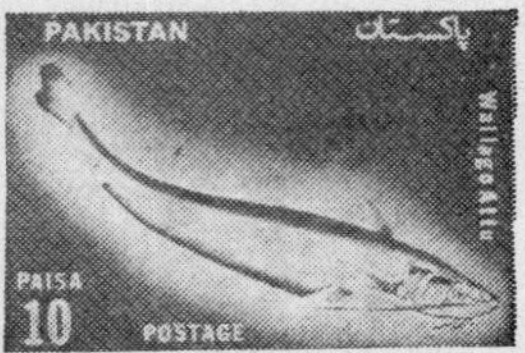

209. " Wallago attu ".

1973. Fishes. Multicoloured.
353. 10 p. Type **209** 80 80
354. 20 p. " Labeo rohita " .. 90 90
355. 60 p. " Tilapia mossambica " 1·00 1·00
356. 1 r. " Catla catla " .. 1·25 1·25

210. Children's Education.

1973. Universal Children's Day.
357. **210.** 20 p. multicoloured .. 15 30

211. Harvesting.

1973. 10th Anniversary of World Food Programme.
358. **211.** 20 p. multicoloured .. 50 30

212. Ankara and Kemal Ataturk.

1973. 50th Anniversary of Turkish Republic.
359. **212.** 50 p. multicoloured .. 45 35

213. Boy Scout. **214.** "Basic Necessities".

1973. National Silver Jubilee Jamboree.
360. **213.** 20 p. multicoloured .. 80 50

1973. 25th Anniversary of Declaration of Human Rights.
361. **214.** 20 p. multicoloured .. 30 30

215. Al-Biruni and Nandana Hill.

1973. Al-Biruni Millennium Congress.
362. **215** 20 p. multicoloured .. 40 20
363 1 r. 25 multicoloured .. 85 75

216. Dr. Hansen, Microscope and Bacillus.

1973. Centenary of Hansen's Discovery of Leprosy Bacillus.
364. **216.** 20 p. multicoloured .. 75 50

217. Family and Emblem.

1974. World Population Year.
365. **217.** 20 p. multicoloured .. 10 10
366. 1 r. 25 multicoloured 30 40

218. Conference Emblem.

1974. Islamic Summit Conference, Lahore. Multicoloured.
367. 20 p. Type **218** 10 10
368. 65 p. Emblem on " Sun " 25 45
No. 368 is larger, size 42 × 30 mm.

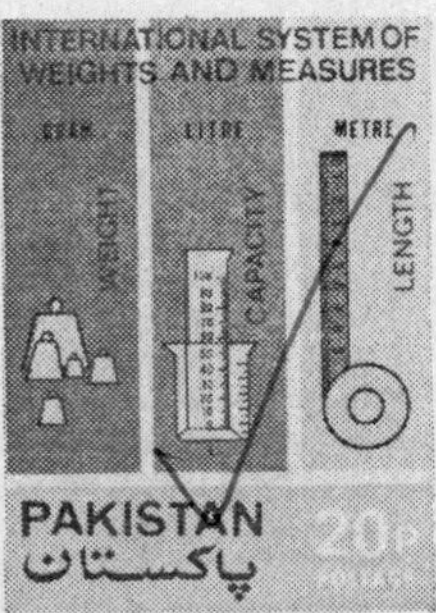

219. Units of Weight and Measurement.

1974. Adoption of Int. Weights and Measures System.
370. **219.** 20 p. multicoloured .. 15 25

220. " Chand Chauthai " Carpet, Pakistan.

1974. 10th Anniversary of Regional Co-operation for Development. Multicoloured.
371. 20 p. Type **220** 15 15
372. 60 p. Persian carpet, 16th-century 45 50
373. 1 r. 25 Anatolian carpet, 15th-century .. .. 65 1·00

221. Hands protecting Sapling.

1974. Tree Planting Day.
374. **221.** 20 p. multicoloured .. 50 30

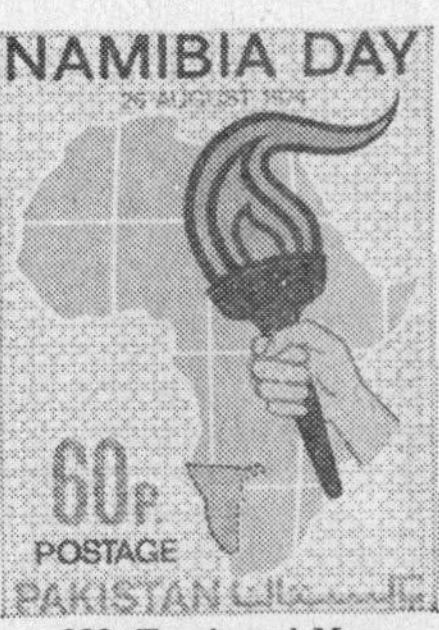

222. Torch and Map.

1974. Namibia Day.
375. **222.** 60 p. multicoloured .. 35 60

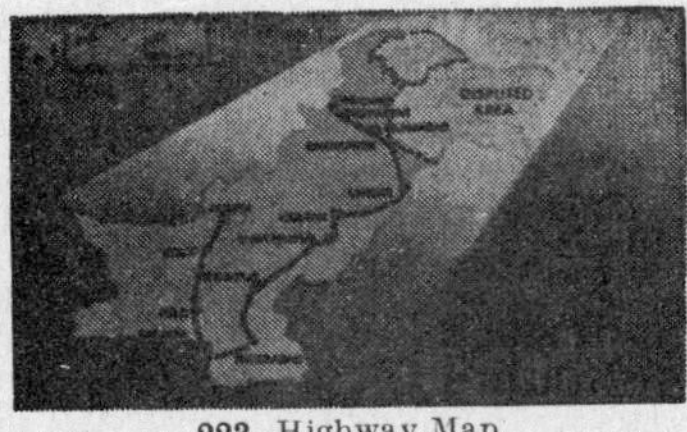

223. Highway Map.

1974. Shahrah-e-Pakistan (Pakistan Highway).
376. **223.** 20 p. multicoloured .. 50 40

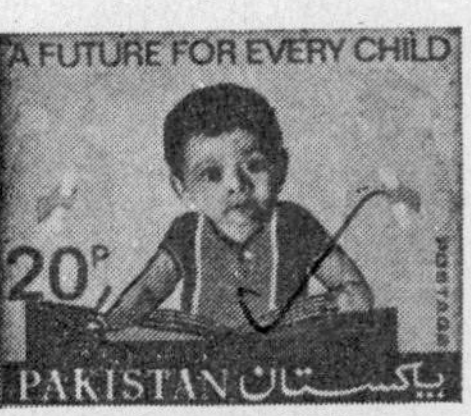

224. Boy at Desk.

1974. Universal Children's Day.
377. **224.** 20 p. multicoloured .. 30 30

225. U.P.U. Emblem. **226.** Liaquat Ali Khan.

1974. Centenary of U.P.U. Multicoloured.
378. 20 p. Type **225** 20 20
379. 2 r. 25 U.P.U. emblem, aeroplane and mail-wagon 55 1·40

1974. Liaquat Ali Khan (First Prime Minister of Pakistan).
381. **226.** 20 p. black and red .. 30 30

227. Dr. Mohammed Iqbal (poet and philosopher).

1974. Birth Centenary of Dr. Iqbal. (1977) (1st issue).
382. **227.** 20 p. multicoloured .. 30 30
See also Nos. 399, 433 and 445/9.

228. Dr. Schweitzer and River Scene.

1975. Birth Cent. of Dr. Albert Schweitzer.
383. **228.** 2 r. 25 multicoloured 1·75 2·00

229. Tourism Year Symbol.

1975. South East Asia Tourism Year.
384. **229.** 2 r. 25 multicoloured 55 80

230. Assembly Hall, Flags and Prime Minister Bhutto.

1975. 1st Anniversary of Islamic Summit Conference, Lahore.
385. 230. 20 p. multicoloured .. 35 25
386. 1 r. multicoloured .. 90 1·00

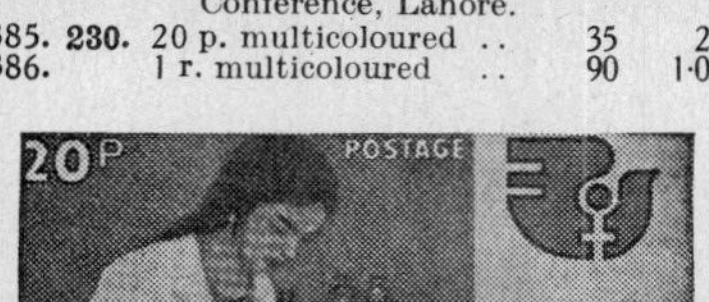

231. " Scientific Research ".

1975. International Women's Year. Mult.
387. 20 p. Type 231 .. .. 20 25
388. 2 r. 25 Girl teaching woman (" Adult Education ") 1·10 1·75

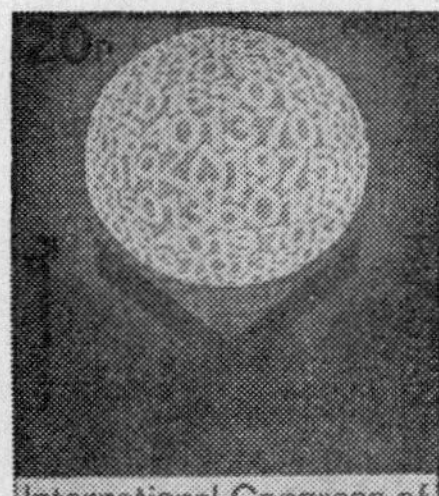

232. " Globe " and Algebraic Symbol.

1975. Int. Congress of Mathematical Sciences, Karachi.
389. 232. 20 p. multicoloured .. 40 30

233. Pakistani Camel-skin Vase.

1975. 11th Anniversary of Regional Co-operation for Development. Multicoloured.
390. 20 p. Type 233 .. .. 25 30
391. 60 p. Iranian tile (horiz.) 50 70
392. 1 r. 25 Turkish porcelain vase .. .. 75 1·25

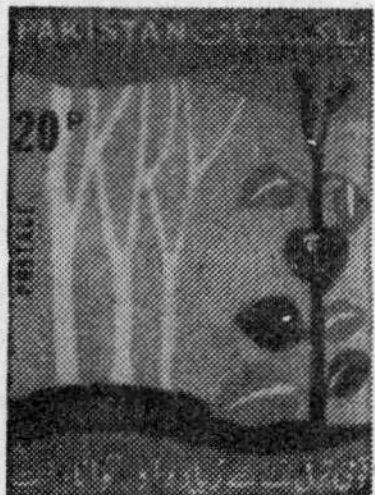

234. Sapling and Dead Trees.

1975. Tree Planting Year.
393. 234. 20 p. multicoloured .. 30 30

235. Black Partridge.

1975. Wildlife Protection (1st series).
394. 235. 20 p. multicoloured .. 1·00 35
395. 2 r. 25 multicoloured 3·75 3·50
See also Nos. 400/1, 411/12, 417/18, 493/6, 560, 572/3, 581/2, 599, 600, 605, 621/2, 691, 702, 780/3 and 853.

236. " Today's Girls ".

1975. Universal Children's Day.
396. 236. 20 p. multicoloured .. 25 30

237. Hazrat Amir Khusrau, Sitar and Tabla.
(Reduced size illustration—actual size 74 × 23 mm.)

1975. 700th Birth Anniversary of Hazrat Amir Khusrau (poet and musician).
397. 237. 20 p. multicoloured .. 20 45
398. 2 r. 25 multicoloured .. 75 1·60

238. Dr. Mohammed Iqbal.

1975. Birth Cent. (1977) of Dr. Iqbal. (2nd issue).
399. 238. 20 p. multicoloured .. 30 30

239. Urial (wild sheep).

1975. Wildlife Protection (2nd series).
400. 239. 20 p. multicoloured .. 40 30
401. 3 r. multicoloured .. 2·50 3·00

240. Moenjodaro Remains.

1976. " Save Moenjodaro " (1st issue). Multicoloured.
402. 10 p. Type 240 .. .. 65 75
403. 20 p. Remains of houses .. 75 85
404. 65 p. Citadel area and stupa 75 85
405. 3 r. Well inside a house .. 75 85
406. 4 r. The " Great Bath " .. 85 95
See also Nos. 414 and 430.

241. Dome and Minaret of the Rauza-e-Mubarak.

1976. Int. Congress on Seerat.
407. 241. 20 p. multicoloured .. 20 20
408. 3 r. multicoloured .. 70 90

242. Alexander Graham Bell and Modern Dial.

1976. Centenary of First Telephone.
409. 242. 3 r. multicoloured .. 1·25 2·00

243. College Arms within " Sun ".

1976. Cent. of National College of Arts, Lahore.
410. 243. 20 p. multicoloured .. 30 40

244. Common Peafowl.

1976. Wildlife Protection (3rd series).
411. 244. 20 p. multicoloured .. 75 35
412. 3 r. multicoloured .. 3·25 4·00

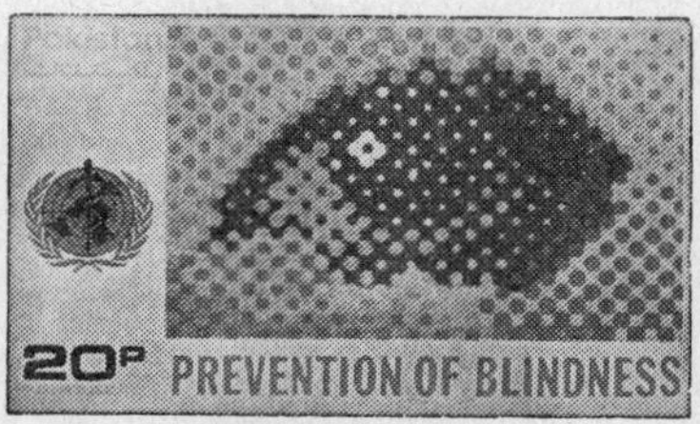

245. Human Eye.

1976. Prevention of Blindness.
413. 245. 20 p. multicoloured .. 40 40

246. Unicorn and Ruins.

1976. " Save Moenjodaro " (2nd series).
414. 246. 20 p. multicoloured .. 30 35

247. Jefferson Memorial.

1976. Bicent. of American Revolution. Mult.
415. 90 p. Type 247 .. .. 1·00 60
416. 4 r. " Declaration of Independence " .. 3·75 4·50
No. 416 is larger, 47 × 36 mm.

248. Ibex.

1976. Wildlife Protection (4th series).
417. 248. 20 p. multicoloured .. 30 35
418. 3 r. multicoloured .. 1·75 2·50

249. Mohammed Ali Jinnah.

1976. 12th Anniv. of Regional Co-operation for Development. Multicoloured.
419. 20 p. Type 249 .. .. 50 50
420. 65 p. Reza Shah the Great (Iran) 50 50
421. 90 p. Kemal Ataturk (Turkey) 50 50

250. Urdu Text.

251. Mohammed Ali Jinnah and Wazir Mansion.

1976. Birth Cent. of Mr. Jinnah. (1st issue).
(a) Type 250.
422. 250. 5 p. black, blue & yell. 20 25
423. 10 p. black, yell. & pur. 20 25
424. 15 p. black, and blue .. 20 25
425. 1 r. black, yell. & blue 30 30

(b) Type 251. Background Buildings given. Multicoloured
426. 20 p. Type 251 .. .. 20 25
427. 40 p. Sind Madressah 20 25
428. 50 p. Minar Qarardad-e-Pakistan 20 25
429. 3 r. Mausoleum 45 50
See also No. 436.

252. Dancing-girl, Ruins and King Priest.
(Illustration reduced. Actual size 64 × 22 mm.).

1976. "Save Moenjodaro" (3rd series).
430. **252.** 65 p. multicoloured .. 35 35

253. U.N. Racial Discrimination Emblem.

1976. U.N. Decade to Combat Racial Discrimination.
431. **253.** 65 p. multicoloured .. 30 40

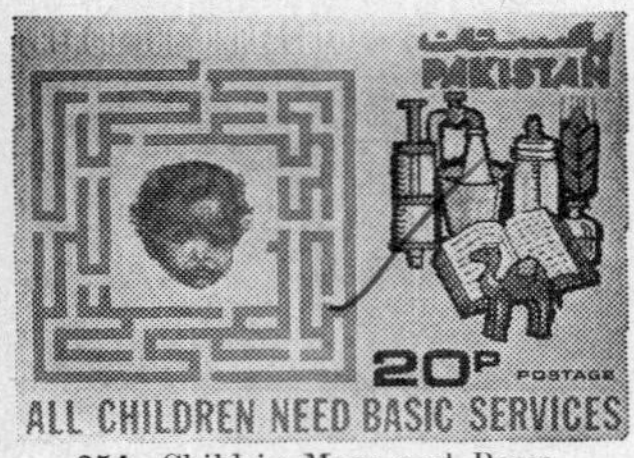

254. Child in Maze and Basic Services.

1976. Universal Children's Day.
432. **254.** 20 p. multicoloured .. 20 30

255. Verse from "Allama Iqbal".

1976. Birth Centenary (1977) of Dr. Iqbal (3rd issue).
433. **255.** 20 p. multicoloured .. 15 20

256. Mohammed Ali Jinnah giving Scout Salute.

1976. Quaid-i-Azam Centenary Jamboree.
434. **256.** 20 p. multicoloured .. 45 30

257. Children Reading.

1976. Children's Literature.
435. **257.** 20 p. multicoloured .. 20 30

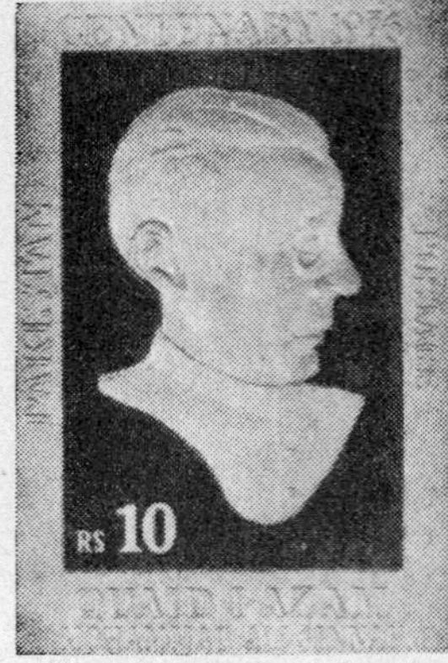

258. Mohammed Ali Jinnah.

1976. Birth Centenary of Quaid-i-Azam (Mohammed Ali Jinnah) (2nd issue).
436. **258.** 10 r. green and gold .. 2·50 3·50

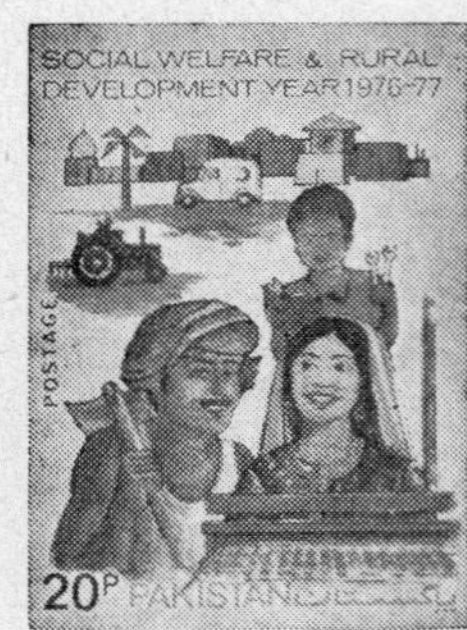

259. Rural Family.

1977. Social Welfare and Rural Development Year.
437. **259.** 20 p. multicoloured .. 15 10

260. Turkish Vase, 1800 B.C.

1977. 13th Anniv. of Regional Co-operation for Development.
438. **260.** 20 p. orge., blue & blk. 25 10
439. – 65 p. multicoloured .. 35 15
440. – 90 p. multicoloured .. 45 30

DESIGNS: 60 p. Pakistani toy bullock cart from Moenjodaro. 90 p. Pitcher with spout from Sialk Hill, Iran.

261. Forest.

1977. Nat. Tree Plantation Campaign.
441. **261.** 20 p. multicoloured .. 10 10

262. Desert Scene.

1977. U.N. Conf. on Desertification, Nairobi.
442. **262.** 65 p. multicoloured .. 30 20

263. "Water for Children of the World".

1977. Universal Children's Day.
443. **263.** 50 p. multicoloured .. 40 20

264. Aga Khan III.

1977. Birth Centenary of Aga Khan III.
444. **264.** 2 r. multicoloured .. 55 85

265. Iqbal and Spirit of the Poet Roomi (from painting by Behzad).

1977. Birth Centenary of Allama Mohammed Iqbal (4th issue). Multicoloured.
445. 20 p. Type **265** 25 35
446. 65 p. "Iqbal looking at Jamaluddin Afghani and Saeed Haleem Pasha at prayer" (Behzad).. 25 35
447. 1 r. 25 Urdu verse .. 30 40
448. 2 r. 25 Persian verse .. 35 45
449. 3 r. Iqbal 40 50

266. The Holy "Khana-Kaaba" (House of God, Mecca).

1977. Haj.
450. **266.** 65 p. multicoloured .. 30 30

267. Rheumatic Patient and Healthy Man.

1977. World Rheumatism Year.
451. **267.** 65 p. blue, blk. & yell. 30 20

268. Woman in Costume of Rawalpindi-Islamabad.

1978. Indonesia-Pakistan Economic and Cultural Cooperation Organization.
452. **268.** 75 p. multicoloured .. 30 20

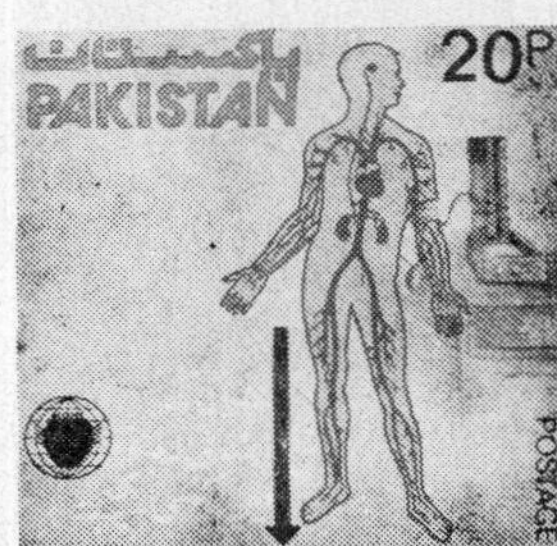

269. Human Body and Sphygmomanometer.

1978. World Hypertension Month.
453. **269.** 20 p. multicoloured .. 15 10
454. – 2 r. multicoloured .. 60 60

The 2 r. value is as Type **269**, but has the words "Down with high blood pressure" instead of the Urdu inscription at the bottom left.

270. Henri Dunant.

1978. 100th Birth Anniv. of Henri Dunant (founder of the Red Cross).
455. **270.** 1 r. multicoloured .. 45 20

271. Red Roses (Pakistan).

1978. 14th Anniv. of Regional Co-operation for Development. Roses. Multicoloured.
456. 20 p. Type **271** 35 20
457. 90 p. Pink roses (Iran) .. 50 20
458. 2 r. Yellow roses (Turkey) 75 25

272. "Pakistan, World Cup Hockey Champions".

1978. "Riccione '78" International Stamp Fair. Multicoloured.
459. 1 r. Type **272** .. .. 1·00 25
460. 2 r. Fountain, Piazza Turismo .. .. .. 1·25 35

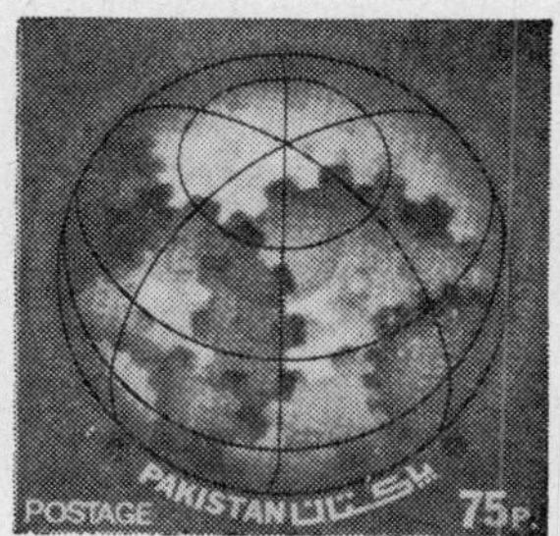

273. Cogwheels within Globe Symbol.

1978. U.N. Technical Co-operation amongst Developing Countries Conference.
461. **273.** 75 p. multicoloured .. 15 10

274. St. Patrick's Cathedral.

1978. Centenary of St. Patrick's Cathedral, Karachi. Multicoloured.
462. 1 r. Type **274** 10 10
463. 2 r. Stained glass window 25 25

275. Minar-i-Qarardad-e-Pakistan.

1978.
464. **275.** 2 p. green 10 10
465. 3 p. black 10 10
466. 5 p. blue 10 10
467. – 10 p. blue & turquoise 10 10
468. – 20 p. green 50 10
469. – 25 p. green and mauve 50 10
470. – 40 p. blue and mauve 10 10
471. – 50 p. lilac and green .. 30 10
472. – 60 p. black 10 10
473b. – 75 p. red 45 10
474. – 90 p. mauve and blue 20 10
475. – 1 r. green 10 10
476. – 1 r. 50 orange 10 10
477. – 2 r. red 15 10
478. – 3 r. blue 20 10
479. – 4 r. black 30 10
480. – 5 r. brown 30 10

DESIGNS—HORIZ. (25 × 20 mm.) 10 p. to 90 p. Tractor. VERT. (21 × 25 mm.) 1 r. to 5 r. Mausoleum of Ibrahim Khan.

277. Emblem and "United Races" Symbol.

1978. International Anti-Apartheid Year.
481. **277.** 1 r. multicoloured .. 15 15

278. Maulana Mohamed Ali Jauhar.

1978. Birth Centenary of Maulana Mohamed Ali Jauhar (patriot).
482. **278.** 50 p. multicoloured .. 40 20

279. "Tornado", "Rapide" and Wright "Flyer".
(Illustration reduced, actual size 52 × 52 mm.).

1978. 75th Anniv. of Powered Flight. Mult.
483. 65 p. Type **279** 75 75
484. 1 r. "Phantom F4F", "Tristar" and Wright "Flyer" 90 90
485. 2 r. "X15", "Tu. 104" and Wright "Flyer" 1·10 1·10
486. 2 r. 25 "Mig 15", "Concorde" and Wright "Flyer" .. .. 1·25 1·25

280. "Holy Koran illuminating Globe" and Raudha-e-Mubarak (mausoleum).

1979. "12th Rabi-ul-Awwal" (Prophet Mohammed's birthday).
487. **280.** 20 p. multicoloured .. 30 15

281. "Aspects of A.P.W.A.".

1979. 30th Anniv. of A.P.W.A. (All Pakistan Women's Association.)
488. **281.** 50 p. multicoloured .. 40 15

282. Tippu Sultan Shaheed of Mysore.

1979. Pioneers of Freedom (1st series). Multicoloured
490. 10 r. Type **282** 50 55
491. 15 r. Sir Syed Ahmad Khan 70 75
492. 25 r. Altaf Hussain Hali .. 1·25 1·40
See also No. 757.

283. Himalayan Monal Pheasant.

1979. Wildlife Protection (5th series). Pheasants. Multicoloured.
493. 20 p. Type **283** 75 40
494. 25 p. Kalij Pheasant .. 75 45
495. 40 p. Koklass Pheasant .. 1·00 75
496. 1 r. Cheer Pheasant .. 2·00 1·50

284. "Pakistan Village Scene" (Ustad Bakhsh).

1979. 15th Anniv. of Regional Co-operation for Development. Multicoloured.
497. 40 p. Type **284** .. 20 25
498. 75 p. "Iranian Goldsmith" (Kamal al Molk) .. 20 25
499. 1 r. 60 "Turkish Harvest" (Namik Ismail) .. 25 30

285. Guj Embroidered Shirt (detail).

1979. Handicrafts (1st series). Multicoloured.
500. 40 p. Type **285** 20 20
501. 1 r. Enamel inlaid brass plate 25 25
502. 1 r. 50 Baskets 30 30
503. 2 r. Chain-stitch embroidered rug (detail) .. 40 40
See also Nos. 578/9, 595/6 and 625/8.

286. Children playing on Climbing-frame.

1979. S.O.S. Children's Village, Lahore.
504. **286.** 50 p. multicoloured .. 30 30

287. "Island" (Z. Maloof).

1979. International Year of the Child. Children's Paintings. Multicoloured.
505. 40 p. Type **287** 15 15
506. 75 p. "Playground" (R. Akbar) 25 25
507. 1 r. "Fairground" (M. Azam) 25 25
508. 1 r. 50 "Hockey Match" (M. Tayyab) 30 30

288. Warrior attacking Crab.

1979. "Fight Against Cancer".
510. **288.** 40 p. multicoloured .. 40 30

289. Pakistan Customs Emblem. **291.** Islamic Pattern.

290. Boeing "747 (Jumbo)" and Douglas "DC–3" Airliners.

1979. Centenary of Pakistan Customs Service.
511. **289.** 1 r. multicoloured .. 20 30

1980. 25th Anniv. of Pakistan International Air Lines.
512. **290.** 1 r. multicoloured .. 50 50

1980.
513. **291.** 10 p. green and yellow 10 10
514. 15 p. deep green & green 10 10
515. 25 p. violet and red .. 10 10
516. 35 p. red and green .. 10 10
517. – 40 p. red and brown .. 15 10
518. – 50 p. violet and green 10 10
519. – 80 p. green and black .. 15 15

The 40 to 80 p. values also show different Islamic patterns, the 40 p. being horizontal and the remainder vertical.

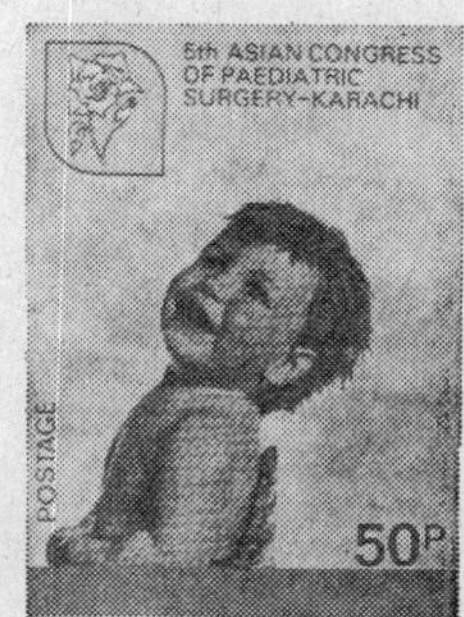

292. Young Child.

1980. Fifth Asian Congress of Paediatric Surgery, Karachi.
530. **292.** 50 p. multicoloured .. 40 40

293. Conference Emblem.

1980. 11th Islamic Conference of Foreign Ministers, Islamabad.
531. 293. 1 r. multicoloured .. 30 45

294. Karachi Port. (Illustration reduced, actual size 75 × 16 mm.)

1980. Centenary of Karachi Port Authority.
532. 294. 1 r. multicoloured .. 60 60

1980. "Riccione 80" International Stamp Exhibition. Nos. 505/8 optd. **RICCIONE 80.**
533. 287. 40 p. multicoloured .. 25 25
534. – 75 p. multicoloured .. 30 30
535. – 1 r. multicoloured .. 35 35
536. – 1 r. 50 multicoloured 45 45

296. Old and New Staff College Buildings.

1980. 75th Anniv. of Quetta Staff College.
537. 296. 1 r. multicoloured .. 10 15

1980. World Tourism Conference, Manila. No. 496 optd. **WORLD TOURISM CONFERENCE, MANILA 80.**
538. 1 r. Cheer Pheasant .. 30 15

298. Birth Centenary Emblem.

1980. Birth Cent. of Hafiz Mahmood Shairani.
539. 298. 40 p. multicoloured .. 30 40

299. Shalimar Gardens, Lahore.

1980. Aga Khan Award for Architecture.
540. 299. 2 r. multicoloured .. 30 60

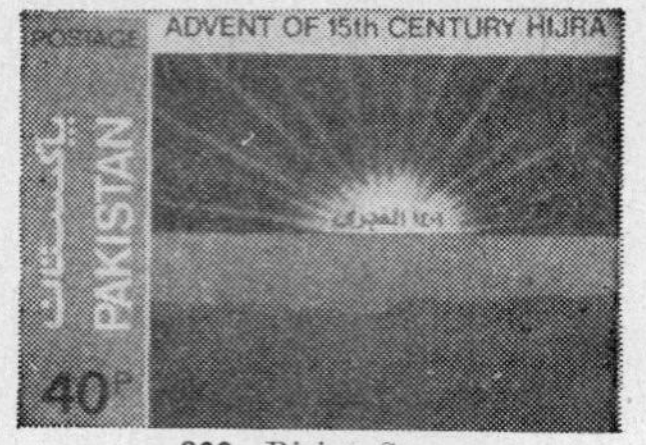

300. Rising Sun.

1980. 1400th Anniv. of Hegira (1st issue). Multicoloured.
541. 40 p. Type 300 .. .. 5 5
542. 2 r. Ka'aba and symbols of Muslim achievement (33 × 33 mm.) .. 25 40
543. 3 r. Koran illuminating the world (30 × 54 mm.) .. 30 60

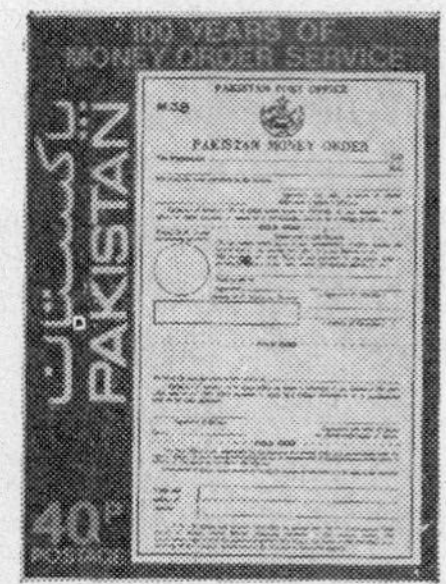

301. Money Order Form.

1980. Centenary of Money Order Service.
545. 301. 40 p. multicoloured .. 15 30

302. Postcards encircling Globe.

1980. Centenary of Postcard Service.
546. 302. 40 p. multicoloured .. 15 30

303. Heinrich von Stephan and U.P.U. Emblem.

1981. 150th Birth Anniv. of Heinrich von Stephan (U.P.U. founder).
547. 303. 1 r. multicoloured .. 20 15

304. Aircraft and Airmail Letters.

1981. 50th Anniv. of Airmail Service.
548. 304. 1 r. multicoloured .. 20 15

305. Mecca.

1981. 1400th Anniv. of Hegira (2nd issue).
549. 305. 40 p. multicoloured .. 15 20

306. Conference Emblem and Afghan Refugees.

1981. Islamic Summit Conference (1st issue). Multicoloured.
550. 40 p. Type 306 .. .. 25 10
551. 40 p. Conference emblem encircled by flags and Afghan refugees (28 × 58 mm.) 25 10
552. 1 r. Type 306 .. .. 40 10
553. 1 r. As No. 551 .. .. 40 10
554. 2 r. Conference emblem and map showing Afghanistan (48 × 32 mm.) .. 55 50

307. Conference Emblem.

1981. Islamic Summit Conference (2nd issue). Multicoloured.
555. 40 p. Type 307 .. .. 10 10
556. 40 p. Conference emblem and flags (28 × 46 mm.) 10 10
557. 85 p. Type 307 .. .. 20 15
558. 85 p. As No. 556 .. .. 20 15

308.

1981. Birth Centenary of Kemal Ataturk (Turkish statesman).
559. 308. 1 r. multicoloured .. 20 15

309. Green Turtle.

1981. Wildlife Protection (6th series).
560. 309. 40 p. multicoloured .. 65 20

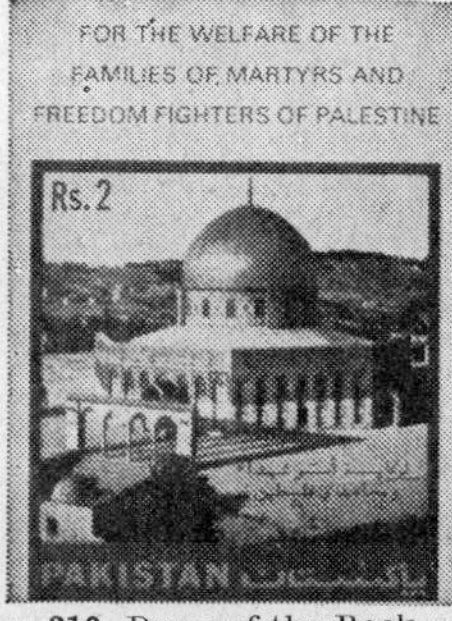

310. Dome of the Rock.

1981. Palestinian Welfare.
561. 310. 2 r. multicoloured .. 35 35

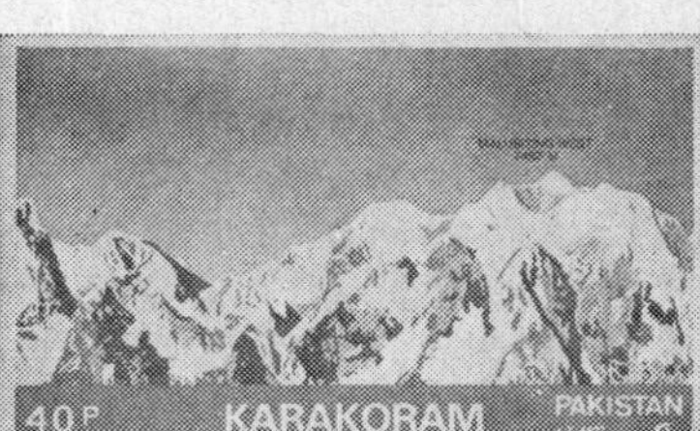

311. Malubiting West.

1981. Mountain Peaks (1st series). Mult.
562. 40 p. Type 311 .. .. 40 35
563. 40 p. Malubiting West (24 × 31 mm.) 40 35
564. 1 r. Haramosh 75 55
565. 1 r. Haramosh (24 × 31 mm.) 75 55
566. 1 r. 50 K6 .. .. 90 70
567. 1 r. 50 K6 (24 × 31 mm.) .. 90 70
568. 2 r. K2, Broad Peak, Gasherbrum 4 and Gasherbrum 2 .. .. .. 1·00 1·00
569. 2 r. K2 (24 × 31 mm.) .. 1·00 1·00

See also Nos. 674/5.

312. Pakistan Steel "Furnace No. 1".

1981. First Firing of Pakistan Steel "Furnace No. 1", Karachi.
570. 312. 40 p. multicoloured .. 15 10
571. 2 r. multicoloured .. 35 30

313. Western Tragopan.

1981. Wildlife Protection (7th series).
572. 313. 40 p. multicoloured .. 1·25 50
573. – 2 r. multicoloured .. 3·00 3·25

DESIGN: 2 r. As Type 313 but with background showing a winter view.

314. Disabled People and I.Y.D.P. Emblem.

1981. International Year for Disabled Persons.
574. 314. 40 p. multicoloured .. 20 20
575. 2 r. multicoloured .. 70 90

315. World Hockey Cup below Flags of participating Countries.

1982. Pakistan—World Cup Hockey Champions. Multicoloured.

576.	1 r. Type **315**	1·50	90
577.	1 r. World Hockey Cup above flags of participating countries	1·50	90

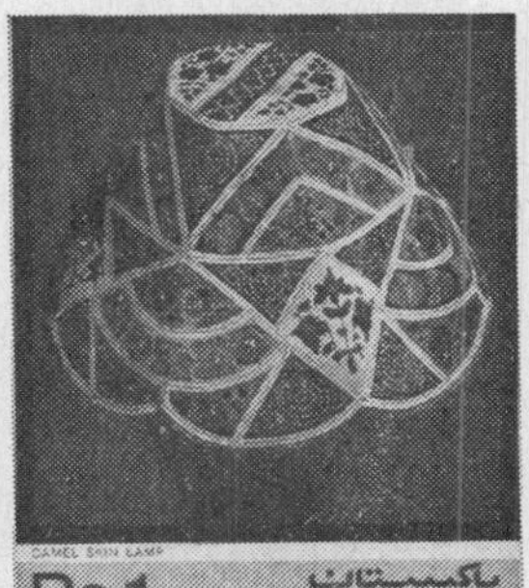

316. Camel Skin Lamp.

1982. Handicrafts (2nd series). Multicoloured.

578.	1 r. Type **316**	30	25
579.	1 r. Hala pottery	50	25

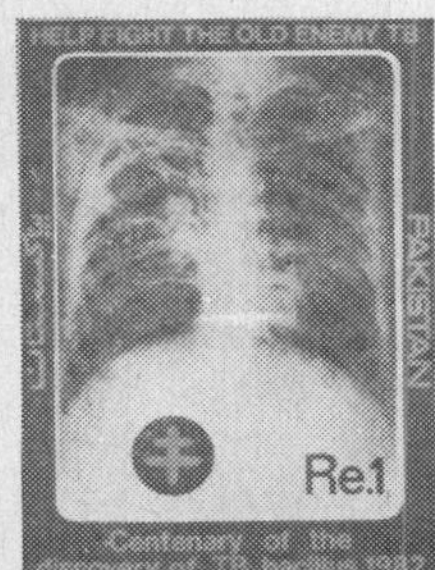

317. Chest X-Ray of Infected Person.

1982. Centenary of Robert Koch's Discovery of Tubercle Bacillus.

580. **317.**	1 r. multicoloured ..	70	60

318. Indus Dolphin.

1982. Wildlife Protection (8th series).

581. **318.**	40 p. multicoloured ..	1·25	90
582. –	1 r. multicoloured ..	2·25	2·10

DESIGN: 1 r. As Type **318** but with design reversed.

319. "Apollo-Soyuz" Linkup, 1975.

1982. Peaceful Use of Outer Space.

583. **319.**	1 r. multicoloured ..	90	55

320. Sukkur Barrage.

1982. 50th Anniv. of Sukkur Barrage.

584. **320.**	1 r. multicoloured ..	30	20

321. Pakistan National Flag and Stylised Sun.

1982. Independence Day. Multicoloured.

585.	40 p. Type **321** ..	10	20
586.	85 p. Map of Pakistan and stylised torch ..	20	40

1982. "Riccione 82" Stamp Exhibition. No. 583. optd **RICCIONE-82.**

587. **320.**	1 r. multicoloured ..	15	15

323. Arabic Inscription and University Emblem.
(Illustration reduced. Actual size 67 × 23 mm.)

1982. Centenary of Punjab University.

588. **323.**	40 p. multicoloured ..	15	15

324. Scout Emblem and Tents.

1983. 75th Anniv. of Boy Scout Movement.

589. **324.**	2 r. multicoloured ..	30	30

325. Laying Pipeline.

1983. Inauguration of Quetta Natural Gas Pipeline Project.

590. **325.**	1 r. multicoloured ..	15	20

326. "Papilio polyctor".

1983. Butterflies. Multicoloured.

591	40 p. Type **326**	70	20
592	50 p. "Atrophaneura aristolochiae" (inscr "Polydorus")	70	20
593	60 p. "Danaus chrysippus"	80	30
594	1 r. 50 "Papilio demoleus"	1·10	70

1983. Handicrafts (3rd series). As T **316.** Multicoloured.

595.	1 r. Five flower motif needlework, Sind ..	15	15
596.	1 r. Straw mats	15	15

327. School of Nursing and University Emblem.

1983. Presentation of Charter to Aga Khan University, Karachi.

597. **327.**	2 r. multicoloured ..	30	30

328. Yak Caravan crossing Zindiharam-Darkot Pass, Hindu Kush.

1983. Trekking in Pakistan.

598. **328.**	1 r. multicoloured ..	40	30

329. Marsh Crocodile.

1983. Wildlife Protection (9th series).

599. **329.**	3 r. multicoloured ..	1·75	1·25

330. Goitred Gazelle.

1983. Wildlife Protection (10th series).

600. **330.**	1 r. multicoloured ..	1·25	75

331. Floral Design.

1983. 36th Anniv. of Independence. Mult.

601.	60 p. Type **331**	10	10
602.	4 r. Hand holding flaming torch	40	45

332. Traditional Weaving, Pakistan.

1983. Indonesian—Pakistan Economic and Cultural Co-operation Organization, 1969–1983. Multicoloured.

603.	2 r. Type **332**	20	25
604.	2 r. Traditional Weaving, Indonesia	20	25

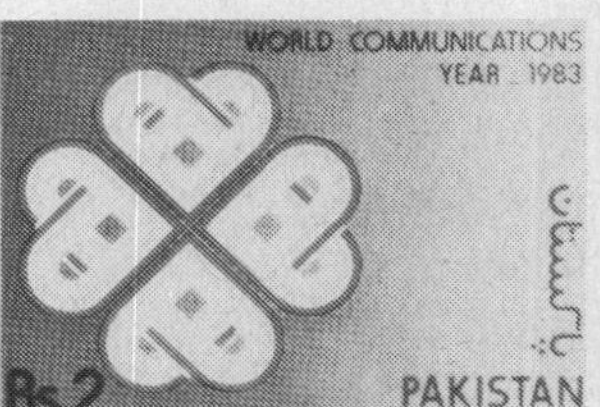

333. "Siberian Cranes" (Great White Cranes). (Sir Peter Scott).

1983. Wildlife Protection (11th series).

605. **333.**	3 r. multicoloured ..	1·75	90

334. W.C.Y. Emblem.

1983. World Communications Year. Multicoloured.

606.	2 r. Type **334**	20	25
607.	3 r. W.C.Y. emblem (different) (33 × 33 mm.) ..	30	35

335. Farm Animals.

1983. World Food Day. Multicoloured.

608.	3 r. Type **335**	1·00	1·00
609.	3 r. Fruit	1·00	1·00
610.	3 r. Crops	1·00	1·00
611.	3 r. Sea food	1·00	1·00

336. Agriculture Produce and Fertilizer Factory.

1983. National Fertilizer Corporation.

612. **336.**	60 p. multicoloured ..	15	20

INDEX

Countries can be quickly located by referring to the index at the end of this volume.

337. Lahore, 1852

1983. National Stamp Exhibition, Lahore. Multicoloured.

613. 60 p. Musti Durwaza Dharmsala 15 15
614. 60 p. Khabgha 15 15
615. 60 p. Type 337 .. .. 15 15
616. 60 p. Summan Burj Hazuri 15 15
617. 60 p. Flower Garden, Samadhi Northern Gate 15 15
618. 60 p. Budda Darya, Badshahi Masjid 15 15

338. Winner of "Enterprise" Event.

1983. Yachting Champions, Asian Games, Delhi. Multicoloured.

619. 60 p. Type 338 .. .. 75 40
620. 60 p. Winner of "OK" Dinghy event 75 40

339. Snow Leopard.

1984. Wildlife Protection (12th series).

621. 339. 40 p. multicoloured .. 1·25 50
622. 1 r. 60 multicoloured .. 2·75 3·00

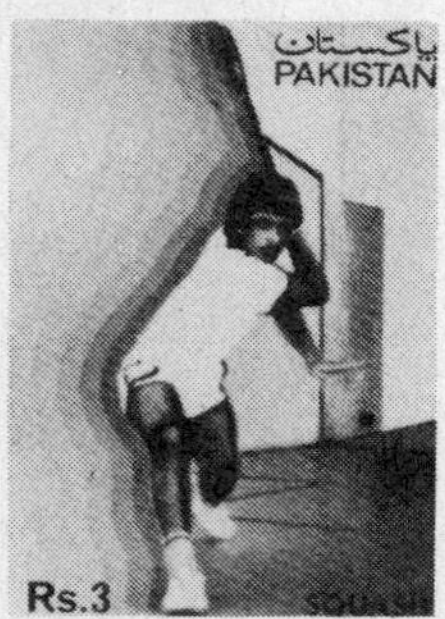

340. Jahangir Khan (world squash champion).

1984. Squash.

623. 340. 3 r. multicoloured .. 1·00 75

341. P.I.A. Airliner.

1984. 20th Anniv. of Pakistan International Airways Service to China.

624. 341. 3 r. multicoloured .. 3·00 3·00

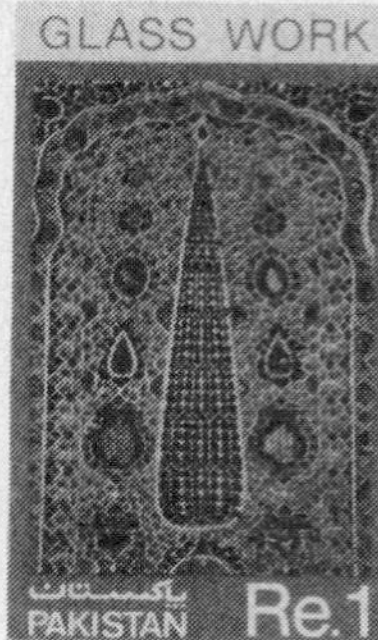

342. Glass-work.

1984. Handicrafts (4th series). Multicoloured, frame colours given.

625. 342. 1 r. blue 10 15
626. – 1 r. red 10 15
627. – 1 r. green 10 15
628. – 1 r. violet 10 15

DESIGNS: showing glass-work in Sheesh Mahal, Lahore Fort. Nos. 627/8 are horizontal designs.

343. Attock Fort.

1984. Forts.

629 – 5 p. black and purple 10 10
630 – 10 p. black and red .. 10 10
631 – 15 p. violet and brown 10 10
632 343 20 p. black and violet 10 10
633 – 50 p. brown and red .. 10 10
634 – 60 p. lt brown & brown 10 10
635 – 70 p. blue 10 10
636 – 80 p. brown and red .. 10 10

DESIGNS: 5 p. Kot Diji Fort. 10 p. Rohtas Fort. 15 p. Bala Hissar Fort. 50 p. Hyderabad Fort. 60 p. Lahore Fort. 70 p. Sibi Fort. 80 p. Ranikot Fort.

344. Shah Rukn i Alam's Tomb, Multan.

1984. Aga Khan Award for Architecture.

647. 344. 60 p. multicoloured .. 60 60

345. Radio Mast and Map of World.

1984. 20th Anniv. of Asia-Pacific Broadcasting Union.

648. 345. 3 r. multicoloured .. 80 60

346. Wrestling.

1984. Olympic Games, Los Angeles. Mult.

649. 3 r. Type 346 .. .. 85 55
650. 3 r. Boxing 85 55
651. 3 r. Athletics 85 55
652. 3 r. Hockey 85 55
653. 3 r. Yachting 85 55

347. Jasmine (National flower) and Inscription.

1984. Independence Day. Multicoloured.

654. 60 p. Type 347 .. .. 10 10
655. 4 r. Symbolic torch .. 45 50

348. Gearwheel Emblem and Flags of Participating Nations.

1984. Pakistan International Trade Fair.

656. 348. 60 p. multicoloured .. 30 20

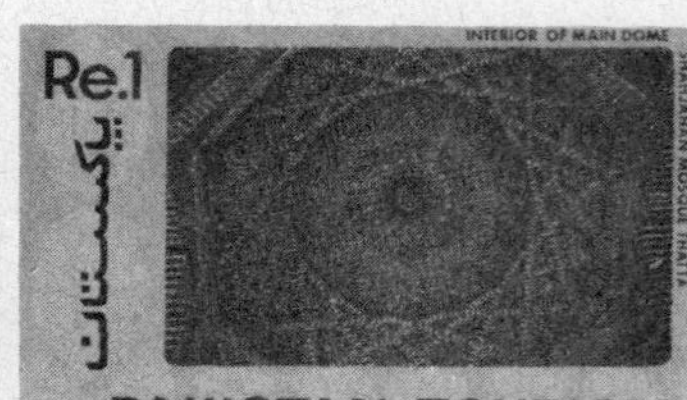

349. Interior of Main Dome.

1984. Tourism Convention. Shahjahan Mosque, Thatta. Multicoloured.

657. 1 r. Type 349 .. .. 20 20
658. 1 r. Brick and glazed tile work 20 20
659. 1 r. Gateway 20 20
660. 1 r. Symmetrical archways 20 20
661. 1 r. Interior of a dome .. 20 20

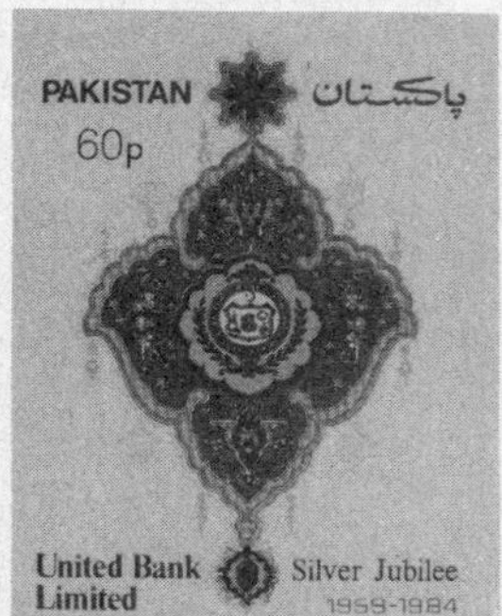

350. Bank Emblem in Floral Pattern.

1984. 25th Anniv. of United Bank Ltd.

662. 350. 60 p. multicoloured .. 40 40

351. Conference Emblem.

1984. 20th United Nations Conference of Trade and Development.

663. 351. 60 p. multicoloured .. 40 20

352. Postal Life Insurance Emblem within Hands.

1984. Centenary of Postal Life Insurance. Multicoloured.

664. 60 p. Type 352 .. .. 25 15
665. 1 r. "100" and Postal Life Insurance emblem .. 35 15

353. Bull (wall painting).

1984. U.N.E.S.C.O. Save Moenjadoro Campaign. Multicoloured.

666. 2 r. Type 353 .. .. 70 70
667. 2 r. Bull (seal) 70 70

354. International Youth Year Emblem and "75".

1985. 75th Anniv. of Girl Guide Movement.

668. 354. 60 p. multicoloured .. 1·00 30

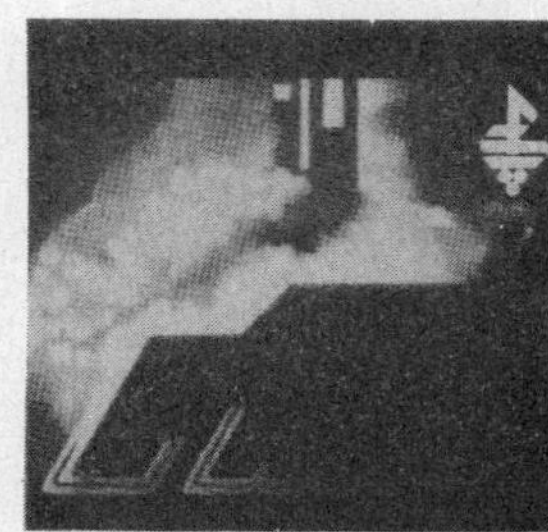

355. Smelting Ore.

1985. Inauguration of Pakistan Steel Corporation. Multicoloured.

669. 60 p. Type 355 .. .. 30 10
670. 1 r. Pouring molten steel from ladle (28 × 46 mm.) 40 20

356. Map of Pakistan and Rays of Sun.

1985. Presidential Referendum of 19 December 1984.

671. 356. 60 p. multicoloured .. 40 20

357. Ballot Box and Voting Paper.

1985. March Elections. Multicoloured.
672. 1 r. Type **357** 30 15
673. 1 r. Minar-e-Qarardad-e-Pakistan Tower, and word "Democracy" (31 × 43 mm.) 30 15

1985. Mountain Peaks (2nd series). As T **311.** Multicoloured.
674. 40 p. Rakaposhi (Karakoram Range) .. 75 35
675. 2 r. Nangaparbat (Western Himalayas) .. .. 1·75 1·75

358. Trophy and Medals from Olympic Games 1984, Asia Cup 1985 and World Cup 1982. (Illustration reduced, actual size 58 × 28 mm.).

1985. Pakistan Hockey Team "Grand Slam" Success.
676. **358.** 1 r. multicoloured .. 90 80

359. King Edward Medical College. (Illustration reduced, actual size 57 × 27 mm.).

1985. 125th Anniv. of King Edward Medical College, Lahore.
677. **359.** 3 r. multicoloured .. 70 40

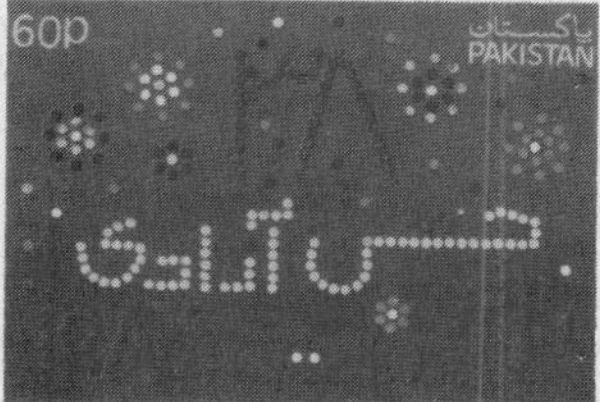

360. Illuminated Inscription in Urdu.

1985. Independence Day. Multicoloured.
678. 60 p. Type **360** 15 15
679. 60 p. Illuminated "XXXVIII" (inscr. in English) 15 15

361. Sind Madressah-tul-Islam, Karachi. (illustration reduced, actual size 56 × 27 mm).

1985. Centenary of Sind Madressah-tul-Islam (theological college), Karachi.
680. **361.** 2 r. multicoloured .. 80 55

362. Jamia Masjid Mosque by Day. (Illustration reduced, actual size 47 × 32 mm.).

1985. Inauguration of New Jamia Masjid Mosque, Karachi. Multicoloured.
681. 1 r. Type **362** 45 30
682. 1 r. Jamia Masjid illuminated at night .. 45 30

363. Lawrence College, Murree.

1985. 125th Anniv. of Lawrence College, Murree.
683. **363.** 3 r. multicoloured .. 75 45

364. United Nations Building, New York.

1985. 40th Anniv. of United Nations Organization. Multicoloured.
684. 1 r. Type **364** 15 15
685. 2 r. U.N. Building and Emblem 25 25

365. Tents and Jamboree Emblem.

1985. 10th National Scout Jamboree.
686. **365.** 60 p. multicoloured .. 90 50

366. Islamabad.

1985. 25th Anniv. of Islamabad.
687. **366.** 3 r. multicoloured .. 65 35

367. Map of S.A.A.R.C. Countries and National Flags.

1985. 1st Summit Meeting of South Asian Association for Regional Co-operation, Dhaka, Bangladesh. Multicoloured.
688. 1 r. Type **367** .. .. 1·25 2·50
689. 2 r. National flags (39 × 39 mm) 75 75

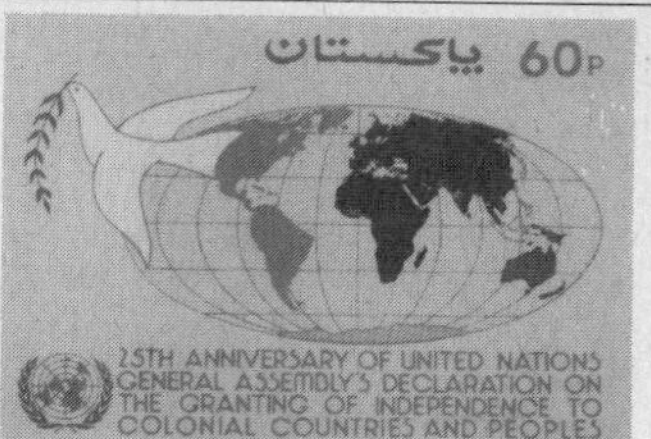

368. Globe and Peace Dove.

1985. 25th Anniv. of U.N. General Assembly's Declaration on Independence for Colonial Territories.
690. **368.** 60 p. multicoloured .. 40 30

369. Peregrine Falcon.

1986. Wildlife Protection (13th series). Peregrine Falcon.
691. **369.** 1 r. 50 multicoloured 2·00 1·75

370. A.D.B.P. Building, Islamabad.

1986. 25th Anniv. of Agricultural Development Bank of Pakistan.
692. **370.** 60 p. multicoloured .. 40 30

371. Government S.E. College.

1986. Centenary of Government Sadiq Egerton College, Bahawalpur.
693. **371.** 1 r. multicoloured .. 45 30

372. Emblem and Bar Graph.

1986. 25th Anniv. of Asian Productivity Organization.
694. **372.** 1 r. multicoloured .. 30 30

373. "1947 1986".

1986. 39th Anniv. of Independence. Multicoloured.
695. 80 p. Type **373** 15 15
696. 1 r. Illuminated inscription in Urdu 15 15

374. Open Air Class.

1986. International Literacy Day.
697. **374.** 1 r. multicoloured .. 20 20

375. Mother and Child.

1986. U.N.I.C.E.F. Child Survival Campaign.
698. **375.** 80 p. multicoloured .. 30 20

376. Aitchison College.

1986. Centenary of Aitchison College, Lahore.
699. **376.** 2 r. 50 multicoloured 30 30

377. Two Doves carrying Olive Branches.

1986. International Peace Year.
700. **377.** 4 r. multicoloured .. 50 10

378. Table Tennis Players.

1986. 4th Asian Cup Table Tennis Tournament, Karachi.
701. **378.** 2 r. multicoloured .. 50 30

379. Argali.

1986. Wildlife Protection (14th series). Argali.
702. **379.** 2 r. multicoloured .. 1·50 65

380. Selimiye Mosque, Erdine, Turkey.

1986. "Ecophilex '86" International Stamp Exhibition, Islamabad. Multicoloured.
703. 3 r. Type **380** 70 70
704. 3 r. Gawhar Shad Mosque, Mashhad, Iran 70 70
705. 3 r. Grand Mosque, Bhong, Pakistan 70 70

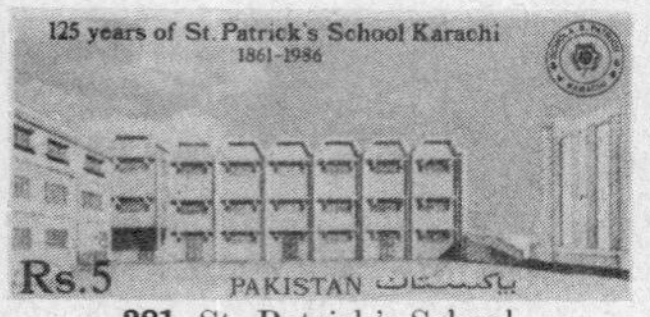

381. St. Patrick's School.

1987. 125th Anniv. of St. Patrick's School, Karachi.
706. **381.** 5 r. multicoloured .. 85 70

382. Mistletoe Flowerpecker and Defence Symbols.

1987. Post Office Savings Bank Week. Multicoloured.
707. 5 r. Type **382** 70 45
708. 5 r. Spotted pardalote and laboratory apparatus .. 70 45
709. 5 r. Black-throated blue warbler and agriculture symbols 70 45
710. 5 r. Red-capped manakin and industrial skyline .. 70 45

383. New Parliament House, Islamabad (illustration reduced, actual size 56 × 27 mm).

1987. Inauguration of New Parliament House, Islamabad.
711. **383.** 3 r. multicoloured .. 30 30

384. Opium Poppies and Flames.

1987. Campaign Against Drug Abuse.
712. **384.** 1 r. multicoloured .. 30 20

385. Flag and National Anthem Score.

1987. 40th Anniv. of Independence. Mult.
713. 80 p. Type **385** 10 10
714. 3 r. Text of speech by Mohammed Ali Jinnah, Minar-e-Qardad-e-Pakistan Tower and arms 20 25

386. "Tempest II".

1987. Air Force Day. Military Aircraft. Multicoloured.
715. 3 r. Type **386** 40 40
716. 3 r. Hawker "Fury" .. 40 40
717. 3 r. Supermarine "Attacker" 40 40
718. 3 r. "F86 Sabre" 40 40
719. 3 r. "F104 Star Fighter" .. 40 40
720. 3 r. "C130 Hercules" .. 40 40
721. 3 r. "F6" 40 40
722. 3 r. "Mirage III" 40 40
723. 3 r. "A5" 40 40
724. 3 r. "F16 Fighting Falcon" 40 40

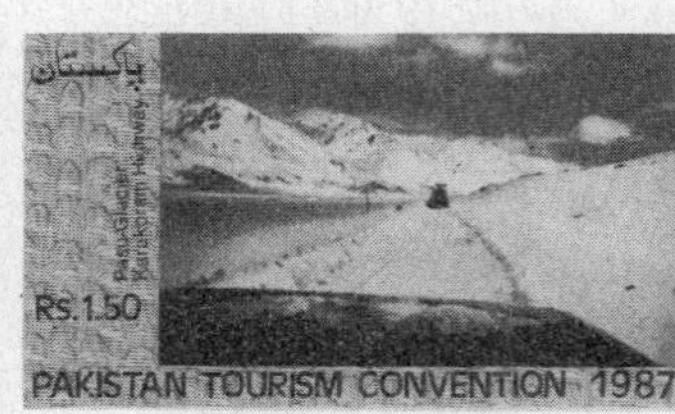

387. Pasu Glacier.

1987. Pakistan Tourism Convention. Views along Karakoram Highway. Multicoloured.
725. 1 r. 50 Type **387** 20 20
726. 1 r. 50 Apricot trees .. 20 20
727. 1 r. 50 Karakoram Highway 20 20
728. 1 r. 50 View from Khunjerab Pass .. 20 20

388. Shah Abdul Latif Bhitai Mausoleum. (Illustration reduced, actual size 53 × 53 mm.).

1987. Shah Abdul Latif Bhitai (poet) Commemoration.
729. **388.** 80 p. multicoloured .. 20 20

389. D. J. Sind Science College, Karachi.

1987. Centenary of D. J. Sind Science College, Karachi.
730. **389.** 80 p. multicoloured .. 20 20

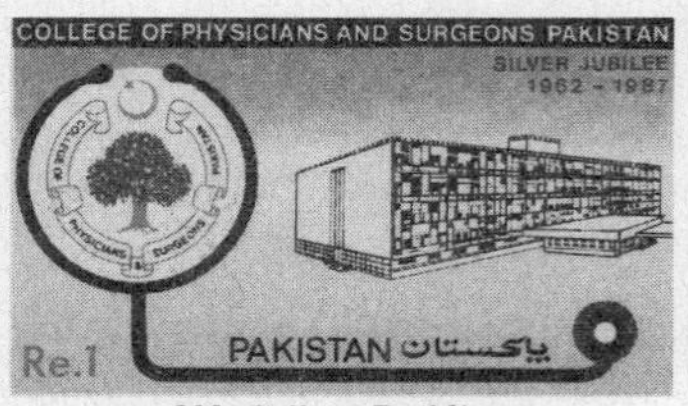

390. College Building.

1987. 25th Anniv. of College of Physicians and Surgeons.
731. **390.** 1 r. multicoloured .. 20 20

391. Homeless People, Houses and Rising Sun.

1987. International Year of Shelter for the Homeless.
732. **391.** 3 r. multicoloured .. 30 30

392. Cathedral Church of the Resurrection, Lahore.

1987. Centenary of Cathedral Church of the Resurrection, Lahore.
733. **392.** 3 r. multicoloured .. 30 30

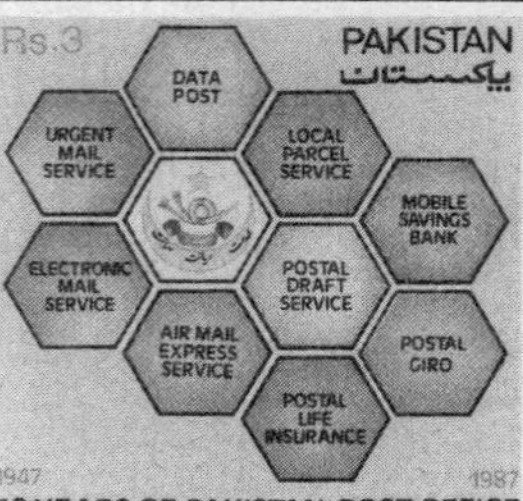

393. Honeycomb and Arms.

1987. 40th Anniv. of Pakistan Post Office.
734. **393.** 3 r. multicoloured .. 30 30

394. Corporation Emblem.

1987. Radio Pakistan's New Programme Schedules.
735. **394.** 80 p. multicoloured .. 15 15

395. Jamshed Nusserwanjee Mehta and Karachi Municipal Corporation Building.

1988. Birth Centenary (1986) of Jamshed Nusserwanjee Mehta (former President of Karachi Municipal Corporation).
736. **395.** 3 r. multicoloured .. 30 30

396. Leprosy Symbols within Flower.

1988. World Leprosy Day.
737. **396.** 3 r. multicoloured .. 35 30

397 W.H.O. Building, Geneva

1988. 40th Anniv of W.H.O.
738 **397** 4 r. multicoloured .. 35 35

398 Globe

1988. 125th Anniv of International Red Cross and Crescent.
739 **398** 3 r. multicoloured . . 30 30

399 Crescent, Leaf Pattern and Archway

1988. Independence Day.
740 **399** 80 p. multicoloured . . 10 10
741 4 r. multicoloured . . 25 30

400 Field Events

1988. Olympic Games, Seoul. Multicoloured.
742 10 r. Type **400** 75 75
743 10 r. Track events . . 75 75
744 10 r. Jumping and pole vaulting 75 75
745 10 r. Gymnastics . . 75 75
746 10 r. Table tennis, tennis, hockey and baseball . . 75 75
747 10 r. Volleyball, football, basketball and handball 75 75
748 10 r. Wrestling, judo, boxing and weightlifting 75 75
749 10 r. Shooting, fencing and archery 75 75
750 10 r. Water sports . . 75 75
751 10 r. Equestrian events and cycling 75 75

401 Markhor

1988. Wildlife Protection (15th series).
752 **401** 2 r. multicoloured . . 30 30

402 Islamia College, Peshawar

1988. 75th Anniv of Islamia College, Peshawar.
753 **402** 3 r. multicoloured . . 30 30

403 Symbols of Agriculture, Industry and Education with National Flags

1988. South Asian Association for Regional Co-operation, 4th Summit Meeting, Islamabad. Multicoloured.
754 25 r. Type **403** . . . . 1·40 1·50
755 50 r. National flags on globe and symbols of communications (33 × 33 mm) . . . . 3·00 3·25
756 75 r. Stamps from member countries (52 × 29 mm) . . 4·25 4·50

1989. Pioneers of Freedom (2nd series). As T **282**. Multicoloured.
757 3 r. Maulana Hasrat Mohani 15 20

404 Logo

1989. "Adasia 89" 16th Asian Advertising Congress, Lahore.
758 **404** 1 r. multicoloured ("Pakistan" in yellow) 15 15
759 1 r. multicoloured ("Pakistan" in blue) 15 15
760 1 r. multicoloured ("Pakistan" in white) 15 15

405 Zulfikar Ali Bhutto

1989. 10th Death Anniv of Zulfikar Ali Bhutto (statesman). Multicoloured.
761 1 r. Type **405** 15 10
762 2 r. Zulfikar Ali Bhutto (different) 20 20

406 "Daphne" Class Submarine (illustration reduced, actual size 61 × 24 mm)

1989. 25 Years of Pakistan Navy Submarine Operations. Multicoloured.
763 1 r. Type **406** 20 20
764 1 r. "Fleet Snorkel" class submarine 20 20
765 1 r. "Agosta" class submarine 20 20

407 "The Oath of the Tennis Court" (David)

1989. Bicentenary of French Revolution.
766 **407** 7 r. multicoloured . . 60 70

408 Pitcher, c. 2200 B.C.

1989. Archaeological Artefacts. Terracotta pottery from Baluchistan Province. Mult.
767 1 r. Type **408** 15 15
768 1 r. Jar, c. 2300 B.C. . . 15 15
769 1 r. Vase, c. 3600 B.C. . . 15 15
770 1 r. Jar, c. 2600 B.C. . . 15 15

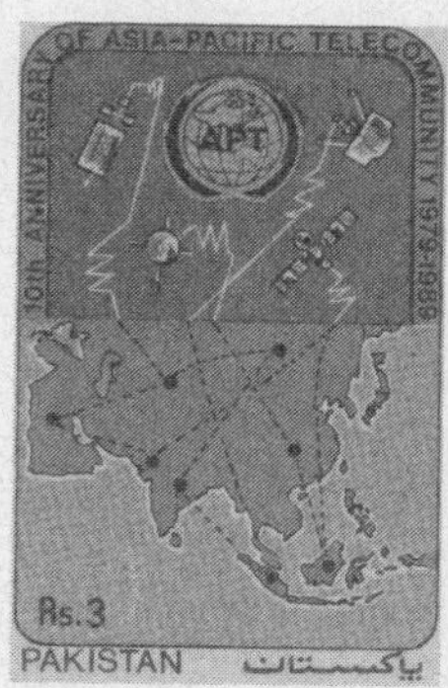

409 Satellites and Map of Asian Telecommunications Network

1989. 10th Anniv of Asia Pacific Telecommunity.
771 **409** 3 r. multicoloured . . 30 30

410 Container Ship at Wharf

1989. Construction of Integrated Container Terminal, Port Qasim.
772 **410** 6 r. multicoloured . . 1·00 1·25

411 Mohammad Ali Jinnah

1989.
773 **411** 1 r. multicoloured . . 10 10
774 1 r. 50 multicoloured . . 10 10
775 2 r. multicoloured . . 10 15
776 3 r. multicoloured . . 15 20
777 4 r. multicoloured . . 20 25
778 5 r. multicoloured . . 25 30

412 Mausoleum of Shah Abdul Latif Bhitai

1989. 300th Birth Anniv of Shah Abdul Latif Bhitai (poet).
779 **412** 2 r. multicoloured . . 20 20

COMMONWEALTH MEMBER

413 Asiatic Black Bear

1989. Wildlife Protection (15th series). Asiatic Black Bear. Multicoloured.
780 4 r. Type **413** 45 45
781 4 r. Bear among boulders 45 45
782 4 r. Standing on rock . . 45 45
783 4 r. Sitting by trees . . 45 45

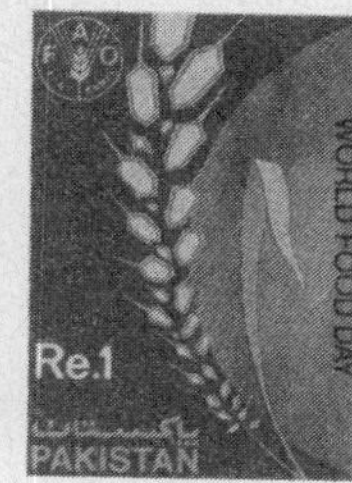

414 Ear of Wheat encircling Globe

1989. World Food Day.
784 **414** 1 r. multicoloured . . 35 35

415 Games Emblem and Flags of Member Countries

1989. 4th South Asian Sports Federation Games, Islamabad.
785 **415** 1 r. multicoloured . . 35 35

416 Patchwork Kamblee (cloth) entering Gate of Heaven

1989. 800th Birth Anniv of Baba Farid (Muslim spiritual leader).
786 **416** 3 r. multicoloured . . 25 30

417 Pakistan Television Logo

1989. 25th Anniv of Television Broadcasting in Pakistan.
787 **417** 3 r. multicoloured .. 25 30

418 Family of Drug Addicts in Poppy Bud

1989. South Asian Association for Regional Co-operation Anti-Drugs Campaign.
788 **418** 7 r. multicoloured .. 55 60

419 Murray College, Sialkot

1989. Centenary of Murray College, Sialkot.
789 **419** 6 r. multicoloured .. 50 50

420 Government College, Lahore

1989. 125th Anniv of Government College, Lahore.
790 **420** 6 r. multicoloured .. 50 50

421 Fields, Electricity Pylons and Rural Buildings

1989. 10th Anniv of Centre for Asia and Pacific Integrated Rural Development.
791 **421** 3 r. multicoloured .. 30 30

422 Emblem and Islamic Patterns

1990. 20th Anniv of Organization of the Islamic Conference.
792 **422** 1 r. multicoloured .. 20 20

423 Hockey Match (illustration reduced, actual size 59 × 27 mm)

1990. 7th World Hockey Cup, Lahore.
793 **423** 2 r. multicoloured .. 70 70

424 Mohammed Iqbal addressing Crowd and Liaquat Ali Khan taking Oath

1990. 50th Anniv of Passing of Pakistan Resolution. Multicoloured.
794 1 r. Type **424** 30 30
795 1 r. Maulana Mohammad Ali Jauhar and Mohammed Ali Jinnah with banner 30 30
796 1 r. Women with Pakistan flag, and Mohammed Ali Jinnah taking Governor-General's oath, 1947 .. 30 30
797 7 r. Minar-i-Qarardad-e-Pakistan Monument and Resolution in Urdu and English (86 × 42 mm) 75 75
Nos. 794/6 were printed together, se-tenant, forming a composite design.

425 Pregnant Woman resting

1990. "Safe Motherhood" South Asia Conference, Lahore.
798 **425** 5 r. multicoloured .. 50 50

426 "Decorated Verse by Ghalib" (Shakir Ali) (illustration reduced, actual size 59 × 27mm)

1990. Painters of Pakistan (1st series). Shakir Ali.
799 **426** 1 r. multicoloured .. 20 20
See also Nos. 856/7.

427 Satellite in Night Sky

1990. Launch of "Badr 1" Satellite.
800 **427** 3 r. multicoloured .. 30 30

428 Allama Mohammed Iqbal

1990. Pioneers of Freedom (3rd series). Each brown and green.
801 1 r. Type **428** 10 10
802 1 r. Mohammed Ali Jinnah 10 10
803 1 r. Sir Syed Ahmad Khan 10 10
804 1 r. Nawab Salimullah .. 10 10
805 1 r. Mohtarma Fatima Jinnah 10 10
806 1 r. Aga Khan III .. 10 10
807 1 r. Nawab Mohammad Ismail Khan 10 10
808 1 r. Hussain Shaheed Suhrawardy 10 10
809 1 r. Syed Ameer Ali .. 10 10
810 1 r. Nawab Bahadur Yar Jung 10 10
811 1 r. Khawaja Nazimuddin 10 10
812 1 r. Maulana Obaidullah Sindhi 10 10
813 1 r. Sahibzada Abdul Qaiyum Khan 10 10
814 1 r. Begum Jahanara Shah Nawaz 10 10
815 1 r. Sir Ghulam Hussain Hidayatullah 10 10
816 1 r. Qazi Mohammad Isa 10 10
817 1 r. Sir M. Shahnawaz Khan Mamdot 10 10
818 1 r. Pir Sahib of Manki Sharif 10 10
819 1 r. Liaquat Ali Khan .. 10 10
820 1 r. Maulvi A.K. Fazl-ul-Haq 10 10
821 1 r. Allama Shabbir Ahmad Usmani .. 10 10
822 1 r. Sadar Abdur Rab Nishtar 10 10
823 1 r. Bi Amma 10 10
824 1 r. Sir Abdullah Haroon 10 10
825 1 r. Chaudhry Rahmat Ali 10 10
826 1 r. Raja Sahib of Mahmudabad 10 10
827 1 r. Hassanally Effendi .. 10 10
See also Nos. 838/46.

429 Cultural Aspects of Indonesia and Pakistan

1990. Indonesia–Pakistan Economic and Cultural Co-operation Organization.
828 **429** 7 r. multicoloured .. 50 50

430 Globe, Open Book and Pen

1990. International Literacy Year.
829 **430** 3 r. multicoloured .. 20 20

431 College Crests

1990. Joint Meeting between Royal College of Physicans, Edinburgh, and College of Physicians and Surgeons, Pakistan.
830 **431** 2 r. multicoloured .. 15 20

432 Children and Globe

1990. U. N. World Summit for Children, New York.
831 **432** 7 r. multicoloured .. 55 65

433 Girl within Members' Flags

1990. South Asian Association for Regional Co-operation Year of Girl Child.
832 **433** 2 r. multicoloured .. 15 20

434 Paper passing over Rollers

1990. 25th Anniv of Security Papers Limited.
833 **434** 3 r. mulitocoloured .. 20 30

435 Civil Defence Worker protecting Islamabad

1991. International Civil Defence Day.
834 **435** 7 r. multicoloured .. 35 40

436 Logo and Flags of Member Countries

1991. South and West Asia Postal Union Commemoration.
835 **436** 5 r. multicoloured .. 25 30

437 Globe and Figures

1991. World Population Day.
836 **437** 10 r. multicoloured .. 50 55

438 Mentally Handicapped Athlete

1991. Pakistan Participation in Special Olympic Games.
837 **438** 7 r. multicoloured .. 35 40

1991. Pioneers of Freedom (4th series). As T **428**. Each brown and green.
838 1 r. Maulana Zafar Ali Khan 10 10
839 1 r. Maulana Mohamed Ali Jauhar 10 10
840 1 r. Chaudhry Khali-quzzaman 10 10
841 1 r. Hameed Nizami .. 10 10
842 1 r. Begum Ra'ana Liaquat Ali Khan 10 10
843 1 r. Mirza Abol Hassan Ispahani 10 10
844 1 r. Raja Ghazanfar Ali Khan 10 10
845 1 r. Malik Barkat Ali .. 10 10
846 1 r. Mir Jaffer Khan Jamali 10 10

439 Habib Bank Headquarters and Emblem

1991. 50th Anniv of Habib Bank.
847 **439** 1 r. multicoloured .. 10 10
848 5 r. multicoloured .. 25 30

440 St. Joseph's Convent School

1991. 130th Anniv (1992) of St. Joseph's Convent School, Karachi.
849 **440** 5 r. multicoloured .. 25 30

441 Emperor Sher Shah Suri

1991. Emperor Sher Shah Suri (founder of road network) Commemoration.
850 **441** 5 r. multicoloured .. 25 30

442 Jinnah Antarctic Research Station

1991. Pakistan Scientific Expedition to Antarctica.
852 **442** 7 r. multicoloured .. 35 40

443 Houbara Bustard

1991. Wildlife Protection (16th series).
853 **443** 7 r. multicoloured .. 35 40

444 Mosque

1991. 300th Death Anniv of Hazrat Sultan Bahoo.
854 **444** 7 r. multicoloured .. 35 40

445 Development Symbols and Map of Asia

1991. 25th Anniv of Asian Development Bank.
855 **445** 7 r. multicoloured .. 35 40

1991. Painters of Pakistan (2nd series). As T **426**. Multicoloured.
856 1 r. "Procession" (Haji Muhammad Sharif) .. 10 10
857 1 r. "Women harvesting" (Ustad Allah Bux) .. 10 10

446 American Express Travellers Cheques of 1891 and 1991 (½-size illustration)

1991. Centenary of American Express Travellers Cheques.
858 **446** 7 r. multicoloured .. 35 40

447 Flag, Banknote and Banking Equipment

1992. 1st Anniv of Muslim Commercial Bank Privatisation. Multicoloured.
859 1 r. Type **447** 10 10
860 7 r. Flag with industrial and commercial scenes 35 40

OFFICIAL STAMPS

1947. King George VI official stamps of India optd. **PAKISTAN.**
O 1. O **20.** 3 p. slate 30 10
O 2. ½ a. purple 20 10
O 3. 9 p. green .. .. 1·00 2·25
O 4. 1 a. red 20 10
O 5. 1½ a. violet 20 10
O 6. 2 a. orange 20 10
O 7. 2½ a. violet .. .. 1·75 2·50
O 8. 4 a. brown 20 10
O 9. 8 a. violet 30 35
O 10. **93.** 1 r. slate and brown (No. O 138) .. 80 50
O 11. 2 r. purple and brown (No. O 139) .. 3·50 1·25
O 12. 5 r. green and blue (No. O 140) .. 13·00 18·00
O 13. 10 r. purple and red (No. O 141) .. 24·00 50·00

1948. Optd. **SERVICE.** Crescent moon pointing to right.
O 14 **7** 3 p. red 10 10
O 15 6 p. violet 10 10
O 37 9 p. green 10 10
O 17 – 1 a. blue .. .. 2·75 10
O 18 – 1½ a. green .. .. 2·25 10
O 19 – 2 a. red .. .. .. 1·25 10
O 20 – 3 a. green .. .. 7·00 1·75
O 21 **9** 4 a. brown 80 10
O 22 – 8 a. black .. .. 80 2·75
O 23 **12** 1 r. blue .. .. 1·00 10
O 42 2 r. brown .. .. 2·25 10
O 61 5 r. red .. .. .. 3·00 15
O 26a **13** 10 r. mauve .. .. 8·50 22·00

1949. Optd. **SERVICE.** Crescent moon pointing to left.
O 38 – 1 a. blue 10 10
O 39 – 1½ a. green 10 10
O 40 – 2 a. red 15 10
O 30 – 3 a. green .. .. 5·50 2·25
O 31 – 8 a. black .. .. 14·00 6·25

1951. 4th Anniv. of Independence. As Nos. 56, 58 and 60 but inscr. "SERVICE" instead of "PAKISTAN POSTAGE".
O 32. 3 a. purple .. .. 1·25 3·00
O 33. 4 a. green 60 10
O 34. 8 a. sepia .. .. 3·00 85

1954. 7th Anniv. of Independence. Nos. 65/71 optd. **SERVICE.**
O 53 6 p violet 10 10
O 54 9 p. blue 10 30
O 55 1 a. red 10 10
O 56 1½ a. red 10 10
O 57 14 a. myrtle .. .. 40 1·75
O 58 1 r. green 40 10
O 51 2 r. orange .. .. 1·25 15

1955. 8th Anniv. of Independence. Nos. 74/5 optd. **SERVICE.**
O 63. 6 a. blue 10 10
O 64. 8 a. violet 10 10

1959. 9th Anniv. of Independence. Optd. **SERVICE.**
O 65. **37.** 2 a. red 10 10

1961. 1st Anniv. of Republic issue optd. **SERVICE.**
O 62. **41.** 10 r. green and orange 6·00 6·00

1961. Optd. **SERVICE.**
O 66. **51.** 8 a. green 10 10
O 67. 1 r. blue 10 10

1961. New currency. Provisional stamps, Nos. 122, etc., optd. **SERVICE.**
O 68. – 1 p. on 1½ a. red .. 10 10
O 69. **7.** 2 p. on 3 p. red .. 10 10
O 70. **51.** 3 p. on 6 p. purple .. 10 10
O 71. – 7 p. on 1 a. red .. 10 10
O 72. **51.** 13 p. on 2 a. red .. 10 10
O 73. **37.** 13 p. on 2 a. red .. 10 10

1961. Definitive issue optd. **SERVICE.**
O 74 **60.** 1 p. violet 10 10
O 75 2 p. red 10 10
O 79 3 p. purple 10 10
O 94 5 p. blue 10 10
O 81 7 p. green 10 10
O 82 **61.** 10 p. brown 10 10
O 83 13 p. violet 10 10
O 98 15 p. purple 10 40
O 99 20 p. green 10 30
O 100 25 p. blue .. .. 2·75 65
O 85 40 p. purple 10 10
O 102 50 p. turquoise .. 10 15
O 87 75 p. red 20 10
O 104 90 p. green .. .. 2·00 2·00
O 88 **62.** 1 r. red 35 10
O 89 2 r. orange .. .. 1·25 20
O 108 5 r. green .. .. 7·00 2·25

1979. Optd. **SERVICE.**
O 109. **275.** 2 p. green 10 10
O 110. – 3 p. black 10 10
O 111. – 5 p. blue 10 10
O 112. – 10 p. blue and turq. 10 10
O 113. – 20 p. green (No. 468) .. 10 10
O 114. – 25 p. green and mauve (No. 489) 10 10
O 115. – 40 p. blue and mauve (No. 470) 30 10
O 116. – 50 p. lilac and green (No. 471) 10 10
O 117. – 60 p. black (No. 472) .. .. 1·00 10
O 118. – 75 p. red (No. 473) 75 10
O 119. – 1 r. green (No. 475) 75 10
O 120. – 1 r. 50 orange (No. 476) 10 10
O 121. – 2 r. red (No. 477) .. 15 10
O 122. – 3 r. blue (No. 478) 20 20
O 123. – 4 r. black (No. 479) 30 25
O 124. – 5 r. brown (No. 480) 25 30

1980. As Nos. 513/19 but inscr. "SERVICE".
O 125. **291.** 10 p. green & yellow 40 10
O 126. 15 p. deep grn. & grn. 10 10
O 127. 25 p. violet and red 10 10
O 128. 35 p. red and green 10 10
O 129. – 40 p. red and brown 15 10
O 130. – 50 p. red and green 20 20
O 131. – 80 p. green and black 80 45

1984. Nos. 629/30 and 632/6 optd **SERVICE.**

O132	–	5 p. black and purple	10	10
O133	–	10 p. black and red	10	10
O135	343	20 p. black and violet	10	10
O136	–	50 p. brown and red	10	10
O137	–	60 p. lt brown & brn	10	10
O138	–	70 p. blue	10	10
O139	–	80 p. brown and red	10	10

1989. No. 773 optd **SERVICE.**

O140	411	1 r. multicoloured ..	10	10

O 7 State Bank of Pakistan Building, Islamabad

1990.

O141	O 7	1 r. red and green ..	10	10
O142		2 r. red and pink ..	15	20
O143		3 r. red and blue ..	15	20
O144		4 r. red and brown ..	20	25
O145		5 r. red and purple ..	25	30

PALESTINE

A territory at the extreme E. of the Mediterranean Sea, captured from the Turks by Great Britain in 1917 and under Military Occupation till 1920, Palestine became a League of Nations Mandate in 1923.

1918. 10 milliemes = 1 piastre.
1927. 1,000 mils = £P1.

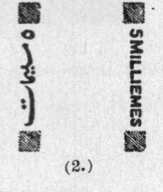

1.

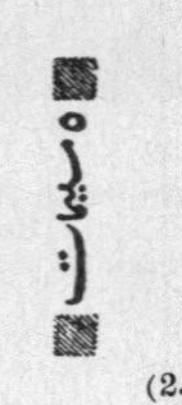

(2.)

1918.

3	1	1 p. blue	2·50	2·50

1918. Surch with T 2.

4	1	5 m. on 1 p. blue ..	5·00	4·00

3.

("E.E.F." = Egyptian Expeditionary Force).

فلسطين

PALESTINE

פלשתינה א״י

(4.)

1918.

5.	3.	1 m. brown	30	40
6.		2 m. green	30	35
7.		3 m. brown	35	35
8.		4 m. red	35	40
9.		5 m. orange	35	30
10.		1 p. blue	35	25
11.		2 p. olive	60	60
12.		5 p. purple	1·75	2·25
13.		9 p. ochre	2·25	4·00
14.		10 p. blue	2·25	3·00
15.		20 p. grey	9·00	15·00

Nos. 1/15 were also valid in Transjordan, Cilicia, Northern Egypt and Syria.

1920. Optd with T 4.

71	3	1 m. brown	30	30
61		2 m. green	35	30
72		2 m. yellow	35	30
62		3 m. brown	35	30
73		3 m. blue	30	15
74		4 m. red	30	20
75		5 m. orange	35	20
76		6 m. green	65	30
77		7 m. brown	65	30
78		8 m. red	65	30
79		1 p. grey	65	30
65		1 p. blue	60	35
80		13 m. blue	50	15
66		2 p. olive	70	40
67		5 p. purple	4·00	5·00
68		9 p. ochre	12·00	14·00
88		10 p. blue	7·50	2·50
26		20 p. grey	15·00	32·00
89		20 p. violet	9·00	5·50

9. Rachel's Tomb.

10. Dome of the Rock.

11. Citadel, Jerusalem.

12. Sea of Galilee.

1927.

90	9	2 m. blue	30	10
91		3 m. green	30	10
92	10	4 m. red	2·75	1·25
104		4 m. purple	30	10
93	11	5 m. orange	45	10
94a	10	6 m. green	50	20
95	11	7 m. red	4·00	1·00
105		7 m. violet	45	10
96	10	8 m. brown	11·00	5·00
106		8 m. red	60	20
97b	9	10 m. grey	40	10
98	10	13 m. blue	3·75	30
107		13 m. brown	40	10
108a		15 m. blue	50	10
99	11	20 m. olive	1·40	15
100a	12	50 m. purple	1·00	20
101		90 m. bistre	75·00	75·00
102		100 m. blue	2·00	50
103b		200 m. violet	5·50	3·00
109		250 m. brown	2·50	2·00
110		500 m. red	4·50	2·75
111		£P1 black	5·00	3·25

POSTAGE DUE STAMPS

D 1.

D 2.

1920.

D 1.	D 1.	1 m. brown	25·00	42·00
D 2.		2 m. green	22·00	32·00
D 3.		4 m. red	22·00	38·00
D 4.		8 m. mauve	17·00	26·00
D 5.		13 m. blue	15·00	26·00

1924.

D 6.	D 2.	1 m. brown	90	1·75
D 7.		2 m. yellow	1·00	1·75
D 8.		4 m. green	1·10	1·25
D 9.		8 m. red	2·50	90
D 10.		13 m. blue	2·50	2·50
D 11.		5 p. violet	7·00	1·75

1928. As Type D 2, but inscr. "MIL" instead of "MILLIEME".

D 12.	D 2.	1 m. brown	45	75
D 13.		2 m. yellow	55	60
D 14.		4 m. green	70	1·25
D 15.		6 m. brown	7·00	7·00
D 16.		8 m. red	1·50	70
D 17.		10 m. grey	1·25	60
D 18.		13 m. blue	1·50	1·50
D 19.		20 m. olive	1·60	1·25
D 20.		50 m. violet	2·50	1·25

PAPUA

(Formerly **BRITISH NEW GUINEA**).

The eastern portion of the island of New Guinea, to the N. of Australia, a territory of the Commonwealth of Australia, now combined with New Guinea. Australian stamps were used after the Japanese defeat in 1945 until the combined issue appeared in 1952.

12 pence = 1 shilling.
20 shillings = 1 pound.

1. Lakatoi (native canoe) with Hanuabada Village in Background.

1901.

9	1	½d. black and green ..	3·00	3·75
10		1d. black and red ..	3·00	2·00
11		2d. black and violet ..	4·75	4·00
12		2½d. black and blue ..	8·00	12·00
5		4d. black and brown ..	45·00	35·00
6		6d. black and green ..	42·00	35·00
7		1s. black and orange ..	60·00	65·00
8		2s. 6d. black and brown ..	£600	£550

1906. Optd. **Papua.**

40	1.	½d. black and green ..	3·50	5·50
41		1d. black and red ..	3·75	6·00
42		2d. black and violet ..	4·50	2·25
27		2½d. black and blue ..	3·75	13·00
43		4d. black and brown ..	25·00	45·00
29		6d. black and green ..	18·00	38·00
25		1s. black and orange ..	20·00	38·00
37		2s. 6d. black and brown ..	30·00	50·00

6.

1907.

66	6	½d. black and green ..	1·40	2·00
100a		1d. black and red ..	1·60	30
68		2d. black and purple ..	3·00	2·50
51a		2½d. black and blue ..	5·50	6·50
63		4d. black and brown ..	3·50	6·50
80		6d. black and green ..	5·50	7·50
81		1s. black and orange ..	5·50	15·00
48		2s. 6d. black and brown ..	48·00	60·00

1911.

84a.	6.	½d. green	30	2·00
85.		1d. red	70	40
86.		2d. mauve	70	75
87.		2½d. blue	4·75	8·50
88.		4d. olive	2·00	11·00
89.		6d. brown	3·75	5·00
90.		1s. yellow	8·50	14·00
91.		2s. 6d. red	28·00	38·00

1917. Surch. **ONE PENNY.**

93a.	6.	1d. on ½d. green ..	50	1·00
94.		1d. on 2d. mauve ..	12·00	14·00
95.		1d. on 2½d. blue ..	1·25	3·75
96.		1d. on 4d. olive ..	1·00	4·50
97.		1d. on 6d. brown ..	8·00	13·00
98.		1d. on 2s. 6d. red ..	1·50	8·00

1919.

99a	6	½d. green and olive ..	55	80
101		1½d. blue and brown ..	1·00	50
102		2d. purple and red ..	1·25	75
103		2½d. green and blue ..	4·25	9·00
104		3d. black and turquoise	1·25	1·75
105		4d. brown and orange ..	2·50	4·50
106		5d. grey and brown ..	4·25	15·00
107		6d. purple	2·75	8·50
127		9d. lilac and violet ..	4·00	25·00
108		1s. brown and olive ..	3·50	6·00
128		1s. 3d. lilac and blue ..	7·00	30·00
109		2s. 6d. red and pink ..	18·00	35·00
110		5s. black and green ..	40·00	45·00
111		10s. green and blue ..	£140	£180

1929. Air. Optd **AIR MAIL.**

114	6	3d. black and turquoise ..	80	6·50

(11.)

1930. Air. Optd. with T 11.

118.	6.	3d. black and turquoise ..	55	5·00
119.		6d. purple	7·00	10·00
120.		1s. brown and olive ..	4·00	15·00

1931. Surch. in words or figs. and words.

122.	6.	2d. on 1½d. blue & brown	80	2·00
125.		5d. on 1s. brown & olive	60	1·75
126.		9d. on 2s. 6d. red & pink	5·00	8·50
123.		1s. 3d. on 5d. blk. & grn.	4·00	9·00

15. Motuan Girl. **18.** Raggiana Bird of Paradise.

20. Native Mother and Child.

1932.

130.	15.	½d. black and orange ..	35	2·50
131.	–	1d. black and green ..	50	30
132.	–	1½d. black and red ..	60	5·00
133.	18.	2d. red	5·50	30
134.	–	3d. black and blue ..	2·00	6·50
135.	20.	4d. olive	3·00	8·50
136.	–	5d. black and green ..	2·00	4·00
137.	–	6d. brown	4·00	7·00
138.	–	9d. black and violet ..	7·00	17·00
139.	–	1s. green	2·50	11·00
140.	–	1s. 3d. black and purple	8·50	20·00
141.	–	2s. black and green ..	11·00	20·00
142.	–	2s. 6d. black and mauve	24·00	38·00
143.	–	5s. black and brown ..	48·00	55·00
144.	–	10s. violet	75·00	75·00
145.	–	£1 black and grey ..	£170	£170

DESIGNS—VERT. As Type **15.** 1d. Chieftain's son. 1½d. Tree houses. 3d. Papuan dandy. 5d. Masked dancer. 9d. Shooting fish. 1s. Ceremonial platform. 1s. 3d. Lakatoi. 2s. Papuan art. 2s. 6d. Pottery-making. 5d. Native policeman. £1, Delta house. VERT. As Type **18**: 6d. Papuan mother. HORIZ. 10s. Lighting fire.

31. Hoisting the Union Jack.

1934. 50th Anniv. of Declaration of British Protectorate. Inscr. "1884 1834".

No.	Type	Description		
146.	**31.**	1d green	80	2·25
147.	–	2d. red	1·75	2·25
148.	**31.**	3d. blue	1·50	3·00
149.	–	5d. purple	5·50	7·00

DESIGN: 2d., 5d. Scene on H.M.S. "Nelson".

1935. Silver Jubilee. Optd. **HIS MAJESTY'S JUBILEE 1910-1935.**

No.	Type	Description		
150.	–	1d. black & green (No. 131)	55	80
151.	**18.**	2d. red	1·25	60
152.	–	3d. black & blue (No. 134)	1·25	2·50
153.	–	5d. black & green (No. 136)	2·75	2·75

35. King George VI.

1937. Coronation.

No.	Type	Description		
154.	35.	1d. green	40	15
155.		2d. red	40	15
156.		3d. blue	40	20
157.		5d. purple	40	45

36. Port Moresby.

1938. Air. 50th Anniv. of Declaration of British Possession.

No.	Type	Description		
158.	**36.**	2d. red	3·75	2·25
159.		3d. blue	3·75	2·25
160.		5d. green	3·75	3·25
161.		8d. red	9·00	9·50
162.		1s. mauve	22·00	13·00

37. Natives poling Rafts.

1939. Air.

No.	Type	Description		
163.	**37.**	2d. red	5·00	2·50
164		3d. blue	5·00	4·00
165.		5d. green	8·00	1·50
166.		8d. red	9·00	2·50
167.		1s. mauve	12·00	5·00
168.		1s. 6d. olive	42·00	30·00

OFFICIAL STAMPS

1931. Optd. **O.S.**

No.	Type	Description		
O 55.	**6.**	½d. green and olive	1·00	4·00
O 56a.		1d. black and red ..	3·00	4·00
O 57.		1½d. blue and brown	1·40	8·50
O 58.		2d. brown & purple	2·25	8·00
O 59.		3d. black & turq.	2·25	14·00
O 60.		4d. brown & orange	2·25	13·00
O 61.		5d. grey and brown	6·00	30·00
O 62.		6d. purple and red	4·00	8·50
O 63.		9d. lilac and violet	35·00	50·00
O 64.		1s. brown and olive	8·00	24·00
O 65.		1s. 3d. lilac and blue	35·00	55·00
O 66.		2s. 6d. red and pink	38·00	80·00

PAPUA NEW GUINEA

Combined territory on the island of New Guinea administered by Australia under trusteeship. Self-government was established during 1973.

1952. 12 pence = 1 shilling;
20 shillings = 1 pound.
1966. 100 cents = $1 Australian.
1975. 100 toea = 1 kina.

1. Tree Kangaroo.

7. Kiriwina Chief House.

1952.

No.	Type	Description		
1.	**1.**	½d. green	30	10
2.	–	1d. brown	20	10
3.	–	2d. blue	35	10
4.	–	2½d. orange	1·75	40
5.	–	3d. myrtle	1·25	10
6.	–	3½d. red	60	10
6a.	–	3½d. black	9·50	4·25
18.	–	4d. red	1·00	10
19.	–	5d. green	1·75	10
7.	**7.**	6½d. purple	2·25	10
20.	–	7d. green	10·00	10
8.	–	7½d. blue	10·00	4·50
21.	–	8d. blue	1·50	2·00
9.	–	9d. brown	6·00	60
10.	–	1s. green	2·75	10
11.	–	1s. 6d. myrtle	12·00	80
22.	–	1s. 7d. brown	30·00	20·00
12.	–	2s. blue	8·00	10
23.	–	2s. 5d. red	4·25	3·25
13.	–	2s. 6d. purple	7·50	40
24.	–	5s. red and olive	11·00	1·50
14.	–	10s. slate	60·00	11·00
15.	–	£1 brown	75·00	11·00

DESIGNS—AS TYPE **1:** 1 d. Buka head-dresses. 2 d. Native youth. 2½d. Greater Bird of Paradise. 3d. Native policeman. 3½d. Papuan head-dress. 4d., 5d. Cacao plant. As Type **7.** VERT. 7½d. Kiriwina Yam house. 1s. 6d. Rubber tapping. 2s. Sepik dancing masks. 5s. Coffee beans. £1. Native shooting fish. HORIZ. 7d., 8d. Klinki plymill. 9d. Copra making. 1s. Lakatoi (trading canoe). 1s. 7d., 2s. 5d. Cattle. 2s. 6d. Native shepherd and flock. 10s. Map of Papua and New Guinea.

1957. Nos. 4, 1 and 10 surch.

No.	Type	Description		
16.	–	4d. on 2½d. orange ..	30	10
25.	1.	5d. on ½d. green	50	10
17.	–	7d. on 1s. green	20	10

23. Council Chamber, Port Moresby.

1961. Reconstitution of Legislative Council.

No.	Type	Description		
26.	**23.**	5d. green and yellow ..	1·50	25
27.		2s. 3d. green and salmon	5·50	1·50

24. Female, Goroka, New Guinea.

26. Female Dancer.

38. Waterfront, Port Moresby.

28. Traffic Policeman.

1961.

No.	Type	Description		
28.	**24.**	1d. lake	1·00	10
29.	–	3d. blue	30	10
47.	**38.**	8d. green	40	15
30.	**26.**	1s. green	3·25	15
31.	–	2s. purple	45	15
48.	–	2s. 3d. blue	30	15
32.	**28.**	3s. green	1·75	1·00

DESIGNS—As Type **24:** 3d. Tribal elder, Tari, Papua. As Type **38:** 2s. 3d. Piaggio P-166 Aircraft landing at Tapini. As Type **26:** 2s. Male dancer.

29. Campaign Emblem.

1962. Malaria Eradication.

No.	Type	Description		
33.	**29.**	5d. lake and blue ..	45	15
34.		1s. red and brown ..	1·00	25
35.		2s. black and green ..	1·40	70

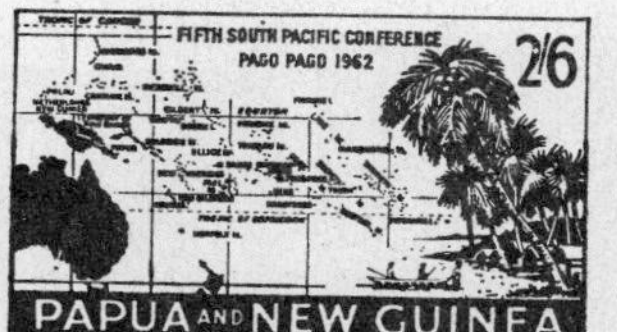

30. Map of South Pacific.

1962. 5th South Pacific Conf., Pago Pago.

No.	Type	Description		
36.	**30.**	5d. red and green ..	70	15
37.		1s. 6d. violet and yellow	2·00	60
38.		2s. 6d. green and blue ..	2·00	1·00

SPORTS: No. 40, High jump. No. 41, Runners.

31. Throwing the Javelin.

1962. 7th British Empire and Commonwealth Games, Perth.

No.	Type	Description		
39.	**31.**	5d. brown and blue ..	30	10
40.	–	5d. brown and orange ..	30	10
41.	–	2s. 3d. brown and green	1·75	75

34. Raggiana Bird of Paradise.

37. Queen Elizabeth II.

DESIGN—As Type **34:** 6d. Golden Opossum.

36. Rabaul.

1963.

No.	Type	Description		
42.	**34.**	5d. yellow, brown & sepia	1·75	10
43.	–	6d. red, brown and grey	1·00	90
44.	**36.**	10s. multicoloured ..	17·00	2·50
45.	**37.**	£1 brown, gold and green	12·00	9·50

1963. Cent. of Red Cross. As T **163** of Australia.

No.	Type	Description		
46.		5 d. red, grey and green ..	60	10

40. Games Emblem.

1963. 1st South Pacific Games, Suva.

No.	Type	Description		
49.	**40.**	5d. brown	10	10
50.		1s. green	20	20

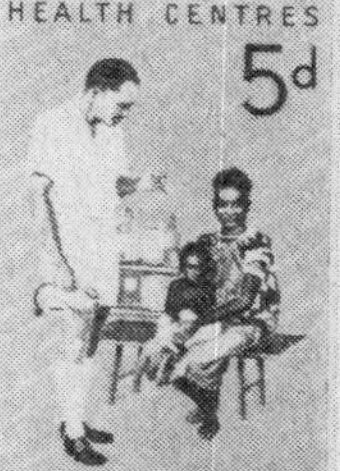

41. Watam Head.

45. Casting Vote.

1964. Native Artifacts. Multicoloured.

No.	Type	Description		
51.		11d. Type **41**	1·00	10
52.		2s. 5d. Watam Head (diff.)	1·00	75
53.		2s. 6d. Bosmun Head ..	1·00	10
54.		5s. Medina Head	1·25	15

1964. Common Roll Elections.

No.	Type	Description		
55.	**45.**	5d. brown and drab ..	10	10
56.		2s. 3d. brown and blue	20	25

HEALTH CENTRES

5d

PAPUA & NEW GUINEA

46. "Health Centres".

PAPUA &
NEW GUINEA
AMBLYORNIS SUBALARIS
1d

50. Striped Gardener Bowerbird.

1964. Health Services.

No.	Type	Description		
57.	**46.**	5d. violet	10	10
58.	–	8d. green	10	10
59.	–	1s. blue	10	10
60.	–	1s. 2d. red	15	30

DESIGNS: 8d. "School Health". 1s. "Infant Child and Maternal Health". 1s. 2d. "Medical Training".

1964. Multicoloured.

No.	Description		
61.	1d. Type **50**	40	10
62.	3d. Adelbert bowerbird ..	50	10
63.	5d. Blue bird of paradise ..	55	10
64.	6d. Lawes's parotia ..	75	10
65.	8d. Black-billed sicklebill ..	1·25	20
66.	1s. Emperor of Germany bird of paradise	1·25	10
67.	2s. Brown sicklebill ..	1·00	30
68.	2s. 3d. Lesser bird of paradise	1·00	85
69.	3s. Magnificent bird of paradise	1·25	1·25
70.	5s. Twelve-wired bird of paradise	16·00	2·00
71.	10s. Magnificent rifle-bird ..	11·00	4·00

Nos. 66/71 are larger (25½ × 36½ mm.).

61. Canoe Prow.

1965. Sepik Canoe Prows in Port Moresby Museum.

72. **61.** 4d. multicoloured .. 40 10
73. – 1s. 3d. multicoloured .. 1·75 85
74. – 1s. 6d. multicoloured .. 50 10
75. – 4s. multicoloured .. 1·50 25

Each show different carved canoe prows as **Type 61.**

1965. 50th Anniv. of Gallipoli Landing. As T **184** of Australia, but slightly larger (22 × 34½ mm.).

76. 2s. 3d. brown, black and green 20 10

65. Urban Plan and Native House.

1965. 6th South Pacific Conf., Lae.

77. **65.** 6d. multicoloured .. 10 10
78. – 1s. multicoloured .. 10 10

No. 78 is similar to Type **65** but with the plan on the right and the house on the left. Also " URBANISATION " reads downwards.

66. Mother and Child.

1965. 20th Anniv. of U.N.O.

79. **66.** 6d. sepia, blue & turquoise 10 10
80. – 1s. brown, blue & violet 10 10
81. – 2s. blue, green and olive 10 10

DESIGNS—VERT. 1s. Globe and U.N. Emblem. 2s. U.N. Emblem and Globes.

69. 'Papilio ulysses".

1966. Decimal Currency. Multicoloured.

82 1 c. Type **69** 30 30
83 3 c. "Marpesia acilia" .. 40 40
84 4 c. "Graphium weiskei" .. 40 20
85 5 c. "Terinos alurgis" .. 40 10
86 10 c. "Ornithoptera priamus" 50 30
86a 12 c. "Euploea callithoe" 2·25 2·25
87 15 c. "Papilio euchenor" .. 4·25 80
88 20 c. "Parthenos sylvia" .. 2·50 25
89 25 c. "Delias aruna" .. 4·50 70
90 50 c. "Apatarina erminea" 12·00 1·25
91 $1 "Doleschallia dascylus" 3·50 1·25
92 $2 "Ornithoptera paradisea" .. .. 6·50 5·00

Nos. 86/92 are horiz.

80. " Molala Harai ".

84. Throwing the Discus.

1966. Folklore. Elema Art (1st series).

93. **80.** 2 c. black and red 10 10
94. – 7 c. black, yellow and blue 10 10
95. – 30 c. black, red and green 15 10
96. – 60 c. black, red & yellow 40 20

DESIGNS: 7 c. " Marai ". 30 c. " Meavea Kivovia ". 60 c. " Toivita Tapaivita ".

1966. South Pacific Games, Noumea. Mult.

97. 5 c. Type **84** 10 10
98. 10 c. Football 10 10
99. 20 c. Tennis 15 10

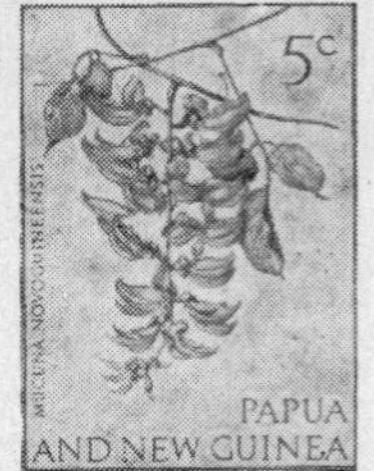

87. " Mucuna novoguineensis ".

1966. Flowers. Multicoloured.

100. 5 c. Type **87** 15 10
101. 10 c. " Tecomanthe dendrophila " 15 10
102. 20 c. " Rhododendron macgregoriae " 25 10
103. 60 c. " Rhododendron konori " 55 40

91. " Fine Arts ".

1967. Higher Education. Multicoloured.

104. 1 c. Type **91** 10 10
105. 3 c. " Surveying " 10 10
106. 4 c. " Civil Engineering " 10 10
107. 5 c. " Science " 10 10
108. 20 c. " Law " 10 10

96. " Sagra speciosa ".

100. Laloki River.

1967. Fauna Conservation (Beetles). Mult.

109. 5 c. Type **96** 20 10
110. 10 c. " Eupholus schoenherri " 30 10
111. 20 c. " Sphingnotus albertisi " 50 10
112. 25 c. " Cyphogastra albertisi " 55 10

1967. Laloki River Hydro-Electric Scheme, and " New Industries ". Multicoloured.

113. 5 c. Type **100** 10 10
114. 10 c. Pyrethrum 10 10
115. 20 c. Tea Plant 10 10
116. 25 c. Type **100** 10 10

103. Air Attack at Milne Bay.

1967. 25th Anniv. of Pacific War. Mult.

117. 2 c. Type **103** 10 10
118. 5 c. Kokoda Trail (vert.) .. 10 10
119. 20 c. The Coast Watchers .. 15 10
120. 50 c. Battle of the Coral Sea 50 25

107. Papuan Lory.

111. Chimbu Head-dress.

1967. Christmas. Territory Parrots. Mult.

121. 5 c. Type **107** 20 10
122. 7 c. Pesquet's Parrot .. 25 15
123. 30 c. Dusky Lory 60 10
124. 25 c. Edward's Fig Parrot 60 10

1968. " National Heritage ". Designs showing different Head-dresses. Multicoloured.

125. 5 c. Type **111** 10 10
126. 10 c. Southern Highlands (horiz.) 10 10
127. 20 c. Western Highlands (horiz.) 15 10
128. 60 c. Chimbu (different) .. 40 20

115. " Hyla thesaurensis ".

1968. Fauna Conservation (Frogs). Mult.

129. 5 c. Type **115** 15 15
130. 10 c. " Hyla iris " 15 10
131. 15 c. " Ceratobatrachus guentheri " 15 10
132. 20 c. " Nyctimystes narinosa " 20 10

119. Human Rights Flame and Papuan Head-dress (abstract).

1968. Human Rights Year. Multicoloured.

133. 5 c. Type **119** 10 10
134. 10 c. Human Rights in the World (abstract) .. 10 10

121. Leadership (abstract).

1968. Universal Suffrage. Multicoloured.

135. 20 c. Type **121** 15 10
136. 25 c. Leadership of the Community (abstract) .. 15 10

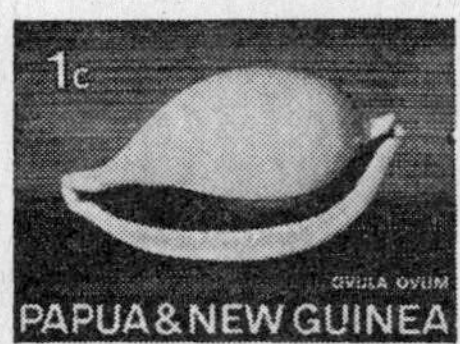

123. Egg Cowry.

1968. Seashells. Multicoloured.

137. 1 c. Type **123** 10 10
138. 3 c. Lancinated Conch .. 30 20
139. 4 c. Lithograph Cone .. 20 30
140. 5 c. Marbled Cone .. 25 10
141. 7 c. Episcopal Mitre .. 35 10
142. 10 c. Red Volute .. 45 10
143. 12 c. Areola Bonnet .. 1·50 90
144. 15 c. Scorpion Conch .. 80 30
145. 20 c. Fluted Clam .. 90 10
146. 25 c. Chocolate Flamed Venus Shell .. 90 30
147. 30 c. Giant Murex .. 1·25 45
148. 40 c. Chambered Nautilus 1·00 40
149. 60 c. Pacific Triton .. 1·25 20
150. $1 Emerald Snail .. 3·00 50
151. $2 Glory of the Sea .. 19·00 4·25

138. Tito Myth.

142. " Fireball " Class Yacht.

1969. Folklore. Elema Art (2nd series).

152. **138.** 5 c. black, yellow & red 10 10
153. – 5 c. black, yellow & red 10 10
154. – 10 c. black, grey and red 15 20
155. – 10 c. black, grey and red 15 20

DESIGNS: No. 153, Iko Myth. No. 154, Luvuapo Myth. No. 155, Miro Myth.

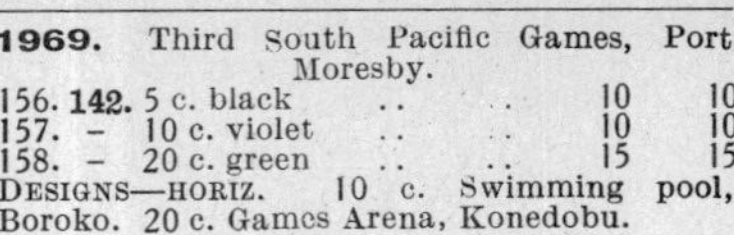

1969. Third South Pacific Games, Port Moresby.

156. **142.** 5 c. black 10 10
157. – 10 c. violet 10 10
158. – 20 c. green 15 15

DESIGNS—HORIZ. 10 c. Swimming pool, Boroko. 20 c. Games Arena, Konedobu.

145. " Dendrobium ostrinoglossum ".

149. Bird of Paradise.

1969. Flora Conservation (Orchids). Multicoloured.

159. 5 c. Type **145** 25 10
160. 10 c. "Dendrobium lawesii" 35 40
161. 20 c. "Dendrobium pseudofrigidum" 55 60
162. 30 c. "Dendrobium conanthum" 70 40

1969. Coil Stamps.

162a. **149.** 2 c. blue, blk. & red .. 10 15
163. 5 c. grn., brn. & orange 10 10

150. Native Potter.

1969. 50th Anniv. of I.L.O.

164. **150.** 5 c. multicoloured .. 10 10

151. Tareko.

1969. Musical Instruments.

165. **151.** 5 c. multicoloured .. 10 10
166. – 10 c. black, grn. & yellow 10 10
167. – 25 c. blk., yellow & brn. 15 10
168. – 30 c. multicoloured .. 25 10

DESIGNS: 10 c. Garamut. 25 c. Iviliko. 30 c. Kundu.

155. Prehistoric Ambun Stone.

1970. "National Heritage". Multicoloured.

169. 5 c. Type **155** 15 10
170. 10 c. Masawa canoe of Kula Cicuit 20 15
171. 25 c. Torres' map, 1606 .. 45 15
172. 30 c. H.M.S. "Basilisk" (paddle-sloop), 1873 .. 60 20

159. King of Saxony Bird of Paradise.

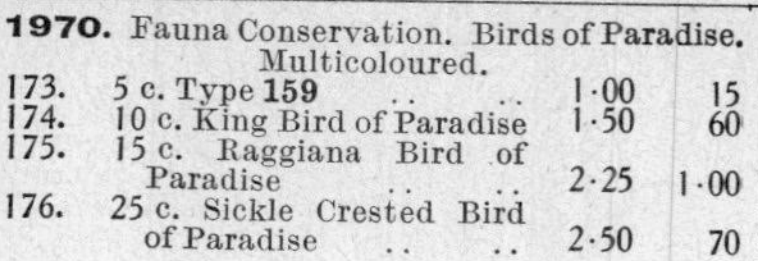
1970. Fauna Conservation. Birds of Paradise. Multicoloured.

173. 5 c. Type **159** .. .. 1·00 15
174. 10 c. King Bird of Paradise 1·50 60
175. 15 c. Raggiana Bird of Paradise .. .. 2·25 1·00
176. 25 c. Sickle Crested Bird of Paradise .. .. 2·50 70

163. McDonnell Douglas "D.C. 6B" and Mt. Wilhelm.

1970. Australian and New Guinea Air Services. Multicoloured.

177. 5 c. Type **163** 25 10
178. 5 c. "Lockheed Electra" (turbo-prop), and Mt. Yule 25 10
179. 5 c. Boeing "727" (jet), and Mt. Giluwe 25 10
180. 5 c. Fokker "Friendship" and Manam Island .. 25 10
181. 25 c. "D.C. 3." and Matupi Volcano 60 40
182. 30 c. Boeing "707" and Hombrom's Bluff .. 70 60

169. N. Miklouho-Maclay (scientist) and Effigy.

1970. 42nd A.N.Z.A.A.S. Congress, Port Moresby. Multicoloured.

183. 5 c. Type **169** 10 10
184. 10 c. B. Malinowski (anthropologist) and native hut 15 10
185. 15 c. T. Salvadori (ornithologist) and Dwarf Cassowary 50 15
186. 20 c. F. R. R. Schlechter (botanist) and flower .. 50 15

A.N.Z.A.A.S. = Australian–New Zealand Association for the Advance of Science.

170. Wogeo Island Food Bowl.

171. Eastern Highlands Dwelling.

1970. Native Artifacts. Multicoloured.

187. 5 c. Type **170** 10 10
188. 10 c. Lime Pot 20 10
189. 15 c. Albom Sago Storage Pot 20 10
190. 30 c. Manus Island Bowl (horiz.) 25 20

1971. Native Dwellings. Multicoloured.

191. 5 c. Type **171** 15 10
192. 7 c. Milne Bay Stilt Dwelling 15 15
193. 10 c. Purari Delta Dwelling 15 10
194. 40 c. Sepik Dwelling .. 35 60

172. Spotted Phalanger.

174. Bartering Fish for Vegetables.

173. "Basketball".

1971. Fauna Conservation. Multicoloured.

195. 5 c. Type **172** 30 10
196. 10 c. Long-fingered Possum 60 15
197. 15 c. Feather-tailed Possum .. .. .. 1·25 1·00
198. 25 c. Long-nosed Echidna 1·75 1·00
199. 30 c. Ornate Tree Kangaroo (horiz) .. 1·75 70

1971. 4th South Pacific Games, Papeete. Multicoloured.

200. 7 c. Type **173** 10 10
201. 14 c. "Sailing" 15 20
202. 21 c. "Boxing" 15 25
203. 28 c. "Athletics" 15 35

1971. Primary Industries. Multicoloured.

204. 7 c. Type **174** 15 10
205. 9 c. Man stacking yams 20 25
206. 14 c. Vegetable market .. 30 10
207. 30 c. Highlanders cultivating garden 50 50

175. Sia Dancer.

1971. Native Dancers. Multicoloured.

208. 7 c. Type **175** 20 10
209. 9 c. Urasena dancer .. 30 20
210. 20 c. Siassi Tubuan dancers (horiz.) 80 90
211. 28 c. Sia dancers (horiz.) .. 1·00 1·10

176. Papuan Flag over Australian Flag.

1971. Constitutional Development.

212. **176.** 7 c. multicoloured .. 30 10
213. – 7 c. multicoloured .. 30 10

DESIGN: No. 213, Crest of Papua New Guinea and Australian coat of arms.

177. Map of Papua New Guinea and Flag of South Pacific Commission.

1972. 25th Anniv. of South Pacific Commission.

214. **177.** 15 c. multicoloured .. 65 55
215. – 15 c. multicoloured .. 65 55

DESIGN: No. 215, Man's face and flag of the Commission.

178. Turtle.

1972. Fauna Conservation (Reptiles). Mult.

216. 7 c. Type **178** 40 10
217. 14 c. Rainforest Dragon .. 1·00 1·25
218. 21 c. Green Python .. 1·25 1·50
219. 30 c. Salvador's Monitor .. 1·75 1·25

179. Curtiss "Seagull MF-6" and "Eureka" (schooner).

1972. 50th Anniv. of Aviation. Multicoloured.

220. 7 c. Type **179** 40 10
221. 14 c. De Havilland "37" and native porters .. 1·00 1·25
222. 20 c. Junkers "G-31" and gold dredger .. .. 1·10 1·25
223. 25 c. Junkers "F-13" and mission church .. .. 1·10 1·25

180. New National Flag.

1972. National Day. Multicoloured.

224. 7 c. Type **180** 30 10
225. 10 c. Native drum 35 25
226. 30 c. Blowing the conch-shell 60 50

181. Rev. Copland King.

1972. Christmas. Missionaries. Mult.

227. 7 c. Type **181** 25 40
228. 7 c. Rev. Dr. Flierl 25 40
229. 7 c. Bishop Verjus 25 40
230. 7 c. Pastor Ruatoka 25 40

182. Mt. Tomavatur Station.

1973. Completion of Telecommunications Project, 1968-72. Multicoloured.

231. 7 c. Type **182** 45 20
232. 7 c. Mt. Kerigomma Station 45 20
233. 7 c. Sattelburg Station .. 45 20
234. 7 c. Wideru Station .. 45 20
235. 9 c. Teleprinter 45 55
236. 30 c. Network map .. 1·25 1·50

Nos. 235/6 are larger, 36 × 26 mm.

183. Queen Carola's Parotia.

1973. Birds of Paradise. Multicoloured.

237. 7 c. Type **183** .. .. 1·50 35
238. 14 c. Goldies' Bird of Paradise .. .. 2·75 1·25
239. 21 c. Ribbon-tailed Bird of Paradise .. .. 3·25 2·00
240. 28 c. Princess Stephanie's Bird of Paradise .. 4·50 2·50

Nos. 229/40 are size 18 × 49 mm.

184. Wood Carver.

1973. Multicoloured.

241. 1 c. Type **184** 10 10
242. 3 c. Wig-makers 40 10
243. 5 c. Mt. Bagana 55 10
244. 6 c. Pig Exchange 70 80
245. 7 c. Coastal village .. 30 10
246. 8 c. Arawe mother .. 35 20
247. 9 c. Fire dancers 30 20
248. 10 c. Tifalmin hunter .. 55 10
249. 14 c. Crocodile hunters .. 45 60
250. 15 c. Mt. Elimbari .. 50 30
251. 20 c. Canoe-racing, Manus 1·50 40
252. 21 c. Making sago 65 65
253. 25 c. Council House .. 70 45
254. 28 c. Menyamya bowmen 80 75
255. 30 c. Shark-snaring .. 1·25 75
256. 40 c. Fishing canoes, Madang .. .. .. 1·50 80
257. 60 c. Tapa cloth-making .. 3·50 1·00
258. $1 Asaro Mudmen .. 5·00 3·25
259. $2 Enga "Sing Sing" .. 10·00 8·50

185. Stamps of German New Guinea, 1897. (Illustration reduced. Actual size 51 × 31 mm.)

1973. 75th Anniv. of Papua New Guinea Stamps.

260. **185.** 1 c. multicoloured .. 15 15
261. – 6 c. indigo, blue & silver 25 35
262. – 7 c. multicoloured .. 30 35
263. – 9 c. multicoloured .. 35 45
264. – 25 c. orange and gold .. 60 1·00
265. – 30 c. plum and silver .. 75 1·25

DESIGNS—As Type **185**. 6 c. 2 mark stamp of German New Guinea, 1900. 7 c. Surcharged registration label of New Guinea, 1914. 46 × 35 mm. 9 c. Papuan 1 s. stamp, 1901. 45 × 38 mm. 25 c. ½ d. stamp of New Guinea, 1925. 30 c. Papuan 10 s. stamp, 1932.

186. Native Carved Heads.

1973. Self-Government.

266. **186.** 7 c. multicoloured .. 30 15
267. 10 c. multicoloured .. 50 65

187. Queen Elizabeth II (from photo by Karsh).

1974. Royal Visit.

268. **187.** 7 c. multicoloured .. 25 15
269. 30 c. multicoloured .. 1·00 1·75

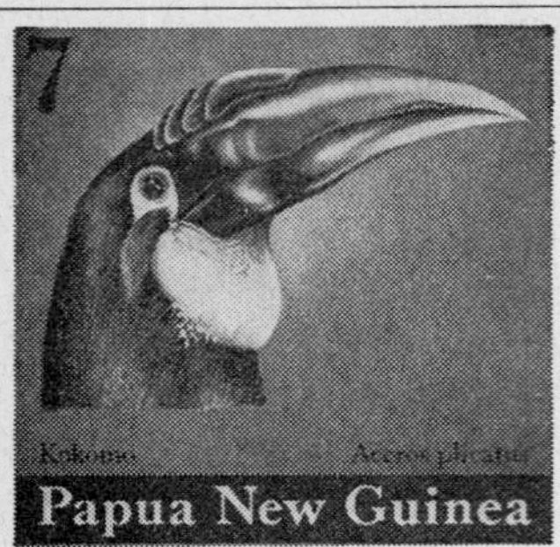

188. Blyth's Hornbill.

1974. Bird's Heads. Multicoloured.

270.	7 c. Type 188	1·50	70
271.	10 c. Double-wattled Cassowary (33 × 49 mm.) ..	2·50	2·75
272.	30 c. New Guinea Harpy Eagle	6·00	7·50

189. "Dendrobium bracteosum".

1974. Flora Conservation. Multicoloured.

273.	7 c. Type 189	50	10
274.	10 c. "D. anosmum" ..	1·00	50
275.	20 c. "D. smillieae" ..	1·40	1·25
276.	30 c. "D. insigne" ..	1·75	1·75

190. Motu Lakatoi.

1974. National Heritage. Canoes. Mult.

277.	7 c. Type 190	30	10
278.	10 c. Tami two-mast morobe	45	60
279.	25 c. Aramia racing canoe	1·10	1·75
280.	30 c. Buka Island canoe ..	1·10	1·25

191. 1-toea Coin.

1975. New Coinage. Multicoloured.

281.	1 t. Type 191	10	10
282.	7 t. New 2 t. and 5 t. coins	40	10
283.	10 t. New 10 t. coin ..	60	30
284.	20 t. New 20 t. coin ..	1·00	80
285.	1 k. New 1 k. coin ..	3·50	4·00

SIZES: 10 t., 20 t. As Type 191. 7 t., 1 k. 45 × 26 mm.

192. "Ornithoptera alexandrae".

193. Boxing.

1975. Fauna Conservation (Birdwing Butterflies). Multicoloured.

286.	7 t. Type 192	50	10
287.	10 t. "O. victoriae regis"	80	65
288.	30 t. "O. allottei" ..	1·75	2·00
289.	40 t. "O. chimaera" ..	2·25	2·75

1975. 5th South Pacific Games, Guam. Multicoloured.

290.	7 t. Type 193	15	10
291.	20 t. Running	25	30
292.	25 t. Basketball	30	45
293.	30 t. Swimming	35	50

194. Map and National Flag.

1975. Independence. Multicoloured.

294.	7 t. Type 194	20	10
295.	30 t. Map and National emblem	40	65

195. M.V. "Bulolo".

1976. Ships of the 1930's. Multicoloured.

297.	7 t. Type 195	30	10
298.	15 t. M.V. "Macdhui" ..	45	30
299.	25 t. M.V. "Malaita" ..	65	65
300.	60 t. S.S. "Montoro" ..	1·75	2·50

196. Rorovana Carvings.

1976. Bougainville Artifacts. Multicoloured.

301.	7 t. Type 196	20	10
302.	20 t. Upe hats	40	75
303.	25 t. Kapkaps	50	85
304.	30 t. Canoe paddles ..	55	90

197. Rabaul House.

1976. Native Dwellings. Multicoloured.

305.	7 t. Type 197	20	10
306.	15 t. Aramia House ..	35	30
307.	30 t. Telefomin house ..	70	75
308.	40 t. Tapini house ..	80	1·00

198. Landscouts.

1976. 50th Anniv. of Survey Flight and Scouting in Papua New Guinea. Multicoloured.

309.	7 t. Type 198	30	10
310.	10 t. D.H. floatplane ..	40	30
311.	15 t. Seascouts	50	65
312.	60 t. Floatplane on water	1·25	2·25

199. Father Ross and New Guinea Highlands.

1976. William Ross Commemoration.

313. 199.	7 t. multicoloured ..	40	15

200. Clouded Rainbow Fish.

1976. Fauna Conservation (Tropical Fish). Multicoloured.

314.	5 t. Type 200	30	10
315.	15 t. Emperor or Imperial Angel Fish	60	45
316.	30 t. Freckled Rock Cod ..	1·10	70
317.	40 t. Threadfin Butterfly Fish	1·40	1·00

201. Man from Kundiawa.

202. Headdress, Wasara Tribe.

1977. Headdresses. Multicoloured.

318.	1 t. Type 201	10	10
319.	5 t. Masked dancer, Abelam area of Maprik ..	10	10
320.	10 t. Headdresses from Koiari	30	15
321.	15 t. Woman with face paint, Hanuabada	30	20
322.	20 t. Orokaiva dancer ..	50	30
323.	25 t. Haus Tambaran dancer, Abelam area of Maprik	40	30
324.	30 t. Asaro Valley headdress	45	35
325.	35 t. Singsing costume, Garaina	70	45
326.	40 t. Waghi Valley headdress	60	35
327.	50 t. Trobriand Island dancer	1·25	60
328.	1 k. Type 202	1·50	1·50
329.	2 k. Headdress, Meko tribe	3·00	3·00

SIZES: 1, 5, 20 t. 25 × 31 mm. 35, 40 t. 23 × 38 mm. 1 k. 28 × 35 mm. 2 k. 33 × 23 mm. Others 26 × 26 mm.

203. National Flag and Queen Elizabeth II.

1977. Silver Jubilee. Multicoloured.

330.	7 t. Type 203	25	10
331.	15 t. The Queen and national emblem	35	35
332.	35 t. The Queen and map of P.N.G.	65	70

204. White-breasted Ground Pigeon.

1977. Fauna Conservation (Birds). Mult.

333.	5 t. Type 204	35	10
334.	7 t. Victoria Crowned Pigeon	35	10
335.	15 t. Pheasant Pigeon ..	65	65
336.	30 t. Orange-fronted Fruit Dove	1·00	1·00
337.	50 t. Banded Imperial Pigeon	1·60	2·00

205. Guides and Gold Badge.

1977. 50th Anniv. of Guiding in Papua New Guinea. Multicoloured.

338.	7 t. Type 205	20	10
339.	15 t. Guides mapping ..	35	20
340.	30 t. Guides washing ..	55	50
341.	35 t. Guides cooking ..	60	60

206. Kari Maruppi Myth.

1977. Folklore. Elema Art (3rd series).

342. 206.	7 t. multicoloured ..	20	10
343. –	20 t. multicoloured ..	45	35
344. –	30 t. red, blue and black	50	75
345. –	35 t. red, yellow & black	50	75

DESIGNS: 20 t. Savoripi clan myth. 30 t. Oa-Laea myth. 35 t. Oa-Iriarapo myth.

207. Blue-tailed Skink.

1978. Fauna Conservation (Skinks). Mult.

346.	10 t. Type 207	30	10
347.	15 t. Green Tree Skink ..	35	20
348.	35 t. Crocodile Skink ..	55	55
349.	40 t. New Guinea Blue-tongued Skink	75	70

208. "Roboastra arika".

1978. Sea Slugs. Multicoloured.

350.	10 t. Type 208	30	10
351.	15 t. "Chromodoris fidelis"	35	30
352.	35 t. "Flabellina macassarana"	70	90
353.	40 t. "Chromodoris trimarginata"	75	1·25

209. Present Day Royal Papua New Guinea Constabulary.

1978. History of Royal Papua New Guinea Constabulary. Uniformed Police and Constabulary Badges. Multicoloured.

354.	10 t. Type 209	30	10
355.	15 t. Mandated New Guinea Constabulary, 1921–1941	40	15
356.	20 t. British New Guinea Armed Constabulary, 1890–1906	45	40
357.	25 t. German New Guinea Police, 1899–1914 ..	50	45
358.	30 t. Royal Papua and New Guinea Constabulary, 1906–1964	60	60

210. Ocarina.

1979. Musical Instruments. Multicoloured.

359.	7 t. Type **210**	15	10
360.	20 t. Musical bow (horiz.)	25	20
361.	28 t. Launut	30	30
362.	35 t. Nose flute (horiz.) ..	40	45

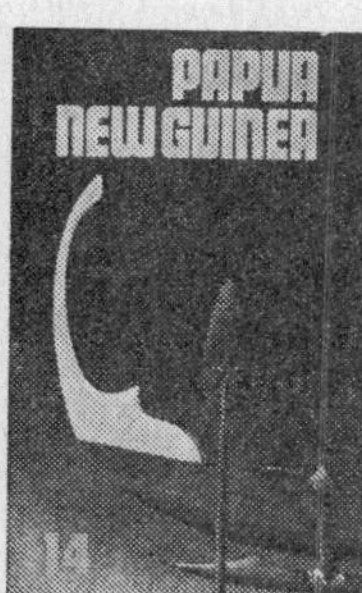

211. East New Britain Canoe Prow.

1979. Traditional Canoe Prows and Paddles. Multicoloured.

363.	14 t. Type **211**	15	15
364.	21 t. Sepik war canoe ..	25	25
365.	25 t. Trobriand Island canoe	25	30
366.	40 t. Milne Bay canoe ..	40	60

212. Katudababila (waist belt).

1979. Traditional Currency. Multicoloured.

367.	7 t. Type **212**	10	10
368.	15 t. Doga (chest ornament)	20	30
369.	25 t. Mwali (armshell) ..	35	55
370.	35 t. Soulava (necklace) ..	45	75

213. "Aenetus cyanochlora".

1979. Fauna Conservation. Moths. Mult.

371	7 t. Type **213**	20	10
372	15 t. "Celerina vulgaris" ..	30	35
373	20 t. "Alcidis aurora" (vert)	40	60
374	25 t. "Phyllodes conspicillator"	45	70
375	30 t. "Lyssa patroclus" (vert)	55	75

214. "The Right to Affection and Love".

1979. International Year of the Child. Multicoloured.

376.	7 t. Type **214**	10	10
377.	15 t. "The right to adequate nutrition and medical care"	15	15
378.	30 t. "The right to play"	20	20
379.	60 t. "The right to a free education"	45	60

215. "Post Office Service".

1980. Admission to U.P.U. (1979). Mult.

380.	7 t. Type **215**	10	10
381.	25 t. "Wartime mail" ..	25	25
382.	35 t. "U.P.U. emblem"	35	40
383.	40 t. "Early postal services"	40	50

216. Betrothal Ceremony, Minj District, Western Highlands Province (detail).

1980. Third South Pacific Festival of Arts.

384. **216.**	20 t. yell., orge. and blk.	25	35
385. –	20 t. multicoloured ..	25	35
386. –	20 t. multicoloured ..	25	35
387. –	20 t. multicoloured ..	25	35
388. –	20 t. multicoloured ..	25	35

DESIGNS: Nos. 385/8, further details of Betrothal Ceremony. Nos. 384/8 were issued together in horizontal se-tenant strips of five within the sheet, forming a composite design.

217. Family being Interviewed.

1980. National Census. Multicoloured.

389.	7 t. Type **217**	10	10
390.	15 t. Population symbol ..	15	15
391.	40 t. Papua New Guinea map	30	40
392.	50 t. Heads symbolising population growth ..	35	50

218. Donating Blood.

1980. Red Cross Blood Bank. Multicoloured.

393.	7 t. Type **218**	15	10
394.	15 t. Receiving transfusion	20	20
395.	30 t. Map of Papua New Guinea showing blood transfusion centres ..	25	25
396.	60 t. Blood and its components	40	60

219. Dugong

1980. Mammals. Multicoloured.

397.	7 t. Type **219**	10	10
398.	30 t. New Guinea Marsupial Cat (vert.) ..	40	40
399.	35 t. Tube-nosed Bat (vert.)	40	40
400.	45 t. Rufescent Bandicoot	50	50

220. White-headed Kingfisher. **221.** Native Mask.

1981. Kingfishers. Multicoloured.

401.	3 t. Type **220**	15	20
402.	7 t. Forest Kingfisher ..	15	10
403.	20 t. Sacred Kingfisher ..	50	50
404.	25 t. White-tailed Kingfisher (26 × 46 mm.) ..	60	85
405.	60 t. Blue-winged Kookaburra	1·40	2·00

1981. Coil Stamps.

406 **221**	2 t. violet and orange	10	20
407 –	5 t. red and green ..	10	20

DESIGN: 5 t. Hibiscus flower.

222. Mortar Team.

1981. Defence Force. Multicoloured.

408.	7 t. Type **222**	15	10
409.	15 t. Aeroplane & aircrew	30	25
410.	40 t. "Aitape" (patrol boat) and seamen ..	70	65
411.	50 t. Medical team examining children	75	75

223. M.A.F. (Missionary Aviation Fellowship) Aeroplane.

1981. "Mission Aviation". Multicoloured.

412.	10 t. Type **223**	20	10
413.	15 t. Catholic mission aeroplane	25	25
414.	20 t. S.I.L. (Summer Institute of Linguistics) helicopter	35	35
415.	30 t. Lutheran mission aeroplane	55	55
416.	35 t. S.D.A. (Seventh Day Adventist Church) aeroplane	65	65

224. Scoop Net Fishing.

1981. Fishing. Multicoloured.

417.	10 t. Type **224**	15	10
418.	15 t. Kite fishing ..	30	30
419.	30 t. Rod fishing ..	50	50
420.	60 t. Scissor net fishing ..	95	85

225. "Forcartia buhleri".

1981. Land Snail Shells. Multicoloured.

421.	5 t. Type **225**	10	10
422.	15 t. "Naninia citrina"	25	25
423.	20 t. "Papuina adonis" and "papuina hermione"	35	35
424.	30 t. "Papustyla hindei" and "papustyla novaepommeraniae" ..	50	50
425.	40 t. "Rhynchotrochus strabo"	70	80

226. Lord Baden-Powell and Flag-raising Ceremony.

1981. 75th Anniv. of Boy Scout Movement. Multicoloured.

426.	15 t. Type **226**	40	25
427.	25 t. Scout leader and camp	60	50
428.	35 t. Scout, and hut building	75	65
429.	50 t. Percy Chaterton and Scouts administering first aid	90	85

227. Yangoru and Boiken Bowls, East Sepik.

1981. Native Pottery. Multicoloured.

430.	10 t. Type **227**	15	10
431.	20 t. Utu cooking pot and small Gumalu pot, Madang	30	30
432.	40 t. Wanigela pots, Northern (37 × 23 mm.) ..	55	55
433.	50 t. Ramu Valley pots, Madang (37 × 23 mm.) ..	70	80

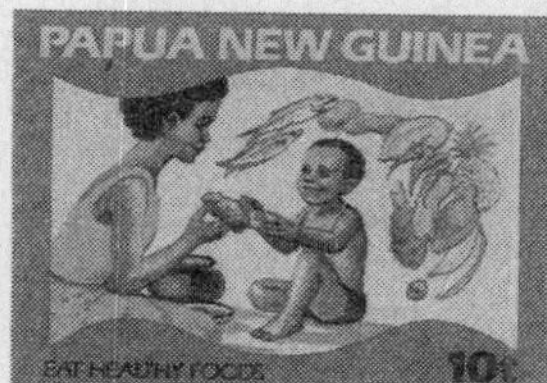

228. "Eat Healthy Foods".

1982. Food and Nutrition. Multicoloured.

434.	10 t. Type **228**	15	10
435.	15 t. Protein foods ..	30	30
436.	30 t. Protective foods ..	55	55
438.	40 t. Energy foods ..	65	70

229. "Stylophora sp.".

1982. Multicoloured.

438.	1 t. Type **229**	10	10
439.	3 t. "Dendrophyllia sp." (vert.)	50	20
440.	5 t. "Acropora humilis" ..	15	10
441.	10 t. "Dendronephthya sp." (vert.)	60	10
442.	12 t. As 10 t.	2·50	1·50
443.	15 t. "Distichopora sp." ..	30	20
444.	20 t. "Isis sp." (vert.) ..	60	25
445.	25 t. "Acropora sp." (vert.)	40	30

446. 30 t. "Dendronephthya sp." (different) (vert.) .. 1·25 60
447. 35 t. "Stylaster elegans" (vert.) 80 50
448. 40 t. "Antipathes sp." (vert.) .. .. .. 1·50 50
449. 45 t. "Turbinarea sp." (vert.) .. .. .. 1·50 60
450. 1 k. "Xenia sp." .. .. 1·25 1·25
451. 3 k. "Distichopora sp." (vert.) .. .. .. 3·75 3·50
452. 5 k. Raggiana Bird of Paradise (33 × 33 mm.). 6·00 6·50

230. Missionaries landing on Beach.

1982. Centenary of Catholic Church in Papua New Guinea. Mural on Wall of Nordup Catholic Church, East New Britain. Mult.
457 10 t. Type **230** 25 20
458 10 t. Missionaries talking to natives 25 20
459 10 t. Natives with slings and spears ready to attack .. 25 20
Nos. 457/9 were issued together, setenant, forming a compsite design.

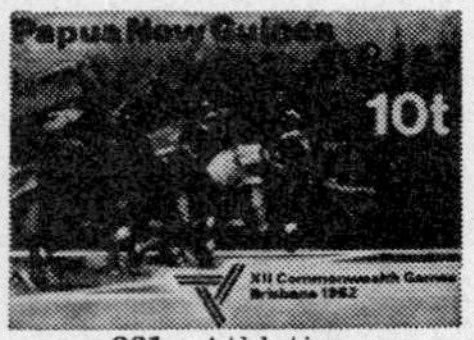

231. Athletics.

1982. Commonwealth Games and "Anpex 82" Stamp Exhibition, Brisbane. Mult.
460. 10 t. Type **231** 15 10
461. 15 t. Boxing 25 25
462. 45 t. Rifle-shooting .. 55 70
463. 50 t. Bowls 65 75

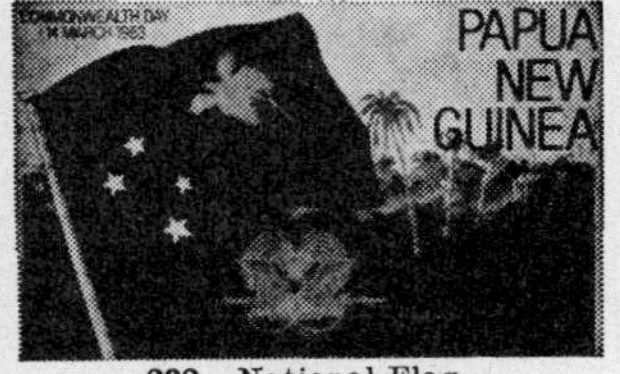

232. National Flag.

1983. Commonwealth Day. Multicoloured.
464. 10 t. Type **232** 15 10
465. 15 t. Basket-weaving and cabbage-picking .. 20 30
466. 20 t. Crane hoisting roll of material 25 35
467. 50 t. Lorries and ships .. 60 75

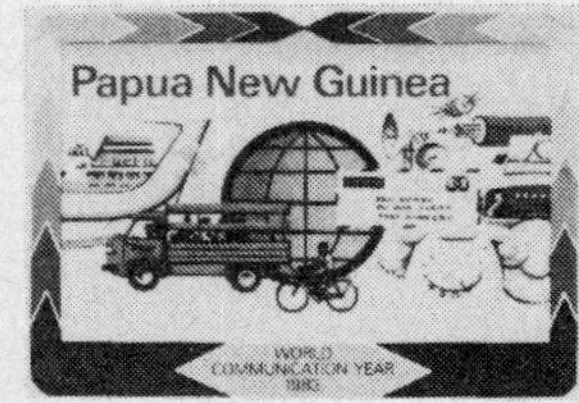

233. Transport Communications.

1983. World Communications Year. Mult.
468. 10 t. Type **233** 30 10
469. 25 t. "Postal service" .. 70 45
470. 30 t. "Telephone service" 80 50
471. 60 t. "Transport service" 1·50 90

234. "Chelonia depressa".

1984. Turtles. Multicoloured.
472. 5 t. Type **234** 20 10
473. 10 t. "Chelonia mydas" 35 10
474. 15 t. "Eretmochelys imbricata" 50 30
475. 20 t. "Lepidochelys olivacea" 65 35
476. 25 t. "Caretta caretta" .. 70 50
477. 40 t. "Dermochelys coriacea" 95 75

235. Avro "X VH-UXX" "Faith in Australia".

1984. 50th Anniv. of First Airmail Australia-Papua New Guinea. Multicoloured.
478. 20 t. Type **235** 40 30
479. 25 t. "DH86B VH-UYU" "Carmania" 50 45
480. 40 t. Westland "Widgeon VH-UGI" 90 80
481. 60 t. Consolidated "Catalina NC777" "Guba" 1·40 1·25

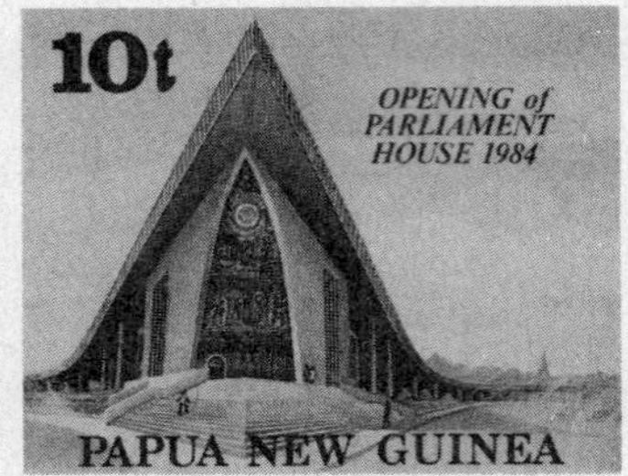

236. Parliament House.

1984. Opening of Parliament House.
482. **236.** 10 t. multicoloured .. 30 30

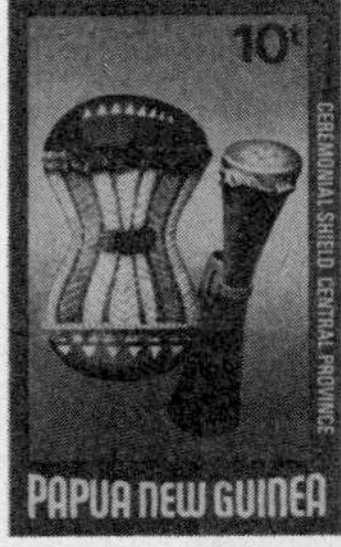

237. Ceremonial Shield and Club, Central Province. **239.** Fergusson Island.

238. H.M.S. "Nelson" at Port Moresby, 1884.

1984. Ceremonial Shields. Multicoloured.
483. 10 t. Type **237** 30 10
484. 20 t. Ceremonial shield, West New Britian .. 50 50
485. 30 t. Ceremonial shield, Madang Province .. 75 90
486. 50 t. Ceremonial shield, East Sepik .. .. 1·25 1·50
See also Nos. 558/61.

1984. Centenary of Protectorate Proclamations for British New Guinea and German New Guinea. Multicoloured.
487. 10 t. Type **238** 35 35
488. 10 t. Papua New Guinea flag and Port Moresby, 1984 .. .. .. 70 70
489. 45 t. Papua New Guinea flag and Rabaul, 1984 .. 1·25 1·50
490. 45 t. "Elisabeth" German warship at Rabaul, 1884 1·25 1·50
Nos. 487/8 and 489/90 were issued in setenant pairs, each pair forming a composite picture.

1985. Tourist Scenes. Multicoloured.
491. 10 t. Type **239** 30 10
492. 25 t. Sepik River 65 55
493. 40 t. Chimbu Gorge (horiz.) 95 80
494. 60 t. Dali Beach, Vanimo (horiz.) .. .. .. 1·40 1·40

1985. No. 408 surch.
495. **222.** 12 t. on 7 t. mult. .. 50 50

241. Dubu Platform, Central Province.

1985. Ceremonial Structures. Multicoloured.
496. 15 t. Type **241** 45 15
497. 20 t. Tamuniai House, West New Britain .. 60 50
498. 30 t. Traditional Yam Tower, Trobriand Island 85 80
499. 60 t. Huli Grave, Tari .. 1·25 1·75

242. Head of New Britain Sparrow Hawk.

1985. Birds of Prey. Multicoloured.
500. 12 t. Type **242** 55 55
501. 12 t. New Britain Sparrow Hawk in flight 55 55
502. 30 t. Doria's Goshawk .. 80 80
503. 30 t. Doria's Goshawk in flight 80 80
504. 60 t. Long-tailed Honey Buzzard .. .. .. 1·50 1·50
505. 60 t. Long-tailed Honey Buzzard in flight .. 1·50 1·50

243. National Flag and Parliament House.

1985. 10th Anniv. of Independence.
506. **243.** 12 t. multicoloured .. 50 40

244. Early Postcard, Aerogramme, Inkwell and Spectacles.

1985. Centenary of Papua New Guinea Post Office. Multicoloured.
507. 12 t. Type **244** 40 10
508. 30 t. Queensland 1897 1d. die with proof and modern press printing stamps 85 70
509. 40 t. Newspaper of 1885 announcing shipping service and loading mail into aircraft .. .. 1·10 85
510. 60 t. Friedrich-Wilhelmshafen postmark of 1892 and Port Moresby F.D.C. postmark of 9 Oct 1985 .. 1·60 1·75

245. Figure with Eagle.

1985. Nombowai Wood Carvings. Mult.
512. 12 t. Type **245** 50 10
513. 30 t. Figure with clam shell 1·25 75
514. 60 t. Figure with dolphin 2·00 2·00
515. 80 t. Figure of woman with cockerel .. .. .. 2·50 2·75

246. "Cypraea valentia".

1986. Seashells. Multicoloured.
516. 15 t. Type **246** 55 15
517. 35 t. "Oliva buelowi" .. 1·25 1·00
518. 45 t. "Oliva parkinsoni" .. 1·50 1·40
519. 70 t. "Cypraea aurantium" 2·00 2·50

1986. 60th Birthday of Queen Elizabeth II. As T **110** of Ascension. Multicoloured.
520. 15 t. Princess Elizabeth in A.T.S. uniform, 1945 .. 20 15
521. 35 t. Silver Wedding Anniversary photograph (by Patrick Lichfield), Balmoral, 1972 .. .. 50 55
522. 50 t. Queen inspecting guard of honour, Port Moresby, 1982 .. .. 70 75
523. 60 t. On board Royal Yacht "Britannia", Papua New Guinea, 1982 85 90
524. 70 t. At Crown Agents' Head Office, London, 1983 .. .. .. 95 1·10

247. Rufous Fantail.

1986. "Ameripex '86" International Stamp Exhibition, Chicago. Small Birds (1st series). Multicoloured.
525. 15 t. Type **247** 70 15
526. 35 t. Streaked berrypecker 1·40 65
527. 45 t. Red-breasted pitta .. 1·50 80
528. 70 t. Olive-yellow robin (vert.) .. .. .. 2·00 2·00
See also Nos. 597/601.

248. Martin Luther nailing Theses to Cathedral Door, Wittenberg, and Modern Lutheran Pastor.

1986. Centenary of Lutheran Church in Papua New Guinea. Multicoloured.
529. 15 t. Type **248** 75 15
530. 70 t. Early church, Finschhafen, and modern Martin Luther Chapel, Lae Seminary .. 2·00 1·50

249. "Dendrobium vexillarius".

1986. Orchids. Multicoloured.
531. 15 t. Type **249** 75 15
532. 35 t. "Dendrobium lineale" 1·40 75
533. 45 t. "Dendrobium johnsoniae" .. .. 1·50 1·10
534. 70 t. "Dendrobium cuthbertsonii" .. .. 2·40 1·75

250. Maprik Dancer.

1986. Papua New Guinea Dancers. Mult.
535. 15 t. Type **250** 65 15
536. 35 t. Kiriwina .. .. 1·40 75
537. 45 t. Kundiawa .. .. 1·50 95
538. 70 t. Fasu .. .. .. 2·40 2·25

251. White Cap Anemonefish.

1987. Anemonefish. Multicoloured.
539. 17 t. Type **251** 70 25
540. 30 t. Black anemonefish .. 1·40 80
541. 35 t. Tomato clownfish .. 1·50 90
542. 70 t. Spine cheek anemonefish .. .. .. 2·50 2·50

252. "Roebuck" (Dampier), 1700.

1987. Ships. Multicoloured.
543. 1 t. "Boudeuse" (De Bougainville, 1768 .. 10 10
544. 5 t. Type **252** 10 10
545. 10 t. H.M.S. "Swallow" (Philip Carteret), 1767 .. 10 15
546. 15 t. H.M.S. "Fly" (Blackwood), 1845 .. 20 25
547. 17 t. As No. 54b 20 25
548. 20 t. H.M.S. "Rattlesnake" (Owen Stanley), 1849 .. 25 30
549. 30 t. "Vitiaz" (Maday), 1871 .. .. .. 35 40
550. 35 t. "San Pedrico" (Torres) and zabra, 1606 45 50
551. 40 t. "L'Astrolabe" (d'Urville), 1872 .. .. 50 55
552. 45 t. "Neva" (D'Albertis), 1876 .. .. .. 55 60
553. 60 t. Spanish galleon (Jorge de Meneses), 1526 65 70
554. 70 t. "Eendracht" (Schouten and Le Maire), 1616 .. .. 85 90
555. 1 k. H.M.S. "Blanche" (Simpson), 1872 .. .. 1·25 1·40
556. 2 k. "Merrie England" (steamer), 1889 .. .. 2·50 2·75
557. 3 k. "Samo" (German colonial steamer), 1884 3·75 4·00

1987. War Shields. As T **237**. Multicoloured.
558. 15 t. Gulf Province 20 25
559. 35 t. East Sepik 45 50
560. 45 t. Madang Province .. 55 60
561. 70 t. Telefomin 85 90

1987. No. 442. surch. **15 t.**
562. 15 t. on 12 t. "Dendronephthya sp." (vert.) .. 40 40

254. "Prototeaster nodosus".

1987. Starfish. Multicoloured.
563. 17 t. Type **254** 35 25
564. 35 t. "Gomophia egeriae" 65 50
565. 45 t. "Choriaster granulatus" 75 70
566. 70 t. "Neoferdina ocellata" 1·25 1·00

255. Cessna "Stationair 6" taking off, Rabaraba.

1987. Aircraft in Papua New Guinea. Multicoloured.
567. 15 t. Type **255** 50 25
568. 35 t. Britten-Norman "Islander" over Hombrum Bluff .. 90 60
569. 45 t. DHC "Twin Otter" Over Highlands.. .. 1·10 80
570. 70 t. Fokker "F28" over Madang .. .. .. 1·90 1·40

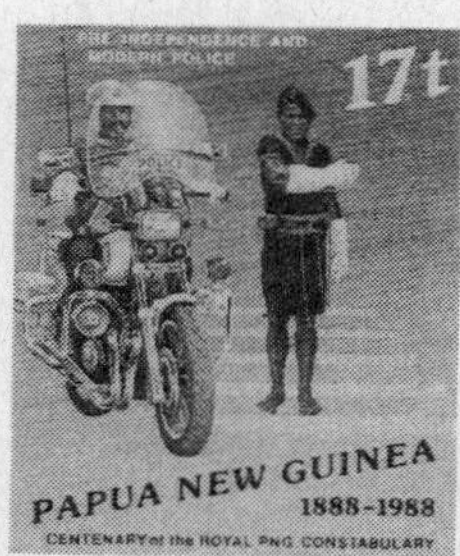

256 Pre-Independence Policeman on Traffic Duty and Present-day Motorcycle Patrol

1988. Centenary of Royal Papua New Guinea Constabulary. Multicoloured.
571 17 t. Type **256** 30 25
572 35 t. British New Guinea Armed Constabulary, 1890, and Governor W. MacGregor 60 50
573 45 t. Police badges .. 75 65
574 70 t. German New Guinea Police, 1888, and Dr. A. Hahl (founder) .. 1·25 1·50

257 Lagatoi (canoe) and Sydney Opera House (Illustration reduced, actual size 53 × 26mm)

1988. "Sydpex '88" National Stamp Exhibition, Sydney.
575 **257** 35 t. multicoloured .. 70 50

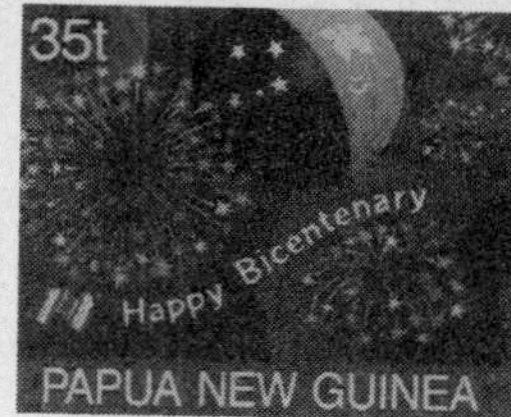

258 Papua New Guinea Flag on Globe and Fireworks

1988. Bicentenary of Australian Settlement. Multicoloured.
576 35 t. Type **258** 55 65
577 35 t. Australian flag on globe and fireworks .. 55 65
Nos. 576/7 were printed together, se-tenant, forming a composite design.

259 Male and Female Butterflies in Courtship

1988. "Ornithoptera alexandrae" (butterfly). Multicoloured.
579 5 t. Type **259** 30 10
580 17 t. Female laying eggs and mature larva (vert) 65 25
581 25 t. Male emerging from pupa (vert) 85 55
582 35 t. Male feeding .. 1·00 85

260 Athletics

1988. Olympic Games, Seoul. Multicoloured.
583 17 t. Type **260** 20 25
584 45 t. Weightlifting .. 60 65

261 "Rhododendron zoelleri"

1989. Rhododendrons. Multicoloured.
585 3 t. Type **261** 10 10
586 20 t. "Rhododendron cruttwellii" .. 35 30
587 60 t. "Rhododendron superbum" .. 1·00 1·00
588 70 t. "Rhododendron christianae" .. .. 1·10 1·10

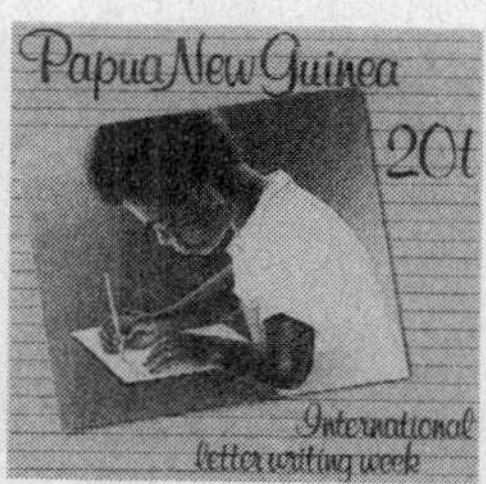

263 Writing Letter

1989. International Letter Writing Week. Multicoloured.
589 20 t. Type **263** 30 30
590 35 t. Stamping letter .. 55 50
591 60 t. Posting letter .. 90 1·10
592 70 t. Reading letter .. 1·10 1·40

264 Village House, Buka Island, North Solomons

1989. Traditional Dwellings. Multicoloured.
593 20 t. Type **264** 35 35
594 35 t. Tree house, Koiari, Central Province .. 60 60
595 60 t. Longhouse, Lauan, New Ireland .. .. 1·00 1·25
596 70 t. Decorated house, Basilaki, Milne Bay .. 1·25 1·50

265 Tit Berrypecker (female)

1989. Small Birds (2nd issue). Multicoloured.
597 20 t. Type **265** 70 55
598 20 t. Tit berrypecker (male) 70 55
599 35 t. Blue-capped babbler 90 75
600 45 t. Black-throated robin 1·10 1·00
601 70 t. Large mountain sericornis .. .. 1·60 1·60

1989. No. 539 surch **20 t.**
602 20 t. on 17 t. Type **251** .. 60 60

266 Motu Motu Dancer, Gulf Province

1989. Traditional Dancers. Multicoloured.
603 20 t. Type **266** 50 35
604 35 t. Baining, East New Britain 85 85
605 60 t. Vailala River, Gulf Province .. .. 1·50 1·75
606 70 t. Timbunke, East Sepik Province .. .. 1·75 2·00

267 Hibiscus, People going to Church and Gope Board

1989. Christmas. Designs showing flowers and carved panels. Multicoloured.
607 20 t. Type **267** 40 35
608 35 t. Rhododendron, Virgin and Child and mask .. 60 60
609 60 t. D'Albertis creeper, Christmas candle and warshield .. .. 1·25 1·50
610 70 t. Pacific frangipani, peace dove and flute mask .. .. .. 1·40 1·75

268 Guni Falls

1990. Waterfalls. Multicoloured.

611	20 t. Type **268**	50	35
612	35 t. Rouna Falls	75	75
613	60 t. Ambua Falls ..	1·25	1·50
614	70 t. Wawoi Falls ..	1·50	1·75

269 Boys and Census Form

1990. National Census. Multicoloured.

615	20 t. Type **269**	40	30
616	70 t. Family and census form	1·50	1·60

270 Gwa Pupi Dance Mask

1990. Gogodala Dance Masks. Multicoloured.

617	20 t. Type **270**	50	30
618	35 t. Tauga paiyale	80	60
619	60 t. A: ga	1·40	1·50
620	70 t. Owala	1·75	2·00

271 Sepik and Maori Kororu Masks

1990. "New Zealand 1990" International Stamp Exhibition, Auckland.

621	**271**	35 t. multicoloured ..	75	75

272 Dwarf Cassowary and Great Spotted Kiwi

1990. 150th Anniv of Treaty of Waitangi. Multicoloured.

622	20 t. Type **272**	70	40
623	35 t. Double-wattled cassowary and Brown kiwi	1·10	1·25

273 Whimbrel

1990. Migratory Birds. Multicoloured.

624	20 t. Type **273**	55	30
625	35 t. Sharp-tailed sandpiper	85	70
626	60 t. Turnstone ..	1·50	1·60
627	70 t. Terek sandpiper ..	1·75	1·90

274 Jew's Harp

1990. Musical Instruments. Multicoloured.

628	20 t. Type **274**	35	30
629	35 t. Musical bow ..	60	50
630	60 t. Wantoat drum ..	1·00	1·10
631	70 t. Gogodala rattle ..	1·10	1·25

275 "Rhynchotrochus weigmani"

1991. Land Shells. Multicoloured.

632	21 t. Type **275**	35	30
633	40 t. "Forcartia globula" and "Canefriula azonata" ..	60	50
634	50 t. "Planispira deaniana"	90	70
635	80 t. "Papuina chancel" and "Papuina xanthocheila" ..	1·25	1·50

276 Lesser Bird of Paradise

1991. Birds of Paradise. Multicoloured.

642	21 t. Crinkle collared manucode (26½ × 32 mm)	25	30
643	45 t. King bird of paradise (26½ × 32 mm) ..	55	60
644	60 t. Queen Carola's parotia (26½ × 32 mm) ..	65	70
645	90 t. Emperor of Germany bird of paradise (26½ × 32 mm) ..	1·10	1·25
650	10 k. Type **276**	12·00	13·00

277 Cricket

1991. 9th South Pacific Games. Multicoloured.

651	21 t. Type **277**	40	30
652	40 t. Athletics	75	60
653	50 t. Baseball	85	70
654	80 t. Rugby Union ..	1·50	1·60

278 Cathedral of St. Peter and St. Paul, Dogura

1991. Cent of Anglican Church in Papua New Guinea. Multicoloured.

655	21 t. Type **278**	35	30
656	40 t. Missionaries landing, 1891, and Kaieta shrine	70	70
657	80 t. First church and Modawa tree	1·40	1·50

279 Rambusto Headdress, Manus Province

1991. Tribal Headdresses. Multicoloured.

658	21 t. Type **279**	35	30
659	40 t. Marawaka, Eastern Highlands	70	70
660	50 t. Tufi, Oro Province ..	80	80
661	80 t. Sina Sina, Simbu Province	1·40	1·50

POSTAGE DUE STAMPS

1960. Stamps of 1952 surch. **POSTAL CHARGES** and value.

D 2.	1d. on 6½d. purple ..	14·00	5·50
D 3.	3d. on ½d. green ..	16·00	5·50
D 1.	6d. on 7½d. blue (A) ..	£700	£375
D 4.	6d. on 7½d. blue (B) ..	30·00	13·00
D 5.	1s. 3d. on 3½d. black ..	24·00	13·00
D 6.	3s. on 2½d. orange.. ..	40·00	26·00

In (A) value and "POSTAGE" is obliterated by a solid circle and a series of "IX's" but these are omitted in (B).

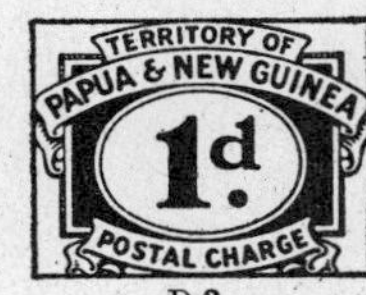

D 3.

1960.

D 7.	D 3.	1d. orange	55	35
D 8.		3d. brown	70	45
D 9.		6d. blue	75	40
D 10.		9d. red	75	1·40
D 11.		1s. green	75	50
D 12.		1s. 3d. violet ..	1·40	1·40
D 13.		1s. 6d. pale blue ..	5·50	5·00
D 14.		3s. yellow	6·00	1·00

PATIALA

A "convention" state in the Punjab, India.

12 pies = 1 anna; 16 annas = 1 rupee.

1884. Stamps of India (Queen Victoria) with curved opt. **PUTTIALLA STATE** vert.

1.	**23.**	½ a. turquoise	80	70
2.	–	1 a. purple	22·00	18·00
3.	–	2 a. blue	5·00	5·00
4.	–	4 a. green (No. 96) ..	20·00	22·00
5.	–	8 a. mauve	£150	£350
6.	–	1 r. grey (No. 101) ..	75·00	£160

1885. Stamps of India (Queen Victoria) optd. **PUTTIALLA STATE** horiz.

7.	**23.**	½ a. turquoise	30	20
11.	–	1 a. purple	15	15
8.	–	2 a. blue	95	35
9.	–	4 a. green (No. 96) ..	1·00	1·10
12.	–	8 a. mauve	7·50	13·00
10.	–	1 r. grey (No. 101) ..	4·75	23·00

Stamps of India optd. **PATIALA STATE.**

1891. Queen Victoria.

32.	**40.**	3 p. red	10	10
13.	**23.**	½ a. turquoise (No. 84)..	10	10
33.		½ a. green (No. 114) ..	20	15
14.	–	9 p. red	25	60
15.	–	1 a. purple	30	15
34.	–	1 a. red	35	20
17.	–	1½ a. brown	30	45
18.	–	2 a. blue	40	20
20.	–	3 a. orange	40	35
22.	–	4 a. green (No. 96) ..	40	40
23.	–	6 a. brown (No. 80) ..	40	2·00
26.	–	8 a. mauve	65	2·50
27.	–	12 a. purple on red ..	65	3·00
28.	**37.**	1 r. green and red ..	3·50	11·00
29.	**38.**	2 r. red and orange ..	80·00	£225
30.		3 r. brown and green ..	95·00	£250
31.		5 r. blue and violet ..	£110	£275

1903. King Edward VII.

36.	3 p. grey	10	10
37.	½ a. green (No. 122) ..	30	10
38.	1 a. red (No. 123) ..	10	10
39.	2 a. lilac	30	30
40.	3 a. orange	30	20
41.	4 a. olive..	1·10	60
42.	6 a. bistre	70	2·25
43.	8 a. mauve	1·50	90
44.	12 a. purple on red ..	1·75	4·50
45.	1 r. green and red ..	1·25	1·75

1912. King Edward VII inscr. "INDIA POSTAGE & REVENUE".

46.	½ a. green (No. 149) ..	10	10
47.	1 a. red (No. 150) ..	25	25

1912. King George V. Optd. in two lines.

48	**55.**	3 p. grey	10	10
49	**56.**	½ a. green	15	10
50	**57.**	1 a. red	20	10
61		1 a. brown	30	10
51	**58.**	1½ a. brown (A).. ..	30	50
52	**59.**	2 a. lilac	[illegible]	20
53	**62.**	3 a. orange	45	60
62		3 a. blue	[illegible]	1·75
54	**63.**	4 a. olive..	70	[illegible]
55a	**64.**	6 a. bistre	60	1·25
56	**65.**	8 a. mauve	65	65
57	**66.**	12 a. red	85	2·50
58	**67.**	1 r. brown and green ..	2·50	4·25
59		2 r. red and orange ..	6·00	38·00
60		5 r. blue and violet ..	16·00	40·00

1928. King George V. Optd. in one line.

63.	**55.**	3 p. grey	35	10
64.	**56.**	½ a. green	15	10
75.	**79.**	½ a. green	20	10
65.	**80.**	9 p. green	20	20
66.	**57.**	1 a. brown	20	15
76.	**81.**	1 a. brown	20	10
67.	**82.**	1¼ a. mauve	50	15
77.	**59.**	2 a. red	15	20
68.	**70.**	2 a. lilac	20	20
69.	**61.**	2½ a. orange	60	1·00
70.	**62.**	3 a. blue	40	75
78.		3 a. red	1·25	1·50
71.	**71.**	4 a. green	75	65
79.	**63.**	4 a. olive..	40	85
72.	**65.**	8 a. mauve	1·50	1·40
73.	**66.**	1 r. brown and green ..	1·75	2·75
74.		2 r. red and orange ..	3·25	17·00

1937. King George VI. Optd. in one line.

80.	**91.**	3 p. grey	23·00	30
81.		½ a. brown	3·75	20
82.		9 p. green	1·60	40
83.		1 a. red	60	20
84.	**92.**	2 a. red	1·00	2·75
85.	–	2½ a. violet	1·40	6·00
86.	–	3 a. green	1·40	3·00
87.	–	3½ a. blue	1·75	8·50
88.	–	4 a. brown	6·00	6·00
89.	–	6 a. green	9·50	13·00
90.	–	8 a. violet	9·50	13·00
91.	–	12 a. red	9·50	17·00
92.	**93.**	1 r. grey and brown ..	15·00	22·00
93.		2 r. purple and brown ..	20·00	45·00
94.		5 r. green and blue ..	32·00	75·00
95.		10 r. purple and red ..	55·00	£140
96.		15 r. brown and green ..	95·00	£225
97.		25 r. grey and purple ..	£140	£300

1943. King George VI. Optd. **PATIALA** only. (a) Issue of 1938.

98.	**94.**	3 p. grey	7·50	50
99.		½ a. brown	7·50	20
100.		9 p. green	75·00	2·50
101.		1 a. red	15·00	20
102.	**93.**	1 r. grey and brown ..	7·00	25·00

(b) Issue of 1940.

103. 92. 3 p. grey 60 15
104. ½ a. mauve 60 15
105. 9 p. green 60 15
106. 1 a. red 40 10
107. 101. 1 a. 3 p. bistre .. .. 1·40 1·00
108. 1½ a. violet .. .. 2·00 45
109. 2 a. red .. .. .. 2·50 20
110. 3 a. violet .. .. 1·75 70
111. 3½ a. blue .. .. 6·50 11·00
112. 102. 4 a. brown .. .. 1·75 7·00
113. 6 a. green .. .. 1·75 7·00
114. 8 a. violet .. .. 2·25 4·50
115. 12 a. purple .. .. 4·75 13·00

OFFICIAL STAMPS

Overprinted **SERVICE.**

1884. Nos. 1 to 3 (Queen Victoria).
O 1. 23. ½ a. turquoise .. .. 4·25 15
O 2. – 1 a. purple 30 10
O 3. – 2 a. blue .. .. £1800 50·00

1885. Nos. 7, 11 and 8 (Queen Victoria).
O 4 23. ½ a. turquoise 20 10
O 5 – 1 a. purple 30 10
O 7 – 2 a. blue 15 10

1891. Nos. 13 to 28 and No. 10 Q.V.
O 8. 23. ½ a. turquoise (No. 13) 10 10
O 9. – 1 a. purple .. .. 1·50 10
O 20. – 1 a. red 10 10
O 10. – 2 a. blue .. .. 1·50 60
O 12. – 3 a. orange 20 70
O 13a. – 4 a. green 20 15
O 15. – 6 a. brown 60 35
O 16a. – 8 a. mauve 45 55
O 18. – 12 a. purple on red .. 45 50
O 19. – 1 r. grey 55 55
O 21. 37. 1 r. green and red .. 5·00 9·00

1903. Nos. 36 to 45 (King Edward VII).
O22 3 p. grey 10 10
O24 ½ a. green 10 10
O25 1 a. red 10 10
O26a 2 a. lilac 15 10
O28 3 a. brown .. .. .. 1·25 1·50
O29 4 a. olive 30 20
O30 8 a. mauve 45 50
O32 1 r. green and red .. 70 70

1907. Nos. 46/7 (King Edward VII) inscr. "INDIA POSTAGE & REVENUE".
O 33. ½ a. green 10 10
O 34. 1 a. red 10 10

1913. Official stamps of India (King George V) optd. **PATIALA STATE** in two lines.
O 35. 55. 3 p. grey 10 10
O 36. 56. ½ a. green 10 10
O 37. 57. 1 a. red 10 10
O 38. 1 a. brown .. .. 1·90 45
O 39. 59. 2 a. mauve 30 15
O 40. 63. 4 a. olive 20 30
O 41. 64. 6 a. bistre .. .. 45 1·75
O 42. 65. 8 a. purple 35 40
O 43. 67. 1 r. brown & green .. 1·00 1·40
O 44. 2 r. red and brown .. 4·50 17·00
O 45. 5 r. blue and violet 8·00 17·00

1927. Postage stamps of India (King George V) optd. **PATIALA STATE SERVICE** in two lines.
O 47 55. 3 p. grey 10 10
O 48 56. ½ a. green 15 30
O 58 79. ½ a. green 10 10
O 49 57. 1 a. brown 10 10
O 59 81. 1 a. brown 10 20
O 50 82. 1¼ a. mauve 10 10
O 51 70. 2 a. purple 15 25
O 52 2 a. red 30 30
O 60 59. 2 a. red 15 15
O 53 61. 2½ a. orange 30 30
O 54 71. 4 a. green 30 30
O 62 63. 4 a. olive 30 20
O 55 65. 8 a. purple 50 55
O 56 66. 1 r. brown & green 1·60 1·10
O 57 2 r. red and orange 3·25 14·00

1938. Postage stamps of India (King George VI) optd. **PATIALA STATE SERVICE.**
O 63. 91. ½ a. brown .. .. 1·00 20
O 64. 9 p. green .. .. 13·00 42·00
O 65. 1 a. red .. .. 1·00 20
O 66. 93. 1 r. grey and brown 2·00 3·50
O 67. 2 r. purple & brown 8·00 5·00
O 68. 5 r. green and blue 20·00 40·00

1939. Surch. **1 A SERVICE 1 A.**
O 70. 82. 1 a. on 1¼ a. mauve .. 1·50 1·40

1940. Official stamps of India optd. **PATIALA.**
O 71. O 20. 3 p. grey 30 10
O 72. ½ a. brown .. .. 1·25 10
O 73. ½ a. purple 30 10
O 74. 9 p. green 30 15
O 75. 1 a. red 40 10
O 76. 1 a. 3 p. bistre .. 60 25
O 77. 1½ a. violet .. .. 1·00 15
O 78. 2 a. orange .. .. 2·50 15
O 79. 2½ a. violet 50 60
O 80. 4 a. brown 60 40
O 81. 8 a. violet .. .. 1·10 2·25

1940. Postage stamps of India (King George VI) optd. **PATIALA SERVICE.**
O 82. 93. 1 r. slate and brown .. 7·50 4·00
O 83. 2 r. purple and brown 13·00 25·00
O 84. 5 r. green and blue .. 20·00 42·00

PENANG

A British Settlement which became a state of the Federation of Malaya, incorporated in Malaysia in 1963.

100 cents = 1 dollar (Straits or Malayan).

1948. Silver Wedding. As T **10/11** of Aden.
1. 10 c. violet 25 15
2. $5 brown .. .. .. 24·00 24·00

1949. As T **58** of Straits Settlements.
3. 1 c. black 10 10
4. 2 c. orange 10 10
5. 3 c. green 10 15
6. 4 c. brown 10 10
7. 5 c. purple 40 80
8. 6 c. grey 15 10
9. 8 c. red .. .. .. 30 2·25
10. 8 c. green .. .. .. 65 1·00
11. 10 c. mauve 15 10
12. 12 c. red .. .. .. 65 2·25
13. 15 c. blue 20 30
14. 20 c. black and green .. 20 1·00
15. 20 c. blue 55 15
16. 25 c. purple and orange .. 30 10
17. 35 c. red and purple .. 60 70
18. 40 c. red and purple .. 55 4·75
19. 50 c. black and blue .. 40 15
20. $1 blue and purple .. 3·50 30
21. $2 green and red .. .. 6·00 60
22. $5 green and brown .. 27·00 80

1949. U.P.U. As T **20/23** of Antigua.
23. 10 c. purple 15 10
24. 15 c. blue 35 40
25. 25 c. orange 35 50
26. 50 c. black .. .. .. 1·00 1·40

1953. Coronation. As T **13** of Aden.
27 10 c. black and purple .. 30 10

1954. As T **1** of Malacca but inscr. "PENANG".
28. 1 c. black 10 30
29. 2 c. orange 30 30
30. 4 c. brown 15 10
31. 5 c. mauve 85 60
32. 6 c. grey 15 10
33. 8 c. green .. .. .. 20 1·75
34. 10 c. purple 15 10
35. 12 c. red .. .. .. 30 1·75
36. 20 c. blue 30 10
37. 25 c. purple and orange .. 30 10
38. 30 c. red and purple .. 20 10
39. 35 c. red and purple .. 30 15
40. 50 c. black and blue .. 30 10
41. $1 blue and purple .. 2·00 10
42. $2 green and red .. .. 4·50 2·50
43. $5 green and brown .. 19·00 3·00

1957. As Nos. 92/102 of Kedah but inset portrait of Queen Elizabeth II.
44. 1 c. black 10 20
45. 2 c. red 10 30
46. 4 c. sepia 10 10
47. 5 c. lake 10 10
48. 8 c. green 80 50
49. 10 c. brown 15 10
50. 20 c. blue 20 30
51. 50 c. black and blue .. 25 10
52. $1 blue and purple .. 2·25 25
53. $2 green and red .. .. 3·50 4·00
54. $5 brown and green .. 7·50 4·00

1. Copra.

1960. As Nos. 44/54 but with inset Arms of Penang as in T **1**.
55. 1 c. black 10 15
56. 2 c. red 10 20
57. 4 c. brown 10 10
58. 5 c. lake 10 10
59. 8 c. green .. .. .. 1·00 1·25
60. 10 c. purple 15 10
61. 20 c. blue 20 10
62. 50 c. black and blue .. 20 10
63. $1 blue and purple .. 1·25 10
64. $2 green and red .. .. 2·25 1·25
65. $5 brown and green .. 6·50 2·50

2. "Vanda hookeriana".

1965. As Nos. 115/21 of Kedah but with Arms of Penang inset and inscr. "PULAU PINANG as in T **2**.
66. 2. 1 c. multicoloured .. 10 30
67. – 2 c. multicoloured .. 10 30
68. – 5 c. multicoloured .. 20 10
69. – 6 c. multicoloured .. 20 20
70. – 10 c. multicoloured .. 15 10
71. – 15 c. multicoloured .. 90 10
72. – 20 c. multicoloured .. 1·40 20

The higher values used in Penang were Nos. 20/7 of Malaysia (National Issues).

3. "Valeria valeria".

1971. Butterflies. As Nos. 124/30 of Kedah but with Arms of Penang inset and inscr. "pulau pinang" as in T **3**.
75. – 1 c. multicoloured .. 15 30
76. – 2 c. multicoloured .. 40 30
77. – 5 c. multicoloured .. 55 10
78. – 6 c. multicoloured .. 55 20
79. – 10 c. multicoloured .. 55 10
80. – 15 c. multicoloured .. 55 10
81. 3. 20 c. multicoloured .. 65 30

The higher values in use with this issue were Nos. 64/71 of Malaysia (National Issues).

4. "Etlingera elatior" (inscr "Phaeomeria speciosa").

1979. Flowers. As Nos. 135/41 of Kedah but with Arms of Penang and inscr. "pulau pinang" as in T **4**.
86. 1 c. "Rafflesia hasseltii" .. 10 10
87. 2 c. "Pterocarpus indicus" 10 10
88. 5 c. "Lagerstroemia speciosa" 10 10
89. 10 c. "Durio zibethinus" .. 10 10
90. 15 c. "Hibiscus rosa-sinensis" 15 10
91. 20 c. "Rhododendron scortechinii" 15 10
92. 25 c. Type **4** 15 10

5. Cocoa.

1986. As Nos. 152/8 of Kedah but with Arms of Penang and inscr. "PULAU PINANG" as in T **5**.
100. 1 c. Coffee 10 10
101. 2 c. Coconuts 10 10
102. 5 c. Type **5** 10 10
103. 10 c. Black pepper .. 10 10
104. 15 c. Rubber 10 10
105. 20 c. Oil palm 10 10
106. 30 c. Rice 10 15

PENRHYN ISLAND

One of the Cook Is. in the S. Pacific. A dependency of New Zealand. Used Cook Is. stamps until 1973 when further issues for use in the Northern group of the Cook Is. issues appeared.

A. NEW ZEALAND DEPENDENCY.

1902. Stamps of New Zealand (Pictorials) surch. **PENRHYN ISLAND** and value in native language.
4 23. ½d. green .. .. 80 3·50
10 40. 1d. red .. .. 90 2·75
1 26. 2½d. blue (No. 253) .. 1·50 3·75
14 28. 3d. brown .. .. 9·00 16·00
15 31. 6d. red .. .. 15·00 28·00
17 34. 1s. orange .. .. 45·00 48·00

1914. Stamps of New Zealand (King Edward VII) surch **PENRHYN ISLAND** and value in native language.
20 51 ½d. green .. .. 70 4·00
22 6d. red .. .. 27·00 60·00
23 1s. orange .. .. 45·00 80·00

1917. Stamps of New Zealand (King George V) optd. **PENRHYN ISLAND.**
28 62 ½d. green .. .. 65 1·25
29 1½d. grey .. .. 5·00 8·50
30 1½d. brown .. .. 60 7·50
24 2½d. blue .. .. 1·50 4·00
31 3d. brown .. .. 3·00 10·00
26 6d. red .. .. 5·00 14·00
27 1s. orange .. .. 12·00 27·00

1920. Pictorial types as Cook Islands (1920), but inscr. "PENRHYN".
32 9 ½d. black and green .. 1·00 5·50
33 – 1d. black and red .. 1·25 5·50
34 – 1½d. black and violet .. 6·50 11·00
40 – 2½d. brown and black .. 1·75 13·00
35 – 3d. black and red .. 2·25 5·00
36 – 6d. brown and red .. 3·25 17·00
37 – 1s. black and blue .. 9·00 17·00

B. PART OF COOK ISLANDS.

1973. Nos. 228/9, 231, 233/6, 239/40 and 243/5 of Cook Is. optd. **PENRHYN NORTHERN** or **PENRHYN** ($1).
41. 1 c. multicoloured .. 10 10
42. 2 c. multicoloured .. 10 10
43. 3 c. multicoloured .. 20 10
44. 4 c. multicoloured .. 10 10
45. 5 c. multicoloured .. 10 10
46. 6 c. multicoloured .. 20 30
47. 8 c. multicoloured .. 30 40
48. 15 c. multicoloured .. 45 50
49. 20 c. multicoloured .. 1·50 80
50. 50 c. multicoloured .. 1·75 1·75
51. $1 multicoloured .. 2·50 2·25
52. $2 multicoloured .. 2·50 2·50

1973. Nos. 450/2 of Cook Is. optd. with **PENRHYN NORTHERN.**
53. 138. 25 c. multicoloured .. 85 20
54. – 30 c. multicoloured .. 85 20
55. – 50 c. multicoloured .. 85 20

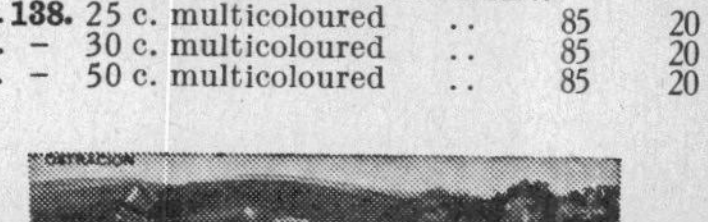

10. "Ostracion sp".

1974. Fishes. Multicoloured.
56. ½ c. Type **10** 50 40
57. 1 c. "Monodactylus argenteus" 70 40
58. 2 c. "Pomacanthus imperatar" 80 40
59. 3 c. "Chelmon rostratus" .. 80 40
60. 4 c. "Chaetodon ornatissimus" 80 40
61. 5 c. "Chaetodon melanotus" 80 40
62. 8 c. "Chaetodon raffessi" .. 80 40
63. 10 c. "Chaetodon ephippium" 85 40
64. 20 c. "Pygoplites diacanthus" 1·75 45
65. 25 c. "Heniochus acuminatus" 1·75 45
66. 60 c. "Plectorhynchus chaetodonoides" .. .. 2·50 90
67. $1 "Belistipus undulatus" 2·75 1·25
68. $2 Bird's-eye view of Penrhyn .. .. 6·00 8·50
69. $5 Satellite view of Australasia .. .. 6·50 6·00

Nos. 68/9 are size 63 × 25 mm.

11. Penrhyn Stamps of 1902.

1974. Centenary of Universal Postal Union. Multicoloured.
70. 25 c. Type **11** 20 20
71. 50 c. Stamps of 1920 .. 35 35

12. " Adoration of the Kings " (Memling).

1974. Christmas. Multicoloured.

72.	5 c. Type **12**	20	10
73.	10 c. "Adoration of the Shepherds" (Hugo van der Goes)	25	10
74.	25 c. "Adoration of the Magi" (Rubens)	40	15
75.	30 c. "The Holy Family" (Borianni)	50	25

13. Churchill giving "V" Sign.

1974. Birth Cent. of Sir Winston Churchill.

76. **13.**	30 c. brown and gold ..	90	70
77. –	50 c. green and gold ..	1·10	80

DESIGN: 50 c. Full-face portrait.

1975. " Apollo-Soyuz " Space Project. **Optd. KIA ORANA ASTRONAUTS and emblem.**

78.	$5 Satellite view of Australasia	3·50	4·50

15. " Virgin and Child " (Bouts).

1975. Christmas. Paintings of the "Virgin and Child" by artists given below. Mult.

79.	7 c. Type **15**	30	10
80.	15 c. Leonardo da Vinci ..	60	20
81.	35 c. Raphael	95	35

16. " Pieta ".

1976. Easter. 500th Birth Anniversary of Michelangelo.

82. **16.**	15 c. brown and gold ..	25	15
83. –	20 c. lilac and gold ..	30	20
84. –	35 c. green and gold ..	40	45

DESIGNS: Nos. 83/4 show different **views of** the " Pieta ".

17. " Washington crossing the Delaware " (E. Leutze).

1976. Bicent. of American Revolution.

86.	30 c.	Type 17	50	15
87.	30 c.		50	15
88.	30 c.		50	15
89.	50 c.	" The Spirit of '76 " (A. M. Willard)	60	20
90.	50 c.		60	20
91.	50 c.		60	20

Type **17** shows the left-hand stamp of the 30 c. design.

18. Running.

1976. Olympic Games, Montreal. **Mult.**

93.	25 c. Type **18**	25	15
94.	30 c. Long jump	30	15
95.	75 c. Throwing the javelin	55	25

19. " The Flight into Egypt ".

1976. Christmas. Durer Engravings.

97. **19.**	7 c. black and silver ..	10	10
98. –	15 c. blue and silver ..	20	15
99. –	35 c. violet and silver ..	30	25

DESIGNS: 15 c. " Adoration of the **Magi** ". 35 c. " The Nativity ".

20. The Queen in Coronation Robes.

1977. Silver Jubilee. Multicoloured.

100.	50 c. Type **20**	60	70
101.	$1 The Queen and Prince Philip	70	75
102.	$2 Queen Elizabeth II ..	1·00	1·00

21. " The Annunciation ".

1977. Christmas. Illustrations by J. S. von Carolsfeld.

104. **21.**	7 c. brn., pur. and gold	30	15
105. –	15 c. red, purple & gold	50	15
106. –	35 c. deep green, green and gold	90	30

DESIGNS: 15 c. " The Announcement to the Shepherds ". 35 c. " The Nativity ".

22. Iiwi.

1978. Bicentenary of Discovery of Hawaii. Birds and Artefacts. Multicoloured.

107.	20 c. Type **22**	70	30
108.	20 c. Elgin cloak	70	30
109.	30 c. Apapane	80	40
110.	30 c. Feather image of a god	80	40
111.	35 c. Moorhen	80	45
112.	35 c. Feather cape, helmet and staff	80	45
113.	75 c. Hawaii Oo	1·25	80
114.	75 c. Feather image and cloak	1·25	80

23. " The Road to Calvary ". 24. Royal Coat of arms.

1978. Easter. 400th Birth Anniv. of Rubens. Multicoloured.

116.	10 c. Type **23**	10	10
117.	15 c. " Christ on the Cross "	15	15
118.	35 c. " Christ with Straw "	25	25

1978. 25th Anniv. of Coronation.

121. **24.**	90 c. black, gold & mauve	55	75
122. –	90 c. multicoloured ..	55	75
123. –	90 c. black, gold & green	55	75

DESIGNS: No. 122, Queen Elizabeth II. No. 123, New Zealand coat of arms.

25. " Madonna of the Pear ".

1978. Christmas. 450th Death Anniv. of Albrecht Durer. Multicoloured.

125.	30 c. Type **25**	50	30
126.	35 c. " The Virgin with St. Anne and Child " (Durer)	50	30

26. Sir Rowland Hill and G.B. Penny Black Stamp.

1979. Death Centenary of Sir Rowland Hill. Multicoloured.

128.	75 c. Type **26**	75	65
129.	75 c. 1974 U.P.U. Centenary 25 c. and 50 c. commemoratives ..	75	65
130.	90 c. Sir Rowland Hill ..	90	80
131.	90 c. 1978 Coronation Anniversary 90 c. commemorative	90	80

27. Max and Moritz.

INDEX

Countries can be quickly located by referring to the index at the end of this volume.

1979. Int. Year of the Child. **Illustrations** from " Max and Moritz " stories **by Wilhelm** Busch. Multicoloured.

133.	12 c. Type **27**	20	10
134.	12 c. Max and Moritz looking down chimney ..	20	10
135.	12 c. Max and Moritz taking food	20	10
136.	12 c. Cook about to beat dog	20	10
137.	15 c. Max sawing through bridge	25	10
138.	15 c. Pursuer approaching bridge	25	10
139.	15 c. Collapse of bridge ..	25	10
140.	15 c. Pursuer in river ..	25	10
141.	20 c. Baker locking shop ..	30	20
142.	20 c. Max and Moritz emerge from hiding ..	30	20
143.	20 c. Max and Moritz falling in dough ..	30	20
144.	20 c. Max and Moritz made into buns	30	20

28. " Christ carrying Cross " (Book of Ferdinand II).

1980. Easter. Scenes from **15th-cent.** Prayer Books. Multicoloured.

145.	12 c. Type **28** ..	10	10
146.	20 c. " The Crucifixion " (William Vrelant, Book of Duke of Burgundy) ..	15	15
147.	35 c. " Descent from the Cross " (Book of Ferdinand II)	25	25

29. "Queen Elizabeth, 1937" (Sir Gerald Kelly).

1980. 80th Birthday of The Queen Mother.

150. **29.**	$1 multicoloured ..	2·00	1·50

30. Falk Hoffman, D.D.R. (platform diving) (gold).

1980. Olympic Medal Winners. **Multicoloured.**

152.	10 c. Type **30**	10	10
153.	10 c. Martina Jaschke (platform diving) ..	10	10
154.	20 c. Tomi Polkolainen (archery)	15	15
155.	20 c. Kete Losaberidse (archery)	15	15
156.	30 c. Czechoslovakia (football)	20	20
157.	30 c. East Germany (football)	20	20
158.	50 c. Barbel Wockel (200 metres)	30	30
159.	50 c. Pietro Mennea (200 metres)	30	30

31. " The Virgin of Counsellers " (Luis Dalmau).

1980. Christmas. Multicoloured.

161. 20 c. Type **31** 15 15
162. 35 c. " Virgin and Child " (Serra Brothers) .. 20 20
163. 50 c. " The Virgin of Albocacer " (Master of the Porciuncula) .. 30 30

32. Amatasi.

1981. Sailing Ships (1st series). Mult.

166. 1 c. Type **32** 20 15
167. 1 c. Ndrua 20 15
168. 1 c. Waka 20 15
169. 1 c. Tongiaki 20 15
170. 3 c. Va'a Teu'ua 40 15
171. 3 c. "Victoria", 1500 .. 40 15
172. 3 c. "Golden Hind", 1560 40 15
173. 3 c. "Boudeuse", 1760 .. 40 15
174. 4 c. H.M.S. "Bounty", 1787 40 15
175. 4 c. "Astrolabe", 1871 .. 40 15
176. 4 c. "Star of India", 1861 40 15
177. 4 c. "Great Republic", 1853 40 15
178. 6 c. "Balcutha", 1866 .. 40 15
179. 6 c. "Coonatoo", 1863 .. 40 15
180. 6 c. "Antiope", 1866 .. 40 15
181. 6 c. "Teaping", 1863 .. 40 15
182. 10 c. "Preussen", 1902 .. 45 35
183. 10 c. "Pamir", 1921 .. 45 35
184. 10 c. "Cap Hornier", 1910 .. 45 35
185. 10 c. "Patriarch", 1869 .. 45 35
186. 15 c. Type **22** 45 50
187. 15 c. As No. 167 .. .. 45 50
188. 15 c. As No. 168 .. .. 45 50
189. 15 c. As No. 169 .. .. 45 50
190. 20 c. As No. 170 .. .. 45 50
191. 20 c. As No. 171 .. .. 45 50
192. 20 c. As No. 172 .. .. 45 50
193. 20 c. As No. 173 .. .. 45 50
194. 30 c. As No. 174 .. .. 45 60
195. 30 c. As No. 175 .. .. 45 60
196. 30 c. As No. 176 .. .. 45 60
197. 30 c. As No. 177 .. .. 45 60
198. 50 c. As No. 178 .. .. 85 1·25
199. 50 c. As No. 179 .. .. 85 1·25
200. 50 c. As No. 180 .. .. 85 1·25
201. 50 c. As No. 181 .. .. 85 1·25
202. $1 As No. 182 .. .. 1·50 1·25
203. $1 As No. 183 .. .. 1·50 1·25
204. $1 As No. 184 .. .. 1·50 1·25
205. $1 As No. 185 .. .. 1·50 1·25
206. $2 "Cutty Sark", 1869 .. 4·00 2·75
207. $4. "Mermerus", 1872 .. 8·00 5·00
208. $6 H.M.S. "Resolution" and "Discovery" 1776–80 .. 12·00 10·00

Nos. 186/201 are 41 × 35 mm., Nos. 202/5 41 × 25 mm. and Nos. 206/8 47 × 33 mm. in size.
See also Nos. 337/55.

33. " Jesus at the Grove " (Veronese).

1981. Easter. Paintings. Multicoloured.

218. 30 c. Type **33** 25 20
219. 40 c. " Christ with Crown of Thorns " (Titian) .. 30 25
220. 50 c. " Pieta " (Van Dyck) 40 30

34. Prince Charles as Young Child.

1981. Royal Wedding. Multicoloured.

223. 40 c. Type **34** 35 40
224. 50 c. Prince Charles as schoolboy 40 45
225. 60 c. Prince Charles as young man 45 50
226. 70 c. Prince Charles in ceremonial Naval uniform 50 55
227. 80 c. Prince Charles as Colonel-in-Chief, Royal Regiment of Wales .. 55 60

1981. International Year for Disabled Persons. Nos. 223/7 surch. **+5 c.**

229. **34.** 40 c. + 5 c. multicoloured 50 75
230. – 50 c. + 5 c. multicoloured 60 85
231. – 60 c. + 5 c. multicoloured 70 95
232. – 70 c. + 5 c. multicoloured 75 85
233. – 80 c. + 5 c. multicoloured 75 1·10

35. Footballers.

1981. World Cup Football Championships, Spain (1982). Multicoloured.

235. 15 c. Type **35** 15 15
236. 15 c. Footballer wearing orange jersey with black and mauve stripes .. 15 15
237. 15 c. Player in blue jersey 15 15
238. 35 c. Player in blue jersey 25 25
239. 35 c. Player in red jersey 25 25
240. 35 c. Player in yellow jersey with green stripes .. 25 25
241. 50 c. Player in orange jersey 35 35
242. 50 c. Player in mauve jersey 35 35
243. 50 c. Player in black jersey 35 35

36. " The Virgin on a Crescent ".

1981. Christmas. Engravings by Durer.

245. **36.** 30 c. violet, purple and stone 65 65
246. – 40 c. vio., pur. and stone 80 80
247. – 50 c. vio., pur. and stone 90 90

DESIGNS: 40 c. " The Virgin at the Fence ". 50 c. " The Holy Virgin and Child ".

37. Lady Diana Spencer as Baby.

1982. 21st Birthday of Princess of Wales. Multicoloured.

250. 30 c. Type **37** 30 30
251. 50 c. As young child .. 45 45
252. 70 c. As schoolgirl .. 60 60
253. 80 c. As teenager 80 80
254. $1·40 As young lady .. 1·25 1·25

1982. Birth of Prince William of Wales (1st issue). Nos. 223/7 optd. **BIRTH OF PRINCE WILLIAM OF WALES 21 JUNE 1982.**

256. 40 c. Type **34** 90 80
257. 50 c. Prince Charles as schoolboy .. .. 1·25 90
258. 60 c. Prince Charles as young man .. .. 1·40 1·00
259. 70 c. Prince Charles in ceremonial Naval Uniform .. .. 1·60 1·25
260. 80 c. Prince Charles as Colonel-in-Chief, Royal Regiment of Wales .. 2·00 1·60

1982. Birth of Prince William of Wales (2nd issue). As Nos. 250/4 but with changed inscriptions. Multicoloured.

262. 30 c. As Type **37** (inscr "21 JUNE 1982. BIRTH OF PRINCE WILLIAM OF WALES") 25 30
263. 30 c. As Type **37** (inscr "COMMEMORATING THE BIRTH OF PRINCE WILLIAM OF WALES") 25 30
264. 50 c. As No. 251 (inscr "21 JUNE 1982. BIRTH OF PRINCE WILLIAM OF WALES") 40 45
265. 50 c. As No. 251 (inscr "COMMEMORATING THE BIRTH OF PRINCE WILLIAM OF WALES") 40 45
266. 70 c. As No. 252 (inscr "21 JUNE 1982. BIRTH OF PRINCE WILLIAM OF WALES") 60 65
267. 70 c. As No. 252 (inscr "COMMEMORATING THE BIRTH OF PRINCE WILLIAM OF WALES") 60 65
268. 80 c. As No. 253 (inscr "21 JUNE 1982. BIRTH OF PRINCE WILLIAM OF WALES") 60 65
269. 80 c. As No. 253 (inscr "COMMEMORATING THE BIRTH OF PRINCE WILLIAM OF WALES") 60 65
270. $1·40 As No. 254 (inscr "21 JUNE 1982. BIRTH OF PRINCE WILLIAM OF WALES") .. .. 1·10 1·25
271. $1·40 As No. 252 (inscr "COMMEMORATING THE BIRTH OF PRINCE WILLIAM OF WALES") 1·10 1·25

39. " Virgin and Child ". (detail from painting by Joos Van Cleve).

1982. Christmas. Detail from Renaissance Paintings of " Virgin and Child ". Mult.

273. 25 c. Type **39** 30 40
274. 48 c. " Virgin and Child " (Filippino Lippi) .. 45 55
275. 60 c. " Virgin and Child " (Cima da Conegliano) .. 60 70

40. Red Coral.

1983. Commonwealth Day. Multicoloured.

278. 60 c. Type **40** 50 60
279. 60 c. Aerial view of Penrhyn atoll 50 60
280. 60 c. Eleanor Roosevelt on Penrhyn during Second World War 50 60
281. 60 c. Map of South Pacific 50 60

41. Scout Emblem and Blue Tropical Flower.

1983. 75th Anniv. of Boy Scout Movement. Multicoloured.

282. 36 c. Type **41** .. .. 1·00 45
283. 48 c. Emblem & pink flower 1·25 55
284. 60 c. Emblem and orange flower .. .. .. 1·40 75

1983. 15th World Scout Jamboree, Alberta, Canada. Nos 282/4 optd **XV WORLD JAMBOREE CANADA 1983.**

286. 36 c. Type **41** .. .. 1·00 40
287. 48 c. Emblem and pink flower .. .. .. 1·25 55
288. 60 c. Emblem and orange flower .. .. .. 1·40 75

43. School of Sperm Whales.

1983. Whale Conservation. Multicoloured.

290. 8 c. Type **43** 65 30
291. 15 c. Harpooner preparing to strike 90 45
292. 35 c. Whale attacking boat 1·40 75
293. 60 c. Dead whales marked with flags .. .. 2·25 1·00
294. $1 Dead whales on slipway 2·50 1·40

44. "Mercury" (cable ship).

1983. World Communications Year. Mult.

295. 36 c. Type **44** 40 35
296. 48 c. Men watching cable being laid 50 45
297. 60 c. "Mercury" (different) 70 60

1983. Various stamps surch. (a) Nos. 182/5, 190/7 and 206.

299. 18 c. on 10 c. "Preussen", 1902 .. .. .. 20 20
300. 18 c. on 10 c. "Pamir", 1902 20 20
301. 18 c. on 10 c. "Cap Hornier", 1910 .. .. 20 20
302. 18 c. on 10 c. "Patriarch", 1869 .. .. .. 20 20
303. 36 c. on 20 c. "Va'a Teu'ua" 35 35
304. 36 c. on 20 c. "Victoria", 1500 .. .. .. 35 35
305. 36 c. on 20 c. "Golden Hind", 1560 .. .. 35 35
306. 36 c. on 20 c. "Boudeuse", 1760 .. .. .. 35 35
307. 36 c. on 30 c. H.M.S. "Bounty", 1787 .. .. 35 35
308. 36 c. on 30 c. "Astrolabe", 1811 .. .. .. 35 35
309. 36 c. on 30 c. "Star of India", 1861 .. .. 35 35
310. 36 c. on 30 c. "Great Republic", 1853 .. .. 35 35
311. $1.20 on $2 "Cutty Sark", 1869 .. .. .. 1·40 1·40

(b) Nos. 252/3.

312. 72 c. on 70 c. Princess Diana as schoolgirl .. 2·00 1·50
313. 96 c. on 80 c. Princess Diana as teenager .. 2·25 1·75

1983. Nos. 225/6, 268/9, 254 and 208 surch.

314	48 c. on 60 c. Prince Charles as young man	3·50	1·50
315	72 c. on 70 c. Prince Charles in ceremonial Naval uniform	4·00	1·75
316	96 c. on 80 c. As No. 253 (inscr "21 JUNE 1982...")	2·75	1·00
317	96 c. on 80 c. As No. 253 (inscr "COMMEMORATING...")	1·75	1·00
318	$1.20 on $4.40 As young lady	3·25	1·50
319	$5.60 on $6 H.M.S. "Resolution" and "Discovery"	12·00	6·50

45. George Cayley's Airship Design, 1837.

1983. Bicentenary of Manned Flight. Mult.
A. Inscr. "NORTHERN COOK ISLANS".
B. Corrected spelling optd. in black on silver, over original inscription.

		A		B	
320.	36 c. Type **45** ..	75	60	30	35
321.	48 c. Dupuy De Lome's man-powered air-ship, 1872 ..	1·00	70	40	45
322.	60 c. Santos Dumont's sixth airship, 1901 ..	1·25	1·00	45	50
323.	96 c. Lebaudy's practical air-ship, 1902 ..	2·00	1·50	75	80
324.	$1.32 Graf Zeppelin "LZ 127", 1929	3·00	2·00	1·00	1·10

46. " Madonna in the Meadow ".

1983. Christmas. 500th Birth Anniv. of Raphael. Multicoloured.

326.	36 c. Type **46**	35	40
327.	42 c. " Tempi Madonna "	35	40
328.	48 c. " The Smaller Cowper Madonna "	45	50
329.	60 c. " Madonna della Tenda "	55	60

1983. Nos. 266/7, 227 and 270 surch.

331.	72 c. on 70 c. As No. 252 (inscr. " 21 JUNE 1982 . . . ")	2·00	1·25
332.	72 c. on 70 c. As No. 252 (inscr. " COMMEMORATING . . . ")	1·25	90
333.	96 c. on 80 c. Prince Charles as Colonel-in-chief, Royal Regiment of Wales	2·00	1·00
334.	$1.20 on $1.40 As No. 254 (inscr. " 21 JUNE 1982 . . . ")	2·25	1·25
335.	$1.20 on $1.40 As No. 254 (inscr. " COMMEMORATING . . . ")	1·75	1·00

47. Waka.

1984. Sailing Craft and Ships (2nd series). Multicoloured.

337.	2 c. Type **47**	10	10
338.	4 c. Amatasi	10	10
339.	5 c. Ndrua	10	10
340.	8 c. Tongiaki	10	10
341.	10 c. "Victoria"	10	10
342.	18 c. "Golden Hind" ..	10	10
343.	20 c. "Boudeuse"	10	15
344.	30 c. H.M.S. "Bounty" ..	20	25
345.	36 c. "Astrolabe"	25	30
346.	48 c. "Great Republic" ..	30	35
347.	50 c. "Star of India" ..	35	40
348.	60 c. "Coonatto"	40	45
349.	72 c. "Antiope"	50	55
350.	80 c. "Balcutha"	55	60
351.	96 c. "Cap Hornier" ..	65	70
352.	$1.20 "Pamir"	80	85
353.	$3 "Mermerus"	2·00	2·25
354.	$5 "Cutty Sark"	3·25	3·50
355.	$9.50 H.M.S. "Resolution and Discovery	6·25	6·50

Nos. 353/5 are larger; 41 × 31 mm.

48. Olympic Flag.

1984. Olympic Games, Los Angeles. Mult.

356.	35 c. Type **48**	30	35
357.	60 c. Olympic torch and flags	50	55
358.	$1.80 Ancient athletes and Coliseum	1·50	1·60

49. Penrhyn Stamps of 1978, 1979 and 1981.

1984. "Ausipex" International Stamp Exhibition, Melbourne. Multicoloured.

360.	60 c. Type **49**	50	75
361.	$1.20 Location map of Penrhyn	1·00	1·25

1984. Birth of Prince Henry. Nos. 223/4 and 250/1 surch. **Birth of Prince Henry 15 Sept. 1984.**

363.	$2 on 30 c. Type **37** ..	2·25	1·50
364.	$2 on 40 c. Type **34** ..	2·75	1·75
365.	$2 on 50 c. Prince Charles as schoolboy	2·75	1·75
366.	$2 on 50 c. Lady Diana as young child	2·25	1·50

51. "Virgin and Child" (Giovanni Bellini).

1984. Christmas. Paintings of the Virgin and Child by different artists. Multicoloured.

367.	36 c. Type **51**	30	35
368.	48 c. Lorenzo di Credi ..	40	45
369.	60 c. Palma the Older ..	50	55
370.	96 c. Raphael	75	80

52. Harlequin Duck.

1985. Birth Bicentenary of John J. Audubon (ornithologist). Multicoloured.

373.	20 c. Type **52**	70	70
374.	55 c. Sage grouse	1·25	1·25
375.	65 c. Solitary sandpiper ..	1·40	1·40
376.	75 c. Dunlin	1·75	1·75

Nos. 373/6 show original paintings.

53. Lady Elizabeth Bowes-Lyon, 1921.

1985. Life and Times of Queen Elizabeth the Queen Mother. Each violet, silver and yellow.

378.	75 c. Type **53**	60	65
379.	95 c. With baby Princess Elizabeth, 1926	75	80
380.	$1.20, Coronation Day, 1937	95	1·00
381.	$2.80, On her 70th birthday	2·10	2·25

54. "The House in the Wood".

1985. International Youth Year. Birth Centenary of Jacob Grimm (folklorist). Multicoloured.

383.	75 c. Type **54**	80	70
384.	95 c. "Snow-White and Rose-Red"	90	85
385.	$1.15 "The Goose Girl" ..	1·25	1·10

55. "The Annunciation".

1985. Christmas. Paintings by Murillo. Mult.

386.	75 c. Type **55**	70	70
387.	$1.15, "Adoration of the Shepherds"	1·00	1·00
388.	$1.80, "The Holy Family"	1·75	1·75

56. Halley's Comet.

1986. Appearance of Halley's Comet. Design showing details of the painting "Fire and Ice" by Camille Rendal. Multicoloured.

391	$1.50 Type **56**	1·10	1·25
392	$1.50 Stylized "Giotto" spacecraft	1·10	1·25

Nos. 391/2 were printed together, forming a composite design of the complete painting.

57. Princess Elizabeth aged Three, 1929, and Bouquet.

1986. 60th Birthday of Queen Elizabeth II. Multicoloured.

394.	95 c. Type **57**	80	80
395.	$1.45 Profile of Queen Elizabeth and St. Edward's Crown ..	1·25	1·25
396.	$2.50 Queen Elizabeth aged three and in profile with Imperial State Crown (56 × 30 mm.)	2·00	2·00

58. Statue of Liberty under Construction, Paris.

1986. Centenary of Statue of Liberty. Each black, gold and yellow-green.

397.	95 c. Type **58**	65	70
398.	$1.75 Erection of Statue, New York	1·10	1·25
399.	$3 Artist's impression of Statue, 1876	2·10	2·25

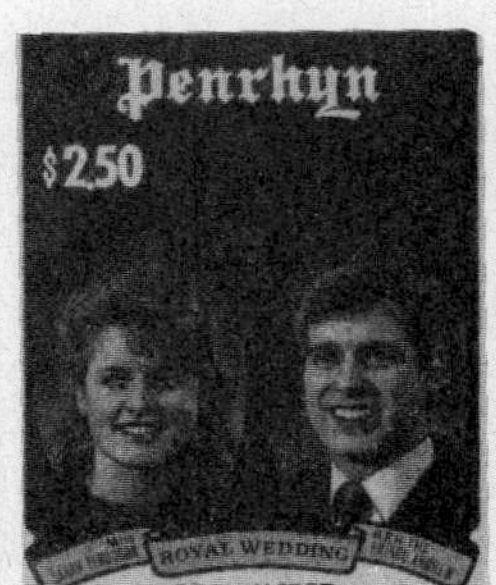

59. Prince Andrew and Miss Sarah Ferguson.

1986. Royal Wedding. Multicoloured.

400.	$2.50 Type **59**	2·50	2·50
401.	$3.50 Profiles of Prince Andrew and Miss Sarah Ferguson	3·25	3·25

61. "Adoration of the Shepherds".

1986. Christmas. Engravings by Rembrandt. Each brown, ochre and gold.
404. 65 c. Type **61** 80 80
405. $1.75 "Virgin and Child" .. 2·00 2·00
406. $2.50 "The Holy Family" .. 2·50 2·50

1986. Visit of Pope John Paul II to South Pacific. Nos. 404/6 surch. **SOUTH PACIFIC VISIT 21 TO 24 NOVEMBER 1986.**
408. 65 c. + 10 c. Type **61** .. 1·50 1·50
409. $1.75 + 10 c. "Virgin and Child" .. .. 2·75 2·75
410. $2.50 + 10 c. "The Holy Family" .. .. .. 3·25 3·25

1987. Royal Ruby Wedding. Nos. 68/9 optd. **Fortieth Royal Wedding Anniversary 1947–87.**
413. $2 Birds-eye view of Penrhyn .. .. .. 1·75 1·75
414. $5 Satellite view of Australasia .. .. 3·75 3·75

65. "The Garvagh Madonna".

1987. Christmas. Religious Paintings by Raphael. Multicoloured.
415. 95 c. Type **65** 70 70
416. $1.60 "The Alba Madonna" 1·25 1·25
417. $2.25 "The Madonna of the Fish" .. .. .. 1·75 1·75

66 Athletics

1988. Olympic Games, Seoul. Multicoloured.
420 55 c. Type **66** 45 45
421 95 c. Pole vault (vert) .. 70 70
422 $1.25 Shot put 95 95
423 $1.50 Tennis (vert) .. 1·25 1·25

1988. Olympic Gold Medal Winners, Seoul. Nos. 420/3 optd.
425 55 c. Type **66** (optd **CARL LEWIS UNITED STATES 100 METERS**) .. 40 45
426 95 c. Pole vault (optd **LOUISE RITTER UNITED STATES HIGH JUMP**) .. 65 70
427 $1.25 Shot put (optd **ULF TIMMERMANN EAST GERMANY SHOT-PUT**) 90 95
428 $1.50 Tennis (optd **STEFFI GRAF WEST GERMANY WOMEN'S TENNIS**) 1·10 1·25

67 "Virgin and Child"

1988. Christmas. Designs showing different "Virgin and Child" paintings by Titian.
430 **67** 70 c. multicoloured .. 65 65
431 – 85 c. multicoloured .. 70 70
432 – 95 c. multicoloured .. 75 75
433 – $1.25 multicoloured .. 90 95

68 Neil Armstrong stepping onto Moon

1989. 20th Anniv of First Manned Moon Landing. Multicoloured.
435 55 c. Type **68** 40 45
436 75 c. Astronaut on Moon carrying equipment .. 55 60
437 95 c. Conducting experiment on Moon 70 75
438 $1.25 Crew of "Apollo 11" 95 1·00
439 $1.75 Crew inside "Apollo 11" .. .. .. 1·40 1·50

69 Virgin Mary

1989. Christmas. Details from "The Nativity" by Durer. Multicoloured.
440 55 c. Type **69** 60 60
441 70 c. Christ Child and cherubs 70 70
442 85 c. Joseph 85 85
443 $1.25 Three women .. 1·25 1·25

70 Queen Elizabeth the Queen Mother

1990. 90th Birthday of Queen Elizabeth the Queen Mother.
445 **70** $2.25 multicoloured .. 1·50 1·60

71 "Adoration of the Magi" (Veronese)

1990. Christmas. Religious Paintings. Mult.
447 55 c. Type **71** 45 45
448 70 c. "Virgin and Child" (Quentin Metsys) .. 60 60
449 85 c. "Virgin and Child Jesus" (Hugo van der Goes) 70 70
450 $1.50 "Adoration of the Kings" (Jan Gossaert) 1·25 1·25

1990. "Birdpex '90" Stamp Exhibition, Christchurch, New Zealand. Nos 373/6 surch **Birdpex '90** and logo.
452 $1.50 on 20 c. Type **52** .. 1·25 1·25
453 $1.50 on 55 c. Sage grouse 1·25 1·25
454 $1.50 on 65 c. Solitary sandpiper .. .. 1·25 1·25
456 $1.50 on 75 c. Dunlin .. 1·25 1·25

1991. 65th Birthday of Queen Elizabeth II. No. 208 optd **COMMEMORATING 65th BIRTHDAY OF H.M. QUEEN ELIZABETH II.**
456 $6 H.M.S. "Resolution" and "Discovery", 1776–80 .. .. .. 4·75 5·00

74 "The Virgin and Child with Saints" (G. David)

1991. Christmas. Religious Paintings. Mult.
457 55 c. Type **74** 35 40
458 85 c. "Nativity" (Tintoretto) 55 60
459 $1.15 "Mystic Nativity" (Botticelli) 75 80
460 $1.85 "Adoration of the Shepherds" (B. Murillo) 1·25 1·40

OFFICIAL STAMPS

1978. Optd. or surch. **O.H.M.S.**
O 1. 1 c. multicoloured (No. 57) 15 10
O 2. 2 c. multicoloured (No. 58) 15 10
O 3. 3 c. multicoloured (No. 59) 25 10
O 4. 4 c. multicoloured (No. 60) 25 10
O 5. 5 c. multicoloured (No. 61) 30 10
O 6. 8 c. multicoloured (No. 62) 35 15
O 7. 10 c. multicoloured (No. 63) 40 15
O 8. 15 c. on 60 c. mult. (No. 66) 45 25
O 9. 18 c. on 60 c. mult. (No. 66) 50 25
O 10. 20 c. multicoloured (No. 64) 50 25
O 11. 25 c. multicoloured (No. 65) 55 30
O 12. 30 c. on 60 c. mult. (No. 66) 55 35
O 13. 50 c. multicoloured (No. 89) 70 55
O 14. 50 c. multicoloured (No. 90) 70 55
O 15. 50 c. multicoloured (No. 91) 70 55
O 16. $1 multicoloured (No. 101) 2·25 1·40
O 17. $2 multicoloured (No. 102) 4·50 2·75

These stamps were originally only sold to the public cancelled-to-order and not in unused condition. They were made available to overseas collectors in mint condition during 1980.

1985. Nos. 206/8, 278/81, 337/47 and 349/55 optd. **O.H.M.S.** or surch also.
O 18. 2 c. Type **47** 10 10
O 19. 4 c. Amatasi 10 10
O 20. 5 c. Ndrua 10 10
O 21. 8 c. Tongiaki 10 10
O 22. 10 c. "Victoria" 10 10
O 23. 18 c. "Golden Hind" .. 10 10
O 24. 20 c. "Boudeuse" 10 15
O 25. 30 c. H.M.S. "Bounty" .. 20 25
O 26. 40 c. on 36 c. "Astrolabe" 25 30
O 27. 50 c. "Star of India" .. 35 40
O 28. 55 c. on 48 c. "Great Republic" 35 40
O 39. 65 c. on 60 c. Type **40** 45 50
O 40. 65 c. on 60 c. Aerial view of Penrhyn atoll 45 50
O 41. 65 c. on 60 c. Eleanor Roosevelt on Penrhyn during Second World War 45 50
O 42. 65 c. on 60 c. Map of South Pacific 45 50
O 29. 75 c. on 72 c. "Antiope" .. 50 55
O 30. 75 c. on 96 c. "Cap Hornier" 50 55
O 31. 80 c. "Balcutha" 55 60
O 32. $1.20 "Pamir" 80 85
O 33. $2 "Cutty Sark" .. .. 1·25 1·40
O 34. $3 "Mermerus" .. .. 2·00 2·10
O 35. $4 "Mermerus" .. .. 2·75 3·00
O 36. $5 "Cutty Sark" .. .. 3·25 3·50
O 37. $6 H.M.S. "Resolution" and "Discovery" .. 4·00 4·25
O 38. $9.60 H.M.S. "Resolution" and "Discovery" .. 6·25 6·50

PERAK

A state of the Federation of Malaya, incorporated in Malaysia in 1963.

100 cents = 1 dollar (Straits or Malayan).

Stamps of Straits Settlements optd. or surch.

1878. No. 11 optd. with crescent, star and **P** in oval.
1. 2 c. brown £950 £850

1880. Optd. **PERAK.**
10. **9.** 2 c. brown .. .. 13·00 19·00
17. 2 c. red 70 70

1883. Surch. **2 CENTS PERAK.**
16. 2 c on 4 c. red £350 £225

1886. No. 63a surch. **ONE CENT PERAK.**
30 1 c. on 2 c. red .. .. 17·00 23·00

1886. No. 63a surch. **1 CENT PERAK.**
28 1 c. on 2 c. red .. .. 50·00 60·00

1886. No. 63a surch **One CENT PERAK.**
33 1 c. on 2 c. red .. .. 45 1·25

1889. Surch. **PERAK ONE CENT.**
41. 1 c. on 2 c. red .. .. 90·00 90·00

1891. Surch. **PERAK One CENT.**
57. 1 c. on 2 c. red .. .. 55 1·75
43. 1 c on 6 c. lilac .. .. 30·00 24·00

1891. Surch. **PERAK Two CENTS.**
48 2 c. on 24 c. green .. .. 8·50 8·50

42. Tiger.

44. Tiger.

45. Elephants.

1892.
61. **42.** 1 c. green .. .. 2·25 15
62. 2 c. red .. .. .. 1·25 30
63. 2 c. orange .. .. 35 3·25
64. 5 c. blue .. .. .. 2·75 6·00

1895. Surch. **3 CENTS.**
65. **42.** 3 c. on 5 c. red .. .. 50 1·40

1895.
66. **44.** 1 c. purple and green .. 70 40
67. 2 c. purple and brown 75 40
68. 3 c. purple and red .. 1·50 20
69. 4 c. purple and red .. 5·50 4·25
70. 5 c. purple and yellow .. 2·50 55
71. 8 c. purple and blue .. 26·00 65
72. 10 c. purple and orange 6·00 45
73. 25 c. green and red .. 90·00 11·00
74. 50 c. purple and black .. 25·00 25·00
75. 50 c. green and black .. £110 £110
76. **45.** $1 green .. .. 65·00 75·00
77. $2 green and red .. £130 £130
78. $3 green and yellow .. £100 £120
79. $5 green and blue .. £300 £275
80. $25 green and orange .. £4000 £1100

1900. Surch. in words.
81. **44.** 1 c. on 2 c. purple & brown 40 1·25
82. 1 c. on 4 c. purple and red 55 3·50
83. 1 c. on 5 c. purple & yellow 70 5·50
84. 3 c. on 8 c. purple & blue 2·50 3·25
85. 3 c. on 50 c. green & black 1·00 3·75
86. **45.** 3 c. on $1 green .. .. 50·00 95·00
87. 3 c. on $2 green and red .. 26·00 65·00

50. Sultan Iskandar. **51.**

1935.
88. **50.** 1 c. black 15 10
89. 2 c. green 30 10
90. 4 c. orange 30 10
91. 5 c. brown 30 10
92. 6 c. red .. .. 5·00 2·50
93. 8 c. grey 40 10
94. 10 c. purple 30 15
95. 12 c. blue 60 90
96. 25 c. purple and red .. 75 85
97. 30 c. purple and orange 80 1·50
98. 40 c. red and purple .. 2·00 4·25
99. 50 c. black on green .. 3·25 80
100. $1 blk. & red on blue 2·00 80
101. $2 green and red .. 8·00 8·50
102. $5 grn. & red on grn. 35·00 22·00

1938.

103. 51.	1 c. black	2·50	10
104.	2 c. green	2·00	10
105.	2 c. orange	50	4·75
106.	3 c. green	75	55
107.	4 c. orange	23·00	10
108.	5 c. brown	1·50	10
109.	6 c. red	16·00	10
110.	8 c. grey	16·00	10
111.	8 c. red	1·00	30·00
112.	10 c. purple	17·00	10
113.	12 c. blue	11·00	2·00
114.	15 c. blue	1·75	13·00
115.	25 c. purple and red ..	65·00	4·25
116.	30 c. purple and orange ..	8·00	3·00
117.	40 c. red and purple ..	35·00	2·00
118.	50 c. black on green ..	18·00	75
119.	$1 black and red on blue	80·00	14·00
120.	$2 green and red ..	90·00	50·00
121.	$5 green and red on green	£170	£190

1948. Silver Wedding. As T **10/11** of Aden.

122.	10 c. violet	15	10
123.	$5 green	20·00	20·00

1949. U.P.U. As T **20/23** of Antigua.

124.	10 c. purple	15	10
125.	15 c. blue	45	35
126.	25 c. orange	45	45
127.	50 c. black	1·25	1·50

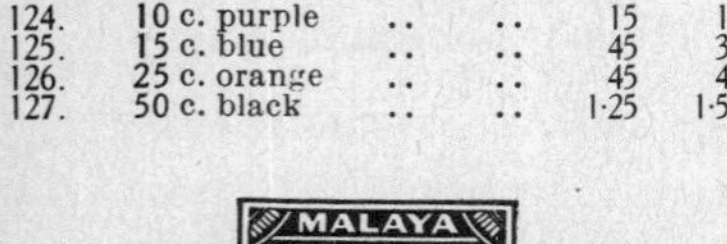

52. Sultan Yussuf 'Izzuddin Shah.

1950.

128. 52.	1 c. black	10	10
129	2 c. orange	10	10
130	3 c. green	85	10
131	4 c. brown	10	10
132a	5 c. purple	35	30
133	6 c. grey	10	10
134	8 c. red	30	75
135	8 c. green	1·00	60
136	10 c. purple	10	10
137	12 c. red	1·00	80
138	15 c. blue	30	10
139	20 c. black and green ..	30	20
140	20 c. blue	75	10
141	25 c. purple and orange	30	10
142	30 c. red and purple ..	1·25	20
143	35 c. red and purple ..	70	25
144	40 c. red and purple ..	85	3·00
145	50 c. black and blue ..	40	10
146	$1 blue and purple ..	3·75	15
147	$2 green and red ..	7·50	70
148	$5 green and brown ..	27·00	7·50

1953. Coronation. As T **13** of Aden.

149.	10 c. black and purple ..	20	10

1957. As Nos. 92/102 of Kedah but portrait of Sultan Yussuf 'Izzuddin Shah.

150.	1 c. black	10	15
151.	2 c. orange	10	10
152.	4 c. brown	10	10
153.	5 c. lake	10	10
154.	8 c. green	1·40	30
155.	10 c. sepia	15	10
156.	10 c. purple	30	10
157.	20 c. blue	20	10
158a.	50 c. black and blue ..	20	10
159.	$1 blue and purple ..	1·75	10
160a.	$2 green and red ..	2·50	1·50
161a.	$5 brown and green ..	6·50	3·00

53. Sultan Idris Shah.

1963. Installation of Sultan of Perak.

162. 53.	10 c. multicoloured ..	10	10

54. "Vanda hookeriana".

1965. As Nos. 115/21 of Kedah but with inset portrait of Sultan Idris as in T **54**.

163. 54.	1 c. multicoloured ..	10	20
164. –	2 c. multicoloured ..	10	25
165. –	5 c. multicoloured ..	10	10
166. –	6 c. multicoloured ..	15	10
167. –	10 c. multicoloured ..	15	10
168. –	15 c. multicoloured ..	65	10
169. –	20 c. multicoloured ..	1·00	10

The higher values used in Perak were Nos. 20/7 of Malaysia (National Issues).

55. "Delias ninus".

1971. Butterflies. As Nos. 124/30 of Kedah but with portrait of Sultan Idris as in T **55**.

172. 55.	1 c. multicoloured ..	15	30
173. –	2 c. multicoloured ..	40	40
174. –	5 c. multicoloured ..	50	10
175. –	6 c. multicoloured ..	50	15
176. –	10 c. multicoloured ..	50	10
177. –	15 c. multicoloured ..	70	10
178. –	20 c. multicoloured ..	85	15

The higher values in use with this issue were Nos. 64/71 of Malaysia (National Issues).

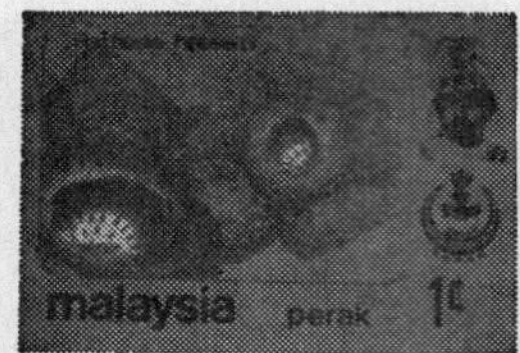

56. "Rafflesia hasseltii".

1979. Flowers. As Nos. 135/41 of Kedah, but with portraits of Sultan Idris as in T **56**.

184	1 c. Type **56**	10	10
185	2 c. "Pterocarpus indicus"	10	10
186	5 c. "Lagerstroemia speciosa"	10	10
187	10 c. "Durio zibethinus" ..	10	10
188	15 c. "Hibiscus rosa-sinensis" ..	15	10
189	20 c. "Rhododendron scortechinii" ..	15	10
190	25 c. "Etlingera elatior" (inscr "Phaeomeria speciosa")	15	10

57. Coffee.

1986. As Nos. 152/8 of Kedah but with portrait of Sultan Azlan Shah as in T **57**.

198.	1 c. Type **57**	10	10
199.	2 c. Coconuts	10	10
200.	5 c. Cocoa	10	10
201.	10 c. Black pepper	10	10
202.	15 c. Rubber	10	10
203.	20 c. Oil palm ..	10	10
204.	30 c. Rice	10	15

OFFICIAL STAMPS

1889. Stamps of Straits Settlements optd. **P.G.S.**

O 1. 30.	2 c. red	2·00	2·50
O 2.	4 c. brown	6·50	12·00
O 3.	6 c. lilac	18·00	28·00
O 4.	8 c. orange	22·00	25·00
O 5. 38.	10 c. grey	65·00	55·00
O 6. 30.	12 c. blue	£110	£120
O 7.	12 c. purple	£110	£190
O 9.	24 c. green	£100	£120

1894. No. 64 optd. **Service.**

O 10. 30.	5 c. blue	24·00	80

1895. No. 70 optd. **Service.**

O 11. 31.	5 c. purple and yellow	1·40	35

PERLIS

A state of the Federation of Malaya, incorporated in Malaysia in 1963.

100 cents = 1 dollar (Straits or Malayan).

1948. Silver Wedding. As T **10/11** of Aden.

1	10 c. violet	30	1·75
2	$5 brown	25·00	42·00

1949. U.P.U. As T **20/23** of Antigua.

3	10 c. purple	25	60
4	15 c. blue	50	2·00
5	25 c. orange	55	1·75
6	50 c. black	90	3·50

1. Raja Syed Putra.

1951.

7. 1.	1 c. black	10	40
8.	2 c. orange	10	40
9.	3 c. green	40	1·25
10.	4 c. brown	20	20
11.	5 c. purple	30	65
12.	6 c. grey	20	25
13.	8 c. red	30	2·00
14.	8 c. green	75	1·50
15.	10 c. purple	15	20
16.	12 c. red	75	1·75
17.	15 c. blue	70	1·50
18.	20 c. black and green ..	70	2·25
19.	20 c. blue	85	65
20.	25 c. purple and orange ..	50	90
21.	30 c. red and purple ..	1·75	4·25
22.	35 c. red and purple ..	75	2·50
23.	40 c. red and purple ..	1·25	9·00
24.	50 c. black and blue ..	1·00	1·75
25.	$1 blue and purple ..	3·00	7·00
26.	$2 green and red	9·50	17·00
27.	$5 green and brown ..	42·00	48·00

1953. Coronation. As T **13** of Aden.

28	10 c. black and purple ..	30	1·50

1957. As Nos. 92/102 of Kedah but inset portrait of Raja Syed Putra.

29	1 c. black	10	20
30	2 c. red	10	20
31	4 c. brown	10	10
32	5 c. lake	10	10
33	8 c. green	1·25	80
34	10 c. brown	15	30
35	10 c. purple	80	35
36	20 c. blue	20	50
37	50 c. black and blue ..	20	60
38	$1 blue and purple ..	2·50	3·50
39	$2 green and red	3·75	5·00
40	$5 brown and green ..	6·50	7·50

2. "Vanda hookeriana".

1965. As Nos. 115/21 of Kedah but with inset portrait of Tunku Bendahara Abu Bakar as in T **2**.

41. 2.	1 c. multicoloured ..	10	60
42. –	2 c. multicoloured ..	10	70
43. –	5 c. multicoloured ..	15	15
44. –	6 c. multicoloured ..	40	30
45. –	10 c. multicoloured ..	45	15
46. –	15 c. multicoloured ..	75	35
47. –	20 c. multicoloured ..	1·00	85

The higher values used in Perlis were Nos. 20/7 of Malaysia (National Issues).

3. "Danaus melanippus".

1971. Butterflies. As Nos 124/30 of Kedah but with portrait of Raza Syed Putra as in T **3**.

48. –	1 c. multicoloured ..	15	60
49. 3.	2 c. multicoloured ..	20	70
50. –	5 c. multicoloured ..	55	20
51. –	6 c. multicoloured ..	55	40
52. –	10 c. multicoloured ..	55	20
53. –	15 c. multicoloured ..	55	25
54. –	20 c. multicoloured ..	65	80

The higher values in use with this issue were Nos. 64/71 of Malaysia (National Issues).

4. Raja Syed Putra.

1971. 25th Anniv. of Installation of Raja Syed Putra.

56. 4.	10 c. multicoloured ..	20	50
57.	15 c. multicoloured ..	20	30
58.	50 c. multicoloured ..	70	1·75

5. " Pterocarpus indicus ".

1979. Flowers. As Nos. 135/41 of Kedah, but with portrait of Raja Syed Putra as in T **5**.

59	1 c. "Rafflesia hasseltii" ..	10	30
60	2 c. Type **5**	10	30
61	5 c. "Lagerstroemia speciosa"	10	10
62	10 c. "Durio zibethinus" ..	10	10
63	15 c. "Hibiscus rosa-sinensis" ..	15	10
64	20 c. "Rhododendron scortechinii"	15	10
65	25 c. "Etlingera elatior" (inscr "Phaeomeria speciosa")	65	1·10

6. Coconuts.

1986. As Nos. 152/8 of Kedah but with portrait of Raja Syed Putra as in T **6**.

73.	1 c. Coffee	10	10
74.	2 c. Type **6**	10	10
75.	5 c. Cocoa	10	10
76.	10 c Black pepper ..	10	10
77.	15 c. Rubber	10	10
78.	20 c. Oil palm	10	10
79.	30 c. Rice	10	15

PITCAIRN ISLANDS

An island group in the Pacific Ocean, nearly midway between Australia and America.

1940. 12 pence = 1 shilling;
20 shillings = 1 pound.
1967. 100 cents = 1 New Zealand dollar.

4. Lt. Bligh and the "Bounty".

1940.

1. – ½d. orange and green .. 40 60
2. – 1d. lilac and mauve .. 55 70
3. – 1½d. grey and red .. 55 50
4. 4. 2d. green and brown .. 1·75 1·40
5. – 3d. green and blue .. 1·25 1·40
5a.– 4d. black and green .. 11·00 7·00
6. – 6d. brown and blue .. 5·00 2·25
6a.– 8d. olive and mauve .. 11·00 7·00
7. – 1s. violet and grey .. 3·00 2·00
8. – 2s. 6d. green and brown .. 7·00 4·25

DESIGNS—HORIZ. ½d. Oranges. 1d. Fletcher Christian, crew and Pitcairn Is. 1½d. John Adams and house. 3d. Map of Pitcairn Is. and Pacific. 4d. Bounty Bible. 6d. H.M.S. "Bounty" 8d. School, 1949. 1s. Christian and Pitcairn Is. 2s. 6d. Christian, crew and Pitcairn Coast.

1946. Victory. As T 9 of Aden.

9. 2d. brown 30 15
10. 3d. blue 30 15

1949. Silver Wedding. As T 10/11 of Aden.

11 1½d. red .. .. .. 1·50 1·00
12 10s. mauve .. .. 80·00 65·00

1949. U.P.U. As T 20/23 of Antigua.

13. 2½d. brown .. .. 2·00 3·00
14. 3d. blue .. .. 8·50 4·00
15. 6d. green .. .. 11·00 5·00
16. 1s. purple .. .. 11·00 5·00

1953. Coronation. As T 13 of Aden.

17 4d. black and green .. 2·00 2·75

4d. Type I is inscribed "PITCAIRN SCHOOL"; Type II is inscribed "SCHOOL-TEACHER'S HOUSE".

12. Handicrafts: Bird Model.

1957.

33 – ½d. green and mauve .. 30 60
19 – 1d. black and green .. 1·25 80
20 – 2d. brown and blue .. 75 60
21 12 2½d. brown and pink .. 50 40
22 – 3d. green and blue .. 80 40
23 – 4d. red and blue (I) .. 90 40
23a – 4d. red and blue (II) .. 5·00 1·50
24 12 6d. buff and blue .. 1·25 55
25 – 8d. green and red .. 60 40
26 – 1s. black and brown .. 1·00 40
27 – 2s. green and orange .. 25·00 10·00
28 – 2s. 6d. blue and red .. 12·00 6·00

DESIGNS—HORIZ. ½d. "Cordyline terminalis". 3d. Bounty Bay. 4d. Pitcairn School. 6d. Map of Pacific. 8d. Inland scene. 1s. Model of the "Bounty". 2s. 6d. Launching new whaleboat. VERT. 1d. Map of Pitcairn. 2d. John Adams and "Bounty" bible. 2s. Island wheelbarrow.

20. Pitcairn Island and Simon Young.

1961. Cent. of Return of Pitcairn Islanders.

29. 20. 3d. black and yellow .. 20 15
30. – 6d. brown and blue .. 50 20
31. – 1s. orange and green .. 60 25

DESIGNS: 6d. Maps of Norfolk and Pitcairn Is. 1s. Migrant brigantine "Mary Ann".

1963. Freedom from Hunger. As T 28 of Aden.

32. 2s. 6d. blue .. .. .. 22·00 3·00

1963. Cent of Red Cross. As T 33 of Antigua.

34. 2d. red and black .. .. 2·00 1·00
35. 2s. 6d. red and blue .. 11·00 5·50

23. Pitcairn Is. Longboat.

24. Queen Elizabeth II (after Anthony Buckley).

1964. Multicoloured.

36. ½d. Type 23 .. .. .. 10 30
37. 1d. H.M.S. "Bounty" .. 30 30
38. 2d. "Out from Bounty Bay" 30 30
39. 3d. Great frigate bird .. 30 30
40. 4d. White tern .. 30 30
41. 6d. Pitcairn warbler .. 30 30
42. 8d. Red-footed booby .. 30 30
43. 10d. Red-tailed tropic bird 30 30
44. 1s. Henderson Island crake 30 30
45. 1s 6d. Stephen's lory .. 5·50 1·25
46. 2s 6d. Murphy's petrel .. 5·00 1·50
47. 4s. Henderson Island fruit dove .. .. .. 7·00 1·75
48. 8s. Type 24 .. .. .. 2·50 1·75

1965. Cent of I.T.U. As T 36 of Antigua.

49. 1d. mauve and brown .. 1·00 40
50. 2s. 6d. turquoise and blue 14·00 3·50

1965. I.C.Y. As T 37 of Antigua.

51. 1d. purple and turquoise 1·00 40
52. 1s. 6d. green and lavender 14·00 4·00

1966. Churchill Commem. As T 38 of Antigua.

53. 2d. blue .. .. .. 2·00 60
54. 3d. green .. .. .. 4·50 80
55. 6d. brown .. .. .. 7·50 1·50
56. 1s. violet .. .. .. 10·00 2·00

1966. World Cup Football Championship. As T 40 of Antigua.

57. 4d. multicoloured .. .. 2·00 1·00
58. 2s. 6d. multicoloured .. 5·00 1·75

1966. Inauguration of W.H.O. Headquarters, Geneva. As T 41 of Antigua.

59. 8d. black, green and blue .. 4·50 1·25
60. 1s. 6d. black, purple & ochre 7·50 1·50

1966. 20th Anniv U.N.E.S.C.O. As T 54/6 of Antigua.

61. ½d. multicoloured 20 30
62. 10d. yellow, violet and olive 5·00 1·75
63. 2s. black, purple and orange 11·00 2·25

36. Mangarevan Canoe, c. 1325.

1967. Bicentenary of Pitcairn Islands' Discovery. Multicoloured.

64. ½d. Type 36 .. .. .. 10 10
65. 1d. P.F. de Quiros and "San Pedro y Pablo", 1606 15 10
66. 8d. "San Pedro y Pablo" and "Los Tres Reyes" 1606 .. .. .. 25 10
67. 1s. Carteret and H.M.S. "Swallow", 1767 .. .. 25 10
68. 1s. 6d. "Hercules", 1819 .. 30 10

1967. Decimal Currency. Nos. 36/48 surch. with "Bounty" anchor and value.

69. 23. ½ c. on ½d. multicoloured .. 10 10
70. – 1 c. on 1d. multicoloured .. 30 30
71. – 2 c. on 2d. multicoloured .. 25 30
72. – 2½ c. on 3d. multicoloured 25 30
73. – 3 c. on 4d. multicoloured .. 25 15
74. – 5 c. on 6d. multicoloured 30 30
75. – 10 c. on 8d. multicoloured 30 30
76. – 15 c. on 10d. multicoloured 70 40
77. – 20 c. on 1s. multicoloured 80 55
78. – 25 c. on 1s. 6d. mult. .. 2·50 1·25
79. – 30 c. on 2s. 6d. mult. .. 2·75 1·25
80. – 40 c. on 4s. multicoloured 4·25 1·25
81. 24. 45 c. on 8s. multicoloured 4·25 1·50

42. Bligh and "Bounty's" Launch.

1967. 150th Death Anniv. of Admiral Bligh.

82. 42. 1 c. black, ultram. & blue 10 10
83. – 8 c. black, yellow & mauve 20 10
84. – 20 c. black, brown & buff 20 15

DESIGNS: 8 c. Bligh and Followers cast adrift. 20 c. Bligh's Tomb.

45. Human Rights Emblem.

1968. Int. Human Rights Year.

85. 45. 1 c. multicoloured .. 10 10
86. 2 c. multicoloured .. 10 10
87. 25 c. multicoloured .. 20 20

46. Moro Wood and Flower.

1968. Handicrafts (1st series).

88. 46. 5 c. multicoloured .. 15 10
89. – 10 c. green, brown & orge. 20 20
90. – 15 c. violet, brn. & salmon 20 20
91. – 20 c. multicoloured .. 25 20

DESIGNS—HORIZ. 10 c. Flying Fish Model. VERT. 15 c. "Hand" Vases. 20 c. Woven Baskets.

See also Nos. 207/10.

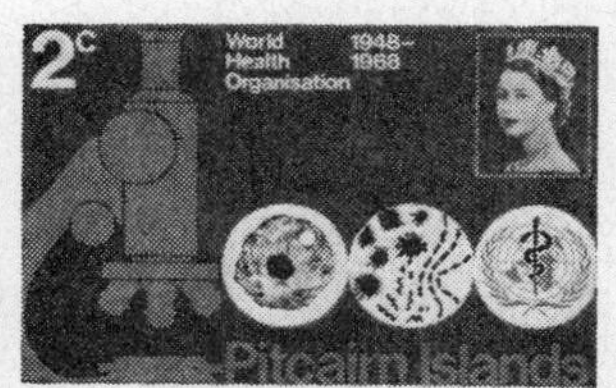

50. Microscope and Slides.

1968. 20th Anniv. of World Health Organization.

92. 50. 2 c. black, turq. & blue 10 10
93. – 20 c. black, orange & pur. 25 20

DESIGN: 20 c. Hypodermic syringe and jars of tablets.

64b. Queen Elizabeth II.

52. Pitcairn Island.

1969. Multicoloured.

94 1 c. Type 52 .. .. 35 15
95 2 c. Captain Bligh and "Bounty" Chronometer 25 15
96 3 c. "Bounty" Anchor .. 25 15
97 4 c. Plans and drawing of "Bounty" 30 15
98 5 c. Breadfruit containers and plant 30 15
99 6 c. Bounty Bay 30 20
100 8 c. Pitcairn Longboat .. 35 20
101 10 c. Ship Landing Point .. 2·00 85
102 15 c. Fletcher Christian's Cave 60 50
103 20 c. Thursday October Christian's house .. 60 40
104 25 c. "Flying Fox" cable system 70 40
105 30 c. Radio Station, Taro Ground 55 45
106 40 c. "Bounty" Bible .. 75 60
106a 50 c. Pitcairn Coat-of-Arms 11·00 10·00
106b $1 Type 64b .. .. 16·00 15·00

The 3 c. and 25 c. are vert.

65. Lantana.

1970. Flowers. Multicoloured.

107. 1 c. Type 65 .. .. 20 20
108. 2 c. "Indian Shot" .. 45 25
109. 5 c. Pulau 85 40
110. 25 c. Wild Gladiolus .. 2·00 1·10

69. Auntie and Ann (grouper).

1970. Fishes. Multicoloured.

111. 5 c. Type 69 .. .. 2·75 70
112. 10 c. Dream Fish (rudder fish) .. .. .. 2·75 85
113. 15 c. Elwyn's Trousers (wrasse) .. .. .. 3·25 1·00
114. 20 c. Whistling Daughter (wrasse) .. .. .. 3·50 1·25

1971. Royal Visit. No. 101a. optd. **ROYAL VISIT 1971.**

115. 10 c. multicoloured .. 2·25 3·00

71. Polynesian Rock Carvings.

1971. Polynesian Pitcairn. Multicoloured.

116. 5 c. Type 71 .. .. 1·75 1·00
117. 10 c. Polynesian artifacts (horiz.) .. .. .. 2·25 1·25
118. 15 c. Polynesian stone fish-hook (horiz.) .. .. 2·50 1·25
119. 20 c. Polynesian stone deity 2·50 1·50

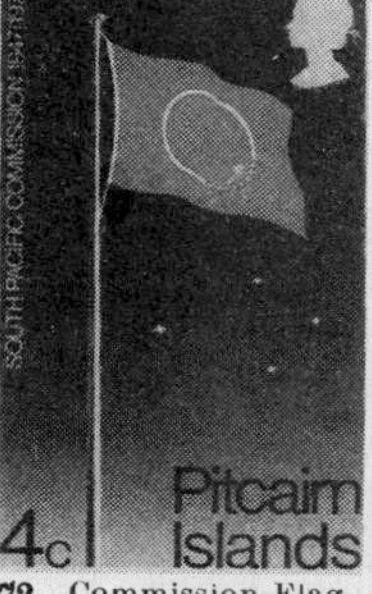

72. Commission Flag.

74. Rose-apple.

1972. 25th Anniv. of South Pacific Commission. Multicoloured.
120. 4 c. Type **72** .. .. 1·00 1·00
121. 8 c. Young and Elderly (Health) .. .. 1·00 1·00
122. 18 c. Junior School (Education) .. .. 1·50 1·50
123. 20 c. Goods Store (Economy) .. .. 2·00 2·00

1972. Royal Silver Wedding. As T **52** of Ascension, but with Red-tailed tropic birds and longboat in background.
124. 4 c. green 40 60
125. 20 c. blue 60 90

1973. Flowers. Multicoloured.
126. 4 c. Type **74** .. .. 1·25 55
127. 8 c. Mountain-apple .. .. 1·75 75
128. 15 c. "Lata" .. .. 3·00 1·00
129. 20 c. "Dorcas-flower" .. 3·25 1·25
130. 35 c. Guava .. .. 4·00 1·75

1973. Royal Wedding. As T **47** of Anguilla. Multicoloured, background colours given.
131. 10 c. mauve 30 15
132. 25 c. green 35 30

75. Horn-shell and Mitres.

1974. Shells. Multicoloured.
147. 4 c. Type **75** .. .. 1·50 60
148. 10 c. Dove-shell .. .. 1·75 80
149. 18 c. Limpet and False Limpet .. .. 2·00 1·00
150. 50 c. Lucine shell .. .. 2·75 1·25

76. Island Post Office.

1974. Centenary of U.P.U.
152. **76.** 4 c. multicoloured .. 25 30
153. – 20 c. pur., brn. & blk. 40 50
154. – 35 c. multicoloured .. 50 60
DESIGNS: 20 c. Pre-stamp letter, 1922. 35 c. Mailship and Pitcairn Longboat.

77. Churchill and Text " Lift up your Hearts . . . ".

1974. Birth Cent. of Sir Winston Churchill.
155. **77.** 20 c. olive, grn. & grey 50 85
156. – 35 c. brn., grn. and grey 75 90
DESIGN: 35 c. Text " Give us the tools . . . ".

78. H.M.S. " Seringapatam ", 1830.

1975. Mailboats. Multicoloured.
157. 4 c. Type **78** 65 60
158. 10 c. "Pitcairn" (missionary schooner), 1890 .. 70 85
159. 18 c. R.M.S. "Athenic", 1901 .. .. 80 1·40
160. 50 c. S.S. "Gothic", 1948 .. 2·00 2·75

79. "Polistes jadwigae" (wasp).

1975. Pitcairn Insects. Multicoloured.
162 4 c. Type **79** 50 45
163 6 c. "Euconocephalus sp." (grasshopper) 70 55
164 10 c. "Anomis flavia" and "Chasmina tibialis" (moth) 80 70
165 15 c. "Pantala flavescens" (skimmer) .. .. 1·25 1·25
166 20 c. "Gnathothlibus erotus" (banana moth) 1·50 1·50

80. Fletcher Christian.

1976. Bicent. of American Revolution. Mult.
167. 5 c. Type **80** 40 65
168. 10 c. H.M.S. "Bounty" .. 50 80
169. 30 c. George Washington .. 75 95
170. 50 c. "Mayflower", 1620 .. 1·00 1·50

81. Chair of Homage.

1977. Silver Jubilee. Multicoloured.
171. 8 c. Prince Philip's visit, 1971 .. .. 20 20
172. 20 c. Type **81** 30 30
173. 50 c. Enthronement .. 50 50

82. The Island's Bell.

1977. Multicoloured.
174. 1 c. Type **82** 30 40
175. 2 c. Building a longboat .. 30 40
176. 5 c. Landing cargo .. 35 40
177. 6 c. Sorting supplies .. 30 40
178. 9 c. Cleaning wahoo (fish) .. 30 40
179. 10 c. Cultivation 30 40
179a. 15 c. Sugar Mill .. .. 1·25 1·00
180. 20 c. Grating coconut and bananas 30 40
181. 35 c. The Island church .. 35 70
182. 50 c. Fetching miro logs, Henderson Is. .. 45 80
182a. 70 c. Burning obsolete stamp issues .. 1·25 1·25
183. $1 Prince Philip, Bounty Bay and Royal Yacht " Britannia " .. 65 1·10
184. $2 Queen Elizabeth II (Photograph by Reginald Davis) .. .. 1·25 1·75
The 1 c., 9 c., 70 c. and $2 are vert. designs.

83. Building a " Bounty " Model.

1978. " Bounty " Day. Multicoloured.
185. 6 c. Type **83** 40 35
186. 20 c. The model at sea .. 70 60
187. 35 c. Burning the model .. 85 70

85. Harbour before Development.

1978. "Operation Pallium" (Harbour Development Project). Multicoloured.
190. 15 c. Type **85** 30 40
191. 20 c. Unloading R.F.A. "Sir Geraint" .. 40 50
192. 30 c. Work on the jetty .. 45 55
193. 35 c. Harbour after improvements 50 60

86. John Adams and Diary Extract.

1979. 150th Death Anniv. of John Adams. Multicoloured.
194. 35 c. Type **86** 40 70
195. 70 c. John Adams' grave and diary extract .. 60 90

87. Pitcairn's Island sketched from H.M.S. " Amphitrite ".

1979. 19th-century Engravings.
196. **87.** 6 c. black, brown & stone 15 20
197. – 9 c. black, vio. & pale vio. 15 25
198. – 20 c. black, green & yell. 15 40
199. – 70 c. black, scarlet & red 50 1·00
DESIGNS: 9 c. Bounty Bay and Village of Pitcairn. 20 c. Lookout Ridge. 70 c. Church and School House.

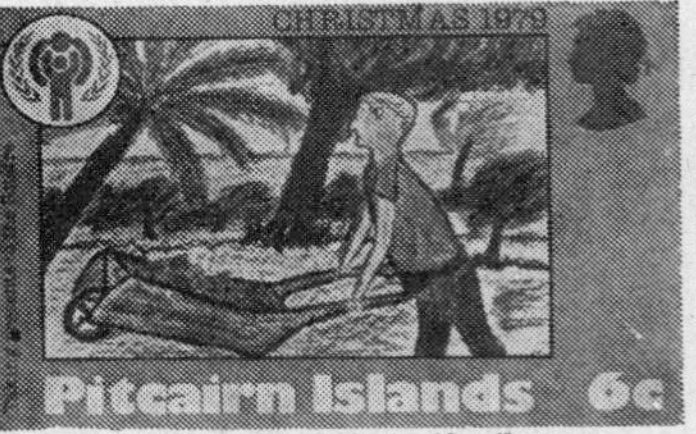

88. Taking Presents to the Square.

1979. Christmas. International Year of the Child. Multicoloured.
200. 6 c. Type **88** 15 20
201. 9 c. Decorating trees with presents 15 20
202. 20 c. Chosen men distributing gifts 25 35
203. 35 c. Carrying presents home 30 40

90. Queen Elizabeth the Queen Mother at Henley Regatta.

1980. 80th Birthday of The Queen Mother.
206. **90.** 50 c. multicoloured .. 50 70

1980. Handicrafts (2nd series). As T **46.** Multicoloured.
207. 9 c. Turtles (wood carvings) 10 10
208. 20 c. Pitcairn wheelbarrow (wood carving) .. 10 15
209. 35 c. Gannet (wood carving) (vert.) 15 25
210. 40 c. Woven bonnet and fan (vert.) 15 25

91. Part of Adamstown.

1981. Scenic Views. Multicoloured.
211. 6 c. Type **91** 10 10
212. 9 c. Big George 10 15
213. 20 c. Christian's Cave, Gannets Ridge 15 20
214. 35 c. Radio Station from Pawala Valley Ridge .. 20 30
215. 70 c. Tatrimoa 30 45

92. Islanders preparing for Departure.

1981. 125th Anniv. of Pitcairn Islanders' Migration to Norfolk Island. Multicoloured.
216. 9 c. Type **92** 15 20
217. 35 c. View of Pitcairn Island from " Morayshire " .. 30 45
218. 70 c. " Morayshire " .. 45 65

93. Prince Charles as Colonel-in-Chief, Cheshire Regiment.

1981. Royal Wedding. Multicoloured.
219. 20 c. Wedding bouquet from Pitcairn Islands .. 25 25
220. 35 c. Type **93** 40 40
221. $1·20 Prince Charles and Lady Diana Spencer .. 75 85

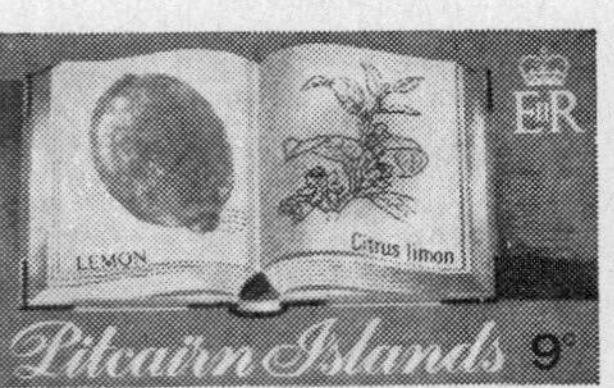

94. Lemon.

1982. Fruit. Multicoloured.
222. 9 c. Type **94** 10 10
223. 20 c. Pomegranate .. 15 20
224. 35 c. Avocado .. 25 30
225. 70 c. Pawpaw 50 65

95. Pitcairn Islands Coat of Arms.

1982. 21st Birthday of Princess of Wales. Multicoloured.
226. 6 c. Type **95** 10 20
227. 9 c. Princess at Royal Opera House, Covent Garden, December, 1981 10 20
228. 70 c. Balcony Kiss .. 50 75
229. $1.20 Formal portrait .. 80 1·10

96. Raphael's Angels.

1982. Christmas. Raphael's Angels.

230. **96.** 15 c. black, silver and pink 15 15
231. – 20 c. black, silver and yellow 20 20
232. – 50 c. brown, silver and stone 45 45
233. – $1 black, silver and blue 85 85

Designs: 20 c. to $1 Different details, the 50 c. and $1 being vertical.

97. Radio Operator.

1983. Commonwealth Day. Multicoloured.

234. 6 c. Type **97** 10 10
235. 9 c. Postal Clerk 10 10
236. 70 c. Fisherman 50 65
237. $1 20 Artist .. .. 80 1·10

98. " Topaz " sights Smoke on Pitcairn.

1983. 175th Anniv. of Folger's Discovery of the Settlers. Multicoloured.

238. 6 c. Type **98** 20 15
239. 20 c. Three islanders approach the "Topaz" .. 30 30
240. 70 c. Capt. Mayhew Folger welcomed by John Adams 75 75
241. $1.20 Folger presented with "Bounty" chronometer 1·10 1·10

99. Hattie-Tree.

1983. Trees of Pitcairn Islands (1st series). Multicoloured.

242. 35 c. Type **99** 30 55
243. 35 c. Leaves from Hattie-Tree 30 55
244. 70 c. Pandanus 65 90
245. 70 c. Pandanus and basket weaving 65 90

See also Nos. 304/7.

100. " Pseudojuloides atavai ".

1984. Fishes. Multicoloured.

246 1 c. Type **100** 20 30
247 4 c. "Halichoeres melasmopomus 30 35
248 6 c. "Scarus longipinnis" 30 35
249 9 c. "Variola louti" .. 30 35
250 10 c. "Centropyge hotumatua" 30 40
251 15 c. "Stegastes emeryi" .. 30 40
252 20 c. "Chaetodon smithi" 40 50
253 35 c. "Xanthichthys mento" 50 60
254 50 c. "Chrysiptera galba" 50 75
255 70 c. "Genicanthus spinus" 70 95
312 90 c. As 9 c. .. .. 1·75 1·75
256 $1 "Myripristis tiki" .. 90 1·25
257 $1.20 "Anthias ventralis" 1·75 2·00
258 $2 "Pseudocaranx dentex" 2·25 2·50
313 $3 "Gymnothorax eurostus" 4·25 4·25

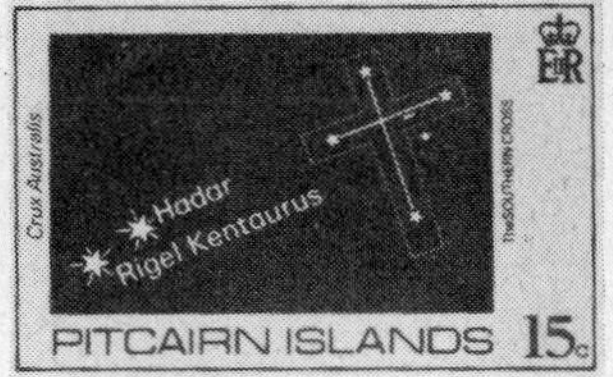

101. Southern Cross.

1984. Night Sky.

259. **101.** 15 c. blue, lilac & gold 20 20
260. – 20 c. blue, green & gold 30 30
261. – 70 c. blue, brown & gold 75 75
262. – $1 blue, lt. blue & gold 1·00 1·00

Designs: 20 c. Southern Fish. 70 c. Lesser Dog. $1 The Virgin.

103. "H.M.S. "Portland" standing off Bounty Bay". (J. Linton Palmer).

1985. 19th-Century Paintings (1st series). Multicoloured.

264. 6 c. Type **103** 30 20
265. 9 c. "Christian's Look Out" (J. Linton Palmer) .. 30 20
266. 35 c. "The Golden Age" (J. Linton Palmer) .. 70 50
267. $2 "A View of the Village, 1825" (William Smyth) (48×31) mm.) .. .. 2·00 1·60

See also Nos. 308/11.

104. The Queen Mother with the Queen and Princess Margaret, 1980.

1985. Life and Times of Queen Elizabeth the Queen Mother. Multicoloured.

268 6 c. Receiving the Freedom of Dundee, 1964 .. 10 20
269 35 c. Type **104** 40 55
270 70 c. The Queen Mother in 1983 .. .. .. 70 90
271 $1·20 With Prince Henry at his christening (from photo by Lord Snowdon) 1·10 1·40

105. "Act 6" (container ship).

1985. Ships (1st issue). Multicoloured.

273. 50 c. Type **105** .. .. 1·00 1·25
274. 50 c. "Columbus Lousiana" (container ship) .. .. 1·00 1·25
275. 50 c. "Essi Gina" (tanker) (48×35 mm.) .. .. 1·00 1·25
276. 50 c. "Stolt Spirit" tanker (48×35 mm.) .. 1·00 1·25

See also Nos. 296/9.

106. "Madonna and Child" (Raphael).

1985. Christmas. Designs showing "Madonna and Child" paintings. Multicoloured.

277. 6 c. Type **106** 30 20
278. 9 c. Krause (after Raphael) 30 20
279. 35 c. Andreas Mayer .. 65 50
280. $2 Unknown Austrian master .. .. .. 2·25 2·50

107. Green Turtle.

1986. Turtles. Multicoloured.

281. 9 c. Type **107** 75 75
282. 20 c. Green Turtle and Pitcairn Island .. .. 1·25 1·25
283. 70 c. Hawksbill Turtle .. 2·50 2·50
284. $1.20 Hawksbill Turtle and Pitcairn Island .. .. 3·25 3·25

1986. 60th Birthday of Queen Elizabeth II. As T **110** of Ascension. Multicoloured.

285. 6 c. Princess Elizabeth at Royal Lodge, Windsor, 1946 .. .. .. 15 15
286. 9 c. Wedding of Princess Anne, 1973 .. .. 15 15
287. 20 c. At Order of St. Michael and St. George service, St. Paul's Cathedral, 1961 .. .. 30 30
288. $1.20 At Electrical Engineering Concert, Royal Festival Hall, 1971 1·10 1·25
289. $2 At Crown Agents Head Office, London, 1983 .. 1·75 2·00

1986. Royal Wedding. As T **112** of Ascension. Multicoloured.

290 20 c. Prince Andrew and Miss Sarah Ferguson .. 50 50
291 $1.20 Prince Andrew aboard "Bluenose II" off Halifax, Canada, 1985 .. 1·75 1·75

108. John I. Tay (pioneer missionary) and First Church.

1986. Centenary of Seventh-Day Adventist Church on Pitcairn. Multicoloured.

292. 6 c. Type **108** 40 40
293. 20 c. "Pitcairn" (mission schooner) and second church (1907) .. .. 1·00 1·00
294. 35 c. Baptism at Down Isaac and third church (1945) .. .. .. 1·50 1·50
295. $2 Islanders singing farewell hymn and present church (1954) .. .. 3·25 3·25

1987. Ships (2nd series). As T **105**. Multicoloured.

296. 50 c. "Samoan Reefer" (freighter) .. .. 1·25 1·50
297. 50 c. "Brussel" (container ship) .. .. .. 1·25 1·50
298. 50 c. "Australian Exporter" (container ship) (48×35 mm.) .. 1·25 1·50
299. 50 c. "Taupo" (cargo liner) (48×35 mm.) .. 1·25 1·50

109. Pitcairn Island Home.

1987. Pitcairn Island Homes.

300. **109.** 70 c. black, deep violet and violet 75 60
301. – 70 c. black, yellow and brown 75 60
302. – 70 c. black, blue and deep blue 75 60
303. – 70 c. black, green and deep green 75 60

Designs: Nos. 301/3 different houses.

1987. Trees of Pitcairn Islands (2nd series). As T **99.** Multicoloured.

304. 40 c. Leaves and flowers from "Erythrina variegata" 70 70
305. 40 c. "Erythrina variegata" tree 70 70
306. $1.80 Leaves from "Aleurites moluccana" and nut torch .. .. 2·00 2·00
307. $1.80 "Aleurites moluccana" tree .. 2·00 2·00

1987. 19th-Century Paintings (2nd series). Paintings by Lt. Conway Shipley in 1848. As T **103.** Multicoloured.

308. 20 c. "House and Tomb of John Adams" 45 45
309. 40 c. "Bounty Bay" .. 70 70
310. 90 c. "School House and Chapel" .. .. .. 1·25 1·25
311. $1.80 "Pitcairn Island" (48×31 mm.) .. .. 2·00 2·00

111 H.M.S. "Swallow" (survey ship), 1767

1988. Ships. Multicoloured.

315 5 c. Type **111** 10 10
316 10 c. H.M.S. "Pandora" (frigate), 1791 .. .. 10 10
317 15 c. H.M.S. "Briton" and H.M.S. "Tagus" (frigates), 1814 .. .. 10 15
318 20 c. H.M.S. "Blossom" (survey ship), 1825 .. 10 15
319 30 c. "Lucy Anne" (barque), 1831 .. .. 20 25
320 35 c. "Charles Doggett" (whaling ship), 1831 .. 25 30
321 40 c. H.M.S. "Fly" (sloop), 1838 .. .. .. 25 30
322 60 c. "Camden" (missionary brig), 1840 .. .. 40 45
323 90 c. H.M.S. "Virago" (paddle-sloop), 1853 .. 60 65
324 $1.20 "Rakaia" (screw-steamer), 1867 .. .. 80 85
325 $1.80 H.M.S. "Sappho" (screw-sloop), 1882 .. 1·25 1·40
326 $5 H.M.S. "Champion" (corvette), 1893 .. 3·25 3·50

INDEX

Countries can be quickly located by referring to the index at the end of this volume.

112 Raising the Union Jack, 1838

1988. 150th Anniv of Pitcairn Island Constitution. Each showing different extract from original Constitution. Multicoloured.

327	20 c. Type **112**	15	20
328	40 c. Signing Constitution on board H.M.S. "Fly", 1838	30	35
329	$1.05 Voters at modern polling station	75	80
330	$1.80 Modern classroom ..	1·25	1·40

113 Angel

1988. Christmas. Multicoloured.

331	90 c. Type **113**	65	70
332	90 c. Holy Family ..	65	70
333	90 c. Two Polynesian Wise Men	65	70
334	90 c. Polynesian Wise Man and shepherd	65	70

114 Loading Stores, Deptford

1989. Bicentenary of Pitcairn Island Settlement (1st issue). Multicoloured.

335	20 c. Type **114**	30	30
336	20 c. H.M.S. "Bounty" leaving Spithead ..	30	30
337	20 c. H.M.S. "Bounty" at Cape Horn	30	30
338	20 c. Anchored in Adventure Bay, Tasmania	30	30
339	20 c. Crew collecting breadfruit	30	30
340	20 c. Breadfruit in cabin ..	30	30

See also Nos. 341/7, 356/61 and 389/94.

1989. Bicentenary of Pitcairn Island Settlement (2nd issue). As T **114**. Mult.

341	90 c. H.M.S. "Bounty" leaving Tahiti	1·10	1·10
342	90 c. Bligh awoken by mutineers	1·10	1·10
343	90 c. Bligh before Fletcher Christian	1·10	1·10
344	90 c. Provisioning "Bounty's" launch ..	1·10	1·10
345	90 c. "Mutineers casting Bligh adrift" (Robert Dodd)	1·10	1·10
346	90 c. Mutineers discarding breadfruit plants ..	1·10	1·10

115 R.N.Z.A.F. "Orion" making Mail Drop, 1985

1989. Aircraft. Multicoloured.

348	20 c. Type **115**	25	25
349	80 c. Beechcraft "Queen Air" on photo-mission, 1983	80	80
350	$1.05 Helicopter landing diesel fuel from U.S.S. "Breton", 1969 ..	1·10	1·10
351	$1.30 R.N.Z.A.F. "Hercules" dropping bulldozer, 1983	1·25	1·25

116 Ducie Island

1989. Islands of Pitcairn Group. Mult.

352	15 c. Type **116**	15	15
353	90 c. Henderson Island ..	90	90
354	$1.05 Oeno Island ..	1·00	1·00
355	$1.30 Pitcairn Island ..	1·25	1·25

1990. Bicentenary of Pitcairn Island Settlement (3rd issue). As T **114**. Multicoloured.

356	40 c. Mutineers sighting Pitcairn Island ..	40	40
357	40 c. Ship's boat approaching landing ..	40	40
358	40 c. Exploring island ..	40	40
359	40 c. Ferrying goods ashore	40	40
360	40 c. Burning of H.M.S. "Bounty"	40	40
361	40 c. Pitcairn Island village	40	40

117 Ennerdale, Cumbria, and Peter Heywood

1990. "Stamp World London 90" International Stamp Exhibition, London. Designs showing English landmarks and "Bounty" crew members. Multicoloured.

362	80 c. Type **117**	75	80
363	90 c. St. Augustine's Tower, Hackney, and John Adams ..	85	90
364	$1.05 Citadel Gateway, Plymouth, and William Bligh	1·00	1·25
365	$1.30 Moorland Close, Cockermouth, and Fletcher Christian ..	1·25	1·40

1990. 90th Birthday of Queen Elizabeth the Queen Mother. As T **134** of Ascension.

378	40 c. multicoloured	50	50
379	$3 black and red	2·50	2·50

DESIGNS—21 × 36 mm. 40 c. Queen Elizabeth, 1937. 29 × 37 mm. $3 King George VI and Queen Elizabeth on way to Silver Wedding Service, 1948.

118 "Bounty" Chronometer and 1940 1d. Definitive

1990. 50th Anniv of Pitcairn Islands Stamps. Multicoloured.

380	20 c. Type **118**	30	30
381	80 c. "Bounty" Bible and 1958 4d. definitive ..	80	80
382	90 c. "Bounty" Bell and 1969 30 c. definitive ..	90	90
383	$1.05 Mutiny on the "Bounty" and 1977 $1 definitive	1·00	1·00
384	$1.30 Penny Black and 1988 15 c. definitive ..	1·40	1·40

119 Stephen's Lory ("Red-breast")

1990. "Birdpex '90" International Stamp Exhibition, Christchurch, New Zealand. Multicoloured.

385	20 c. Type **119**	30	30
386	90 c. Grey-green fruit dove ("Wood pigeon") ..	1·10	1·10
387	$1.30 Pitcairn warbler ("Sparrow")	1·40	1·40
388	$1.80 Henderson Island crake ("Chicken bird")	1·60	1·60

1991. Bicent of Pitcairn Islands Settlement (4th issue). Celebrations. As T **114**. Mult.

389	80 c. Re-enacting landing of mutineers	90	1·10
390	80 c. Commemorative plaque	90	1·10
391	80 c. Memorial church service	90	1·10
392	80 c. Cricket match ..	90	1·10
393	80 c. Burning model of "Bounty"	90	1·10
394	80 c. Firework display ..	90	1·10

120 "Europa"

1991. Cruise Liners. Multicoloured.

395	15 c. Type **120** ..	20	20
396	80 c. "Royal Viking Star"	85	85
397	$1.30 "World Discoverer"	1·25	1·25
398	$1.80 "Sagafjord" ..	1·90	1·90

1991. 65th Birthday of Queen Elizabeth II and 70th Birthday of Prince Philip. As T **280** of Antigua. Multicoloured.

399	20 c. Prince Philip (vert) ..	40	30
400	$1.30 Queen in robes of the Order of St. Michael and St. George (vert) ..	1·60	1·25

121 Bulldozer

1991. Island Transport. Multicoloured.

401	20 c. Type **121**	20	20
402	80 c. Two-wheeled motor-cycle	75	75
403	$1.30 Tractor	1·25	1·25
404	$1.80 Three-wheeled motor-cycle	1·90	1·90

122 The Annunciation

1991. Christmas. Multicoloured.

405	20 c. Type **122** ..	20	20
406	80 c. Shepherds and lamb	75	75
407	$1.30 Holy Family ..	1·10	1·10
408	$1.80 Three Wise Men ..	1·75	1·75

1992. 40th Anniv of Queen Elizabeth II's Accession. As T **143** of Ascension. Mult.

409	20 c. Bounty Bay ..	15	15
410	60 c. Sunset over Pitcairn	60	60
411	90 c. Pitcairn coastline ..	85	85
412	$1 Three portraits of Queen Elizabeth ..	90	90
413	$1.80 Queen Elizabeth II	1·60	1·60

POONCH

A state in Kashmir, India. Now uses Indian stamps.

12 pies = 1 anna; 16 annas = 1 rupee.

1.

4.

1876. Imperf.

1.	**1.**	6 pies red	£2000	85·00
2.		½ a. red	—	£950

1880. Imperf.

32.	**1.**	1 pice red	40	80
12	**4.**	½ a. red	1·25	2·00
50.		1 a. red	40	75
52.		2 a. red (22 × 22 mm.) ..	60	1·00
31.		4 a. red (28 × 27 mm.) ..	2·25	2·25

These stamps were printed on various coloured papers.

OFFICIAL STAMPS

1888. Imperf.

O 1.	**1.**	1 pice black	80	90
O 2.	**4.**	½ a. black	80	1·25
O 3.		1 a. black	70	1·00
O 4.		2 a. black	1·25	1·25
O 5.		4 a. black	3·00	3·50

PRINCE EDWARD ISLAND

An island off the E. coast of Canada, now a province of that Dominion, whose stamps it uses.

1861. 12 pence = 1 shilling.
1872. 100 cents = 1 dollar.

1.

7.

1861. Queen's portrait in various frames. Values in pence.

9	1	1d. orange	8·50	13·00
28		2d. red	5·50	8·00
30		3d. blue	6·00	8·50
16		4d. black	12·00	15·00
18		6d. green	17·00	17·00
20		9d. mauve	16·00	16·00

1870.

32.	**7.**	4½d. (3d. stg.) brown ..	13·00	26·00

8.

1872. Queen's portrait in various frames. Values in cents.

35	**8.**	1 c. orange	1·60	7·00
38		2 c. blue	8·00	24·00
37		3 c. red	3·25	7·00
40		4 c. green	2·50	10·00
41		6 c. black	1·60	10·00
42		12 c. mauve	1·60	20·00

QATAR

An independent Arab Shaikhdom with British postal administration until May 23, 1963; later issues by the Qatar Post Department. The stamps of Muscat were formerly used at the Capital, Doha and at Umm Said.

100 naye paise = 1 rupee.
Stamps of Great Britain surcharged **QATAR** and value in Indian currency.

1957. Queen Elizabeth II and pictorials.

1.	**157.**	1 n.p. on 5d. brown ..	10	10
2.	**154.**	3 n.p. on ½d. orange ..	15	15
3.		6 n.p. on 1d. blue ..	15	15
4.		9 n.p. on 1½d. green ..	15	10
5.		12 n.p. on 2d. pale brown	20	30
6.	**155.**	15 n.p. on 2½d. red ..	15	10
7.		20 n.p. on 3d. lilac ..	15	10
8.		25 n.p. on 4d. blue ..	40	40
9.	**157.**	40 n.p. on 6d. purple ..	15	10
10.	**158.**	50 n.p. on 9d. olive ..	40	15
11.	**159.**	75 n.p. on 1s. 3d. green	50	50
12.		1 r. on 1s. 6d. blue ..	5·50	10
13.	**166.**	2 r. on 2s. 6d. brown ..	4·00	1·00
14.	–	5 r. on 5s. red ..	7·00	2·75
15.	–	10 r. on 10s. blue ..	8·50	8·50

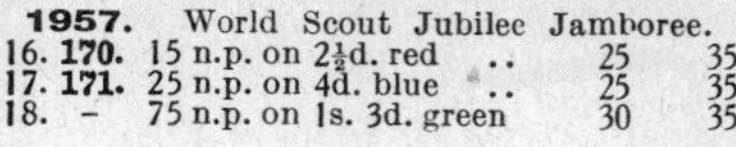

1957. World Scout Jubilee Jamboree.

16.	**170.**	15 n.p. on 2½d. red ..	25	35
17.	**171.**	25 n.p. on 4d. blue ..	25	35
18.	–	75 n.p. on 1s. 3d. green	30	35

8. Shaikh Ahmed bin Ali al Thani.

9. Peregrine Falcon.

11. Oil Derrick.

1961.

27.	**8.**	5 n.p. red	10	10
28.		15 n.p. black	10	10
29.		20 n.p. purple	10	10
30.		30 n.p. green	10	10
31.	**9.**	40 n.p. red	85	10
32.		50 n.p. brown	1·25	10
33.	–	75 n.p. blue	60	60
34.	**11.**	1 r. red	70	10
35.		2 r. blue	2·00	25
36.	–	5 r. green	9·00	80
37.	–	10 r. black	19·00	1·75

DESIGNS—As Type **9**; 75 n.p. Dhow. As Type **11**: 5 r., 10 r. Mosque.

QUEENSLAND

The N.E. state of the Commonwealth of Australia whose stamps it now uses.

12 pence = 1 shilling
20 shillings = 1 pound.

1.

7.

1860. Imperf.

1.	**1.**	1d. red	£2250	£800
2.		2d. blue	£5000	£1500
3.		6d. green	£3500	£800

1860. Perf.

94	1	1d. red	38·00	5·00
99		2d. blue	22·00	1·00
101		3d. brown	60·00	9·00
65		3d. green	80·00	5·00
53		4d. grey	£150	20·00
55		4d. lilac	90·00	16·00
103		4d. yellow	£600	20·00
27		6d. green	80·00	12·00
108		1s. purple	40·00	9·00
29		1s. grey	£130	22·00
119		2s. blue	60·00	22·00
121		2s. 6d. red	£110	40·00
58		5s. red	£200	55·00
123		5s. yellow	£150	60·00
125		10s. brown	£350	£110
127		20s. red	£700	£130

1879.

134.	**7.**	1d. brown	32·00	5·00
135.		1d. orange	9·00	3·00
136.		1d. red	12·00	1·75
138.		2d. blue	25·00	1·00
141.		4d. yellow	£100	10·00
142.		6d. green..	55·00	4·50
145.		1s. mauve	45·00	5·50

1880. No. 136 surch. **Half-penny.**

151.	**7.**	½d. on 1d. brown ..	£160	90·00

9.

13.

12.

14.

1882.

152.	**9.**	2s. blue	60·00	17·00
162.		2s. 6d. orange	38·00	20·00
163.		5s. red	35·00	28·00
164.		10s. brown	95·00	40·00
165.		£1 green	£170	60·00

1882. Shaded background around head.

184	**13.**	½d. green..	2·75	50
206	**12.**	1d. orange	2·00	15
204		2d. blue	3·00	20
191	**14.**	2½d. red	10·00	55
192	**12.**	3d. brown	8·50	1·40
169		4d. yellow	12·00	1·40
170		6d. green..	9·00	70
173		1s. mauve	11·00	1·40
197		2s. brown	38·00	7·50

15.

16.

17.

1895. Head on white background.

208	15	½d. green	1·00	45
211	16	1d. red	2·00	20
212		2d. blue	3·25	35
213	17	2½d. red	8·00	3·00
215		5d. brown	10·00	2·75

19.

21.

1896.

229.	**19.**	1d. red	7·50	40

1897. Same designs, but figures in all four corners, as T **21**.

286		½d. green	1·00	20
288		1d. red	1·00	15
234		2d. blue	1·25	15
236		2½d. red	15·00	6·00
238		2½d. purple on blue ..	8·50	85
241		3d. brown	8·00	80
244		4d. yellow	8·00	80
294		4d. black	12·00	1·50
246		5d. brown	7·00	80
250		6d. green	6·00	1·25
298		1s. mauve	11·00	1·60
300		2s. green	30·00	6·50

26.

28.

27.

1899.

287.	**26.**	½d. green	1·00	20

1900. S. African War Charity. Inscr. "PATRIOTIC FUND 1900".

264a.	**27.**	1d. (1s.) mauve ..	£100	£100
264b.	–	2d. (2s.) violet (horiz.)	£225	£225

1903.

265.	**28.**	9d. brown and blue ..	10·00	1·75

REGISTRATION STAMP

1861. Inscr. "REGISTERED".

20.	**1.**	(No value) yellow ..	45·00	35·00

RAJASTHAN

Formed in 1948 from states in Rajputana, India, which included Bundi, Jaipur and Kishangarh whose separate posts functioned until 1 April 1950. Now uses Indian stamps.

12 pies = 1 anna; 16 annas = 1 rupee.

BUNDI

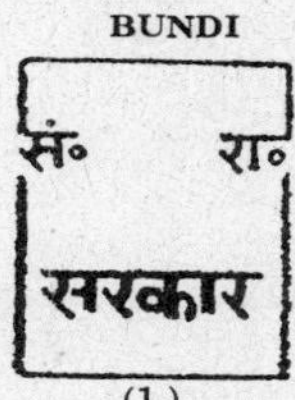

(1.)

1949. Nos. 86/92 of Bundi handstamped or optd. by machine with T **1**.

1.	**21.**	¼ a. green	2·25	
2.		½ a. violet	2·25	
3.		1 a. green	2·25	
11.	–	2 a. red	1·75	22·00
12.	–	4 a. orange	2·00	22·00
6.	–	8 a. blue	2·50	
14.	–	1 r. brown	7·00	

Nos. 1, 2, 3 and 6 used are worth about three times the unused prices.

JAIPUR

राजस्थान

RAJASTHAN
(2.)

1949. Stamps of Jaipur optd. with T **2**.

15.	**7.**	¼ a. black and purple ..	3·00	7·50
16.		½ a. black and violet ..	2·50	7·50
17.		¾ a. black and orange ..	3·00	8·00
18.		1 a. black and blue ..	3·50	13·00
19.		2 a. black and orange ..	3·25	14·00
20.		2½ a. black and red ..	4·25	11·00
21.		3 a. black and green ..	4·25	24·00
22.		4 a black and green ..	4·25	28·00
23		6 a. black and blue ..	5·50	35·00
24.		8 a. black and brown ..	8·00	45·00
25.		1 r. black and bistre ..	10·00	65·00

KISHANGARH

1949. Stamps of Kishangarh handstamped with T **1**.

(a) On stamps of 1899.

26a	**2**	¼ a. pink	—	70·00
27		½ a. blue	85·00	
29		1 a. lilac	14·00	27·00
30		4 a. brown	32·00	45·00
31		1 r. green	95·00	£100
31a		2 r. red	£120	
32		5 r. mauve	£120	£120

(b) On stamps of 1904.

33	**13**	½ a. brown	—	45·00
33a		1 a. blue	—	65·00
34		4 a. brown	12·00	
35	**2**	8 a. grey	45·00	70·00
36	**13**	8 a. violet	11·00	
37		1 r. green	11·00	
38		2 r. yellow	17·00	
39		5 r. brown	17·00	

(c) On stamps of 1912.

40.	**14.**	½ a. green	—	50·00
41.	–	1 a. red	—	50·00
43.		2 a. purple	1·40	5·00
44.		4 a. blue	—	£160
45.		8 a. brown	5·00	
46.		1 r. mauve	10·00	
47.		2 r. green	10·00	
48		5 r. brown	£130	

(d) On stamps of 1928.

55	**16**	¼ a. blue	27·00	27·00
57		½ a. green	14·00	14·00
58	–	1 a. red	17·00	17·00
59	–	2 a. purple	42·00	42·00
61	**16**	4 a. brown	1·75	5·00
51		8 a. violet	6·00	35·00
62		1 r. green	6·00	
53		2 r. yellow	14·00	
54		5 r. red	14·00	

RAJPIPLA

A state of Bombay, India. Now uses Indian stamps.

12 pies = 1 anna; 12 annas = 1 rupee.

1. (1 pice).

2. (2 a.).

1880.

No.	Type	Description	Unused	Used
1.	1.	1 p. blue	60	12·00
2.	2.	2 a. green	11·00	32·00
3.		4 a. red	4·25	20·00

REDONDA

A dependency of Antigua.

The following stamps were issued in anticipation of commercial and tourist development, philatelic mail being handled by a bureau in Antigua. Since at the present time the island is uninhabited, we do not list or stock these items. It is understood that the stamps are valid for the prepayment of postage in Antigua. Miniature sheets, imperforate stamps etc., are excluded from this section.

1979.

Antigua 1976 definitive issue optd. **REDONDA.** 3, 5, 10, 25, 35, 50, 75 c., $1, 2.50, 5, 10.

Antigua Coronation Anniversary issue optd. **REDONDA.** 10, 30, 50, 90 c., $2.50.

Antigua World Cup Football Championship issue optd. **REDONDA.** 10, 15 c., $3.

Death Centenary of Sir Rowland Hill. 50, 90 c., $2.50, 3.

International Year of the Child. 25, 50 c., $1, 2.

Christmas. Paintings. 8, 50, 90 c., $3.

1980.

Marine Life. 8, 25, 50 c., $4.

Rotary International. 75th Anniv. 25, 50 c., $1, 2.

Birds of Redonda. 8, 10, 15, 25, 30, 50 c., $1, 2, 5.

Olympic Medal Winners, Lake Placid and Moscow. 8, 25, 50 c., $3.

80th Birthday of Queen Elizabeth the Queen Mother. 10 c., $2.50.

Christmas. Paintings. 8, 25, 50 c., $4.

1981.

Royal Wedding 25, 55 c., $4.

Christmas. Walt Disney Cartoon Characters. ½, 1, 2, 3, 4, 5, 10 c., $2·50, $3.

World Cup Football Championship, Spain (1982). 30 c. × 2, 50 c. × 2. $1 × 2, $2 × 2.

1982.

Boy Scout Annivs. 8, 25, 50 c. $3, $5.

Butterflies. 8, 30, 50 c.; $2.

21st Birthday of Princess of Wales. $2, $4.

Birth of Prince William of Wales. Optd on Princess of Wales 21st Birthday issue. $2, $4.

Christmas. Walt Disney's " One Hundred and One Dalmations ". ½, 1, 2, 3, 4, 5, 10; $2.50, $3.

1983.

Easter. 500th Birth Anniv. of Raphael. 10, 50, 90 c., $5.

Bicent. of Manned Flight. 10, 50, 90 c., $2.50.

Christmas. Walt Disney Cartoon Characters. "Deck the Halls". ½, 1, 2, 3, 4, 5, 10 c., $2.50, $3.

1984.

Easter. Walt Disney Cartoon Characters. ½, 1, 2, 3, 4, 5, 10 c., $2, $4.

Olympic Games, Los Angeles. 10, 50, 90 c., $2.50.

Christmas. 50th Birthday of Donald Duck. 45, 60, 90 c., $2, $4.

1985.

Birth Bicentenary of John J. Audubon (ornithologist) (1st issue). 60, 90 c., $1, $3.

Life and Times of Queen Elizabeth the Queen Mother, $1, $1.50, $2.50.

Royal Visit. 45 c., $1, $4.

150th Birth Anniv. of Mark Twain (author). 25, 50 c., $1.50, $3.

Birth Bicentenaries of Grimm Brothers (folklorists). Walt Disney cartoon characters. 30, 60, 70 c., $4.

1986.

Birth Bicentenary of John J. Audubon (ornithologist) (2nd issue). 90 c., $1, $1.50, $3.

Appearance of Halley's Comet. 5, 15, 55 c., $4.

Centenary of Statue of Liberty (1st issue). 20, 25, 30 c., $4.

60th Birthday of Queen Elizabeth II. 50, 60 c., $4.

Royal Wedding. 60 c., $1, $4.

Christmas (1st issue). Disney characters in Hans Andersen Stories. 30, 60, 70 c., $4.

Christmas (2nd issue). "Wind in the Willows" (by Kenneth Grahame). 25, 50 c., $1.50, $3.

1987.

"Capex '87" International Stamp Exhibition, Toronto. Disney characters illustrating Art of Animation. 25, 30, 50, 60, 70 c., $1.50, $3, $4.

Birth Centenary of Marc Chagall (artist). 10, 30, 40, 60, 90 c., $1, $3, $4.

Centenary of Statue of Liberty (2nd issue). 10, 15, 25, 30, 40, 60, 70, 90 c., $1, $2, $3, $4.

250th Death Anniv. of Sir Isaac Newton (scientist) 20 c., $2.50.

750th Anniv. of Berlin. $1, $4.

Bicentenary of U.S. Constitution. 30 c., $3.

16th World Scout Jamboree, Australia. 10 c., $4.

1988.

500th Anniv. (1992) of Discovery of America by Columbus. 15, 30, 45, 60, 90 c., $1, $2, $3.

"Finlandia '88" International Stamp Exhibition, Helsinki. Disney characters in Finnish scenes. 1, 2, 3, 4, 5, 6 c., $5, $6.

Olympic Games, Seoul. 25, 60 c., $1.25, $3.

500th Birth Anniv. of Titian. 10, 25, 40, 70, 90 c., $2, $3, $4.

1989.

20th Anniv of First Manned Landing on Moon. Disney characters on moon. ½, 1, 2, 3, 4, 5 c., $5, $6.

500th Anniv (1992) of Discovery of America by Columbus (2nd issue). Pre-Columbian Societies. 15, 45, 45, 50 c., $2, $2, $3, $3.

Christmas. Disney Characters and Cars of 1950's. 25, 35, 45, 60 c., $1, $2, $3, $4.

1990.

Christmas. Disney Characters and Hollywood cars. 25, 35, 40, 60 c., $1, $2, $4, $5.

1991.

Nobel Prize Winners. 5, 15, 25, 40, 50 c., $1, $2, $4.

RHODESIA

A Br. territory in S. Central Africa, formerly administered by the Br. S. Africa Co., and in 1924 divided into the territories of N. and S. Rhodesia which issued their own stamps (q.v.).

1890. 12 pence = 1 shilling
20 shillings = 1 pound.
1970. 100 cents = 1 dollar.

1. Arms of the Company.

1890. The pound values are larger.

No.	Type	Description	Unused	Used
18.	1.	½d. blue and red	2·50	1·00
1.		1d. black	9·00	1·25
20.		2d. green and red ..	8·00	1·75
21.		3d. black and green ..	8·00	1·75
22.		4d. brown and black ..	8·00	1·75
3.		6d. blue	22·00	2·50
23.		8d. red and blue	10·00	5·00
4.		1s. brown	28·00	7·50
5.		2s. red	40·00	25·00
6.		2s. 6d. purple	24·00	25·00
25.		3s. brown and green ..	95·00	65·00
26.		4s. black and red.. ..	30·00	40·00
8.	1.	5s. yellow	42·00	48·00
9.		10s. green	60·00	90·00
10.	–	£1 blue	£160	£130
11.	–	£2 red	£375	£150
12.	–	£5 green	£1500	£450
13.	–	£10 brown..	£2750	£700

1891. Surch. in figures.

No.	Type	Description	Unused	Used
14.	1.	½d. on 6d. blue	65·00	£110
15.		2d. on 6d. blue	60·00	£140
16.		4d. on 6d. blue	80·00	£180
17.		8d. on 1s. brown	90·00	£250

5. 9.

1896. The ends of ribbons containing motto cross the animals' legs.

No.	Type	Description	Unused	Used
41	5.	½d. grey and mauve ..	1·00	1·50
42		1d. red and green ..	1·50	2·25
43		2d. brown and mauve ..	4·00	3·50
31		3d. brown and blue ..	2·25	80
44a		4d. blue and mauve ..	6·00	40
46		6d. mauve and red ..	4·50	45
34		8d. green & mauve on buff	4·50	45
35		1s. green and blue ..	15·00	2·25
47		2s. blue and green on buff	20·00	3·00
48		2s. 6d. brn. & pur. on yell.	55·00	38·00
36		3s. green & mauve on blue	48·00	29·00
37		4s. red and blue on green	40·00	2·00
49		5s. brown and green ..	35·00	12·00
50		10s. grey and red on rose	80·00	60·00

1896. Surch. in words.

No.	Type	Description	Unused	Used
51.	1.	1d. on 3d. black and green	£350	£375
52.		1d. on 4s. black and red..	£250	£225
53.		3d. on 5s. yellow ..	£150	£200

1896. Cape of Good Hope stamps optd. **BRITISH SOUTH AFRICA COMPANY.**

No.	Type	Description	Unused	Used
58.	6.	½d. black (No. 48) ..	6·00	11·00
59.	17.	1d. red (No. 58a).. ..	9·50	12·00
60.	6.	2d. brown (No. 60) ..	10·00	7·50
61.		3d. red (No. 40)	45·00	55·00
62.		4d. blue (No. 51) ..	12·00	12·00
63.	4.	6d. violet (No. 52a) ..	42·00	60·00
64.	6.	1s. yellow (No. 65 ..	80·00	£110

1897. The ends of motto ribbons do not cross the animals' legs.

No.	Type	Description	Unused	Used
66.	9.	½d. grey and mauve ..	1·60	3·00
67.		1d. red and green ..	3·00	3·75
68.		2d. brown and mauve ..	3·25	60
69.		3d. brown and blue ..	2·50	30
70.		4d. blue and mauve ..	5·00	1·25
71.		6d. mauve and red ..	5·50	3·50
72.		8d. grn. and mve. on buff	8·50	40
73.		£1 black & brown on green	£400	£225

10.

11.

1898. Nos. 90/3 are larger (24 × 28½ mm.).

No.	Type	Description	Unused	Used
75.	10.	½d. green	75	20
77.		1d. red	1·00	15
79.		2d. brown	1·25	10
80.		2½d. blue	3·75	30
81.		3d. red	3·75	40
82.		4d. olive	3·75	15
83.		6d. purple	6·50	1·75
84.	11.	1s. brown	7·50	1·25
85.		2s. 6d. grey	28·00	55
86.		3s. violet	9·00	50
87.		5s. orange	24·00	8·50
88.		7s. 6d. black	45·00	14·00
89.		10s. green	15·00	1·50
90.		£1 purple	£150	60·00
91.		£2 brown	65·00	6·50
92.	–	£5 blue	£3000	£2250
93.	–	£10 lilac	£3000	£2250
93a.	–	£20 brown	£8500	

13. Victoria Falls.

1905. Visit of British Assn. and Opening of Victoria Falls Bridge across Zambesi.

No.	Type	Description	Unused	Used
94.	13.	1d. red	2·75	3·00
95.		2½d. blue	7·50	3·75
96.		5d. red	18·00	40·00
97.		1s. green	18·00	23·00
98.		2s. 6d. black	£100	£150
99.		5s. violet	85·00	45·00

1909. Optd. **RHODESIA** or surch. also.

No.	Type	Description	Unused	Used
100	10	½d. green	1·25	20
101		1d. red	1·25	20
102		2d. brown	1·60	2·00
103		2½d. blue	1·00	20
104		3d. red	1·60	20
105		4d. olive	2·75	35
114		5d. on 6d. purple ..	6·50	7·00
106		6d. purple	5·00	1·25
116	11	7½d. on 2s. 6d. grey ..	3·50	2·25
117a		10d. on 2s. violet ..	4·00	3·25
107c		1s. brown	8·50	1·00
118		2s. on 5s. orange ..	12·00	7·00
108		2s. 6d. grey	15·00	4·00
109		3s. violet	15·00	4·00
110		5s. orange	25·00	13·00
111		7s. 6d. black	55·00	11·00
112		10s. green	26·00	8·50
113	–	£1 purple	£100	
113d	–	£2 brown	£3000	
113e	–	£5 blue	£5000	

17.

1910.

No.	Type	Description	Unused	Used
119	17.	½d. green..	6·50	85
123		1d. red	10·00	30
126		2d. black and grey ..	27·00	5·50
131a		2½d. blue..	13·00	5·00
135		3d. purple and yellow ..	22·00	6·00
140		4d. black and orange ..	23·00	10·00
141		5d. purple and olive ..	20·00	32·00
145		6d. purple and mauve ..	18·00	8·00
148		8d. black and purple ..	£110	55·00
149		10d. red and purple ..	26·00	48·00
152		1s. black and green ..	25·00	9·00
153		2s. black and blue ..	55·00	50·00
157		2s. 6d. black and red ..	£275	£275
158		3s. green and violet ..	£130	£130
159		5s. red and green ..	£225	£200
160b		7s. 6d. red and blue ..	£600	£500
164		10s. green and orange ..	£425	£250
165		£1 red and black ..	£900	£375

18.

1913.

No.	Type	Description	Unused	Used
187	18.	½d. green	1·50	40
192		1d. red	2·25	30
197		1½d. brown	2·00	40
291		2d. black and grey ..	1·75	1·00
200		2½d. blue..	3·00	11·00
259		3d. black and yellow ..	3·50	1·40
225		4d. black and orange ..	5·50	3·25
212		5d. black and green ..	3·50	5·00
266		6d. black and mauve ..	3·25	2·25
230		8d. violet and green ..	9·50	25·00
247		10d. blue and red ..	4·00	17·00
300		1s. black and blue ..	2·25	3·25
273		2s. black and brown ..	12·00	14·00
236		2s. 6d. blue and brown..	35·00	14·00
304		3s. brown and blue ..	50·00	75·00
239		5s. blue and green ..	42·00	48·00
252		7s. 6d. mauve and grey	75·00	£130
309		10s. red and green ..	£140	£170
242		£1 black and purple ..	£400	£450

1917. Surch. **Half Penny.**

281. 18. ½d. on 1s. red .. .. 1·25 3·25

RHODESIA

The following stamps are for the former Southern Rhodesia, renamed Rhodesia.

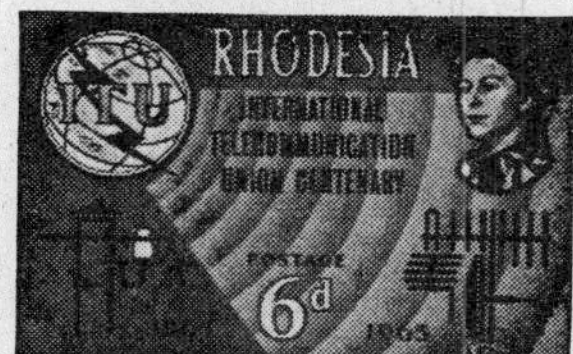

59. "Telecommunications".

1965. Centenary of I.T.U.

351. 59. 6d. violet and olive .. 1·00 25
352. 1s. 3d. violet and lilac 1·00 35
353. 2s. 6d. violet and brown 2·00 3·00

60. Bangala Dam.

1965. Water Conservation. Multicoloured.

354. 3d. Type **60** 20 10
355. 4d. Irrigation canal 75 60
356. 2s. 6d. Cutting sugar cane 1·50 1·75

63. Sir Winston Churchill, Quill, Sword and Houses of Parliament.

1965. Churchill Commem.

357. 63. 1s. 3d. black and blue 50 35

64. Coat of Arms.

1965. "Independence".

358. 64. 2s. 6d. multicoloured .. 15 15

1966. Optd. **INDEPENDENCE. 11th November 1965.** (a) On Nos. 92/105 of Southern Rhodesia.

359. 45. ½d. yellow, green & blue 10 10
360. – 1d. violet and ochre .. 10 10
361. – 2d. yellow and violet .. 10 10
362. – 3d. brown and blue .. 10 10
363. – 4d. orange and green .. 15 10
364. 50. 6d. red, yellow & green 15 10
365. – 9d. brown, yellow & grn. 20 10
366. – 1s. green and ochre .. 25 10
367. – 1s. 3d. red, violet & grn. 80 10
368. – 2s. blue and ochre .. 90 2·25
369. – 2s. 6d. blue and red .. 60 25
370. 56. 5s. multicoloured .. 8·00 5·00
371. – 10s. multicoloured .. 3·25 1·25
372. – £1 multicoloured .. 1·50 1·50

(b) Surch on No. 357.

373. 63. 5s. on 1s. 3d. black & blue 20·00 35·00

67. Emeralds.

1966. As Nos. 92/8 and 100/105 of Southern Rhodesia, but inscr. "RHODESIA" as in T 67. Some designs and colours changed.

374. – 1d. violet and ochre .. 10 10
375. – 2d. orange and green (As No. 96) .. 10 10
376. – 3d. brown and blue .. 10 10
377. 67. 4d. green and brown .. 30 10
378. 50. 6d. red yellow & green, 15 10
379. – 9d. yellow and violet (As No. 94) .. 15 20
380. 45. 1s. yellow, green & blue 15 10
381. – 1s. 3d. blue and ochre (As No. 101).. .. 25 15
382. – 1s. 6d. brown, yellow and green (As No. 98) .. 75 25
383. – 2s. red, violet and green (As No. 100).. .. 40 80
384. – 2s. 6d. blue, red & turq. 40 20
385. 56. 5s. multicoloured .. 40 90
386. – 10s. multicoloured .. 2·50 4·00
387. – £1 multicoloured .. 17·00 10·00

Nos. 379/80 are in larger format as Type **50**.

Stamps in these designs were later printed locally. These vary only slightly from the above in details and shade.

For Nos. 376, 380 and 382/4 in dual currency see Nos. 408/12.

68. Zeederberg Coach, c. 1895.

1966. 28th Congress of Southern Africa Philatelic Federation ("Rhopex").

388. 68. 3d. multicoloured .. 30 10
389. – 9d. multicoloured .. 40 35
390. – 1s. 6d. blue and black 60 50
391. – 2s. 6d. pink, grn. & blk. 70 80

Designs: 9d. Sir Rowland Hill. 1s. 6d. The Penny Black. 2s. 6d. Rhodesian stamp of 1892 (No. 12).

69. De Havilland "Rapide" (1946).

1966. 20th Anniv. of Central African Airways.

393. 69. 6d. multicoloured .. 1·00 35
394. – 1s. 3d. multicoloured .. 1·25 55
395. – 2s. 6d. multicoloured .. 3·50 1·75
396. – 5s. black and blue .. 6·00 3·50

Aircraft: 1s. 3d. Douglas "D.C.3" (1953). 2s. 6d. Vickers "Viscount" (1956). 5s. Modern jet.

70. Kudu.

1967. Dual Currency Issue. As Nos. 376, 380 and 382/4 but value in dual currency as T 70.

408. 70. 3d./2½ c. brn. & blue .. 60 20
409. – 1s./10 c. yellow, green and blue (No. 380) .. 70 45
410. – 1s. 6d./15 c. brown, yellow & green (No. 382) 4·75 90
411. – 2s./20 c. red, violet and green (No. 383) .. 10·00 9·00
412. – 2s. 6d./25 c. ultram., red and blue (No. 384) .. 50·00 60·00

71. Dr. Jameson (administrator).

1967. Famous Rhodesians (1st series). 50th Death Anniv. of Dr. Jameson.

413. 71. 1s. 6d. multicoloured .. 30 35

See also Nos. 426, 430, 457, 458, 469, 480, 488, and 513.

72. Soapstone Sculpture (Joram Mariga).

1967. 10th Anniv. of Opening of Rhodes National Gallery.

414. 72. 3d. brn., green & black 10 10
415. – 9d. blue, brn. & black 20 20
416. – 1s. 3d. multicoloured .. 20 25
417. – 2s. 6d. multicoloured .. 25 35

Designs: 9d. "The Burgher of Calais" (detail, Rodin). 1s. 3d. "The Knight" (stamp wrongly inscr.) (Roberto Crippa). 2s. 6d. "John the Baptist" (Tossini).

73. Baobab Tree.

1967. Nature Conservation.

418. 73. 4d. brown and black.. 20 25
419. – 4d. green and black .. 20 25
420. – 4d. grey and black .. 20 25
421. – 4d. orange and black .. 20 25

Designs—horiz. No. 419, White Rhinoceros No. 420, African Elephants. vert. No. 421, Wild Gladiolus.

74. Wooden Hand Plough.

1968. 15th World Ploughing Contest, Norton, Rhodesia.

422. 74. 3d. orange, red & brn... 10 10
423. – 9d. multicoloured .. 20 20
424. – 1s. 6d. multicoloured .. 30 45
425. – 2s. 6d. multicoloured .. 35 70

Designs: 9d. Early wheel plough. 1s. 6d. Steam powered tractor, and ploughs. 2s. 6d. Modern tractor, and plough.

75. Alfred Beit (national benefactor).

1968. Famous Rhodesians. (2nd issue).

426. 75. 1s. 6d. orge., blk. & brn. 30 30

76. Raising the Flag, Bulawayo, 1893.

1968. 75th Anniv. of Matabeleland.

427. 76. 3d. orge., red, & black.. 10 10
428. – 9d. multicoloured .. 15 20
429. – 1s. 6d. grn., emerald & black 20 35

Designs: 9d. View and coat of arms of Bulawayo. 1s. 6d. Allan Wilson (combatant in the Matabele War).

77. Sir William Henry Milton (administrator).

1969. Famous Rhodesians (3rd issue).

430. 77. 1s. 6d. multicoloured .. 20 45

78. 2 ft. Gauge Steam Locomotive, Beira-Salisbury Line, 1899.

1969. 70th Anniv. of Opening of Beira-Salisbury Railway. Multicoloured.

431. 3d. Type **78** .. .. 1·00 10
432. 9d. Steam locomotive, 1904 2·00 75
433. 1s. 6d. Articulated steam locomotive, 1950 .. 6·50 3·25
434. 2s. 6d. Diesel locomotive, 1955 .. .. .. 8·50 6·50

79. Low Level Bridge.

1969. Bridges of Rhodesia. Multicoloured.

435. 3d. Type **79** 75 10
436. 9d. Mpudzi bridge .. 1·25 25
437. 1s. 6d. Umniati bridge .. 3·50 1·00
438. 2s. 6d. Birchenough bridge 4·50 1·50

80. Harvesting Wheat. 81. Devil's Cataract, Victoria Falls.

1970. Decimal Currency.

439. 80. 1 c. multicoloured .. 10 10
440. – 2 c. multicoloured .. 10 10
441. – 2½ c. turquoise, bl. & blk. 10 10
441c. – 3 c. multicoloured .. 1·25 10
442. – 3½ c. multicoloured .. 10 10
442b. – 4 c. multicoloured .. 1·50 30
443. – 5 c. multicoloured .. 15 10
443b. – 6 c. multicoloured .. 4·50 3·00
443c. 81. 7½ c. multicoloured .. 9·00 1·25
444. – 8 c. multicoloured .. 1·75 20
445. – 10 c. multicoloured .. 60 10
446. – 12½ c. multicoloured .. 1·25 10
446a. – 14 c. multicoloured .. 16·00 1·50
447. – 15 c. multicoloured .. 3·50 15
448. – 20 c. multicoloured .. 2·50 15
449. – 25 c. orge., grey & blk. 3·75 65
450. – 50 c. turquoise & blue 2·75 70
451. – $1 blue, turq. & black 4·00 4·00
452. – $2 multicoloured .. 15·00 25·00

Designs: Size as Type **80.** 2 c. Pouring molten metal. 2½ c. Zimbabwe Ruins. 3 c. Articulated lorry. 3½ c., 4 c. Statue of Cecil Rhodes. 5 c. Mine headgear. 6 c. Hydrofoil "Seaflight". Size as Type **81.** 10 c. Yachting on Lake Mcllwaine. 12½ c. Hippopotamus in river. 14 c., 15 c. Kariba Dam. 20 c. Irrigation canal. Larger (31 × 26 mm.). 25 c. Bateleur eagles. 50 c. Radar antenna and Vickers "Viscount". $1, "Air Rescue", $2, Rhodesian flag.

82. Despatch Rider c. 1890.

1970. Inauguration of Posts and Telecommunications Corporation. Mult.

453. 2½ c. Type **82** 25 10
454. 3½ c. Loading mail at Salisbury airport .. 40 25
455. 15 c. Constructing telegraph line, c. 1890 .. 1·25 2·00
456. 25 c. Telephone and modern telecommunications equipment .. .. .. 2·00 3·50

83. Mother Patrick (Dominican nurse and teacher).

1971. Famous Rhodesians (4th issue).

457. **83.** 15 c. multicoloured .. 40 40

84. Fredrick Courteney Selous (Big-game hunter, explorer and pioneer).

1971. Famous Rhodesians (5th issue).

458. **84.** 15 c. multicoloured .. 40 40

85. Hoopoe.

86. Porphyrite Granite.

1971. Birds of Rhodesia (1st series). Mult.

459. 2 c. Type **85** .. .. 1·25 20
460. $2\frac{1}{2}$ c. Half-collared kingfisher (horiz.) .. .. 1·25 20
461. 5 c. Golden-breasted bunting .. .. .. 3·50 60
462. $7\frac{1}{2}$ c. Carmine bee eater .. 4·00 1·00
463. 8 c. Red-eyed bulbul .. 4·00 1·25
464. 25 c. Senegal wattled plover (horiz.) .. .. 8·50 2·75

See also Nos. 537/42.

1971. "Granite 71" Geological Symposium. Multicoloured.

465. $2\frac{1}{2}$ c. Type **86** 75 10
466. $7\frac{1}{2}$ c. Muscovite mica seen through microscope .. 1·75 80
467. 15 c. Granite seen through microscope .. .. 2·50 3·25
468. 25 c. Geological map of Rhodesia.. .. .. 3·25 4·75

87. Dr. Robert Moffat (missionary).

1972. Famous Rhodesians (6th issue).

469. **87.** 13 c. multicoloured .. 1·00 90

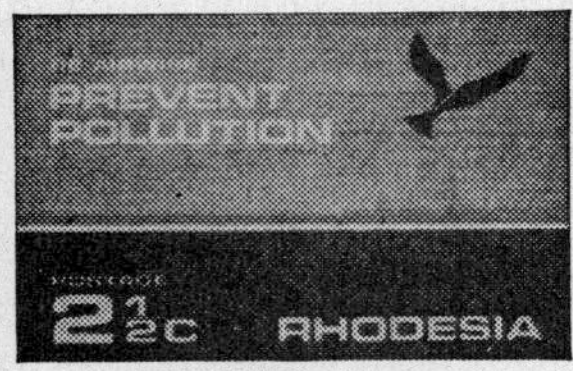

88. Bird (" Be Airwise").

1972. "Prevent Pollution". Mult.

470. $2\frac{1}{2}$ c. Type **88** 20 10
471. $3\frac{1}{2}$ c. Antelope ("Be Countrywise").. .. 20 10
472. 7 c. Fish ("Be Waterwise") 30 45
473. 13 c. City ("Be Citywise") 45 70

HAVE YOU READ THE NOTES AT THE BEGINNING OF THIS CATALOGUE?

These often provide answers to the enquiries we receive.

89. "The Three Kings".

91. W.M.O. Emblem.

90. Dr. David Livingstone.

1972. Christmas.

477. **89.** 2 c. multicoloured .. 10 10
478. 5 c. multicoloured .. 20 15
479. 13 c. multicoloured .. 50 45

1973. Famous Rhodesians (7th issue).

480. **90.** 14 c. multicoloured .. 70 75

1973. Centenary of I.M.O./W.M.O.

481. **91.** 3 c. multicoloured .. 15 10
482. 14 c. multicoloured .. 50 60
483. 25 c. multicoloured .. 1·00 1·50

92. Arms of Rhodesia.

1973. 50th Anniv. of Responsible Government.

484. **92.** $2\frac{1}{2}$ c. multicoloured .. 15 10
485. 4 c. multicoloured .. 20 20
486. $7\frac{1}{2}$ c. multicoloured .. 35 70
487. 14 c. multicoloured .. 60 1·75

93. George Pauling (construction engineer).

1974. Famous Rhodesians (8th issne).

488. **93.** 14 c. multicoloured .. 1·00 1·50

94. Greater Kudu.

95. Thunbergia.

96. "Charaxes varanes".

1974. Multicoloured.

(a) Antelopes.

489. 1 c. Type **94** 10 10
490. $2\frac{1}{2}$ c. Eland 75 10
491. 3 c. Roan Antelope 10 10
492. 4 c. Reedbuck 10 10
493. 5 c. Bushbuck 30 10

(b) Wild Flowers.

494. 6 c. Type **95** 40 10
495. $7\frac{1}{2}$ c. Flame Lily .. .. 3·00 35
496. 8 c. As $7\frac{1}{2}$ c. 40 10
497. 10 c. Devil Thorn.. .. 30 10
498. 12 c. Hibiscus 70 60
499. $12\frac{1}{2}$ c. Pink Sabi Star .. 4·50 50
500. 14 c. Wild Pimpernel .. 7·50 70
501. 15 c. As $12\frac{1}{2}$ c. 70 60
502. 16 c. As 14 c. 70 45

(c) Butterflies.

503 20 c. Type **96** .. 1·50 35
504 24 c. "Precis hierta" .. 1·50 40
505 25 c. As 24 c. .. 8·50 3·00
506 50 c. "Colotis regina" .. 70 90
507 $1 "Papilio antheus" .. 70 1·25
508 $2 "Hamanumida daedalus" 80 1·50

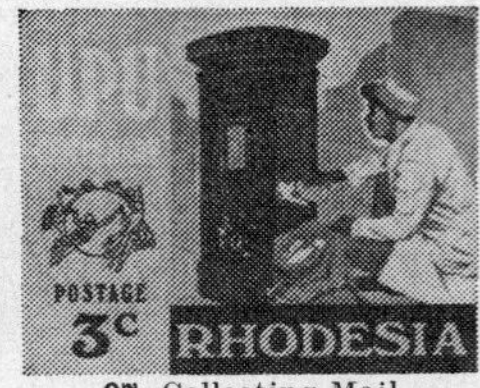

97. Collecting Mail.

1974. Centenary of U.P.U. Multicoloured.

509. 3 c. Type **97** 15 10
510. 4 c. Sorting mail 20 10
511. $7\frac{1}{2}$ c. Mail delivery .. 50 65
512. 14 c. Weighing parcel .. 1·00 1·75

98. Thomas Baines (artist).

1975. Famous Rhodesians (9th issue).

513. **98.** 14 c. multicoloured .. 80 1·25

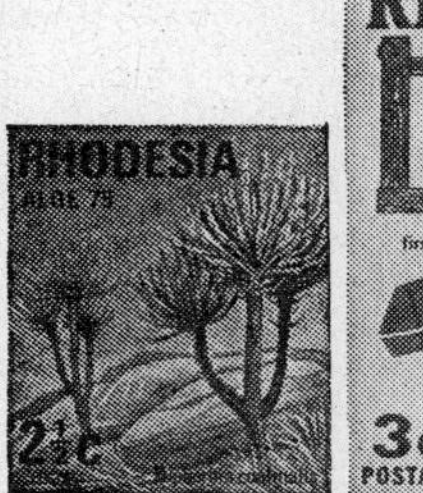

99. " Euphorbia confinalis".

101. Telephones, 1876 and 1976.

100. Prevention of Head Injuries.

1975. Int. Succulent Congress, Salisbury ("Aloe '75"). Multicoloured.

514. $2\frac{1}{2}$ c. Type **99** 20 10
515. 3 c. "Aloe excelsa" .. 20 10
516. 4 c. "Hoodia lugardii" .. 30 15
517. $7\frac{1}{2}$ c. "Aloe ortholopha" 55 55
518. 14 c. "Aloe musapana" 1·50 1·25
519. 25 c. "Aloe saponaria" 2·00 2·00

1975. Occupational Safety. Multicoloured.

520. $2\frac{1}{2}$ c. Type **100** 15 10
521. 4 c. Bandaged hand and gloved hand 20 10
522. $7\frac{1}{2}$ c. Broken glass and eye 35 20
523. 14 c. Blind man and welder with protective mask .. 50 60

1976. Centenary of Telephone.

524. **101.** 3 c. grey and blue .. 10 10
525. – 14 c. black and brown.. 20 35

DESIGN: 14 c. Alexander Graham Bell.

1976. Nos. 495, 500 and 505 surch.

526. 8 c. on $7\frac{1}{2}$ c. multicoloured 15 15
527. 16 c. on 14 c. multicoloured 20 25
528. 24 c. on 25 c. multicoloured 30 50

103. Roan Antelope.

1976. Vulnerable Wildlife. Multicoloured.

529. 4 c. Type **103** 20 10
530. 6 c. Brown Hyena .. 25 10
531. 8 c. Wild Dog 35 25
532. 16 c. Cheetah 45 45

104. Msasa.

1976. Trees of Rhodesia. Multicoloured.

533. 4 c. Type **104** 15 10
534. 6 c. Red Mahogany .. 15 10
535. 8 c. Mukwa 20 30
536. 16 c. Rhodesian Teak .. 25 50

105. Common Bulbul.

1977. Birds of Rhodesia (2nd series). Mult.

537. 3 c. Type **105** 20 10
538. 4 c. Yellow-mantled whydah 20 10
539. 6 c. Cape longclaw .. 25 35
540. 8 c. Eastern long-tailed shrike 45 50
541. 16 c. Lesser blue-eared glossy starling .. .. 75 1·00
542. 24 c. Green wood hoopoe.. 95 1·25

106. "Lake Kyle" (Joan Evans).

1977. Landscape Paintings. Multicoloured.

543. 3 c. Type **106** 15 10
544. 4 c. "Chimanimani Mountains" (Joan Evans) .. 15 10
545. 6 c. "Rocks near Bonsor Reef" (Alice Balfour).. 15 10
546. 8 c. "A Dwala near Devil's Pass" (Alice Balfour).. 25 10
547. 16 c. "Zimbabwe" (Alice Balfour).. .. 35 40
548. 24 c. "Victoria Falls" (Thomas Baines) .. 40 45

107. Virgin and Child.

1977. Christmas.

549. **107.** 3 c. multicoloured .. 10 10
550. 6 c. multicoloured .. 15 10
551. 8 c. multicoloured .. 30 10
552. 16 c. multicoloured .. 30 50

MORE DETAILED LISTS

are given in the Stanley Gibbons Catalogues referred to in the country headings.

For lists of current volumes see Introduction.

108. Fair Spire.

109. Morganite.

1978. Trade Fair Rhodesia, Bulawayo. Mult.
553. 4 c. Type 108 .. .. 15 10
554. 8 c. Fair Spire (different) .. 20 25

1978. Gemstones, Wild Animals and Waterfalls. Multicoloured.
555. 1 c. Type 109 .. .. 20 10
556. 3 c. Amethyst 30 10
557. 4 c. Garnet 30 10
558. 5 c. Citrine 30 10
559. 7 c. Blue Topaz 30 10
560. 9 c. White Rhinoceros .. 20 10
561. 11 c. Lion 20 15
562. 13 c. Warthog 20 15
563. 15 c. Giraffe 20 15
564. 17 c. Common Zebra .. 20 10
565. 21 c. Odzani Falls .. 20 30
566. 25 c. Goba Falls 20 40
567. 30 c. Inyangombi Falls .. 25 30
568. $1 Bridal Veil Falls .. 50 80
569. $2 Victoria Falls .. 75 1·00

Nos. 560/4 are 26×23 mm., and Nos. 565/9 32×27 mm.

112. Wright "Flyer".

1978. 75th Anniv. of Powered Flight. Mult.
570. 4 c. Type 112 .. .. 10 10
571. 5 c. Bleriot "XI" .. 10 10
572. 7 c. Vickers "Vimy" "Silver Queen II" .. 10 10
573. 9 c. "A.W.15 Atalanta" .. 10 10
574. 17 c. Vickers "Viking 1B" .. 15 15
575. 25 c. Boeing "720B" .. 20 30

POSTAGE DUE STAMPS

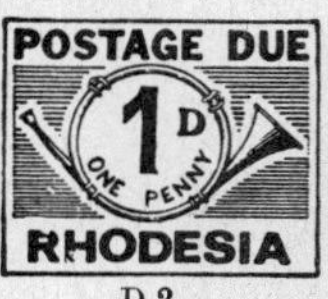
D 2.

D 3. Zimbabwe Bird. (soapstone sculpture).

1965. Roul.
D 8 D 2 1d. red .. .. 1·25 4·00
D 9 2d. blue .. .. 50 8·00
D10 4d. green .. .. 60 8·00
D11 6d. plum .. .. 60 6·00

1966.
D12 D 3 1d. red .. .. 1·25 2·50
D13 2d. blue .. .. 1·50 2·75
D14 4d. green .. .. 1·75 4·50
D15 6d. violet .. .. 1·75 2·75
D16 1s. brown .. .. 2·00 3·00
D17 2s. black .. .. 3·00 6·50

1970. Decimal Currency. As Type D 3 but larger (26×22½ mm.).
D18 D 3 1 c. green .. .. 1·00 1·40
D19 2 c. blue .. .. 1·00 80
D20 5 c. violet .. .. 2·50 2·00
D21 6 c. yellow .. .. 3·75 2·75
D22 10 c. red .. .. 2·50 3·50

RHODESIA AND NYASALAND

Stamps for the Central African Federation of Northern and Southern Rhodesia and Nyasaland Protectorate. The stamps of the Federation were withdrawn on 19 February 1964, when all three constituent territories had resumed issuing their own stamps.

12 pence = 1 shilling.
20 shillings = 1 pound.

1. Queen Elizabeth II. 2.

1954.
1. 1. ½d. red 15 10
2. 1d. blue 15 10
3. 2d. green 15 10
3a. 2½d. ochre .. .. .. 2·00 10
4. 3d. red 20 10
5. 4d. brown 60 15
6. 4½d. green 15 25
7. 6d. purple 60 10
8. 9d. violet 65 70
9. 1s. grey .. .. .. 1·00 10
10. 2. 1s. 3d. red and blue .. 2·25 10
11. 2s. blue and brown .. 5·00 65
12. 2s. 6d. black and red .. 5·50 65
13. 5s. violet and olive .. 11·00 2·00
14. – 10s. turquoise and orange 13·00 7·00
15. – £1 olive and lake .. .. 22·00 20·00

The 10s. and £1 are as Type 2 but larger (31×17 mm). and have the name at top and foliage on either side of portrait.

4. Aeroplane over Victoria Falls.

5. Livingstone and Victoria Falls.

1955. Cent. of Discovery of Victoria Falls.
16. 4. 3d. blue and turquoise .. 20 20
17. 5. 1s. purple and blue .. 30 30

6. Tea Picking.

11. Lake Bangweulu.

17. Rhodes' Statue.

1959.
18. 6. ½d. black and green .. 40 30
19. – 1d. red and black .. 15 10
20. – 2d. violet and buff .. 40 20
21. – 2½d. purple and blue .. 30 40
22. – 3d. black and blue .. 15 10
23. 11. 4d. purple and olive .. 70 10
24. – 6d. blue and green .. 35 10
24a. – 9d. brown and violet .. 4·50 1·75
25. – 1s. green and blue .. 60 10
26. – 1s. 3d. green and brown .. 1·75 10
27. – 2s. green and red .. 3·25 45
28. – 2s. 6d. blue and buff .. 3·75 30
29. 17. 5s. brown and green .. 5·50 2·25
30. – 10s. bistre and red .. 23·00 12·00
31. – £1 black and violet .. 32·00 25·00

DESIGNS—As Type 6: VERT. 1d. V.H.F. mast. 2d. Copper mining. 2½d. Fairbridge Memorial. HORIZ. 3d. Rhodes' grave. As Type 11: VERT. 6 d. Eastern Cataract, Victoria Falls. HORIZ. 9d. Rhodesian railway trains. 1s. Tobacco. 1s. 3d. Lake Nyasa. 2s. Chirundu Bridge. 2s. 6d. Salisbury Airport. As Type 17: HORIZ. 10s. Mlanje. £1, Federal Coat of Arms.

20. Kariba Gorge, 1955.

1960. Opening of Kariba Hydro-Electric Scheme.
32. 20. 3d. green and orange .. 35 10
33. – 6d. brown & bistre .. 70 20
34. – 1s. blue and green .. 1·75 1·50
35. – 1s.3d. blue and brown .. 2·50 1·00
36. – 2s. 6d. purple and red .. 3·25 7·00
37. – 5s. violet and turquoise .. 6·50 11·00

DESIGNS: 6d. 330 k.V. power lines. 1s. Barrage wall. 1s. 3d. Barrage and lake. 2s. 6d. Interior of power station. 5s. Queen Mother and barrage wall (inscr. "ROYAL OPENING").

26. Miner Drilling.

1961. 7th Commonwealth Mining and Metallurgical Congress.
38. 26. 6d. green and brown .. 30 15
39. – 1s. 3d. black and blue .. 40 60

DESIGN: 1s. 3d. Surface installations, Nchanga mine.

28. D.H. "Hercules" on Rhodesian Airstrip.

1962. 30th Anniv. of 1st London-Rhodesian Airmail Service.
40. 28. 6d. green and red .. 35 25
41. – 1s. 3d. blue, blk. & yell. 1·00 50
42. – 2s. 6d. red and violet .. 6·00 4·25

DESIGNS: 1s. 3d. Empire "C" Class flying-boat taking-off from Zambesi. 2s. 6d. D.H. "Comet" at Salisbury Airport.

31. Tobacco Plant.

DESIGNS: 6d. Tobacco field. 1s. 3d. Auction floor. 2s. 6d. Cured tobacco.

1963. World Tobacco Congress, Salisbury.
43. 31. 3d. green and olive .. 15 10
44. – 6d. green, brown & blue 20 35
45. – 1s. 3d. brown and blue .. 30 45
46. – 2s. 6d. yellow and brown 75 2·50

35.

1963. Centenary of Red Cross.
47. 35. 3d. red 30 10

36. African "Round Table" Emblem.

1963. World Council of Young Men's Service Clubs, Salisbury.
48. 36. 6d. black, gold and green 20 50
49. 1s. 3d. multicoloured .. 30 40

POSTAGE DUE STAMPS

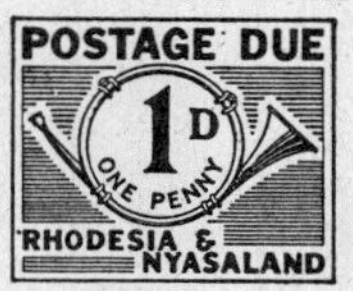
D 1.

1961.
D 1. D 1. 1d. red .. .. .. 1·25 3·00
D 2. 2d. blue .. .. .. 1·75 3·00
D 3. 4d. green .. .. .. 1·75 4·50
D 4. 6d. purple .. .. .. 2·50 7·00

ROSS DEPENDENCY

A dependency of New Zealand in the Antarctic on the Ross Sea.

1957. 12 pence = 1 shilling.
20 shillings = 1 pound.
1967. 100 cents = 1 dollar.

3. Map of Ross Dependency and New Zealand.

DESIGNS—HORIZ. as Type 3: 3d. H.M.S. "Erebus". 4d. Shackleton and Scott.

4. Queen Elizabeth II.

1957.
1. – 3d. blue .. .. .. 2·50 75
2. – 4d. red .. .. .. 2·50 75
3. 3. 8d. red and blue .. .. 2·50 1·00
4. 4. 1s. 6d. purple .. .. 2·50 1·25

5. H.M.S. "Erebus".

1968. Nos. 1/4 with values inscr. in decimal currency as T 5.
5. 5. 2 c. blue .. .. .. 8·00 4·75
6. – 3 c. red .. .. .. 9·00 4·75
7. 3. 7 c. red and blue .. .. 11·00 7·50
8. 4. 15 c. purple .. .. 12·00 12·00

6. Great Skua.

7. Scott Base.

1972.
9a. 6. 3 c. blk., grey and blue .. 65 85
10a. – 4 c. blk., blue & violet .. 40 80
11a. – 5 c. blk., grey and lilac .. 30 80
12a. – 8 c. black, grey & brown 40 85
13a. 7. 10 c. black, green & grey 40 90
14a. – 18 c. black, violet and bright violet .. 1·50 1·25

DESIGNS: Size as Type 6. 4 c. "Hercules" aeroplane at Williams Field. 5 c. Shackleton's Hut. 8 c. Supply ship H.M.N.Z.S. "Endeavour". Size as Type 7. 18 c. Tabular ice floe.

8. Adelie Penguins.

1982. Multicoloured.
15. 5 c. Type 8 .. .. 65 40
16. 10 c. Tracked vehicles .. 30 30
17. 20 c. Scott Base 40 30
18. 30 c. Field party 40 30
19. 40 c. Vanda Station .. 40 30
20. 50 c. Scott's hut, Cape Evans 50 35

The post office closed on 30 September 1987.

SABAH

Formerly North Borneo, now part of Malaysia

100 cents = 1 Malaysian dollar.

1964. Nos. 391/406 of North Borneo optd. **SABAH.**

No.	Description		Unused	Used
408.	1 c. green and red	..	10	10
409.	4 c. olive and orange	..	15	50
410.	5 c. sepia and violet	..	15	10
411.	6 c. black and turquoise	..	10	10
412.	10 c. green and red	..	15	10
413.	12 c. brown and myrtle	..	15	10
414.	20 c. turquoise and blue	..	1·25	10
415.	25 c. black and red	..	45	80
416.	30 c. sepia and olive	..	25	10
417.	35 c. slate and brown	..	30	20
418.	50 c. green and bistre	..	30	10
419.	75 c. blue and purple	..	2·25	65
420.	$1 brown and green	..	3·50	50
421.	$2 brown and slate	..	6·00	2·75
422.	$4 green and purple	..	8·00	10·00
423.	$10 red and blue ..	..	13·00	15·00

138. "Vanda hookeriana".

1965. As No. 115/21 of Kedah but with Arms of Sabah inset as in T **138.**

No.	Type	Description		Unused	Used
424.	138.	1 c. multicoloured	..	10	30
425.	–	2 c. multicoloured	..	10	40
426.	–	5 c. multicoloured	..	10	10
427.	–	6 c. multicoloured	..	20	40
428.	–	10 c. multicoloured	..	20	10
429.	–	15 c. multicoloured	..	1·00	10
430.	–	20 c. multicoloured	..	1·40	30

The higher values used in Sabah were Nos. 20/7 of Malaysia.

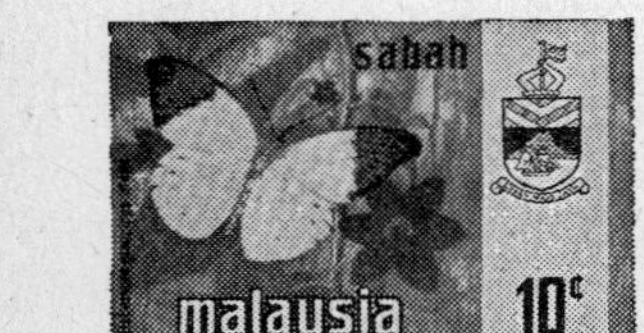

139. "Hebomoia glaucippe".

1971. Butterflies. As Nos. 124/30 of Kedah, but with Sabah Arms inset as T **139**.

No.	Type	Description		Unused	Used
432.	–	1 c. multicoloured	..	10	50
433.	–	2 c. multicoloured	..	30	50
434.	–	5 c. multicoloured	..	45	10
435.	–	6 c. multicoloured	..	45	40
436.	139.	10 c. multicoloured	..	45	10
437.	–	15 c. multicoloured	..	60	10
438.	–	20 c. multicoloured	..	70	40

The higher values in use with this issue were Nos. 64/71 of Malaysia.

140. "Hibiscus rosa-sinensis".

1979. As Nos. 135/41 of Kedah but with Arms of Sabah as T **140**.

No.	Description	Unused	Used
445	1 c. "Rafflesia hasseltii" ..	10	20
446	2 c. "Pterocarpus indicus"	10	20
447	5 c. "Lagerstroemia speciosa"	10	10
448	10 c. "Durio zibethinus" ..	10	10
449	15 c. Type **140**	20	10
450	20 c. "Rhododendron scortechinii"	25	10
451	25 c. "Etlingera elatior" (inscr "Phaeomeria speciosa")	25	10

The higher values in use with this issue were Nos. 190/7 of Malaysia.

141. Coffee.

1986. As Nos. 152/8 of Kedah but with Arms of Sabah as in T **141.**

No.	Description			Unused	Used
458.	1 c. Type **141**	..	..	10	10
459.	2 c. Coconuts	..	..	10	10
460.	5 c. Cocoa ..	..	..	10	10
461.	10 c. Black pepper		..	10	10
462.	15 c. Rubber	..	..	10	10
463.	20 c. Oil palm	..	..	10	10
464.	30 c. Rice ..	..	..	10	15

ST. CHRISTOPHER

One of the Leeward Is. Stamps superseded in 1890 by Leeward Islands general issue.

12 pence = 1 shilling.

1.

1870.

No.	Type	Description			Unused	Used
11	1	½d. green ..	..	..	50	80
2		1d. mauve ..	..	..	38·00	26·00
13		1d. red	..	..	60	60
14		2½d. brown	..	..	£170	55·00
16		2½d. blue ..	..	..	1·50	1·50
10		4d. blue	..	..	£150	15·00
18		4d. grey	..	..	1·25	80
9		6d. green ..	..	..	50·00	5·00
19		6d. olive ..	..	..	80·00	£200
20		1s. mauve ..	..	..	90·00	65·00

1885. Surch. in words.

No.	Type	Description		Unused	Used
22.	1.	½d. on half of 1d. red	..	24·00	32·00
26.		1d. on ½d. green ..	..	28·00	38·00
28.		1d. on 2½d. blue ..	..	38·00	42·00
24.		1d. on 6d. green ..	..	16·00	28·00
23.		4d. on 6d. green ..	..	48·00	48·00

1886. Surch. in figures.

No.	Type	Description		Unused	Used
25.	1.	4d. on 6d. green ..	..	48·00	90·00

ST. HELENA

An island in the S. Atlantic Ocean, W. of Africa.

1856. 12 pence = 1 shilling,
20 shillings = 1 pound.
1971. 100 pence = 1 pound.

1.

11.

The early stamps of St. Helena, other than the 6d. were formed by printing the 6d. in various colours and surcharging it with new values in words or (in the case of the 2½d.) in figures.

1856. Imperf.

No.	Type	Description			Unused	Used
4.	1.	1d. on 6d. red	..	..	£110	£140
5.		4d. on 6d. red	..	..	£500	£250
1.		6d. blue ..	..	..	£500	£180

1861. Perf.

No.	Type	Description		Unused	Used
36	1.	½d. on 6d. green	..	90	1·10
38		1d. on 6d. red ..	..	2·75	2·00
39		2d. on 6d. yellow ..	..	1·25	3·50
40		2½d. on 6d. blue ..	..	2·00	5·00
41		3d. on 6d. purple	..	2·00	2·75
14		4d. on 6d. red ..	..	70·00	45·00
43b		4d. on 6d. brown	..	14·00	8·00
25		6d. blue	..	£250	30·00
44		6d. grey	..	10·00	3·50
30		1s. on 6d. green ..	..	20·00	12·00
20		5s. on 6d. yellow	..	35·00	45·00

1890.

No.	Type	Description			Unused	Used
46.	11.	½d. green ..	..	..	2·75	4·50
47.		1d. red ..	..	..	6·50	1·00
48.		1½d. brown and green		..	4·25	6·00
49.		2d. yellow ..	..	..	4·00	8·50
50.		2½d. blue ..	..	..	5·00	9·00
51.		5d. violet ..	..	..	11·00	23·00
52.		10d. brown	..	..	15·00	42·00

12.

13. Government House.

14. The Wharf.

1902. Inscr. "POSTAGE POSTAGE".

No.	Type	Description			Unused	Used
53.	12.	½d. green ..	..	..	1·50	90
54.		1d. red	..	..	3·50	70

1903.

No.	Type	Description		Unused	Used
55.	13.	½d. brown and green	..	2·00	2·25
56.	14.	1d. black and red	..	1·50	35
57.	13.	2d. black and green	..	6·00	1·25
58.	14.	8d. black and brown	..	14·00	32·00
59.	13.	1s. brown and orange	..	14·00	27·00
60.	14.	2s. black and violet	..	42·00	70·00

1908. Inscr. "POSTAGE & REVENUE".

No.	Type	Description	Unused	Used
64	12	2½d. blue	1·00	1·40
66a		4d. black and red on yellow	1·25	4·25
67a		6d. purple	2·75	9·50
71		10s. green & red on green	£180	£225

1912. As T **13/14,** but with medallion of King George V.

No.	Type	Description		Unused	Used
72.	13.	½d. black and green	..	1·25	5·00
73.	14.	1d. black and red	..	1·25	1·00
89.		1d. green	..	50	15·00
74.		1½d. black and orange	..	2·00	4·25
90.		1½d. red	..	6·00	25·00
75.	13.	2d. black and grey	..	2·00	1·75
76.	14.	2½d. black and blue	..	1·75	5·00
77.	13.	3d. black & purple on yell.		2·00	5·00
91.		3d. blue	..	12·00	35·00
78.	14.	8d. black and purple	..	5·50	38·00
79.	13.	1s. black on green	..	8·00	19·00
80.	14.	2s. black and blue on blue		27·00	55·00
81.		3s. black and violet	..	48·00	85·00

18.

22. Badge of St. Helena.

1912. Inscr. "POSTAGE & REVENUE".

No.	Type	Description	Unused	Used
83.	18.	4d. black & red on yellow	4·00	13·00
84.		6d. purple	2·50	5·00

1913. Inscr. "POSTAGE POSTAGE".

No.	Type	Description	Unused	Used
85.	18.	4d. black & red on yellow	5·50	3·50
86.		6d. purple	9·50	20·00

1916. Surch. **WAR TAX ONE PENNY.**

No.	Description	Unused	Used
87.	1d. + 1d. black & red (No. 73)	85	2·25

1919. Surch. **WAR TAX 1d.**

No.	Description	Unused	Used
88.	1d. + 1d. black & red (No. 73)	40	3·00

1922.

No.	Type	Description		Unused	Used
97.	22.	½d. grey and black	..	90	1·25
98.		1d. grey and green	..	1·50	80
99.		1½d. red	..	2·50	7·00
100.		2d. grey and brown	..	1·50	2·00
101.		3d. blue	..	1·75	4·00
92.		4d. grey & black on yell.		5·00	7·00
103.		5d. green & red on green		2·50	5·50
104.		6d. grey and purple	..	3·25	8·00
105.		8d. grey and violet	..	3·25	6·50
106.		1s. grey and brown	..	4·75	8·50
107.		1s. 6d. grey & grn. on grn.		10·00	35·00
108.		2s. purple & blue on blue		10·00	30·00
109.		2s. 6d. grey & red on yell.		12·00	40·00
110.		5s. grey & green on yell.		30·00	60·00
111.		7s. 6d. grey and orange ..		75·00	£120
112.		10s. grey and green	..	£110	£160
113.		15s. grey & pur. on blue		£850	£1400
96.		£1 grey & purple on red ..		£400	£450

23. Lot and Lots wife.

1934. Centenary of British Colonization.

No.	Type	Description		Unused	Used
114.	23.	½d. black and purple	..	45	80
115.	–	1d. black and green	..	50	85
116.	–	1½d. black and red	..	2·00	2·50
117.	–	2d. black and orange	..	1·75	1·25
118.	–	3d. black and blue	..	1·40	4·50
119.	–	6d. black and blue	..	3·25	3·00
120.	–	1s. black and brown	..	6·00	18·00
121.	–	2s. 6d. black and red	..	32·00	48·00
122.	–	5s. black and brown	..	75·00	85·00
123.	–	10s. black and purple	..	£200	£250

DESIGNS—HORIZ. 1d. "Plantation". 1½d. Map of St. Helena. 2d. Quay, Jamestown. 3d. James Valley. 6d. Jamestown. 1s. Mundens Promontory. 5s. High Knoll. 10s. Badge of St. Helena. VERT. 2s. 6d. St. Helena.

1935. Silver Jubilee. As T **13** of Antigua.

No.	Description		Unused	Used
124.	1½d. blue and red	..	75	2·00
125.	2d. blue and grey	..	1·25	90
126.	6d. green and blue	..	5·50	1·75
127.	1s. grey and purple	..	6·50	10·00

1937. Coronation. As T **2** of Aden.

No.	Description			Unused	Used
128.	1d. green	..	..	30	15
129.	2d. orange	..	..	75	15
130.	3d. blue ..	..	..	1·00	25

33. Badge of St. Helena.

1938.

No.	Type	Description			Unused	Used
131.	33.	½d. violet	..	..	10	30
132.		1d. green	..	..	20·00	4·00
132a.		1d. orange	..	..	15	20
149.		1d. black and green		..	40	80
133.		1½d. red ..	..	..	15	30
150.		1½d. black and red		..	40	80
134.		2d. orange	..	..	15	10
151.		2d. black and red		..	40	80
135.		3d. blue ..	..	..	90·00	30·00
135a.		3d. grey ..	..	..	30	15
135b.		4d. blue ..	..	..	70	20
136.		6d. blue ..	..	..	80	15
136a.		8d. green	..	..	2·00	75
137.		1s. brown	..	..	35	25
138.		2s. 6d. purple ..		..	8·00	2·75
139.		5s. brown	..	..	11·00	7·50
140.		10s. purple	..	..	11·00	15·00

1946. Victory. As T **9** of Aden.

No.	Description			Unused	Used
141.	2d. orange	..	..	10	10
142.	4d. blue ..	..	..	10	10

1948. Silver Wedding. As T **10/11** of Aden.

No.	Description			Unused	Used
143.	3d. black	..	..	30	20
144.	10s. blue	..	..	18·00	23·00

1949. U.P.U. As T **20/23** of Antigua.

No.	Description			Unused	Used
145	3d. red ..	..	..	75	30
146	4d. blue ..	..	..	1·50	90
147	6d. green ..	..	..	1·75	90
148	1s. black ..	..	..	1·75	1·10

1953. Coronation. As T **13** of Aden.

No.	Description		Unused	Used
152.	3d. black and lilac	..	70	65

34. Badge of St. Helena.

1953.

No.	Type	Description		Unused	Used
153.	34.	½d. black and green	..	30	30
154.	–	1d. black and green	..	15	20
155.	–	1½d. black and purple	..	1·25	60
156.	–	2d. black and red	..	50	30
157.	–	2½d. black and red	..	40	30
158.	–	3d. black and brown	..	2·50	30
159.	–	4d. black and blue	..	40	40
160.	–	6d. black and violet	..	40	30
161.	–	7d. black ..	..	65	1·25
162.	–	1s. black and red	..	40	40
163.	–	2s. 6d. black and violet		8·50	6·50
164.	–	5s. black and sepia	..	12·00	9·00
165.	–	10s. black and yellow	..	40·00	20·00

DESIGNS—HORIZ. 1d. Flax plantation, 2d. Lace-making. 2½d. Drying flax. 3d. St. Helena Sand Plover. 4d. Flagstaff and the Barn (hills). 6d. Donkeys carrying flax. 7d. Map. 1s. The Castle. 2s. 6d. Cutting flax. 5s. Jamestown. 10s. Longwood House. VERT. 1½d. Heart-shaped Waterfall.

45. Stamp of 1856.

1956. Cent. of First St. Helena Postage Stamp.

No.	Type	Description		Unused	Used
166.	45.	3d. blue and red	..	10	10
167.		4d. blue and brown	..	10	10
168.		6d. blue and purple	..	15	15

47. East Indiaman "London" off James Bay.

1959. Tercent of Settlement.

No.	Type	Description		Unused	Used
169.	–	3d. black and red	..	10	10
170.	47.	6d. green and blue	..	30	25
171.	–	1s. black and orange	..	30	25

DESIGNS—HORIZ. 3d. Arms of East India Company. 1s. Commemoration Stone.

1961. Tristan Relief Fund. Nos. 46 and 49/51 of Tristan da Cunha surch. **ST. HELENA Tristan Relief** and premium.

No.	Description	Unused	Used
172.	2½ c. + 3d. black and red ..	—	£400
173.	5 c. + 6d. black and blue ..	—	£400
174.	7½ c. + 9d. black and red ..	—	£475
175.	10 c. + 1s. black and brown	—	£550

50. Cunning Fish.

63. Queen Elizabeth II with Prince Andrew (after Cecil Beaton).

1961.

176 **50** 1d. multicoloured .. 10 10
177 – 1½d. multicoloured .. 30 10
178 – 2d. red and grey .. 15 10
179 – 3d. multicoloured .. 50 20
180 – 4½d. multicoloured .. 60 30
181 – 6d. red, sepia and olive 2·25 35
182 – 7d. brown, blk. & violet 35 50
183 – 10d. purple and blue.. 35 40
184 – 1s. lemon, grn. & brn. 35 40
185 – 1s. 6d. grey and blue.. 7·50 3·00
186 – 2s. 6d. red, yell. & turq. 2·50 1·50
187 – 5s. yell., brown & grn. 8·50 2·75
188 – 10s. red, black & blue 17·00 8·50
189 **63** £1 brown and blue .. 22·00 17·00

Designs—As Type **50**—vert. 1½d. Yellow canary. 3d. Queen Elizabeth II. 4½d. Redwood flower. 6d. Madagascar red fody. 1s. Gum-wood flower. 1s 6d. White tern. 5s. Night-blooming Cereus. horiz. 2d. Brittle starfish. 7d. Trumpet fish. 10d. Feather starfish. 2s 6d. Orange starfish. 10s. Deep-water bull's-eye.

1963. Freedom from Hunger. As T **28** of Aden.
190. 1s. 6d. blue .. .. 2·50 40

1963. Cent of Red Cross. As T **33** of Antigua.
191. 3d. red and black.. .. 75 25
192. 1s. 6d. red and blue .. 3·00 75

1965. 1st Local Post. Optd. **FIRST LOCAL POST 4th JANUARY 1965.**
193. **50.** 1d. 10 10
194. 3d. (No. 179) 10 10
195. 6d. (No. 181) 20 10
196. 1s. 6d. (No. 185) .. 25 15

1965. Cent of I.T.U. As T **36** of Antigua.
197. 3d. blue and brown .. 35 15
198. 6d. purple and green .. 55 15

1965. Cent of I.C.Y. As T **37** of Antigua.
199. 1d. purple and turquoise.. 20 15
200. 6d. green and lavender .. 55 15

1966. Churchill Commem. As T **38** of Antigua.
201. 1d. blue 15 10
202. 3d. green 35 10
203. 6d. brown.. .. .. 50 10
204. 1s. 6d. violet 70 30

1966. World Cup Football Championship. As T **40** of Antigua.
205. 3d. multicoloured .. 50 15
206. 6d. multicoloured .. 75 15

1966. Inauguration of W.H.O. Headquarters, Geneva. As T **41** of Antigua.
207. 3d. black, green and blue 50 15
208. 1s. 6d. blk., purple & ochre 2·75 40

1966. 20th Anniv of U.N.E.S.C.O. As T **54/6** of Antigua.
209. 3d. multicoloured .. 1·50 20
210. 6d. yellow, violet and olive 2·50 30
211. 1s. 6d. blk., purple & orge. 4·00 1·00

65. Badge of St. Helena.

1967. New Constitution.
212. **65.** 1s. multicoloured .. 10 10
213. 2s. 6d. multicoloured .. 20 20

66. Fire of London.

1967. 300th Anniv. of Arrival of Settlers after Great Fire of London.
214. **66.** 1d. red and black .. 10 10
215. – 3d. blue and black .. 10 10
216. – 6d. violet and black .. 10 10
217. – 1s. 6d. green and black 10 10

Design: 3d. East Indiaman "Charles". 6d. Settlers landing at Jamestown. 1s. 6d. Settlers clearing scrub.

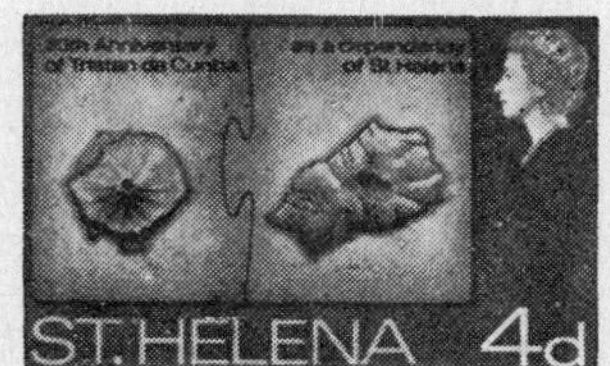

70. Interlocking Maps of Tristan and St. Helena.

1968. 30th Anniv. of Tristan da Cunha as a Dependency of St. Helena.
218. **70.** 4d. purple and brown.. 10 10
219. – 8d. olive and brown .. 10 10
220. **70.** 1s. 9d. blue and brown 10 15
221. – 2s. 3d. blue & brown 15 15

Design: 8d. and 2s. 3d. Interlocking Maps of Tristan and St. Helena (different).

72. Queen Elizabeth and Sir Hudson Lowe.

1968. 150th Anniversary of Abolition of Slavery in St. Helena.
222. **72.** 3d. multicoloured .. 10 10
223. 9d. multicoloured .. 10 10
224. – 1s. 6d. multicoloured .. 15 15
225. – 2s. 6d. multicoloured .. 25 15

Design: Nos. 224 and 225, Queen Elizabeth and Sir George Bingham.

74. Blue Gum Eucalyptus and Road Construction.

1968. Multicoloured.
226. ½d. Type **74** 10 10
227. 1d. Electricity Development 10 10
228. 1½d. Dental Unit.. .. 15 10
229. 2d. Post Control 15 10
230. 3d. Flats in Jamestown .. 30 10
231. 4d. Blue gum Eucalyptus and Livestock Improvement 20 10
232. 6d. Schools Broadcasting 40 10
233. 8d. County Cottages .. 30 10
234. 10d. New School Buildings 30 10
235. 1s. Reafforestation .. 25 10
236. 1s. 6d. Heavy Lift Crane.. 70 1·25
237. 2s. 6d. Lady Field Children's Home .. .. 80 1·40
238. 5s. Agricultural Training.. 90 1·75
239. 10s. New General Hospital 2·25 3·00
240. £1 Lifeboat "John Dutton" 10·00 15·00

Plants shown: 4d., 1s. 6d. Blue gum Eucalyptus. 1d., 6d., 2s. 6d. Cabbage-tree. 1½d., 8d., 5s. St. Helena Redwood. 2d., 10d., 10s. Scrubweed. 3d., 1s., £1, Tree-fern.

89. Brig "Perseverance".

1969. Mail Communications. Multicoloured.
241. 4d. Type **89** 20 15
242. 8d. R.M.S. "Dane" .. 30 15
243. 1s. 9d. S.S. "Llandovery Castle" 40 25
244. 2s. 3d. R.M.S. "Good Hope Castle" 45 30

93. W.O. and Drummer of the 53rd Foot, 1815.

1969. Military Uniforms. Multicoloured.
245. 6d. Type **93** 30 15
246. 8d. Officer and Surgeon, 20th Foot, 1816 .. 40 15
247. 1s. 8d. Drum Major, 66th Foot, 1816, and Royal Artillery Officer, 1920.. 50 15
248. 2s. 6d. Private, 91st Foot, and 2nd Corporal, Royal Sappers & Miners, 1832 60 20

97. Dickens, Mr. Pickwick and Job Trotter ("Pickwick Papers").

1970. Death Cent. of Charles Dickens. Mult.
249. 4d. Type **97** 15 10
250. 8d. Mr. Bumble and Oliver ("Oliver Twist") .. 15 10
251. 1s. 6d. Sairey Gamp and Mark Tapley ("Martin Chuzzlewit") 35 15
252. 2s. 6d. Jo and Mr. Turveydrop ("Bleak House") 45 30

All designs include a portrait of Dickens as Type **97**.

98. "Kiss of Life".

1970. Centenary of British Red Cross.
253. **98.** 6d. bistre, red and black 10 10
254. – 9d. green, red and black 10 10
255. – 1s. 9d. grey, red & black 15 10
256. – 2s. 3d. lilac, red & black 20 20

Designs: 9d. Nurse with girl in wheelchair. 1s. 9d. Hurse bandaging child's knee. 2s. 3d. Red Cross emblem.

99. Officer's Shako Plate (20th Foot).

1970. Military Equipment (1st issue). Mult.
257. 4d. Type **99** 80 20
258. 9d. Officer's Breast Plate (66th Foot) .. 1·25 30
259. 1s. 3d. Officer's Full Dress Shako (91st Foot) 1·50 40
260. 2s. 11d. Ensign's Shako (53rd Foot) .. .. 2·00 60

See also Nos. 281/4, 285/8 and 291/4.

100. Electricity Development.

1971. Decimal Currency. Designs as Nos. 227/39, inscr. as T **100.**
261. ½p. multicoloured .. 10 10
262. 1p. multicoloured .. 10 10
263. 1½p. multicoloured .. 10 10
264. 2p. multicoloured .. 1·75 90
265. 2½p. multicoloured .. 10 10
266. 3½p. multicoloured .. 15 10
267. 4½p. multicoloured .. 10 10
268. 5p. multicoloured .. 10 10
269. 7½p. multicoloured .. 30 35
270. 10p. multicoloured .. 30 35
271. 12½p. multicoloured .. 30 50
272. 25p. multicoloured .. 60 1·25
273. 50p. multicoloured .. 1·25 2·00

101. St. Helena holding the "True Cross".

1971. Easter.
275. **101.** 2p. multicoloured .. 10 10
276. 5p. multicoloured .. 15 15
277. 7½p. multicoloured .. 20 20
278. 12½p. multicoloured .. 25 25

102. Napoleon (after painting by J. L. David), and Tomb on St. Helena.

1971. 150th Death Anniv. of Napoleon. Mult.
279. 2p. Type **102** 50 40
280. 34p. "Napoleon at St. Helena" (H. Delaroche) 2·00 85

1971. Military Equipment (2nd issue). As T **99.** Multicoloured.
281. 1½p. Artillery Private's hanger .. .. 1·25 30
282. 4p. Baker rifle and socket bayonet .. .. 2·00 60
283. 6p. Infantry Officer's sword 2·00 80
284. 22½p. Baker rifle and sword bayonet .. .. 2·50 1·25

1972. Military Equipment (3rd issue). As T **99.** Multicoloured.
285. 2p. multicoloured .. 60 20
286. 5p. lilac, blue and black .. 1·25 50
287. 7½p. multicoloured .. 1·50 60
288. 12½p. sepia, brn. & black.. 2·00 75

Designs: 2p. Royal Sappers and Miners breast-plate, post 1823. 5p. Infantry sergeant's spontoon, c. 1830. 7½p. Royal Artillery Officer's breast-plate, c. 1830. 12½p. English military pistol, c. 1800.

1972. Royal Silver Wedding. As T **52** of Ascension but with St. Helena Sand Plover and White Tern in background.
289. 2p. green 25 35
290. 16p. brown 50 65

1973. Military Equipment (4th issue). As T **99.** Multicoloured.
291. 2p. Other Rank's shako, 53rd Foot, 1815 .. 1·00 55
292. 5p. Band and Drums sword, 1830 .. .. 2·00 1·00
293. 7½p. Royal Sappers and Miners Officer's hat, 1830 2·25 1·25
294. 12½p. General's sword, 1831 3·50 1·50

1973. Royal Wedding. As T **47** of Anguilla. Multicoloured, background colours given.
295. 2p. blue 15 10
296. 18p. green 25 20

104. "Westminster" and "Claudine" Beached, 1849.

1973. Tercentenary of East India Company Charter. Multicoloured.

297.	1½p. Type 104	50	35
298.	4p. "True Briton", 1790	60	65
299.	6p. "General Goddard" in action, 1795 ..	60	65
300.	22½p. "Kent" burning in the Bay of Biscay, 1825,	1·50	2·00

105. U.P.U. Emblem and Ships.

1974. Centenary of U.P.U. Multicoloured.

301.	5p. Type 105	25	25
302.	25p. U.P.U. emblem and letters	55	55

106. Churchill in Sailor Suit and Blenheim Palace.

1974. Birth Cent. of Sir Winston Churchill.

304. 106.	5 p. multicoloured	25	55
305. –	25 p. black, pink & purple	55	75

DESIGN: 25 p. Churchill and River Thames.

107. Capt. Cook and H.M.S. "Resolution".

1975. Bicentenary of Capt. Cook's Return to St. Helena.

307.	5p. Type 107	50	50
308.	25p. Capt. Cook and Jamestown	1·00	1·50

108. "Mellissia begonifolia" (tree).

1975. Centenary of Publication of "St. Helena" by J. C. Melliss. Multicoloured.

310.	2p. Type 108	25	40
311.	5p. "Mellissius adumbratus" (beetle) ..	35	60
312.	12p. St. Helena Sand Plover (bird) (horiz.) ..	90	1·50
313.	25p. "Scorpaenia mellissii" (fish) (horiz.)	1·00	1·75

109. £1 Note.

1976. Currency Notes. First Issue. Mult.

314.	8p. Type 109	40	35
315.	33p. £5 Note	85	1·25

110. 1d. Stamp of 1863.

1976. Festival of Stamps, London.

316. 110.	5p. brn., blk. and pink ..	15	15
317. –	8p. blk., grn. & lt. grn.	25	30
318. –	25p. multicoloured ..	40	45

DESIGNS—VERT. 8p. 1d. stamp of 1922. HORIZ. 25p. Mail carrier "Good Hope Castle".

111. "High Knoll, 1806" (Capt. Barnett).

1976. Views of St. Helena. Multicoloured.

319.	1p. Type 111	30	40
320.	3p. "The Friar Rock. 1815" (G. Bellasis) ..	30	40
321.	5p. "The Column Lot, 1815" (G. Bellasis) ..	20	40
322.	6p. "Sandy Bay Valley, 1809" (H. Salt) ..	20	40
323.	8p. "Scene from Castle Terrace, 1815" (G. Bellasis)	30	45
324.	9p. "The Briars, 1815"	30	50
325.	10p. "Plantation House, 1821" (J. Wathen) ..	50	60
326.	15p. "Longwood House, 1821" ((J. Wathen) ..	35	45
327.	18p. "St. Paul's Church" (V. Brooks)	35	65
328.	26p. "St. James's Valley, 1815" (Capt. Hastings)	40	65
329.	40p. "St Matthew's Church, 1860" (V. Brooks)	70	1·25
330.	£1 "St. Helena, 1815" (G. Bellasis)	1·50	3·00
331.	£2 "Sugar Loaf Hill, 1821" (J. Wathen) ..	3·50	5·50

Nos. 330/1 are larger; 47 × 34 mm.
Nos. 319, 325 and 331 come with or without date imprint.

112. Duke of Edinburgh paying Homage.

1977. Silver Jubilee. Multicoloured.

332.	8p. Royal visit, 1947 ..	20	35
333.	15p. Queen's sceptre with dove	25	45
334.	26p. Type 112	35	50

113. Halley's Comet (from Bayeux Tapestry).

1977. Tercentenary of Halley's Visit. Mult.

335.	5p. Type 113	35	20
336.	8p. Late 17th-century sextant	50	20
337.	27p. Halley and Halley's Mount, St. Helena ..	1·00	60

114. Sea Lion.

1978. 25th Anniv. of Coronation.

338.	25p. agate, red & silver	40	50
339. –	25p. multicoloured ..	40	50
340. 114.	25p. agate, red & silver	40	50

DESIGNS: No. 338, Black Dragon of Ulster. No. 339, Queen Elizabeth II.

115. Period Engraving of St. Helena.

1978. Wreck of the "Witte Leeuw". Multicoloured.

341.	3p. Type 115	15	15
342.	5p. Chinese porcelain ..	20	20
343.	8p. Bronze cannon ..	25	30
344.	9p. Chinese porcelain ..	30	35
345.	15p. Pewter mug and ceramic flasks	50	55
346.	20p. Dutch East Indiaman	60	70

116. H.M.S. "Discovery".

1979. Bicentenary of Captain Cook's Voyages, 1768–79. Multicoloured.

347.	3p. Type 116	20	15
348.	8p. Cook's portable observatory	30	25
349.	12p. "Pharnaceum acidum" (sketch by Joseph Banks)	35	35
350.	25p. Flaxman/Wedgwood medallion of Capt. Cook	55	90

117. Sir Rowland Hill.

1979. Death Centenary of Sir Rowland Hill.

351. 117.	5p. multicoloured ..	15	15
352. –	8p. multicoloured ..	20	20
353. –	20p. multicoloured ..	40	40
354. –	32p. blk., mag. and mve.	55	55

DESIGNS—HORIZ. 8p. 1965 1d. "FIRST LOCAL POST 4th JANUARY 1965" overprinted stamp. 20p. 1863 1d. on 6d. surcharged stamp. 32p. 1902 1d. stamp.

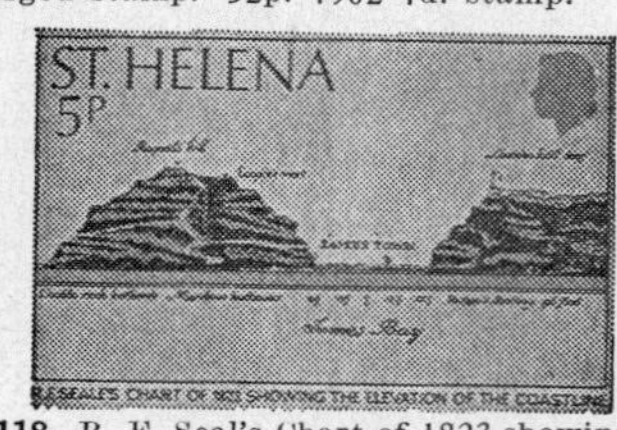

118. R. F. Seal's Chart of 1823 showing the Elevation of the Coastline.

1979. 150th Anniv. of Inclined Plane

355. 118.	5p. black, grey & stone	20	15
356. –	8p. black, grey & stone	20	20
357. –	50p. multicoloured ..	70	75

DESIGNS—HORIZ. 8p. The Inclined Plane in 1829. VERT. 50p. The Inclined Plane in 1979.

119. Napoleon's Tomb, 1848.

1980. Centenary of Visit of Empress Eugenie of France.

358. 119.	5p. brown, pink & gold	20	20
359. –	8p. brown, stone & gold	25	25
360. –	62p. brown, flesh & gold	95	1·10

DESIGNS: 8p. Landing at St. Helena. 62p. The Empress at Napoleon's Tomb.

120. East Indiaman.

1980. "London 1980" International Stamp Exhibition. Multicoloured.

362.	5p. Type 120	15	15
363.	8p. "Dolphin" Postal Stone	15	20
364.	47p. Postal Stone outside Castle entrance, Jamestown	60	80

121. Queen Elizabeth the Queen Mother in 1974.

1980. 80th Birthday of The Queen Mother.

366. 121.	24p. multicoloured ..	50	50

122. The Briars, 1815.

1980. 175th Anniv. of Wellington's Visit. Multicoloured.

367.	9p. Type 122	15	15
368.	30p. "Wellington" (Goya) (vert.)	45	45

123. Redwood.

1981. Endemic Plants. Multicoloured.

369.	5p. Type 123	15	15
370.	8p. Old Father Live Forever ..	20	20
371.	15p. Gumwood ..	25	25
372.	27p. Black Cabbage ..	45	45

124. Detail from Reinel Portolan Chart, c. 1530.

1981. Early Maps.

373. 124.	5p. multicoloured ..	25	15
374. –	8p. black, red and grey	30	20
375. –	20p. multicoloured ..	50	35
376. –	30p. multicoloured ..	55	50

DESIGNS: 8p. John Thornton Map of St. Helena, c. 1700. 20p. Map of St. Helena, 1815. 30p. Map of St. Helena, 1817.

125. Prince Charles as Royal Navy Commander.

1981. Royal Wedding. Multicoloured.

378.	14p. Wedding bouquet from St. Helena	25	25
379.	29p. Type **125**	35	35
380.	32p. Prince Charles and Lady Diana Spencer	50	50

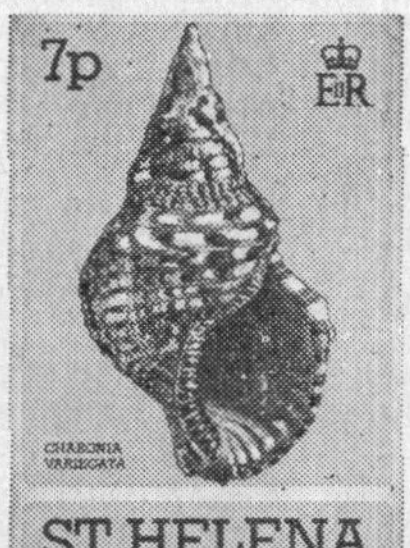

126. " Charonia Variegata ".

1981. Seashells. Multicoloured.

381.	7p. Type **126**	35	20
382.	10p. " Cypraea spurca sanctaehelenae "	40	25
383.	25p. " Janthina janthina "	70	60
384.	53p. " Pinna rudis "	1·25	1·25

127. Traffic Duty.

1981. 25th Anniv. of Duke of Edinburgh Award Scheme. Multicoloured.

385.	7p. Type **127**	15	15
386.	11p. Signposting	15	15
387.	25p. Animal care	35	35
388.	50p. Duke of Edinburgh in ceremonial dress, on horse-back	70	70

128. "Sympetrum dilatatum" (dragonfly).

1981. Insects (1st series). Multicoloured.

389	7p. Type **128**	30	25
390	10p. "Aplothorax burchelli" (beetle)	40	35
391	25p. "Ampulex compressa" (wasp)	70	60
392	32p. "Labidura herculeana" (earwig)	80	75

See also Nos. 411/14.

129. Charles Darwin.

1982. 150th Anniv. of Charles Darwin's Voyage. Multicoloured.

393.	7p. Type **129**	30	30
394.	14p. Flagstaff Hill and Darwin's hammer	45	60
395.	25p. Ring-necked Pheasant and Chukar Partridge	75	1·00
396.	29p. H.M.S. "Beagle" off St. Helena	95	1·25

130. Prince and Princess of Wales at Balmoral, Autumn, 1981.

1982. 21st Birthday of Princess of Wales. Multicoloured.

397.	7p. St. Helena coat of arms	15	15
398.	11p. Type **130**	25	25
399.	29p. Bride on Palace balcony	55	70
400.	55p. Formal portrait	1·00	1·40

1982. Commonwealth Games, Brisbane. Nos. 326 and 328 optd. **1st PARTICIPATION COMMONWEALTH GAMES 1982.**

401.	15p. " Longwood House, 1821 " (G. Wathen)	25	25
402.	26p. " St. James's Valley 1815 " (Capt. Hastings)	45	45

132. Lord Baden-Powell.

1982. 75th Anniv. of Boy Scout Movement.

403. **132.**	3p. brn., grey and yellow	15	15
404. –	11p. brn., grey and green	35	25
405. –	29p. brn., grey and orge.	70	60
406. –	59p. brn., grey and green	1·25	1·25

DESIGNS—HORIZ. 11p. Boy Scout (drawing by Lord Baden Powell). 59p. Camping at Thompsons Wood. VERT—29p. Canon Walcott.

133. King and Queen Rocks.

1982. Views of St. Helena by Roland Svensson. Multicoloured.

407.	7p. Type **133**	20	20
408.	11p. " Turks' Cap "	25	25
409.	29p. Coastline from Jamestown (horiz.)	65	65
410.	59p. " Mundens Point " (horiz.)	1·40	1·40

1983. Insects (2nd series). As T **128**. Mult.

411	11p. "Acherontia atropos" (hawk moth)	35	30
412	15p. "Helenasaldula aberrans" (shore-bug)	40	35
413	29p. "Anchastus compositarum" (click beetle)	65	55
414	59p. "Lamprochrus cossonoides" (weevil)	1·40	1·25

134. " Coriolus versicolor ".

135. Java Sparrow.

1983. Fungi. Multicoloured.

415.	11p. Type **134**	20	20
416.	15p. " Pluteus brunneisucus "	30	30
417.	29p. " Polyporus induratus " (horiz.)	55	55
418.	59p. " Coprinus angulatus "	1·25	1·25

1983. Birds. Multicoloured.

419.	7p. Type **135**	30	20
420.	15p. Madagascar red fody	45	35
421.	33p. Common waxbill	80	70
422.	59p. Yellow canary	1·50	1·40

136. Birth of St. Helena.

1983. Christmas. Life of St. Helena (1st series). Multicoloured.

423.	10p. Type **136**	25	35
424.	15p. St. Helena being taken to convent	30	35

See also Nos. 450/3 and 468/71.

137. 1934 Centenary ½d. Stamp.

1984. 150th Anniv. of St. Helena as a British Colony. Multicoloured.

425.	1p. Type **137**	10	20
426.	3p. 1934 1d. stamp	10	20
427.	6p. 1934 1½d. stamp	10	30
428.	7p. 1934 2d. stamp	15	30
429.	11p. 1934 3d. stamp	20	40
430.	15p. 1934 6d. stamp	25	45
431.	29p. 1934 1s. stamp	50	95
432.	33p. 1934 5s. stamp	55	1·25
433.	59p. 1934 10s. stamp	1·10	2·00
434.	£1 1934 2s. 6d. stamp	1·75	3·25
435.	£2 St. Helena Coat of Arms	3·50	5·00

138. Prince Andrew and H.M.S. "Invincible" (aircraft carrier).

1984. Visit of Prince Andrew. Mult.

436.	11p. Type **138**	25	25
437.	60p. Prince Andrew and H.M.S. "Herald" (survey ship)	1·25	1·40

139. "St. Helena" (schooner).

1984. 250th Anniv. of "Lloyd's List" (newspaper). Multicoloured.

438.	10p. Type **139**	20	20
439.	18p. Solomons Facade (local agent)	35	35
440.	25p. Lloyd's Coffee House, London	50	55
441.	50p. "Papanui" (freighter)	1·00	1·00

140. Twopenny Coin and Donkey.

1984. New Coinage. Multicoloured.

442.	10p. Type **140**	35	35
443.	15p. Five pence coin and St. Helena sand plover	45	45
444.	29p. Penny coin and yellowfin tuna	75	75
445.	50p. Ten pence coin and arum lily	1·25	1·25

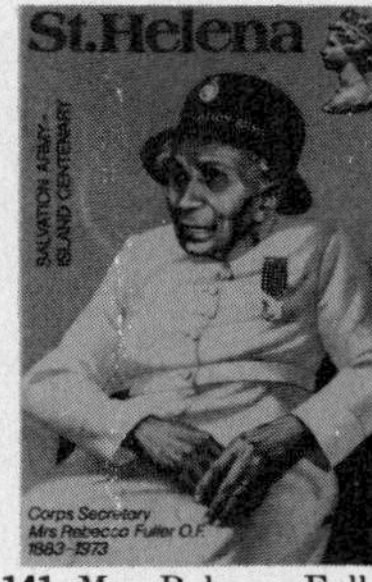

141. Mrs. Rebecca Fuller (Former Corps Secretary).

1984. Centenary of Salvation Army on St. Helena. Multicoloured.

446.	7p. Type **141**	35	25
447.	11p. Meals-on-wheels service (horiz.)	45	30
448.	25p. Salvation Army Citadel, Jamestown (horiz.)	80	60
449.	60p. Salvation Army band at Jamestown Clock Tower	1·75	1·60

1984. Christmas. Life of St. Helena (2nd series). As T **136**. Multicoloured.

450.	6p. St. Helena visits prisoners	20	20
451.	10p. Betrothal of St. Helena	30	30
452.	15p. Marriage of St. Helena to Constantius	40	40
453.	33p. Birth of Constantine	70	70

142. Queen Elizabeth the Queen Mother aged Two.

1985. Life and Times of Queen Elizabeth the Queen Mother. Multicoloured.

454.	11p. Type **142**	20	25
455.	5p. At Ascot with the Queen	30	35
456.	29p. Attending Gala Ballet at Covent Garden	60	65
457.	55p. With Prince Henry at his christening	1·10	1·25

143. Rock Bullseye.

1985. Marine Life. Multicoloured.

459.	7p. Type **143**	25	25
460.	11p. Mackerel	30	30
461.	15p. Skipjack Tuna	40	40
462.	33p. Yellowfin Tuna	75	75
463.	50p. Stump	1·25	1·25

144. John J. Audubon.

1985. Birth Bicentenary of John J. Audubon (ornithologist).
464. **144.** 11p. black and brown 45 25
465. – 15p. multicoloured .. 55 35
466. – 25p. multicoloured .. 75 55
467 – 60p. multicoloured .. 1·40 1·40

Design—horiz (from original Audubon paintings). 15p. Common gallinule (moorhen). 25p. White-tailed tropic bird. 68p. Common noddy.

1985. Christmas. Life of St Helena (3rd series). As T **136**. Multicoloured.
468. 7p. St. Helena journeys to the Holy Land 25 25
469. 10p. Zambres slays the bull 30 30
470. 15p. The bull restored to life: conversion of St. Helena 40 40
471. 60p. Resurrection of the corpse: the true Cross identified .. .. 1·50 1·50

145. Church Provident Society for Women Banner.

1986. Friendly Societies Banners. Mult.
472. 10p. Type **145** 25 25
473. 11p. Working Men's Christian Association .. 25 25
474. 25p. Church Benefit Society for Children .. 55 55
475. 29p. Mechanics and Friendly Benefit Society 65 65
476. 33p. Ancient Order of Foresters 70 70

1986. 60th Birthday of Queen Elizabeth II. As T **110** of Ascension. Multicoloured.
477. 10p. Princess Elizabeth making 21st birthday broadcast, South Africa, 1947 .. .. .. 20 25
478. 15p. Silver Jubilee photograph, 1977 .. .. 30 35
479. 20p. Princess Elizabeth on board H.M.S. "Implacable" 1947 .. 40 45
480. 50p. In the U.S.A., 1976 .. 1·00 1·10
481. 65p. At Crown Agents Head Office, London, 1983 .. .. .. 1·25 1·40

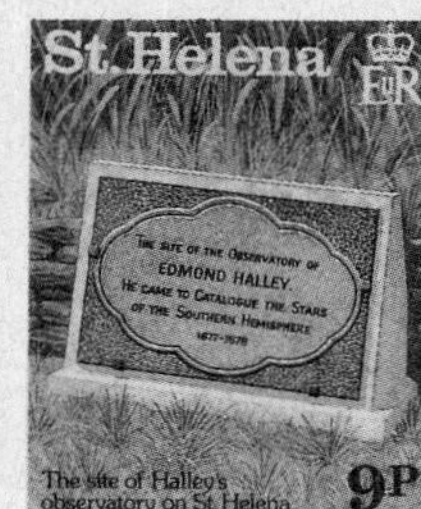

146. Plaque at Site of Halley's Observatory on St. Helena.

1986. Appearance of Halley's Comet. Multicoloured.
482. 9p. Type **146** 25 25
483. 12p. Edmond Halley .. 30 30
484. 20p. Halley's planisphere of the southern stars .. 45 45
485. 65p. "Unity" on passage to St. Helena, 1676 .. 1·40 1·40

1986. Royal Wedding. As T **112** of Ascension. Multicoloured.
486. 10p. Prince Andrew and Miss Sarah Ferguson .. 20 25
487. 40p. Prince Andrew with Governor J. Massingham on St. Helena 80 85

147. James Ross and H.M.S. "Erebus".

1986. Explorers.
488. **147.** 1p. brown and pink .. 10 10
489. – 3p. deep blue and blue 10 10
490. – 5p. deep grn. & grn. 10 15
491. – 9p. brown and red .. 20 25
492. – 10p. deep brn. & brn. 20 25
493. – 12p. green & light grn. 25 30
494. – 15p. brown and pink 30 35
495. – 20p. blue and lt. blue 40 45
496. – 25p. sepia and pink .. 50 55
497. – 40p. deep grn. & grn. 80 85
498. – 60p. deep brn. & brn. 1·25 1·40
499. – £1 deep blue and blue 2·00 2·10
500. – £2 deep lilac & lilac .. 4·00 4·25

Designs: 3p. Robert FitzRoy and H.M.S. "Beagle". 5p. Adam Johann von Krusenstern and "Nadezhda". 9p. William Bligh and H.M.S. "Resolution". 10p. Otto von Kotzebue and "Rurik". 12p. Philip Carteret and H.M.S. "Swallow". 15p. Thomas Cavendish and "Desire". 20p. Louis-Antoine de Bougainville and "La Boudeuse" 25p. Fyodor Petrovich Lütke and "Senyavin". 40p. Louis Isidore Duperrey and "La Coquille" 60p. John Byron and H.M.S. "Dolphin". £1 James Cook and H.M.S. "Endeavour". £2 Jules Dumont d'Urville and L'Astrolabe".

148. Prince Edward and H.M.S. "Repulse" (battle cruiser), 1925.

1987. Royal Visits to St. Helena. Mult.
501. 9p. Type **148** 50 40
502. 13p. King George VI and H.M.S. "Vanguard" (battleship), 1947 .. 70 60
503. 38p. Prince Philip and Royal Yacht "Britannia", 1957 .. 1·40 1·50
504. 45p. Prince Andrew and H.M.S. "Herald" (survey ship), 1984 1·60 1·75

149. St. Helena Tea Plant.

1987. Rare Plants (1st series). Multicoloured.
505. 9p. Type **149** 65 35
506. 13p. Baby's toes 80 45
507. 38p. Salad plant .. 1·50 1·00
508. 45p. Scrubwood .. .. 1·75 1·25

See also Nos. 531/4.

150. Lesser Rorqual.

1987. Marine Mammals. Multicoloured.
509. 9p. Type **150** 60 35
510. 13p. Risso's dolphin .. 75 50
511. 45p. Sperm whale .. 1·75 1·40
512. 60p. Euphrosyne dolphin 2·00 1·60

1987. Royal Ruby Wedding. Nos. 477/81 optd.. **40TH WEDDING ANNIVERSARY.**
514. 10p. Princess Elizabeth making 21st birthday broadcast, South Africa, 1947 .. .. .. 20 25
515. 15p. Silver Jubilee photograph, 1977 .. .. 30 35
516. 20p. Princess Elizabeth on board H.M.S. "Implacable", 1947 .. 40 45
517. 50p. In the U.S.A., 1976 .. 1·00 1·10
518. 65p. At Crown Agents Head Office, London, 1983 .. .. .. 1·25 1·40

151. "Defence" and Dampier's Signature, 1691.

1988. Bicentenary of Australian Settlement. Ships and signatures. Multicoloured.
519. 9p. Type **151** 75 65
520. 13p. H.M.S. "Resolution" (Cook), 1775 .. .. 1·25 90
521. 45p. H.M.S. "Providence" (Bligh), 1792 .. .. 2·25 2·00
522. 60p. H.M.S. "Beagle" (Darwin), 1836 .. .. 2·75 2·50

152 "The Holy Virgin with the Child"

1988. Christmas. Religious paintings. Mult.
523 5p. Type **152** 10 15
524 20p. "Madonna" 40 45
525 38p. "The Holy Family with St. John" .. 75 80
526 60p. "The Holy Virgin with the Child" .. 1·25 1·40

1988. 300th Anniv of Lloyd's of London. As T **123** of Ascension.
527 9p. deep brown and brown 20 25
528 20p. multicoloured .. 40 45
529 45p. multicoloured .. 90 95
530 60p. multicoloured .. 1·25 1·40

DESIGNS; VERT—9p. Lloyd's Underwriting Room, 1886; 60p. "Spangereid" (full-rigged ship) on fire, St. Helena, 1920. HORIZ—20p. "Edinburgh Castle" (liner); 45p. "Bosun Bird" (freighter).

153 Ebony

1989. Rare Plants (2nd series). Multicoloured.
531 9p. Type **153** 30 30
532 20p. St. Helena lobelia .. 55 55
533 45p. Large bellflower .. 1·10 1·10
534 60p. She cabbage tree .. 1·40 1·40

INDEX

Countries can be quickly located by referring to the index at the end of this volume.

154 Private, 53rd Foot

1989. Military Uniforms of 1815. Mult.
535 9p. Type **154** 35 35
536 13p. Officer, 53rd Foot .. 40 40
537 20p. Royal Marine .. 55 55
538 45p. Officer, 66th Foot .. 1·25 1·25
539 60p. Private, 66th Foot .. 1·50 1·50

1989. "PHILEXFRANCE 89" International Stamp Exhibition, Paris. Nos. 535/9 optd **PHILEXFRANCE 89**.
540 9p. Type **154** 35 35
541 13p. Officer, 53rd Foot .. 40 40
542 20p. Royal Marine .. 55 55
543 45p. Officer, 66th Foot .. 1·25 1·25
544 60p. Private, 66th Foot .. 1·50 1·50

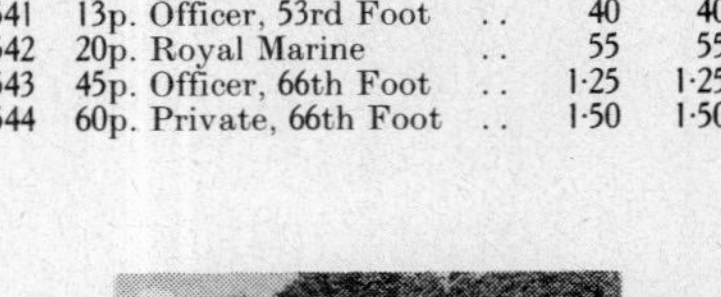

156 Agricultural Studies

1989. New Prince Andrew Central School. Multicoloured.
545 13p. Type **156** 35 35
546 20p. Geography lesson .. 55 55
547 25p. Walkway and classroom block 65 65
548 60p. Aerial view of School 1·50 1·50

157 "The Madonna with the Pear" (Durer)

1989. Christmas. Religious Paintings. Mult.
549 10p. Type **157** 40 30
550 20p. "The Holy Family under the Appletree" (Rubens) 65 55
551 45p. "The Virgin in the Meadow" (Raphael) .. 1·40 1·25
552 60p. "The Holy Family with St. John" (Raphael) .. .. 1·75 1·60

158 Chevrolet "6" 30 cwt Lorry, 1930

1989. Early Vehicles. Multicoloured.
553 9p. Type **158** 30 30
554 20p. Austin "Seven", 1929 50 50
555 45p. Morris "Cowley" 11.9 h.p., 1929 .. .. 1·00 1·00
556 60p. Sunbeam 25 h.p., 1932 1·40 1·40

159 Sheep

1990. Farm Animals. Multicoloured.

No.	Description		
558	9p. Type **159**	30	30
559	13p. Pigs	35	35
560	45p. Cow and calf ..	1·00	1·25
561	60p. Geese	1·40	1·60

160 1840 Twopence Blue

1990. "Stamp World London 90" International Stamp Exhibition, London.

No.	Description		
562	**160** 13p. black and blue ..	40	40
563	– 20p. multicoloured ..	65	65
564	– 38p. multicoloured ..	1·10	1·10
565	– 45p. multicoloured ..	1·40	1·40

DESIGNS: 20p. 1840 Penny Black and 19th-century St. Helena postmark; 38p. Delivering mail to sub post office; 45p. Mail van and Post Office, Jamestown.

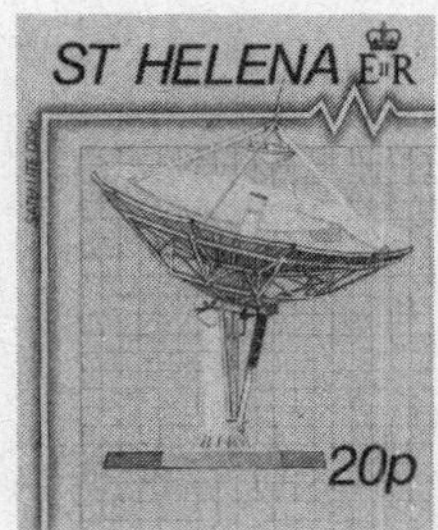

161 Satellite Dish

1990. Modern Telecommunications Links. Multicoloured.

No.	Description		
566	20p. Type **161**	60	60
567	20p. Digital telephone exchange	60	60
568	20p. Public card phone ..	60	60
569	20p. Facsimile machine ..	60	60

1990. 90th Birthday of Queen Elizabeth the Queen Mother. As T **134** of Ascension.

No.	Description		
570	25p. multicoloured ..	75	75
571	£1 black and brown ..	2·50	2·75

DESIGNS—21 × 36 mm. 25p. Lady Elizabeth Bowes-Lyon, April 1923. 29 × 37 mm. £1 Queen Elizabeth visiting communal kitchen, 1940.

1990. Maiden Voyage of "St. Helena II". As T **137** of Ascension. Multicoloured.

No.	Description		
572	13p. "Dane" (mail ship), 1857	40	40
573	20p. "St. Helena I" off-loading at St. Helena ..	65	65
574	38p. Launch of "St. Helena II"	1·10	1·10
575	45p. The Duke of York launching "St. Helena II"	1·25	1·40

163 Baptist Chapel, Sandy Bay

1990. Christmas. Local Churches. Mult.

No.	Description		
577	10p. Type **163**	30	30
578	13p. St. Martin in the Hills Church	35	35
579	20p. St. Helena and the Cross Church ..	55	55
580	38p. St. James Church ..	1·00	1·00
581	45p. St. Paul's Cathedral, Jamestown	1·25	1·25

164 "Funeral Cortege, Jamestown Wharf" (detail, V. Adam)

1990. 150th Anniv of Removal of Napoleon's Body.

No.	Description		
582	**164** 13p. black, brn & grn	40	40
583	– 20p. black, brown & bl	70	70
584	– 38p. black, brn & mve	1·25	1·25
585	– 45p. multicoloured	1·50	1·50

DESIGNS: 20p. "Coffin being conveyed to the 'Belle Poule'", (detail V. Adam); 38p. "Transfer of the Coffin to the 'Normandir', Cherbourg", (detail, V. Adam); 45p. "Napoleon's Tomb, St. Helena", (T. Sutherland).

165 Officer, Leicestershire Regiment

1991. Military Uniforms of 1897. Mult.

No.	Description		
586	13p. Type **165**	40	40
587	15p. Officer, York & Lancaster Regiment ..	45	45
588	20p. Colour-sergeant, Leicestershire Regiment	65	65
589	38p. Bandsman, York & Lancaster Regiment ..	1·25	1·25
590	45p. Lance-corporal, York & Lancaster Regiment	1·50	1·50

1991. 65th Birthday of Queen Elizabeth II and 70th Birthday of Prince Philip. As T **139** of Ascension. Multicoloured.

No.	Description		
591	25p. Queen Elizabeth II ..	75	75
592	25p. Prince Philip in naval uniform	75	75

166 "Madonna and Child" (T. Vecellio)

1991. Christmas. Religious Paintings. Mult.

No.	Description		
593	10p. Type **166**	35	35
594	13p. "The Holy Family" (A. Mengs)	45	45
595	20p. "Madonna and Child" (W. Dyce)	65	65
596	38p. "The Two Trinities" (B. Murillo)	1·10	1·10
597	45p. "The Virgin and Child" (G. Bellini) ..	1·60	1·60

167 Matchless (346cc) Motorcycle, 1947

1991. "Philanippon '91" International Stamp Exhibition, Tokyo. Motorcycles. Mult.

No.	Description		
598	13p. Type **167**	35	35
599	20p. Triumph "Tiger 100" (500cc), 1950	55	55
600	38p. Honda "CD" (175cc), 1967	95	95
601	45p. Yamaha "DTE 400", 1976	1·40	1·40

168 "Eye of the Wind" (cadet ship) and Compass Rose

1992. 500th Anniv of Discovery of America by Columbus and Re-enactment Voyages. Multicoloured.

No.	Description		
603	15p. Type **168**	50	50
604	25p. "Soren Larsen" (cadet ship) and map of re-enactment voyages ..	80	80
605	35p. "Santa Maria", "Nina" and "Pinta" ..	1·25	1·25
606	50p. Columbus and "Santa Maria"	1·60	1·60

1992. 40th Anniv of Queen Elizabeth II's Accession. As T **143** of Ascension. Mult.

No.	Description		
607	11p. Prince Andrew Central School	30	30
608	15p. Plantation House ..	45	45
609	25p. Jamestown	70	70
610	35p. Three portraits of Queen Elizabeth ..	95	95
611	50p. Queen Elizabeth II ..	1·25	1·25

POSTAGE DUE STAMPS

D 1. Outline Map of St. Helena.

1986.

No.	Description		
D 1.	D **1.** 1p. deep brn. & brn.	10	10
D 2.	2p. brown & orange	10	10
D 3.	5p. brown and red ..	10	15
D 4.	7p. black & violet ..	15	20
D 5.	10p. black & blue ..	20	25
D 6.	25p. black & green ..	50	50

ST. KITTS

On 23 June 1980 separate postal administrations were formed for St. Kitts and for Nevis, although both islands remained part of the State of St. Kitts–Nevis.

100 cents = 1 West Indian dollar.

1980. As Nos. 394/406 of St. Kitts–Nevis optd. **St. Kitts.**

No.	Description		
29.	5 c. multicoloured	10	10
30.	10 c. multicoloured ..	10	10
31.	12 c. multicoloured ..	80	80
32.	15 c. multicoloured ..	10	10
33.	25 c. multicoloured ..	10	10
34.	30 c. multicoloured ..	10	10
35.	40 c. multicoloured ..	10	15
36.	45 c. multicoloured ..	15	15
37.	50 c. multicoloured ..	15	15
38.	55 c. multicoloured ..	15	15
39.	$1 multicoloured ..	25	25
40.	$5 multicoloured	1·00	1·00
41.	$10 multicoloured	1·75	1·75

9. H.M.S. "Vanguard", 1762.

1980. Ships. Multicoloured.

No.	Description		
42.	4 c. Type **9**	10	10
43.	10 c. H.M.S. "Boreas", 1787	10	10
44.	30 c. H.M.S. "Druid", 1827	15	10
45.	55 c. H.M.S. "Winchester", 1831	20	15
46.	$1.50 Harrison Line "Philosopher", 1857	40	30
47.	$2 Harrison Line "Contractor", 1930 ..	50	40

10. Queen Elizabeth the Queen Mother at Royal Variety Performance, 1978.

1980. 80th Birthday of The Queen Mother.

No.	Description		
48.	**10.** $2 multicoloured	60	60

11. The Three Wise Men.

1980. Christmas. Multicoloured.

No.	Description		
49.	5 c. Type **11** ..	10	10
50.	15 c. The Shepherds ..	10	10
51.	30 c. Bethlehem ..	10	10
52.	$4 Nativity scene	60	60

12. Purple-throated Carib.

13. Bananaquit.

1981. Birds. Multicoloured.

53 1 c. Magnificent frigate bird 15 15
54 4 c. Wied's crested fly-catcher 25 15
55 5 c. Type **12** 25 15
56 6 c. Burrowing owl .. 35 25
57 8 c. Caribbean martin .. 30 25
58 10 c. Yellow-crowned night heron 25 15
59 15 c. Type **13** 25 15
60 20 c. Scaly-breasted thrasher 30 15
61 25 c. Grey kingbird .. 30 15
62 30 c. Green-throated carib 30 15
63 40 c. Turnstone 35 20
64 45 c. Black-faced grassquit 35 25
65 50 c. Cattle egret 40 30
66 55 c. Brown pelican .. 40 30
67 $1 Lesser Antillean bull-finch 60 50
68 $2.50 Zenaida dove .. 1·25 1·25
69 $5 American kestrel .. 2·25 2·50
70 $10 Antillean crested hummingbird .. .. 4·50 4·75

The 1 c. to 10 c. are vertical as Type **12**. The remainder are horizontal as Type **13**.

14. Battalion Company Sergeant, 3rd Regt. of Foot (" The Buffs "), c. 1801.

1981. Military Uniforms. Multicoloured.

71. 5 c. Type **14** 10 10
72. 30 c. Battalion Company Officer, 45th Regt. of Foot, 1796-97 20 10
73. 55 c. Battalion Company Officer, 9th Regt. of Foot, 1790 30 10
74. $2.50 Grenadier, 38th Regt. of Foot, 1751 .. .. 90 35

1981. Royal Wedding. Royal Yachts. As T **26/27** of Kiribati. Multicoloured.

75 55 c. " Saudadoes " .. 15 15
82 55 c. Prince Charles and Lady Diana Spencer .. 30 30
77 $2.50 " Royal George " .. 35 35
78 $2.50 As No. 76 .. .. 70 70
79 $4 " Britannia " 50 50
80 $4 As No. 76 .. .. 1·00 1·00

15. Miriam Pickard (first Guide Commissioner).

1981. 50th Anniv. of St. Kitts Girl Guide Movement. Multicoloured.

84. 5 c. Type **15** 10 10
85. 30 c. Lady Baden-Powell's visit, 1964 .. .. 15 10
86. 55 c. Visit of Princess Alice, 1960 .. .. 30 10
87. $2 Thinking-Day parade, 1980's 60 35

16. Stained-glass Windows.

1981. Christmas.

88. **16.** 5 c. multicoloured .. 10 10
89. – 30 c. multicoloured .. 20 10
90. – 55 c. multicoloured .. 30 10
91. – $3 multicoloured .. 1·00 50

DESIGNS: 30 c. to $3, Various designs showing stained-glass windows.

17. Admiral Samuel Hood.

1982. Bicentenary of Brimstone Hill Siege.

92. **17.** 15 c. multicoloured .. 10 10
93. – 55 c. multicoloured .. 20 10

DESIGNS—55 c. Marquis De Bouille.

18. Alexandra, Princess of Wales, 1863.

1982. 21st Birthday of Princess of Wales. Multicoloured.

95. 15 c. Type **18** 10 10
96. 55 c. Coat of arms of Alexandra of Denmark .. 40 35
97. $6 Diana, Princess of Wales 1·50 1·50

1982. Birth of Prince William of Wales. Nos. 95/7 optd. **ROYAL BABY.**

98. 15 c. Type **18** 10 10
99. 55 c. Coat of arms of Alexandra of Denmark 40 35
100. $6 Diana, Princess of Wales 1·50 1·50

20. Naturalist Badge.

1982. 75th Anniv. of Boy Scout Movement. Multicoloured.

101. 5 c. Type **20** 10 10
102. 55 c. Rescuer badge .. 40 15
103. $2 First Aid badge .. 1·10 80

21. Santa with Christmas Tree and Gifts.

1982. Christmas. Children's Paintings. Multicoloured.

104. 5 c. Type **21** 10 10
105. 55 c. The Inn 15 10
106. $1.10 Three Kings .. 30 15
107. $3 Annunciation 80 40

22. Cruise Ship "Stella Oceanis" at Basseterre.

1983. Commonwealth Day. Multicoloured.

108. 55 c. Type **22** 20 10
109. $2 "Queen Elizabeth 2" at Basseterre 50 40

1983. Military Uniforms (2nd series). As T **14**. Multicoloured.

110. 15 c. Light Company Private, 15th Regt. of Foot, c. 1814 .. .. 20 10
111. 30 c. Battalion Company Officer, 15th Regt. of Foot, c. 1780 .. 35 15
112. 55 c. Light Company Officer, 5th Regt. of Foot, c. 1822 .. .. 55 20
113. $2.50 Battalion Company Officer, 11th Regt. of Foot, c. 1804 .. .. 1·40 1·60

23. Sir William Smith (founder).

1983. Centenary of Boys' Brigade. Mult.

114. 10 c. Type **23** 25 10
115. 45 c. B.B. members on steps of Sandy Point Methodist Church 55 20
116. 50 c. Brigade drummers .. 65 25
117. $3 Boys' Brigade badge .. 2·50 2·75

1983. Nos. 55, 59/63 and 66/70 optd. **INDEPENDENCE 1983.**

118 5 c. Type **12** 15 10
119 15 c. Type**13** 20 10
120 20 c. Scaly-breasted thrasher 25 10
121 25 c. Grey kingbird .. 30 10
122 30 c. Green-throated carib 35 15
123 40 c. Turnstone 40 20
124 55 c. Brown pelican .. 45 30
125 $1 Lesser Antillean bull-finch 80 50
126 $2.50 Zenaida dove .. 1·50 1·25
127 $5 American kestrel .. 2·50 2·50
128 $10 Antillean crested hummingbird .. .. 5·00 5·00

25. Montgolfier Balloon, 1783.

1983. Bicentenary of Manned Flight. Mult.

129. 10 c. Type **25** 10 10
130. 45 c. Sikorsky " Russian Knight " biplane (horiz.) 15 10
131. 50 c. Lockheed " Tristar " (horiz.) 20 15
132. $2.50 Bell " XS-1 " (horiz.) 60 75

26. Star over West Indian Town.

1983. Christmas. Multicoloured.

134. 15 c. Type **26** 10 10
135. 30 c. Shepherds watching Star 10 10
136. 55 c. Mary and Joseph .. 15 10
137. $2.50 The Nativity .. 40 40

27. Parrot in Tree.

1984. Batik Designs. (1st series).

139. **27.** 45 c. multicoloured .. 15 10
140. – 50 c. multicoloured .. 15 10
141. – $1.50 blue, yell & pur. 45 50
142. – $3 multicoloured .. 80 1·00

DESIGNS: 50 c. Man under coconut tree. $1.50, Women with fruit. $3 Butterflies.

See also Nos 169/72.

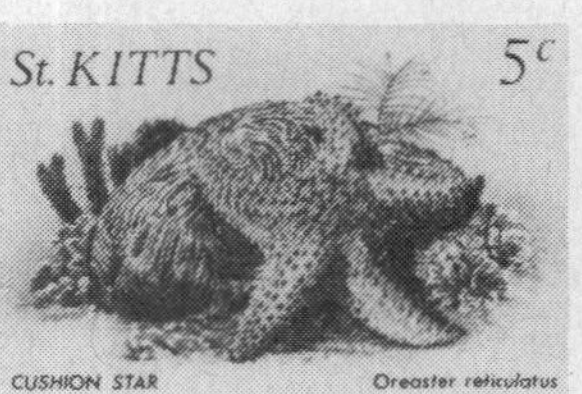

28. Cushion Star.

1984. Marine Life. Multicoloured.

143 5 c. Type **28** 25 20
144 10 c. Rough file shell .. 35 20
145 15 c. Red-lined cleaning shrimp 35 15
146 20 c. Bristleworm 35 15
147 25 c. Flamingo tongue .. 30 15
148 30 c. Christmas tree worm 30 20
149 40 c. Pink-tipped anemone 45 25
150 50 c. Smallmouth grunt .. 45 30
151 60 c. Glasseye snapper .. 1·00 40
152 75 c. Reef squirrelfish .. 75 45
153 $1 Sea fans and flamefish (vert.) 85 50
155 $2·50 Reef butterflyfish (vert.) .. .. .. 2·00 2·25
156 $5 Blackbar soldierfish (vert.) .. .. .. 4·75 5·50
206 $10 Cocoa damselfish (vert.) .. .. .. 8·50 10·00

The 10 c., 60 c., $5 and $10 come with or without imprint date.

29. Agriculture.

1984. 25th Anniv. of The 4-H Organisation. Multicoloured.

157. 30 c. Type **29** 30 10
158. 55 c. Animal husbandry .. 40 15
159. $1.10 The 4-H Pledge .. 70 60
160. $3 On parade .. .. 1·25 1·25

30. Construction of Royal St. Kitts Hotel.

1984. First Anniv. of Independence of St. Kitts-Nevis. Multicoloured.

161. 15 c. Type **30** 20 10
162. 30 c. Independence celebrations 30 15
163. $1.10 National Anthem and aerial view (vert.) .. 70 60
164. $3 "Dawn of a New Day" (vert.) .. .. .. 1·60 1·40

31. Opening Presents.

1984. Christmas. Multicoloured.

165.	15 c. Type **31**	15	10
166.	60 c. Singing carols ..	45	35
167.	$1 Nativity play	75	60
168.	$2 Leaving church on Christmas Day	1·40	1·10

1985. Batik Designs (2nd series). Horiz. designs as T **27**.

169.	15 c. black, green and light green	15	10
170.	40 c. black, blue and light blue	30	15
171.	60 c. black, orange and red	45	20
172.	$3 black, brown and light brown	1·75	2·00

DESIGNS: 15 c. Country bus. 40 c. Donkey cart. 60 c. Rum shop, and man on bicycle. $3 S.V. "Polynesia" (tourist yacht).

32. Container Ship "Tropic Jade".

1985. Ships. Multicoloured.

173.	40 c. Type **32**	75	30
174.	$1.20 "Atlantic Clipper" (schooner)	1·50	1·25
175.	$2 "Mandalay" (schooner)	2·25	2·25
176.	$2. "Cunard Countess" (liner)	2·25	2·25

33. James Derrick Cardin (leading Freemason).

1985. 150th Anniv. of Mount Olive S. C. Masonic Lodge. Multicoloured.

177.	15 c. Type **33**	50	20
178.	75 c. Banner of Mount Olive Lodge	1·50	1·10
179.	$1·20 Masonic symbols (horiz.)	2·25	2·25
180.	$3 Lodge Charter, 1835 ..	3·75	3·75

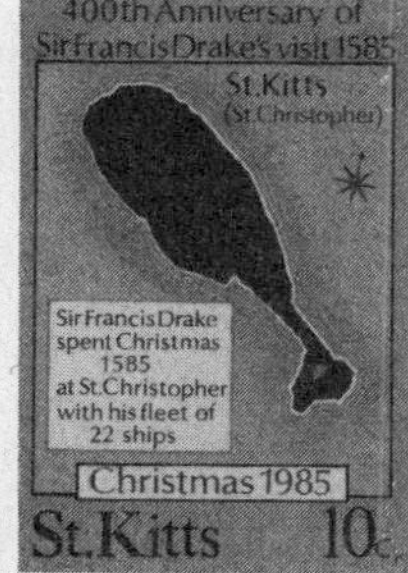

34. Map of St. Kitts.

1985. Christmas. 400th Anniv. of Sir Francis Drake's Visit. Multicoloured.

181.	10 c. Type **34**	30	15
182.	40 c. "Golden Hind" ..	75	35
183.	60 c. Sir Francis Drake ..	85	50
184.	$3 Drake's heraldic shield	2·50	2·25

35. Queen Elizabeth and Prince Philip on St. Kitts.

1986. 60th Birthday of Queen Elizabeth. Multicoloured.

185.	10 c. Type **35**	15	10
186.	20 c. Queen Elizabeth on St. Kitts	25	15
187.	40 c. At Trooping the Colour	50	30
188.	$3 In Sweden	2·00	2·25

1986. Royal Wedding. As T **112** of Ascension. Multicoloured.

189	15 c. Prince Andrew and Miss Sarah Ferguson ..	15	10
190	$2.50 Prince Andrew ..	1·50	2·00

36. Family on Smallholding.

1986. Agriculture Exhibition. Multicoloured.

191.	15 c. Type **36**	20	10
192.	$1.20 Hands holding people, computers and crops	1·25	1·40

1986. 40th Anniv. of U.N. Week. Nos. 185/8 optd. **40th ANNIVERSARY U.N. WEEK 19–26 OCT.**

207.	10 c. Type **35**	20	15
208.	20 c. Queen Elizabeth on St. Kitts	30	20
209.	40 c. At Trooping the Colour	40	30
210.	$3 In Sweden	2·25	2·75

38. Adult Green Monkey with Young.

1986. Green Monkeys on St. Kitts. Multicoloured.

211.	15 c. Type **38**	30	15
212.	20 c. Adult on ground ..	35	20
213.	60 c. Young monkey in tree	85	65
214.	$1 Adult grooming young monkey	1·40	1·75

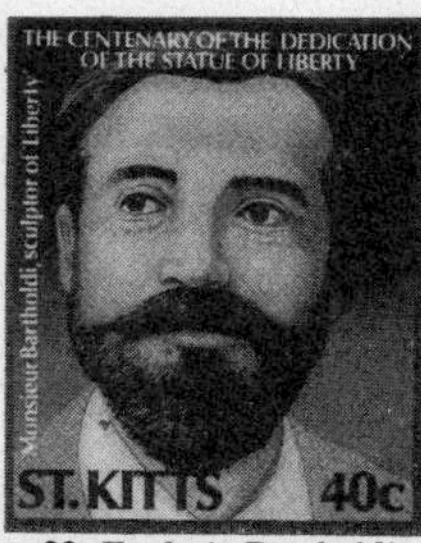

39. Frederic Bartholdi (sculptor).

1986. Centenary of Statue of Liberty. Mult.

215.	40 c. Type **39**	40	30
216.	60 c. Torch (1876) and head (1878) on exhibition (horiz.)	65	50
217.	$1.50 French ship "Isere" carrying statue (horiz.)	1·50	1·50
218.	$3 Statue of Liberty, Paris, 1884	2·40	2·50

40. Officer, 9th Regt (East Norfolk), 1792.

1987. Military Uniforms (3rd series). Mult.

220	15 c. Type **40**	40	30
221	15 c. Officer, Regt de Neustrie, 1779	40	30
222	40 c. Sergeant, 3rd Regt of Foot ("The Buffs"), 1801	75	45
223	40 c. Officer, French Artillery, 1812	75	45
224	$2 Light Company Private, 5th Regt, 1778	2·25	2·50
225	$2 Grenadier of the Line, 1796	2·25	2·50

41. Sugar Cane Warehouse.

1987. Sugar Cane Industry. Multicoloured (colour of panel behind "ST. KITTS" given).

227.	**41.**	15 c. yellow	20	20
228.	–	15 c. brown	20	20
229.	–	15 c. lilac	20	20
230.	–	15 c blue	20	20
231.	–	15 c. turquoise ..	20	20
232.	–	75 c. bright geeen ..	75	75
233.	–	75 c. lilac	75	75
234.	–	75 c. dull green ..	75	75
235.	–	75 c. yellow	75	75
236.	–	75 c. turquoise ..	75	75

DESIGNS: Nos. 227/31, Sugar cane factory. Nos. 232/6, Loading sugar train.

Nos. 227/31 and 232/6 were each printed together, se-tenant, forming composite designs.

42. B.W.I.A. "L-1011-500 TriStar".

1987. Aircraft visiting St. Kitts. Mult.

237.	40 c. Type **42**	65	30
238.	60 c. L.I.A.T. BAe "Super 748"	85	60
239.	$1.20 W.I.A. "DHC-6 Twin Otter"	1·50	1·50
240.	$3 American Eagle Aerospatiale "ATR-42" ..	2·75	3·25

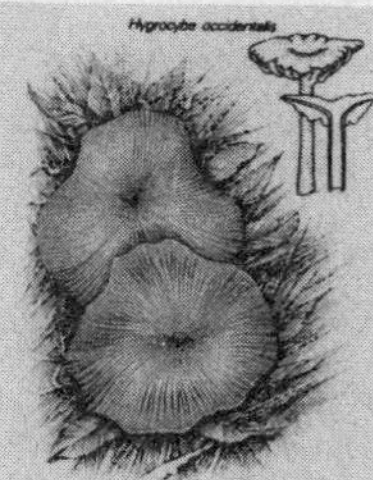

43. "Hygrocybe occidentalis".

1987. Fungi. Multicoloured.

241.	15 c. Type **43**	45	20
242.	40 c. "Marasmius haematocephalus"	75	40
243.	$1.20 "Psilocybe cubensis"	1·50	1·50
244.	$2 "Hygrocybe acutoconica"	2·25	2·25
245.	$3 "Boletellus cubensis" ..	2·75	3·00

44. Carnival Clown.

1987. Christmas. Designs showing different clowns.

246.	**44.**	15 c. multicoloured ..	25	15
247.	–	40 c. multicoloured ..	55	30
248.	–	$1 multicoloured ..	1·25	80
249.	–	$3 multicoloured ..	2·50	3·00

See also Nos. 266/9.

45. Ixora.

1988. Flowers. Multicoloured.

250.	15 c. Type **45**	30	15
251.	40 c. Shrimp plant ..	55	30
252.	$1 Poinsettia	1·00	75
253.	$3 Honolulu rose	2·50	3·00

46. Fort Thomas Hotel.

1988. Tourism (1st series). Hotels. Mult.

254.	60 c. Type **46**	40	40
255.	60 c. Fairview Inn ..	40	40
256.	60 c. Frigate Bay Beach Hotel	40	40
257.	60 c. Ocean Terrace Inn ..	40	40
258.	$3 The Golden Lemon ..	1·75	2·00
259.	$3 Royal St. Kitts Casino and Jack Tar Village ..	1·75	2·00
260.	$3 Rawlins Plantation Hotel and Restaurant ..	1·75	2·00

See also Nos. 270/5.

47 Ball, Wicket and Leeward Islands Cricket Association Emblem

1988. 75th Anniv of Leeward Islands Cricket Tournament. Multicoloured.

261	40 c. Type **47**	75	30
262	$3 Cricket match at Warner Park	3·25	3·75

48 Flag of St. Kitts–Nevis

1988. 5th Anniv of Independence. Mult.

263	15 c. Type **48**	15	10
264	60 c. Arms of St. Kitts . .	50	50

1988. Christmas. As T **44** showing carnival masqueraders.

266	15 c. multicoloured . .	10	10
267	40 c. multicoloured . .	20	25
268	80 c. multicoloured . .	40	45
269	$3 multicoloured . .	1·25	1·75

1989. Tourism (2nd series). Colonial Architecture. As T **46**. Multicoloured.

270	20 c. Georgian house . .	20	15
271	20 c. Colonial-style house	20	15
272	$1 Romney Manor . .	70	75
273	$1 Lavington Great House	70	75
274	$2 Government House . .	1·25	1·40
275	$2 Treasury Building . .	1·25	1·40

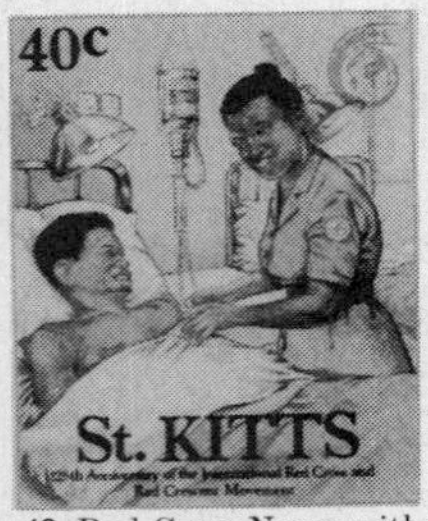

49 Red Cross Nurse with Hospital Patient

1989. 125th Anniv of International Red Cross.

276	**49**	40 c. multicoloured . .	30	30
277	–	$1 multicoloured . .	65	65
278	–	$3 red and black . .	1·75	2·00

DESIGNS: $1 Loading patient into ambulance; $3 125th anniversary logo.

1989. 20th Anniv of First Manned Landing on Moon. As T **126** of Ascension. Multicoloured.

280	10 c. Lunar rover on Moon	10	10
281	20 c. Crew of "Apollo 13" (30 × 30 mm)	10	10
282	$1 "Apollo 13" emblem (30 × 30 mm)	45	60
283	$2 "Apollo 13" splash-down, South Pacific . .	95	1·25

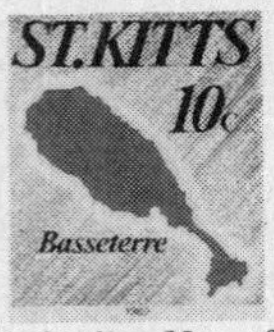

51 Outline Map of St. Kitts

1989.

285	**51**	10 c. mauve and black	10	10
286		15 c. red and black . .	10	10
287		20 c. orange and black	15	10
288		40 c. yellow and black	20	20
289		60 c. blue and black . .	30	30
290		$1 green and black . .	50	60

52 "Santa Mariagalante" passing St. Kitts, 1493

1989. 500th Anniv (1992) of Discovery of America by Columbus. Multicoloured.

291	15 c. Type **52**	35	20
292	80 c. Arms of Columbus and map of fourth voyage, 1502–04 . .	1·00	1·00
293	$1 Navigation instruments, c. 1500	1·25	1·25
294	$5 Columbus and map of second voyage, 1493–96	4·00	4·50

53 Poinciana Tree

1989. "World Stamp Expo '89" International Stamp Exhibition, Washington. Multicoloured.

295	15 c. Type **53**	20	10
296	40 c. Fort George Citadel, Brimstone Hill . .	45	30
297	$1 Private, Light Company, 5th Foot, 1778	95	70
298	$3 St. George's Anglican Church	2·50	2·75

54 "Junonia evarete"

1990. Butterflies. Multicoloured.

299	15 c. Type **54**	25	15
300	40 c. "Anartia jatrophae"	25	25
301	60 c. "Heliconius charitonia"	65	45
302	$3 "Biblis hyperia" . .	2·25	2·75

1990. "Expo '90" International Garden and Greenery Exhibition, Osaka. Nos. 299/302 optd **EXPO '90** and logo.

303	15 c. Type **54**	25	15
304	40 c. "Anartia jatrophae"	45	25
305	60 c. "Heliconius charitoia"	65	45
306	$3 "Biblis hyperia" . .	2·25	2·75

56 Brimstone Hill

1990. 300th Anniv of English Bombardment of Brimstone Hill. Multicoloured.

307	15 c. Type **56**	20	10
308	40 c. Restored Brimstone Hill fortifications . .	35	25
309	60 c. 17th-century English marine and Fort Charles under attack	50	50
310	$3 English sailors firing cannon	2·25	2·25

No. 309 exists se-tenant, as a horizontal pair, with No. 310, each pair showing a composite design.

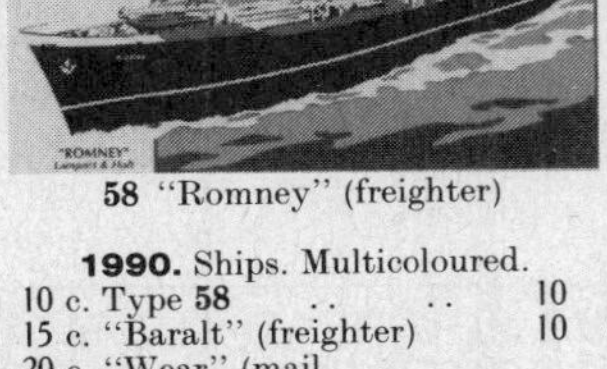

58 "Romney" (freighter)

1990. Ships. Multicoloured.

312	10 c. Type **58**	10	10
313	15 c. "Baralt" (freighter)	10	10
314	20 c. "Wear" (mail steamer)	10	10
315	25 c. "Sunmount" (freighter)	10	15
316	40 c. "Inanda" (cargo liner)	15	20
317	50 c. "Alcoa Partner" (freighter)	20	25
318	60 c. "Dominica" (freighter)	25	30
319	80 c. "C.G.M Provence" (container ship)	35	40
320	$1 "Director" (freighter) . .	40	45
321	$1.20 Sailing barque . .	50	55
322	$2 "Chignecto" (mail steamer)	85	90
323	$3 "Berbice" (mail steamer)	1·25	1·40
324	$5 "Vamos" (freighter) . .	2·10	2·25
325	$10 "Federal Maple" (freighter)	4·25	4·50

59 Single Fork Game

1990. Christmas. Traditional Games. Mult.

326	10 c. Type **59**	15	10
327	15 c. Boulder breaking . .	15	10
328	40 c. Double fork . .	30	30
329	$3 The run up	1·75	1·75

60 White Periwinkle

1991. Flowers. Multicoloured.

330	10 c. Type **60**	15	10
331	40 c. Pink oleander . .	25	25
332	60 c. Pink periwinkle (vert)	40	40
333	$2 White oleander (vert) . .	1·25	1·25

61 Census Logo

1991. Nationl Census.

334	**61**	15 c. multicoloured . .	15	10
335		$2.40 multicoloured . .	1·60	1·60

The $2.40 differs from Type **61** by showing "ST. KITTS" in a curved panel.

1991. 65th Birthday of Queen Elizabeth II and 70th Birthday of Prince Philip. As T **139** of Ascension. Multicoloured.

336	$1.20 Prince Philip . .	75	75
337	$1.80 Queen holding bouquet of flowers . .	1·00	1·00

62 Nassau Grouper

1991. Fishes. Multicoloured.

338	10 c. Type **62**	15	10
339	60 c. Hogfish	40	40
340	$1 Red hind	70	70
341	$3 Porkfish	2·00	2·00

63 School of Continuing Studies, St. Kitts, and Chancellor Sir Shridath Ramphal

1991. 40th Anniv of University of West Indies. Multicoloured.

342	15 c. Type **63**	15	10
343	50 c. Administration Building, Barbados . .	35	35
344	$1 Engineering Building, Trinidad and Tobago . .	65	65
345	$3 Mona Campus, Jamaica, and Sir Shridath Ramphal	2·00	2·00

64 Whipping The Bull

1991. Christmas. "The Bull" (Carnival play). Multicoloured.

346	10 c. Type **64**	15	10
347	15 c. Death of The Bull . .	15	10
348	60 c. Cast of characters and musicians	45	45
349	$3 The Bull in procession	1·60	1·60

1992. 40th Anniv of Queen Elizabeth II's Accession. As T **143** of Ascension. Mult.

350	10 c. St. Kitts coastline . .	15	10
351	40 c. Warner Park Pavilion	25	25
352	60 c. Brimstone Hill . .	40	40
353	$1 Three portraits of Queen Elizabeth . .	70	70
354	$3 Queen Elizabeth II . .	1·90	1·90

65 Map of St. Kitts-Nevis

1992. 50th Anniv of St. Kitts-Nevis Red Cross Society. Multicoloured.

355	10 c. Type **65**	15	10
356	20 c. St. Kitts-Nevis flag	20	20
357	50 c. Red Cross House, St. Kitts	35	35
358	$2.40 Henri Dunant . .	1·50	1·50

OFFICIAL STAMPS

1980. Nos. 32/41 optd. **OFFICIAL.**

O 1.	15 c. multicoloured . .	10	10
O 2.	25 c. multicoloured . .	10	10
O 3.	30 c. multicoloured . .	10	10
O 4.	40 c. multicoloured . .	10	15
O 5.	45 c. multicoloured . .	15	15
O 6.	50 c. multicoloured . .	15	15
O 7.	55 c. multicoloured . .	15	15
O 8.	$1 multicoloured . .	25	25
O 9.	$5 multicoloured . .	1·00	1·50
O 10.	$10 multicoloured . .	1·75	2·50

1981. Nos. 59/70 optd. **OFFICIAL.**

O 11.	15 c. Bananaquit . .	20	10
O 12.	20 c. Scaly-breasted Thrasher	20	10
O 13.	25 c. Grey Kingbird . .	25	10
O 14.	30 c. Green-throated Carib	25	10
O 15.	40 c. Turnstone	35	15
O 16.	45 c. Black-faced Grassquit	40	20
O 17.	50 c. Cattle-Egret . .	40	20
O 18.	55 c. Brown Pelican . .	50	25
O 19.	$1 Lesser Antillean Bull-finch	75	45
O 20.	$2.50 Zenaida Dove . .	1·60	1·00
O 21.	$5 American Kestrel . .	2·75	2·00
O 22.	$10 Antillean Crested Hummingbird . .	5·00	4·25

1983. Nos. 75/80 optd. **OFFICIAL** and surch.

O 23.	45 c. on $2.50 " Royal George "	25	25
O 24.	45 c. on $2.50 Prince Charles and Lady Diana Spencer	25	25
O 25.	55 c. " Saudadoes "	30	30
O 26.	55 c. Prince Charles and Lady Diana Spencer	30	30
O 27.	$1.10 on $4 " Britannia "	60	70
O 28.	$1.10 on $4 Prince Charles and Lady Diana Spencer	60	70

1984. Nos. 145/56 optd. **OFFICIAL.**

O29.	15 c. Red-lined Cleaning Shrimp	25	25
O30.	20 c. Bristleworm	30	30
O31.	25 c. Flamingo Tongue	35	35
O32.	30 c. Christmas Tree Worm	40	40
O33.	40 c. Pink-tipped Anemone	50	50
O34.	50 c. Smallmouth Grunt	60	60
O35.	60 c. Glasseye Snapper	70	70
O36.	75 c. Reef Squirrelfish	80	80
O37.	$1 Sea Fans and Flame-fish (vert.)	1·00	1·00
O38.	$2.50 Reef Butterflyfish (vert.)	2·25	2·50
O39.	$5 Blackbar Soldierfish (vert.)	4·00	4·50
O40.	$10 Cocoa Damselfish (vert.)	7·50	8·50

ST. KITTS-NEVIS

Islands of the Leeward Is., Br. W. Indies. The general issues for Leeward Is. were in concurrent use until 1 July 1956. From 1952 the stamps are inscribed " St. Christopher, Nevis and Anguilla ". Achieved Associated Statehood on 27 February 1967. St. Kitts and Nevis had separate postal administrations from 23 June 1980.

1903. 12 pence = 1 shilling;
20 shillings = 1 pound.
1951. 100 cents = 1 West Indian dollar.

1. Christopher Columbus. 2. Medicinal Spring.

1903.

1	1	½d. purple and green	1·50	70
12	–	½d. green	30	35
13	2	1d. grey and red	1·00	25
14a	–	1d. red	35	20
15a	1	2d. purple and brown	80	1·75
4		2½d. black and blue	9·00	3·50
17		2½d. blue	60	40
18a	2	3d. green and orange	80	2·00
6	1	6d. black and purple	3·25	15·00
20		1s. green and orange	4·00	12·00
8		2s. green and black	9·00	14·00
9	1	2s. 6d. black and violet	16·00	30·00
21	2	5s. purple and green	23·00	55·00

1916. Optd **WAR TAX.**

22a	1	½d. green	10	30

1918. Optd **WAR STAMP.**

23	1	1½d. orange	15	30

4.

5.

1920.

37	4	½d. green	40	65
38	5	1d. red	20	15
39		1d. violet	1·25	35
26	4	1½d. yellow	1·25	80
40		1½d. red	75	2·50
40a		1½d. brown	30	15
41	5	2d. grey	30	60
42	4	2½d. blue	2·00	2·25
43		2½d. brown	75	4·50
45a	5	3d. purple on yellow	50	2·50
45		3d. blue	40	2·50
46	4	6d. purple and mauve	2·00	4·50
31	5	1s. black on green	1·25	3·00
47	4	2s. purple & blue on blue	3·50	12·00
33	5	2s. 6d. black & red on bl	5·00	25·00
34	4	5s. green & red on yellow	5·00	35·00
35	5	10s. green & red on green	12·00	45·00
36	4	£1 purple & black on red	£200	£275

6. Old Road Bay and Mount Misery.

1923. Tercent. Commem.

48.	6.	½d. black and green	2·00	6·00
49.		1d. black and violet	1·75	1·50
50.		1½d. black and red	3·75	7·00
51.		2d. black and grey	1·75	1·50
52.		2½d. black and brown	3·00	18·00
53.		3d. black and blue	3·25	12·00
54.		6d. black and purple	8·00	22·00
55.		1s. black and green	12·00	27·00
56.		2s. black and blue on blue	24·00	48·00
57.		2s. 6d. black & red on blue	38·00	65·00
59.		5s. black and red on yellow	60·00	£150
58.		10s. black and red on green	£225	£325
60.		£1 black and purple on red	£850	£1300

1935. Silver Jubilee. As T **13** of Antigua.

61	1d. blue and red	75	20
62	1½d. blue and grey	60	75
63	2½d. brown and blue	1·00	80
64	1s. grey and purple	4·75	9·50

1937. Coronation. As T **2** of Aden.

65.	1d. red	30	15
66.	1½d. brown	35	10
67.	2½d. blue	40	35

Nos. 61/7 are inscribed " ST. CHRISTOPHER NEVIS ".

7. King George VI. 8. King George VI and Medicinal Spring.

10. King George VI and Anguilla Island.

1938.

68a	7	½d. green	10	10
69a		1d. red	30	20
70		1½d. orange	15	20
71b	8	2d. red and grey	50	70
72a	7	2½d. blue	15	15
73ba	8	3d. purple and red	1·00	1·00
74bb	–	6d. green and purple	1·25	1·00
75c	8	1s. black and green	75	70
76ab		2s. 6d. black and red	5·00	3·00
77b	–	5s. green and red	13·00	6·00
77c	10	10s. black and blue	12·00	18·00
77d		£1 black and brown	15·00	12·00

The 6d. and 5s. are as Type **8**, but with the Christopher Columbus device as in Type **4**.

1946. Victory. As T **9** of Aden.

78.	1½d. orange	10	10
79.	3d. red	10	10

1949. Silver Wedding. As T **10/11** of Aden.

80.	2½d. blue	10	10
81.	5s. red	3·50	2·50

1949. U.P.U. As T **20/23** of Antigua.

82	2½d. blue	25	10
83	3d. red	35	25
84	6d. mauve	35	25
85	1s. green	35	25

1950. Tercent. Br. Settlement in Anguilla. Optd. **ANGUILLA TERCENTENARY 1650-1950.**

86.	7.	1d. red	10	10
87.		1½d. orange	10	10
88.		2½d. blue	10	10
89.	8.	3d. purple and red	10	10
90.	–	6d. green & purple (No. 74ab)	10	10
91.	8.	1s. black and green	10	10

1951. Inauguration of B.W.I. University College. As T **24/25** of Antigua.

92.	22.	3 c. black and orange	15	10
93.	23.	12 c. green and mauve	15	20

ST. CHRISTOPHER, NEVIS AND ANGUILLA

13. Bath House and Spa.

1952.

94.	13.	1 c. green and ochre	15	25
95.	–	2 c. green	20	30
96.	–	3 c. red and violet	25	30
97.	–	4 c. red	20	20
98.	–	5 c. blue and grey	20	10
99.	–	6 c. blue	20	15
100.	–	12 c. blue and brown	20	10
101.	–	24 c. black and red	20	10
102.	–	48 c. olive and brown	1·50	1·50
103.	–	60 c. ochre and green	1·50	1·50
104.	–	$1.20 green and blue	4·50	1·75
105.	–	$4.80 green and red	10·00	16·00

DESIGNS—HORIZ. 2 c. Warner Park. 4 c. Brimstone Hill. 5 c. Nevis from the sea, North. 6 c. Pinney's Beach, Nevis. 24 c. Old Road Bay. 48 c. Sea Island cotton, Nevis. 60 c. The Treasury. $1.20, Salt pond, Anguilla. $4.80, Sugar factory. VERT. Map of the islands. 12 c. Sir Thomas Warner's tomb.

1953. Coronation. As T **13** of Aden.

106	2 c. black and green	10	10

1954. As 1952 but with portrait of Queen Elizabeth II.

106a	½ c. olive (as $1.20)	20	10
107	1 c. green and ochre	15	10
108	2 c. green	30	10
109	3 c. red and violet	50	10
110	4 c. red	15	10
111	5 c. blue and grey	15	10
112	6 c. blue	30	10
112b	8 c. black	3·00	10
113	12 c. blue and brown	15	10
114	24 c. black and red	15	10
115	48 c. olive and brown	60	50
116	60 c. ochre and green	2·00	85
117	$1.20 green and blue	7·00	90
117b	$2.40 black and orange	8·00	11·00
118	$4.80 green and red	12·00	11·00

DESIGNS (new values)—VERT. 8 c. Sombrero Lighthouse. HORIZ. $2.40 Map of Anguilla and Dependencies.

27. Alexander Hamilton and View of Nevis.

1956. Birth Bicent. of Alexander Hamilton.

119.	27.	24 c. green and blue	15	10

1958. British Caribbean Federation. As T **28** of Antigua.

120.	3 c. green	30	10
121.	6 c. blue	55	60
122.	12 c. red	80	15

28. 1d. Stamp of 1861.

1961. Centenary of Nevis Stamp.

123.	28.	2 c. dp. red and green	15	15
124.		8 c. red and blue	15	10
125.		12 c. lilac and red	20	10
126.		24 c. green and orange	25	15

The 8 c., 12 c. and 24 c. show the original 4d., 6d. and 1s. stamps of Nevis respectively.

1963. Cent of Red Cross. As T **33** of Antigua.

127	3 c. red and black	10	10
128	12 c. red and blue	20	40

33. Loading Sugar Cane, St. Kitts.

1963. Multicoloured.

129.	½ c. New Lighthouse Sombrero	10	10
130.	1 c. Type **33**	10	10
131.	2 c. Pall Mall Square, Basseterre	10	10
132.	3 c. Gateway, Brimstone Hill Fort, St. Kitts	10	10
133.	4 c. Nelson's Spring, Nevis	10	10
134.	5 c. Grammar School, St. Kitts	10	10
135.	6 c. Crater, Mt. Misery, St. Kitts	10	10
136.	10 c. Hibiscus	15	10
137.	15 c. Sea Island cotton, Nevis	35	10
138.	20 c. Boat-building, Anguilla	20	10
139.	25 c. White-crowned pigeon	65	10
140.	50 c. St. George's Church Tower, Basseterre	40	25
141.	60 c. Alexander Hamilton	1·00	25
142.	$1 Map of St. Kitts-Nevis	2·25	40
143.	$2.50 Map of Anguilla	2·25	2·00
144.	$5 Arms of St. Christopher, Nevis and Anguilla	3·50	3·00

The ½, 2, 3, 15, 25, 60 c., $1 and $5 are vert. the rest horiz.

1964. Arts Festival. Optd. **ARTS FESTIVAL ST. KITTS 1964.**

145.	3 c. mult. (No. 132)	10	10
146.	25 c. mult. (No. 139)	20	10

1965. Cent of I.T.U. As T **36** of Antigua.

147.	2 c. bistre and red	10	10
148.	50 c. blue and olive	40	35

1965. I.C.Y. As T **37** of Antigua.

149	2 c. purple and green	10	10
150	25 c. green and violet	20	10

1966. Churchill Commem. As T **38** of Antigua.

151.	½ c. blue	10	10
152.	3 c. green	15	10
153.	15 c. brown	30	15
154.	25 c. violet	35	15

1966. Royal Visit. As T **39** of Antigua.

155. 3 c. black and blue .. 10 10

156. 25 c. black and mauve .. 30 10

1966. World Cup Football Championship. As T **40** of Antigua

157. 6 c. multicoloured .. 10 10

158. 25 c. multicoloured .. 30 10

49. Festival Emblem.

1966. Arts Festival.

159. **49.** 3 c. multicoloured .. 10 10

160. – 25 c. multicoloured .. 10 10

1966. Inauguration of W.H.O. Headquarters, Geneva. As T **41** of Antigua.

161 3 c. black, green and blue 10 10

162 40 c. black, purple & brown 20 20

1966. 20th Anniv of U.N.E.S.C.O. As T **54/6** of Antigua.

163. 3 c. multicoloured .. 10 10

164. 6 c. yellow, violet and olive 10 10

165. 40 c. black, purple & orge. 20 35

50. Government Headquarters, Basseterre.

1967. Statehood. Multicoloured.

182. 3 c. Type **50** .. 10 10

183. 10 c. National Flag .. 10 10

184. 25 c. Coat of Arms .. 15 10

53. John Wesley and Cross.

1967. West Indies Methodist Conf.

185. **53.** 3 c. black, red and violet 10 10

186. – 25 c. black, turq. & blue 15 10

187. – 40 c. black, yell. & orge. 15 10

DESIGNS: 25 c. Charles Wesley and cross. 40 c. Thomas Coke and cross.

56. "Herald" Aircraft over "Jamaica Producer" (freighter).

1968. Caribbean Free Trade Area.

188. **56.** 25 c. multicoloured .. 15 10

189. 50 c. multicoloured .. 15 10

57. Dr. Martin Luther King.

1968. Martin Luther King Commem.

190. **57.** 50 c. multicoloured .. 10 10

58. "Mystical Nativity" (Botticelli).

1968. Christmas.

191. **58.** 12 c. multicoloured .. 10 10

192. – 25 c. multicoloured .. 10 10

193. **58.** 40 c. multicoloured .. 10 10

194. – 50 c. multicoloured .. 10 10

DESIGN: 25 c., 50 c. "The Adoration of the Magi" (Rubens).

60. Tarpon.

1968. Fishes.

195. **60.** 6 c. multicoloured .. 10 10

196. – 12 c. black, green & blue 15 10

197. – 40 c. multicoloured .. 20 10

198. – 50 c. multicoloured .. 25 15

FISHES: 12 c. Garfish. 40 c. Horse-eye Jack. 50 c. Redsnapper.

64. The Warner Badge and Islands.

1969. Sir Thomas Warner Commem. Mult.

199. 20 c. Type **64** 10 10

200. 25 c. Sir Thomas Warner's tomb 10 10

201. 40 c. Charles I's Commission 15 15

67. "The Adoration of the Kings" (Mostaert).

1969. Christmas. Multicoloured.

202. 10 c. Type **67** 10 10

203. 25 c. As 10 c. 10 10

204. 40 c. "The Adoration of the Kings" (Geertgen).. 10 10

205. 50 c. As 40 c. 10 10

73. Portuguese Caravels (16th-cent.).

1970. Multicoloured (except ½ c.).

206. ½ c. Pirates and treasure at Frigate Bay (black, orge. and green) .. 10 10

207. 1 c. English Two-decker warship, 1650 .. .. 30 10

208. 2 c. Naval flags of colonising nations 15 10

209. 3 c. Rapier hilt (17th-cent.) 15 10

210. 4 c. Type **73** .. 20 10

211. 5 c. Sir Henry Morgan and fireships, 1669 .. .. 30 10

212. 6 c. L'Ollonois and pirate carrack 16th-cent. 30 10

213. 10 c. 17th-century smugglers' ship 20 10

214a. 15 c. "Piece of Eight" .. 50 10

215. 20 c. Cannon (17th-cent.).. 35 10

216. 25 c. Humphrey Cole's astrolabe, 1574 .. .. 40 10

217. 50 c. Flintlock pistol (17th-cent). .. 85 80

218. 60 c. Dutch Flute (17th-cent.) .. .. 2·25 70

219. $1 Capt. Bartholomew Roberts and his crew's death sentence .. .. 2·50 75

220. $2.50 Railing Piece (gun) (16th-cent.) .. .. 2·00 3·00

221. $5 Drake, Hawkins and sea battle .. .. 2·50 4·25

280. $10 The Apprehension of Blackbeard (Edward Teach) .. .. 20·00 13·00

The ½ c. to 3 c., 15 c., 25 c., 60 c. and $1 are vert. designs.

85. Graveyard Scene ("Great Expectations").

1970. Death Cent. of Charles Dickens.

222. **85.** 4 c. brown, gold & green 10 10

223. – 20 c. brn., gold and purple 10 10

224. – 25 c. brown, gold & green 10 10

225. – 40 c. brown, gold & blue 10 15

DESIGNS—HORIZ. 20 c. Miss Havisham and Pip ("Great Expectations"). VERT. 25 c. Dickens' Birthplace. 40 c. Charles Dickens.

86. Local Steel Band.

1970. Festival of Arts. Multicoloured.

226. 20 c. Type **86** 10 10

227. 25 c. Local string band .. 10 10

228. 40 c. Scene from "A Midsummer Night's Dream" 15 15

87. 1d. Stamp of 1870 and Post Office, 1970.

1970. Stamp Cent.

229. **87.** ½ c. green and red .. 10 10

230. – 20 c. blue, green & red 10 10

231. – 25 c. purple, grn. & red 10 10

232. – 50 c. red, green and blk. 30 45

DESIGNS: 20 c., 25 c., 1d. and 6d. stamps of 1870. 50 c. 6d. stamp of 1870 and early postmark.

88. "Adoration of the Shepherds" (Frans van Floris).

1970. Christmas. Multicoloured.

233. 3 c. Type **88** 10 10

234. 20 c. "The Holy Family" (Van Dyck) .. 10 10

235. 25 c. As 20 c. 10 10

236. 40 c. Type **88** 15 10

89. Monkey Fiddle.

1971. Flowers. Multicoloured.

237. ½ c. Type **89** 10 10

238. 20 c. Tropical Mountain Violet 20 10

239. 30 c. Trailing Morning Glory 20 10

240. 50 c. Fringed Epidendrum 40 40

90. Royal Poinciana.

1971. Philippe de Poincy Commem. **Mult.**

241. 20 c. Type **90** 10 10

242. 30 c. Chateau de Poincy .. 10 10

243. 50 c. De Poincy's badge (vert.) 20 15

91. The East Yorks.

1971. Siege of Brimstone Hill, 1782. **Mult.**

244. ½ c. Type **91** 10 10

245. 20 c. Royal Artillery .. 45 10

246. 30 c. French infantry .. 55 10

247. 50 c. The Royal Scots .. 75 20

92. "Crucifixion" (Massys).

1972. Easter.

248. **92.** 4 c. multicoloured .. 10 10

249. 20 c. multicoloured .. 10 10

250. 30 c. multicoloured .. 10 10

251. 40 c. multicoloured .. 10 10

93. "Virgin and Child" (Borgognone).

1972. Christmas. Multicoloured.

252. 3 c. Type **93** 10 10

253. 20 c. "Adoration of the Kings" (J. Bassano) (horiz.) 15 10

254. 25 c. "Adoration of the Shepherds" (Domenichino) 15 10

255. 40 c. "Virgin and Child" (Fiorenzo di Lorenzo) .. 20 10

1972. Royal Silver Wedding. As T **52** of Ascension, but with Brown Pelicans in background.

256. 20 c. red 15 15

257. 25 c. blue 15 15

95. Landing on St. Christopher 1623.

1973. 300th Anniv. of Sir Thomas Warner's Landing on St. Christopher. Multicoloured.

258. 4 c. Type **95** 15 10
259. 25 c. Growing tobacco .. 15 10
260. 40 c. Building fort at Old Road 20 10
261. £2.50 "Concepcion" .. 80 1·10

96. "The Last Supper" (Titian).

1973. Easter. Paintings of "The Last Supper" by the artists listed. Mult.

262. 4 c. Type **96** 10 10
263. 25 c. Ascribed to Roberti .. 10 10
264. $2. 50 Juan de Juanes (horiz.) 70 60

1973. Royal Visit Nos. 258/61 optd. **VISIT OF HRH THE PRINCE OF WALES 1973.**

265. **95.** 4 c. multicoloured .. 10 15
266. – 25 c. multicoloured .. 10 15
267. – 40 c. multicoloured .. 15 15
268. – $2.50 multicoloured .. 45 50

99. Harbour Scene and 2d. Stamp of 1903.

1973. 70th Anniv. of 1st St. Kitts-Nevis Stamps. Multicoloured.

285. 4 c. Type **99** 10 10
286. 25 c. Sugar-mill and 1d. stamp of 1903 .. .. 15 10
287. 40 c. Unloading boat and ½d. stamp of 1903 .. 35 10
288. $2.50 Rock-carvings and 3d. stamp of 1903 .. 2·00 1·00

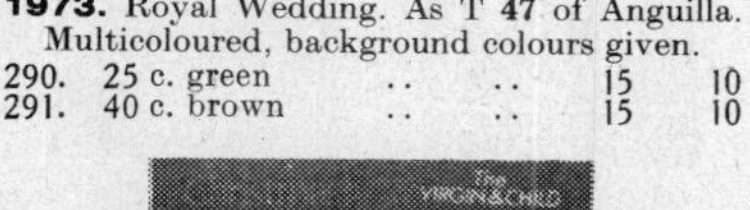

1973. Royal Wedding. As T **47** of Anguilla. Multicoloured, background colours given.

290. 25 c. green 15 10
291. 40 c. brown 15 10

100. "Madonna and Child" (Murillo).

1973. Christmas. Paintings of "The Holy Family" by the artists listed. Mult.

292. 4 c. Type **100** 10 10
293. 40 c. Mengs 20 10
294. 60 c. Sassoferrato 25 15
295. $1 Filippino Lippi (horiz.) 35 30

101. "Christ Carrying the Cross" (S. del Piombo).

1974. Easter. Multicoloured.

296. 4 c. Type **101** 10 10
297. 25 c. "The Crucifixion" (Goya) 15 10
298. 40 c. "Trinity" (Ribera) .. 15 10
299. $2.50 "The Deposition" (Fra Bartolomeo) (horiz.) 1·00 75

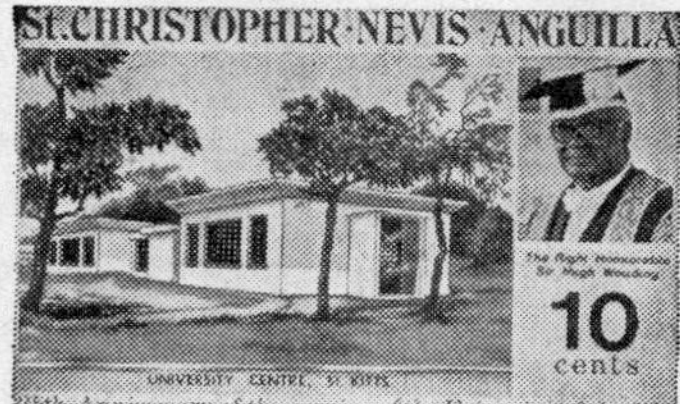

102. University Centre, St. Kitts.

1974. 25th Anniv. of University of West Indies. Multicoloured.

300. 10 c. Type **102** 10 10
301. $1 As Type **102** but showing different buildings .. 20 25

103. Hands reaching for Globe.

1974. Family Planning.

303. **103.** 4 c. brn., blue & black .. 10 10
304. – 25 c. multicoloured .. 10 10
305. – 40 c. multicoloured .. 10 10
306. – $2.50 multicoloured .. 35 55

DESIGNS—HORIZ. 25 c. Instruction by nurse. $2.50, Emblem and globe on scales. VERT 40 c. Family group.

104. Churchill as Army Lieutenant.

1974. Birth Centenary of Sir Winston Churchill. Multicoloured.

307. 4 c. Type **104** 10 10
308. 25 c. Churchill as Prime Minister 15 10
309. 40 c. Churchill as Knight of the Garter 25 10
310. 60 c. Churchill's statue, London 35 15

106. "The Last Supper" (Dore).

1975. Easter. Paintings by Dore. Mult.

314. 4 c. Type **106** 10 10
315. 25 c. "Christ Mocked" .. 10 10
316. 40 c. "Jesus Falling beneath the Cross" 10 10
317. $1 "The Erection of the Cross" 25 30

INDEX

Countries can be quickly located by referring to the index at the end of this volume.

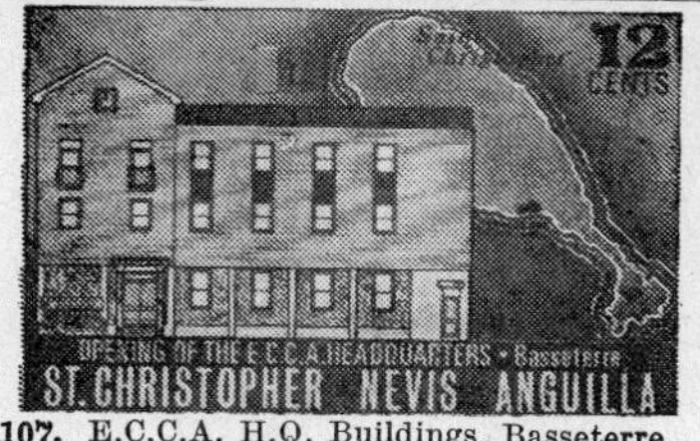

107. E.C.C.A. H.Q. Buildings, Basseterre.

1975. Opening of East Caribbean Currency Authority's Headquarters.

318. **107.** 12 c. multicoloured .. 10 10
319. – 25 c. multicoloured .. 10 10
320. – 40 c. red, silver and grey 15 10
321. – 45 c. multicoloured .. 15 15

DESIGNS: 25 c. Specimen one-dollar banknote. 40 c. Half-dollar of 1801 and current 4-dollar coin. 45 c. Coins of 1801 and 1960.

108. Evangeline Booth (Salvation Army General).

1975. International Women's Year. Mult.

338. 4 c. Type **108** 10 10
339. 25 c. Sylvia Pankhurst .. 25 10
340. 40 c. Marie Curie 50 30
341. $2.50 Lady Annie Allen (teacher and guider) .. 2·00 2·75

109. Golfer.

1975. Opening of Frigate Bay Golf Course.

342. **109.** 4 c. black and red .. 20 10
343. 25 c. black and yellow .. 35 10
344. 40 c. black and green .. 45 10
345. $1 black and blue .. 1·00 70

110. "St. Paul" (Pier Francesco Sacchi).

1975. Christmas. Religious Paintings. Mult.

346. 25 c. Type **110** .. 20 10
347. 40 c. "St. James" (Bonifazio di Pitati) .. 35 10
348. 45 c. "St. John the Baptist" (Mola) 35 10
349. $1 "St. John" (Raphael) 70 60

111. "Crucifixion" (detail).

1976. Easter. Stained Glass Windows. Mult.

350. 4 c. } Type **111** 10 10
351. 4 c. } 10 10
352. 4 c. } 10 10
353. 25 c. "Last Supper" .. 30 10
354. 40 c. "Last Supper" .. 35 10
355. $1 "Baptism of Christ" 60 55

Type **111** shows the left-hand stamp of the 4 c. design.
Nos. 353/5 are size 27 × 35 mm.

1976. West Indian Victory in World Cricket Cup. As Nos 559/60 of Barbados.

356. 12 c. Map of the Caribbean 60 20
357. 40 c. Prudential Cup .. 1·40 50

112. Crispus Attucks and the Boston Massacre.

1976. Bicent. of American Revolution. Mult.

359. 20 c. Type **112** .. 15 10
360. 40 c. Alexander Hamilton and Battle of Yorktown 30 10
361. 45 c. Jefferson and Declaration of Independence .. 30 10
362. $1 Washington and the Crossing of the Delaware 60 80

113. "The Nativity" (Storza Book of Hours).

1976. Christmas. Multicoloured.

363. 20 c. Type **113** 10 10
364. 40 c. "Virgin and Child with St. John" (Pintoricchio) 15 10
365. 45 c. "Our Lady of Good Children" (Ford Maddox-Brown) 15 10
366. $1 "Little Hands Outstretched to Bless" (M. Tarrant) 35 50

114. Royal Visit, 1966.

1977. Silver Jubilee. Multicoloured.

367. 50 c. Type **114** 15 10
368. 55 c. The Sceptre 15 10
369. $1.50 Bishops paying homage 30 50

115. "Christ on the Cross" (Niccolo di Liberatore).

1977. Easter. Paintings from National Gallery, London. Multicoloured.
370. 25 c. Type **115** 10 10
371. 30 c. " The Resurrection " (imitator of Mantegna) 10 10
372. 50 c. " The Resurrection " (Ugolino da Siena) (horiz.) 15 10
373. $1 " Christ Rising from the Tomb " (Gaudenzio Ferrari) 25 30

116. Estridge Mission.

1977. Bicentenary of Moravian Mission.
374. **116.** 4 c. black, green & blue 10 10
375. – 20 c. blk., mauve & violet 10 10
376. – 40 c. blk., yell. & orge. 15 15
DESIGNS: 20 c. Mission symbol. 40 c. Basseterre Mission.

117. Laboratory Instruments.

1977. 75th Anniv. of Pan-American Health Organisation.
377. **117.** 3 c. multicoloured .. 10 10
378. – 12 c. multicoloured .. 15 10
379. – 20 c. multicoloured .. 20 10
380. – $1 brn., orge. and black 70 40
DESIGNS: 12 c. Fat cells, blood cells and nerve cells. 20 c. " Community participation in health ". $1, Inoculation.

118. " Nativity " (West Window).

1977. Christmas. Stained-glass windows from Chartres Cathedral. Multicoloured.
381. 4 c. Type **118** 10 10
382. 6 c. " Three Magi " (west window) 10 10
383. 40 c. " La Belle Verriere " 35 10
384. $1 " Virgin and Child " (Rose window) 75 45

119. Savanna Monkey with Vervet.

120. Falcon of Edward III.

1978. The Savanna Monkey.
385. **119.** 4 c. brown, red & black 10 10
386. – 5 c. multicoloured 10 10
387. **119.** 55 c. brn., green and blk. 30 10
388. – $1.50 multicoloured .. 75 60
DESIGN: 5 c., $1.50, Savanna Monkeys on branch.

1978. 25th Anniv. of Coronation.
389. **120.** $1 brown and red .. 20 20
390. – $1 multicoloured .. 20 20
391. – $1 brown and red .. 20 20
DESIGNS: No. 390, Queen Elizabeth II. No. 391, Brown pelican.

121. Tomatoes.

1978. Multicoloured.
392. 1 c. Type **121** 10 15
393. 2 c. Defence Force band .. 10 15
394. 5 c. Radio and T.V. station 10 10
395. 10 c. Technical college .. 10 10
396. 12 c. T.V. assembly plant 10 15
397. 15 c. Sugar cance harvesting 15 10
398. 25 c. Crafthouse (craft centre) 15 10
399. 30 c. "Europa" (liner) .. 40 30
400. 40 c. Lobster and sea crab 30 10
401. 45 c. Royal St. Kitts Hotel and golf course .. 75 30
402. 50 c. Pinney's Beach, Nevis 30 10
403. 55 c. New runway at Golden Rock .. 30 10
404. $1 Cotton picking 35 30
405. $5 Brewery .. .. 1·00 1·25
406. $10 Pineapples and peanuts .. .. .. 2·25 2·50

122. Investiture.

1978. 50th Anniv. of Boy Scout Movement on St. Kitts and Nevis. Multicoloured.
407. 5 c. Type **122.** 10 10
408. 10 c. Map reading .. 10 10
409. 25 c. Pitching tent .. 20 15
410. 40 c. Cooking 35 25
411. 50 c. First Aid 40 35
412. 55 c. Rev. W. A. Beckett (founder of Scouting in St. Kitts) 45 45

123. Wise Man with Gift of Gold.

1978. Christmas. Multicoloured.
413. 5 c. Type **123** 10 10
414. 15 c. Wise Man with gift of Frankincense .. 10 10
415. 30 c. Wise Man with gift of Myrrh 10 10
416. $2.25 Wise Man paying homage to the infant Jesus 35 50

124. " Canna coccinea ".

1979. Local Flowers (1st series). Multicoloured.
417. 5 c. Type **124** 10 10
418. 30 c. " Heliconia bihai " .. 30 20
419. 55 c. " Ruellia tuberosa " 50 30
420. $1.50 " Gesneria ventricosa " .. .. .. 1·10 1·40
See also Nos. 430/3.

125. St. Christopher 1870–76 1d. Stamp and Sir Rowland Hill.

1979. Death Centenary of Sir Rowland Hill. Multicoloured.
421. 5 c. Type **125** 10 10
422. 15 c. 1970 Stamp Centenary 50 c. commemorative .. 10 10
423. 50 c. Great Britain 1841 2d. blue 35 35
424. $2.50, St. Kitts–Nevis 1923 300th Anniv. of Colony £1 commemorative 90 1·10

126. " The Woodman's Daughter ".

1979. Christmas. International Year of the Child. Paintings by Sir John Millais. Multicoloured.
425. 5 c. Type **126** 10 10
426. 25 c. " Cherry Ripe " .. 25 20
427. 30 c. " The Rescue " .. 25 20
428. 55 c. " Bubbles " 30 25

1980. Local Flowers (2nd series). As T **124.** Multicoloured.
430. 4 c. " Clerodendrum aculeatum " 30 10
431. 55 c. " Inga laurina " .. 40 20
432. $1. 50 " Epidendrum difforme " .. .. 1·00 50
433. $2 " Salvia serotina " .. 1·10 90

127. Nevis Lagoon.

1980. " London 1980 " International Stamp Exhibition. Multicoloured.
434. 5 c. Type **127** 10 10
435. 30 c. Fig Tree Church (vert.) 20 10
436. 55 c. Nisbet Plantation .. 45 25
437. $3 " Nelson " (Fuger) (vert.) 1·00 1·00

OFFICIAL STAMPS

1980. Nos. 396, 398 and 400/6 optd. **OFFICIAL.**
O 1. 12 c. multicoloured .. 1·25 1·00
O 2. 25 c. multicoloured .. 15 20
O 3. 40 c. multicoloured .. 50 50
O 4. 45 c. multicoloured .. 45 45
O 5. 50 c. multicoloured .. 30 40
O 6. 55 c. multicoloured .. 30 40
O 7. $1 multicoloured .. 1·25 2·25
O 8. $5 multicoloured .. 1·00 2·50
O 9. $10 multicoloured .. 2·00 3·50

ST. LUCIA

One of the Windward Is., Br. W. Indies Achieved Associated Statehood on 1 March 1967.

1860. 12 pence = 1 shilling;
20 shillings = 1 pound.
1949. 100 cents = 1 West Indian dollar.

1.

HALFPENNY
(3.)

1860. No value on stamps.
5. **1.** (1d.) red .. .. .. 55·00 80·00
11a. (1d.) black .. .. 15·00 11·00
7. (4d.) blue £100 £100
16. (4d.) yellow .. .. 60·00 18·00
8. (6d.) green £200 £200
17a. (6d.) violet .. .. 60·00 18·00
14c. (1s.) orange .. .. £150 25·00

1881. With value added by surch. as T **2.**
25. **1.** ½d. green .. .. .. 12·00 22·00
26. 1d. black .. .. .. 18·00 8·00
24. 2½d. red .. .. .. 19·00 18·00
27. 4d. yellow .. .. .. £170 17·00
28. 6d. violet .. .. .. 22·00 25·00
29. 1s. orange £250 £160

5.

9.

1882.
43. **5.** ½d. green 50 30
32. 1d. red .. .. .. 23·00 7·50
46. 2½d. blue .. .. .. 1·75 30
48. 4d. brown .. .. .. 1·40 2·25
35. 6d. lilac £250 £200
36. 1s. brown £400 £140

1886.
44. **5.** 1d. mauve 90 15
45. 2d. blue and orange .. 70 1·00
47. 3d. mauve and green .. 3·25 5·50
41. 6d. mauve and blue .. 3·25 7·00
50. 1s. mauve and red .. 2·75 5·00
51. 5s. mauve and orange .. 27·00 70·00
52. 10s. mauve and black .. 50·00 70·00

1891. Surch. in words.
56. **5.** ½d. on 3d. mauve & green 30·00 14·00
55. 1d. on 4d. brown .. .. 3·00 3·00

1891. Surch. in figures.
54. **5.** ½d. on half 6d. (No. 41) .. 14·00 3·25

1902.
64 **9** ½d. purple and green .. 1·25 20
66 1d. purple and red .. 1·75 20
68a 2½d. purple and blue .. 2·75 2·00
70 3d. purple and yellow .. 3·50 3·00
72 6d. purple .. .. .. 5·50 4·75
62 1s. green and black .. 7·50 12·00
76 5s. green and red .. .. 30·00 70·00

11. The Pitons.

12.

13.

14.

1902. 400th Anniv. of Discovery.
63. **11.** 2 d. green and brown .. 6·50 1·75

1907.
65. **9.** ½d. green .. .. .. 1·00 30
67. 1d. red .. .. .. 1·00 10
69. 2½d. blue .. .. .. 3·00 1·25
71. 3d. purple on yellow .. 1·75 7·50
75. 1s. black on green .. 2·75 4·50
77. 5s. green & red on yellow 35·00 48·00

1912.
91 **12** ½d. green 20 15
79 1d. red .. .. .. 1·90 10
93 1d. brown 20 15
94 **14** 1½d. red 40 90
95 **13** 2d. grey 20 15
98 **12** 2½d. blue .. .. .. 90 2·50
97 2½d. orange .. .. 5·50 26·00
82 3d. purple on yellow .. 60 2·00
99a 3d. blue .. .. .. 1·00 9·00
83a **14** 4d. black & red on yellow 60 1·50
102 **12** 6d. purple .. .. 1·25 4·75
85 1s. black on green .. 2·50 4·25
103 1s. brown .. .. 1·75 4·00
87 **13** 2s. 6d. black & red on blue 14·00 20·00
88 **12** 5s. green & red on yellow 18·00 55·00

1916. No. 79a optd. **WAR TAX** in two lines.
89. **12.** 1d. red .. .. .. 3·25 3·25

1916. No. 79a optd. **WAR TAX** in one line.
90. **12.** 1d. red 15 15

1935. Silver Jubilee. As T **13** of Antigua.
109. ½d. black and green .. 15 25
110. 2d. blue and grey .. 45 25
111. 2½d. brown and blue .. 90 65
112. 1s. grey and purple .. 3·00 3·75

19. Port Castries.

1936. King George V.
113. 19. ½d. black and green .. 20 45
114. – 1d. black and brown .. 25 10
115. – 1½d. black and red .. 55 30
116. 19. 2d. black and grey .. 25 15
117. – 2½d. black and blue .. 30 15
118. – 3d. black and green .. 1·25 70
119. 19. 4d. black and brown .. 30 1·00
120. – 6d. black and orange .. 65 1·00
121. – 1s. black and blue .. 70 2·00
122. – 2s. 6d. black and blue .. 3·50 13·00
123. – 5s. black and violet .. 8·00 20·00
124. – 10s. black and red .. 40·00 50·00
DESIGNS—HORIZ. 1d., 2½d., 6d. Columbus Square, Castries. 1s. Fort Rodney, Pigeon Island. 5s. Govt. House. 10s. Badge of Colony. VERT. 1½d., 3d. Ventine Falls. 2s. 6d. Inniskilling Monument.

1937. Coronation. As T **2** of Aden.
125. 1d. violet 20 15
126. 1½d. red 30 15
127. 2½d. blue 30 15

26. King George VI.

DESIGNS — HORIZ. As Type **27**: 1s. Govt. House. 2s. The Pitons. 5s. Loading bananas. VERT. 10s. Device of St. Lucia as Type **33**.

27. Columbus Square.

1938. King George VI.
128a 26 ½d. green 10 10
129a 1d. violet 10 15
129b 1d. red 10 10
130a 1½d. red 10 30
131a 2d. grey 10 10
132a 2½d. blue 10 10
132b 2½d. violet 10 10
133 3d. orange 10 10
133b 3½d. blue 30 15
134 27 6d. red 35 40
134c 26 8d. brown .. .. 1·25 30
135 – 1s. brown 15 30
136 – 2s. blue and red .. 3·25 1·25
136a 26 3s. purple .. .. 8·00 2·75
137 – 5s. black and purple .. 8·00 4·00
138 – 10s. black on yellow .. 3·50 9·00
141 26 £1 brown .. .. 11·00 8·00

1946. Victory. As T **9** of Aden.
142. 1d. violet 10 10
143. 3½d. blue 10 10

1948. Silver Wedding. As T **10/11** of Aden.
144 1d. red 15 10
145 £1 purple .. .. .. 11·00 30·00

33. Device of St. Lucia. 34. Phoenix rising from Burning Buildings.

1949. New Currency.
146. 26. 1 c. green 10 10
147. 2 c. mauve 10 10
148. 3 c. red 10 20
149. 4 c. grey 10 10
150. 5 c. violet 10 10
151. 6 c. orange 10 20
152. 7 c. blue 50 30
153. 12 c. red 90 15
154. 16 c. brown 75 15
155. 33. 24 c. blue 30 10
156. 48 c. olive .. .. 1·50 50
157. $1.20 purple .. .. 2·25 4·00
158. $2.40 green .. .. 3·00 14·00
159. $4.80 red .. .. 7·00 18·00

1949. U.P.U. As T **20/23** of Antigua.
160 5 c. violet 15 15
161 6 c. orange 35 25
162 12 c. mauve 25 20
163 24 c. green 50 20

1951. Inauguration of B.W.I. University College. As T **24/25** of Antigua.
164 3 c. black and red .. 20 10
165 12 c. black and red .. 20 10

1951. Reconstruction of Castries.
166. 34. 12 c. red and blue .. 15 30

1951. New Constitution. Optd. **NEW CONSTITUTION 1951.**
167. 26. 2 c. mauve 10 15
168. 4 c. grey 10 15
169. 5 c. violet 10 15
170. 12 c. red 10 25

1953. Coronation. As T **13** of Aden.
171. 3 c. black and red 15 10

1953. As 1949 but portrait of Queen Elizabeth II facing left and new Royal Cypher.
172. 26. 1 c. green 10 10
173. 2 c. purple 10 10
174. 3 c. red 10 10
175. 4 c. grey 10 10
176. 5 c. violet 10 10
177. 6 c. orange 15 10
178. 8 c. red 10 10
179. 10 c. blue 10 10
180. 15 c. brown 30 10
181. 33. 25 c. blue 20 10
182. 50 c. olive .. .. 3·50 35
183. $1 green .. .. 3·25 85
184. $2.50 red .. .. 4·50 3·00

1958. British Caribbean Federation. As T **28** of Antigua.
185 3 c. green 30 15
186 6 c. blue 55 65
187 12 c. red 70 55

38. Columbus's "Santa Maria" off the Pitons.

1960. New Constitution for the Windward and Leeward Islands.
188. 38. 8 c. red 25 15
189. 10 c. orange 25 15
190. 25 c. blue 35 20

39. Stamp of 1860.

1960. Stamp Cent.
191. 39. 5 c. red and blue .. 10 10
192. 16 c. blue and green .. 15 25
193. 25 c. green and red .. 15 10

1963. Freedom from Hunger. As T **28** of Aden.
194. 25 c. green 30 10

1963. Cent of Red Cross. As T **33** of Antigua.
195 4 c. red and black .. 15 10
196 25 c. red and blue .. 40 70

40. Queen Elizabeth II. 41. (after A. C. Davidson-Houston).

42 Fishing Boats.

1964.
197. 40. 1 c. red 10 10
198. 2 c. violet 30 10
199. 4 c. green 35 10
200. 5 c. blue 30 10
201. 6 c. brown 45 10
202. 41. 8 c. multicoloured .. 10 10
203. 10 c. multicoloured .. 40 10
204. 42. 12 c. multicoloured .. 15 10
205. – 15 c. multicoloured .. 20 10
206. – 25 c. multicoloured .. 20 10
207. – 35 c. blue and buff .. 1·25 10
208. – 50 c. multicoloured .. 1·10 10
209. – $1 multicoloured .. 1·25 25
210. – $2.50 multicoloured .. 2·00 1·50
DESIGNS—As Type **42**: HORIZ. 15 c. Pigeon Island. 25 c. Reduit Beach. VERT. $1, Vigie Beach. As Type **42** but "E. II R" in place of portrait. HORIZ. 35 c. Castries Harbour. 50 c. The Pitons. As Type **41**: $2·50, Queen Elizabeth II, head and shoulders.

1964. 400th Birth Anniv of Shakespeare. As T **34** of Antigua.
211. 42a. 10 c. green 10 10

1965. Cent of I.T.U. As T **36** of Antigua.
212. 2 c. mauve and purple .. 10 10
213. 50 c. lilac and green .. 90 35

1965. I.C.Y. As T **37** of Antigua.
214 1 c. purple and green .. 10 10
215 25 c. green and violet .. 20 20

1966. Churchill Commem. As T **38** of Antigua.
216. 4 c. blue 10 10
217. 6 c. green 15 10
218. 25 c. brown 20 15
219. 35 c. violet 30 20

1966. Royal Visit. As T **39** of Antigua.
220 4 c. black and blue .. 10 10
221 25 c. black and mauve .. 40 25

1966. World Cup Football Championship. As T **40** of Antigua.
222 4 c. multicoloured .. 10 10
223 25 c. multicoloured .. 30 20

1966. Inauguration of W.H.O. Headquarters, Geneva. As T **41** of Antigua.
224 4 c. black, green and blue 10 10
225 25 c. black, purple & brown 25 20

1966. 20th Anniv of U.N.E.S.C.O. As T **54/6** of Antigua.
226. 4 c. multicoloured .. 10 10
227. 12 c. yellow, violet & olive 20 15
228. 25 c. black, purple & orge. 35 30

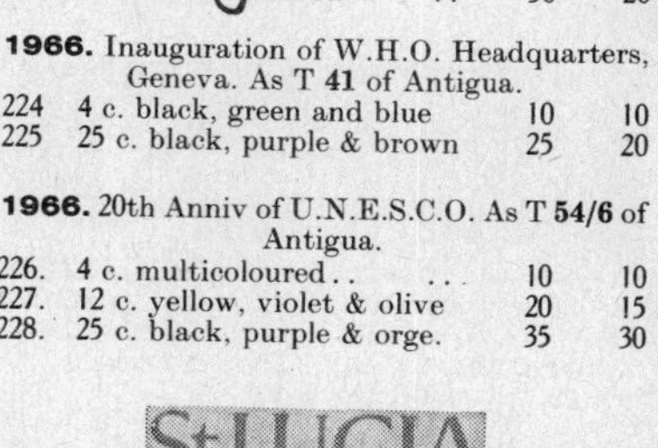

51. Map of St. Lucia.

1967. Statehood. Nos. 198, 202/9 and 257 optd. **STATEHOOD 1st MARCH 1967.**
(a) Postage.
229. 40. 2 c. violet 20 15
230. 5 c. blue 10 10
231. 6 c. brown 10 10
232. 41. 8 c. multicoloured .. 20 10
233. 10 c. multicoloured .. 25 10
234. 42. 12 c. multicoloured .. 20 10
235. – 15 c. multicoloured .. 25 30
236. – 25 c. multicoloured .. 30 30
237. – 35 c. blue and buff .. 50 35
238. – 50 c. multicoloured .. 50 55
239. – $1 multicoloured .. 50 55
(b) Air.
240. 51. 15 c. blue 10 10

52. "Madonna and Child with the Infant Baptist" (Raphael).

1967. Christmas.
241. 52. 4 c. multicoloured .. 10 10
242. 25 c. multicoloured .. 20 10

53. Batsman and Sir Frederick Clarke (Governor).

1968. M.C.C.'s West Indies Tour.
243. 53. 10 c. multicoloured .. 20 15
244. 35 c. multicoloured .. 45 40

54. "The Crucified Christ with the Virgin Mary, Saints and the Angels". (Raphael.) 56. Dr. Martin Luther King.

1968. Easter Commem.
245. 54. 10 c. multicoloured .. 10 10
246. – 15 c. multicoloured .. 10 10
247. 54. 25 c. multicoloured .. 15 10
248. – 35 c. multicoloured .. 15 10
DESIGN: 15 c., 35 c. "Noli me tangere" (detail by Titian).

1968. Martin Luther King Commem.
250. 56. 25 c. blue, black & flesh 10 10
251. 35 c. blue, black & flesh 10 10

57. "Virgin and Child in Glory" (Murillo).

1968. Christmas.
252. 57. 5 c. multicoloured .. 10 10
253. – 10 c. multicoloured .. 10 10
254. 57. 25 c. multicoloured .. 10 10
255. – 35 c. multicoloured .. 15 10
DESIGN: 10 c., 35 c. "Madonna and Child" (Murillo).

59. Purple-throated Carib.

1969. Birds. Multicoloured.
256. 10 c. Type **59** 45 20
257. 15 c. St. Lucia amazon .. 55 25
258. 25 c. Type **59** 75 30
259. 35 c. As 15 c. 90 30

HAVE YOU READ THE NOTES AT THE BEGINNING OF THIS CATALOGUE?
These often provide answers to the enquiries we receive.

61. "Head of Christ Crowned with Thorns" (Reni).

1969. Easter Commem. Multicoloured.

260.	10 c. Type **61**	10	10
261.	15 c. "Resurrection of Christ" (Sodoma) ..	10	10
262.	25 c. Type **61**	10	10
263.	35 c. As the 15 c. ..	10	10

63. Map showing "CARIFTA" Countries.

1969. 1st Anniv. of "CARIFTA".

264. **63.**	5 c. multicoloured ..	10	10
265.	10 c. multicoloured ..	10	10
266. –	25 c. multicoloured ..	10	10
267. –	35 c. multicoloured ..	10	10

DESIGN: 25 c., 35 c. Handclasp and names of "CARIFTA" countries.

65. Emperor Napoleon and Empress Josephine.

1969. Birth Bicent. of Napoleon Bonaparte.

268. **65.**	15 c. multicoloured ..	10	10
269.	25 c. multicoloured ..	10	10
270.	35 c. multicoloured ..	10	10
271.	50 c. multicoloured .	15	15

66. "Virgin and Child" (P. Delaroche).

1969. Christmas. Paintings. Multicoloured; background colours given.

272. **66.**	5 c. gold and purple ..	10	10
273. –	10 c. gold and blue ..	10	10
274. **66.**	25 c. gold and red ..	10	10
275. –	35 c. gold and green ..	10	10

DESIGN: 10 c. and 35 c. "Holy Family" (Rubens).

68. House of Assembly.

1970. Multicoloured.

276.	1 c. Type **68**	10	10
277.	2 c. Roman Catholic Cathedral	10	10
278.	4 c. The Boulevard, Castries	15	10
279.	5 c. Castries Harbour ..	15	10
280.	6 c. Sulphur Springs ..	15	10
281.	10 c. Vigie Airport ..	20	10
282.	12 c. Reduit Beach ..	20	10
283.	15 c. Pigeon Island ..	25	10
284.	25 c. The Pitons and yacht	40	10
285.	35 c. Marigot Bay ..	40	10
286.	50 c. Diamond Waterfall..	70	60
287.	$1 Flag of St. Lucia ..	75	70
288.	$2.50 St. Lucia Coat of Arms	1·50	1·75
289.	$5 Queen Elizabeth II ..	3·25	4·75
289a.	$10 Map of St. Lucia ..	9·00	11·00

Nos. 286/9a are vert.

69. "The Sealing of the Tomb" (Hogarth).

1970. Easter. Multicoloured.

290.	25 c. Type **69**	15	20
291.	35 c. "The Three Marys at the Tomb" (Hogarth) ..	15	20
292.	$1 "The Ascension (Hogarth)	30	40

The $1 is larger (39 × 54 mm.).

Nos. 290/2 were issued in a triptych, with the $1 value 10 mm. higher than the other values.

72. Charles Dickens and Dickensian Characters.

1970. Death Cent. of Charles Dickens.

293. **72.**	1 c. multicoloured ..	10	10
294.	25 c. multicoloured ..	10	10
295.	35 c. multicoloured ..	15	10
296.	50 c. multicoloured ..	20	20

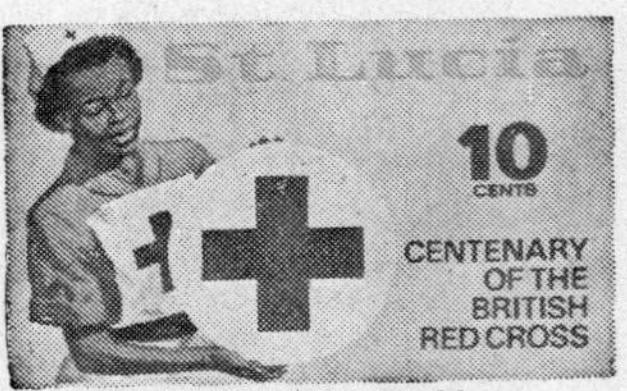

73. Nurse and Emblem.

1970. Cent. of British Red Cross. Mult.

297.	10 c. Type **73**	10	10
298.	15 c. Flags of Great Britain, Red Cross and St. Lucia	15	10
299.	25 c. Type **73**	25	10
300.	35 c. As 15 c.	30	10

74. "Madonna with the Lilies" (Luca della Robbia).

1970. Christmas.

301. **74.**	5 c. multicoloured ..	10	10
302.	10 c. multicoloured ..	10	10
303.	35 c. multicoloured ..	20	10
304.	40 c. multicoloured ..	20	15

75. "Christ on the Cross" (Rubens).

1971. Easter. Multicoloured.

305.	10 c. Type **75**	10	10
306.	15 c. "Descent from the Cross" (Rubens) ..	10	10
307.	35 c. Type **75**	20	10
308.	40 c. As 15 c.	20	15

76. Moule a Chique Lighthouse.

1971. Opening of Beane Field Airport. Mult.

309.	5 c. Type **76**	20	15
310.	25 c. Aircraft landing at Beane Field	35	15

77. Morne Fortune.

78. Morne Fortune, Modern View.

1971. Old and New Views of St. Lucia. Multicoloured.

311.	5 c. Type **77**	10	10
312.	5 c. Type **78**	10	10
313.	10 c. } Castries City ..	10	10
314.	10 c. } ..	10	10
315.	25 c. } Pigeon Island ..	20	20
316.	25 c. } ..	20	20
317.	50 c. } View from grounds	40	40
318.	50 c. } of Govt. House ..	40	40

Each value of this issue was printed horizontally and vertically se-tenant in two designs showing respectively old and new views of St. Lucia.

The old views are taken from printings by J. H. Caddy.

79. "Virgin and Child with two Angels". (Verrocchio).

1971. Christmas. Multicoloured.

319.	5 c. Type **79**	10	10
320.	10 c. "Virgin and Child, St. John the Baptist and an Angel" (Morando) ..	10	10
321.	35 c. "Madonna and Child" (Battista)	15	10
322.	40 c. Type **79**	20	25

80. "St. Lucia" (Dolci School) and Coat of Arms.

1971. National Day.

323. **80.**	5 c. multicoloured ..	10	10
324.	10 c. multicoloured ..	10	10
325.	25 c. multicoloured ..	20	10
326.	50 c. multicoloured ..	40	30

81. "The Dead Christ Mourned" (Carracci).

1972. Easter. Multicoloured.

327.	10 c. Type **81**	10	10
328.	25 c. "Angels weeping over the dead Christ" (Guercino) ..	20	10
329.	35 c. Type **81**	30	10
330.	50 c. As 25 c.	40	40

82. Science Block and Teachers' College.

1972. Morne Educational Complex. Mult.

331.	5 c. Type **82**	10	10
332.	15 c. University Centre ..	10	10
333.	25 c. Secondary School ..	10	10
334.	35 c. Technical College ..	15	10

83. Steamship Stamp and Map.

1972. 1st Postal Service by St. Lucia Steam Conveyance Co. Ltd. Cent.

335. **83.**	5 c. multicoloured ..	15	10
336. –	10 c. blue, mauve & blk.	20	10
337. –	35 c. red, blue and black	45	10
338. –	50 c. multicoloured ..	1·00	1·00

DESIGNS: 10 c. Steamship stamp and Castries Harbour. 35 c. Steamship stamp and Soufriere. 50 c. Steamship stamps.

84. "The Holy Family" (Sebastiano Ricci).

1972. Christmas.

339. **84.**	5 c. multicoloured ..	10	10
340.	10 c. multicoloured ..	10	10
341.	35 c. multicoloured ..	20	10
342.	40 c. multicoloured ..	25	15

1972. Royal Silver Wedding. As T **52** of Ascension but with Arms and St. Lucia Amazon.

343 **85**	15 c. red	20	10
344	35 c. green	20	10

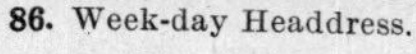

86. Week-day Headdress. **87.** Coat of Arms.

1973. Local Headdresses. Multicoloured.
345. 5 c. Type **86** 10 10
346. 10 c. Formal style 10 10
347. 25 c. Unmarried girl's style 10 10
348. 50 c. Ceremonial style .. 20 20

1973.
349 **87** 5 c. green 10 15
350 10 c. blue 15 15
953 10 c. green 30 30
351 25 c. brown 15 20

88. H.M.S. "St. Lucia", 1830.

1973. Historic Ships. Multicoloured.
352. 15 c. Type **88** 15 10
353. 35 c. H.M.S. "Prince of Wales", 1765 .. .. 20 10
354. 50 c. "Oliph Blossom", 1605 .. .. .. 30 15
355. $1 H.M.S. "Rose", 1757 .. 45 55

89. Plantation and Flower.

1973. Banana Industry. Multicoloured.
357. 5 c. Type **89** 10 10
358. 15 c. Aerial spraying .. 15 10
359. 35 c. Boxing plant .. 20 10
360. 50 c. Loading a boat .. 40 40

90. "The Virgin with Child" (Maratta).

1973. Christmas. Multicoloured.
361. 5 c. Type **90** 10 10
362. 15 c. "Madonna in the Meadow" (Raphael) .. 10 10
363. 35 c. "The Holy Family" (Bronzino) 15 10
364. 50 c. "Madonna of the Pear" (Durer) 20 25

1973. Royal Wedding. As T **47** of Anguilla. Multicoloured, background colours given.
365 40 c. green 10 10
366 50 c. lilac 10 10

91. "The Betrayal".

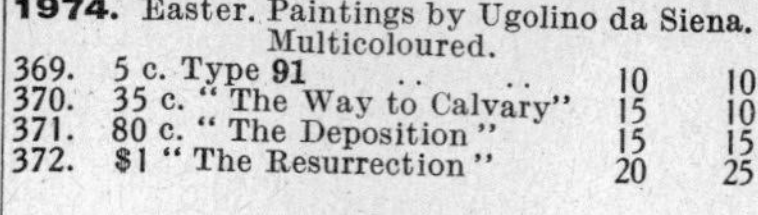

1974. Easter. Paintings by Ugolino da Siena. Multicoloured.
369. 5 c. Type **91** 10 10
370. 35 c. "The Way to Calvary" 15 10
371. 80 c. "The Deposition" 15 15
372. $1 "The Resurrection" 20 25

92. 3-Escalins Coins, 1798.

1974. Coins of Old St. Lucia. Multicoloured.
374. 15 c. Type **92** 15 10
375. 35 c. 6-escalins coins, 1798 20 10
376. 40 c. 2-livres, 5-sols coins, 1813 .. .. .. 20 10
377. $1 6-livres, 15-sols coins, 1813 .. .. .. 55 65

93. Baron de Laborie. **94.** "Virgin and Child", (Andrea del Verrocchio).

1974. Past Governors of St. Lucia. Mult.
379. 5 c. Type **93** 10 10
380. 35 c. Sir John Moore .. 10 10
381. 80 c. Sir Dudley Hill .. 15 10
382. $1 Sir Frederick Clarke .. 25 35

1974. Christmas. Multicoloured.
384. 5 c. Type **94** 10 10
385. 35 c. "Virgin and Child" (Andrea della Robbia) .. 10 10
386. 80 c. "Madonna and Child" (Luca della Robbia) .. 15 15
387. $1 "Virgin and Child" (Rossellino) 20 25

95. Churchill and Montgomery.

1974. Birth Centenary of Sir Winston Churchill.
389. 5 c. Type **95** 10 10
390. $1 Churchill and Truman 30 35

96. "Christ on the Cross" (School of Van der Weyden).

1975. Easter. Multicoloured.
391. 5 c. Type **96** 10 10
392. 35 c. "Noli me tangere" (Romano) 10 10
393. 80 c. "Calvary" (Gallego) 15 15
394. $1 "Noli me tangere" (Correggio) 20 25

97. "Nativity" (French Book of Hours).

1975. Christmas. Multicoloured.
399. 5 c. Type **97** 10 10
400. 10 c. } "Epiphany scene" 10 10
401. 10 c. } (stained glass 10 10
402. 10 c. } window) .. 10 10
403. 40 c. "Nativity" (Hastings Book of Hours) .. 30 20
404. $1 "Virgin and Child with Saints" (Borgognone) .. 70 50

98. American Schooner "Hanna".

1975. Bicentenary of American Revolution. Ships. Multicoloured.
406. ½ c. Type **98** 10 10
407. 1 c. Mail Packet "Prince of Orange" 10 10
408. 2 c. H.M.S. "Edward" .. 10 10
409. 5 c. Merchantman "Millern" 30 10
410. 15 c. American lugger "Surprise" 60 10
411. 35 c. H.M.S. "Serapis" .. 1·10 20
412. 50 c. American frigate "Randolph" .. .. 1·25 40
413. $1 American frigate "Alliance" .. .. 2·25 1·00

99. Laughing Gull.

1976. Birds. Multicoloured.
415 1 c. Type **99** 20 40
416 2 c. Little blue heron .. 30 40
417 4 c. Belted kingfisher .. 35 40
418 5 c. St. Lucia amazon .. 1·25 40
419 6 c. St. Lucia oriole .. 1·25 50
420 8 c. Brown trembler .. 1·25 50
421 10 c. American kestrel .. 1·25 35
422 12 c. Red-billed tropic bird 1·25 55
423 15 c. Moorhen .. .. 1·25 15
424a 25 c. Common noddy .. 1·00 30
425 35 c. Sooty tern .. .. 1·75 55
426 50 c. Osprey .. .. 3·25 1·00
427 $1 White-breasted trembler 3·25 1·10
428 $2.50 St. Lucia black finch 3·50 3·25
429 $5 Red-necked pigeon .. 4·25 3·50
430 $10 Caribbean elaenia .. 6·00 7·50

1976. West Indian Victory in World Cricket Cup. As Nos. 599/60 of Barbados. Mult.
431 50 c. Caribbean map .. 1·00 1·00
432 $1 Prudential Cup .. 1·50 2·25

100. H.M.S. "Ceres".

1976. Royal Navy Crests. Multicoloured.
434. 10 c. Type **100** 30 10
435. 20 c. H.M.S. "Pelican" .. 50 10
436. 40 c. H.M.S. "Ganges" .. 75 10
437. $2 H.M.S. "Ariadne" .. 1·75 2·00

101. "Madonna and Child" (Murillo).

1976. Christmas. Multicoloured.
438. 10 c. Type **101** 10 10
439. 20 c. "Madonna and Child with Angels" (Costa) .. 10 10
440. 50 c. "Madonna and Child Enthroned" (Isenbrandt) 15 10
441. $2 "Madonna and Child with St. John" (Murillo) 50 65

102. Queen Elizabeth II.

1977. Silver Jubilee.
443. **102.** 10 c. multicoloured .. 10 10
444. 20 c. multicoloured .. 15 15
445. 40 c. multicoloured .. 20 25
446. $2 multicoloured 60 90

103. Scouts from Tapion School.

1977. Caribbean Boy Scout Jamboree. Multicoloured.
448. ½ c. Type **103** 10 10
449. 1 c. Sea scouts 10 10
450. 2 c. Scout from Micoud .. 10 10
451. 10 c. Two scouts from Tapion School 15 10
452. 20 c. Venture scout .. 20 15
453. 50 c. Scout from Gros Islet 45 35
454. $1 Sea scouts in motor boat 75 90

104. "Nativity" (Giotto).

1977. Christmas. Multicoloured.
456. ½ c. Type **104** 10 10
457. 1 c. "Perugia triptych" (Fra Angelico) 10 10
458. 2 c. "Virgin and Child" (El Greco) 10 10
459. 20 c. "Madonna of the Rosary" (Caravaggio) 10 10
460. 50 c. "Adoration of the Magi" (Velazquez) .. 20 10
461. $1 "Madonna of Carmel" (Tiepolo) 30 40
462. $2.50 "Adoration of the Magi" (Tiepolo) .. 55 80

105. " Susan Lunden ".

1977. 400th Birth Anniv. of Rubens. Mult.
463. 10 c. Type 105 .. .. 10 10
464. 35 c. " The Rape of the Sabine Women " (detail) 15 10
465. 50 c. " Ludovicus Nonnius " 25 10
466. $2·50 " Minerva protects Pax from Mars " (detail) 65 80

106. Yeoman of the Guard and Life Guard.

1978. 25th Anniv. of Coronation. Mult.
468. 15 c. Type 106 .. .. 10 10
469. 20 c. Groom and postillion 10 10
470. 50 c. Footman and coachman 15 10
471. $3 State trumpeter and herald 60 80

107. Queen Angelfish.

1978. Fish. Multicoloured.
473. 10 c. Type 107 .. .. 10 10
474. 20 c. Foureye Butterfly-fish 20 10
475. 50 c. French Angelfish .. 40 20
476. $2 Yellowtail Damselfish 1·00 1·25

108. French Grenadier and Map of the Battle.

1978. Bicentenary of Battle of Cul-de-Sac. Multicoloured.
478. 10 c. Type 108 .. .. 15 10
479. 30 c. British Grenadier Officer and Map of St. Lucia (Bellin), 1762 .. 30 10
480. 50 c. Coastline from Gros Islet to Cul-de-Sac and British Fleet opposing French landings .. 40 15
481. $2.50 General James Grant, 1798 and Light Infantrymen of the 46th Regiment 1·50 1·25

109. The Annunciation.

1978. Christmas. Multicoloured.
482. 30 c. Type 109 .. .. 10 10
483. 50 c. Type 109 .. .. 15 10
484. 55 c. The Nativity .. 15 10
485. 80 c. As 55 c. 20 20

110. Hewanorra International Air Terminal.

1979. Independence. Multicoloured.
486. 10 c. Type 110 .. .. 10 10
487. 30 c. New coat of arms .. 10 10
488. 50 c. Government House and Sir Allen Lewis (first Governor-General) .. 15 10
489. $2 French, St. Lucia and Union flags on map of St. Lucia 30 45

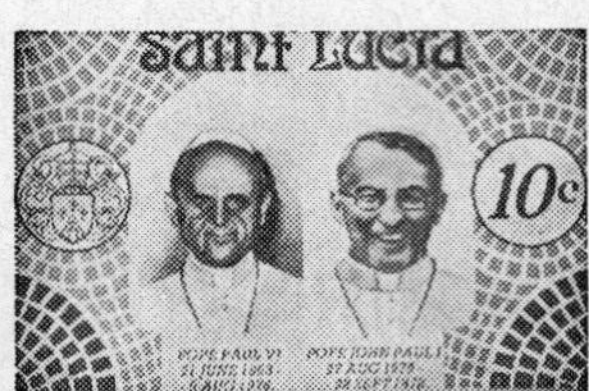

111. Popes Paul VI and John Paul I.

1979. Pope Paul VI Commemoration. Mult.
491. 10 c. Type 111 .. .. 10 10
492. 30 c. Pres. Sadat of Egypt with Pope Paul .. 20 10
493. 50 c. Pope Paul with Secretary-General U Thant 35 20
494. 55 c. Pope Paul and Prime Minister Golda Meir of Israel 40 25
495. $2 Martin Luther King received in audience by Pope Paul .. .. 1·00 80

112. Dairy Farming.

1979. Agricultural Diversification. Mult.
496. 10 c. Type 112 .. .. 10 10
497. 35 c. Fruit and vegetables 10 10
498. 50 c. Water conservation 10 10
499. $3 Copra industry .. 35 50

113. Lindbergh and Flying-boat.

1979. 50th Anniv. of Lindbergh's Inaugural Airmail Flight via St. Lucia.
500. 113. 10 c. blk., red & orge... 10 10
501. – 30 c. multicoloured .. 10 10
502. – 50 c. multicoloured .. 10 10
503. – $2 multicoloured .. 30 40

DESIGNS: 30 c. Flying-boat and route map. 50 c. Arrival at La Toc, September, 1929. $2, First flight covers.

114. " A Prince of Saxony " (Cranach the Elder).

1979. International Year of the Child. Famous Paintings. Multicoloured.
504. 10 c. Type 114 .. .. 10 10
505. 50 c. " The Infanta Margarita " (Velazquez) 15 10
506. $2 " Girl playing Badminton " (Chardin) .. 30 40
507. $2.50 " Mary and Francis Wilcox " (Stock) .. 35 45

115. Notice of Introduction of Penny Post.

1979. Death Centenary of Sir Rowland Hill. Multicoloured.
509. 10 c. Type 115 .. .. 10 10
510. 50 c. Wyon essay 20 10
511. $2 First St. Lucia stamp .. 45 50
512. $2.50 G.B. 1840 Penny Black 55 60

116. " Madonna and Child " (Bernardino Fungai).

1979. Christmas. Int. Year of the Child. Paintings of the " Madonna and Child " by artists named. Multicoloured.
514. 10 c. Type 116 .. .. 10 10
515. 50 c. Carlo Dolci 25 10
516. $2 Titian 70 40
517. $2.50 Giovanni Bellini .. 75 50

117. St. Lucia Steam Conveyance Co. Ltd. Cover of 1873.

1980. " London 1980 " International Stamp Exhibition. Multicoloured.
519. 10 c. Type 117 .. .. 10 10
520. 30 c. 1879 S.S. " Assistance " 1d. postmark 10 10
521. 50 c. 1929 Postage Due handstamp 15 10
522. $2 1844 Crown Circle Paid stamp 40 55

118. Mickey Mouse astride Rocket.

1980. 10th Anniv. (1979) of Moon Landing. Disney Characters in Space Scenes. Mult.
524. ½ c. Type 118 .. .. 10 10
525. 1 c. Donald Duck being towed by rocket (horiz.) 10 10
526. 2 c. Minnie Mouse on Moon 10 10
527. 3 c. Goofy hitching lift to Mars 10 10
528. 4 c. Goofy and Moondog (horiz.) 10 10
529. 5 c. Pluto burying bone on Moon (horiz.) 10 10
530. 10 c. Donald Duck and love-sick Martian (horiz.) 10 10
531. $2 Donald Duck paddling spaceship (horiz.) .. 1·75 1·00
532. $2·50 Mickey Mouse driving moonbuggy (horiz.) .. 2·00 1·10

119. Queen Elizabeth the Queen Mother.

1980. 80th Birthday of The Queen Mother.
534. 119. 10 c. multicoloured .. 20 10
535. $2·50 multicoloured .. 1·40 1·50

120. Hawker Siddeley " HS 748 ".

1980. Transport. Multicoloured.
537. 5 c. Type 120 .. .. 25 10
538. 10 c. McDonnell Douglas "DC-10" airliner .. 35 10
539. 15 c. Local bus 35 10
540. 20 c. Refrigerated freighter 35 10
541. 25 c. "Islander" aeroplane 50 10
542. 30 c. Pilot boat 40 20
543. 50 c. Boeing "727" airliner 65 40
544. 75 c. "Cunard Countess" (liner) 65 75
545. $1. Lockheed "Tristar" airliner 85 85
546. $2 Cargo liner .. .. 1·25 1·50
547. $5 Boeing "707" airliner .. 4·50 4·50
548. $10 "Queen Elizabeth 2" liner .. .. .. 5·50 6·50

121. Shot-putting.

1980. Olympic Games, Moscow. Mult.
549. 10 c. Type 121 .. .. 10 10
550. 50 c. Swimming 15 10
551. $2 Gymnastics 60 50
552. $2·50 Weight-lifting .. 70 60

122. Coastal Landscape within Cogwheel.

1980. 75th Anniv. of Rotary International. Different coastal landscapes within cogwheels.
554. 122. 10 c. multicoloured .. 10 10
555. – 50 c. multicoloured .. 15 10
556. – $2 black, red and yellow 40 40
557. – $2.50 multicoloured .. 50 55

123. Sir Arthur Lewis.

1980. Nobel Prize Winners. Multicoloured.
559. 10 c. Type 123 .. .. 10 10
560. 50 c. Martin Luther King Jnr. 20 15
561. $2 Ralph Bunche 50 60
562. $2.50 Albert Schweitzer .. 70 80

1980. Hurricane Relief. Nos. 538/9 and 542 surch. **1980 $1·50 HURRICANE RELIEF.**
564. $1·50 on 15 c. mult. .. 30 40
565. $1·50 on 20 c. mult. .. 30 40
566. $1·50 on 50 c. mult. .. 30 40

125. " The Nativity " (Giovanni Battista).

1980. Christmas. Paintings. **Multicoloured.**

567. 10 c. Type **125** 10 10
568. 30 c. " Adoration of the Kings " (Pieter the Elder) 10 10
569. $2 " Adoration of the Shepherds " (ascribed to Murillo) 40 60

126. Brazilian Agouti.

1981. Wildlife. Multicoloured.

571. 10 c. Type **126** 15 10
572. 50 c. St. Lucia Amazon .. 75 10
573. $2 Purple-throated Carib 1·00 80
574. $2.50 Fiddler Crab .. 1·10 1·00

127. Prince Charles at Balmoral.

1981. Royal Wedding. Multicoloured.

576. 25 c. Prince Charles and Lady Diana Spencer .. 15 10
577. 50 c. Clarence House .. 20 10
578. $4 Type **127** 75 80

128. Lady Diana Spencer.

1981. Royal Wedding. Booklet stamps. Multicoloured. Self-adhesive.

580. 50 c. Type **128** 15 30
581. $2 Prince Charles .. 50 80
582. $5 Prince Charles and Lady Diana Spencer .. .. 1·75 2·50

MINIMUM PRICE

The minimum price quoted is 10p which represents a handling charge rather than a basis for valuing common stamps. For further notes about prices see introductory pages.

129. " The Cock ".

1981. Birth Bicentenary of Picasso. Mult.

583. 30 c. Type **129** 25 10
584. 50 c. " Man with an Ice-cream " 35 10
585. 55 c. " Woman dressing her Hair " 35 10
586. $3 " Seated Woman " .. 95 85

130. " Industry ".

1981. 25th Anniv. of Duke of Edinburgh Award Scheme. Multicoloured.

588. 10 c. Type **130** 10 10
589. 35 c. " Community service " 15 10
590. 50 c. " Physical recreation " 20 10
591. $2.50 Duke of Edinburgh speaking at Caribbean Conference, 1975 .. 70 70

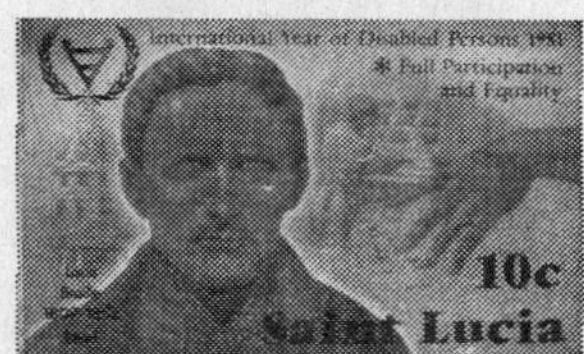

131. Louis Braille.

1981. International Year of Disabled People. Famous Disabled People. Multicoloured.

592. 10 c. Type **131** 15 10
593. 50 c. Sarah Bernhardt .. 30 15
594. $2 Joseph Pulitzer .. 1·00 90
595. $2.50 Henri de Toulouse-Lautrec .. .. 1·10 1·00

132. " Portrait of Fanny Travis Cochran " (Cecilia Beaux).

1981. Decade for Women. Paintings. **Mult.**

597. 10 c. Type **132** 10 10
598. 50 c. " Women with Dove " (Marie Laurencin) .. 35 15
599. $2 " Portrait of a Young Pupil of David " (Aimee Duvivier) .. .. 1·00 90
600. $2.50 " Self-portrait " (Rosalba Carriera) .. 1·10 1·00

133. "Adoration of the Magi" (Sfoza).

1981. Christmas. Paintings. Multicoloured.

602. 10 c. Type **133** 15 10
603. 30 c. " The Adoration of the Kings " (Orcanga) 30 10
604. $1.50 " The Adoration of the Kings " (Gerard) .. 1·10 60
605. $2.50 " The Adoration of the Kings " (Foppa) .. 1·75 1·25

134. 1860 1d. Stamp.

1981. 1st Anniversary of U.P.U. Membership. Multicoloured.

606. 10 c. Type **134** 15 10
607. 30 c. 1969 First anniversary of Caribbean Free Trade Area 25 c. commemorative 35 10
608. 50 c. 1979 Independence $2 commemorative .. 50 40
609. $2 U.P.U. emblem with U.P.U. and St. Lucia flags 1·60 2·25

135. Scene from Football Match.

1982. World Cup Football Championship, Spain.

611. **135.** 10 c. multicoloured .. 20 10
612. – 50 c. multicoloured .. 70 15
613. – $2 multicoloured .. 1·75 90
614. – $2.50 multicoloured .. 2·00 1·00

DESIGNS: 50 c. to $2.50, Scenes from different matches.

136. Pigeon Island National Park.

1982. Bicentenary of Battle of the Saints. Multicoloured.

616. 10 c. Type **136** 25 15
617. 35 c. Battle scene 80 15
618. 50 c. Rodney (English admiral) and De Grasse (French admiral) .. 1·10 35
619. $2.50 Map of the Saints, Martinique and St. Lucia 3·25 3·50

137. Map-reading.

1982. 75th Anniv. of Boy Scout Movement. Multicoloured.

621. 10 c. Type **137** 10 10
622. 50 c. First Aid practice .. 30 15
623. $1.50 Camping 75 80
624. $2.50 Campfire singsong .. 1·25 1·50

138. Leeds Castle.

1982. 21st Birthday of Princess of Wales. Multicoloured.

625. 50 c. Type **138** 30 20
626. $2 Princess Diana boarding aircraft 90 75
627. $4 Wedding .. .. .. 1·60 1·40

139. " Adoration of the Kings " (detail, Jan Breughel).

1982. Christmas. Multicoloured.

629. 10 c. Type **139** 10 10
630. 30 c. " Nativity " (Lorenzo Costa) 15 10
631. 50 c. " Virgin and Child " (Fra Filippo Lippi) .. 25 15
632. 80 c. " Adoration of the Shepherds " (Nicolas Poussin) 40 55

140. The Pitons.

1983. Commonwealth Day. Multicoloured.

633. 10 c. Type **140** 10 10
634. 30 c. Tourist Beach .. 15 10
635. 50 c. Banana harvesting .. 20 15
636. $2 Flag of St. Lucia .. 60 1·00

141. Crown Agents Headquarters, Millbank, London.

1983. 150th Anniv. of Crown Agents. Mult.

637. 10 c. Type **141** 10 10
638. 15 c. Road construction .. 10 10
639. 50 c. Road network map .. 20 25
640. $2 First St. Lucia stamp .. 60 1·00

142. **Communications at Sea.**

1983. **World Communications Year. Mult.**

641. 10 c. Type **142** 15 10
642. 50 c. Communications in the air 40 15
643. $1.50 T.V. transmission via satellite 90 75
644. $2.50 Computer communications .. .. .. 1·40 1·25

143. **Longspine Squirrelfish.**

1983. Coral Reef Fishes. Multicoloured.

646. 10 c. Type **143** 10 10
647. 50 c. Banded Butterflyfish 20 15
648. $1.50 Blackbar Soldierfish 70 75
649. $2.50 Yellowtail Snapper 1·10 1·25

144. " Duke of Sutherland " (1930).

1983. Leaders of the World. Railway Locomotives (1st series).

No.	Type	Description		
651.	144.	35 c. multicoloured ..	25	20
652.	–	35 c. multicoloured ..	25	20
653.	–	35 c. multicoloured ..	25	20
654.	–	35 c. multicoloured ..	25	20
655.	–	50 c. multicoloured ..	35	30
656.	–	50 c. multicoloured ..	35	30
657.	–	50 c. multicoloured ..	35	30
658.	–	50 c. multicoloured ..	35	30
659.	–	$1 multicoloured ..	70	50
660.	–	$1 multicoloured ..	70	50
661.	–	$1 multicoloured ..	70	50
662.	–	$1 multicoloured ..	70	50
663.	–	$2 multicoloured ..	90	80
664.	–	$2 multicoloured ..	90	80
665.	–	$2 multicoloured ..	90	80
666.	–	$2 multicoloured ..	90	80

DESIGNS: (The first in each pair shows technical drawings and the second the locomotive at work). Nos. 651/2, "Duke of Sutherland", Great Britain (1930). 653/4, "City of Glasgow", Great Britain (1940). 655/6, "Lord Nelson", Great Britain (1926). 657/8, "Leeds United", Great Britain (1928). 659/60, "Bodmin", Great Britain (1945). 661/2, "Eton", Great Britain (1930). 663/4, "Flying Scotsman", Great Britain (1923). 665/6, "Rocket", Great Britain (1923).

See also Nos. 715/26, 761/76, 824/31 and 858/73.

145. " The Niccolini-Cowper Madonna ".

1983. Christmas. 500th Birth Anniversary of Raphael. Multicoloured.

No.	Description		
667.	10 c. Type **145**	10	10
668.	30 c. " The Holy Family with a Palm Tree " ..	20	10
669.	50 c. "The Sistine Madonna"	35	20
670.	$5 " The Alba Madonna "	2·50	2·25

146. George III.

1984. Leaders of the World. British Monarchs. Multicoloured.

No.	Description		
671.	5 c. Battle of Waterloo ..	10	10
672.	5 c. Type **146** ..	10	10
673.	10 c. George III at Kew ..	10	10
674.	10 c. Kew Palace	10	10
675.	35 c. Coat of Arms of Elizabeth I	20	20
676.	35 c. Elizabeth I	20	20
677.	60 c. Coat of Arms of George III	30	30
678.	60 c. George III (different)	30	30
679.	$1 Elizabeth I at Hatfield	40	40
680.	$1 Hatfield Palace ..	40	40
681.	$2.50 Spanish Armada ..	75	75
682.	$2.50 Elizabeth I (different)	75	75

MORE DETAILED LISTS
are given in the Stanley Gibbons Catalogues referred to in the country headings.
For lists of current volumes see Introduction.

147. Clarke & Co's Drug Store.

1984. Historic Buildings. Multicoloured.

No.	Description		
683.	10 c. Type **147**	10	10
684.	45 c. Colonial architecture (horiz.)	30	25
685.	65 c. Colonial " chattel " house (horiz.)	45	35
686.	$2.50 Treasury after 1906 earthquake (horiz.) ..	1·75	1·60

148. Logwood.

1984. Forestry Resources. Multicoloured.

No.	Description		
699.	10 c. Type **148**	15	10
700.	45 c. Calabash	60	30
701.	65 c. Gommier (vert.) ..	80	55
702.	$2.50 Raintree	2·25	2·75

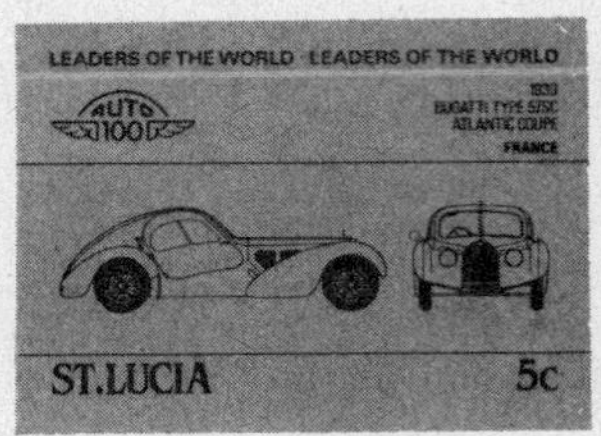

149. Bugatti Type "578C Atlantic Coupe".

1984. Leaders of the World. Automobiles (1st series) the first in each pair showing technical drawings and the second paintings.

No.	Type	Description		
703	149	5 c. blk., lav. & yell.	10	10
704	–	5 c. multicoloured ..	10	10
705	–	10 c. black, bl. & red	10	10
706	–	10 c. multicoloured ..	10	10
707	–	$1 black, grn. & brn.	35	35
708	–	$1 multicoloured ..	35	35
709	–	$2.50 black, pink & bl.	60	60
710	–	$2.50 multicoloured ..	60	60

DESIGNS: Nos. 703/4, Bugatti Type "578C Atlantic Coupe". 705/6, Chevrolet "Bel Air Convertible". 707/8, Alfa Romeo "1750 GS (Zagato)". 709/10, Dusenberg "SJ Roadster".

See also Nos. 745/60.

150. Pygmy Gecko.

1984. Endangered Wildlife. Multicoloured.

No.	Description		
711.	10 c. Type **150**	40	10
712.	45 c. Maria Island Ground Lizard	1·00	50
713.	65 c. Green Iguana ..	1·25	85
714.	$2.50 Couresse Snake ..	3·00	3·50

1984. Leaders of the World. Railway Locomotives (2nd series). As T **144**, the first in each pair showing technical drawings and the second the locomotive at work.

No.	Description		
715.	1 c. multicoloured	10	10
716.	1 c. multicoloured	10	10
717.	15 c. multicoloured ..	15	15
718.	15 c. multicoloured ..	15	15
719.	50 c. multicoloured ..	30	30
720.	50 c. multicoloured ..	30	30
721.	75 c. multicoloured ..	35	35
722.	75 c. multicoloured ..	35	35
723.	$1 multicoloured	40	40
724.	$1 multicoloured	40	40
725.	$2 multicoloured	70	70
726.	$2 multicoloured	70	70

DESIGNS: Nos. 715/16, "Taw", Great Britain (1897). 717/18, "Crocodile I.C.C.I.", Switzerland (1920). 719/20, "The Countess", Great Britain (1903). 721/2, Class "GE6/6 C.C.", Switzerland (1921). 723/4, Class "P8", Germany (1906). 725/6, "Der Adler", Germany (1835).

151. Men's Volleyball.

1984. Leaders of the World. Olympic Games, Los Angeles. Multicoloured.

No.	Description		
727.	5 c. Type **151**	10	10
728.	5 c. Women's volleyball ..	10	10
729.	10 c. Women's hurdles ..	10	10
730.	10 c. Men's hurdles ..	10	10
731.	65 c. Show jumping ..	20	20
732.	65 c. Dressage	20	20
733.	$2.50 Women's gymnastics	50	50
734.	$2.50 Men's gymnastics ..	50	50

152. Glass of Wine and Flowers.

1984. Christmas. Multicoloured.

No.	Description		
735.	10 c. Type **152**	10	10
736.	35 c. Priest and decorated altar	20	15
737.	65 c. Nativity scene ..	35	35
738.	$3 Holy Family	1·50	1·60

153. Slaves preparing Manioc.

1984. 150th Anniv. of Abolition of Slavery. Each black and brown.

No.	Description		
740.	10 c. Type **153**	10	10
741.	35 c. Sifting and cooking cassava flour	15	20
742.	55 c. Cooking pot, and preparing tobacco ..	25	30
743.	$5 Stripping tobacco leaves for twist tobacco ..	2·25	2·50

1984. Leaders of the World. Automobiles (2nd series). As T **149**, the first in each pair showing technical drawings and the second paintings.

No.	Description		
745.	10 c. black green & brn. ..	10	10
746.	10 c. multicoloured ..	10	10
747.	30 c. black, blue and green	15	15
748.	30 c. multicoloured ..	15	15
749.	55 c. black, yellow & brn.	30	30
750.	55 c. multicoloured ..	30	30
751.	65 c. black, grey and lilac	35	35
752.	65 c. multicoloured ..	35	35
753.	75 c. black, brown and red	35	35
754.	75 c. multicoloured ..	35	35
755.	$1 black, brown and blue	40	40
756.	$1 multicoloured	40	40
757.	$2 black, green and red ..	50	50
758.	$2 multicoloured	50	50
759.	$3 black, brown and red ..	60	60
760.	$3 multicoloured	60	60

DESIGNS: Nos. 754/6, Panhard and Levassor. 747/8, N.S.U. "RO-80" Saloon. 749/50, Abarth "Bialbero". 751/2, TVR "Vixen 2500M". 753/4, Ford "Mustang" Convertible. 755/6, Ford "Model T". 757/8, Aston Martin DB35". 759/60, Chrysler "Imperial CG Dual Cowl" Phaeton.

1985. Leaders of the World. Railway Locomotives (3rd series). As T **144**, the first in each pair showing technical drawings and the second the locomotive at work.

No.	Description		
761.	5 c. multicoloured	10	10
762.	5 c. multicoloured	10	10
763.	15 c. multicoloured ..	15	10
764.	15 c. multicoloured ..	15	10
765.	35 c. multicoloured ..	20	20
766.	35 c. multicoloured ..	20	20
767.	60 c. multicoloured ..	25	25
768.	60 c. multicoloured ..	25	25
769.	75 c. multicoloured ..	25	25
770.	75 c. multicoloured ..	25	25
771.	$1 multicoloured	30	30
772.	$1 multicoloured	30	30
773.	$2 multicoloured	55	55
774.	$2 multicoloured	55	55
775.	$2.50 multicoloured ..	75	75
776.	$2.50 multicoloured ..	75	75

DESIGNS: Nos. 761/2, Class "C53", Japan (1928). 763/4, Class "Heavy L", India (1885). 765/6, Class "B18¼", Australia (1926). 767/8, "Owain Glyndwr", Great Britain (1923). 769/70, "Lion", Great Britain (1838). 771/2, Coal engine, Great Britain (1873). 773/4, No. 2238, Class "Q6", Great Britain (1921). 775/6, Class "H", Great Britain (1920).

154. Girl Guide Badge in Shield and Crest of St. Lucia.

1985. 75th Anniv. of Girl Guide Movement and 60th Anniv. of Guiding in St. Lucia.

No.	Type	Description		
777.	154.	10 c. multicoloured ..	20	10
778.		35 c. multicoloured ..	60	15
779.		65 c. multicoloured ..	1·00	35
780.		$3 multicoloured ..	3·00	1·90

155. "Clossiana selene".

1985. Leaders of the World. Butterflies. Multicoloured.

No.	Description		
781	15 c. Type **155**	15	10
782	15 c. "Inachis io" ..	15	10
783	40 c. "Philaethria dido" ..	30	30
784	40 c. "Callicore sorana" ..	30	30
785	60 c. "Kallima inachus" ..	40	40
786	60 c. "Hypanartia paullus"	40	40
787	$2.25 "Morpho helena" ..	1·25	1·25
788	$2.25 "Ornithoptera meridionalis"	1·25	1·25

1985. Leaders of the World. Automobiles (3rd series). As T **149**, the first in each pair showing technical drawings and the second paintings.

No.	Description		
789.	15 c. black, blue and red ..	10	10
790.	15 c. multicoloured ..	10	10
791.	50 c. black, orange and red	20	25
792.	50 c. multicoloured ..	20	25
793.	$1 black, green and orange	30	40
794.	$1 multicoloured	30	40
795.	$1.50 black, grn. & brn. ..	40	55
796.	$1.50 multicoloured ..	40	55

DESIGNS: Nos. 789/90, Hudson "Eight" (1940). 791/2, KdF (1937). 793/4, Kissel "Goldbug" (1925). 795/6, Ferrari "246 GTS" (1973).

156. Grenadier, 70th Regiment *c.* 1775.

1985. Military Uniforms. Multicoloured.

797 5 c. Type **156** 25 15
798 10 c. Officer, Grenadier Company, 14th Regiment, 1780 .. .. 25 15
930 15 c. Private, Battalion Company, 2nd West India Regiment, 1803 .. 35 35
799 20 c. Officer, Battalion Company, 46th Regiment, 1781 .. .. 40 15
800 25 c. Officer, Royal Artillery, c. 1782 .. 40 15
801 30 c. Officer, Royal Engineers, 1782 .. .. 60 15
802 35 c. Officer, Battalion Company, 54th Regiment, 1782 .. .. 50 20
935 45 c. Private, Grenadier Company, 14th Regiment, 1782 .. .. 50 50
936 50 c. Gunner, Royal Artillery, 1796 .. .. 60 60
937 60 c. Officer, Battalion Company, 5th Regiment, 1778 .. .. .. 70 70
805 65 c. Private, Battalion Company, 85th Regiment, c. 1796 .. .. 70 50
806 75 c. Private, Battalion Company, 76th Regiment, 1796 .. .. 75 55
940 80 c. Officer, Battalion Company, 27th Regiment, c. 1780 .. .. 90 90
807 90 c. Private, Battalion Company, 81st Regiment, c. 1796 .. .. 85 60
808 $1 Sergeant, 74th (Highland) Regiment, 1796 .. 90 60
943 $2.50 Private, Light Company, 93rd Regiment, 1803 .. .. 3·00 3·25
944 $5 Private, Battalion Company, 1st West India Regiment, 1803 .. 5·50 6·00
811 $15 Officer, Royal Artillery, 1850 .. .. 11·00 13·00
1003 $20 Private, Grenadier Company, 46th Regiment, 1778 .. .. 16·00 18·00

157. Messerschmitt "109-E".

1985. Leaders of the World. Military Aircraft. The first in each pair shows paintings and the second technical drawings.

812. **157.** 5 c. multicoloured .. 10 10
813. – 5 c. blk., bl. & yell. 10 10
814. – 55 c. multicoloured .. 40 35
815. – 55 c. blk., bl. & yell. 40 35
816. – 60 c. multicoloured .. 40 40
817. – 60 c. blk., bl. & yell. 40 40
818. – $2 multicoloured .. 80 80
819. – $2 blk., bl. & yell. 80 80

Designs: Nos. 812/13, Messerschmitt "109-E". 814/15, Avro "683 Lancaster Mark I". 816/17, North American "P.51-D Mustang". 818/19, Supermarine "Spitfire Mark II".

158. Magnificent Frigate Birds, Frigate Island Bird Sanctuary.

1985. Nature Reserves. Multicoloured.

820. 10 c. Type **158** 45 20
821. 35 c. Mangrove cuckoo, Scorpion Island, Savannes Bay .. .. 1·40 45
822. 65 c. Lesser yellowlegs, Maria Island Reserve .. 2·00 85
823. $3 Audubon's shearwaters; Lapins Island Reserve .. 4·00 5·00

1985. Leaders of the World Railway Locomotives (4th series). As T **144**. The first in each pair shows technical drawings and the second the locomotive at work.

824. 10 c. multicoloured .. 15 10
825. 10 c. multicoloured .. 15 10
826. 30 c. multicoloured .. 20 20
827. 30 c. multicoloured .. 20 20
828. 75 c. multicoloured .. 30 30
829. 75 c. multicoloured .. 30 30
830. $2.50 multicoloured .. 75 75
831. $2.50 multicoloured .. 75 75

Designs: Nos. 824/5, No. 28 Tank locomotive, Great Britain (1897). 826/7, No. 1621 Class "M", Great Britain (1893). 828/9, Class "Dunalastair", Great Britain (1896). 830/1, No. 2290 "Big Bertha" type, Great Britain (1919).

159. Queen Elizabeth the Queen Mother.

1985. Leaders of the World. Life and Times of Queen Elizabeth the Queen Mother. Various portraits.

832. **159.** 40 c. multicoloured .. 20 25
833. – 40 c. multicoloured .. 20 25
834. – 75 c. multicoloured .. 30 40
835. – 75 c. multicoloured .. 30 40
836. – $1.10 multicoloured .. 40 55
837. – $1.10 multicoloured .. 40 55
838. – $1.75 multicoloured .. 65 80
839. – $1.75 multicoloured .. 65 80

Each value issued in pairs showing a floral pattern across the bottom of the portraits which stops short of the left-hand edge on the first stamp and of the right-hand edge on the second.

160. "Youth playing Banjo" (Wayne Whitfield).

1985. International Youth Year. Paintings by Young St. Lucians.

841. **160.** 10 c. black, blue & mauve 10 10
842. – 45 c. multicoloured .. 30 25
843. – 75 c. multicoloured .. 50 40
844. – $3.50 multicoloured .. 2·00 1·75

Designs—vert. (as T **160**). 45 c. "Motorcyclist" (Mark Maragh). 75 c. "Boy and Girl at Pitons" (Bartholomew Eugene). $3.50 "Abstract" (Lyndon Samuel). horiz. (80 × 55 mm). $5 Young people and St. Lucia landscapes.

1985. Royal Visit Nos. 649, 685/6, 702, 713, 778 and 836/7 optd. **CARIBBEAN ROYAL VISIT–1985.**

846. **154.** 35 c. multicoloured .. 3·50 2·50
847. – 65 c. mult. (685) .. 3·00 3·00
848. – 65 c. mult. (713) .. 3·00 3·00
849. – $1.10 mult. (836) .. 4·00 4·00
850. – $1.10 mult. (837) .. 4·00 4·00
851. – $2.50 mult. (649) .. 4·00 4·00
852. – $2.50 mult. (686) .. 3·50 3·50
853. – $2.50 mult. (702) .. 3·50 3·50

161. "Papa Jab".

1985. Christmas. Masqueraders. Mult.

854. 10 c. Type **161** 10 10
855. 45 c. "Paille Bananne" .. 20 25
856. 65 c. "Cheval Bois" .. 30 35

1986. Leaders of the World. Railway Locomotives (5th series). As T **144**. The first in each pair shows technical drawings and the second the locomotive at work.

858. 5 c. multicoloured 15 15
859. 5 c. multicoloured 15 15
860. 15 c. multicoloured .. 15 15
861. 15 c. multicoloured .. 15 15
862. 30 c. multicoloured .. 30 30
863. 30 c. multicoloured .. 30 30
864. 60 c. multicoloured .. 45 45
865. 60 c. multicoloured .. 45 45
866. 75 c. multicoloured .. 50 50
867. 75 c. multicoloured .. 50 50
868. $1 multicoloured 65 65
869. $1 multicoloured 65 65
870. $2.25 multicoloured .. 1·25 1·25
871. $2.25 multicoloured .. 1·25 1·25
872. $3 multicoloured .. .. 1·60 1·60
873. $3 multicoloured .. .. 1·60 1·60

Designs: Nos. 858/9, Rack loco "Tip Top", U.S.A (1983). 860/1, "Stephenson", Great Britain (1975). 862/3, No. 737 Class "D", Great Britain (1901). 864/5, No. 13 Class "2-CO2", Great Britain (1922). 866/7, "Electra", Great Britain (1954). 868/9, "City of Newcastle", Great Britain (1922). 870/1, Von Kruckenburg propeller-driven railcar, Germany (1930). 872/3, No. 860, Japan (1893).

1986. 60th Birthday of Queen Elizabeth II (1st issue). As T **167** of British Virgin Islands. Multicoloured.

876. 5 c. Queen Elizabeth II .. 10 10
877. $1 Princess Elizabeth .. 40 45
878. $3.50 Queen Elizabeth II (different) .. .. 1·10 1·50
879. $6 In Canberra, 1982 (vert.) 1·75 2·25

163. Queen Elizabeth and Marian Home.

1986. 60th Birthday of Queen Elizabeth II (2nd issue). Multicoloured.

881. 10 c. Type **163** 15 15
882. 45 c. Queen addressing rally, Mindoo Phillip Park, 1985 .. .. 35 35
883. 50 c. Queen opening Leon Hess Comprehensive School, 1985 .. .. 40 40
884. $5 Queen Elizabeth and Government House, Castries .. .. .. 2·50 2·75

164. Pope John Paul II kissing Ground, Castries Airport.

1986. Visit of Pope John Paul II. Multicoloured.

886. 55 c. Type **164** 70 60
887. 60 c. Pope and St. Joseph's Convent 70 60
888. 80 c. Pope and Castries Catholic Cathedral (vert.) .. .. .. 1·10 95

1986. Royal Wedding (1st issue). As T **168** of British Virgin Islands. Multicoloured.

890. 80 c. Miss Sarah Ferguson 45 50
891. 80 c. Prince Andrew .. 45 50
892. $2 Prince Andrew and Miss Sarah Ferguson (horiz.) 1·25 1·40
893. $2 Prince Andrew with Mrs Nancy Reagan (horiz.) 1·25 1·40

See also Nos. 897/900.

165. Peace Corps Teacher with Students.

1986. 25th Anniv. of United States Peace Corps. Multicoloured.

894. 80 c. Type **165** 35 40
895. $2 President John Kennedy (vert.) .. 1·10 1·25
896. $3.50 Peace Corps emblem between arms of St. Lucia and U.S.A. .. 1·60 2·00

166. Prince Andrew in Carriage.

1986. Royal Wedding (2nd issue). Mult.

897. 50 c. Type **166** 30 30
898. 80 c. Miss Sarah Ferguson in coach 40 40
899. $1 Duke and Duchess of York at altar .. 45 50
900. $3 Duke and Duchess of York in carriage .. 1·25 1·75

1986. Automobiles (4th series). As T **149**, the first in each pair showing technical drawings and the second paintings.

902. 20 c. multicoloured .. 10 15
903. 20 c. multicoloured .. 10 15
904. 50 c. multicoloured .. 15 20
905. 50 c. multicoloured .. 15 20
906. 60 c. multicoloured .. 15 20
907. 60 c. multicoloured .. 15 20
908. $1 multicoloured 25 30
909. $1 multicoloured 25 30
910. $1.50 multicoloured .. 30 35
911. $1.50 multicoloured .. 30 35
912. $3 multicoloured 60 75
913. $3 multicoloured 60 75

Designs: Nos. 902/3, AMC "AMX" (1969). 904/5, Russo-Baltique (1912). 906/7, Lincoln "K.B." (1932). 908/9, Rolls Royce "Phantom II Continental" (1933). 910/11, Buick "Century" (1939). 912/13, Chrysler "300 C" (1957).

167. Chak-Chak Band.

1986. Tourism (1st series). Multicoloured.

914. 15 c. Type **167** 15 10
915. 45 c. Folk dancing .. 35 30
916. 80 c. Steel band 70 60
917. $5 Limbo dancing .. .. 2·75 3·00

See also Nos. 988/91.

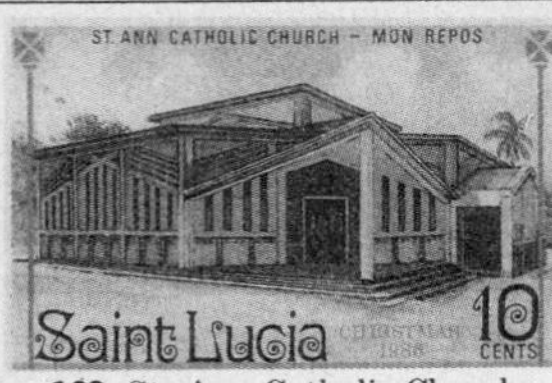

168. St. Ann Catholic Church, Mon Repos.

1986. Christmas. Multicoloured.

919.	10 c. Type **168**	10	10
920.	40 c. St. Joseph the Worker Catholic Church, Gros Islet	35	25
921.	80 c. Holy Trinity Anglican Church, Castries	60	45
922.	$4 Our Lady of the Assumption Catholic Church, Soufriere (vert.)	2·25	2·75

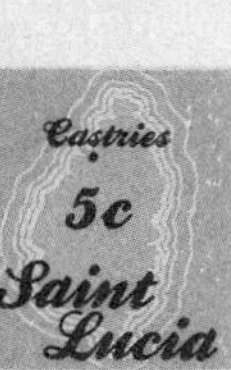

169. Outline Map of St. Lucia. **170.** Statue of Liberty and Flags of France and U.S.A.

1987.

924.	**169.**	5 c. black and brown	15	15
925.		10 c. black and green	15	15
926.		45 c. black & orange	45	45
927.		50 c. black and blue ..	45	45
927c.		$1 black and red ..	65	65

1987. Centenary of Statue of Liberty (1986). Multicoloured.

947.	15 c. Type **170**	15	10
948.	80 c. Statue of Liberty and liner	75	55
949.	$1 Statue and "Concorde"	1·10	75
950.	$5 Statue and flying boat at sunset	3·00	3·50

171. First Cadastral Survey Map and Surveying Instruments, 1775.

1987. New Cadastral Survey of St. Lucia. Multicoloured.

955	15 c. Type **171**	30	30
956	60 c. Map and surveying instruments, 1814 ..	70	55
957	$1 Map and surveying instruments, 1888 ..	90	90
958	$2.50 Cadastral survey map and surveying instruments, 1987	2·25	2·50

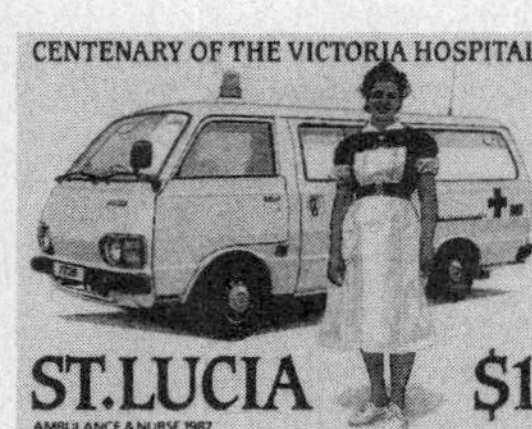

172. Ambulance and Nurse, 1987.

1987. Centenary of Victoria Hospital, Castries. Multicoloured.

959.	**172.**	$1 multicoloured ..	1·00	1·00
960.	–	$1 blue	1·00	1·00
961.	–	$2 multicoloured ..	1·50	1·50
962.	–	$2 blue	1·50	1·50

DESIGNS: No. 960, Nurse and carrying hammock, 1913. No. 961, $2 Victoria Hospital, 1987. No. 962, Victoria Hospital, 1887.

173. "The Holy Family".

1987. Christmas. Paintings. Multicoloured.

964	15 c. Type **173**	30	10
965	50 c. "Adoration of the Shepherds"	60	30
966	60 c. "Adoration of the Magi"	70	55
967	90 c. "Madonna and Child"	1·25	1·50

174. St. Lucia Amazon perched on Branch.

1987. St. Lucia Amazon. Multicoloured.

969	15 c. Type **174**	35	20
970	35 c. Pair in flight	75	35
971	50 c. Perched on branch (rear view)	1·10	85
972	$1 Emerging from tree ..	2·00	2·50

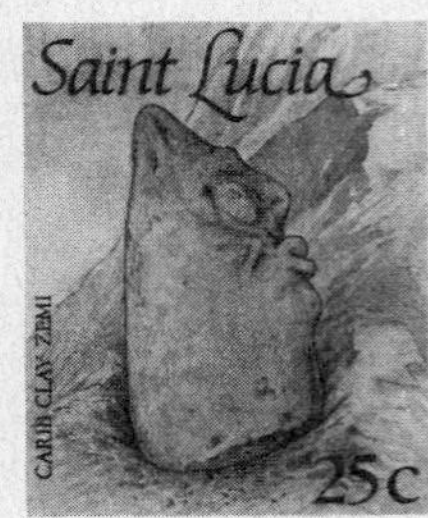

175. Carib Clay Zemi.

1988. Amerindian Artefacts. Multicoloured.

973	25 c. Type **175**	15	10
974	30 c. Troumassee cylinder	20	15
975	80 c. Three pointer stone ..	55	45
976	$3.50 Dauphine petroglyph	2·25	2·50

176. East Caribbean Currency.

1988. 50th Anniv. of St. Lucia Co-operative Bank. Multicoloured.

977.	10 c. Type **176**	20	10
978.	45 c. Castries branch ..	55	35
979.	60 c. As 45 c.	75	80
980.	80 c. Vieux Fort branch ..	1·25	1·50

177 Rural Telephone Exchange

1988. 50th Anniv of Cable and Wireless (West Indies) Ltd. Multicoloured.

981	15 c. Type **177**	10	10
982	25 c. Early and modern telephones	15	15
983	80 c. St. Lucia Teleport dish aerial	40	45
984	$2.50 Map showing Eastern Caribbean Microwave System	1·00	1·10

178 Stained Glass Window

1988. Centenary of Methodist Church in St. Lucia. Multicoloured.

985	15 c. Type **178**	10	10
986	80 c. Church interior ..	40	45
987	$3.50 Methodist Church, Castries	1·50	1·60

179 Garnished Lobsters

1988. Tourism (2nd series). Designs showing local delicacies. Multicoloured.

988	10 c. Type **179**	30	30
989	30 c. Cocktail and tourists at buffet	45	45
990	80 c. Fresh fruits and roasted breadfruit ..	80	80
991	$2.50 Barbecued red snappers (fish) ..	1·75	1·75

Nos. 988/91 were printed together, se-tenant, forming a composite design of tourists at beach barbecue.

1988. 300th Anniv of Lloyd's of London. As T **123** of Ascension.

1004	10 c. black, lilac & brown	20	10
1005	60 c. multicoloured ..	60	45
1006	80 c. multicoloured ..	90	75
1007	$2.50 multicoloured ..	2·25	2·50

DESIGNS: VERT—10 c. San Francisco earthquake, 1906; $2.50, Castries fire, 1948. HORIZ—60 c. Castries Harbour; 80 c. "Lady Nelson" (liner), 1942.

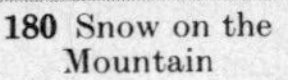

180 Snow on the Mountain **181** Princess Alexandra presenting Constitution Document to Prime Minister

1988. Christmas. Flowers. Multicoloured.

1008	15 c. Type **180**	30	10
1009	45 c. Christmas candle ..	55	40
1010	60 c. Balisier	70	70
1011	80 c. Poinsettia	1·00	1·25

1989. 10th Anniv of Independence. Mult.

1013	15 c. Type **181**	10	10
1014	80 c. Geothermal well ..	40	45
1015	$1 Sir Arthur Lewis Community College ..	45	50
1016	$2.50 Pointe Seraphine shopping centre ..	1·00	1·10

182 "Gerronema citrinum"

1989. Fungi. Multicoloured.

1022	15 c. Type **182**	35	15
1023	25 c. "Lepiota spiculata"	50	15
1024	50 c. "Calocybe cyanocephala" ..	90	65
1025	$5 "Russula puiggarii"	4·50	4·75

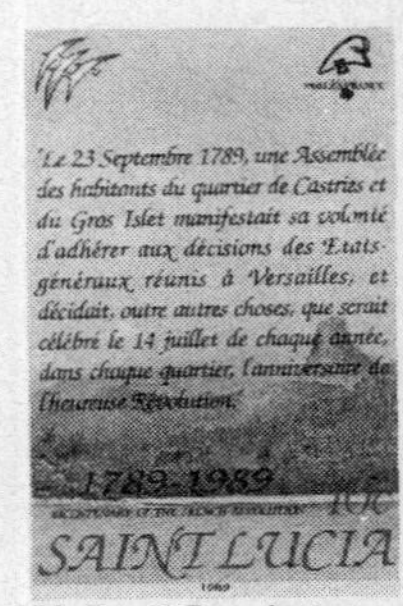

183 Local Revolutionary Declaration, 1789 and View of St. Lucia

1989. Bicentenary of the French Revolution. Designs include the "PHILEXFRANCE" International Stamp Exhibition logo. Mult.

1026	10 c. Type **183**	20	15
1027	60 c. Hoisting Revolutionary flag, Morne Fortune, 1791 (horiz) ..	80	60
1028	$1 Declaration of Rights of Man and view of St. Lucia	1·10	85
1029	$3.50 Arrival of Capt. La Crosse, Gros Islet, 1792 (horiz)	3·50	3·75

184 Red Cross Headquarters, St. Lucia

1989. 125th Anniv of International Red Cross. Multicoloured.

1030	50 c. Type **184**	75	75
1031	80 c. Red Cross seminar, Castries, 1987	1·25	1·25
1032	$1 Red Cross ambulance	1·40	1·40

185 Christmas Lantern

1989. Christmas.

1033	**185**	10 c. multicoloured ..	10	10
1034	–	50 c. multicoloured ..	25	30
1035	–	90 c. multicoloured ..	40	45
1036	–	$1 multicoloured ..	45	50

DESIGNS: 50c. to $1 various decorative "building" lanterns.

HAVE YOU READ THE NOTES AT THE BEGINNING OF THIS CATALOGUE?
These often provide answers to the enquiries we receive.

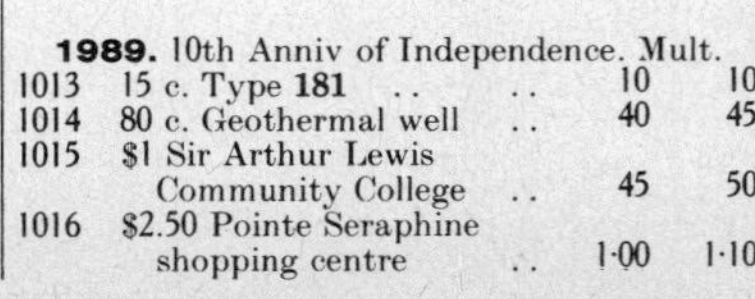

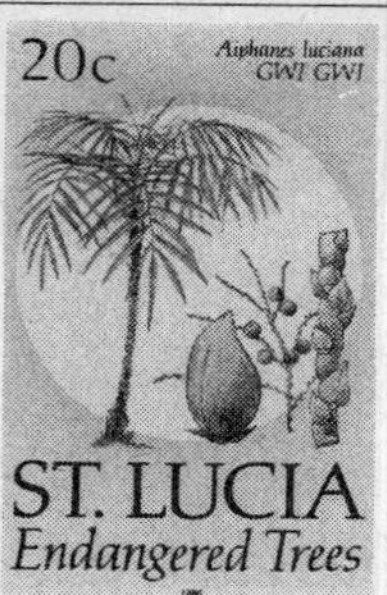

186 Gwi Gwi

1990. Endangered Trees. Multicoloured.

1037	10 c. Chinna	10	10
1038	15 c. Latanier	10	10
1039	20 c. Type **186**	10	10
1040	25 c. L'Encens	10	15
1041	50 c. Bois Lele	20	25
1042	80 c. Bois D'Amande ..	35	40
1043	95 c. Mahot Piman Grand Bois	40	45
1044	$1 Balata	40	45
1045	$1.50 Pencil cedar ..	65	70
1046	$2.50 Bois Cendre ..	1·00	1·10
1047	$5 Lowye Cannelle ..	2·10	2·25
1048	$25 Chalantier Grand Bois	10·50	11·00

187 Father Tapon and Original College Building

1990. International Literacy Year. Cent of St. Mary's College, Castries. Multicoloured.

1049	30 c. Type **187**	15	15
1050	45 c. Brother M. C. Collins and St. Mary's College	25	25
1051	75 c. Literacy class ..	45	45
1052	$2 Children approaching "door to knowledge" ..	1·50	1·50

1990. 90th Birthday of Queen Elizabeth the Queen Mother. As T **134** of Ascension.

1053	50 c. multicoloured ..	35	35
1054	$5 black and blue ..	2·75	3·00

DESIGNS—21 × 36 mm. 50 c. Crowning of Queen Consort, 1937. 29 × 37 mm. $5 Queen Elizabeth arriving at New Theatre, London, 1949.

1990. "EXPO 90" International Garden and Greenery Exhibition, Osaka. No. 1047 optd **EXPO '90** and logo.

1055	$5 Lowye cannelle ..	2·75	3·00

189 "Adoration of the Magi" (Rubens)

1990. Christmas. Religious Painting. Mult.

1056	10 c. Type **189**	15	10
1057	30 c. "Adoration of the Shepherds" (Murillo) ..	20	15
1058	80 c. "Adoration of the Magi" (Rubens) (different)	50	50
1059	$5 "Adoration of the Shepherds" (Philippe de Champaigne) ..	2·75	3·00

190 "Vistafjord" (liner)

1991. Cruise Ships. Multicoloured.

1060	50 c. Type **190**	35	30
1061	80 c. "Windstar" (schooner)	55	50
1062	$1 "Unicorn" (brig) ..	70	65
1063	$2.50 Game-fishing launch	2·00	2·25

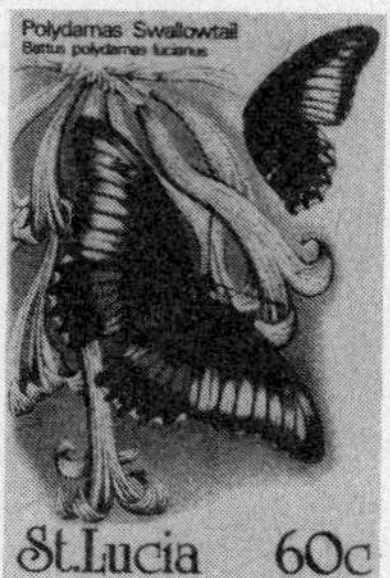

191 "Battus polydamas"

1991. Butterflies. Multicoloured.

1065	60 c. Type **191**	50	40
1066	80 c. "Strymon simaethis"	75	60
1067	$1 "Mestra cana" ..	85	70
1068	$2.50 "Allosmaitia piplea"	1·90	2·00

192 Mural, Jacmel Church

1991. Christmas. Paintings by Duncan St. Omer. Multicoloured.

1069	10 c. Type **192**	15	10
1070	15 c. "Red Madonna" (vert)	15	10
1071	80 c. Mural, Monchy Church	50	45
1072	$5 "Blue Madonna" (vert)	2·50	2·75

193 Yacht and Map

1991. Atlantic Rally for Cruising Yachts. Multicoloured.

1073	60 c. Type **193**	35	35
1074	80 c. Yachts off St. Lucia	50	50

OFFICIAL STAMPS.

1983. Nos. 537/48 optd. **OFFICIAL.**

O 1.	5 c. Type **120**	15	10
O 2.	10 c. McDonnell Douglas "DC-10"	15	10
O 3.	15 c. Local Bus	20	15
O 4.	20 c. Refrigerator ship ..	30	20
O 5.	25 c. "Islander" aeroplane	35	20
O 6.	30 c. Pilot boat	40	25
O 7.	50 c. Boeing "727" ..	55	35
O 8.	75 c. Cruise ship	75	50
O 9.	$1 Lockheed "Tristar"	95	75
O 10.	$2 Cargo liner	1·75	1·75
O 11.	$5 Boeing "707" ..	3·50	3·50
O 12.	$10 "Queen Elizabeth 2"	6·50	7·50

1985. Nos. 797/811 optd. **OFFICIAL.**

O 13.	5 c. Type **156**	20	20
O 14.	10 c. Officer, Grenadier Company, 14th Regiment, 1780	20	20
O 15.	20 c. Officer, Battalion Company, 46th Regiment 1781	20	20
O 16.	25 c. Officer, Royal Artillery, c 1782 ..	20	20
O 17.	30 c. Officer, Royal Engineers, 1782	30	30
O 18.	35 c. Officer, Battalion Company, 54th Regiment, 1782	30	30
O 19.	45 c. Private, Grenadier Company, 14th Regiment, 1782	40	40
O 20.	50 c. Gunner, Royal Artillery, 1796 ..	40	40
O 21.	65 c. Private, Battalion Company, 85th Regiment, c 1796	50	50
O 22.	75 c. Private, Battalion Company, 76th Regiment, 1796	60	60
O 23.	90 c. Private, Battalion Company, 81st Regiment, c. 1796	65	65
O 24.	$1 Sergeant, 74th (Highland) Regiment, 1796	70	70
O 25.	$2.50, Private, Light Company, 93rd Regiment, 1803	1·75	1·75
O 26.	$5 Private, Battalion Company, 1st West India Regiment, 1803	3·50	4·00
O 27.	$15 Officer, Royal Artillery, 1850 ..	8·00	9·00

POSTAGE DUE STAMPS

No. 4545
ST. LUCIA.
1d.
POSTAGE DUE

D 1.

1930.

D 1.	D 1.	1d. black on blue ..	2·25	7·50
D 2.		2d. black on yellow ..	6·00	24·00

D 2.

D 3.

1933.

D 3.	D 2.	1d. black	4·00	4·00
D 4.		2d. black	9·00	6·50
D 5.		4d. black	3·50	21·00
D 6.		8d. black	3·50	25·00

1949.

D 7a	D 2	2 c. black	10	3·75
D 8a		4 c. black	40	4·75
D 9a		8 c. black	90	15·00
D10a		16 c. black	1·75	20·00

D 4. St. Lucia Coat of Arms.

1981.

D13	D 4	5 c. purple	10	15
D17		5 c. red	10	10
D18		15 c. green	10	10
D19		25 c. orange	10	15
D20		$1 blue	40	45

ST. VINCENT

One of the Windward Is., Br. W. Indies.
1861. 12 pence = 1 shilling;
20 shillings = 1 pound.
1949. 100 cents = 1 West Indian dollar.

7.

1.

3.

1861.

36	7.	½d. orange	7·00	2·50
47		½d. green	60	20
48b	1.	1d. red	1·60	35
18		1d. black	38·00	7·50
29		1d. olive	85·00	3·25
39		1d. drab	35·00	90
61		2½d. blue	2·50	2·25
43		4d. blue	£275	18·00
56		4d. yellow	1·60	4·75
51		4d. brown..	38·00	75
62		5d. sepia	5·50	17·00
4		6d. green	50·00	18·00
57		6d. violet	2·00	4·75
11		1s. grey	£225	£120
13		1s. blue	£325	90·00
14		1s. brown	£425	£160
45		1s. red	80·00	48·00
58		1s. orange	5·50	9·00
53	3.	5s. red	27·00	48·00

1880. Surch. in figures.

33.	1.	½d. on half 6d. green ..	£160	£160
28.		1d. on half 6d. green ..	£375	£250

1881. Surch. in words.

34.	1.	1d. on 6d. green	£400	£275
63.		3d. on 1d. mauve ..	7·50	15·00
60a.		5d. on 6d. red	80	1·75

1881. Surch. in figures.

54.	1.	2½d. on 4d. brown ..	48·00	65·00
35.		4d. on 1s. orange.. ..	£1300	£700

1882. Surch. in figures and words.

40.	1.	2½d. on 1d. red	7·50	40
55a.		2½d. on 1d. blue	75	35
59.		5d. on 4d. brown.. ..	9·00	18·00

1885. No. 40 surch. **1d.** and bars.

46.	1.	1d. on 2½d. on 1d. red ..	10·00	11·00

13.

17. Seal of the Colony.

1899.

67.	13.	½d. mauve and green ..	1·00	75
68.		1d. mauve and red ..	3·25	45
69.		2½d. mauve and blue ..	4·00	2·00
70.		3d. mauve and green ..	4·00	8·50
71.		4d. mauve and orange ..	4·00	13·00
72.		5d. mauve and black ..	7·00	13·00
73.		6d. mauve and brown ..	13·00	27·00
74.		1s. green and red.. ..	13·00	38·00
75.		5s. green and blue ..	70·00	£120

1902. As T **13**, but portrait of King Edward VII.

76	½d. purple and green ..	1·00	60
77	1d. purple and red ..	1·25	20
78	2d. purple and black ..	1·75	2·25
79	2½d. purple and blue ..	2·00	3·25
80	3d. purple and green ..	2·00	2·00
81	6d. purple and brown ..	9·00	22·00
90a	1s. green and red.. ..	9·00	27·00
83	2s. green and violet ..	22·00	45·00
91	2s. purple & blue on blue	22·00	42·00
84	5s. green and blue ..	45·00	90·00
92	5s. green and red on yellow	17·00	45·00
93	£1 purple and black on red	£300	£350

1907.

94.	17.	½d. green	1·25	80
95.		1d. red	2·50	15
96.		2d. orange	1·00	5·50
97.		2½d. blue	11·00	8·50
98.		3d. violet	4·25	14·00

18. Seal of the Colony.

19.

1909.
102 18 ½d. green .. .. .. 1·25 40
99 1d. red .. .. .. 1·25 25
104 2d. grey .. .. .. 1·75 8·00
105 2½d. blue .. .. .. 5·00 2·00
106 3d. purple on yellow .. 2·00 3·25
107 6d. purple .. .. 2·00 5·00
101 1s. black on green .. 3·75 7·00
139 2s. blue and purple .. 4·00 13·00
140 5s. red and green .. 10·00 30·00
141 £1 mauve and black .. 70·00 £110

1913.
131 19. ½d. green 30 20
132a 1d. red 30 15
132b 1½d. brown 60 15
133 2d. grey 40 30
111 2½d. blue 35 40
135 3d. purple on yellow .. 45 1·50
134 3d. blue .. .. .. 90 6·00
113 4d. red on yellow .. 80 2·00
136 5d. green .. .. .. 70 5·00
137 6d. red .. .. .. 80 3·50
116 1s. black on green .. 1·50 3·25
138a 1s. brown .. .. 1·50 10·00

1915. Surch. **ONE PENNY.**
121. 19. 1d. on 1s. black on green 3·00 15·00

1916. Optd. **WAR STAMP** in two lines.
122 19 1d. red .. .. .. 1·50 2·75

1916. Optd. **WAR STAMP** in one line.
128. 19. 1d. red 15 50

1935. Silver Jubilee. As T **13** of Antigua.
142. 1d. blue and red 40 55
143. 1½d. blue and grey .. 1·00 65
144. 2½d. brown and blue .. 1·50 65
145. 1s. grey and purple .. 2·00 3·50

1937. Coronation. As T **2** of Aden.
146. 1d. violet 35 15
147. 1½d. red 55 10
148. 2½d. blue 65 45

25.

26. Young's Island and Fort Duvernette.

1938.
149. 25. ½d. blue and green .. 10 10
150. 26. 1d. blue and brown .. 10 10
151. – 1½d. green and red .. 15 10
152. 25. 2d. green and black .. 40 35
153. – 2½d. black and green .. 10 40
153a. – 2½d. green and brown .. 15 15
154. 25. 3d. orange and purple .. 15 10
154a. – 3½d. blue and green .. 40 75
155. 25. 6d. black and red .. 50 40
156. – 1s. purple and green .. 50 40
157. 25. 2s. blue and purple .. 4·50 55
157a. 2s. 6d. brown and blue 1·00 3·50
158. 5s. red and green .. 8·50 2·50
158a. 10 s. violet and brown 3·50 7·50
159. £1 purple and black .. 16·00 15·00
DESIGNS—HORIZ. 1½d. Kingstown and Fort Charlotte. 2½d. (No. 153) and 3½d. Bathing Beach at Villa. 2½d. (No. 153a) and 1s. Victoria Park, Kingstown.

1946. Victory. As T **9** of Aden.
160. 1½d. red 10 10
161. 3½d. blue 10 10

1948. Silver Wedding. As T **10/11** of Aden.
162. 1½d. red 10 10
163. £1 mauve .. .. 15·00 12·00

1949. As 1938 issue, but values in cents and dollars.
164. 25. 1 c. blue and green .. 20 15
164a. 1 c. green and black .. 30 40
165. 26. 2 c. blue and brown .. 15 20
166. – 3 c. green and red .. 40 15
166a. 25. 3 c. orange and purple .. 30 35
167. 4 c. green and black .. 35 20
167a. 4 c. blue and green .. 25 15
168. 5 c. green and brown .. 15 10
169. 6 c. orange and purple .. 40 35
169a. – 6 c. green and red .. 25 15
170. – 7 c. black and blue .. 2·50 30
170a. – 10 c. black & turquoise 50 20
171. 25. 12 c. black and red .. 35 15
172. – 24 c. purple and green .. 35 30
173. 25. 48 c. blue and purple .. 1·50 1·50
174. 60 c. brown and blue .. 1·75 1·75
175. $1.20 red and green .. 4·25 4·00
176. $2.40 violet and brown 6·50 9·00
177. $4.80 purple and black 11·00 17·00
DESIGNS—HORIZ. 3 c. (No. 166), 6 c. (No. 169a) Kingstown and Fort Charlotte. 5 c., 24 c. Victoria Park, Kingstown. 7 c., 10 c. Bathing Beach at Villa.

1949. U.P.U. As T **20/23** of Antigua.
178. 5 c. blue 15 15
179. 6 c. purple 25 25
180. 12 c. mauve 30 30
181. 24 c. green 40 25

1951. Inauguration of B.W.I. University College. As T **24/25** of Antigua.
182. 18. 3 c. green and red .. 20 15
183. 19. 12 c. black and purple 25 15

1951. New Constitution. Optd. **NEW CONSTITUTION 1951.**
184. – 3 c. green and red (No. 166) 10 15
185. 25. 4 c. green and black .. 10 15
186. – 5 c. grn. & brn. (No. 168) 10 15
187. 25. 12 c. black and red .. 10 15

1953. Coronation. As T **13** of Aden.
188. 4 c. black and green .. 30 15

30. 31.

1955.
198. 30. 1 c. orange 10 10
190 – 2 c. blue 10 10
191 3 c. grey 30 10
192 4 c. brown 15 10
215 5 c. red 15 10
216 10 c. lilac 15 10
195 15 c. blue 55 20
218 20 c. green 45 10
197 25 c. sepia 50 10
198a 31. 50 c. brown .. .. 2·75 75
199 $1 green .. .. .. 4·25 1·00
200 $2.50 blue .. .. .. 12·00 6·50

1958. British Caribbean Federation. As T **28** of Antigua.
201. 3 c. green 40 20
202. 6 c. blue 55 35
203. 12 c. red 80 35

1963. Freedom from Hunger. As T **28** of Aden.
204. 8 c. violet 60 50

1963. Cent of Red Cross. As T **33** of Antigua.
205. 4 c. red and black .. 15 20
206. 8 c. red and blue 35 50

32. Scout Badge and Proficiency Badges.

1964. 50th Anniversary of St. Vincent Boy Scouts Association.
221. 32. 1 c. green and brown .. ·10 10
222. 4 c. blue and purple .. 10 10
223. 20 c. yellow and violet .. 30 10
224. 50 c. red and green .. 45 20

33. Tropical Fruits.

1965. Bicent. of Botanic Gardens. Mult.
225. 1 c. Type **33** 10 10
226. 4 c. Breadfruit and H.M.S. "Providence", 1791 .. 10 10
227. 25 c. Doric Temple and Pond (vert.) 15 10
228. 40 c. Talipot Palm and Doric Temple (vert.) .. 30 40

1965. Cent of I.T.U. As T **36** of Antigua.
229. 4 c. blue and green .. 25 10
230. 48 c. ochre and orange .. 1·00 45

37. Boat-building, Bequia (inscr. "BEOUIA").

1965. Multicoloured.
231 1 c. Type **37** 10 40
231a 1 c. Type **37** (inscr. "BEQUIA") 10 10
232 2 c. Friendship Beach, Bequia 10 10
233 3 c. Terminal Building, Arnos Vale Airport .. 15 10
261 4 c. Woman with Bananas 30 30
235 5 c. Crater Lake 15 10
236 6 c. Carib Stone 15 30
237 8 c. Arrowroot 30 10
238 10 c. Owia Salt Pond .. 20 10
239 12 c. Deep Water Wharf .. 30 10
240 20 c. Sea Island Cotton .. 30 10
241 25 c. Map of St. Vincent and Islands 35 10
242 50 c. Breadfruit 50 25
243 $1 Baleine Falls .. .. 4·00 30
244 $2.50 St. Vincent Amazon 16·00 4·00
245 $5 Arms of St. Vincent .. 7·00 5·50
Nos. 234, 236/7 and 240/5 vert.

1966. Churchill Commem. As T **38** of Antigua.
246. 1 c. blue 10 10
247. 4 c. green 35 10
248. 20 c. brown 75 45
249. 40 c. violet .. .. .. 1·50 1·25

1966. Royal Visit. As T **39** of Antigua.
250. 4 c. black and blue .. 1·50 25
251. 25 c. black and mauve .. 4·00 1·25

1966. Inauguration of W.H.O. Headquarters, Geneva. As T **41** of Antigua.
252. 4 c. black, green and blue .. 30 10
253. 25 c. black, purple & ochre 95 80

1966. 20th Anniv of U.N.E.S.C.O. As T **54/6** of Antigua.
254. 4 c. multicoloured .. 40 10
255. 8 c. yellow, violet & olive 75 10
256. 25 c. black, purple & orge. 1·50 60

38. Coastal View of Mount Coke Area.

1967. Autonomous Methodist Church. Mult.
257. 2 c. Type **38** 10 10
258. 8 c. Kingstown Methodist Church 10 10
259. 25 c. First Licence to perform Marriages 20 10
260. 35 c. Conference Arms .. 20 10

39. Meteorological Institute.

1968. World Meteorological Day.
262. 39. 4 c. multicoloured .. 10 10
263. 25 c. multicoloured .. 15 10
264. 35 c. multicoloured .. 15 10

40. Dr. Martin Luther King and Cotton Pickers.

1968. Dr. Martin Luther King Commem.
265. 40. 5 c. multicoloured .. 10 10
266. 25 c. multicoloured .. 10 10
267. 35 c. multicoloured .. 10 10

41. Speaker addressing Demonstrators.

1968. Human Rights Year.
268. 41. 3 c. multicoloured .. 10 10
269. – 35 c. blue 20 10
DESIGN—VERT. 35 c. Scales of Justice and Human Rights Emblem.

43. Male Masquerader.

1969. St. Vincent Carnival.
270. 43. 1 c. multicoloured .. 10 10
271. – 5 c. red and brown .. 10 10
272. – 8 c. multicoloured .. 10 10
273. – 25 c. multicoloured .. 15 15
DESIGNS—VERT. 5 c. Steel Bandsman. 25 c. Queen of Bands. HORIZ. 8 c. Carnival Revellers.

1969. Methodist Conf. Nos. 241, 257/8 and 260 optd. **METHODIST CONFERENCE MAY 1969.**
274 38 2 c. multicoloured .. 10 15
275 – 8 c. multicoloured .. 30 40
276 – 25 c. multicoloured .. 35 40
277 – 35 c. multicoloured .. 1·50 3·00

48. "Strength in Unity".

1969. 1st Anniv. of "CARIFTA".
278. 48. 2 c. black, buff and red 10 10
279. – 5 c. multicoloured .. 10 10
280. 48. 8 c. black, buff & green 10 10
281. – 25 c. multicoloured .. 15 15
DESIGN—VERT. 5 c., 25 c. Map.

50. Flag of St. Vincent.

1969. Statehood.
282. 50. 4 c. multicoloured .. 10 10
283. – 10 c. multicoloured .. 10 10
284. – 50 c. grey, black & orange 25 10
DESIGNS: 10 c. Battle scene with insets of Petroglyph and Carib Chief Chatoyer. 50 c. Carib House with maces and scales.

51. Green Heron.

1970. Multicoloured.
285. ½ c. House Wren 10 10
286a. 1 c. Type **51** 30 80
287. 2 c. Lesser Antillean Bullfinches 15 30
288. 3 c. St. Vincent Amazon .. 15 30
289. 4 c. Rufous-throated Solitaire 20 30
364. 5 c. Red-necked Pigeon .. 50 20
291. 6 c. Bananaquit 25 20
292. 8 c. Purple-throated Carib 25 20
293. 10 c. Mangrove Cuckoo .. 30 10
294. 12 c. Common Black Hawk 40 10
295. 20 c. Bare-eyed Thrush .. 60 15
296. 25 c. Hooded Tanager (Prince) 70 20
297. 50 c. Blue Hooded Euphonia 1·50 75
298. $1 Barn Owl .. .. 6·50 3·50
299. $2.50 Yellow-bellied Elaenia 7·00 4·00
300. $5 Ruddy Quail Dove .. 11·00 5·50
Nos. 285, 289, 364, 293/4, and 298/9 are vert.

52. "DHC-6" Twin Otter.

1970. 20th Anniv. of Regular Air Services. Multicoloured.
301. 5 c. Type **52** 10 10
302. 8 c. "Grumman Goose" .. 15 10
303. 10 c. Hawker Siddeley "HS-748" 20 10
304. 25 c. Douglas "DC-3" .. 65 30

53. "Children's Nursery".

1970. Cent. of British Red Cross. Mult.

305.	3 c. Type **53**	10	10
306.	5 c. "First Aid"	15	10
307.	12 c. "Voluntary Aid Detachment"	20	15
308.	25 c. "Blood Transfusion"	30	15

54. "Angel and the two Marys at the tomb" (stained-glass window).

1970. 150th Anniv. of St. George's Cathedral, Kingstown. Multicoloured.

309.	½ c. Type **54**	10	10
310.	5 c. St. George's Cathedral	10	10
311.	25 c. Tower, St. George's Cathedral	10	10
312.	35 c. Interior, St. George's Cathedral	15	10
313.	50 c. Type **54**	20	30

Nos. 310 and 312 are horiz.

55. "The Adoration of the Shepherds" (Le Nain).

1970. Christmas. Multicoloured.

314.	8 c. "The Virgin and Child" (G. Bellini) (vert.)	10	10
315.	25 c. Type **55**	10	10
316.	35 c. As 8 c.	10	10
317.	50 c. Type **55**	15	20

56. New Post Office and 6d. Stamp of 1861.

1971. 110th Anniv. of 1st St. Vincent Stamps. Multicoloured.

318.	2 c. Type **56**	10	10
319.	4 c. 1d. stamp of 1861 and new Post Office	10	10
320.	25 c. Type **56**	10	10
321.	$1 As 4 c.	35	45

57. Trust Seal and Wildlife.

1971. St. Vincent's National Trust. Mult.

322.	12 c. Type **57**	25	10
323.	30 c. Old Cannon, Fort Charlotte	40	15
324.	40 c. Type **57**	55	25
325.	45 c. As 30 c.	55	30

58. "Madonna appearing to St. Anthony" (Tiepolo).

1971. Christmas. Multicoloured.

326.	5 c. Type **58**	10	10
327.	10 c. "The Holy Family on the flight into Egypt" (detail, Pietro da Cortona)	10	10
328.	25 c. Type **58**	10	10
329.	$1 As 10 c.	30	35

59. Careening.

1971. The Grenadines of St. Vincent. Multicoloured.

330.	1 c. Type **59**	10	10
331.	5 c. Seine fishermen ..	10	10
332.	6 c. Map of the Grenadines	10	10
333.	15 c. Type **59**	10	10
334.	20 c. As 5 c.	15	10
335.	50 c. As 6 c.	30	60

60. Private, Grenadier Company, 32nd Foot (1764).

1972. Military Uniforms.

337.	**60.**	12 c. multicoloured ..	90	15
338.	–	30 c. multicoloured ..	1·75	65
339.	–	50 c. multicoloured ..	2·50	1·00

DESIGNS: 30 c. Officer, Battalion Company, 31st. Foot (1772). 50 c. Private, Grenadier Company, 6th Foot (1772).

61. Breadnut Fruit.

1972. Fruit. Multicoloured.

340.	3 c. Type **61**	10	10
341.	5 c. Pawpaw	10	10
342.	12 c. Plumrose or Roseapple	30	30
343.	25 c. Mango	70	70

62. Candlestick Cassia.

1972. Flowers. Multicoloured.

344.	1 c. Type **62**	10	10
345.	30 c. Lobster Claw ..	20	10
346.	40 c. White Trumpet ..	25	15
347.	$1 Soufriere tree ..	70	80

63. Sir Charles Brisbane and Coat of Arms.

1972. Birth Bicent. of Sir Charles Brisbane.

348.	**63.**	20 c. brn., gold & red ..	15	10
349.	–	30 c. yellow, mauve & blk.	40	10
350.	–	$1 multicoloured ..	1·40	70

DESIGNS: 30 c. H.M.S. "Arethusa", 1807. $1 H.M.S. "Blake", 1808.

1972. Royal Silver Wedding. As T **52** of Ascension, but with Arrowroot and Bread-fruit in background.

352.	30 c. brown	10	10
353.	$1 green	40	20

65. Sighting of St. Vincent.

1973. 475th Anniv. of Columbus's Visit to the West Indies. Multicoloured.

354.	5 c. Type **65**	25	15
355.	12 c. Caribs watching Columbus's fleet ..	45	20
356.	30 c. Christopher Columbus	1·00	70
357.	50 c. "Santa Maria" ..	1·50	1·10

66. "The Last Supper" (French stained-glass Window).

1973. Easter.

358.	**66.**	15 c. multicoloured ..	10	10
359.	–	60 c. multicoloured ..	20	20
360.	–	$1 multicoloured ..	20	20

Nos. 358/60 are in the form of a triptych which make a composite design depicting "The Last Supper".

67. William Wilberforce and Poster.

1973. 140th Death Anniv. of William Wilberforce. Multicoloured.

369.	30 c. Type **67**	15	10
370.	40 c. Slaves cutting cane ..	20	15
371.	50 c. Wilberforce and medallion	20	15

68. P.P.F. Symbol.

1973. 21st Anniv. of International Planned Parenthood Federation. Multicoloured.

372.	12 c. Type **68**	10	10
373.	40 c. "IPPF" and symbol	20	20

1973. Royal Wedding. As T **47** of Anguilla. Multicoloured, background colours given.

374.	50 c. blue	15	10
375.	70 c. green	20	10

69. Administration Block, Mona.

1973. 25th Anniv. of West Indies University. Multicoloured.

376.	5 c. Type **69**	10	10
377.	10 c. University Centre, Kingstown	10	10
378.	30 c. Aerial view, Mona University ..	15	10
379.	$1 University coat of arms (vert.)	50	60

1973. Nos. 297, 292 and 298 surch.

380.	30 c. on 50 c. multicoloured	1·75	70
381.	40 c. on 8 c. multicoloured	1·75	70
382.	$10 on $1 multicoloured ..	10·00	6·50

71. "The Descent from the Cross" (Sansovino).

1974. Easter. Multicoloured.

383.	5 c. Type **71**	10	10
384.	30 c. "The Deposition" (English, 14th-century)	10	10
385.	40 c. "Pieta" (Fernandez)	10	10
386.	$1 "The Resurrection" (French, 16th-century)	20	25

72. "Istra".

1974. Cruise Ships. Multicoloured.
387. 15 c. Type **72** 20 10
388. 20 c. "Oceanic" 25 10
389. 30 c. "Aleksandr Pushkin" 25 10
390. $1 "Europa" 50 30

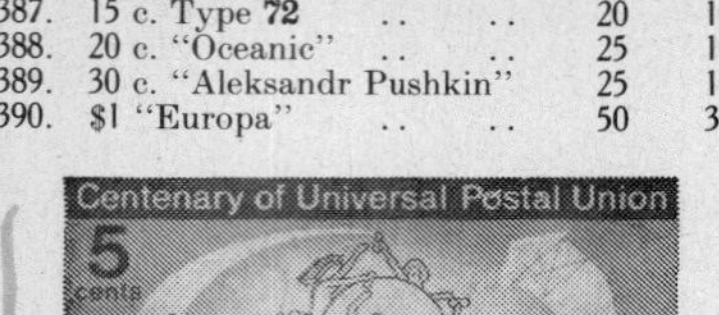

73. U.P.U. Emblem.

1974. Centenary of U.P.U. Multicoloured.
392. 5 c. Type **73** 10 10
393. 12 c. Globe within posthorn 10 10
394. 60 c. Map of St. Vincent and hand-cancelling .. 20 10
395. 90 c. Map of the World .. 25 30

74. Royal Tern.

1974. Multicoloured.
396. 30 c. Type **74** .. .. 2·00 75
397. 40 c. Brown pelican .. 2·00 75
398. $10 Magnificent Frigate Bird .. .. .. 18·00 9·00

75. Scout Badge and Emblems.

1974. Diamond Jubilee of Scout Movement in St. Vincent.
399. **75.** 10 c. multicoloured .. 10 10
400. 25 c. multicoloured .. 20 10
401. 45 c. multicoloured .. 35 25
402. $1 multicoloured .. 75 50

76. Sir Winston Churchill.

1974. Birth Cent. of Sir Winston Churchill. Multicoloured.
403. 25 c. Type **76** 15 10
404. 35 c. Churchill in military uniform 20 10
405. 45 c. Churchill in naval uniform 25 10
406. $1 Churchill in air force uniform 45 50

77. The Shepherds.

1974. Christmas.
407. **77.** 3 c. blue and black .. 10 10
408. – 3 c. blue and black .. 10 10
409. – 3 c. blue and black .. 10 10
410. – 3 c. blue and black .. 10 10
411. **77.** 8 c. green and black .. 10 10
412. – 35 c. pink and black .. 20 10
413. – 45 c. brown and black 20 10
414. – $1 mauve and black .. 40 50

DESIGNS: Nos. 408, 411, Mary and crib. Nos. 409, 413, Joseph, ox and ass. Nos. 410, 414, The Magi.

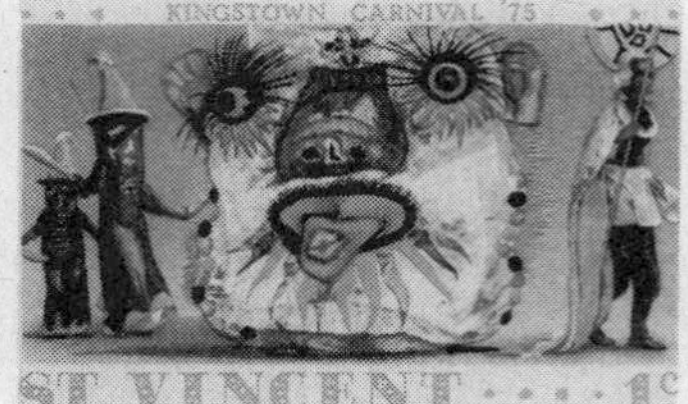

78. Faces.

1975. Kingstown "Carnival '75". Mult.
415. 1 c. Type **78** 10 10
416. 15 c. Pineapple women .. 20 15
417. 25 c. King of the Bands .. 20 20
418. 35 c. Carnival dancers .. 25 15
419. 45 c. Queen of the Bands 25 20
420. $1.25 "African Splendour" 35 55

79. French Angelfish.

1975. Multicoloured.
422. 1 c. Type **79** 15 40
423. 2 c. Spotfin Butterfly-fish 15 40
424. 3 c. Horse-eyed Jack .. 15 15
425. 4 c. Mackerel 20 10
426. 5 c. French Grunt .. 20 30
427. 6 c. Spotted Goatfish .. 20 40
428. 8 c. Ballyhoo 20 40
429. 10 c. Sperm Whale .. 30 10
430. 12 c. Humpback Whale .. 40 50
431. 15 c. Cowfish 70 45
432. 15 c. Skipjack .. .. 3·00 35
433. 20 c. Queen Angelfish .. 40 10
434. 25 c. Princess Parrotfish .. 45 10
435. 35 c. Red Hind 50 30
436. 45 c. Atlantic Flying-fish 65 30
437. 50 c. Porkfish 65 35
438. 70 c. "Albacore" or Yellow-fin Tuna .. .. 4·25 70
439. 90 c. Pompano .. .. 4·25 70
440. $1 Queen Triggerfish .. 90 20
441a. $2.50 Sailfish .. .. 3·50 1·50
442. $5 Dolphin Fish .. .. 5·00 2·50
443. $10 Blue Marlin .. .. 5·00 8·00

80. Cutting Bananas.

1975. Banana Industry. Multicoloured.
447. 25 c. Type **80** 15 10
448. 35 c. Packaging Station, La Croix 15 10
449. 45 c. Cleaning and boxing 20 15
450. 70 c. Shipping bananas aboard "Geest Tide" .. 40 30

81. Snorkel Diving.

1975. Tourism. Multicoloured.
451. 15 c. Type **81** 15 10
452. 20 c. Aquaduct Golf Course 20 10
453. 35 c. Steel Band at Mariner's Inn 35 15
454. 45 c. Sunbathing at Young Island 45 25
455. $1.25 Yachting marina .. 1·25 1·50

82. George Washington, John Adams, Thomas Jefferson and James Madison.

1975. Bicentenary of American Revolution.
456. **82.** ½ c. black and mauve .. 10 10
457. – 1 c. black and green .. 10 10
458. – 1½ c. black and mauve 10 10
459. – 5 c. black and green .. 10 10
460. – 10 c. black and blue .. 15 10
461. – 25 c. black and yellow .. 25 10
462. – 35 c. black and blue .. 30 15
463. – 45 c. black and red .. 35 15
464. – $1 black and orange .. 55 40
465. – $2 black and green .. 90 75

PRESIDENTS: 1 c. Monroe, Quincy Adams, Jackson, van Buren. 1½ c. W. Harrison, Tyler, Polk, Taylor. 5 c. Fillmore, Pierce, Buchanan, Lincoln. 10 c. Andrew Johnson, Grant, Hayes, Garfield. 25 c. Arthur, Cleveland, B. Harrison, McKinley. 35 c. Theodore Roosevelt, Taft, Wilson, Harding. 45 c. Coolidge, Hoover, Franklin Roosevelt, Truman, $1, Eisenhower, Kennedy, Lyndon Johnson, Nixon. $2, Pres. Ford and White House.

83/4. "Shepherds".

1975. Christmas.
467. – 3 c. black and mauve .. 10 10
468. – 3 c. black and mauve .. 30 30
469. – 3 c. black and mauve .. 10 10
470. – 3 c. black and mauve .. 10 10
471. – 8 c. black and blue .. 10 10
472. – 8 c. black and blue .. 10 10
473. – 35 c. black and yellow .. 20 20
474. – 35 c. black and yellow .. 20 20
475. **83.** 45 c. black and green .. 30 30
476. **84.** 45 c. black and green .. 30 30
477. – $1 black and purple .. 65 65
478. – $1 black and purple .. 65 65

DESIGNS: No. 467, "Star of Bethlehem". No. 468, "Holy Trinity". No. 469, As Type **83**. No. 470. "Three Kings". No. 471/2, As No. 467. No. 473/4, As No. 468. No. 475/6, Types **83/4**. No. 477/8, As No. 470. The two designs of each value (Nos. 471/8) differ in that the longest side is at the foot and at the top respectively, as in Types **83/4**.

85. Carnival Dancers.

1976. Kingstown "Carnival '76". Mult.
479. 1 c. Type **85** 10 10
480. 2 c. Humpty-Dumpty people 10 10
481. 5 c. Smiling faces 10 10
482. 35 c. Dragon worshippers 20 10
483. 45 c. Carnival tableau .. 25 15
484. $1.25 Bumble-bee dancers 45 45

1976. Nos. 424 and 437 surch.
485. 70 c. on 3 c. Horse-eyed Jack 1·25 1·25
486. 90 c. on 50 c. Porkfish .. 1·40 1·40

87. Blue-headed Hummingbird and Yellow Hibiscus.

1976. Hummingbirds and Hibiscuses. Mult.
487. 5 c. Type **87** 35 10
488. 10 c. Antillean Crested Hummingbird and Pink Hibiscus 60 15
489. 35 c. Purple-throated Carib and White Hibiscus .. 1·40 55
490. 45 c. Blue-headed Humming-bird and Red Hibiscus 1·50 65
491. $1.25 Green-throated Carib and Peach Hibiscus .. 9·50 5·50

1976. West Indian Victory in World Cricket Cup. As Nos. 431/2 of St. Lucia.
492. 15 c. Map of the Caribbean 75 25
493. 45 c. Prudential Cup .. 1·75 1·00

88. St. Mary Church, Kingstown.

1976. Christmas. Multicoloured.
494. 35 c. Type **88** 15 10
495. 45 c. Anglican Church, Georgetown 15 10
496. 50 c. Methodist Church, Georgetown 20 10
497. $1.25 St. George's Cathedral, Kingstown 40 60

89. Barrancoid Pot-stand.

1977. National Trust. Multicoloured.
498. 5 c. Type **89** 10 10
499. 45 c. National Museum .. 15 10
500. 70 c. Carib sculpture .. 25 20
501. $1 Ciboney petroglyph .. 45 50

90. William I, William II, Henry I and Stephen.

1977. Silver Jubilee. Multicoloured.
502. ½ c. Type **90** 10 10
503. 1 c. Henry II, Richard I, John, Henry III .. 10 10
504. 1½ c. Edward I, Edward II, Edward III, Richard II 10 10
505. 2 c. Henry IV, Henry V, Henry VI, Edward IV 10 10
506. 5 c. Edward V, Richard III, Henry VII, Henry VIII 10 10
507. 10 c. Edward VI, Lady Jane Grey, Mary I, Elizabeth I 10 10
508. 25 c. James I, Charles I, Charles II, James II .. 20 15
509. 35 c. William III, Mary II, Anne, George I .. 30 20
510. 45 c. George II, George III, George IV 35 25
511. 75 c. William IV, Victoria, Edward VII 45 35
512. $1 George V, Edward VIII, George VI 55 45
513. $2 Elizabeth II leaving Westminster Abbey .. 95 70

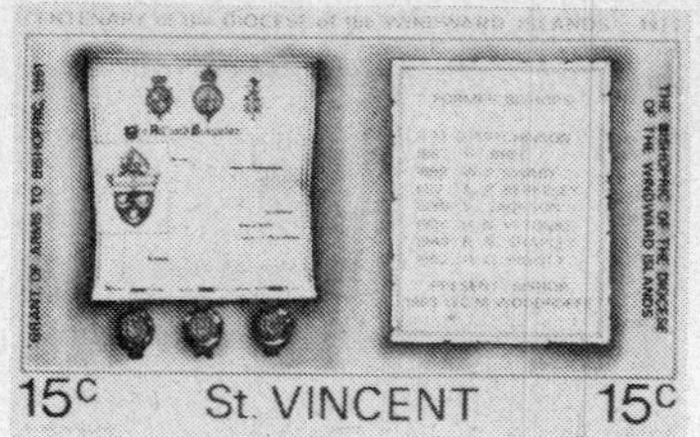

91. Grant of Arms.

1977. Centenary of Windward Islands Diocese. Multicoloured.

527. 15 c. Type **91** 10 10
528. 35 c. Bishop Berkeley and mitres 10 10
529. 45 c. Map and arms of diocese 10 10
530. $1.25 St. George's Cathedral and Bishop Woodroffe .. 30 45

1977. Carnival '77. Nos. 426, 429, 432/3 and 440 optd. **CARNIVAL 1977 JUNE 25th. — JULY 5th.**

531. 5 c. French Grunt .. 10 10
532. 10 c. Sperm Whale .. 10 10
533. 15 c. Skipjack .. 10 10
534. 20 c. Queen Angelfish .. 10 10
535. $1 Queen Triggerfish .. 40 40

93. Guide and Emblem.

1977. 50th Anniv. of St. Vincent Girl Guides. Multicoloured.

536. 5 c. Type **93** 10 10
537. 15 c. Early uniform, ranger, guide and brownie .. 15 10
538. 20 c. Early uniform and guide 15 10
539. $2 Lady Baden-Powell .. 70 60

1977. Royal Visit. No. 513 optd. **CARIBBEAN VISIT 1977.**

540. $2 Queen Elizabeth leaving Westminster Abbey .. 40 30

95. Map of St. Vincent.

1977. Surch. as in T **95.**

541. **95.** 20 c. pale blue and blue 15 15
542. 40 c. pale orange & orge. 25 20
543. 40 c. pink and mauve .. 20 15

Nos. 541/3 were originally printed without face values.

96. Opening Verse and Scene.

1977. Christmas. Scenes and Verses from the carol " While Shepherds Watched their Flocks by Night ". Multicoloured.

544. 5 c. Type **96** 10 10
545. 10 c. Angel consoling shepherds 10 10
546. 15 c. View of Bethlehem .. 10 10
547. 25 c. Nativity scene .. 10 10
548. 50 c. Throng of Angels .. 10 10
549. $1.25 Praising God .. 30 45

97. "Vanessa cardui" and "Bougainvillea glubra var. alba".

1978. Butterflies and Bougainvilleas. Mult.

551 5 c. Type **97** 10 10
552 25 c. "Dione juno" and (Golden Glow) .. 15 10
553 40 c. "Anartia amathea" and "Mrs McLean" .. 25 10
554 50 c. "Hypolimnas misippus" and "Cyphen" .. 30 10
556 $1.25 "Pseudolycaena marsyas" and "Thomasii" .. 65 55

1978. 25th Anniv. of Coronation. Horiz. designs as Nos. 422/5 of Montserrat. Multicoloured.

556. 40 c. Westminster Abbey 10 10
557. 50 c. Gloucester Cathedral 10 10
558. $1.25 Durham Cathedral 20 15
559. $2.50 Exeter Cathedral .. 30 25

98. Rotary International Emblem and Motto.

1978. International Service Clubs. Emblems and mottos. Multicoloured.

561. 40 c. Type **98** 25 10
562. 50 c. Lions International 25 10
563. $1 Jaycees 50 35

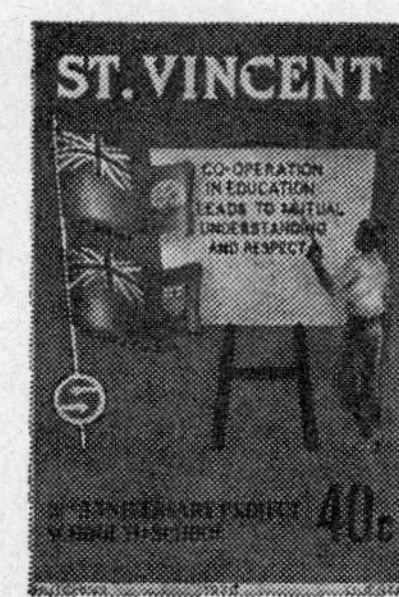

99. " Co-operation in Education Leads to Mutual Understanding and Respect ".

1978. 10th Anniv. of Project School to School (St. Vincent–Canada school twinning project). Multicoloured.

564. 40 c. Type **99** 10 10
565. $2 " Co-operation in Education Leads to the Elimination of Racial Intolerance " (horiz.) .. 40 50

100. Arnos Vale Airport.

1978. Powered Flight. 75th Anniv. Mult.

566. 10 c. Type **100** 10 10
567. 40 c. Wilbur Wright and " Flyer " 15 10
568. 50 c. " Flyer " 15 10
569. $1.25 Orville Wright and " Flyer " 45 35

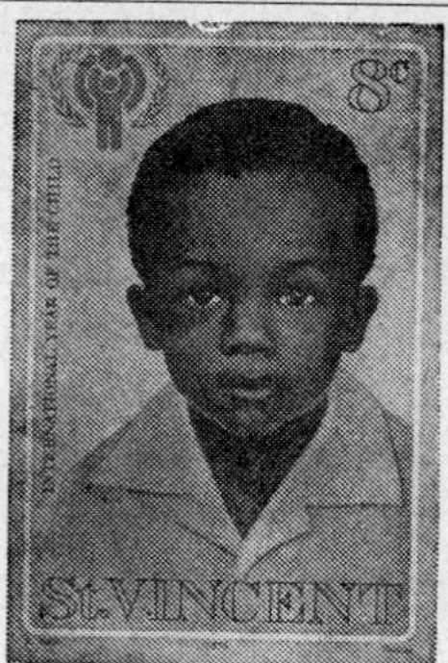

101. Young Child.

1979. International Year of the Child.

570. **101.** 8 c. black, gold and green 10 10
571. – 20 c. black, gold and lilac 15 10
572. – 50 c. black, gold and blue 25 10
573. – $2 black, gold and flesh 75 50

DESIGNS: 20 c., 50 c., $2, Different portraits of young children.

1979. Soufriere Eruption Relief Fund. As T **95,** but surch. **SOUFRIERE RELIEF FUND 1979** and premium.

574. **95.** 10 c.+5 c. blue and lilac 10 15
575. 50 c.+25 c. brn. & buff 20 20
576. $1+50 c. brown & grey 30 30
577. $2+$1 green and light green 50 50

103. Sir Rowland Hill.

1979. Death centenary of Sir Rowland Hill. Multicoloured.

578. 40 c. Type **103** 15 10
579. 50 c. Penny Black and Two Penny Blue stamps .. 20 15
580. $3 1861 1d. and 6d. stamps 1·00 1·10

104. First and latest Buccament Postmarks and Map of St. Vincent.

1979. Post Offices of St. Vincent. Early and modern postmarks. Multicoloured.

582. 1 c. Type **104** 10 10
583. 2 c. Sion Hill 10 10
584. 3 c. Cumberland 10 10
585. 4 c. Questelles 10 10
586. 5 c. Layou 10 10
587. 6 c. New Ground 10 10
588. 8 c. Mesopotamia 10 10
589. 10 c. Troumaca 10 10
590. 12 c. Arnos Vale 15 10
591. 15 c. Stubbs 15 10
592. 20 c. Orange Hill 15 10
593. 25 c. Calliaqua 15 10
594. 40 c. Edinboro 25 20
595. 50 c. Colonarie 30 25
596. 80 c. Biabou 40 35
597. $1 Chateaubelair 50 50
598. $2 Head P.O., Kingstown 60 80
599. $3 Barrouallie .. .. 75 1·25
600. $5 Georgetown .. .. 1·25 2·00
601. $10 Kingstown .. .. 2·25 4·00

1979. Opening of St. Vincent and the Grenadines Air Service. Optd. **ST. VINCENT AND THE GRENADINES AIR SERVICE 1979.**

602. 10 c. Type **100** 10 10

106. National Flag and " Ixora coccinea " (flower).

1979. Independence. Multicoloured.

603. 20 c. Type **106** 15 10
604. 50 c. House of Assembly and " ixora stricta " (flower) 20 10
605. 80 c. Prime Minister R. Milton Cato and " ixora williamsii" (flower) .. 25 20

1979. Independence. Nos. 422, 425/30, 432 437/41 and 443. Optd. **INDEPENDENCE, 1979.**

606. 1 c. Type **79** 10 10
607. 4 c. Mackerel 10 10
608. 5 c. French Grunt .. 10 10
609. 6 c. Spotted Goatfish .. 10 10
610. 8 c. Ballyhoo 10 10
611. 10 c. Sperm Whale .. 15 15
612. 12 c. Humpback Whale .. 15 15
613. 15 c. Skipjack 15 15
614. 25 c. Princess Parrotfish .. 20 20
615. 50 c. Porkfish 35 35
616. 70 c. " Albacore " or Yellowfin Tuna .. 45 45
617. 90 c. Pompano 60 50
618. $1 Queen Triggerfish .. 60 50
619. $2.50, Sailfish .. .. 1·75 1·00
620. $10 Blue Marlin .. .. 4·75 4·25

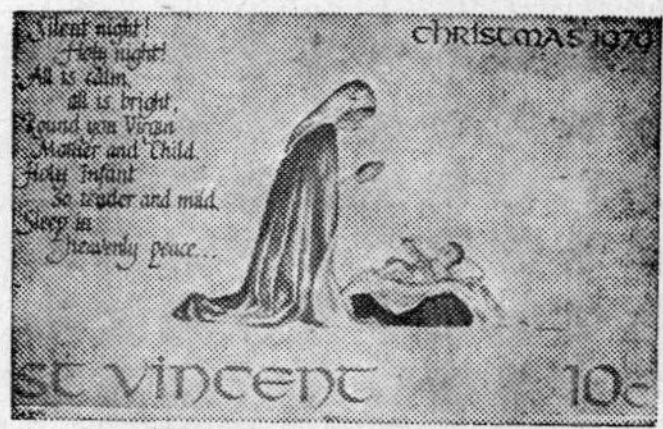

108. Virgin and Child.

1979. Christmas. Scenes and quotations from " Silent Night " (carol). Multicoloured.

621. 10 c. Type **108** 10 10
622. 20 c. Jesus sleeping .. 10 10
623. 25 c. Shepherds 10 10
624. 40 c. Angel 10 10
625. 50 c. Angels holding Jesus 10 10
626. $2 Nativity 40 30

109. "Polistes cinctus" (wasp) and Oleander.

1979. Flowers and Insects. Designs showing different varieties of oleander. Multicoloured.

628 5 c. Type **109** 10 10
629 10 c. "Pyrophorus noctiluca" (click beetle) .. 10 10
630 25 c. "Stagmomantis limbata" (mantid) .. 10 10
631 50 c. "Psiloptera lampetis" (beetle) 10 10
632 $2 "Diaprepies abbreviatus" (weevil) 30 30

110. Queen Elizabeth II.

1980. " London 1980 " International Stamp Exhibition. Multicoloured.

634. 80 c. Type **110** 20 20
635. $1 Great Britain 1954 3d. and St. Vincent 1954 5 c. definitives 30 30
636. $2 Unadopted postage stamp design, 1971 .. 60 60

111. Steel Band.

1980. Kingstown Carnival. Multicoloured.

638. 20 c. Type **111** 15 15
639. 20 c. Steel band (different) 15 15

112. Football.

1980. " Sport for All ". Multicoloured.
640. 10 c. Type **112** 10 10
641. 60 c. Cycling 20 15
642. 80 c. Basketball 30 20
643. $2.50 Boxing 40 70

1980. Hurricane Relief. Nos. 640/3 surch. **HURRICANE RELIEF 50 c.**
644. **112.** 10 c.+50 c. mult. .. 15 15
645. – 60 c.+50 c. mult. .. 25 25
646. – 80 c.+50 c. mult. .. 35 35
647. – $2.50+50 c. mult. .. 60 60

114. Brazilian Agouti.

1980. Wildlife. Multicoloured.
648. 25 c. Type **114** 10 10
649. 50 c. Giant Toad 15 10
650. $2 Small Indian Mongoose 40 55

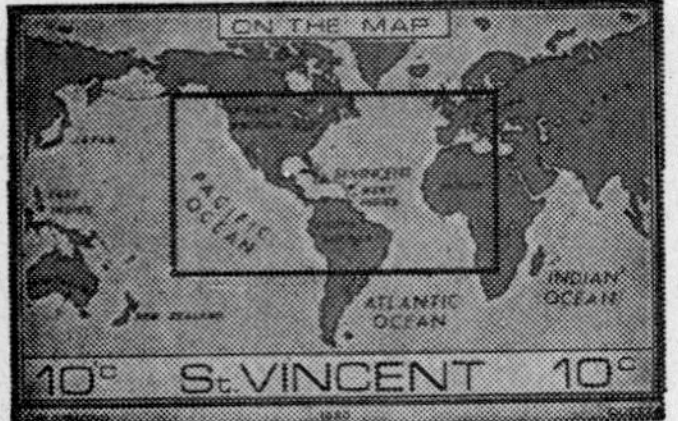

115. Map of World showing St. Vincent.

1980. St. Vincent " On the Map ". Maps showing St. Vincent. Multicoloured.
651. 10 c. Type **115** 10 10
652. 50 c. Western hemisphere 10 10
653. $1 Central America .. 25 15
654. $2 St. Vincent 40 30

116. "Ville de Paris", 1782.

1981. Historical Sailing Ships. Mult.
656. 50 c. Type **116** 30 20
657. 60 c. H.M.S. "Ramillies", 1782 .. .. .. 35 30
658. $1.50 H.M.S. "Providence", 1793 .. .. 80 1·25
659. $2 "Dee" (paddle-steamer packet) .. .. 1·10 1·50

117. Arrowroot Cultivation.

1981. Agriculture. Multicoloured.
660. 25 c. Type **117** 10 15
661. 25 c. Arrowroot processing 10 15
662. 50 c. Banana cultivation 20 25
663. 50 c. Banana export packaging station 20 25
664. 60 c. Coconut plantation .. 25 30
665. 60 c. Copra drying frames 25 30
666. $1 Cocoa cultivation .. 50 45
667. $1 Cocoa beans and sun drying frames 50 45

1981. Royal Wedding. Royal Yachts. As T **26/27** of Kiribati. Multicoloured.
668. 60 c. " Isabella " 15 15
669. 60 c. Prince Charles and Lady Diana Spencer .. 30 30
670. $2.50 " Alberta " (Tender) 30 30
671. $2.50 As No. 669 .. .. 70 70
672. $4 " Britannia " 40 40
673. $4 As No. 669 .. .. 1·25 1·25

118. Kingstown General Post Office. 119. (Actual size 85 × 24 mm.)

1981. U.P.U. Membership.
677. **118.** $2 multicoloured .. 70 90
678. **119.** $2 multicoloured .. 70 90
Nos. 677/8 were printed together, se-tenant, in horizontal pairs throughout the sheet, forming a composite design.

120. St. Vincent Flag with Flags of other U.N. Member Nations.

1981. 1st Anniv. of U.N. Membership. Mult.
679. $1.50 Type **120** 55 25
680. $2.50 Prime Minister Robert Milton Cato 85 50
Nos. 679/80 are inscribed " ST VINCENT and the GRENADINES ".

121. Silhouettes of Figures at Old Testament Reading, and Bible Extract.

1981. Christmas. Designs showing silhouettes of Figures. Multicoloured.
681. 50 c. Type **121** 15 10
682. 60 c. Madonna and angel 15 10
683. $1 Madonna and Bible extract 25 25
684. $2 Joseph and Mary travelling to Bethlehem .. 50 50

122. Sugar Boilers.

1982. 1st Anniv. of Re-introduction of Sugar Industry. Multicoloured.
686. 50 c. Type **122** 25 15
687. 60 c. Sugar drying plant .. 25 20
688. $1.50 Sugar mill machinery 70 80
689. $2 Crane loading suger cane 95 1·25

123. Butterfly Float.

1982. Carnival 1982. Multicoloured.
690. 50 c. Type **123** 20 15
691. 60 c. Angel dancer (vert.) 20 15
692. $1.50 Winged dancer (vert) 50 70
693. $2 Eagle float .. .. 70 1·00

INDEX

Countries can be quickly located by referring to the index at the end of this volume.

124. Augusta of Saxe-Gotha, Princess of Wales, 1736.

1982. 21st Birthday of Princess of Wales. Multicoloured.
694. 50 c. Type **124** 25 20
695. 60 c. Coat of arms of Augusta of Saxe-Gotha 25 25
696. $6 Diana, Princess of Wales 1·75 1·75

125. Scout Emblem.

1982. 75th Anniv. of Boy Scout Movement. Multicoloured.
697. $1.50 Type **125** .. .. 70 1·00
698. $2.50 75th anniversary emblem .. .. 90 1·25

1982. Birth of Prince William of Wales. Nos. 694/6 optd. **ROYAL BABY.**
699. 50 c. Type **124** 20 20
700. 60 c. Coat of arms of Augusta of Saxe-Gotha 25 25
701. $6 Diana, Princess of Wales 1·75 2·00

126. De Havilland " Moth ", 1932.

1982. 50th Anniv. of Airmail Service. Mult.
702. 50 c. Type **126** 45 30
703. 60 c. Grumman " Goose ", 1952 .. .. .. 50 40
704. $1.50 Hawker-Siddeley " 748 ", 1968 .. .. 95 1·00
705. $2 Britten-Norman " Trislander ", 1982 .. 1·10 1·60

127. "Geestport" (freighter).

1982. Ships. Multicoloured.
706. 45 c. Type **127** 25 25
707. 60 c. "Stella Oceanic" (liner) 30 35
708. $1.50 "The Victoria" (liner) 70 1·00
709. $2 "Queen Elizabeth 2" (liner) .. .. 95 1·50

128. " Pseudocorynactis caribbeorum ".

1983. Marine Life. Multicoloured.
710. 50 c. Type **128** 45 25
711. 60 c. " Actinoporus elegans " (vert.) 50 35
712. $1.50 " Arachnanthus nocturnus " (vert.) .. 1·00 75
713. $2 " Hippocampus reidi " (vert.) .. .. 1·25 1·00

129. Satellite View of St. Vincent.

1983. Commonwealth Day. Multicoloured.
714. 45 c. Type **129** 20 20
715. 60 c. Flag of St. Vincent 25 25
716. $1·50 Prime Minister R. Milton Cato 50 65
717. $2 Harvesting bananas .. 75 90
Nos. 714/17 are inscribed "ST. VINCENT and the GRENADINES".

1983. No. 681 surch.
718. 45 c. on 50 c. Type **121** .. 40 30

131. Symbolic Handshake. 132. William A. Smith (founder).

1983. 10th Anniv. of Treaty of Chaguaramas. Multicoloured.
719. 45 c. Type **131** 25 20
720. 60 c. Commerce emblem .. 30 25
721. $1.50 Caribbean map .. 60 65
722. $2 Flags of member countries and map of St. Vincent 85 90

1983. Centenary of Boy's Brigade. Mult.
723. 45 c. Type **132** 25 25
724. 60 c. On parade 30 35
725. $1.50 Craftwork .. .. 70 1·10
726. $2 Community service .. 95 1·60

133. Ford " Model T " (1908).

1983. Leaders of the World. Automobiles (1st series).
727. **133.** 10 c. multicoloured .. 10 10
728. – 10 c. multicoloured .. 10 10
729. – 60 c. multicoloured .. 20 20
730. – 60 c. multicoloured .. 20 20
731. – $1.50 multicoloured .. 25 25
732. – $1.50 multicoloured .. 25 25
733. – $1.50 multicoloured .. 25 25
734. – $1.50 multicoloured .. 25 25
735. – $2 multicoloured .. 40 40
736. – $2 multicoloured .. 40 40
737. – $2 multicoloured .. 40 40
738. – $2 multicoloured .. 40 40

DESIGNS: (the first in each pair shows technical drawings and the second, paintings of the cars). Nos. 727/8, Ford "Model T" (1908). 729/30, "Supercharged" Cord "812" (1937). 731/2, Citroen "Open Tourer" (1937). 733/4, Mercedes Benz "300SL Gull-Wing" (1954). 735/6, Rolls Royce "Phantom I" (1925). 737/8, Ferrari "Boxer 512BB" (1967).

See also Nos. 820/9, 862/7, 884/91 and 952/63.

134. Shepherds see Nativity Star.

1983. Christmas.

739. 10 c. Type **134** 10 10
740. 50 c. Message of the Angel 20 10
741. $1.50 The Heavenly Host 45 45
742. $2.40 Shepherds worship Jesus 65 75

135. " King Henry VIII ".

1983. Leaders of the World. Railway Locomotives (1st series). First in each pair shows technical drawings and the second the locomotive at work.

744. 10 c. multicoloured .. 10 10
745. 10 c. multicoloured .. 10 10
746. 10 c. multicoloured .. 10 10
747. 10 c. multicoloured .. 10 10
748. 25 c. multicoloured .. 10 10
749. 25 c. multicoloured .. 10 10
750. 50 c. multicoloured .. 20 20
751. 50 c. multicolured .. 20 20
752. 60 c. multicoloured .. 25 25
753. 60 c. multicoloured .. 25 25
754. 75 c. multicoloured .. 35 35
755. 75 c. multicoloured .. 35 35
756. $2.50 multicoloured .. 75 75
757. $2.50 multicoloured .. 75 75
758. $3 multicoloured 90 90
759. $3 multicoloured 90 90

Designs: Nos. 744/5, "King Henry VIII", Great Britain (1927). 746/7, "Royal Scots Greys", Great Britain (1961). 748/9, "Hagley Hall", Great Britain (1928). 750/1, "Sir Lancelot", Great Britain (1926). 752/3, Class "B12", Great Britain (1912). 754/5, Deeley "Compound" type, Great Britain (1902). 756/7, "Cheshire", Great Britain (1927). 758/9, Bullied "Austerity" Class Q1, Great Britain (1942).

See also Nos. 792/807, 834/41, 872/83, 893/904 and 1001/8.

136. Fort Duvernette.

1984. Fort Duvernette. Multicoloured.

760. 35 c. Type **136** 20 30
761. 45 c. Soldiers on fortifications 25 30
762. $1 Canon facing bay .. 40 60
763. $3 Map of St. Vincent and mortar .. .. .. 1·25 1·75

137. White Frangipani.

1984. Flowering Trees and Shrubs. Mult.

764. 5 c. Type **137** 10 10
765. 10 c. Genip 15 10
766. 15 c. Immortelle 20 10
767. 20 c. Pink Poui 25 10
768. 25 c. Buttercup 30 10
769. 35 c. Sandbox 40 20
770. 45 c. Locust 50 25
771. 60 c. Colville's Glory .. 65 30
772. 75 c. Lignum Vitae .. 75 40
773. $1 Golden Shower .. .. 1·00 60
774. $5 Angelin .. .. 3·50 4·00
775. $10 Roucou .. .. 5·50 7·50

138. Trench Warfare, First World War.

1984. Leaders of the World. British Monarchs. Multicoloured.

776. 1 c. Type **138** 10 10
777. 1 c. George V and trenches 10 10
778. 5 c. Battle of Bannockburn 10 10
779. 5 c. Edward II and battle 10 10
780. 60 c. George V 25 25
781. 60 c. York Cottage, Sandringham 25 25
782. 75 c. Edward II 30 30
783. 75 c. Berkeley Castle .. 30 30
784. $1 Coat of Arms of Edward II 35 35
785. $1 Edward II (different) .. 35 35
786. $4 Coat of Arms of George V .. .. 1·00 1·00
787. $4 George V and Battle of Jutland .. .. .. 1·00 1·00

Nos. 776/7, 778/9, 780/1, 782/3, 784/5 and 786/7 were printed together, se-tenant, each pair forming a composite design.

139. Musical Fantasy Costume.

1984. Carnival 1984. Costumes. Mult.

788. 35 c. Type **139** 15 15
789. 45 c. African princess .. 20 20
790. $1 Market woman 40 40
791. $3 Carib hieroglyph .. 1·25 1·40

1984. Leaders of the World. Railway Locomotives (2nd series). As T **135**, the first in each pair shows technical drawings and the second the locomotive at work.

792. 1 c. multicoloured 10 10
793. 1 c. multicoloured 10 10
794. 2 c. multicoloured 10 10
795. 2 c. multicoloured 10 10
796. 3 c. multicoloured 10 10
797. 3 c. multicoloured 10 10
798. 50 c. multicoloured .. 30 30
799. 50 c. multicoloured .. 30 30
800. 75 c. multicoloured .. 35 35
801. 75 c. multicoloured .. 35 35
802. $1 multicoloured 40 40
803. $1 multicoloured 40 40
804. $2 multicoloured 55 55
805. $2 multicoloured 55 55
806. $3 multicoloured 65 65
807. $3 multicoloured 65 65

Designs: Nos. 792/3, "Liberation" Class, France (1945). 794/5, "Dreadnought", Great Britain (1967). 796/7, No. 242A1, France (1946). 798/9, Class "Dean Goods", Great Britain (1883). 800/1, Hetton colliery No. 1, Great Britain (1822). 802/3, "Penydarren", Great Britain (1804). 804/5, "Novelty", Great Britain (1829). 806/7, Class "44" Germany (1925).

140. Slaves tilling Field.

1984. 150th Anniv. of Emancipation of Slaves on St. Vincent. Multicoloured.

808. 35 c. Type **140** 20 20
809. 45 c. Sugar-cane harvesting 25 25
810. $1 Cutting sugar-cane .. 45 45
811. $3 William Wilberforce and African slave caravan .. 1·25 1·40

141. Weightlifting

1984. Leaders of the World. Olympic Games, Los Angeles. Multicoloured.

812. 1 c. Judo 10 10
813. 1 c. Type **141** 10 10
814. 3 c. Pursuit cycling .. 10 10
815. 3 c. Cycle road-racing .. 10 10
816. 60 c. Women's backstroke swimming 20 20
817. 60 c. Men's butterfly swimming 20 20
818. $3 Sprint start 75 75
819. $3 Finish of long distance race 75 75

1984. Leaders of the World. Automobiles (2nd series). As T **133**, the first in each pair shows technical drawings and the second paintings.

820. 5 c. black, drab and green 10 10
821. 5 c. multicoloured 10 10
822. 20 c. black, pink and blue 15 15
823. 20 c. multicoloured .. 15 15
824. 55 c. black, green & brn. .. 25 25
825. 55 c. multicoloured .. 25 25
826. $1.50 black, light turquoise and turquoise 35 35
827. $1.50 multicoloured .. 35 35
828. $2.50 black, turq. & lilac .. 40 40
829. $2.50 multicoloured .. 40 40

Designs: Nos. 820/1, Austin-Healey "Sprite" (1958). 822/3, Maserati "Ghibli Coupe" (1971). 824/5, Pontiac "GTO" (1964). 826/7, Jaguar "D-Type" (1957). 828/9, Ferrari "365 GTB4 Daytona" (1970).

142. Grenadier, 70th Regt of Foot, 1773.

1984. Military Uniforms. Multicoloured.

830. 45 c. Type **142** 25 30
831. 60 c. Grenadier, 6th Regt of Foot, 1775 .. .. 30 35
832. $1.50 Grenadier, 3rd Regt of Foot, 1768 .. .. 75 80
833. $2 Battalion Company officer, 14th Regt of Foot, 1780 .. .. 1·00 1·10

1984. Leaders of the World. Railway Locomotives (3rd series). As T **135**, the first in each pair shows technical drawings and the second the locomotive at work.

834. 5 c. multicoloured 10 10
835. 5 c. multicoloured 10 10
836. 40 c. multicoloured .. 20 35
837. 40 c. multicoloured .. 20 35
838. 75 c. multicoloured .. 30 40
839. 75 c. multicoloured .. 30 40
840. $2.50 multicoloured .. 1·00 1·25
841. $2.50 multicoloured .. 1·00 1·25

Designs: Nos. 834/5, Class "20", Rhodesia (1954). 836/7, "Southern Maid", Great Britain (1928). 838/9, "Prince of Wales", Great Britain (1911). 840/1, German "05", Germany (1935).

143. N. S. Taylor.

1985. Leaders of the World. Cricketers. The first in each pair shows a head portrait and the second the cricketer in action.

842. 5 c. multicoloured 10 10
843. 5 c. multicoloured 10 10
844. 35 c. multicoloured .. 25 25
845. 35 c. multicoloured .. 25 25
846. 50 c. multicoloured .. 35 35
847. 50 c. multicoloured .. 35 35
848. $3 multicoloured .. .. 1·50 1·50
849. $3 multicoloured .. .. 1·50 1·50

Designs: Nos. 842/3, N. S. Taylor. 844/5, T. W. Graveney. 846/7, R. G. D. Willis. 848/9, S. D. Fletcher.

144. Eye Lash Orchid.

1985. Orchids. Multicoloured.

850. 35 c. Type **144** 40 30
851. 45 c. "Ionopsis utricularioides" 50 30
852. $1 "Epidendrum secundum" 80 65
853. $3 "Oncidium altissimum" 1·75 2·00

145. Brown Pelican.

1985. Leaders of the World. Birth Bicentenary of John J. Audubon (ornithologist). Multicoloured.

854. 15 c. Type **145** 15 10
855. 15 c. Green heron 15 10
856. 40 c. Pileated woodpecker 40 30
857. 40 c. Common flicker .. 40 30
858. 60 c. Painted bunting .. 50 40
859. 60 c. White-winged crossbill 50 40
860. $2.25 Red-shouldered hawk .. .. .. 1·75 1·50
861. $2.25 Common caracara .. 1·75 1·50

1985. Leaders of the World. Automobiles (3rd series). As T **133**, the first in each pair shows technical drawings and the second paintings.

862. 1 c. black, yellow & green 10 10
863. 1 c. multicoloured 10 10
864. 55 c. black, blue and grey 20 20
865. 55 c. multicoloured .. 20 20
866. $2 black, yellow and purple 55 55
867. $2 multicoloured 55 55

Designs: Nos. 862/3, Lancia "Aprilia", (1937). 864/5, Pontiac "Firebird Trans Am", (1973). 866/7, Cunningham "C-5R", (1953).

146. Pepper.

1985. Herbs and Spices. Multicoloured.

868. 25 c. Type **146** 15 15
869. 35 c. Sweet Marjoram .. 20 25
870. $1 Nutmeg 50 60
871. $3 Ginger .. .. .. 1·50 2·00

1985. Leaders of the World. Railway Locomotives (4th series). As T **135**, the first in each pair shows technical drawings and the second the locomotive at work.

872. 1 c. multicoloured 10 10
873. 1 c. multicoloured 10 10
874. 10 c. multicoloured . . 10 10
875. 10 c. multicoloured . . 10 10
876. 40 c. multicoloured . . 25 30
877. 40 c. multicoloured . . 25 30
878. 60 c. multicoloured . . 35 40
879. 60 c. multicoloured . . 35 40
880. $1 multicoloured 45 50
881. $1 multicoloured 45 50
882. $2.50 multicoloured . . 90 1·25
883. $2.50 multicoloured . . 90 1·25

DESIGNS: Nos. 872/3, "Glen Douglas", Great Britain (1913). 874/5, "Fenchurch", Great Britain (1872). 876/7, No. 1 "Stirling Single", Great Britain (1870). 878/9, No. 158A, Great Britain (1866). 880/1, No. 103 Class "Jones Goods", Great Britain (1893). 882/3, "The Great Bear", Great Britain (1908).

1985. Leaders of the World. Automobiles (4th series). As T **133**, the first in each pair shows technical drawings and the second paintings.

884. 25 c. black, grey and red . . 15 15
885. 25 c. multicoloured . . 15 15
886. 60 c. black, pink & orange 25 25
887. 60 c. multicoloured . . 25 25
888. $1 black, blue and violet . . 30 30
889. $1 multicoloured 30 30
890. $1.50 black, blue and red 40 40
891. $1.50 multicoloured . . 40 40

DESIGNS: Nos. 884/5, Essex "Coach" (1922). 886/7, Nash "Rambler" (1950). 888/9, Ferrari "Tipo 156" (1961). 890/1, Eagle-Weslake "Type 58" (1967).

1985. Leaders of the World. Railway Locomotives (5th series). As T **135**. The first in each pair shows technical drawings and the second the locomotive at work.

893. 5 c. multicoloured 10 10
894. 5 c. multicoloured 10 10
895. 30 c. multicoloured . . 15 20
896. 30 c. multicoloured . . 15 20
897. 60 c. multicoloured . . 30 40
896. 60 c. multicoloured . . 30 40
899. 75 c. multicoloured . . 30 40
900. 75 c. multicoloured . . 30 40
901. $1 multicoloured 40 50
902. $1 multicoloured 40 50
903. $2.50 multicoloured . . 80 1·00
904. $2.50 multicoloured . . 80 1·00

DESIGNS: Nos. 893/4, Tank locomotive "Loch", Great Britain (1874). 895/6, Class "47XX", Great Britain (1919). 897/8, P.L.M. Class "121", France (1876). 899/900, Class "24", Germany (1927). 90/2, No. 1008 tank locomotive, Great Britain (1889). 903/4, Class "PS-4", U.S.A. (1926).

147. Bamboo Flute.

1985. Traditional Musical Instruments. Mult.

905. 25 c. Type **147** 15 15
906. 35 c. Quatro (four-stringed guitar) 20 25
907. $1 Ba-ha (bamboo pipe) (vert.) 50 55
908. $2 Goat-skin drum (vert.) 1·00 1·10

148. Queen Elizabeth the Queen Mother.

1985. Leaders of the World. Life and Times of Queen Elizabeth the Queen Mother. Various portraits.

910. **148.** 35 c. multicoloured . . 15 20
911. – 35 c. multicoloured . . 15 20
912. – 85 c. multicoloured . . 35 45
913. – 85 c. multicoloured . . 35 45
914. – $1.20 multicoloured . . 40 60
915. – $1.20 multicoloured . . 40 60
916. – $1.60 multicoloured . . 50 80
917. – $1.60 multicoloured . . 50 80

Each value issued in pairs showing a floral pattern across the bottom of the portraits which stops short of the left-hand edge on the first stamp and of the right-hand edge on the second.

149. Elvis Presley.

1985. Leaders of the World. Elvis Presley (entertainer). Various portraits Mult., background colours given.

919. **149.** 10 c. multicoloured . . 30 10
920. – 10 c. mult. (blue) . . 30 10
921. – 60 c. mult. (brown) . . 65 35
922. – 60 c. mult. (grey) . . 65 35
923. – $1 mult. (brown) . . 1·00 55
924. – $ mult. (blue) . . 1·00 55
925. – $5 mult. (light blue) 3·25 2·75
926. – $5 mult. (blue) . . 3·25 2·75

150. Silos and Conveyor Belt.

1985. St. Vincent Flour Milling Industry. Multicoloured.

928. 20 c. Type **150** 15 15
929. 30 c. Roller mills 15 20
930. 75 c. Administration building 40 45
931. $3 Bran finishers . . . . 1·60 1·75

1985. Royal Visit. Nos. 672/3, 697/8, 711, 724 and 912/3 optd. **CARIBBEAN ROYAL VISIT 1985** or surch. also.

932. – 60 c. mult. (711) . . 2·50 2·00
933. – 60 c. mult. (724) . . 3·00 2·50
934. – 85 c. mult. (912) . . 4·00 3·50
935. – 85 c. mult. (913) . . 4·00 3·50
936. **125.** $1.50 multicoloured . . 4·00 4·00
937. – $1.60 on $4 mult. (672) 2·00 2·50
938. – $1.60 on $4 mult. (673) 9·00 9·00
939. – $2.50 mult. (698) . . 5·50 4·50

No. 938 shows a new face value only; "Caribbean Royal Visit—1985" is omitted from the surcharge.

151. Michael Jackson.

1985. Leaders of the World. Michael Jackson (entertainer). Various portraits. Mult.

940. 60 c. multicoloured . . 25 30
941. 60 c. multicoloured . . 25 30
942. $1 multicoloured 40 45
943. $1 multicoloured 40 45
944. $2 multicoloured 85 90
945. $2 multicoloured 85 90
946. $5 multicoloured . . . . 2·10 2·25
947. $5 multicoloured . . . . 2·10 2·25

Each value issued in pairs, the left-hand design showing the face value at top left (as on Type **151**) and the right-hand design at top right.

152. "The Serenaders" (Kim de Freitas).

1985. Christmas. Children's Paintings. Mult.

949. 25 c. Type **152** 15 15
950. 75 c. "Poinsettia" (Jackie Douglas) 35 40
951. $2.50 "Jesus our Master" (Bernadette Payne) . . 1·25 1·40

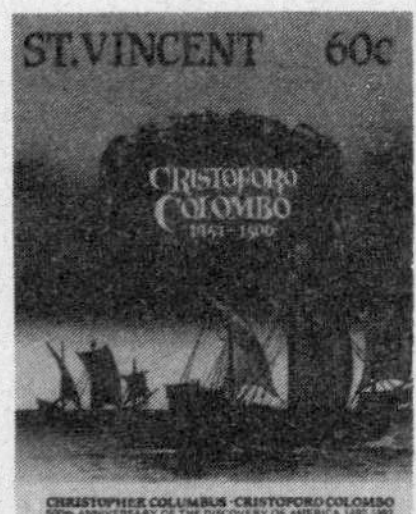

153. "Santa Maria".

1986. 500th Anniv. (1992) of Discovery of America by Columbus (1st issue). Mult.

952. 60 c. Type **153** 30 35
953. 60 c. Christopher Columbus 30 35
954. $1.50 Columbus at Spanish Court 75 80
955. $1.50 King Ferdinand and Queen Isabella of Spain 75 80
956. $2.75 "Santa Maria" and fruits . . . . . . 1·40 1·50
957. $2.75 Maize and fruits . . 1·40 1·50

See also Nos. 1125/31, 1305/24, 1639/56 and 1677/84.

1986. Leaders of the World. Automobiles (5th series). As T **133**, the first in each pair shows technical drawings and the second paintings.

959. 30 c. black, blue & orange 15 15
960. 30 c. multicoloured . . 15 15
961. 45 c. black, grey and blue 20 20
962. 45 c. multicoloured . . 20 20
963. 60 c. black, blue and red . . 25 25
964. 60 c. multicoloured . . 25 25
965. 90 c. black, yellow and blue 30 30
966. 90 c. multicoloured . . 30 30
967. $1.50 black, lilac & mauve 40 40
968. $1.50 multicoloured . . 40 40
969. $2.50 black, blue & lt. blue 50 50
970. $2.50 multicoloured . . 50 50

DESIGNS: Nos. 959/60, Cadillac "Type 53" (1916). 961/2, Triumph "Dolomite" (1939). 963/4, Panther "J-72" (1972). 965/6, Ferrari "275 GTB/4" (1967). 967/8, Packard "Caribbean" (1953). 969/70, Bugatti "Type 41 Royale" (1931).

155. Halley's Comet.

1986. Appearance of Halley's Comet. Multicoloured.

973. 45 c. Type **155** 50 30
974. 60 c. Edmond Halley . . 60 40
975. 75 c. Newton's telescope and astronomers . . 75 55
976. $3 Amateur astronomer on St. Vincent . . . . 2·25 2·25

1986. 60th Birthday of Queen Elizabeth II (1st issue). As T **117a** of Montserrat. Mult.

978. 10 c. Queen Elizabeth II . . 10 10
979. 90 c. Princess Elizabeth . . 40 40
980. $2·50 Queen gathering bouquets from crowd . . 1·00 1·00
981. $8 In Canberra, 1982 (vert.) . . 3·00 3·50

See also Nos. 996/9.

156. Mexican Player.

1986. World Cup Football Championship, Mexico. Multicoloured.

983. 1 c. Football and world map (horiz.) 10 10
984. 2 c. Type **156** 10 10
985. 5 c. Mexican player (different) 10 10
986. 5 c. Hungary v Scotland . . 10 10
987. 10 c. Spain v Scotland . . 10 10
988. 30 c. England v U.S.S.R. (horiz.) 20 20
989. 45 c. Spain v France . . 30 30
990. 75 c. Mexican team (56×36 mm.) 45 40
991. $1 England v Italy . . 75 55
992. $2 Scottish team (56×36 mm.) . . . . 1·40 1·10
993. $4 Spanish team (56×36 mm.) . . . . 2·50 2·10
994. $5 English team (56×36 mm.) . . . . 3·00 2·75

157. Queen Elizabeth at Victoria Park, Kingstown.

1986. 60th Birthday of Queen Elizabeth II (2nd issue). Scenes from 1985 Royal Visit. Multicoloured.

996. 45 c. Type **157** 25 30
997. 60 c. Queen and Prime Minister James Mitchell, Bequia 30 35
998. 75 c. Queen, Prince Philip and Mr. Mitchell, Port Elizabeth, Bequia . . 35 40
999. $2·50 Queen, Prince Philip and Mr Mitchell watching Independence Day parade, Victoria Park . . 1·25 1·40

1986. Leaders of the World. Railway Locomotives (6th series). As T **135**. Mult.

1001. 30 c. multicoloured . . 15 15
1002. 30 c. multicoloured . . 15 15
1003. 50 c. multicoloured . . 20 20
1004. 50 c. multicoloured . . 20 20
1005. $1 multicoloured . . 30 30
1006. $1 multicoloured . . 30 30
1007. $3 multicoloured . . 80 80
1008. $3 multicoloured . . 80 80

DESIGNS: Nos. 1001/2, Class "ED41 BZZB" rack and adhesion locomotive, Japan (1926). 1003/4, Locomotive "The Judge", Chicago Railroad Exposition, U.S.A. (1883). 1005/6, Class "E60C" electric locomotive, U.S.A. (1973). 1007/8, Class "SD40-2" diesel locomotive, U.S.A. (1972).

1986. Royal Wedding (1st issue). As T **168** of British Virgin Islands. Multicoloured.

1009. 60 c. Profile of Prince Andrew 20 25
1010. 60 c. Miss Sarah Ferguson 20 25
1011. $2 Prince Andrew with Mrs. Nancy Reagan (horiz.) 65 85
1012. $2 Prince Andrew in naval uniform (horiz.) 65 85

See aslo Nos. 1022/5.

158. "Acrocomia aculeata".

1986. Timber Resources of St. Vincent. Multicoloured.

1014.	10 c. Type **158**	30	15
1015.	60 c. "Pithecellobium saman"	90	60
1016.	75 c. White cedar	1·25	75
1017.	$3 "Andira inermis" ..	3·25	3·50

159. Cadet Force Emblem and Cadets of 1936 and 1986.

1986. 50th Anniv. of St. Vincent Cadet Force (45 c., $2) and 75th Anniv. of St. Vincent Girls' High School (others). Multicoloured.

1018.	45 c. Type **159**	30	30
1019.	60 c. Grimble Building, Girls' High School (horiz.)	35	35
1020.	$1.50 High School pupils (horiz.)	80	80
1021.	$2 Cadets on parade (horiz.)	1·25	1·10

1986. Royal Wedding (2nd issue). Nos. 1009/12 optd. **Congratulations to T.R.H. The Duke and Duchess of York.**

1022.	60 c. Profile of Prince Andrew	30	35
1023.	60 c. Miss Sarah Ferguson	30	35
1024.	$2 Prince Andrew with Mrs. Nancy Reagan (horiz.)	1·00	1·10
1025.	$2 Prince Andrew in naval uniform (horiz.)	1·00	1·10

160. King Arthur.

1986. The Legend of King Arthur. Multicoloured.

1026.	30 c. Type **160**	40	40
1027.	45 c. Merlin taking baby Arthur	50	50
1028.	60 c. Arthur pulling sword from stone ..	60	60
1029.	75 c. Camelot	70	70
1030.	$1 Arthur receiving Excalibur from the Lady of the Lake ..	80	80
1031.	$1.50 Knights at the Round Table ..	1·25	1·25
1032.	$2 The Holy Grail ..	1·50	1·50
1033.	$5 Sir Lancelot jousting	2·75	2·75

MINIMUM PRICE

The minimum price quoted is 10p which represents a handling charge rather than a basis for valuing common stamps. For further notes about prices see introductory pages.

161. Statue of Liberty Floodlit.

1986. Centenary of Statue of Liberty. Designs showing aspects of the Statue.

1034. **161.**	15 c. multicoloured ..	10	10
1035. –	25 c. multicoloured ..	15	15
1036. –	40 c. multicoloured ..	20	25
1037. –	55 c. multicoloured ..	25	30
1038. –	75 c. multicoloured ..	35	40
1039. –	90 c. multicoloured ..	45	50
1040. –	$1.75 multicoloured	90	95
1041. –	$2 multicoloured ..	1·00	1·10
1042. –	$2.50 multicoloured	1·25	1·40
1043. –	$3 multicoloured ..	1·50	1·60

162. Fishing for Tri Tri.

1986. Freshwater Fishing. Multicoloured.

1045.	75 c. Type **162**	35	40
1046.	75 c. Tri Tri	35	40
1047.	$1.50 Crayfishing ..	75	80
1048.	$1.50 Crayfish	75	80

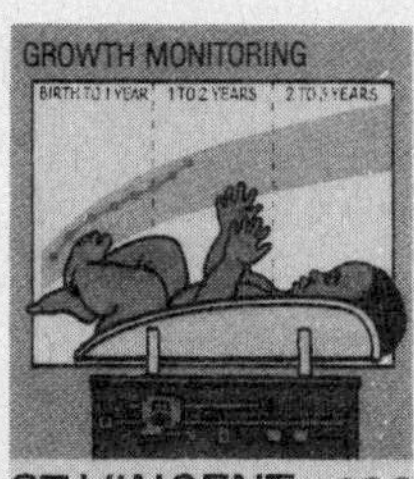

163. Baby on Scales.

1987. Child Health Campaign. Multicoloured.

1049.	10 c. Type **163**	10	10
1050.	50 c. Oral rehydration therapy	35	40
1051.	75 c. Breast feeding ..	50	55
1052.	$1 Nurse giving injection	75	80

1987. World Population Control. Nos. 1049/52 optd. **WORLD POPULATION 5 BILLION 11TH JULY 1987.**

1053.	10 c. Type **163**	10	10
1054.	50 c. Oral rehydration therapy	40	40
1055.	75 c. Breast feeding ..	55	55
1056.	$1 Nurse giving injection	70	70

165. Hanna Mandlikova.

1987. International Lawn Tennis Players. Multicoloured.

1057.	40 c. Type **165**	25	25
1058.	60 c. Yannick Noah ..	35	35
1059.	80 c. Ivan Lendl ..	40	40
1060.	$1 Chris Evert	50	50
1061.	$1.25 Steffi Graf	60	60
1062.	$1.50 John McEnroe ..	75	75
1063.	$1.75 Martina Navratilova with Wimbledon trophy	85	85
1064.	$2 Boris Becker with Wimbledon trophy ..	95	95

166. Miss Prima Donna, Queen of the Bands, 1986.

1987. 10th Anniv. of Carnival. Multicoloured.

1066.	20 c. Type **166**	10	15
1067.	45 c. Donna Young, Miss Carnival, 1985 ..	20	25
1068.	55 c. Miss St. Vincent and the Grenadines, 1986	25	30
1069.	$3.70 "Spirit of Hope" costume, 1986	1·60	1·75

The 45 c. value is inscribed "Miss Carival" in error.

1987. 10th Death Anniv. of Elvis Presley (entertainer). Nos. 919/26 optd. **THE KING OF ROCK AND ROLL LIVES FOREVER AUGUST 16th 1977-1987.**

1070. **149.**	10 c. mult.	10	10
1071. –	10 c. mult. (blue) ..	10	10
1072. –	60 c. mult. brown ..	25	30
1073. –	60 c. mult. (grey) ..	25	30
1074. –	$1 mult. (brown) ..	40	45
1075. –	$1 mult. (blue) ..	40	45
1076. –	$5 mult. (light blue)	2·10	2·25
1078. –	$5 mult. (blue) ..	2·10	2·25

168. Queen Victoria, 1841.

1987. Royal Ruby Wedding and 150th Anniv. of Queen Victoria's Accession. Mult.

1079.	15 c. Type **168**	15	10
1080.	75 c. Queen Elizabeth and Prince Andrew, 1960	45	40
1081.	$1 Coronation, 1953 ..	60	50
1082.	$2.50 Duke of Edinburgh, 1948 ..	1·40	1·50
1083.	$5 Queen Elizabeth II, c. 1980	2·50	2·75

MORE DETAILED LISTS

are given in the Stanley Gibbons Catalogues referred to in the country headings.
For lists of current volumes see Introduction.

169. Karl Benz and Benz Three-wheeler (1886). (Illustration reduced. Actual size 60 × 40 mm.).

1987. Century of Motoring. Multicoloured.

1085.	$1 Type **169**	60	60
1086.	$2 Enzo Ferrari and Ferrari "Dino 206SP" (1966)	1·25	1·25
1087.	$4 Charles Rolls and Sir Henry Royce and Rolls-Royce "Silver Ghost" (1907)	2·00	2·00
1088.	$5 Henry Ford and Ford "Model T" (1908) ..	2·50	2·50

170. Everton Football Team. (Illustration reduced. Actual size 60 × 40 mm.).

1987. English Football Teams. Mult.

1090.	$2 Type **170**	1·25	1·25
1091.	$2 Manchester United ..	1·25	1·25
1092.	$2 Tottenham Hotspur	1·25	1·25
1093.	$2 Arsenal	1·25	1·25
1094.	$2 Liverpool	1·25	1·25
1095.	$2 Derby County ..	1·25	1·25
1096.	$2 Portsmouth	1·25	1·25
1097.	$2 Leeds United ..	1·25	1·25

171. Five Cent Coins. 172. Charles Dickens.

1987. East Caribbean Currency. Mult.

1098	5 c. Type **171**	10	10
1099	6 c. Two cent coins ..	10	10
1100	10 c. Ten cent coins ..	10	10
1101	12 c. Two and ten cent coins	10	10
1102	15 c. Five cent coins ..	10	10
1103	20 c. Ten cent coins ..	10	10
1104	25 c. Twenty-five cent coins	10	15
1105	30 c. Five and twenty-five cent coins	10	15
1106	35 c. Twenty-five and ten cent coins	15	20
1107	45 c. Twenty-five and two ten cent coins	20	25
1108	50 c. Fifty cent coins ..	20	25
1109	65 c. Fifty, ten and five cent coins	25	30
1110	75 c. Fifty and twenty-five cent coins ..	30	35
1111	$1 One dollar note (horiz)	40	45
1112	$2 Two one dollar notes (horiz)	85	90
1113	$3 Three one dollar notes (horiz)	1·25	1·40
1114	$5 Five dollar note (horiz)	2·10	2·25
1115	$10 Ten dollar note (horiz)	4·25	4·50
1115a	$20 Twenty-dollar note (horiz)	8·50	8·75

1987. Christmas. 175th Birth Anniv. of Charles Dickens. Multicoloured.

1116.	6 c. Type **172**	10	10
1117.	6 c. Mr. Fezziwig's Ball	10	10
1118.	25 c. Type **172**	15	15
1119.	25 c. Scrooge's Third Visitor	15	15

1120. 50 c. Type **172** 30 30
1121. 50 c. The Cratchits' Christmas 30 30
1122. 75 c. Type **172** 45 45
1123. 75 c. "A Christmas Carol" 45 45

Nos. 1116/17, 1118/19, 1120/1 and 1122/3 were printed together, se-tenant, each pair forming a composite design showing an open book. The first design in each pair shows Type **172** and the second a scene from "A Christmas Carol".

173. "Santa Maria".

1988. 500th Anniv. (1992) of Discovery of America by Columbus (2nd issue). Mult.
1125. 15 c. Type **173** 15 15
1126. 75 c. "Nina" and "Pinta" 50 50
1127. $1 Compass and hour-glass 70 70
1128. $1.50 Claiming the New World for Spain .. 90 90
1129. $3 Arawak village .. 1·50 1·50
1130. $4 Parrot, hummingbird, pineapple and maize .. 2·00 2·00

174. Brown Pelican. **175.** Windsurfing.

1988.
1132. **174.** 45 c. multicoloured .. 20 25

1988. Tourism. Multicoloured.
1133. 10 c. Type **175** 10 10
1134. 45 c. Scuba diving .. 20 25
1135. 65 c. Aerial view of Young Island (horiz.) 30 35
1136. $5 Charter yacht (horiz.) 2·10 2·25

176 "Nuestra Senora del Rosario" (galleon) and Spanish Knight's Cross (Illustration reduced, actual size 56 × 36 mm)

1988. 400th Anniv of Spanish Armada. Mult.
1137 15 c. Type **176** 15 10
1138 75 c. "Ark Royal" and English Armada medal 30 35
1139 $1.50 English fleet and Drake's dial .. 60 65
1140 $2 Dismasted Spanish ship and 16th-century shot 80 85
1141 $3.50 Attack of English fireships at Calais and 16th-century grenade .. 1·50 1·60
1142 $5 "Revenge" and Drake's Drum .. 2·10 2·25

177 D. K. Lillee

1988. Cricketers of 1988 International Season. Multicoloured.
1144 15 c. Type **177** 30 30
1145 50 c. G. A. Gooch .. 50 50
1146 75 c. R. N. Kapil Dev .. 70 70
1147 $1 S. M. Gavaskar .. 85 85
1148 $1.50 M. W. Gatting .. 1·25 1·25
1149 $2.50 Imran Khan .. 1·75 1·75
1150 $3 I. T. Botham .. 2·00 2·00
1151 $4 I. V. A. Richards .. 2·25 2·25

178 Athletics

1988. Olympic Games, Seoul. Multicoloured.
1153 10 c. Type **178** 10 10
1154 50 c. Long jumping (vert) 20 25
1155 $1 Triple jumping .. 40 45
1156 $5 Boxing (vert) .. 2·10 2·25

179 Babe Ruth

1988. Famous Baseball Players (1st series).
1158 **179** $2 multicoloured .. 85 90

See also Nos. 1264/75, 1407 and 1408/88.

1988. Christmas. "Mickey's Christmas Train". As T **246** of Antigua. Multicoloured.
1160 1 c. Minnie Mouse in rail-way van loaded with candy (horiz) 10 10
1161 2 c. Mordie and Ferdie in wagon with toys (horiz) 10 10
1162 3 c. Chip n'Dale in wagon with Christmas trees (horiz) 10 10
1163 4 c. Donald Duck's nephews riding with reindeer (horiz) .. 10 10
1164 5 c. Donald and Daisy Duck in restaurant car (horiz) 10 10
1165 10 c. Grandma Duck, Uncle Scrooge McDuck, Goofy and Clarabelle carol singing in carriage (horiz) 10 10
1166 $5 Mickey Mouse driving locomotive (horiz) .. 2·10 2·25
1167 $6 Father Christmas in guard's van (horiz) .. 2·50 2·75

181 Mickey Mouse as Snake Charmer

1989. "India-89" International Stamp Exhibition, New Delhi. Multicoloured.
1169 1 c. Type **181** 10 10
1170 2 c. Goofy with chow-singha antelope .. 10 10
1171 3 c. Mickey and Minnie Mouse with blue peacock .. 10 10
1172 5 c. Goofy with Briolette Diamond and Mickey Mouse pushing mine truck 10 10
1173 10 c. Clarabelle with Orloff Diamond .. 10 10
1174 25 c. Mickey Mouse as tourist and Regent Diamond, Louvre, Paris 10 15
1175 $4 Minnie and Mickey Mouse with Kohinoor Diamond .. .. 1·75 1·90
1176 $5 Mickey Mouse and Goofy with Indian rhinoceros .. .. 2·10 2·25

182 Harry James

1989. Jazz Musicians. Multicoloured.
1178 10 c. Type **182** 10 10
1179 15 c. Sidney Bechet .. 10 10
1180 25 c. Benny Goodman .. 10 15
1181 35 c. Django Reinhardt .. 15 20
1182 50 c. Lester Young .. 20 25
1183 90 c. Gene Krupa .. 40 45
1184 $3 Louis Armstrong .. 1·25 1·40
1185 $4 Duke Ellington .. 1·75 1·90

183 Head of St. Vincent Amazon

1989. Wildlife Conservation. St. Vincent Amazon ("St. Vincent Parrot"). Multicoloured.
1187 10 c. Type **183** 10 10
1188 20 c. St. Vincent amazon in flight 10 10
1189 40 c. Feeding (vert) .. 15 20
1190 70 c. At entrance to nest (vert) 30 35

184 Blue-hooded Euphonia

1989. Birds of St. Vincent. Multicoloured.
1191 25 c. Type **184** 10 15
1192 75 c. Common black hawk 30 35
1193 $2 Mangrove cuckoo .. 85 90
1194 $3 Hooded tanager .. 1·25 1·40

185 Birds in Flight

1989. Wildlife Conservation. Noah's Ark. Multicoloured.
1196 40 c. Type **185** 15 20
1197 40 c. Rainbow (left side) 15 20
1198 40 c. Noah's Ark on mountain .. 15 20
1199 40 c. Rainbow (right side) 15 20
1200 40 c. Birds in flight (different) 15 20
1201 40 c. Cow elephant .. 15 20
1202 40 c. Bull elephant .. 15 20
1203 40 c. Top of eucalyptus tree 15 20
1204 40 c. Kangaroos 15 20
1205 40 c. Hummingbird .. 15 20
1206 40 c. Lions 15 20
1207 40 c. White-tailed deer .. 15 20
1208 40 c. Koala in fork of tree 15 20
1209 40 c. Koala on branch .. 15 20
1210 40 c. Hummingbird approaching flower .. 15 20
1211 40 c. Toucan and flower 15 20
1212 40 c. Toucan facing right 15 20
1213 40 c. Camels 15 20
1214 40 c. Giraffes 15 20
1215 40 c. Mountain sheep .. 15 20
1216 40 c. Ladybirds on leaf .. 15 20
1217 40 c. "Eurytides sp." (butterfly) 15 20
1218 40 c. "Eurytides sp." (butterfly) behind leaves 15 20
1219 40 c. Pythons 15 20
1220 40 c. Dragonfiles 15 20

Nos. 1187/1211 were printed together, se-tenant, forming a composite design showing Noah's Ark and animals released after the Flood.

1989. Easter. 500th Birth Anniv of Titian (artist). As T **238** of Antigua. Multicoloured.
1221 5 c. "Baptism of Christ" (detail) 10 10
1222 30 c. "Temptation of Christ" 10 15
1223 45 c. "Ecce Homo" .. 20 25
1224 65 c. "Noli Me Tangere" (fragment) 25 30
1225 75 c. "Christ carrying the Cross" (detail) .. 30 35
1226 $1 "Christ crowned with Thorns" (detail) .. 40 45
1227 $4 "Lamentation over Christ" (detail) .. 1·75 1·90
1228 $5 "The Entombment" (detail) .. .. 2·10 2·25

186 "Ile de France"

1989. Ocean Liners. Multicoloured.
1230 10 c. Type **186** 10 10
1231 40 c. "Liberte" .. 15 20
1232 50 c. "Mauretania" (launched 1906) .. 20 25
1233 75 c. "France" 30 35
1234 $1 "Aquitania" .. 40 45
1235 $2 "United States" .. 85 90
1236 $3 "Olympic" .. 1·25 1·40
1237 $4 "Queen Elizabeth" .. 1·75 1·90

187 Space Shuttle deploying West German Satellite, 1983

1989. International Co-operation in Space. Multicoloured.
1239 40 c. Type **187** 15 20
1240 60 c. Vladimir Remeck (Czech cosmonaut) and "Soyuz 28", 1978 .. 25 30
1241 $1 Projected "Hermes" space plane and "Columbus" Space Station 40 45
1242 $4 Ulf Merbold (West German astronaut), 1983, and proposed European Spacelab .. 1·75 1·90

188 "Mercury 9" Capsule and Astronaut L. Gordon Cooper

1989. 25th Anniv of Launching of "Telstar II" Communications Satellite (1988). Each showing satellite and T.V. screen. Mult.

1244 15 c. Type **188** 10 10
1245 35 c. Martin Luther King addressing crowd, 1963 15 20
1246 50 c. Speedskater, Winter Olympic Games, Innsbruck, 1964 .. .. 20 25
1247 $3 Pope John XXIII blessing crowd .. 1·25 1·40

1989. Japanese Art. As T **250** of Antigua. Multicoloured.

1249 10 c. "Autumn Flowers in Front of the Full Moon" (Hiroshige) .. 10 10
1250 40 c. "Hibiscus" (Hiroshige) 15 20
1251 50 c. "Iris" (Hiroshige) .. 20 25
1252 75 c. "Morning Glories" (Hiroshige) 30 35
1253 $1 "Dancing Swallows" (Hiroshige) 40 45
1254 $2 "Sparrow and Bamboo" (Hiroshige) 85 90
1255 $3 "Yellow Bird and Cotton Rose" (Hiroshige) .. 1·25 1·40
1256 $4 "Judos Chrysanthemums in a Deep Ravine in China" (Hiroshige) 1·75 1·90

189 Schooner

1989. "Philexfrance 89" International Stamp Exhibition, Paris, and Bicentenary of French Revolution. 18th-century French Naval Vessels. Multicoloured.

1258 30 c. Type **189** 10 15
1259 55 c. Corvette 25 30
1260 75 c. Frigate 30 35
1261 $1 Ship of the line .. 40 45
1262 $3 "Ville de Paris" (ship of the line) .. .. 1·25 1·40

190 Johnny Bench

1989. Famous Baseball Players (2nd series). Multicoloured.

1264 $2 Type **190** 85 90
1265 $2 Red Schoendienst .. 85 90
1266 $2 Carl Yastrezmski .. 85 90
1267 $2 Ty Cobb 85 90
1268 $2 Willie Mays 85 90
1269 $2 Stan Musial 85 90
1270 $2 Ernie Banks 85 90
1271 $2 Lou Gehrig 85 90
1272 $2 Jackie Robinson .. 85 90
1273 $2 Bob Feller 85 90
1274 $2 Ted Williams 85 90
1275 $2 Al Kaline 85 90

191 Dante Bichette, 1989

1989. Major League Baseball Rookies. Mult.

1276 60 c. Type **191** 25 30
1277 60 c. Carl Yastrzemski, 1961 .. .. .. 25 30
1278 60 c. Randy Johnson, 1989 25 30
1279 60 c. Jerome Walton, 1989 25 30
1280 60 c. Ramon Martinez, 1989 .. .. .. 25 30
1281 60 c. Ken Hill, 1989 .. 25 30
1282 60 c. Tom McCarthy, 1989 25 30
1283 60 c. Gaylord Perry, 1963 25 30
1284 60 c. John Smoltz, 1989 .. 25 30
1285 60 c. Bob Milacki, 1989 .. 25 30
1286 60 c. Babe Ruth, 1915 .. 25 30
1287 60 c. Jim Abbott, 1989 .. 25 30
1288 60 c. Gary Sheffield, 1989 25 30
1289 60 c. Gregg Jeffries, 1989 25 30
1290 60 c. Kevin Brown, 1989 25 30
1291 60 c. Cris Carpenter, 1989 25 30
1292 60 c. Johnny Bench, 1968 25 30
1293 60 c. Ken Griffey Jr, 1989 25 30

192 Chris Sabo

1989. Major League Baseball Award Winners. Multicoloured.

1294 60 c. Type **192** 25 30
1295 60 c. Walt Weiss .. 25 30
1296 60 c. Willie Mays .. 25 30
1297 60 c. Kirk Gibson .. 25 30
1298 60 c. Ted Williams .. 25 30
1299 60 c. Jose Canseco .. 25 30
1300 60 c. Gaylord Perry .. 25 30
1301 60 c. Orel Hershiser .. 25 30
1302 60 c. Frank Viola .. 25 30

194 St. Vincent Amazon

1989.

1304 **194** 55 c. multicoloured .. 25 30

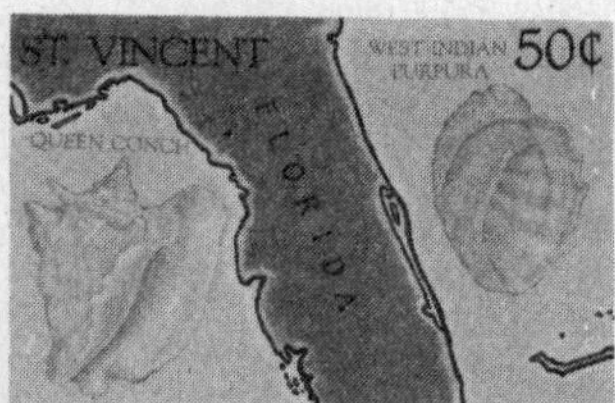

195 Queen Conch and West Indian Purpura Shells

1989. 500th Anniv (1992) of Discovery of America by Columbus (3rd issue).

1305 – 50 c. multicoloured .. 20 25
1306 – 50 c. multicoloured .. 20 25
1307 – 50 c. ultram, blk & bl 20 25
1308 – 50 c. ultram, blk & bl 20 25
1309 – 50 c. multicoloured .. 20 25
1310 – 50 c. multicoloured .. 20 25
1311 – 50 c. multicoloured .. 20 25
1312 – 50 c. black and blue 20 25
1313 – 50 c. multicoloured .. 20 25
1314 – 50 c. multicoloured .. 20 25
1315 – 50 c. multicoloured .. 20 25
1316 – 50 c. multicoloured .. 20 25
1317 – 50 c. multicoloured .. 20 25
1318 – 50 c. multicoloured .. 20 25
1319 – 50 c. multicoloured .. 20 25
1320 – 50 c. multicoloured .. 20 25
1321 – 50 c. multicoloured .. 20 25
1322 – 50 c. multicoloured .. 20 25
1323 – 50 c. multicoloured .. 20 25
1324 – 50 c. multicoloured .. 20 25

DESIGNS: No. 1305, Type **195**; 1306, Caribbean reef fishes; 1307, Sperm whale; 1308, Fleet of Columbus; 1309, Remora (fish); 1310, Columbus planting flag; 1311, Navigational instruments; 1312, Sea monster; 1313, Kemp's ridley turtle; 1314, Magnificent frigate bird; 1315, Caribbean manatee; 1316, Caribbean monk seal; 1317, Mayan Chief, dugout canoe and caravel; 1318, Masked boobies; 1319, Venezuelan pile village; 1320, Atlantic wing oyster and lion's paw scallop; 1321, Great hammerhead and mako sharks; 1322, Brown pelican and hyacinthine macaw; 1323, Venezuelan bowmen; 1324, Capuchin and squirrel monkeys.

Nos. 1305/24 were printed together, se-tenant, forming a composite design of a map of the Caribbean showing the voyages of Columbus.

196 Command Module "Columbia" returning to Earth

1989. 20th Anniv of First Manned Landing on Moon. Multicoloured.

1325 35 c. Type **196** 15 20
1326 75 c. Lunar module "Eagle" landing .. 30 35
1327 $1 "Apollo 11" launch .. 40 45
1328 $2 Buzz Aldrin on Moon 85 90
1329 $2 Lunar module "Eagle" 85 90
1330 $2 Earth rise from the Moon 85 90
1331 $2 Neil Armstrong .. 85 90
1332 $3 "Eagle" and "Columbia" in Moon orbit .. .. .. 1·25 1·40

197 Jay Howell and Alejandro Pena

1989. Centenary of the Los Angeles Dodgers (1st issue). Baseball Players. Multicoloured.

1334 60 c. Type **197** 25 30
1335 60 c. Mike Davis and Kirk Gibson 25 30
1336 60 c. Fernando Valenzuela and John Shelby .. 25 30
1337 60 c. Jeff Hamilton and Franklin Stubbs .. 25 30
1338 60 c. Aerial view of Dodger Stadium (no inscription) 25 30
1339 60 c. Ray Searage and John Tudor 25 30
1340 60 c. Mike Sharperson and Mickey Hatcher .. 25 30
1341 60 c. Coaching staff .. 25 30
1342 60 c. John Wetteland and Ramon Martinez .. 25 30
1343 60 c. Tim Belcher and Tim Crews 25 30
1344 60 c. Orel Hershiser and Mike Morgan 25 30
1345 60 c. Mike Scioscia and Rick Dempsey 25 30
1346 60 c. Dave Anderson and Alfredo Griffin .. 25 30
1347 60 c. Anniversary emblem 25 30
1348 60 c. Kal Daniels and Mike Marshall .. 25 30
1349 60 c. Eddie Murray and Willie Randolph .. 25 30
1350 60 c. Tom Lasorda and Jose Gonzalez .. 25 30
1351 60 c. Lenny Harris, Chris Gwynn and Billy Bean 25 30

See also Nos. 1541/58.

198 "Eurema venusta"

1989. Butterflies. Multicoloured.

1352 6 c. Type **198** 10 10
1353 10 c. "Historis odius" .. 10 10
1354 15 c. "Cynthia virginiensis" 10 10
1355 75 c. "Leptotes cassius" 30 35
1356 $1 "Battus polydamas" 40 45
1357 $2 "Astraptes talus" .. 85 90
1358 $3 "Danaus gilippus" .. 1·25 1·40
1359 $5 "Myscelia antholia" .. 2·10 2·25

199 Young Footballers

1989. World Cup Football Championship, Italy (1990) (1st issue). Multicoloured.

1361 10 c. Type **199** 10 10
1362 55 c. Youth football teams 25 30
1363 $1 St. Vincent team in training 40 45
1364 $5 National team with trophies .. .. 2·10 2·25

See also Nos. 1559/62.

200 St. Vincent Amazon

1989. Wildlife. Multicoloured.

1366 65 c. Type **200** 25 30
1367 75 c. Whistling warbler .. 30 35
1368 $5 Black snake .. .. 2·10 2·25

1989. California Earthquake Relief Fund. Nos. 1276/302 surch +10 **CALIF. EARTHQUAKE RELIEF.**

1370 60 c.+10 c. Type **191** .. 35 35
1371 60 c.+10 c. Carl Yastrzemski 35 35
1372 60 c.+10 c. Randy Johnson 35 35
1373 60 c.+10 c. Jerome Walton 35 35
1374 60 c.+10 c. Ramon Martinez 35 35
1375 60 c.+10 c. Ken Hill .. 35 35
1376 60 c.+10 c. Tom McCarthy 35 35
1377 60 c.+10 c. Gaylord Perry 35 35
1378 60 c.+10 c. John Smoltz 35 35
1379 60 c.+10 c. Bob Milacki 35 35
1380 60 c.+10 c. Babe Ruth .. 35 35
1381 60 c.+10 c. Jim Abbott .. 35 35
1382 60 c.+10 c. Gary Sheffield 35 35
1383 60 c.+10 c. Gregg Jeffries 35 35
1384 60 c.+10 c. Kevin Brown 35 35
1385 60 c.+10 c. Cris Carpenter 35 35
1386 60 c.+10 c. Johnny Bench 35 35
1387 60 c.+10 c. Ken Griffey Jr 35 35
1388 60 c.+10 c. Type **192** .. 35 35
1389 60 c.+10 c. Walt Weiss .. 35 35
1390 60 c.+10 c. Willie Mays 35 35
1391 60 c.+10 c. Kirk Gibson 35 35
1392 60 c.+10 c. Ted Williams 35 35
1393 60 c.+10 c. Jose Canseco 35 35
1394 60 c.+10 c. Gaylord Perry 35 35
1395 60 c.+10 c. Orel Hershiser 35 35
1396 60 c.+10 c. Frank Viola 35 35

1989. "World Stamp Expo '89" International Stamp Exhibition, Washington (1st issue). As T **256** of Antigua showing Walt Disney cartoon characters and U.S. monuments. Multicoloured.

1397 1 c. Mickey and Minnie Mouse by Seagull Monument, Utah (vert) 10 10
1398 2 c. Mickey Mouse and Goofy at Lincoln Memorial (vert) .. 10 10
1399 3 c. Mickey and Minnie Mouse at Crazy Horse Memorial, South Dakota (vert) 10 10
1400 4 c. Mickey Mouse saluting "Uncle Sam" Wilson statue, New York (vert) 10 10
1401 5 c. Goofy and Mickey Mouse at Benjamin Franklin Memorial, Philadelphia (vert) .. 10 10
1402 10 c. Goofy and Mickey Mouse at George Washington statue, New York (vert) 10 10
1403 $3 Mickey Mouse at John F. Kennedy's birth-place, Massachusetts (vert) .. .. .. 1·25 1·40
1404 $6 Mickey and Minnie Mouse at Mount Vernon, Virginia (vert) 2·50 2·75

202 Nolan Ryan

1989. Famous Baseball Players (3rd series).
1407 **202** $2 multicoloured .. 85 90

203 Early Wynn

1989. Famous Baseball Players (4th series).
1408/88 30 c. × 81 mult
Set of 81 .. .. 10·00 10·50

204 Arms and 1979 Independence 50 c. Stamp

1989. 10th Anniv of Independence.
1489 **204** 65 c. multicoloured .. 25 30

1989. Christmas. Paintings by Botticelli and Da Vinci. As T **259** of Antigua. Multicoloured.

1491 10 c. Holy Family (detail, "The Adoration of the Magi") (Botticelli) .. 10 10
1492 25 c. Crowd (detail, "The Adoration of the Magi") (Botticelli) 10 15
1493 30 c. "The Madonna of the Magnificat" (detail) (Botticelli) 10 15
1494 40 c. "The Virgin and Child with St. Anne and St. John the Baptist" (detail) (Da Vinci) .. 15 20
1495 55 c. Angel (detail, "The Annunciation") (Da Vinci) 25 30
1496 75 c. Virgin Mary (detail, "The Annunciation") (Da Vinci) 30 35
1497 $5 "Madonna of the Carnation" (detail) (Da Vinci) .. .. .. 2·10 2·25
1498 $6 "The Annunciation" (detail) (Botticelli) .. 2·50 2·75

205 Boy Scout, 1989

1989. 75th Anniv of Boy Scout and 60th Anniv of Girl Guide Movements in St. Vincent. Mult.

1500 35 c. Type **205** 15 20
1501 35 c. Guide, ranger and brownie 15 20
1502 55 c. Boy scout in original uniform 25 30
1503 55 c. Mrs. Jackson (founder of St. Vincent Girl Guides) 25 30
1504 $2 Scouts' 75th Anniv logo 85 90
1505 $2 Mrs. Russell (Girl Guide leader, 1989) .. 85 90

206 Man and Blind Girl

1990. 25th Anniv (1989) of Lions Club of St. Vincent. Multicoloured.

1507 10 c. Type **206** 10 10
1508 65 c. Handing out school books (horiz) 25 30
1509 75 c. Teacher explaining diabetes (horiz) .. 30 35
1510 $2 Blood sugar testing machine (horiz) .. 85 90
1511 $4 Distributing book on drugs (horiz) .. .. 1·75 1·90

1990. 50th Anniv of Second World War. As T **98** of Grenada Grenadines. Mult.

1512 5 c. Scuttling of "Admiral Graf Spee", 1939 .. 10 10
1513 10 c. General De Gaulle and French resistance, 1940 .. .. .. 10 10
1514 15 c. British tank, North Africa, 1940 .. .. 10 10
1515 25 c. U.S.S "Reuben James" in periscope sight, 1941 .. .. 10 15
1516 30 c. General MacArthur and map of S.W. Pacific, 1942 .. .. 10 15
1517 40 c. American parachute drop on Corregidor, 1945 .. .. .. 15 20
1518 55 c. H.M.S. "King George V" engaging "Bismarck", 1941 .. 25 30
1519 75 c. American battleships entering Tokyo Bay, 1945 .. .. .. 30 35
1520 $5 Hoisting the Soviet flag on the Reichstag, Berlin, 1945 .. .. 2·10 2·25
1521 $6 American carriers, Battle of Philippine Sea, 1944 .. .. 2·50 2·75

207 Two Pence Blue

1990. 150th Anniv of the Penny Black.
1523 **207** $2 black, green & mve 85 90
1524 – $4 black and mauve 1·75 1·90
DESIGN: $4, Penny Black.

1990. "Stamp World London 90" International Stamp Exhibition. British Uniforms. As T **193** of Gambia showing Walt Disney cartoon characters. Multicoloured.

1526 5 c. Scrooge McDuck as 18th-century Admiral 10 10
1527 10 c. Huey as Light Infantry bugler, 1854 .. 10 10
1528 15 c. Minnie Mouse as Irish Guards drummer, 1900 .. .. .. 10 10
1529 25 c. Goofy as Seaforth Highlanders lance-corporal, 1944 .. .. 10 15
1530 $1 Mickey Mouse as 58th Regiment ensign, 1879 40 45
1531 $2 Donald Duck as Royal Engineers officer, 1813 85 90
1532 $4 Mickey Mouse as Duke of Edinburgh's Royal Regiment drum major 1·75 1·90
1533 $5 Goofy as Cameronians sergeant piper, 1918 .. 2·10 2·25

1990. Nolan Ryan—Sixth No-hitter. No. 1407 optd **Sixth No-Hitter 11 June 90 Oakland Athletics**.
1535 **202** $2 multicoloured .. 85 90

1990. 90th Birthday of Queen Elizabeth the Queen Mother. As T **99** of Grenada Grenadines.
1536 $2 black, green & mauve 85 90
1537 $2 black, green & mauve 85 90
1538 $2 black, green & mauve 85 90
DESIGNS: No. 1536, Queen Elizabeth signing visitors' book; 1537, Queen Elizabeth in evening dress; 1538, Queen Elizabeth the Queen Mother in Coronation robes, 1953.

1990. Nolan Ryan—300th Win. No. 1407 optd **300th Win Milwaukee Brewers July 31, 1990**.
1540 **202** $2 multicoloured .. 85 90

1990. Cent of Los Angeles Dodgers (2nd issue). Baseball Players. As T **197**. Multicoloured.

1541 60 c. Mickey Hatcher and Jay Howell 25 30
1542 60 c. Juan Samuel and Mike Scioscia 25 30
1543 60 c. Lenny Harris and Mike Hartley 25 30
1544 60 c. Ramon Martinez and Mike Morgan 25 30
1545 60 c. Aerial view of Dodger Stadium (inscr "DODGER STADIUM") 25 30
1546 60 c. Stan Javier and Don Aase 25 30
1547 60 c. Ray Searage and Mike Sharperson .. 25 30
1548 60 c. Tim Belcher and Pat Perry 25 30
1549 60 c. Dave Walsh, Jose Vizcaino, Jim Neidlinger, Jose Offerman and Carlos Hernandez 25 30
1550 60 c. Hubie Brooks and Orel Hershiser .. 25 30
1551 60 c. Tom Lasorda and Tim Crews 25 30
1552 60 c. Fernando Valenzuela and Eddie Murray .. 25 30
1553 60 c. Kal Daniels and Jose Gonzalez 25 30
1554 60 c. Dodgers emblem .. 25 30
1555 60 c. Chris Gwynn and Jeff Hamilton .. 25 30
1556 60 c. Kirk Gibson and Rick Dempsey .. 25 30
1557 60 c. Jim Gott and Alfredo Griffin .. 25 30
1558 60 c. Ron Perranoski, Bill Russell, Joe Ferguson, Joe Amalfitano, Mark Cresse, Ben Hines and Manny Mota .. 25 30

210 Maradona, Argentina

1990 World Cup Football Championship, Italy (2nd issue). Multicoloured.

1559 10 c. Type **210** 10 10
1560 75 c. Valderrama, Colombia 30 35
1561 $1 Francescoli, Uruguay 40 45
1562 $5 Beulemans, Belgium .. 2·00 2·10

1990. 95th Anniv of Rotary International. Nos. 1230/7 optd with Rotary emblem.

1564 10 c. Type **186** 10 10
1565 40 c. "Liberte" .. 15 20
1566 50 c. "Mauretania" (launched 1906) .. 20 25
1567 75 c. "France" .. 30 35
1568 $1 "Aquitania" 40 45
1569 $2 "United States" .. 85 90
1570 $3 "Olympic" .. 1·25 1·40
1571 $4 "Queen Elizabeth" .. 1·75 1·90

1990. Olympic Medal Winners, Seoul. Nos. 1153/6 optd.

1573 10 c. Type **178** (optd **JOE DELOACH U.S.A STEVE LEWIS U.S.A. PAUL ERANG KENYA**) .. 10 10
1574 50 c. Long jumping (optd **CARL LEWIS U.S.A.**) 20 25
1575 $1 Triple jumping (optd **HRISTO MARKOV BULGARIA**) .. 40 45
1576 $5 Boxing (optd **HENRY MASKE E. GERMANY**) .. 2·00 2·10

213 "Dendrophylax funalis" and "Dimerandra emarginata"

1990. "EXPO 90" International Garden and Greenery Exposition, Osaka. Orchids. Mult.

1578 10 c. Type **213** 10 10
1579 15 c. "Epidendrum elongatum" 10 10
1580 45 c. "Comparettia falcata" 20 25
1581 60 c. "Brassia maculata" 25 30
1582 $1 "Encyclia cochleata" and "Encyclia cordigera" 40 45
1583 $2 "Cyrtopodium punctatum" 85 90
1584 $4 "Cattleya labiata" .. 1·75 1·90
1585 $5 "Bletia purpurea" .. 2·10 2·25

214 "Miraculous Draught of Fishes" (detail, Rubens)

1990. Christmas. 350th Death Anniv of Rubens. Multicoloured.

No.	Description		
1587	10 c. Type **214**	10	10
1588	45 c. "Crowning of Holy Katherine" (detail)	20	25
1589	50 c. "St. Ives of Treguier" (detail)	20	25
1590	65 c. "Allegory of Eternity" (detail)	25	30
1591	$1 "St. Bavo receives Monastic Habit of Ghent" (detail)	40	45
1592	$2 "Crowning of Holy Katherine" (different detail)	85	90
1593	$4 "St. Bavo receives Monastic Habit of Ghent" (different detail)	1·75	1·90
1594	$5 "Communion of St. Francis" (detail)	2·10	2·25

215 Geoffrey Chaucer

1990 International Literacy Year. Chaucer's "Canterbury Tales". Multicoloured.

No.	Description		
1596	40 c. Type **215**	15	20
1597	40 c. "When April with his showers..."	15	20
1598	40 c. "When Zephyr also has..."	15	20
1599	40 c. "And many little birds..."	15	20
1600	40 c. "And palmers to go seeking out..."	15	20
1601	40 c. Quill in ink well and open book	15	20
1602	40 c. Green bird in tree	15	20
1603	40 c. Brown bird in tree and franklin's head	15	20
1604	40 c. Purple bird in tree and banner	15	20
1605	40 c. Canterbury	15	20
1606	40 c. Knight's head	15	20
1607	40 c. Black bird in tree and squire's head	15	20
1608	40 c. Friar	15	20
1609	40 c. Franklin	15	20
1610	40 c. Prioress and monk holding banner	15	20
1611	40 c. Summoner, Oxford clerk and parson	15	20
1612	40 c. Serjeant-at-Law and knight on horseback	15	20
1613	40 c. Squire	15	20
1614	40 c. "In fellowship..."	15	20
1615	40 c. Cockerel and horse's legs	15	20
1616	40 c. Hens	15	20
1617	40 c. Hen and rabbit	15	20
1618	40 c. Horses' legs and butterfly	15	20
1619	40 c. "And briefly, when the sun..."	15	20

Nos. 1596/1619 were printed together, se-tenant, forming a composite design.

216 Self-portrait, 1889

1990. Death Cent of Van Gogh (painter). Mult.

No.	Description		
1620	1 c. Type **216**	10	10
1621	5 c. Self-portrait, 1886	10	10
1622	10 c. Self-portrait with hat and pipe, 1888	10	10
1623	15 c. Self-portrait at easel, 1888	10	10
1624	20 c. Self-portrait, 1887	10	10
1625	45 c. Self-portrait, 1889 (different)	20	25
1626	$5 Self-portrait with pipe, 1889	2·10	2·25
1627	$6 Self-portrait wearing straw hat, 1887	2·50	2·75

217 "The Photographer"

1990. Hummel Figurines. Multicoloured.

No.	Description		
1628	10 c. Type **217**	10	10
1629	15 c. "Ladder and Rope"	10	10
1630	40 c. "Druggist"	15	20
1631	60 c. "Hello"	25	30
1632	$1 "Boots"	40	45
1633	$2 "The Artist"	80	85
1634	$4 "Waiter"	1·75	1·90
1635	$5 "The Postman"	2·10	2·25

218 U.S.A. 1893 1 c. Columbus Stamp

1991. 500th Anniv (1992) of Discovery of America by Columbus (4th issue). Designs showing U.S.A 1893 Columbian Exposition, Chicago, stamps (Nos.1639/54) or ships (others). Multicoloured.

No.	Description		
1639	1 c. Type **218**	10	10
1640	2 c. Columbus 2 c.	10	10
1641	3 c. Columbus 3 c.	10	10
1642	4 c. Columbus 4 c.	10	10
1643	5 c. Columbus 5 c.	10	10
1644	6 c. Columbus 6 c.	10	10
1645	8 c. Columbus 8 c.	10	10
1646	10 c. Columbus 10 c.	10	10
1647	15 c. Columbus 15 c.	10	10
1648	30 c. Columbus 30 c.	10	15
1649	50 c. Columbus 50 c.	20	25
1650	$1 Columbus $1	40	45
1651	$2 Columbus $2	80	85
1652	$3 Columbus $3	1·25	1·40
1653	$4 Columbus $4	1·75	1·90
1654	$5 Columbus $5	2·10	2·25
1655	$10 "Santa Maria", parrot and tropical flower	4·25	4·50
1656	$10 Logo, "Santa Maria" and Amerindian hut	4·25	4·50

219 Pebbles and Hoppy boxing

1991. Sports. Characters from the "Flintstones" cartoons. Multicoloured.

No.	Description		
1658	10 c. Type **219**	10	10
1659	15 c. Fred Flintstone and Dino playing football	10	10
1660	45 c. Fred losing rowing race to Barney Rubble	20	25
1661	55 c. Betty Rubble, Wilma Flintstone and Pebbles in dressage competition	25	30
1662	$1 Fred playing basketball	40	45
1663	$2 Bamm Bamm wrestling Barney with Fred as referee	85	90
1664	$4 Fred and Barney playing tennis	1·75	1·90
1665	$5 Fred, Barney and Dino cycling	2·10	2·25

220 Board Meeting

1991. "The Jetsons" (cartoon film). Mult.

No.	Description		
1667	5 c. Type **220**	10	10
1668	20 c. Jetsons with Dog	10	10
1669	45 c. Judy and Apollo Blue	20	25
1670	50 c. Cosmo Spacely and George Jetson	20	25
1671	60 c. George and Elroy catching cogs (horiz)	25	30
1672	$1 Judy, Apollo, Elroy and Teddy in cavern (horiz)	40	45
1673	$2 Drill destroying the cavern (horiz)	85	90
1674	$4 Jetsons celebrating with the Grungees	1·75	1·90
1675	$5 The Jetsons returning home	2·10	2·25

1991. 500th Anniv (1992) of Discovery of America by Columbus, (5th issue). History of Exploration. As T **64** of Nevis. Mult.

No.	Description		
1677	5 c. "Sanger 2" (projected space shuttle)	10	10
1678	10 c. "Magellan" satellite, 1990	10	10
1679	25 c. "Buran" space shuttle	10	15
1680	75 c. Projected "Freedom" space station	30	35
1681	$1 Projected Mars mission space craft	40	45
1682	$2 "Hubble" telescope, 1990	85	90
1683	$4 Projected Mars mission "sailship"	1·75	1·90
1684	$5 Projected "Craf" satellite	2·10	2·25

1991. 65th Birthday of Queen Elizabeth II. As T **280** of Antigua. Multicoloured.

No.	Description		
1686	5 c. Queen and Prince Philip during visit to Spain, 1988	10	10
1687	60 c. Queen and Prince Philip in landau	25	30
1688	$2 Queen at Caen Hill Waterway, 1990	85	90
1689	$4 Queen at Badminton, 1983	1·75	1·90

1991. 10th Wedding Anniv of the Prince and Princess of Wales. As T **280** of Antigua. Multicoloured.

No.	Description		
1691	20 c. Prince and Princess in hard hats, 1987	10	10
1692	25 c. Portraits of Prince and Princess and sons	10	15
1693	$1 Prince Henry and Prince William, both in 1988	40	40
1694	$5 Princess Diana in France and Prince Charles in 1987	2·10	2·25

221 Class "D 51" Steam Locomotive

1991. "Philanippon '91" International Stamp Exhibition, Tokyo. Japanese Trains. Mult.

No.	Description		
1696	75 c. Type **221**	30	35
1697	75 c. Class "9600" steam locomotive	30	35
1698	75 c. Goods wagons and chrysanthemum emblem	30	35
1699	75 c. Passenger coach	30	35
1700	75 c. Decorated class "C 57" steam locomotive	30	35
1701	75 c. Oil tanker wagon	30	35
1702	75 c. Class "C 53" steam locomotive	30	35
1703	75 c. First Japanese steam locomotive	30	35
1704	75 c. Class "C 11" steam locomotive	30	35
1705	$1 Class "181" electric train	40	45
1706	$1 Class "EH-10" electric locomotive	40	45
1707	$1 Passenger coaches and Special Express symbol	40	45
1708	$1 Sendai City class "1" tram	40	45
1709	$1 Class "485" electric train	40	45
1710	$1 Sendai City street cleaning tram	40	45
1711	$1 Hakari "Bullet" train	40	45
1712	$1 Class "ED-11" electric locomotive	40	45
1713	$1 Class "EF-66" electric locomotive	40	45

222 Marcello Mastroianni (actor)

1991. Italian Entertainers. Multicoloured.

No.	Description		
1715	$1 Type **222**	40	45
1716	$1 Sophia Loren (actress)	40	45
1717	$1 Mario Lanza (singer)	40	45
1718	$1 Federico Fellini (director)	40	45
1719	$1 Arturo Toscanini (conductor)	40	45
1720	$1 Anna Magnani (actress)	40	45
1721	$1 Giancarlo Giannini (actor)	40	45
1722	$1 Gina Lollobrigida (actress)	40	45
1723	$1 Enrico Caruso (operatic tenor)	40	45

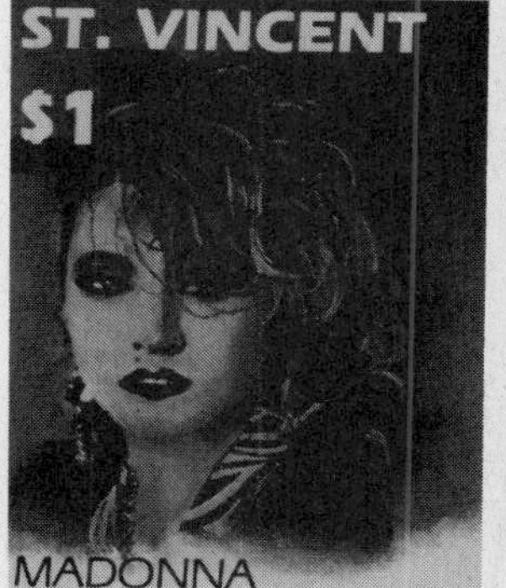

223 Madonna

1991. Madonna (American singer). Mult.

No.	Description		
1725	$1 Type **223**	40	45
1726	$1 In strapless dress	40	45
1727	$1 Wearing necklaces, looking right	40	45
1728	$1 In green dress	40	45
1729	$1 Wearing necklaces, looking to front	40	45
1730	$1 With wrist bangles	40	45
1731	$1 With hand to face	40	45
1732	$1 In purple dress	40	45
1733	$1 With microphone	40	45

224 John Lennon

1991. John Lennon (British musician). Mult.
1735 $1+2 c. Type **224** 40 45
1736 $1+2 c. With Beatle hair cut 40 45
1737 $1+2 c. In cap 40 45
1738 $1+2 c. In red polka-dot shirt 40 45
1739 $1+2 c. In green polo-neck jumper and jacket 40 45
1740 $1+2 c. In glasses and magenta jacket .. 40 45
1741 $1+2 c. With long hair and glasses 40 45
1742 $1+2 c. In black jumper 40 45
1743 $1+2 c. In polo-neck jumper 40 45

225 Tales around the Camp Fire

1991. 50th Death Anniv of Lord Baden-Powell and World Scout Jamboree, Korea. Mult.
1744 65 c. Type **225** 25 30
1745 $1.50 British trenches and Mafeking Siege 3d. stamp (horiz) 60 65
1746 $3. 50 Queen angelfish and scout diver (horiz) .. 1·50 1·75

226 Free French Resistance Fighters, 1944

1991. Birth Centenary (1990) of Charles de Gaulle (French statesman). Multicoloured.
1748 10 c. Type **226** 10 10
1749 45 c. De Gaulle with Churchill, 1944 .. 20 25
1750 75 c. Liberation of Paris, 1944 .. .. 30 35

227 Protester with Banner

1991. Bicentenary of Brandenburg Gate, Berlin. Multicoloured.
1752 50 c. Type **227** 20 25
1753 75 c. Building Berlin Wall 30 35
1754 90 c. German flag and shadows of protesters 40 45
1755 $1 Presidents Bush and Gorbachev shaking hands 40 45

1991. Death Bicentenary of Mozart. As T **226**. Multicoloured.
1757 $1 "Marriage of Figaro" 40 45
1758 $3 "The Clemency of Titus" .. .. 1·25 1·50

228 Myrvyn Bennion

1991. 50th Anniv of Japanese Attack on Pearl Harbor. Designs showing recipients of Congressional Medal of Honor. Mult.
1760 $1 Type **228** 40 45
1761 $1 George Cannon .. 40 45
1762 $1 John Finn 40 45
1763 $1 Francis Flaherty .. 40 45
1764 $1 Samuel Fuqua .. 40 45
1765 $1 Edwin Hill 40 45
1766 $1 Herbert Jones .. 40 45
1767 $1 Isaac Kidd 40 45
1768 $1 Jackson Pharris .. 40 45
1769 $1 Thomas Reeves .. 40 45
1770 $1 Donald Ross 40 45
1771 $1 Robert Scott 40 45
1772 $1 Franklin van Valkenburgh 40 45
1773 $1 James Ward 40 45
1774 $1 Cassin Young .. 40 45

1992. International Literacy Year (1st issue). As T **269** of Antigua, but horiz, showing scenes from Disney cartoon film "The Prince and The Pauper". Multicoloured.
1775 5 c. Mickey Mouse, Goofy and Pluto as pauper pals 10 10
1776 10 c. Mickey as the bored prince 10 10
1777 15 c. Donald Duck as the valet 10 10
1778 25 c. Mickey as the prince and the pauper .. 10 10
1779 60 c. Exchanging clothes 25 30
1780 75 c. Prince and pauper with suit of armour .. 30 35
1781 80 c. Throwing food from the battlements .. 35 40
1782 $1 Pete as Captain of the Guard 40 45
1783 $2 Mickey and Donald in the dungeon .. 85 90
1784 $3 Mickey and Donald at dungeon window .. 1·25 1·40
1785 $4 Goofy rescuing Mickey and Donald .. 1·75 1·90
1786 $5 Crowning the real prince .. .. 2·10 2·25

1991. International Literacy Year (2nd issue). As T **269** of Antigua but horiz, showing scenes from Disney cartoon film "The Rescuers Down Under". Multicoloured.
1788 5 c. Miss Bianca 10 10
1789 10 c. Bernard 10 10
1790 15 c. Matre d'Francoise .. 10 10
1791 25 c. Wilbur the Albatross 10 10
1792 60 c. Jake the Kangaroo Mouse 25 30
1793 75 c. Bernard, Bianca and Jake in the outback 30 35
1794 80 c. Bianca and Bernard to the rescue .. 35 40
1795 $1 Marahute the Eagle .. 40 45
1796 $2 Cody and Marahute with eggs 85 90
1797 $3 McLeach and his pet Joanna the Goanna .. 1·25 1·40
1798 $4 Frank the Frill-necked Lizard .. .. 1·75 1·90
1799 $5 Red Kangaroo, Krebbs Koala and Polly Platypus .. .. .. 2·10 2·25

1991. Centenary of Trans-Siberian Railway. As T **286** of Antigua. Multicoloured.
1801 $1.50 Modern Trans-Siberian steam locomotive (horiz) .. 60 65

1991. 700th Anniv of Swiss Confederation. As T **285** of Antigua. Multicoloured.
1802 $1.50 Map of Switzerland and woman in national costume 60 65

1991. Cent of Otto Lilienthal's Gliding Experiments. As T **285** of Antigua. Mult.
1803 $1.65 Lilienthal's signature and "Flugzeug Nr.13 Doppeldecker" .. 80 85

1991. 50th Anniv of Capture of Kiev. As T **285** of Antigua. Multicoloured.
1804 $2 Street fighting .. 85 90

1991. 750th Anniv of Hanover. As T **285** of Antigua. Multicoloured.
1805 $2 Gottfried Leibniz (mathematician) .. 85 90

1.

2. Palm trees.

3. King Malietoa Laupepa.

8.

229 Hans-Dietrich Genscher and "Winged Victory" Statue

1991. European History. Multicoloured.
1806 $1 Type **229** 40 45
1807 $1 Destruction of Berlin Wall 40 45
1808 $1 Churchill, De Gaulle and Appeal to the French, 1940 .. .. 40 45
1809 $1 Eisenhower, De Gaulle and D-Day, 1944 .. 40 45
1810 $1 Brandenburg Gate, Berlin (bicentenary) .. 40 45
1811 $1 Chancellor Helmut Kohl and meeting of Berlin mayors, 1989 .. 40 45
1812 $1 De Gaulle with Chancellor Adenauer .. 40 45
1813 $1 Pres. Kennedy's visit to Europe, 1961, Washington and Lafayette .. 40 45

1991. Famous Golfers. As T **229**. Mult.
1815 $1 Gary Player 40 45
1816 $1 Nick Faldo 40 45
1817 $1 Severiano Ballesteros 40 45
1818 $1 Ben Hogan 40 45
1819 $1 Jack Nicklaus .. 40 45
1820 $1 Greg Norman .. 40 45
1821 $1 Jose-Maria Olazabal .. 40 45
1822 $1 Bobby Jones 40 45

OFFICIAL STAMPS.

1982. Nos. 668/73 optd. **OFFICIAL.**
O 1. 60 c. "Isabella" 25 30
O 2. 60 c. Prince Charles and Lady Diana Spencer .. 50 50
O 3. $2.50 "Alberta" (tender) 80 90
O 4. $2.50 Prince Charles and Lady Diana Spencer .. 1·25 1·40
O 5. $4 "Britannia" .. .. 1·25 1·60
O 6. $4 Prince Charles and Lady Diana Spencer .. .. 2·00 2·25

SAMOA

Islands in the W. Pacific administered jointly from 1889–99 by Gt. Britain, Germany and the U.S.A. In 1889 the eastern islands were assigned to the U.S.A. and the western to Germany (for issues see Vol. 2). The latter were occupied by British forces in 1914 and were taken over by New Zealand, under mandate, in 1920. W. Samoa was under United Nations trusteeship but became independent on 1 January 1962.

1877. 12 pence = 1 shilling,
20 shillings = 1 pound.
1967. 100 sene or cents = 1 tale or dollar.

INDEPENDENT KINGDOM.

1877.
15. 1. 1d. blue .. .. .. 24·00 40·00
16. 3d. red .. .. .. 45·00 65·00
17. 6d. violet .. .. .. 40·00 48·00
20. 9d. brown .. .. 55·00 £110
7b. 1s. yellow .. .. 70·00 85·00
18. 2s. brown £130 £200
19a. 5s. green £375 £550

The majority of the stamps of T **1** found in old collections are worthless reprints. A 2d. stamp exists but was never issued.

1886.
57a 2 ½d. brown .. .. 65 1·75
88 ½d. green .. .. .. 65 1·40
58 1d. green .. .. .. 1·25 1·75
89 1d. brown .. .. 55 1·25
59c 2d. orange .. .. 4·50 1·00
60 3 2½d. red .. .. .. 70 4·50
81 2½d. black .. .. .. 90 3·00
61 2 4d. blue .. .. .. 5·75 2·00
72a 8 5d. red .. .. .. 1·25 13·00
62 2 6d. lake .. .. .. 5·50 4·00
63 1s. red .. .. .. 5·50 4·50
64b 2s. 6d. violet .. .. 4·75 9·50

1893. Surch. **FIVE PENCE** and bar.
65. 2. 5d. on 4d. blue .. .. 45·00 42·00

1893. Surch. **5d.** and bar.
69. 2. 5d. on 4d. blue .. .. 17·00 25·00

1895. Surch. **Surcharged** and **value in figures.**
75. 2. 1½d. on 2d. orange .. 1·50 3·00
84. 2½d. on 1d. green .. .. 55 2·00
85. 2½d. on 1s. red .. .. 3·50 8·50
87. 2½d. on 2s. 6d. violet .. 4·75 11·00

1895. Surch. R **3d.**
76. 2 3d. on 2d. orange .. .. 5·00 7·50

1899. Optd. **PROVISIONAL GOVT.**
90. 2. ½d. green .. .. .. 30 1·25
91. 1d. brown .. .. 90 2·50
92. 2d. orange .. .. 55 2·50
93. 4d. blue .. .. .. 45 2·25
94. 8. 5d. red .. .. .. 90 4·50
95. 2. 6d. lake .. .. .. 1·10 3·75
96. 1s. red .. .. .. 1·50 9·50
97. 2s. 6d. violet .. .. 4·75 17·00

NEW ZEALAND DEPENDENCY.
(under Mandate from League of Nations and United Nations).

1914. "Yacht" key-types as German Cameroons, but inscr "Samoa" surch **G.R.I.** and value in British currency.
101. N. ½d. on 3 pf. brown .. 16·00 8·50
102. ½d. on 5 pf. green .. 35·00 10·00
103. 1d. on 10 pf. red .. 95·00 40·00
104. 2½d. on 20 pf. blue .. 30·00 10·00
105. 3d. on 25 pf. black and red on yellow .. .. 50·00 35·00
106. 4d. on 30 pf. black and orange on buff .. £100 60·00
107. 5d. on 40 pf. black & red £110 70·00
108. 6d. on 50 pf. black and purple on buff .. 55·00 35·00
109. 9d. on 80 pf. black and red on rose .. .. £190 95·00
110. O. 1s. on 1 m. red .. £3000 £3250
112. 2s. on 2 m. blue £3000 £2750
113. 3s. on 3 m. black .. £1400 £1200
114. 5s. on 5 m. red and black £1000 £950

1914. Stamps of New Zealand (King Edward VII) optd. **SAMOA.**

115. **50.** ½d. green 30 30
116. **51.** 1d. red 30 10
117. **50.** 2d. mauve 60 95
118. **27.** 2½d. blue .. .. 1·50 1·75
119. **50.** 6d. red .. .. .. 1·50 1·75
121. 1s. red .. .. .. 3·50 9·00

1914. Large stamps of New Zealand (Queen Victoria) optd. **SAMOA.**

127 F 4 2s. blue .. .. 4·00 5·50
123 2s. 6d. brown .. .. 4·50 8·50
129 3s. violet .. .. 12·00 26·00
124 5s. green .. .. 9·50 11·00
125 10s. brown .. .. 20·00 28·00
126 £1 red .. .. .. 60·00 50·00

1916. Stamps of New Zealand (King George V) overprinted **SAMOA.**

134. **60a.** ½d. green 20 40
135. 1½d. grey 25 25
136. 1½d. brown 15 40
137. 2d. yellow 40 15
139a. 2½d. blue 35 35
140. 3d. brown 35 90
141. 6d. red .. .. 1·25 90
142a. 1s. red .. .. 1·25 1·25

1920. Stamps of New Zealand (Victory issue. Nos. 511/16) optd. **SAMOA.**

143. **62.** ½d. green .. .. 1·25 2·25
144. **63.** 1d. red .. .. 1·25 1·00
145. – 1½d. orange .. .. 1·25 4·00
146. – 3d. brown .. .. 3·50 7·00
147. – 6d. violet .. .. 4·00 6·50
148. – 1s. orange .. .. 12·00 11·00

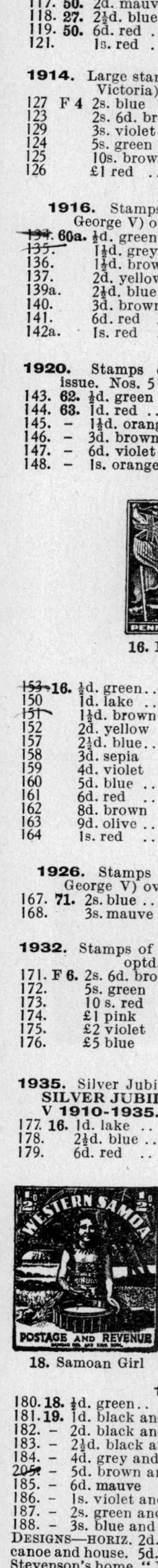

16. Native Hut.

1921.

153. **16.** ½d. green .. .. 1·00 1·75
150 1d. lake 40 20
151 1½d. brown .. .. 40 4·75
152 2d. yellow .. .. 60 1·90
157 2½d. blue.. .. .. 70 3·50
158 3d. sepia .. .. 75 3·00
159 4d. violet .. .. 80 3·00
160 5d. blue .. .. 75 5·00
161 6d. red .. .. 80 3·50
162 8d. brown .. .. 1·25 9·00
163 9d. olive .. .. 1·25 10·00
164 1s. red .. .. 1·25 11·00

1926. Stamps of New Zealand (King George V) overprinted **SAMOA.**

167. **71.** 2s. blue .. .. 4·50 12·00
168. 3s. mauve .. .. 7·00 22·00

1932. Stamps of New Zealand (Arms type) optd. **SAMOA.**

171. **F 6.** 2s. 6d. brown .. 15·00 27·00
172. 5s. green .. .. 20·00 35·00
173. 10 s. red .. .. 45·00 70·00
174. £1 pink .. .. 60·00 85·00
175. £2 violet £700
176. £5 blue £1800

1935. Silver Jubilee. Stamps of 1921 optd. **SILVER JUBILEE OF KING GEORGE V 1910-1935.**

177. **16.** 1d. lake 30 30
178. 2½d. blue 60 65
179. 6d. red .. .. 2·10 2·50

18. Samoan Girl **19.** Apia.

1935.

180. **18.** ½d. green 10 35
181. **19.** 1d. black and red .. 10 10
182. – 2d. black and orange .. 2·00 1·25
183. – 2½d. black and blue .. 10 10
184. – 4d. grey and brown .. 40 15
205. – 5d. brown and blue .. 20 50
185. – 6d. mauve 40 10
186. – 1s. violet and brown .. 30 10
187. – 2s. green and purple .. 50 50
188. – 3s. blue and orange .. 1·50 3·50

DESIGNS—HORIZ. 2d. River scene. 4d. Samoan canoe and house. 5d. Apia post office. 6d. R. L. Stevenson's home, "Vailima". 1s. Stevenson's tomb. VERT. 2½d. Samoan chief and wife. 2s. Lake Lanuto'o. 3s. Falefa Falls.

1935. Stamps of New Zealand (Arms types) optd. **WESTERN SAMOA.**

207. **F 6.** 2s. 6d. brown .. .. 2·25 5·50
208. 5s. green .. .. 5·00 7·50
209. 10s. red .. .. 16·00 17·00
234. £1 pink .. .. 27·00 35·00
211. 30s. brown £140 £225
235. £2 violet .. .. 70·00 £130
213. £3 green £170 £300
214. £5 blue £250 £350

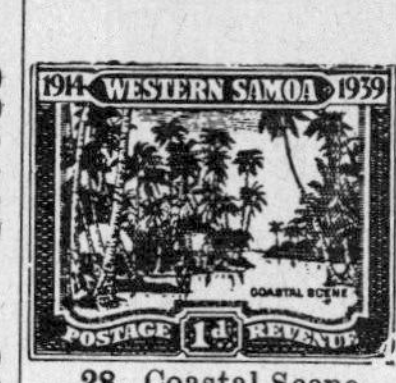

28. Coastal Scene.

31. Robert Louis Stevenson.

1939. 25th Anniv. of New Zealand Control.

195. **28.** 1d. olive and red .. 30 10
196. – 1½d. blue and brown .. 35 30
197. – 2½d. brown and blue .. 90 65
198. **31.** 7d. violet and green .. 4·50 1·50

DESIGNS—HORIZ. 1½d. Map of Western Samoa. 2½d. Samoan dancing party.

32. Samoan Chief.

35. Making Siapo Cloth.

36. Native Houses and Flags.

1940. Surch.

199. **32.** 3d. on 1½d. brown .. 10 10

1946. Peace stamps of New Zealand optd. **WESTERN SAMOA.**

215. **132.** 1d. green 10 10
216. – 2d. purple (No. 670) .. 10 10
217. – 6d. brown and red (674) 10 10
218. **139.** 8d. black and red .. 10 10

1952.

219. **35.** ½d. red and brown .. 10 40
220. **36.** 1d. olive and green .. 10 10
221. – 2d. red 10 10
222. – 3d. blue and indigo .. 40 10
223. – 5d. brown and green .. 3·50 70
224. – 6d. blue and mauve .. 40 10
225. – 8d. red 30 30
226. – 1s. sepia and blue .. 15 10
227. – 2s. brown .. .. 1·40 60
228. – 3s. brown and olive .. 3·00 2·00

DESIGNS: As Type **35**—VERT. 2d. Seal of Samoa. 5d. Tooth-billed Pigeon. HORIZ. 1s. Thatching native hut. As Type **36**—HORIZ. 3d. Malifa Falls, wrongly inscr. on stamp "Aleisa Falls". 6d. Bonito fishing canoe. 8d. Cacao harvesting. 2s. Preparing copra. VERT. 3s. Samoan chieftainess.

1953. Coronation. As Types of New Zealand.

229. **164.** 2d. brown 75 15
230. **166.** 6d. grey .. .. 1·00 35

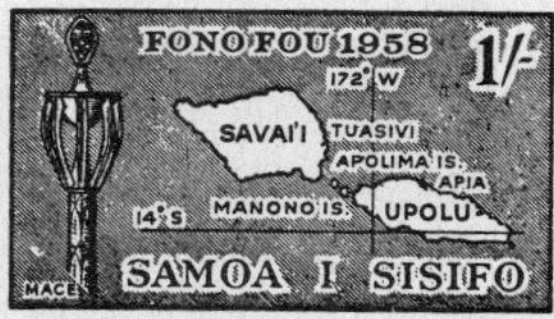

48. Map of Samoa, and the Mace.

1958. Inaug. of Samoan Parliament. Inscr. "FONO FOU 1958" and "SAMOA I SISIFO".

236. – 4d. red (As T 36) .. 15 10
237. – 6d. violet (As No. 221) 15 15
238. **48.** 1s. blue 25 15

INDEPENDENT STATE.

49. Samoan Fine Mat.

DESIGNS — HORIZ. 2d. Samoa College. 3d. Public library. 4d. Fono house. 6d. Map of Samoa. 8d. Airport. 1s. 3d. "Vailima". 2s. 6d. Samoan flag. 5s. Samoan Seal. VERT. 1s. Samoan orator.

1962. Independence.

239. **49.** 1d. brown and red .. 10 10
240. – 2d multicoloured .. 10 10
241. – 3d. brown, green & blue 10 10
242. – 4d. multicoloured .. 15 10
243. – 6d. yellow and blue .. 20 10
244. – 8d. turq., green & blue 20 10
245. – 1s. brown and green .. 20 10
246. – 1s. 3d. green and blue .. 75 35
247. – 2s. 6d. red and blue .. 1·50 1·25
248. – 5s. multicoloured .. 3·25 2·50

59. Seal and Joint Heads of State.

1963. 1st Anniv. of Independence.

249. **59.** 1d. sepia and green .. 10 10
250. 4d. sepia and blue .. 10 10
251. 8d. sepia and pink .. 10 10
252. 2 s. sepia and orange .. 20 10

60. Signing the Treaty.

1964. 2nd Anniv. of New Zealand-Samoa Treaty of Friendship.

253. **60.** 1d. multicoloured .. 10 10
254. 8d. multicoloured .. 10 10
255. 2s. multicoloured .. 20 10
256. 3s. multicoloured .. 20 20

62. Red-tailed Tropic Bird.

1965. Air.

263. **62.** 8d. black, orge & blue 40 10
264. – 2s. black and blue .. 55 20

DESIGN: 2s. Flying Fish.

64. Aerial View of Deep Sea Wharf.

1966. Opening of 1st Deep Sea Wharf, Apia. Multicoloured.

265. 1d. Type **64** 10 10
266. 8d. Aerial View of Wharf and Bay 15 10
267. 2s. Aerial View of Wharf and Bay 25 15
268. 3s. Type **64** 30 15

66. W.H.O. Building.

1966. Inaug. of W.H.O. Headquarters, Geneva.

269. **66.** 3d. ochre ,blue and slate 30 10
270. – 4d. multicoloured .. 35 10
271. **66.** 6d. lilac, green & olive.. 40 15
272. – 1s. multicoloured .. 60 20

DESIGNS: 4d. and 1s. W.H.O. Building on flag.

1966. Huurricane Relief Fund. No. 244 surch **HURRICANE RELIEF** and value.

273 8d.+6d. turqoise, grn & bl 10 10

69. Hon. Tuatagaloa L.S. (Minister of Justice).

1967. 5th Anniv. of Independence.

274. **69.** 3d. sepia and violet .. 10 10
275. – 8d. sepia and blue .. 10 10
276. – 2s. sepia and olive .. 10 10
277. – 3s. sepia and mauve .. 15 15

DESIGNS: 8d. Hon. F. C. F. Nelson (Minister of Works, Marine and Civil Aviation). 2s. Hon. To'omata T.L. (Minister of Lands). 3s. Hon. Fa'alava'au G. (Minister of Post Office, Radio and Broadcasting).

73. Samoan Fales (houses), 1890.

1967. Cent. of Mulinu'u as Seat of Government.

278. **73.** 8d. multicoloured .. 15 10
279. – 1s. multicoloured .. 15 10

DESIGN: 1s. Fono (Parliament) House, 1967.

74. Caruncalated Honeyeater.

1967. Decimal Currency. Multicoloured.

280. 1 s. Type **74** 10 10
281. 2 s. Pacific Pigeon .. 10 10
282. 3 s. Samoan Starling .. 10 10
283. 5 s. White-vented Fly-catcher 15 10
284. 7 s. Red-headed Parrot Finch 15 10
285. 10 s. Purple Swamphen .. 20 10
286. 20 s. Barn Owl .. 2·25 40
287. 25 s. Tooth-billed Pigeon 1·50 15
288. 50 s. Island Thrush .. 1·50 25
289. $1 Samoan Fantail .. 1·75 1·50
289a. $2 Black-breasted Honey-eater .. .. 5·50 7·00
289b. $4 Savaii White eye .. 40·00 45·00

85. Nurse and Child.

1967. South Pacific Health Service. Mult.

290. 3 s. Type **85** 10 10
291. 7 s. Leprosarium .. 10 10
292. 20 s. Mobile X-ray Unit .. 20 10
293. 25 s Apia Hospital .. 25 15

89. Thomas Trood.

1968. 6th Anniv. of Independence. Mult.

294. 2 s. Type **89** 10 10
295. 7 s. Dr. Wilhelm Solf .. 10 10
296. 20 s. J. C. Williams .. 10 10
297. 25 s. Fritz Marquardt .. 15 10

HAVE YOU READ THE NOTES AT THE BEGINNING OF THIS CATALOGUE?
These often provide answers to the enquiries we receive.

93. Cocoa.

1968. Agricultural Development.
298. 93. 3 s. brown, green & black 10 10
299. – 5 s. green, yellow & brn. 10 10
300. – 10 s. red, brown & yellow 10 10
301. – 20 s. bistre, yell. & olive 15 10
DESIGNS: 5 s. Breadfruit. 10 s. Copra. 20 s. Bananas.

97. Women Weaving Mats.

1968. 21st Anniv. of South Pacific Commission. Multicoloured.
302. 7 s. Type 97 .. .. 10 10
303. 20 s. Palm trees and bay .. 15 10
304. 25 s. Sheltered cove .. 15 15

1968. Kingsford-Smith's Trans-Pacific Flight. 40th Anniv. No. 285 surch. **1928-1968 KINGSFORD-SMITH TRANS-PACIFIC FLIGHT** and new value.
305. 20 s. on 10 s. multicoloured 10 10

101. Bougainville's Route.

1968. Bicent. of Bougainville's Visit to Samoa.
306. 101. 3 s. blue and black .. 10 10
307. – 7 s. ochre and black .. 15 10
308. – 20 s. multicoloured .. 45 15
309. – 25 s. multicoloured .. 60 25
DESIGNS: 7 s. Louis de Bougainville. 20 s. Bougainvillea flower. 25 s. Ships "La Boudeuse" and "L'Etoile".

105. Globe and Human Rights Emblem.

1968. Human Rights Year.
310. 105. 7 s. blue, brown & gold 10 10
311. 20 s. orge., green & gold 10 10
312. 25 s. violet, grn. & gold 15 10

106. Dr. Martin Luther King.
107. Polynesian Version of Madonna and Child.

1968. Martin Luther King. Commem.
313. 106. 7 s. black and green .. 10 10
314. 20 s. black and purple .. 10 10

1968. Christmas.
315. 107. 1 s. multicoloured .. 10 10
316. 3 s. multicoloured .. 10 10
317. 20 s. multicoloured .. 10 10
318. 30 s. multicoloured .. 15 15

108. Frangipani—"Plumeria acuminata".

1969. 7th Anniv. of Independence. Mult.
319. 2 s. Type 108 .. .. 10 10
320. 7 s. Hibiscus (vert.) .. 25 10
321. 20 s. Red-Ginger (vert.) .. 65 10
322. 30 s. Moso'oi 80 35

109. R. L. Stevenson and "Treasure Island".

1969. 75th Death Anniv. of Robert Louis Stevenson. Multicoloured.
323. 3 s. Type 109 .. .. 15 10
324. 7 s. R. L. Stevenson and "Kidnapped" 20 10
325. 20 s. R. L. Stevenson and "Dr. Jekyll and Mr. Hyde" 45 10
326. 22 s. R. L. Stevenson and "Weir of Hermiston" .. 55 15

110. Weightlifting.

1969. 3rd South Pacific Games, Port Moresby.
327. 110. 3 s. black and green .. 10 10
328. – 20 s. black and blue .. 10 10
329. – 22 s. black and orange .. 15 15
DESIGNS: 20 s. Yachting. 22 s. Boxing.

113. U.S. Astronaut on the Moon and the Splashdown near Samoan Islands.

1969. 1st Man on the Moon.
330. 113. 7 s. multicoloured .. 15 15
331. 20 s. multicoloured .. 15 15

114. "Virgin with Child" (Murillo).

1969. Christmas. Multicoloured.
332. 1 s. Type 114 .. .. 10 10
333. 3 s. "The Holy Family" (El Greco) 10 10
334. 20 s. "The Nativity" (El Greco) 20 10
335. 30 s. "The Adoration of the Magi" (detail) (Velazquez) 20 15

115. Seventh Day Adventists' Sanatorium, Apia.

1970. 8th Anniv. of Independence.
337. 115. 2 s. brown, slate & black 10 10
338. – 7 s. violet, buff & black 10 10
339. – 20 s. rose, lilac & black 15 10
340. – 22 s. green, buff & black 15 15
DESIGNS—HORIZ. 7 s. Rev. Father Violette and Roman Catholic Cathedral, Apia. 22 s. John Williams, 1797-1839, and London Missionary Society Church. Sapapali'i. VERT. 20 s. Mormon Church of Latter Day Saints, Tuasivi-on-Safotulafai.

119. Wreck of S.M.S. "Adler".

1970. Great Apia Hurricane of 1889. Mult.
341. 5 s. Type 119 .. .. 45 10
342. 7 s. U.S.S. "Nipsic" .. 50 10
343. 10 s. H.M.S. "Calliope" .. 65 25
344. 20 s. Apia after the hurricane .. .. .. 2·00 1·25

120. Sir Gordon Taylor's "Frigate Bird III".

1970. Air. Multicoloured.
345. 3 s. Type 120 .. .. 35 10
346. 7 c. Polynesian Airlines "DC-3" 70 10
347. 20 s. Pan-American Airways "Samoan Clipper" 1·75 60
348. 30 s. Air Samoa Britten-Norman "Islander" .. 2·00 1·25

121. Kendal's Chronometer and Cook's Sextant.

1970. Cook's Exploration of the Pacific.
349. 121. 1 s. red, silver and black 20 15
350. – 2 s. multicoloured 35 25
351. – 10 s. black, blue & gold 1·75 1·00
352. – 30 s. multicoloured 2·75 1·75
DESIGNS—VERT. 2 s. Cook's statue, Whitby. 10 s. Cook's head. HORIZ. 30 s. Cook, H.M.S. "Endeavour" and island (83 × 25 mm.).

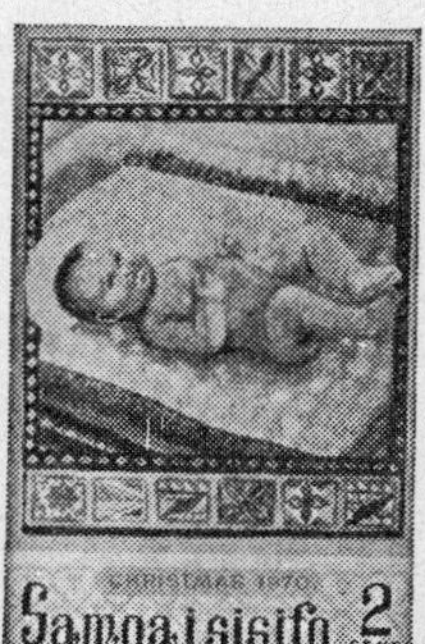

122. "Peace for the World" (F. B. Eccles).

1970. Christmas. Multicoloured.
353. 2 s. Type 122 .. .. 10 10
354. 3 s. "The Holy Family" (W. E. Jahnke) 10 10
355. 20 s. "Mother and Child" (F. B. Eccles) 15 10
356. 30 c. "Prince of Peace" (Meleane Fe'ao) 20 15

123. Pope Paul VI.

1970. Visit of Pope Paul to Samoa.
358. 123. 8 s. black and blue .. 15 15
359. 20 s. black and red .. 35 15

124. Native and Tree.

1971. Timber Industry. Multicoloured.
360. 3 s. Type 124 .. .. 10 10
361. 8 s. Bulldozer in clearing .. 15 10
362. 20 s. Log in Sawmill .. 30 10
363. 22 s. Floating Logs, and Harbour. .. 30 15
The 8 s. and 20 s. are horiz.

126. Siva Dance.

1971. Tourism. Multicoloured.
365. 5 s. Type 126 .. .. 40 10
366. 7 s. Samoan cricket .. 1·00 60
367. 8 s. Hideaway Hotel .. 1·00 35
368. 10 s. Aggie Grey and her hotel .. .. .. 1·00 60

127. "Queen Salamasina".

1971. Myths and Legends of Old Samoa (1st series). Multicoloured.
369. 3 s. Type 127 .. .. 10 10
370. 8 s. "Lu and his Sacred Hens" .. 15 10
371. 10 s. "God Tagaloa fishes Samoa from the sea" .. 20 10
372. 22 s. "Mount Vaea and the Pool of Tears" 35 20
See also Nos. 426/9.

128. "The Virgin and Child" (Bellini).

1971. Christmas.

373. 128.	2 s. multicoloured ..	10	10
374.	3 s. multicoloured ..	10	10
375. –	20 s. multicoloured ..	20	10
376. –	30 s. multicoloured ..	30	20

DESIGN: 20 s., 30 s. "The Virgin and Child with St. Anne and John the Baptist" (Leonardo da Vinci).

129. Map and Scales of Justice.

1972. First South Pacific Judicial Conference.

377. 129.	10 s. multicoloured ..	15	15

130. Asau Wharf, Savaii.

1972. 10th Anniv. of Independence. Mult.

378.	1 s. Type 130	10	10
379.	8 s. Parliament Building	10	10
380.	10 s. Mothers' Centre ..	10	10
381.	22 s. "Vailima" Residence and Rulers	20	25

131. Flags of Member Countries.

1972. 25th Anniv. of South Pacific Commission. Multicoloured.

382.	3 s. Type 131	10	15
383.	7 s. Flag and Afoafouvale Misimoa (Sec. Gen.) ..	10	15
384.	8 s. H.Q. building, Noumea (horiz.) ..	15	15
385.	10 s. Flags and area map (horiz.)	15	15

132. Expedition Ships.

1972. 250th Anniv. of Sighting of Western Samoa by Jacob Roggeveen. Multicoloured.

386.	2 c. Type 132	15	10
387.	8 s. Ships in storm (horiz.)	45	10
388.	10 s. Ships passing island (horiz.)	50	10
389.	30 s. Route of Voyage (horiz.) (85 × 25 mm.) ..	1·75	1·50

133. Bull Conch.

1972. Multicoloured.

390	1 s. Type 133	20	10
391	2 s. "Oryctes rhinoceros" (beetle)	1·50	1·50
392	3 s. Skipjack (fish) ..	1·50	1·50
393	4 s. Painted crab ..	30	10
394	5 s. Butterfly fish ..	35	10
395	7 s. "Danaus neomelissia" (butterfly)	1·25	30
396	10 s. Triton shell ..	80	40
397	20 s. "Cyphogastra abodominali" (beetle)	1·25	30
398	50 s. Spiny lobster ..	2·00	1·25
399	$1 "Gnathothlibus erotus" (moth) (29 × 45 mm)	7·00	2·50
399a	$2 Green turtle (29 × 45 mm)	8·00	4·00
399b	$4 Black marlin (29 × 45 mm)	5·00	7·00
399c	$5 Green tree lizard (29 × 45 mm)	5·50	7·50

134. "The Ascension".

1972. Christmas. Multicoloured.

400.	1 s. Type 134	10	10
401.	4 s. "The Blessed Virgin, and Infant Christ" ..	10	10
402.	10 s. "St. Andrew blessing Samoan canoe" ..	10	10
403.	30 s. "The Good Shepherd"	40	30

135. Erecting a Tent.

1973. Boy Scout Movement. Multicoloured.

405.	2 s. Saluting the flag ..	10	10
406.	3 s. First-aid ..	10	10
407.	8 s. Type 135 ..	25	10
408.	20 s. Samoan action-song	90	85

136. Hawker Siddeley "748".

1973. Air. Multicoloured.

409.	8 s. Type 136	45	15
410.	10 s. Hawker Siddeley "748" in flight ..	55	15
411.	12 s. Hawker Siddeley "748" on runway ..	65	35
412.	22 s. "B.A.C. 1-11" aircraft	1·00	60

137. Apia General Hospital.

1973. 25th Anniv. of W.H.O. Multicoloured.

413.	2 s. Type 137	10	10
414.	8 s. Baby clinic	20	10
415.	20 s. Filariasis research ..	45	20
416.	22 s. Family welfare ..	45	30

138. Mother and Child, and Map.

1973. Christmas. Multicoloured.

417.	3 s. Type 138	10	10
418.	4 s. Mother and Child, and village	10	10
419.	10 s. Mother and child, and beach	10	10
420.	30 s. Samoan stable ..	45	50

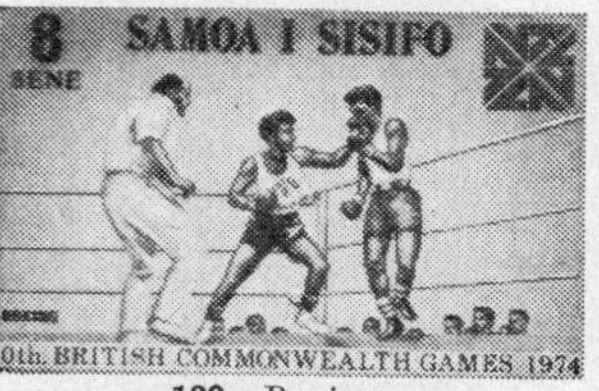

139. Boxing.

1973. Commonwealth Games, Christchurch. Multicoloured.

422.	8 s. Type 139 ..	10	10
423.	10 s. Weight-lifting ..	10	10
424.	20 s. Bowls	20	10
425.	30 s. Athletics stadium ..	35	45

1974. Myths and Legends of Old Samoa (2nd series). As T 127. Multicoloured.

426.	2 s. Tigilau and sacred dove	10	10
427.	8 s. Pili, his sons and fishing net	10	10
428.	20 s. Sina and the origin of the coconut ..	30	10
429.	30 s. The warrior, Nafanua	45	45

140. Mail-van at Faleolo Airport.

1974. Centenary of U.P.U. Multicoloured.

430.	8 s. Type 140	15	10
431.	20 s. Cargo liner at Apia Wharf	35	15
432.	22 s. Early Post Office, Apia, and letter ..	40	25
433.	50 s. William Willis and "Age Unlimited" (sailing-raft) (87 × 29 mm.)	80	1·00

141. "Holy Family" (Sebastiano).

1974. Christmas. Multicoloured.

435.	3 s. Type 141	10	10
436.	4 s. "Virgin and Child with Saints" (Lotto)	10	10
437.	10 s. "Madonna and Child with St. John" (Titian)	10	10
438.	30 s. "Adoration of the Shepherds" (Rubens) ..	35	45

142. Winged Passion Flower.

1975. Tropical Flowers. Multicoloured.

440.	8 s. Type 142	20	10
441.	20 s. Gardenia (vert.) ..	50	45
442.	22 s. "Barringtonia samoensis" (vert.) ..	55	50
443.	30 s. Malay apple	85	85

143. "Joyita" loading at Apia.

1975. "Interpex 1975" Stamp Exhibition, New York, and "Joyita" Mystery. Mult.

444.	1 s. Type 143	10	10
445.	8 s. "Joyita" sails for Tokelau Islands ..	15	10
446.	20 s. Taking to rafts ..	35	25
447.	25 s. "Joyita" abandoned	40	30
448.	50 s. Discovery of "Joyita" north of Fiji	1·00	1·25

144. "Pate" Drum.

1975. Musical Instruments. Multicoloured.

450.	8 s. Type 144	10	10
451.	20 s. "Lali" drum ..	20	10
452.	22 s. "Logo" drum ..	20	10
453.	30 s. "Pu" shell horn ..	35	30

145. "Mother and Child" (Meleane Fe'ao).

1975. Christmas. Multicoloured.

454.	3 s. Type 145	10	10
455.	4 s. "The Saviour" (Polataia Tuigamala) ..	10	10
456.	10 s. "A Star is Born" (Iosua Tovafa)	10	10
457.	30 s. "Madonna and Child" (Ernesto Coter) ..	30	45

146. "The Boston Massacre, 1770" (Paul Revere).

1976. Bicent. of American Revolution. Mult.

459. 7 s. Type **146** 20 15
460. 8 s. " The Declaration of Independence " (John Trumbull) 20 15
461. 20 s. " The Ship that Sank in Victory, 1779 " (J. L. G. Ferris) 60 35
462. 22 s. " Pitt addressing the Commons, 1782 " (R. A. Hickel) 60 35
463. 50 s. " Battle of Princeton " (William Mercer) .. 1·50 1·75

147. Mullet Fishing.

1976. Fishing. Multicoloured.

465. 10 s. Type **147** 10 10
466. 12 s. Fish traps 15 10
467. 22 s. Samoan fisherman .. 30 10
468. 50 s. Net fishing 85 70

149. Boxing.

1976. Olympic Games, Montreal. Mult.

470. 10 s. Type **149** 10 10
471. 12 s. Wrestling 10 10
472. 22 s. Javelin 15 10
473. 50 s. Weightlifting .. 45 50

150. Mary and Joseph going to Bethlehem.

1976. Christmas. Multicoloured.

474. 3 s. Type **150** 10 10
475. 5 s. The Shepherds .. 10 10
476. 22 s. The Holy Family .. 15 10
477. 50 s. The Magi 55 65

151. Queen Elizabeth and View of Apia.

1977. Silver Jubilee and Royal Visit. **Mult.**

479. 12 s. Type **151** 20 10
480. 26 s. Presentation of Spurs of Chivalry 35 20
481. 32 s. Queen and Royal Yacht " Britannia " 50 25
482. 50 s. Queen leaving Abbey 55 80

152. Map of Flight Route.

1977. 50th Anniv. of Lindbergh's Transatlantic Flight. Multicoloured.

483. 22 s. Type **152** 25 10
484. 24 s. In flight 35 15
485. 26 s. Landing 35 15
486. 50 s. Col. Lindbergh .. 80 75

Designs show the " Spirit of St. Louis ".

153. 3d. Express Stamp and First Mail Notice.

1977. Stamp Centenary.

488. **153.** 12 s. yell., red and brn. 20 10
489. – 13 s. multicoloured .. 20 15
490. – 26 s. multicoloured .. 45 30
491. – 50 s. multicoloured .. 80 1·00

DESIGNS: 13 s. Early cover and 6d. Express. 26 s. Apia P.O. and 1d. Express. 50 s. Schooner " Energy " (1877) and 6d. Express.

154. Apia Automatic Telephone Exchange.

1977. Telecommunications Project. Mult.

492 12 s. Type **154** 15 10
493 13 s. Mulinuu radio terminal 15 10
494 26 s. Old and new telephones 30 20
495 50 s. "Global communication" 50 70

155. "Samoan Nativity" (P. Feata).

1977. Christmas. Multicoloured.

496 4 s. Type **155** 10 10
497 6 s. "The Offering" (E. Saofaiga) 10 10
498 26 s. "Madonna and Child" (F. Tupou) 20 10
499 50 s. "Emmanuel" (M. Sapa'u) 35 40

156. Polynesian Airlines Boeing "737".

1978. Aviation Progress. Multicoloured.

501. 12 s. Type **156** 20 10
502. 24 s. Wright brothers' " Flyer " 40 20
503. 26 s. Kingsford Smith's " Southern Cross " .. 40 20
504. 50 s. " Concorde " .. 1·10 85

157. Hatchery, Aleipata.

1978. Hawksbill Turtle Conservation Project. Multicoloured.

506. 24 s. Type **157** 35 30
507. $1 Hawksbill turtle .. 1·60 1·60

158. Pacific Pigeon.

1978. 25th Anniv. of Coronation.

508. – 26 s. blk., brn. and mve. 25 30
509. – 26 s. multicoloured .. 25 30
510. **158.** 26 s. blk., brn. and mve. 25 30

DESIGNS: No. 508, King's Lion. No. 509, Queen Elizabeth II.

160. Captain Cook.

1978. 250th Birth Anniv. of Captain Cook. Multicoloured.

512. 12 s. Type **160** 30 15
513. 24 s. Cook's Cottage, Gt. Ayton, Yorkshire .. 60 35
514. 26 s. Old drawbridge over the river Esk, Whitby, 1766–1833 .. .. 70 35
515. 50 s. H.M.S. " Resolution " 1·25 1·50

161. Thick-edged Cowry.

1978. Shells. Multicoloured.

516. 1 s. Type **161** 15 10
517. 2 s. Isabella cowry .. 15 10
518. 3 s. Money cowry .. 25 10
519. 4 s. Eroded cowry .. 30 10
520. 6 s. Honey cowry .. 30 10
521. 7 s. Banded cowry .. 35 10
522. 10 s. Globe cowry .. 40 10
523. 11 s. Mole cowry .. 40 10
524. 12 s. Children's cowry .. 40 10
525. 13 s. Flag cone 40 10
526. 14 s. Soldier cone .. 40 10
527. 24 s. Cloth-of-gold cone .. 40 10
528. 26 s. Lettered cone .. 45 10
529. 50 s. Tiled cone 50 15
530. $1 Black Marble cone .. 95 60
530a. $2 Marlin-spike auger .. 1·50 90
530b. $3 Scorpion Spider Conch 2·25 1·50
530c. $5 Common harp .. 3·75 3·00

162. " Madonna on the Crescent ".

1978. Christmas. Woodcuts by Durer. Multicoloured.

531. **162.** 4 s. black and brown .. 10 10
532. – 6 s. black and green .. 10 10
533. – 26 s. black and blue .. 15 10
534. – 50 s. black and violet .. 35 50

DESIGNS: 6 s. " Nativity ". 26 s. " Adoration of the Kings ". 50 s. " Annunciation ".

163. Boy with Coconuts.

1979. International Year of the Child. Multicoloured.

536. 12 s. Type **163** 15 10
537. 24 s. White Sunday .. 30 15
538. 26 s. Children at pump .. 35 15
539. 50 s. Girl with ukulele .. 70 80

164. " Charles W. Morgan."

1979. Sailing Ships (1st series). Whalers. Multicoloured.

540. 12 s. Type **164** 30 10
541. 14 s. " Lagoda " 35 10
542. 24 s. " James T. Arnold " 50 20
543. 50 s. " Splendid " .. .. 1·10 85

See also Nos. 561/4 and 584/7.

165. Launch of " Apollo 11 ".

1979. 10th Anniv. of Moon Landing.

544. **165.** 12 s. brown and red .. 20 10
545. – 14 s. multicoloured .. 25 10
546. – 24 s. multicoloured .. 30 15
547. – 26 s. multicoloured .. 30 15
548. – 50 s. multicoloured .. 55 55
549. – $1 multicoloured .. 1·25 1·50

DESIGNS—HORIZ. 14 s. Lunar module and astronaut on Moon. 26 s. Astronaut on Moon. $1 Command module after splash-down. VERT. 24 s. View of Earth from Moon. 50 s. Lunar and Command modules in Space.

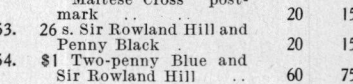

166. Sir Rowland Hill (statue) and Penny Black.

1979. Death Centenary of Sir Rowland Hill. Multicoloured.

551. 12 s. Type **166** 15 10
552. 24 s. Two-penny Blue with " Maltese Cross " postmark 20 15
553. 26 s. Sir Rowland Hill and Penny Black .. 20 15
554. $1 Two-penny Blue and Sir Rowland Hill .. 60 75

167. Anglican Church, Apia.

1979. Christmas. Churches.

556. **167.** 4 s. black and blue .. 10 10
557. – 6 s. black and yellow .. 10 10
558. – 26 s. black and brown .. 15 10
559. – 50 s. black and lilac .. 30 30

DESIGNS: 6 s. Congregational Christian, Leulumoega. 26 s. Methodist, Piula. 50 s. Protestant, Apia.

1980. Sailing Ships (2nd series). Whalers. As T **164**.

561. 12 s. " William Hamilton " 30 10
562. 14 s. " California " .. 35 15
563. 24 s. " Liverpool II " .. 50 25
564. 50 s. " Two Brothers " .. 1·10 70

168. " Equipment for a Hospital ".

1980. Anniversaries. Multicoloured.

565. 12 s. Type **168** 30 10
566. 13 s. John Williams, dove with olive twig and commemorative inscription 30 15
567. 14 s. Dr. Wilhelm Solf (instigator), flag and commemorative inscription 35 15
568. 24 s. Cairn Monument .. 45 25
569. 26 s. Williams Memorial, Savai'i 45 25
570. 50 s. Paul P. Harris (founder) 75 60

COMMEMORATIONS: 12 s., 50 s. Rotary International. 75th Anniv. 13 s., 26 s. John Williams' (missionary) arrival in Samoa. 150th Anniv. 14 s., 24 s. Raising of German flag. 80th Anniv.

170. Queen Elizabeth the Queen Mother in 1970.

1980. 80th Birthday of The Queen Mother.

572. **170.** 50 s. multicoloured .. 50 35

172. Afiamalu Satellite Earth Station.

1980. Afiamalu Satellite Earth Station. Multicoloured.

574. 12 s. Type **172** 15 10
575. 14 s. Satellite station (different) 20 10
576. 24 s. Satellite station and map of Savai'i and Upolu 30 15
577. 50 s. Satellite and globe .. 60 60

174. " The Saviour " (J. Poynton).

1980. Christmas. Paintings. Multicoloured.

579. 8 s. Type **174** 10 10
580. 14 s. " Madonna and Child " (Lealofi F. Siaopo) 10 10
581. 27 s. " Nativity " (Pasila Feata) 15 10
582. 50 s. " Yuletide " (R. P. Aiono) 25 40

1981. Sailing Ships (3rd series). As T **164**. Multicoloured.

584. 12 s. "Ocean" (whaling ship) 20 10
585. 18 s. "Horatio" (whaling ship) 30 15
586. 27 s. H.M.S. "Calliope" .. 45 25
587. 32 s. H.M.S. "Calypso" .. 50 50

175. President Franklin D. Roosevelt and Hyde Park (family home).

1981. International Year for Disabled Persons. President Franklin D. Roosevelt Commemoration. Multicoloured.

588. 12 s. Type **175** 15 10
589. 18 s. Roosevelt's Inauguration, 4 March 1933 .. 25 15
590. 27 s. Franklin and Eleanor Roosevelt 35 20
591. 32 s. Roosevelt's Lend-lease Bill (Atlantic convoy, 1941) 40 30
592. 38 s. Roosevelt the philatelist 45 35
593. $1 Campobello House (summer home) .. 1·00 1·00

176. Hotel Tusitala.

1981. Tourism. Multicoloured.

594. 12 s. Type **176** 15 10
595. 18 s. Apia Harbour .. 25 15
596. 27 s. Aggie Grey's Hotel 25 20
597. 32 s. Preparation for Ceremonial Kava 30 30
598. 54 s. Piula water pool .. 55 55

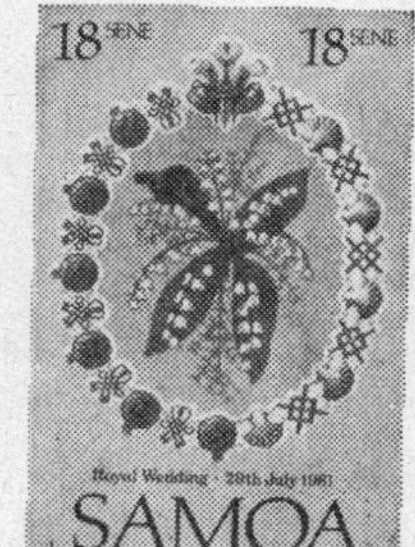

177. Wedding Bouquet from Samoa.

1981. Royal Wedding. Multicoloured.

599. 18 s. Type **177** 25 10
600. 32 s. Prince Charles as Colonel-in-Chief, Gordon Highlanders 35 20
601. $1 Prince Charles and Lady Diana Spencer 70 90

178. Tattooing Instruments.

1981. Tattooing. Multicoloured.

602. 12 s. Type **178** 20 20
603. 18 s. First stage of tattooing 25 25
604. 27 s. Progressive stage .. 30 30
605. $1 Completed tattoo .. 70 70

180. " Thespesia populnea ".

1981. Christmas. Flowers. Multicoloured.

607. 11 s. Type **180** 15 10
608. 15 s. Copper Leaf .. 20 15
609. 23 s. " Allamanda cathartica " 30 25
610. $1 Mango .. .. 1·00 1·00

181. George Washington's Pistol.

1982. 250th Birth Anniversary of George Washington.

612. **181.** 23 s. blk., brn. and stone 30 30
613. – 25 s. blk., brn. and stone 30 30
614. – 34 s. blk., brn. and stone 40 40

DESIGNS: 25 s. Mount Vernon (Washington's home). 34 s. George Washington.

182. "Forum Samoa" (container ship).

1982. 20th Anniv. of Independence. Mult.

616. 18 s. Type **182** 30 20
617. 23 s. " Air services " .. 40 30
618. 25 s. N.P.F. (National Provident Fund) Building, Apia 40 30
619. $1 " Telecommunications " 1·10 1·00

183. Scouts Map-reading and " 75 ".

1982. 75th Anniv. of Boy Scout Movement. Multicoloured.

620. 5 s. Type **183** 10 10
621. 38 s. Scout salute and " 75 " 40 40
622. 44 s. Scout crossing river by rope, and " 75 " .. 50 50
623. $1 " Tower " of Scouts and " 75 " .. .. .. 1·00 1·00

184. Boxing.

1982. Commonwealth Games. Brisbane. Multicoloured.

625. 23 s. Type **184** 25 20
626. 25 s. Hurdling 25 20
627. 34 s. Weightlifting .. 35 40
628. $1 Bowling .. .. 95 1·75

185. " Mary and Joseph " (Emma Dunlop).

1982. Christmas. Children's Pictures. Mult.

629. 11 s. Type **185** 15 10
630. 15 s. " Mary, Joseph and Baby Jesus " (Marie Tofaeono) 15 15
631. 38 s. " Madonna and Child " (Ralph Laban and Fetalaiga Fareni) .. 40 30
632. $1 " Mother and Child " (Panapa Pouesi) .. 90 1·10

186. Satellite View of Australasia.

1983. Commonwealth Day. Multicoloured.

634. 14 s. Type **186** 10 10
635. 29 s. Flag of Samoa .. 15 20
636. 43 s. Harvesting copra .. 25 25
637. $1 Head of State Malietoa Tanumafili II 50 80

188. Pole Vaulting.

189. Lime.

1983. South Pacific Games. Multicoloured.

639. 8 s. Type **188** 30 10
640. 15 s. Netball 40 20
641. 25 s. Tennis 60 40
642. 32 s. Weightlifting .. 60 60
643. 35 s. Boxing 65 60
644. 46 s. Football 80 70
645. 48 s. Golf 90 85
646. 56 s. Rugby .. .. 1·00 95

1983. Fruit. Multicoloured.

647. 1 s. Type **189** 10 10
648. 2 s. Star fruit 10 10
649. 3 s. Mangosteen 10 10
650. 4 s. Lychee 10 10
651. 7 s. Passion fruit .. 10 10
652. 8 s. Mango 10 10
653. 11 s. Pawpaw 10 10
654. 13 s. Pineapple 15 15
655. 14 s. Breadfruit 15 15
656. 15 s. Banana 20 15
657. 21 s. Cashew Nut .. 60 20
658. 25 s. Guava 80 20
659. 32 s. Water Melon .. 65 35
660. 48 s. Sasalapa 80 60
661. 56 s. Avocado 85 60
662. $1 Coconut .. .. 1·00 65
663. $2 Vi Apple .. .. 1·25 1·50
664. $4 Grapefruit .. .. 2·00 2·75
665. $5 Orange .. .. .. 2·50 3·00

191. Togitogiga Falls, Upolu.

1984. Scenic Views. Multicoloured.

669. 25 s. Type **191** 30 15
670. 32 s. Lano Beach, Savai'i .. 50 50
671. 48 s. Mulinu'u Point, Upolu 75 85
672. 56 s. Nu'utele Island .. 80 1·10

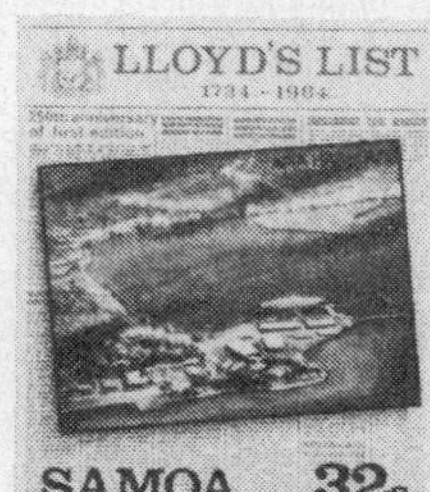

192. Apia Harbour.

1984. 250th Anniv. of "Lloyd's List" (newspaper). Multicoloured.

673. 32 s. Type **192** 25 20
674. 48 s. Apia hurricane, 1889 40 45
675. 60 s. "Forum Samoa" (container ship) 45 50
676. $1 "Matua" (cargo liner) .. 75 80

1984. Universal Postal Union Congress, Hamburg. No. 662 optd. **19th U.P.U. CONGRESS HAMBURG 1984.**

677. $1 Coconut 90 80

194. Olympic Stadium.

1984. Olympic Games, Los Angeles. Multicoloured.

678. 25 s. Type **194** 20 20
679. 32 s. Weightlifting .. 25 25
680. 48 s. Boxing 40 45
681. $1 Running 75 80

196. "Faith".

1984. Christmas. "The Three Virtues" (Raphael). Multicoloured.

684. 25 s. Type **196** 20 15
685. 35 s. "Hope" 25 20
686. $1 "Charity" 75 90

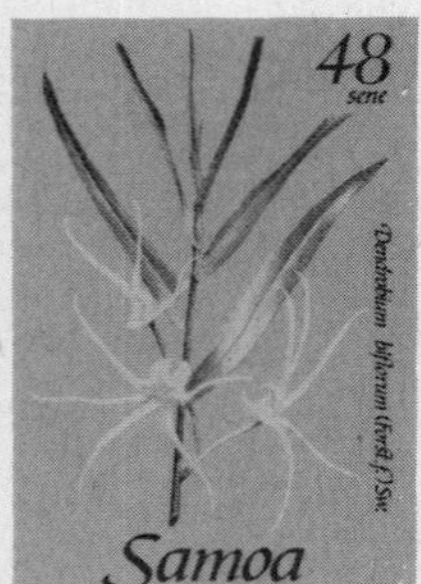

197. "Dendrobium biflorum".

1985. Orchids (1st series). Multicoloured.

688. 48 s. Type **197** 55 35
689. 56 s. "Dendrobium vaupelianum Kraenzl" 65 45
690. 67 s. "Glomera montana" 80 60
691. $1 "Spathoglottis plicata" 1·10 1·10

See also Nos. 818/21.

198. Ford "Model A", 1903.

1985. Veteran and Vintage Cars. Mult.

692. 48 s. Type **198** 60 35
693. 56 s. Chevrolet "Tourer", 1912 .. .. .. 70 40
694. 67 s. Morris "Oxford", 1913 80 45
695. $1 Austin "Seven", 1923 .. 1·00 70

199. "Dictyophora indusiata".

1985. Fungi. Multicoloured.

696. 48 s. Type **199** 35 35
697. 56 s. "Ganoderma tornatum" 40 40
698. 67 s. "Mycena chlorophos" 45 45
699. $1 "Mycobonia flava" .. 70 70

200. The Queen Mother at Liverpool Street Station.

1985. Life and Times of Queen Elizabeth the Queen Mother. Multicoloured.

700. 32 s. At Glamis Castle, aged 9 .. .. .. 20 25
701. 48 s. At Prince Henry's Christening with other members of the Royal Family 30 35
702. 56 s. Type **200** 35 40
703. $1 With Prince Henry at his christening (from photo by Lord Snowdon) .. 65 70

202. I.Y.Y. Emblem and Map (Alaska–Arabian Gulf).

1985. International Youth Year. Designs showing background map and emblem (Nos. 706 and 710) or raised arms (others). Multicoloured.

706. 60 s. Type **202** 40 45
707. 60 s. Raised arms (Pakistan–Mexico) .. 40 45
708. 60 s. Raised arms (Central America–China) .. 40 45
709. 60 s. Raised arms (Japan–Greenland) 40 45
710. 60 s. Type **202** (Iceland–Siberia) 40 45

Nos. 706/10 were printed together in horizontal strips of 5, the background forming a composite design of three continuous world maps.

203. "System".

1985. Christmas. Designs showing illustrations by Millicent Sowerby for R. L. Stevenson's "A Child's Garden of Verses". Multicoloured.

711. 32 s. Type **203** 20 25
712. 48 s. "Time to Rise" .. 30 35
713. 56 s. "Auntie's Skirts" .. 35 40
714. $1 "Good Children" .. 65 70

204. "Hypolimnas bolina".

1986. Butterflies. Multicoloured.

716 25 s. Type **204** 25 15
717 32 s. "Belenois java" .. 30 20
718 48 s. "Deudorix epijarbas" 50 35
719 56 s. "Badamia exclamationis" 55 40
720 60 s. "Danaus hamata" .. 55 40
721 $1 "Catochrysops taitensis" 80 65

205. Halley's Comet over Apia.

1986. Appearance of Halley's Comet. Mult.

722. 32 s. Type **205** 15 20
723. 48 s. Edmond Halley .. 30 35
724. 60 s. Comet passing Earth 35 40
725. $2 Preparing "Giotto" spacecraft .. .. 1·10 1·25

1986. 60th Birthday of Queen Elizabeth II. As T **110** of Ascension. Multicoloured.

726. 32 s. Engagement photograph, 1947 .. .. 15 20
727. 48 s. Queen with Liberty Bell, U.S.A., 1976 .. 30 35
728. 56 s. At Apia, 1977 .. 35 40
729. 67 s. At Badminton Horse Trials, 1978 .. .. 40 45
730. $2 At Crown Agents Head Office, London, 1983 .. 1·10 1·25

206. U.S.S. "Vincennes".

1986. "Ameripex '86" International Stamp Exhibition, Chicago. Multicoloured.

731. 48 s. Type **206** 30 35
732. 56 s. Sikorsky "S-42" flying boat 35 40
733. 60 s. U.S.S. "Swan" .. 35 40
734. $2 "Apollo 10" descending 1·10 1·25

208. Spotted Grouper.

1986. Fishes. Multicoloured.

736. 32 s. Type **208** 25 20
737. 48 s. Sabel squirrelfish .. 40 35
738. 60 s. Lunartail grouper .. 45 40
739. 67 s. Longtail snapper .. 50 45
740. $1 Berndt's soldierfish .. 75 65

209. Samoan Prime Ministers, American Presidents and Parliament House.

1986. Christmas, 25th Anniv. of United States Peace Corps. Multicoloured.

741. 45 s. Type **209** 25 30
742. 60 s. French and American Presidents, Samoan Prime Minister and Statue of Liberty .. 35 40

210. "Hibiscus rosa-sinensis" and Map of Samoa.

1987. 25th Anniv. of Independence. Mult.

744. 15 s. Type **210** 30 10
745. 45 s. Parliament Building, Apia 50 30
746. 60 s. Boat race at Independence celebration .. 65 40
747. 70 s. Peace dove and laurel wreath 75 50
748. $2 Head of State Malietoa Tanumafili II and national flag (horiz.) .. 1·60 1·75

211. Gulper.

1987. Deep Ocean Fishes. Multicoloured.

749. 45 s. Type **211** 45 30
750. 60 s. Hatchet fish 50 35
751. 70 s. Angler fish 60 45
752. $2 Gulper .. .. .. 1·40 1·40

213. Lefaga Beach, Upolu.

1987. Coastal Scenery. Multicoloured.

754. 45 s. Type **213** 35 30
755. 60 s. Vaisala Beach, Savaii 40 35
756. 70 s. Solosolo Beach, Upolu 55 45
757. $2 Neiafu Beach, Savaii .. 1·40 1·25

214. Abel Tasman.

1987. Bicentenary of Australian Settlement (1988) (1st issue). Explorers of the Pacific. Multicoloured.

758. 40 s. Type **214** 30 25
759. 45 s. Capt. James Cook .. 45 30
760. 80 s. Comte Louis-Antoine de Bougainville 50 50
761. $2 Comte Jean de la Perouse .. .. .. 1·10 1·25

See also Nos. 768/72.

216. Christmas Tree.

1987. Christmas. Multicoloured.

764. 40 s. Type **216** 20 25
765. 45 s. Family going to church 25 30
766. 50 s. Bamboo fire-gun .. 25 30
767. 80 s. Inter-island transport 45 50

217. Samoa Coat of Arms and Australia Post Logo.

1988. Bicentenary of Australian Settlement (2nd issue). Postal Services. Multicoloured.

768.	45 s. Type **217**	40	40
769.	45 s. Samoan mail van and aircraft	40	40
770.	45 s. Loading mail plane ..	40	40
771.	45 s. Australian mail van and aircraft	40	40
772.	45 s. "Congratulations Australia" message on airmail letter	40	40

Nos. 768/72 were printed together, se-tenant, Nos. 769/71 forming a composite design.

218. Airport Terminal and Airliner taking off.

1988. Opening of Faleolo Airport. Mult.

773.	40 s. Type **218**	35	25
774.	45 s. Boeing "727"	40	30
775.	60 s. DHC "Twin Otter" ..	45	35
776.	70 s. Boeing "737"	55	50
777.	80 s. Boeing "727" and control tower	70	60
778.	$1 "DC9" over "fale" (house)	80	70

219. "Expo '88" Pacific Islands Village.

1988. "Expo '88" World Fair, Brisbane. Multicoloured.

779.	45 s. Type **219**	25	30
780.	70 s. Expo Complex and monorail	35	40
781.	$2 Map of Australia showing Brisbane ..	1·00	1·10

221 Athletics

1988. Olympic Games, Seoul. Multicoloured.

783	15 s. Type **221**	10	10
784	60 s. Weightlifting ..	30	35
785	80 s. Boxing	40	45
786	$2 Olympic stadium ..	1·00	1·10

222 Spotted Triller

1988. Birds. Multicoloured.

788	10 s. Type **222**	10	10
789	15 s. Samoan wood rail ..	10	10
790	20 s. Flat-billed kingfisher	10	10
791	25 s. Samoan fantail ..	10	10
792	35 s. Scarlet robin ..	15	20
793	40 s. Black-breasted honeyeater ("Mao") ..	20	25
794	50 s. Cardinal honeyeater	25	30
795	65 s. Yellow-fronted whistler	30	35
796	75 s. Many-coloured fruit dove	35	40
798	75 s. Silver gull (45 × 28mm)	40	45
797	85 s. White-throated pigeon	35	40
799	85 s. Great frigate bird (45 × 28 mm) ..	40	45
800	90 s. Eastern reef heron (45 × 28 mm)	45	50
801	$3 Short-tailed albatross (45 × 28 mm)	1·50	1·60
802	$10 White tern (45 × 28 mm)	5·00	5·25
803	$20 Shy albatross (45 × 28 mm)	10·00	10·50

223 Forest

1988. National Conservation Campaign. Mult.

807	15 s. Type **223**	10	10
808	40 s. Samoan handicrafts	20	25
809	45 s. Forest wildlife ..	25	30
810	50 s. Careful use of water (horiz)	25	30
811	60 s. Fishing (horiz) ..	30	35
812	$1 Coconut plantation (horiz)	55	60

224 Congregational Church of Jesus, Apia

1988. Christmas. Samoan Churches. Mult.

813	15 s. Type **224**	10	10
814	40 s. Roman Catholic Church, Leauva'a ..	20	25
815	45 s. Congregational Christian Church, Moataa	25	30
816	$2 Baha'i Temple, Vailima	1·00	1·25

225 "Phaius flavus"

1989. Orchids (2nd series). Multicoloured.

818	15 s. Type **225**	15	10
819	45 s. "Calanthe triplicata"	35	30
820	60 s. "Luisia teretifolia" ..	40	35
821	$3 "Dendrobium mohlianum"	1·50	1·75

226 "Eber" (German warship)

1989. Cent of Great Apia Hurricane. Mult.

822	50 s. Type **226**	40	40
823	65 s. "Olga" (German warship)	55	55
824	85 s. H.M.S. "Calliope" (screw corvette) ..	70	70
825	$2 U.S.S. "Vandalia" ..	1·50	1·75

227 Samoan Red Cross Youth Group on Parade

1989. 125th Anniv of International Red Cross. Multicoloured.

826	50 s. Type **227**	35	30
827	65 s. Blood donors ..	45	40
828	75 s. Practising first aid ..	55	45
829	$3 Red Cross volunteers carrying patient ..	1·75	2·25

1989. 20th Anniv of First Manned Landing on Moon. As T **126** of Ascension. Multicoloured.

830	18 s. Saturn rocket on mobile launcher ..	15	10
831	50 s. Crew of "Apollo 14" (30 × 30 mm)	30	30
832	65 s. "Apollo 14" emblem (30 × 30 mm)	45	45
833	$2 Tracks of lunar transporter	1·25	1·75

228 Virgin Mary and Joseph

1989. Christmas. Multicoloured.

835	18 s. Type **228**	10	10
836	50 s. Shepherds	30	30
837	55 s. Donkey and ox ..	35	35
838	$2 Three Wise Men ..	1·50	1·50

229 Pao Pao Outrigger

1990. Local Transport. Multicoloured.

840	18 s. Type **229**	15	15
841	55 s. Fautasi (large canoe)	35	40
842	60 s. Polynesian Airlines aircraft	40	45
843	$3 "Lady Samoa" (ferry)	1·75	2·00

230 Bismarck and Brandenburg Gate, Berlin

1990. Treaty of Berlin, 1889, and Opening of Berlin Wall, 1989. Multicoloured.

844	75 s. Type **230**	1·00	1·00
845	$3 "Adler" (German steam gunboat)	2·00	2·00

Nos. 844/5 were printed together, se-tenant, forming a composite design showing Berliners on the Wall near the Brandenburg Gate.

231 Penny Black and Alexandra Palace, London (Illustration reduced, actual size 78 × 24 mm)

1990. "Stamp World London 90" International Stamp Exhibition.

846	**231** $3 multicoloured ..	2·40	2·75

232 Visitors' Bureau

1990. Tourism. Multicoloured.

847	18 s. Type **232**	20	10
848	50 s. Village resort ..	35	30
849	65 s. Aggie's Hotel ..	50	40
850	$3 Swimming pool, Tusitala Hotel	1·75	2·00

234 "Virgin and Child" (Bellini)

1990. Christmas. Paintings. Multicoloured.

852	18 s. Type **234**	20	10
853	50 s. "Virgin and Child with St. Peter and St. Paul" (Bouts)	40	25
854	55 s. "School of Love" (Correggio)	45	30
855	$3 "Virgin and Child" (Cima)	2·00	2·50

The 55 s. value should have shown "The Madonna of the Basket" by the same artist and is so inscribed.

235 William Draper III (administrator) and 40th Anniv Logo

1990. 40th Anniv of United Nations Development Programme.

856	235	$3 multicoloured ..	2·00	2·25

236 Black-capped Lory

1991. Parrots. Multicoloured.

857	18 s. Type **236**	20	10
858	50 s. Eclectus parrot ..	45	35
859	65 s. Scarlet macaw ..	55	40
860	$3 Palm cockatoo ..	2·50	2·50

1991. 65th Birthday of Queen Elizabeth II and 70th Birthday Of Prince Philip. As T **139** of Ascension. Multicoloured.

861	75 s. Prince Philip in the countryside	60	60
862	$2 Queen wearing yellow lei	1·50	1·50

238 "O Come All Ye Faithful"

1991. Christmas. Carols. Multicoloured.

864	20 s. Type **238**	20	15
865	60 s. "Joy to the World"	55	40
866	75 s. "Hark the Herald Angels sing"	65	50
867	$4 "We wish you a Merry Christmas"	2·75	3·00

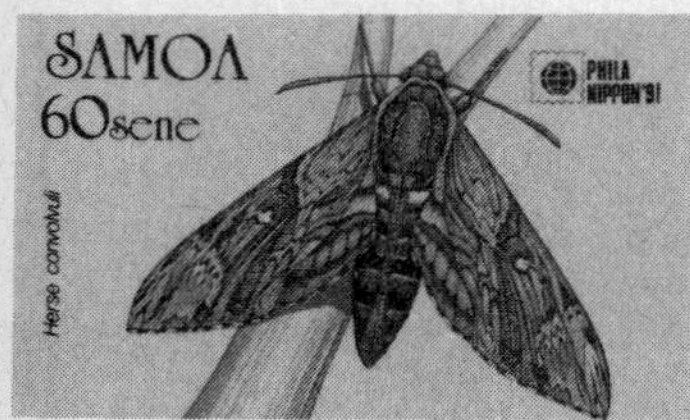

239 "Herse convolvuli"

1991. "Philanippon '91" International Stamp Exhibition, Tokyo. Samoan Hawkmoths. Multicoloured.

868	60 s. Type **239**	50	50
869	75 s. "Gnathothlibus erotus"	55	55
870	85 s. "Hippotion celerio"	60	60
871	$3 "Cephonodes armatus"	2·00	2·00

240 Head of State inspecting Guard of Honour

1992. 30th Anniv of Independence. Mult.

872	50 s. Type **240**	35	30
873	65 s. Siva ceremony ..	45	40
874	$1 Commemorative float	70	70
875	$3 Raising Samoan flag ..	2·00	2·00

1992. 40th Anniv of Queen Elizabeth II's Accession. As T **143** of Ascension. Mult.

876	20 s. Queen and Prince Philip with umbrellas ..	15	10
877	60 s. Queen and Prince Philip on Royal Yacht	40	35
878	75 s. Queen in multi-coloured hat	50	40
879	85 s. Three portraits of Queen Elizabeth ..	60	50
880	$3 Queen Elizabeth II ..	2·00	2·00

SARAWAK

Formerly an independent state on the N. coast of Borneo under British protection. Under Japanese occupation from 1941 until 1945. A Crown Colony from 1946 until September 1963, when it became a state of the Federation of Malaysia.

100 cents = 1 dollar (Malayan or Malaysian).

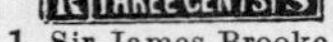

1. Sir James Brooke. 2. Sir Charles Brooke.

1869.

1.	1.	3 c. brown on yellow ..	40·00	£200

1871.

3.	2.	2 c. mauve on lilac	2·50	11·00
2.		3 c. brown on yellow ..	1·25	3·00
4.		4 c. brown on yellow ..	2·75	3·00
5.		6 c. green on green	2·75	3·50
6.		8 c. blue on blue	2·50	3·50
7.		12 c. red on red	6·50	6·50

4. Sir Charles Brooke. 11.

1888.

8.	4.	1 c. mauve and black ..	80	45
9.		2 c. mauve and red ..	85	65
10.		3 c. mauve and blue ..	1·25	1·00
11.		4 c. mauve and yellow ..	9·50	24·00
12.		5 c. mauve and green ..	8·00	1·50
13.		6 c. mauve and brown ..	7·00	28·00
14.		8 c. green and red ..	4·50	2·50
15.		10 c. green and violet ..	22·00	13·00
16.		12 c. green and blue ..	4·00	6·50
17.		16 c. green and orange ..	28·00	42·00
18.		25 c. green and brown ..	28·00	32·00
19.		32 c. green and black ..	24·00	35·00
20.		50 c. green	25·00	55·00
21.		$1 green and black ..	35·00	50·00

1889. Surch. in words or figures.

27	2	1 c. on 3 c. brown on yell.	50	90
23	4	1 c. on 3 c. mauve & blue	2·75	2·75
24		2 c. on 8 c. green and red	2·25	5·00
25a		5 c. on 12 c. green & blue	17·00	26·00

1895. Various frames.

28c.	11.	2 c. red	3·75	4·50
29.		4 c. black	3·75	2·50
30.		6 c. violet	3·25	7·00
31.		8 c. green	12·00	6·00

1899. Surch. in figures and words.

32.	2.	2 c. on 3 c. brown on yell.	80	90
33.		2 c. on 12 c. red on red ..	2·50	3·00
34.		4 c. on 6 c. green on green	15·00	38·00
35.		4 c. on 8 c. blue on blue ..	2·50	4·50

1899. As T **4**, but inscr. "POSTAGE POSTAGE".

36.		1 c. blue and red ..	30	50
37.		2 c. green	40	30
38.		3 c. purple	2·50	15
39a.		4 c. red	1·75	15
40.		8 c. yellow and black ..	1·75	70
41.		10 c. blue	1·75	50
42.		12 c. mauve	2·00	1·50
43.		16 c. brown and green ..	1·75	1·50
44.		20 c. olive and mauve ..	4·00	2·25
45.		25 c. brown and blue ..	2·75	3·50
46.		50 c. olive and red ..	11·00	18·00
47.		$1 red and green ..	27·00	45·00

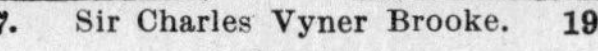

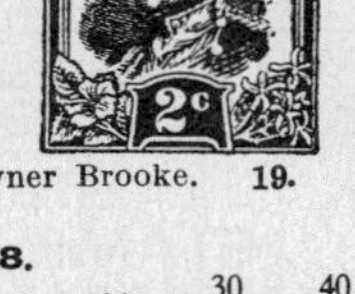

17. Sir Charles Vyner Brooke. 19.

1918.

50	17	1 c. blue and red ..	30	40
51		2 c. green	75	65
77		2 c. purple	50	40
52		3 c. purple	1·75	1·40
64		3 c. green	45	65
53a		4 c. red	1·40	1·40
65	17	4 c. purple	60	15
66		5 c. orange	40	90
81		6 c. red	70	30
54		8 c. yellow and black ..	4·50	23·00
82		8 c. red	1·75	5·50
55		10 c. blue	2·00	2·25
83		10 c. black	1·25	1·75
56		12 c. purple	6·00	8·00
84		12 c. blue	1·75	6·50
85		16 c. brown and green ..	1·75	2·50
86		20 c. olive and lilac ..	1·75	2·75
87		25 c. brown and blue ..	2·50	6·00
71		30 c. brown and blue ..	3·50	3·75
89		50 c. olive and red ..	3·50	5·50
90		$1 red and green ..	8·50	18·00

1923. Surch. in words.

72.	17.	1 c. on 10 c. blue	12·00	40·00
73.		2 c. on 12 c. purple ..	5·00	23·00

1932.

91.	19.	1 c. blue	70	35
92.		2 c. green	70	30
93.		3 c. violet	2·25	60
94.		4 c. orange	80	15
95.		5 c. red	2·25	60
96.		6 c. red	3·00	5·00
97.		8 c. yellow	3·00	4·50
98.		10 c. black	2·25	2·50
99.		12 c. blue	2·75	5·00
100.		15 c. brown	3·50	6·00
101.		20 c. orange and violet ..	3·00	6·00
102.		25 c. yell. and brown ..	4·50	7·00
103.		30 c. brown and red ..	4·50	12·00
104.		50 c. red and olive ..	4·50	6·00
105.		$1 green and red ..	7·00	18·00

21. Sir Charles Vyner Brooke.

1934.

106.	21.	1 c. purple	15	10
107.		2 c. green	15	10
107a.		2 c. black	80	1·40
108.		3 c. black	[illegible]	[illegible]
108a.		3 c. green	70	[illegible]
109.		4 c. purple	15	[illegible]
110.		5 c. violet	20	[illegible]
111.		6 c. red	15	[illegible]
111a.		6 c. brown	1·40	[illegible]
112.		8 c. brown	15	[illegible]
112a.		8 c. red	1·00	10
113.		10 c. red	75	40
114.		12 c. blue	30	25
114a.		12 c. orange	80	3·75
115.		15 c. orange	40	2·75
115a.		15 c. blue	1·25	4·25
116.		20 c. green and red ..	90	40
117.		25 c. violet and orange ..	50	1·00
118.		30 c. brown and violet ..	60	1·25
119.		50 c. violet and red ..	60	60
120.		$1 red and brown ..	60	50
121.		$2 purple and violet ..	4·00	6·00
122.		$3 red and green ..	15·00	12·00
123.		$4 blue and red ..	15·00	15·00
124.		$5 red and brown ..	16·00	23·00
125.		$10 black and yellow ..	16·00	27·00

1945. Optd. **BMA.**

126.	21.	1 c. purple	20	40
127.		2 c. black	20	40
128.		3 c. green	20	30
129.		4 c. purple	20	30
130.		5 c. violet	30	50
131.		6 c. brown	50	75
132.		8 c. red	9·00	9·00
133.		10 c. red	50	60
134.		12 c. orange	60	3·75
135.		15 c. blue	85	40
136.		20 c. green and red ..	1·25	1·40
137.		25 c. violet and orange ..	1·25	1·75
138.		30 c. brown and violet	1·25	2·75
139.		50 c. violet and red ..	1·25	35
140.		$1 red and brown ..	2·50	1·25
141.		$2 purple and violet ..	9·00	4·50
142.		$3 red and green ..	17·00	22·00
143.		$4 blue and red ..	25·00	25·00
144.		$5 red and brown ..	75·00	90·00
145.		$10 black and yellow ..	90·00	£110

23. Sir James Brooke, Sir Chas. Vyner Brooke and Sir Charles Brooke.

1946. Centenary Issue.

146.	23.	8 c. red	20	15
147.		15 c. blue	20	90
148.		50 c. black and red ..	35	80
149.		$1 black and brown ..	50	7·00

1947. Optd. with the Royal Cypher.

150.	21.	1 c. purple	15	20
151.		2 c. black	15	10
152.		3 c. green	15	15
153.		4 c. purple	15	15
154.		6 c. brown	20	50
155.		8 c. red	20	10
156.		10 c. red	20	20
157.		12 c. orange	15	70
158.		15 c. blue	15	40
159.		20 c. green and red	30	50
160.		25 c. violet and orange	30	30
161.		50 c. violet and red	30	30
162.		$1 red and brown	60	80
163.		$2 purple and violet	90	3·00
164.		$5 red and brown	1·75	3·00

1948. Silver Wedding. As T **10/11** of Aden.

165.	8 c. red	30	20
166.	$5 brown	23·00	24·00

1949. U.P.U. As T **20/23** of Antigua.

167	8 c. red	60	50
168	15 c. blue	1·40	2·25
169	25 c. green	1·40	1·50
170	50 c. violet	2·00	3·00

25. "Trogonoptera brookiana".

26. Western Tarsier.

27. Kayan Tomb.

1950.

171.	25.	1 c. black	30	30
172.	26.	2 c. orange	20	40
173.	27.	3 c. green	10	50
174.	–	4 c. brown	10	20
175.	–	6 c. blue	10	15
176.	–	8 c. red	10	30
177.	–	10 c. orange	50	2·50
186.	–	10 c. orange	20	30
178.	–	12 c. violet	1·50	1·25
179.	–	15 c. blue	70	10
180.	–	20 c. brown and orange	60	20
181.	–	25 c. green and red	70	30
182.	–	50 c. brown and violet	70	15
183.	–	$1 green and brown	4·50	1·25
184.	–	$2 blue and red	12·00	4·50
185.	–	$5 multicoloured	16·00	7·00

DESIGNS—VERT. 4 c. Kayan boy and girl. 6 c. Beadwork. 50 c. Iban woman. HORIZ. 8 c. Dayak dancer. 10 c. (No. 177) Malayan Pangolin. 10 c. (No. 186), Map of Sarawak. 12 c. Kenyah boys. 15 c. Fire making. 20 c. Kelemantan rice barn. 25 c. Pepper vines. $1, Kelabit smithy. $2 Map of Sarawak. $5 Arms of Sarawak.

1953. Coronation. As T **13** of Aden.

187	10 c. black and blue	85	55

47. Barong Panau (sailing prau).

51. Queen Elizabeth II.

52. Queen Elizabeth II (after Annigoni).

1955.

188.	–	1 c. green	10	30
189.	–	2 c. orange	20	55
190.	–	4 c. brown	30	30
191.	–	6 c. blue	2·75	35
192.	–	8 c. red	20	30
193.	–	10 c. green	15	10
194.	47.	12 c. plum	2·75	55
195.	–	15 c. blue	80	15
196.	–	20 c. olive and brown	80	10
197.	–	25 c. sepia and green	4·25	15
198.	51.	30 c. brown and lilac	1·75	15
199.		50 c. black and red	1·75	15
200.	52.	$1 myrtle and brown	2·00	40
201.		$2 violet and green	4·50	1·75
202.	–	$5 multicoloured	13·00	5·50

DESIGNS—As Type **47**—VERT. 1 c. Logging. 2 c. Young Orang-Utan. 4 c. Kayan dancing. HORIZ. 6 c. Malabar Pied Hornbill. 8 c. Shield with spears. 10 c. Kenyah ceremonial carving. 15 c. Turtles. 20 c. Melanan basket-making. 25 c. Astana, Kuching. $5, Arms of Sarawak.

1963. Freedom from Hunger. As T **28** of Aden.

203.	12 c. sepia	1·50	35

53. "Vanda hookeriana".

1965. As Nos. 155/21 of Kedah, but with Arms of Sarawak inset as in T **53**.

212.	53.	1 c. multicoloured	10	50
213.	–	2 c. multicoloured	15	50
214.	–	5 c. multicoloured	35	10
215.	–	6 c. multicoloured	50	40
216.	–	10 c. multicoloured	55	10
217.	–	15 c. multicoloured	1·25	10
218.	–	20 c. multicoloured	1·75	40

The higher values used in Sarawak were Nos. 20/7 of Malaysia (National Issues).

54. "Precis orithya".

1971. Butterflies. As Nos. 124/30 of Kedah, but with Sarawak Arms as in T **54**.

219.	–	1 c. multicoloured	15	55
220.	–	2 c. multicoloured	35	60
221.	–	5 c. multicoloured	55	10
222.	–	6 c. multicoloured	70	40
223.	–	10 c. multicoloured	70	10
224.	54.	15 c. multicoloured	1·00	10
225.	–	20 c. multicoloured	1·25	45

The higher values in use with this issue were Nos. 64/71 of Malaysia (National Issues).

55. "Precis orithya" (different crest at right).

1977. As Nos. 219/21 and 223/5, but showing new State Crest.

226.		1 c. multicoloured	4·25	5·50
227.	–	2 c. multicoloured	3·50	4·50
228.	–	5 c. multicoloured	80	55
230.	–	10 c. multicoloured	65	20
231.	55.	15 c. multicoloured	1·00	20
232.	–	20 c. multicoloured	5·50	3·50

56. "Rhododendron scortechinii".

1979. As Nos. 135/41 of Kedah, but with Arms of Sarawak as in T **56**.

233	1 c. "Rafflesia hasseltii"	10	20
234	2 c. "Pterocarpus indicus"	10	20
235	5 c. "Lagerstroemia speciosa"	10	10
236	10 c. "Durio zibethinus"	10	10
237	15 c. "Hibiscus rosa-sinensis"	20	10
238	20 c. Type **56**	25	10
239	25 c. "Etlingera elatior" (inscr "Phaeomeria speciosa")	25	10

57. Coffee.

1986. As Nos. 152/8 of Kedah, but with Arms of Sarawak as in T **57**.

247.	1 c. Type **57**	10	10
248.	2 c. Coconuts	10	10
249.	5 c. Cocoa	10	10
250.	10 c. Black pepper	10	10
251.	15 c. Rubber	10	10
252.	20 c. Oil palm	10	10
253.	30 c. Rice	10	15

JAPANESE OCCUPATION

府政国帝本日大

(1. "Imperial Japanese Government".)

1942. Stamps of Sarawak optd. with T **1**.

J 1.	21.	1 c. purple	22·00	27·00
J 2.		2 c. green	60·00	75·00
J 3.		2 c. black	38·00	50·00
J 4.		3 c. black	£110	£130
J 5.		3 c. green	32·00	38·00
J 6.		4 c. purple	24·00	30·00
J 7.		5 c. violet	26·00	30·00
J 8.		6 c. red	45·00	55·00
J 9.		6 c. brown	30·00	38·00
J 10.		8 c. brown	£100	£130
J 11.		8 c. red	90·00	£110
J 12.		10 c. red	30·00	38·00
J 13.		12 c. blue	70·00	75·00
J 14.		12 c. orange	80·00	£100
J 15.		15 c. orange	£120	£130
J 16.		15 c. blue	40·00	50·00
J 17.		20 c. green and red	28·00	38·00
J 18.		25 c. violet and orange	32·00	38·00
J 19.		30 c. brown and violet	32·00	42·00
J 20.		50 c. violet and red	32·00	42·00
J 21.		$1 red and brown	38·00	55·00
J 22.		$2 purple and violet	90·00	£110
J 23.		$3 red and green	£550	£650
J 24.		$4 blue and red	£100	£130
J 25.		$5 red and brown	£100	£130
J 26.		$10 black and yellow	£110	£150

SELANGOR

A state of the Federation of Malaya, incorporated in Malaysia in 1963.

100 cents = 1 dollar (Straits or Malayan).

1881. Stamps of Straits Settlements optd. **SELANGOR.**

3.	5.	2 c. brown	55·00	60·00
35.		2 c. red	3·00	2·25

1882. Straits Settlements stamp optd. **S.**

8.	5.	2 c. brown	—	£1300

1891. Stamp of Straits Settlements surch. **SELANGOR Two CENTS.**

44.	5.	2 c. on 24 c. green	12·00	30·00

40.

42.

43.

1891.

49.	40.	1 c. green	70	25
50.		2 c. red	2·50	45
51.	–	2 c. orange	75	40
52.		5 c. blue	9·00	3·75

1894. Surch. **3 CENTS.**

53.	40.	3 c. on 5 c. red	1·00	30

1895.

54	42	3 c. purple and red	4·25	20
55		5 c. purple and yellow	80	30
56		8 c. purple and blue	50·00	7·00
57		10 c. purple and orange	5·50	35
58		25 c. green and red	60·00	35·00
60		50 c. green and black	£150	85·00
59		50 c. purple and black	21·00	15·00
61	43	$1 green	32·00	50·00
62		$2 green and red	£100	£100
63		$3 green and yellow	£200	£150
64		$5 green and blue	95·00	£130
65		$10 green and purple	£275	£275
66		$25 green and orange	£1200	

1900. Surch. in words.

66a.	2.	1 c. on 5 c. purple & yell.	50·00	65·00
66b.		1 c. on 50 c. green & black	90	14·00
67.		3 c. on 50 c. green & black	6·00	15·00

46. Mosque at Palace, Klang.

47. Sultan Suleiman.

1935.

68.	46.	1 c. black	20	10
69.		2 c. green	30	10
70.		2 c. orange	30	1·10
71.		3 c. green	3·00	2·50
72.		4 c. orange	30	10
73.		5 c. brown	30	10
74.		6 c. red	3·25	10
75.		8 c. grey	40	10
76.		10 c. purple	40	10
77.		12 c. blue	1·50	10
78.		15 c. blue	4·25	23·00
79.		25 c. purple and red	1·50	60
80.		30 c. purple and orange	1·25	85
81.		40 c. red and purple	1·75	1·25
82.		50 c. black on green	1·50	15
83.	47.	$1 black and red on blue	4·00	40
84.		$2 green and red	15·00	7·00
85.		$5 green and red on green	45·00	23·00

48. Sultan Hisamud-din Alam Shah. **49.**

1941.

86.	48.	$1 black and red on blue	7·00	5·00
87.		$2 green and red	40·00	27·00

1948. Silver Wedding. As T **10/11** of Aden.

88.	10 c. violet	20	10
89.	$5 green	23·00	14·00

1949.

No.	Type	Description	Unused	Used
90	49	1 c. black	10	10
91		2 c. orange	10	10
92		3 c. green	20	65
93		4 c. brown	10	10
94a		5 c. purple	30	10
95		6 c. grey	10	10
96		8 c. red	25	65
97		8 c. green	65	50
98		10 c. purple	10	10
99		12 c. red	80	1·25
100		15 c. blue	35	10
101		20 c. black and green	30	10
102		20 c. blue	80	10
103		25 c. purple and orange	30	10
104		30 c. red and purple	1·25	50
105		35 c. red and purple	70	80
106		40 c. red and purple	1·25	2·00
107		50 c. black and blue	40	10
108		$1 blue and purple	2·00	10
109		$2 green and red	5·00	15
110		$5 green and brown	30·00	80

1949. U.P.U. As T **20/23** of Antigua.

No.	Description	Unused	Used
111	10 c. purple	15	10
112	15 c. blue	45	45
113	25 c. orange	50	90
114	50 c. black	1·10	80

1953. Coronation. As T **13** of Aden.

No.	Description	Unused	Used
115	10 c. black and purple	30	10

1957. As Nos. 92/102 of Kedah but inset portrait of Sultan Hisamud-din Alam Shah.

No.	Description	Unused	Used
116.	1 c. black	10	30
117.	2 c. red	10	20
118.	4 c. sepia	10	10
119.	5 c. lake	10	10
120.	8 c. green	1·10	25
121.	10 c. sepia	15	10
122.	10 c. purple	1·25	10
123.	20 c. blue	25	10
124a.	50 c. black and blue	25	10
125.	$1 blue and purple	1·25	10
126.	$2 green and red	2·25	85
127a.	$5 brown and green	4·25	1·00

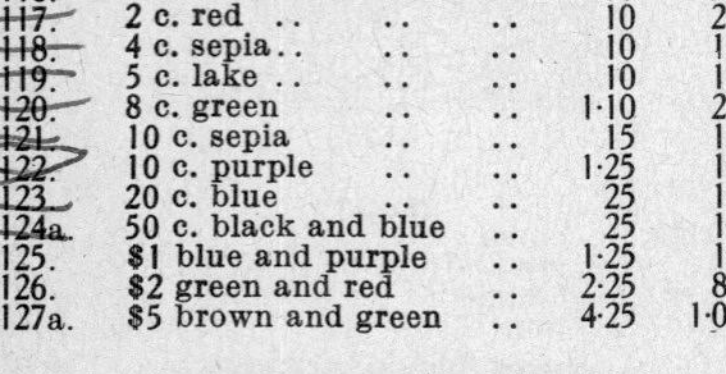

50. Sultan Salahuddin Abdul Aziz Shah.

1961. Installation of the Sultan.

No.	Type	Description	Unused	Used
128.	**50.**	10 c. multicoloured	10	10

51. Sultan Salahuddin Abdul Aziz Shah.

1961. As Nos. 116, etc., but with inset portrait of Sultan Salahuddin Abdul Aziz as in T **51**.

No.	Description	Unused	Used
129.	1 c. black	10	30
130.	2 c. red	10	30
131.	4 c. sepia	10	10
132.	5 c. lake	10	10
133.	8 c. green	70	80
134.	10 c. purple	10	10
135.	20 c. blue	40	10

52. "Vanda hookeriana".

1965. As Nos. 115/21 of Kedah, but with inset portrait of Sultan Salahuddin Abdul Aziz Shah as in T **52**.

No.	Type	Description	Unused	Used
136.	**52.**	1 c. multicoloured	10	10
137.	–	2 c. multicoloured	10	30
138.	–	5 c. multicoloured	15	10
139.	–	6 c. multicoloured	15	10
140.	–	10 c. multicoloured	15	10
141.	–	15 c. multicoloured	85	10
142.	–	20 c. multicoloured	1·25	15

The higher values used in Selangor were Nos. 20/7 of Malaysia (National Issues).

INDEX

Countries can be quickly located by referring to the index at the end of this volume.

53. "Parthenos sylvia".

1971. Butterflies. As Nos. 124/30 of Kedah, but with portrait of Sultan Salahuddin Abdul Aziz Shah as in T **53**.

No.	Type	Description	Unused	Used
146.	–	1 c. multicoloured	15	30
147.	–	2 c. multicoloured	40	40
148.	**53.**	5 c. multicoloured	50	10
149.	–	6 c. multicoloured	50	15
150.	–	10 c. multicoloured	50	10
151.	–	15 c. multicoloured	55	10
152.	–	20 c. multicoloured	90	15

The higher values in use with this issue were Nos. 64/71 of Malaysia (National Issues).

54. "Lagerstroemia speciosa".

1979. Flowers. As Nos. 135/41 of Kedah, but with portrait of Sultan Salahuddin Abdul Shah as in T **54**.

No.	Description	Unused	Used
158	1 c. "Rafflesia hasseltii"	10	10
159	2 c. "Pterocarpus indicus"	10	10
160	5 c. Type **54**	10	10
161	10 c. "Durio zibethinus"	10	10
162	15 c. "Hibiscus rosa-sinensis"	15	10
163	20 c. "Rhododendron scortechinii"	15	10
164	25 c. "Etlingera elatior" (inscr "Phaeomeria speciosa")	15	10

55. Sultan Salahuddin Abdul Aziz Shah and Royal Crest.

1985. 25th Anniv. of Sultan's Coronation.

No.	Type	Description	Unused	Used
173.	**55.**	15 c. multicoloured	55	10
174.		20 c. multicoloured	70	15
175.		$1 multicoloured	1·90	2·00

56. Black Pepper.

1986. As Nos. 152/8 of Kedah, but with portrait of Sultan Salahuddin Abdul Aziz Shah as in T **56**.

No.	Description	Unused	Used
176.	1 c. Coffee	10	10
177.	2 c. Coconuts	10	10
178.	5 c. Cocoa	10	10
179.	10 c Type **56**	10	10
180.	15 c. Rubber	10	10
181.	20 c. Oil palm	10	10
182.	30 c. Rice	10	15

SEYCHELLES

A group of islands in the Indian Ocean, E. of Africa.

100 cents = 1 rupee.

1.

6.

1890.

No.	Type	Description	Unused	Used
9.	**1.**	2 c. green and red	65	90
28.		2 c. brown and green	30	45
22.		3 c. purple and orange	55	30
10.		4 c. red and green	90	85
29.		6 c. red	2·25	40
11.		8 c. purple and blue	2·50	1·40
12.		10 c. blue and brown	2·75	2·00
23.		12 c. brown and green	55	40
13.		13 c. grey and black	85	1·50
24.		15 c. olive and lilac	3·25	2·00
30.		15 c. blue	2·50	2·50
6.		16 c. brown and blue	2·00	2·75
31.		18 c. blue	1·40	90
32.		36 c. brown and red	15·00	4·00
25.		45 c. brown and red	22·00	25·00
7.		48 c. bistre & grn.	16·00	16·00
33.		75 c. yellow and violet	35·00	55·00
8.		96 c. mauve and red	38·00	45·00
34.		1 r. mauve and red	8·50	3·50
35.		1 r. 50 grey and red	48·00	75·00
36.		2 r. 25 mauve and green	48·00	75·00

1893. Surch. in figures and words in two lines.

No.	Type	Description	Unused	Used
15	1	3 c. on 4 c. red and green	75	1·10
17		12 c. on 16 c. brn. & blue	2·50	1·25
19		15 c. on 16 c. brn. & blue	7·00	1·75
20		45 c. on 48 c. brn. & grn.	8·50	4·00
21		90 c. on 96 c. mauve & red	23·00	25·00

1896. Surch. in figures and words in one line.

No.	Type	Description	Unused	Used
26.	**1.**	18 c. on 45 c. brown & red	6·50	2·50
27.		36 c. on 45 c. brown & red	10·00	32·00

1901. Surch. in figures and words.

No.	Type	Description	Unused	Used
41.	**1.**	2 c. on 4 c. red and green	90	2·75
37.		3 c. on 10 c. blue & brown	30	60
38.		3 c. on 16 c. brown & blue	30	85
39.		3 c. on 36 c. brown and red	30	50
40.		6 c. on 8 c. purple and blue	30	1·50
42.		30 c. on 75 c. yellow & vio.	80	4·00
43.		30 c. on 1 r. mauve and red	3·25	16·00
44.		45 c. on 1 r. mauve and red	3·25	16·00
45.		45 c. on 2 r. mve. & green	21·00	35·00

1903.

No.	Type	Description	Unused	Used
46	**6**	2 c. brown and green	40	40
61		3 c. green	70	30
62		6 c. red	80	10
49		12 c. brown and green	1·50	1·00
64		15 c. blue	1·60	2·00
65		18 c. olive and red	3·00	5·50
66		30 c. violet and green	6·00	7·50
67		45 c. brown and red	3·00	5·00
54		75 c. yellow and violet	9·00	16·00
69		1 r. 50 black and red	35·00	35·00
70		2 r. 25 purple and green	30·00	35·00

1903. Surch. **3 cents.**

No.	Type	Description	Unused	Used
57.	**6.**	3 c. on 15 c. blue	55	1·00
58.		3 c. on 18 c. olive and red	1·75	21·00
59.		3 c. on 45 c. brown and red	55	1·50

9.

11.

1912. Inscr. "POSTAGE POSTAGE."

No.	Type	Description	Unused	Used
71.	**9.**	2 c. brown and green	20	1·10
72.		3 c. green	35	30
73a.		6 c. red	2·25	40
74.		12 c. brown and green	80	3·50
75.		15 c. blue	1·25	40
76.		18 c. olive and red	1·25	3·50
77.		30 c. violet and green	5·00	90
78.		45 c. brown and red	2·50	22·00
79.		75 c. yellow and violet	2·50	5·50
80.		1 r. 50 black and red	5·50	85
81a.		2 r. 25 purple and green	30·00	2·50

1917. Inscr. "POSTAGE & REVENUE".

No.	Type	Description	Unused	Used
98	**11.**	2 c. brown and green	10	15
99		3 c. green	20	15
100		3 c. black	50	30
101		4 c. green	60	40
102		4 c. olive and red	3·50	9·50
84		5 c. brown	45	2·50
85		6 c. red	55	40
105		6 c. mauve	30	10
106		9 c. red	1·25	2·75
107		12 c. grey	50	15
108		12 c. red	45	15
87		15 c. blue	30	85
111		15 c. yellow	50	2·50
112		18 c. purple on yellow	2·00	6·50
113		20 c. blue	1·25	35
89b		25 c. blk. & red on yell.	1·00	5·00
90		30 c. purple and olive	1·50	5·50
116		45 c. purple and orange	80	5·00
117		50 c. purple and black	90	2·25
93		75 c. black on green	1·25	7·00
119		1 r. purple and red	7·00	17·00
121		1 r. 50 pur. & bl. on bl.	8·00	15·00
122		2 r. 25 green & violet	8·00	14·00
123		5 r. green and blue	48·00	90·00

1935. Silver Jubilee. As T **13** of Antigua.

No.	Description	Unused	Used
128.	6 c. blue and black	70	40
129.	12 c. green and blue	2·00	30
130.	20 c. brown and blue	2·00	40
131.	1 r. grey and purple	3·00	7·75

1937. Coronation. As T **2** of Aden.

No.	Description	Unused	Used
132.	6 c. olive	35	15
133.	12 c. orange	50	30
134.	20 c. blue	70	40

14. Coco-de-mer Palm.

DESIGNS—VERT. 3, 12, 15, 30, 75 c., 2 r. 25, Giant Tortoise. HORIZ. 6, 20, 45 c., 1 r., 5 r. Fishing Pirogue.

1938.

No.	Type	Description	Unused	Used
135a	**14**	2 c. brown	20	30
136	–	3 c. green	4·00	1·00
136a	–	3 c. orange	35	30
137ab	–	6 c. orange	3·50	2·50
137b	–	6 c. green	30	40
138	**14**	9 c. red	7·00	1·75
138ab	–	9 c. blue	40	40
139	–	12 c. mauve	24·00	70
139ab	–	15 c. red	50	45
139c	**14**	18 c. red	1·75	40
140	–	20 c. blue	32·00	5·50
140ab	–	20 c. yellow	60	40
141	**14**	25 c. brown	45·00	9·50
142	–	30 c. red	55·00	6·50
142ab	–	30 c. blue	40	60
143a	–	45 c. brown	75	55
144a	**14**	50 c. violet	30	70
145	–	75 c. blue	75·00	38·00
145ab	–	75 c. mauve	40	50
146	–	1 r. green	95·00	48·00
146a	–	1 r. black	50	45
147a	**14**	1 r. 50 blue	1·50	90
148a	–	2 r. 25 olive	2·50	3·00
149	–	5 r. red	3·50	2·75

1946. Victory. As T **9** of Aden.

No.	Description	Unused	Used
150	9 c. blue	10	10
151	30 c. blue	10	10

1948. Silver Wedding. As T **10/11** of Aden.

No.	Description	Unused	Used
152.	9 c. blue	15	25
153.	5 r. red	6·50	9·50

1949. U.P.U. As T **20/23** of Antigua.

No.	Description	Unused	Used
154.	18 c. mauve	15	15
155.	50 c. purple	35	40
156.	1 r. grey	30	15
157.	2 r. 25 olive	50	40

17. Sail-fish.

21. "La Pierre de Possession".

1952. Full-face portrait.

No.	Type	Description	Unused	Used
158.	**17.**	2 c. lilac	40	40
159.	–	3 c. orange	40	30
160.	–	9 c. blue	40	40
161.	–	15 c. green	30	50
162.	–	18 c. lake	55	20
163.	–	20 c. yellow	80	60
164.	–	25 c. red	60	70
165.	**17.**	40 c. blue	60	70
166.	–	45 c. brown	60	30
167.	–	50 c. violet	1·00	60
168.	–	1 r. black	1·75	1·25
169.	–	1 r. 50 blue	3·25	6·00
170.	–	2 r. 25 olive	3·50	7·50
171.	–	5 r. red	3·75	10·00
172.	**17.**	10 r. green	7·00	15·00

DESIGNS—VERT. 2 c., 25 c., 2 r. 25, Giant tortoise. 9 c., 50 c., 1 r. 50, Coco-de-Mer Palm. HORIZ. 15 c., 20 c., 45 c. Fishing pirogue. 18 c., 1 r., 5 r. Map of Indian Ocean.

1953. Coronation. As T **13** of Aden.

No.	Description	Unused	Used
173.	9 c. black and blue	10	20

1954. Designs as 1952 but with portrait of Queen Elizabeth II.

No.	Description	Unused	Used
174.	2 c. lilac	10	10
175.	3 c. orange	10	10
175a.	5 c. violet	30	30
176.	9 c. blue	10	10
176a.	10 c. blue (as 9 c.)	30	30
177.	15 c. green	15	15
178.	18 c. lake	10	10
179.	20 c. yellow	30	20
180.	25 c. red	50	50
180a.	35 c. lake (as 18 c.)	1·50	90
181.	40 c. blue	30	25
182.	45 c. brown	20	15
183.	50 c. violet	30	20
183a.	70 c. brown (as 45 c.)	1·50	1·25
184.	1 r. black	50	40
185.	1 r. 50 blue	3·25	2·50
186.	2 r. 25 olive	3·25	6·00
187.	5 r. red	10·00	6·00
188.	10 r. green	21·00	16·00

NEW DESIGN: 5 c. Seychelles Flying Fox.

1956. Bicent. of La Pierre de Possession.
189. **21.** 40 c. blue 10 10
190. 1 r. black 10 10

1957. No. 182 surch. **5 cents** and bars.
191. 5 c. on 45 c. brown .. 10 10

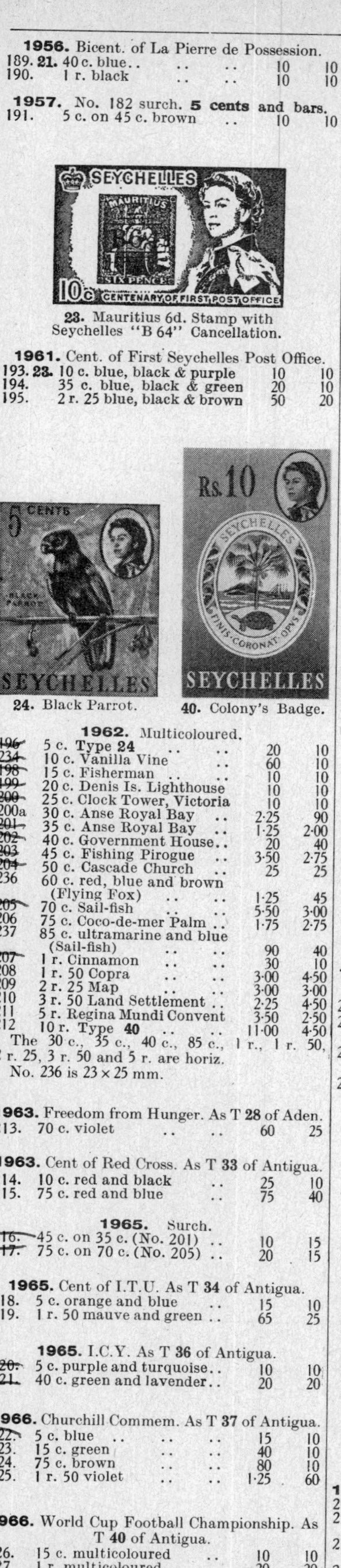

23. Mauritius 6d. Stamp with Seychelles "B 64" Cancellation.

1961. Cent. of First Seychelles Post Office.
193. **23.** 10 c. blue, black & purple 10 10
194. 35 c. blue, black & green 20 10
195. 2 r. 25 blue, black & brown 50 20

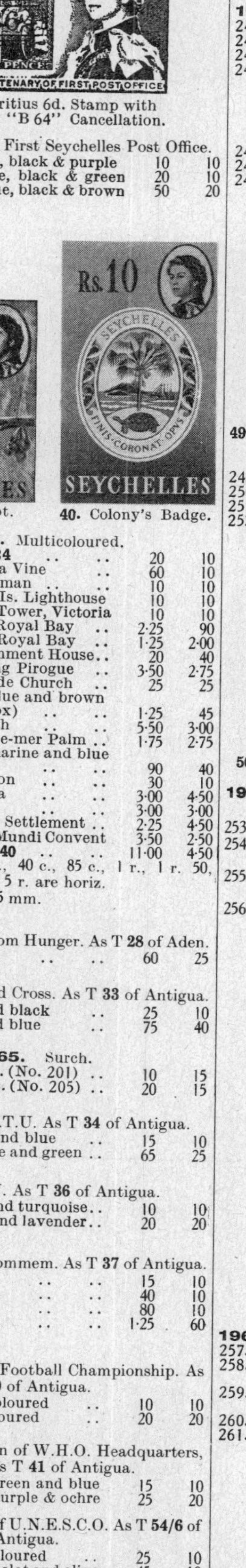

24. Black Parrot. **40.** Colony's Badge.

1962. Multicoloured.
196 5 c. Type **24** 20 10
234 10 c. Vanilla Vine .. 60 10
198 15 c. Fisherman 10 10
199 20 c. Denis Is. Lighthouse 10 10
200 25 c. Clock Tower, Victoria 10 10
200a 30 c. Anse Royal Bay .. 2·25 90
201 35 c. Anse Royal Bay .. 1·25 2·00
202 40 c. Government House .. 20 40
203 45 c. Fishing Pirogue .. 3·50 2·75
204 50 c. Cascade Church .. 25 25
236 60 c. red, blue and brown (Flying Fox) .. .. 1·25 45
205 70 c. Sail-fish .. .. 5·50 3·00
206 75 c. Coco-de-mer Palm .. 1·75 2·75
237 85 c. ultramarine and blue (Sail-fish) 90 40
207 1 r. Cinnamon 30 10
208 1 r. 50 Copra .. .. 3·00 4·50
209 2 r. 25 Map .. .. 3·00 3·00
210 3 r. 50 Land Settlement .. 2·25 4·50
211 5 r. Regina Mundi Convent 3·50 2·50
212 10 r. Type **40** .. .. 11·00 4·50

The 30 c., 35 c., 40 c., 85 c., 1 r., 1 r. 50, 2 r. 25, 3 r. 50 and 5 r. are horiz.
No. 236 is 23 × 25 mm.

1963. Freedom from Hunger. As T **28** of Aden.
213. 70 c. violet 60 25

1963. Cent of Red Cross. As T **33** of Antigua.
214. 10 c. red and black .. 25 10
215. 75 c. red and blue .. 75 40

1965. Surch.
216. 45 c. on 35 c. (No. 201) .. 10 15
217. 75 c. on 70 c. (No. 205) .. 20 15

1965. Cent of I.T.U. As T **34** of Antigua.
218. 5 c. orange and blue .. 15 10
219. 1 r. 50 mauve and green .. 65 25

1965. I.C.Y. As T **36** of Antigua.
220. 5 c. purple and turquoise .. 10 10
221. 40 c. green and lavender .. 20 20

1966. Churchill Commem. As T **37** of Antigua.
222. 5 c. blue 15 10
223. 15 c. green 40 10
224. 75 c. brown 80 10
225. 1 r. 50 violet .. .. 1·25 60

1966. World Cup Football Championship. As T **40** of Antigua.
226. 15 c. multicoloured .. 10 10
227. 1 r. multicoloured .. 20 20

1966. Inauguration of W.H.O. Headquarters, Geneva. As T **41** of Antigua.
228. 20 c. black, green and blue 15 10
229. 50 c. black, purple & ochre 25 20

1966. 20th Anniv of U.N.E.S.C.O. As T **54/6** of Antigua.
230. 15 c. multicoloured .. 25 10
231. 1 r. yellow, violet and olive 45 10
232. 5 r. black, purple & orange 1·25 1·00

1967. Universal Adult Suffrage. Nos. 198, 203, 206 and 210 optd. **UNIVERSAL ADULT SUFFRAGE 1967.**
238. 15 c. multicoloured .. 10 10
239. 45 c. multicoloured .. 10 10
240. 75 c. multicoloured .. 10 10
241. 3 r. 50 multicoloured .. 20 15

44. Cowrie Shells.

1967. Int. Tourist Year. Multicoloured.
242. 15 c. Type **44** 15 10
243. 40 c. Cone Shells 20 10
244. 1 r. Arthritic Spider Conch 25 10
245. 2 r. 25 "Subulate auger" and Triton Shells .. 55 40

1968. Nos. 202/3 and 206 surch.
246. 30 c. on 40 c. multicoloured 10 10
247. 60 c. on 45 c. multicoloured 10 10
248. 85 c. on 75 c. multicoloured 15 15

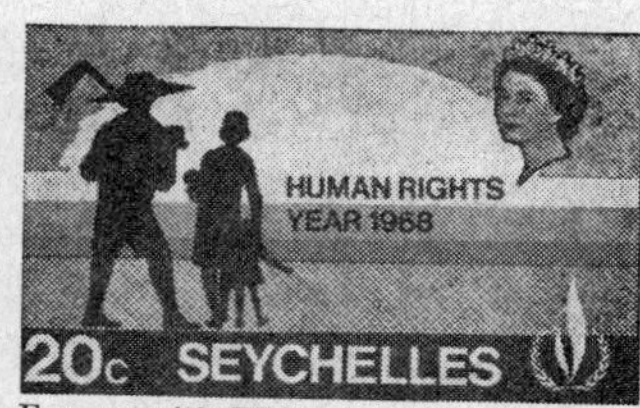

49. Farmer with Wife and Children at Sunset.

1968. Human Rights Year.
249. **49.** 20 c. multicoloured .. 10 10
250. 50 c. multicoloured .. 10 10
251. 85 c. multicoloured .. 10 10
252. 2 r. 25 multicoloured .. 20 30

50. Expedition landing at Anse Possession.

1968. Bicentenary of First Landing on Praslin. Multicoloured.
253. 20 c. Type **50** 15 10
254. 50 c. French warships at Anchor 20 15
255. 85 c. Coco-de-mer and Black Parrot 45 20
256. 2 r. 25 French warships under Sail 55 50

54. Apollo Launch.

1969. 1st Man on the Moon. Multicoloured.
257. 5 c. Type **54** 10 10
258. 20 c. Module leaving mother-ship for the moon .. 15 10
259. 50 c. Astronauts and Space Module on the moon .. 20 15
260. 85 c. Tracking Station .. 25 15
261. 2 r. 25 Moon craters with Earth on the "Horizon" 45 65

59. Picault's Landing, 1742.

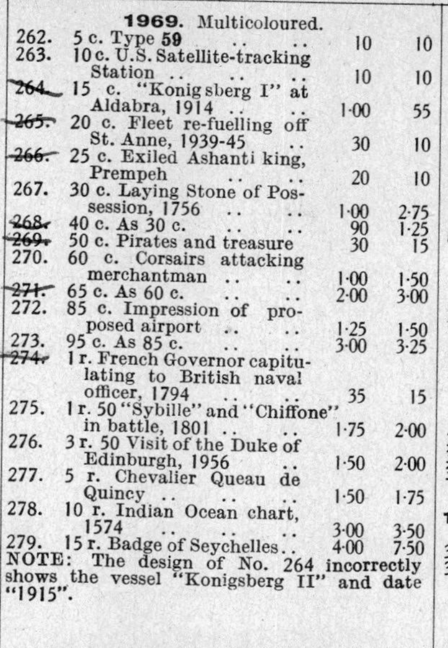

1969. Multicoloured.
262. 5 c. Type **59** 10 10
263. 10 c. U.S. Satellite-tracking Station 10 10
264. 15 c. "Konigsberg I" at Aldabra, 1914 .. .. 1·00 55
265. 20 c. Fleet re-fuelling off St. Anne, 1939-45 .. 30 10
266. 25 c. Exiled Ashanti king, Prempeh 20 10
267. 30 c. Laying Stone of Possession, 1756 .. .. 1·00 2·75
268. 40 c. As 30 c. .. .. 90 1·25
269. 50 c. Pirates and treasure 30 15
270. 60 c. Corsairs attacking merchantman .. .. 1·00 1·50
271. 65 c. As 60 c. .. .. 2·00 3·00
272. 85 c. Impression of proposed airport .. .. 1·25 1·50
273. 95 c. As 85 c. .. .. 3·00 3·25
274. 1 r. French Governor capitulating to British naval officer, 1794 .. .. 35 15
275. 1 r. 50 "Sybille" and "Chiffone" in battle, 1801 .. .. 1·75 2·00
276. 3 r. 50 Visit of the Duke of Edinburgh, 1956 .. 1·50 2·00
277. 5 r. Chevalier Queau de Quincy .. .. 1·50 1·75
278. 10 r. Indian Ocean chart, 1574 .. .. 3·00 3·50
279. 15 r. Badge of Seychelles .. 4·00 7·50

NOTE: The design of No. 264 incorrectly shows the vessel "Konigsberg II" and date "1915".

74. White Tern, French Warship and Island.

1970. Bicentenary of 1st Settlement, St. Anne Island. Multicoloured.
280. 20 c. Type **74** 15 10
281. 50 c. Flying Fish, ship and island 15 10
282. 85 c. Compass and chart .. 15 10
283. 3 r. 50 Anchor on sea-bed .. 30 45

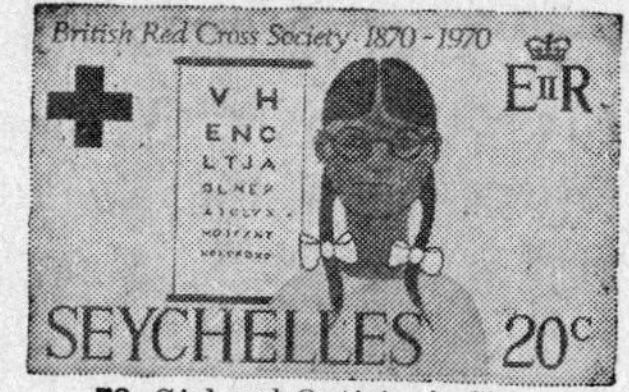

78. Girl and Optician's Chart.

1970. Cent. of British Red Cross. Mult.
284. 20 c. Type **78** 10 10
285. 50 c. Baby, scales and milk bottles 15 10
286. 85 c. Woman with child and umbrella (vert.) .. 15 10
287. 3 r. 50 Red Cross local headquarters building .. 80 60

79. Pitcher Plant. **81.** Piper "Navajo".

1970. Flowers. Multicoloured.
288. 20 c. Type **79** 45 15
289. 50 c. Wild Vanilla .. 55 15
290. 85 c. Tropic-Bird Orchid .. 1·40 30
291. 3 r. 50 Vare Hibiscus .. 2·50 1·50

1971. Airport Completion. Multicoloured.
294. 5 c. Type **81** 10 10
295. 20 c. Westland "Wessex" 20 10
296. 50 c. "Catalina" flying-boat (horiz.) 40 10
297. 60 c. Grumman "Albatross" 45 10
298. 85 c. Short "G" Class Flying-boat (horiz.) .. 65 10
299. 3 r. 50 Vickers Supermarine "Walrus" (horiz.) .. 3·50 3·00

82. Santa Claus delivering Gifts (Jean-Claude Waye Hive).

1971. Christmas. Multicoloured.
300. 10 c. Type **82** 10 10
301. 15 c. Santa Claus seated on turtle (Edison Theresine) 10 10
302. 3 r. 50 Santa Claus landing on island (Isabelle Tirant) 40 70

1971. Nos. 267, 270 and 272 surch.
303. 40 c. on 30 c. multicoloured 30 55
304. 65 c. on 60 c. multicoloured 40 75
305. 95 c. on 85 c. multicoloured 45 1·00

1972. Royal Visit. Nos. 265a and 277 optd. **ROYAL VISIT, 1972.**
306. 20 c. multicoloured .. 15 20
307. 5 r. multicoloured .. .. 1·50 2·50

85. Seychelles Brush Warbler.

1972. Rare Seychelles Birds. Multicoloured.
308. 5 c. Type **85** 30 10
309. 20 c. Bare-legged Scops Owl 1·00 20
310. 50 c. Seychelles Blue Pigeon .. .. 1·25 65
311. 65 c. Seychelles Magpie Robin .. .. 1·50 75
312. 95 c. Seychelles Paradise Flycatcher .. .. 2·25 2·00
313. 3 r. 50 Seychelles Kestrel 6·50 8·00

86. Fireworks Display.

1972. "Festival '72". Multicoloured.
315. 10 c. Type **86** 10 10
316. 15 c. Pirogue race (horiz.) 10 10
317. 25 c. Floats and costumes 10 10
318. 5 r. Water skiing (horiz.) .. 60 80

1972. Royal Silver Wedding. As T **52** of Ascension, but with Giant Tortoise and Sailfish in background.
319. 95 c. blue 15 10
320. 1 r. 50 brown 15 10

1973. Royal Wedding. As T **47** of Anguilla. Multicoloured, background colours given.
321. 95 c. brown 10 10
322. 1 r. 50 blue 10 10

88. Soldier Fish.

1974. Fishes. Multicoloured.
323. 20 c. Type **88** 15 10
324. 50 c. File Fish 25 10
325. 95 c. Butterfly Fish .. 30 20
326. 1 r. 50 Gaterin .. .. 75 1·00

89. Globe and Letter.

1974. Centenary of U.P.U. Multicoloured.

327. 20 c. Type **89** 10 10
328. 50 c. Globe and radio beacon 20 10
329. 95 c. Globe and postmark 35 40
330. 1 r. 50 Emblems within "UPU" 50 70

90. Sir Winston Churchill.

1974. Birth Centenary of Sir Winston Churchill. Multicoloured.

331. 95 c. Type **90** 20 15
332. 1 r. 50 Profile portrait .. 35 40

1975. Visit of Liner "Queen Elizabeth II". Nos. 265a, 269a, 273a and 275a optd. **VISIT OF Q.E. II.**

334. 20 c. multicoloured .. 15 15
335. 50 c. multicoloured .. 20 20
336. 95 c. multicoloured .. 25 35
337. 1 r. 50 multicoloured .. 35 60

1975. Internal Self-Government. Nos. 265a 271a, 274a and 276a optd. **INTERNAL SELF-GOVERNMENT OCTOBER 1975.**

338. 20 c. multicoloured .. 15 15
339. 65 c. multicoloured .. 25 30
340. 1 r. multicoloured .. 30 35
341. 3 r. 50 multicoloured .. 1·00 1·50

93. Queen Elizabeth I.

1975. International Women's Year. Mult.

342. 10 c. Type **93** 10 10
343. 15 c. Gladys Aylward .. 10 10
344. 20 c. Elizabeth Fry .. 10 10
345. 25 c. Emmeline Pankhurst 10 10
346. 65 c. Florence Nightingale 25 20
347. 1 r. Amy Johnson.. .. 40 35
348. 1 r. 50 Joan of Arc.. .. 50 60
349. 3 r. 50 Eleanor Roosevelt 1·50 2·25

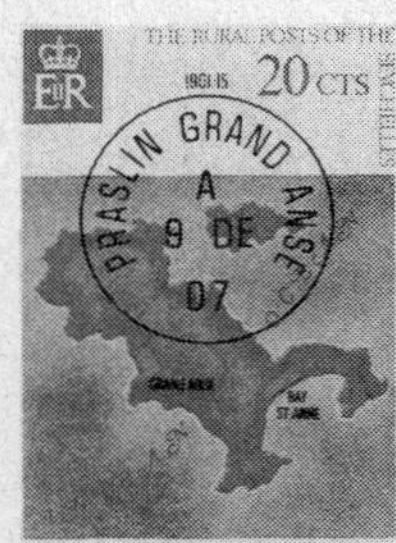

94. Map of Praslin and Postmark.

1976. Seychelles Rural Posts. Multicoloured.

350. 20 c. Type **94** 15 10
351. 65 c. La Digue 25 20
352. 1 r. Mahe with Victoria postmark 30 25
353. 1 r. 50 Mahe Anse Royale postmark 45 70

Nos. 350/53 show maps and postmarks.

95. First Landing, 1609 (Inset portrait of Premier James Mancham).

1976. Independence. Multicoloured.

355. 20 c. Type **95** 10 10
356. 25 c. The possession Stone 10 10
357. 40 c. First settlers, 1770.. 15 15
358. 75 c. Chevalier Queau de Quincy 20 20
359. 1 r. Sir Bickham Sweet-Escott 25 20
360. 1 r. 25 Legislative Building 40 50
361. 1 r. 50 Seychelles badge.. 45 60
362. 3 r. 50 Seychelles flag .. 90 1·40

96. Flags of Seychelles and U.S.A.

1976. Bicent. of Seychelles Independence and American Independence. Multicoloured.

363. 1 r. Type **96** 25 15
364. 10 r. Statehouses of Seychelles and Philadelphia 1·25 1·50

97. Swimming.

1976. Olympic Games, Montreal.

365. **97.** 20 c. blue, light blue and brown 10 10
366. – 65 c. dark green, green and grey 20 10
367. – 1 r. brown, blue & grey 25 10
368. – 3 r. 50 light red, red and grey 50 80

DESIGNS: 65 c. Hockey. 1 r. Basketball. 3 r. 50 Football.

98. Seychelles Paradise Flycatcher.

1976. 4th Pan-African Ornithological Congress, Seychelles. Multicoloured.

369. 20 c. Type **98** 15 10
370. 1 r. 25 Seychelles Sunbird (horiz.) 65 65
371. 1 r. 50 Seychelles Brown White Eye (horiz.) .. 80 80
372. 5 r. Black Parrot .. .. 2·00 2·00

1976. Independence. Nos. 265, 269, 271, 273, 274, 276 and 277/9 optd. **Independence 1976** or surch. also.

374. 20 c. Fleet re-fuelling at St. Anne, 1939–45 .. 25 55
375. 50 c. Pirates and treasure 40 75
376. 95 c. Impressions of proposed airport .. .. 55 1·00
377. 1 r. French Governor capitulating to British naval officer, 1794 .. .. 55 1·00
378. 3 r. 50 Visit of the Duke of Edinburgh, 1956 .. 2·75 3·50
379. 5 r. Chevalier Queau de Quincy .. .. .. 3·00 3·50
380. 10 r. Indian Ocean chart, 1574 .. .. .. 5·50 9·00
381. 15 r. Badge of Seychelles 7·50 9·00
382. 25 r. on 65 c. Corsairs attacking merchantmen 11·00 16·00

100. Inauguration of George Washington.

1976. Bicentenary of American Revolution.

383. **100.** 1 c. deep red and red .. 10 10
384. – 2 c. violet and lilac .. 10 10
385. – 3 c. light blue and blue 10 10
386. – 4 c. brown and yellow.. 10 10
387. – 5 c. green and yellow .. 10 10
388. – 1 r. 50 brown and light brown 60 35
389. – 3 r. 50 blue and green.. 80 80
390. – 5 r. brown and yellow.. 1·00 1·00
391. – 10 r. blue and light blue 1·75 1·75

DESIGNS: 2 c. Jefferson and Louisiana Purchase. 3 c. William Seward and Alaska Purchase. 4 c. Pony express, 1860. 5 c. Lincoln's Emancipation Proclamation. 1 r. 50, Transcontinental Railroad, 1869. 3 r. 50, Wright Brothers flight, 1903. 5 r. Henry Ford's assembly-line, 1913. 10 r. J. F. Kennedy and 1969 Moon-landing.

101. Silhouette of the Islands.

1977. Silver Jubilee. Multicoloured.

393. 20 c. Type **101** 10 10
394. 40 c. Silhouette (different) 10 10
395. 50 c. The Orb 10 10
396. 1 r. St. Edward's Crown.. 15 10
397. 1 r. 25 Ampulla and Spoon 20 15
398. 1 r. 50 Sceptre with Cross 20 20
399. 5 r. Silhouette (different) 50 50
400. 10 r. Silhouette (different) 90 90

The 50 c. to 1 r. 50 are vertical designs.

102. Cruiser "Aurora" and Flag.

1977. 60th Anniv. of Russian Revolution.

402. **102.** 1 r. 50 milticoloured .. 35 30

103. Coral Stone.

1977. Marine Life. Rupee face value shown as "Re" or "Rs". Multicoloured.

404 5 c. Reef fish 10 10
405 10 c. Hawksbill turtle .. 10 10
406 15 c. Coco-de-Mer .. 10 10
407 20 c. Wild vanilla orchid 10 10
408 25 c. "Hypolimnas misippus" (butterfly) .. 10 10
409 40 c. Type **103** 10 10
410 50 c. Giant tortoise .. 10 10
411 75 c. Crayfish 20 10
412 1 r. Madagascar red fody 1·25 10
413 1 r. 25 White tern .. 1·00 15
414 1 r. 50 Seychelles flying fox 1·50 15
415 3 r. 50 Green gecko .. 75 80
416 5 r. Octopus .. .. 2·00 40
417 10 r. Giant tiger cowrie .. 2·25 2·00
418 5 r. Pitcher plant .. 2·25 2·50
419 20 r. Coat of arms .. 2·50 2·50

The 40 c. 1 r., 1 r.25 and 1 r.50 values are horizontal, 31 × 27 mm. The 5, 10, 15 and 20 r. are vertical, 28 × 36 mm. The others are horizontal, 29 × 25 mm.

Nos. 405/12 and 414 exist with or without imprint date at foot.

For similiar designs with rupee face values shown as "R"see Nos. 487/94.

104. St. Roch Roman Catholic Church, Bel Ombre.

1977. Christmas. Multicoloured.

420. 20 c. Type **104** 10 10
421. 1 r. Anglican cathedral, Victoria.. .. .. 10 10
422. 1 r. 50 Roman Catholic cathedral, Victoria .. 15 10
423. 5 r. St. Mark's Anglican church, Praslin .. 30 45

105. Liberation Day ringed on Calendar.

1978. Liberation Day. Multicoloured.

424. 40 c. Type **105** 10 10
425. 1 r. 25 Hands holding bayonet, torch and flag 15 10
426. 1 r. 50 Fisherman and farmer 15 15
427. 5 r. Soldiers and rejoicing people 35 40

106. Stamp Portraits of Edward VII, George V and George VI.

1978. 25th Anniv. of Coronation. Mult.

428. 40 c. Type **106** 10 10
429. 1 r. 50 Queen Victoria and Elizabeth II 10 10
430. 3 r. Queen Victoria Monument 20 25
431. 5 r. Queen's Building, Victoria.. .. .. 30 35

107. Gardenia.

1978. World Wildlife. Multicoloured

433. 40 c. Type **107** 10 10
434. 1 r. 25 Seychelles Magpie Robin 40 25
435. 1 r. 50 Seychelles Paradise Flycatcher 45 35
436. 5 r. Green Turtle 70 85

108. Possession Stone.

1978. Bicentenary of Victoria. Multicoloured.

437 20 c. Type **108** 10 10
438 1 r. 25 Plan of 1782 "L'Etablissement" 15 15
439 1 r. 50 Clock Tower 15 15
440 5 r. Bust of Pierre Poivre 40 50

109. Seychelles Fody.

1979. Birds (1st series). Multicoloured.

441. 2 r. Type **109** 50 50
442. 2 r. Green heron 50 50
443. 2 r. Thick-billed Bulbul 50 50
444. 2 r. Seychelles cave swiftlet 50 50
445. 2 r. Grey-headed lovebird 50 50

See also Nos. 463/7, 500/4 and 523/7.

110. Patrice Lumumba.

1979. African Liberation Heroes.

446. **110.** 40 c. blk., violet & lilac 10 10
447. – 2 r. blk., blue & pale blue 25 25
448. – 2 r. 25 blk., brn. & orge. 30 30
449. – 5 r. black, olive & green 65 80

DESIGNS: 2 r. Kwame Nkrumah. 2 r. 25, Dr. Eduardo Mondlane. 5 r. Hamilcar Cabral.

111. 1978 5 r. Liberation Day Commemorative and Sir Rowland Hill.

1979. Death Centenary of Sir Rowland Hill. Multicoloured.

450. 40 c. Type **111** 10 10
451. 2 r. 25 1972 50 c. Seychelles Blue Pigeon commemorative 45 40
452. 3 r. 1962 50 c. definitive 50 55

112. Child with Book.

1979. International Year of the Child Multicoloured.

454. 40 c. Type **112** 10 10
455. 2 r. 25 Children of different races 20 30
456. 3 r. Young child with ball (vert.) 30 45
457. 5 r. Girl with glove-puppet (vert.) 40 65

113. The Herald Angel.

1979. Christmas. Multicoloured.

458. 20 c. Type **113** 10 10
459. 2 r. 25 The Virgin and Child 30 30
460. 3 r. The Three Kings (horiz.) 40 45

1980. No. 415 surch.

462. 1 r. 10 on 3 r. 50 Green Gecko 30 30

115. Seychelles Kestrel.

1980. Birds (2nd series). Seychelles Kestrel. Multicoloured.

463. 2 r. Type **115**. 60 50
464. 2 r. Pair of Seychelles Kestrels 60 50
465. 2 r. Seychelles Kestrel with eggs 60 50
466. 2 r. Seychelles Kestrel on nest with chick 60 50
467. 2 r. Seychelles Kestrel chicks in nest 60 50

116. 10 Rupees Banknote.

1980. "London 1980" International Stamp Exhibition. Currency Notes. Multicoloured.

468. 40 c. Type **116** 10 10
469. 1 r. 50 25 rupees 20 15
470. 2 r. 25 50 rupees (vert.) 30 25
471. 5 r. 100 rupees (vert.) 60 55

117. Sprinting.

1980. Olympic Games, Moscow. Mult.

473. 40 c. Type **117** 10 10
474. 2 r. 25 Weightlifting 20 20
475. 3 r. Boxing 30 30
476. 5 r. Yachting 60 40

118. "Jumbo Jet" Airliner.

1980. International Tourism Conference, Manila. Multicoloured.

478. 40 c. Type **118** 10 10
479. 2 r. 25 Bus 35 35
480. 3 r. Cruise liner 50 50
481. 5 r. "La Belle Caralline" (tourist launch) 70 75

119. Female Palm.

1980. Coco-de-Mer (palms). Multicoloured.

482. 40 c. Type **119**. 10 10
483. 2 r. 25 Male Palm 25 20
484. 3 r. Artefacts 40 35
485. 5 r. Fisherman's gourd 55 55

1981. As Nos. 412/14, 415 (with new value), and 416/19, but face values redrawn as "R" instead of "Re" or "Rs".

487a 1 r. Madagascar fody 20 25
488 1 r. 10 Green gecko 25 30
735 1 r. 25 White tern 25 30
490 1 r. 50 Seychelles flying fox 35 40
736 3 r. Green gecko 90 90
738 5 r. Octopus 1·10 1·25
492 10 r. Giant tiger cowrie 2·25 2·40
493 15 r. Pitcher plant 3·25 3·50
494 20 r. Seychelles coat of arms 4·50 4·75

120. Vasco da Gama's "Sao Gabriel", 1497.

1981. Ships. Multicoloured.

495. 40 c. Type **120** 15 10
496. 2 r. 25 Mascarenhas' caravel, 1505 60 55
497. 3 r. 50 Darwin's H.M.S. "Beagle", 1831 90 1·00
498. 5 r. "Queen Elizabeth 2" (liner), 1968 1·10 1·40

121. White Tern.

1981. Birds (3rd series). White Tern. Multicoloured.

500. 2 r. Type **121** 85 65
501. 2 r. Pair of White Terns 85 65
502. 2 r. Female White Tern 85 65
503. 2 r. Female White Tern on nest, and egg 85 65
504. 2 r. White Tern and chick 85 65

1981. Royal Wedding, Royal Yachts. As T **26/27** of Kiribati. Multicoloured.

505 1 r. 50 "Victoria and Albert I" 20 25
506 1 r. 50 Prince Charles and Lady Diana Spencer 50 50
507 5 r. "Cleveland" 60 60
513 5 r. As No. 506 1·00 1·60
509 10 r. "Britannia" 1·00 1·50
510 10 r. As No. 506 2·25 2·25

122. Britten-Norman "Islander".

1981. 10th Anniv. of Opening of Seychelles International Airport. Aircraft. Mult.

514. 40 c. Type **122** 15 10
515. 2 r. 25 Britten-Norman "Trislander" 55 45
516. 3 r. 50 BAC (Vickers) "VC10" airliner 80 70
517. 5 r. Boeing "747" airliner 1·00 1·00

123. Seychelles Flying Foxes in Flight.

1981. Seychelles Flying Fox (Roussette). Multicoloured.

518. 40 c. Type **123** 10 10
519. 2 r. 25 Flying Fox eating 45 45
520. 3 r. Flying Fox climbing across tree branch 70 70
521. 5 r. Flying Fox hanging from tree branch 1·00 1·00

124. Chinese Little Bittern (male).

1982. Birds (4th series). Chinese Bittern. Multicoloured.

523. 3 r. Type **124** 1·75 65
524. 3 r. Chinese Little Bittern (female) 1·75 65
525. 3 r. Hen on Nest 1·75 65
526. 3 r. Nest and eggs 1·75 65
527. 3 r. Hen and chicks 1·75 65

125. Silhouette Island and La Digue.

1982. Modern Maps. Multicoloured.

528. 40 c. Type **125** 15 10
529. 1 r. 50 Denis and Bird Islands 40 25
530. 2 r. 75 Praslin 65 65
531. 7 r. Mahe 1·60 2·00

126. " Education ".

1982. 5th Anniv. of Liberation. Mult.

533.	40 c. Type **126**	10	10
534.	1 r. 75 " Health " ..	25	25
535.	2 r. 75 " Agriculture " ..	45	45
536.	7 r. " Construction " ..	1·40	1·40

127. Tourist Board Emblem.

1982. Tourism. Multicoloured.

538.	1 r. 75 Type **127**	40	35
539.	1 r. 75 Northolme Hotel ..	40	35
540.	1 r. 75 Reef Hotel	40	35
541.	1 r. 75 Barbarons Beach Hotel	40	35
542.	1 r. 75 Coral Strand Hotel	40	35
543.	1 r. 75 Beau Vallon Bay Hotel	40	35
544.	1 r. 75 Fisherman's Cove Hotel	40	35
545.	1 r. 75 Mahe Beach Hotel	40	35

128. Tata Bus.

1982. Land Transport. Multicoloured.

546.	20 c. Type **128**	10	10
547.	1 r. 75 Mini-moke	30	25
548.	2 r. 75 Ox-cart	50	55
549.	7 r. Truck	1·40	1·75

129. Radio Seychelles Control Room.

1983. World Communications Year. Mult

550.	40 c. Type **129**	10	10
551.	2 r. 75 Satellite Earth station	45	50
552.	3 r. 50 Radio Seychelles televison control ..	70	75
553.	5 r. Postal services sorting office	1·00	1·25

130. Agricultural Experimental Station.

1983. Commonwealth Day. Multicoloured.

554.	40 c. Type **130**	10	10
555.	2 r. 75 Food processing plant	45	50
556.	3 r. 50 Unloading fish catch	70	75
557.	7 r. Seychelles flag ..	1·40	1·50

131. Denis Island Lighthouse.

1983. Famous Landmarks. Multicoloured.

558.	40 c. Type **131**	10	10
559.	2 r. 75 Victoria Hospital ..	40	45
560.	3 r. 50 Supreme Court ..	60	65
561.	7 r. State House	1·25	1·40

132. " Royal Vauxhall " Balloon, 1836.

1983. Bicentenary of Manned Flight. Mult.

563.	40 c. Type **132**	10	10
564.	1 r. 75 De Havilland " D.H.50J "	40	30
565.	2 r. 75 Grumman " Albatross "	55	55
566.	7 r. Swearingen " Merlin "	1·40	1·75

133. Jet Plane.

1983. 1st International Flight of Air Seychelles.

567.	**133.** 2 r. multicoloured ..	60	60

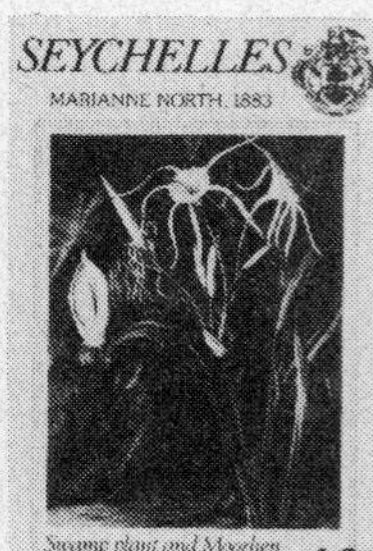

134. Swamp Plant and Moorhen.

1983. Centenary of Marianne North's Visit. Multicoloured.

568.	40 c. Type **134** ..	15	10
569.	1 r. 75 " Wormia flagellaria "	50	30
570.	2 r. 75 Asiatic Pancratium	65	60
571.	7 r. Pitcher Plant ..	1·50	1·60

1983. Nos. 505/10 surch.

573.	50 c. on 1 r. 50 " Victoria and Albert I " ..	15	15
574.	50 c. on 1 r. 50 Prince Charles and Lady Diana Spencer	40	45
575.	2 r. 25 on 5 r. " Cleveland "	45	50
576.	2 r. 25 on 5 r. As No. 574	1·00	1·25
577.	3 r. 75 on 10 r. " Britannia "	75	80
578.	3 r. 75 on 10 r. As No. 574	1·40	1·75

136. Coconut Vessel.

1984. Traditional Handicrafts. Multicoloured.

579.	50 c. Type **136**	15	10
580.	2 r. Scarf and doll ..	50	60
581.	3 r. Coconut-fibre roses ..	70	80
582.	10 r. Carved fishing boat and doll	2·00	3·00

137. Victoria Port.

1984. 250th Anniv. of "Lloyd's List" (newspaper). Multicoloured.

583.	50 c. Type **137**	20	10
584.	2 r. Cargo liner	55	55
585.	3 r. "Sun Viking" (liner) ..	80	80
586.	10 r. Loss of R.F.A. "Ennerdale II"	2·25	2·75

138. Old S.P.U.P. Office.

1984. 20th Anniv. of Seychelles Peoples' United Party. Multicoloured.

587.	50 c. Type **138**	15	10
588.	2 r. Liberation statue (vert.)	40	50
589.	3 r. New S.P.U.D. office ..	60	80
590.	10 r. President Rene (vert.)	2·00	3·00

140. Long jumping.

1984. Olympic Games, Los Angeles. Mult.

592.	50 c. Type **140**	10	10
593.	2 r. Boxing	40	45
594.	3 r. Swimming	60	75
595.	10 r. Weightlifting ..	1·75	2·50

141. Sub-aqua Diving.

1984. Water Sports. Multicoloured.

597.	50 c. Type **141**	20	10
598.	2 r. Paragliding	60	45
599.	3 r. Sailing	80	75
600.	10 r. Water-skiing	2·25	2·50

142. Humpback Whale.

1984. Whale Conservation. Multicoloured.

601.	50 c. Type **142**	75	15
602.	2 r. Sperm Whale	1·75	85
603.	3 r. Black Right Whale ..	2·00	1·25
604.	10 r. Blue Whale	4·00	4·50

143. Two Bare-legged Scops Owls in Tree.

1985. Birth Bicentenary of John J. Audubon (ornithologist). Bare-legged Scops Owl. Multicoloured.

605.	50 c. Type **143**	75	15
606.	2 r. Owl on branch ..	1·75	1·25
607.	3 r. Owl in flight	2·00	1·25
608.	10 r. Owl on ground ..	3·25	4·00

144. Giant Tortoises.

1985. "Expo '85" World Fair, Japan. Multicoloured.

609.	50 c. Type **144**	30	10
610.	2 r. White terns	1·00	60
611.	3 r. Windsurfing	1·00	75
612.	5 r. Coco-de-Mer	1·25	1·40

145. The Queen Mother with Princess Anne and Prince Andrew, 1970.

1985. Life and Times of Queen Elizabeth the Queen Mother. Multicoloured.

614.	50 c. The Queen Mother in 1930	10	10
615.	2 r. Type **145** ..	45	50
616.	3 r. On her 75th Birthday	65	70
617.	5 r. With Prince Henry at his christening (from photo by Lord Snowdon)	1·10	1·25

146. Boxing.

1985. 2nd Indian Ocean Islands Games. Multicoloured.

619.	50 c. Type **146**	15	10
620.	2 r. Football	55	50
621.	3 r. Swimming	75	70
622.	10 r. Windsurfing	2·40	2·40

1985. Acquisition of 1st Air Seychelles "Airbus" As No. 735, but additionally inscribed "AIR SEYCHELLES FIRST AIRBUS".

623.	1 r. 25 White Tern ..	75	75

147. Agriculture Students.

1985. International Youth Year. Mult.

624. 50 c. Type **147** 10 10
625. 2 r. Construction students building wall 45 50
626. 3 r. Carpentry students .. 65 70
627. 10 r. Science students .. 2·25 2·40

148. Ford "Model T" (1919).

1985. Vintage Cars. Multicoloured.

628. 50 c. Type **148** 30 10
629. 2 r. Austin "Seven" (1922) 1·00 50
630. 3 r. Morris "Oxford" (1924) 1·25 70
631. 10 r. Humber "Coupe" (1929) .. .. .. 2·75 2·40

149. Five Foot Transit Instrument.

1986. Appearance of Halley's Comet. Mult.

632. 50 c. Type **149** 30 10
633. 2 r. Eight foot quadrant .. 1·00 50
634. 3 r. Comet's orbit .. .. 1·25 75
635. 10 r. Edmond Halley .. 2·75 2·40

150. Ballerina.

1986. Visit of Ballet du Louvre Company. "Giselle". Multicoloured.

636. 2 r. Type **150** 75 60
637. 3 r. Male dancer .. .. 1·00 90

1986. 60th Birthday of Queen Elizabeth II. As T **110** of Ascension. Multicoloured.

639. 50 c. Wedding photograph, 1947 .. .. .. 10 10
640. 1 r. 25 At State Opening of Parliament, 1982 .. 30 35
641. 2 r. Queen accepting bouquet, Seychelles, 1972 45 50
642. 3 r. On board Royal Yacht "Britannia", Qatar, 1979 70 75
643. 5 r. At Crown Agents Head Office, London, 1983 .. 1·10 1·25

151. Ferry to La Digue.

1986. "Ameripex '86" International Stamp Exhibition, Chicago. Inter-island Communication. Multicoloured.

644. 50 c. Type **151** 40 10
645. 2 r. Telephone kiosk (vert.) 85 50
646. 3 r. Post Office Counter, Victoria (vert.) .. .. 1·25 75
647. 7 r. Air Seychelles Britten-Norman "Trislander" aircraft .. .. .. 2·50 1·75

152. Crests of Seychelles and Knights of Malta.

1986. Seychelles Knights of Malta Day.

648. **152.** 5 r. multicoloured .. 1·10 1·25

1986. Royal Wedding. As T **112** of Ascension. Multicoloured.

651. 2 r. Prince Andrew and Miss Sarah Ferguson .. 45 50
652. 10 r. Prince Andrew boarding Wessex helicopter, 1983 .. .. 2·25 2·40

1986. International Creole Day. No. 487 optd. **LAZOURNEN ENTERNASYONAL KREOL.**

653. 1 r. Madagascar red fody 1·00 50

154. Pope John Paul at Seychelles Airport.

1986. Visit of Pope John Paul II. Designs showing Pope and Seychelles scene. Multicoloured.

654. 50 c. Type **154** 50 10
655. 2 r. Catholic Cathedral, Victoria .. .. .. 1·50 60
656. 3 r. Baie Lazare Parish Church .. .. .. 2·00 90
657. 10 r. Aerial view of Peoples' Stadium .. 6·50 2·75

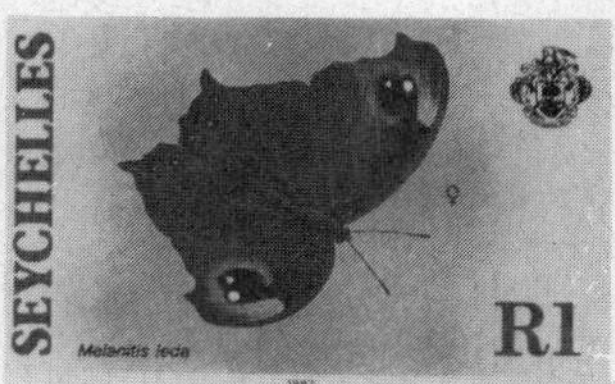

155. "Melanitis leda".

1987. Butterflies. Multicoloured.

659. 1 r. Type **155** 55 25
660. 2 r. "Phalanta philiberti" 90 60
661. 3 r. "Danaus chrysippus" 1·25 1·00
662. 10 r. "Euploea mitra" .. 3·50 3·50

156. "Gloripallium pallium".

1987. Seashells. Multicoloured.

663. 1 r. Type **156** 60 25
664. 2 r. "Spondylus aurantius" 1·00 60
665. 3 r. "Harpa ventricosa" and "Lioconcha ornata" 1·50 90
666. 10 r. "Strombus lentiginosus" .. .. 3·25 3·00

157. Statue of Liberation.

1987. 10th Anniv. of Liberation. Mult.

667. 1 r. Type **157** 20 25
668. 2 r. Seychelles hospital (horiz.) 45 50
669. 3 r. Orphanage village (horiz.) 70 75
670. 10 r. Proposed sail-fish monument .. .. 2·25 2·50

158. Seychelles Savings Bank, Praslin.

1987. Centenary of Banking in Seychelles.

671. **158.** 1 r. dp. grn. & grn. .. 20 25
672. – 2 r. brown and orange 45 50
673. – 10 r. dp. bl. & bl. .. 2·25 2·50

DESIGNS: 2 r. Development bank. 10 r. Central bank.

1987. Royal Ruby Wedding. Nos. 639/43 optd. **40TH WEDDING ANNIVERSARY.**

674. 50 c. Wedding photograph, 1947 .. .. .. 15 15
675. 1 r. 25 At State Opening of Parliament, 1982 .. 30 35
676. 2 r. Queen accepting bouquet, Seychelles, 1972 45 50
677. 3 r. On board Royal Yacht "Britannia", Qatar, 1979 70 75
678. 5 r. At Crown Agents Head Office, London, 1983 .. 1·10 1·25

159. Tuna Canning Factory.

1987. Seychelles Fishing Industry. Mult.

679. 50 c. Type **159** 15 15
680. 2 r. Trawler 45 50
681. 3 r. Weighing catch .. 70 75
682. 10 r. Unloading net .. 2·25 2·40

160. Water Sports.

1988. Tourism. Multicoloured.

683. 1 r. Type **160** 20 25
684. 2 r. Speedboat and yachts 45 50
685. 3 r. Yacht at anchor .. 70 75
686. 10 r. Hotel at night .. 2·25 2·40

161. Young Turtles making for Sea.

1988. The Green Turtle. Multicoloured.

687. 2 r. Type **161** .. .. 1·00 1·00
688. 2 r. Young turtles hatching 1·00 1·00
689. 3 r. Female turtle leaving sea .. .. .. 1·50 1·50
690. 3 r. Female laying eggs .. 1·50 1·50

Nos. 687/8 and 689/90 were printed together, se-tenant, each pair forming a composite design.

162 Shot Put

1988. Olympic Games, Seoul. Multicoloured.

691 1 r. Type **162** 20 25
692 2 r. Type **162** 40 45
693 2 r. High jump 40 45
694 2 r. Gold medal winner on podium 40 45
695 2 r. Athletics 40 45
696 2 r. Javelin 40 45
697 3 r. As No. 694 .. .. 60 65
698 4 r. As No. 695 .. .. 80 85
699 5 r. As No. 696 .. .. 1·00 1·10

1988. 300th Anniv of Lloyd's of London. As T **123** of Ascension. Multicoloured.

701 1 r. Leadenhall Street, London, 1928 .. .. 50 25
702 2 r. "Cinq Juin" (travelling post office) (horiz) .. 1·00 45
703 3 r. "Queen Elizabeth 2" (liner) (horiz) .. .. 1·50 65
704 10 r. Loss of "Hindenburg" (airship), 1937 .. .. 3·50 2·75

163 Police Motorcyclists

1988. 1st Anniv of Defence Forces Day. Mult.

705 1 r. Type **163** 60 25
706 2 r. Air Wing helicopter .. 1·00 90
707 3 r. Patrol boat .. .. 1·50 1·40
708 10 r. BRDM armoured car 3·50 4·00

164 Father Christmas with Basket of Presents

1988. Christmas. Multicoloured.
709 50 c. Type **164** 10 10
710 2 r. Bird and gourd filled with presents 40 45
711 3 r. Father Christmas basket weaving . . 60 65
712 10 r. Christmas bauble and palm tree . . . . 2·00 2·10

165 "Dendrobium sp."

1988. Orchids (1st series). Multicoloured.
713 1 r. Type **165** 30 25
714 2 r. "Arachnis" hybrid (horiz) 50 45
715 3 r. "Vanda caerulea" . . 70 65
716 10 r. "Dendrobium phalaenopsis" (horiz) 2·00 2·50
See also Nos. 767/70 and 795/8.

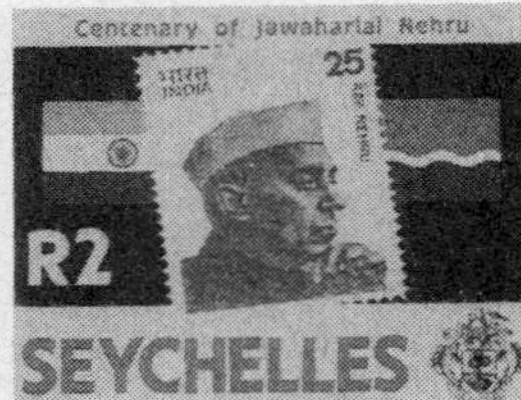

166 India 1976 25 p. Nehru Stamp

1989. Birth Centenary of Jawaharlal Nehru (Indian statesman). Each showing flags of Seychelles and India. Multicoloured.
724 2 r. Type **166** 40 50
725 10 r. Jawaharlal Nehru . . 2·00 2·50

167 Pres. Rene addressing Rally at Old Party Office

1989. 25th Anniv of Seychelles People's United Party. Multicoloured.
742 1 r. Type **167** 20 25
743 2 r. Women with Party flags and Maison Du Peuple 40 45
744 3 r. President Rene making speech and Torch of Freedom 60 65
745 10 r. President Rene, Party flag and Torch of Freedom . . . . 2·00 2·25

1989. 20th Anniv of First Manned Landing on Moon. As T **126** of Ascension. Multicoloured.
746 1 r. Lift off of "Saturn 5" rocket 20 25
747 2 r. Crew of "Apollo 15" (30×30 mm) 40 45
748 3 r. "Apollo 15" emblem (30×30 mm) 60 65
749 5 r. James Irwin saluting U.S. flag on Moon . . 1·00 1·10

168 British Red Cross Ambulance, Franco-Prussian War, 1870

1989. 125th Anniv of International Red Cross.
751 **168** 1 r. black and red . . 40 25
752 – 2 r. black, green & red 80 70
753 – 3 r. black and red . . 1·25 1·00
754 – 10 r. black and red . . 3·50 4·00
DESIGNS: 2 r. H.M. Hospital Ship "Liberty", 1914–18; 3 r. Sunbeam "Standard" army ambulance, 1914–18; 10 r. "White Train", South Africa, 1899–1902.

169 Black Parrot and Map of Praslin

1989. Island Birds. Multicoloured.
755 50 c. Type **169** 50 15
756 2 r. Sooty tern and Ile aux Vaches . . . . . . 1·25 1·00
757 3 r. Magpie robin and Fregate . . . . . . 1·60 1·40
758 5 r. Roseate tern and Aride 2·25 2·50

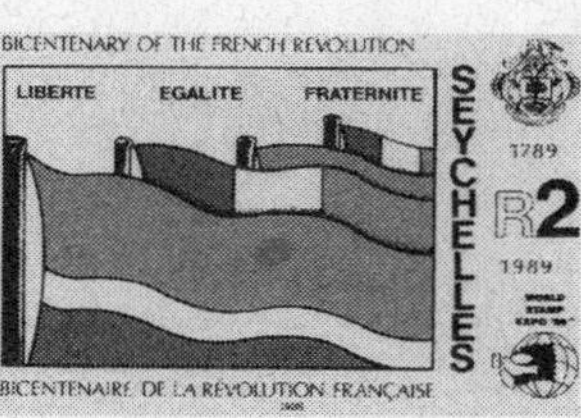

170 Flags of Seychelles and France

1989. Bicentenary of French Revolution and "World Stamp Expo '89", International Stamp Exhibition, Washington.
760 **170** 2 r. multicoloured . . 1·00 1·00
761 – 5 r. black, blue and red 2·25 2·25
DESIGN: 5 r. Storming the Bastille, Paris, 1789.

171 Beau Vallon School

1989. 25th Anniv of African Development Bank. Multicoloured.
763 1 r. Type **171** 40 25
764 2 r. Seychelles Fishing Authority Headquarters 75 65
765 3 r. "Variola" (fishing boat) (vert) . . 1·10 1·00
766 10 r. "Deneb" (fishing boat) (vert) . . . . 3·25 3·75

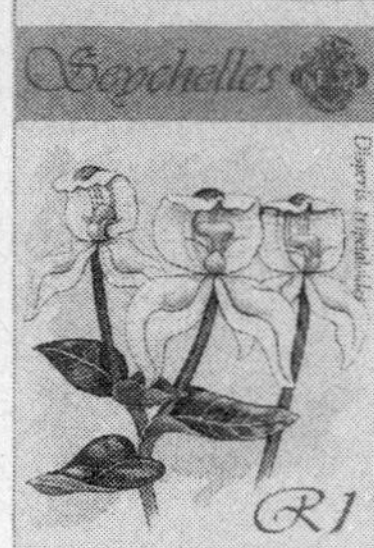

172 "Disperis tripetaloides"

1990. Orchids (2nd series). Multicoloured.
767 1 r. Type **172** 40 25
768 2 r. "Vanilla phalaenopsis" 75 65
769 3 r. "Angraecum eburneum" subsp. "superbum" 95 85
770 10 r. "Polystachya concreta" . . . . 2·50 3·00

173 Seychelles 1903 2 c. and Great Britain 1880 1½d. Stamps

1990. "Stamp World London 90" International Stamp Exhibition. Each showing stamps. Multicoloured.
771 1 r. Type **173** 40 25
772 2 r. Seychelles 1917 25 c. and G.B. 1873 1s. . . 75 65
773 3 r. Seychelles 1917 2 c. and G.B. 1874 6d. . . . . 1·10 1·00
774 5 r. Seychelles 1890 2 c. and G.B. 1841 1d. brown . . 1·75 2·00

174 Fumiyo Sako

1990. "EXPO 90" International Garden and Greenery Exhibition, Osaka. Multicoloured.
776 2 r. Type **174** 75 75
777 3 r. Male and female coco-de-mer palms . . 1·00 1·00
778 5 r. Pitcher plant and aldabra lily . . . . 1·60 1·60
779 7 r. Arms of Seychelles and gardenia . . . . 2·25 2·25

175 Air Seychelles Boeing "767-200ER" over Island

1990. Air Seychelles "Boeing 767-200ER" World Record-breaking Flight (1989).
781 **175** 3 r. multicoloured . . 1·40 1·40

1990. 90th Birthday of Queen Elizabeth the Queen Mother. As T **134** of Ascension.
782 2 r. multicoloured . . 75 60
783 10 r. black and violet . . 2·75 3·00
DESIGNS—21 × 36 mm. 2 r. Queen Elizabeth in Coronation robes, 1937. 29 × 37 mm. 10 r. Queen Elizabeth visiting Lord Roberts Workshops, 1947.

176 Adult Class

1990. International Literacy Year. Mult.
784 1 r. Type **176** 40 25
785 2 r. Reading a letter . . 75 65
786 3 r. Following written instructions . . . . 1·00 85
787 10 r. Typewriter, calculator and crossword . . . . 3·25 3·50

177 Sega Dancers

1990. Kreol Festival. Sega Dancing. Mult.
788 2 r. Type **177** 65 70
789 2 r. Dancing couple (girl in yellow dress) . . 65 70
790 2 r. Female Sega dancer . . 65 70
791 2 r. Dancing couple (girl in floral pattern skirt) . . 65 70
792 2 r. Dancing couple (girl in red patterned skirt) . . 65 70

178 Beach

1990. 1st Indian Ocean Regional Seminar on Petroleum Exploration. Multicoloured.
793 3 r. Type **178** . . . . 1·00 1·00
794 10 r. Geological map . . 3·00 3·00

1991. Orchids (3rd series). As T **172**. Mult.
795 1 r. "Bulbophyllum intertextum" 40 25
796 2 r. "Agrostophyllum occidentale" 75 60
797 3 r. "Vanilla planifolia" . . 1·10 85
798 10 r. "Malaxis seychellarum" . . . . 3·25 3·50

1991. 65th Birthday of Queen Elizabeth II and 70th Birthday of Prince Philip. As T **139** of Ascension. Multicoloured.
799 4 r. Queen in evening dress 1·40 1·50
800 4 r. Prince Philip in academic robes . . 2·75 3·00

179 "Precis rhadama"

1991. "Philanippon '91" International Stamp Exhibition, Tokyo. Butterflies. Mult.
801 1 r. 50 Type **179** 50 40
802 3 r. "Lampides boeticus" 95 85
803 3 r. 50 "Zizeeria knysna" 1·10 1·00
804 10 r. "Phalanta phalanta" 3·00 3·00

180 "The Holy Virgin, Joseph, The Holy Child and St. John" (S. Vouillemont after Raphael)

1991. Christmas. Woodcuts.

806	180	50 c. black, brn & red	20	15
807	–	1 r. black, brown & grn	35	25
808	–	2 r. black, brown & bl	60	60
809	–	7 r. black, brown & bl	2·00	2·25

DESIGNS: 1 r. "The Holy Virgin, the Child and Angel" (A. Blooting after Van Dyck); 2 r. "The Holy Family, St. John and St. Anna" (L. Vorsterman after Rubens); 7 r. "The Holy Family, Angel and St. Cathrin" (C. Bloemaert).

1992. 40th Anniv of Queen Elizabeth II's Accession. As T **143** of Ascension. Mult.

810	1 r. Seychelles coastline	35	25
811	1 r. 50 Clock Tower, Victoria	50	40
812	3 r. Victoria harbour	90	90
813	3 r. 50 Three portraits of Queen Elizabeth	1·00	1·00
814	5 r. Queen Elizabeth II	1·40	1·60

POSTAGE DUE STAMPS

D 1.

1951. Value in red.

D 1.	D 1.	2 c. red and carmine	80	1·50
D 2.		3 c. red and green	1·25	1·50
D 3.		6 c. red and bistre	1·25	1·25
D 4.		9 c. red and orange	1·50	1·25
D 5.		15 c. red and violet	1·75	7·50
D 6.		18 c. red and blue	1·75	7·50
D 7.		20 c. red and brown	1·75	7·50
D 8.		30 c. red and claret	1·75	7·50

1980. As D 1 but 18×22 mm.

D 11.	D 1.	5 c. red and mauve	10	15
D 12.		10 c. red and green	10	15
D 13.		15 c. red and bistre	15	20
D 14.		20 c. red and brown	15	25
D 15.		25 c. red and violet	15	25
D 16.		75 c. red and maroon	25	35
D 17.		80 c. red and blue	25	35
D 18.		1 r. red and purple	30	40

SHAHPURA

One of the Indian Feudatory States. Now uses Indian stamps.

12 pies = 1 anna; 12 annas = 1 rupee.

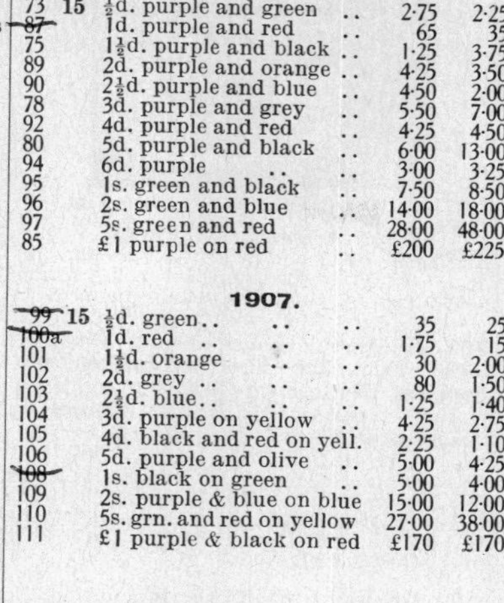

1

1914. Perf (No. 1) or imperf (No. 2).

1	1	1 p. red/grey	—	£110
2		1 p. red/brown	—	£160

1919. As T 1 but postage omitted. Imperf.

3	1	1 p. red/brown	—	£225
4		1 a. black/pink	—	£225

SIERRA LEONE

A Br. colony on the W. coast of Africa. Achieved independence within the Br. Commonwealth in 1961. By vote of the Assembly on 19 April, 1971, Sierra Leone was proclaimed a Republic.

1859. 12 pence = 1 shilling.
20 shillings = 1 pound.
1964. 100 cents = 1 leone.

1.

2.

1859.

16	2	½d. brown	2·00	4·75
27		½d. green	30	30
28		1d. red	1·40	35
29		1½d. lilac	2·00	5·00
25		2d. mauve	35·00	6·50
30		2d. grey	16·00	2·00
31		2½d. blue	7·00	55
32		3d. yellow	1·75	3·50
21		4d. blue	90·00	6·50
33		4d. brown	1·50	1·00
37	1	6d. purple	2·00	6·50
22	2	1s. green	50·00	6·00
34		1s. brown	12·00	9·00

1893. Surch. **HALF PENNY**

39.	2.	½d. on 1½d. lilac	2·75	3·00

4.

15

6.

1896.

41.	4.	½d. mauve and green	65	85
42.		1d. mauve and red	65	40
43.		1½d. mauve and black	2·25	6·00
44.		2d. mauve and orange	2·25	5·00
45.		2½d. mauve and blue	1·40	80
46.		3d. mauve and grey	7·00	7·00
47.		4d. mauve and red	7·00	13·00
48.		5d. mauve and black	7·00	11·00
49.		6d. mauve	7·00	12·00
50.		1s. green and black	6·00	15·00
51.		2s. green and blue	20·00	26·00
52.		5s. green and red	38·00	75·00
53.		£1 purple on red	£140	£250

1897. T **6** optd. **POSTAGE AND REVENUE**

54.	6.	1 d. purple and green	1·60	1·75

1897. T **6** optd. **POSTAGE AND REVENUE** and surch. **2½d.** and bars.

55.	6.	2½d. on 3d. purple & green	11·00	12·00
59.		2½d. on 6d. purple & green	8·50	11·00
63.		2½d. on 1s. purple	80·00	60·00
67.		2½d. on 2s. purple	£1300	£1600

1903.

73	15	½d. purple and green	2·75	2·25
87		1d. purple and red	65	35
75		1½d. purple and black	1·25	3·75
89		2d. purple and orange	4·25	3·50
90		2½d. purple and blue	4·50	2·00
78		3d. purple and grey	5·50	7·00
92		4d. purple and red	4·25	4·50
80		5d. purple and black	6·00	13·00
94		6d. purple	3·00	3·25
95		1s. green and black	7·50	8·50
96		2s. green and blue	14·00	18·00
97		5s. green and red	28·00	48·00
85		£1 purple on red	£200	£225

1907.

99	15	½d. green	35	25
100a		1d. red	1·75	15
101		1½d. orange	30	2·00
102		2d. grey	80	1·50
103		2½d. blue	1·25	1·40
104		3d. purple on yellow	4·25	2·75
105		4d. black and red on yell.	2·25	1·10
106		5d. purple and olive	5·00	4·25
108		1s. black on green	5·00	4·00
109		2s. purple & blue on blue	15·00	12·00
110		5s. grn. and red on yellow	27·00	38·00
111		£1 purple & black on red	£170	£170

17

20

1912.

131	17	½d. green	55	15
113		1d. red	1·00	10
132a		1d. violet	1·25	10
114		1½d. orange	80	85
133		1½d. red	50	30
134		2d. grey	40	10
116a		2½d. blue	85	65
116b	20	3d. purple on yellow	2·75	2·50
136	17	3d. blue	40	25
137		4d. blk. & red on yell.	1·75	1·25
138		5d. purple and olive	50	55
139		6d. purple	1·25	2·00
120		7d. purple and orange	1·75	4·00
141		9d. purple and black	2·50	7·50
142		10d. purple and red	2·00	13·00
124a	20	1s black on green	3·25	2·50
125		2s. blue & pur. on bl.	7·50	3·25
126		5s. red & grn. on yell.	11·00	17·00
127		10s. red & grn. on grn.	45·00	70·00
128		£1 blk. & pur. on red	£110	£140
147		£2 blue and purple	£425	£600
130		£5 orange and green	£1200	£1400

21 Rice Field

22 Palms and Cola Tree

1932.

155	21	½d. green	15	20
156		1d. violet	15	10
157		1½d. red	20	1·25
158		2d. brown	20	10
159		3d. blue	40	85
160		4d. orange	40	2·00
161		5d. green	50	1·40
162		6d. blue	40	1·50
163		1s. red	80	2·50
164	22	2s. brown	2·75	3·50
165		5s. blue	7·00	15·00
166		10s. green	45·00	80·00
167		£1 purple	75·00	£140

23 Arms of Sierra Leone

DESIGNS VERT. 1d. "Freedom". 1½d. Map of Sierra Leone. 4d. Government Sanatorium. 5s. African Elephant. HORIZ. 2d. Old Slave Market, Freetown. 3d. Native Fruitseller. 5d. Bullom canoe. 6d. Punting near Banana Is. 1s. Govt. Buildings, Freetown. 2s. Bunce Is. 10s. King George V. £1, Freetown Harbour.

1933. Cent. of Abolition of Slavery and Death of William Wilberforce. Dated "1833 1933".

168	23	½d. green	35	60
169	–	1d. black and brown	30	10
170	–	1½d. brown	3·25	4·00
171	–	2d. purple	2·50	20
172	–	3d. blue	2·00	1·50
173	–	4d. brown	6·00	10·00
174	–	5d. green and brown	6·50	16·00
175	–	6d. black and orange	6·50	8·00
176	–	1s. violet	4·50	13·00
177	–	2s. brown and blue	19·00	26·00
178	–	5s. black and purple	£120	£150
179	–	10s. black and olive	£130	£180
180	–	£1 violet and orange	£375	£450

1935. Silver Jubilee. As T **13** of Antigua.

181	1d. blue and black	50	40
182	3d. brown and blue	1·00	2·75
183	5d. green and blue	1·40	4·75
184	1s. grey and purple	4·75	2·75

1937. Coronation. As T **2** of Aden.

185.	1d. orange	70	25
186.	2d. purple	80	30
187.	3d. blue	1·40	1·25

30. Freetown from the Harbour.

1938. King George VI.

188.	30.	½d. black and green	10	15
189.		1d. black and red	20	10
190.	–	1½d. red	15·00	20
190a.	–	1½d. mauve	10	10
191.	–	2d. mauve	35·00	1·25
191a.	–	2d. red	10	30
192.	30.	3d. black and blue	20	20
193.		4d. black and brown	50	60
194.	–	5d. olive	4·00	2·50
195.	–	6d. grey	40	20
196.	30.	1s. black and olive	35	20
196a.	–	1s. 3d. orange	30	20
197.	30.	2s. black and brown	1·50	70
198.	–	5s. brown	4·50	2·25
199.	–	10s. green	8·00	5·50
200.	30.	£1 blue	15·00	8·50

DESIGN: 1½d., 2d., 5d., 6d., 1s. 3d., 5s., 10s. Rice harvesting.

1946. Victory. As T **9** of Aden.

201.	1½d. lilac	10	10
202.	3d. blue	15	10

1948. Silver Wedding. As T **10/11** of Aden.

203	1½d. mauve	15	15
204	£1 blue	14·00	13·00

1949. 75th Anniv of U.P.U. As T **20/23** of Antigua.

205	1½d. purple	15	15
206	3d. blue	35	70
207	6d. grey	35	70
208	1s. green	35	80

1953. Coronation. As T **13** of Aden.

209.	1½d. black and lilac	15	15

32. Cape Lighthouse.

1956. Centres in black.

210.	32.	½d. lilac	40	70
211.	–	1d. olive	45	20
212.	–	1½d. blue	60	1·75
213.	–	2d. brown	40	10
214.	–	3d. blue	75	10
215.	–	4d. slate	1·75	60
216.	–	6d. violet	70	15
217.	–	1s. red	50	10
218.	–	1s. 3d. sepia	6·00	10
219.	–	2s. 6d. brown	6·50	2·00
220.	–	5s. green	1·00	80
221.	–	10s. mauve	3·00	2·00
222.	–	£1 orange	9·00	16·00

DESIGNS—HORIZ. 1d. Queen Elizabeth II Quay. 1½d. Piassava workers. 4d. Iron ore production, Marampa. 6d. Whale Bay, York Village. 1s. 3d. Aeroplane and map. 10s. Law Courts, Freetown. £1 Government House. VERT. 2d. Cotton tree, Freetown. 3d. Rice harvesting. 1s. Bullom canoe. 2s. 6d. Orugu railway bridge. 5s. Kuranko chief.

46. Licensed Diamond Miner.

1961. Independence.

No.	Type	Description	Unused	Used
223.	–	½d. brown and turquoise	10	10
224.	46.	1d. brown and green	50	10
225.	–	1½d. black and green	10	10
226.	–	2d. black and blue	10	10
227.	–	3d. brown and blue	10	10
228.	–	4d. blue and red	10	10
229.	–	6d. black and purple	10	10
230.	–	1s. brown and orange	10	10
231.	–	1s. 3d. blue and violet	15	10
232.	46.	2s. 6d. green and black	1·75	10
233.	–	5s. black and red	90	90
234.	–	10 s. black and green	1·00	1·25
235.	–	£1 red and yellow	6·00	4·00

DESIGNS—VERT. ½d., 1s. Palm fruit gathering. 1½d., 5s. Bundu mask. 2d., 10s. Bishop Crowther and Old Fourah Bay College. £1, Forces bugler. HORIZ. 3d., 6d. Sir Milton Margai. 4d., 1s. 3d. Lumley Beach, Freetown.

DESIGNS—As Type **53**: 4d. King's Yard Gate, Freetown, 1817. As Type **55**: 1s. 3d. Royal Yacht "Britannia" at Freetown.

53. Royal Charter, 1799.

55. Old House of Representatives, Freetown, 1924.

1961. Royal Visit.

No.	Type	Description	Unused	Used
236.	53.	3d. black and red	10	10
237.	–	4d. black and violet	10	20
238.	55.	6d. black and orange	10	10
239.	–	1s. 3d. black and blue	1·25	20

57. Campaign Emblem. 58. Fireball Lily.

1962. Malaria Eradication.

No.	Type	Description	Unused	Used
240.	57.	3d. red	10	10
241.		1s. 3d. green	10	10

1963. Flowers in natural colours; background colours given below.

No.	Type	Description	Unused	Used
242.	58.	½d. bistre	10	10
243.	–	1d. red	10	10
244.	–	1½d. green	10	10
245.	–	2d. olive	10	10
246.	–	3d. green	10	10
247.	–	4d. blue	10	10
248.	–	6d. blue	15	10
249.	–	1s. green	30	10
250.	–	1s. 3d. green	60	20
251.	–	2s. 6d. purple	60	30
252.	–	5s. violet	80	80
253.	–	10s. purple	2·00	1·50
254.	–	£1 blue	7·50	7·00

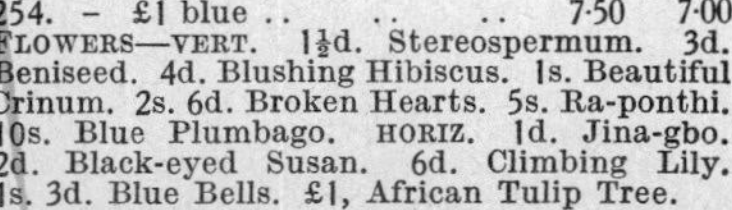

FLOWERS—VERT. 1½d. Stereospermum. 3d. Beniseed. 4d. Blushing Hibiscus. 1s. Beautiful Crinum. 2s. 6d. Broken Hearts. 5s. Ra-ponthi. 10s. Blue Plumbago. HORIZ. 1d. Jina-gbo. 2d. Black-eyed Susan. 6d. Climbing Lily. 1s. 3d. Blue Bells. £1, African Tulip Tree.

71. Threshing Machine and Corn Bins.

1963. Freedom from Hunger.

No.	Type	Description	Unused	Used
255.	71.	3d. black and ochre	15	10
256.	–	1s. 3d. sepia and green	35	10

DESIGN: 1s. 3d. Girl with onion crop.

1963. 2nd Anniv. of Independence. Stamp of 1956 surch. **2nd Year of Independence Progress Development 1963** and value in various types (except 2s. 6d.). Centres in black. (a) Postage.

No.	Type	Description	Unused	Used
257.		3d. on ½d. lilac	20	10
258.		4d. on 1½ d. blue	10	10
259.		6d. on ½d. lilac	20	10
260.		10d. on 3d. blue	40	10
261.		1s. 6d. on 3d. blue	20	10
262.		3s. 6d. on 3d. blue	30	15

(b) Air. Optd. **AIRMAIL** in addition.

No.	Type	Description	Unused	Used
263.		7d. on 1½d. blue	10	10
264.		1s. 3d. on 1½d. blue	10	10
265.		2s. 6d. brown	40	15
266.		3s. on 3d. blue	30	15
267.		6s. on 3d. blue	80	20
268.		11s. on 10s. mauve	1·25	75
269.		11s. on £1 orange	£500	£170

DESIGNS: 6d. Red Cross emblem. 1s. 3d. As Type **75** but with lined background and value on left.

75. Centenary Emblem.

1963. Centenary of Red Cross.

No.	Type	Description	Unused	Used
270.	75.	3d. red and violet	30	10
271.	–	6d. red and black	30	15
272.	–	1s. 3d. red and green	45	20

1963. Postal Commemorations. (a) Postage. Optd. or surch. **1853-1859-1963 Oldest Postal Service Newest G.P.O. in West Africa** and value.

No.	Type	Description	Unused	Used
273.	–	3d. (No. 214)	10	10
274.	–	4d. on 1½d. (No. 212)	10	10
275.	–	9d. on 1½d. (No. 212)	10	10
276.	–	1s. on 1s. 3d. (No. 231)	10	10
277.	32.	1s. 6d. on ½d.	15	10
278.	–	2s. on 3d. (No. 214)	15	10

(b) Air. Optd. or surch. as above but **Postage Stamp** instead of **Postal Service** and **AIRMAIL** in addition.

No.	Type	Description	Unused	Used
279.	53.	7d. on 3d.	10	20
280.	–	1s. 3d. (No. 239)	75	40
281.	–	2s. 6d. on 4d. (No. 228)	40	20
282.	53.	3s. on 3d.	75	90
283.	55.	6s. on 6d.	60	60
284.	–	£1 (No. 222)	11·00	13·00

Commemoration dates:—
1853—"First Post Office".
1859—"First Postage Stamps".
1963—"Newest G.P.O." in West Africa.

80. Lion Emblem and Map.

81. Globe and Map.

1964. World's Fair, New York. Imperf. Self-adhesive.

No.	Type	Description	Unused	Used
285.	80.	1d. mult. (postage)	10	10
286.		3d. multicoloured	10	10
287.		4d. multicoloured	10	10
288.		6d. multicoloured	10	10
289.		1s. multicoloured	10	10
290.		2s. multicoloured	15	10
291.		5s. multicoloured	25	20
292.	81.	7d. multicoloured (air)	10	10
293.		9d. multicoloured	10	10
294.		1s. 3d. multicoloured	10	10
295.		2s. 6d. multicoloured	15	10
296.		3s. 6d. multicoloured	15	10
297.		6s. multicoloured	25	25
298.		11s. multicoloured	35	50

Warning.—These self-adhesive stamps should be kept mint on their backing paper and used on cover or piece.

82. Inscription and Map.

83. Pres. Kennedy and Map.

1964. President Kennedy Memorial Issue. Imperf. Self-adhesive.

No.	Type	Description	Unused	Used
299.	82.	1d. mult. (postage)	10	10
300.		3d. multicoloured	10	10
301.		4d. multicoloured	10	10
302.		6d. multicoloured	10	10
303.		1s. multicoloured	10	10
304.		2s. multicoloured	10	10
305.		5s. multicoloured	25	20
306.	83.	7d. multicoloured (air)	10	10
307.		9d. multicoloured	10	10
308.		1s. 3d. multicoloured	10	10
309.		2s. 6d. multicoloured	15	20
310.		3s. 6d. multicoloured	15	20
311.		6s. multicoloured	30	40
312.		11s. multicoloured	45	60

The note below No. 298 applies also to the above issue.

1964. Decimal Currency. Various stamps surch.

(i) 1st issue. Surch. in figures.

(a) Postage.

No.	Type	Description	Unused	Used
313.	–	1 c. on 6d. (No. 248)	10	10
314.	53.	2 c. on 3d. (No. 236)	10	10
315.	–	3 c. on 3d. (No. 246)	10	10
316.	–	5 c. on ½d. (No. 223)	10	10
317.	71.	8 c. on 3d. (No. 255)	10	10
318.	–	10 c. on 1s. 3d. (No. 250)	10	10
319.	–	15 c. on 1s. (No. 249)	15	10
320.	55.	25 c. on 6d. (No. 238)	25	25
321.	46.	50 c. on 2s. 6d. (No. 232)	50	50

(b) Air. Nos. 322/5 additionally optd. **AIRMAIL.**

No.	Type	Description	Unused	Used
322.	–	7 c. on 1s. 3d. (No. 256)	10	10
323.	–	20 c. on 4d. (No. 228)	20	15
324.	–	30 c. on 10s. (No. 234)	30	30
325.	–	40 c. on 5s. (No. 233)	40	40
326.	83.	1 l. on 1s. 3d. (No. 308)	60	80
327.		2 l. on 11s. (No. 312)	1·10	1·40

(ii) 2nd issue. Surch. in figures or figures and words (Nos. 332/3).

No.	Type	Description	Unused	Used
328.	–	1 c. on 3d. (No. 227) (postage)	10	10
329.	82.	2 c. on 1d. (No. 299)	10	10
330.		4 c. on 3d. (No. 300)	10	10
331.	–	5 c. on 2d. (No. 245)	10	10
332.	–	1 l. on 5s. (No. 252)	1·25	1·25
333.	–	2 l. on £1 (No. 235)	2·25	2·25
334.	83.	7 c. on 7d. (No. 306) (air)	10	10
335.		60 c. on 9d. (No. 307)	50	45

(iii) Third issue. Surch. in figures.

No.	Type	Description	Unused	Used
336.	–	1 c. on 1½d. (No. 225) (postage)	10	10
337.	82.	2 c. on 3d. (No. 300)	10	10
338.	80.	2 c. on 4d. (No. 287)	10	10
339.	–	3 c. on 1d. (No. 243)	10	10
340.	–	3 c. on 2d. (No. 226)	10	10
341.		5 c. on 1s. 3d. (No. 231)	10	10
342.	82.	15 c. on 6d. (No. 302)	80	50
343.		15 c. on 1s. (No. 303)	1·25	90
344.	–	20 c. on 6d. (No. 229)	30	15
345.	–	25 c. on 6d. (No. 248)	35	20
346.	–	50 c. on 3d. (No. 227)	80	55
347.	80.	60 c. on 5s. (No. 291)	3·00	1·75
348.	82.	1 l. on 4d. (No. 301)	3·25	2·75
349.	–	2 l. on £1 (No. 235)	5·00	3·75
350.	81.	7 c. on 9d. (air)	15	10

(iv) Fourth issue. Surch in figures.

No.	Type	Description	Unused	Used
351.	80.	1 c. on 6d. (postage)	2·75	7·00
352.		1 c. on 2s.	2·75	7·00
353.	82.	1 c. on 2s.	2·75	7·00
354.		1 c. on 5s.	2·75	7·00
355.	81.	2 c. on 1s. 3d. (air)	2·75	7·00
356.	83.	2 c. on 1s. 3d.	2·75	7·00
357.		2 c. on 3s. 6d.	2·75	7·00
358.	81.	3 c. on 7d.	2·75	7·00
359.	83.	3 c. on 9d.	2·75	7·00
360.	81.	5 c. on 2s. 6d.	2·75	7·00
361.	83.	5 c. on 2s. 6d.	2·75	7·00
362.	81.	5 c. on 3s. 6d.	2·75	7·00
363.		5 c. on 6s.	2·75	7·00
364.	83.	5 c. on 6s.	2·75	7·00

(v) Fifth issue. No. 374 further surch. **TWO Leones.**

No.	Type	Description	Unused	Used
365.	–	2 l. on 30 c. on 6d. (air)	2·50	2·00

(91. Margai and Churchill).

1965. Sir Milton Margai and Sir Winston Churchill Commem. Flower stamps of 1963 surch. as T **91** on horiz. designs or with individual portraits on vert. designs as indicated. Multicoloured.

(a) Postage.

No.	Type	Description	Unused	Used
366.	–	2 c. on 1d.	10	10
367.	–	3 c. on 3d. Margai	10	10
368.	–	10 c. on 1s. Churchill	20	10
369.	–	20 c. on 1s. 3d.	40	10
370.	–	50 c. on 4d. Margai	90	35
371.	–	75 c. on 5s. Churchill	2·25	1·25

(b) Air. Additionally optd. **AIR MAIL.**

No.	Type	Description	Unused	Used
372.	–	7 c. on 2d.	20	10
373.	58.	15 c. on ½d. Margai	35	10
374.	–	30 c. on 6d.	1·25	25
375.	–	1 l. on £1	4·00	1·50
376.	–	2 l. on 10s. Churchill	11·00	5·00

92. Cola Plant and Nut.

1965. Various shapes, backed with paper bearing advertisements. Imperf. Self-adhesive.

A. Printed in green, yellow and red on silver foil. Values in colours given.

No.	Type	Description	Unused	Used
377.	92.	1 c. green (postage)	25	10
378.		2 c. red	25	10
379.		3 c. yellow	25	10
380.		4 c. silver on green	30	10
381.		5 c. silver on red	30	10

B. Designs 45 × 49 mm. showing Arms of Sierra Leone.

No.	Type	Description	Unused	Used
382.	–	20 c. mult. on cream (postage)	1·00	35
383.	–	50 c. mult. on cream	2·50	1·60
384.	–	40 c. mult. on cream (air)	2·25	1·60

C. Designs 48 × 44½ mm. showing inscription and necklace.

No.	Type	Description	Unused	Used
385.	–	7 c. multicoloured post.)	55	15
386.	–	15 c. multicoloured	85	50

1966. 5th Anniv. of Independence. Surch. **FIVE YEARS INDEPENDENCE 1961-1966** and value.

(a) Postage.
387. – 1 c. on 6d. (No. 248) .. 10 10
388. – 2 c. on 4d. (No. 247) .. 10 10
389. – 3 c. on 1½d. (No. 212) .. 10 10
390. – 8 c. on 1s. (No. 249) .. 15 10
391. – 10 c. on 2s. 6d. (No. 251) 15 10
392. – 20 c. on 2d. (No. 213) .. 20 10

(b) Air. Surch. **AIRMAIL** also.
393. **75.** 7 c. on 3d. 10 10
394. – 15 c. on 1s. (No. 249) .. 20 10
395. – 25 c. on 2s. 6d. (No. 251) 40 60
396. – 50 c. on 1½d. (No. 244) .. 60 80
397. – 1 l. on 4d. (No. 247) .. 1·00 1·60

97. Lion's Head.

1966. 1st Sierra Leone Gold Coinage Commem. Circular designs, embossed on gold foil, backed with paper bearing advertisements. Imperf. (a) Postage.

(i) ¼ golde coin. Diameter 1½ in.
398. **97.** 2 c. mauve and orange 10 10
399. – 3 c. green and purple .. 10 10

(ii) ½ golde coin. Diameter 2⅛ in.
400. **97.** 5 c. red and blue .. 10 10
401. – 8 c. turquoise and black 15 15

(ii) 1 golde coin. Diameter 3¼ in.
402. **97.** 25 c. violet and green .. 35 35
403. – 1 l. orange and red .. 2·25 2·25

(b) Air (i) ¼ golde coin. Diameter 1½ in.
404. **97.** 7 c. orange and red .. 10 10
405. – 10 c. red and blue .. 15 15

(ii) ½ golde coin. Diameter 2⅛ in.
406. **97.** 15 c. orange and red .. 25 25
407. – 30 c. purple and black .. 40 45

(iii) 1 golde coin. Diameter 3¼ in.
408. **97.** 50 c. green and purple .. 75 75
409. – 2 l. black and green .. 3·50 3·50

DESIGN: Nos. 399, 401, 403, 405, 407 and 409 Map of Sierra Leone.

1967. Decimal Currency Provisionals. Nos. 347/8, 369/71 and 383/4 surch.
410. 6½ c. on 75 c. on 5s. (post) 15 15
411. 7½ c. on 75 c. on 5s. .. 15 15
412. 9½ c. on 50 c. on 4d. .. 20 20
413. 12½ c. on 20 c. on 1s. 3d. .. 25 25
414. 17½ c. on 50 c. .. .. 1·40 1·40
415. 17½ c. on 1 l. on 4d. .. 1·40 1·40
416. 18½ c. on 1 l. on 4d. .. 1·40 1·40
417. 18½ c. on 60 c. on 5s. .. 4·00 4·00
418. 25 c. on 50 c. 60 60
419. 11½ c. on 40 c. (air) .. 20 20
420. 25 c. on 40 c. 60 60

1967. Decimal Currency. Imperf. Self-adhesive. As **T 92**, but embossed on white paper, backed with paper bearing advertisements. Background colours given first, and value tablet colours in brackets.
421. **92.** ½ c. red (red on white) .. 10 10
422. 1 c. red (red on white) 15 10
423. 1½ c. yellow (grn. on white) 20 15
424. 2 c. red (grn. on white) 35 10
425. 2½ c. grn. (yell. on white) 50 30
426. 3 c. red (white on red) .. 30 10
427. 3½ c. pur. (white on grn.) 50 30
428. 4 c. red (white on green) 50 15
429. 4½ c. grn. (grn. on white) 50 30
430. 5 c. red (yell. & white) 50 15
431. 5½ c. red (grn. on white) 50 40

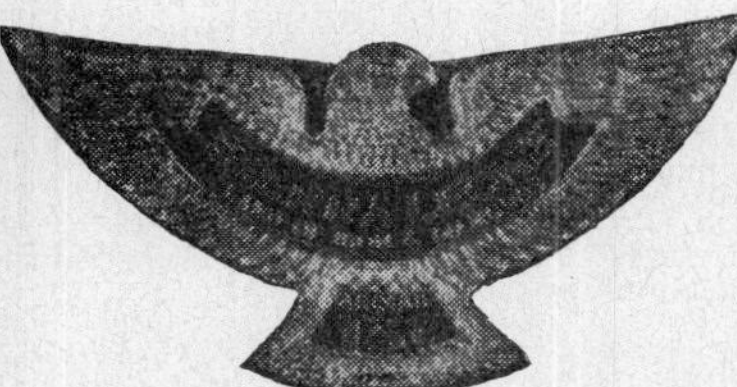

102. Eagle.

1967. T 102 Embossed on black paper, backed with paper bearing advertisements; or, (No. 433/a), as No. 382, also with advertisements.
432. **102.** 9½ c. red & gold on black 60 60
432a. 9½ c. blue & gold on blk. 3·50 3·00
433. 10 c. mult. (red frame) 65 65
433b. 10 c. mult. (black frame) 3·75 3·25
434. **102.** 15 c. green & gold on blk. 85 85
434a. 15 c. red and gold on black 4·00 4·00

See also Nos. 538/44.

1968. No advertisements on back, and colours in value tablet reversed. Background colours given first, and value tablet colours in brackets.
435. **92.** ½ c. red (white on green) 10 10
436. 1 c. red (white on red) .. 15 10
437. 2 c. red (white in green) 4·00 4·00
438. 2½ c. grn. (white on yell.) 4·50 4·50
439. 3 c. red (red on white) .. 1·75 65

On Nos. 435 and 438, the figure "½" is larger than in Nos. 421 and 425.

1968. No advertisements on back, colours changed and new value (7 c.). Background colours given.
440. **92.** 2 c. pink (postage) .. 1·50 90
441. 2½ c. green .. .. 1·50 90
442. 3½ c. yellow .. .. 2·00 1·10
442a. 7 c. yellow (air) .. 6·00 3·00

On Nos. 441/2 the fraction "½" is larger than on Nos. 425 and 427.

103. Outline Map of Africa.

1968. Human Rights Year. Each value comes in six types, showing the following territories: Portuguese Guinea; South Africa: Mozambique; Rhodesia; South West Africa and Angola. Imperf. Self-adhesive.
443 **103** ½ c. multicoloured (post) 10 10
444 2 c. multicoloured .. 10 10
445 2½ c. multicoloured .. 10 10
446 3½ c. multicoloured .. 10 10
447 10 c. multicoloured .. 15 15
448 11½ c. multicoloured .. 20 20
449 15 c. multicoloured .. 25 25
450 **103** 7½ c. multicoloured (air) 15 15
451 9½ c. multicoloured .. 20 20
452 14½ c. multicoloured .. 25 25
453 18½ c. multicoloured .. 30 30
454 25 c. multicoloured .. 40 40
455 1 l. multicoloured .. 6·50 5·50
456 2 l. multicoloured .. 14·00 12·00
Set of 84 (6 different territories) £120 £100

Nos. 443/56 were issued in sheets of 30 (6 × 5) on backing paper depicting diamonds or the coat-of-arms on the reverse. The six types occur once in each horiz. row.

1968. Mexico Olympics Participation. Nos. 383/4 surch. or optd. (Nos. 461 and 466) **OLYMPIC PARTICIPATION 1968 MEXICO** etc.
457. 6½ c. on 50 c. mult. (post.) 15 10
458. 17½ c. on 50 c. mult. .. 20 15
459. 22½ c. on 50 c. mult. .. 35 25
460. 28½ c. on 50 c. mult. .. 45 35
461. 50 c. multicoloured .. 70 40
462. 6½ c. on 40 c. mult. (air) .. 15 10
463. 17½ c. on 40 c. mult. .. 20 15
464. 22½ c. on 40 c. mult. .. 35 25
465. 28½ c. on 40 c. mult. .. 45 35
466. 40 c. multicoloured .. 70 50

105. 1859 6d. Stamp.

111. 1965 15 c. Self-adhesive.

1969. 5th Anniv. of World's First Self-adhesive Postage Stamps. Stamp Multicoloured. Self-adhesive. Imperf.
467. 1 c. Type **105** (postage) .. 10 10
468. 2 c. 1965 2 c. self-adhesive 10 10
469. 3½ c. 1961 Independence 2 c. 10 10
470. 5 c. 1965 20 c. self-adhesive 10 10
471. 12½ c. 1948 Royal Silver Wedding £1 .. .. 30 15
472. 1 l. 1923 £2 .. .. 3·50 2·75
473. 7½ c. Type **111** (air) .. 20 10
474. 9½ c. 1967 9½ c. self-adhesive 20 10
475. 20 c. 1964 1s. 3d. self-adhesive 40 25
476. 30 c. 1964 President Kennedy Memorial 6s. self-adhesive 55 35
477. 50 c. 1933 Centenary of Abolition of Slavery £1 1·75 1·00
478. 2 l. 1963 2nd Anniv. of Independence 11s. .. 15·00 13·00

DESIGNS—As Type **105**. Nos. 468/72. As Type **111**, Nos. 474/8.

All values are on white backing paper with advertisement printed on the reverse.

117. Ore Carrier, Globe and Flags of Sierra Leone and Japan.

118. Ore Carrier, Map of Europe and Africa and Flags of Sierra Leone and Netherlands.

1969. Pepel Port Improvements. Imperf. Self-adhesive, backed with paper bearing advertisements.
479. **117.** 1 c. mult. (postage) .. 10 10
480. **118.** 2 c. multicoloured .. 10 10
481. – 3½ c. multicoloured .. 10 10
482. – 10 c. multicoloured .. 10 10
483. **118.** 18½ c. multicoloured .. 20 25
484. – 50 c. multicoloured .. 70 85
485. **117.** 7½ c. multicoloured (air) 10 10
486. 9½ c. multicoloured .. 15 10
487. **117.** 15 c. multicoloured .. 20 25
488. **118.** 25 c. multicoloured .. 30 35
489. – 1 l. multicoloured .. 1·25 1·50
490. – 2 l. multicoloured .. 2·50 3·75

The 3½, 9½ c., 2 l. and 10, 50 c., 1 l. show respectively the flags of Great Britain and West Germany instead of the Netherlands.

119. African Development Bank Emblem.

1969. 5th Anniv. of African Development Bank. Imperf. Self-adhesive, backed with paper bearing advertisements.
491. **119.** 3½ c. green, gold and black (post.) .. 25 20
492. 9½ c. violet, gold and green (air) 30 45

120. Boy Scouts Emblem in "Diamond".

1969. Boy Scouts Diamond Jubilee. Imperf. Self-adhesive.
493. **120.** 1 c. multicoloured (postage) 10 10
494. 2 c. multicoloured .. 10 10
495. 3½ c. multicoloured .. 15 10
496. 4½ c. multicoloured .. 15 15
497. 5 c. multicoloured .. 15 15
498. 75 c. multicoloured .. 9·00 5·00
499. – 7½ c. multicoloured (air) 35 30
500. – 9½ c. multicoloured .. 45 35
501. – 15 c. multicoloured .. 70 50
502. – 22 c. multicoloured .. 1·25 70
503. – 55 c. multicoloured .. 7·50 4·00
504. – 3 l. multicoloured .. 85·00 60·00

DESIGN—OCTAGONAL (65 × 51 mm.): Nos. 499/504, Scout saluting, Baden-Powell and badge.

1970. Air. No. 443 surch. **AIRMAIL** twice and new value.
505. **103.** 7½ c. on ½ c. mult. .. 20 10
506. 9½ c. on ½ c. mult. .. 20 10
507. 15 c. on ½ c. mult. .. 40 25
508. 28 c. on ½ c. mult. .. 70 55
509. 40 c. on ½ c. mult. .. 1·25 1·40
510. 2 l. on ½ c. mult. .. 6·00 7·50
Set of 36 (6 different territories) 45·00 48·00

122. Expo Symbol and Maps of Sierra Leone and Japan.

1970. World Fair, Osaka. Imperf. Self-adhesive.
511. **122.** 2 c. mult. (postage) .. 10 10
512. 3½ c. multicoloured .. 10 10
513. 10 c. multicoloured .. 15 10
514. 12½ c. multicoloured .. 15 10
515. 20 c. multicoloured .. 20 10
516. 45 c. multicoloured .. 45 45
517. – 7½ c. multicoloured (air) 10 10
518. – 9½ c. multicoloured .. 15 10
519. – 15 c. multicoloured .. 20 10
520. – 25 c. multicoloured .. 40 20
521. – 50 c. multicoloured .. 55 50
522. – 3 l. multicoloured .. 3·00 4·00

DESIGN—CHRYSANTHEMUM (43 × 42 mm.): Nos. 517/22, Maps of Sierra Leone and Japan.

123. Diamond.

124. Palm Nut.

1970. Imperf. Self-adhesive.

No.	Type	Description		
523.	123.	1 c. multicoloured ..	10	10
524.		1½ c. multicoloured ..	10	10
525.		2 c. multicoloured ..	10	10
526.		2½ c. multicoloured ..	10	10
527.		3 c. multicoloured ..	15	10
528.		3½ c. multicoloured ..	15	10
529.		4 c. multicoloured ..	15	10
530.		5 c. multicoloured ..	20	10
531.	124.	6 c. multicoloured ..	25	10
532.		7 c. multicoloured ..	30	15
533.		8½ c. multicoloured ..	40	15
534.		9 c. multicoloured ..	40	15
535.		10 c. multicoloured ..	45	15
536.		11½ c. multicoloured ..	55	20
537.		18½ c. multicoloured ..	75	45

1970. Air. As T **102**, but on white paper.

No.	Type	Description		
538.	102.	7½ c. gold and red (air)	35	10
539.		9½ c. silver and green ..	40	10
540.		15 c. silver and blue ..	55	20
541.		25 c. gold and purple ..	90	50
542.		50 c. green and orange ..	2·00	1·50
543.		1 l. blue and silver ..	5·00	6·50
544.		2 l. blue and gold ..	10·00	15·00

126. "Jewellery Box" and Sewa Diadem.

1970. Diamond Industry. Imperf. Self-adhesive.

No.	Type	Description		
545.	126.	2 c. mult. (postage) ..	30	10
546.		3½ c. multicoloured ..	30	10
547.		10 c. multicoloured ..	55	15
548.		12½ c. multicoloured ..	75	25
549.		40 c. multicoloured ..	1·75	1·00
550.		1 l. multicoloured ..	9·50	8·00
551.	–	7½ c. multicoloured (air)	50	10
552.	–	9½ c. multicoloured ..	60	10
553.	–	15 c. multicoloured ..	95	30
554.	–	25 c. multicoloured ..	1·40	60
555.	–	75 c. multicoloured ..	5·00	4·00
556.	–	2 l. multicoloured ..	22·00	17·00

DESIGN—HORIZ. (63 × 61 mm.) Nos. 551/6 Diamond and curtain.

127. "Traffic Changeover".

1971. Changeover to Driving on the Right of the Road. Imperf. Self-adhesive.

No.	Type	Description		
557.	127.	3½ c. orange, blue and black (postage)	1·25	40
558.		9½ c. blue, orange and black (air)	1·75	1·60

1971. Air. Various stamps surch. **AIRMAIL** and value (Nos. 559/61) or value only (Nos. 562/3).

No.	Description		
559.	10 c. on 2d. (No. 226) ..	40	20
560.	20 c. on 1s. (No. 230) ..	70	45
561.	50 c. on 1d. (No. 243) ..	1·25	1·10
562.	70 c. on 30 c. (No. 476) ..	2·00	2·75
563.	1 l. on 30 c. (No. 476) ..	3·00	3·75

129. Flag and Lion's Head.

1971. 10th Anniv. of Independence. Imperf. Self-adhesive.

No.	Type	Description		
564.	129.	2 c. mult. (postage) ..	10	10
565.		3½ c. multicoloured ..	10	10
566.		10 c. multicoloured ..	15	10
567.		12½ c. multicoloured ..	20	10
568.		40 c. multicoloured ..	70	40
569.		1 l. multicoloured ..	1·50	2·25
570.	–	7½ c. multicoloured (air)	15	10
571.	–	9½ c. multicoloured ..	15	10
572.	–	15 c. multicoloured ..	25	10
573.	–	25 c. multicoloured ..	35	35
574.	–	75 c. multicoloured ..	1·25	1·50
575.	–	2 l. multicoloured ..	4·00	6·00

DESIGN: "Map" shaped as Type **129**. Nos. 570/5, Bugles and lion's head.

130. Pres. Siaka Stevens.

1972. Multicoloured. Background colour given.

No.	Type	Description		
576.	130.	1 c. lilac	10	10
577.		2 c. lavender	10	10
578.		4 c. blue	10	10
579.		5 c. brown	10	10
580.		7 c. pink	15	10
581.		10 c. brown	15	10
582.		15 c. green	25	15
583.		18 c. yellow	25	15
584.		20 c. blue	30	15
585.		25 c. orange	35	15
586.		50 c. green	1·00	55
587.		1 l. mauve	1·50	1·00
588.		2 l. pink	3·50	3·50
589.		5 l. cream	8·00	8·50

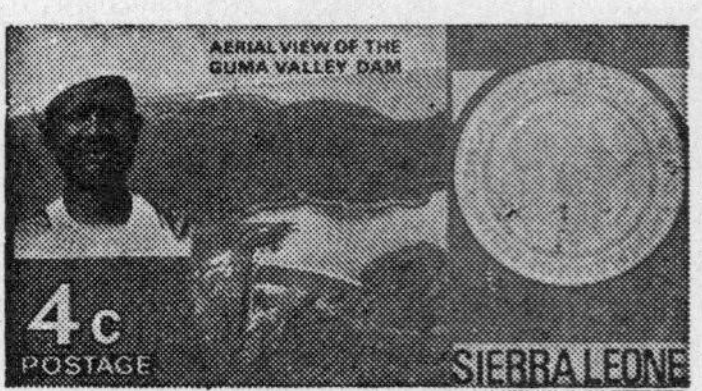

131. Guma Valley Dam and Bank Emblem.

1975. 10th Anniv. of African Development Bank.

No.	Type	Description		
590.	131.	4 c. multicoloured (postage)	45·00	28·00
591.		15 c. multicoloured (air)	1·00	80

132. Opening Ceremony.

1975. New Congo Bridge Opening and 70th Birthday of President Stevens.

No.	Type	Description		
592.	132.	5 c. multicoloured (postage) ..	5·00	1·75
593.		20 c. multicoloured (air)	70	25

133. Presidents Tolbert and Stevens, and Handclasp.

1975. 1st Anniv. of Mano River Union.

No.	Type	Description		
594.	133.	4 c. multicoloured (postage)	75	50
595.		15 c. multicoloured (air)	35	25

134. "Quaid-i-Azam" (Mohammed Ali Jinnah).

1977. Birth Centenary of Mohammed Ali Jinnah (Quaid-i-Azam).

No.	Type	Description		
596.	134.	30 c. multicoloured ..	75	30

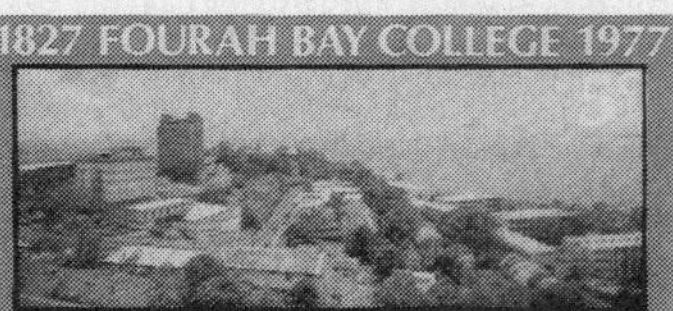

135. Queen Elizabeth II.

1977. Silver Jubilee.

No.	Type	Description		
597.	135.	5 c. multicoloured ..	10	10
598.		1 l. multicoloured ..	90	80

136. College Buildings.

1977. 150th Anniv. of Fourah Bay College. Multicoloured.

No.	Description		
599.	5 c. Type **136**	10	10
600.	20 c. The old college (vert.)	35	30

137. St. Edward's Crown and Sceptres.

1978. 25th Anniv. of Coronation. Mult.

No.	Description		
601.	5 c. Type **137**	10	10
602.	50 c. Queen Elizabeth II in Coronation Coach	30	40
603.	1 l. Queen Elizabeth II and Prince Philip	40	60

138. "Myrina silenus".

1979. Butterflies (1st series). Multicoloured.

No.	Description		
604	5 c. Type **138**	10	10
605	15 c. "Papilio nireus" ..	25	15
606	25 c. "Catacroptera cloanthe"	40	15
607	1 l. "Papilio antimachus"	2·00	1·50

See also Nos. 646/9.

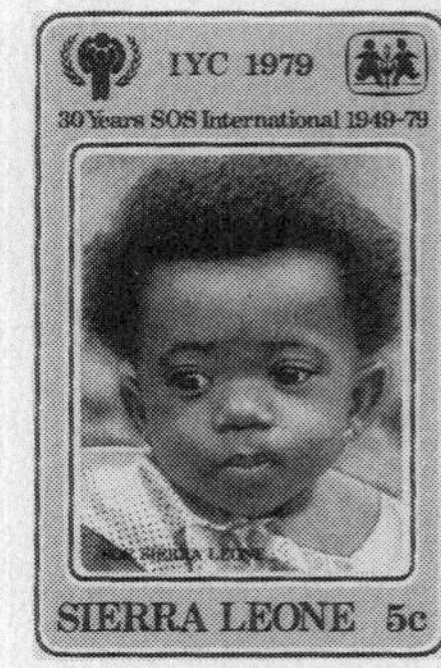

139. Young Child's Face.

1979. International Year of the Child. 30th Anniv. of S.O.S. International. Multicoloured.

No.	Description		
608.	5 c. Type **139**	10	10
609.	27 c. Young child with baby	20	25
610.	1 l. Mother with young child	50	1·10

140. Presidents Stevens (Sierra Leone) and Tolbert (Liberia), Dove with Letter and Bridge.

1979. 5th Anniv. of Mano River Union and 1st Anniv. of Postal Union.

No.	Type	Description		
612.	140.	5 c. brn., orge. & yell.	10	10
613.		22 c. brn., yell. & violet	10	15
614.		27 c. brn., blue & orge.	10	15
615.		35 c. brown, green & red	15	20
616.		1 l. brown, violet & blue	50	1·00

141. Great Britain 1848 10d. Stamp.

1979. Death Centenary of Sir Rowland Hill.

No.	Type	Description		
618.	141.	10 c. black, brn. & blue	15	10
619.	–	15 c. black, brn. & blue	25	15
620.	–	50 c. black, red & yell.	60	70

DESIGNS: 15 c. 1872 4d. stamp. 50 c. 1961 £1 Independence commemorative.

142. Knysna Turaco.

1980. Birds. Multicoloured.

No.	Description		
622	1 c. Type **142**	20	30
623	2 c. Olive-bellied sunbird ..	20	30
624	3 c. Western Black-headed oriole	30	50
625	5 c. Spur-winged goose ..	30	30
626	7 c. Didric cuckoo	40	20
627	10 c. Grey parrot (vert.) ..	30	35
628	15 c. Blue quail (vert.) ..	40	75
629	20 c. African wood owl (vert.)	40	75
630	30 c. Greater blue turaco (vert.)	50	1·00
631	40 c. Blue-breasted kingfisher (vert.) ..	60	1·25
632	50 c. Black crake (vert.) ..	60	1·50
633	1 l. Hartlaub's duck ..	60	1·75
634	2 l. Black bee eater ..	2·50	3·50
635	5 l. Barrow's bustard ..	4·25	8·50

143. Paul P. Harris (founder), President Stevens of Sierra Leone and Rotary Emblem.

1980. 75th Anniv. of Rotary International

No.	Description		
636. **143**	5 c. multicoloured ..	10	10
637.	27 c. multicoloured ..	10	10
638.	50 c. multicoloured ..	20	25
639.	1 l. multicoloured ..	40	55

144. " Maria ", 1884.

1980. " London 1980 " International Stamp Exhibition. Multicoloured.

No.	Description		
640.	6 c. Type **144**	10	10
641.	31 c. "Tarquah", 1902 ..	25	30
642.	50 c. " Aureol ", 1951 ..	40	60
643.	1 l. " Africa Palm ", 1974	55	95

145. Organization for African Unity Emblem.

1980. African Summit Conference, Freetown.

No.	Description		
644. **145.**	20 c. black, bl. & purple	10	10
645.	1 l. black, purple & blue	45	45

146. "Graphium policenes".

1980. Butterflies (2nd series). Multicoloured.

No.	Description		
646	5 c. Type **146**	10	10
647	27 c. "Charaxes varanes"	30	15
648	35 c. "Charaxes brutus" ..	35	25
649	1 l. "Euphaedra zaddachi"	1·10	1·40

147. Arrival at Freetown Airport.

1980. Tourism. Multicoloured.

No.	Description		
650.	6 c. Type **147**	10	10
651.	26 c. Welcome to tourists	20	20
652.	31 c. Freetown cotton tree	25	25
653.	40 c. Beinkongo Falls ..	30	30
654.	50 c. Sports facilities ..	40	40
655.	1 l. African Elephant ..	95	95

148. Servals.

1981. Wild Cats. Multicoloured.

No.	Description		
656.	6 c. Type **148**	10	10
657.	6 c. Serval cubs ..	10	10
658.	31 c. African Golden Cats	30	30
659.	31 c. African Golden Cat cubs	30	30
660.	50 c. Leopards	45	45
661.	50 c. Leopard cubs ..	45	45
662.	1 l. Lions	80	80
663.	1 l. Lion cubs	80	80

The two designs of each value were printed together, se-tenant, in horizontal pairs, forming composite designs.

149. Soldiers (Defence).

1981. 20th Anniv of Independence and 10th Anniv of Republic. National Services. Mult.

No.	Description		
664.	6 c. Type **149**	30	10
665.	31 c. Nurses administering first aid, and ambulance (health) (horiz.) ..	75	20
666.	40 c. Traffic (Police Force)	1·25	30
667.	1 l. Patrol boat (coastguard) (horiz.)	2·00	1·25

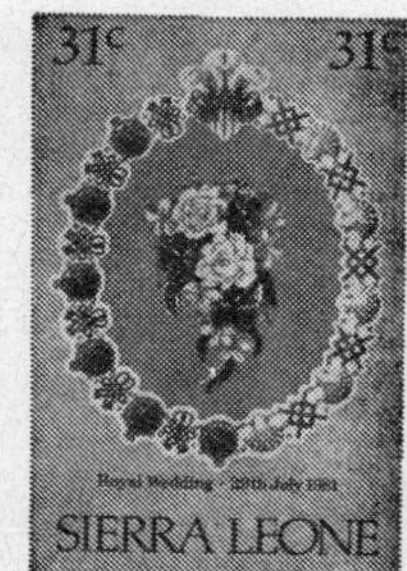

150. Wedding Bouquet from Sierra Leone.

1981. Royal Wedding (1st issue). Mult.

No.	Description		
668.	31 c. Type **150**	20	20
669.	45 c. Prince Charles as helicopter pilot ..	25	30
670.	1 l. Prince Charles and Lady Diana Spencer ..	45	1·10

151. Sandringham.

1981. Royal Wedding (2nd issue). **Mult.**

No.	Description		
671.	35 c. Type **151**	30	35
672.	60 c. Prince Charles in out-door clothes	50	40
675.	70 c. Type **151**	75	90
676.	1 l. 30 As 60 c.	1·00	1·25
673.	1 l. 50 Prince Charles and Lady Diana Spencer ..	1·00	1·40
677.	2 l. As 1 l. 50	3·25	3·50

152. " Physical Recreation ".

1981. 25th Anniv. of Duke of Edinburgh Award Scheme and President's Award Scheme Publicity. Multicoloured.

No.	Description		
678.	6 c. Type **152**	10	10
679.	31 c. " Community service "	15	10
680.	1 l. Duke of Edinburgh ..	40	40
681.	1 l. President Siaka Stevens	40	40

153. Pineapples.

1981. World Food Day. Multicoloured.

No.	Description		
682.	6 c. Type **153**	10	10
683.	31 c. Groundnuts	15	10
684.	50 c. Cassava fruits ..	20	15
685.	1 l. Rice plants	50	50

154. Groundnut.

1981. World Food Day (2nd issue). Agricultural Industry. Multicoloured.

No.	Description		
686.	6 c. Type **154**	10	10
687.	31 c. Cassava	25	10
688.	50 c. Rice	45	25
689.	1 l. Pineapple	90	70

155. Scouts with Cattle.

1982. 75th Anniv. of Boy Scout Movement. Multicoloured.

No.	Description		
690.	20 c. Type **155**	25	10
691.	50 c. Scouts picking flowers	50	40
692.	1 l. Lord Baden-Powell ..	90	1·00
693.	2 l. Scouts fishing	1·90	2·00

1982. Nos. 668/74 surch.

No.	Description		
695.	50 c. on 31 c. Type **150** ..	40	40
696.	50 c. on 35 c. Type **151** ..	40	40
697.	50 c. on 45 c. Prince Charles as helicopter pilot	40	40
698.	50 c. on 60 c. Prince Charles in outdoor clothes	40	40
699.	90 c. on 1 l. Prince Charles and Lady Diana Spencer ..	75	75
699a.	1 l. 30 on 60 c. Prince Charles in outdoor clothes	1·75	1·75
699b.	2 l. on 35 c. Type **151** ..	2·75	2·75
700.	2 l. on 1 l. 50 Prince Charles and Lady Diana Spencer ..	1·50	1·50
700a.	8 l. on 1 l. 50 Prince Charles and Lady Diana Spencer ..	8·75	8·75

157. Heading.

1982. World Cup Football Championship. Spain. Multicoloured.

No.	Description		
702.	20 c. Type **157**	35	15
703.	30 c. Dribbling	50	20
704.	1 l. Tackling	1·60	1·40
705.	2 l. Goalkeeping ..	2·75	3·00

158. Prince and Princess of Wales.

1982. 21st Birthday of Princess of Wales. Multicoloured.

No.	Description		
707.	31 c. Caernarvon Castle ..	35	15
708.	50 c. Type **158**	50	25
709.	2 l. Princess of Wales ..	1·40	1·50

1982. Birth of Prince William of Wales. Nos. 707/9 optd. **ROYAL BABY 21.6.82.**

No.	Description		
711.	31 c. Caernarvon Castle ..	35	15
712.	50 c. Type **158**	50	25
713.	2 l. Princess of Wales ..	1·40	1·50

159. Washington with Troops.

1982. 250th Birth Anniv. of George Washington. Multicoloured.

No.	Description		
715.	6 c. Type **159**	10	10
716.	31 c. Portrait of Washington (vert.)	20	20
717.	50 c. Washington with horse	35	35
718.	1 l. Washington standing on battlefield (vert.) ..	65	80

160. Temptation of Christ.

1982. Christmas. Stained-Glass Windows. Multicoloured.

720. 6 c. Type **160** 10 10
721. 31 c. Baptism of Christ .. 15 20
722. 50 c. Annunciation .. 20 40
723. 1 l. Nativity 55 90

1982. World Cup Football Championship Winners. Nos. 702/5 optd. **WORLD CUP WINNERS ITALY 3 W. GERMANY 1.**

725. 20 c. Type **157** 15 20
726. 30 c. Dribbling 20 30
727. 1 l. Tackling 55 85
728. 2 l. Goalkeeping .. .. 1·00 1·75

162. Long Snouted Crocodile.

1982. Death Centenary of Charles Darwin. Multicoloured.

730. 6 c. Type **162** 30 10
731. 31 c. Rainbow Lizard .. 85 55
732. 50 c. River Turtle .. 1·25 95
733. 1 l. Chameleon .. .. 2·00 2·50

163. Diogenes.

1983. 500th Birth Anniv. of Raphael. Details from painting "The School of Athens". Multicoloured.

735. 6 c. Type **163** 10 10
736. 31 c. Euclid, Ptolemy, Zoroaster, Raphael and Sodoma 20 30
737. 50 c. Euclid and his pupils 35 45
738. 2 l. Pythagoras, Francesco Maria della Rovere and Heraclitus .. .. 1·25 1·40

164. Agricultural Training.

1983. Commonwealth Day. Multicoloured.

740. 6 c. Type **164** 10 10
741. 10 c. Tourism development 10 10
742. 50 c. Broadcasting training 45 45
743. 1 l. Airport services .. 90 90

165. Map of Africa and Flag of Sierra Leone.

1983. 25th Anniv. of Economic Commission for Africa.

744. **165.** 1 l. multicoloured .. 80 1·10

166. Chimps in Tree.

1983. Endangered Species. Multicoloured.

745. 6 c. Type **166** 50 15
746. 10 c. Three chimps (vert.) 60 15
747. 31 c. Chimps swinging in tree (vert.) .. .. 1·40 50
748. 60 c. Group of chimps .. 2·50 2·75

167. Traditional Communications.

1983. World Communications Year. Mult.

750. 6 c. Type **167** 10 10
751. 10 c. Mail via Mano River 10 10
752. 20 c. Satellite ground station 10 10
753. 1 l. British packet, circa 1805 .. .. .. 55 65

168. Montgolfier Balloon, Paris, 1783.

1983. Bicentenary of Manned Flight. Mult.

755. 6 c. Type **168** 20 10
756. 20 c. "Deutschland" air-ship, Berlin, 1879 (horiz.) 35 20
757. 50 c. "Norge I", North Pole, 1926 (horiz.) .. 70 60
758. 1 l. "Cape Sierra" sport balloon, Freetown, 1983 1·10 1·40

169. Mickey Mouse.

1983. Space Ark Fantasy. Multicoloured.

774. 1 c. Type **169** 10 10
775. 1 c. Huey, Dewey and Louie 10 10
776. 3 c. Goofy in spaceship .. 10 10
777. 3 c. Donald Duck 10 10
778. 10 c. Ludwig Von Drake .. 10 10
779. 10 c. Goofy 10 10
780. 2 l. Mickey Mouse and Giraffe in spaceship .. 1·10 1·25
781. 3 l. Donald Duck floating in space .. .. .. 1·60 1·75

170. Graduates from Union Training Programme.

1984. 10th Anniv. of Mano River Union. Mult.

783. 6 c. Type **170** 10 10
784. 25 c. Intra-Union trade .. 10 10
785. 31 c. Member Presidents on map 15 15
786. 41 c. Signing ceremony marking Guinea's accession 20 20

171. Gymnastics.

1984. Olympic Games, Los Angeles. Mult.

788. 90 c. Type **171** 30 40
789. 1 l. Hurdling 30 40
790. 3 l. Javelin throwing .. 75 1·25

172. "Apollo II" Liftoff.

1984. 15th Anniv. of First Moonwalk. Mult.

792. 50 c. Type **172** 20 20
793. 75 c. Lunar module .. 30 30
794. 1 l.25 First Moonwalk .. 45 45
795. 2 l.50 Lunar exploration .. 85 85

173. Concorde.

1984. Universal Postal Union Congress, Hamburg.

797 **173** 4 l. multicoloured .. 2·50 1·75

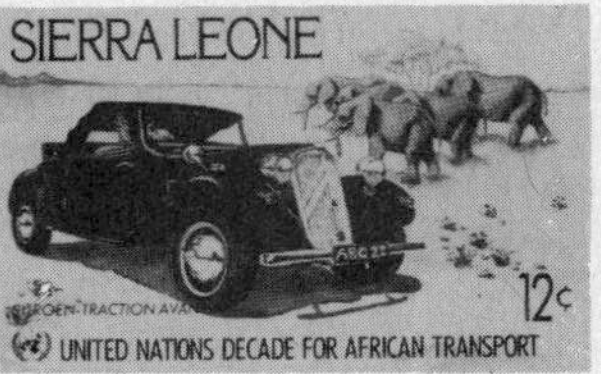

174. Citroen "Traction Avante".

1984. United Nations Decade of African Transport. Multicoloured.

799. 12 c. Type **174** 20 10
800. 60 c. Locomobile 40 25
801. 90 c. A.C. "Ace" 55 35
802. 1 l. Vauxhall "Prince Henry" 55 35
803. 1 l. 50 Delahaye "135" .. 70 50
804. 2 l. Mazda "1105" 90 65

1984. Nos. 625, 627 and 634 surch.

811. 25 c. on 10 c. Grey Parrot (vert.) 75 85
812. 40 c. on 10 c. Grey Parrot (vert.) 50 70
813. 50 c. on 2 l. Black Bee Eater 50 70
814. 70 c. on 5 c. Spur-winged Goose 50 70
815. 10 l. on 5 c. Spur-winged Goose .. .. .. 3·00 3·50

1984. "Ausipex" International Stamp Exhibition. Melbourne. Nos. 632 and 635 optd. **AUSIPEX 84.**

818. 50 c. Black Crake (vert.) .. 1·00 75
819. 5 l. Barrow's Bustard .. 2·25 2·00

177. Portuguese Caravel.

1984. History of Shipping. Multicoloured.

820. 2 c. Type **177** 15 20
821. 5 c. "Merlin" of Bristol .. 20 20
822. 10 c "Golden Hind" .. 30 20
823. 15 c. "Mordaunt" .. 55 40
824. 20 c. "Atlantic" (sail transport) 30 20
825. 25 c. H.M.S. "Lapwing" (frigate), 1785 .. .. 30 20
826. 30 c. "Traveller" (brig) .. 30 25
827. 40 c. "Amistad" (schooner) 35 25
828. 50 c. H.M.S. "Teazer" (gun vessel), 1868 .. .. 40 25
829. 70 c. "Scotia" (cable ship) 55 35
830. 1 l. H.M.S. "Alecto" (paddle-steamer), 1882 .. 60 35
831. 2 l. H.M.S. "Blonde" (cruiser), 1889 .. .. 85 55
832. 5 l. H.M.S. "Fox" (cruiser), 1895 .. .. .. 1·25 85
833. 10 l. "Accra" (liner) .. 1·75 1·40
833c. 15 l. H.M.S. "Favourite" (sloop), 1829 .. .. 1·25 1·25
833d. 25 l. H.M.S. "Euryalus" (screw frigate), 1883 .. 1·75 1·75

Nos. 820/2 and 824/33 come both with and without imprint dates.

178. Mail Runner approaching Mano River Depot, c1843.

1984. 125th Anniv. of First Postage Stamps. Multicoloured.

834. 50 c. Type **178** 30 15
835. 2 l. Isaac Fitzjohn, first Postmaster, receiving letters, 1855 .. .. 1·00 65
836. 3 l. 1859 packet franked with four 6d. stamps .. 1·50 1·00

179. "Madonna and Child" (Pisanello).

1984. Christmas. Madonna and Child paintings by artist named. Multicoloured.

838. 20 c. Type **179** 10 10
839. 1 l. Memling 40 30
840. 2 l. Raphael 75 55
841. 3 l. Van der Werff .. 1·10 80

180. Donald Duck in "The Wise Little Hen" (Illustration reduced, actual size 50 × 38 mm.).

1984. 50th Birthday of Donald Duck. Walt Disney Cartoon Characters. Multicoloured.

843. 1 c. Type **180** 10 10
844. 2 c. Mickey Mouse and Donald Duck in "Boat Builders" 10 10
845. 3 c. Panchito, Donald Duck and Jose Carioca in "The Three Caballeros" 10 10
846. 4 c. Donald Duck meeting Pythagoras in "Mathmagic Land" 10 10
847. 5 c. Donald Duck and nephew in "The Mickey Mouse Club" 10 10
848. 10 c. Mickey Mouse, Goofy and Donald Duck in "Donald on Parade" .. 10 10
849. 1 l. Donald Duck riding donkey in "Don Donald" 75 75
850. 2 l. Donald Duck in "Donald Gets Drafted" 1·50 1·50
851. 4 l. Donald Duck meeting children in Tokyo Disneyland .. .. 2·50 2·50

181. Fischer's Whydah.

1985. Birth Bicentenary of John J. Audubon (ornithologist). Songbirds of Sierra Leone. Multicoloured.

853. 40 c. Type **181** .. .. 1·00 40
854. 90 c. Spotted Flycatcher .. 2·00 1·10
855. 1 l. 30 Garden Warbler .. 2·25 2·00
856. 3 l. Speke's Weaver .. 3·50 4·00

182. Fishing.

1985. International Youth Year. Mult.

858. 1 l. 15 Type **182** 30 35
859. 1 l. 50 Sawing timber .. 40 45
860. 2 l. 15 Rice farming .. 55 60

183. Eddie Rickenbacker and Spad "XIII", 1918.

1985. 40th Anniv. of International Civil Aviation Organization. Multicoloured.

862. 70 c. Type **183** .. .. 1·00 60
863. 1 l. 25 Samuel P. Langley and "Aerodrome No. 5", 1903 .. .. .. 1·40 1·25
864. 1 l. 30 Orville and Wilbur Wright with "Flyer No. 1", 1903 .. .. .. 1·40 1·25
865. 2 l. Charles Lindberg and "Spirit of St. Louis", 1927 .. .. .. 1·75 2·00

184. "Temptation of Christ" (Botticelli).

1985. Easter. Religious Paintings. Mult.

867. 45 c. Type **184** 30 15
868. 70 c. "Christ at the Column" (Velasquez) .. 55 25
869. 1 l. 55 "Pieta" (Botticelli) (vert.) 90 45
870. 10 l. "Christ on the Cross" (Velasquez) (vert.) .. 4·25 3·25

185. The Queen Mother at St. Paul's Cathedral.

1985. Life and Times of Queen Elizabeth the Queen Mother. Multicoloured.

872. 1 l. Type **185** 25 30
873. 1 l. 70 With her racehorse, "Double Star", at Sandown (horiz.) .. 45 50
874. 10 l. At Covent Garden, 1971 .. .. .. 3·00 3·25

1985. 75th Anniv. of Girl Guide Movement. Nos. 690/3 surch. **75th ANNIVERSARY OF GIRL GUIDES.**

876. 70 c. on 20 c. Type **155** .. 20 25
877. 1 l. 30 on 50 c. Scouts picking flowers 35 40
878. 5 l. on 1 l. Lord Baden-Powell .. .. .. 1·25 1·40
879. 7 l. on 2 l. Scouts fishing .. 1·75 1·90

1985. Olympic Gold Medal Winners, Los Angeles. Nos. 788/90 surch.

881. 2 l. on 90 c. Type **171** (surch. **MA YANHONGJ CHINA GOLD MEDAL**) 50 55
882. 4 l. on 1 l. Hurdling (surch. **E. MOSES U.S.A. GOLD MEDAL**) .. .. 1·00 1·25
883. 8 l. on 3 l. Javelin-throwing (surch. **A. HAERKOENEN FINLAND GOLD MEDAL**) .. .. .. 2·00 2·10

188. Chater-Lea (1905) at Hill Station House.

1985. Centenary of Motor Cycle and Decade for African Transport. Multicoloured.

885. 1 l. 40 Type **188** .. .. 1·00 1·00
886. 2 l. Honda "XR 350 R" at Queen Elizabeth II Quay, Freetown .. 1·40 1·40
887. 4 l. Kawasaki "Vulcan" at Bo Clock Tower .. 2·50 2·50
888. 5 l. Harley-Davidson "Electra-Glide" in Makeni village .. .. 2·75 2·75

1985. 300th Birth Anniv of Johann Sebastian Bach (composer). As T **206** of Antigua. Mult.

890. 70 c. Viola pompose .. 40 25
891. 3 l. Spinet .. .. 1·10 80
892. 4 l. Lute .. .. 1·40 1·10
893. 5 l. Oboe .. .. 1·60 1·40

1985. Nos. 707/9 and 711/13 surch.

895. 70 c. on 31 c. Caernarvon Castle (707) 30 30
899. 1 l. 30 on 31 c. Caernarvon Castle (711) 80 80
896. 4 l. on 50 c. Type **158** (708) 2·50 2·50
897. 5 l. on 2 l. Princess of Wales (709) .. .. 3·00 3·00
900. 5 l. on 50 c. Type **158** (712) 3·00 3·00
901. 7 l. on 2 l. Princess of Wales (713) .. .. 4·00 4·00

190. "Madonna and Child" (Crivelli).

1985. Christmas. "Madonna and Child" Paintings by artists named. Multicoloured.

903. 70 c. Type **190** 20 10
904. 3 l. Bouts 70 40
905. 4 l. Da Messina 85 55
906. 5 l. Lochner .. .. 1·00 65

1985. 150th Birth Anniv of Mark Twain (author). As T **118** of Anguilla showing Walt Disney cartoon characters illustrating Mark Twain quotations. Multicoloured.

908. 1 l. 50 Snow White and Bashful 20 25
909. 3 l. Three Little Pigs .. 35 40
910. 4 l. Donald Duck and nephew 50 55
911. 5 l. Pinocchio and Figaro the cat 60 65

1985. Birth Bicentenaries of Grimm Brothers (folklorists). Walt Disney cartoon characters in scenes from "Rumpelstiltskin". As T **119** of Anguilla. Multicoloured.

913. 70 c. The Miller (Donald Duck) and his daughter (Daisy Duck) meet the King (Uncle Scrooge) .. 20 25
914. 1 l. The King puts the Miller's daughter to work 35 40
915. 2 l. Rumpelstiltskin demands payment .. 50 55
916. 10 l. The King with gold spun from straw .. 2·75 3·00

1985. 40th Anniv of U.N.O. As T **208** of Antigua showing United Nations (New York) stamps. Multicoloured.

918 2 l. John Kennedy and 1954 Human Rights 8 c. stamp 70 70
919 4 l. Albert Einstein (scientist) and 1958 Atomic Energy 3 c. .. 1·40 1·40
920 7 l. Maimonides (physician) and 1956 W.H.O. 8 c. .. .. 3·25 3·25

191. Player kicking Ball.

1986. World Cup Football Championship, Mexico. Multicoloured.

922. 70 c. Type **191** 20 10
923. 3 l. Player controlling ball 60 50
924. 4 l. Player chasing ball .. 75 70
925. 5 l. Player kicking ball (different) .. .. 1·00 80

1966. Centenary of Statue of Liberty. As T **163b** of Lesotho. Multicoloured.

927. 40 c. Times, Square, 1905 (vert.) 10 10
928. 70 c. Times Square, 1986 (vert.) 15 10
929. 1 l. "Tally Ho" coach, c 1880 .. .. .. 20 15
930. 10 l. Express bus, 1986 .. 1·60 1·40

1986. Appearance of Halley's Comet (1st issue). As T **123** of Anguilla. Multicoloured.

932. 15 c. Johannes Kepler (astronomer) and Paris Observatory 10 10
933. 50 c. N.A.S.A. Space Shuttle landing, 1985 .. 10 10
934. 70 c. Halley's Comet (from Bayeux Tapestry) .. 10 10
935. 10 l. Comet of 530 A.D. and Merlin predicting coming of King Arthur .. .. 1·25 1·40

See also Nos. 988/91.

1986. 60th Birthday of Queen Elizabeth II. As T **125** of Anguilla.

937. 10 c. black and yellow .. 10 10
938. 1 l. 70 multicoloured .. 25 30
939. 10 l. multicoloured .. 1·25 1·40

DESIGNS: 10 c. Princess Elizabeth inspecting guard of honour, Cranwell, 1951. 1 l. 70, In Garter robes. 10 l. Braemar Games, 1970.

192. Chicago-Milwaukee "Hiawatha Express".

1986. "Ameripex" International Stamp Exhibition. Chicago. American Trains. Multicoloured.

941. 50 c. Type **192** 60 25
942. 2 l. Rock Island Line "The Rocket" .. .. 1·25 80
943. 4 l. Rio Grande "Prospector" .. .. 2·00 1·60
944. 7 l. Southern Pacific "Daylight Express" .. 2·50 2·50

1986. Royal Wedding. As T **213** of Antigua. Multicoloured.

946. 10 c. Prince Andrew and Miss Sarah Ferguson .. 10 10
947. 1 l. 70 Prince Andrew at clay pigeon shoot .. 30 35
948. 10 l. Prince Andrew in naval uniform .. .. 1·40 1·75

193. "Monodora myristica".

1986. Flowers of Sierra Leone. Multicoloured.

950. 70 c. Type **193** 15 10
951. 1 l. 50 "Gloriosa simplex" .. 20 15
952. 4 l. "Mussaenda erythrophylla" 35 25
953. 6 l. "Crinum ornatum" .. 50 40
954. 8 l. "Bauhinia purpurea" .. 60 60
955. 10 l. "Bombax costatum" .. 70 70
956. 20 l. "Hibiscus rosasinensis" .. .. 1·25 1·50
957. 30 l. "Cassia fistula" .. 1·75 2·00

194. Handshake and Flags of Sierra Leone and U.S.A.

1986. 25th Anniv. of United States Peace Corps.

959. **194.** 4 l. multicoloured .. 70 70

195. Transporting Goods by Canoe.

1986. International Peace Year. Mult.

960. 1 l. Type **195** 10 10
961. 2 l. Teacher and class .. 15 15
962. 5 l. Rural post office .. 30 30
963. 10 l. Fishermen in longboat 55 55

1986. Various stamps surch.

968. 70 c. on 10 c. Princess Elizabeth inspecting guard of honour, Cranwell (No. 937) .. 10 10
971. 70 c. on 10 c. Prince Andrew and Miss Sarah Ferguson (No. 946) .. 10 10
964. 30 l. on 2 c. Type **177** (No. 820).. .. 1·50 1·60
965. 40 l. on 30 c. "Traveller" (brig) (No. 826).. .. 2·10 2·25
969. 45 l. on 10 l. Queen at Braemar Games, 1970 (No. 934).. .. .. 2·40 2·50
972. 45 l. on 10 l. Prince Andrew in naval uniform (No. 948).. .. .. 2·40 2·50
966. 45 l. on 40 c. "Amistad" (schooner) (No. 827) .. 2·40 2·50
967. 50 l. on 70 c. "Scotia" (cable ship) (No. 829) .. 2·60 2·75

1986. World Cup Football Championship Winners, Mexico. Nos. 922/5 optd. **WINNERS Argentina 3 W. Germany 2** or surch. also.

974. 70 c. Type **191** 15 10
975. 3 l. Player controlling ball 30 30
976. 4 l. Playing chasing ball .. 40 40
977. 40 l. on 5 l. Player kicking ball (different) .. .. 3·00 3·50

198. Mickey and Minnie Mouse as Jack and Jill.

1986. "Stockholmia '86" International Stamp Exhibition, Sweden. Walt Disney cartoon characters in scenes from nursery rhymes. Multicoloured.

979. 70 c. Type **198** 10 10
980. 1 l. Donald Duck as Wee Willie Winkie 10 10
981. 2 l. Minnie Mouse as Little Miss Muffet 15 15
982. 4 l. Goofy as Old King Cole 30 30
983. 5 l. Clarabelle as Mary Quite Contrary 40 40
984. 10 l. Daisy Duck as Little Bo Peep 70 70
985. 25 l. Daisy Duck and Minnie Mouse in "Polly put the Kettle on" .. 1·75 1·75
986. 35 l. Goofy, Mickey Mouse and Donald Duck as the Three Men in a Tub .. 2·25 2·25

1986. Appearance of Halley's Comet (2nd issue). Nos. 932/5 optd as T **218** of Antigua.

988. 50 c. N.A.S.A. Space Shuttle landing, 1985 .. 10 10
989. 70 c. Halley's Comet (from Bayeux Tapestry) .. 10 10
990. 1 l. 50 on 15 c. Johannes Kepler (astronomer) and Paris Observatory .. 10 10
991. 45 l. on 10 l. Comet of 530 A.D. and Merlin predicting coming of King Arthur .. .. 3·00 3·50

199. "Virgin and Child with St. Dorothy".

1986. Christmas. Paintings by Titian. Mult.

993. 70 c. Type **199** 10 10
994. 1 l. 50 "The Gypsy Madonna" (vert.) .. 15 10
995. 20 l. "The Holy Family" .. 1·75 1·75
996. 30 l. "Virgin and Child in an Evening Landscape" (vert.) .. .. .. 2·25 2·50

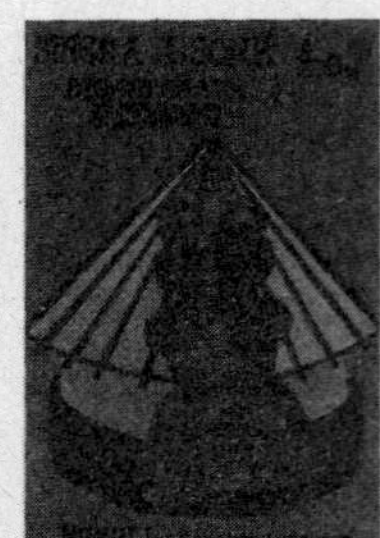

200. Nomoli (soapstone figure).

1987. Bicentenary of Sierra Leone. Mult.

998. 2 l. Type **200** 10 15
999. 5 l. King's Yard Gate, Royal Hospital, 1817 .. 20 30

201. Removing Top of Statue's Torch.

1987. Centenary of Statue of Liberty (1986) (2nd issue). Multicoloured.

1001. 70 c. Type **201** 10 10
1002. 1 l. 50 View of statue's torch and New York harbour (horiz.) .. 10 10
1003. 2 l. Crane lifting torch .. 10 10
1004. 3 l. Workman steadying torch 10 15
1005. 4 l. Statue's crown (horiz.) 15 20
1006. 5 l. Statue of Liberty (side view) and fireworks 20 25
1007. 10 l. Statue of Liberty and fireworks 40 45
1008. 25 l. Bedloe Island, statue and fireworks (horiz.) .. .. 1·00 1·25
1009. 30 l. Statue's face .. 1·25 1·60

202. Emblem, Mother and Child and Syringe.

1987. 40th Anniv.of U.N.I.C.E.F.

1010. **202.** 10 l. multicoloured .. 40 55

MINIMUM PRICE

The minimum price quoted is 10p which represents a handling charge rather than a basis for valuing common stamps. For further notes about prices see introductory pages.

203. "U.S.A.", 1987.

1987. America's Cup Yachting Championship. Multicoloured.

1011. 1 l. Type **203** 10 10
1012. 1 l. 50 "New Zealand", 1987 (horiz.) 10 10
1013. 2 l. 50 "French Kiss", 1987 .. .. .. 10 10
1014. 10 l. "Stars and Stripes", 1987 (horiz.) 40 45
1015. 15 l. "Australia II", 1983 60 65
1016. 25 l. "Freedom", 1980 .. 1·00 1·10
1017. 30 l. "Kookaburra III", 1987 (horiz.) .. .. 1·75 1·40

204. Mickey Mouse as Mountie and Parliament Building, Ottawa (Illustration reduced. Actual size 50 × 37 mm.).

1987. "Capex '87" International Stamp Exhibition, Toronto. Walt Disney cartoon characters in Canada. Multicoloured.

1019. 2 l. Type **204** 10 10
1020. 5 l. Goofy dressed as Mountie and totem poles 20 25
1021. 10 l. Goofy windsurfing and Donald Duck fishing off Perce Rock 40 45
1022. 20 l. Goofy with mountain goat in Rocky Mountains 80 85
1023. 25 l. Donald Duck and Mickey Mouse in Old Quebec .. .. 1·00 1·10
1024. 45 l. Goofy emerging from igloo and "Aurora Borealis" .. 1·75 1·90
1025. 50 l. Goofy as gold prospector and post office, Yukon .. .. .. 2·00 2·10
1026. 75 l. Dumbo flying over Niagara Falls .. .. 3·25 3·25

205. "Salamis temora".

1987. Butterflies. Multicoloured.

1028 10 c. Type **205** 10 10
1029 20 c. "Iolaus marmorea" 10 10
1030 40 c. "Graphium ridleyanus" 10 10
1031 1 l. "Papilio bromius" .. 10 10
1032 2 l. "Papilio zalmoxis" .. 10 10
1033 3 l. "Cymothoe sangaris" 10 10
1034 5 l. "Graphium tynderaeus" 10 10
1035 10 l. "Graphium policenes" 10 10
1036 20 l. "Iolaus timon" .. 10 10
1037 25 l. "Danaus limniace" 10 10
1038 30 l. "Papilio hesperus" 10 10
1039 45 l. "Charaxes smaragdalis" 10 15
1040 60 l. "Charaxes lucretius" 20 25
1041 75 l. "Antanartia delius" 20 25
1042 100 l. "Abisara talantus" 30 35

206. Cycling.

1987. Olympic Games, Seoul (1988) (1st series). Multicoloured.

1043. 5 l. Type **206** 20 25
1044. 10 l. Three day eventing 40 45
1045. 45 l. Athletics .. .. 1·75 1·90
1046. 50 l. Tennis .. .. 2·00 2·10

See also Nos. 1137/41.

1987. Birth Centenary of Marc Chagall (artist). As T **225** of Antigua. Multicoloured.

1048 3 l. "The Quarrel" .. 10 15
1049 5 l. "Rebecca giving Abraham's Servant a Drink" 15 15
1050 10 l. "The Village" .. 20 25
1051 20 l. "Ida at the Window" 40 45
1052 25 l. "Promenade" .. 80 85
1053 45 l. "Peasants" .. 1·00 1·10
1054 50 l. "Turquoise Plate" (ceramic) .. .. 1·75 1·90
1055 75 l. "Cemetery Gate" .. 2·00 2·10

1987. Milestones of Transportation. As T **226** of Antigua. Multicoloured.

1057 3 l. "Apollo 8" spacecraft (first manned Moon orbit), 1968 .. .. 15 15
1058 5 l. Blanchard's balloon (first U.S. balloon flight), 1793 .. .. 20 20
1059 10 l. Amelia Earhart's Lockheed "Vega" (first solo transatlantic flight by woman), 1932 .. 40 40
1060 15 l. Vicker's "Vimy" (first non-stop transatlantic flight), 1919 .. 60 60
1061 20 l. British "Mk I" tank (first combat tank), 1916 .. .. .. 80 80
1062 25 l. Sikorsky "VS-300" (first U.S. helicopter flight), 1939 .. .. 90 90
1063 30 l. Wright brothers' "Flyer I" (first powered flight), 1903 .. .. 1·10 1·10
1064 35 l. Bleriot "XI" (first cross Channel flight), 1909 .. .. .. 1·25 1·25
1065 40 l. Paraplane (first flexible-wing ultralight), 1983 .. .. 1·50 1·50
1066 50 l. Daimler's first motorcycle, 1885 .. 1·75 1·75

Nos. 1058/64 are horiz.

207 Evonne Goolagong

1987. Wimbledon Tennis Champions. Mult.

1068 2 l. Type **207** 20 20
1069 5 l. Martina Navratilova 35 35
1070 10 l. Jimmy Connors .. 60 60
1071 15 l. Bjorn Borg 90 90
1072 30 l. Boris Becker .. 1·75 1·75
1073 40 l. John McEnroe .. 2·00 2·00
1074 50 l. Chris Evert Lloyd .. 2·25 2·25
1075 75 l. Virginia Wade .. 3·00 3·00

208 Ducats, "Santa Maria" and Issac Abravanel (financier)

1987. 500th Anniv (1992) of Discovery of America by Columbus. Multicoloured.

1077 5 l. Type **208** 15 20
1078 10 l. Astrolabe, "Pinta" and Abraham Zacuto (astronomer) 30 35
1079 45 l. Maravedis (coins), "Nina" and Luis de Santangel (financier) .. 1·25 1·40
1080 50 l. Carib and Spaniard with tobacco plant and Luis de Torres (translator) .. .. 1·50 1·60

209 Cotton Tree

1987. Flora and Fauna. Multicoloured.

1082 3 l. Type **209** 10 10
1083 5 l. Dwarf crocodile .. 15 20
1084 10 l. Kudu 30 35
1085 20 l. Yellowbells .. 60 65
1086 25 l. Hippopotamus and calf 75 80
1087 45 l. Comet orchid .. 1·25 1·40
1088 50 l. Baobab tree .. 1·50 1·60
1089 75 l. Elephant and calf 2·25 2·40

210 Scouts at Ayers Rock

1987. World Scout Jamboree, Australia. Mult.

1091 5 l. Type **210** 15 20
1092 15 l. Scouts sailing yacht 45 50
1093 40 l. Scouts and Sydney skyline .. .. 1·25 1·40
1094 50 l. Scout, Sydney Harbour Bridge and Opera House .. .. 1·50 1·60

1987. Bicentenary of U.S. Constitution. As T **232** of Antigua. Multicoloured.

1096 5 l. White House .. 15 20
1097 10 l. George Washington (Virginia delegate) (vert) 30 35
1098 30 l. Patrick Henry (statesman) (vert) .. 90 95
1099 65 l. State Seal, New Hampshire .. .. 1·90 2·00

1987. 60th Anniv of Mickey Mouse (Walt Disney cartoon character). Cartoon characters at Tokyo Disneyland. As T **220** of Dominica. Multicoloured.

1101 20 c. Mickey and Minnie Mouse on Space Mountain 10 10
1102 40 c. Mickey Mouse at Country Bear Jamboree 10 10
1103 80 c. Mickey Mouse as bandleader and Minnie Mouse, Goofy and Pluto as musicians 10 10
1104 1 l. Goofy, Mickey Mouse and children in canoe and Mark Twain's river boat 10 10
1105 2 l. Mickey Mouse, Goofy and Chip n'Dale on Western River Railroad 10 10
1106 3 l. Goofy and Mickey Mouse as Pirates of the Caribbean 10 10
1107 10 l. Mickey Mouse, Goofy and children aboard "Big Thunder Mountain" train .. 30 35
1108 20 l. Mickey Mouse, Morty and Ferdie in boat and Goofy on flying carpet 60 65
1109 30 l. Mickey and Minnie Mouse in kimonos at Disneyland entrance .. 90 95

211 "The Annunciation" (detail) (Titian)

1987. Christmas. Religious Paintings by Titian. Multicoloured.

1111 2 l. Type **211** 10 10
1112 10 l. "Madonna and Child with Saints" 40 35
1113 20 l. "Madonna and Child with Saints Ulfus and Brigid" 75 75
1114 35 l. "The Madonna of the Cherries" .. .. 1·40 1·50

1988. Royal Ruby Wedding. As T **234** of Antigua.

1116 2 l. brown, black and grey 10 10
1117 3 l. multicoloured .. 10 10
1118 10 l. brown, black & orge 30 35
1119 50 l. multicoloured .. 1·50 1·60

DESIGNS: 2 l. Wedding of Princess Elizabeth and Duke of Edinburgh; 3 l. Prince Charles's christening photograph, 1949; 10 l. Queen Elizabeth II with Prince Charles and Princess Anne, c. 1951; 50 l. Queen Elizabeth, c. 1960.

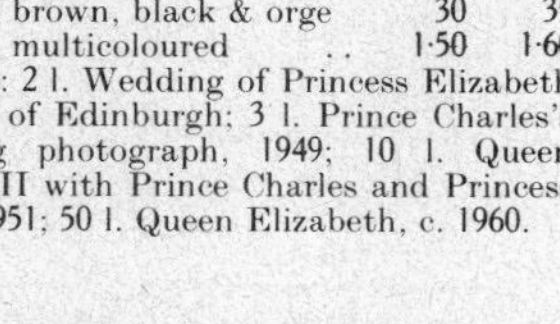

212 "Russula cyanoxantha"

1988. Fungi. Multicoloured.

1121 3 l. Type **212** 30 20
1122 10 l. "Lycoperdon perlatum" 70 50
1123 20 l. "Lactarius deliciosus" .. .. 1·25 1·25
1124 30 l. "Boletus edulis" .. 1·75 2·00

213 Golden Pheasant Fish

1988. Fishes of Sierra Leone. Multicoloured.

1126 3 l. Type **213** 10 10
1127 10 l. Banded toothcarp .. 30 35
1128 20 l. Jewel fish 60 65
1129 35 l. Butterfly fish .. 1·00 1·10

1988. Stamp Exhibitions. Nos. 1016, 1072 and 1079 optd.

1131 25 l. Freedom, 1980 (optd **Independence 40**, Israel) 75 80
1132 30 l. Boris Becker (optd **OLYMPHILEX '88**, Seoul) 90 95
1133 45 l. Maravedis (coins), "Nina" and Luis de Santangel (financier) (optd **PRAGA 88**, Prague) .. .. 1·25 1·40

214 Hands holding Coffee Beans and Woman with Cocoa

1988. International Fund for Agricultural Development. Multicoloured.

1134 3 l. Type **214** 10 10
1135 15 l. Tropical fruits and man climbing palm tree 45 50
1136 25 l. Sheaf of rice and harvesters 75 80

215 Basketball

1988. Olympic Games, Seoul (2nd issue). Mult.

1137 3 l. Type **215** 10 10
1138 10 l. Judo 30 35
1139 15 l. Gymnastics .. 45 50
1140 40 l. Synchronized swimming .. .. 1·25 1·40

216 Swallow-tailed Bee Eater

1988. Birds. Multicoloured.

1142 3 l. Type **216** 15 15
1143 5 l. Double-toothed barbet 25 25
1144 8 l. African golden oriole 35 35
1145 10 l. Red bishop 40 40
1146 12 l. Red-billed shrike .. 45 45
1147 20 l. European bee eater 80 80
1148 35 l. Common gonolek ("Barbary Shrike") .. 1·40 1·40
1149 40 l. Western black-headed oriole .. .. 1·50 1·50

217 "Aureol" (cargo liner)

1988. Ships. Multicoloured.

1151 3 l. Type **217** 30 30
1152 10 l. "Dunkwa" (freighter) 80 80
1153 15 l. "Melampus" (container ship) .. 1·10 1·10
1154 30 l. "Dumbaia" (freighter) .. .. 1·90 1·90

1988. 500th Birth Anniv of Titian (artist). As T **238** of Antigua. Multicoloured.

1156 1 l. "The Concert" (detail) 10 10
1157 2 l. "Philip II of Spain" 10 10
1158 3 l. "Saint Sebastian" (detail) 10 10
1159 5 l. "Martyrdom of St. Peter Martyr" .. 15 20
1160 15 l. "St. Jerome" .. 45 50
1161 20 l. "St. Mark enthroned with Saints" .. 60 65
1162 25 l. "Portrait of a Young Man" 75 80
1163 30 l. "St. Jerome in Penitence" 90 95

218 Helicopter lowering "Mercury" Capsule to Flight Deck

1988. 25th Death Anniv of John F. Kennedy (American statesman). U.S. Space Achievements. Multicoloured.

1165 3 l. Type **218** 10 10
1166 5 l. "Liberty Bell 7" capsule descending (vert) 15 20
1167 15 l. Launch of first manned American capsule (vert) 45 50
1168 40 l. "Freedom 7" orbiting Earth) .. .. 1·25 1·40

219 Famine Relief Convoy crossing Desert

1988. 125th Anniv of Int Red Cross. Mult.

1170 3 l. Type **219** 20 20
1171 10 l. Rifle and map of Battle of Solferino, 1859 50 50
1172 20 l. World War II hospital ship in Pacific 90 90
1173 40 l. Red Cross tent and World War I German biplanes .. .. 1·75 1·75

1988. Christmas. "Mickey's Christmas Dance". As T **228** of Dominica showing Walt Disney cartoon characters. Multicoloured.

1175 10 l. Donald Duck's nephews playing as band 35 35
1176 10 l. Clarabelle 35 35
1177 10 l. Goofy 35 35
1178 10 l. Scrooge McDuck and Grandma Duck .. 35 35
1179 10 l. Donald Duck .. 35 35
1180 10 l. Daisy Duck .. 35 35
1181 10 l. Minnie Mouse .. 35 35
1182 10 l. Mickey Mouse .. 35 35

Nos. 1175/82 were printed together, se-tenant, forming a composite design.

220 "Adoration of the Magi" (detail)

1988. Christmas. Religious Paintings by Rubens. Multicoloured.

1184 3 l. Type **220** 10 10
1185 3 l. 60 "Adoration of the Shepherds" (detail) .. 10 10
1186 5 l. "Adoration of the Magi" (detail) .. 15 20
1187 10 l. "Adoration of the Shepherds" (diff detail) 30 35
1188 20 l. "Virgin and Child surrounded by Flowers" 60 65
1189 40 l. "St. Gregory the Great and Other Saints" (detail) .. 1·25 1·40
1190 60 l. "Adoration of the Magi" (detail) .. 1·75 1·90
1191 80 l. "Madonna and Child with Saints" (detail) 2·25 2·40

222 Brazil v. Sweden, 1958

1989. World Cup Football Championship, Italy. Designs showing action from previous World Cup finals. Multicoloured.

1194 3 l. Type **222** 10 10
1195 6 l. West Germany v. Hungary, 1954 .. 10 10
1196 8 l. England v. West Germany, 1966 .. 10 10
1197 10 l. Argentina v. Netherlands, 1978 .. 10 10
1198 12 l. Brazil v. Czechoslovakia, 1962 .. 10 10
1199 20 l. West Germany v. Netherlands, 1974 .. 10 10
1200 30 l. Italy v. West Germany, 1982 .. 10 15
1201 40 l. Brazil v. Italy, 1970 10 15

223 Decathlon (Gold, C. Schenk, East Germany)

1989. Olympic Medal Winners, Seoul (1988). Multicoloured.

1203 3 l. Type **223** 10 10
1204 6 l. Men's heavyweight judo (Gold, H. Saito, Japan) 10 10
1205 10 l. Women's cycle road race (Silver, J. Niehaus, West Germany) .. 10 10
1206 15 l. Men's single sculls (Gold, T. Lange, East Germany) 10 10
1207 20 l. Men's 50 metres freestyle swimming (Gold, M. Biondi, U.S.A.) 10 10
1208 30 l. Men's 100 metres (Gold, C. Lewis, U.S.A.) 10 15
1209 40 l. Dressage (Gold, West Germany) 10 15
1210 50 l. Greco-Roman wrestling (57 kg) (Gold, A. Sike, Hungary) .. 15 20

224 Map of Union States, Mail Lorry and Post Office

1989. 15th Anniv of Mano River Union. Mult.

1212 1 l. Type **224** 10 10
1213 3 l. Map of West Africa and Presidents Momoh, Conte and Doe .. 10 10
1214 10 l. Construction of Freetown–Monrovia Highway 10 10

225 "Richard III" (illustration reduced, actual size 49 × 36 mm)

1989. 425th Birth Anniv of Shakespeare. Mult.

1216 15 l. Type **225** 10 10
1217 15 l. "Othello" (Iago) .. 10 10
1218 15 l. "Two Gentlemen of Verona" 10 10
1219 15 l. "Macbeth" (Lady Macbeth) 10 10
1220 15 l. "Hamlet" 10 10
1221 15 l. "The Taming of the Shrew" 10 10
1222 15 l. "The Merry Wives of Windsor" 10 10
1223 15 l. "Henry IV" (Sir John Falstaff) .. 10 10
1224 15 l. "Macbeth" (The Witches) 10 10
1225 15 l. "Romeo and Juliet" 10 10
1226 15 l. "Merchant of Venice" 10 10
1227 15 l. "As You Like It" .. 10 10
1228 15 l. "The Taming of the Shrew" (banquet scene) 10 10
1229 15 l. "King Lear" .. 10 10
1230 15 l. "Othello" (Othello and Desdemona) .. 10 10
1231 15 l. "Henry IV" (Justice Shallow) 10 10

226 Centenary Logo

1989. Cent of Ahmadiyya Muslim Society.

1233 **226** 3 l. black and blue .. 10 10

1989. Japanese Art (1st series). Paintings by Seiho. As T **250** of Antigua. Multicoloured.

1234 3 l. "Lapping Waves" .. 10 10
1235 6 l. "Hazy Moon" (vert) 10 10
1236 8 l. "Passing Spring" (vert) 10 10
1237 10 l. "Mackerels" .. 10 10
1238 12 l. "Calico Cat" .. 10 10
1239 30 l. "The First Time to be a Model" (vert) .. 10 15
1240 40 l. "Kingly Lion" .. 10 15
1241 75 l. "After a Shower" (vert) 20 25

See also Nos. 1321/50.

227 Robespierre and Bastille

1989. "Philexfrance 89" International Stamp Exhibition, Paris, and Bicentenary of French Revolution. Multicoloured.

1243 6 l. Type **227** 10 10
1244 20 l. Danton and Louvre 10 10
1245 45 l. Queen Marie Antoinette and Notre Dame 10 15
1246 80 l. Louis XVI and Palace of Versailles .. 25 30

228 "Sputnik" Satellite in Orbit, 1957

1989. History of Space Exploration.

1248/301 10 l. × 27, 15 l. × 27 multicoloured .. set of 54 2·00 2·10

229 "Bulbophyllum barbigerum"

1989. Orchids of Sierra Leone. Multicoloured.

1303 3 l. Type **229** 10 10
1304 6 l. "Bulbophyllum falcatum" 10 10
1305 12 l. "Habenaria macrara" 10 10
1306 20 l. "Eurychone rothchildiana" .. 10 10
1307 50 l. "Calyptrochilum christyanum" 15 20
1308 60 l. "Bulbophyllum distans" 20 25
1309 70 l. "Eulophia guineensis" 20 25
1310 80 l. "Diaphananthe pellucida" 25 30

230 "Salamis temora"

1989. Butterflies. Multicoloured.

1312 6 l. Type **230** 10 10
1313 12 l. "Pseudacraea lucretia" 10 10
1314 18 l. "Charaxes boueti" (vert) 10 10
1315 30 l. "Graphium antheus" (vert) 10 15
1316 40 l. "Colotis protomedia" 10 15
1317 60 l. "Asterope pechueli" (vert) 20 25
1318 72 l. "Coenura aurantiaca" 20 25
1319 80 l. "Precis octavia" (vert) 25 30

1989. Japanese Art (2nd series). Paintings by Hiroshige of "The Fifty-three Stations on the Tokaido Road". As T **250** of Antigua. Mult.

1321 25 l. "Ferry-boat to Kawasaki" 10 10
1322 25 l. "The Hilly Town of Hodogaya" .. 10 10
1323 25 l. "Lute Players at Fujisawa" .. 10 10
1324 25 l. "Mild Rainstorm at Oiso" 10 10
1325 25 l. "Lake Ashi and Mountains of Hakone" 10 10
1326 25 l. "Twilight at Numazu" 10 10
1327 25 l. "Mount Fuji from Hara" 10 10
1328 25 l. "Samurai Children riding through Yoshiwara" 10 10
1329 25 l. "Mountain Pass at Yui" 10 10
1330 25 l. "Harbour at Ejiri" 10 10
1331 25 l. "Halt at Fujieda" .. 10 10
1332 25 l. "Misty Kanaya on the Oi River" .. 10 10
1333 25 l. "The Bridge to Kakegawa" 10 10
1334 25 l. "Teahouse at Fukuroi" 10 10
1335 25 l. "The Ford at Mistuke" 10 10
1336 25 l. "Coolies warming themselves at Hamamatsu" .. 10 10
1337 25 l. "Imakiri Ford at Maisaka" 10 10
1338 25 l. "Pacific Ocean from Shirasuka" 10 10
1339 25 l. "Futakawa Street-singers" 10 10
1340 25 l. "Repairing Yoshida Castle" 10 10
1341 25 l. "The Inn at Akasaka" 10 10
1342 25 l. "The Bridge to Okazaki" 10 10
1343 25 l. "Samurai's Wife entering Narumi" .. 10 10
1344 25 l. "Harbour at Kuwana" 10 10
1345 25 l. "Autumn in Ishiyakushi" 10 10
1346 25 l. "Snowfall at Kameyama" 10 10
1347 25 l. "The Frontier-station of Seki" 10 10
1348 25 l. "Teahouse at Sakanoshita" 10 10
1349 25 l. "Kansai Houses at Minakushi" 10 10
1350 25 l. "Kusatsu Station" 10 10

231 Formosan Sika Deer

1989. "World Stamp Expo '89" International Stamp Exhibition, Washington (2nd issue). Endangered Fauna. Multicoloured.

1353 6 l. Humpback whale .. 10 10
1354 9 l. Type **231** 10 10
1355 16 l. Spanish lynx .. 10 10
1356 20 l. Goitred gazelle .. 10 10
1357 30 l. Japanese sea lion .. 10 15
1358 50 l. Long-eared owl .. 15 20
1359 70 l. Lady Amherst's ("Chinese Copper") pheasant 20 25
1360 100 l. Siberian tiger .. 30 35

1989. Christmas. Walt Disney cartoon characters with cars. As T **183** of Gambia Multicoloured.

1362 3 l. Mickey Mouse and Goofy in Rolls-Royce "Phantom II Roadstar", 1934 .. 10 10
1363 6 l. Mickey and Minnie Mouse in Mercedes-Benz "500K", 1935 .. 10 10
1364 10 l. Mickey and Minnie Mouse with Jaguar "SS-100", 1938 .. 10 10
1365 12 l. Mickey Mouse and Goofy with U.S. army jeep, 1941 .. .. 10 10
1366 20 l. Mickey and Minnie Mouse with Buick Roadmaster Sedan "Model 91", 1937 .. 10 10
1367 30 l. Mickey Mouse driving 1948 Tucker .. 10 15
1368 40 l. Mickey and Minnie Mouse in Alfa Romeo, 1933 .. .. .. 10 15
1369 50 l. Mickey and Minnie Mouse with 1937 Cord 15 20

1989. Christmas. Paintings by Rembrandt. As T **259** of Antigua. Multicoloured.

1371 3 l. "The Adoration of the Magi" 10 10
1372 6 l. "The Holy Family with a Cat" 10 10
1373 10 l. "The Holy Family with Angels" .. 10 10
1374 15 l. "Simeon in the Temple" 10 10
1375 30 l. "The Circumcision" 10 15
1376 90 l. "The Holy Family" 25 30
1377 100 l. "The Visitation" .. 30 35
1378 120 l. "The Flight into Egypt" 35 40

232 Johann Kepler (astronomer)

1990. Exploration of Mars. Designs showing astronomers, spacecraft and Martian landscapes.

1380/1415 175 l. × 36 mult Set of 36 .. .. 19·00 20·00

1990. 50th Anniv of Second World War. American Aircraft. As T **188** of Gambia. Multicoloured.

1417 1 l. Dolittle's B-25 "Ruptured Duck", 1942 .. 10 10
1418 2 l. B-24 Liberator .. 10 10
1419 3 l. A-20 Boston attacking Japanese convoy, Bismark Sea, 1943 .. 10 10
1420 9 l. P-38 Lightning .. 10 10
1421 12 l. B-26 bomber .. 10 10
1422 16 l. Two B-17 F bombers .. 10 10
1423 50 l. B-25 D bomber .. 15 20
1424 80 l. B-29 Superfortress .. 25 30
1425 90 l. B-17 G bomber .. 25 30
1426 100 l. B-29 Superfortress "Enola Gay" 30 35

233 Mickey Mouse at Bauxite Mine

1990. Sierra Leone Sites and Scenes. Walt Disney cartoon characters. Multicoloured.

1428 3 l. Type **233** 10 10
1429 6 l. Scrooge McDuck panning for gold .. 10 10
1430 10 l. Minnie Mouse at Lungi Airport .. 10 10
1431 12 l. Mickey Mouse at Old Fourah Bay College .. 10 10
1432 16 l. Mickey Mouse mining bauxite 10 10
1433 20 l. Huey, Dewey and Louie harvesting rice .. 10 10
1434 30 l. Mickey and Minnie Mouse admire the Freetown Cotton Tree 10 15
1435 100 l. Mickey Mouse flying over Rutile Mine .. 30 35
1436 200 l. Mickey Mouse fishing at Goderich .. 60 65
1437 225 l. Mickey and Minnie Mouse at Bintumani Hotel 65 70

234 Olivier as Antony in "Antony and Cleopatra", 1951

1990. Sir Laurence Olivier (actor) Commemoration. Multicoloured.

1439 3 l. Type **234** 10 10
1440 9 l. As King Henry V in "Henry V", 1943 .. 10 10
1441 16 l. As Oedipus in "Oedipus", 1945 .. 10 10
1442 20 l. As Heathcliffe in "Wuthering Heights", 1939 .. .. 10 10
1443 30 l. As Szell in "Marathon Man", 1976 10 15
1444 70 l. As Othello in "Othello", 1964 .. 20 25
1445 175 l. As Michael in "Beau Geste", 1929 .. 50 55
1446 200 l. As King Richard III in "Richard III", 1956 60 65

235 Penny Black

1990. 150th Anniv of the Penny Black.

1448 **235** 50 l. blue 15 20
1449 100 l. brown 30 35

236 Cameroons World Cup Team

1990. World Cup Football Championship, Italy. Finalists. Multicoloured.

1451/74 15 l. × 8 (Type **236**, Colombia, Costa Rica, Egypt, Rumania, South Korea, U.A.E., Yugoslavia), 30 l. × 8 (Austria, Belgium, Czechoslovakia, Netherlands, Scotland, Sweden, Uruguay, U.S.S.R.), 45 l. × 8 (Argentina, Brazil, England, Ireland, Italy, Spain, U.S.A., West Germany) Set of 24 .. 2·10 2·25

237 Great Crested Grebe

1990. Birds. Multicoloured.

1475 3 l. Type **237** 10 10
1476 6 l. Green wood hoopoe .. 10 10
1477 10 l. African jacana .. 10 10
1478 12 l. Avocet 10 10
1479 20 l. Peters's finfoot .. 10 15
1480 80 l. Glossy ibis .. 25 30
1481 150 l. Hamerkop .. 45 50
1482 200 l. Black-throated honeyguide 60 65

1990. "Stamp World London 90" International Stamp Exhibition. British Costumes. As T **193** of Gambia showing Walt Disney cartoon characters. Multicoloured.

1484 3 l. Mickey Mouse as a Yeoman Warder .. 10 10
1485 6 l. Scrooge McDuck as a lamplighter .. 10 10
1486 12 l. Goofy as a medieval knight 10 10
1487 15 l. Clarabell as Ann Boleyn 10 10
1488 75 l. Minnie Mouse as Queen Elizabeth I 20 25
1489 100 l. Donald Duck as a chimney sweep .. 30 35
1490 125 l. Pete as King Henry VIII 35 40
1491 150 l. Clarabell, Minnie Mouse and Daisy Duck as May dancers .. 45 50

1990. 90th Birthday of Queen Elizabeth the Queen Mother. As T **99** of Grenada Grenadines. Multicoloured.

1493 75 l. Queen Mother on Remembrance Sunday 20 25
1494 75 l. Queen Mother in yellow hat 20 25
1495 75 l. Waving to crowds on 85th birthday .. 20 25

238 Golden Cat

1990. Wildlife. Multicoloured.

1497 25 l. Type **238** 10 10
1498 25 l. White-backed night heron 10 10
1499 25 l. Bateleur eagle .. 10 10
1500 25 l. Marabou stork .. 10 10
1501 25 l. White-faced whistling duck .. 10 10
1502 25 l. Aardvark 10 10
1503 25 l. Royal antelope .. 10 10
1504 25 l. Pygmy hippopotamus 10 10
1505 25 l. Leopard 10 10
1506 25 l. Sacred ibis .. 10 10
1507 25 l. Mona monkey .. 10 10
1508 25 l. Darter 10 10
1509 25 l. Chimpanzee .. 10 10
1510 25 l. African elephant .. 10 10
1511 25 l. Potto 10 10
1512 25 l. African manatee .. 10 10
1513 25 l. African fish eagle .. 10 10
1514 25 l. African spoonbill .. 10 10

239 Rabbit

1990. Fairground Carousel Animals. Mult.

1516 5 l. Type **239** 10 10
1517 10 l. Horse with panther saddle 10 10
1518 20 l. Ostrich 10 10
1519 30 l. Zebra 10 15
1520 50 l. Horse 15 20
1521 80 l. Sea monster .. 25 30
1522 100 l. Giraffe 30 35
1523 150 l. Armoured horse .. 45 50
1524 200 l. Camel 60 65

1990. Olympic Games, Barcelona (1992). As T **268** of Antigua.

1526 5 l. Start of Men's 100 metres 10 10
1527 10 l. Men's 4 × 400 metres relay 10 10
1528 20 l. Men's 100 metres in progress 10 10
1529 30 l. Weightlifting .. 10 15
1530 40 l. Freestyle wrestling 10 15
1531 80 l. Water polo .. 25 30
1532 150 l. Women's gymnastics 45 50
1533 200 l. Cycling 60 65

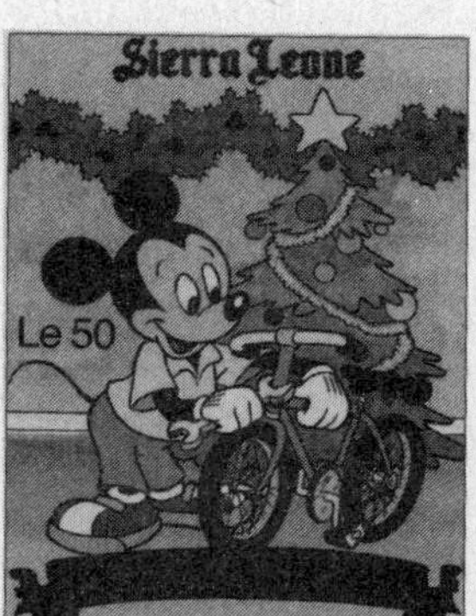

240 Morty assembling Bicycle by Christmas Tree

1990. Christmas. "The Night before Christmas". Walt Disney cartoon characters in scenes from Clement Moore's poem.

1535/58 50 l. × 8, 75 l. × 8, 100 l. × 8 mult Set of 24 .. .. 5·50 5·75

241 "Holy Family with St. Elizabeth" (Mantegna)

1990. Christmas. Paintings. Multicoloured.

1560 10 l. "Holy Family resting" (Rembrandt) 10 10
1561 20 l. Type **241** 10 10
1562 30 l. "Virgin and Child with an Angel" (Correggio) 10 15
1563 50 l. "Annunciation" (Bernardo Strozzi) .. 15 20
1564 100 l. "Madonna and Child appearing to St. Anthony" (Lippi) .. 30 35
1565 175 l. "Virgin and Child" (Giovanni Boltraffio) 50 55
1566 200 l. "Esterhazy Madonna" (Raphael) 60 65
1567 300 l. "Coronation of Mary" (Andrea Orcagna) 90 95

1990. 350th Death Anniv of Rubens. As T **273** of Antigua, but vert. Multicoloured.

1569 5 l. "Helena Fourment as Hagar in the Wilderness" (detail) .. 10 10
1570 10 l. "Isabella Brant" .. 10 10
1571 20 l. "Countess of Arundel and her Party" (detail) 10 10
1572 60 l. "Countess of Arundel and her Party" (different detail) .. 20 25
1573 80 l. "Nicolaas Rockox" 35 30
1574 100 l. "Adriana Perez" .. 30 35
1575 150 l. "George Villiers, Duke of Buckingham" (detail) 45 50
1576 300 l. "Countess of Buckingham" .. 90 95

SINGAPORE

An island at the south of the Malay peninsula, formerly part of the Straits Settlements but became a Crown Colony on 1 April, 1946, when the stamps of Malaya were used until 1948. From 1 August, 1958, an internally self-governing territory designated the State of Singapore. From 16 September, 1963, part of the Malaysian Federation until 9th August, 1965, when it became an independent republic within the Commonwealth.

100 cents = 1 dollar.

1948. As T **58** of Straits Settlements, but inscr. "MALAYA SINGAPORE".

No.		Description	Unused	Used
1		1 c. black	15	10
2		2 c. orange	15	10
3		3 c. green	20	10
4		4 c. brown	20	40
19a		5 c. purple	2·50	55
5		6 c. grey	25	15
6		8 c. red	25	15
21a		8 c. green	4·00	2·25
7		10 c. mauve	20	10
22a		12 c. red	4·00	3·75
8		15 c. blue	2·75	10
9		20 c. black and green	2·75	20
24a		20 c. blue	4·00	10
25		25 c. purple and orange	80	10
25a		35 c. red and purple	4·00	90
11		40 c. red and purple	4·75	5·00
12		50 c. black and blue	3·25	10
13		$1 blue and purple	10·00	60
14		$2 green and red	48·00	2·50
15		$5 green and brown	£100	2·50

1948. Silver Wedding. As T **10/11** of Aden.

No.		Description	Unused	Used
31.		10 c. violet	75	10
32.		$5 brown	95·00	27·00

1949. U.P.U. As T **20/23** of Antigua.

No.		Description	Unused	Used
33.		10 c. purple	75	10
34.		15 c. blue	3·25	1·40
35.		25 c. orange	3·75	1·25
36.		50 c. black	5·50	2·50

1953. Coronation. As T **13** of Aden.

No.		Description	Unused	Used
37.		10 c. black and purple	1·00	10

1. Chinese Sampan.

3. Singapore River.

1955.

No.	Type	Description	Unused	Used
38.	1.	1 c. black	10	40
39.	–	2 c. orange	60	1·00
40.	–	4 c. brown	35	15
41.	–	5 c. purple	35	15
42.	–	6 c. grey	35	30
43.	–	8 c. turquoise	55	70
44.	–	10 c. lilac	2·00	10
45.	–	12 c. red	2·25	2·50
46.	–	20 c. blue	90	10
47.	–	25 c. orange and violet	75	10
48.	–	30 c. violet and lake	2·00	10
49.	–	50 c. blue and black	1·25	10
50.	–	$1 blue and purple	22·00	10
51.	3.	$2 green and red	26·00	65
52.	–	$5 yell., red, brn. & black	35·00	3·00

DESIGNS—As Type **1** (2 c. to 20 c. are sailing craft); 2 c. Malay kolek. 4 c. Twa-kow lighter. 5 c. Lombok sloop. 6 c. Trengganu pinas. 8 c. Palari. 10 c. Timber tongkong. 12 c. Hainan junk. 20 c. Cocos-Keeling schooner. 25 c. "Argonaut" aircraft. 30 c. Oil tanker. 50 c. "Chusan III" (liner). As Type **3**—VERT. $1, Raffles statue. $5, Arms of Singapore.

16. The Singapore Lion.

1959. New Constitution. Lion in yellow and sepia.

No.	Type	Description	Unused	Used
53.	16.	4 c. red	30	30
54.		10 c. purple	40	20
55.		20 c. blue	1·10	2·00
56.		25 c. green	1·10	1·25
57.		30 c. violet	1·25	2·00
58.		50 c. slate	1·50	2·00

17. State Flag.

1960. National Day.

No.	Type	Description	Unused	Used
59.	17.	4 c. red, yellow and blue	20	40
60.		10 c. red, yellow and grey	40	10

18. Clasped Hands.

1961. National Day.

No.	Type	Description	Unused	Used
61.	18.	4 c. black, brown & yellow	20	40
62.		10 c. black, green & yellow	35	10

19. "Arachnis—Maggie Oei" (orchid).

20. Sea-Horse.

1962. Orchids, Fishes and Birds.

No.	Type	Description	Unused	Used
63.	19	1 c. multicoloured	10	75
64	20	2 c. brown and green	10	75
65	–	4 c. black and red	10	30
66	–	5 c. red and black	10	10
67	–	6 c. black and yellow	45	60
68	–	8 c. multicoloured	55	2·25
69	–	10 c. orange and black	15	10
70	–	12 c. multicoloured	55	2·25
70a	–	15 c. multicoloured	80	10
71	–	20 c. orange and blue	30	10
72	–	25 c. black and orange	35	10
73	–	30 c. multicoloured	1·00	10
74	–	50 c. multicoloured	95	10
75	–	$1 multicoloured	10·00	30
76	–	$2 multicoloured	13·00	75
77	–	$5 multicoloured	27·00	2·75

DESIGNS—VERT. (As Type **19**). 8 c. "Vanda-Tan Chay Yan" (orchid). 12 c. "Grammatophyllum speciosum" (orchid). 15 c. Black-naped tern. 30 c. "Vanda-Miss Joaquim" (orchid). $2 Yellow-bellied sunbird. $5 White-bellied sea eagle. (As Type **20**). 6 c. Archer fish. 20 c. Butterfly fish. HORIZ. (as Type **19**). 50 c. White-rumped shama. $1 White-breasted kingfisher. (As Type **20**). 4 c. Six-banded barb. 5 c. Clown fish. 10 c. Harlequin. 25 c. Two-spot gourami.

34. "The Role of Labour in Nation-Building".

1962. National Day.

No.	Type	Description	Unused	Used
78.	34.	4 c. yellow, red & black	15	40
79.		10 c. yellow, blue & black	35	10

35. Blocks of Flats, Singapore.

1963. National Day.

No.	Type	Description	Unused	Used
80.	35.	4 c. multicoloured	15	40
81.		10 c. multicoloured	35	10

36. Dancers in National Costume.

1963. South East Asia Cultural Festival.

No.	Type	Description	Unused	Used
82.	36.	5 c. multicoloured	15	20

37. Workers.

1966. 1st Anniv. of Republic.

No.	Type	Description	Unused	Used
89.	37.	15 c. multicoloured	40	30
90.		20 c. multicoloured	60	70
91.		30 c. multicoloured	80	95

38. Flag Procession.

1967. National Day.

No.	Type	Description	Unused	Used
92.	38.	6 c. red, brown & slate	20	40
93.		15 c. purple, brn. & slate	40	10
94.		50 c. blue, brown & slate	75	1·10

Nos. 92/4 are respectively inscr. "Build a Vigorous Singapore" in Chinese, Malay, and Tamil, in addition to the English inscr.

39. Skyscrapers and Afro-Asian Map.

1967. 2nd Afro-Asian Housing Congress.

No.	Type	Description	Unused	Used
95.	39.	10 c. multicoloured	25	10
96.		25 c. multicoloured	45	80
97.		50 c. multicoloured	70	1·40

40. Symbolical Figure wielding Hammer, and Industrial outline of Singapore.

45. Sword Dance.

43. Mirudhangam.

1968. National Day. Inscription at top in Chinese (6 c.), Malay (15 c.) or Tamil (50 c.).

No.	Type	Description	Unused	Used
98.	40.	6 c. red, black and gold	20	20
99.		15 c. green, black & gold	25	15
100.		50 c. blue, black & gold	65	60

1968.

No.	Type	Description	Unused	Used
101.	43.	1 c. multicoloured	15	1·50
102.	–	4 c. multicoloured	30	1·75
103.	45.	5 c. multicoloured	40	40
104.	–	6 c. blk., lemon & orge.	15	60
105.	–	10 c. multicoloured	10	10
106.	–	15 c. multicoloured	30	10
107.	–	20 c. multicoloured	15	20
108.	–	25 c. multicoloured	40	40
109.	–	30 c. multicoloured	30	40
110.	–	50 c. black, red & brown	50	40
111.	–	75 c. multicoloured	1·00	70
112.	–	$1 multicoloured	2·00	70
113.	–	$2 multicoloured	3·50	1·00
114.	–	$5 multicoloured	9·00	2·00
115.	–	$10 multicoloured	30·00	12·00

DESIGNS—As Type **43**—VERT. 4 c. Pi Pa. $2 Rebab. $10 Ta Ku. HORIZ. $5 Vina. As Type **45**—VERT. 6 c. Lion Dance. 10 c. Bharatha Natyam. 15 c. Tari Payong. 20 c. Kathak Kali. 25 c. Lu Chih Shen and Lin Chung. 50 c. Tari Lilin. 75 c. Tarian Kuda Kepang. $1, Yao Chi. HORIZ. 30 c. Dragon Dance.

58. E.C.A.F.E. Emblem.

1969. Plenary Session of Economic Commission for Asia and the Far East.

No.	Type	Description	Unused	Used
116.	58.	15 c. black, silver & blue	35	15
117.		30 c. black, silver & red	70	80
118.		75 c. black, silver & violet	1·25	1·50

59. "100000" and Slogan as Block of Flats.

60. Aircraft over Silhouette of Singapore Docks.

1969. Completion of "100,000 Homes for the People" Project.

No.	Type	Description	Unused	Used
119.	59.	25 c. black and green	70	50
120.		50 c. black and blue	90	1·00

1969. 150th Anniv. of Founding of Singapore.

No.	Type	Description	Unused	Used
121.	60.	15 c. black, red & yellow	1·25	30
122.	–	30 c. black and blue	1·75	75
123.	–	75 c. multicoloured	3·00	2·00
124.	–	$1 black and red	3·50	3·25
125.	–	$5 red and black	35·00	45·00
126.	–	$10 black and green	48·00	48·00

DESIGNS: 30 c. U.N. Emblem and outline of Singapore. 75 c. Flags and outline of Malaysian Federation. $1, Uplifted hands holding crescent and stars. $5, Tail of Japanese aircraft and searchlight beams. $10, Bust from statue of Sir Stamford Raffles.

61. Sea Shells.

1970. World Fair, Osaka. Multicoloured

No.		Description	Unused	Used
128.		15 c. Type **61**	90	15
129.		30 c. Tropical fish	1·75	90
130.		75 c. Greater Flamingo and Helmeted Horn-bill	4·75	3·75
131.		$1 Orchid	4·75	6·00

INDEX

Countries can be quickly located by referring to the index at the end of this volume.

62. "Kindergarten".

1970. 10th Anniv. of People's Assn.

133.	62.	15 c. agate and orange . .	50	15
134.	–	50 c. blue and orange . .	1·40	1·40
135.	–	75 c. purple and black . .	2·25	2·75

DESIGNS: 50 c. "Sport". 75 c. "Culture".

63. Soldier Charging.

1970. National Day. Multicoloured.

136.	15 c. Type 63	70	15
137.	50 c. Soldier on assault course	2·75	2·50
138.	$1 Soldier jumping . .	3·75	5·00

64. Sprinters.

1970. Festival of Sports.

139.	64.	10 c. mve., blk. and blue	90	1·25
140.	–	15 c. black and orange	1·25	1·60
141.	–	25 c. blk., orge. and grn.	1·40	1·75
142.	–	50 c. blk., grn. and mve.	1·50	2·00

DESIGNS: 15 c. Swimmers. 25 c. Tennis-players. 50 c. Racing-cars.

65. "Neptune Aquamarine" (freighter).

1970. Singapore Shipping.

143.	65.	15 c. multicoloured . .	1·10	55
144.	–	30 c. yellow and blue . .	3·25	3·75
145.	–	75 c. yellow and red . .	5·00	6·00

DESIGNS: 30 c. Container berth. 75 c. Ship-building.

66. Country Names in Circle.

1971. Commonwealth Heads of Government Meeting, Singapore. Multicoloured.

146.	15 c. Type 66	60	15
147.	30 c. Flags in Circle . .	1·10	65
148.	75 c. Commonwealth Flags	2·50	2·75
149.	$1 Commonwealth Flags linked to Singapore (63 × 61 mm.)	3·00	3·75

67. Bicycle Rickshaws.

DESIGNS—SQUARE: 20 c. Houseboat "Village" and boats. 30 c. Bazaar. HORIZ. (68 × 18 mm.): 50 c. Modern harbour Skyline. 75 c. Religious buildings.

1971. Tourism. ASEAN Year. (ASEAN = Association of South East Asian Nations).

150.	67.	15 c. black, violet & orge.	40	25
151.	–	20 c. indigo, orge. & blue	55	40
152.	–	30 c. red and purple . .	80	1·00
153.	–	50 c. multicoloured . .	2·75	4·50
154.	–	75 c. multicoloured . .	3·50	6·00

68. Chinese New Year.

1971. Singapore Festivals. Multicoloured.

155.	15 c. Type 68	70	15
156.	30 c. Hari Raya	2·00	2·00
157.	50 c. Deepavali	2·75	4·00
158.	75 c. Christmas	3·25	5·00

69. "Dish" Aerial.

1971. Opening of Satellite Earth Station.

160.	69.	15 c. multicoloured . .	2·75	75
161.	–	30 c. multicoloured . .	8·00	8·00
162.	–	30 c. multicoloured . .	8·00	8·00
163.	–	30 c. multicoloured . .	8·00	8·00
164.	–	30 c. multicoloured . .	8·00	8·00

DESIGNS: Nos. 161/4 were printed in se-tenant blocks of four throughout the sheet, the four stamps forming a composite design similar to Type 69. They can be identified by the colour of the face value which is: yellow (No. 161), green (No. 162), red (No. 163) or orange (No. 614).

70. "Singapore River and Fort Canning, 1843–7" (Lieut. E. A. Porcher). (Illustration reduced. Actual size 53 × 46 mm.)

1971. Art. Multicoloured.

165	10 c. Type 70	1·50	1·00
166	15 c. "The Padang, 1851" (J.T. Thomson) . .	2·25	1·75
167	20 c. "Singapore Water-front, 1848–9" . .	2·75	2·50
168	35 c. "View from Fort Canning, 1846" (J.T. Thomson) . .	5·50	4·75
169	50 c. "View from Mt. Wallich, 1857" (P. Carpenter)	8·00	8·00
170	$1 "Singapore Waterfront, 1861" (W. Gray) . .	11·00	14·00

The 50 c. and $1 are larger, 69 × 47 mm.

71. One Dollar of 1969.

1972. Coins.

171.	–	15 c. orange, blk. & grn.	45	15
172.	71.	35 c. black and red . .	1·00	1·25
173.	–	$1 yellow, black & blue	3·25	4·25

DESIGNS: 15 c. One-cent coin of George V. $1 One hundred and fifty dollar gold coin of 1969.

72. "Moon Festival" (Seah Kim Joo).

1972. Contemporary Art. Multicoloured.

174.	15 c. Type 72	40	20
175.	35 c. "Complimentary Forces" (Thomas Yeo)	1·25	1·50
176.	50 c. "Rhythm in Blue" (Yusman Aman) . .	2·00	2·25
177.	$1 "Gibbons" (Chen Wen Hsi)	3·75	4·75

Nos. 175/6 are 36 × 54 mm.

73. Lanterns and Fish.

1972. National Day. Designs symbolising Festivals. Multicoloured.

178.	15 c. Type 73 . .	45	15
179.	35 c. Altar and candles . .	1·00	1·25
180.	50 c. Jug, bowl and gifts	1·40	2·50
181.	75 c. Candle	2·25	4·00

74. Student Welding.

1972. Youth.

182.	74.	15 c. multicoloured . .	50	10
183.	–	35 c. multicoloured . .	1·00	1·50
184.	–	$1 orge., violet & green	3·00	5·50

DESIGNS: 35 c. Sport. $1, Dancing.

75. "Maria Rickmers".

1972. Shipping. Multicoloured.

185.	15 c. "Neptune Ruby" (container ship) (42 × 29 mm.)	70	40
186.	75 c. Type 75	3·75	4·75
187.	$1 Chinese junk	5·00	6·00

76. P.Q.R. Slogan.

1973. "Prosperity Through Quality and Reliability" Campaign. Multicoloured.

189.	15 c. Type 76	40	15
190.	35 c. Badge	85	75
191.	75 c. Text (diff.)	1·40	2·50
192.	$1 Seal	1·75	3·25

77. Jurong Bird Park.

1973. Singapore Landmarks.

193.	77.	15 c. black and orange	55	15
194.	–	35 c. black and green	1·00	1·00
195.	–	50 c. black and brown	2·00	2·50
196.	–	$1 black and purple . .	3·25	4·00

DESIGNS: 35 c. National Theatre. 50 c. City Hall. $1, Fullerton Building and Singapore River.

78. Aircraft Tail-fins.

1973. Aviation. Multicoloured.

197.	10 c. Type 78	25	10
198.	35 c. Emblems of Singapore Airlines and destinations	75	75
199.	75 c. Emblem on tail-fin . .	1·40	1·60
200.	$1 Emblems encircling the globe	2·00	2·25

79. "Culture".

1973. National Day.

201.	79.	10 c. orange and black	1·25	55
202.	–	35 c. orange and black	1·50	1·25
203.	–	50 c. orange and black	1·75	1·50
204.	–	75 c. orange and black	2·00	1·75

Nos. 201/204 were printed in se-tenant blocks of four within the sheet. and form a composite design representing Singapore's culture.

80. Athletics, Judo and Boxing.

1973. Seventh S.E.A.P.* Games.

205.	80.	10 c. gold, silver and blue	25	20
206.	–	15 c. gold and black . .	50	30
207.	–	25 c. gold, silver and blk.	65	65
208.	–	35 c. gold, silver and blue	1·10	90
209.	–	50 c. multicoloured . .	1·75	2·25
210.	–	$1 silver, blue and green	3·25	5·00

DESIGNS—As Type 80. 15 c. Cycling, weight-lifting, pistol-shooting and sailing. 25 c. Foot-balls. 35 c. Table-tennis bat, shuttlecock, tennis ball and hockey stick. HORIZ. (41 × 25 mm.). 50 c. Swimmers. $1, Stadium.

*S.E.A.P. = South East Asian Peninsular.

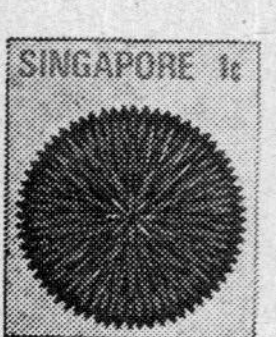

81. Agave. **82.** Mangosteen.

1973. Multicoloured.
(a) Flowers and plants as T **81.**

212. 1 c. Type **81** 20 40
213. 5 c. " Coleus blumei " .. 10 25
214. 10 c. " Vinca rosea " .. 15 10
215. 15 c. " Helianthus angustifolius " .. 15 10
216. 20 c. " Licuala grandis " .. 25 40
217. 25 c. " Wedelia trilobata " 30 30
218. 35 c. " Chrysanthemum frutescens " 50 55
219. 50 c. " Costus malortieanus " 75 30
220. 75 c. " Gerbera jamesonii " 1·75 70

(b) Fruits as T **82.**

221. $1 Type **82** .. .. 1·50 30
222. $2 Jackfruit .. .. 3·25 1·25
223. $5 Coconut .. .. 6·00 5·00
224. $10 Pineapple .. .. 12·00 5·00

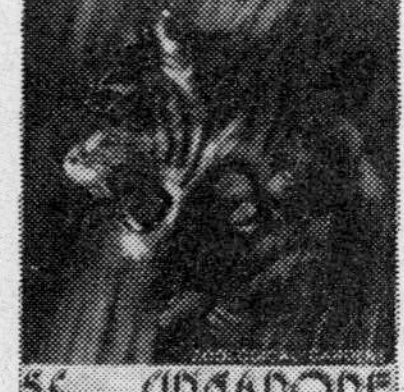

83. Tiger and Orang-Utans.

1973. Singapore Zoo. Multicoloured.

225. 5 c. Type **83** 25 10
226. 10 c. Leopard and Waterbuck 45 20
227. 35 c. Leopard and Thamin 1·75 1·75
228. 75 c. Horse and Lion .. 2·75 4·50

84. Multicolour Guppy. **86.** U.P.U. Emblem and Multiple "Centenary".

85. Scout Badge within "9".

1974. Tropical Fish. Multicoloured.

229. 5 c. Type **84** 20 10
230. 10 c. Half Black Guppy .. 40 15
231. 35 c. Multicolour Guppy (different) .. .. 1·10 1·40
232. $1 Black Guppy .. 2·75 4·00

1974. Ninth Asia-Pacific Scout Conference.

233. **85.** 10 c. multicoloured .. 40 10
234. 75 c. multicoloured .. 1·60 1·40

1974. Centenary of U.P.U.

235. **86.** 10 c. brn., pur. & gold .. 20 10
236. – 35 c. bl., dark bl. & gold 55 75
237. – 75 c. multicoloured .. 1·25 2·50

DESIGNS: 35 c. U.P.U. emblem and multiple U.N. symbols. 75 c. U.P.U. emblem and multiple peace doves.

87. Family Emblem.

1974. World Population Year. Multicoloured.

238. 10 c. Type **87** 20 10
239. 35 c. Male and female symbols 80 1·00
240. 75 c. World Population Map 1·75 3·00

88. "Tree and Sun" (Chia Keng San).

1974. Universal Children's Day. Mult.

241. 5 c. Type **88** 20 10
242. 10 c. "My Daddy and Mummy" (Angeline Ang) 35 10
243. 35 c. "A Dump Truck" (Si-Hoe Yeen Joong) .. 1·75 2·25
244. 50 c. "My Aunt" (Raymond Teo) .. .. .. 2·25 3·25

89. Street Scene.

1975. Singapore Views. Multicoloured.

246. 15 c. Type **89** 45 10
247. 20 c. Singapore River .. 60 70
248. $1 "Kelong" (fish-trap) .. 2·75 5·50

90. Emblem and Lighters' Prows.

1975. 9th Biennial Conference of Int., Association of Ports and Harbours, Singapore. Multicoloured.

249. 5 c. Type **90** 15 10
250. 25 c. Freighter and ship's wheel 70 80
251. 50 c. Oil-tanker and flags .. 1·40 2·00
252. $1 Container-ship and propellers .. .. 2·25 4·25

91. Satellite Earth Station, Sentosa.

1975. "Science and Industry". Mult.

253. 10 c. Type **91** 25 10
254. 35 c. Oil refineries (vert.) .. 75 1·00
255. 75 c. " Medical Sciences " 1·50 2·75

92. " Homes and Gardens".

1975. 10th National Day. Multicoloured.

256. 10 c. Type **92** 20 10
257. 35 c. " Shipping and Ship-building " 75 75
258. 75 c. " Communications and Technology " .. 1·90 3·00
259. $1 " Trade, Commerce and Industry " .. 2·10 3·50

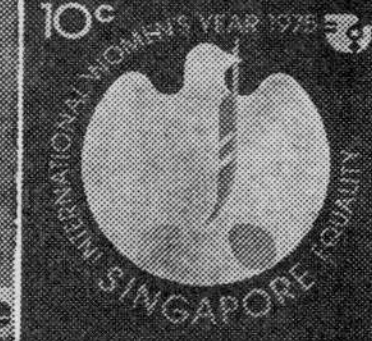

93. South African Crowned Cranes. **94.** " Equality ".

1975. Birds. Multicoloured.

260. 5 c. Type **93** .. .. 1·00 20
261. 10 c. Great Indian Hornbill 1·50 10
262. 35 c. White-breasted Kingfishers and White-collared Kingfisher .. .. 4·00 3·00
263. $1 Sulphur-crested Cockatoo, and Blue and Yellow Macaw .. .. 10·00 12·00

1975. International Women's Year. **Mult.**

264. 10 c. Type **94** 25 10
265. 35 c. " Development " .. 1·50 1·50
266. 75 c. " Peace " .. .. 2·75 4·50

95. Yellow Flame. **96.** " Arachnis hookeriana x Vanda " Hilo Blue.

1976. Wayside Trees. Multicoloured.

268. 10 c. Type **95** 50 10
269. 35 c. Cabbage Tree .. 1·25 1·00
270. 50 c. Rose of India .. 2·00 2·50
271. 75 c. Variegated Coral Tree 2·25 4·00

1976. Singapore Orchids. Multicoloured.

272. 10 c. Type **96** 70 10
273. 35 c. " Arachnis Maggie Oei x Vanda insignis " .. 1·75 1·10
274. 50 c. " Arachnis Maggei Oei x Vanda " Rodman .. 3·00 3·25
275. 75 c. " Arachnis hookeriana x Vanda " Dawn Nishimura .. .. .. 3·25 5·50

97. Festival Symbol and Band.

1976. 10th Anniv. of Singapore Youth Festival. Multicoloured.

276. 10 c. Type **97** 20 10
277. 35 c. Athletes 60 60
278. 75 c. Dancers .. .. 1·40 1·40

98. " Queen Elizabeth Walk ".

1976. Paintings of Old Singapore. Mult.

279. 10 c. Type **98** 30 10
280. 50 c. " The Padang " .. 1·75 1·75
281. $1 " Raffles Place " .. 3·25 3·50

99. Chinese Costume.

1976. Bridal Costumes. Multicoloured.

283. 10 c. Type **99** 25 10
284. 35 c. Indian costume .. 1·00 1·00
285. 75 c. Malay costume .. 1·75 2·00

100. Radar, Missile and Soldiers.

1977. 10th Anniv. of National Service. Multicoloured.

286. 10 c. Type **100** 30 10
287. 50 c. Tank and soldiers .. 1·25 90
288. 75 c. Soldiers, wireless operators, pilot and aircraft 2·00 1·75

101. Lyrate Cockle. **102.** Spotted Hermit Crab.

1977. Multicoloured.
(a) Shells as T **101.**

289. 1 c. Type **101** 30 60
290. 5 c. Folded Scallop .. 20 10
291. 10 c. Marble cone .. 20 10
292. 15 c. Scorpion Conch .. 45 10
293. 20 c. Amplustre Bubble .. 70 10
294. 25 c. Spiral Babylon .. 80 30
295. 35 c. Regal Thorny Oyster 1·00 70
296. 50 c. Winged Frog Shell .. 1·25 10
297. 75 c. Troschel's Murex .. 2·00 20

(b) Fish and Crustaceans as T **102.**

298. $1 Type **102** .. .. 1·75 15
299. $2 Stingray .. .. 1·75 50
300. $5 Cuttlefish .. .. 4·00 2·25
301. $10 Lionfish .. .. 7·50 5·50

103. Shipbuilding.

1977. Labour Day. Multicoloured.

302. 10 c. Type **103** 15 10
303. 50 c. Building construction 75 60
304. 75 c. Road construction .. 1·00 1·00

104. Keyhole and Banknotes. **105.** Flags of Member Nations.

1977. Centenary of Post Office Savings Bank. Multicoloured.

305. 10 c. Type **104** 15 10
306. 35 c. On-line banking service 75 50
307. 75 c. GIRO service .. 1·50 1·25

1977. 10th Anniv. of ASEAN (Assn. of South-East Asian Nations). Multicoloured.

308. 10 c. Type **105** 15 10
309. 35 c. " Agriculture " .. 60 50
310. 75 c. " Industry " .. 1·25 1·10

106. " Chingay Procession " (Liang Yik Yin).

1977. Children's Art. Multicoloured.

311.	10 c. Type **106**	20	10
312.	35 c. " At the Bus Stop " (Chong Khing Ann) (horiz.)	75	50
313.	75 c. " Playground " (Yap Li Hwa) (horiz.) ..	1·60	1·40

107. " Life Sciences ".

1977. Singapore Science Centre. Mult.

315.	10 c. Type **107**	10	10
316.	35 c. " Physical sciences "	45	30
317.	75 c. " Science and technology "	1·00	85
318.	$1 Singapore Science Centre	1·25	1·00

108. Botanical Gardens and Esplanade, Jurong Bird Park.

1978. Park and Gardens. Multicoloured.

319.	10 c. Type **108**	15	10
320.	35 c. Lagoon, East Coast Park (vert.) ..	45	35
321.	75 c. Botanical Gardens (vert.)	75	75

109. Red-whiskered Bulbul.

1978. Singing Birds. Multicoloured.

322.	10 c. Type **109**	35	10
323.	35 c. Oriental white eye ..	85	45
324.	50 c. White-rumped shama	1·10	85
325.	75 c. White-crested laughing thrush and hwamei	1·50	1·60

110. Thian Hock Keng Temple.

1978. National Monuments. Multicoloured.

326.	10 c. Type **110**	20	20
327.	10 c. Hajjah Fatimah Mosque	20	20
328.	10 c. Armenian Church ..	20	20
329.	10 c. Sri Mariamman Temple	20	20

111. Map of South East Asia showing Cable Network.

1978. A.S.E.A.N. Submarine Cable (1st issue). Philippines–Singapore Section.

331. **111.**	10 c. multicoloured ..	10	10
332.	35 c. multicoloured ..	40	40
333.	50 c. multicoloured ..	50	50
334.	75 c. multicoloured ..	80	1·00

See also Nos. 385/8 and 458/61.

112. "Neptune Spinel" (bulk carrier).

1978. 10th Anniv. of Neptune Orient Shipping Lines. Multicoloured.

335	10 c. Type **112**	15	10
336	35 c. "Neptune Aries" (tanker)	40	50
337	50 c. "Anro Temasek" (container ship) ..	45	75
338	75 c. "Neptune Pearl" (container ship) ..	80	1·40

113. " Concorde ".

1978. Aviation. Multicoloured.

339.	10 c. Type **113**	35	15
340.	35 c. Boeing " 747B " ..	50	30
341.	50 c. Vickers " Vimy " ..	70	90
342.	75 c. Wright Brothers' " Flyer 1 "	80	1·75

114. 10-Kilometre Marker.

1979. Metrication. Multicoloured.

343.	10 c. Type **114**	10	10
344.	35 c. Tape measure ..	20	20
345.	75 c. Weighing scales ..	45	45

115. Vanda Hybrid.

1979. Orchids.

346. **115.**	10 c. multicoloured ..	15	10
347. –	35 c. multicoloured ..	35	20
348. –	50 c. multicoloured ..	50	30
349. –	75 c. multicoloured ..	70	45

DESIGNS—HORIZ. 35 c. VERT. 50, 75 c. Different varieties of Vanda Hybrid.

116. Envelope with new Singapore Postcode.

1979. Postal Code Publicity.

350. **116.**	10 c. multicoloured ..	10	10
351. –	50 c. multicoloured ..	30	35

The 50 c. design is as Type **116**, but the envelope is addressed to the Philatelic Bureau, General Post Office and has the postcode " Singapore 0104 ".

117. Early Telephone and Overhead Cables.

1979. Centenary of Telephone Service.

352. **117.**	10 c. brown and blue ..	10	10
353. –	35 c. orange and violet	20	25
354. –	50 c. blue, turq. & grn.	35	40
355. –	75 c. green and orange ..	50	80

DESIGNS: 35 c. Telephone dial and world map. 50 c. Modern telephone and city scene. 75 c. Latest computerised telephone and circuit diagram.

118. " Lantern Festival " (Eng Chun-Ngan).

1979. International Year of the Child. Children's Drawings. Multicoloured.

356.	10 c. Type **118**	10	10
357.	35 c. " Singapore Harbour " (Wong Chien Chien) ..	30	30
358.	50 c. " Use Your Hands " (Leong Choy Yeen) ..	40	45
359.	75 c. " Soccer " (Tan Cheong Hin)	60	75

119. View of Gardens.

1979. 120th Anniv. of Botanic Gardens.

361. **119.**	10 c. multicoloured ..	15	10
362. –	50 c. multicoloured ..	60	75
363. –	$1 multicoloured ..	1·10	2·00

DESIGNS: 50 c., $1, Different views of Botanic Gardens.

120. Hainan Junk.

1980. Ships. Multicoloured.

364.	1 c. Type **120**	30	60
365.	5 c. Clipper	10	35
366.	10 c. Fujian junk	10	10
367.	15 c. Golekkan	15	15
368.	20 c. Palari schooner ..	20	30
369.	25 c. East Indiaman ..	25	30
370.	35 c. Galleon	30	30
371.	50 c. Caravel	50	30
372.	75 c. Jiangsu trading junk	65	65
373.	$1 "Keduh" (coaster) ..	70	45
374.	$2 "Murex" (oil tanker) ..	1·25	90
375.	$5 "Chusan" screw steamer)	3·00	3·00
376.	$10 "Braganza" (paddle-steamer)	6·00	6·00

Nos. 373/6 are 42 × 25 mm.

121. Straits Settlements 1867 1½ c. Stamp and Map of Singapore, 1843.

1980. " London 1980 " International Stamp Exhibition. Multicoloured.

377.	10 c. Type **121** ..	20	10
378.	35 c. Straits Settlements 1906 $500 stamp and treaty between Johore and British Colony of Singapore	35	25
379.	$1 1948 $2 stamp and map of Malaysia	70	90
380.	$2 1969 150th Anniv. of Singapore $10 commemorative and letter to Col. Addenbrooke from Sir Stamford Raffles ..	1·25	2·00

HAVE YOU READ THE NOTES AT THE BEGINNING OF THIS CATALOGUE?

These often provide answers to the enquiries we receive.

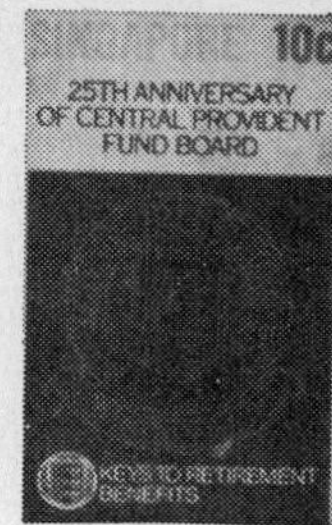

122. C.P.F. Emblem and " Keys to Retirement Benefits ".

1980. 25th Anniv. of Central Provident Fund Board. Multicoloured.

382.	10 c. Type **122**	10	10
383.	50 c. "C.P.F. savings for home ownership" ..	40	30
384.	$1 " C.P.F. savings for old-age "	75	80

123. Map of South East Asia showing Cable Network.

1980. A.S.E.A.N. (Association of South-East Asian Nations) Submarine Cable Network (2nd issue). Completion of Indonesia—Singapore Section.

385. **123.**	10 c. multicoloured ..	10	10
386.	35 c. multicoloured ..	40	25
387.	50 c. multicoloured ..	50	40
388.	75 c. multicoloured ..	65	1·00

124. A.S.E.A.N. Trade Fair Emblem.

1980. A.S.E.A.N. (Association of South-East Asian Nations) Trade Fair.

389. **124.**	10 c. multicoloured ..	10	10
390.	35 c. multicoloured ..	30	20
391.	75 c. multicoloured ..	60	80

125. Ixora.

1980. National Tree Planting Day. Flowers. Multicoloured.

392.	10 c. Type **125**	10	10
393.	35 c. Allamanda	40	25
394.	50 c. Sky Vine	50	40
395.	75 c. Bougainvillea ..	60	75

126. International Currency Symbols.

1981. 10th Anniv. of Singapore Monetary Authority.

396. **126.**	10 c. blk., red & yell..	10	10
397.	35 c. multicoloured ..	30	20
398.	75 c. multicoloured ..	55	60

1981. No. 65 surch. **10 CENTS.**

399	10 c. on 4 c. black and red	15	30

128. Woodwork.

1981. Technical Training. Multicoloured.
400. 10 c. Type **128** 10 10
401. 35 c. Building construction 25 20
402. 50 c. Electronics 40 30
403. 75 c. Precision machining 50 60

singapore 10¢
International Year of Disabled Persons
The Right to Environmental Aids

129. Figures representing various Sports. 130. " The Right to Environmental Aids ".

1981. " Sports for All ".
404. **129.** 10 c. multicoloured .. 15 10
405. – 75 c. multicoloured .. 1·40 1·60
406. – $1 multicoloured .. 1·60 2·25
DESIGNS: 75 c. and $1 Figures representing different sports.

1981. International Year for Disabled Persons. Multicoloured.
407. 10 c. Type **130**. 10 10
408. 35 c. " The right to social integration " 40 20
409. 50 c. " The right to education " 60 35
410. 75 c. " The right to work " 80 70

131. Control Tower and Passenger Terminal Building, Changi Airport.

1981. Opening of Changi Airport.
411. **131.** 10 c. multicoloured .. 10 10
412. 35 c. multicoloured .. 35 20
413. 50 c. multicoloured .. 45 30
414. 75 c. multicoloured .. 70 65
415. $1 multicoloured .. 80 1·00
The background emblem differs for each value.

132. "Parthenos sylvia".

1982. Butterflies. Multicoloured.
417 10 c. Type **132** 15 10
418 50 c. "Danaus vulgaris" .. 60 40
419 $1 "Trogonoptera brookiana" .. .. 90 1·25

133. A.S.E.A.N. Emblem.

1982. 15th Anniv. of A.S.E.A.N. (Association of South-East Asian Nations).
420. **133.** 10 c. multicoloured .. 10 10
421. – 35 c. multicoloured .. 25 30
422. 50 c. multicoloured .. 35 40
423. – 75 c. multicoloured .. 50 75
The 50 and 75 c. values are as Type **133** but inscribed "15th ASEAN Ministerial Meeting".

134. Football and Stylised Player.

1982. World Cup Football Championship, Spain.
424. **134.** 10 c. black, bright blue and blue 20 10
425. – 75 c. multicoloured .. 75 1·00
426. – $1 multicoloured .. 95 1·40
DESIGNS: 75 c. Football and World Cup, Asian Four emblem. $1 Football and globe.

135. Sultan Shoal Lighthouse, 1896.

1982. Lighthouses of Singapore. Mult.
427. 10 c. Type **135** 10 10
428. 75 c. Horsburgh Lighthouse, 1855 .. .. 55 1·00
429. $1 Raffles Lighthouse, 1855 .. .. .. 75 1·40

136. Yard Gantry Cranes.

1982. 10th Anniv. of Container Terminal. Multicoloured.
431. 10 c. Type **136** 10 10
432. 35 c. Computer 20 25
433. 50 c. Freightlifter .. 30 30
434. 75 c. Straddle carrier .. 45 50

137. Scouts on Parade.

1982. 75th Anniv. of Boy Scout Movement. Multicoloured.
435. 10 c. Type **137** 15 10
436. 35 c. Scouts hiking .. 45 25
437. 50 c. Scouts building tower 65 35
438. 75 c. Scouts canoeing .. 95 80

138. Productivity Movement Slogans.

1983. Productivity Movement.
439. **138.** 10 c. orange and green 10 10
440. – 35 c. brown and blue .. 35 30
441. – 50 c. red, yellow & grey 55 55
442. – 75 c. red and yellow .. 75 75
DESIGNS: 35 c. Family and housing (" Benefits of Productivity "). 50 c. Works meeting (" Quality Control Circles "). 75 c. Aspects of Singapore business (" Everybody's Business ").

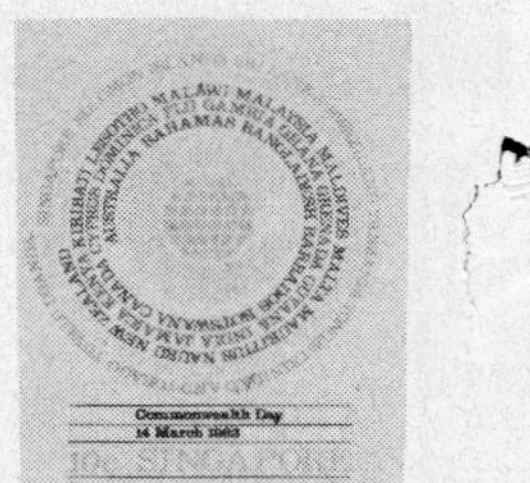

139. Commonwealth Logo and Country Names.

1983. Commonwealth Day.
443. **139.** 10 c. multicoloured .. 10 10
444. 35 c. multicoloured .. 20 25
445. 75 c. multicoloured .. 45 60
446. $1 multicoloured .. 65 80

140. Soccer.

1983. 12th South-East Asia Games. Mult.
447. 10 c. Type **140** 10 10
448. 35 c. Racket games .. 20 25
449. 75 c. Athletics 45 50
450. $1 Swimming 65 70

141. Policeman and Family.

1983. Neighbourhood Watch Scheme. Mult.
451. 10 c. Type **141** 15 10
452. 35 c. Policeman and children 45 30
453. 75 c. Policeman and inhabitants with linked arms .. 80 70

142. 1977 A.S.E.A.N. Stamps and Statue of King Chulalongkorn.

1983. Bangkok International Stamp Exn. Multicoloured.
454. 10 c. Type **142** 10 10
455. 35 c. 1980 A.S.E.A.N. stamps and map of south-east Asia 25 35
456. $1 1982 A.S.E.A.N. stamps and signatures of Heads of State .. .. .. 65 1·10

143. Map of South-East Asia showing Cable Network.

1983. A.S.E.A.N. (Association of South-East Asian Nations) Submarine Cable Network (3rd issue). Completion of Malaysia–Singapore–Thailand section.
458. **143.** 10 c. multicoloured .. 10 10
459. 35 c. multicoloured .. 20 25
460. 50 c. multicoloured .. 35 35
461. 75 c. multicoloured .. 45 50

144. Teletex Service
(Illustration reduced, actual size 74 × 24 mm.).

1983. World Communications Year.
463. **144.** 10 c. yell., grn. & blk. 10 10
464. – 35 c. yellow, red & brn. 20 30
465. – 75 c. grn., bl. & dp. bl. 45 65
466. – $1 yellow, brn. & blk. 50 85
DESIGNS: 35 c. World telephone numbering plan. 75 c. Satellite transmission. $1 Sea communications.

145. Blue-breasted Banded Rail.

1984. Coastal Birds. Multicoloured.
467. 10 c. Type **145** 30 10
468. 35 c. Black bittern .. 70 40
469. 50 c. Brahminy kite .. 85 70
470. 75 c. Moorhen .. .. 1·10 1·50

146. House of Tan Yeok Nee.

1984. National Monuments. Multicoloured.
471. 10 c. Type **146** 10 10
472. 35 c. Thong Chai building 30 35
473. 50 c. Telok Ayer market .. 40 50
474. $1 Nagore Durgha shrine 80 1·25

147. 1970 $1 National Day Stamp.

1984. "25 Years of Nation Building". Multicoloured.
475. 10 c. Type **147** 10 10
476. 35 c. 1981 $1 "Sports for All" stamp 30 35
477. 50 c. 1969 25 c. "100,000 Homes for the People" stamp 40 55
478. 75 c. 1976 10 c. Wayside Trees stamp 60 75
479. $1 1981 $1 Opening of Changi Airport stamp .. 80 1·00
480. $2 1981 10 c. Monetary Authority stamp .. 1·75 2·75

148. School children.

1984. "Total Defence".

482. **148.** 10 c. brown and red .. 10 15
483. – 10 c. brn., olive & bl. 10 15
484. – 10 c. brown, violet and salmon .. 10 15
485. – 10 c. brown, light brown and mauve 10 15
486. – 10 c. brn., yell. & olive 10 15

DESIGNS: No. 483, People of Singapore. 484, Industrial workers. 485, Civil Defence first aid worker. 486, Anti-aircraft gun crew.

149. Coleman Bridge.

1985. Bridges of Singapore.

487. 10 c. black (Type **149**) .. 15 10
488. 35 c. blk. (Cavenagh Bridge) 30 30
489. 75 c. black (Elgin Bridge) 55 55
490. $1 black (Benjamin Sheares Bridge) 70 70

150. "Ceriagrion cerinorubellum" (damselfly).

1985. Insects. Multicoloured.

5 c. Type **150** 25 10
10 c. "Apis javana" (bee) 30 10
15 c. "Delta arcuata" (wasp) 35 10
20 c. "Xylocopa caerulea" (bee) 40 10
495 25 c. "Donacia javana" (water beetle) .. 40 20
496 35 c. "Heteroneda reticulata" (ladybird) .. 50 25
497 50 c. "Catacanthus nigripes" (bug) .. 70 35
498 75 c. "Chremistica pontianaka" (cicadu) .. 80 45
499 $1 "Homoexipha lycoides" (cricket) .. .. 1·00 60
500 $2 "Traulia azureipennis" (grasshopper) .. .. 1·50 1·25
501 $5 "Trithemis aurora" (dragonfly) .. .. 2·75 3·00
502 $10 "Scambophyllum sanguinolentum" (grasshopper) .. .. 5·75 6·00

Nos. 499/502 are larger, 35 × 30 mm.

151. Tennis, canoeing, Judo and Children Playing (Illustration reduced, actual size 50 × 20 mm.)

1985. 25th Anniv. of People's Association. Multicoloured.

503. 10 c. Type **151** 15 10
504. 35 c. Lion dance, martial arts and athletes with flags 30 30
505. 50 c. Tae-kwon-do, Indian dance and Dragon dance 40 40
506. 75 c. Boxing, table tennis, basketball and dancing 55 55

152. Modern Housing Estate and Squatter Settlement (Illustration reduced, actual size 50 × 20 mm.)

1985. 25th Anniv. of Housing and Development Board. Designs show different aspects of housing at left. Multicoloured.

507. 10 c. Type **152** 15 10
508. 35 c. Singapore family (Home-ownership) .. 30 30
509. 50 c. Group of residents (Community development) 40 40
510. 75 c. Construction workers (Building technology) .. 55 55

153. Brownies.

1985. 75th Anniv. of Girl Guide Movement. Multicoloured.

512. 10 c. Type **153** 10 10
513. 35 c. Guides practising first aid 30 30
514. 50 c. Senior Branch .. 40 40
515. 75 c. Adult leaders and guides 55 55

154. Badges and Emblems of Singapore Youth Organizations.

1985. International Youth Year. Mult.

516. 10 c. Type **154** .. 10 10
517. 75 c. Hand protecting sapling 50 55
518. $1 Stylised figures and dove 65 70

155. Guava.

1986. Singapore Fruits. Multicoloured.

519. 10 c. Type **155** 10 10
520. 35 c. Jambu Air 25 30
521. 50 c. Rambutan 30 35
522. 75 c. Ciku 50 55

156. Laboratory Technician and Salesmen with Bar Graph.

1986. 25th Anniv. of National Trades Union Congress. Multicoloured.

523. 10 c. Type **156** 20 20
524. 10 c. Computer operator and welder 20 20
525. 10 c. Draughtsmen and surveyors 20 20
526. 10 c. Group of workers .. 20 20

157. Calligraphy.

1986. "Expo '86" World Fair, Vancouver. Multicoloured.

528. 50 c. Type **157** 45 55
529. 75 c. Garland maker .. 60 75
530. $1 Batik printer 75 95

158. Industrial Automation.

1986. 25th Anniv. of Economic Development Board. Multicoloured.

531. 10 c. Type **158** 10 10
532. 35 c. Manufacture of aircraft components .. 25 30
533. 50 c. Electronics industry 30 40
534. 75 c. Biotechnology industry 50 70

159. Map showing Route of Cable and "Vercors" (cable ship).

1986. SEA-ME-WE Submarine Cable Project.

535. **159.** 10 c. multicoloured .. 15 10
536. 35 c. multicoloured .. 35 30
537. 50 c. multicoloured .. 45 45
538. 75 c. multicoloured .. 65 75

160. Stylized Citizens.

1986. 21st Anniv. of Citizens' Consultative Committees.

539. **160.** 10 c. multicoloured .. 20 20
540. – 35 c. multicoloured .. 35 35
541. – 50 c. multicoloured .. 40 40
542. – 75 c. multicoloured .. 60 60

DESIGNS: 35 c. to 75 c. Citizens.

Nos. 539/42 were printed together, se-tenant, forming a composite design.

161. Peace Doves and People of Different Races.

1986. International Peace Year. Mult.

543. 10 c. Type **161** 10 10
544. 35 c. Doves and map of ASEAN countries .. 25 25
545. $1 Doves and globe .. 60 60

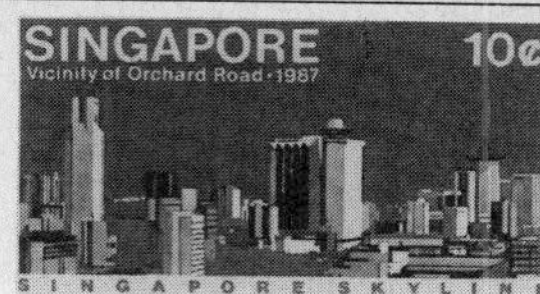

162. Orchard Road.

1987. Singapore Skyline. Multicoloured.

546. 10 c. Type **162** 15 10
547. 50 c. Central Business District 40 30
548. 75 c. Marina Centre and Raffles City 60 45

163. Flags of Members Nations and Logo.

164. Soldier with Rocket Launcher and Tank.

1987. 20th Anniv. of Association of South-east Asian Nations.

549. **163.** 10 c. multicoloured .. 10 10
550. 35 c. multicoloured .. 25 25
551. 50 c. multicoloured .. 30 30
552. 75 c. multicoloured .. 45 45

1987. 20th Anniv. of National Service. Multicoloured.

553. 10 c. Type **164** 20 25
554. 10 c. Radar operator and patrol boat 20 25
555. 10 c. Fighter pilot and aircraft 20 25
556. 10 c. Servicemen pledging allegiance 20 25

165. Singapore River and Dragon Boats.

1987. River Conservation. Multicoloured.

558. 10 c. Type **165** 10 10
559. 50 c. Kallang Basin, canoe and fishing punt .. 35 30
560. $1 Kranji Reservoir, athletes and cyclist .. 70 60

166. Majapahit Gold Bracelet and Museum.

1987. Centenary of National Museum. Each showing different drawings of Museum. Multicoloured.

561. 10 c. Type **166** 10 10
562. 75 c. Ming fluted kendi (water vessel) 40 45
563. $1 Patani hulu pekakak keris (sword) 55 60

167. Omni-theatre.

1987. 10th Anniv. of Singapore Science Centre. Multicoloured.

564. 10 c. Type **167** 10 10
565. 35 c. Omni-planetarium .. 30 25
566. 75 c. Model of body cell .. 50 45
567. $1 Physical sciences exhibits 70 60

168 Modern Anti-aircraft Gun

1988. Cent of Singapore Artillery. Mult.

568 10 c. Type **168** 25 10
569 35 c. 25-pounder field gun firing salute 55 30
570 50 c. Gunner and 12-pounder gun, c. 1920 .. 80 45
571 $1 Gunner and Maxim gun, 1889 .. .. .. 1·25 75

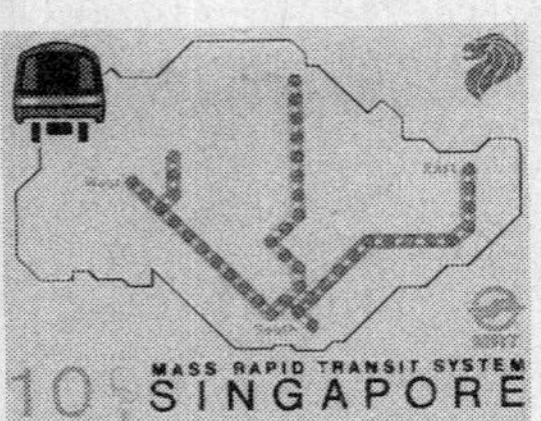

169 Route Map

1988. Singapore Mass Rapid Transit System. Multicoloured.

572 10 c. Type **169** 15 10
573 50 c. Train on elevated section 45 35
574 $1 Train in tunnel .. 80 60

170 Camera, Film and Outside Broadcast Van

1988. 25th Anniv of Television in Singapore. Multicoloured.

575 10 c. Type **170** 10 10
576 35 c. Camera, studio lights and microphone .. 20 25
577 75 c. Television set and transmitter 40 45
578 $1 Globe on TV screen and dish aerial 55 60

171 Water Droplet and Blocks of Flats

1988. 25th Anniv of Public Utilities Board. Multicoloured.

579 10 c. Type **171** 10 10
580 50 c. Electric light bulb and city centre .. 35 35
581 $1 Gas flame and factories 65 65

172 Greeting Neighbours

1988. 10th Anniv of National Courtesy Campaign. Each showing campaign mascot "Singa". Multicoloured.

583 10 c. Type **172** 10 10
584 30 c. Queueing at checkout 15 20
585 $1 Helping the elderly .. 55 60

173 Modern 30 Metre Turntable Fire Appliance

1988. Centenary of Fire Service. Mult.

586 10 c. Type **173** 20 10
587 $1 Steam fire engine, c. 1890 .. .. .. 1·25 75

174 Container Ships and Warehouses

1989. 25th Anniv of Singapore Port Authority. Multicoloured.

588 10 c. Type **174** 15 10
589 30 c. Shipping and oil storage depot 30 30
590 75 c. Container ships and Singapore skyline .. 70 75
591 $1 Container port at night 80 90

175 "Sago Street"

1989. Paintings of Chinatown by Choo Keng Kwang. Multicoloured.

592 10 c. Type **175** 15 10
593 35 c. "Pagoda Street" .. 40 40
594 75 c. "Trengganu Street" 90 90
595 $1 "Temple Street" .. 1·00 1·00

176 North-west Singapore City, 1920

1989. Maps of Singapore. Multicoloured.

596 15 c. Type **176** (top left) .. 20 20
597 15 c. North-east Singapore (top right) 20 20
598 15 c. South-west Singapore (bottom left) 20 20
599 15 c. South-east Singapore (bottom right) 20 20
600 50 c. Singapore Island and Dependencies, 1860's .. 65 65
601 $1 British Settlement of Singapore, 1820's .. 1·10 1·10

Nos. 596/9 were printed together, se-tenant, forming a composite design. Individual stamps can be identified by the position of the lion emblem which is quoted in brackets.

177 Clown Triggerfish

1989. Fishes. Multicoloured.

602 15 c. Type **177** 30 10
603 30 c. Majestic angelfish .. 60 40
604 75 c. Emperor angelfish .. 1·40 90
605 $1 Royal empress angelfish .. .. .. 1·60 1·10

178 "Hari Raya Puasa" (Loke Yoke Yun)

1989. Festivals of Singapore. Children's Drawings. Multicoloured.

606 15 c. Type **178** 15 10
607 35 c. "Chinese New Year" (Simon Koh) 30 30
608 75 c. "Thaipusam" (Henry Setiono) 70 70
609 $1 "Christmas" (Wendy Ang Lin Min) .. .. 90 1·00

179 North Entrance of Stadium

1989. Opening of Singapore Indoor Stadium. Multicoloured.

611 30 c. Type **179** 40 25
612 75 c. Arena 80 65
613 $1 East entrance .. 1·10 90

180 "Singapore River, 1839" (Louis le Breton)

1990. Lithographs of 19th-century Singapore. Multicoloured.

615 15 c. Type **180** 15 10
616 30 c. "Chinatown, 1837" (Barthelemy Lauvergne) 30 30
617 75 c. "Singapore Harbour, 1837" (Barthelemy Lauvergne) .. 70 70
618 $1 "View from the French Resident's House, 1824" (Deroy) 85 90

181 1969 150th Anniv of Singapore Stamp Issue

1990. 150th Anniv of the Penny Black. Mult.

619 50 c. Type **181** 55 40
620 75 c. Indian stamps, including bisect, used from Singapore in 1859 80 70
621 $1 Indian stamps used from Singapore in 1854 1·25 90
622 $2 Penny Black and Two Pence Blue .. .. 2·00 2·00

182 Zoological Gardens

183 Chinese Opera Singer and Siong Lim Temple

1990. Tourism. Multicoloured.

(a) As T **182**

624 5 c. Type **182** 10 10
625 15 c. Sentosa Island .. 10 10
626 20 c. Singapore River .. 15 20
627 25 c. Dragon Boat Festival 15 20
628 30 c. Raffles Hotel .. 20 25
629 35 c. Coffee shop bird singing contest .. 25 30
630 40 c. Jurong Bird Park .. 30 35
631 50 c. Chinese New Year boat float 35 40
632 75 c. Peranakan Place .. 50 55

(b) As T **183**

633 $1 Type **183** .. 70 75
634 $2 Malay dancer and Sultan Mosque .. .. 1·40 1·50
635 $5 Indian dancer and Sri Mariamman Temple .. 3·50 3·75
636 $10 Ballet dancer and Victoria Memorial Hall 7·00 7·25

184 Armed Forces Personnel

1990. 25th Anniv of Independence. Mult.

637 15 c. Type **184** 20 15
638 35 c. Inhabitants of Singapore 40 40
639 75 c. Workers and technological achievements 80 80
640 $1 Cultural activities .. 1·00 1·00

185 Stag's Horn Fern

1990. Ferns. Multicoloured.

641 15 c. Type **185** 15 10
642 35 c. Maiden Hair fern .. 35 35
643 75 c. Bird's Nest fern .. 70 70
644 $1 Rabbit's Foot fern .. 90 90

186 Carved Dragon Pillar, Hong San See Temple

1991. National Monuments. Multicoloured.

No.	Description		
645	20 c. Type **186**	25	25
646	20 c. Hong San See Temple (40 × 25 mm)	25	25
647	50 c. Interior of dome, Abdul Gaffoor Mosque	45	45
648	50 c. Abdul Gaffoor Mosque (40 × 25 mm) ..	45	45
649	75 c. Statue of Vishnu, Sri Perumal Hindu Temple	65	65
650	75 c. Sri Perumal Temple (40 × 25 mm)	65	65
651	$1 Stained glass window, St. Andrew's Cathedral	80	80
652	$1 St. Andrew's Cathedral (40 × 25 mm)	80	80

187 "Vanda Miss Joaquim"

1991. "Singapore '95" International Stamp Exhibition. Orchids (1st issue). Mult.

No.	Description		
653	$2 Type **187**	1·90	1·90
654	$2 "Dendrobium anocha" ..	1·90	1·90

See also Nos. 674/5.

188 Changi Airport Terminal II, 1991, and "B747-400"

1991. Singapore Civil Aviation. Mult.

No.	Description		
656	20 c. Type **188**	25	20
657	75 c. Changi Airport Terminal I, 1981, and "B747-200"	75	75
658	$1 Paya Lebar Airport, 1955–1981, and "Concorde"	95	95
659	$2 Kallang Airport, 1937–1955, and "DC-2"	1·75	1·40

189 "Arachnopsis Eric Holttum"

1991. Orchid Dress Motifs. Multicoloured.

No.	Description		
660	20 c. Type **189** ..	25	20
661	30 c. "Cattleya meadii" ..	35	30
662	$1 "Calanthe vestita" ..	75	75

INDEX

Countries can be quickly located by referring to the index at the end of this volume.

190 Long-Tailed Tailorbird

1991. Garden Birds. Multicoloured.

No.	Description		
663	20 c. Type **190**	25	20
664	35 c. Scarlet-backed flower-pecker	40	40
665	75 c. Black-naped oriole ..	80	80
666	$1 Common iora	95	95

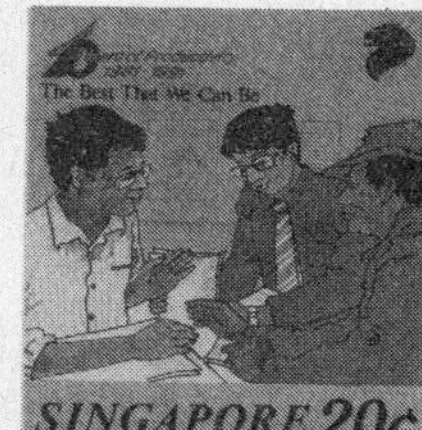

191 Productivity Discussion

1991. 10th Anniv of Productivity Movement. Multicoloured.

No.	Description		
667	20 c. Type **191**	15	20
668	$1 Construction workers ..	70	75

192 Railway Creeper

1992. "Philanippon '91" International Stamp Exhibition, Tokyo. Wild Flowers. Mult.

No.	Description		
669	30 c. Type **192**	20	25
670	75 c. Asystasia	50	55
671	$1 Singapore rhododendron	70	75
672	$2 Coat buttons	1·40	1·50

1992. "Singapore '95" International Stamp Exhibition. Orchids (2nd issue). As T **187**. Multicoloured.

No.	Description		
674	$2 "Dendrobium Sharifah Fatimah"	1·40	1·50
675	$2 "Phalaenopsis Shim Beauty"	1·40	1·50

193 "Singapore Waterfront" (Georgette Chen Liying)

1992. Local Artists. Multicoloured.

No.	Description		
677	20 c. Type **193**	15	20
678	75 c. "Kampung Hut" (Lim Cheng Hoe) ..	50	55
679	$1 "The Bridge" (Poh Siew Wah)	70	75
680	$2 "Singapore River" (Lee Boon Wang)	1·40	1·50

194 Football

1992. Olympic Games, Barcelona. Mult.

No.	Description		
681	20 c. Type **194**	15	20
682	35 c. Athletics	20	25
683	50 c. Swimming	35	40
684	75 c. Basketball ..	50	55
685	$1 Tennis	70	75
686	$2 Sailing	1·40	1·50

POSTAGE DUE STAMPS

The postage due stamps of Malayan Postal Union were in use in Singapore from 1948 until replaced by the following issue.

D 1.

D 2.

1968.

No.	Description		
D 1.	D **1.** 1 c. green	30	1·50
D 2.	2 c. red	30	1·75
D 3.	4 c. orange	45	2·50
D 4.	8 c. brown	40	90
D 5.	10 c. mauve	50	90
D 6.	12 c. violet	1·00	1·50
D 7.	20 c. blue	2·00	3·00
D 8.	50 c. green	4·75	4·75

1978.

No.	Description		
D16a.	D **2.** 1 c. green	10	30
D17a.	4 c. orange	15	40
D18a.	10 c. blue	30	50
D19a.	20 c. blue	40	75
D20a.	50 c. green	70	1·25

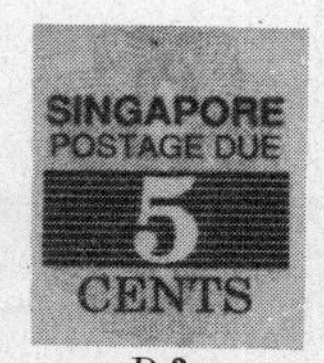

D 3

1989.

No.	Description		
D21	D **3** 5 c. mauve	10	10
D22	10 c. red	10	10
D23	20 c. blue	15	20
D24	50 c. green	35	40

SIRMOOR

A state of the Punjab, India. Now uses Indian stamps.

12 pies = 1 anna; 16 annas = 1 rupee.

1.

2.

1876.

No.	Description		
1.	**1.** 1 pice green	5·00	
2.	1 pice blue	4·00	70·00

1892.

No.	Description		
3b.	**2.** 1 pice green	35	40
4.	1 pice blue	45	45

3. Raja Sir Shamsher Parkash.

4.

1885.

No.	Description		
6.	**3.** 3 p. brown	15	20
8.	3 p. orange	15	15
12.	6 p. green	30	20
14.	1 a. blue	65	90
20.	2 a. red	3·50	3·00

1895.

No.	Description		
22.	**4.** 3 p. orange	50	30
23.	6 p. green	50	30
24.	1 a. blue	1·10	30
25.	2 a. red	1·00	1·00
26.	3 a. green	7·00	12·00
27.	4 a. green	4·50	6·50
28.	8 a. blue	6·00	8·00
29.	1 r. red	13·00	25·00

5. Raja Sir Surendar Bikram Parkash.

1899.

No.	Description		
30.	**5.** 3 a. green	1·25	10·00
31.	4 a. green	1·75	7·00
32.	8 a. blue	2·25	8·50
33.	1 r. red	4·25	15·00

OFFICIAL STAMPS

1890. Optd. **ON S.S.S.**

No.	Description		
60	**3.** 3 p. orange	40	40
79	6 p. green	40	45
80	1 a. blue	35	50
63	2 a. red	7·00	7·00

SOLOMON ISLANDS

A group of islands in the W. Pacific, E. of New Guinea, under Br. protection.

1907. 12 pence = 1 shilling;
20 shillings = 1 pound.
1966. 100 cents = $1 Australian.

1.

1907.

No.	Description		
1.	**1.** ½d. blue	6·50	12·00
2.	1d. red	20·00	30·00
3.	2d. blue	24·00	30·00
4.	2½d. yellow	30·00	35·00
5.	5d. green	50·00	65·00
6.	6d. brown	55·00	60·00
7.	1s. purple	75·00	75·00

2.

3.

1908.

8.	2.	½d. green	50	80
9.		1d. red	1·00	50
10.		2d. grey	1·25	1·00
11.		2½d. blue	2·00	2·50
11a.		4d. red on yellow.. ..	3·00	11·00
12.		5d. olive	8·50	9·00
13.		6d. red	7·00	7·50
14.		1s. black on green ..	9·50	12·00
15.		2s. purple on blue ..	27·00	50·00
16.		2s. 6d. red on blue ..	40·00	70·00
17.		5s. green on yellow ..	70·00	£100

1913. Inscr. "POSTAGE POSTAGE".

18.	3.	½d. green	80	3·50
19.		1d. red	80	10·00
42.		1½d. red	1·60	30
20.		3d. purple on yellow ..	80	4·00
21.		11d. purple and red ..	3·00	14·00

1914. Inscr. "POSTAGE REVENUE".

39	3	½d. green	30	1·75
24		1d. red	70	80
41		1d. violet	1·00	5·00
26		2d. grey	1·25	9·00
27		2½d. blue	2·00	5·00
28		3d. purple on yellow ..	18·00	60·00
44		3d. blue	60	2·50
29		4d. black & red on yellow	2·00	2·50
45a		4½d. brown	3·00	14·00
46		5d. purple and green ..	2·75	20·00
47		6d. purple..	3·75	15·00
33		1s. black on green ..	3·00	7·00
34		2s. purple and blue on blue	6·50	10·00
35		2s. 6d. black & red on blue	7·50	20·00
36		5s. green and red on yellow	25·00	38·00
37		10s. green and red on green	75·00	80·00
38		£1 purple & black on red	£225	£160

1935. Silver Jubilee. As T **13** of Antigua.

53	1½d. blue and red	75	50
54	3d. brown and blue ..	2·75	4·00
55	6d. blue and green ..	6·00	8·50
56	1s. grey and purple ..	6·00	7·00

1937. Coronation. As T **2** of Aden.

57.	1d. violet	30	40
58.	1½d. red	30	50
59.	3d. blue	40	40

5. Spears and Shield.

1939. Portrait of King George VI.

60.	5.	½d. blue and green ..	15	50
61.	–	1d. brown and violet ..	15	30
62.	–	1½d. green and red ..	35	70
63.	–	2d. brown and black ..	30	85
64.	–	2½d. mauve and olive ..	70	55
65.	–	3d. black and blue ..	30	60
66.	–	4½d. green and brown ..	8·00	13·00
67.	–	6d. violet and purple ..	35	50
68.	–	1s. green and black ..	50	30
69.	–	2s. black and orange ..	6·00	3·00
70.	–	2s. 6d. black and violet ..	23·00	4·50
71.	–	5s. green and red.. ..	22·00	7·50
72	–	10s. green and mauve ..	7·00	8·50

DESIGNS—VERT. 1d. Native constable and Chief. 4½d., 10s. Native house, Reef Islands. 6d. Coconut plantation. HORIZ. 1½d. Artificial Is., Malaita. 2½d. Roviana canoe. 1s. Breadfruit. 5s. Malaita canoe. LARGER—35½ × 22 mm. 2d. Canoe house. 3d. Roviana canoes. 2s. Tinakula Volcano. 2s. 6d. Common Scrub Hen.

1946. Victory. As T **9** of Aden.

73	1½d. red	15	30
74	3d. blue	15	10

1949. Silver Wedding. As T **10/11** of Aden.

75	2d. grey	50	30
76	10s. mauve	11·00	8·00

1949. U.P.U. As T **20/23** of Antigua.

77.	2d. brown	75	50
78.	3d. blue	1·25	70
79.	5d. green	1·25	75
80.	1s. black	1·75	50

1953. Coronation. As T **13** of Aden.

81.	2d. black and grey ..	30	45

17. Ysabel Canoe.

1956. Portrait of Queen Elizabeth II.

82	17	½d. orange and purple ..	15	50
83	–	1d. grn. & brn. (As No. 65)	15	15
84	–	1½d. slate & red (No. 62)..	15	40
105	–	2d. sepia & green (No. 63)	20	30
86	–	2½d. black and blue ..	25	45
87	–	3d. green and red (No. 71)	25	15
88	–	5d. black and blue ..	30	55
89	–	6d. black and green ..	50	25
90	–	8d. blue and black ..	25	15
108	–	9d. green and black ..	20	35
91	–	1s. slate and brown ..	50	50
109	–	1s. 3d. black and blue ..	60	70
110	–	2s. black and red (No. 69)	1·00	4·50
93	–	2s. 6d. grn. & pur. (No. 66)	7·50	45
94	–	5s. brown	12·00	1·75
95	–	10s. sepia (No. 61) ..	16·00	2·50
96	–	£1 black and blue ..	42·00	35·00

DESIGNS—VERT. 2½d. Prow of Roviana canoe. HORIZ. 5d., 1s. 3d. Map. 6d. Trading schooner. 8d., 9d. Henderson Airfield, Guadalcanal. 1s. Chart showing voyage of H.M.S. "Swallow" in 1767. 5s. Mendana and Ship. 10s. Similar to No. 61, but constable in different uniform, without rifle. £1, Arms.

32. Great Frigate Bird.

1961. New Constitution, 1960.

97.	32.	2d. black and turquoise ..	10	15
98.		3d. black and red ..	10	10
99.		9d. black and purple ..	15	15

1963. Freedom from Hunger. As T **28** of Aden.

100.	1s. 3d. blue	2·50	35

1963. Cent of Red Cross. As T **33** of Antigua.

101.	2d. red and black ..	60	20
102.	9d. red and blue	1·40	70

33. Makira Food Bowl.

1965. Central design in black; background colours given.

112.	33.	½d. slate and blue ..	10	30
113.	–	1d. orange and yellow ..	50	20
114.	–	1½d. blue and green ..	25	35
115.	–	2d. ultramarine and blue	40	30
116.	–	2½d. brown & light brown	10	35
117.	–	3d. green and light green	10	10
118.	–	6d. mauve and orange..	35	20
119.	–	9d. turquoise and yellow	40	15
120.	–	1s. brown and mauve ..	80	15
121.	–	1s. 3d. red	3·50	2·25
122.	–	2s. purple and lilac ..	5·50	2·75
123.	–	2s. 6d. olive and brown..	1·00	70
124.	–	5s. blue and violet ..	10·00	4·50
125.	–	10s. olive and yellow ..	11·00	4·00
126.	–	£1 violet and pink ..	11·00	5·00

DESIGNS: 1d. "Dendrobium veratrifolium" (orchid). 1½d. Scorpion shell. 2d. Blyth's Hornbill. 2½d. Ysabel shield. 3d. Rennellese club. 6d. Moorish Idol (fish). 9d. Lesser Frigate Bird. 1s. "Dendrobium macrophyllum (orchid). 1s. 3d. "Dendrobium spectabilis" (orchid). 2s. Sanford's Sea Eagle. 2s. 6d. Malaita belt. 5s. "Ornithoptera victoreae" (butterfly). 10s. Ducorp's Cockatoo. £1, Western Canoe Figurehead.

1965. Cent of I.T.U. As T **36** of Antigua.

127.	2d. red and turquoise ..	20	10
128.	3d. turquoise and drab ..	20	10

1965. I.C.Y. As T **37** of Antigua.

129.	1d. purple and turquoise..	15	10
130.	2s. 6d. green and lavender	60	15

1966. Churchill Commem. As T **38** of Antigua.

131.	2d. blue	15	10
132.	9d. green	25	10
133.	1s. 3d. brown	35	10
134.	2s. 6d. violet	40	15

1966. Decimal Currency. Nos. 112/26 surch.

135.	1 c. on ½d.	10	10
136.	2 c. on 1d.	10	10
137.	3 c. on 1½d.	10	10
138.	4 c. on 2d.	15	10
139.	5 c. on 6d.	15	10
140.	6 c. on 2½d.	10	10
141.	7 c. on 3d.	10	10
142.	8 c. on 9d.	15	10
143.	10 c. on 1s.	30	10
144.	12 c. on 1s. 3d.	65	10
145.	13 c. on 1s. 3d.	1·50	15
146.	14 c. on 3d.	40	10
147.	20 c. on 2s.	75	25
148.	25 c. on 2s. 6d.	60	40
149.	35 c. on 2d.	1·75	25
150.	50 c. on 5s.	5·50	2·75
151.	$1 on 10s.	4·00	1·25
152.	$2 on £1	5·00	3·00

1966. World Cup Football Championship. As T **40** of Antigua.

153.	8 c. multicoloured ..	15	10
154.	35 c. multicoloured ..	30	10

1966. Inauguration of W.H.O. Headquarters, Geneva. As T **41** of Antigua.

155.	3 c. black, green and blue	25	10
156.	50 c. black, purple & ochre	1·00	20

1966. 20th Anniv of U.N.E.S.C.O. As T **54/6** of Antigua.

157.	3 c. multicoloured ..	20	10
158.	25 c. yellow, violet & olive	55	15
159.	$1 black, purple & orange	1·50	70

49. Henderson Field.

1967. 25th Anniv. of Guadalcanal Campaign (Pacific War). Multicoloured.

160.	8 c. Type **49**	10	10
161.	35 c. Red Beach Landings	10	10

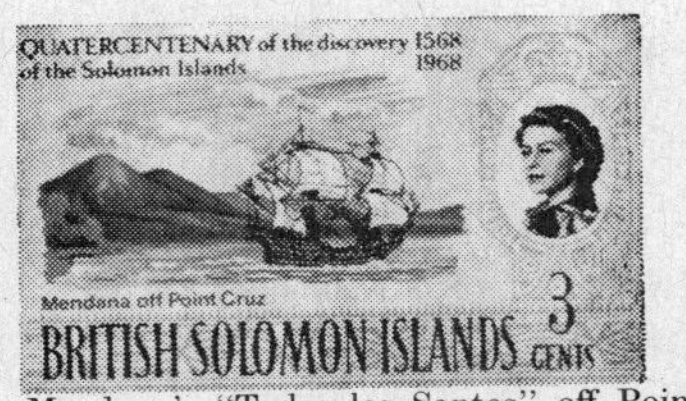

51. Mendana's "Todos los Santos" off Point Cruz.

1968. 400th Anniv. of Discovery of the Solomon Is. Multicoloured.

162.	3 c. Type **51**	15	10
163.	8 c. Arrival of missionaries	15	10
164.	35 c. Pacific Campaign, World War II ..	30	10
165.	$1 Proclamation of the Protectorate ..	50	80

55. Vine Fishing.

1968.

166.	55.	1 c. blue, black & brown	10	10
167.	–	2 c. green, black & brown	10	10
168.	–	3 c. grn., myrtle & black	10	10
169.	–	4 c. purple, black & brn.	15	10
170.	–	6 c. multicoloured ..	15	10
171.	–	8 c. multicoloured ..	25	10
172.	–	12 c. ochre, red & black	65	40
173.	–	14 c. red, brn. & black	1·25	90
174.	–	15 c. multicoloured ..	80	50
175.	–	20 c. blue, red & black	2·25	1·00
176.	–	24 c. red, black & yellow	2·00	1·25
177.	–	35 c. multicoloured ..	1·75	70
178.	–	45 c. multicoloured ..	1·50	75
179.	–	$1 blue, green and black	2·50	2·00
180.	–	$2 multicoloured ..	4·00	5·00

DESIGNS: 2 c. Kite Fishing. 3 c. Platform Fishing. 4 c. Net Fishing. 6 c. Gold Lip Shell Diving. 8 c. Night Fishing. 12 c. Boat Building. 14 c. Cocoa. 15 c. Road Building. 20 c. Geological Survey. 24 c. Hauling Timber. 35 c. Copra. 45 c. Harvesting Rice. $1, Honiara Port. $2, Internal Air Service.

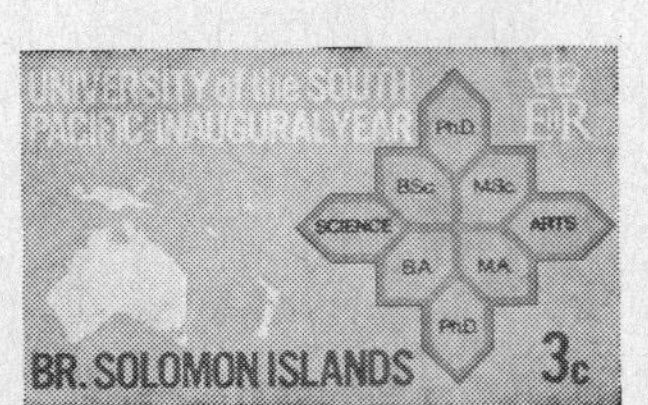

70. Map of Australasia and Diagram.

1969. Inaugural Year of South Pacific University.

181.	70.	3 c. multicoloured ..	10	10
182.		12 c. multicoloured ..	10	10
183.		35 c. multicoloured ..	15	10

71. Basketball Player.

75. South Sea Island with Star of Bethlehem.

1969. 3rd South Pacific Games, Port Moresby. Multicoloured.

184.	3 c. Type **71**	10	10
185.	8 c. Footballer	10	10
186.	14 c. Sprinter	10	10
187.	45 c. Rugby player ..	20	15

1969. Christmas.

189.	75.	8 c. black, violet & green	10	10
190.	–	35 c. multicoloured ..	20	10

DESIGN: 35 c. Southern Cross, "PAX" and Frigate Bird (stained glass window).

77. "Paid" Stamp, New South Wales 1896–1906 2d. Stamp and 1906–07 Tulagi Postmark.

1970. New G.P.O., Honiara.

191.	77.	7 c. mve., blue and black	20	15
192.	–	14 c. green, blue & black	25	15
193.	–	18 c. multicoloured ..	25	15
194.	–	23 c. multicoloured ..	30	20

DESIGNS: 14 c. 1906–07 2d. stamp and C. M. Woodford. 18 c. 1910–14 5s. stamp and Tulagi Postmark, 1913. 23 c. New G.P.O., Honiara.

81. Coat of Arms.

1970. New Constitution.

195.	81.	18 c. multicoloured ..	15	10
196.	–	35 c. green, blue & ochre	30	20

DESIGN—HORIZ. 35 c. Map.

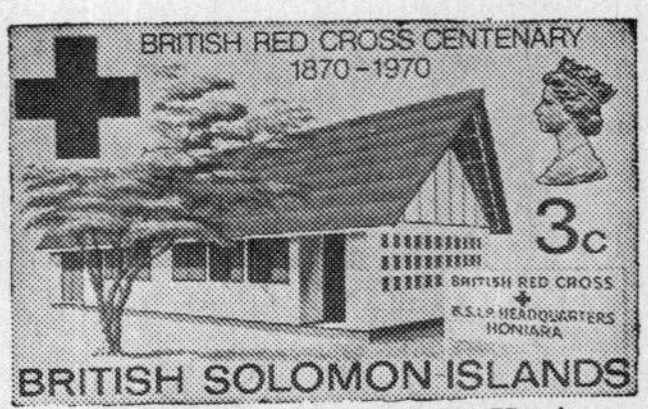

83. British Red Cross H.Q., Honiara.

1970. Centenary of British Red Cross.

197.	83.	3 c. multicoloured ..	10	10
198.	–	35 c. blue, red & blk.	25	20

DESIGN—VERT. 35 c. Wheelchair and map.

86. Reredos (Altar Screen).

1970. Christmas.

199.	–	8 c. ochre and violet ..	10	10
200.	86.	45 c. chestnut, orange and brown	25	20

DESIGN—HORIZ. 8 c. Carved angel.

87. La Perouse and "La Boussole".

1971. Ships and Navigators (1st series). Multicoloured.

201. 3 c. Type **87** 55 20
202. 4 c. Astrolabe and Polynesian reed map 65 20
203. 12 c. Abel Tasman and "Heemskerk" .. .. 1·50 45
204. 35 c. Te puki canoe .. 3·00 75

See also Nos. 215/18, 236/9, 254/7 and 272/5.

88. J. Atkin, Bishop Patteson and S. Taroaniara.

1971. Death Cent. of Bishop Patteson. Mult.

205. 2 c. Type **88** 10 10
206. 4 c. Last landing at Nukapu 10 10
207. 14 c. Memorial Cross and Nukapu (vert.) .. 10 10
208. 45 c. Knotted leaf and canoe (vert.) 20 10

89. Torch Emblem and Boxers.

1971. South Pacific Games, Tahiti. Mult.

209. 3 c. Type **89** 10 10
210. 8 c. Emblem and Footballers 10 10
211. 12 c. Emblem and Runner 10 10
212. 35 c. Emblem and Skin-diver 10 10

90. Melanesian Lectern.

1971. Christmas. Multicoloured.

213. 9 c. Type **90** 10 10
214. 45 c. "United we Stand" (Margarita Bara) .. 15 15

1972. Ships and Navigators (2nd series). As T **87**. Multicoloured.

215. 4 c. Bougainville and "La Boudeuse" 30 10
216. 9 c. Horizontal planisphere and ivory backstaff .. 60 10
217. 15 c. Philip Carteret and H.M.S. "Swallow" .. 85 15
218. 45 c. Malaita canoe .. 3·75 1·25

91. "Cupha woodfordi".

1972. Multicoloured.

219 1 c. Type **91** 15 30
220 2 c. "Ornithoptera priamus" .. 25 40
221 3 c. "Vindula sapor" .. 25 40
222 4 c. "Papilio ulysses" .. 25 40
223 5 c. Great trevally .. 25 30
224 8 c. Little bonito .. 40 50
225 9 c. Sapphire demoiselle 50 55
226 12 c. "Costus speciosus" .. 1·25 80
227 15 c. Orange anemone fish 1·25 1·00
228 20 c. "Spathoglottis plicata" .. .. 3·25 1·75
229 25 c. "Ephemerantha comata" .. .. 3·25 1·50
230 35 c. "Dendrobium cuthbertsonii" .. 3·50 2·25
231 45 c. "Heliconia salomonica" .. .. 3·50 3·00
232 $1 Blue finned triggerfish 6·00 4·50
233 $2 "Ornithoptera alottei" 13·00 12·00
233a $5 Great frigate bird .. 10·00 10·00

The 2, 3, 4 c and $2 are butterflies; the 5, 8, 9, 15 c. and $1 are fishes, and the 12, 20, 25, 35, 45 c. are flowers.

1972. Royal Silver Wedding. As T **52** of Ascension, but with Greetings and Message Drum in background.

234. 8 c. red 10 10
235. 45 c. green 20 20

1973. Ships and Navigators (3rd series). As T **87**. Multicoloured.

236. 4 c. D. Entrecasteaux and "Recherche", 1791 30 15
237. 9 c. Ship's Hour-glass and Chronometer, 1761 60 15
238. 15 c. Lt. Shortland and "Alexander", 1788 75 20
239. 35 c. Tomoko (war canoe) 3·25 1·75

93. Pan Pipes.

1973. Musical Instruments. Multicoloured.

240. 4 c. Type **93** 10 10
241. 9 c. Castanets 10 10
242. 15 c. Bamboo flute .. 15 10
243. 35 c. Bauro gongs .. 35 25
244. 45 c. Bamboo band .. 35 30

1973. Royal Wedding. As T **47** of Anguilla.

245. 4 c. blue 10 10
246. 35 c. blue 15 10

94. "Adoration of the Kings" (Jan Brueghel).

1973. Christmas. "Adoration of the Kings" by the artists listed. Multicoloured.

247. 8 c. Type **94** 10 10
248. 22 c. Peter Brueghel .. 25 25
249. 45 c. Botticelli (49 × 35 mm.) 50 50

95. Queen Elizabeth II and Map.

1974. Royal Visit.

250. **95.** 4 c. multicoloured .. 25 10
251. 9 c. multicoloured .. 50 10
252. 15 c. multicoloured .. 60 20
253. 35 c. multicoloured .. 1·10 1·25

1974. Ships and Navigators (4th series). As T **87**. Multicoloured.

254. 4 c. Commissioner landing from "S.S. Titus" .. 20 10
255. 9 c. Radar scanner .. 25 10
256. 15 c. Natives being transported to a "Blackbirder" 40 15
257. 45 c. Lieut. John F. Kennedy's "P.T. 109" .. 2·00 1·25

96. "Postman".

1974. Centenary of U.P.U.

258. **96.** 4 c. grn., dp. grn. & blk. 10 10
259. – 9 c. lt. brn., brn. & blk. 10 10
260. – 15 c. mauve, pur. & blk. 15 10
261. – 45 c. bl., dp. bl. & blk... 35 60

DESIGNS (Origami figures)—HORIZ. 9 c. Carrier-pigeon. 45 c. Pegasus. VERT. 15 c. St. Gabriel.

97. "New Constitution" Stamp of 1970.

1974. New Constitution.

262. **97.** 4 c. multicoloured .. 10 10
263. – 9 c. red, black & brown 10 10
264. – 15 c. red, blk. & brown 15 10
265. **97.** 35 c. multicoloured .. 45 50

DESIGN: 9 c., 15 c. "New Constitution" stamp of 1961 (inscr. "1960").

98. Golden Whistler.

1975. Birds. Multicoloured.

267. 1 c. Type **98** 45 45
268. 2 c. Common Kingfisher .. 50 50
269. 3 c. Red-bibbed Fruit Dove 55 55
270. 4 c. Little Button Quail .. 55 55
271. $2 Duchess Lorikeet .. 11·00 9·00

See also Nos. 305/20.

1975. Ships and Navigators (5th series). As T **87**. Multicoloured.

272. 4 c. M.V. "Walande" .. 25 10
273. 9 c. M.V. "Melanesian" .. 30 10
274. 15 c. M.V. "Marsina" .. 35 15
275. 45 c. S.S. "Himalaya" .. 1·00 1·50

99. 800 Metres Race.

1975. South Pacific Games. Multicoloured.

276. 4 c. Type **99** 10 10
277. 9 c. Long jump 10 10
278. 15 c. Javelin-throwing .. 15 10
279. 45 c. Football 45 45

100. Nativity Scene and Candles.

1975. Christmas. Multicoloured.

281. 15 c. Type **100** 20 10
282. 35 c. Shepherds, angels and candles 40 15
283. 45 c. The Magi and candles 50 40

1975. Nos. 267/70, 223/32, 271 and 233a with obliterating bar over "BRITISH". Mult.

285. 1 c. Type **98** 25 45
286. 2 c. Common Kingfisher .. 30 45
287. 3 c. Red-bibbed Fruit Dove 30 45
288. 4 c. Little Button Quail .. 35 45
289. 5 c. Great Trevally .. 35 45
290. 8 c. Little Bonito .. 50 60
291. 9 c. Sapphire Demoiselle .. 50 60
292. 12 c. "Costus speciosus" .. 1·50 1·00
293. 15 c. Orange Anemone Fish 1·50 1·25
294. 20 c. "Spathoglottis plicata" .. .. 2·75 1·50
295. 25 c. "Ephemerantha comata" .. .. 2·75 1·75
296. 35 c. "Dendrobium cuthbertsonii" .. 3·50 1·75
297. 45 c. "Heliconia salomonica" .. 3·50 3·00
298. $1 Blue Finned Triggerfish 3·00 2·50
299. $2 Duchess Lorikeet .. 8·00 10·00
300. $5 Great Frigate Bird .. 15·00 18·00

102. Ceremonial Food-bowl.

1975. Artefacts (1st series). Multicoloured.

301. 4 c. Type **102** 10 10
302. 15 c. Chieftains' money .. 10 10
303. 35 c. Nguzu-nguzu (canoe protector spirit) (vert.) 25 20
304. 45 c. Nguzu-nguzu canoe prow 30 25

See also Nos. 337/40, 353/6 and 376/9.

103. Golden Whistler.

1976. Multicoloured.

305. 1 c. Type **103** 20 40
306. 2 c. Common kingfisher .. 25 45
307. 3 c. Red-bibbed fruit dove 25 40
308. 4 c. Little button quail .. 30 40
309. 5 c. Willie wagtail .. 30 40
310. 6 c. Golden cowrie .. 60 50
311. 10 c. Glory-of-the-sea cone 60 50
312. 12 c. Rainbow lory .. 60 70
313. 15 c. Pearly nautilus .. 65 40
314. 20 c. Venus comb murex .. 1·00 45
315. 25 c. Commercial trochus 85 50
316. 35 c. Melon or baler shell 1·00 70
317. 45 c. Orange spider conch 1·50 1·25
318. $1 Pacific triton .. 3·25 3·00
319. $2 Duchess lorikeet .. 6·50 4·75
320. $5 Great frigate bird .. 6·50 6·00

104. Coastwatchers, 1942.

1976. Bicent. of American Revolution. Mult.

321. 6 c. Type **104** 20 10
322. 20 c. "Amagiri" ramming PT 109 and Lt. J. F. Kennedy .. 60 30
323. 35 c. Henderson Airfield .. 1·00 40
324. 45 c. Map of Guadalcanal 1·10 70

105. Alexander Graham Bell.

1976. Centenary of Telephone.

326. **105.** 6 c. multicoloured .. 10 10
327. – 20 c. multicoloured .. 15 10
328. – 35 c. brown, orge. & red 30 15
329. – 45 c. multicoloured .. 40 35

DESIGNS: 20 c. Radio telephone via satellite. 35 c. Ericson's magneto telephone. 45 c. Stick telephone and first telephone.

106. B.A.C. "1-11".

1976. 50th Anniv. of 1st Flight to Solomon Is. Multicoloured.
330. 6 c. Type **106** 20 10
331. 20 c. Britten-Norman "Islander" 35 10
332. 35 c. "Dakota DC3" .. 65 15
333. 45 c. De Havilland "DH50A" 75 45

107. The Communion Plate.

1977. Silver Jubilee. Multicoloured.
334. 6 c. Queen's Visit, 1974.. 10 10
335. 35 c. Type **107** . .. 15 20
336. 45 c. The Communion .. 25 45

108. Carving from New Georgia.

1977. Artefacts (2nd series). Carvings.
337. **108.** 6 c. multicoloured .. 10 10
338. – 20 c. multicoloured .. 10 10
339. – 35 c. black, grey and red 20 15
340. – 45 c. multicoloured .. 25 30
DESIGNS: 20 c. Sea adaro (spirit). 35 c. Shark-headed man. 45 c. Man from Ulawa or Malaita.

109. Spraying Roof and Mosquito.

1977. Malaria Eradication. Multicoloured.
341. 6 c. Type **109** 10 10
342. 20 c. Taking blood samples 20 10
343. 35 c. Microscope and map 30 15
344. 45 c. Delivering drugs .. 40 40

110. The Shepherds.

1977. Christmas. Multicoloured.
345. 6 c. Type **110** 10 10
346. 20 c. Mary and Jesus in stable.. .. 10 10
347. 35 c. The Three Kings .. 20 15
348. 45 c. "The Flight into Egypt" 25 25

111. Feather Money.

1977. New Currency. Multicoloured.
349. 6 c. Type **111** 10 10
350. 6 c. New currency coins .. 10 10
351. 45 c. New currency notes 35 25
352. 45 c. Shell money 35 25

112. Figure from Shortland Is.

1977. Artefacts (3rd series).
353. **112.** 6 c. multicoloured .. 10 10
354. – 20 c. multicoloured .. 10 10
355. – 35 c. brn., blk. and orge. 20 15
356. – 45 c. multicoloured .. 25 30
DESIGNS: 20 c. Ceremonial shield. 35 c. Santa Cruz ritual figure. 45 c. Decorative combs.

113. Sandford's Sea Eagle. **114.** National Flag.

1978. 25th Anniv. of Coronation. Mult.
357. – 45 c. black, red & silver 25 30
358. – 45 c. multicoloured .. 25 30
359. **113.** 45 c. black, red & silver 25 30
DESIGNS: No. 357, King's Dragon. No. 358, Queen Elizabeth II.

1978. Independence. Multicoloured.
360. 6 c. Type **114** 10 10
361. 15 c. Governor-General's flag 20 10
362. 35 c. The Cenotaph, Honiara 35 30
363. 45 c. National coat of arms 40 50

115. John.

1978. 450th Death Anniv. of Durer. Mult.
364. 6 c. Type **115** 10 10
365. 20 c. Peter 10 10
366. 35 c. Paul 15 15
367. 45 c. Mark 20 30

116. Firelighting.

1978. 50th Anniv. of Scouting in Solomon Islands. Multicoloured.
368. 6 c. Type **116** 15 10
369. 20 c. Camping 20 20
370. 35 c. Solomon Islands Scouts 40 40
371. 45 c. Canoeing 50 70

MORE DETAILED LISTS
are given in the Stanley Gibbons Catalogues referred to in the country headings.
For lists of current volumes see Introduction.

117. " Discovery ".

1979. Bicentenary of Captain Cook's Voyages, 1768–79.
372. **117.** 8 c. multicoloured .. 30 10
373. – 18 c. multicoloured .. 40 15
374. – 35 c. black, green & grey 55 25
375. – 45 c. multicoloured .. 60 40
DESIGNS: 18 c. Portrait of Captain Cook by Nathaniel Dance. 35 c. Sextant. 45 c. Flaxman/Wedgwood medallion.

118. Fish Net Float.

1979. Artefacts (4th series).
376. **118.** 8 c. multicoloured .. 10 10
377. – 20 c. multicoloured .. 10 10
378. – 35 c. black, grey and red 15 15
379. – 45 c. blk., brn. and grn. 20 30
DESIGNS—VERT. 20 c. Armband of shell money. 45 c. Forehead ornament. HORIZ. 35 c. Ceremonial food bowl.

119. Running.

1979. South Pacific Games, Fiji. Multicoloured.
380. 8 c. Type **119** 10 10
381. 20 c. Hurdling 10 10
382. 35 c. Football 15 15
383. 45 c. Swimming 25 35

120. 1908 6d. Stamp.

1979. Death Centenary of Sir Rowland Hill.
384. **120.** 8 c. red and pink .. 10 10
385. – 20 c. mauve & pale mauve 20 30
386. – 35 c. multicoloured .. 35 45
DESIGNS: 20 c. Great Britain 1856 6d. Stamp. 35 c. 1978 45 c. Independence commemorative.

121. Sea Snake.

1979. Animals. Multicoloured.
388. 1 c. Type **121** 10 15
389. 3 c. Red-banded tree snake 10 15
390. 4 c. Whip snake.. .. 10 15
391. 6 c. Pacific boa 10 15
392. 8 c. Skink 10 10
393. 10 c. Gecko 10 10
394. 12 c. Monitor 15 30
395. 15 c. Anglehead 30 15
396. 20 c. Giant toad.. .. 30 20
397. 25 c. Marsh frog.. .. 20 40
398. 30 c. Horned frog .. 85 85
399. 35 c. Tree frog 30 35
399a. 40 c. Burrowing snake .. 35 90
400. 45 c. Guppy's snake .. 30 60
400a. 50 c. Tree gecko.. .. 40 40
401. $1 Large skink .. .. 1·00 70
402. $2 Guppy's frog .. .. 1·25 2·00
403. $5 Estuarine crocodile .. 4·00 4·00
403a. $10 Hawksbill turtle .. 6·50 6·75

122. " Madonna and Child " (Morando).

1979. International Year of the Child. " Madonna and Child " paintings by various artists. Multicoloured.
404. 4 c. Type **122** 10 10
405. 20 c. Luini 20 15
406. 35 c. Bellini 30 15
407. 50 c. Raphael 35 50

123. H.M.S. " Curacoa ", 1839.

1980. Ships and Crests (1st series). Mult.
409. 8 c. Type **123** 20 10
410. 20 c. H.M.S. "Herald", 1854 .. .. 35 15
411. 35 c. H.M.S. "Royalist", 1889 .. .. 55 35
412. 45 c. H.M.S. "Beagle", 1878 70 55
See also Nos. 430/3.

124. Steel Fishery Training Vessel.

1980. Fishing. Ancillary Craft. Mult.
413. 8 c. Type **124** 15 10
414. 20 c. F.R.P. Fishery Training Vessel 20 15
415. 45 c. Refrigerated Fish Carrier 35 35
416. 80 c. Research Vessel .. 60 75

125. "Comliebank" (cargo-ship) and 1935 Tulagi Registered Letter Postmark.

1980. "London 1980" International Stamp Exhibition. Mail-carrying Transport. Mult.
417. 45 c. Type **125** 35 50
418. 45 c. Douglas "C-47" aeroplane (U.S. Army Postal Service, 1943) 35 50
419. 45 c. B.A.C. "1-11" airliner and 1979 Honiara postmark 35 50
420. 45 c. "Corabank" (container ship) and 1979 Auki postmark 35 50

126. Queen Elizabeth the Queen Mother.

1980. 80th Birthday of The Queen Mother.
421. **126.** 45 c. multicoloured .. 40 35

127. Angel with Trumpet.

1980. Christmas. Multicoloured.
422. 8 c. Type **127** 10 10
423. 20 c. Angel with fiddle .. 10 10
424. 45 c. Angel with trumpet (different) 25 25
425. 80 c. Angel with lute .. 40 45

128. " Parthenos sylvia ".

1980. Butterflies (1st series). Multicoloured.
426. 8 c. Type **128** 10 10
427. 20 c. " Delias schoenbergi " 25 20
428. 45 c. " Jamides cephion " 40 40
429. 80 c. " Ornithoptera victoriae" 1·00 1·00
See also. Nos. 456/9 and 610/13.

1981. Ships and crests (2nd series). As T **123**. Multicoloured.
430. 8 c. H.M.S. "Mounts Bay" 15 10
431. 20 c. H.M.S. "Charybdis" 25 15
432. 45 c. H.M.S. "Hydra" .. 50 35
433. $1 Royal Yacht "Britannia" 1·25 1·00

129. Francisco Antonio Maurelle.

1981. Bicentenary of Maurelle's Visit and Bauche's Chart.
434. **129.** 8 c. brown, yellow & blk. 15 10
435. – 10 c. yellow, black & red 20 10
436. – 45 c. multicoloured .. 60 65
437. – $1 multicoloured .. 1·00 1·10
DESIGNS—VERT. $1, Spanish compass cards, 1745. HORIZ. 10 c. Map by Belling of 1742 showing Maurelle's route. 45 c. " La Princesa ".

130. Netball.

1981. Mini South Pacific Games. Multicoloured.
439. 8 c. Type **130** 10 10
440. 10 c. Tennis 15 15
441. 25 c. Running 25 25
442. 30 c. Football 25 25
443. 45 c. Boxing 40 40

131. Prince Charles as Colonel-in-Chief, Royal Regiment of Wales.

1981. Royal Wedding. Multicoloured.
445. 8 c. Wedding bouquet from Solomon Islands .. 10 10
446. 45 c. Type **131** 30 40
447. $1 Prince Charles and Lady Diana Spencer .. 60 1·00

132. " Music ".

1981. 25th Anniv. of Duke of Edinburgh Award Scheme. Multicoloured.
448. 8 c. Type **132** 10 10
449. 25 c. " Handicrafts " .. 10 10
450. 45 c. " Canoeing " .. 20 20
451. $1 Duke of Edinburgh .. 50 70

133. Primitive Church.

1981. Christmas. Churches.
452. **133.** 8 c. black, buff and blue 10 10
453. – 10 c. multicoloured .. 10 10
454. – 25 c. black, buff and grn. 15 10
455. – $2 multicoloured .. 1·00 1·25
DESIGNS: 10 c. St. Barnabas Anglican Cathedral, Honiara. 25 c. Early church. $2, Holy Cross Cathedral, Honiara.

1982. Butterflies (2nd series). As T **128**. Mult.
456 10 c. "Doleschallia bisaltide" 15 10
457 25 c. "Papilio bridgei" .. 35 25
458 35 c. "Taenaris phorcas" 40 30
459 $1 "Graphium sarpedon" 1·50 1·50

1982. Cyclone Relief Fund. No. 447 surch. **50 CENTS SURCHARGE CYCLONE RELIEF FUND 1982.**
460. $1+50 c. Prince Charles and Lady Diana Spencer 2·50 2·75

135. Pair of Sanford's Sea Eagles constructing Nest.

1982. Sanford's Sea Eagle. Multicoloured.
461. 12 c. Type **135** 35 35
462. 12 c. Egg and chick .. 35 35
463. 12 c. Hen feeding chicks .. 35 35
464. 12 c. Fledgelings 35 35
465. 12 c. Young bird in flight 35 35
466. 12 c. Pair of birds and village dwellings .. 35 35

136. Wedding Portrait.

1982. 21st Birthday of Princess of Wales. Multicoloured.
467. 12 c. Solomon Islands coat of arms 15 10
468. 40 c. Lady Diana Spencer at Broadlands, May 1981 30 30
469. 50 c. Type **136** 35 35
470. $1 Formal portrait .. 65 65

137. Flags of Solomon Islands and United Kingdom.

1982. Royal Visit. (Nos. 471/2) and Commonwealth Games, Brisbane. (Nos. 473/4. Multicoloured.
471. 12 c. Type **137** 15 20
472. 12 c. Queen and Prince Philip 15 20
473. 25 c. Running 30 45
474. 25 c. Boxing 30 45

138. Boy Scouts.

1982. 75th Anniv. of Boy Scout Movement. (Nos. 477, 479, 481, 483) and Centenary of Boys Brigade (others). Multicoloured.
477. 12 c. Type **138** 20 15
478. 12 c. Boys Brigade cadets 20 15
479. 25 c. Lord Baden-Powell 35 40
480. 25 c. Sir William Smith .. 35 40
481. 35 c. Type **138** 40 50
482. 35 c. As No. 478 .. .. 40 50
483. 50 c. As. No. 479 .. .. 60 90
484. 50 c. As No. 480 .. .. 60 90

139. Leatherback Turtle.

1983. Turtles. Multicoloured.
485. 18 c. Type **139** 25 25
486. 35 c. Loggerhead turtle .. 45 45
487. 45 c. Pacific Ridley turtle 60 60
488. 50 c. Green turtle 65 65

140. "Oliva vidum, Conus generalis and Murex tribulus".

1983. Commonwealth Day. Shells. Mult.
489. 12 c. Type **140** 15 15
490. 35 c. Romu, Kurila, Kakadu and money belt .. 35 40
491. 45 c. Shells from " Bride-price " necklaces .. 50 60
492. 50 c. " Trochus niloticus " polished and in natural state 55 65

141. Montgolfier Balloon.

1983. Bicentenary of Manned Flight. Mult.
493. 30 c. Type **141** 55 40
494. 35 c. R.A.A.F. Lockheed " Hercules " 60 45
495. 40 c. Wright brothers' " Flyer III " 70 55
496. 45 c. Space shuttle " Columbia " 75 60
497. 50 c. Beechcraft " Baron–Solair " 80 65

142. Weto Dancers.

1983. Christmas. Multicoloured.
498. 12 c. Type **142** 15 10
499. 15 c. Custom wrestling .. 20 20
500. 18 c. Girl dancers 20 20
501. 20 c. Devil dancers .. 20 20
502. 25 c. Bamboo band .. 30 35
503. 35 c. Gilbertese dancers .. 40 45
504. 40 c. Pan pipers 45 55
505. 45 c. Girl dancers 50 65
506. 50 c. Cross surrounded by flowers 55 70

143. Earth Satellite Station.

1983. World Communications Year. Mult.
508. 12 c. Type **143** 20 15
509. 18 c. Ham radio operator 25 20
510. 25 c. 1908 2½d. Canoe stamp 35 30
511. $1 1908 6d. Canoe stamp .. 1·25 1·40

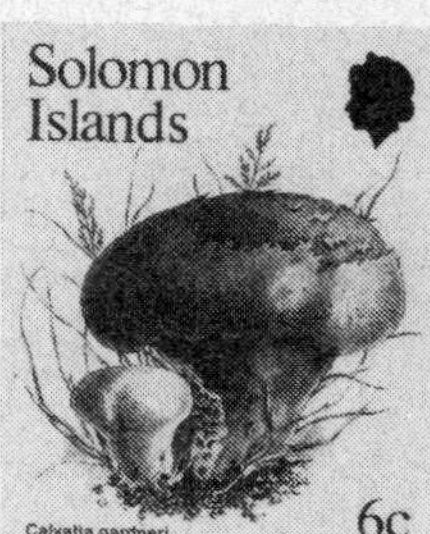

144. " Calvatia gardneri ".

1984. Fungi. Multicoloured.
513. 6 c. Type **144** 10 10
514. 18 c. " Marasmiellus inoderma " 20 25
515. 35 c. " Pycnoporus sanguineus " 35 45
516. $2 " Filoboletus manipularis " .. .. .. 2·25 2·50

145. Cross surrounded by Flowers.

1984. Visit of Pope John Paul II.
517. **145.** 12 c. multicoloured .. 20 10
518. 50 c. multicoloured .. 65 80

146. " Olivebank ", 1892.

1984. 250th Anniv. of "Lloyd's List" (newspaper).

519. 12 c. Type **146** 30 10
520. 15 c. S.S. " Tinhow ", 1906 35 30
521. 18 c. " Oriana " at Point Cruz, Honiara 40 40
522. $1 Point Cruz, Honiara .. 1·40 2·25

147. Village Drums.

1984. 20th Anniv. of Asia–Pacific Broadcasting Union. Multicoloured.

524. 12 c. Type **147** 15 15
525. 45 c. Radio City, Guadalcanal 60 60
526. 60 c. S.I.B.C. studios, Honiara 75 80
527. $1 S.I.B.C. Broadcasting House .. .. .. 1·25 1·40

148. Solomon Islands Flag and Torch-bearer.

1984. Olympic Games, Los Angeles. Multicoloured.

528. 12 c. Type **148** 15 20
529. 25 c. Lawson Tama stadium, Honiara (horiz.) .. 30 35
530. 50 c. Honiara community centre (horiz.) 65 70
531. 95 c. Alick Wickham inventing crawl stroke, Bronte Baths, New South Wales, 1898 (horiz.) .. .. 1·75 2·00
532. $1 Olympic stadium, U.S.A. (horiz.) .. .. .. 1·25 1·40

149. Little Pied Cormorant.

1984. "Ausipex" International Stamp Exhibition, Melbourne. Birds. Multicoloured.

533. 12 c. Type **149** 20 15
534. 18 c. Spotbill duck 30 30
535. 35 c. Rufous night heron .. 50 50
536. $1 Eastern broad-billed roller .. .. .. 1·25 2·00

150. The Queen Mother with Princess Margaret at Badminton Horse Trials.

1985. Life and Times of Queen Elizabeth the Queen Mother. Multicoloured.

538. 12 c. With Winston Churchill at Buckingham Palace, VE Day 1945 .. .. .. 10 10
539. 25 c. Type **150** 25 30
540. 35 c. At St. Patrick's Day parade 30 35
541. $1 With Prince Henry at his christening (from photo by Lord Snowdon) 90 95

151. Japanese Memorial Shrine, Mount Austen, Guadalcanal.

1985. "Expo '85" World Fair, Japan. Multicoloured.

543. 12 c. Type **151** 10 10
544. 25 c. Digital telephone exchange equipment .. 25 30
545. 45 c. Fishing vessel "Soltai No. 7" 40 45
546. 85 c. Coastal village scene 75 80

152. Titiana Village.

1985. Christmas. "Going Home for the Holiday". Multicoloured.

547. 12 c. Type **152** 10 10
548. 25 c. Sigana, Santa Isabel 25 30
549. 35 c. Artificial Island and Langa Lagoon 30 35

153. Girl Guide Activities.

1985. 75th Anniv. of Girl Guide Movement (12, 45 c.) and International Youth Year (others). Multicoloured.

550. 12 c. Type **153** 35 10
551. 15 c. Boys playing and child in wheelchair (Stop Polio) 40 20
552. 25 c. Runners and Solomon Island scenes 60 30
553. 35 c. Runners and Australian scenes ("Run Round Australia") .. 75 35
554. 45 c. Guide colour party and badges 85 45

INDEX

Countries can be quickly located by referring to the index at the end of this volume.

156. Building Red Cross Centre, Gizo.

1986. Operation Raleigh (volunteer project). Multicoloured.

558. 18 c. Type **156** 50 20
559. 30 c. Exploring rainforest 75 30
560. 60 c. Observing Halley's Comet .. .. .. 1·25 75
561. $1 "Sir Walter Raleigh" and "The Zebu" .. 1·75 1·25

1986. 60th Birthday of Queen Elizabeth II. As T **110** of Ascension. Multicoloured.

562. 5 c. Princess Elizabeth and Duke of Edinburgh at Clydebank Town Hall, 1947 .. .. 10 10
563. 18 c. At St. Paul's Cathedral for Queen Mother's 80th birthday service, 1980 .. .. 15 20
564. 22 c. With children, Solomon Islands, 1982 .. 20 25
565. 55 c. At Windsor Castle on 50th birthday, 1976 .. 40 45
566. $2 At Crown Agents Head Office, London, 1983 .. 1·40 1·50

1986. Royal Wedding. As T **112** of Ascension. Multicoloured.

568. 55 c. Prince Andrew and Miss Sarah Ferguson .. 40 45
569. 60 c. Prince Andrew at helm of yacht "Bluenose II" off Nova Scotia, 1985 45 50

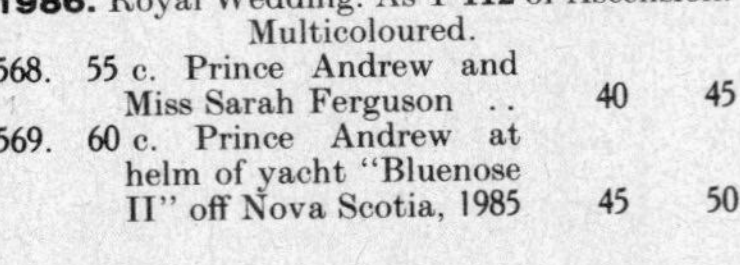

158. "Freedom" (winner 1980).

1986. America's Cup Yachting Championship (1987).

570. **158.** 18 c. multicoloured .. 15 20
571. – 30 c. multicoloured .. 50 70
572. – $1 multicoloured .. 75 80

Nos. 570/2 were issued as a sheet of 50, each horizontal strip of 5 being separated by gutter margins. The sheet contains 20 different designs at 18 c., 10 at 30 c. and 20 at $1. Individual stamps depict yachts, charts, the America's Cup or the emblem of the Royal Perth Yacht Club.

1986. Cyclone Relief Fund. No. 541 surch. **+ 50c Cyclone Relief Fund 1986.**

573. $1 + 50 c. Queen Mother with Prince Henry at his christening .. .. 1·10 1·25

160. Dendrophyllia gracilis".

1987. Corals. Multicoloured.

576. 18 c. Type **160** 20 15
577. 45 c. "Dendronephthya sp." .. 60 50
578. 60 c. "Clavularia sp." .. 80 80
579. $1.50 "Melithaea squamata" .. .. 1·60 1·75

161. "Cassia fistula".

1987. Flowers. Multicoloured.

580. 1 c. Type **161** 10 10
581. 5 c. "Allamanda cathartica" 10 10
582. 10 c. "Catharanthus roseus" 10 10
583. 18 c. "Mimosa pudica" .. 10 10
584. 20 c. "Hibiscus rosa-sinensis" 10 10
585. 22 c. "Clerodendrum thomsonae" 10 10
586. 25 c. "Bauhinia variegata" 10 15
587. 28 c. "Gloriosa rothschildiana" 10 15
588. 30 c. "Heliconia solomonensis" 10 15
589. 40 c. "Episcia" hybrid .. 15 20
590. 45 c. "Bougainvillea" hybrid 20 25
591. 50 c. "Alpinia purpurata" 20 25
592. 55 c. "Plumeria rubra" .. 25 30
593. 60 c. "Acacia farnesiana" 25 30
594. $1 "Ipomea purpurea" .. 40 45
595. $2 "Dianella ensifolia" .. 85 90
596. $5 "Passiflora foetida" .. 2·10 2·25
597. $10 "Hemigraphis sp." .. 4·25 4·50

162. Mangrove Kingfisher on Branch.

1987. Mangrove Kingfisher. Multicoloured.

598. 60 c. Type **162** .. .. 1·00 1·25
599. 60 c. Kingfisher diving .. 1·00 1·25
600. 60 c. Entering water .. 1·00 1·25
601. 60 c. Kingfisher with prey 1·00 1·25

Nos. 598/601 were printed together, se-tenant, forming a composite design.

163. "Dendrobium conanthum".

1987. Christmas. Orchids (1st series). Mult.

602. 18 c. Type **163** 40 10
603. 30 c. "Spathoglottis plicata" 65 20
604. 55 c. "Dendrobium gouldii" 85 50
605. $1.50 "Dendrobium goldfinchii" .. .. 2·00 1·75

See also Nos. 640/3.

164. Telecommunications Control Room and Satellite.

1987. Asia–Pacific Transport and Communications Decade. Multicoloured.

606. 18 c. Type **164** 10 15
607. 30 c. De Havilland "Twin Otter" mail plane .. 15 20
608. 60 c. Guadalcanal road improvement project .. 35 40
609. $2 Beechcraft "Queen Air" and Henderson Control Tower .. .. .. 1·10 1·25

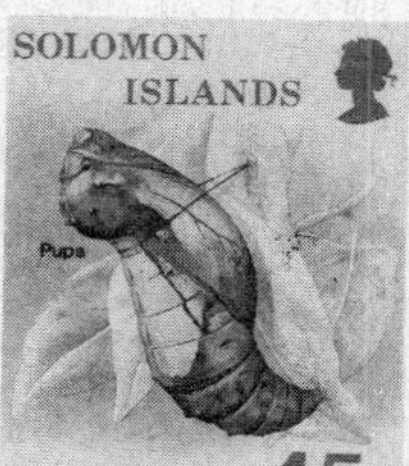

165. Pupa of "Ornithoptera victoriae".

1987. Butterflies (3rd series). "Ornithoptera victoriae" (Queen Victoria's Birdwing). Mult.

610. 45 c. Type **165** 90 90
611. 45 c. Larva 90 90
612. 45 c. Female butterfly .. 90 90
613. 45 c. Male butterfly .. 90 90

166. Student and National Agriculture Training Institute.

1988. 10th Anniv. of International Fund for Agricultural Development. Multicoloured.

614. 50 c. Type **166** 30 35
615. 50 c. Students working in fields 30 35
616. $1 Transport by lorry .. 55 60
617. $1 Canoe transport .. 55 60

Nos. 614/15 and 616/17 were printed together, se-tenant, each pair forming a composite design.

167 Building a Fishing Boat

1988. "Expo '88" World Fair, Brisbane. Mult.

618 22 c. Type **167** 15 15
619 80 c. War canoe 40 45
620 $1.50 Traditional village .. 80 85

168 "Todos los Santos" in Estrella Bay, 1568

1988. 10th Anniv of Independence. Mult.

622 22 c. Type **168** 25 15
623 55 c. Raising the Union Jack, 1893 .. .. 50 35
624 80 c. High Court Building 70 50
625 $1 Dancers at traditional celebration 90 80

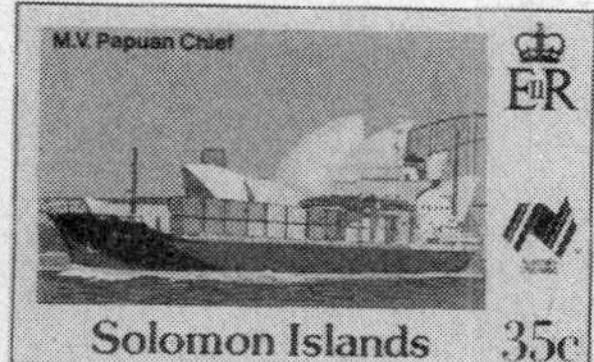

169 "Papuan Chief" (container ship)

1988. "Sydpex '88" National Stamp Exhibition, Sydney and Bicentenary of Australian Settlement. Multicoloured.

626 35 c. Type **169** 20 25
627 60 c. "Nimos" (container ship) 30 35
628 70 c. "Malaita" (liner) .. 40 45
629 $1.30 "Makambo" (freighter) 70 75

170 Archery

1988. Olympic Games, Seoul. Multicoloured.

631 22 c. Type **170** 30 15
632 55 c. Weightlifting .. 50 40
633 70 c. Athletics 60 55
634 80 c. Boxing 70 60

1988. 300th Anniv of Lloyd's of London. As T **123** of Ascension.

636 22 c. black and brown .. 20 15
637 50 c. multicoloured .. 35 30
638 65 c. multicoloured .. 50 45
639 $2 multicoloured .. 1·40 1·50

DESIGNS: VERT—22 c. King George V and Queen Mary laying foundation stone of Leadenhall Street Building, 1925; $2 "Empress of China", 1911. HORIZ—50 c. "Forthbank" (container ship); 65 c. Soltel satellite communications station.

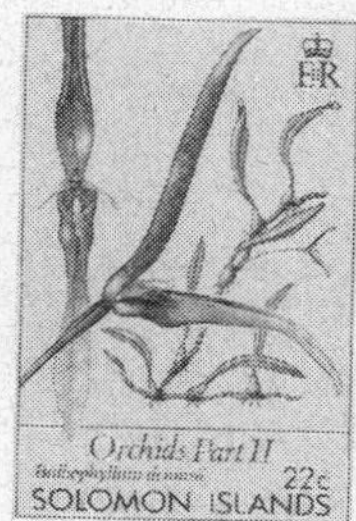

171 "Bulbophyllum dennisii"

1989. Orchids (2nd series). Multicoloured.

640 22 c. Type **171** 35 15
641 35 c. "Calanthe langei" .. 45 30
642 55 c. "Bulbophyllum blumei" 65 45
643 $2 "Grammatophyllum speciosum" .. .. 1·60 1·75

172 Red Cross Workers with Handicapped Children

1989. 125th Anniv of International Red Cross. Multicoloured.

644 35 c. Type **172** 15 20
645 35 c. Handicapped Children Centre minibus .. 15 20
646 $1.50 Blood donor .. 65 70
647 $1.50 Balance test .. 65 70

Nos. 644/5 and 646/7 were each printed together, se-tenant, each pair forming a composite design.

173 "Phyllidia varicosa"

1989. Nudibranchs (Sea Slugs). Multicoloured.

648 22 c. Type **173** 10 10
649 70 c. "Chromodoris bullocki" 30 35
650 80 c. "Chromodoris leopardus" 35 40
651 $1.50 "Phidiana indica" .. 65 70

1989. 20th Anniv of First Manned Landing on Moon. As T **126** of Ascension. Multicoloured.

652 22 c. "Apollo 16" descending by parachute .. 10 10
653 35 c. Launch of "Apollo 16" (30 × 30 mm) .. 15 20
654 70 c. "Apollo 16" emblem (30 × 30 mm) 30 35
655 80 c. Ultra-violet colour photograph of Earth .. 35 40

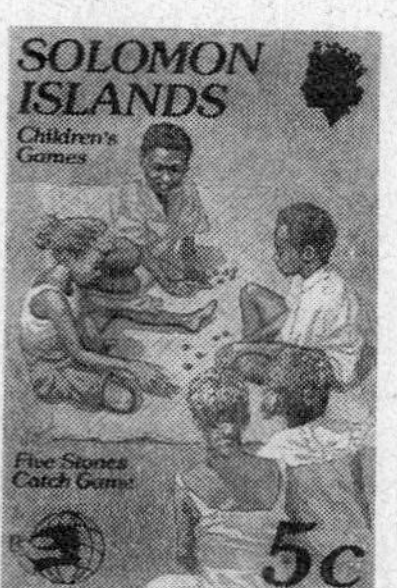

174 Five Stones Catch

1989. "World Stamp Expo '89", International Stamp Exhibition, Washington. Children's Games. Multicoloured.

657 5 c. Type **174** 10 10
658 67 c. Blowing soap bubbles (horiz) 30 35
659 73 c. Coconut shell game (horiz) 30 35
660 $1 Seed wind sound .. 40 45

175 Fishermen and Butterfly

1989. Christmas. Multicoloured.

662 18 c. Type **175** 10 10
663 25 c. The Nativity .. 10 15
664 45 c. Hospital ward at Christmas 20 25
665 $1.50 Village tug-of-war .. 65 70

176 Man wearing Headband, Necklace and Sash

1990. Personal Ornaments. Multicoloured.

666 5 c. Type **176** 10 10
667 12 c. Pendant 10 10
668 18 c. Man wearing medallion, nose ring and earrings 10 10
669 $2 Forehead ornament .. 85 90

177 Spindle Cowrie

1990. Cowrie Shells. Multicolored.

670 4 c. Type **177** 10 10
671 20 c. Map cowrie 10 15
672 35 c. Sieve cowrie .. 15 20
673 50 c. Egg cowrie 20 25
674 $1 Prince cowrie 40 45

1990. 90th Birthday of Queen Elizabeth the Queen Mother. As T **134** of Ascension.

675 25 c. multicoloured .. 10 15
676 $5 black and red .. .. 2·10 2·25

DESIGNS—21 × 36 mm. 25 c. Queen Mother, 1987. 29 × 37 mm. $5 King George VI and Queen Elizabeth inspecting bomb damage to Buckingham Palace, 1940.

178 Postman with Mail Van

1990. 150th Anniv of the Penny Black. Mult.

677 35 c. Type **178** 15 20
678 45 c. General Post Office .. 20 25
679 50 c. 1907 ½d. Stamp .. 20 25
680 55 c. Child collecting stamps 25 30
681 60 c. Penny Black and Solomon Islands 1913 1d. stamp 25 30

179 Purple Swamphen

1990. "Birdpex '90" Stamp Exhibition, Christchurch, New Zealand. Multicoloured.

682 10 c. Type **179** 10 10
683 25 c. Mackinlay's cuckoo dove ("Rufous brown pheasant dove") .. 10 10
684 30 c. Superb fruit dove .. 10 15
685 45 c. Cardinal honeyeater 20 25
686 $2 Finsch's pygmy parrot 85 90

180 "Cylas formicarius" (weevil)

1991. Crop Pests. Multicoloured.

687 7 c. Type **180** 10 10
688 25 c. "Dacus cucurbitae" (fruit-fly) 10 10
689 40 c. "Papuana uninodis" (beetle) 15 20
690 90 c. "Pantorhytes biplagiatus" (weevil) .. 35 40
691 $1.50 "Scapanes australis" (beetle) 65 70

1991. 65th Birthday of Queen Elizabeth II and 70th Birthday of Prince Philip. As T **139** of Ascension. Multicoloured.

692 90 c. Prince Philip in evening dress .. 35 40
693 $2 Queen Elizabeth II .. 85 90

181 Child drinking from Coconut

1991. Health Campaign. Multicoloured.

694 5 c. Type **181** 10 10
695 75 c. Mother feeding child 30 35
696 80 c. Breast feeding .. 35 40
697 90 c. Local produce .. 35 40

182 Volley Ball

1991. 9th South Pacific Games. Multicoloured.

698	25 c. Type **182**	10	10
699	40 c. Judo	15	20
700	65 c. Squash	25	30
701	90 c. Bowling	35	40

183 Preparing Food for Christmas

1991. Christmas. Multicoloured.

703	10 c. Type **183**	10	10
704	25 c. Christmas Day church service	10	15
705	65 c. Christmas Day feast	25	30
706	$2 Cricket match	85	90

184 Yellowfin Tuna

1991. "Philanippon '91" International Stamp Exhibition, Tokyo. Tuna Fishing. Mult.

708	5 c. Type **184**	10	10
709	30 c. Pole and line tuna fishing boat	10	15
710	80 c. Pole and line fishing	35	40
711	$2 Processing "arabushi" (smoked tuna) ..	85	90

1992. 40th Anniv of Queen Elizabeth II's Accession. As T **143** of Ascension. Mult.

713	5 c. Aerial view of Honiara	10	10
714	20 c. Sunset across lagoon	10	10
715	40 c. Honiara harbour ..	15	20
716	60 c. Three portraits of Queen Elizabeth ..	25	20
717	$5 Queen Elizabeth II ..	2·10	2·25

185 Mendana's Fleet in Thousand Ships Bay

1992. "Granada '92" International Stamp Exhibition, Spain. Mendana's Discovery of Solomon Islands. Multicoloured.

718	10 c. Type **185**	10	10
719	65 c. Map of voyage ..	25	30
720	80 c. Alvaro Mendana de Niera	35	40
721	$1 Settlement at Graciosa Bay	40	45
722	$5 Mendana's fleet at sea	2·10	2·25

186 Sgt-Major Jacob Vouza

1992. Birth Centenary of Sgt-Major Jacob Vouza (war hero). Multicoloured.

723	25 c. Type **186**	10	15
724	70 c. Vouza in U.S. Marine corps battle dress ..	30	35
725	90 c. Vouza in U.S. Marine corps uniform	35	40
726	$2 Statue of Vouza ..	85	90

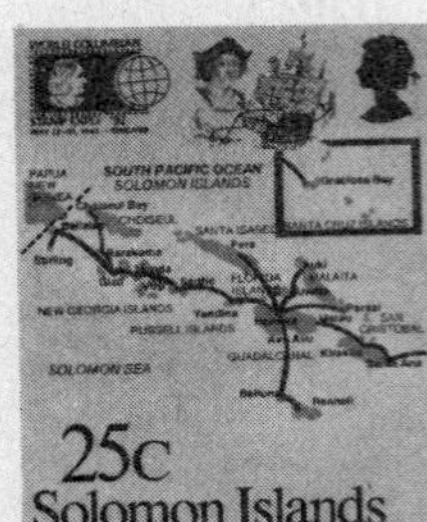

187 Solomon Airlines Domestic Routes

1992. 500th Anniv of Discovery of America by Columbus and "World Columbian Stamp EXPO '92" Exhibition, Chicago. Mult.

728	25 c. Type **187**	10	15
729	80 c. Solomon Airlines Boeing 737-400 "Guadalcanal" ..	35	40
730	$1.50 Solomon Airlines international routes ..	65	70
731	$5 Columbus and "Santa Maria"	2·10	2·25

POSTAGE DUE STAMPS

D 1.

1940.

D 1.	D 1.	1d. green	3·75	6·50
D 2.		2d. red	4·25	6·50
D 3.		3d. brown	4·50	10·00
D 4.		4d. blue	7·00	11·00
D 5.		5d. olive	8·00	14·00
D 6.		6d. purple	8·50	15·00
D 7.		1s. violet	12·00	26·00
D 8.		1s. 6d. green	22·00	45·00

SOMALILAND PROTECTORATE

A Br. protectorate in N.E. Africa on the Gulf of Aden. Amalgamated with the Somalia Republic on 1st July, 1960, whose stamps it now uses.

1903. 16 annas = 1 rupee.
1951. 100 cents = 1 shilling.

1903. Stamps of India (Queen Victoria) optd. **BRITISH SOMALILAND.**

1.	**23.**	½ a. green	1·25	1·75
2.	–	1 a. red	1·25	1·50
3.	–	2 a. lilac	75	40
4.	–	2½ a. blue..	2·00	1·75
5.	–	3 a. orange	1·25	1·75
6.	–	4 a. green (No. 96) ..	1·50	2·75
19.	–	6 a. brown (No. 80) ..	2·00	4·25
8.	–	8 a. mauve	1·50	5·00
9.	–	12 a. purple on red ..	1·75	7·00
21.	**37.**	1 r. green and red ..	2·00	10·00
11.	**38.**	2 r. red and orange ..	22·00	32·00
12.		3 r. brown and green ..	17·00	35·00
13.		5 r. blue and violet ..	20·00	45·00

1903. Stamps of India of 1902 (King Edward VII) with same opt.

25.	½ a. green (No. 122) ..	75	55
26.	1 a. red (No. 123)	60	30
27.	2 a. lilac	1·00	2·50
28.	3 a. orange..	1·00	2·50
29.	4 a. olive	1·00	4·00
30.	8 a. mauve..	1·25	2·25

2.

1904.

32	2	½ a. green..	30	2·50
33		1 a. black and red ..	1·25	1·75
59		1 a. red	2·50	75
34		2 a. purple	1·50	1·00
35		2½ a. blue	1·75	3·00
36		3 a. brown and green ..	1·00	2·25
37		4 a. green and black ..	1·50	2·75
38		6 a. green and violet ..	3·00	8·50
39		8 a. black and blue ..	2·75	5·50
53		12 a. black and orange ..	2·75	10·00
41		1 r. green	12·00	28·00
42		2 r. purple	28·00	55·00
43		3 r. green and black ..	28·00	60·00
44		5 r. black and red ..	30·00	60·00

The rupee values are larger (26 × 31 mm.)

1912. As 1904, but portrait of King George V.

60.–	½ a green	20	3·50
74.	1 a. red	80	30
75.–	2 a. purple	1·00	1·00
76.	2½ a blue	50	3·50
64.	3 a. brown and green ..	80	3·75
65.	4 a. green and black ..	80	4·75
66.	6 a. green and violet ..	80	3·25
80.	8 a. black and blue ..	1·50	5·00
68.	12 a. black and orange ..	1·25	13·00
69.	1 r. green	4·75	8·00
83.	2 r. purple	14·00	32·00
84.	3 r. green and black ..	26·00	80·00
72.	5 r. black and red	48·00	£100

1935. Silver Jubilee. As T **13** of Antigua.

86.	1 a. blue and red	1·25	1·50
87.	2 a. blue and grey	1·25	1·50
88.	3 a. brown and blue ..	2·00	3·50
89.	1 r. grey and purple ..	5·00	7·00

1937. Coronation. As T **2** of Aden.

90.	1 a. red	10	10
91.	2 a. grey	30	45
92.	3 a. blue	45	50

6. Berbera Blackhead Sheep. 9.

8. Somaliland Protectorate.

DESIGN—As T **6**; 4 a. to 12 a. Greater Kudu Antelope.

1938. Portrait faces left.

93.	**6.**	½ a. green	15	1·25
94.		1 a. red	15	10
95.		2 a. purple	15	15
96.		3 a. blue	3·00	3·50
97.	–	4 a. brown	1·25	2·25
98.	–	6 a. violet	2·50	6·00
99.	–	8 a. grey..	65	5·00
100.	–	12 a. orange	65	6·50
101.	**8.**	1 r. green	6·00	20·00
102.		2 r. purple	8·50	20·00
103.		3 r. blue	9·00	17·00
104.		5 r. black	13·00	17·00

1942. As Nos. 93/104 but with full-face portraits as in T **9**.

105.	**9.**	½ a. green	10	10
106.	–	1 a. red	10	10
107.	–	2 a. purple	40	10
108.		3 a. blue	50	10
109.	–	4 a. brown	50	10
110.	–	6 a. violet	70	10
111.	–	8 a. grey	45	10
112.	–	12 a. orange	1·00	10
113.	–	1 r. green	45	25
114.	–	2 r. purple	1·00	1·75
115.	–	3 r. blue	1·10	5·50
116.	–	5 r. black	3·25	4·00

1946. Victory. As T **9** of Aden.

117.	1 a. red	10	10
118.	3 a. blue	10	10

1949. Silver Wedding. As T **10/11** of Aden.

119.	1 a. red	10	10
120.	5 r. black	3·00	3·25

1949. U.P.U. As T **20/23** of Antigua.

121.	1 a. on 10 c. red ..	10	10
122.	3 a. on 30 c. blue ..	25	30
123.	6 a. on 50 c. purple ..	25	30
124.	12 a. on 1 s. orange ..	35	30

1951. 1942. issue surch. with figures and **Cents** or **Shillings.**

125.	5 c. on ½ a. green	10	10
126.	10 c. on 2 a. purple ..	10	10
127.	15 c. on 3 a. blue	20	10
128.	20 c. on 4 a. brown ..	30	10
129.	30 c. on 6 a. violet ..	45	10
130.	50 c. on 8 a. grey	40	10
131.	70 c. on 2 a. orange ..	60	1·25
132.	1 s. on 1 r. green	40	10
133.	2 s. on 2 r. purple	70	3·25
134.	2 s. on 3 r. blue	1·25	2·50
135.	5 s. on 5 r. black	2·25	4·00

1953. Coronation. As T **13** of Aden.

136.	15 c. black and green ..	10	15

12. Camel and Gurgi. **13.** Askari.

1953.

137.	**12.**	5 c. black	10	20
138.	**13.**	10 c. orange	90	20
139.	**12.**	15 c. green	40	30
140.		20 c. red	40	30
141.	**13.**	30 c. brown	1·25	30
142.	–	35 c. blue	1·00	60
143.	–	50 c. brown and red ..	1·00	35
144.	–	1 s. blue	50	20
145.	–	1 s. 30 blue and black	4·50	3·00
146.	–	2 s. brown and violet	10·00	2·00
147.	–	5 s. brown and green ..	10·00	5·50
148.	–	10 s. brown and violet	5·50	11·00

DESIGNS—HORIZ. 35 c., 2 s. Somali Stock Dove. 50 c., 5 s. Martial Eagle. 1 s. Berbera Blackhead Sheep. 1 s. 30, Sheikh Isaaq's Tomb, Mait. 10 s. Taleh Fort.

1957. Opening of Legislative Council. Optd. **OPENING OF THE LEGISLATIVE COUNCIL 1957.**

149.	**12.**	20 c. red	10	10
150.		1 s. blue (No. 144) ..	10	10

1960. Legislative Council's Unofficial Majority Optd. **LEGISLATIVE COUNCIL UNOFFICIAL MAJORITY. 1960.**

151.	**12.**	20 c. red	10	10
152.	-	1 s. 30, bl. & blk. (No. 145)	10	10

OFFICIAL STAMPS

1903. Official stamps of India (Queen Victoria) (optd **On H.M.S.**) further optd **BRITISH SOMALILAND.**

O 1.	**23.**	½ a. turquoise	3·50	48·00
O 2.	–	1 a. red	10·00	7·50
O 3.	–	2 a. lilac	8·00	48·00
O 4.	–	8 a. mauve	10·00	£350
O 5.	**37.**	1 r. green and red ..	10·00	£475

1904. Stamps of 1904 optd. **O.H.M.S.**

O 10. 2.	½ a. green	3·25	48·00
O 11.	1 a. black and red	3·25	7·00
O 12.	2 a. purple	£120	48·00
O 13.	8 a. black and blue	60·00	£130
O 15. –	1 r. green (No. 41)	£150	£450

SORUTH

A state of India. In 1948 the Saurashtra Union was formed which included Jasdan, Morvi, Nawanagar and Wadhwan as well as Soruth. Now uses Indian stamps.

12 pies = 1 anna; 16 annas = 1 rupee.

A. JUNAGADH

1.

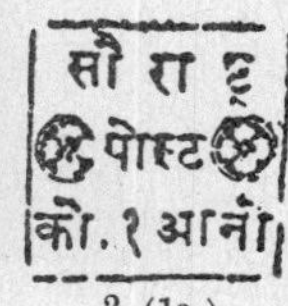

2. (1a.)

1864 (?) On paper of various colours. Imperf.

1. 1.	1 a. black	£650	40·00

1867. (Nos. 11 and 13 are on paper of various colours.) Imperf.

11	2	1 a. black	50·00	8·00
13		1 a. red	12·00	14·00
14		4 a. black	£100	£120

6.

7.

1877. Imperf. or perf.

40	7.	3 p. green	35	35
24	6.	1 a. green	15	15
41		1 a. red	60	60
26	7.	4 a. red	90	60

1913. Surch. in words in English and in native characters.

34. 6.	3 p. on 1 a. green	10	15
39. 7.	1 a. on 4 a. red	90	2·00

ત્રણ પાઇ

(14.)

13. Nawab Sir Mahabatkhanji III.

1923. Surch. as T **14.**

43. 13.	3 p. on 1 a. red	2·50	6·00

1924. Imperf. or perf.

44	13	3 p. mauve	35	40
46		1 a. red	3·00	3·75

The 1 a. is smaller.

15. Junagadh City.

17. Nawab Sir Mahabatkhanji III.

DESIGNS—HORIZ. ½ a., 4 a. Gir lion. 2 a., 8 a. Kathi horse.

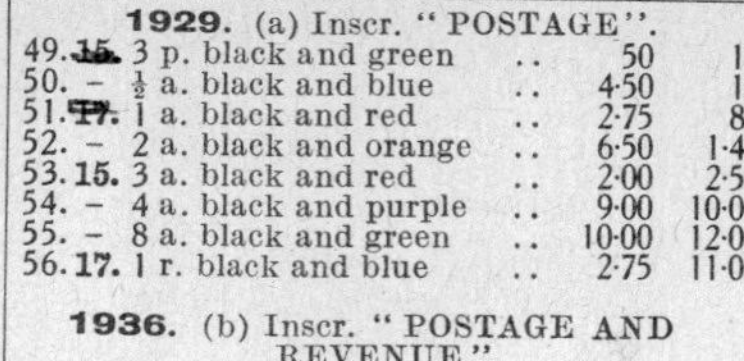

1929. (a) Inscr. " POSTAGE ".

49. 15.	3 p. black and green	50	10
50. –	½ a. black and blue	4·50	10
51. 17.	1 a. black and red	2·75	85
52. –	2 a. black and orange	6·50	1·40
53. 15.	3 a. black and red	2·00	2·50
54. –	4 a. black and purple	9·00	10·00
55. –	8 a. black and green	10·00	12·00
56. 17.	1 r. black and blue	2·75	11·00

1936. (b) Inscr. " POSTAGE AND REVENUE ".

57. 17.	1 a. black and red	2·50	90

OFFICIAL STAMPS

1929. Nos. 49/56 optd. **SARKARI.**

O 1. 15.	3 p. black and green	50	10
O 2. –	½ a. black and blue	1·25	10
O 3. 17.	1 a. black and red	1·00	10
O 4. –	2 a. black and orange	2·00	30
O 5. 15.	3 a. black and red	60	20
O 6. –	4 a. black and purple	1·50	40
O 7. –	8 a. black and green	1·75	80
O 8. 17.	1 r. black and blue	2·25	8·50

1938. No. 57 optd. **SARKARI.**

O 13. 17.	1 a. black and red	4·50	60

B. UNION OF SAURASHTRA

1949. Surch. **POSTAGE & REVENUE ONE ANNA.**

61. 15.	1 a. on 3 p. black & green	30·00	30·00
58. –	1 a. on ½ a. black and blue (No. 50)	5·50	2·75

Surch. **Postage and Revenue ONE ANNA.**

59.	1 a. on 2 a. grey and yellow (No. 52)	3·75	12·00

21.

1949.

60	21	1 s. purple	5·00	5·00

OFFICIAL STAMPS

1948. Official stamps of 1929 surch **ONE ANNA.**

O 14	1 a. on 2 a. grey & yellow	£2000	18·00
O 15	1 a. on 3 a. black & red	£1700	32·00
O 16	1 a. on 4 a. black & purple	£170	24·00
O 17	1 a. on 8 a. black & green	£170	20·00
O 19	1 a. on 1 r. black & blue	£180	27·00

1949. No. 59 optd. **SARKARI.**

O 22.	1 a. on 2 a. grey & yellow	32·00	10·00

SOUTH AFRICA

The Union of S. Africa consists of the provinces of the Cape of Good Hope, Natal, the Orange Free State and the Transvaal. Became an independent republic on 31st May, 1961.

1910. 12 pence = 1 shilling;
20 shillings = 1 pound.
1961. 100 cents = 1 rand.

1.

2.

1910.

2. 1.	2½d. blue	2·00	1·25

1913.

3. 2.	½d. green	60	25
4.	1d. red	60	10
5.	1½d. brown	30	10
6.	2d. purple	1·25	10
7.	2½d. blue	2·50	85
8.	3d. black and red	6·50	25
9.	3d. blue	4·50	1·50
10a.	4d. orange and green	7·50	45
11.	6d. black and violet	5·50	15
12.	1s. orange	15·00	55
13.	1s. 3d. violet	12·00	7·00
14.	2s. 6d. purple and green	55·00	1·00
15.	5s. purple and blue	£130	5·00
16.	10s. blue and olive	£225	5·50
17.	£1 green and red	£700	£350

5.

1925. Air.

26.	5.	1d. red	3·50	6·00
27.		3d. blue	7·00	8·00
28.		6d. mauve	10·00	13·00
29.		9d. green	18·00	45·00

NOTE—"Bilingual" in heading indicates that the stamps are inscribed alternately in English and Afrikaans throughout the sheet. Our prices for such issues are for mint bilingual pairs and used single stamps of either inscription.

6. Springbok.

7. Van Riebeeck's Ship.

8. Orange Tree.

11. Union Buildings, Pretoria.

12. Groot Schuur.

10. " Hope ".

1926. Bilingual Pairs. No. 33 is imperf.

114	6	½d. black and green	30	10
135	7	1d. black and red	30	10
34	11	2d. grey and purple	8·00	50
44		2d. grey and lilac	15·00	20
58		2d. blue and violet	55·00	1·00
35	12	3d. black and red	18·00	50
45b		3d. blue	4·50	10
33	10	4d. blue	1·00	60
118	–	4d. brown	80	10
119	8	6d. green and orange	1·50	10
120	–	1s. brown and blue	6·00	10
121	–	2s. 6d. green and brown	8·50	30
49a	–	2s. 6d. blue and brown	14·00	20
64a	–	5s. black and green	32·00	50
39	–	10s. blue and brown	£150	9·00

DESIGNS—As Type **11:** 4d. (No. 118) A native kraal. 1s. Gnus. 2s. 6d. Ox-wagon crossing river. 5s. Ox-wagon outspanned. 10s. Cape Town and Table Bay.

On No. 33 the English and Afrikaans inscriptions are on separate sheets, and our price is for single stamps of either language.

For ½d., 1d., 2d. 3d. and 10s. in similar designs see Nos. 105/6, 107a, 116/7 and 64ba respectively.

17. D.H. " Moth ".

1929. Air.

40. 17.	4d. green	5·00	2·50
41.	1s. orange	9·00	11·00

18. Church of the Vow.

1933. Voortrekker Memorial Fund. Inscr. as in T **18.** Bilingual pairs.

50. 18.	½d.+½d. green	3·25	50
51. –	1d.+½d. black and pink	3·25	25
52. –	2d.+1d. green & purple	4·00	55
53. –	3d.+1½d. green and blue	6·00	70

DESIGNS: 1d. The " Great Trek ". 2d Voortrekker man. 3d. Voortrekker woman.

24.

1935. Silver Jubilee. Bilingual pairs.

65	24	½d. black and green	2·50	10
66		1d. black and red	2·75	10
67		3d. blue	23·00	2·25
68		6d. green and orange	42·00	3·25

The positions of Afrikkaans and English inscriptions are transposed on alternate stamps.

22. Gold Mine.

25. King George VI.

1936. Bilingual pair.

57. 22.	1½d. green and gold	1·50	10

1937. Coronation. Bilingual pairs.

71. 25.	½d. grey and green	25	10
72.	1d. grey and red	35	10
73.	1½d. orange and green	50	10
74.	3d. blue	3·00	10
75.	1s. brown and blue	5·50	15

27. Wagon crossing Drakensberg.

28. Signing of Dingaan-Retief Treaty

1938. Voortrekker Centenary Fund. Dated " 1838 1938 ". Bilingual pairs.

76. –	½d.+½d. blue and green	9·00	30
77. 27.	1d.+1d. blue and red	10·00	40
78. 28.	1½d.+1½d. brown & grn.	12·00	70
79. –	3d.+3d. blue	13·00	90

DESIGNS—As T **27:** ½d. Voortrekker ploughing. As T **28:** Voortrekker Monument.

31. Voortrekker Family.

1938. Voortrekker Commem. Bilingual pairs.

80. –	1 d. blue and red	2·75	20
81. 31.	1½d. blue and brown	4·25	20

DESIGN: 1d. Wagon wheel.

22a. Groot Schuur.

23. Groot Constantia.

1939. Bilingual pairs.

117a	**22a**	3d. blue	1·25	10
64ba	**23**	10s. blue and brown	35·00	30

32. Old Vicarage, Paarl, now a Museum.

33. Symbol of the Reformation.

34. Huguenot Dwelling, Drakenstein Mountain Valley.

1939. 250th Anniv. of Landing of Huguenots in S. Africa. Bilingual pairs.

82.	**32.**	½d.+½d. brown and green	4·50	30
83.	**33.**	1d.+1d. green and red	8·50	30
84.	**34.**	1½d.+1½d. green and pur.	14·00	70

34a. Gold Mine.

1941. Bilingual pair.

87.	**34a.**	1½d. green and buff	25	10

35. Infantry. **38.** Sailor, Destroyer and Lifebelts.

39. Women's Auxiliary Services.

1941. War Effort. Bilingual pairs except the 2d. and 1s. which are inscr. in both languages on each stamp.

88.	**35.**	½d. green	75	10
89.	–	1d. red	1·25	10
90.	–	1½d. green	65	10
95.	**38.**	2d. violet	45	10
91.	**39.**	3d. blue	11·00	50
92.	–	4d. brown	10·00	10
93.	–	6d. orange	7·50	10
96.	–	1s. brown	2·50	50
94a.	–	1s. 3d. brown	5·50	15

DESIGNS—As Type **35**: 1d. Nurse and ambulance. 1½d. Airman. 1s. 3d. Signaller. As Type **38**: 4d. Artillery. 6d. Welding. As Type **39**: 1s. Tank corps.

43. Infantry.

DESIGNS—As Type **43**. VERT. 1d. Nurse. 1½d. Airman. 2d. Sailor. 6d. Welder. HORIZ. 3d. Women's Auxiliary Services. 6d. Heavy gun. 1s. Tanks.

1942. War Effort. Bilingual except 4d. and 1s., which are inscr. in both languages on each stamp.

97.	**43.**	½d. green	70	10
98.	–	1d. red	70	10
99.	–	1½d. brown	65	10
100.	–	2d. violet	90	10
101.	–	3d. blue	7·00	10
103.	–	4d. green	10·00	10
102.	–	6d. orange	2·00	10
104.	–	1s. brown	7·00	10

Our prices for Nos. 97, 98, 101 and 103 are for units of three. The other stamps are in units of two.

1943. As 1926, but in single colours and with plain background to central oval. Bilingual pairs.

105.	**6.**	½d. green	60	15
106.	**7.**	1d. red	80	10

54. Union Buildings, Pretoria.

1945. Type 11 redrawn. Bilingual pairs.

107a	**54**	2d. slate and violet	2·00	15
116		2d. blue and purple	30	10

55. "Victory". **58.** King George VI.

59. King George VI and Queen Elizabeth.

1945. Victory. Bilingual pairs.

108.	**55.**	1d. brown and red	20	10
109.	–	2d. blue and violet	20	10
110.	–	3d. blue	20	10

DESIGNS: 2d. Man and oxen ploughing ("Peace"). 3d. Man and woman gazing at a star ("Hope").

1947. Royal Visit. Bilingual pairs.

111.	**58.**	1d. black and red	10	10
112.	**59.**	2d. violet	15	10
113.	–	3d. blue	15	10

DESIGN—As Type **59**: 3d. Queen Elizabeth II when Princess and Princess Margaret.

61. Gold Mine. **62.** King George VI and Queen Elizabeth.

1948. Bilingual.

124.	**61.**	1½d. green and buff	50	10

The price for No. 124 is for a unit of four stamps.

1948. Royal Silver Wedding. Bilingual pair.

125.	**62.**	3d. blue and silver	50	10

63. "Wanderer" entering Durban.

1949. Centenary of Arrival of British Settlers in Natal. Bilingual pair.

127.	**63.**	1½d. brown	15	10

64. Hermes.

1949. U.P.U. 75th Anniv. Bilingual pairs.

128.	**64.**	½d. green	50	10
129.		1½d. red	60	10
130.		3d. blue	1·25	10

65. Wagons approaching Bingham's Berg.

1949. Inauguration of Voortrekker Monument, Pretoria.

131.	**65.**	1d. mauve	10	10
132.	–	1½d. green	10	10
133.	–	3d. blue	10	10

DESIGNS: 1½d. Voortrekker Monument, Pretoria. 3d. Bible, candle and Voortrekkers.

68. Union Bldgs., Pretoria.

1950. Bilingual pair.

134.	**68.**	2d. blue and violet	15	10

INSCRIPTIONS. In all later issues except Nos. 167 and 262/5, the stamps are inscribed in both Afrikaans and English. Our prices are for single copies, unused and used.

70. " Maria de la Quellerie " (D. Craey). **76.** Queen Elizabeth II.

1952. Tercentenary of Landing of Van Riebeeck. Dated "1652–1952".

136.	–	½d. purple and sepia	10	10
137.	**70.**	1d. green	10	10
138.	–	2d. violet	20	10
139.	–	4½d. blue	10	10
140.	–	1s. brown	15	10

DESIGNS—HORIZ. ½d. Seal and monogram. 2d. Arrival of Van Riebeeck's ships. 1s. Landing at the Cape. VERT. 4½d. Jan Van Riebeeck.

1952. S. African Tercentenary Stamp Exn., Cape Town. No. 137 optd. **SATISE** and No. 138 optd. **SADIPU**.

141.	**70.**	1d. green	15	50
142.	–	2d. violet	15	10

1953. Coronation.

143.	**76.**	2d. blue	20	10

77. 1d. Cape Triangular Stamp.

1953. Stamp Cent. of Cape of Good Hope.

144.	**77.**	1d. sepia and red	10	10
145.	–	4d. indigo and blue	10	10

DESIGN: 4d. as Type **77** but reproducing "Triangular".

79. Merino Ram.

1953.

146.	**79.**	4½d. purple and yellow	20	10
147.	–	1s. 3d. brown	80	10
148.	–	1s. 6d. red and green	70	25

DESIGNS: 1s. 3d. Springbok. 1s. 6d. Aloes.

82. Arms of Orange Free State and Scroll.

1954. Centenary of Orange Free State.

149.	**82.**	2d. sepia and red	10	10
150.		4½d. purple and grey	10	25

83. Warthog. **87.** Rhinoceros.

1954. Wild Animals.

151.	**83.**	½d. turquoise	10	10
152.	–	1d. lake	10	10
153.	–	1½d. sepia	10	10
154.	–	2d. plum	10	10
155.	**87.**	3d. brown and blue	15	10
156.	–	4d. blue and green	40	10
157.	–	4½d. indigo and blue	60	1·25
158.	–	6d. sepia and orange	50	10
159.	–	1s. brown and red	60	10
160.	–	1s. 3d. brown and green	1·00	10
161.	–	1s. 6d. brown and pink	1·75	60
162.	–	2s. 6d. sepia & light green	3·50	20
163.	–	5s. sepia and buff	10·00	90
164.	–	10s. black and blue	17·00	4·50

DESIGNS: As Type **83**—VERT. 1d. Black Wildebeest. 1½d. Leopard. 2d Mountain Zebra. As Type **87**—VERT. 4d. African Elephant. 4½d. Hippopotamus. 1s. Greater Kudu 1s. 6d. Gemsbok. 2s. 6d. Nyala. 5s. Giraffe. 10s. Sable Antelope. HORIZ. 6d. Lion. 1s. 3d. Springbok.

97. President Kruger. **99.** A. Pretorius, Church of the Vow and Flag.

1955. Cent. of Pretoria.

165.	**97.**	3d. green	10	10
166.	–	6d. pur. (Pres. Pretorius)	10	20

1955. Voortrekker Covenant Celebrations Pietermaritzburg. Bilingual pair.

167.	**99.**	2d. blue and red	45	10

100. Settlers' Block-wagon and House.

1958. Centenary of Arrival of German Settlers in S. Africa.
168. 100. 2d. brown and purple .. 10 10

101. Arms of the Academy.

1959. 50th Anniv. S. African Academy of Science and Art, Pretoria.
169. 101. 3d. blue and turquoise .. 10 10

103. Globe and Antarctic Scene. **104.** Union Flag.

1959. S. African National Antarctic Expedition.
178. 103. 3d. turquoise & orange 15 10

1960. 50th Anniv. of Union of S. Africa.
179. 104. 4d. orange and blue .. 25 10
180. – 6d. red, brown & green 20 10
181. – 1s. blue and yellow .. 20 10
182. – 1s. 6d. black and blue .. 1·00 1·75
DESIGNS—VERT. 6d. Union Arms. HORIZ. 1s. "Wheel of progress". 1s. 6d. Union Festival emblem.
See also Nos. 190 and 192/3.

108. Locomotives of 1860 and 1960.

1960. Centenary of S. African Railways.
183. 108. 1s. 3d. blue .. .. 1·25 30

109. Prime Ministers Botha, Smuts Hertzog, Malan, Strijdom and Verwoerd.

1960. Union Day.
184. 109. 3d. brown & light brown 10 10

1961. Types as before but new currency
185. 83. ½ c. turquoise 10 10
186. – 1 c. lake (as No. 152) .. 10 10
187. – 1½ c. sepia (as No. 153) 10 10
188. – 2 c. plum (as No. 154) 10 10
189. 109. 2½ c. brown 10 10
190. 104. 3½ c. orange and blue .. 15 80
191. – 5 c. sep. & orge. (as 158) 20 10
192. – 7½ c. red, brown and green (as No. 180) .. 20 1·00
193. – 10 c. bl. & yell. (as 181) 20 15
194. – 12½ c. brn. & grn. (as 160) 1·00 1·60
195. – 20 c. brn. & pk. (as 161) 2·00 2·75
196. – 50 c. sep. & buff (as 163) 6·00 10·00
197. – 1 r. blk. & blue (as 164) 17·00 22·00

For later issues see Volume 2.

OFFICIAL STAMPS

1926. Optd. **OFFICIAL OFFISIEEL.**
(a) On Stamp of 1913.
O1. 3. 2d. purple .. .. 17·00 1·75

(b) On various pictorial issues.
O35b 6 ½d. black and green 70 15
O25 7 1d. black and red .. 65 15
O26 22 1½d. green and gold 12·00 1·50
O37 34a 1½d. green and buff 1·40 25
O 6 11 2d. grey and purple 3·25 1·50
O15 2d. grey and lilac .. 6·00 1·50
O27 2d. blue and violet 45·00 2·00
O27a 54 2d. slate and violet 2·25 1·50
O38 68 2d. blue and violet .. 1·00 20
O39 8 6d. green and orange 1·00 35
O40 – 1s. brown & blue. (No. 120) 5·50 1·60
O41 – 2s. 6d. green & brown (No. 121) 8·50 3·25
O20a – 2s. 6d. blue & brown (No. 49a) .. 24·00 6·50
O41b – 5s. black and green (No. 122) .. 22·00 5·50
O42 23 10s. blue and brown 55·00 16·00

POSTAGE DUE STAMPS

D 1. D 2.

1914. Perf. or roul.
D 11. D 1. ½d. black and green 30 1·75
D 12. 1d. black and red .. 35 15
D 13. 1½d. black & brown 50 1·25
D 14. 2d. black and violet .. 55 60
D 4. 3d. black and blue .. 2·25 35
D 5. 5d. black and brown 3·50 13·00
D 16. 6d. black and grey .. 9·00 6·00
D 7. 1s. red and black .. 60·00 £110

1927.
D 17 D 2. ½d. black and green .. 35 2·00
D 18 1d. black and red .. 35 30
D 19 2d. black and mauve 1·25 30
D 23 2d. black and purple 3·50 1·10
D 20 3d. black and blue .. 5·50 14·00
D 28 3d. indigo and blue .. 4·00 15
D 21 6d. black and grey .. 8·50 6·00
D 29 6d. green and brown 15·00 4·00
D 29a 6d. green and orange 7·00 2·25

D 3. D 5.

1943.
D 30. D 3. ½d. green .. .. 4·50 30
D 31. 1d. red .. .. 6·00 10
D 32. 2d. violet .. .. 6·00 15
D 33. 3d. blue .. .. 35·00 1·25
The above mint prices are for horiz units of three.

1948. Frame as Type D 2, but with bolder figures of value and capital "D".
D 34. ½d. black and green .. 4·25 6·00
D 39. 1d. black and red .. 70 30
D 40. 2d. black and violet .. 50 20
D 41. 3d. indigo and blue .. 4·00 1·50
D 42. 4d. turquoise and green .. 6·00 6·50
D 43. 6d. green and orange .. 7·00 6·50
D 44. 1s. brown and purple .. 8·00 9·00

1961.
D 45. D 5. 1 c. black and red .. 20 2·50
D 46. 2 c. black and violet 35 2·50
D 47. 4 c. turquoise & green 80 5·50
D 48. 5 c. indigo and blue .. 1·75 5·50
D 49. 6 c. green and orange 4·50 4·75
D 50. 10 c. sepia and brown 5·50 7·50

SOUTH ARABIAN FEDERATION

Comprising Aden and most of the territories of the former Western Aden Protectorate plus one from the Eastern Aden Protectorate. The South Arabian Federation became fully independent on 30 November 1967.

1963. 100 cents = 1 shilling.
1965. 1000 fils = 1dinar.

1963. Cent of Red Cross. As T 30 of Antigua, but without portrait. Value in English and Arabic.
1. 15 c. red and black .. 20 15
2. 1s. 25 c. red and blue .. 40 35

2. Federal Crest.

3. Federal Flag.

1965.
3. 3. 5 f. blue 10 10
4. 10 f. lavender 10 10
5. 15 f. green 10 10
6. 20 f. green 10 10
7. 25 f. brown 10 10
8. 30 f. bistre 10 10
9. 35 f. brown 10 10
10. 50 f. red 10 10
11. 65 f. green 30 30
12. 75 f. red 30 10
13. 3. 100 f. multicoloured .. 30 10
14. 250 f. multicoloured .. 1·00 25
15. 500 f. multicoloured .. 2·50 50
16. 1 d. multicoloured .. 4·50 2·75

4. I.C.Y. Emblem.

1965. Int. Co-operation Year.
17. 4. 5 f. purple and turquoise .. 20 10
18. 65 f. green and lavender .. 50 20

5. Sir Winston Churchill and St. Paul's Cathedral in Wartime.

1966. Churchill Commem. Designs in black, cerise and gold with background in colours given.
19. 5. 5 f. blue 10 10
20. 10 f. green 25 10
21. 65 f. brown 65 10
22. 125 f. violet 90 75

6. Footballer's Legs, Ball and Jules Rimet Cup.

1966. World Cup Football Championships.
23. 6. 10 f. multicoloured .. 25 10
24. – 50 f. multicoloured .. 65 20

7. W.H.O. Building.

1966. Inaug. of W.H.O. Headquarters, Geneva.
25. 7. 10 f. black, green and blue 25 10
26. 75 f. black, purple & brown 45 30

8. "Education".

1966. 20th Anniv. of U.N.E.S.C.O.
27. 8. 10 f. multicoloured .. 15 10
28. – 65 f. yellow, violet & olive 60 55
29. – 125 f. blk., purple & orge. 2·00 1·50
DESIGNS: 65 f. "Science". 125 f. "Culture".

For later issues see **SOUTHERN YEMEN**, and **YEMEN PEOPLE'S DEMOCRATIC REPUBLIC** in Volume 2.

SOUTH AUSTRALIA

A state of the Australian Commonwealth whose stamps it now uses.

12 pence = 1 shilling.
20 shillings = 1 pound.

1.

1855. Imperf.
1. 1. 1d. green £2500 £350
9. 2d. red .. .. .. £650 55·00
3. 6d. blue £2000 £150
12. 1s. orange £3750 £325

3. **4.**

1858. Roul. or perf.
20 1 1d. green .. .. 40·00 23·00
26 2d. red .. .. 38·00 2·75
112 3 3d. on 4d. blue .. 50·00 15·00
138 4d. violet .. 25·00 2·00
141 1 6d. blue .. 35·00 1·75
118 4 8d. on 9d. brown .. 48·00 4·50
123 9d. purple .. 9·00 2·25
35 10d. on 9d. orange .. 90·00 24·00
38 1 1s. yellow .. £450 28·00
130 1s. brown .. 24·00 3·00
151 3 2s. red .. .. 19·00 8·00
The 3d., 8d. and 10d. are formed by surcharges: **3-PENCE, 8 PENCE** and **TEN PENCE** (curved).

15. **11.** **12.**

1868. Various frames.
183 15. ½d. brown .. .. 2·00 35
238 11. 1d. green .. .. 3·00 1·25
294a 1d. red .. .. 1·75 10
251 12. 2d. orange .. .. 3·50 10
295a 2d. violet .. .. 1·60 10
230 – 2½d. on 4d. green .. 6·00 1·75
255 – 3d. green .. .. 5·00 50
256 – 4d. violet .. .. 6·00 40
232 – 5d. on 6d. brown .. 14·00 3·25
260 – 6d. blue .. .. 7·00 40
Nos. 230 and 231 are surch. in figures over straight or curved line.

1882. Surch. **HALF-PENNY** in two lines.
181. 11. ½d. on 1d. green .. .. 8·50 3·00

19. **24.** G.P.O., Adelaide.

22. Red Kangaroo.

23.

1886.

195a.	**19.**	2s. 6d. mauve.. ..	24·00	6·00
196.		5s. pink	32·00	12·00
197.		10s. green	80·00	35·00
198.		15s. brown	£300	£120
199.		£1 blue	£150	80·00

1894.

~~262~~.	**24.**	½d. green	1·25	20
~~252~~.	**22.**	2½d. violet	4·50	45
266.		2½d. blue	4·50	30
258.	**23.**	5d. purple	6·50	45

1902. Inscr. "POSTAGE" at top.

268	**19.**	3d. green	3·25	45
269		4d. orange	5·00	70
~~284~~		6d. green	5·50	70
285		8d. blue..	7·00	2·00
273		9d. red	7·00	1·00
274		10d. orange	10·00	3·25
303b		1s. brown	10·00	1·00
276a		2s. 6d. violet	20·00	7·00
290		5s. red	40·00	20·00
278		10s. green	£110	60·00
292a		£1 blue	£130	80·00

OFFICIAL STAMPS

1874. Various postage issues optd. **O.S.**

A. Issue of 1858.

O 6.	**1.**	1d. green	—	16·00
O 7.	**3.**	3d. on 4d. blue ..	£1000	£375
O 17.		4d. violet	25·00	2·50
O 19.	**1.**	6d. blue..	35·00	4·00
O 26.	**4.**	8d. on 9d. brown ..	£450	£180
O 11.		9d. purple	£350	£110
O 33.	**1.**	1s. brown	20·00	3·50
O 35.	**3.**	2s. red	40·00	7·00

B. Issues of 1868-82.

O 66	**15.**	½d. brown	5·50	2·25
O 50	**11.**	½d. on 1d. green ..	35·00	14·00
~~O 67~~		1d. green	5·00	25
O 81		1d. red	4·75	50
~~O 74~~		2d. orange	5·00	25
O 82		2d. violet	7·00	50
O 58	–	2½d. on 4d. green ..	28·00	4·00
O 84	–	4d. violet	18·00	90
O 61	–	5d. on 6d. brown ..	35·00	11·00
O 62	–	6d. blue	8·50	1·25

C. Issue of 1886.

O 86.	**19.**	2s. 6d. mauve.. ..	£2000	£1600
O 87.		5s. pink	£2000	£1600

D. Issue of 1894.

O 80.	**24.**	½d. green	6·00	2·75
O 83.	**22.**	2½d. blue	20·00	2·25
O 77.	**23.**	5d. purple	40·00	4·25

SOUTH GEORGIA

An island in the Antarctic, one of the Falkland Islands Dependencies. From May 1980, used stamps inscribed FALKLAND ISLANDS DEPENDENCIES.

1963. 12 pence = 1 shilling,
20 shillings = 1 pound.
1971. 100 pence = 1 pound.

1. Reindeer.

1963.

1.	**1.**	½d. red	50	30
2.	–	1d. blue	70	15
3.	–	2d. turquoise	70	15
4.	–	2½d. black..	2·75	80
5.	–	3d. bistre	1·25	15
6.	–	4d. bronze	2·25	30
7.	–	5½d. violet	1·25	15
8.	–	6d. orange	75	15
9.	–	9d. blue	2·75	30
10.	–	1s. purple..	75	15
11.	–	2s. olive and blue ..	11·00	4·00
12.	–	2s. 6d. blue	12·00	4·00
13.	–	5s. brown	16·00	4·00
14.	–	10s. mauve	38·00	10·00
15.	–	£1 blue	95·00	48·00
16.	–	£1 black	10·00	16·00

DESIGNS—HORIZ. 2½d. King penguin and chinstrap penguin. 4d. Fin whale. 5½d. Elephant seal. 9d. Whale-catcher. 1s. Leopard seal. 2s. Shackleton's Cross. 2s 6d. Wandering albatross. 5s. Elephant and fur seal. £1 (No. 15), Blue whale. VERT. 1d. South Sandwich Islands. 2d. Sperm whale. 3d. Fur seal. 6d. Light-mantled sooty albatross. 10s. Plankton and krill. £1, (No. 16) King penguins.

1971. Decimal Currency. Nos 1/14 surch.

18a	½p. on ½d. red	1·00	90
19	1p. on 1d. blue	1·50	55
55	1½p. on 5½d. violet ..	90	1·75
21	2p. on 2d. turquoise ..	70	40
22	2½p. on 2½d. black ..	1·50	40
23	3p. on 3d. bistre	1·00	50
24	4p. on 4d. bronze	90	50
25	5p. on 6d. orange	90	30
26	6p. on 9d. blue	1·50	70
27	7½p. on 1s. purple	2·00	70
63	10p. on 2s. olive and blue..	4·00	8·00
64	15p. on 2s. 6d. blue ..	4·00	8·00
65	25 p. on 5s. brown	4·50	8·00
66	50p. on 10s. mauve ..	3·00	8·50

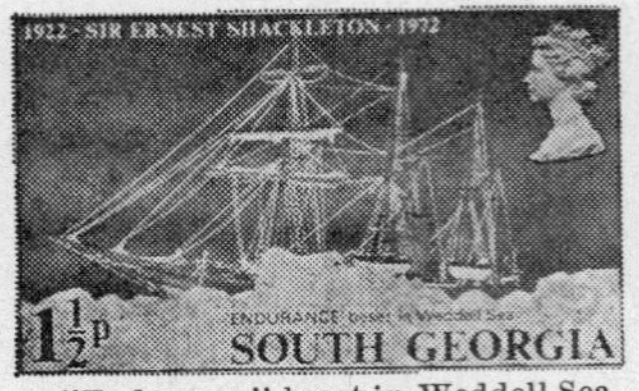

6. "Endurance" beset in Weddell Sea.

1972. 50th Death Anniv. of Sir Ernest Shackleton. Multicoloured.

32.	1½p. Type **6**..	1·00	60
33.	5p. Launching of the long-boat "James Caird" ..	1·25	85
34.	10p. Route of the "James Caird"	1·75	1·00
35.	20p. Sir Ernest Shackleton and the "Quest".. ..	2·00	1·25

1972. Royal Silver Wedding. As T **52** of Ascension, but with Elephant Seal and King Penguins in background.

36.	5p. green	1·00	35
37.	10p. violet	1·00	35

1973. Royal Wedding. As T **47** of Anguilla. Background colours given. Multicoloured.

38.	5p. brown	25	10
39.	15 p. lilac	35	20

8. Churchill and Westminster Skyline.

1974. Birth Cent. of Sir Winston Churchill. Multicoloured.

40.	15p. Type **8**	1·75	1·00
41.	25p. Churchill and warship	2·00	1·00

9. Captain Cook.

1975. Bicentenary of Possession by Captain Cook.

43.	2p. Type **9**	1·60	1·00
44.	8p. H.M.S. "Resolution"	2·75	1·50
45.	16p. Possession Bay ..	3·25	1·75

Nos 44/5 are horiz.

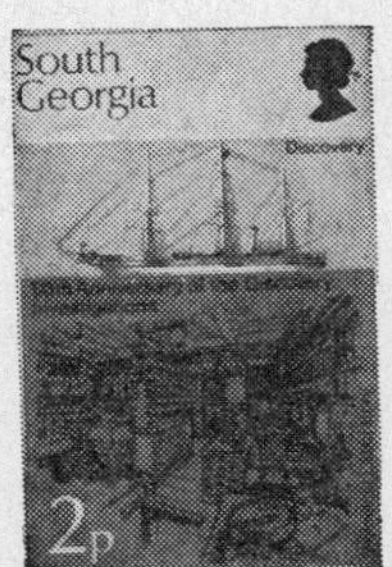

10. "Discovery" and Biological Laboratory.

1976. 50th Anniv. of "Discovery" Investigations. Multicoloured.

46.	2p. Type **10**	1·00	35
47.	8p. "William Scoresby" and water-sampling bottles	1·40	50
48.	11p. "Discovery 11" and plankton net	1·75	55
49.	25p. Biological Station and krill	2·50	85

11. The Queen and Retinue after Coronation.

1977. Silver Jubilee. Multicoloured.

50.	6p. Visit by Prince Philip, 1957	80	30
51.	11p. The Queen and Westminster Abbey	90	35
52.	33p. Type **11**	1·25	50

12. Fur Seal.

1978. 25th Anniv. of Coronation.

67.	–	25p. deep blue, blue and silver	75	1·00
68.	–	25p. multicoloured ..	75	1·00
69.	**12.**	25p. deep blue, blue and silver	75	1·00

DESIGNS: No. 67, Panther of Henry VI. No. 68, Queen Elizabeth II.

13. H.M.S. "Resolution".

1979. Bicentenary of Captain Cook's Voyages, 1768–79. Multicoloured.

70.	3p. Type **13**	1·50	80
71.	6p. "Resolution" and Map of South Georgia and S. Sandwich Isles showing route	1·50	70
72.	11p. King Penguin (from drawing by George Forster)	2·50	2·00
73.	25p. Flaxman/Wedgwood medallion of Capt. Cook	2·75	2·25

SOUTH GEORGIA AND THE SOUTH SANDWICH ISLANDS

Under the new constitution, effective 3 October 1985, South Georgia and the South Sandwich Islands ceased to be dependencies of the Falkland Islands.

100 pence = 1 pound.

1986. 60th Birthday of Queen Elizabeth II. As T **110** of Ascension. Multicoloured.

153.	10p. Four generations of Royal Family at Prince Charles's christening, 1948	25	25
154.	24p. With Prince Charles and Lady Diana Spencer, Buckingham Palace, 1981	55	55
155.	29p. In robes of Order of the British Empire, St. Paul's Cathedral, London	60	60
156.	45p. At banquet, Canada, 1976	95	95
157.	58p. At Crown Agents Head Office London, 1983	1·25	1·25

1986. Royal Wedding. As T **153** of Falkland Islands. Multicoloured.

158	17p. Prince Andrew and Miss Sarah Ferguson at Ascot	75	75
159	22p. Wedding photograph	85	85
160	29p. Prince Andrew with Lynx helicopter on board H.M.S. "Brazen"	1·00	1·00

26. Southern Black-backed Gull.

1987. Birds. Multicoloured.

161.	1p. Type **26**	10	10
162.	2p. Blue-eyed cormorant ..	10	10
163.	3p. Snowy sheathbill (vert.)	10	10
164.	4p. Great skua (vert.) ..	10	10
165.	5p. Pintado petrel.. ..	10	15
166.	6p. Georgian diving petrel	10	15
167.	7p. South Georgia pipit (vert.)	15	20
168.	8p. Georgian teal (vert.) ..	15	20
169.	9p. Fairy prion	20	25
170.	10p. Bearded penguin ..	20	25
171.	20p. Macaroni penguin (vert.)	40	45
172.	25p. Light-mantled sooty albatross (vert.) ..	50	55
173.	50p. Giant petrel (vert.) ..	1·00	1·10
174.	£1 Wandering albatros ..	2·00	2·10
175.	£3 King penguin (vert.) ..	6·00	6·25

1987. 30th Anniv of Int. Geophysical Year. As T **39** of British Antarctic Territory.

176	24p. black and blue ..	50	55
177	29p. multicoloured ..	55	60
178	58p. multicoloured ..	1·10	1·25

DESIGNS: 24p. I.G.Y. Logo; 29p. Grytviken; 58p. Glaciologist using hand-drill to take core sample.

27. "Gaimardia trapesina".

1988. Sea Shells. Multicoloured.

179.	10p. Type **27**	30	30
180.	24p. "Margarella tropidophoroides"	50	60
181.	29p. "Trophon scotianus"	55	65
182.	58p. "Chlanidota densesculpta"	1·10	1·25

1988. 300th Anniv of Lloyd's of London. As T **123** of Ascension.

183	10p. black and brown ..	30	30
184	24p. multicoloured ..	50	55
185	29p. black and green ..	60	65
186	58p. black and red ..	1·10	1·25

DESIGNS—VERT. 10p. Queen Mother at opening of new Lloyd's building, 1957; 58p. "Horatio" (tanker) on fire, 1916. HORIZ. 24p. "Lindblad Explorer" (cruise liner); 29p. Whaling station, Leith Harbour.

28 Glacier Headwall

1989. Glacier Formations. Multicoloured.

187	10p. Type **28**	35	35
188	24p. Accumulation area ..	70	70
189	29p. Ablation area ..	80	80
190	58p. Calving front ..	1·40	1·40

29 Retracing Shackleton's Trek

1989. 25th Anniv of Combined Services Expedition to South Georgia. Multicoloured.

191	10p. Type **29**	35	35
192	24p. Surveying at Royal Bay	70	70
193	29p. H.M.S. "Protector" (ice patrol ship) ..	80	80
194	58p. Raising Union Jack on Mount Paget ..	1·40	1·40

1990. 90th Birthday of Queen Elizabeth the Queen Mother. As T **134** of Ascension.

195	26p. multicoloured ..	75	75
196	£1 black and blue ..	2·75	2·75

DESIGNS—21 × 36 mm. 26p. Queen Mother. 29 × 37 mm. King George VI and Queen Elizabeth with A.R.P. wardens, 1940.

30 "Brutus", Prince Olav Harbour

1990. Wrecks and Hulks. Multicoloured.

197	12p. Type **30**	40	40
198	26p. "Bayard", Ocean Harbour	80	80
199	31p. "Karrakatta", Husvik	95	95
200	62p. "Louise", Grytviken	1·75	1·75

1991. 65th Birthday of Queen Elizabeth II and 70th Birthday of Prince Philip. As T **139** of Ascension. Multicoloured.

201	31p. Queen Elizabeth II ..	1·00	1·00
202	31p. Prince Philip in Grenadier Guards uniform	1·00	1·00

31. Contest between two Bull Elephant Seals.

1991. Elephant Seals. Multicoloured.

203	12p. Type **31**	40	40
204	26p. Adult elephant seal ..	85	85
205	29p. Seal throwing sand ..	95	95
206	31p. Head of elephant seal	1·00	1·00
207	34p. Seals on beach ..	1·10	1·10
208	62p. Cow seal with pup ..	1·75	1·75

1992. 40th Anniv of Queen Elizabeth II's Accession. As T **143** of Ascension. Mult.

209	7p. Ice-covered mountains	30	30
210	14p. Zavodovski Island ..	55	55
211	29p. Gulbrandsen Lake ..	95	95
212	34p. Three portraits of Queen Elizabeth ..	1·10	1·10
213	68p. Queen Elizabeth II	1·75	1·75

32 Adult Teal and Young Bird

1992. Endangered Species. South Georgia Teal. Multicoloured.

214	2p. Type **32**	10	10
215	6p. Adult with eggs ..	10	10
216	12p. Teals swimming	25	30
217	20p. Adult and two chicks	40	45

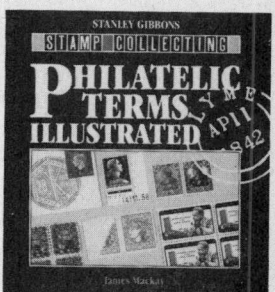

SOUTH WEST AFRICA

A territory in S.W. Africa, formerly the German Colony of German South West Africa (q.v. in Volume 1). Administered by South Africa until 1990 when it became independent as Namibia.

1923. 12 pence = 1 shilling;
20 shillings = 1 pound.
1961. 100 cents = 1 rand.

NOTE.—Stamps overprinted for South West Africa are always South African Stamps, except where otherwise indicated. "Bilingual" in heading indicates that the stamps are inscribed alternately in English and Afrikaans throughout the sheet. "Bilingual" is not repeated in the heading where bilingual stamps of South Africa are overprinted.
Our prices for such issues are for mint bilingual pairs and used single stamps of either inscription.

1923. Optd. alternately **South West Africa** or **Zuidwest Afrika.**

1	2	½d. green	1·25	1·00
2		1d. red	1·50	1·00
3		2d. purple	2·25	1·50
19		3d. blue	3·50	1·25
20		4d. orange and green ..	4·75	2·50
34		6d. black and violet ..	6·50	3·75
35		1s. yellow	11·00	4·25
36		1s. 3d. violet	14·00	5·00
37		2s. 6d. purple and green	35·00	10·00
38		5s. purple and blue ..	55·00	14·00
39		10 s. blue and green ..	85·00	20·00
40a		£1 green and red ..	£300	90·00

1926. Optd. **South West Africa** or **Suidwes Afrika** alternately.

45.	6.	½d. black and green ..	1·40	75
46.	7.	1d. black and red ..	1·40	50
49.	11.	2d. grey and purple ..	3·75	1·75
50.	–	3d. black and red ..	3·75	2·25
47.	8.	6d. green and orange ..	13·00	3·00
51.	–	1s. brown and blue ..	14·00	4·00
52.	–	2s. 6d. green and brown	45·00	12·00
53.	–	5s. black and green ..	75·00	20·00
54.	–	10s. blue and brown ..	85·00	20·00

1926. Triangular optd. **SOUTH WEST AFRIKA** in two lines (E), or **SUIDWES-AFRIKA** in one line (A). Imperf. or perf.

			E.		A.	
44.	10.	4d. blue ..	65	2·00	65	2·00

1927. Triangular optd. **SOUTH WEST AFRIKA** in one line. Imperf.

48.	10.	4d. blue	7·50	19·00

1927. Optd. **S.W.A.**

56.	2.	1s. 3d. violet	1·25	6·00
57.		£1 olive and red ..	£140	£180

1927. Optd. **S.W.A**

58.	6.	½d. black and green ..	1·50	70
59.	7.	1d. black and red ..	1·25	55
60.	11.	2d. grey and purple ..	4·50	1·10
61.	–	3d. black and red ..	6·00	3·25
62.	–	4d. brown	18·00	7·00
63.	8.	6d. green and orange ..	13·00	2·75
64.	–	1s. brown and blue ..	24·00	5·00
65.	–	2s. 6d. green and brown	45·00	10·00
66.	–	5s. black and green ..	65·00	18·00
67.	–	10s. blue and brown ..	£120	28·00

1930. Air. Optd. **S.W.A.**

72.	17.	4d. green	1·25	5·00
73.		1s. orange	1·50	13·00

12 Kori Bustard

1931. Bilingual pairs.

74.	12.	½d. black and green ..	1·40	10
75.	–	1d. blue and red	1·00	10
76.	–	2d. blue and brown ..	50	15
77.	–	3d. dull blue and blue ..	50	15
78.	–	4d. green and purple ..	80	20
79.	–	6d. blue and brown ..	60	20
80.	–	1s. brown and blue ..	1·00	25
81.	–	1s. 3d. violet and yellow ..	8·50	50
82.	–	2s. 6d. red and grey ..	19·00	1·75
83.	–	5s. green and brown ..	20·00	2·75
84.	–	10s. brown and green ..	55·00	7·00
85.	–	£1 red and green	£110	12·00

DESIGNS: 1d. Cape Cross. 2d. Begenfels. 3d. Windhoek. 4d. Waterberg. 6d. Luderitz Bay. 1s. Bush scene. 1s. 3d. Elands. 2s. 6d. Mountain Zebra and Wildebeests. 5s. Herero huts. 10s. Welwitschia plant. £1, Okuwahaken Falls.

24 Monoplane over Windhoek

1931. Air. Bilingual pairs.

86.	24.	3d. brown and blue ..	32·00	3·00
87.	–	10d. black and brown ..	55·00	8·50

DESIGN: 10d. Biplane over Windhoek.

26

1935. Silver Jubilee.

88.	26.	1d. black and red ..	40	25
89.		2d. black and brown ..	90	25
90.		3d. black and blue ..	9·00	13·00
91.		6d. black and purple ..	4·50	3·50

1935. Voortrekker Memorial. As Nos. 50/3 of South Africa optd **S.W.A.**

92	½d.+½d. black and green ..	1·00	65
93	1d.+½d. black and pink ..	1·50	40
94	2d.+1d. green and purple ..	5·00	80
95	3d.+1½d. green and blue ..	15·00	3·25

27 Mail Transport

1937. Bilingual pair.

96	27	1½d. brown	8·00	15

28

1937. Coronation. Bilingual pairs.

97.	28.	½d. black and green ..	45	15
98.		1d. black and red ..	45	15
99.		1½d. black and orange	55	15
100.		2d. black and brown ..	60	15
101.		3d. black and blue ..	65	15
102.		4d. black and purple ..	70	20
103.		6d. black and yellow ..	80	20
104.		1s. black and grey ..	1·25	20

1938. Cent. of Voortrekker. Fund. Optd. **S.W.A.**

105.	–	½d.+½d. blue and green	5·50	1·00
106.	27.	1d.+1d. blue and red	12·00	60
107.	28.	1½d.+1½d. brown & grn.	14·00	2·00
108.	–	3d.+3d. blue	35·00	3·75

1938. Voortrekker Commem. Optd. **S.W.A.**

109.	–	1d. blue and red ..	5·50	75
110.	31.	1½d. blue and brown ..	7·50	1·00

1939. 250th Anniv. of Landing of Huguenots in S. Africa. Optd. **S.W.A.**

111.	32.	½d.+½d. brown & green	4·75	70
112.	33.	1d.+1d. green and red	7·00	85
113.	34.	1½d.+1½d. grn. & purple	10·00	1·25

1941. War Effort. Optd. **S W A.**

(a) Bilingual pairs.

114a	35.	½d. green	65	15
115	–	1d. red	55	15
116	–	1½d. green	55	15
117	39.	3d. blue	9·50	75
118	–	4d. brown	6·50	60
119	–	6d. orange	2·50	50
120	–	1s. 3d. brown	7·00	75

(b) Inscr. in both English and Afrikaans.

121.	38.	2d. violet	40	30
122.	–	1s. brown	60	40

1943. War Effort. Optd. **S W A.**

123.	43.	½d. green (T)	40	10
124.	–	1d. red (T)	70	10
125.	–	1½d. brown (P) ..	45	10
126.	–	2d. violet (P) ..	2·00	10
127.	–	3d. blue (T)	2·50	30
129.	–	4d. green (T)	2·00	40
128.	–	6d. orange (P)	2·00	30
130b.	–	1s. brown (P)	3·25	30

The units referred to above consist of pairs (P), or triplets (T).

1945. Victory. Optd. **S W A.**

131.	55.	1d. brown and red ..	25	10
132.	–	2d. blue and violet ..	30	10
133.	–	3d. blue	65	10

1947. Royal Visit. Optd. **S W A.**

134.	58.	1d. black and red ..	10	10
135.	59.	2d. violet	10	10
136.	–	3d. blue	15	10

1948. Silver Wedding Optd. **S W A.**

137.	62.	3d. blue and silver ..	1·25	10

1949. 75th Anniv. of U.P.U. Optd. **S.W.A.**

138.	64.	½d. green	1·25	20
139.		1½d. red	1·25	15
140.		3d. blue	1·75	20

1949. Inaug. of Voortrekker Monument Pretoria. Optd. **S W A.**

141.	65.	1d. mauve	10	10
142.	–	1½d. green	10	10
143.	–	3d. blue	10	20

1952. Tercentenary of Landing of Van Riebeeck. Optd. **S W A.**

144.	–	½d. purple and sepia ..	10	30
145.	70.	1d. green	10	10
146.	–	2d. violet	50	10
147.	–	4½d. blue	30	90
148.	–	1s. brown	1·00	10

33 Queen Elizabeth II and "Catophracies alexandri"

1953. Coronation. Native Flowers.

149.	33.	1d. red	75	10
150.	–	2d. green ("Banhinia machrantha")	75	10
151.	–	4d. mauve ("Caralluma nebrownii") ..	1·60	55
152.	–	6d. blue ("Gloriosa virescens")	1·75	1·25
153.	–	1s. brown ("Rhigozum tricholotum" ..	1·75	40

34 "Two Bucks" (rock painting)

1954.

154.	34.	1d. lake	30	10
155.	–	2d. brown	35	10
156.	–	3d. purple	2·00	10
157.	–	4d. black	1·75	10
158.	–	4½d. blue	1·25	15
159.	–	6d. green	1·25	10
160.	–	1s. mauve	1·25	30
161.	–	1s. 3d. red	5·00	30
162.	–	1s. 6d. purple ..	5·00	35
163.	–	2s. 6d. brown ..	9·00	60
164.	–	5 s. blue	14·00	2·75
165.	–	10s. green	42·00	15·00

DESIGNS—VERT. 2d. "White Lady" (rock painting). 4½d. Karakul lamb. 6d. Ovambo woman blowing horn. 1s. Ovambo woman. 1s. 3d. Herero woman. 1s. 6d. Ovambo girl. 2s. 6d. Lioness. 5s. Gemsbok. 10s. African elephant. HORIZ. 3d. "Rhinoceros Hunt" (rockpainting). 4 d. "White Elephant and Giraffe" (rock painting).

46 G.P.O., Windhoek

59 "Agricultural Development"

1961.

171	46.	½ c. brown and blue ..	60	10
172	–	1 c. sepia and mauve ..	15	10
173	–	1½ c. violet and salmon ..	20	10
174	–	2 c. green and yellow ..	75	10
175	–	2½ c. brown and blue ..	35	10
176	–	3 c. blue and red ..	3·75	15
177	–	3½ c. blue and green ..	70	15
209	–	4 c. brown and blue ..	1·50	1·25
210	–	5 c. red and blue ..	3·50	10
211	–	6 c. sepia and yellow ..	8·00	7·50
179	–	7½ c. sepia and lemon ..	70	15
213	–	9 c. blue and yellow ..	8·00	7·50
180	–	10 c. blue and yellow ..	1·75	15
181	–	12½ c. blue and lemon ..	85	30
182	–	15 c. brown and blue ..	14·00	3·25
183	–	20 c. brown and orange ..	6·00	30
184	–	50 c. green and orange ..	10·00	1·50
185	–	1 r. yellow, purple & blue	16·00	12·00

DESIGNS—VERT. 1 c. Finger Rock. 1½ c. Mounted Soldier Monument. 2 c. Quivertree. 3 c. Greater flamingoes and Swakopmund Lighthouse. 3½ c. Fishing industry. 5 c. Greater flamingo. 6 c., 7½ c. German Lutheran Church, Windhoek. 10 c. Diamond. 20 c. Topaz. 50 c. Tourmaline. 1 r. Heliodor. HORIZ. 2½ c., 4 c. S.W.A. House, Windhoek. 9 c., 12½ c. Fort Namutoni, 15 c. Hardap Dam.
See also Nos. 224/26.

1963. Opening of Hardap Dam.

192.	59.	3 c. brown and green ..	30	15

61 Centenary Emblem and part of Globe

62 Interior of Assembly Hall

1963. Centenary of Red Cross.

193.	–	7½ c. red, black & blue	7·00	3·00
194.	61.	15 c. red, blk. & salmon	10·00	5·00

DESIGN: 7½ c. Centenary emblem and Map.

1964. Opening of Legislative Assembly Hall, Windhoek.

195.	62.	3 c. blue and salmon ..	50	30

63 Calvin

64 Mail Runner of 1890

1965. 400th Death Anniv. of Calvin (Protestant reformer).

196.	63.	2½ c. purple and gold ..	50	15
197.		15 c. green and gold ..	2·50	1·25

1965. 75th Anniv. of Windhoek.

198.	64.	3 c. sepia and red ..	50	15
199.	–	15 c. brown and green ..	1·25	85

DESIGN: 15 c. Kurt von Francois (founder).

66 Dr. H. Vedder

70 Pres. Swart

67 Camelthorn Tree

1966. 90th Birth Anniv of Vedder (philosopher and writer).

200	66	3 c. green and pink ..	50	15
201		15 c. brown and blue ..	1·25	65

1967. Verwoerd Commemoration.

217 **67** 2½ c. black and green .. 20 10
218 – 3 c. brown and blue .. 30 10
219 – 15 c. brown and purple 1·10 45

DESIGNS—VERT. 3 c. Waves breaking against rock. 15 c. Dr. H. F. Verwoerd.

1968. Swart Commem. Inscr. in German, Afrikaans or English.

220. **70.** 3 c. red, blue and black 45 15
221. – 15 c. red, green and olive 1·50 1·75

DESIGN: 15 c. Pres. and Mrs. Swart.

1970. Water 70 Campaign. As Nos. 299/300 of South Africa, but inscr "SWA".

222. 2½ c. green, blue & brown 75 30
223. 3 c. blue and buff .. 75 30

1970. As Nos. 171 etc., but with "POSGELD" "INKOMSTE" omitted and larger figure of value.

224. **46.** ½ c. brown and blue .. 1·25 30
225. – 1½ c. violet and salmon .. 13·00 13·00
226. – 2 c. green and yellow .. 5·00 40

1970. 150th Anniv. of Bible Soc. of South Africa. As Nos. 301/2 of South Africa.

228. 2½ c. multicoloured .. 1·50 10
229. 12½ c. gold, black and blue 8·00 6·50

1971. "Interstex" Stamp Exhibition, Cape Town. As No. 303 of South Africa. Inscr. "SWA".

230. 5 c. blue black and yellow 4·75 1·50

1971. 10th Anniv of Antarctic Treaty. As No. 401 of South Africa. Inscr "SWA".

231. 12½ c. black, blue and red 45·00 25·00

1971. 10th Anniv. of South African Republic As Nos. 305/6 of South Africa. Inscr. "SWA".

232 2 c. flesh and red .. .. 3·25 75
233 4 c. green and black .. 3·25 75

1972. Centenary of S.P.C.A. As No. 312 of South Africa. Inscr. "SWA".

234. 5 c. multicoloured .. .. 3·50 55

73 "Red sand-dunes, Eastern South-West Africa"

1973. Scenery. Paintings by Adolph Jentsch. Multicoloured.

235. 2 c. Type **73** 75 75
236. 4 c. "After the Rain" .. 1·25 1·25
237. 5 c. "Barren Country" .. 1·50 1·50
238. 10 c. "Schaap River" (vert.) .. .. 2·75 2·75
239. 15 c. "Namib Desert" (vert.) .. .. .. 4·00 4·00

74 "Sarcocaulon rigidum"

75 "Euphorbia virosa"

1973. Multicoloured.

(a) As T **74.**

241 1 c. Type **74** 15 10
242a 2 c. "Lapidaria margaretae" 20 10
243 3 c. "Titanopsis schwantesii" 20 10
244 4 c. "Lithops karasmontana" 25 10
245b 5 c. "Caralluma lugardii" 40 20
246 6 c. "Dinteranthus microspermus" .. 70 40
247 7 c. "Conophytum gratum" 55 45
248 9 c. "Huernia oculata" .. 65 40
249b 10 c. "Gasteria pillansii" 40 30
250 14c. "Stapelia pedunculata" 1·25 90
251 15c. "Fenestraria aurantiaca" 65 30
252 20c. "Decabelonc grandiflora" 3·75 80
253 25 c. "Hoodia bainii" .. 2·25 1·25

(b) As T **75.**

254 30 c. Type **75** .. .. 1·00 50
255a 50 c. "Pachypodium namaquanum" (vert.) 1·50 1·50
256 1 r. "Welwitschia bainesii" 2·00 4·00

1973. Coil Stamps. As Nos 241/2a and 245. Colours changed.

257a **18** 1 c. black and mauve .. 60 30
258 – 2 c. black and yellow .. 40 40
259a – 5 c. black and red .. 90 45

76 Chat-shrikes

77 Giraffe, Antelope and Spoor

1974. Rare Bird Species of South West Africa. Multicoloured.

260. 4 c. Type **76** .. .. 2·75 75
261. 5 c. Peach-faced Lovebirds 3·50 1·25
262. 10 c. Damaraland Rock Jumper .. .. 9·00 3·00
263. 15 c. Ruppell's Parrots .. 13·00 8·50

1974. Twyfelfontein Rock Engravings. Mult.

264. 4 c. Type **77** .. .. 1·50 50
265. 5 c. Elephant, hyena, antelope and spoor .. .. 1·50 80
266. 15 c. Kudu cow .. .. 7·00 6·00

No. 266 is horizontal, size 38×21 mm.

78 Cut Diamond

80 Peregrine Falcon

79 Wagons and Map of the Trek

1974. Diamond Mining. Multicoloured.

267. 10 c. Type **78** .. .. 4·00 3·00
268. 15 c. Diagram of shore workings .. .. 4·50 4·00

1974. Centenary of Thirstland Trek.

269 **79** 4 c. multicoloured .. 1·00 75

1975. Protected Birds of Prey. Mult.

270. 4 c. Type **80** .. .. 2·00 70
271. 5 c. Verreaux's Eagle .. 2·25 1·25
272. 10 c. Martial Eagle .. 6·00 4·00
273. 15 c. Egyptian Vulture .. 7·50 7·00

81 Kolmannskop (ghost town)

1975. Historic Monuments. Multicoloured.

274. 5 c. Type **81** 30 15
275. 9 c. "Martin Luther" (steam tractor) .. 50 50
276. 15 c. Kurt von Francois and Old Fort, Windhoek 1·00 80

82 "View of Luderitz"

1975. Otto Schroder (painter). Multicoloured.

277. 15 c. Type **82** 55 45
278. 15 c. "View of Swakopmund" 55 45
279. 15 c. "Harbour Scene" .. 55 45
280. 15 c. "Quayside, Walvis Bay" 55 45

83 Elephants

1976. Prehistoric Rock Paintings. Mult.

282. 4 c. Type **83** 40 10
283. 10 c. Rhinoceros 65 30
284. 15 c. Antelope 80 60
285. 20 c. Man with bow and arrow .. .. 1·10 85

84 Schwerinsburg

1976. Castles. Multicoloured.

287. 10 c. Type **84** 50 30
288. 15 c. Schloss Duwisib .. 70 50
289. 20 c. Heynitzburg .. 1·00 80

85 Large-toothed Rock Hyrax

1976. Fauna Conservation. Multicoloured.

290. 4 c. Type **85** 50 20
291. 10 c. Kirk's Dik-Dik .. 1·50 75
292. 15 c. Kahl's Tree Squirrel 2·25 1·40

86 The Augustineum, Windhoek

1976. Modern Buildings.

293. **86.** 15 c. black and yellow .. 40 40
294. – 20 c. black and yellow .. 50 50

DESIGN: 20 c. Katutura Hospital, Windhoek.

87 Ovambo Water Canal System

1976. Water and Electricity Supply. Mult.

295. 15 c. Type **87** 30 30
296. 20 c. Ruacana Falls Power Station 40 40

88 Coastline, near Pomona. (illustration reduced, actual size 57×21 mm)

1977. Namib Desert. Multicoloured.

297. 4 c. Type **88** 20 15
298. 10 c. Bush and Dunes, Sossusvlei 30 30
299. 15 c. Plain near Brandberg 50 50
300. 20 c. Dunes, Sperr Gebiet 60 60

89 Kraal

1977. The Ovambo People.

301. **89.** 4 c. multicoloured .. 10 10
302. – 10 c. blk., orge. & brn. 30 20
303. – 15 c. multicoloured .. 30 25
304. – 20 c. multicoloured .. 35 45

DESIGNS: 10 c. Grain baskets. 15 c. Pounding grain. 20 c. Women in tribal dress.

90 Terminal Buildings (illustration reduced, actual size 57×21 mm)

1977. J. G. Strijdom Airport, Windhoek.

305. **90.** 20 c. multicoloured .. 30 30

91 Drostdy, Luderitz

1977. Historic Houses. Multicoloured.

306. 5 c. Type **91** 15 10
307. 10 c. Woermannhaus, Swakopmund 40 30
308. 15 c. Neu-Heusis, Windhoek 45 35
309. 20 c. Schmelenhaus, Bethanie 65 40

92 Side-winding Adder

1978. Small Animals. Multicoloured.

311. 4 c. Type **92** 15 10
312. 10 c. Grant's Desert Golden mole 35 30
313. 15 c. Palmato Gecko .. 50 30
314. 20 c. Namaqua Chameleon 65 40

93 Ostrich Hunting

1978. The Bushmen. Each brown, stone and black.

315. 4 c. Type **93** 15 10
316. 10 c. Woman carrying fruit 25 20
317. 15 c. Hunters kindling fire 35 30
318. 20 c. Woman with musical instrument 40 40

94 Lutheran Church, Windhoek

1978. Historic Churches.

319 **94** 4 c. black and brown .. 10 10
320 – 10 c. black and brown .. 15 20
321 – 15 c. black and pink .. 20 25
322 – 20 c. black and blue .. 30 35

DESIGNS: 10 c. Lutheran Church, Swakopmund. 15 c. Rhenish Mission Church Otjimbingwe. 20 c. Rhenish Missionary Church, Keetmanshoop.

1978. Universal Suffrage. Nos 244/5, 249b and 251/3 optd **ALGEMENE STEMREG** (Afrikaans) **UNIVERSAL SUFFRAGE** (English) or **ALLGEMEINES WAHLRECHT** (German).

324. 4 c. "Lithops karasmontana" 10 10
325. 5 c. "Caralluma lugardii" 10 10
326. 10 c. "Gasteria pillansii" 10 10
327. 15 c. "Fenestraria aurantiaca" 15 15
328. 20 c. "Decabelone grandiflora" 20 20
329. 25 c. "Hoodia bainii" .. 25 25

Nos. 324/9 were issued in se-tenant strips of three, each stamp in the strip being optd. in either Afrikaans, English or German. The same prices apply for any of the three languages

96 Greater Flamingo

1979. Water Birds. Multicoloured.

330.	4 c. Type **96**	20	10
331.	15 c. White-breasted cormorant	45	25
332.	20 c. Chestnut-banded sand plover	50	35
333.	25 c. Eastern white pelican	55	40

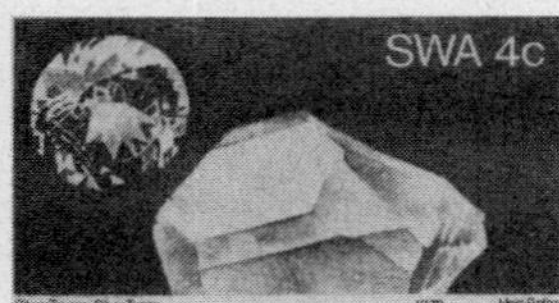

97 Silver Topaz

1979. Gemstones. Multicoloured.

334.	4 c. Type **97**	25	10
335.	15 c. Aquamarine	55	20
336.	20 c. Malachite	60	25
337.	25 c. Amethyst	60	30

98 Killer Whale

1980. Whales. Multicoloured.

338.	4 c. Type **98**	35	10
339.	5 c. Humpback Whale (38 × 22 mm.)	40	10
340.	10 c. Black Right Whale (38 × 22 mm.)	55	30
341.	15 c. Sperm Whale (58 × 22 mm.)	1·00	60
342.	20 c. Fin Whale (58 × 22 mm.)	1·25	80
343.	25 c. Blue Whale (88 × 22 mm.)	1·60	1·10

99 Impala

1980. 25th Anniv. of Division of Nature Conservation and Tourism. Antelopes. Mult.

345.	5 c. Type **99**	15	10
346.	10 c. Topi	20	10
347.	15 c. Roan Antelope ..	40	15
348.	20 c. Sable Antelope ..	50	20

100 Black-backed Jackal

101 Meerkat

1980. Wildlife. Multicoloured.

349	1 c. Type **100**	15	10
350	2 c. Hunting dog	30	10
351	3 c. Brown hyena	20	10
352	4 c. Springbok	20	10
353	5 c. Gemsbok	20	10
354	6 c. Greater kudu	20	10
355	7 c. Mountain zebra (horiz.)	40	20
356	8 c. Cape porcupine (horiz.)	30	10
357	9 c. Ratel (horiz.)	30	10
358	10 c. Cheetah (horiz.) ..	30	10
358a	11 c. Blue wildebeest ..	40	30
358b	12 c. African buffalo (horiz.)	60	45
358c	14 c. Caracal (horiz.) ..	1·50	70
359	15 c. Hippopotamus (horiz.)	30	10
359b	16 c. Warthog (horiz.) ..	1·00	80
360	20 c. Eland (horiz.) ..	30	10
361	25 c. Black rhinoceros (horiz.)	40	20
362	30 c. Lion (horiz.)	60	20
363	50 c. Giraffe	50	30
364	1 r. Leopard	90	55
365	2 r. African elephant ..	1·00	90

1980. Coil stamps. Wildlife.

366.	**101.**	1 c. brown	10	10
367.	–	2 c. blue	10	10
368.	–	5 c. green	15	15

DESIGNS: 2 c. Savanna Monkey 5 c. Chacma Baboon.

102 Von Bach

(Illustration reduced, actual size 57 × 21 mm)

1980. Water Conservation. Dams. Mult.

369.	5 c. Type **102**	10	10
370.	10 c. Swakoppoort ..	15	10
371.	15 c. Naute	20	20
372.	20 c. Hardap	25	25

103 View of Fish River Canyon

1981. Fish River Canyon.

373.	–	5 c. multicoloured ..	10	10
374.	–	15 c. multicoloured ..	20	20
375.	–	20 c. multicoloured ..	25	25
376.	**103.**	25 c. multicoloured ..	30	30

DESIGNS: 5 c. to 20 c. Various views of canyon.

104 "Aloe erinacea"

1981. Aloes. Multicoloured.

377.	5 c. Type **104**	10	10
378.	15 c. " Aloe viridiflora " ..	30	25
379.	20 c. " Aloe pearsonii " ..	35	25
380.	25 c. " Aloe littoralis " ..	40	30

105 Paul Weiss-Haus

1981. Historic Buildings of Luderitz. Mult.

381.	5 c. Type **105**	10	10
382.	15 c. Deutsche Afrika Bank	20	20
383.	20 c. Schroederhaus ..	30	30
384.	25 c. Altes Postamt ..	30	35

106 Salt Plain

1981. Salt Industry. Multicoloured.

386.	5 c. Type **106**	10	10
387.	15 c. Dumping and washing	20	20
388.	20 c. Loading by conveyor	25	30
389.	25 c. Dispatch to refinery	30	35

107 Kalahari Starred Tortoise ("psammobates oculifer")

1982. Tortoises. Multicoloured.

390.	5 c. Type **107**	10	10
391.	15 c. Leopard Tortoise (" geochelone pardalis ")	20	20
392.	20 c. Angulate Tortoise (" chersina angulata ")	25	30
393.	25 c. Speckled Padloper (" homopus signatus ")	30	35

108 Mythical Sea-monster

1982. Discoverers of South West Africa (1st series). Multicoloured.

394.	15 c. Type **108**	20	20
395.	20 c. Bartolomeu Dias and map of Africa showing voyage	30	30
396.	25 c. Dias' caravel ..	45	40
397.	30 c. Dias erecting commemorative cross, Angra das Voltas, 25 July, 1488	45	45

See also Nos. 455/8.

109 Brandberg

1982. Mountains of South West Africa. Mult.

398.	6 c. Type **109**	10	10
399.	15 c. Omatako	20	20
400.	20 c. Die Nadel	25	30
401.	25 c. Spitzkuppe	30	35

110 Otjikaeva Head-dress of Herero Woman

1982. Traditional Head-dresses of South Africa (1st series). Multicoloured.

402.	6 c. Type **110**	10	10
403.	15 c. Ekori head-dress of Himba	25	35
404.	20 c. Oshikoma hair-piece and iiponda plaits of Ngandjera	35	45
405.	25 c. Omhatela head-dress of Kwanyama	35	60

See also Nos 427/30.

111 Fort Vogelsang

1983. Centenary of Luderitz.

406	**111**	6 c. black and red ..	10	10
407	–	20 c. black and brown	25	30
408	–	25 c. black and brown	30	35
409	–	30 c. black and purple	35	40
410	–	40 c. black and green	50	55

DESIGNS—VERT. (23 × 29 mm.) 20 c. Chief Joseph Fredericks. 30 c. Heinrich Vogelsang (founder). 40 c. Adolf Luderitz (colonial promoter). HORIZ. (As T **111**) 25 c. Angra Pequena.

112 Searching for Diamonds, Kolmanskop, 1908

1983. 75th Anniv. of Discovery of Diamonds.

411.	**112.**	10 c. dp. brn. & brn...	15	15
412.	–	20 c. red and brown ..	30	30
413.	–	25 c. blue and brown ..	35	35
414.	–	40 c. black and brown	55	55

DESIGNS—HORIZ. (34 × 19 mm.). 20 c. Digging for diamonds, Kolmanskop, 1908. VERT. (19 × 26 mm.). 25 c. Sir Ernest Oppenheimer (industrialist). 40 c. August Stauch (prospector).

113 "Common Zebras drinking" (J. van Ellinckhuijzen)

1983. Painters of South West Africa. Mult.

415.	10 c. Type **113**	15	15
416.	20 c. "Rossing Mountain" (H. Henckert)	25	30
417.	25 c. "Stampeding African buffalo" (F. Krampe) ..	30	35
418.	40 c. "Erongo Mountains" (J. H. Blatt)	50	55

114 The Rock Lobster

1983. The Lobster Industry. Multicoloured.

419.	10 c. Type **114**	15	15
420.	20 c. Mother ship and fishing dinghies	25	30
421.	25 c. Netting lobsters from a dinghy	30	35
422.	40 c. Packing lobsters ..	50	55

115 Hohenzollern House

1984. Historic Buildings of Swakopmund.

423.	**115.**	10 c. black & brown ..	15	15
424.	–	20 c. black and blue ..	30	25
425.	–	25 c. black & green ..	30	30
426.	–	30 c. black & brown ..	35	30

DESIGNS: 20 c. Railway Station. 25 c. Imperial District Bureau. 30 c. Ritterburg.

1984. Traditional Head-dresses of South West Africa (2nd series). As T **110**. Mult.

427.	11 c. Eendjushi head-dress of Kwambi	25	15
428.	20 c. Bushman woman ..	40	25
429.	25 c. Omulenda head-dress of Kwaluudhi	45	30
430.	30 c. Mbukushu women ..	45	30

116 Map and German Flag

1984. Centenary of German Colonisation. Multicoloured.

431 11 c. Type **116** 25 15
432 25 c. Raising the German flag, 1884 .. .. 50 50
433 30 c. German Protectorate boundary marker .. 50 50
434 45 c. "Elizabeth" and "Leipzig" (German Corvettes .. .. 1·25 1·40

117 Sweet Thorn

1984. Spring in South West Africa. Mult.

435. 11 c. Type **117** 20 15
436. 25 c. Camel Thorn .. 40 35
437. 30 c. Hook Thorn 45 35
438. 45 c. Candle-pod Acacia .. 60 50

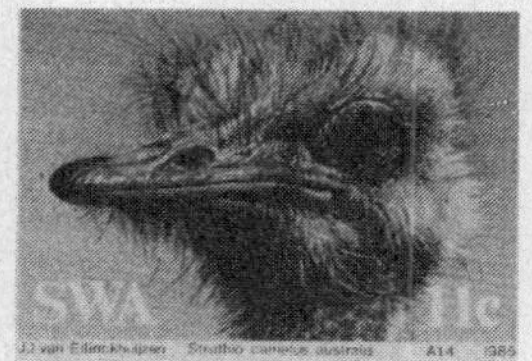

118 Head of Ostrich

1985. Ostriches. Multicoloured.

439. 11 c. Type **118** 35 10
440. 25 c. Ostrich on eggs .. 60 30
441. 30 c. Newly-hatched chick and eggs 70 50
442. 50 c. Mating dance .. 1·00 75

119 Kaiserstrasse

1985. Historic Buildings of Windhoek.

443. **119.** 12 c. black and brown 20 10
444. – 25 c. black and green 35 25
445. – 30 c. black and brown 35 30
446. – 50 c. black and brown 80 70

DESIGNS: 25 c. Turnhalle. 30 c. Old Supreme Court Building. 50 c. Railway Station.

120 Zwilling Locomotive

1985. Narrow-gauge Railway Locomotives. Multicoloured.

447. 12 c. Type **120** 30 10
448. 25 c. Feldspur side-tank locomotive .. 60 25
449. 30 c. Jung and Henschel side-tank locomotive .. 70 35
450. 50 c. Henschel Hd locomotive 90 60

121 Lidumu-dumu (keyboard instrument)

1985. Traditional Musical Instrument. Mult.

451. 12 c. Type **121** 10 10
452. 25 c. Ngoma (drum) .. 20 20
453. 30 c. Okambulumbumbwa (stringed instrument) .. 25 25
454. 50 c. Gwashi (stringed instrument) 35 35

122 Erecting Commemorative Pillar at Cape Cross, 1486

1986. Discoverers of South West Africa (2nd series). Diogo Cao.

455. **122.** 12 c. black, grey and green 25 10
456. – 20 c. black, grey and brown 40 20
457. – 25 c. black, grey and blue 50 30
458. – 30 c. black, grey & purple 60 40

DESIGNS: 20 c. Diogo Cao's coat of arms. 25 c. Caravel. 30 c. Diogo Cao.

123 Ameib Erongo Mountains

1986. Rock Formations. Multicoloured.

459. 14 c. Type **123** 50 15
460. 20 c. Vingerklip, near Outjo 60 25
461. 25 c. Petrified sand dunes, Kuiseb River .. 70 40
462. 30 c. Orgelpfeifen, Twyfelfontein 85 55

124 Model wearing Swakara Coat

1986. Karakul Industry. Multicoloured.

463. 14 c. Type **124** 30 15
464. 20 c. Weaving karakul wool carpet .. 45 20
465. 25 c. Flock of karakul ewes in veld 45 30
466. 30 c. Karakul rams .. 65 40

125 Pirogue, Lake Liambezi

1986. Life in the Caprivi Strip. Mult.

467. 14 c. Type **125** 40 15
468. 20 c. Ploughing with oxen 65 40
469. 25 c. Settlement in Eastern Caprivi 85 65
470. 30 c. Map of Caprivi Strip 95 80

126 "Gobabis Mission Station", 1863

1987. Paintings by Thomas Baines. Multicoloured.

471. 14 c. Type **126** 40 15
472. 20 c. "Outspan at Koobie". 1861 .. .. .. 65 50
473. 25 c. "Outspan under Oomahaama Tree", 1862 85 70
474. 30 c. "Swakop River", 1861 95 85

127 "Garreta nitens" (beetle)

1987. Useful Insects. Multicoloured.

475 16 c. Type **127** 40 15
476 20 c. "Alcimus stenurus" (fly) 60 50
477 25 c. "Anthophora caerulea" (bee) .. 80 70
478 30 c. "Hemiempusa capensis" (mantid) .. 90 85

128 Okaukuejo

1987. Tourist Camps. Multicoloured.

479. 16 c. Type **128** 40 15
480. 20 c. Daan Viljoen .. 50 35
481. 25 c. Ai-Ais 60 50
482. 30 c. Hardap 65 55

129 Wreck of "Hope" (whaling schooner, 1804)

1987. Shipwrecks. Multicoloured.

483. 16 c. Type **129** 50 15
484. 30 c. "Tilly", 1885 .. .. 80 65
485. 40 c. "Eduard Bohlen", 1909 .. .. .. 1·00 90
486. 50 c. "Dunedin Star", 1942 1·25 1·00

130 Bartolomeu Dias

1988. 500th Anniv. of Discovery of Cape of Good Hope by Bartolomeu Dias. Mult.

487. 16 c. Type **130** 25 15
488. 30 c. Caravel 50 35
489. 40 c. Map of South West Africa, c. 1502 .. .. 60 50
490. 50 c. King Joao II of Portugal 75 60

131 Sossusvlei

1988. Landmarks of South West Africa. Multicoloured.

491. 16 c. Type **131** 30 15
492. 30 c. Sesriem Canyon .. 55 40
493. 40 c. Hoaruseb "clay castles" 70 50
494. 50 c. Hoba meteorite .. 85 65

132 1st Postal Agency, Otyimbingue, 1888

1988. Centenary of Postal Service in South West Africa. Multicoloured.

495 16 c. Type **132** 30 15
496 30 c. Post Office, Windhoek, 1904 .. 50 30
497 40 c. Mail-runner and map 65 40
498 50 c. Camel mail, 1904 .. 75 55

133 Herero Chat

1988. Birds of South West Africa. Mult.

499 16 c. Type **133** 30 15
500 30 c. Gray's lark 50 30
501 40 c. Ruppell's bustard .. 60 40
502 50 c. Monteiro's hornbill .. 75 55

134 Dr. C. H. Hahn and Gross-Barmen Mission

1989. Missionaries. Multicoloured.

503 16 c. Type **134** 30 10
504 30 c. Revd. J. G. Kronlein and Berseba Mission .. 50 30
505 40 c. Revd. F. H. Kleinschmidt and Rehoboth Mission .. 60 40
506 50 c. Revd. J. H. Schmelen and Bethanien Mission 70 55

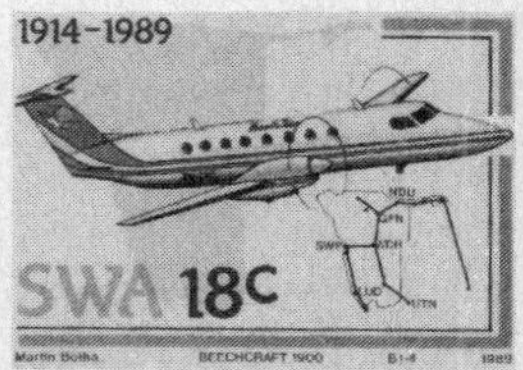

135 Beechcraft "1900"

1989. 75th Anniv of Aviation in South West Africa. Multicoloured.

507 18 c. Type **135** 20 15
508 30 c. Ryan "Navion" .. 30 30
509 40 c. Junkers "F13" .. 40 40
510 50 c. Pfalz "Otto" biplane 50 50

136 Barchan Dunes (illustration reduced, actual size 57×21 mm)

1989. Namib Desert Sand Dunes. Mult.

No.	Description	Unused	Used
511	18 c. Type **136**	20	15
512	30 c. Star dunes (36×20 mm)	40	40
513	40 c. Transverse dunes	50	50
514	50 c. Crescentic dunes (36×20 mm)	70	70

137 Ballot Box and Outline Map of South West Africa

1989. South West Africa Constitutional Election.

No.	Type	Description	Unused	Used
515	**137**	18 c. brown and orange	20	15
516		35 c. blue and green	40	40
517		45 c. purple and yellow	55	55
518		60 c. green and ochre	70	70

138 Gypsum **140** Arrow Poison

139 Oranjemund Alluvial Diamond Field

1989. Minerals. Multicoloured

No.	Description	Unused	Used
519	1 c. Type **138**	10	10
520	2 c. Fluorite	10	10
521	5 c. Mimetite	10	10
522	7 c. Cuprite	10	10
523	10 c. Azurite	10	10
524	18 c. Boltwoodite	20	10
525	20 c. Dioptase	20	15
526	25 c. Type **139**	25	15
527	30 c. Tsumeb lead and copper complex	35	20
528	35 c. Rosh Pinah zinc mine	35	20
529	40 c. Diamonds	50	30
530	45 c. Wulfenite	50	30
531	50 c. Uis tin mine	60	30
532	1 r. Rossing uranium mine	1·10	80
533	2 r. Gold	1·50	1·50

The 1, 2, 5, 7, 10, 18, 20, 40, 45 c. and 2 r. are vert as T **138**, and the 25, 30, 35, 50 c. and 1 r. horiz as T **139**.

1990. Flora. Multicoloured.

No.	Description	Unused	Used
534	18 c. Type **140**	30	10
535	35 c. Baobab flower	55	35
536	45 c. Sausage tree flowers	60	40
537	60 c. Devil's claw	75	75

MINIMUM PRICE

The minimum price quoted is 10p which represents a handling charge rather than a basis for valuing common stamps. For further notes about prices see introductory pages.

OFFICIAL STAMPS

1927. Pictorial and portrait (2d.) stamps alternately optd. **OFFICIAL South West Africa** or **OFFISIEEL Suidwes Afrika.**

No.	Type	Description	Unused	Used
O 1.	**6.**	½d. black and green	65·00	30·00
O 2.	**7.**	1d. black and red	65·00	30·00
O 3.	**2.**	2d. purple	£140	45·00
O 4.	**8.**	6d. green and orange	85·00	30·00

Mint prices are for pairs.

1929. Pictorial stamps alternately optd **OFFICIAL S.W.A.** or **OFFISIEEL. S.W.A.** horizontally or vertically

No.	Type	Description	Unused	Used
O 9.	**6.**	½d. black and green	65	2·50
O 10.		1d. black and red	75	2·50
O 11.	**11.**	2d. grey and purple	90	3·00
O 12.	**8.**	6d. green and orange	3·00	6·50

1931. Optd. alternately **OFFICIAL** or **OFFISIEEL** in small capital letters.

No.	Type	Description	Unused	Used
O 13.	**12.**	½d. black and green	6·00	3·25
O 14.	–	1d. blue and red	75	3·25
O 15.	–	2d. blue and brown	70	3·25
O 16.	–	6d. blue and brown	2·25	3·00

1938. Optd. alternately **OFFICIAL** or **OFFISIEEL** in large capital letters.

No.	Type	Description	Unused	Used
O18	**12**	½d. black and green	6·00	3·75
O24	–	1d. blue & red (No. 75)	1·00	1·60
O25	**27**	1½d. brown	20·00	4·00
O26	–	2d. blue & brn. (No. 76)	1·00	3·00
O22	–	6d. blue & brn. (No. 79)	6·50	4·50

POSTAGE DUE STAMPS

1923. Postage Due stamps of Transvaal optd. **South West Africa,** or **Zuidwest Afrika.**

No.	Type	Description	Unused	Used
D 25.	D 1.	5d. black and violet	2·00	3·00
D 2.		6d. black and brown	17·00	9·00

1923. Postage Due stamps of S. Africa optd as last.

No.	Type	Description	Unused	Used
D23	D 1.	½d. black and green	2·00	4·75
D28		1d. black and red	1·10	1·50
D 8		1½d. black and brown	75	2·25
D30		2d. black and violet	2·50	2·75
D31		3d. black and blue	2·50	3·00
D20		6d. black and grey	2·25	8·00

1927. Postage Due stamp of Transvaal optd. **Suidwes Afrika.***

No.	Type	Description	Unused	Used
D33	D 1	5d. black and violet	16·00	18·00

*The corresponding English overprint used here is the same, for the purposes of this catalogue, as that on No. D 25.

1927. Postage Due Stamps of S. Africa optd as last*.

No.	Type	Description	Unused	Used
D 39.	D **2.**	1d. black and red	1·00	2·25
D 34.	D **1.**	1½d. black and brown	55	3·00
D 35.		2d. black and violet	2·50	2·50
D 37.		3d. black and blue	8·50	9·00
D 38.		6d. black and grey	5·50	6·50

*The corresponding English overprint used here is the same, for the purposes of this catalogue, as that on Nos. D 28, D 7, D 30/1 and D 20.

1928. Postage Due stamps of S. Africa (Type D 1) optd. **S.W.A.**

No.	Type	Description	Unused	Used
D 40.	D **1.**	3d. black and blue	50	10·00
D 41.		6d. black and grey	7·50	20·00

1928. Postage Due stamps of S. Africa (Type D 2) optd. **S.W.A.**

No.	Type	Description	Unused	Used
D 42.	D **2.**	½d. black and green	40	7·00
D 43.		1d. black and red	40	3·25
D 44.		2d. black and mauve	40	3·50
D 45.		3d. black and blue	1·75	17·00
D 46.		6d. black and grey	1·00	17·00

D 3

1931. Size 19×23½ mm.

No.	Type	Description	Unused	Used
D 47.	D **3.**	½d. black and green	60	5·00
D 48.		1d. black and red	60	1·25
D 49.		2d. black and violet	70	2·50
D 50.		3d. black and blue	1·50	14·00
D 51.		6d. black and slate	7·00	20·00

1959. As Type D **3** but smaller (17¾×21 mm.).

No.	Description	Unused	Used
D55	1d. black and red	2·50	4·50
D53	2d. black and violet	1·00	11·00
D56	3d. black and blue	2·50	6·50

1961. As Nos. D 52, etc., but value in cents.

No.	Description	Unused	Used
D 57.	1 c. black and turquoise	30	2·50
D 58.	2 c. black and red	30	2·50
D 59.	4 c. black and violet	40	2·50
D 60.	5 c. black and blue	65	3·25
D 61.	6 c. black and green	65	4·50
D 62.	10 c. black and yellow	1·25	6·00

1972. As Type D **8** of South Africa. Inscr. "SWA".

No.	Description	Unused	Used
D 63.	1 c. green	75	3·50
D 64.	8 c. blue	3·00	6·50

For subsequent issues see NAMIBIA.

SOUTHERN CAMEROONS

The southern area of that part of the Cameroun which was formerly under British trusteeship. Following a plebiscite it became an autonomous state on 1st October, 1960, but after another plebiscite it became part of the independent republic of Cameroun on 30th September, 1961.

12 pence = 1 shilling.
20 shillings = 1 pound.

1960. Stamps of Nigeria of 1953 optd. **CAMEROONS U.K.T.T.**

No.	Type	Description	Unused	Used
1	**18**	½d. black and orange	10	20
2	–	1d. black and bronze	10	10
3	–	1½d. turquoise	10	15
4	–	2d. slate	10	15
5	–	3d. black and lilac	15	10
6	–	4d. black and blue	10	40
7	–	6d. brown and black	15	10
8	–	1s. black and purple	15	10
9	**26**	2s. 6d. black and green	80	80
10	–	5s. black and red	90	2·75
11	–	10s. black and brown	2·25	3·00
12	**29**	£1 black and violet	6·50	11·00

This issue was also on sale in Northern Cameroons.

SOUTHERN NIGERIA

A Br. possession on the W. coast of Africa now incorp. in Nigeria, whose stamps it uses.

12 pence = 1 shilling.
20 shillings = 1 pound.

1.

1901.

No.	Type	Description	Unused	Used
1a.	**1.**	½d. black and green	45	50
2.		1d. black and red	50	50
3.		2d. black and brown	1·75	3·50
4.		4d. black and green	1·75	6·00
5.		6d. black and purple	1·75	3·50
6.		1s. green and black	7·00	13·00
7.		2s. 6d. black and brown	28·00	50·00
8.		5s. black and yellow	38·00	70·00
9.		10s. black & pur. on yellow	65·00	£130

2. 3.

1903.

No.	Type	Description	Unused	Used
21	**2**	½d. black and green	40	10
11		1d. black and red	1·25	15
23		2d. black and brown	2·00	45
24		2½d. black and blue	80	95
25		3d. brown and purple	8·50	1·25
14		4d. black and green	1·75	3·25
27		6d. black and purple	5·00	1·00
28		1s. green and black	2·25	1·25
29		2s. 6d. black and brown	15·00	9·00
30		5s. black and yellow	30·00	45·00
19		10s. black & pur. on yellow	25·00	60·00
32a		£1 green and violet	£100	£140

1907.

No.	Type	Description	Unused	Used
33a.	**2.**	½d. green	30	20
34a.		1d. red	30	10
35.		2d. grey	70	70
36.		2½d. blue	1·00	3·50
37.		3d. purple on yellow	90	30
38.		4d. black & red on yellow	60	80
39.		6d. purple	10·00	3·00
40.		1s. black on green	6·00	40
41.		2s. 6d. black & red on blue	4·00	90
42.		5s. green & red on yellow	24·00	42·00
43.		10s. green & red on green	55·00	80·00
44.		£1 purple & black on red	£140	£150

1912.

No.	Type	Description	Unused	Used
45.	**3.**	½d. green	40	10
46.		1d. red	50	10
47.		2d. grey	50	85
48.		2½d. blue	2·00	2·75
49.		3d. purple on yellow	75	30
50.		4d. black & red on yellow	70	2·00
51.		6d. purple	75	90
52.		1s. black on green	2·00	60
53.		2s. 6d. blk. & red on bl.	4·50	11·00
54.		5s. green & red on yellow	8·00	40·00
55.		10s. green & red on grn.	32·00	70·00
56.		$1 purple & blk. on red	£140	£150

SOUTHERN RHODESIA

A Br. territory in the N. part of S. Africa, S. of the Zambesi. In 1954 became part of the Central African Federation which issued its own stamps inscribed "Rhodesia and Nyasaland" (q.v.), until 1964 when it resumed issuing its own stamps after the break-up of the Federation. In October, 1964, Southern Rhodesia was renamed Rhodesia.

12 pence = 1 shilling.
20 shillings = 1 pound.

1.

1924.

No.	Type	Description	Unused	Used
1.	**1.**	½d. green	70	10
2.		1d. red	90	10
3.		1½d. brown	70	30
4.		2d. black	55	30
5.		3d. blue	1·50	2·00
6.		4d. black and red	1·10	2·75
7.		6d. black and mauve	1·10	2·25
8.		8d. purple and green	10·00	32·00
9.		10d. blue and red	11·00	35·00
10.		1s. black and blue	3·25	3·00
11.		1s. 6d. black and yellow	18·00	27·00
12.		2s. black and brown	17·00	17·00
13.		2s. 6d. blue and brown	32·00	48·00
14.		5s. blue and green	55·00	85·00

2. King George V. 3. Victoria Falls.

1931.

No.	Type	Description	Unused	Used
15a.	**2.**	½d. green	20	10
16.		1d. red	20	10
16d		1½d. brown	1·25	45
17.	**3.**	2d. black and brown	3·25	70
18		3d. blue	8·50	11·00
19.	**2.**	4d. black and red	1·10	70
20		6d. black and mauve	2·00	75
21		8d. violet and green	1·75	3·25
21b		9d. red and green	6·00	7·50
22		10d. blue and red	6·00	3·00
23		1s. black and blue	1·75	2·00
24		1s 6d. black and yellow	10·00	16·00
25		2s. black and brown	13·00	4·50
26a		2s. 6d. blue and brown	28·00	30·00
27		5s. blue and green	48·00	48·00

4.

1932.

No.	Type	Description	Unused	Used
29.	**4.**	2d. green and brown	2·50	30
30.		3d. blue	3·25	1·75

5. Victoria Falls.

1935. Silver Jubilee.

No.	Type	Description	Unused	Used
31.	**5.**	1d. green and red	1·50	60
32.		2d. green and brown	3·00	2·75
33.		3d. violet and blue	5·00	10·00
34.		6d. black and purple	7·00	8·50

1935. As Nos. 29/30, but inscr. "POSTAGE AND REVENUE".

No.	Type	Description	Unused	Used
35a.	**4.**	2d. green and brown	30	10
35b.		3d. blue	75	10

6. Victoria Falls and Railway Bridge.

1937. Coronation.

No.	Type	Description	Unused	Used
36.	**6.**	1d. olive and red	65	30
37.		2d. green and brown	65	30
38.		3d. violet and blue	3·25	4·00
39.		6d. black and purple	2·25	1·75

7. King George VI.

10. Cecil John Rhodes (after S. P. Kendrick).

8. British South Africa Co's Arms.

1937.

40.	7.	½d. green ..	30	10
41.		1d. red	20	10
42.		1½d. brown	45	10
43.		4d. orange	75	10
44.		6d. black	80	10
45.		8d. green	1·60	80
46.		9d. blue	1·00	20
47.		10d. purple	1·10	1·75
48.		1s. black and green	75	10
49.		1s. 6d. black and yellow	6·00	1·25
50.		2s. black and brown	8·00	55
51.		2s. 6d. blue and purple	6·00	2·00
52.		5s. blue and green	24·00	2·00

1940. Golden Jubilee of British South Africa Co's.

53.	8.	½d. violet and green	10	10
54.	–	1d. blue and red	10	10
55.	10.	1½d. black and brown	10	10
56.	–	2d. green and violet	30	20
57.	–	3d. black and blue	30	30
58.	–	4d. green and brown	95	80
59.	–	6d. brown and green	30	70
60.	–	1s. blue and green	35	1·25

DESIGNS—HORIZ. 1d. Hoisting the flag; Fort Salisbury, 1890. 2d. Pioneer Fort and mail coach, Fort Victoria. 3d. Rhodes makes peace, 1896. 1s. Queen Victoria, King George VI, Lobengula's kraal and Govt. House, Salisbury. VERT. 4d. Victoria Falls Bridge. 6d. Statue of Sir Charles Coghlan.

16. Mounted Pioneer.

20. King George VI.

17. Queen Elizabeth II when Princess, and Princess Margaret.

1943. 50th Anniv. of Occupation of Matabeleland.

61.	16.	2d. brown and green	10	15

1947. Royal Visit.

62.	17.	½d. black and green	10	15
63.	–	1d. black and red	10	15

DESIGN: 1d. King George VI and Queen Elizabeth.

1947. Victory.

64.	–	1d. red	10	10
65.	20.	2d. slate	10	10
66.	–	3d. blue	15	15
67.	–	6d. orange	15	15

PORTRAITS: 1d. Queen Elizabeth. 3d. Queen Elizabeth II when Princess. 6d. Princess Margaret.

1949. U.P.U. As T 18/21 of Antigua.

68.	2d. green	65	20
69.	3d. blue	1·10	2·50

23. Queen Victoria, Arms and King George VI.

1950. Diamond Jubilee of S. Rhodesia.

70.	23.	2d. green and brown	15	20

24. "Medical Services".

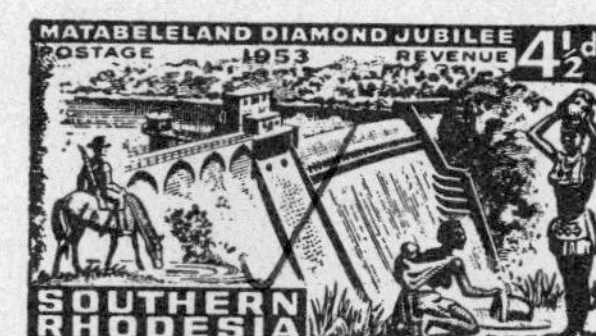

27. "Water Supplies".

1953. Birth Cent. of Cecil Rhodes. Inscr. "RHODES CENTENARY".

71.	24.	½d. blue and sepia	15	50
72.	–	1d. chestnut and green	15	10
73.	–	2d. green and violet	15	10
74.	27.	4½d. green and blue	75	1·75
75.	–	1s. black and brown	3·00	60

DESIGNS: 1d. Agricultural scene and wild animals. 2d. Township and Rhodes. 1s. Ox-cart, train and aeroplane. No. 74 also commemorates the Diamond Jubilee of Matabeleland.

1953. Rhodes Centenary Exhibition, Bulawayo. As No. 59 of Northern Rhodesia.

76.	6d. violet	15	15

30. Queen Elizabeth II.

1953. Coronation.

77.	30.	2s. 6d. red	5·50	5·00

31. Sable Antelope.

33. Rhodes's Grave.

43. Balancing Rocks.

1953.

78.	31.	½d. grey and claret	15	30
79.	–	1d. green and brown	15	10
80.	33.	2d. brown and violet	15	10
81.	–	3d. brown and red	45	50
82.	–	4d. red, green and blue	1·50	10
83.	–	4½d. black and blue	1·25	1·25
84.	–	6d. olive and turquoise	2·00	20
85.	–	9d. blue and brown	3·25	1·50
86.	–	1s. violet and blue	75	10
87.	–	2s. purple and red	6·50	3·25
88.	–	2s. 6d. olive and brown	5·50	3·75
89.	–	5s. brown and green	14·00	7·50
90.	43.	10s. brown and olive	16·00	35·00
91.	–	£1 red and black	25·00	35·00

DESIGNS—As Type 31: 1d. Tobacco planter. As Type 33—HORIZ. 3d. Farm worker. 4d. Flame lily. 4½d. Victoria Falls. 9d. Lion. 1s. Zimbabwe Ruins. 2s. Birchenough Bridge. 2s. 6d. Kariba Gorge. VERT 6d. Baobab tree. 5s. Basket maker. As Type 43: £1, Coat of Arms.

45. Maize.

50. Flame Lily.

56. Cattle.

1964.

92.	45.	½d. yell., green & blue	15	40
93.	–	1d. violet and ochre	15	10
94.	–	2d. yellow and violet	15	10
95.	–	3d. brown and blue	15	10
96.	–	4d. orange and green	30	10
97.	50.	6d. red, yellow and green	40	10
98.	–	9d. brown, yell. & green	2·00	80
99.	–	1s. green and ochre	2·25	10
100.	–	1s. 3d. red, violet & grn.	3·00	10
101.	–	2s. blue and ochre	2·25	85
102.	–	2s. 6d. blue and red	2·75	70
103.	56.	5s. multicoloured	4·50	2·00
104.	–	10s. multicoloured	11·00	6·50
105.	–	£1 multicoloured	7·00	13·00

DESIGNS—As Type 45: 1d. African buffalo. 2d. Tobacco. 3d. Greater kudu. 4d. Citrus. As Type 50: 9d. Ansellia orchid. 1s. Emeralds. 1s. 3d. Aloe. 2s. Lake Kyle. 2s. 6d. Tiger fish. As Type 56: 10s. Helmet guineafowl. £1 Coat of Arms.

Similar designs inscribed "RHODESIA" are listed under that heading.

POSTAGE DUE STAMPS

1951. Postage due stamps of Great Britain optd. SOUTHERN RHODESIA.

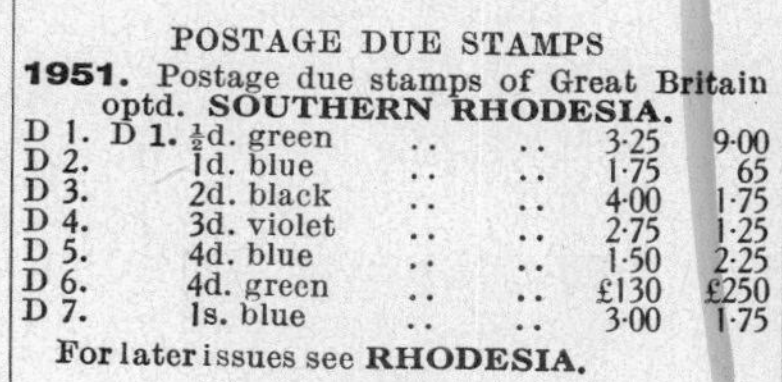

D 1.	D 1.	½d. green	3·25	9·00
D 2.		1d. blue	1·75	65
D 3.		2d. black	4·00	1·75
D 4.		3d. violet	2·75	1·25
D 5.		4d. blue	1·50	2·25
D 6.		4d. green	£130	£250
D 7.		1s. blue	3·00	1·75

For later issues see **RHODESIA**.

SRI LANKA

Ceylon became a republic within the British Commonwealth in 1972 and changed its name to Sri Lanka (="Resplendent Island").

100 cents = 1 rupee.

208. National Flower and Mountain of the Illustrious Foot.

1972. Inaug. of Republic of Sri Lanka.

591.	208.	15 c. multicoloured	15	20

209. Map of World with Buddhist Flag.

1972. 10th World Fellowship of Buddhists. Conference.

592.	209.	5 c. multicoloured	10	30

210. Book Year Emblem.

1972. Int. Book Year.

593.	210.	20 c. orange & brown	20	30

211. Imperial Angelfish.

1972. Fish. Multicoloured.

594.	2 c. Type 211	10	40
595.	3 c. Green Chromide	10	40
596.	30 c. Skipjack	75	15
597.	2 r. Black Ruby Barb	1·50	2·00

212. Memorial Hall.

1973. Opening of Bandaranaike Memorial Hall.

598.	212.	15 c. cobalt and blue	20	15

213. King Vessantara giving away his Children.

1973. Rock and Temple Paintings. Mult.

599.	35 c. Type 213	30	10
600.	50 c. The Prince and the Grave-digger	35	10
601.	90 c. Bearded old man	50	55
602.	1 r. 55 Two female figures	65	1·00

214. Bandaranaike Memorial Conference Hall.

1974. 20th Commonwealth Parliamentary Conf., Colombo.

604.	214.	85 c. multicoloured	20	20

215. Prime Minister Bandaranaike.

1974.

605.	215.	15 c. multicoloured	15	10

216. "UPU" and "100".

1974. Centenary of U.P.U.

606. **216.** 50 c. multicoloured .. 65 65

217. Sri Lanka Parliament Building.

1975. Inter-Parliamentary Meeting.

607. **217.** 1 r. multicoloured .. 30 50

218. Sir Ponnambalam Ramanathan (politician).

1975. Ramanathan Commem.

608. **218.** 75 c. multicoloured .. 30 50

219. D. J. Wimalasurendra (engineer).

1975. Wimalasurendra Commemoration.

609. **219.** 75 c. black and blue .. 30 50

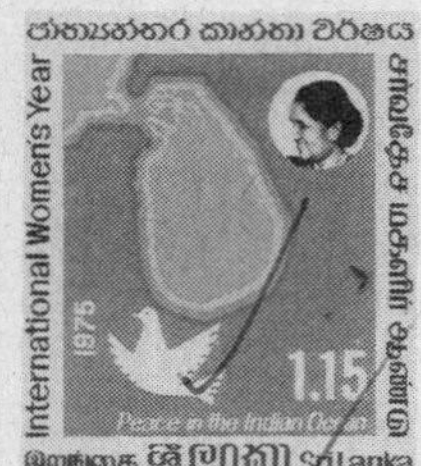

220. Mrs. Bandaranaike, Map and Dove.

1975. International Women's Year.

610. **220.** 1 r. 15 multicoloured .. 1·25 1·25

221. Ma-ratmal

1976. Indigenous Flora. Multicoloured.

611.	25 c. Type **221**	10	10
612.	50 c. Binara	10	10
613.	75 c. Daffodil orchid	15	15
614.	10 r. Diyapara	3·00	4·00

222. Mahaweli Dam.

1976. Mahaweli River Diversion.

616. **222.** 85 c. turq., blue & violet 30 50

223. Dish Aerial.

1976. Opening of Satellite Earth Station, Padukka.

617. **223.** 1 r. multicoloured .. 65 65

224. Conception of the Buddha.

1976. Vesek. Multicoloured.

618.	5 c. Type **224**	10	10
619.	10 c. King Suddhodana and the astrologers	10	10
620.	1 r. 50 The astrologers being entertained ..	20	30
621.	2 r. The Queen in a palanquin	25	35
622.	2 r. 25 Royal procession ..	30	70
623.	5 r. Birth of the Buddha ..	70	1·40

Nos. 618/23 show paintings from the Dambava Temple.

225. Blue Sapphire.

1976. Gems of Sri Lanka. Multicoloured.

625.	60 c. Type **225**	2·25	30
626.	1 r. 15 Cat's Eye	3·25	1·25
627.	2 r. Star sapphire ..	3·75	3·25
628.	5 r. Ruby	5·50	6·00

226. Prime Minister Mrs. S. Bandaranaike.

1976. Non-aligned Summit Conf., Colombo.

630. **226.**	1 r. 15 multicoloured ..	25	20
631.	2 r. multicoloured ..	40	35

227. Statue of Liberty.

1976. Bicent. of American Revolution.

632. **227.** 2 r. 25 light blue and deep blue 65 75

228. Bell, Early Telephone and Telephone lines.

229. Maitreya (pre-carnate Buddha).

1976. Centenary of Telephone.

633. **228.** 1 r. multicoloured .. 30 20

1976. Cent. of Colombo Museum. Mult.

634.	50 c. Type **229**	15	15
635.	1 r. Sundra Murti Swami (Tamil psalmist) ..	30	30
636.	5 r. Tara (goddess) ..	1·10	2·00

230. Kandyan Crown.

1977. Regalia of the Kings of Kandy. Multicoloured.

637.	1 r. Type **230**	35	40
638.	2 r. Throne and footstool	75	2·00

231. Sri Rahula Thero (poet).

1977. Sri Rahula Commemoration.

639. **231.** 1 r. multicoloured .. 40 55

232. Sir Ponnambalam Arunachalam.

1977. Sir Ponnambalam Arunachalam (social reformer). Commemoration.

640. **232.** 1 r. multicoloured .. 30 55

233. Brass Lamps.

1977. Handicrafts. Multicoloured.

641.	20 c. Type **233**	15	15
642.	25 c. Jewellery box ..	15	15
643.	50 c. Caparisoned elephant	30	15
644.	5 r. Mask	1·60	2·75

234. Siddi Lebbe (author and educationalist).

1977. Siddi Lebbe Commemoration.

646. **234.** 1 r. multicoloured .. 30 60

235. Girl Guide.

1977. 60th Anniv. of Sri Lanka Girl Guides Association.

647. **235.** 75 c. multicoloured .. 85 30

236. Parliament Building and "Wheel of Life".

1978. Election of New President.

648. **236.** 15 c. gold, grn. & emer. 20 10

For similar design in a smaller format, see Nos. 680/c.

237. Youths Running.

1978. National Youth Service Council.

649. **237.** 15 c. multicoloured .. 20 20

238. Prince Siddhartha's Renunciation.

1978. Vesak. Rock Carvings from Borobudur Temple.

650. **238.**	15 c. buff, brn. & blue	25	10
651. –	50 c. buff, brn. & blue	45	40

DESIGN: 50 c. Prince Siddhartha shaving his hair.

1978. Surch.

652.	5 c. on 90 c. Bearded old man. (No. 601)	20	10
653.	10 c. on 35 c. Type **213** ..	20	40
654.	25 c. on 15 c. Type **215** ..	2·00	1·50
655.	25 c. on 15 c. Type **236** ..	2·00	1·50
656.	25 c. on 15 c. Type **237** ..	2·00	1·50
657.	1 s. on 1 r. 55 Two female figures. (No. 602) ..	60	45

240. Veera Puran Appu.

241. "Troides helena".

1978. 130th Death Anniv. of Veera Puran Appu (revolutionary).

658. **240.** 15 c. multicoloured .. 15 20

1978. Butterfiles. Multicoloured.

659. 25 c. Type **241** 15 10
660. 50 c. "Cethosia nietneri" .. 40 10
661. 5 r. "Kallima horsfieldi" .. 1·00 1·00
662. 10 r. "Papilio polymnestor" .. .. 1·25 1·50

1979. No. 486 of Ceylon surch. **SRI LANKA 15.**

664. 15 c. on 10 c. green .. 80 55

243. Prince Danta and Princess Hema Mala bringing the Sacred Tooth Relic from Kalinga. **244.** Piyadasa Sirisena.

1979. Vesak. Kelaniya Temple Paintings. Multicoloured.

665. 25 c. Type **243** 10 10
666. 1 r. Theri Sanghamitta bringing the Bodhi Tree branch to Sri Lanka .. 15 15
667. 10 r. King Kirti Sri Rajasinghe offering fan of authority to the Sangha Raja .. .. 95 1·10

1979. Piyadasa Sirisena (writer) Commem.

669. **244.** 1 r. 25 multicoloured .. 20 20

245. Wrestlers. **246.** Dudley Senanayake.

1979. Wood Carvings from Embekke Temple.

670. **245.** 20 r. brn., ochre & grn. 95 1·50
671. – 50 r. agate, yell. & grn. 2·25 3·00

DESIGN: 50 r. Dancer.

1979. Dudley Senanayake (former Prime Minister) Commemoration.

672. **246.** 1 r. 25 green 15 20

247. Mother with Child.

1979. International Year of the Child. Multicoloured.

673. 5 c. Type **247** 10 10
674. 3 r. Superimposed heads of children of different races 30 70
675. 5 r. Children playing .. 40 80

248. Ceylon 1857 6d. Stamp and Sir Rowland Hill.

1979. Death Centenary of Sir Rowland Hill.

676. **248.** 3 r. multicoloured .. 25 45

249. Conference Emblem and Parliament Building.

1979. International Conference of Parliamentarians on Population and Development, Colombo.

677. **249.** 2 r. multicoloured .. 30 50

250. Airline Emblem on Aircraft Tail-fin. **251.** Coconut Tree.

1979. Inauguration of "Airlanka" Airline.

678. **250.** 3 r. blk., blue and red 15 50

1979. 10th Anniv. of Asian and Pacific Coconut Community.

679. **251.** 2 r. multicoloured .. 30 45

1979. As No. 648, but 20 × 24 mm.

680. **236.** 25 c. gold, green and emerald 15 20
680a. 50 c. gold, green and emerald .. .. 1·00 10
680b. 60 c. gold, green and emerald .. .. 2·00 1·25
680c. 75 c. gold, green and emerald 10 10

252. Swami Vipulananda.

1979. Swami Vipulananda (philosopher). Commemoration.

681. **252.** 1 r. 25 multicoloured .. 20 30

253. Inscription and Crescent.

1979. 1500th Anniv. of Hegira (Mohammedan Religion).

682. **253.** 3 r. 75 black, green and blue-green .. .. 35 1·00

254. "The Great Teacher" (Institute emblem). **255.** Ceylon Blue Magpie.

1979. 50th Anniv. of Institute of Ayurveda (school of medicine).

683. **254.** 15 c. multicoloured .. 20 30

1979. Birds (1st series). Multicoloured.

684. 10 c. Type **255** 10 10
685. 15 c. Ceylon Hanging Parrot 10 10
686. 75 c. Ceylon Whistling Thrush 15 15
687. 1 r. Ceylon Spurfowl .. 15 15
688. 5 r. Yellow fronted Barbet 60 1·00
689. 10 r. Yellow tufted Bulbul 75 1·75

See also Nos. 827/30 and 985/8.

256. Rotary International Emblem and Map of Sri Lanka.

1980. 75th Anniv. of Rotary International and 50th Anniv. of Sri Lanka Rotary Movement.

691. **256.** 1 r. 50 multicoloured 30 45

257. A. Ratnayake.

1980. 80th Birth Anniv. of A. Ratnayake (politician).

692. **257.** 1 r. 25 green 20 30

1980. No. 680 surch.

693. **236.** 35 c. on 25 c. gold, green and emerald .. 15 15

259. Tank and Stupa (symbols of Buddhist culture).

1980. 60th Anniv. of All Ceylon Buddhist Congress. Multicoloured.

694. 10 c. Type **259** 10 20
695. 35 c. Bo-leaf wheel and Fan 10 20

260. Colonel Olcott.

1980. Centenary of Arrival of Colonel Olcott (campaigner for Buddhism).

696. **260.** 2 r. multicoloured .. 40 50

261. Patachara's Journey through Forest.

1980. Vesak. Details from Temple Paintings, Purvaramaya, Kataluwa. Multicoloured.

697. 35 c. Type **261** 15 15
698. 1 r. 60 Patachara crossing river 40 65

262. George E. de Silva.

1980. George E. de Silva (politician). Commemoration.

699. **262.** 1 r. 60 multicoloured .. 15 20

263. Dalada Maligawa.

1980. U.N.E.S.C.O. – Sri Lanka **Project.**

700. **263.** 35 c. claret 10 15
701. – 35 c. grey 10 15
702. – 35 c. red 10 15
703. – 1 r. 60 olive 20 40
704. – 1 r. 60 green 20 40
705. – 1 r. 60 brown 20 40

DESIGNS: No. 701, Dambulla. No. 702, Alahana Pirivena. No. 703, Jetavanarama. No. 704, Abhayagiri. No. 705, Sigiri.

264. Co-operation Symbols.

1980. 50th Anniv. of co-operative Department.

707. **264.** 20 c. multicoloured .. 10 10

265. Lanka Mahila Samiti Emblem.

1980. 50th Anniv. of Lanka Mahila Samiti (Rural Women's Movement).

708. **265.** 35 c. vio., red & yellow 10 10

266. The Holy Family.

1980. Christmas. Multicoloured.

709. 35 c. Type **266** 10 10
710. 3 r. 75 The Three Wise Men 25 40

267. Colombo Public Library.

1980. Opening of Colombo Public Library.

712. **267.** 35 c. multicoloured .. 10 10

268. Flag of Walapane Disawa.

1980. Ancient Flags.

713. **268.** 10 c. blk., grn. & pur. 10 10
714. – 25 c. blk., yell. & pur. 10 10
715. – 1 r. 60 blk., yell. & pur. 15 20
716. – 20 r. blk., yell. & pur. 1·25 2·25

DESIGNS: 25 c. Flag of the Gajanayaka, Huduhumpola, Kandy. 1 r. 60, Sinhala royal flag. 20 r. Sinhala royal flag, Ratnapura.

269. Fishing Cat.

1981. Animals. Multicoloured.
718. 2 r. 50 on 1 r. 60 Type **269** 15 15
719. 3 r. on 1 r. 50 Golden palm civet 15 20
720. 4 r. on 2 r. Indian spotted chevrotain 25 30
721. 5 r. on 3 r. 15 Rusty-spotted cat 35 45

Nos. 718/21 are previously unissued stamps surcharged as in T **269**.

For stamps with revised face values see Nos. 780/2.

270. Heads and Houses on Map of Sri Lanka.

1981. Population and Housing Census.
723. **270.** 50 c. multicoloured .. 15 30

271. Sri Lanka Light Infantry Regimental Badge.

1981. Centenary of Sri Lanka Light Infantry.
724. **271.** 2 r. multicoloured .. 55 30

272. Panel from " The Great Stupa " in Honour of the Buddha, Sanci, India, 1st-century A.D.

1981. Vesak. Festival.
725. **272.** 35 c. blk., dk. gn. & grn. 10 10
726. – 50 c. multicoloured .. 10 10
727. – 7 r. black and pink .. 40 1·00

DESIGNS: 50 c. Silk banner representing a Bodhisattva from " Thousand Buddhas ", Tun-Huang, Central Asia. 7 r. Bodhisattva from Fondukistan, Afghanistan.

273. St. John Baptist de la Salle.

1981. 300th Anniv. of De La Salle Brothers (Religious Order of the Brothers of the Christian Schools).
729. **273.** 2 r. pink, light bl. & bl. 70 50

274 .Rev. Polwatte Sri Buddadatta

1981. National Heroes.
730. **274.** 50 c. brown 30 45
731. – 50 c. pink 30 45
732. – 50 c. mauve 30 45

DESIGNS: No. 731, Rev. Mohottiwatte Gunananda. No. 732, Dr. Gnanaprakasar. (each a scholar, writer and Buddhist campaigner).

275. Dr. Al-Haj T. B. Jayah.

1981. Dr. Al-Haj T. B. Jayah (statesman) Commemoration.
733. **275.** 50 c. green 30 40

276. Dr. N. M. Perera.

1981. Dr. N. M. Perera (campaigner for social reform) Commemoration.
734. **276.** 50 c. red 30 40

277. Stylised Disabled Person and Globe.

1981. International Year for Disabled Persons.
735. **277.** 2 r. red, black and grey 40 50

278. Hand placing Vote into Ballot Box.

1981. 50th Anniv. of Universal Franchise. Multicoloured.
736. 50 c. Type **278** 15 10
737. 7 r. Ballot box, and people forming map of Sri Lanka (vert.) .. .. .. 1·00 60

279. T. W. Rhys Davids (founder).

1981. Centenary of Pali Text Society.
738. **279.** 35 c. stone, dp. brn. & brn. 50 20

MINIMUM PRICE

The minimum price quoted is 10p which represents a handling charge rather than a basis for valuing common stamps. For further notes about prices see introductory pages.

280. Federation Emblem and " 25 ".

1981. 25th Anniv. of All-Ceylon Buddhist Students' Federation.
739. **280.** 2 r. blk. yellow and red 60 30

281. " Plan for Happiness ".

1981. Population and Family Planning.
740. **281.** 50 c. multicoloured .. 50 30

282. Dove Symbol with Acupuncture Needle and " Yin-Yang " (Chinese universe duality emblem).

1981. World Acupuncture Congress.
741. **282.** 2 r. blk. yell., and orge. 1·75 2·00

283. Union and Sri Lanka Flags.

1981. Royal Visit.
742. **283.** 50 c. multicoloured .. 30 20
743. 5 r. multicoloured .. 1·25 1·50

284. " Conserve our Forests ".

1981. Forest Conservation.
745. **284.** 35 c. multicoloured .. 10 10
746. – 50 c. brown and stone, 10 15
747. – 5 r. multicoloured .. 1·25 1·75

DESIGN: 50 c. " Plant a tree ", 5 r. Jak (tree).

285. Sir James Peiris.

1981. Birth Centenary of Sir James Peiris (politician).
749. **285.** 50 c. brown 45 40

286. F. R. Senanayaka.

1982. Birth Centenary of F. R. Senanayaka (national hero).
750. **286.** 50 c. brown 45 45

287. Philip Gunawardhane.

1982. 10th Death Anniv. of Philip Gunawardhane (politician).
751. **287.** 50 c. red 45 45

288. Department of Inland Revenue Building, Colombo.

1982. 50th Anniv. of Department of Inland Revenue.
752. **288.** 50 c. blue, blk. & orge. 45 45

289. Rupavahini Emblem.

1982. Inauguration of Rupavahini (national television).
753. **289.** 2 r. 50 yell., brn. and grey 1·50 1·75

290. Cricketer and Ball.

1982. First Sri Lanka—England Test Match, Colombo.
754. **290.** 2 r. 50 multicoloured 3·00 3·00

291. " Obsbeckia wightiana ".

1982. Flowers. Multicoloured.

755. 35 c. Type **291** 10 10
756. 2 r. " Mesua nagassarium " 20 20
757. 7 r. " Rhodomyrtus tomentosa " 50 90
758. 20 r. " Phaius tancarvilleae " 1·40 2·50

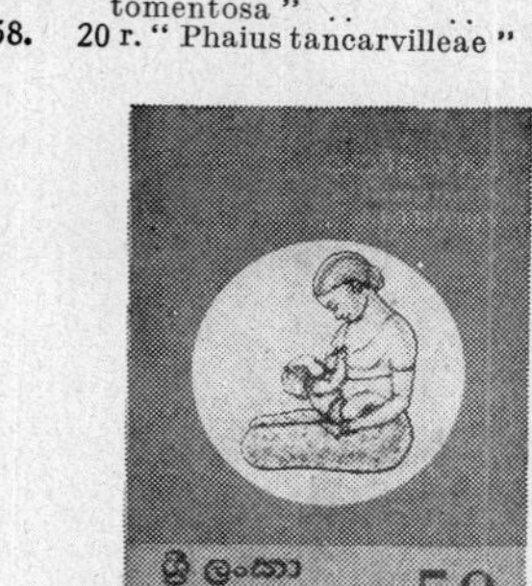

292. Mother breast-feeding Child.

1982. Food and Nutrition Policy Planning.

760. **292.** 50 c. multicoloured .. 60 60

293. Conference Emblem.

1982. World Hindu Conference.

761. **293.** 50 c. multicoloured .. 60 60

294. King Vessantara giving away Magical, Rain-making White Elephant.

1982. Vesak. Legend of Vessantara Jataka. Details of Cloth Painting from Arattana Rajamaha Vihara (temple), Hanguranketa, District of Nuwara Eliya. Multicoloured.

762. 35 c. Type **294** 30 10
763. 50 c. King Vessantara with family in Vankagiri Forest 40 15
764. 2 r. 50 Vessantara giving away his children as slaves .. .. .. 1·25 1·50
765. 5 r. Vessantara and family arriving back in Jetuttara in royal chariot .. 2·00 2·75

295. Parliament Buildings, Sri Jayawardanapura.

1982. Opening of Parliament Building Complex, Sri Jayawardanapura, Kotte.

767. **295.** 50 c. multicoloured .. 60 60

296. Dr. C. W. W. Kannangara.

1982. Dr. C. W. W. Kannangara (" Father of Free Education ") Commemoration.

768. **296.** 50 c. olive 60 60

297. Lord Baden-Powell.

1982. 125th Birth Anniv. of Lord Baden-Powell.

769. **297.** 50 c. multicoloured .. 90 60

298. Dr. G. P. Malalasekara.

1982. Dr. G. P. Malalasekara (founder of World Fellowship of Buddhists). Commem.

770. **298.** 50 c. green 60 60

299. Wheel encircling Globe.

1982. World Buddhist Leaders Conference.

771. **299.** 50 c. multicoloured .. 60 60

300. Wildlife.

1982. World Environment Day.

772. **300.** 50 c. multicoloured .. 1·00 60

301. Sir Waitialingam Duraiswamy.

1982. Sir Waitialingam Duraiswamy (statesman and educationalist) Commemoration.

773. **301.** 50 c. deep brown and brown 55 55

302. Y.M.C.A. Emblem.

1982. Centenary of Colombo Y.M.C.A.

774. **302.** 2 r. 50 multicoloured 2·00 2·25

303. Rev. Weliwita Sri Saranankara Sangharaja.

1982. Rev. Weliwita Sri Saranankara Sangharaja (Buddhist leader) Commemoration.

775. **303.** 50 c. brown and orange 60 60

304. Maharagama Sasana Sevaka Samithiya Emblem.

1982. 25th Anniv. of Maharagama Sasana Sevaka Samithiya (Buddhist Social Reform Movement).

776. **304.** 50 c. multicoloured .. 60 60

305. Dr. Robert Koch.

1982. Centenary of Robert Koch's Discovery of Tubercle Bacillus.

777. **305.** 50 c. multicoloured .. 1·00 60

306. Sir John Kotelawala.

1982. 2nd Death Anniv. of Sir John Kotelawala.

778. **306.** 50 c. olive 60 60

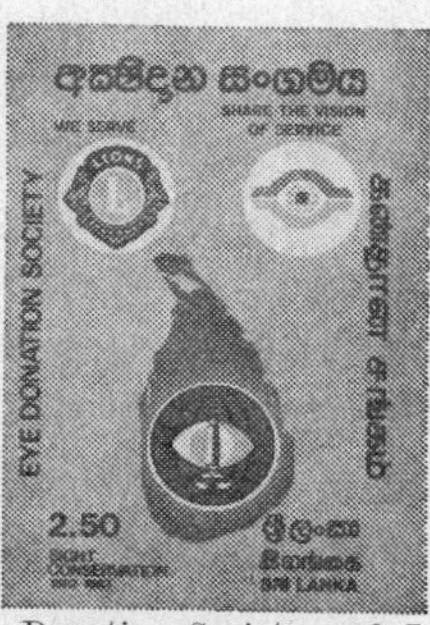

307. Eye Donation Society and Lions Club Emblems.

1982. World-wide Sight Conservation Project.

779. **307.** 2 r. 50 multicoloured 1·40 1·60

1982. As Nos. 718/20, but without surcharges and showing revised face values.

780. 2 r. 50 Type **269** 10 10
781. 3 r. Golden palm civet .. 30 30
782. 4 r. Indian spotted chevrotain 10 15

308. 1859 4 d. Rose and 1948 15 c. Independence Commemorative.

1982. 125th Anniv. of First Postage Stamps. Multicoloured.

784. 50 c. Type **308** 15 25
785. 2 r. 50 1859 1 s. 9 d. green and 1981 50 c. " Just Society " stamps .. 50 85

309. Sir Oliver Goonetilleke.

1983. 4th Death Anniv. of Sir Oliver Goonetilleke (statesman).

787. **309.** 50 c. grey, brn. & blk. 30 40

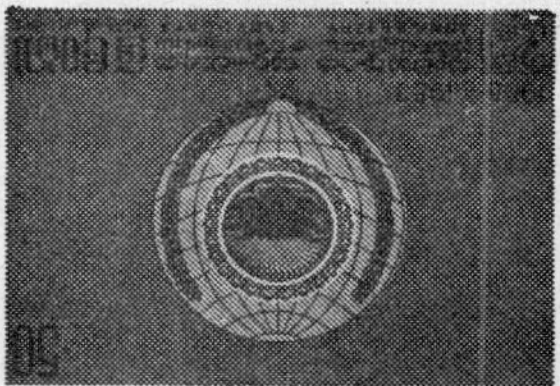

310. Sarvodaya Emblem.

1983. 25th Anniv. of Sarvodaya Movement.

788. **310.** 50 c. multicoloured .. 60 60

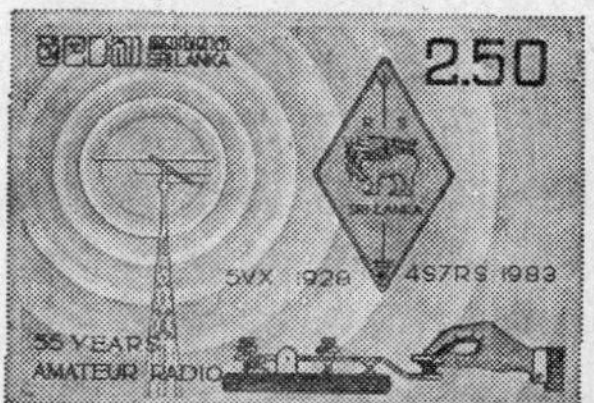

311. Morse Key, Radio Aerial and Radio Amateur Society Emblem.

1983. Radio Amateur Society.

789. **311.** 2 r. 50 multicoloured 2·00 2·50

312. Customs Co-operation Council Emblem and Sri Lanka Flag.

1983. 30th Anniv. of International Customs Day.

790. **312.** 50 c. multicoloured .. 30 30
791. 5 r. multicoloured .. 2·25 2·50

313. Bottle-nosed Dolphin.

1983. Marine Mammals.

792. **313.** 50 c. blk., blue & grn. 25 15
793. – 2 r. multicoloured .. 40 55
794. – 2 r. 50 blk., bl. & grey 50 55
795. – 10 r. multicoloured .. 1·40 1·75

DESIGNS: 2 r. Dugongs. 2 r. 50, Humpback whale. 10 r. Sperm whale.

314. "Lanka Athula" (container ship).

1983. Ships of the Ceylon Shipping Corporation. Multicoloured.

796. 50 c. Type **314** 10 10
797. 2 r. 50 Map of routes .. 15 30
798. 5 r. "Lanka Kalyani" (freighter) 25 65
799. 20 r. "Tammanna" (tanker) .. .. .. 1·10 2·25

315. Woman with I.W.D. Emblem and Sri Lanka Flag.

1983. International Women's Day. Mult.

800. 50 c. Type **315** 10 15
801. 5 r. Woman, emblem, map and symbols of progress 25 60

316. Waterfall.

1983. Commonwealth Day. Multicoloured.

802. 50 c. Type **316** 10 10
803. 2 r. 50, Tea plucking .. 15 25
804. 5 r. Harvesting rice .. 25 40
805. 20 r. Decorated elephants 80 2·00

317. Lions Club International Badge.

1983. 25th Anniv. of Lions Club International in Sri Lanka.

806. **317.** 2 r. 50 multicoloured 1·25 1·25

318. "The Dream of Queen Mahamaya".

1983. Vesak. Life of Prince Siddhartha from murals by George Keyt and Gotami Vihara. Multicoloured.

807. 35 c. Type **318** 10 10
808. 50 c. "Prince Siddhartha given to Maha Brahma" 10 10
809. 5 r. "Prince Siddhartha and the Sleeping Dancers" 25 60
810. 10 r. "The Meeting with Mara" .. .. .. 55 1·50

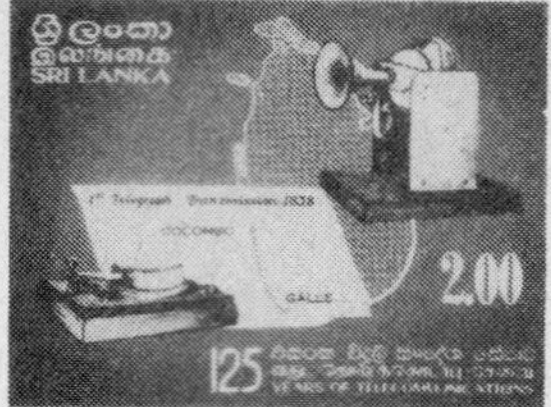

319. First Telegraph Transmission, Colombo to Galle, 1858.

1983. 125th Anniv. of Telecommunications in Sri Lanka (2 r.), and World Communications Year (10 r.). Multicoloured.

812. 2 r. Type **319** 10 35
813. 10 r. World Communications Year emblem .. 55 1·40

320. Henry Woodward Amarasuriya (philanthropist).

1983. National Heroes.

814. **320.** 50 c. green 20 35
815. – 50 c. blue 20 35
816. – 50 c. magenta 20 35
817. – 50 c. green 20 35

DESIGNS: No. 815, Father Simon Perera (historian). No. 816, Charles Lorenz (lawyer and newspaper editor). No. 817. Noordeen Abdul Cader (first President of All-Ceylon Muslim League).

321. Family and Village.

1983. Gam Udawa (Village Re-awakening Movement). Multicoloured.

818. 50 c. Type **321** 10 15
819. 5 r. Village view 25 65

322. Caravan of Bulls.

1983. Transport. Multicoloured.

820. 35 c. Type **322** 10 10
821. 2 r. Steam train 50 65
822. 2 r. 50 Ox and cart .. 50 80
823. 5 r. Ford motor car .. 85 1·60

323. Sir Tikiri Banda Panabokke.

1983. 20th Death Anniv. of Adigar Sir Tikiri Banda Panabokke.

824. **323.** 50 c. red 60 60

324. C. W. Thamotheram Pillai.

1983. C. W. Thamotheram Pillai (Tamil scholar).

825. **324.** 50 c. brown 60 60

325. Arabi Pasha.

1983. Centenary of Banishment of Arabi Pasha (Egyptian nationalist).

826. **325.** 50 c. green 60 60

326. Sri Lanka Wood Pigeon.

1983. Birds (2nd series). Multicoloured.

827. 25 c. Type **326** 10 10
828. 35 c. Large Sri Lanka white eye 10 10
829. 2 r. Sri Lanka Dusky blue flycatcher 10 10
829a. 7 r. As 35 c. 20 25
830. 20 r. Ceylon coucal .. 55 60

327. Pelene Siri Vajiragnana.

1983. Reverend Thero (scholar).

832. **327.** 50 c. brown 60 60

328. Mary praying over Jesus and St. Joseph welcomes Shepherds.

1983. Christmas.

833. **328.** 50 c. multicoloured .. 10 15
834. 5 r. multicoloured .. 25 60

1983. No. 680a. surch.

836. **236.** 60 c. on 50 c. gold, green and emerald 40 40

331. Paddy Field, Globe and F.A.O. Emblem.

1984. World Food Day.

838. **331.** 3 r. multicoloured .. 30 60

332. Modern Tea Factory.

1984. Centenary of Colombo Tea Auctions. Multicoloured.

839 1 r. Type **332** 10 15
840 2 r. Logo 15 35
841 5 r. Girl picking tea .. 30 80
842 10 r. Auction in progress .. 65 1·60

333. Students and University.

1984. 4th Anniv. of Mahapola Scheme for Development and Education. Multicoloured.

843. 60 c. Type **333** 10 15
844. 1 r. Teacher with Gnana Darsana class 10 15
845. 5 r. 50 Student with books and microscope .. .. 35 1·00
846. 6 r. Mahapola lamp symbol 40 1·25

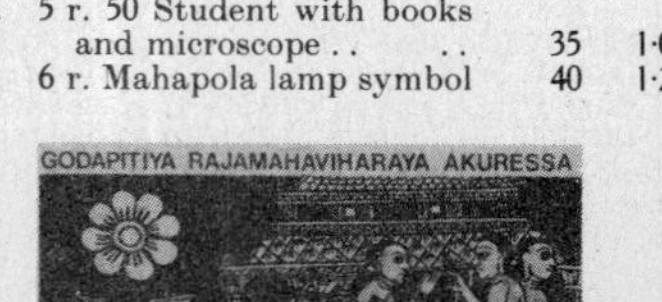

334. King Daham Sonda instructing Angels.

1984. Vesak. The Story of King Daham Sonda from Ancient Casket Paintings. Multicoloured.

847. 35 c. Type **334** 10 10
848. 60 c. Elephant paraded with gift of gold .. 10 25
849. 5 r. King Daham Sonda leaps into mouth of God Sakra 30 85
850. 10 r. God Sakra carrying King Daham Sonda .. 65 1·50

335. Development Programme Logo.

1984. Sri Lanka Lions Clubs' Development Programme.

852. **335.** 60 c. multicoloured .. 60 60

336. Dodanduwe Siri Piyaratana Tissa Mahanayake Thero (Buddhist scholar).

1984. National Heroes.

853. **336.** 60 c. bistre 10 20
854. – 60 c. green 10 20
855. – 60 c. green 10 20
856. – 60 c. red 10 20
857. – 60 c. brown 10 20

DESIGNS: No. 854, G. P. Wickremarachchi (physician). 855, Sir Mohamed Macan Markar (politician). 856, Dr. W. Arthur de Silva (philanthropist). 857, K. Balasingham (lawyer).

337. Association Emblem.

1984. Centenary of Public Service Mutual Provident Association.

858. **337.** 4 r. 60 multicoloured 30 90

338. Sri Lanka Village.

1984. 6th Anniv. of "Gam Udawa" (Village Reawakening Movement).

859. **338.** 60 c. multicoloured .. 20 30

339. World Map showing A.P.B.U. Countries.

1984. 20th Anniv. of Asia-Pacific Broadcasting Union.

860. **339.** 7 r. multicoloured .. 1·10 1·50

340. Drummers and Elephant carrying Royal Instructions.

1984. Esala Perahera (Procession of the Tooth), Kandy. Multicoloured.

861. 4 r. 60 Type **340** 70 90
862. 4 r. 60 Dancers and elephants 70 90
863. 4 r. 60 Elephant carrying Tooth Relic 70 90
864. 4 r. 60 Custodian of the Sacred Tooth and attendants 70 90

Nos. 861/4 were printed together, se-tenant, in horizontal strips of 4 throughout the sheet, forming a composite design.

341. "Vanda Memoria Ernest Soysa" (orchid).

1984. 50th Anniv. of Ceylon Orchid Circle. Multicoloured.

866. 60 c. Type **341** 25 40
867. 4 r. 60 "Acanthephippium bicolor" .. .. 65 1·75
868. 5 r. "Vanda tessellata var. rufescens" .. .. 45 1·75
869. 10 r. "Anectochilus setaceus" .. .. 1·75 2·75

342. Symbolic Athletes and Stadium.

1984. 1st National School Games.

871 **342** 60 c. black, grey & blue 50 50

343. D.S. Senanayake, Temple and Fields.

1984. Birth Centenary of D.S. Senanayake (former Prime Minister). Multicoloured.

872. 35 c. Type **343** 10 10
873. 60 c. Senanayake and statue 10 10
874. 4 r. 60 Senanayake and irrigation project .. 25 50
875. 6 r. Senanayake and House of Representatives .. 30 60

344. Lake House.

1984. 150th Anniv. of "Observer" Newspaper.

876. **344.** 4 r. 60 multicoloured 50 1·10

345. Agricultural Workers and Globe.

1984. 20th Anniv. of World Food Programme.

877. **345.** 7 r. multicoloured .. 70 75

346. College Emblem. **347.** Dove and Stylised Figures.

1984. Centenary of Baari Arabic College, Weligama.

878. **346.** 4 r. 60 grn., turq. & bl. 70 1·00

1985. International Youth Year. Mult.

879. 4 r. 60 Type **347** 30 50
880. 20 r. Dove, stylised figures and flower .. .. 1·25 2·00

348. Religious Symbols.

1985. World Religion Day.

881. **348.** 4 r. 60 multicoloured 35 60

349. College Crest.

1985. 150th Anniv. of Royal College, Colombo.

882. **349.** 60 c. yellow and blue 10 20
883. – 7 r. multicoloured .. 50 1·40

DESIGN: 7 r. Royal College.

350. Banknotes, Buildings, Ship and "Wheel of Life".

1985. 5th Anniv. of Mahapola Scheme.

884. **350.** 60 c. multicoloured .. 40 55

351. Wariyapola Sri Sumangala Thero.

1985. Wariyapola Sri Sumangala Thero (Buddhist priest and patriot). Commem.

885. **351.** 60 c. brn., yell. & blk. 40 55

352. Victoria Dam.

1985. Inauguration of Victoria Hydro-electric Project. Multicoloured.

886. 60 c. Type **352** 40 40
887. 7 r. Map of Sri Lanka enclosing dam and power station (vert.) .. 1·75 2·25

353. Cover of 50th Edition of International Buddhist Annual, "Vesak Sirisara". **354.** Ven. Waskaduwe Sri Subhuthi (priest and scholar).

1985. Centenary of Vesak Poya Holiday. Multicoloured.

888. 35 c. Type **353** 10 10
889. 60 c. Buddhists worshiping at temple 10 10
890. 6 r. Buddhist Theosophical Society Headquarters, Colombo 30 35
891. 9 r. Buddhist Flag .. 50 55

1985. Personalities.

893. **354.** 60 c. brn., orge. & blk. 15 20
894. – 60 c. mve., orge & blk. 15 20
895. – 60 c. brn., orge. & blk. 15 20
896. – 60 c. grn., orge. & blk. 15 20

DESIGNS: 894, Revd. Fr. Peter A. Pillai (educationist and social reformer). 895. Dr. Senarath Paranavitane (scholar). 896. A. M. Wapche Marikar (architect and educationist).

355. Stylised Village and People.

1985. Gam Udawa '85 (Village Re-awakening Movement).

897. **355.** 60 c. multicoloured .. 60 60

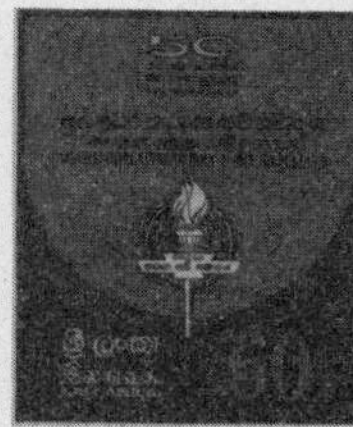

356. Emblem.

1985. 50th Anniv. of Colombo Young Poets' Association.

898. **356.** 60 c. multicoloured .. 20 30

357. Kothmale Dam and Reservoir.

1985. Inauguration of Kothmale Hydro-electric Project. Multicoloured.

899. 60 c. Type **357** 10 15
900. 6 r. Kothmale Power Station 35 60

358. Federation Logo.

1985. 10th Asian and Oceanic Congress of Obstetrics and Gynaecology.
901. **358.** 7 r. multicoloured .. 2·00 1·75

359. Breast Feeding.

1985. U.N.I.C.E.F. Child Survival and Development Programme. Multicoloured.
902. 35 c. Type **359** 10 10
903. 60 c. Child and oral rehydration salts .. 15 20
904. 6 r. Weighing child (growth monitoring) .. 1·00 1·25
905. 9 r. Immunization .. 1·40 1·75

360. Blowing Conch Shell.

1985. 10th Anniv. of World Tourism Organization. Multicoloured.
907. 1 r. Type **360** 10 10
908. 6 r. Parliamentary Complex, Jayawardhanapura, Kotte .. 30 50
909. 7 r. Tea plantation .. 40 65
910. 10 r. Ruwanveliseya (Buddhist shrine), Anuradhapura 60 85

361. Casket containing Land Grant Deed.

1985. 50th Anniv. of Land Development Ordinance.
912. **361.** 4 r. 60 multicoloured 50 95

362. Koran and Map of Sri Lanka.

1985. Translation of The Koran into Sinhala.
913. **362.** 60 c. violet and gold 30 50

363. "Our Lady of Matara" Statue.

1985. Christmas. Multicoloured.
914. 60 c. Type **363** 10 10
915. 9 r. "Our Lady of Madhu" Statue 50 60

1985. Nos. 608b, 780, 828, 860 and 879 surch.
917. **236.** 75 c. on 60 c. gold, green and emerald 10 10
918. **347.** 1 r. on 4 r. 60 mult. .. 60 50
919. **339.** 1 r. on 7 r. mult. .. 90 50
920. **269.** 5 r. 75 on 2 r. 50 mult. 1·00 35
921. – 7 r. on 35 c. multicoloured (No. 828) 1·40 65

365. Linked Arms and Map of S.A.A.R.C. Countries.

1985. 1st Summit Meeting of South Asian Association for Regional Co-operation, Dhaka, Bangladesh. Multicoloured.
922. 60 c. Type **363** .. .. 75 2·00
923. 5 r. 50 Logo and flags of member countries .. 75 1·00

366. "Viceroy Special" Train.

1986. Inaugural Run of "Viceroy Special" Train from Colombo to Kandy.
924. **366.** 1 r. multicoloured .. 1·50 80

367. Girl and Boy Students.

1986. 6th Anniv. of Mahapola Scheme.
925. **367.** 75 c. multicoloured .. 20 40

368. Wijewardena.

1986. Birth Centenary of D. R. Wijewardena (newspaper publisher).
926. **368.** 75 c. brown and green 20 40

369. Ven. Welitara Gnanatilake Maha Nayake Thero.

1986. Ven. Welitara Gnanatillake Maha Nayake Thero (scholar) Commemoration.
927. **369.** 75 c. multicoloured .. 50 50

370. Red Cross Flag and Personnel.

1986. 50th Anniv. of Sri Lanka Red Cross Society.
928. **370.** 75 c. multicoloured .. 75 50

371. Comet depicted as Goddess visiting Sun-god.

1986. Appearance of Halley's Comet. Multicoloured.
929. 50 c. Type **371** 10 10
930. 75 c. Comet and constellations of Scorpius and Sagittarius 10 20
931. 6 r. 50 Comet's orbit .. 45 80
932. 8 r. 50 Edmond Halley .. 60 1·25

372. Woman lighting Lamp.

1986. Sinhalese and Tamil New Year. Multicoloured.
934. 50 c. Type **372** 10 10
935. 75 c. Woman and festive foods 15 15
936. 6 r. 50 Women playing drum .. .. .. 55 1·00
937. 8 r. 50 Anointing and making offerings at temple .. .. .. 75 1·40

373. The King donating Elephant to the Brahmin.

1986. Vesak. Wall paintings from Samudragiri Temple, Mirissa. Multicoloured.
939. 50 c. Type **373** 10 10
940. 75 c. The Bodhisattva in the Vasavarthi heaven 10 15
941. 5 r. The offering of milk rice by Sujatha 35 75
942. 10 r. The offering of parched corn and honey by Thapassu and Bhalluka .. .. 60 1·25

374. Ven. Kalukondayave Sri Prajnasekhara Maha Nayake Thero (Buddhist leader and social reformer).

1986. National Heroes. Multicoloured.
943. 75 c. Type **374** 15 25
944. 75 c. Brahmachari Walisinghe Harischandra (social reformer) (birth centenary) 15 25
945. 75 c. Martin Wickramasinghe (author and scholar) 15 25
946. 75 c. G. G. Ponnambalam (politician) 15 25
947. 75 c. A. M. A. Azeez (Islamic scholar) (75th birth anniv.) 15 25

375. Stylized Village and People.

1986. Gam Udawa '86 (Village Re-awakening Movement).
948. **375.** 75 c. multicoloured .. 45 30

376. Co-op Flag and Emblem.

1986. 75th Anniv. of Sri Lanka Co-operative Movement.
949. **376.** 1 r. multicoloured .. 80 80

377. Arthur V. Dias.

1986. Birth Centenary of Arthur V. Dias (philanthropist).
950. **377.** 1 r. brown and blue .. 55 55

378. Bull Elephant.

1986. Sri Lanka Wild Elephants. Mult.

951.	5 r. Type **378**	1·00	1·25
952.	5 r. Cow elephant and calf	1·00	1·25
953.	5 r. Cow elephant	1·00	1·25
954.	5 r. Elephants bathing ..	1·00	1·25

379. Congress Logo.

1986. 2nd Indo-Pacific Congress on Legal Medicine and Forensic Sciences.

955. **379.** 8 r. 50 multicoloured 70 1·00

380. Map showing Route of Cable and Telephone Receiver.

1986. SEA-ME-WE Submarine Cable Project.

956. **380.** 5 r. 75 multicoloured 50 85

381. Anniversary Logo.

1986. 25th Anniv. of Dag Hammarskjold Award.

957. **381.** 2 r. multicoloured .. 60 40

382. Logo on Flag.

1986. 2nd National School Games.

958. **382.** 1 r. multicoloured .. 60 40

383. Logo.

1986. 60th Anniv. of Surveyors' Institute of Sri Lanka.

959. **383.** 75 c. brn. & lt. brn. 20 30

384. College Building and Crest.

1986. Centenary of Ananda College, Colombo.

960.	**384.**	75 c. multicoloured ..	10	10
961.	–	5 r. multicoloured ..	25	30
962.	–	5 r. 75 multicoloured	25	30
963.	–	6 r. red, gold and lilac	25	30

DESIGNS: 5 r. Sports field and college crest. 5 r. 75, Col. H. S. Olcott (founder), Ven. Migettuwatte Gunananda, Ven. Hikkaduwe Sri Sumangala (Buddhist leaders) and Buddhist flag, 6 r. College flag.

385. Mangrove Swamp.

1986. Mangrove Conservation. Multicoloured.

964.	35 c. Type **385**	10	10
965.	50 c. Mangrove tree ..	15	10
966.	75 c. Germinating mangrove flower	20	15
967.	6 r. Fiddler crab	95	1·00

386. Family and Housing Estate.

1987. International Year of Shelter for the Homeless.

968. **386.** 75 c. multicoloured .. 60 30

387. Ven. Ambagahawatte Indasabhawaragnanasamy Thero.

1987. Ven. Ambagahawatte Indasabhawaragnanasamy Thero (Buddhist monk) Commemoration.

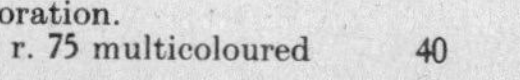

969. **387.** 5 r. 75 multicoloured 40 30

388. Proctor John de Silva.

1987. Proctor John de Silva (playwright) Commemoration.

970. **388.** 5 r. 75 multicoloured 30 30

389. Mahapola Logo and Aspects of Communication.

1987. 7th Anniv. of Mahapola Scheme.

971. **389.** 75 c. multicoloured .. 20 30

390. Dr. R. L. Brohier.

1987. Dr Richard L. Brohier (historian and surveyor) Commemoration.

972. **390.** 5 r. 75 multicoloured 40 30

391. Tyre Corporation Building, Kelaniya, and Logo.

1987. 25th Anniv. of Sri Lanka Tyre Corporation.

973. **391.** 5 r. 75 black, red and orange 30 30

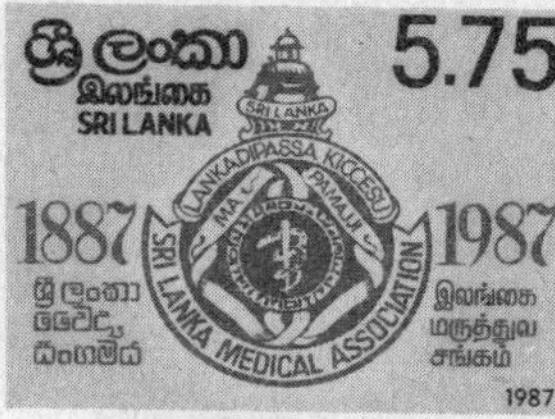

392. Logo.

1987. Centenary of Sri Lanka Medical Association.

974. **392.** 5 r. 75 brown, yellow and black 30 30

MINIMUM PRICE

The minimum price quoted is 10p which represents a handling charge rather than a basis for valuing common stamps. For further notes about prices see introductory pages.

393. Clasped Hands, Farmer and Paddy Field.

1987. Inauguration of Farmers' Pension and Social Security Benefit Scheme.

975. **393.** 75 c. multicoloured .. 15 15

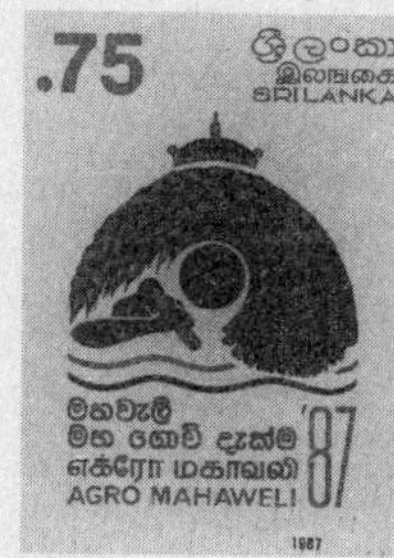

394. Exhibition Logo.

1987. Mahaweli Maha Goviya Contest and Agro Mahaweli Exhibition.

976. **394.** 75 c. multicoloured .. 15 15

395. Young Children with W.H.O. and Immunization Logos.

1987. World Health Day.

977. **395.** 1 r. multicoloured .. 75 30

396. Girls playing on Swing.

1987. Sinhalese and Tamil New Year. Multicoloured.

978.	75 c. Type **396**	10	10
979.	5 r. Girls with oil lamp and sun symbol	30	40

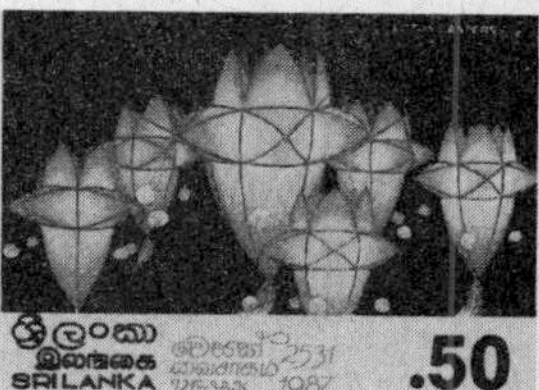

397. Lotus Lanterns.

1987. Vesak. Multicoloured.

980.	50 c. Type **397**	10	10
981.	75 c. Octagonal lanterns ..	10	10
982.	5 r. Star lanterns	30	30
983.	10 r. Gok lanterns	45	55

398. Emerald-collared Parakeet.

1987. Birds (3rd series). Multicoloured.

985.	50 c. Type **398**	10	10
986.	1 r. Legge's flowerpecker ..	10	10
987.	5 r. Ceylon white-headed starling	15	20
988.	10 r. Ceylon jungle babbler	30	35

399. Ven. Heenatiyana Sri Dhammaloka Maha Nayake Thero (Buddhist monk).

1987. National Heroes. Multicoloured.

990.	75 c. Type **399**	15	15
991.	75 c. P. de S. Kularatne (educationist)	15	15
992.	75 c. M. C. Abdul Rahuman (legislator) ..	15	15

400. Peasant Family and Village.

1987. Gam Udawa '87 (Village Re-awakening Movement).

993.	**400.** 75 c. multicoloured ..	15	15

401. "Mesua nagassarium".

1987. Forest Conservation. Multicoloured.

994.	75 c. Type **401**	10	10
995.	5 r. Elephants in forest ..	50	30

402. Dharmaraja College, Crest and Col. H. Olcott (founder).

1987. Centenary of Dharmaraja College, Kandy.

996.	**402.** 75 c. multicoloured ..	50	20

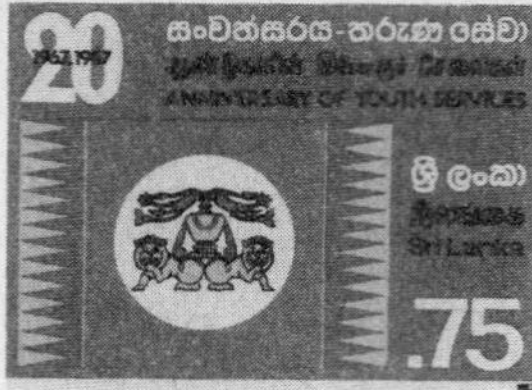

403. Youth Services Logo.

1987. 20th Anniv. of National Youth Services.

997.	**403.** 75 c. multicoloured ..	15	15

404. Arm holding Torch and Mahaweli Logo.

1987. Mahaweli Games.

998.	**404.** 75 c. multicoloured ..	55	55

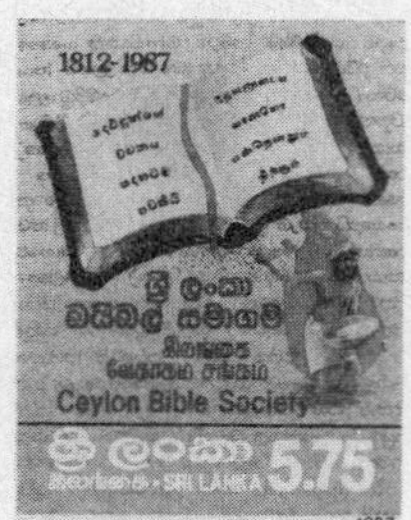

405. Open Bible and Logo.

1987. 175th Anniv. of Ceylon Bible Society.

999.	**405.** 5 r. 75 multicoloured	30	30

406. Hurdler and Committee Symbol.

1987. 50th Anniv. of National Olympic Committee.

1000.	**406.** 10 r. multicoloured ..	60	60

407. Madonna and Child, Flowers and Oil Lamp.

1987. Christmas. Multicoloured.

1001.	75 c. Type **407**	10	10
1002.	10 r. Christ Child in manger, star and dove	35	40

408. Sir Ernest de Silva.

1987. Birth Centenary of Sir Ernest de Silva (philanthropist and philatelist).

1004.	**408.** 75 c. multicoloured	15	15

409. Society Logo.

1987. 150th Anniv. of Kandy Friend-in Need Society.

1005.	**409.** 75 c. multicoloured ..	15	15

410. University Flag and Graduates.

1987. 1st Convocation of Buddhist and Pali University.

1006.	**410.** 75 c. multicoloured ..	15	15

411. Father Joseph Vaz.

1987. 300th Anniv. of Arrival of Father Joseph Vaz in Kandy.

1007.	**411.** 75 c. multicoloured ..	15	15

412. Wheel of Dhamma, Dagaba and Bo Leaf.

1988. 30th Anniv. of Buddhist Publication Society, Kandy.

1008.	**412.** 75 c. multicoloured ..	15	15

413. Dharmayatra Lorry.

1988. 5th Anniv. of Mahapola Dharmayatra Service.

1009.	**413.** 75 c. multicoloured ..	15	15

414. Society Logo.

1988. Centenary of Ceylon Society of Arts.

1010.	**414.** 75 c. multicoloured ..	15	15

415. National Youth Centre, Maharagama.

1988. Opening of National Youth Centre, Maharagama.

1011.	**415.** 1 r. multicoloured ..	50	20

416. Citizens with National Flag and Map of Sri Lanka.

1988. 40th Anniv. of Independence. Mult.

1012.	75 c. Type **416**	10	10
1013.	8 r. 50 "40" in figures and lion emblem	50	50

417. Graduates, Clay Lamp and Open Book.

1988. 8th Anniv. of Mahapola Scheme.

1014.	**417.** 75 c. multicoloured ..	15	15

418. Bus and Logo.

1988. 30th Anniv. of Sri Lanka Transport Board.

1015. **418.** 5 r. 75 multicoloured 30 30

419. Ven. Weligama Sri Sumangala Maha Nayake Thero.

1988. Ven. Weligama Sri Sumangala Maha Nayake Thero (Buddhist monk). Commemoration.

1016. **419.** 75 c. multicoloured .. 15 15

420. Regimental Colour.

1988. Centenary of Regiment of Artillery.

1017. **420.** 5 r. 75 multicoloured 40 30

421 Chevalier I.X. Pereira

1988. Birth Centenary of Chevalier I.X. Pereira (politician).

1018 **421** 5 r. 75 multicoloured 30 30

422 Invitation to the Deities and Brahmas

1988. Vesak. Paintings from Narendrarama Rajamaha Temple, Suriyagoda. Multicoloured.

1019 50 c. Type **422** 15 15
1020 75 c. Bodhisathva at the Seventh Step 15 15

423 Father Ferdinand Bonnel (educationist)

1988. National Heroes. Multicoloured.

1022 75 c. Type **423** 15 15
1023 75 c. Sir Razik Fareed (politician) 15 15
1024 75 c. W. F. Gunawardhana (scholar) .. 15 15
1025 75 c. Edward Nugawela (politician) .. 15 15
1026 75 c. Chief Justice Sir Arthur Wijeyewardene 15 15

424 Stylized Figures and Reawakened Village

1988. 10th Anniv of Gam Udawa (Village Reawakening Movement).

1027 **424** 75 c. multicoloured .. 15 15

425 Maliyadeva College, Kurunegala, and Crest

1988. Centenary of Maliyadeva College, Kurunegala.

1028 **425** 75 c. multicoloured .. 15 15

426 M.J.M. Lafir, Billiard Game and Trophy

1988. Mohamed Junaid Mohamed Lafir (World Amateur Billiards Champion, 1973) Commemoration.

1029 **426** 5 r. 75 multicoloured 30 30

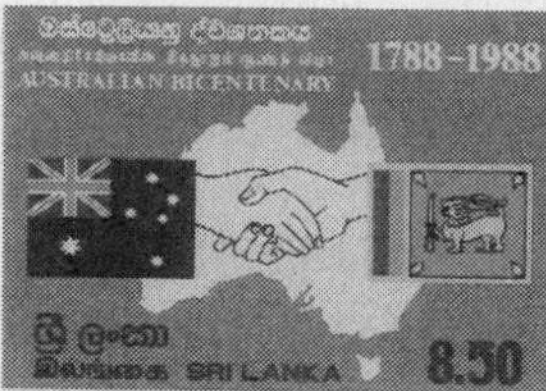

427 Flags of Australia and Sri Lanka, Handclasp and Map of Australia

1988. Bicentenary of Australian Settlement.

1030 **427** 8 r. 50 multicoloured 30 35

428 Ven. Kataluwe Sri Gunaratana Maha Nayake Thero

1988. Ven. Kataluwe Sri Gunaratana Maha Nayake Thero (Buddhist monk) Commem.

1031 **428** 75 c. multicoloured .. 15 15

429 Athlete, Rice and Hydro-electric Dam

1988. Mahaweli Games.

1032 **429** 75 c. multicoloured .. 15 15

430 Athletics

1988. Olympic Games, Seoul. Multicoloured.

1033 75 c. Type **430** 10 10
1034 1 r. Swimming 10 10
1035 5 r. 75 Boxing 20 25
1036 8 r. 50 Map of Sri Lanka and logos of Olympic Committee and Seoul Games 30 35

431 Outline Map of Sri Lanka and Anniversary Logo

1988. 40th Anniv of W.H.O.

1038 **431** 75 c. multicoloured .. 15 15

432 Games Logo

1988. 3rd National School Games.

1039 **432** 1 r. black, gold & mve 50 15

433 Mahatma Gandhi

1988. 40th Death Anniv of Mahatma Gandhi.

1040 **433** 75 c. multicoloured .. 30 15

434 Globe with Forms of Transport and Communications

1988. Asia–Pacific Transport and Communications Decade.

1041 **434** 75 c. multicoloured .. 10 10
1042 – 5 r. 75 mve, bl & blk 40 30

DESIGN: 5 r. 75, Antenna tower with dish aerials and forms of transport.

435 Woman with Rice Sheaf and Hydro-electric Project

1988. Commissioning of Randenigala Project. Multicoloured.

1043 75 c. Type **435** 10 10
1044 5 r. 75 Randenigala Dam and reservoir 20 25

436 Handicrafts and Centre Logo in Cupped Hands

1988. Opening of Gramodaya Folk Art Centre, Colombo.

1045 **436** 75 c. multicoloured .. 15 15

437 Angel, Dove, Olive Branch and Globe

1988. Christmas. Multicoloured.

1046 75 c. Type **437** 10 10
1047 8 r. 50 Shepherds and Star of Bethlehem 30 35

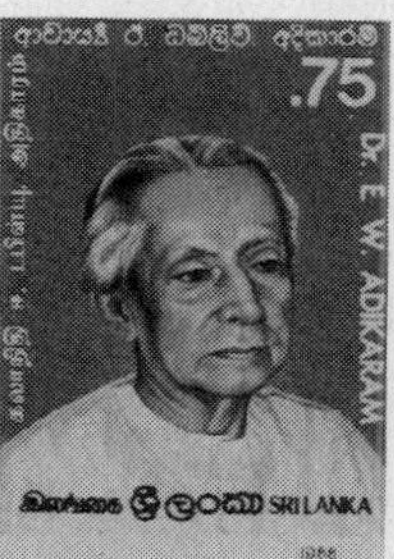

438 Dr. E. W. Adikaram

1988. Dr. E. W. Adikaram (educationist) Commemoration.

1049 **438** 75 c. multicoloured .. 15 15

439 Open Book in Tree and Children reading

1989. 10th Anniv of Free Distribution of School Text Books.

1050	**439**	75 c. multicoloured ..	15	15

440 Wimalaratne Kumaragama

1989. Poets of Sri Lanka. Multicoloured.

1051	75 c. Type **440**	10	10
1052	75 c. G. H. Perera ..	10	10
1053	75 c. Sagara Palansuriya	10	10
1054	75 c. P. B. Alwis Perera	10	10

441 Logo and New Chamber of Commerce Building

1989. 150th Anniv of Ceylon Chamber of Commerce.

1055	**441**	75 c. multicoloured ..	15	15

442 Bodhisatva at Lunch and Funeral Pyre

1989. Vesak. Wall Paintings from Medawala Monastery, Harispattuwa. Multicoloured.

1056	50 c. Type **442**	10	10
1057	75 c. Rescue of King Vessantara's children by god Sakra ..	10	10
1058	5 r. Bodhisatva ploughing and his son attacked by snake	20	25
1059	5 r. 75 King Vessantara giving away his children	20	25

443 Parawahera Vajiragnana Thero (Buddhist monk)

1989. National Heroes. Multicoloured.

1061	75 c. Type **443**	15	15
1062	75 c. Fr. Maurice Jacques Le Goc (educationist)	15	15
1063	75 c. Hemapala Munidasa (author)	15	15
1064	75 c. Ananda Samarakoon (composer)	15	15
1065	75 c. Simon Casie Chitty (scholar) (horiz) ..	15	15

444 College Crest

1989. 150th Anniv of Hartley College, Point-Pedro (1988).

1066	**444**	75 c. multicoloured ..	15	15

445 Dramachakra, Lamp, Buddhist Flag and Map

1989. Establishment of Ministry of Buddha Sasana.

1067	**445**	75 c. multicoloured ..	15	15

446 Hands holding Brick and Trowel, House and Family

1989. Gam Udawa '89 (Village Re-awakening Movement).

1068	**446**	75 c. multicoloured ..	15	15

447 Two Families and Hand turning Cogwheel

1989. Janasaviya Development Programme.

1069	**447**	75 c. multicoloured ..	15	15
1070		1 r. multicoloured ..	15	15

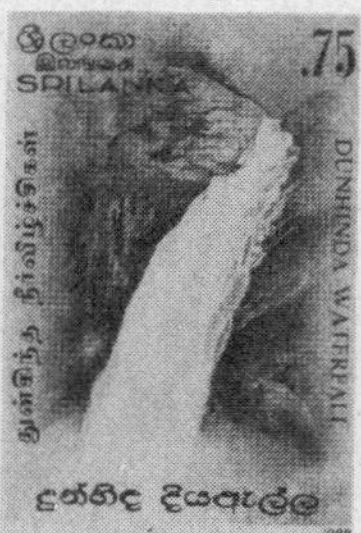

448 Dunhinda Falls

1989. Waterfalls. Multicoloured.

1071	75 c. Type **448**	10	10
1072	1 r. Rawana Falls ..	15	10
1073	5 r. 75 Laxapana Falls ..	25	25
1074	8 r. 50 Diyaluma Falls ..	35	35

449 Rev. James Chater (missionary) and Baptist Church

1989. 177th Anniv of Baptist Church in Sri Lanka.

1075	**449**	5 r. 75 multicoloured	15	20

450 Bicentenary Logo

1989. Bicentenary of French Revolution.

1076	**450**	8 r. 50 black, bl & red	20	25

451 Old and New Bank Buildings and Logo

1989. 50th Anniv of Bank of Ceylon. Mult.

1077	75 c. Type **451**	10	10
1078	5 r. "Bank of Ceylon" orchid and logo ..	20	20

452 Water Lily, Dharma Chakra and Books

1989. State Literary Festival.

1079	**452**	75 c. multicoloured ..	15	15

453 Wilhelm Geiger

1989. Wilhelm Geiger (linguistic scholar) Commemoration.

1080	**453**	75 c. multicoloured ..	15	15

454 H. V. Perera, Q.C.

1989. Constitutional Pioneers. Multicoloured.

1082	75 c. Type **454**	15	15
1083	75 c. Prof. Ivor Jennings	15	15

455 Sir Cyril de Zoysa

1989. Sir Cyril de Zoysa (Buddhist philanthropist) Commemoration.

1084	**455**	75 c. multicoloured ..	15	15

456 Map of South-east Asia and Telecommunications Equipment

1989. 10th Anniv of Asia–Pacific Telecommunity.

1085	**456**	5 r. 75 multicoloured	20	20

457 Members with Offerings and Water Lily on Map of Sri Lanka

1989. 50th Anniv of Sri Sucharitha Welfare Movement.

1086	**457**	75 c. multicoloured ..	15	15

458 "Apollo 11" Blast-off and Astronauts

1989. 20th Anniv of First Manned Landing on Moon. Multicoloured.

1087	75 c. Type **458**	10	10
1088	1 r. Armstrong leaving lunar module "Eagle"	10	10
1089	2 r. Astronaut on Moon ..	10	10
1090	5 r. 75 Lunar surface and Earth from Moon ..	15	20

459 Shepherds

1989. Christmas. Multicoloured.
1092 75 c. Type **459** 10 10
1093 8 r. 50 Magi with gifts .. 20 40

460 Ven. Sri Devananda Nayake Thero

1989. Ven. Sri Devananda Nayake Thero (Buddhist monk) Commemoration.
1095 **460** 75 c. multicoloured .. 10 10

461 College Building, Crest and Revd. William Ault (founder)

1989. 175th Anniv of Methodist Central College, Batticaloa.
1096 **461** 75 c. multicoloured .. 10 10

462 Golf Ball, Clubs and Logo

1989. Cent of Nuwara Eliya Golf Club. Mult.
1097 75 c. Type **462** 15 10
1098 8 r. 50 Course and club house 40 40

463 "Raja"

1989. "Raja" Royal Ceremonial Elephant, Kandy, Commemoration.
1099 **463** 75 c. multicoloured .. 10 10

464 College Building and G. Wickremarachchi (founder)

1989. 60th Anniv of Gampaha Wickremarachchi Institute of Ayurveda Medicine.
1100 **464** 75 c. multicoloured .. 10 10

465 Ven. Udunuwara Sri Sarananda Thero

1989. Ven. Udunuwara Sri Sarananda Thero (Buddhist monk) Commemoration.
1101 **465** 75 c. multicoloured .. 10 10

466 Diesel Train on Viaduct, Ella-Demodara

1989. 125 Years of Sri Lanka Railways. Mult.
1102 75 c. Type **466** 10 10
1103 2 r. Diesel train at Maradana Station .. 15 15
1104 3 r. Steam train 20 20
1105 7 r. Steam train, 1864 .. 40 40

467 Cardinal Thomas Cooray

1989. Cardinal Thomas Cooray Commem.
1106 **467** 75 c. multicoloured .. 30 15

468 Farmer and Wife with Dagaba and Dam

1989. Agro Mahaweli Development Programme.
1107 **468** 75 c. multicoloured .. 10 10

469 Justin Wijayawardena

1990. Justin Wijayawardena (scholar) Commemoration.
1108 **469** 1 r. multicoloured .. 40 20

470 Ven. Induruwe Uttarananda Mahanayake Thero

1990. 4th Death Anniv of Ven. Induruwe Uttarananda Mahanayake Thero (Buddhist theologian).
1109 **470** 1 r. multicoloured .. 15 20

471 Two Graduates, Lamp and Open Book

1990. 9th Anniv of Mahapola Scheme.
1110 **471** 75 c. multicoloured .. 10 10

472 Traditional Drums

1990. 25th Anniv of Laksala Traditional Handicrafts Organization. Multicoloured.
1111 1 r. Type **472** 10 10
1112 2 r. Silverware 15 15
1113 3 r. Lacquerware .. 15 20
1114 8 r. Dumbara mats .. 35 40

473 King Maha Prathapa visiting Queen Chandra

1990. Vesak. Wall Paintings from Buduraja Maha Viharaya, Wewurukannala. Mult.
1115 75 c. Type **473** 10 10
1116 1 r. Execution of Prince Dharmapala 10 10
1117 2 r. Prince Mahinsasaka with the Water Demon 15 15
1118 8 r. King Dahamsonda with the God Sakra disguised as a demon .. 35 35

474 Father T. Long (educationist)

1990. National Heroes. Multicoloured.
1120 1 r. Type **474** 10 10
1121 1 r. Prof. M. Ratnasuriya (37 × 25 mm) 10 10
1122 1 r. D. Wijewardene (patriot) (37 × 25 mm) 10 10
1123 1 r. L. Manjusri (artist) (37 × 25 mm) 10 10

475 Janasaviya Workers

1990. 12th Anniv of Gam Udawa and Opening of Janasaviya Centre, Pallekele.
1124 **475** 1 r. multicoloured .. 10 10

476 Gold Reliquary

1990. Cent of Department of Archaeology.
1125 **476** 1 r. black and yellow 10 10
1126 – 2 r. black and grey .. 15 15
1127 – 3 r. black, grn & brn 15 20
1128 – 8 r. black and brown 30 35
DESIGNS: 2 r. Statuette of Ganesh; 3 r. Terrace of the Bodhi-tree, Isurumuniya Vihara; 8 r. Inscription of King Nissankamalla.

477 Male Tennis Player at Left

1990. 75th Anniv of Sri Lanka Tennis Association. Multicoloured.
1129 1 r. Type **477** 15 15
1130 1 r. Male tennis player at right 15 15
1131 8 r. Male tennis players .. 40 40
1132 8 r. Female tennis players 40 40
Nos. 1129/30 and 1131/2 were each printed together, se-tenant, each pair forming a composite design of a singles (1 r.) or doubles (8 r.) match.

478 Spotted Loach

1990. Endemic Fishes. Multicoloured.
1133 25 c. Type **478** 10 10
1134 2 r. Ornate paradise fish 10 10
1135 8 r. Mountain labeo .. 20 25
1136 20 r. Cherry barb .. 55 60

479 Rukmani Devi

1990. 12th Death Anniv of Rukmani Devi (actress and singer).

1138	**479**	1 r. multicoloured ..	30	20

480 Innkeeper turning away Mary and Joseph

1990. Christmas. Multicoloured.

1139	1 r. Type **480**	10	10
1140	10 r. Adoration of the Magi	35	40

481 Health Worker talking to Villagers

1990. World AIDS Day. Multicoloured.

1142	1 r. Type **481**	10	10
1143	8 r. Emblem and Aids virus	35	45

482 Main College Building and Flag

1990. 50th Anniv of Dharmapala College, Pannipitiya.

1144	**482**	1 r. multicoloured ..	20	20

483 Peri Sundaram

1990. Birth Centenary of Peri Sundaram (lawyer and politician).

1145	**483**	1 r. brown and green	20	20

484 Letter Box, Galle, 1904

1990. 175th Anniv of Sri Lanka Postal Service. Multicoloured.

1146	1 r. Type **484**	10	10
1147	2 r. Mail runner, 1815 ..	10	10
1148	5 r. Mail coach, 1832 ..	20	25
1149	10 r. Nuwara-Eliya Post Office, 1894	35	40

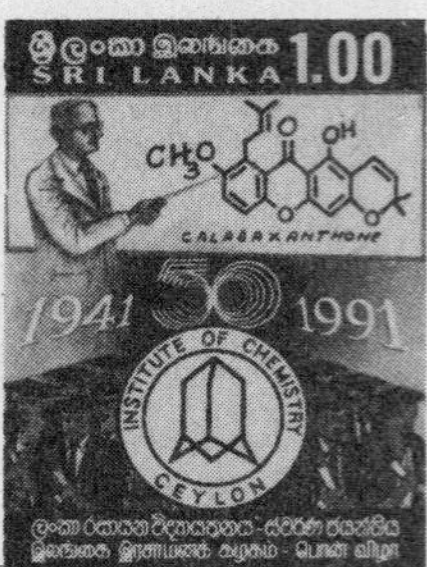

485 Chemical Structure Diagram, Graduating Students and Emblem

1991. 50th Anniv of Institute of Chemistry.

1150	**485**	1 r. multicoloured ..	20	20

486 Kastavahana on Royal Elephant

1991. Vesak. Temple Paintings from Karagampitiya Subodarama. Mult.

1151	75 c. Type **486**	10	10
1152	1 r. Polo Janaka in prison	10	10
1153	2 r. Two merchants offering food to Buddha ..	15	15
1154	11 r. Escape of Queen ..	50	50

487 Narada Thero (Buddhist missionary)

1991. National Heroes. Multicoloured.

1156	1 r. Type **487**	10	10
1157	1 r. Wallewatta Silva (novelist)	10	10
1158	1 r. Sir Muttu Coomaraswamy (lawyer and politician)	10	10
1159	1 r. Dr. Andreas Nell (ophthalmic surgeon) ..	10	10

488 Society Building

1991. Centenary of Maha Bodhi Society.

1160	**488**	1 r. multicoloured ..	10	10

489 Women working at Home

1991. 13th Anniv of Gum Udawa Movement.

1161	**489**	1 r. multicoloured ..	10	10

490 Globe and Plan Symbol

1991. 40th Anniv of Colombo Plan.

1162	**490**	1 r. violet and blue ..	10	10

491 17th-century Map and Modern Satellite Photo of Sri Lanka

1991. 190th Anniv of Sri Lanka Survey Department.

1163	**491**	1 r. multicoloured ..	10	10

492 Ven. Henpitagedera Gnanaseeha Nayake Thero

1991. 10th Death Anniv of Ven. Nayak Henpitagedera Gnanaseeha Nayake Thero (Buddhist theologian).

1164	**492**	1 r. multicoloured ..	10	10

STELLALAND

A temporary Boer republic annexed by the British in 1885 and later incorporated in Br. Bechuanaland.

12 pence = 1 shilling.
20 shillings = 1 pound.

1. Arms of the Republic.

1884.

1.	**1.**	1d. red	£170	£275
2.		3d. orange	14·00	£275
3.		4d. blue	14·00	£300
4.		6d. mauve	14·00	£300
5.		1s. green	32·00	

1885. Surch. **Twee.**

6	1	2d. on 4d. blue	£3250	

STRAITS SETTLEMENTS

A Br. Crown colony which included portions of the mainland of the Malay Peninsula and islands off its coasts, and the island of Labuan off the N. coast of Borneo.

100 cents = 1 dollar (Straits).

1867. Stamps of India surch. with crown and value.

1.	**11.**	1½ c. on ½ a. blue	55·00	£150
2.		2 c. on 1 a. brown ..	55·00	50·00
3.		3 c. on 1 a. brown	60·00	55·00
4.		4 c. on 1 a. brown	£120	£150
5.		6 c. on 2 a. orange ..	£250	£150
6.		8 c. on 2 a. orange ..	75·00	30·00
7.		12 c. on 4 a. green ..	£350	£180
8.		24 c. on 8 a. red	£160	60·00
9.		32 c. on 2 a. orange ..	£160	60·00

1869 (?). No. 1 with "THREE HALF" deleted and "2" written above in manuscript.

10.	**11.**	2 on 1½ c. on ½ a. blue ..	£4000	£2500

5.

8.

9.

1867.

11	**5.**	2 c. brown	13·00	1·75
98		4 c. red	2·50	1·25
66a		6 c. lilac	1·60	1·50
52		8 c. orange	2·00	35
15		12 c. blue	60·00	4·50
68a		24 c. green	2·75	2·75
69	**8.**	30 c. red	7·00	4·50
70	**9.**	32 c. red	5·50	1·50
71		96 c. grey	70·00	32·00

1879. Surch. in words.

20.	**5.**	5 c. on 8 c. orange ..	55·00	80·00
21.	**9.**	7 c. on 32 c. red	60·00	70·00

1880. Surch. in figures and words.

47.	**5.**	5 c. on 4 c. red	£160	£180
42.		5 c. on 8 c. orange ..	55·00	70·00
44.		10 c. on 6 c. lilac	30·00	6·00
45a.		10 c. on 12 c. blue ..	26·00	9·00
23.	**8.**	10 c. on 30 c. red	95·00	40·00

1880. Surch in figures only.

33	8	"10" on 30 c. red ..	70·00	35·00

18.

19.

1882.

63a.	**5.**	2 c. red	1·50	15
64.		4 c. brown	15·00	1·25
99.	**18.**	5 c. brown	2·25	90
65.		5 c. blue	4·50	30
100.		5 c. purple	1·75	2·00
101.	**5.**	8 c. blue	3·50	30
53.	**19.**	10 c. grey	2·00	50
102.	**5.**	12 c. purple	7·50	8·00

1883. Surch in words in one line horiz (No. 109) or vert.

57 5 2 c. on 8 c. orange .. 60·00 45·00
59 9 2 c. on 32 c. orange .. £325 £100
109 18 4 c. on 5 c. red 30 20

1883. Surch. with figures over words in two lines.

61. 5. 2 c. on 4 c. red .. 45·00 50·00
62. 2 c. on 12 c. blue .. £110 60·00
82. 18. 3 c. on 5 c. blue.. .. 75·00 £180
84. 3 c. on 5 c. purple .. £100 £110
106. 4 c. on 5 c. brown .. 75 4·25
73. 4 c. on 5 c. blue (A)* .. 75·00 65·00
107. 4 c. on 5 c. blue (B)* .. 1·25 5·50
108b. 5. 4 c. on 8 c. blue.. .. 50 70
74. 8 c. on 12 c. blue .. £140 75·00
75. 8 c. on 12 c. purple .. £120 85·00

* (A) "Cents" in italics (B) "cents" (with small "c") in roman type.

1884. Surch. **TWO CENTS** vert.

76. 18. 2 c. on 5 c. blue.. .. 65·00 80·00

1884. Nos. 73 and 75 surch. with large figure.

80. 5. "8" on 8 c. on 12 c. purple £130 £140

1885. Surch. with words in one line and thick bar.

93. 5. 1 c. on 8 c. green.. .. 40 75
83a. 9. 3 c. on 32 c. purple .. 90 90
94. 3 c. on 32 c. red .. 2·00 70

1887. Surch. **2 Cents** in one line.

85. 18. 2 c. on 5 c. blue.. .. 13·00 27·00

1891. Surch. **10 CENTS** in one line and thin bar.

86. 5. 10 c. on 24 c. green .. 1·50 1·25

1891. Surch. with words in two lines and thin bar.

88. 5. 1 c. on 2 c. red .. 1·25 1·50
89. 1 c. on 4 c. brown .. 3·75 4·00
90. 1 c. on 6 c. lilac .. 1·00 2·50
91. 1 c. on 8 c. orange .. 1·00 60
92. 1 c. on 12 c. purple .. 4·00 9·00
87. 9. 30 c. on 32 c. orange .. 4·75 3·50

33. 37.

1892.

95. 33. 1 c. green 40 20
96. 3 c. red .. .. 5·50 30
97. 3 c. brown .. .. 2·50 40
103a. 25 c. purple and green .. 12·00 3·75
104. 50 c. olive and red .. 17·00 2·50
105. $5 orange and red .. £275 £275

1902.

110 37 1 c. green 45 90
111 3 c. purple and orange .. 75 15
112 4 c. purple on red .. 2·00 30
113 5 c. purple .. .. 1·75 55
157 5 c. orange .. .. 2·75 30
114 8 c. purple on blue .. 3·00 20
132 10 c. pur. and blk. on yell. 2·50 30
159 10 c. purple on yellow .. 1·00 15
116 25 c. purple and green .. 7·50 3·50
161 25 c. purple .. .. 5·50 2·75
117 30 c. grey and red .. 12·00 8·00
162 30 c. purple and yellow .. 21·00 1·50
135a 50 c. green and red .. 10·00 6·00
164 50 c. black on green .. 3·75 1·75
136a $1 green and black .. 17·00 7·50
165 $1 black and red on blue 9·50 3·50
120 $2 purple and black .. 45·00 45·00
166 $2 green & red on yellow 16·00 16·00
138 $5 green and orange .. 90·00 90·00
167 $5 green and red on green 65·00 48·00
139 $25 green and black .. £800 £800

39. 42.

47. 46.

1903.

127 39 1 c. green .. .. 1·00 10
128 3 c. purple 50 30
153 3 c. red .. .. 1·25 10
125 4 c. purple on red .. 1·00 30
154 4 c. red .. .. 4·75 90
155 4 c. purple .. .. 1·50 10
131 42 8 c. purple on blue .. 5·00 35
158 8 c. blue .. .. 1·50 25
160 47 21 c. purple .. .. 5·50 24·00
163 45 c. black on green .. 2·50 3·50
168 46 $25 purple and blue .. £700 £500

1907. Stamps of Labuan (Crown type) optd. **STRAITS SETTLEMENTS** or surch. in words also.

141. 18. 1 c. black and purple .. 35·00 75·00
142. 2 c. black and green .. £130 £150
143. 3 c. black and brown .. 14·00 65·00
144. 4 c. on 12 c. black & yell. 1·50 5·50
145. 4 c. on 16 c. green & brn. 1·50 4·25
146. 4 c. on 18 c. black & brn. 1·00 4·25
147. 8 c. black and orange .. 1·00 5·50
148. 10 c. brown and blue .. 3·00 4·25
149. 25 c. green and blue .. 4·25 18·00
150. 50 c. purple and lilac .. 9·00 42·00
151. $1 red and orange .. 38·00 70·00

48. 54.

52. 53.

1912.

193 48 1 c. green .. .. 2·75 40
196a 3 c. red 30 10
197 4 c. purple 70 30
225a 54 5 c. orange 85 15
227 52 6 c. purple .. .. 2·00 15
201 8 c. blue 70 30
202 54 10 c. purple on yellow .. 90 30
204 53 21 c. purple .. .. 4·00 7·00
234b 54 25 c. purple and mauve 3·25 1·40
235a 30 c. purple and orange 2·00 40
208a 53 45 c. black on green .. 3·00 9·00
238 54 50 c. black on green .. 1·25 40
239 $1 black and red on blue 4·75 45
240 $2 green & red on yell. 9·00 8·00
212a $5 green & red on green 50·00 24·00
240b – $25 pur. & blue on blue £300 75·00

No. 240b is as Type **46** but with head of King George V.

1917. Surch. **RED CROSS 2c.**

216. 48. 2 c. on 3 c. red .. 1·25 18·00
217. 2 c. on 4 c. purple .. 1·25 18·00

1919.

218 48. 1 c. black 30 10
219 52. 2 c. green 30 10
220 2 c. brown .. .. 5·00 2·25
221 48. 3 c. green .. .. 1·25 60
222 4 c. red .. .. 2·00 2·75
223 4 c. violet 30 10
224 4 c. orange 85 10
226 54. 5 c. brown .. .. 1·00 10
229 52. 6 c. red .. .. 2·00 10
230 54. 10 c. blue .. .. 1·75 30
232 52. 12 c. blue 70 10
236a 53. 35 c. purple and orange 3·50 5·50
237 35 c. red and purple .. 7·50 7·00

1922. Optd. **MALAYA-BORNEO EXHIBITION.**

250 48. 1 c. black .. .. 60 6·50
251 52. 2 c. green .. .. 1·40 11·00
252 48. 4 c. red .. .. 1·75 15·00
243 54. 5 c. orange .. .. 3·50 12·00
244 52. 8 c. blue .. .. 1·75 6·00
254 54. 10 c. blue .. .. 2·25 17·00
245 25 c. purple and mauve 3·00 18·00
246 53. 45 c. black on green .. 3·00 15·00
255 54. $1 black and red on blue 15·00 70·00
248 $2 green & red on yellow 22·00 80·00
249 $5 green & red on green £190 £275

1935. Silver Jubilee. As T **13** of Antigua.

256. 5 c. blue and grey .. 45 20
257. 8 c. green and blue .. 1·25 1·25
258. 12 c. brown and blue .. 2·75 1·50
259. 25 c. grey and purple .. 2·75 3·25

57. 58.

1936.

260. 57. 1 c. black 30 20
261. 2 c. green 30 15
262. 4 c. orange 50 30
263. 5 c. brown 30 10
264. 6 c. red 70 40
265. 8 c. grey 40 20
266. 10 c. purple .. .. 1·00 20
267. 12 c. blue .. .. 2·00 2·00
268. 25 c. purple and red .. 1·00 30
269. 30 c. purple and orange 1·25 2·00
270. 40 c. red and purple .. 1·25 2·00
271. 50 c. black and green .. 1·50 70
272. $1 black & red on blue 8·00 70
273. $2 green and red .. 14·00 10·00
274. $5 green & red on green 30·00 10·00

1937. Coronation. As T **2** of Aden.

275. 4 c. orange 30 10
276. 8 c. grey 55 10
277. 12 c. blue 65 50

1937.

278. 58. 1 c. black .. .. 2·00 10
279. 2 c. green .. .. 9·00 10
294. 2 c. orange .. .. 1·00 3·75
295. 3 c. green .. .. 2·75 2·00
280. 4 c. orange .. .. 8·00 10
281. 5 c. brown .. .. 13·00 10
282. 6 c. red .. .. 5·50 10
283. 8 c. grey .. .. 35·00 10
284. 10 c. purple .. .. 4·50 10
285. 12 c. blue .. .. 4·50 10
298. 15 c. blue .. .. 3·50 6·00
286. 25 c. purple and red .. 35·00 75
287. 30 c. purple and orange 35·00 1·25
288. 40 c. red and purple .. 9·00 2·00
289 50 c. black on green .. 6·00 10
290. $1 black and red on blue 7·00 ·15
291. $2 green and red .. 19·00 3·00
292. $5 green & red on green 23·00 3·00

For subsequent issues see " Malaya ".
For Japanese issues see " Japanese Occupation of Malaya ".

POSTAGE DUE STAMPS

D 1.

1924.

D 1. D 1. 1 c. violet .. .. 3·75 4·75
D 2. 2 c. black .. .. 3·00 1·25
D 3. 4 c. green .. .. 2·00 4·75
D 4. 8 c. red .. .. 4·50 55
D 5. 10 c. orange .. .. 5·00 85
D 6. 12 c. blue .. .. 7·00 65

For later issues see Malayan Postal Union.

SUDAN

A territory in Africa, extending S. from Egypt towards the equator, jointly administered by Gt. Britain and Egypt until 1954 when the territory was granted a large measure of self-government. Became independent 1 Jan. 1956.

1000 milliemes = 100 piastres = £1 Sudanese.

1897. Stamps of Egypt optd. **SOUDAN** in English and Arabic.

1. 18. 1 m. brown.. .. .. 1·25 2·00
3. 2 m. green .. .. 1·25 1·75
4. 3 m. yellow .. .. 1·40 1·50
5. 5 m. red .. .. 2·00 70
6. 10. 1 pi. blue .. .. 7·00 2·00
7. – 2 pi. orange .. .. 40·00 12·00
8. – 5 pi. grey .. .. 40·00 12·00
9. 18. 10 pi. mauve .. .. 30·00 40·00

2. Arab Postman. 6.

1898.

18 2 1 m. brown and red .. 30 10
19 2 m. green and brown .. 1·00 10
20 3 m. mauve and green .. 1·25 25
21 4 m. blue and brown .. 1·50 2·50
22 4 m. red and brown .. 1·50 75
13 5 m. red and black .. 75 30
24 1 pi. blue and brown .. 1·60 15
15 2 pi. black and blue .. 12·00 6·50
44 2 pi. purple and orange .. 30 10
44b 3 pi. brown and blue .. 2·00 10
44c 4 pi. blue and black .. 1·60 10
45 5 pi. brown and green .. 80 10
45b 6 pi. blue and black .. 2·00 20
45c 8 pi. green and black .. 2·50 90
46 10 pi. black and mauve .. 90 10
46ba 20 pi. blue .. .. 1·75 10

1903. Surch. **5 Milliemes.**

29. 2. 5 m. on 5 pi. brown & grn. 6·50 9·00

1921.

37. 6. 1 m. black and orange .. 20 10
38. 2 m. yellow and brown .. 20 10
39. 3 m. mauve and green .. 20 10
40. 4 m. green and brown .. 30 10
41. 5 m. brown and black .. 30 10
42. 10 m. red and black .. 30 10
43. 15 m. blue and brown .. 30 10

For stamps as Type **2** and **6** with different Arabic inscriptions see issue of 1948.

1931. Air. Optd. **AIR MAIL.**

47. 6. 5 m. brown and black .. 35 70
48. 10 m. red and black .. 85 3·25
49. 2. 2 pi. purple and yellow .. 85 3·25

10. Statue of General Gordon.

1931. Air.

49b 10. 3 m. green and brown .. 2·50 5·50
50 5 m. black and green .. 1·00 20
51 10 m. black and red .. 1·00 35
52 15 m. brown 40 10
53 2 pi. black and orange .. 30 10
53c $2\frac{1}{2}$ pi. mauve and blue .. 1·50 15
54 3 pi. black and grey .. 60 15
55 $3\frac{1}{2}$ pi. black and violet .. 1·25 80
56 $4\frac{1}{2}$ pi. brown and grey .. 9·00 15·00
57 5 pi. black and blue .. 1·00 40
57b $7\frac{1}{2}$ pi. green .. .. 4·75 3·50
57d 10 pi. brown and blue .. 8·00 40

1932. Air. Surch. **AIR MAIL** and value in English and Arabic figures.

58. 2. $2\frac{1}{2}$ pi. on 2 pi. pur. & orge. 2·00 3·50

12. General Gordon (after C. Ouless).

13. Gordon Memorial College, Khartoum.

1935. 50th Death Anniv. of Gen. Gordon.

59. 12. 5 m. green 35 10
60. 10 m. brown 55 25
61. 13 m. blue .. .. 85 5·00
62. 15 m. red .. .. 1·25 25
63. 2 pi. blue .. .. 1·25 20
64. 5 pi. orange .. .. 1·25 40
65. 13. 10 pi. purple .. .. 6·50 6·00
66. – 20 pi black .. .. 22·00 45·00
67. – 50 pi. brown .. .. 65·00 80·00

DESIGN—(44 × 20 mm.): **20 pi., 50 pi.** Gordon Memorial Service, Khartoum.

1935. Air. Stamps of 1931 surch. in English and Arabic.

74 10 5 m. on $2\frac{1}{2}$ pi. mauve & bl 1·75 10
68 15 m. on 10 m. blk & red 40 10
69 $2\frac{1}{2}$ pi. on 3 m. grn & brn 85 4·75
70 $2\frac{1}{2}$ pi. on 5 m. blk & grn 40 2·00
75 3 pi. on $3\frac{1}{2}$ pi. black & vio 22·00 25·00
71 3 pi. on $4\frac{1}{2}$ pi. brn & grey 1·75 9·00
76 3 pi. on $7\frac{1}{2}$ pi. green .. 5·00 6·00
77 5 pi. on 10 pi. brown & bl 1·50 4·25
72 $7\frac{1}{2}$ pi. on $4\frac{1}{2}$ pi. brown and grey .. .. 6·00 32·00
73 10 pi. on $4\frac{1}{2}$ pi. brown and grey .. .. 5·00 32·00

1940. Surch. **5 mills** and in Arabic.

78. 6. 5 m. on 10 m. red & black 50 30

1940. Surch. **$4\frac{1}{2}$ Piastres.**

79. 6. $4\frac{1}{2}$ p. on 5 m. brown & blk. 35·00 2·00
80. 2. $4\frac{1}{2}$ p. on 8 p. green & black 23·00 4·50

20. Tuti Island, R. Nile, near Khartoum.

1941.

81. 20. 1 m. black and orange .. 10 1·00
82. 2 m. orange and brown .. 30 75
83. 3 m. mauve and green .. 30 10
84. 4 m. green and brown .. 15 20
85. 5 m. brown and black .. 15 10
86. 10 m. red and black .. 6·00 1·75
87. 15 m. blue and brown .. 20 10
88. 2 pi purple and yellow .. 3·25 60
89. 3 pi. brown and blue .. 70 10
90. 4 pi. blue and black .. 60 10
91. 5 pi. brown and green .. 4·50 5·00
92. 6 pi. blue and black .. 14·00 40
93. 8 pi. green and black .. 11·00 45
94. 10 pi. black and violet .. 40·00 75
95. 20 pi. blue .. .. 40·00 22·00

The piastre values are larger (30 × 25 mm.).

22. Arab Postman. **23.**

1948.

96.	**22.**	1m. black and orange ..	35	75
97.		2 m. orange and brown ..	80	90
98.		3 m. mauve and green ..	30	40
99.		4 m. green and brown ..	30	10
100.		5 m. brown and black ..	75	40
101.		10 m. red and black ..	1·50	10
102.		15 m. blue and brown ..	75	10
103.	**23.**	2 p. purple and yellow ..	3·00	10
104.		3 p. brown and blue ..	2·00	10
105.		4 p. blue and black ..	2·25	65
106.		5 p. orange and green ..	2·25	35
107.		6 p. blue and black ..	2·00	90
108.		8 p. green and black ..	2·25	1·25
109.		10 p. black and mauve ..	4·00	90
110.		20 p. blue	2·75	10
111.		50 p. red and blue ..	5·00	40

In this issue the Arabic inscriptions below the camel differ from those in Types 2 and 6.

24. Arab Postman.

1948. Golden Jubilee of "Camel Postman" design.

112.	**24.**	2 p. black and blue ..	10	10

25. Arab Postman.

1948. Legislative Assembly.

113.	**25.**	10 m. red and black ..	10	10
114.		5 p. orange and green ..	10	30

26. Blue Nile Bridge, Khartoum.

1950. Air.

115.	**26.**	2 p. black and green ..	3·00	20
116.	–	2½ p. blue and orange ..	50	40
117.	–	3 p. purple and blue ..	2·00	10
118.	–	3½ p. sepia and brown	75	2·00
119.	–	4 p. brown and blue ..	70	75
120.	–	4½ p. black and blue ..	2·00	2·75
121.	–	6 p. black and red ..	60	50
122.	–	20 p. black and purple	1·75	2·25

DESIGNS: 2½ p. Kassala Jebel. 3 p. Sagia (water wheel). 3½ p. Port Sudan. 4 p. Gordon Memorial College. 4½ p. "Gordon Pasha" (Nile mail boat). 6 p. Suakin. 20 p. G.P.O. Khartoum.

34. Ibex.

35. Cotton Picking.

1951.

123	**34**	1 m. black and orange	10	80
124	–	2 m. black and blue ..	40	15
125	–	3 m. black and green ..	1·75	1·75
126	–	4 m. black and green ..	30	70
127	–	5 m. black and purple	30	10
128	–	10 m. black and blue ..	15	10
129	–	15 m. black and brown	40	10
130	**35**	2 p. blue	15	10
131	–	3 p. brown and blue ..	1·00	10
132	–	3½ p. green and brown	30	10
133	–	4 p. blue and black ..	30	10
134	–	5 p. brown and green	30	10
135	–	6 p. blue and black ..	2·25	65
136	–	8 p. blue and brown ..	3·25	70
137	–	10 p. black and green	1·00	10
138	–	20 p. turquoise & black	3·00	50
139	–	50 p. red and black ..	7·00	55

DESIGNS—As Type **34**: 2 m. Whale-headed Stork. 3 m. Giraffe. 4 m. Baggara girl. 5 m. Shilluk warrior. 10 m. Hadendowa. 15 m. Policeman. As Type **35**—HORIZ. 3 p. Ambatch canoe 3½ p. Nuba wrestlers. 4 p. Weaving. 5 p. Saluka farming. 6 p. Gum tapping. 8 p. Darfur Chief. 10 p. Stack medical Laboratory. 20 p. Nile Lechwe (antelope). VERT. 50 p. Camel postman.

51. Camel Postman.

1954. Self-Government.

140.	**51.**	15 m. brown & green ..	40	40
141.		3 p. blue and indigo ..	40	60
142.		5 p. black and purple ..	40	30

Stamps as Type 51, but dated "1953" were released in error at the Sudan Agency in London. They had no postal validity.

For later issues see Volume 2.

ARMY SERVICE STAMPS

1905. Optd. **ARMY OFFICIAL.**

A 1.	**2.**	1 m. brown and red ..	2·50	2·00

1906. Optd. **Army Service.**

A 6.	**2.**	1 m. brown and red ..	1·50	20
A 7.		2 m. green and brown ..	5·00	1·00
A 8.		3 m. mauve and green ..	16·00	40
A 9.		5 m. red and black ..	1·25	10
A 10.		1 pi. blue and brown ..	8·50	15
A 11.		2 pi. black and blue ..	22·00	11·00
A 12.		5 pi. brown and green	75·00	42·00
A 16.		10 pi. black and mauve	£120	£150

OFFICIAL STAMPS

1902. Optd. **O.S.G.S.**

O 5	**2.**	1 m. brown and red ..	40	10
O 6		3 m. mauve and green ..	1·50	15
O 7		5 m. red and black ..	1·75	10
O 8		1 pi. blue and brown ..	1·75	10
O 9		2 pi. black and blue ..	11·00	20
O 10		5 pi. brown and green	2·00	30
O 4		10 pi. black and mauve	13·00	15·00

1936. Optd. **S.G.**

O32	**6**	1 m. black and orange ..	35	5·00
O33		2 m. yellow and brown	30	2·00
O34		3 m. mauve and green ..	1·00	10
O35		4 m. green and brown	1·25	2·25
O36		5 m. brown and black ..	40	10
O37		10 m. red and black ..	35	10
O38		15 m. blue and brown ..	1·50	10
O39		2 pi. purple and orange	3·00	10
O39b		3 pi. brown and blue ..	75	50
O39c		4 pi. blue and black ..	3·00	15
O40		5 pi. brown and green	4·50	10
O40b		6 pi. blue and black ..	3·00	1·00
O40c	**2**	8 pi. green and black ..	3·25	10·00
O41		10 pi. black and mauve	9·00	3·50
O42		20 pi. blue	9·50	13·00

1948. Optd. **S.G.**

O 43.	**22.**	1 m. black and orange ..	10	1·00
O 44.		2 m. orange and brown	30	10
O 45.		3 m. mauve and green ..	40	1·75
O 46.		4 m. green and brown ..	40	10
O 47.		5 m. brown and black ..	30	10
O 48.		10 m. red and black ..	30	15
O 49.		15 m. blue and brown ..	30	10
O 50.	**23.**	2 p. purple and yellow ..	35	10
O 51.		3 p. brown and blue ..	35	10
O 52.		4 p. blue and black ..	50	10
O 53.		5 p. orange and green ..	50	10
O 54.		6 p. blue and black ..	50	10
O 55.		8 p. green and black ..	50	30
O 56.		10 p. black and mauve	60	20
O 57.		20 p. blue	2·25	25
O 58.		50 p. red and blue ..	35·00	15·00

1950. Air. Nos. 115/22 optd. **S.G.**

O 59.		2 p. black and green ..	7·50	1·25
O 60.		2½ p. blue and orange ..	1·25	80
O 61.		3 p. purple and blue ..	80	70
O 62.		3½ p. sepia and brown ..	80	3·50
O 63.		4 p. brown and blue ..	80	2·75
O 64.		4½ p. black and blue ..	2·50	7·50
O 65.		6 p. black and red ..	1·00	3·50
O 66.		20 p. black and purple ..	5·00	10·00

1951. Nos. 123/39 optd. **S.G.**

O 67.		1 m. black and orange ..	30	2·00
O 68.		2 m. black and blue ..	30	10
O 69.		3 m. black and green ..	1·50	7·50
O 70.		4 m. black and green ..	10	1·40
O 71.		5 m. black and purple ..	10	10
O 72.		10 m. black and blue ..	10	10
O 73.		15 m. black and brown ..	10	10
O 74.		2 p. blue	10	10
O 75.		3 p. brown and blue ..	75	10
O 76.		3½ p. green and brown ..	25	10
O 77.		4 p. blue and black ..	25	10
O 78.		5 p. brown and green ..	25	10
O 79.		6 p. blue and black ..	30	95
O 80.		8 p. blue and brown ..	45	10
O 81.		10 p. black and green ..	50	10
O 82.		20 p. turquoise and black	1·25	25
O 83.		50 p. red and black ..	3·50	1·25

POSTAGE DUE STAMPS

1897. Postage Due stamps of Egypt optd. **SOUDAN** in English and Arabic.

D 1.	**D 23.**	2 m. green	1·75	8·00
D 2.		4 m. purple	1·75	8·00
D 3.		1 pi. blue	6·00	5·00
D 4.		2 pi. orange	7·50	11·00

D 1. Gunboat "Zafir". **D 2.**

1901.

D 5.	**D 1.**	2 m. black and brown	55	60
D 10.		4 m. brown and green	90	80
D 11.		10 m. green and mauve	1·25	1·60
D 8.		20 m. blue and red ..	3·25	3·25

1948.

D 12.	**D 2.**	2 m. black and brown	80	13·00
D 13.		4 m. brown and green	2·00	16·00
D 394.		10 m. green & mauve	15	15
D 395.		20 m. blue and red ..	15	15

The Arabic inscription in Type **D 2** differs from that in Type **D 1.**

SUNGEI UJONG

A native state of the Malay Peninsula, later incorporated in Negri Sembilan.

100 cents = 1 dollar (Straits).

1878. Stamp of Straits Settlements optd. with Crescent, Star and **SU** in an oval.

1.	**5.**	2 c. brown	£1600	£1400

1881. Stamps of Straits Settlements optd **SUNGEI UJONG.**

28.	**5.**	2 c. brown	28·00	70·00
43.		2 c. red	4·50	6·50
22.		4 c. red	£700	£750
34.		4 c. brown	£110	£140
24.		8 c. orange	£800	£700
26.	**19.**	10 c. grey	£300	£300

1882. Stamps of Strait Settlements optd **S.U.** (2 c. with or without stops).

13	**5**	2 c. brown	£160	£200
14		4 c. red	£1500	£1500

1891. Stamp of Straits Settlements surch. **SUNGEI UJONG Two CENTS.**

49.	**5.**	2 c. on 24 c. green	70·00	95·00

16. Tiger. **17.** Tiger.

1891.

50.	**16.**	2 c. red	20·00	26·00
51.		2 c. orange	1·40	4·25
55.	**17.**	3 c. purple and red ..	5·00	75
52.	**16.**	5 c. blue	4·50	5·50

1894. Surch. in figures and words.

53.	**16.**	1 c. on 5 c. green	65	70
54.		3 c. on 5 c. red	1·75	4·25

SWAZILAND

A kingdom in the E. part of S. Africa. Its early stamps were issued under joint control of G. Britain and the S. Africa Republic. Incorporated into the latter state in 1895 it was transferred in 1906 to the High Commissioner for S. Africa. Again issued stamps in 1933. Achieved Independence in 1968.

1961. 100 cents = 1 rand.
1974. 100 cents = 1 lilangeni (plural-emalangeni).

1889. Stamps of Transvaal optd. **Swazieland.**

10.	**18.**	½d. grey	7·00	13·00
1.		1d. red	14·00	15·00
5.		2d. pale brown	12·00	14·00
6.		6d. blue	15·00	30·00
3.		1s. green	10·00	13·00
7.		2s. 6d. yellow	£110	£150
8.		5s. blue	£110	£150
9.		10s. brown	£4500	£2750

2. King George V. **7.** Swazi Married Woman.

1933.

11.	**2.**	½d. green	25	30
12.		1d. red	25	10
13.		2d. brown	30	45
14.		3d. blue	45	50
15.		4d. red	1·00	1·40
16.		6d. mauve	1·00	80
17.		1s. olive	1·50	2·75
18.		2s. 6d. violet	15·00	28·00
19.		5s. grey	35·00	50·00
20.		10s. brown	£100	£120

1935. Silver Jubilee. As T **13** of Antigua.

21.		1d. blue and red	30	20
22.		2d. blue and black ..	30	30
23.		3d. brown and blue ..	45	1·25
24.		6d. grey and purple ..	60	1·00

1937. Coronation. As T **2** of Aden.

25.		1d. red	65	20
26.		2d. brown	65	10
27.		3d. blue	65	30

1938. As T **2**, but with portrait of King George VI and inscr. "SWAZILAND" only below portrait.

28a.		½d. green	15	80
29a.		1d. red	30	35
30b.		1½d. blue	15	35
31a.		2d. brown	15	15
32b.		3d. blue	60	1·40
33a.		4d. orange	30	80
34b.		6d. purple	1·25	55
35a.		1s. olive	30	20
36a.		2s. 6d. violet	3·75	1·50
37b.		5s. grey	11·00	8·00
38a.		10s. brown	5·00	4·50

1945. Victory, Victory stamps of South Africa optd. **SWAZILAND.** Inscr. alternately in English or Afrikaans.

39.	**55.**	1d. brown and red ..	30	30
40.	–	2d. blue & vio. (No. 109)	30	30
41.	–	3d. blue (No. 110) ..	35	1·00

Prices are for pairs.

1947. Royal Visit. As Nos. 32/5 of Basutoland.

42.		1d. red	10	10
43.		2d. green	10	10
44.		3d. blue	10	10
45.		1s. mauve	10	10

1948. Silver Wedding. As T **10/11** of Aden.

46.		1½d. blue	30	10
47.		10s. purple	17·00	12·00

1949. U.P.U. As T **20/23** of Antigua.

48.		1½d. blue	10	10
49.		3d. blue	40	30
50.		6d. mauve	50	40
51.		1s. olive	50	40

1953. Coronation. As T **13** of Aden.

52.		2d. black and brown ..	10	15

1956.

53.	–	½d. black and orange ..	10	10
54.	–	1d. black and green ..	10	10
55.	**7.**	2d. black and brown ..	10	10
56.	–	3d. black and red ..	10	10
57.	–	4½d. black and blue ..	40	10
58.	–	6d. black and mauve ..	20	10
59.	–	1s. black and olive ..	15	10
60.	–	1s. 3d. black and sepia ..	80	45
61.	–	2s. 6d. green and red ..	1·00	70
62.	–	5s. violet and grey ..	3·50	85
63.	**7.**	10s. black and violet ..	9·00	4·00
64.	–	£1 black and turquoise ..	25·00	24·00

DESIGNS—HORIZ. ½d., 1s. Havelock asbestos mine. 1d., 2s. 6d. Highveld view. VERT. 3d., 1s. 3d. Swazi courting couple. 4½d., 5s. Swazi warrior. 6d., £1 Greater Kudu.

1961. Stamps of 1956 surch. in new currency.

65.	½ c. on ½d. black & orange	2·00	2·00
66.	1 c. on 1d. black & green	10	15
67.	2 c. on 2d. black & brown	10	15
68.	2½ c. on 2d. black & brown	10	10
69.	2½ c. on 3d. black and red	10	10
70.	3½ c. on 2d. black & brown	10	10
71.	4 c. on 4½d. black and blue	10	10
72.	5 c. on 6d. black & mauve	10	10
73.	10 c. on 1s. black & olive	10·00	3·00
74.	25 c. on 2s. 6d. green & red	30	65
75.	50 c. on 5s. violet & grey	30	60
76.	1 r. on 10s. black & violet	1·25	60
77a.	2 r. on £1 black & turquoise	4·50	5·50

1961. As 1956 but values in new currency.

78.	½ c. black and orange (as ½d.)	10	15
79.	1 c. black and green (as 1d.)	10	10
80.	2 c. black and brown (as 2d.)	10	40
81.	2½ c. black and red (as 3d.)	15	10
82.	4 c. black and blue (as 4½d.)	15	40
83.	5 c. black & mauve (as 6d.)	30	15
84.	10 c. black and olive (as 1s.)	15	10
85.	12½ c. blk. & sep. (as 1s. 3d.)	90	40
86.	25 c. green & red (as 2s. 6d.)	1·25	1·25
87.	50 c. violet and grey (as 5s.)	2·00	1·40
88.	1 r. black & violet (as 10s.)	3·00	3·75
89.	2 r. blk. & turquoise (as £1)	9·00	11·00

15. Swazi Shields. 31. Steam Train and Map.

1962.

90. 15.	½ c. black, brown & buff	10	10
91. –	1 c. orange and black	10	10
92. –	2 c. green, black and olive	10	10
93. –	2½ c. black and red	10	10
94. –	3½ c. green and grey	10	10
95. –	4 c. black and turquoise	10	10
96. –	5 c. black, red & deep red	30	10
97. –	7½ c. brown and buff	30	15
98. –	10 c. black and blue	70	10
99. –	12½ c. red and olive	50	70
100. –	15 c. black and mauve	75	50
101. –	20 c. black and green	30	70
102. –	25 c. black and blue	30	60
103. –	50 c. black and red	5·50	2·50
104. –	1 r. green and ochre	2·50	2·25
105. –	2 r. red and blue	8·50	5·50

DESIGNS—VERT. 1 c. Battle axe. 2 c. Forestry. 2½ c. Ceremonial head-dress. 3½ c. Musical instrument. 4 c. Irrigation. 5 c. Long-tailed Whydah. 7½ c. Rock paintings. 10 c. Secretary Bird. 12½ c. Pink Arum. 15 c. Swazi married woman. 20 c. Malaria control. 25 c. Swazi warrior. 1 r. Aloes. HORIZ. 50 c. Southern Ground Hornbill. 2 r. Msinsi in flower.

1963. Freedom from Hunger. As T **28** of Aden.

106.	15 c. violet	40	15

1963. Cent of Red Cross. As T **33** of Antigua.

107.	2½ c. red and black	10	10
108.	15 c. red and blue	40	20

1964. Opening of the Swaziland Railway.

109. 31.	2½ c. green and purple	20	10
110.	3½ c. blue and olive	20	10
111.	15 c. orange and brown	30	30
112.	25 c. yellow and blue	45	25

1965. Cent of I.T.U. As T **36** of Antigua.

113.	2½ c. blue and bistre	10	10
114.	15 c. purple and red	25	20

1965. I.C.Y. As T **37** of Antigua.

115.	½ c. purple and turquoise	10	10
116.	15 c. green and lavender	40	20

1966. Churchill Commem. As T **38** of Antigua.

117.	½ c. blue	10	10
118.	2½ c. green	20	10
119.	15 c. brown	35	15
120.	25 c. violet	50	35

1966. 20th Anniv of U.N.E.S.C.O. As T **54/6** of Antigua.

121.	2½ c. multicoloured	10	10
122.	7½ c. yellow, violet & olive	20	10
123.	15 c. black, purple & orge.	35	20

32. King Sobhuza II and Map.

1967. Protected State.

124. 32.	2½ c. multicoloured	10	10
125. –	7½ c. multicoloured	10	10
126. 32.	15 c. multicoloured	10	10
127. –	25 c. multicoloured	15	10

DESIGN—VERT. 7½ c., 25 c. King Sobhuza II.

1967. First Conferment of University Degrees. As T **66** of Botswana.

128.	2½ c. sepia, blue & orange	10	10
129.	7½ c. sepia, blue & turq.	10	10
130.	15 c. sepia, blue and red	10	10
131.	25 c. sepia, blue and violet	10	10

35. Incwala Ceremony.

1968. Traditional Customs.

132. 35.	3 c. silver, red and black	10	10
133. –	10 c. multicoloured	10	10
134. 35.	15 c. gold, red and black	10	10
135. –	25 c. multicoloured	10	10

DESIGN—VERT. 10 c., 25 c. Reed Dance.

1968. No. 96 Surch.

136. –	3 c. on 5 c. black, red and deep red	15	10

38. Cattle Ploughing.

1968. Independence.

137. 38.	3 c. multicoloured	10	10
138. –	4½ c. multicoloured	10	10
139. –	17½ c. multicoloured	15	10
140. –	25 c. slate, black & gold	45	45

1968. Nos. 90/105 optd. **INDEPENDENCE 1968** and No. 93 additionally surch. **3 c.**

142. 15.	½ c. black, brown & buff	10	10
143. –	1 c. orange and black	10	10
144. –	2 c. green, black & olive	10	10
145. –	2½ c. black and red	30	10
146. –	3 c. on 2½ c. black & red	10	10
147. –	3½ c. green and grey	15	10
148. –	4 c. black and turquoise	10	10
149. –	5 c. black, red & verm.	1·25	10
150. –	7½ c. brown and buff	20	10
151. –	10 c. black and blue	1·25	10
152. –	12½ c. red and olive	25	30
153. –	15 c. black and mauve	25	30
154. –	20 c. black and green	75	1·00
155. –	25 c. black and blue	35	40
159. –	50 c. black and red	4·25	2·50
157. –	1 r. green and ochre	2·50	3·00
160. –	2 r. red and blue	5·50	5·00

43. Porcupine.

1969. Multicoloured.

161.	½ c. Caracal	10	10
162.	1 c. Type **43**	10	10
163.	2 c. Crocodile	20	10
164.	3 c. Lion	60	10
165.	3½ c. African elephant	60	10
166.	5 c. Bush pig	30	10
167.	7½ c. Impala	35	10
168.	10 c. Chacma baboon	45	10
169.	12½ c. Ratel	70	1·25
170.	15 c. Leopard	1·25	70
171.	20 c. Blue wildebeest	95	60
172.	25 c. White rhinoceros	1·40	1·00
173.	50 c. Common zebra	1·50	2·25
174.	1 r. Waterbuck	3·00	4·25
175.	2 r. Giraffe	6·00	8·50

Nos. 174/5 are vert. Nos. 164/5 are larger (35 × 24½ mm.).

For designs as Nos. 174/5, but in new currency, see Nos. 219/20.

44. King Sobhuza II and Flags.

1969. Swaziland's Admission to the U.N. Multicoloured.

176.	3 c. Type **44**	10	10
177.	7½ c. King Sobhuza II, U.N. building and emblem	15	10
178.	12½ c. As Type **44**	20	10
179.	25 c. As 7½ c.	30	30

46. Athlete, Shield and Spears. 47. "Bauhinia galpinii".

1970. 9th Commonwealth Games. Multicoloured.

180.	3 c. Type **46**	10	10
181.	7½ c. Runner	15	10
182.	12½ c. Jumper	20	10
183.	25 c. Procession of Swaziland competitors	30	30

1971. Flowers. Multicoloured.

184.	3 c. Type **47**	20	10
185.	10 c. "Crocosmia aurea"	35	10
186.	15 c. "Gloriosa superba"	50	15
187.	25 c. "Watsonia densiflora"	70	35

48. King Sobhuza II in Ceremonial Dress.

1971. Golden Jubilee of King Sobhuza II's Accession. Multicoloured.

188.	3 c. Type **48**	10	10
189.	3½ c. Sobhuza II in medallion	10	10
190.	7½ c. Sobhuza II attending Incwala ceremony	10	10
191.	25 c. Sobhuza II and aides at opening of Parliament	20	35

49. U.N.I.C.E.F. Emblem.

1972. 25th Anniv. of U.N.I.C.E.F.

192. 49.	15 c. black and lilac	15	10
193. –	25 c. black and green	20	20

DESIGN: 25 c. As Type **49**, but inscription rearranged.

50. Local Dancers.

1972. Tourism. Multicoloured.

194.	3½ c. Type **50**	10	10
195.	7½ c. Swazi beehive hut	15	10
196.	15 c. Ezulwini Valley	30	20
197	25 c. Fishing, Usutu River	80	40

51. Spraying Mosquitoes.

1973. 25th Anniv. of W.H.O. Multicoloured.

198.	3½ c. Type **51**	15	10
199.	7½ c. Anti-malaria vaccination	25	20

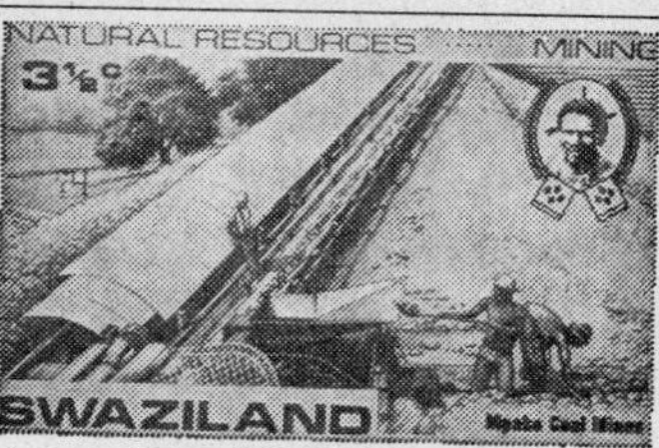

52. Mining.

1973. Natural Resources Multicoloured.

200.	3½ c. Type **52**	20	10
201.	7½ c. Cattle	25	10
202.	15 c. Water	30	15
203.	25 c. Rice	35	30

53. Coat of arms.

1973. 5th Anniv. of Independence.

204. 53.	3 c. pink and black	10	10
205. –	10 c. multicoloured	20	10
206. –	15 c. multicoloured	35	30
207. –	25 c. multicoloured	40	40

DESIGNS: 10 c. King Sobhuza II saluting. 15 c. Parliament buildings. 25 c. National Somhlolo stadium.

54. Flags and Mortarboard.

1973. 10th Anniv. of University of Botswana, Lesotho and Swaziland. Multicoloured.

208.	7½ c. Type **54**	15	10
209.	12½ c. University campus	20	10
210.	15 c. Map of Southern Africa	25	20
211.	25 c. University badge	35	35

55. King Sobhuza as College Student.

1974. 75th Birth Anniv. of King Sobhuza II. Multicoloured.

212.	3 c. Type **55**	10	10
213.	9 c. King Sobhuza in middle-age	10	10
214.	50 c. King Sobhuza at 75 years of age	50	60

56. New Post Office, Lobamba.

1974. Centenary of U.P.U. Multicoloured.

215.	4 c. Type **56**	10	10
216.	10 c. Mbabane Temporary Post Office, 1902	25	15
217.	15 c. Carrying mail by cableway	45	50
218.	25 c. Mule-drawn mail-coach	55	70

1975. As Nos. 174/5, but in new currency.
219. 1 e. Waterbuck .. .. .. 2·00 2·50
220. 2 e. Giraffe .. .. 4·00 4·50

57. Umcwasho Ceremony.

1975. Swazi Youth. Multicoloured.
221. 3 c. Type **57** 10 10
222. 10 c. Butimba (ritual dance) 15 10
223. 15 c. Lusekwane (preparation) (horiz.) 25 15
224. 25 c. Goina Regiment on parade 30 30

58. Control Tower Matsapa Airport.

1975. 10th Anniv. of Internal Air Service. Multicoloured.
225. 4 c. Type **58** 30 10
226. 5 c. Fire engine 40 10
227. 15 c. Douglas "Dakota" 1·60 80
228. 25 c. Hawker Siddeley "748" 1·90 1·25

1975. Nos. 167 and 169 surch.
230. 3 c. on $7\frac{1}{2}$ c. Impala .. 1·25 70
231. 6 c. on $12\frac{1}{2}$ c. Ratel .. 1·75 80

60. Elephant Symbol.

1975. International Women's Year.
232. **60.** 4 c. grey, black and blue 15 10
233. – 5 c. multicoloured .. 15 10
234. – 15 c. multicoloured .. 40 35
235. – 25 c. multicoloured .. 60 50

DESIGNS—HORIZ. 5 c. Queen Labotsibeni. VERT. 15 c. Craftswoman. 25 c. "Women in Service".

61. African Black-headed Oriole.

1976. Birds. Multicoloured.
236. 1 c. Type **61** 60 35
237. 2 c. African Green Pigeon (vert.) 65 30
238. 3 c. Green-winged Pytilla 80 35
239. 4 c. Violet Starling (vert.) 80 15
240. 5 c. Black-headed Heron (vert.) 90 30
241. 6 c. Stonechat (vert.) .. 1·25 30
242. 7 c. Chorister Robin Chat (vert.) 90 30
243. 10 c. Four-coloured Bush-Shrike (vert.) .. .. 1·00 30
244. 15 c. Black-collared Barbet (vert.) .. .. 1·25 55
245. 20 c. Grey Heron (vert.) .. 1·75 75
246. 25 c. Giant Kingfisher (vert.) 1·75 75
247. 30 c. Verreaux's Eagle (vert.) 1·75 95
248a. 50 c. Red Bishop (vert.) .. 90 1·00
249a. 1 e. Pin-tailed Whydah (vert.) .. .. 1·75 2·50
250a. 2 e. Lilac-breasted Roller 3·00 4·50

62. Blindness from Malnutrition.

1976. Prevention of Blindness. Mult.
251. 5 c. Type **62** 15 10
252. 10 c. Infected retina .. 25 10
253. 20 c. Blindness from trachoma 40 35
254. 25 c. Medicines 50 40

63. Marathon.

1976. Olympic Games, Montreal. Mult.
255. 5 c. Type **63** 10 10
256. 6 c. Boxing 15 10
257. 20 c. Football 35 25
258. 25 c. Olympic torch and flame 40 35

64. Footballer Shooting.

1976. F.I.F.A. Membership. Multicoloured.
259. 4 c. Type **64** 15 10
260. 6 c. Heading 15 10
261. 20 c. Goalkeeping .. 40 25
262. 25 c. Player about to shoot 45 30

65. Alexander Graham Bell and Telephone.

1976. Centenary of Telephone.
263. **65.** 4 c. multicoloured .. 10 10
264. – 5 c. multicoloured .. 10 10
265. – 10 c. multicoloured .. 10 10
266. – 15 c. multicoloured .. 30 20
267. – 20 c. multicoloured .. 40 30

Nos. 264/7 as Type **65**, but showing different telephones.

66. Queen Elizabeth II and King Sobhuza II.

1977. Silver Jubilee. Multicoloured.
268. 20 c. Type **66** 20 20
269. 25 c. Coronation Coach at Admiralty Arch 20 20
270. 50 c. Queen in coach .. 30 45

67. Matsapa College.

1977. 50 Years of Police Training. Mult.
271. 5 c. Type **67** 10 10
272. 10 c. Policemen and women on parade 30 10
273. 20 c. Royal Swaziland Police badge (vert.) 45 25
274. 25 c. Dog handling .. 50 35

68. Animals and Hunters.

1977. Rock Paintings. Multicoloured.
275. 5 c. Type **68** 25 10
276. 10 c. Four dancers in a procession 30 10
277. 15 c. Man with cattle .. 40 20
278. 20 c. Four dancers .. 45 30

69. Timber, Highveld Region.

1977. Maps of the Regions. Multicoloured.
280. 5 c. Type **69** 10 10
281. 10 c. Pineapple, Middleveld 20 10
282. 15 c. Orange and lemon, Lowveld 30 20
283. 20 c. Cattle, Lubombo region 40 30

71. Cabbage Tree.

1978. Trees of Swaziland.
285. **71.** 5 c. grn., brn. and blk. 15 10
286. – 10 c. multicoloured .. 35 10
287. – 20 c. multicoloured .. 55 40
288. – 25 c. multicoloured .. 60 50

DESIGNS: 10 c. Marula. 20 c. Kiaat. 25 c. Lucky bean-tree.

72. Rural Electrification at Lobamba.

1978. Hydro-electric Power.
289. **72.** 5 c. black and brown .. 10 10
290. – 10 c. black and green .. 15 10
291. – 20 c. black and blue .. 25 30
292. – 25 c. black and purple .. 30 35

DESIGNS: 10 c. Edwaleni Power Station. 20 c. Switchgear, Magudza Power Station. 25 c. Turbine Hall, Edwaleni.

73. Elephant.

1978. 25th Anniv. of Coronation.
293. – 25 c. blue, black & green 20 30
294. – 25 c. multicoloured .. 20 30
295. **73.** 25 c. blue, black & green 20 30

DESIGNS: No. 293, Queen's Lion. No. 294, Queen Elizabeth II.

74. Clay Pots.

1978. Handicrafts (1st series). Multicoloured.
296. 5 c. Type **74** 10 10
297. 10 c. Basketwork 10 10
298. 20 c. Wooden utensils .. 15 15
299. 30 c. Wooden pot .. 25 30

See also Nos. 310/13.

75. Defence Force.

1978. 10th Anniv. of Independence. Mult.
300. 4 c. Type **75** 10 10
301. 6 c. The King's Regiment 10 10
302. 10 c. Tinkabi tractor (agricultural development) .. 15 10
303. 15 c. Water-pipe laying (self-help scheme) .. 20 10
304. 25 c. Sebenta adult literacy scheme 25 25
305. 50 c. Fire emergency service 40 50

76. Archangel Gabriel appearing before Shepherds.

1978. Christmas. Multicoloured.
306. 5 c. Type **76** 10 10
307. 10 c. Wise Men paying homage to infant Jesus .. 10 10
308. 15 c. Archangel Gabriel warning Joseph .. 10 10
309. 25 c. Flight into Eygpt .. 20 20

1979. Handicrafts (2nd series). As T **74**. Multicoloured.
310. 5 c. Sisal bowls 10 10
311. 15 c. Pottery 10 10
312. 20 c. Basket work .. 15 15
313. 30 c. Hide shield 20 20

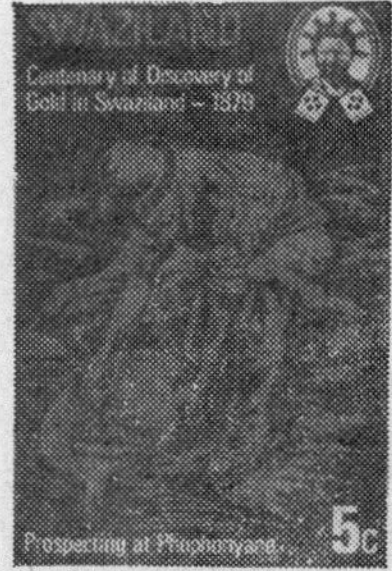

77. Prospecting at Phophonyane.

1979. Centenary of Discovery of Gold in Swaziland.

No.	Type	Description	Unused	Used
314.	77.	5 c. gold and blue ..	15	10
315.	–	15 c. gold and brown ..	30	20
316.	–	25 c. gold and green ..	45	30
317.	–	50 c. gold and red ..	70	90

DESIGNS: 15 c. Early 3-stamp battery mill. 25 c. Cyanide tanks at Piggs Peak. 50 c. Pouring off molten gold.

78. " Girls at the Piano ".

1979. International Year of the Child. Paintings by Renoir. Multicoloured.

No.	Description	Unused	Used
318.	5 c. Type 78	10	10
319.	15 c. " Madame Charpentier and her Children "	25	10
320.	25 c. " Girls Picking Flowers "	35	15
321.	50 c. " Girl with Watering Can "	70	55

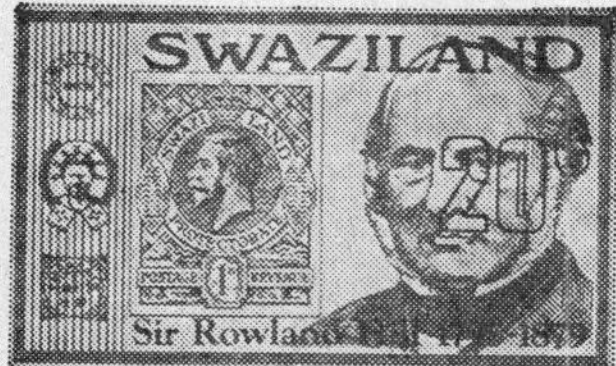

79. 1933 1d. Carmine Stamp and Sir Rowland Hill.

1979. Death Centenary of Sir Rowland Hill. Multicoloured.

No.	Description	Unused	Used
323.	10 c. 1945 3d. Victory commemorative ..	15	10
324.	20 c. Type 79	25	25
325.	25 c. 1968 25 c. Independence commemorative ..	25	30

80. Obverse and Reverse of 5 Cents.

1979. Coins.

No.	Type	Description	Unused	Used
327.	80.	5 c. black and brown ..	10	10
328.	–	10 c. black and blue ..	15	10
329.	–	20 c. black and green ..	25	20
330.	–	50 c. black and orange ..	45	45
331.	–	1 e. black and cerise ..	75	80

DESIGNS: 10 c. Obverse and reverse of 10 cents. 20 c. Obverse and reverse of 20 cents. 50 c. Reverse of 50 cents. 1 e. Reverse of 1 lilangeni.

81. Big Bend Post Office.

1979. Post Office Anniversaries.

No.	Type	Description	Unused	Used
332.	81.	5 c. multicoloured ..	10	10
333.	–	15 c. multicoloured ..	15	10
334.	–	20 c. black, green & red	20	15
335.	–	50 c. multicoloured ..	40	60

DESIGNS AND COMMEMORATIONS—HORIZ. 5 c. Type 81 (25th anniversary of Posts and Telecommunications Services). 20 c. 1949 1s. 75th anniversary of U.P.U. stamp (10th anniversary of U.P.U. membership). 50 c. 1974 25 c. centenary of U.P.U. stamp (10th anniversary of U.P.U. membership). VERT. 15 c. Microwave antenna, Mount Ntondzi (25th anniversary of Posts and Telecommunications Services).

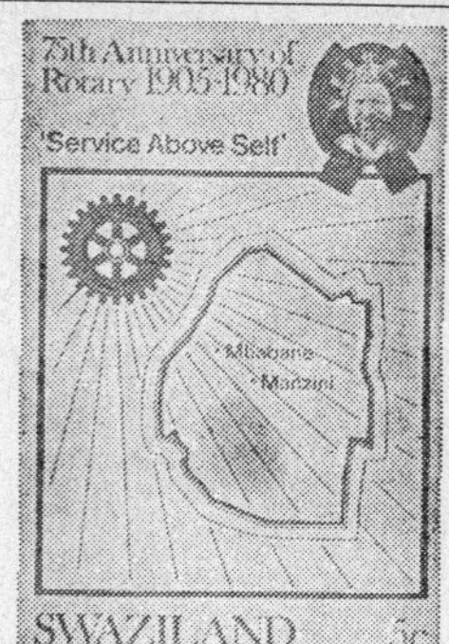

82. Map of Swaziland.

1980. 75th Anniv. of Rotary International.

No.	Type	Description	Unused	Used
336.	82.	5 c. blue and gold ..	10	10
337.	–	15 c. blue and gold ..	15	10
338.	–	50 c. blue and gold ..	40	55
339.	–	1 e. blue and gold ..	80	1·25

DESIGNS: 15 c. Vitreous cutter and optical illuminator. 50 c. Scroll. 1 e. Rotary Headquarters, Evanston, U.S.A.

83. " Brunsvigia radulosa ".

1980. Flowers. Multicoloured.

No.	Description	Unused	Used
340.	1 c. Type 83	15	10
341.	2 c. " Aloe suprafoliata " ..	15	10
342.	3 c. " Haemanthus magnificus "	15	10
343.	4 c. " Aloe marlothii " ..	20	10
344.	5 c. " Dicoma zeyheri " ..	15	10
345.	6 c. " Aloe kniphofioides "	20	20
346.	7 c. " Cyrtanthus bicolor "	15	10
347.	10 c. " Eucomis autumnalis " (horiz.)	25	10
348.	15 c. " Leucospermum gerrardii " (horiz.) ..	15	10
349.	20 c. " Haemanthus multiflorus " (horiz.) ..	40	25
350.	30 c. " Acridocarpus natalitius " (horiz.) ..	20	20
351.	50 c. " Adenium swazicum " (horiz.)	30	30
352.	1 e. " Protea simplex " ..	55	60
353.	2 e. " Calodendrum capense "	1·10	1·25
354.	5 e. " Gladiolus ecklonii " ..	2·75	3·00

Nos. 347/51 are 42 × 45 mm. and Nos. 352/4 28 × 38 mm.

Nos. 340/1, 343, 345, 347 and 349 come with and without date imprint.

84. Mail Runner.

1980. " London 1980 " International Stamp Exhibition. Multicoloured.

No.	Description	Unused	Used
355.	10 c. Type 84	15	10
356.	20 c. Post Office mail truck	25	15
357.	25 c. Mail sorting office ..	30	20
358.	50 c. Ropeway conveying mail at Bulembu ..	70	70

85. Yellow Fish.

1980. River Fishes. Multicoloured.

No.	Description	Unused	Used
359.	5 c. Type 85	10	10
360.	10 c. Silver Barbel ..	15	10
361.	15 c. Tiger Fish ..	20	15
362.	30 c. Squeaker Fish ..	40	30
363.	1 e. Bream	1·10	1·40

86. Oribi.

1980. Wildlife Conservation. Multicoloured.

No.	Description	Unused	Used
364.	5 c. Type 86	10	10
365.	10 c. Nile crocodile (vert.)	15	10
366.	50 c. Temminck's ground pangolin	70	70
367.	1 e. Leopard (vert.) ..	1·25	1·50

87. Public Bus Service.

1981. Transport. Multicoloured.

No.	Description	Unused	Used
368.	5 c. Type 87	10	10
369.	25 c. Royal Swazi National Airways	25	15
370.	30 c. Swaziland United Transport	30	20
371.	1 e. Swaziland Railway ..	1·75	1·75

88. Mantenga Falls.

1981. Tourism. Multicoloured.

No.	Description	Unused	Used
372.	5 c. Type 88	10	10
373.	15 c. Mananga Yacht Club	15	10
374.	30 c. White Rhinoceros in Mlilwane Game Sanctuary	40	30
375.	1 e. Gambling equipment (casinos)	1·40	1·60

89. Prince Charles on Hike.

1981. Royal Wedding. Multicoloured.

No.	Description	Unused	Used
376.	10 c. Wedding bouquet from Swaziland ..	15	10
377.	25 c. Type 89	15	10
378.	1 e. Prince Charles and Lady Diana Spencer ..	60	70

90. Installation of King Sobhuza II, 22 December 1921.

1981. Diamond Jubilee of King Sobhuza II. Multicoloured.

No.	Description	Unused	Used
379.	5 c. Type 90	10	10
380.	10 c. Royal Visit, 1947 ..	15	10
381.	15 c. King Sobhuza II and Coronation of Queen Elizabeth II, 1953 ..	20	15
382.	25 c. King Sobhuza taking Royal Salute, Independence, 1968	25	25
383.	30 c. King Sobhuza in youth	30	30
384.	1 e. King Sobhuza and Parliament Buildings ..	90	1·25

91. " Physical Recreation ".

1981. 25th Anniv. of Duke of Edinburgh Award Scheme. Multicoloured.

No.	Description	Unused	Used
385.	5 c. Type 91	10	10
386.	20 c. " Expeditions " ..	15	10
387.	50 c. " Skills "	40	25
388.	1 e. Duke of Edinburgh in ceremonial dress ..	80	80

92. Disabled Person in Wheelchair.

1981. International Year for the Disabled. Multicoloured.

No.	Description	Unused	Used
389.	5 c. Type 92	15	10
390.	15 c. Teacher with disabled child (vert.) ..	30	15
391.	25 c. Disabled craftsman (vert.)	50	20
392.	1 e. Disabled driver in invalid carriage ..	1·75	1·40

93. "Papilio demodocus".

1981. Butterflies. Multicoloured.

No.	Description	Unused	Used
393	5 c. Type 93	40	10
394	10 c. "Charaxes candiope"	50	10
395	50 c. "Papilio nireus" ..	1·50	85
396	1 e. "Eurema desjardinsii"	2·00	2·00

94. Man holding a Flower, after discarding Cigarettes.

1982. Pan-African Conference on Smoking and Health. Multicoloured.

No.	Description	Unused	Used
397.	5 c. Type 94	30	30
398.	10 c. Smoker and non-smoker	40	40

95. Male Pel's Fishing Owl.

1982. Wildlife Conservation (1st series). Pel's Fishing Owl. Multicoloured.

399.	35 c. Type **95**	1·10	1·25
400.	35 c. Female Pel's Fishing Owl at nest	1·10	1·25
401.	35 c. Pair of Pel's Fishing Owls	1·10	1·25
402.	35 c. Pel's Fishing Owl, nest and eggs	1·10	1·25
403.	35 c. Adult Pel's Fishing Owl with youngster ..	1·10	1·25

See also Nos. 425/29 and 448/52.

96. Swaziland Coat of Arms.

1982. 21st Birthday of Princess of Wales. Multicoloured.

404.	5 c. Type **96**	10	10
405.	20 c. Princess leaving East-leigh Airport, Southampton	15	10
406.	50 c. Bride at Buckingham Palace	35	35
407.	1 e. Formal Portrait ..	80	80

97. Irrigation.

1982. Sugar Industry. Multicoloured.

408.	5 c. Type **97**	10	10
409.	20 c. Harvesting	25	15
410.	30 c. Mhlume mills ..	35	25
411.	1 e. Sugar transportation by train	1·00	1·40

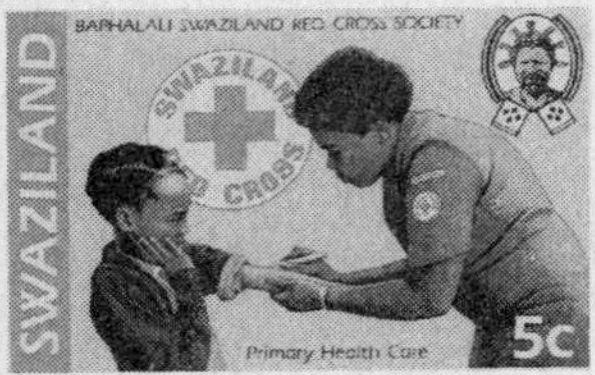

98. Doctor with Child.

1982. Swaziland Red Cross Society (Baphaladi). Multicoloured.

412.	5 c. Type **98**	10	10
413.	20 c. Juniors carrying stretcher	25	15
414.	50 c. Disaster relief ..	55	60
415.	1 e. Henri Dunant (founder of Red Cross)	1·25	1·40

99. Taking the Oath.

1982. 75th Anniv. of Boy Scout Movement. Multicoloured.

416.	5 c. Type **99**	10	10
417.	10 c. Hiking and exploration	15	10
418.	25 c. Community development	30	20
419.	75 c. Lord Baden-Powell	1·00	1·00

MINIMUM PRICE

The minimum price quoted is 10p which represents a handling charge rather than a basis for valuing common stamps. For further notes about prices see introductory pages.

100. Satellite View of Earth.

1982. Commonwealth Day. Multicoloured.

421.	6 c. Type **100**	10	10
422.	10 c. King Sobhuza II ..	10	10
423.	50 c. Swazi woman and beehive huts (horiz.) ..	35	55
424.	1 e. Spraying sugar crops (horiz.)	70	1·00

1983. Wildlife Conservation (2nd series). Lammergeier. As T **95**. Multicoloured.

425.	35 c. Adult male	1·00	1·00
426.	35 c. Pair	1·00	1·00
427.	35 c. Nest and egg ..	1·00	1·00
428.	35 c. Female at nest ..	1·00	1·00
429.	35 c. Adult bird with fledgeling	1·00	1·00

102. Montgolfier Balloon.

1983. Bicentenary of Manned Flight. Mult.

431.	5 c. Type **102**	10	10
432.	10 c. Wright brothers' "Flyer" (horiz.) ..	15	10
433.	25 c. Fokker "Fellowship" (horiz.)	30	35
434.	50 c. Bell "X-1" (horiz.)	60	65

103. Dr. Albert Schweitzer (Peace Prize, 1952).

1983. 150th Birth Anniv. of Alfred Nobel. Multicoloured.

436.	6 c. Type **103**	25	10
437.	10 c. Dag Hammarskjold (Peace Prize, 1961) ..	25	10
438.	50 c. Albert Einstein (Physics Prize, 1921) ..	1·25	70
439.	1 e. Alfred Nobel	1·75	1·50

104. Maize.

1983. World Food Day. Multicoloured.

440.	6 c. Type **104**	10	10
441.	10 c. Rice	10	10
442.	50 c. Cattle herding ..	55	65
443.	1 e. Ploughing	1·10	1·40

105. Women's College.

1984. Education. Multicoloured.

444.	5 c. Type **105**	10	10
445.	15 c. Technical Training School	15	15
446.	50 c. University	45	60
447.	1 e. Primary school ..	90	1·10

106. Male on Ledge.

1984. Wildlife Conservation (3rd series). Bald Ibis. Multicoloured.

448.	35 c. Type **106**	1·40	1·40
449.	35 c. Male and female ..	1·40	1·40
450.	35 c. Bird and egg ..	1·40	1·40
451.	35 c. Female on nest of eggs	1·40	1·40
452.	35 c. Adult and fledgling ..	1·40	1·40

107. Mule-drawn Passenger Coach.

1984. Universal Postal Union Congress Hamburg. Multicoloured.

453.	7 c. Type **107**	20	10
454.	15 c. Ox-drawn post wagon	25	15
455.	50 c. Mule-drawn mail coach	65	60
456.	1 e. Bristol to London mail coach	1·10	1·10

108. Running.

1984. Olympic Games, Los Angeles. Multicoloured.

457.	7 c. Type **108**	10	10
458.	10 c. Swimming	10	10
459.	50 c. Shooting	45	50
460.	1 e. Boxing	90	95

109. "Suillus bovinus".

1984. Fungi. Multicoloured.

462.	10 c. Type **109**	40	10
463.	15 c. "Langermannia gigantea" (vert.)	65	15
464.	50 c. "Coriolus versicolor" (vert.)	1·25	55
465.	1 e. "Boletus edulis" ..	1·75	1·40

110. King Sobhuza opening Railway, 1964.

1984. 20th Anniv. of Swaziland Railways. Multicoloured.

466.	10 c. Type **110**	25	10
467.	25 c. Type "15A" locomotive at Siweni Yard	55	30
468.	30 c. Container loading, Matsapha Station	55	30
469.	1 e. Locomotive No. 268 leaving Alto Tunnel	1·50	95

1985. Nos. 340, 342, 343, 345 and 346 surch.

471a.	10 c. on 4 c. "Aloe marlothii"	20	10
472.	15 c. on 7 c. "Cyrtanthus bicolor"	30	10
473.	20 c. on 3 c. "Haemanthus magnificus"	40	15
474.	25 c. on 6 c. "Aloe kniphofioides"	40	20
475.	30 c. on 1 c. Type **83** ..	50	20
476.	30 c. on 2 c. "Aloe suprafoliata"	55	60

112. Rotary International Logo and Map of World.

1985. 80th Anniv. of Rotary International. Multicoloured.

477.	10 c. Type **112**	25	10
478.	15 c. Teacher and handicapped children	35	20
479.	50 c. Youth exchange ..	80	55
480.	1 e. Nurse and children ..	1·40	1·10

113. Male Southern Ground Hornbill.

1985. Birth Bicentenary of John J. Audubon (ornithologist). Southern Ground Hornbills. Multicoloured.

481.	25 c. Type **113**	85	55
482.	25 c. Male and female Ground hornbills ..	85	55
483.	25 c. Female at nest ..	85	55
484.	25 c. Ground hornbill in nest, and egg	85	55
485.	25 c. Adult and fledgeling	85	55

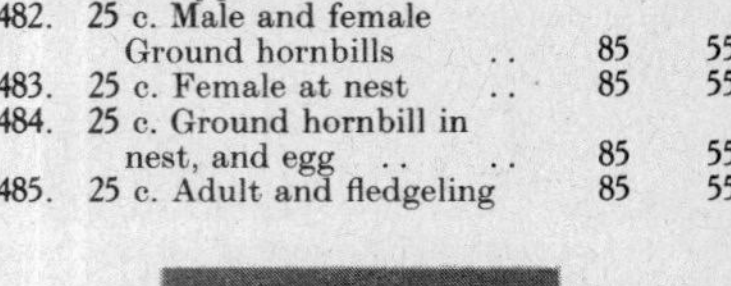

114. The Queen Mother in 1975.

1985. Life and Times of Queen Elizabeth the Queen Mother. Multicoloured.

486	10 c. The Queen Mother in South Africa, 1947 ..	10	10
487	15 c. With the Queen and Princess Margaret, 1985 (from photo by Norman Parkinson)	10	10
488	50 c. Type **114**	30	35
489	1 e. With Prince Henry at his christening (from photo by Lord Snowdon)	65	70

115. Buick "Tourer"

1985. Century of Motoring. Multicoloured.

491.	10 c. Type **115**	30	1
492.	15 c. Four cylinder Rover	45	1
493.	50 c. De Dion Bouton ..	1·00	7
494.	1 e. "Model T" Ford ..	1·60	2·0

116. Youths building Bridge over Ravine.

1985. International Youth Year (10, 50 c.) and 75th Anniv. of Girl Guide Movement (others). Multicoloured.

95.	10 c. Type **116**	15	10
96.	20 c. Girl Guides in camp	20	15
97.	50 c. Youth making model from sticks	45	60
98.	1 e. Guides collecting brushwood	80	1·25

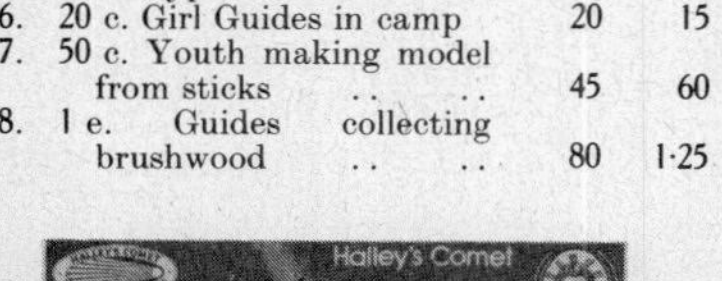

117. Halley's Comet over Swaziland.

1986. Appearance of Halley's Comet.

99.	**117.**	1 e. 50 multicoloured	2·25	2·25

1986. 60th Birthday of Queen Elizabeth II. As T **110** of Ascension. Multicoloured.

00.	10 c. Christening of Princess Anne, 1950	10	10
01.	30 c. On Palace balcony after wedding of Prince and Princess of Wales, 1981	20	25
02.	45 c. Royal visit to Swaziland, 1947	25	30
03.	1 e. At Windsor Polo Ground, 1984	55	60
04.	2 e. At Crown Agents Head Office, London, 1983	1·10	1·25

118 King Mswati III

1986. Coronation of King Mswati III

05.	**118.**	10 c. black and gold	30	10
06.	–	20 c. multicoloured	50	30
07.	–	25 c. multicoloured	55	35
08.	–	30 c. multicoloured	60	40
09.	–	40 c. multicoloured	65	65
10.	–	2 e. multicoloured	2·50	3·50

DESIGNS—HORIZ. 20 c. Prince with King Sobhuza II at Incwala ceremony. 25 c. At primary school. 30 c. At school in England. 40 c. Inspecting guard of honour at Matsapha Airport. 2 e. Dancing the Simemo.

119. Emblems of Round Table and Project Orbis (eye disease campaign).

1986. 50th Anniv. of Round Table Organization. Designs showing branch emblems. Multicoloured.

11.	15 c. Type **119**	10	10
12.	25 c. Ehlanzeni 51	15	20
13.	55 c. Mbabane 30	35	40
14.	70 c. Bulembu 54	45	50
15.	2 e. Manzini 44	1·25	1·40

120. "Junonia hierta".

1987. Butterflies. Multicoloured.

516	10 c. Type **120**	10	10
517	15 c. "Hamanumida daedalus"	10	10
518	20 c. "Charaxes boueti"	10	10
519	25 c. "Abantis paradisea"	10	10
520	30 c. "Acraea anemosa"	10	15
521	35 c. "Graphium lepridas"	15	20
522	45 c. "Graphium antheus"	20	25
523	50 c. "Junonia orithya"	20	25
524	55 c. "Pinacopteryx eriphia"	20	25
525	70 c. "Precis octavia"	30	35
526	1 e. "Mylothris chloris"	40	45
527	5 e. "Colotis regina"	2·00	2·10
528	10 e. "Spindasis natalensis"	4·00	4·25

121. Two White Rhinoceroses.

1987. White Rhinoceros. Multicoloured.

529.	15 c. Type **121**	45	15
530.	25 c. Female and calf	70	55
531.	45 c. Rhinoceros charging	1·25	1·25
532.	70 c. Rhinoceros wallowing	1·75	2·00

122. Hybrid Tea Rose "Blue Moon".

1987. Garden Flowers. Multicoloured.

533.	15 c. Type **122**	45	15
534.	35 c. Rambler rose "Danse du feu"	75	55
535.	55 c. Pompon dahlia "Odin"	1·25	90
536.	2 e. "Lilium davidii var. willmottiae"	3·00	3·50

1987. Royal Ruby Wedding. Nos. 501/4 optd. **40th WEDDING ANNIVERSARY.**

537.	30 c. On Palace balcony after wedding of Prince and Princess of Wales, 1981	20	20
538.	45 c. Royal visit to Swaziland, 1947	30	30
539.	1 e. At Windsor Polo Ground, 1984	80	85
540.	2 e. At Crown Agents Head Office, London, 1983	1·50	1·75

123. "Zabalius aridus".

1988. Insects. Multicoloured.

541.	15 c. Type **123**	45	15
542.	55 c. "Callidea bohemani"	1·25	85
543.	1 e. "Phymateus viridipes"	1·90	2·00
544.	2 e. "Nomadacris septemfasciata"	3·25	3·50

124 Athlete with Swazi Flag and Olympic Stadium

1988. Olympic Games, Seoul. Multicoloured.

545	15 c. Type **124**	25	10
546	35 c. Taekwondo	55	35
547	1 e. Boxing	1·25	1·25
548	2 e. Tennis	2·25	2·50

125 Savanna Monkey

1989. Small Mammals. Multicoloured.

549	35 c. Type **125**	55	25
550	55 c. Large-toothed rock hyrax	75	55
551	1 e. Zorilla	1·40	1·40
552	2 e. African wild cat	2·50	2·75

126 Dr. David Hynd (founder of Swazi Red Cross)

1989. 125th Anniv of International Red Cross. Multicoloured.

553	15 c. Type **126**	20	15
554	60 c. First aid training	55	40
555	1 e. Sigombeni Clinic	90	80
556	2 e. Refugee camp	1·40	1·40

127 King Mswati III with Prince of Wales, 1987

1989. 21st Birthday of King Mswati III. Mult.

557	15 c. Type **127**	10	10
558	60 c. King with Pope John Paul II, 1988	30	35
559	1 e. Introduction of Crown Prince to people, 1983	50	55
560	2 e. King Mswati III and Queen Mother	95	1·00

128 Manzini to Mahamba Road

1989. 25th Anniv of African Development Bank. Multicoloured.

561	15 c. Type **128**	10	10
562	60 c. Microwave Radio Receiver, Mbabane	30	35
563	1 e. Mbabane Government Hospital	50	65
564	2 e. Ezulwini Power Station switchyard	95	1·25

129 International Priority Mail Van

1990. "Stamp World London 90" International Stamp Exhibition. Multicoloured.

565	15 c. Type **129**	15	10
566	60 c. Facsimile Service operators	40	40
567	1 e. Rural post office	75	75
568	2 e. Ezulwini Earth Station	1·40	1·40

1990. 90th Birthday of Queen Elizabeth the Queen Mother. As T **134** of Ascension.

570	75 c. multicoloured	50	50
571	4 e. black and green	2·25	2·25

DESIGNS—21 × 36 mm. 75 c. Queen Mother. 29 × 37 mm. 4 e. King George VI and Queen Elizabeth visiting Civil Resettlement Unit, Hatfield House.

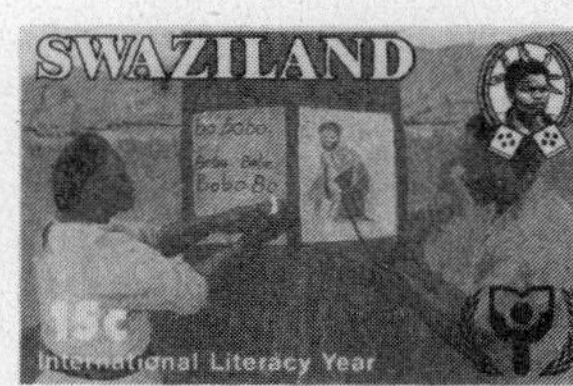

130 Pictorial Teaching

1990. International Literacy Year. Mult.

572	15 c. Type **130**	10	10
573	75 c. Rural class	45	45
574	1 e. Modern teaching methods	60	60
575	2 e. Presentation of certificates	1·10	1·10

131 Rural Water Supply

1990. 40th Anniv of United Nations Development Programme. "Helping People to Help Themselves". Multicoloured.

576	60 c. Type **131**	35	35
577	1 e. Seed multiplication project	60	60
578	2 e. Low-cost housing project	1·10	1·10

1990. Nos. 519/20, 522 and 524 surch.

579	10 c. on 25 c. "Abatis pardisea"	10	10
580	15 c. on 30 c. "Acraea anemosa"	10	10
581	20 c. on 45 c. "Graphium artheus"	10	10
582	40 c. on 55 c. "Piracopteryx eriphia"	15	10

133 Lobamba Hot Spring

1991. National Heritage. Multicoloured.

583	15 c. Type **133**	15	10
584	60 c. Sibebe Rock	40	40
585	1 e. Jolobela Falls	70	70
586	2 e. Mantjolo Sacred Pool	1·25	1·40

134 King Mswati III making Speech

1991. 5th Anniv of King Mswati III's Coronation. Multicoloured.

588	15 c. Type **134**	15	10
589	75 c. Butimba Royal Hunt	50	50
590	1 e. King and visiting school friends, 1986 ..	70	70
591	2 e. King opening Parliament	1·25	1·40

1991. 65th Birthday of Queen Elizabeth II and 70th Birthday of Prince Philip. As T **139** of Ascension. Multicoloured.

592	1 e. Prince Philip ..	70	70
593	2 e. Queen Elizabeth II ..	1·25	1·40

135 "Xerophyta retinervis"

1991. Indigenous Flowers. Multicoloured.

594	15 c. Type **135**	15	10
595	75 c. "Bauhinia galpinii"	50	50
596	1 e. "Dombeya rotundifolia"	70	70
597	2 e. "Kigelia africana" ..	1·40	1·50

136 Father Christmas arriving with Gifts

1991. Christmas. Multicoloured.

598	20 c. Type **136**	15	10
599	70 c. Singing carols ..	45	45
600	1 e. Priest reading from Bible	60	60
601	2 e. The Nativity ..	1·25	1·25

137 Lubombo Flat Lizard

1992 Reptiles. Multicoloured.

602	20 c. Type **137**	15	10
603	70 c. Natal hinged tortoise	45	45
604	1 e. Swazi thick-toed gecko	70	70
605	2 e. Nile monitor	1·25	1·25

POSTAGE DUE STAMPS

D 1.

D 6.

1933.

D 1.	**D 1.**	1d. red	20	4·25
D 2.		2d. violet	1·00	12·00

1961. Surch. **Postage Due 2d.**

D 3.	**7.**	2d. on 2d. blk. & brown	3·00	5·50

These prices apply to stamps with large figure measuring 4½ mm. high.

1961. As Type **D 1** but with value in cents.

D 4.	1 c. red	15	75
D 5.	2 c. violet	15	1·10
D 6.	5 c. green	20	1·10

1961. Surch. **Postage Due** and value in cents.

D 10.	**7.**	1 c. on 2d. black & brown	80	2·25
D 11.		2 c. on 2d. black & brown	55	1·75
D 12.		5 c. on 2d. black & brown	1·00	2·25

1971.

D19	**D 6**	1 c. red	20	30
D23		2 c. purple	10	10
D24		5 c. green	10	10
D25		10 c. blue	10	10
D26		25 c. brown	10	15

TANGANYIKA

Formerly the German colony of German East Africa. After the 1914–18 War it was under British mandate until 1946 and then administered by Britain under United Nations trusteeship until 1961 when it became independent within the British Commonwealth. It had a common postal service with Kenya and Uganda from 1935 to 1961 (for these issues see under Kenya, Uganda and Tanganyika). Renamed Tanzania in 1965.

1915. 16 annas = 1 rupee.
1917. 100 cents = 1 rupee.
1922. 100 cents = 1 shilling.

BRITISH OCCUPATION

1915. Stamps of the Indian Expeditionary Forces optd. **G.R. POST MAFIA.**

M 33	**55.**	3 p. grey	17·00	35·00
M 34	**56.**	½ a. green	27·00	38·00
M 35	**57.**	1 a. red	30·00	38·00
M 36	**59.**	2 a. lilac	42·00	65·00
M 37	**61.**	2½ a. blue	55·00	80·00
M 38	**62.**	3 a. orange	55·00	80·00
M 39	**63.**	4 a. olive	75·00	£100
M 40	**65.**	8 a. mauve	£130	£180
M 41	**66.**	12 a. red	£200	£275
M 52	**67.**	1 r. brown and green	£225	£300

1916. Stamps of Nyasaland (King George V) optd. **N.F.**

N 1.	½d. green	80	4·50
N 2.	1d. red	70	2·50
N 3.	3d. purple on yellow ..	5·00	14·00
N 4.	4d. black and red on yellow	20·00	30·00
N 5.	1s. black on green ..	21·00	32·00

1917. Stamps of Kenya and Uganda (King George V, 1912) optd. **G.E.A.**

45.	1 c. black	15	70
47.	3 c. green	15	15
48.	6 c. red	15	10
49.	10 c. orange	15	30
50.	12 c. grey	15	1·25
51.	15 c. blue	15	1·75
52.	25 c. black and red on yellow	30	2·25
53.	50 c. black and lilac ..	50	2·75
54.	75 c. black on green ..	65	3·00
55.	1 r. black on green	1·00	5·50
56.	2 r. red and black on blue ..	4·50	19·00
57.	3 r. violet and green ..	6·50	32·00
58.	4 r. red and green on yellow	15·00	48·00
59.	5 r. blue and purple ..	26·00	50·00
60.	10 r. red and green on green	45·00	£110
61.	20 r. black and purple on red	£150	£200
62.	50 r. red and green ..	£500	£700

BRITISH MANDATE

4. Giraffe. **5.**

1922.

74.	**4.**	5 c. black and purple ..	65	20
89.		5 c. black and green ..	30	90
75.		10 c. black and green ..	30	20
90.		10 c. black and yellow ..	1·75	1·00
76.		15 c. black and red ..	55	10
77.		20 c. black and orange ..	45	10
78.		25 c. black	3·00	5·50
91.		25 c. black and blue ..	2·00	12·00
79.		30 c. black and blue ..	3·00	2·50
92.		30 c. black and purple ..	75	6·50
80.		40 c. black and brown ..	1·50	3·00
81.		50 c. black and grey ..	1·25	1·50
82.		75 c. black and yellow ..	2·75	11·00
83.	**5.**	1 s. black and green ..	1·25	6·00
84.		2 s. black and purple ..	4·25	9·50
85.		3 s. black	6·50	20·00
86.		5 s. black and red ..	7·50	45·00
87.		10 s. black and blue ..	35·00	70·00
88.		£1 black and orange ..	95·00	£180

6.

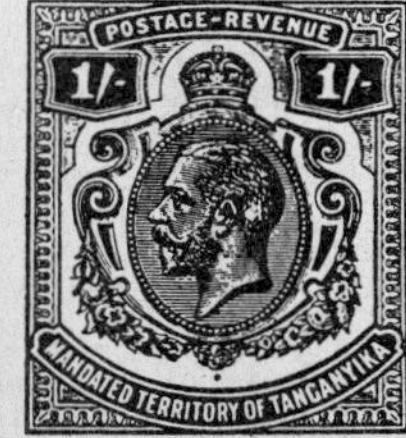

7.

1927.

93.	**6.**	5 c. black and green ..	20	10
94.		10 c. black and yellow	30	10
95.		15 c. black and red ..	20	10
96.		20 c. black and orange	50	10
97.		25 c. black and blue ..	75	75
98.		30 c. black and purple	90	2·50
98a.		30 c. black and blue ..	14·00	30
99.		40 c. black and brown	1·00	2·75
100.		50 c. black and grey ..	75	30
101.		75 c. black and olive ..	1·75	8·50
102.	**7.**	1 s. black and green ..	2·25	90
103.		2 s. black and purple ..	5·00	2·25
104.		3 s. black	8·00	30·00
105.		5 s. black and red ..	9·00	14·00
106.		10 s. black and blue ..	38·00	70·00
107.		£1 black and orange ..	85·00	£120

INDEPENDENT WITHIN THE COMMONWEALTH

8. Teacher and Pupils.

15. Freedom Torch over Mt. Kilimanjaro.

1961. Independence. Inscr. "UHURU 1961"

108.	**8.**	5 c. sepia and green ..	10	10
109.	–	10 c. turquoise ..	10	10
110.	–	15 c. sepia and blue ..	10	10
111.	–	20 c. brown	10	10
112.	–	30 c. blk., grn. & yell.	10	10
113.	–	50 c. black and yellow	10	10
114.	–	1 s. brown, bl. & yell.	15	10
115.	**15.**	1 s. 30 multicoloured ..	1·00	10
116.	–	2 s. multicoloured ..	40	10
117.	–	5 s. turquoise and red	50	40
118.	–	10 s. black, pur. & bl.	10·00	2·75
119.	**15.**	20 s. multicoloured ..	3·00	7·00

DESIGNS—As Type **8.** VERT. 10 c. District nurse and child. 15 c. Coffee-picking. 20 c. Harvesting maize. 50 c. Serengeti lions. HORIZ. 30 c. Tanganyikan Flag. As Type **15.** HORIZ. 1 s. "Maternity" (mother with nurse holding baby). 2 s. Dar-es-Salaam waterfront. 5 s. Land tillage. 10 s. Diamond mine.

19. Mr. Nyerere inaugurating Self-help Project.

DESIGNS: 50 c. Hoisting flag on Mt. Kilimanjaro. 1 s. 30, Presidential emblem. 2 s. 50, Independence monument.

1962. Inauguration of Republic.

120.	**19.**	30 c. green	10	10
121.	–	50 c. multicoloured ..	10	10
122.	–	1 s. 30 multicoloured ..	10	10
123.	–	2 s. 30 black, red & bl.	15	30

23. Map of Republic.

1964. United Republic of Tanganyika and Zanzibar Commem.

124.	**23.**	20 c. green and blue ..	10	10
125.	–	30 c. blue and sepia ..	10	10
126.	–	1 s. 50 purple and blue	10	10
127.	**23.**	2 s. 50 purple and blue	35	30

DESIGN: 30 c., 1 s. 30, Torch and Spear Emblem.

Despite the inscription on the stamps the above issue was only on sale in Tanganyika and had no validity in Zanzibar.

OFFICIAL STAMPS

1961. Independence stamps of 1961 optd. **OFFICIAL.**

O 1.	5 c. brown and green	10	10
O 2.	10 c. turquoise	10	10
O 3.	15 c. brown and blue	10	10
O 4.	20 c. brown	10	10
O 5.	30 c. black, green & yell.	10	10
O 6.	50 c. black and yellow	10	10
O 7.	1 s. brn., blue and yellow	10	10
O 8.	5 s. turquoise and red	65	75

For later issues see **TANZANIA**.

TANZANIA

A republic within the Br. Commonwealth formerly known as Tanganyika and incorporating Zanzibar.

100 cents = 1 shilling.

NOTE.—Stamps inscribed "UGANDA KENYA TANGANYIKA & ZANZIBAR" (or "TANZANIA UGANDA KENYA") will be found listed under Kenya, Uganda and Tanganyika.

A. For use in Tanzania and also valid for use in Kenya and Uganda.

25. Hale Hydro-Electric Scheme.

33. Dar-es-Salaam Harbour.

1965.

128.	25.	5 c. blue and orange	10	10
129.	–	10 c. multicoloured	10	10
130.	–	15 c. multicoloured	10	10
131.	–	20 c. sepia, grn. & bl.	10	10
132.	–	30 c. black and brown	10	10
133.	–	40 c. multicoloured	30	20
134.	–	50 c. multicoloured	30	10
135.	–	65 c. grn, brn. & bl.	1·75	1·25
136.	33.	1 s. multicoloured	50	10
137.	–	1 s. 30 multicoloured	4·00	60
138.	–	2 s. 50 blue and brown	2·75	90
139.	–	5 s. brn., grn. & bl.	80	20
140.	–	10 s. yell., grn. & bl.	1·00	1·75
141.	–	20 s. multicoloured	3·75	10·00

DESIGNS—As Type **25**—HORIZ. 10 c. Tanzania flag. 20 c. Road-building. 50 c. Common Zebras, Manyara National Park. 65 c. Mt. Kilimanjaro. VERT. 15 c. National Servicemen. 30 c. Drum, Spear, Shield and Stool. 40 c. Giraffes, Mikumi National Park. As Type **33**—HORIZ. 1 s. 30, Skull of "Zinjanthropus" and Excavations, Olduvai Gorge. 2 s. 50, Fishing 5 s. Sisal Industry. 10 s. State House, Dar-es-Salaam. VERT. 20 s. Arms of Tanzania.

39. Cardinal.

1967. Fishes. Multicoloured.

142	39.	5 c. mauve, grn. & blk.	10	30
143	–	10 c. brown and bistre	10	10
144	–	15 c. grey, blue & black	10	30
145	–	20 c. brown and green	10	10
146	–	30 c. green and black	10	10
147	–	40 c. yell., brn. & green	15	10
148	–	50 c. multicoloured	15	10
149	–	65 c. yell., grn. & black	3·50	4·00
150	–	70 c. multicoloured	1·00	2·50
151	–	1 s. brn., blue & purple	30	10
152	–	1 s. 30 multicoloured	4·00	10
153	–	1 s. 50 multicoloured	2·25	50
154	–	2 s. 50 multicoloured	3·00	60
155a	–	5 s. yell., black & green	3·25	10
156a	–	10 s. multicoloured	2·50	10
157	–	20 s. multicoloured	4·00	4·00

DESIGNS—As Type **39**: 10 c. Mud skipper. 15 c. White spotted puffer. 20 c. Sea horses. 30 c. Bat fish. 40 c. Sweetlips. 50 c. Blue clubnosed wrasse. 65 c. Bennett's butterfly. 70 c. Striped grouper. 42 × 25 mm. 1 s. Scorpion fish. 1 s. 30, Powder blue surgeon. 1 s. 50, Fusilier. 2 s. 50, Red snapper. 5 s. Moorish idol. 10 s. Picasso fish. 20 s. Squirrel fish.

53. "Papilio hornimani". 54. "Euphaedra neophron".

1973.

(a) As T **53**.

158.	53.	5 c. green, blue & blk.	30	20
159.	–	10 c. multicoloured	40	15
160.	–	15 c. lavender and black	40	15
161.	–	20 c. brn., yellow & blk.	50	15
162.	–	30 c. yellow, orge. & blk.	50	10
163.	–	40 c. multicoloured	60	15
164.	–	50 c. multicoloured	70	15
165.	–	60 c. brown, yell. & lake	1·00	20
166.	–	70 c. green, orge. & blk.	1·00	20

(b) As T **54**.

167.	54.	1 s. multicoloured	1·00	15
168.	–	1 s. 50 multicoloured	2·00	45
169.	–	2 s. 50 multicoloured	2·50	80
170.	–	5 s. multicoloured	2·75	85
171.	–	10 s. multicoloured	3·75	3·50
172.	–	20 s. multicoloured	5·50	8·00

BUTTERFLIES: 10 c. "Colotis ione". 15 c. "Amauris makuyuensis". 20 c. "Libythea laius". 30 c. "Danaus chrysippus." 40 c. "Sallya rosa". 50 c. "Axiocerses styx". 60 c. "Eurema hecabe" 70 c. "Acraea insignis". 1 s. "Euphaedra neophron". 1 s. 50, "Precis octavia". 2 s. 50, "Charaxes eupale". 5 s. "Charaxes pollux". 10 s. "Salamis" parhassus". 20 s. "Papilio ophidicephalus".

1975. Nos. 165 and 172 surch.

173.	80 c. on 60 c. "Eurema hecabe"	1·75	1·00
174.	2 s. on 1 s. 50 "Precis octavia"	3·25	3·25
175.	3 s. on 2 s. 50 "Charaxes eupale"	13·00	19·00
176.	40 s. on 20 s. "Papilio ophidicephalus"	6·00	8·50

1976. Telecommunications Development As Nos. 56/9 of Kenya.

177.	50 c. Microwave Tower	10	10
178.	1 s. Cordless switchboard	15	10
179.	2 s. Telephones	25	30
180.	3 s. Message Switching Centre	30	40

1976. Olympic Games, Montreal. As Nos. 61/4 of Kenya.

182.	50 c. Akii Bua, Ugandan hurdler	15	10
183.	1 s. Filbert Bayi, Tanzanian runner	15	10
184.	2 s. Steve Muchoki, Kenyan boxer	35	40
185.	3 s. Olympic flame and East African flags	45	55

1976. Railway Transport. As Nos. 66/9 of Kenya.

187.	50 c. Tanzania-Zambia Railway	20	10
188.	1 s. Nile Bridge, Uganda	30	10
189.	2 s. Nakuru Station, Kenya	75	40
190.	3 s. Class "A" loco, 1896	90	65

1977. Game Fish of East Africa. As Nos. 71/4 of Kenya.

192.	50 c. Nile Perch	30	10
193.	1 s. Tilapia	40	10
194.	3 s. Sailfish	1·60	60
195.	5 s. Black Marlin	1·75	80

1977. Second World Black and African Festival of Arts and Culture. As Nos. 76/9 of Kenya.

197.	50 c. Maasai Manyatta (village), Kenya	15	10
198.	1 s. "Heartbeat of Africa" (Ugandan dancers)	20	10
199.	2 s. Makonde sculpture	45	60
200.	3 s. "Early Man and Technology" (skinning hippopotamus)	55	85

1977. 25th Anniv. of Safari Rally. As Nos. 81/4 of Kenya. Multicoloured.

202.	50 c. Rally-car and villagers	15	10
203.	1 s. Starting line	20	10
204.	2 s. Car fording river	50	60
205.	5 s. Car and elephants	1·25	1·75

1977. Centenary of Ugandan Church. As Nos. 86/9 of Kenya. Multicoloured.

207.	50 c. Canon Kivebulaya	10	10
208.	1 s. Modern Namirembe Cathedral	15	10
209.	2 s. Old Namirembe Cathedral	30	40
210.	5 s. Early congregation Kigezi	60	90

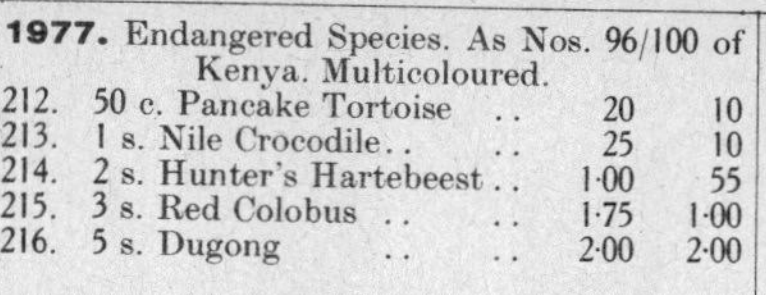

1977. Endangered Species. As Nos. 96/100 of Kenya. Multicoloured.

212.	50 c. Pancake Tortoise	20	10
213.	1 s. Nile Crocodile	25	10
214.	2 s. Hunter's Hartebeest	1·00	55
215.	3 s. Red Colobus	1·75	1·00
216.	5 s. Dugong	2·00	2·00

56. Prince Philip and President Nyerere.

1977. Silver Jubilee. Multicoloured.

218.	50 c. Type **56**	15	10
219.	5 s. Pres. Nyerere with Queen and Prince Philip	35	35
220.	10 s. Jubilee emblem and Commonwealth flags	60	60
221.	20 s. The Crowning	1·00	1·00

57. Improvements in Rural Living Standards.

1978. "Chama Cha Mapinduzi" (New Revolutionary Party). 1st Anniv.

223.	57.	50 c. multicoloured	10	10
224.	–	1 s. multicoloured	10	10
225.	–	3 s. multicoloured	35	60
226.	–	5 s. black, green & yellow	55	85

DESIGNS: 1 s. Flag-raising ceremony, Zanzibar. 3 s. Handing over of TANU headquarters, Dodoma. 5 s. Chairman Julius Nyerere.

1978. World Cup Football Championships. As Nos. 122/5 of Kenya. Multicoloured.

228.	50 c. Joe Kadenge and forwards	15	10
229.	1 s. Mohamed Chuma and cup presentation	15	10
230.	2 s. Omari S. Kidevu and goalmouth scene	40	60
231.	3 s. Polly Ouma and three forwards	50	75

1978. 25th Anniv. of Coronation. Nos. 218/21 optd. **25th ANNIVERSARY CORONATION 2nd JUNE 1953.**

233.	50 c. Type **56**	10	10
234.	5 s. Pres. Nyerere with Queen and Prince Philip	35	45
235.	10 s. Jubilee emblem and Commonwealth flags	50	65
236.	20 s. The Crowning	80	1·25

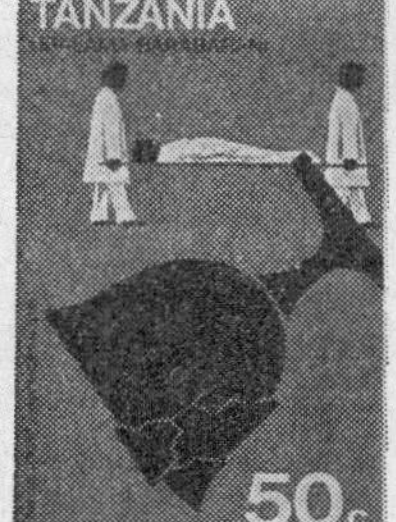

60. "Do not Drink and Drive."

1978. Road Safety.

238.	60.	50 c. multicoloured	15	10
239.	–	1 s. multicoloured	20	10
240.	–	3 s. orange, black & brn.	70	60
241.	–	5 s. multicoloured	1·00	90

DESIGNS: 1 s. "Show courtesy to young, old and crippled". 3 s. "Observe the Highway Code". 5 s. "Do not drive a faulty vehicle"

61. Lake Manyara Hotel.

1978. Game Lodges. Multicoloured.

243.	50 c. Type **61**	10	10
244.	1 s. Lobo Wildlife Lodge	20	10
245.	3 s. Ngorongoro Crater Lodge	40	35
246.	5 s. Ngorongoro Wildlife Lodge	55	55
247.	10 s. Mafia Island Lodge	1·00	1·25
248.	20 s. Mikumi Wildlife Lodge	2·00	3·00

62. "Racial Suppression".

1978. International Anti-Apartheid Year.

250.	62.	50 c. multicoloured	10	10
251.	–	1 s. black, green & yell.	15	10
252.	–	2 s. 50 multicoloured	40	40
253.	–	5 s. multicoloured	70	85

DESIGNS: 1 s. "Racial division". 2 s. 50, "Racial Harmony". 5 s. "Fall of suppression and rise of freedom".

63. Fokker "Friendship".

1978. 75th Anniv. of Powered Flight. Mult.

255.	50 c. Type **63**	20	10
256.	1 s. "Dragon" on Zanzibar Island, 1930's	25	10
257.	2 s. Supersonic "Concorde"	1·00	45
258.	5 s. Wright brothers "Flyer", 1903	1·25	85

64. Corporation Emblem.

1979. 1st Anniv. of Tanzania Posts and Telecommunications Corporation. Mult.

260.	50 c. Type **64**	10	10
261.	5 s. Headquarters buildings	50	70

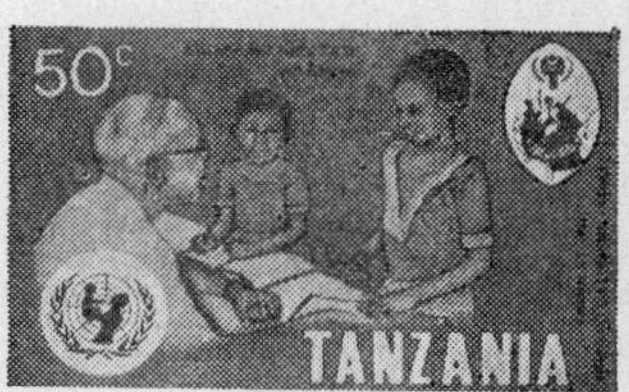

65. Pres. Nyerere (patron of National I.Y.C. Committee) with Children.

1979. Int. Year of the Child. Mult.

263.	50 c. Type **65**	10	10
264.	1 s. Day Care Centre	15	10
265.	2 s. "Immunisation" (child being vaccinated)	25	45
266.	5 s. National I.Y.C. Committee emblem	40	80

1979. Nos. 159 and 166 surch.

268	10 c. + 30 c. multicoloured	50	60
269	50 c. on 70 c. green, orange and black	1·25	1·40

No. 268 was used as a 40 c. value.

67. Planting Young Trees.

1979. Forest Preservation. Multicoloured.

270.	50 c. Type **67**	10	10
271.	1 s. Replacing dead trees with saplings	20	10
272.	2 s. Rainfall cycle ..	50	50
273.	5 s. Forest fire warning ..	80	1·50

68. Mwenge Earth Satellite Station.

1979. Inauguration of Mwenge Earth Satellite Station.

274. **68.**	10 c. multicoloured ..	10	10
275.	40 c. multicoloured ..	10	10
276.	50 c. multicoloured ..	10	10
277.	1 s. multicoloured ..	20	20

69. Tabata Dispensary, Dar-es-Salaam.

1980. 75th Anniv. of Rotary International. Multicoloured.

278.	50 c. Type **69**	10	10
279.	1 s. Ngomvu Village water project	15	10
280.	5 s. Flying Doctor service (plane donation) ..	55	70
281.	20 s. Torch and 75th Anniversary emblem ..	1·75	2·50

70. Zanzibar 1896 2 r. Stamp and 1964 25 c. Definitive.

1980. Death Centenary of Sir Rowland Hill. Multicoloured.

283.	40 c. Type **70**	10	10
284.	50 c. Tanganyika 1962 Independence 50 c. commemorative and man attaching stamp to letter (vert.) ..	10	10
285.	10 s. Tanganyika 1922 25 c. stamp and 1961 1 s. 30 definitive	1·00	1·25
286.	20 s. Penny Black and Sir Rowland Hill (vert.)	1·50	2·00

1980. " London 1980 " International Stamp Exhibition. Nos. 283/6 optd. **'LONDON 1980' PHILATELIC EXHIBITION.**

288. **70.**	40 c. multicoloured ..	10	10
289. –	50 c. multicoloured ..	10	10
290. –	10 s. multicoloured ..	75	1·25
291. –	20 s. multicoloured ..	1·10	1·75

1980. Annual Conference of District 920, Rotary International, Arusha. Nos. 278/81 optd. **District 920—55th Annual Conference, Arusha, Tanzania.**

293. **69.**	50 c. multicoloured ..	20	10
294. –	1 s. multicoloured ..	25	10
295. –	5 s. multicoloured ..	70	70
296. –	20 s. multicoloured ..	2·25	2·50

73. Conference, Tanzanian Posts and Telecommunications Corporation and U.P.U. Emblems.

1980. P.A.P.U. (Pan-African Postal Union) Plenipotentiary Conference, Arusha.

298. **73.**	50 c. black and violet ..	10	10
299.	1 s. black and blue ..	15	10
300.	5 s. black and red ..	65	65
301.	10 s. black and green ..	1·25	1·40

74. Gidamis Shahanga (marathon).

1980. Olympic Games, Moscow. Multicoloured.

302.	50 c. Type **74**	10	15
303.	1 s. Nzael Kyomo (sprints)	15	15
304.	10 s. Zakayo Malekwa (javelin)	80	1·25
305.	20 s. William Lyimo (boxing)	1·50	2·00

75. Spring Hare.

1980. Wildlife. Multicoloured.

307.	10 c. Type **75**	10	15
308.	20 c. Large-spotted Genet	10	15
309.	40 c. Banded Mongoose ..	15	10
310.	50 c. Ratel	15	10
311.	75 c. Large-toothed Rock Hyrax	15	15
312.	80 c. Leopard	20	15
313.	1 s. Impala	15	10
314.	1 s. 50 Giraffe ..	20	15
315.	2 s. Common Zebra ..	20	15
316.	3 s. Buffalo	25	15
317.	5 s. Lion	50	25
318.	10 s. Black Rhinoceros ..	85	70
319.	20 s. African Elephant ..	1·50	1·10
320.	40 s. Cheetah	2·25	2·50

Nos. 313/20 are larger, 40 × 24 mm.

77. Ngorongoro Conservation Area Authority Emblem.

1981. 60th Anniv. of Ngorongoro and Serengeti National Parks.

321. **77.**	50 c. multicoloured ..	10	10
322. –	1 s. black, gold and green	10	10
323. –	5 s. multicoloured ..	55	60
324. –	20 s. multicoloured ..	2·10	2·25

DESIGNS: 1 s. Tanzania National Parks emblem. 5 s. Friends of the Serengeti emblem. 20 s. Friends of Ngorongoro emblem.

1981. Royal Wedding. Nos. 220/1 optd. **ROYAL WEDDING H.R.H. PRINCE CHARLES 29th JULY 1981.**

325.	10 s. Jubilee emblem and Commonwealth flags ..	1·25	1·00
326.	20 s. Crowning	1·75	1·25

79. Mail Runner.

1981. Commonwealth Postal Administrations Conference, Arusha. Multicoloured.

328.	50 c. Type **79**	10	10
329.	1 s. Letter sorting ..	15	15
330.	5 s. Letter Post symbols	65	1·00
331.	10 s. Flags of Commonwealth nations	1·25	2·00

80. Morris Nyunyusa (blind drummer).

1981. International Year for Disabled Persons. Multicoloured.

333.	50 c. Type **80**	20	10
334.	1 s. Mgulani Rehabilitation Centre, Dar-es-Salaam	25	10
335.	5 s. Aids for disabled persons	1·75	2·00
336.	10 s. Disabled children cleaning school compound	2·50	3·00

81. Mwalimu Julius K. Nyerere (President).

1981. 20th Anniv. of Independence. Mult.

337.	50 c. Type **81**	10	10
338.	1 s. Electricity plant, Mtoni	15	10
339.	3 s. Sisal industry ..	45	80
340.	10 s. " Universal primary education "	1·10	2·00

82. Ostrich.

1982. Birds. Multicoloured.

342.	50 c. Type **82**	40	10
343.	1 s. Secretary Bird ..	55	10
344.	5 s. Kori Bustard ..	2·00	2·50
345.	10 s. Saddle-bill Stork ..	3·00	3·50

83. Jella Mtaga.

1982. World Cup Football Championship, Spain. Multicoloured.

346.	50 c. Type **83**	30	10
347.	1 s. Football stadium ..	35	10
348.	10 s. Diego Maradona ..	2·25	2·75
349.	20 s. FIFA emblem ..	4·00	4·50

84. "Jade" of Seronera (cheetah) with Cubs.

1982. Animal Personalities. Multicoloured.

351.	50 c. Type **84**	20	10
352.	1 s. Wild dog featured in film, " Havoc " ..	30	10
353.	5 s. " Fiji " and two sons of " Gombe " (chimpanzees)	1·00	2·00
354.	10 s. " Bahati " of Lake Manyara with twins, " Rashidi " and " Ramadhani "	1·90	3·00

85. Brick-laying.

1982. 75th Anniv. of Boy Scout Movement. Multicoloured.

356.	50 c. Type **85**	15	10
357.	1 s. Camping	20	10
358.	10 s. Tracing signs ..	1·50	2·25
359.	20 s. Lord Baden-Powell ..	2·50	3·75

86. Ploughing Field.

1982. World Food Day. Multicoloured.

361.	50 c. Type **86**	10	10
362.	1 s. Dairy farming ..	15	10
363.	5 s. Maize farming ..	60	75
364.	10 s. Grain storage ..	1·00	1·60

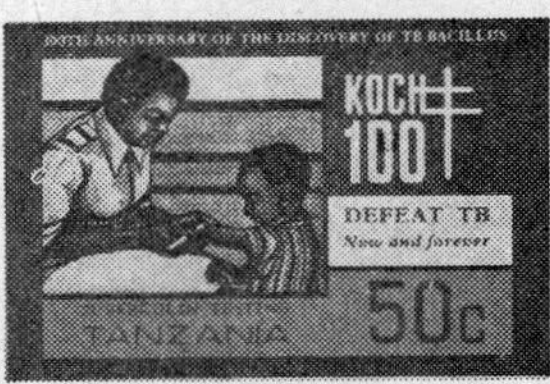

87. Immunization.

1982. Centenary of Robert Koch's Discovery of Tubercle Bacillus. Multicoloured.

366.	50 c. Type **87**	15	10
367.	1 s. Dr. Robert Koch ..	20	10
368.	5 s. International Union against TB emblem ..	65	1·25
369.	10 s. World Health Organization emblem	1·25	2·25

88. Letter Post.

1982. 5th Anniv. of Posts and Telecommunications Corporation. Mult.

370.	50 c. Type **88**	10	10
371.	1 s. Training institute ..	10	10
372.	5 s. Satellite communications	55	90
373.	10 s. U.P.U., I.T.U. and T.P.T.C.C. (Tanzania Post and Telecommunications Corporation) emblems	1·10	2·00

89. Pres. Mwalimu Julius Nyerere.

1982. Commonwealth Day. Multicoloured.

375.	50 c. Type **89**	10	10
376.	1 s. Athletics and boxing	15	10
377.	5 s. Flags of Commonwealth countries	60	80
378.	10 s. Pres. Nyerere and members of British Royal Family	1·25	1·75

INDEX

Countries can be quickly located by referring to the index at the end of this volume.

90. Eastern and Southern African Management Institute, Arusha, Tanzania.

1983. 25th Anniv. of Economic Commission for Africa. Multicoloured.

380.	50 c. Type **90**	15	10
381.	1 s. 25th Anniversary inscription and U.N. logo	20	10
382.	5 s. Mineral collections	2·00	2·00
383.	10 s. E.C.A. Silver Jubilee logo and O.A.U. flag	2·00	3·00

91. Telephone cables.

1983. World Communications Year. Mult.

385.	50 c. Type **91**	15	10
386.	1 s. W.C.Y. logo	20	10
387.	5 s. Postal service	1·00	1·40
388.	10 s. Microwave tower	1·75	2·25

92. Bagamoya Boma.

1983. Historical Buildings of Tanzania. Multicoloured.

390.	1 s. Type **92**	10	10
391.	1 s. 50 Beit El Ajaib, Zanzibar	15	25
392.	5 s. Anglican Cathedral Church, Zanzibar	55	1·00
393.	10 s. Original German Government House and present State House, Dar Es Salaam	1·10	2·00

93. Sheikh Abeid Amani Karume (founder of Afro-Shirazi Party).

1984. 20th Anniv. of Zanzibar Revolution. Multicoloured.

395.	1 s. Type **93**	10	10
396.	1 s. 50 Clove farming	15	25
397.	5 s. Symbol of Industrial Development	55	1·00
398.	10 s. New housing schemes	1·10	2·00

94. Boxing.

1984. Olympic Games, Los Angeles. Multicoloured.

400.	1 s. Type **94**	10	10
401.	1 s. 50 Running	15	10
402.	5 s. Basketball	45	60
403.	20 s. Football	1·50	2·25

95. Icarus in Flight.

1984. 40th Anniv. of International Civil Aviation Organization. Multicoloured.

405.	1 s. Type **95**	10	10
406.	1 s. 50 Aircraft and air traffic controller	15	20
407.	5 s. Aircraft undergoing maintenance	55	1·25
408.	10 s. I.C.A.O. Badge	1·10	2·00

96. Sochi-Conical House.

1984. Traditional Houses. Multicoloured.

410.	1 s. Type **96**	10	10
411.	1 s. 50 Isyenga-circular type	15	20
412.	5 s. Tembe-flatroof type	45	1·25
413.	10 s. Banda-coastal type	90	2·00

97. Production of Cotton Textiles.

1985. 5th Anniv. of Southern African Development Co-ordination Conference. Multicoloured.

415.	1 s. 50 Type **97**	30	15
416.	4 s. Diamond mining	1·75	1·25
417.	5 s. Map of member countries and means of communication	1·75	1·25
418.	20 s. Flags and signatures of member countries	2·50	3·00

98. Tortoise.

1985. Rare Animals of Zanzibar. Mult.

420.	1 s. Type **98**	15	10
421.	4 s. Leopard	60	80
422.	10 s. Civet cat	1·25	2·25
423.	17 s. 50 Red colobus monkey (vert.)	2·00	2·75

99. The Queen Mother.

1985. Life and Times of Queen Elizabeth the Queen Mother. Multicoloured.

425.	20 s. Type **99**	20	35
426.	20 s. Queen Mother waving to crowd	20	35
427.	100 s. Oval portrait with flowers	90	1·40
428.	100 s. Head and shoulders portrait	90	1·40

100. Locomotive No. 3022.

1985. Tanzanian Railway Steam Locomotives (1st issue). Multicoloured

430.	5 s. Type **100**	20	25
431.	10 s. Locomotive No. 3107	35	50
432.	20 s. Locomotive No. 6004	60	80
433.	30 s. Locomotive No. 3129	80	1·10

See also Nos. 445/9.

1985. Olympic Games Gold Medal Winners, Los Angeles. Nos. 400/3 optd.

435.	1 s. Type **94** (optd. **GOLD MEDAL HENRY TILLMAN USA**)	10	10
436.	1 s. 50 Running (optd. **GOLD MEDAL USA**)	15	20
437.	5 s. Basketball (optd. **GOLD MEDAL USA**)	45	1·00
438.	20 s. Football (optd. **GOLD MEDAL FRANCE**)	1·75	2·75

102. Cooking and Water Pots.

1985. Pottery. Multicoloured.

440.	1 s. 50 Type **102**	15	10
441.	2 s. Large pot and frying pot with cover	20	10
442.	5 s. Trader selling pots	50	30
443.	40 s. Beer pot	2·00	2·25

103. Class "64" Locomotive.

1985. Tanzanian Railway Locomotives (2nd series).

445.	**103.**	1 s. 50 multicoloured	20	10
446.	–	2 s. multicoloured	30	20
447.	–	5 s. multicoloured	50	50
448.	–	10 s. multicoloured	85	90
449.	–	30 s. black, deep brown and red	2·25	2·50

DESIGNS: 2 s. Class "36" locomotive. 5 s. "DFH1013" shunting locomotive. 10 s. "DE 1001" diesel-electric locomotive. 15 s. Class "30" steam locomotive. 20 s. Class "11" steam locomotive. 30 s. Steam locomotive, Zanzibar, 1906.

104. Young Pioneers.

1986. International Youth Year.

451.	**104.**	1 s. 50 multicoloured	15	15
452.	–	4 s. brown, light brown and black	30	45
453.	–	10 s. multicoloured	70	1·10
454.	–	20 s. brown, light brown and black	1·40	2·00

DESIGNS: 4 s. Youth health care. 10 s. Uhuru torch race. 20 s. Young workers and globe.

105. Rolls-Royce "20/25" (1936).

1986. Centenary of Motoring. Multicoloured.

456.	1 s. 50 Type **105**	15	10
457.	5 s. Rolls-Royce "Phantom II" (1933)	20	25
458	10 s. Rolls-Royce "Phantom I" (1926)	35	50
459.	30 s. Rolls-Royce "Silver Ghost" (1907)	80	1·10

106. Rotary Logo and Queen Chess Piece.

1986. World Chess Championships, Moscow.

461.	**106.**	20 s. blue and purple	50	50
462.	–	100 s. multicoloured	1·50	2·25

DESIGN: 100 s. Hand moving chess piece. No. 461 also commemorates Rotary International.

107. Mallard.

1986. Birth Bicentenary (1985) of John J. Audubon (ornithologist). Multicoloured.

464.	5 s. Type **107**	30	25
465.	10 s. Eider	55	50
466.	20 s. Scarlet ibis	80	1·25
467.	30 s. Roseate spoonbill	1·00	1·50

108. Pearls.

1986. Tanzanian Minerals. Multicoloured.

469.	1 s. 50 Type **108**	40	15
470.	2 s. Sapphire	55	40
471.	5 s. Tanzanite	85	75
472.	40 s. Diamonds	4·25	4·50

110. "Hibiscus calyphyllus".

1986. Flowers of Tanzania. Multicoloured.

474.	1 s. 50 Type **110**	10	10
475.	5 s. "Aloe graminicola"	15	15
476.	10 s. "Nersium oleander"	25	25
477.	30 s. "Nymphaea caerulea"	65	65

111. Oryx.

1986. Endangered Animals of Tanzania. Multicoloured.

479. 5 s. Type **111** 30 15
480. 10 s. Giraffe 55 45
481. 20 s. Rhinoceros . . . . 1·00 1·00
482. 30 s. Cheetah . . . . 1·10 1·50

112. Immunization.

1986. U.N.I.C.E.F. Child Survival Campaign. Multicoloured.

484. 1 s. 50 Type **112** 10 10
485. 2 s. Growth monitoring . . 10 10
486. 5 s. Oral rehydration therapy 15 15
487. 40 s. Breast feeding . . 1·00 1·25

113. Butterfly Fish.

1986. Marine Life. Multicoloured.

489. 1 s. 50 Type **113** 20 10
490. 4 s. Parrot fish 35 30
491. 10 s. Turtle 70 70
492. 20 s. Octopus . . . . 1·25 1·25

114. Team Captains shaking Hands.

1986. World Cup Football Championship, Mexico. Multicoloured.

494. 1 s. 50 Type **114** 15 10
495. 2 s. Referee sending player off 15 10
496. 10 s. Goalkeeper and ball in net 60 60
497. 20 s. Goalkeeper saving ball . . . . . . 1·00 1·40

115 Pres. Nyerere receiving Beyond War Award

1986. International Peace Year. Mult.

499 1 s. 50 Type **115** 25 10
500 2 s. Children of many races 40 10
501 10 s. African cosmonaut and rocket launch . . 80 90
502 20 s. United Nations Headquarters, New York . . 1·25 1·40

116 Mobile Bank Service

1987. 20th Anniv of National Bank of Commerce. Multicoloured.

504 1 s. 50 Type **116** 20 10
505 2 s. National Bank of Commerce Head Office 30 15
506 5 s. Pres. Mwinyi laying foundation stone . . 45 45
507 20 s. Cotton harvesting . . 1·25 1·50

117 Parade of Young Party Members

1987. 10th Anniv of Chama Cha Mapinduzi Party and 20th Anniv of Arusha Declaration. Multicoloured.

508 2 s. Type **117** 15 10
509 3 s. Harvesting coffee . . 20 10
510 10 s. Pres. Nyerere addressing Second Peace Initiative Reunion . . 30 20
511 30 s. Presidents Julius Nyerere and Ali Hassan Mwinyi 50 60

118 Nungu Nungu Hair Style

1987. Traditional Hair Styles. Multicoloured.

512 1 s. 50 Type **118** 25 10
513 2 s. Upanga wa jogoo style 35 20
514 10 s. Morani style . . 60 60
515 20 s. Twende kilioni style 1·25 1·40

120 Royal Family on Buckingham Palace Balcony after Trooping the Colour

1987. 60th Birthday (1986) of Queen Elizabeth II. Multicoloured.

517 5 s. Type **120** 15 10
518 10 s. Queen and Prince Philip at Royal Ascot . . 25 20
519 40 s. Queen Elizabeth II . . 80 80
520 60 s. Queen Elizabeth with crowd . . . . . . 1·10 1·25

121 "Apis mellifera" (bee)

1987. Insects. Multicoloured.

522 1 s. 50 Type **121** 30 10
523 2 s. "Prostephanus truncatus" (grain borer) 40 20
524 10 s. "Glossina palpalis" (tsetse fly) . . 75 75
525 20 s. "Polistes sp." (wasp) 1·25 1·40

122 Crocodile

1987. Reptiles. Multicoloured.

527 2 s. Type **122** 15 10
528 3 s. Black-striped grass-snake 20 15
529 10 s. Adder 35 30
530 20 s. Green mamba . . 65 70

123 Emblems of Posts/ Telecommunications and Railways

1987. 10th Anniv of Tanzania Communications and Transport Corporations. Mult.

532 2 s. Type **123** 10 10
533 8 s. Emblems of Air Tanzania and Harbours Authority 20 20

124 Basketry

1987. Traditional Handicrafts. Multicoloured.

535 2 s. Type **124** 15 10
536 3 s. Decorated gourds . . 15 15
537 10 s. Stools 25 20
538 20 s. Makonde carvings . . 40 45

1987. 10th Anniv of Tanzania–Zambia Railway (1986). Nos. 445/9 optd **10th Anniversary of TANZANIA ZAMBIA RAILWAY AUTHORITY 1976–1986.**

540 **103** 1 s. 50 multicoloured 10 10
541 – 2 s. multicoloured 15 15
542 – 5 s. multicoloured . . 20 20
543 – 10 s. multicoloured . . 30 30
544 – 30 s. black, brn & red 50 50

126 Mdako (pebble game)

1988. Traditional Pastimes. Multicoloured.

545 2 s. Type **126** 10 10
546 3 s. Wrestling 10 10
547 8 s. Bullfighting, Zanzibar 15 15
548 20 s. Bao (board game) . . 35 35

127 Plateosaurus (illustration reduced, actual size 57 × 29 mm)

1988. Prehistoric and Modern Animals. Mult.

550 2 s. Type **127** 15 10
551 3 s. Pteranodon 15 10
552 5 s. Jurassic brontosaurus 15 10
553 7 s. Lion 20 15
554 8 s. Tiger 20 15
555 12 s. Orang-utan 20 15
556 20 s. Elephant 50 35
557 100 s. Stegosaurus . . 1·50 1·25

128 Marchers with Party Flag

1988. National Solidarity Walk. Mult.

558 2 s.+1 s. Type **128** . . 15 15
559 3 s.+1 s. Pres. Mwinyi leading Walk 15 15

129 Population Symbols on Map

1988. 3rd National Population Census. Mult.

561 2 s. Type **129** 10 10
562 3 s. Census official at work 10 10
563 10 s. Community health care 15 15
564 20 s. Population growth 1967–1988 . . . . 30 30

130 Javelin

1988. Olympic Games, Seoul (1st issue). Mult.

566 2 s. Type **130** 10 10
567 3 s. Hurdling 10 10
568 7 s. Long distance running 15 15
569 12 s. Relay racing . . 25 25

131 Football

1988. Olympic Games, Seoul (2nd issue). Mult.

571 10 s. Type **131** 10 10
572 20 s. Cycling 20 25
573 50 s. Fencing 45 50
574 70 s. Volleyball 60 65

1988. Winter Olympic Games, Calgary. As T **131**. Multicoloured.

576 5 s. Cross-country skiing . . 10 10
577 25 s. Figure skating . . 20 25
578 50 s. Downhill skiing . . 45 50
579 75 s. Bobsleighing . . 65 70

132 Goat

1988. Domestic Animals. Multicoloured.

581 4 s. Type **132** 10 10
582 5 s. Rabbit (horiz) . . 10 10
583 8 s. Cows (horiz) . . 15 15
584 10 s. Kitten (horiz) . . 20 20
585 12 s. Pony 25 25
586 20 s. Puppy 45 45

133 "Love You, Dad" (Pinocchio) (illustration reduced, actual size 50 × 38 mm)

1988. Greetings Stamps. Showing Walt Disney cartoon characters. Multicoloured.

No.	Description		
588	4 s. Type **133**	10	10
589	5 s. "Happy Birthday" (Brer Rabbit and Chip n'Dale)	10	10
590	10 s. "Trick or Treat" (Daisy and Donald Duck)	10	10
591	12 s. "Be kind to Animals" (Ferdie and Mordie with Pluto)	10	10
592	15 s. "Love" (Daisy and Donald Duck)	15	15
593	20 s. "Let's Celebrate" (Mickey Mouse and Goofy)	25	25
594	30 s. "Keep in Touch" (Daisy and Donald Duck)	35	35
595	50 s. "Love you, Mom" (Minnie Mouse with Ferdie and Mordie) ..	60	60

134 "Charaxes varanes"

1988. Butterflies. Multicoloured.

No.	Description		
597	8 s. Type **134**	30	10
598	30 s. "Neptis melicorta" ..	65	30
599	40 s. "Mylothris chloris" ..	75	40
600	50 s. "Charaxes bohemani"	90	50
601	60 s. "Myrina silenus" ..	1·00	70
602	75 s. "Papilio phorcas" ..	1·50	90
603	90 s. "Cyrestis camillus" ..	1·75	1·10
604	100 s. "Salamis temora" ..	2·00	1·25

135 Independence Torch and Mt. Kilimanjaro

1988. National Monuments. Multicoloured.

No.	Description		
606	5 s. Type **135**	10	10
607	12 s. Arusha Declaration Monument	10	10
608	30 s. Askari Monument ..	25	30
609	60 s. Independence Monument	55	60

136 Eye Clinic

1988. 25th Anniv of Dar es Salaam Lions Club. Multicoloured.

No.	Description		
611	2 s. Type **136**	10	10
612	3 s. Family at shallow water well	10	10
613	7 s. Rhinoceros and outline map of Tanzania ..	15	15
614	12 s. Club presenting school desks	15	15

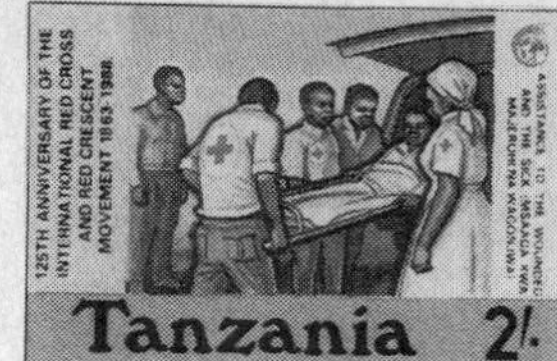

137 Loading Patient into Ambulance

1988. 125th Anniv of International Red Cross and Red Crescent. Multicoloured.

No.	Description		
616	2 s. Type **137**	10	10
617	3 s. Mother and baby health clinic	10	10
618	7 s. Red Cross flag ..	10	10
619	12 s. Henri Dunant (founder)	15	15

138 Paradise Whydah

1989. Birds. Multicoloured.

No.	Description		
621	20 s. Type **138**	10	15
622	20 s. Black-collared barbet	10	15
623	20 s. Bateleur	10	15
624	20 s. Lilac-breasted roller and openbill storks in flight	10	15
625	20 s. Red-tufted malachite sunbird and openbill stork in flight ..	10	15
626	20 s. Dark chanting goshawk	10	15
627	20 s. White-fronted bee eater, carmine bee eater and little bee eaters ..	10	15
628	20 s. Narina trogon and marabou stork in flight	10	15
629	20 s. Grey parrot	10	15
630	20 s. Hoopoe	10	15
631	20 s. Masked lovebird ("Yellow-collared lovebird")	10	15
632	20 s. Yellow-billed hornbill	10	15
633	20 s. Hammerkop ..	10	15
634	20 s. Violet-crested turaco and flamingos in flight	10	15
635	20 s. Malachite kingfisher	10	15
636	20 s. Greater flamingos ..	10	15
637	20 s. Yellow-billed storks	10	15
638	20 s. Whale-headed stork ("Shoebill stork") ..	10	15
639	20 s. Saddle-bill stork and blacksmith plover ..	10	15
640	20 s. Crowned crane ..	10	15

Nos. 622/40 were printed together, se-tenant, forming a composite design of birds at a waterhole.

139 Bushbaby

1989. Fauna and Flora. Multicoloured.

No.	Description		
642	5 s. Type **139**	10	10
643	10 s. Bushbaby holding insect (horiz)	10	10
644	20 s. Bushbaby on forked branch	10	15
645	30 s. Black cobra on umbrella acacia ..	15	20
646	45 s. Bushbaby at night (horiz)	20	25
647	70 s. Red-billed tropic bird and tree ferns	35	40
648	100 s. African tree frog on cocoa tree	50	55
649	150 s. Black-headed heron and Egyptian papyrus	75	80

Nos. 646 and 648/50 are without the World Wildlife Fund logo.

140 Juma Ikangaa (marathon runner)

1989. International Sporting Personalities. Multicoloured.

No.	Description		
651	4 s. Type **140**	10	10
652	8 s. 50 Steffi Graf (tennis player)	10	10
653	12 s. Yannick Noah (tennis player)	10	10
654	40 s. Pelé (footballer) ..	20	25
655	100 s. Erhard Keller (speed skater)	50	55
656	125 s. Sadanoyama (sumo wrestler)	60	65
657	200 s. Taino (sumo wrestler)	1·00	1·10
658	250 s. I. Aoki (golfer) ..	1·25	1·40

141 Drums

1989. Musical Instruments. Multicoloured.

No.	Description		
660	2 s. Type **141**	10	10
661	3 s. Xylophones	10	10
662	10 s. Thumbpiano ..	15	20
663	20 s. Fiddles	30	40

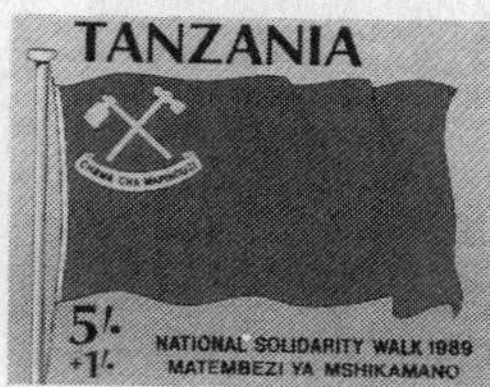

142 Chama Cha Mapinduzi Party Flag

1989. National Solidarity Walk. Mult.

No.	Description		
665	5 s. + 1 s. Type **142** ..	10	10
666	10 s. + 1 s. Marchers with party flag and President Mwinyi	10	10

143 Class "P36" Locomotive, U.S.S.R.

1989. Steam Locomotives. Multicoloured.

No.	Description		
668	10 s. Type **143**	10	10
669	25 s. Class "12", Belgium	10	15
670	60 s. Class "C62", Japan ..	30	35
671	75 s. Pennsylvania Railroad Class "T1", U.S.A.	35	40
672	80 s. Class "WP", India ..	40	45
673	90 s. East African Railways Class "59" ..	45	50
674	150 s. Class "People", China	75	80
675	200 s. Southern Pacific "Daylight Express" U.S.A.	1·00	1·10

144 "Luna 3" Satellite orbiting Moon, 1959

1989. History of Space Exploration and 20th Anniv of First Manned Landing on Moon. Multicoloured.

No.	Description		
678	20 s. Type **144**	10	15
679	30 s. "Gemini 6" and "7", 1965	15	20
680	40 s. Astronaut Edward White in space, 1965 ..	20	25
681	60 s. Astronaut Aldrin on Moon, 1969	30	35
682	70 s. Aldrin performing experiment, 1969 ..	35	40
683	100 s. "Apollo 15" astronaut and lunar rover, 1971	50	55
684	150 s. "Apollo 18" and "Soyuz 19" docking in space, 1975	75	80
685	200 s. Spacelab, 1983 ..	1·00	1·10

1989. Olympic Medal Winners, Calgary and Seoul. Various stamps optd.

(a) Nos. 571/4

No.	Description		
687	10 s. Type **131** (optd **Gold-USSR Silver-Brazil Bronze-W.Germany**)	10	10
688	20 s. Cycling (optd **Men's Match Sprint, Lutz Hesslich, DDR**) ..	10	15
689	50 s. Fencing (optd **Epee, Schmitt, W.Germany**)	25	30
690	70 s. Volleyball (optd **Men's Team, USA**) ..	35	40

(b) Nos. 576/9

No.	Description		
692	5 s. Cross-country skiing (optd **Biathlon, Peter-Roetsch, DDR**) ..	10	10
693	25 s. Figure skating (optd **Pairs, Gordeeva & Grinkov, USSR**) ..	10	15
694	50 s. Downhill skiing (optd **Zubriggen, Switerland**)	25	30
695	75 s. Bobsleighing (optd **Gold—USSR Silver—DDR Bronze—DDR**)	35	40

146 Tiger Tilapia

1989. Reef and Freshwater Fishes of Tanzania. Multicoloured.

No.	Description		
697	9 s. Type **146**	10	10
698	13 s. Picasso fish ..	10	10
699	20 s. Powder-blue surgeonfish	10	15
700	40 s. Butterflyfish ..	20	25
701	70 s. Guenther's notho ..	35	40
702	100 s. Ansorge's neolebias	50	55
703	150 s. Lyretail panchax ..	75	80
704	200 s. Regal angelfish ..	1·00	1·10

147 Rural Polling Station

1989. Cent of Inter-Parliamentary Union.

No.	Type	Description		
706	147	9 s. multicoloured ..	10	10
707	–	13 s. multicoloured ..	10	10
708	–	80 s. multicoloured ..	40	45
709	–	100 s. blk, ultram & bl	50	55

DESIGNS: 13 s. Parliament Building, Dar-es-Salaam; 40 s. Sir William Randal Cremer and Frederic Passy (founders); 80 s. Tanzania Parliament in session; 100 s. Logo.

148 Logo

1990. 10th Anniv of Pan-African Postal Union.

711 **148** 9 s. yellow, green & blk . . 10 10
712 – 13 s. multicoloured . . 10 10
713 – 70 s. multicoloured . . 35 40
714 – 100 s. multicoloured . . 50 55

DESIGNS: 13 s. Collecting mail from post office box; 40 s. Logos of Tanzania Posts and Telecommunications Corporation, P.A.P.U. and U.P.U.; 70 s. Taking mail to post office; 100 s. Mail transport.

149 Admiral's Flag and "Nina"

1990. 500th Anniv (1992) of Discovery of America by Columbus (50, 60, 75, 200 s.) and Modern Scientific Discoveries (others). Multicoloured.

716 9 s. Bell X-1 aircraft (first supersonic flight, 1947 . . 10 10
717 13 s. "Trieste" (bathyscaphe) (first dive to depth of 35,000 ft, 1960) 10 10
718 50 s. Type **149** 25 30
719 60 s. Fleet flag and "Pinta" 30 35
720 75 s. Standard of Castile and Leon and "Santa Maria" 35 40
721 150 s. Transistor technology 75 80
722 200 s. Arms of Columbus and map of First Voyage 1·00 1·10
723 250 s. DNA molecule . . 1·25 1·40

150 Tecopa Pupfish

1990. Extinct Species. Multicoloured.

725 25 s. Type **150** 10 15
726 40 s. Thylacine 20 25
727 50 s. Quagga 25 30
728 60 s. Passenger pigeon . . 30 35
729 75 s. Rodriguez saddleback tortoise 35 40
730 100 s. Toolache wallaby . . 50 55
731 150 s. Texas red wolf . . 75 80
732 200 s. Utah Lake sculpin 1·00 1·10

151 Camping

1990. 60th Anniv of Girl Guides Movement in Tanzania. Multicoloured.

734 9 s. Type **151** 10 10
735 13 s. Guides planting sapling 10 10
736 50 s. Guide teaching woman to write . . 25 30
737 100 s. Guide helping at child-care clinic . . 50 55

152 Fishing

1990. 25th Anniv of Union of Tanganyika and Zanzibar. Multicoloured.

739 9 s. Type **152** 10 10
740 13 s. Vineyard 10 10
741 50 s. Cloves 25 30
742 100 s. Presidents Nyerere and Karume exchanging Union instruments (vert) 55 60

153 Footballer

1990. World Cup Football Championship, Italy (1st issue). Multicoloured.

744 25 s. Type **153** 10 15
745 60 s. Player passing ball . . 30 35
746 75 s. Player turning . . 35 40
747 200 s. Player kicking ball 1·00 1·25

See also Nos. 789/92 and 794/7.

154 Miriam Makeba

1990. Famous Black Entertainers. Mult.

749 9 s. Type **154** 10 10
750 13 s. Manu Dibango . . 10 10
751 25 s. Fela 10 15
752 70 s. Smokey Robinson . . 35 40
753 100 s. Gladys Knight . . 50 55
754 150 s. Eddie Murphy . . 75 80
755 200 s. Sammy Davis Jnr. 1·00 1·10
756 250 f. Stevie Wonder . . 1·25 1·40

155 Ring of People round Party Flag

1990. Solidarity Walk, 1990. Multicoloured.

758 9 s.+1 s. Type **155** . . 10 10
759 13 s.+1 s. President Mwinyi 10 10

156 Passenger Train

1990. 10th Anniv of Southern African Development Co-ordination Conf. Mult.

761 8 s. Type **156** 10 10
762 11 s. 50 Paper-making plant 10 10
763 25 s. Tractor factory and ploughing 10 15
764 100 s. Map and national flags 50 55

157 Pope John Paul II

1990. Papal Visit to Tanzania. Multicoloured.

766 10 s. Type **157** 10 10
767 15 s. Pope in ceremonial robes 10 10
768 20 s. Pope giving blessing 10 10
769 100 s. Papal coat of arms 50 55

158 Mickey and Minnie Mouse in Herby the Love Bug

1990. Motor Cars from Disney Films. Mult.

771 20 s. Type **158** 10 15
772 30 s. The Absent-minded Professor's car 15 20
773 45 s. Chitty-Chitty Bang-Bang 20 25
774 60 s. Mr. Toad's car . . 30 35
775 75 s. Scrooge's limousine . . 35 40
776 100 s. The Shaggy Dog's car 50 55
777 150 s. Donald Duck's nephews cleaning car . . 75 80
778 200 s. Fire engine from "Dumbo" . . . . 1·00 1·10

159 "St. Mary Magdalen in Penitence" (detail)

1990. Paintings by Titian. Multicoloured.

780 5 s. Type **159** 10 10
781 10 s. "Averoldi Polyptych" (detail) 10 10
782 15 s. "Saint Margaret" (detail) 10 10
783 50 s. "Venus and Adonis" (detail) 25 30
784 75 s. "Venus and the Lutenist" (detail) . . 35 40
785 100 s. "Tarquin and Lucretia" (detail) . . 50 55
786 125 s. "Saint Jerome" (detail) 60 65
787 150 s. "Madonna and Child in Glory with Saints" (detail) 75 80

160 Klinsmann of West Germany

1990. World Cup Football Championship, Italy (2nd issue). Multicoloured.

789 10 s. Type **160** 10 10
790 60 s. Serena of Italy . . 30 35
791 100 s. Nicol of Scotland . . 50 55
792 300 s. Susic of Yugoslavia 1·50 1·60

161 Throw-in

1990 World Cup Football Championship, Italy (3rd issue). Multicoloured.

794 9 s. Type **161** 10 10
795 13 s. Penalty kick . . 10 10
796 25 s. Dribbling 10 10
797 100 s. Corner kick . . 50 55

162 Dugout Canoe

1990. Marine Transport. Multicoloured.

799 9 s. Type **162** 10 10
800 13 s. Sailing canoe . . 10 10
801 25 s. Dhow 10 15
802 100 s. Freighter 50 55

163 Lesser Masked Weaver

164 Lesser Flamingo

1990. Birds. Designs as T **163** (5 s. to 25 s.) or T **164** (40 s. to 500 s.). Multicoloured.

804 5 s. Type **163** 10 10
805 9 s. African emerald cuckoo 10 10
806 13 s. Little bee eater . . 10 10
807 15 s. Red bishop 10 10
808 20 s. Bateleur 10 15
809 25 s. Scarlet-chested sunbird 10 15
810 40 s. Type **164** 20 25
811 70 s. Helmet guineafowl . . 35 40
812 100 s. Eastern white pelican 50 55
813 170 s. Saddle-bill stork . . 85 90
814 200 s. South African crowned crane . . 1·00 1·10
815 500 s. Ostrich . . . . 2·50 2·75

165 Athletics

1990. 14th Commonwealth Games, Auckland, New Zealand. Multicoloured.

817	9 s. Type **165**	10	10
818	13 s. Netball (vert) ..	10	10
819	25 s. Pole vaulting ..	10	15
820	100 s. Long jumping (vert)	50	55

OFFICIAL STAMPS

1965. Nos. 128, etc., optd. **OFFICIAL.**

O 9. **25.**	5 c. blue & orange ..	10	10
O 10. –	10 c. multicoloured	10	10
O 11. –	15 c. multicoloured ..	10	10
O 12. –	20 c. sepia, green & blue	10	10
O 13. –	30 c. black and brown	10	10
O 14. –	50 c. multicoloured	15	10
O 15. **33.**	1s. multicoloured ..	30	10
O 16. –	5s. brown, green & blue	1·50	2·25

1967. Nos. 142, etc., optd. **OFFICIAL.**

O 20.	5 c. mauve, grn. & blk.	10	40
O 21.	10 c. brown & bistre ..	10	15
O 22.	15 c. grey, blue & black	10	30
O 23.	20 c. brown and green..	10	10
O 24.	30 c. green and black..	10	10
O 36.	40 c. yell., brn. & green	—	2·00
O 25.	50 c. multicoloured ..	15	20
O 26.	1 s. brn., blue & purple	30	40
O 27.	5 s. yellow, blk. & green	2·25	3·50

1973. Nos. 158 etc. optd. **OFFICIAL.**

O 40. **53.**	5 c. green, blue & blk.	30	40
O 41. –	10 c. multicoloured ..	40	10
O 42. –	20 c. brn., yell. & blk.	50	10
O 43. –	40 c. multicoloured ..	70	20
O 44. –	50 c. multicoloured ..	75	20
O 45. –	70 c. grn., orge. & blk.	1·00	50
O 46. **54.**	1 s. multicoloured ..	1·00	20
O 47. –	1 s. 50 multicoloured..	2·00	1·25
O 48. –	2 s. 50 multicoloured..	2·25	2·25
O 49. –	5 s. multicoloured ..	3·00	3·25

1980. Nos. 307/13 and 315/17 optd. **OFFICIAL.**

O 54.	10 c. Type **75**	15	10
O 55.	20 c. Large-spotted genet	20	15
O 56.	40 c. Banded mongoose	20	15
O 57.	50 c. Ratel	20	15
O 58.	75 c. Large-toothed rock hyrax	30	30
O 59.	80 c. Leopard	35	35
O 60.	1 s. Impala	35	15
O 61.	1 s. 50 Giraffe ..	1·50	1·75
O 62.	2 s. Common zebra ..	55	55
O 63.	3 s. African buffalo ..	65	70
O 64.	5 s. Lion	85	95

1990. Nos. 804/12 optd **OFFICIAL**. Mult.

O65	5 s. Type **163**	10	10
O66	9 s. African emerald cuckoo	10	10
O67	13 s. Little bee eater ..	10	10
O68	15 s. Red bishop	10	10
O69	20 s. Bateleur	10	15
O70	25 s. Scarlet-chested sunbird	10	15
O71	40 s. Type **164**	20	25
O72	70 s. Helmet guineafowl ..	35	40
O73	100 s. Eastern white pelican	50	55

POSTAGE DUE STAMPS

The Postage Due stamps of Kenya, Uganda and Tanganyika were used in Tanganyika until January 2nd, 1967.

D 1.

1967.

D 19. D 1.	5 c. red	10	70
D 20.	10 c. green	10	70
D 21.	20 c. blue	15	90
D 22.	30 c. brown	20	1·25
D 23.	40 c. purple	25	1·40
D 24.	1 s. orange	35	1·75

D 2

1990.

D25 D 2	50 c. green	10	10
D26	80 c. blue	10	10
D27	1 s. brown	10	10
D28	2 s. green	10	10
D29	3 s. purple	10	10
D30	5 s. brown	10	10
D31	10 s. brown	10	10
D32	20 s. brown	10	15

B. For use in Zanzibar only.

Z 39. Pres. Nyerere and First Vice-Pres. Karume within Bowl of Flame.

1966. 2nd Anniv of United Republic. Mult.

Z 142.	30 c. Type Z **39** ..	15	10
Z 143.	50 c. Hands supporting Bowl of Flame ..	15	10
Z 144.	1 s. 30 As 50 c. ..	15	15
Z 145.	2 s. 50 Type Z **39** ..	30	50

APPENDIX

The following stamps have either been issued in excess of postal needs, or have not been made available to the public in reasonable quantities at face value.

1986.

Caribbean Royal Visit. Optd on previous issues. (a) On Nos. 425/8 20 s. ×2, 100 s. ×2. (b) On Nos. 430/3 5, 10, 20, 30 s.

"Ameripex" International Stamp Exhibition, Chicago. Optd on Nos. 425/8. 20 s. ×2, 100 s. ×2.

1988.

Cent of (1986) Statue of Liberty. 1, 2, 3, 4, 5, 6, 7, 8, 10, 12, 15, 18, 20, 25, 30, 35, 40, 45, 50, 60 s.

Royal Ruby Wedding. Optd on No. 378. 10 s.

125th Anniv of Red Cross. Optd on Nos. 486/7. 5, 40 s.

63rd Anniv of Rotary International in Africa. Optd on Nos. 422/3. 10 s., 17 s. 50.

TASMANIA

An island S. of Australia, one of the States of the Australian Commonwealth, whose stamps it now uses.

12 pence = 1 shilling.
20 shillings = 1 pound.

1.

2.

1853. Imperf.

3. **1.**	1d. blue	£3000	£600
8. **2.**	4d. orange..	£1800	£325

3.

7.

8.

1855. Imperf.

28 **3**	1d. red	80·00	15·00
34	2d. green	£120	45·00
36	4d. blue	£100	11·00
47 **7**	6d. purple	£130	40·00
41 **8**	1s. orange	£500	70·00

1864. Perf.

82 **3**	1d. red	25·00	6·50
71	2d. green	£100	38·00
72	4d. blue	70·00	11·00
143 **7**	6d. purple	24·00	11·00
141 **8**	1s. orange	70·00	38·00

11.

20.

1870.

159 **11.**	½d. orange	1·90	1·25
156	1d. red	2·75	25
157	2d. green.. ..	3·00	25
165	3d. brown	7·00	1·75
130	4d. blue	£700	£400
226	4d. yellow	12·00	5·50
158	8d. purple	14·00	3·25
256	9d. blue	7·00	2·50
131	10d. black	20·00	15·00
149b	5s. mauve	£110	30·00

1889. Surch. **Halfpenny.**

167. **11.**	½d. on 1d. red	8·00	6·00

1889. Surch. **2½d.**

169. **11.**	2½d. on 9d. blue ..	5·00	2·25

1892. Various frames.

216. **20.**	½d. orange and mauve ..	1·25	40
217.	2½d. purple	2·50	1·00
218.	5d. blue and brown ..	4·50	1·40
219.	6d. violet and black ..	5·50	1·75
220.	10d. lake and green ..	9·00	6·50
221.	1s. red and green ..	6·00	1·75
222.	2s. 6d. brown and blue..	20·00	9·00
223.	5s. purple and red ..	38·00	18·00
224.	10s. mauve and brown..	75·00	48·00
225.	£1 green and yellow ..	£400	£150

22. Lake Marion.

23. Mount Wellington.

DESIGNS—HORIZ. 2d. Hobart. 3d Spring River, Port Davey. 5d. Mt. Gould, Lake St. Clair. 6d. Dilston Falls. VERT. 2½d. Tasman's Arch. 4d. Russell Falls.

1899.

249 **22**	½d. green	1·25	20
250 **23**	1d. red	1·50	10
239 –	2d. violet ..	2·50	10
232 –	2½d. blue	10·00	4·50
253 –	3d. brown	6·50	1·25
247 –	4d. orange	12·00	1·75
235 –	5d. blue.. ..	14·00	4·50
254a –	6d. lake	15·00	7·00

1904. No. 218 surch. **1½d.**

244. **20.**	1½d. on 5d. blue & brown	1·25	90

1912. No. 251a surch. **ONE PENNY.**

259.	1d. on 2d. violet	90	30

TOBAGO

An island in the Br. W. Indies, N.E. of Trinidad. Now uses stamps of Trinidad and Tobago.

12 pence = 1 shilling.
20 shillings = 1 pound.

1.

2.

1879.

1. **1.**	1d. red	65·00	50·00
2.	3d. blue	55·00	35·00
3.	6d. orange	24·00	38·00
4.	1s. green	£350	60·00
5.	5s. grey	£550	£500
6.	£1 mauve	£5000	

In the above issue only stamps watermarked Crown CC were issued for postal use and our prices are for stamps bearing this watermark. Stamps with watermark Crown CA are fiscals and were never admitted to postal use.

1880. No. 3 divided vertically down the centre and surch. with pen and ink.

7. **1.**	1d. on half of 6d. orange..	£4500	£550

1880. "POSTAGE" added in design.

14. **2.**	½d. lilac	1·00	11·00
20.	½d. green	20	35
21.	1d. red	45	20
16a.	2½d. blue	1·75	75
10.	4d. green	£180	23·00
22.	4d. grey	50	55
11.	6d. buff	£250	90·00
23.	6d. brown..	60	2·50
24.	1s. yellow	70	6·50

1883. Surch. in figures and words.

26 **2**	½d. on 2½d. blue	2·25	6·00
30	½d. on 4d. grey	8·50	26·00
27	½d. on 6d. buff	1·50	13·00
28	½d. on 6d. brown ..	60·00	80·00
29	1d. on 2½d. blue ..	23·00	14·00
31	2½d. on 4d. grey ..	3·00	6·50
13	2½d. on 6d. buff ..	22·00	20·00

1896. Surch ½d. **POSTAGE.**

33. **1.**	½d. on 4d. lilac and red ..	22·00	23·00

TOGO

A territory in W. Africa, formerly a German Colony. Divided between France and Gt. Britain in 1919, the British portion being attached to the Gold Coast for administration and using the stamps of that country. In 1956 the French portion became an autonomous republic within the French Union. Full independence was achieved in April 1960.

100 pfennigs = 1 mark.

BRITISH OCCUPATION

1914. Nos. 7/19 (German Colonial Types) optd. **TOGO Anglo–French Occupation.**

H 1	N.	3 pf. brown	£110	95·00
H 2		5 pf. green	£100	90·00
H 3		10 pf. red	£120	£100
H 17		20 pf. blue	14·00	12·00
H 18		25 pf. blk. & red on yell.	19·00	27·00
H 19		30 pf. black & orange buff	19·00	27·00
H 7		40 pf. black and red	£225	£250
H 33		50 pf. black & purple on buff	£9500	£6500
H 9		80 pf. blk. & red on rose	£250	£275
H 10	O.	1 m. red	£5000	£2500
H 11		2 m. blue	£7500	£8000
H 25		3 m. black	†	£30000
H 26		5 m. lake and black	†	£30000

1914. Nos. 1/2 surch. in words.

H 27.	N.	½d. on 3 pf. brown	26·00	26·00
H 28.		1d. on 5 pf. green	4·00	4·25

1915. Stamps of Gold Coast (King George V) optd. **TOGO ANGLO-FRENCH OCCUPATION.**

H 47	½d. green	15	60
~~H 48~~	1d. red	15	40
H 36	2d. grey	30	40
H 37	2½d. blue	40	60
H 51	3d. purple on yellow	55	70
H 52	6d. purple	55	1·00
H 53	1s. black on green	1·25	1·50
H 54	2s. purple & blue on blue	4·50	5·50
H 55	2s. 6d. black & red on blue	4·50	6·00
H 44	5s. green & red on yellow	8·00	12·00
H 57a	10s. green & red on green	16·00	40·00
H 58	20s. purple & black on red	£120	£120

TOKELAU

Three islands situated north of Samoa. Formerly part of the Gilbert and Ellice Is. and known as the Union Is., they were declared part of New Zealand as from 1 Jan. 1949.

1948. 12 pence = 1 shilling;
20 shillings = 1 pound.
1967. 100 cents = 1 New Zealand dollar.
1982. 100 sene or cents = 1 Samoan tola or dollar.

1. Atafu Village and Map.

1948.

1.	1.	½d. brown and purple	15	20
2.	–	1d. red and green	15	20
3.	–	2d. green and blue	15	20

DESIGNS: 1d. Nukunonu hut and map. 2d. Fakaofo village and map.

1953. Coronation. As T **164** of New Zealand.

4.	3d. brown	3·50	3·75

1956. Surch. **ONE SHILLING.**

5.	1.	1s. on ½d. brown and purple	4·00	3·50

1966. Arms types of New Zealand without value, surch. **TOKELAU ISLANDS** and value in sterling.

6.	F 6.	6d. blue	65	1·25
7.		8d. green	75	1·00
8.		2s. pink	85	1·40

1967. Decimal currency. Nos 1/3 surch.

9.	–	1 c. on 1d. (No. 2)	60	60
10.	–	2 c. on 2d. (No. 3)	1·00	1·00
11.	1.	10 c. on ½d. (No. 1)	2·00	2·00

1968. Arms types of New Zealand without value, surch. **TOKELAU ISLANDS** and value in decimal currency.

12.	F 6.	3 c. lilac	50	30
13.		5 c. blue	50	30
14.		7 c. green	50	30
15.		20 c. pink	65	40

8. British Protectorate (1877).

1969. History of Tokelau Islands

16.	8.	5 c. blue, yellow & black	25	10
17.	–	10 c. red, yellow and black	30	10
18.	–	15 c. green, yellow & black	35	15
19.	–	20 c. brown, yellow & black	40	15

DESIGNS: 10 c. Annexed to Gilbert and Ellice Islands (1916). 15 c. New Zealand Administration (1925). 20 c. New Zealand Territory (1948).

1969. Christmas. As T **301** of New Zealand.

20.	2 c. multicoloured	10	15

1970. Christmas. As T **314** of New Zealand.

21.	2 c. multicoloured	10	20

12. H.M.S. "Dolphin", 1765.

13. Fan.

1970. Discovery of Tokelau Is. Multicoloured.

22.	5 c. Type **12**	1·50	35
23.	10 c. H.M.S. "Pandora", 1791	1·50	35
24.	25 c. "General Jackson", 1835	3·25	70

The 25 c. is horiz.

1971. Handicrafts. Multicoloured.

25.	1 c. Type **13**	20	20
26.	2 c. Hand-bag	30	30
27.	3 c. Basket	40	40
28.	5 c. Hand-bag	50	65
29.	10 c. Shopping-bag	60	80
30.	15 c. Hand-bag	1·00	1·50
31.	20 c. Canoe	1·25	2·00
32.	25 c. Fishing hooks	1·25	2·00

14. Windmill Pump.

15. Horny Coral.

1972. South Pacific Commission. 25th Anniv. Multicoloured.

33.	5 c. Type **14**	35	60
34.	10 c. Community well	45	75
35.	15 c. Pest eradication	55	1·00
36.	20 c. Flags of member nations	60	1·25

In No. 35 "PACIFIC" is spelt "PACFIC".

1973. Coral. Multicoloured.

37.	3 c. Type **15**	1·00	80
38.	5 c. Soft Coral	1·00	90
39.	15 c. Mushroom Coral	1·75	1·50
40.	25 c. Staghorn Coral	2·00	1·75

16. Hump-back Cowrie.

1975. "Shells of the Coral Reef". Mult.

41.	3 c. Type **16**	1·50	1·25
42.	5 c. Tiger Cowrie	1·75	1·50
43.	15 c. Mole Cowrie	3·00	3·00
44.	25 c. Eyed Cowrie	4·00	3·50

17. Moorish Idol.

1975. Fishes. Multicoloured.

45.	5 c. Type **17**	50	1·00
46.	10 c. Long-nosed Butterfly-fish	70	1·25
47.	15 c. Lined Butterfly-fish	85	1·75
48.	25 c. Red Fire-fish	1·10	2·00

18. Canoe Building.

1976. Multicoloured.

49a	1 c. Type **18**	10	15
50	2 c. Reef fishing	20	1·00
51a	3 c. Weaving preparation	10	15
52a	5 c. Uma (kitchen)	10	15
53a	9 c. Carving	10	15
54a	20 c. Husking coconuts (vert.)	15	20
55a	50 c. Wash day (vert.)	20	20
56a	$1 Meal time (vert.)	30	30

19. White Tern.

1977. Birds of Tokelau. Multicoloured.

57.	8 c. Type **19**	30	40
58.	10 c. Turnstone	35	45
59.	15 c. White-capped Noddy	60	70
60.	30 c. Common Noddy	90	1·25

20. Westminster Abbey.

1978. Coronation. 25th Anniv. Mult.

61.	8 c. Type **20**	20	20
62.	10 c. King Edward's Chair	20	20
63.	15 c. Coronation regalia	30	35
64.	30 c. Queen Elizabeth II	50	60

21. Canoe Race.

1978. Canoe Racing.

65.	21.	8 c. multicoloured	20	20
66.	–	12 c. multicoloured	25	25
67.	–	15 c. multicoloured	30	30
68.	–	30 c. multicoloured	50	50

DESIGNS: 12 c. to 30 c. Different scenes of canoe racing.

22. Rugby.

1979. Local Sports. Multicoloured.

69.	10 c. Type **22**	15	15
70.	15 c. Cricket	40	60
71.	20 c. Rugby (different)	40	65
72.	30 c. Cricket (different)	60	80

23. Surfing.

1980. Water Sports. Multicoloured.

73.	10 c. Type **23**	10	10
74.	20 c. Surfing (different)	15	15
75.	30 c. Swimming	20	25
76.	50 c. Swimming (different)	25	35

24. Pole Vaulting. 25. Wood Carving.

1981. Sports. Multicoloured.

77.	10 c. Type **24**	10	10
78.	20 c. Volleyball	20	20
79.	30 c. Athletics (different)	25	30
80.	50 c. Volleyball (different)	30	35

1982. Handicrafts. Multicoloured.

81.	10 s. Type **25**	10	10
82.	22 s. Bow-drilling sea shell	15	25
83.	34 s. Bowl finishing	20	35
84.	60 s. Basket weaving	35	50

26. Octopus Lure.

1982. Fishing Methods. Multicoloured.

85.	5 s. Type **26**	10	10
86.	18 s. Multiple-hook fishing	30	20
87.	23 s. Ruvettus fishing	35	25
88.	34 s. Netting flying fish	40	30
89.	63 s. Noose fishing	50	40
90.	75 s. Bonito fishing	60	45

27. Outrigger Canoe.

1983. Transport. Multicoloured.

91.	5 s. Type **27**	10	10
92.	18 s. Wooden whaleboat	15	15
93.	23 s. Aluminium whaleboat	15	20
94.	34 s. "Alia" (fishing catamaran)	25	25
95.	63 s. "Frysna" (freighter)	35	40
96.	75 s. McKinnon "Goose" flying-boat	45	50

28. Javelin-throwing.

1983. Traditional Pastimes. Multicoloured.

No.	Description	Unused	Used
97.	5 s. Type **28**	10	10
98.	18 s. String game	15	15
99.	23 s. Fire making	15	20
100.	34 s. Shell-throwing ..	25	25
101.	63 s. Hand-ball game ..	35	40
102.	75 s. Mass wrestling ..	45	50

29. Planting and Harvesting.

1984. Copra Industry. Multicoloured.

No.	Description	Unused	Used
103.	48 s. Type **29**	40	45
104.	48 s. Husking and splitting	40	45
105.	48 s. Drying	40	45
106.	48 s. Bagging	40	45
107.	48 s. Shipping	40	45

30. Convict Tang ("Manini").

1984. Fishes. Multicoloured.

No.	Description	Unused	Used
108	1 s. Type **30**	10	10
109	2 s. Flying Fish ("Hahave")	10	10
110	5 s. Fire Wrasse ("Uloulo")	10	10
111	9 s. Unicorn Fish ("Ume iho")	10	10
112	23 s. Napoleon Fish ("Lafilafi")	15	20
113	34 s. Red Snapper ("Fagamea")	20	25
114	50 s. Yellow Fin Tuna ("Kakahi")	35	40
115	75 s. Castor-oil Fish ("Palu po")	50	55
116	$1 Grey Shark ("Mokoha")	65	70
117	$2 Black Marlin ("Hakula")	1·25	1·40

31. "Ficus tinctoria" ("Mati").

1985. Native Trees. Multicoloured.

No.	Description	Unused	Used
118.	5 c. Type **31**	10	10
119.	18 c. "Morinda citrifolia" ("Nonu")	15	15
120.	32 c. Breadfruit Tree ("Ulu")	20	25
121.	48 c. "Pandanus tectorius" ("Fala")	35	40
122.	60 c. "Cordia subcordata" ("Kanava")	40	45
123.	75 c. Coconut Palm ("Niu")	50	55

INDEX

Countries can be quickly located by referring to the index at the end of this volume.

32. Administration Centre, Atafu.

1985. Tokelau Architecture (1st series). Public Buildings. Multicoloured.

No.	Description	Unused	Used
124.	5 c. Type **32**	10	10
125.	18 c. Administration Centre, Nukunonu ..	15	15
126.	32 c. Administration Centre, Fakaofo ..	20	25
127.	48 c. Congregational Church, Atafu	35	40
128.	60 c. Catholic Church, Nukunonu	40	45
129.	75 c. Congregational Church, Fakaofo ..	50	55

See also Nos. 130/5.

33. Atafu Hospital.

1986. Tokelau Architecture (2nd series). Hospitals and Schools. Multicoloured.

No.	Description	Unused	Used
130.	5 c. Type **33**	10	10
131.	18 c. St. Joseph's Hospital, Nukunonu	10	10
132.	32 c. Fenuafala Hospital, Fakaofo	20	25
133.	48 c. Matauala School, Atafu	35	40
134.	60 c. Matiti School, Nukunonu	40	45
135.	75 c. Fenuafala School, Fakaofo	55	60

34. Coconut Crab.

1986. Agricultural Livestock. Multicoloured.

No.	Description	Unused	Used
136.	5 c. Type **34**	10	10
137.	18 c. Pigs	15	15
138.	32 c. Chickens	25	25
139.	48 c. Reef Hawksbill turtle	40	40
140.	60 c. Goats	45	45
141.	75 c. Ducks	60	60

35. "Scaevola taccada" ("Gahu").

1987. Tokelau Flora. Multicoloured.

No.	Description	Unused	Used
142.	5 c. Type **35**	25	20
143.	18 c. "Hernandia nymphaeifolia" ("Puka")	40	30
144.	32 c. "Pandanus tectorius" ("Higano")	60	50
145.	48 c. "Gardenia taitensis" ("Tialetiale")	80	70
146.	60 c. "Pemphis acidula" ("Gagie")	1·00	90
147.	75 c. "Guettarda speciosa" ("Puapua")	1·25	1·00

36. Javelin Throwing.

1987. Tokelau Olympic Sports. Mult.

No.	Description	Unused	Used
148.	5 c. Type **36**	15	15
149.	18 c. Shot putting	30	30
150.	32 c. Long jumping ..	45	45
151.	48 c. Hurdling	60	60
152.	60 c. Sprinting	80	80
153.	75 c. Wrestling	95	95

37 Small Boat Flotilla in Sydney Harbour

1988. Bicentenary of Australian Settlement and "Sydpex '88" National Stamp Exhibition, Sydney. Multicoloured.

No.	Description	Unused	Used
154	50 c. Type **37**	70	70
155	50 c. Sailing ships and liners	70	70
156	50 c. Sydney skyline and Opera House	70	70
157	50 c. Sydney Harbour Bridge	70	70
158	50 c. Sydney waterfront	70	70

Nos. 154/8 were printed together, se-tenant, forming a composite aerial view of the re-enactment of First Fleet's arrival.

38 Island Maps and Ministerial Representatives

1988. Political Development. Multicoloured.

No.	Description	Unused	Used
159	5 c. Type **38** (administration transferred to N.Z. Foreign Affairs Ministry, 1975)	10	10
160	18 c. General Fono (island assembly) meeting, 1977	15	15
161	32 c. Arms of New Zealand (first visit by New Zealand Prime Minister, 1985)	20	25
162	48 c. U.N. logo (first visit by U.N. representative, 1976)	35	40
163	60 c. Canoe and U.N. logo (first Tokelau delegation to U.N., 1987) ..	40	45
164	75 c. Secretary and N.Z. flag (first islander appointed as Official Secretary, 1987) ..	50	55

39 Three Wise Men in Canoe and Star

1988. Christmas. Designs showing Christmas in Tokelau. Multicoloured.

No.	Description	Unused	Used
165	5 c. Type **39**	10	10
166	20 c. Tokelau Nativity ..	20	20
167	40 c. Flight to Egypt by canoe	35	35
168	60 c. Children's presents ..	45	45
169	70 c. Christ child in Tokelauan basket ..	55	55
170	$1 Christmas parade ..	75	75

40 Launching Outrigger Canoe

1989. Food Gathering. Multicoloured.

No.	Description	Unused	Used
171	50 c. Type **40**	60	60
172	50 c. Paddling canoe away from shore	60	60
173	50 c. Fishing punt and sailing canoe	60	60
174	50 c. Canoe on beach ..	60	60
175	50 c. Loading coconuts into canoe	60	60
176	50 c. Tokelauans with produce	60	60

Nos. 171/3 and 174/6 were each printed together, se-tenant, forming composite designs.

41 Basketwork

1990. Womens' Handicrafts. Multicoloured.

No.	Description	Unused	Used
177	5 c. Type **41**	25	25
178	20 c. Preparing cloth ..	55	55
179	40 c. Tokelau fabrics ..	75	75
180	60 c. Mat weaving ..	1·25	1·25
181	80 c. Weaving palm fronds	1·50	1·50
182	$1 Basket making ..	1·60	1·60

42 Man with Adze and Wood Blocks

1990. Men's Handicrafts. Multicoloured.

No.	Description	Unused	Used
183	50 c. Type **42**	75	75
184	50 c. Making fishing boxes	75	75
185	50 c. Fixing handles to fishing boxes ..	75	75
186	50 c. Two men decorating fishing boxes	75	75
187	50 c. Canoe building (two men)	75	75
188	50 c. Canoe building (three men)	75	75

TONGA

(Or Friendly Is.) A group of islands in the S. Pacific Ocean. An independent Polynesian kingdom formerly under British protection, Tonga became a member of the Commonwealth in June 1970.

1886. 12 pence = 1 shilling.
20 shillings = 1 pound.
1967. 100 seniti = 1 pa'anga.

1. King George I.

1886.

1b.	1.	1d. red	10·00	3·25
2b.		2d. violet	24·00	2·75
3ab.		6d. blue	16·00	2·25
9.		6d. orange	11·00	22·00
4ba.		1s. green	40·00	3·25

1891. Surch. with value in words.

5.	1.	4d. on 1d. red	2·00	10·00
6.		8d. on 2d. violet	35·00	70·00

1891. Optd. with stars in upper right and lower left corners.

7.	1.	1d. red	35·00	45·00
8.		2d. violet	42·00	38·00

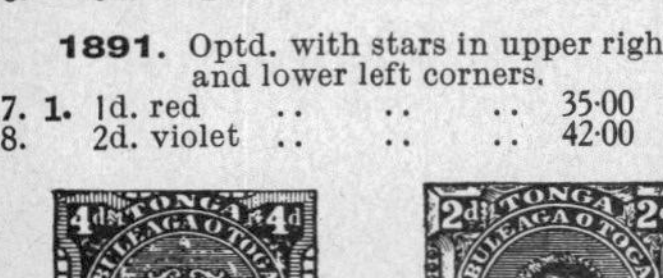

5. Arms of Tonga. 6. King George I.

1892.

10.	5.	1d. red	12·00	16·00
11.	6.	2d. olive	11·00	15·00
12.	5.	4d. brown	32·00	48·00
13.	6.	8d. mauve	48·00	80·00
14.		1s. brown	60·00	80·00

1893. Surch in figures.

15.	5.	½d. on 1d. blue	23·00	23·00
16.	6.	2½d. on 2d. green	14·00	12·00
18.		7½d. on 6d. red	24·00	65·00

1893. Surch. in words.

17.	5.	5d. on 4d. orange	4·00	6·50

1894. Surch. vert. **SURCHARGE** and value in words.

21.	5.	½d. on 4d. brown	1·50	7·00
22.	6.	½d. on 1s. brown	1·50	11·00
25.		1d. on 2d. blue	29·00	22·00

1894. Surch. vert. **SURCHARGE** and value in figures.

26a.	6.	1½d. on 2d. blue	35·00	27·00
27.		2½d. on 2d. blue	40·00	45·00
23.		2½d. on 8d. mauve	5·00	9·50
24b.	1.	2½d. on 1s. green	15·00	28·00
28a.	6.	7½d. on 2d. blue	55·00	45·00

13. King George II. 15. Arms.

16. Ovava tree, Kana-Kubolu.

21. View of Haapai.

1895.

29.	13.	1d. green	15·00	20·00
30.		2½d. red	20·00	20·00
31.		5d. blue	13·00	35·00
32.		7½d. yellow	20·00	35·00

1895. Surch. vert. **SURCHARGE,** and value in words or figures.

33.	13.	½d. on 2½d. red	30·00	32·00
34.		1d. on 2½d. red	35·00	28·00
35.		7½d. on 2½d. red	48·00	48·00

1896. Nos. 26a and 28a surch. with typewritten **Half-Penny** and Tongan inscription.

36.	6.	½d. on 1½d. on 2d. blue	£250	£250
37.		½d. on 7½d. on 2d. blue	50·00	50·00

1897.

38a	15	½d. blue	70	90
74		½d. green	15	75
75	16	1d. black and red	25	65
42a	–	2d. sepia and bistre	4·50	70
43b	–	2½d. black and blue	2·00	1·00
78	–	3d. black and green	15	30
45	–	4d. green and purple	3·75	4·00
46	–	5d. black and orange	18·00	9·50
79	–	6d. red	30	50
48	–	7½d. black and green	8·00	17·00
49	–	10d. black and red	19·00	26·00
50	–	1s. black and brown	9·50	6·00
51a	21	2s. black and blue	18·00	20·00
81	–	2s. 6d. purple	12·00	16·00
82	–	5s. black and red	14·00	27·00

DESIGNS—As Type **26**: 2d., 2½d., 5d., 7½d., 10d., 1s. King George II. As Type **16**: HORIZ. 3d. Prehistoric trilith at Haamonga. 4d. Breadfruit. VERT. 6d. Coral. As Type **21**: VERT. 2s. 6d. Red Shining Parrot. HORIZ. 5s. Vavau Harbour.

1899. Royal Wedding. Optd. **T-L 1 June, 1899.**

54.	16.	1d. black and red	24·00	48·00

26. Queen Salote. 29.

1920.

56.	26.	1½d. black	20	1·50
57.		2d. purple and violet	3·00	12·00
76.		2d. black and purple	30	35
58.		2½d. black and blue	2·75	18·00
77.		2½d. blue	15	30
60.		5d. black and orange	3·25	3·25
61.		7½d. black and green	1·75	1·75
62.		10d. black and red	1·25	4·50
80.		1s. black and brown	20	1·00

1923. Nos. 46 and 48/82 surch. **TWO PENCE PENI-E-UA.**

64	2d. on 5d. black and orange	65	85
65	2d. on 7½d. black and green	12·00	20·00
66	2d. on 10d. black and red	4·75	24·00
67	2d. on 1s. black and brown	24·00	22·00
68a	2d. on 2s. black and blue	3·50	4·50
69	2d. on 2s. 6d. purple	17·00	6·50
70a	2d. on 5s. black and red	2·00	2·50

1938. 20th Anniv of Queen Salote's Accession. Dated "1918–1938" at foot.

71.	29.	1d. black and red	55	2·00
72.		2d. black and purple	4·25	1·50
73.		2½d. black and blue	4·25	2·00

1944. Silver Jubilee of Queen Salote's Accession. Tablet at foot dated "1918–1943".

83.	29.	1d. black and red	15	15
84.		2d. black and violet	15	15
85.		3d. black and green	15	15
86.		6d. black and orange	15	45
87.		1s. black and brown	15	45

1949. U.P.U. As T **20/23** of Antigua.

88.	2½d. blue	30	10
89.	3d. olive	40	90
90.	6d. red	40	20
91.	1s. brown	40	35

31. Queen Salote.

DESIGN — VERT. 1s. Half-length portrait of Queen.

32. Queen Salote.

1950. 50th Birthday of Queen Salote.

92.	31.	1d. red	30	30
93.	32.	5d. green	30	30
94.	–	1s. violet	30	75

34. Map.

DESIGNS—HORIZ. 2½d. Beach scene. 5d. Flag and island. 1s. Arms of Tonga and Great Britain. VERT., 3d. H.M.N.Z.S. "Bellona".

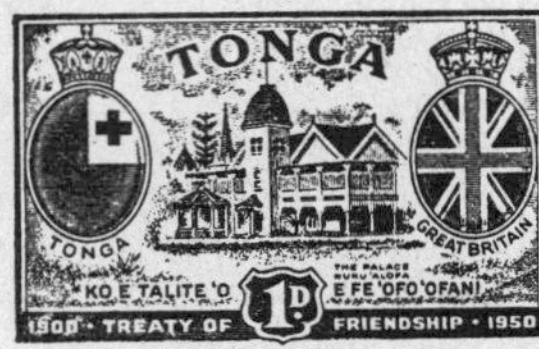

35. Palace, Nuku'alofa.

1951. 50th Anniv. of Treaty of Friendship with Gt. Britain.

95.	34.	½d. green	20	50
96.	35.	1d. black and red	10	30
97.	–	2½d. green and brown	30	50
98.	–	3d. yellow and blue	35	50
99.	–	5d. red and green	30	30
100.	–	1s. orange and violet	30	30

40. Royal Palace, Nuku'alofa.

1953.

101.	40.	1d. black and brown	10	10
102.	–	1½d. blue and green	10	10
103.	–	2d. turquoise and black	40	10
104.	–	3d. blue and green	20	10
105.	–	3½d. yellow and red	30	40
106.	–	4d. yellow and red	45	10
107.	–	5d. blue and brown	30	10
108.	–	6d. black and blue	30	20
109.	–	8d. green and violet	40	30
110.	–	1s. blue and black	40	10
111.	–	2s. olive and brown	45	60
112.	–	5s. yellow and lilac	12·00	4·50
113.	–	10s. yellow and black	5·50	4·50
114.	–	£1 yellow, red and blue	8·00	6·50

DESIGNS—HORIZ. 1½d. Shore fishing with throw net. 2d. "Hilofua" and "Aoniu" (ketches). 3½d. Map of Tongatapu. 4d. Vava'u Harbour. 5d. P.O., Nuku'alofa. 6d. Aerodrome Fua'amotu. 8d. Nuku'alofa Wharf. 2s. Lifuka, Ha'apai. 5s. Mutiny of the "Bounty". VERT. 3d. Swallows' Cave, Vava'u. 1s. Map of Tonga Islands. 10s. Queen Salote. £1, Arms of Tonga.

54. Stamp of 1886.

1961. 75th Anniv. of Tongan Postal Service.

115.	54.	1d. red and orange	10	10
116.	–	2d. blue	20	10
117.	–	4d. turquoise	10	10
118.	–	5d. violet	25	10
119.	–	1s. brown	25	10

DESIGNS: 2d. Whaler and longboat. 4d. Queen Salote and Post Office, Nuku'alofa. 5d. Mail steamer. 1s. Mailplane over Tongatapu.

1962. Cent. of Emancipation. Stamps of 1953 and No. 117 optd. **1862 TAU'ATAINA EMANCIPATION 1962.** or surch. also.

120.	1d. black and brown	10	10
121.	4d. turquoise (No. 117)	10	15
122.	5d. blue and brown	15	15
123.	6d. black and blue	15	20
124.	8d. green and violet	30	25
125.	1s. blue and black	15	20
126.	2s. on 3d. blue and green	40	55
127.	5s. yellow and lilac	50	85

60. "Protein Foods".

1963. Freedom from Hunger.

128.	60.	11d. blue	20	15

61. Coat of Arms.

1963. First Polynesian Gold Coinage Commemoration. Circular designs, backed with paper, inscr. overall "TONGA THE FRIENDLY ISLANDS". Imperf.

(a) Postage. ¼ koula coin. Diameter 1⅝ in.

129.	61.	1d. red on gold	10	10
130.	A.	2d. blue on gold	10	10
131.	61.	6d. green on gold	15	15
132.	A.	9d. purple on gold	15	15
133.	61.	1s. 6d. violet on gold	20	25
134.	A.	2s. green on gold	25	30

(b) Air. (i) ½ koula coin. Diameter 2⅛ in.

135.	B.	10d. red on gold	20	20
136.	61.	11d. green on gold	20	20
137.	B.	1s. 1d. blue on gold	20	20

(ii) 1 koula coin. Diameter 3⅛ in.

138.	B.	2s. 1d. purple on gold	30	30
139.	61.	2s. 4d. green on gold	35	35
140.	B.	2s. 9d. violet on gold	35	40

DESIGNS: A, Queen Salote (head). B. Queen Salote (full length).

64. Red Cross Emblem.

1963. Centenary of Red Cross.

141.	64.	2d. red and black	10	10
142.		11d. red and blue	20	20

65. Queen Salote.

66. Map of Tongatapu.

1964. Pan-Pacific South-East Asia Women's Assn. Meeting, Nuku'alofa. T **65/66** backed with paper inscr. overall "TONGA THE FRIENDLY ISLANDS". Imperf.

143.	65.	3d. pink (postage)	10	10
144.		9d. blue	10	10
145.		2s. green	15	20
146.		5s. lilac	30	40
147.	66.	10d. turquoise (air)	10	10
148.		1s. 2d. black	15	15
149.		3s. 6d. red	20	25
150.		6s. 6d. violet	35	50

1965. "Gold Coin" stamps of 1963 surch. and with star over old value.

151.	61.	1s. 3d. on 1s. 6d. (post.)	15	15
152.	A.	1s. 9d. on 9d.	15	20
153.	61.	2s. 6d. on 6d.	20	35
154.		5s. on 1d.	14·00	16·00
155.	A.	5s. on 2d.	2·50	3·00
156.		5s. on 2s.	60	75
157.	B.	2s. 3d. on 10d. (air)	15	25
158.	61.	2s. 9d. on 11d.	20	35
159.	B.	4s. 6d. on 2s. 1d.	10·00	12·00
160.	61.	4s. 6d. on 2s. 4d.	10·00	12·00
161.	B.	4s. 6d. on 2s. 9d.	7·00	7·00

1966. Tupou College and Secondary Education. Cent. Nos. 115/6 and 118/9 optd. or surch. **1866-1966 TUPOU COLLEGE & SECONDARY EDUCATION.**

162.	54.	1d. red and orge. (postage)	10	10
163.		3d. on 1d. red and orange	10	10
164.	–	6d. on 2d. blue	10	10
165.	–	1s. 2d. on 2d. blue	10	10
166.	–	2s. on 2d. blue	15	10
167.	–	3s. on 2d. blue	15	15

As above optd. but with additional **AIRMAIL & CENTENARY.**

168. – 5d. violet (air) 10 10
169. **54.** 10d. on 1d. red & brown 10 10
170. – 1s. brown 10 10
171. – 2s. 9d. on 2d. blue .. 15 15
172. – 3s. 6d. on 5d. violet .. 15 15
173. – 4s. 6d. on 1s. brown .. 20 15

1966. Queen Salote Commem. "Women's Assn." stamps optd. (a) **IN MEMORIAM QUEEN SALOTE 1900+1965.** (b) **1900 1965**+flower emblem or surch. also. Inscr. and new figures of value in first colour and obliterating shapes in second colour given.

(a) Postage.

174. **65.** 3d. (silver and blue) .. 10 10
175. 5d. on 9d. (silver and black) 10 10
176. 9d. (silver and black).. 15 10
177. 1s. 7d. on 3d. (silver and blue) 20 15
178. 3s. 6d. on 9d. (silver and black 35 20
179. 6s. 6d. on 3d. (silver and blue) 60 30

(b) Air.

180. **66.** 10d. (silver and black).. 10 10
181. 1s. 2d. (black and gold) 15 10
182. 4s. on 10d. (silver & black) 40 20
183. 5s. 6d. on 1s. 2d. (black and gold) 55 30
184. 10s. 6d. on 1s. 2d. (gold and black) 75 45

1967. Various stamps surch. **SENITI** or **Seniti** and value.

(a) Postage.

185 1s. on 1d. (No. 101) .. 10 10
186 2s. on 4d. (No. 106) .. 10 10
230 3s. on 3d. (No. 104) .. 10 10
187 3s. on 5d. (No. 107) .. 10 10
231 4s. on 5d. (No. 107) .. 10 10
232 5s. on 2d. (No. 108) .. 10 10
189 5s. on 3½d. (No. 105) .. 10 10
233 6s. on 6d. (No. 108) .. 10 10
190 6s. on 8d. (No. 109) .. 10 10
191 7s. on 1½d. (No. 102) .. 10 10
192 8s. on 6d.(No. 108) .. 10 10
235 8s. on 8d. (No. 109) .. 10 10
193 9s. on 3d. (No. 104) .. 15 15
236 9s. on 3½d. (No. 105) .. 20 20
194 10s on 1s. (No. 110) .. 15 15
195 11s. on 3d. on 1d. (No. 163) 15 20
238 20s. on 5s. (No. 112) .. 40 40
196 21s. on 3s. on 2d. (No. 167) 25 35
197 23s on 1d. (No. 101) .. 25 35
198 30s. on 2s. (No. 111) .. 1·25 1·75
199 30s. on 2s. (No. 111) .. 1·50 2·00
200 50s. on 6d. (No. 108) .. 85 1·25
201 60s. on 2d (No. 103) .. 1·25 1·75
239 2p. on 2s. (No. 111) .. 1·50 1·50

(b) Air. Surch. with **AIRMAIL** added.

240. 11s. on 10s. (No. 113) .. 25 25
241. 21s. on 10s. (No. 113) .. 40 40
242. 23s. on 10s. (No. 113) .. 40 40

74. Coat of Arms (reverse).

1967. Coronation of King Taufa'ahau IV. Circular designs, backed with paper inscr. overall "TONGA, THE FRIENDLY ISLANDS" etc. Imperf.

Sizes:

(a) Diameter 1½ in. (d) Diameter $2\frac{3}{10}$ in.
(b) Diameter $1\frac{7}{10}$ in. (e) Diameter $2\frac{7}{10}$ in.
(c) Diameter 2 in. (f) Diameter $2\frac{6}{10}$ in.

202. **74.** 1 s. orge. & bl. (b) (post.) 10 10
203. A. 2 s. blue and mauve (c) 10 10
204. **74.** 4 s. green and purple (d) 10 10
205. A. 15 s. turq. & violet (e).. 25 25
206. **74.** 28 s. black & purple (a) 50 40
207. A. 50 s. red and blue (c) .. 85 65
208. **74.** 1 p. blue and red (f) .. 1·50 1·10
209. A. 7 s. red & black (b) (air) 10 10
210. **74.** 9 s. purple and green (c) 10 10
211. A. 11 s. blue & orange (d) 15 15
212. **74.** 21 s. black and green (e) 30 30
213. A. 23 s. purple and green (a) 40 35
214. **74.** 29 s. blue and green (c) 50 40
215. A. 2 p. purple & orge. (f).. 2·00 1·25

DESIGN: A King Taufa'ahau IV (obverse).

The commemorative coins depicted in reverse (type **74**) are inscribed in various denominations as follows: 1 s. – "20 SENITI"; 4 s. – "PA'ANGA"; 9 s. – "50 SENITI"; 21 s. – "TWO PA'ANGA"; 28 s. – "QUARTER HAU"; 29 s. "HALF HAU"; 1 p. "HAU".

1967. Arrival of U.S. Peace Corps in Tonga. As Nos. 101/13 but imperf. in different colours and surch. **The Friendly Islands welcome the United States Peace Corps** and new value (or $ only).

216. 1 s. on 1d. black & yellow (postage) 10 10
217. 2 s. on 2d. blue and red .. 10 10
218. 3 s. on 3d. brown & yellow 10 10
219. 4 s. on 4d. violet & yellow 10 10
220. 5 s. on 5d. green and yellow 10 10
221. 10 s. on 1s. red and yellow 10 10
222. 20 s. on 2s. red and blue.. 15 15
223. 50 s. on 5s. sepia and yellow 30 35
224. 1 p. on 10s. yellow .. 50 55
225. 11 s. on 3½d. blue (air) .. 10 10
226. 21 s. on 1½d. green .. 20 20
227. 23 s. on 3½d. blue .. 20 20

1968. 50th Birthday of King Taufa'ahua IV. Nos. 202/15 optd. **H.M.'s BIRTHDAY 4 JULY 1968.**

243. **74.** 1 s. orange and blue (post.) 10 10
244. A. 2 s. blue and mauve .. 10 10
245. **74.** 4 s. green and purple .. 10 10
246. A. 15 s. turquoise & violet 25 15
247. **74.** 28 s. black and purple.. 55 30
248. A. 50 s. red and blue .. 1·00 60
249. **74.** 1 p. blue and red .. 2·25 1·25
250. A. 7 s. red and black (air).. 10 10
251. **74.** 9 s. purple and green .. 15 10
252. A. 11 s. blue and orange .. 15 10
253. **74.** 21 s. black and green .. 40 25
254. A. 23 s. purple and green.. 40 25
255. **74.** 29 s. blue and green .. 65 35
256. A. 2 p. purple and orange.. 4·50 2·50

1968. South Pacific Games Field and Track Trials. Port Moresby, New Guinea. As Nos. 101/13 surch. **Friendly Islands Field & Track Trials South Pacific Games, Port Moresby 1969** and value.

257. 5 s. on 5d. grn. & yell. (post.) 10 10
258. 10 s. on 1s. red and yellow 10 10
259. 15 s. on 2s. red and blue.. 15 15
260. 25s. on 2d. blue and red.. 15 15
261. 50 s. on 1d. black & yellow 30 30
262. 75 s. on 10s. orge. & yellow 45 45
263. 6 s. on 6d. blk. & yell. (air) 10 10
264. 7 s. on 4d. violet & yellow 10 10
265. 8 s. on 8d. black & yellow 10 10
266. 9 s. on 1½d. green .. 10 10
267. 11 s. on 3d. brown & yellow 10 10
268. 21 s. on 3½d. blue .. 15 15
269. 38 s. on 5s. sepia and yellow 20 20
270. 1 p. on 10s. yellow .. 50 50

1969. Emergency Provisionals. Various stamps (Nos. 273/6 are imperf. and in different colours), surch. (a) Postage.

271. 1 s. on 1s. 2d. blue (No. 165) .. .. .. 1·00 65
272. 1 s. on 2s. on 2d. blue (No. 166) .. .. .. 1·00 65
273. 1 s. on 6d. black and yellow (No. 108) 40 25
274. 2 s. on 3½d. blue (No. 105) 45 30
275. 3 s. on 1½d. green (No. 102) 45 30
276. 4 s. on 8d. black and yellow (No. 109) 70 50

(b) Air. Nos. 171/3 surch.

277. 1 s. on 2s. 9d. on 2d. blue 1·00 65
278. 1 s. on 3s. 6d. on 5d. violet 1·00 65
279. 1 s. on 4s. 6d. on 1s. brown 1·00 65

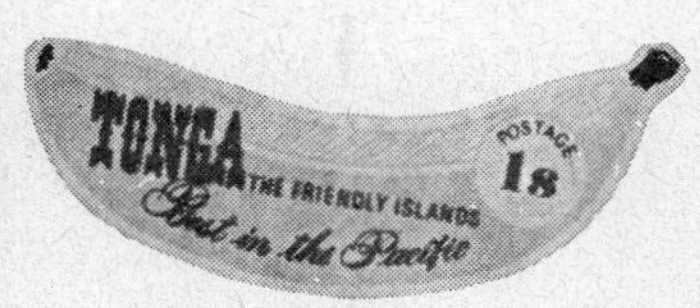

83. Banana.

1969. Coil stamps. Self-adhesive.

280. **83.** 1 s. red, black & yellow 30 35
281. 2 s. green, black & yellow 40 45
282. 3 s. violet, black & yellow 45 50
283. 4 s. blue, black & yellow 55 60
284. 5 s. green, black & yell. 75 80

See also Nos. 325/9, 413/17, 657/89, O 45/9, O 82/6 and O 169/83.

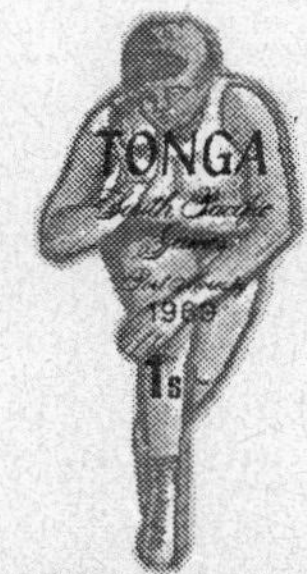

84. Putting the Shot.

1969. 3rd South Pacific Games, Port Moresby. Imperf., Self-adhesive.

285. **84.** 1 s. blk., red & buff (post.) 10 10
286. 3 s. green, red and buff.. 10 10
287. 6 s. blue, red and buff .. 10 10
288. 10s. violet, red & buff.. 10 10
289. 30 s. blue, red and buff.. 15 20
290. – 9 s. black, violet and orange (air) 10 10
291. – 11 s. black, blue, & orge. 10 10
292. – 20 s. blk., grn. & orange 15 15
293. – 60 s. black, red & orge. 45 55
294. – 1 p. black, green & orge. 70 80

DESIGN: Nos. 290/4, Boxing.

86. Oil Derrick and Map.

1969. Oil Search. Imperf. Self-adhesive.

295. **86.** 3 s. multicoloured (post.) 10 10
296. 7 s. multicoloured .. 15 15
297. 20 s. multicoloured .. 40 40
298. 25 s. multicoloured .. 45 45
299. 35 s. multicoloured .. 70 70
300. – 9 s. multicoloured (air) 20 20
301. – 10 s. multicoloured .. 20 20
302. – 24 s. multicoloured .. 45 45
303. – 29 s. multicoloured .. 50 50
304. – 38 s. multicoloured .. 70 70

DESIGN: Nos. 300/4, Oil Derrick and island of Tongatapu.

87. Members of the British and Tongan Royal Families.

(Reduced size illustration. Actual size 54 × 49 mm.)

1970. Royal Visit. Imperf., Self-adhesive.

305. **87.** 3 s. multicoloured (postage) 20 10
306. 5 s. multicoloured .. 25 10
307. 10 s. multicoloured .. 40 20
308. 25 s. multicoloured .. 1·00 55
309. 50 s. multicoloured .. 1·75 90
310. – 7 s. multicoloured (air) 35 15
311. – 9 s. multicoloured .. 40 20
312. – 24 s. multicoloured .. 1·00 55
313. – 29 s. multicoloured .. 1·25 60
314. – 38 s. multicoloured .. 1·50 80

DESIGN: Nos. 310/14, Queen Elizabeth II and King Taufa'aha Tupou IV.

89. Book, Tongan Rulers and Flag.

(Reduced size illustration. Actual size 69 × 38 mm.)

1970. Entry into British Commonwealth. Imperf. Self-adhesive.

315. **89.** 3 s. multicoloured (post.) 10 10
316. 7 s. multicoloured .. 15 15
317. 15 s. multicoloured .. 25 20
318. 25 s. multicoloured .. 35 25
319. 50 s. multicoloured .. 60 50
320. – 9 s. blue, gold & red (air) 15 15
321. – 10 s. pur., gold & blue 15 15
322. – 24 s. yell., gold & green 35 30
323. – 29 s. blue, gold and red 40 30
324. – 38 s. yell., gold & green 50 40

DESIGN: ("Star" shape. Size 44×51 mm.). Nos. 320/24, Star and King Taufa'ahua Tupou IV.

90. Coconut.

1970. Coil stamps. Imperf. Self-adhesive.

(a) As T **83** but colours changed.

325. **83.** 1 s. yell., pur. and black 15 20
326. 2 s. yellow, blue & black 20 30
327. 3 s. yellow, brn. & blk. 25 30
328. 4 s. yell., green & black 25 30
329. 5 s. yell., red and black 30 35

(b) Multicoloured; colour of face values given.

330. **90.** 6 s. red 35 40
331. 7 s. purple 40 45
332. 8 s. violet 45 55
333. 9 s. green 55 65
334. 10 s. orange 55 65

91. "Red Cross".

1970. Centenary of British Red Cross. Imperf. Self-adhesive.

335. **91.** 3 s. red, black & green (postage) 10 10
336. 7 s. red, black and blue 15 15
337. 15 s. red, black & pur. 30 30
338. 25 s. red, black & blue 50 50
339. 75 s. red, black & brown 3·00 3·00
340. – 9 s. red and turq. (air) 20 20
341. – 10 s. red and purple .. 20 20
342. – 18 s. red and green .. 35 35
343. – 38 s. red and blue .. 1·50 1·50
344. – 1 p. red and silver .. 4·00 4·00

DESIGN: As Type **91.** Nos. 340/4 as Nos. 335/9 but with inscription rearranged and coat of arms omitted.

1971. 5th Death Anniv. of Queen Salote. Nos. 174/80, 182/4 with part of old surch. obliterated and further surch. **1965† 1970** and value in seniti. On air values the surch. includes two laurel leaves.

345. **65.** 2 s. on 5d. on 9d. (post.) 10 10
346. 3 s. on 9d. 10 10
347. 5 s. on 3d. 15 15
348. 15 s. on 3s. 6d. on 9d. .. 45 35
349. 25 s. on 6s. 6d. on 3d. .. 80 65
350. 50 s on 1s. 7d. on 3d .. 1·75 1·25
351. **66.** 9 s. on 10d. (air) .. 30 20
352. 24 s. on 4s. on 10d. .. 80 60
353. 29 s. on 5s. 6d. on 1s. 2d. 90 80
354. 38 s. on 10s. 6d. on 1s. 2d. 1·40 1·00

1971. Philatokyo '71 Stamp Exhib., Japan. As Nos. 101, etc., but imperf. with colours changed and surch **PHILATOKYO '71,** emblem and value or **HONOURING JAPANESE POSTAL CENTENARY 1871-1971** (Nos. 357, 362. 364) Nos. 360/4 also surch. **AIRMAIL.**

355. 3 s. on 8d. blk. & yell. (postage) 10 10
356. 7 s. on 4d. violet and yellow 10 10
357. 15 s. on 1s. red and yellow 20 20
358. 25 s. on 1d. black & yellow 30 30
359. 75 s. on 2s. red and blue.. 85 85
360. 9 s. on 1½d. green (air) .. 10 10
361. 10 s. on 4d. violet & yellow 10 10
362. 18 s. on 1s. red and yellow 20 20
363. 38 s. on 1d. black & yellow 40 40
364. 1 p. on 2s. red and blue.. 1·00 1·00

96. Wristwatch.

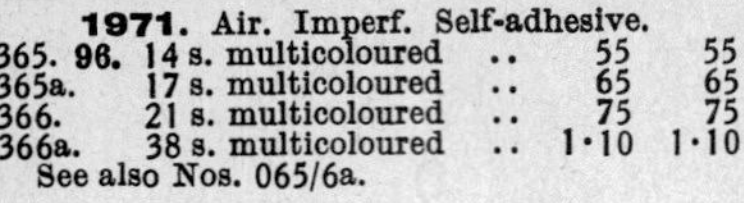

1971. Air. Imperf. Self-adhesive.

365. **96.** 14 s. multicoloured .. 55 55
365a. 17 s. multicoloured .. 65 65
366. 21 s. multicoloured .. 75 75
366a. 38 s. multicoloured .. 1·10 1·10

See also Nos. O65/6a.

97. Pole-vaulter.

1971. 4th South Pacific Games, Tahiti. Imperf. Self-adhesive.

367. **97.** 3 s. multicoloured (postage) 10 10
368. 7 s. multicoloured .. 10 10
369. 15 s. multicoloured .. 15 15
370. 25 s. multicoloured .. 25 30
371. 50 s. multicoloured .. 40 60
372. – 9 s. multicoloured (air) 10 10
373. – 10 s. multicoloured .. 10 10
374. – 24 s. multicoloured .. 25 30
375. – 29 s. multicoloured .. 30 40
376. – 38 s. multicoloured .. 35 50

DESIGN—HORIZ. Nos. 372/6 High-jumper.

98. Medal of Merit (reverse).

1971. Investiture of Royal Tongan Medal of Merit. Multicoloured, colour of medal given. Imperf. Self-adhesive.

377. **98.** 3 s. gold (postage) .. 10 10
378. 24 s. silver 20 20
379. – 38 s. brown 30 30
380. – 10 s. gold (air) 15 15
381. – 75 s. silver 65 65
382. **98.** 1 p. brown 75 75

DESIGN—As Type **98.** Nos. 379/81, Obverse of the Medal of Merit.

99. Child.

1971. 25th Anniv. of U.N.I.C.E.F. Imperf. Self-adhesive.

383. **99.** 2 s. multicoloured (postage) 10 10
384. 4 s. multicoloured .. 10 10
385. 8 s. multicoloured .. 10 10
386. 16 s. multicoloured .. 20 20
387. 30 s. multicoloured .. 30 30
388. – 10 s. multicoloured (air) 15 15
389. – 15 s. multicoloured .. 20 20
390. – 25 s. multicoloured .. 30 30
391. – 50 s. multicoloured .. 60 60
392. – 1 p. multicoloured .. 1·25 1·25

DESIGN—VERT. (21 × 42 mm.). Nos. 388/92. Woman.

100. Map of South Pacific, and " Olovaha ". (Illustration reduced. Actual size 53 × 47 mm.)

1972. Merchant Marine Routes. Imperf. Self-adhesive.

393. **100.** 2 s. mult. (postage) .. 10 10
394. 10 s. multicoloured .. 20 10
395. 17 s. multicoloured .. 40 20
396. 21 s. multicoloured .. 50 25
397. 60 s. multicoloured .. 2·00 1·25
398. – 9 s. mult. (air) .. 20 10
399. – 12 s. multicoloured .. 25 15
400. – 14 s. multicoloured .. 30 15
401. – 75 s. multicoloured .. 2·25 1·50
402. – 90 s. multicoloured .. 2·75 2·00

DESIGN: Nos. 398/402, Map of South Pacific, and " Niuvakai ".

101. ½ Hau Coronation Coin. (Illustration reduced. Actual size 60 × 40 mm.)

1972. 5th Anniv. of Coronation. Imperf. Self-adhesive.

403. **101.** 5 s. multicoloured (post.) 10 10
404. 7 s. multicoloured .. 10 10
405. 10 s. multicoloured .. 15 10
406. 17 s. multicoloured .. 25 15
407. 60 s. multicoloured .. 85 40
408. – 9 s. multicoloured (air) 15 10
409. – 12 s. multicoloured .. 20 10
410. – 14 s. multicoloured .. 25 15
411. – 21 s. multicoloured .. 30 15
412. – 75 s. multicoloured .. 1·10 45

DESIGNS—(47 × 41 mm). Nos. 408/12. As T **101**, but with coins above inscription instead of beneath it.

102. Water Melon.

1972. Imperf. Self-adhesive.

(a) As T **83**, but inscription altered, omitting " Best in the Pacific ", and colours changed.

413. **83.** 1 s. yellow, red & black 15 10
414. 2 s. yellow, blue & black 20 15
415. 3 s. yellow, green & blk. 25 20
416. 4 s. yellow, blue & black 25 20
417. 5 s. yellow, brown & blk. 25 20

(b) As T **90** but colours changed. Multicoloured. Colour of face-value given.

418. **90.** 6 s. orange 25 20
419. 7 s. blue 30 25
420. 8 s. purple 30 25
421. 9 s. orange 30 25
422. 10 s. blue 35 30

(c) Type **102.** Multicoloured. Colour of face-value given.

423. **102.** 15 s. blue 55 45
424. 20 s. orange 70 60
425. 25 s. brown 80 70
426. 40 s. orange .. .. 1·75 1·50
427. 50 s. lemon .. .. 2·00 1·75

1972. Inaug. of Int. Airmail. No. 398 surch. **NOVEMBER 1972 INAUGURAL Internal Airmail Nuku'alofa – Vava'u** and value.

428. 7 s. on 9 s. multicoloured .. 1·10 1·50

104. Hoisting Tongan Flag. (Illustration reduced. Actual size 60 × 41 mm.)

1972. Proclamation of Sovereignty over Minerva Reefs. Imperf. Self-adhesive.

429. **104.** 5 s. multicoloured (post.) 10 10
430. 7 s. multicoloured .. 10 10
431. 10 s. multicoloured .. 15 10
432. 15 s. multicoloured .. 25 15
433. 40 s. multicoloured .. 80 45
434. – 9 s. multicoloured (air) 15 10
435. – 12 s. multicoloured .. 20 10
436. – 14 s. multicoloured .. 25 15
437. – 38 s. multicoloured .. 75 35
438. – 1 p. multicoloured .. 2·00 1·00

DESIGN–SPHERICAL (52 mm. diameter). Nos. 434/8, Proclamation in Govt. Gazette.

105. Coins around Bank. (Illustration reduced. Actual size 53 × 48 mm.)

1973. Bank of Tonga. Foundation. Imperf. Self-adhesive.

439. **105.** 5 s. multicoloured (post.) 10 10
440. 7 s. multicoloured .. 10 10
441. 10 s. multicoloured .. 15 10
442. 20 s. multicoloured .. 25 15
443. 30 s. multicoloured .. 35 25
444. – 9 s. multicoloured (air) 20 10
445. – 12 s. multicoloured .. 20 10
446. – 17 s. multicoloured .. 25 15
447. – 50 s. multicoloured .. 80 40
448. – 90 s. multicoloured .. 1·50 90

DESIGN—HORIZ. (64 × 52 mm.). Nos. 444/8, Bank and banknotes.

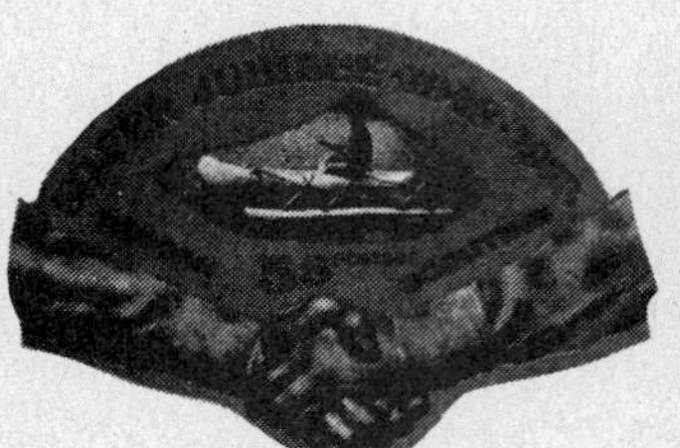

106. Handshake and Scout in Outrigger Canoe. (Illustration reduced. Actual size 61 × 43 mm.)

1973. Silver Jubilee of Scouting in Tonga. Imperf. Self-adhesive.

449. **106.** 5 s. multicoloured (post.) 20 10
450. 7 s. multicoloured .. 30 15
451. 15 s. multicoloured .. 95 40
452. 21 s. multicoloured .. 1·25 50
453. 50 s. multicoloured .. 4·50 1·75
454. – 9 s. multicoloured (air) 50 20
455. – 12 s. multicoloured .. 60 30
456. – 14 s. multicoloured .. 85 50
457. – 17 s. multicoloured .. 95 60
458. – 1 p. multicoloured .. 15·00 5·50

DESIGN—SQUARE (53 × 53 mm.). Nos. 454/8, Scout badge.

107. Excerpt from Cook's Log-book. (Illustration reduced. Actual size 69 × 38 mm.)

1973. Bicentenary of Capt. Cook's Visit to Tonga. Imperf. Self-adhesive.

459. **107.** 6 s. multicoloured (post.) 20 15
460. 8 s. multicoloured .. 25 20
461. 11 s. multicoloured .. 40 25
462. 35 s. multicoloured .. 3·00 1·40
463. 40 s. multicoloured .. 3·00 1·40
464. – 9 s. multicoloured (air) 45 20
465. – 14 s. multicoloured .. 75 30
466. – 29 s. multicoloured .. 2·75 1·25
467. – 38 s. multicoloured .. 3·00 1·50
468. – 75 s. multicoloured .. 6·00 2·75

DESIGNS—VERT. Nos. 464/8, H.M.S. "Resolution".

1973. Commonwealth Games, Christchurch. Various stamps optd. **COMMONWEALTH GAMES CHRISTCHURCH 1974** and No. 474 is optd. **AIRMAIL** in addition.

469. **97.** 5 s. on 50 s. multicoloured (No. 371) (post.) .. 15 10
470. – 12 s. on 38 s. multicoloured (No. 379) .. 30 15
471. – 14 s. on 75 s. multicoloured (No. 381) .. 30 15
472. **98.** 20 s. on 1 p. multicoloured (No. 382) .. 50 25
473. 50 s. on 24 s. multicoloured (No. 378) .. 1·25 65
474. **97.** 7 s. on 25 s. multicoloured (No. 370) (air) .. 15 10
475. – 9 s. on 38 s. multicoloured (No. 376) .. 20 10
476. – 24 s. multicoloured (No. 374) 60 25
477. – 29 s. on 9s. multicoloured (No. 454) 70 35
478. – 40 s. on 14 s. multicoloured (No. 456) .. 1·00 60

109. Red Shining Parrot

1974. Air. Imperf. Self-adhesive.

479. **109.** 7 s. multicoloured .. 30 20
480. 9 s. multicoloured .. 35 25
481. 12 s. multicoloured .. 40 30
482. 14 s. multicoloured .. 45 35
483. 17 s. multicoloured .. 55 50
484. 29 s. multicoloured .. 95 80
485. 38 s. multicoloured .. 1·25 1·00
486. 50 s. multicoloured .. 1·75 1·50
487. 75 s. multicoloured .. 2·25 2·00

110. "Stamped Letter".

1974. Centenary of U.P.U. Imperf. self-adhesive.

488. **110.** 5 s. mult. (postage) .. 15 10
489. 10 s. multicoloured .. 15 10
490. 15 s. multicoloured .. 25 15
491. 20 s. multicoloured .. 30 25
492. 50 s. multicoloured .. 1·25 75
493. – 14 s. multicoloured (air) 25 15
494. – 21 s. multicoloured .. 35 30
495. – 60 s. multicoloured .. 1·40 75
496. – 75 s. multicoloured .. 1·60 85
497. – 1 p. multicoloured .. 1·90 1·10

DESIGNS—HORIZ. Nos. 493/7, Carrier pigeon scattering letters over Tonga.

111. Girl Guides Badges.

1974. Tongan Girl Guides. Imperf. Self-adhesive.

498. **111.** 5 s. mult. (postage) .. 40 10
499. 10 s. multicoloured .. 60 20
500. 20 s. multicoloured .. 1·50 55
501. 40 s. multicoloured .. 3·25 1·25
502. 60 s. multicoloured .. 4·00 2·00
503. – 14 s. multicoloured (air) 1·00 35
504. – 16 s. multicoloured .. 1·00 35
505. – 29 s. multicoloured .. 2·00 80
506. – 31 s. multicoloured .. 2·25 90
507. – 75 s. multicoloured .. 5·50 2·50

DESIGNS—VERT. Nos. 503/7, Girl Guide leaders.

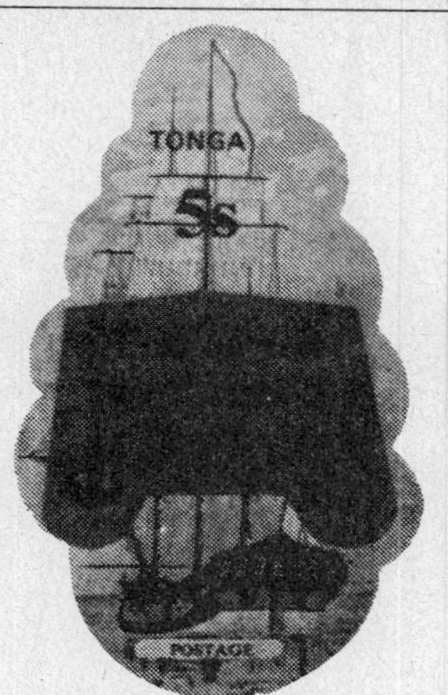

112. H.M.S. "Resolution".

1974. Establishment of Royal Marine Institute. Imperf. Self-adhesive.

No.	Description		
508. 112.	5 s. mult. (postage) ..	55	10
509.	10 s. multicoloured ..	75	20
510.	25 s. multicoloured ..	1·25	45
511.	50 s. multicoloured ..	2·25	1·25
512.	75 s. multicoloured ..	3·25	2·00
513. –	9 s. multicoloured (air)	90	20
514. –	14 s. multicoloured ..	1·25	35
515. –	17 s. multicoloured ..	1·40	40
516. –	60 s. multicoloured ..	3·25	1·75
517. –	90 s. multicoloured ..	4·50	2·75

DESIGNS—HORIZ. (53 × 47 mm.). Nos. 513/17, "James Cook" (bulk carrier).

113. Dateline Hotel, Nuku'alofa.
(Illustration reduced. Actual size 60 × 38 mm.)

1975. South Pacific Forum and Tourism. Imperf. Self-adhesive.

No.	Description		
518. 113.	5 s. multicoloured (postage)	10	10
519.	10 s. multicoloured ..	10	10
520.	15 s. multicoloured ..	20	20
521.	30 s. multicoloured ..	45	45
522.	1 p. multicoloured ..	1·60	1·50
523. –	9 s. multicoloured (air)	10	10
524. –	12 s. multicoloured ..	15	15
525. –	14 s. multicoloured ..	20	20
526. –	17 s. multicoloured ..	20	20
527. –	38 s. multicoloured ..	55	55

DESIGNS (46 × 60 mm.): 9, 12, 14 s. Beach. 17, 38 s. Surf and sea.

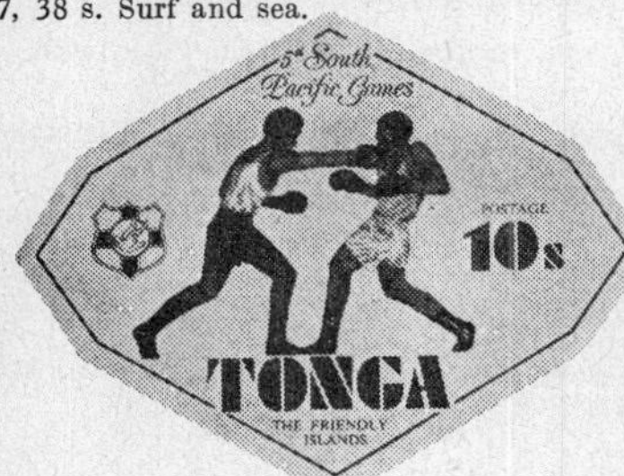

114. Boxing.
(Illustration reduced. Actual size 60 × 47 mm.)

1975. 5th South Pacific Games, Guam. Imperf. Self-adhesive.

No.	Description		
528. 114.	5s. multicoloured (post.)	10	10
529.	10 s. multicoloured ..	15	10
530.	20 s. multicoloured ..	25	20
531.	25 s. multicoloured ..	30	25
532.	65 s. multicoloured ..	70	75
533. –	9 s. multicoloured (air)	15	10
534. –	12 s. multicoloured ..	20	15
535. –	14 s. multicoloured ..	20	15
536. –	17 s. multicoloured ..	25	20
537. –	90 s. multicoloured ..	90	80

DESIGN: (37 × 43 mm.): Nos. 533/7, Throwing the discus.

115. Commemorative Coin.

1975. F.A.O. Commemoration. Imperf. Self-adhesive.

No.	Description		
538. 115.	5 s. mult. (postage) ..	10	10
539. –	20 s. multicoloured ..	30	15
540. –	50 s. blue, black & silver	65	35
541. –	1 p. blue, black & silver	1·25	75
542. –	2 p. black and silver ..	2·25	1·75
543. –	12 s. multicoloured (air)	25	15
544. –	14 s. multicoloured ..	25	15
545. –	25 s. red, black & silver	35	20
546. –	50 s. pur., black & silver	60	40
547. –	1 p. black and silver ..	1·25	75

DESIGNS: Nos. 539/47 are as T 52 but showing different coins. Nos. 542 and 544 are horiz., size 75 × 42 mm.

116. Commemorative Coin.
(Illustration reduced. Actual size 58 × 58 mm.)

1975. Centenary of Tongan Constitution. Multicoloured. Imperf. Self-adhesive.

No.	Description		
548.	5 s. Type 116 (postage) ..	10	10
549.	10 s. King George I ..	15	10
550.	20 s. King Taufa'ahau IV	30	20
551.	50 s. King George II ..	60	35
552.	75 s. Tongan arms ..	1·00	70
553.	9 s. King Taufa'ahau IV (air)	15	10
554.	12 s. Queen Salote ..	20	10
555.	14 s. Tongan arms ..	20	10
556.	38 s. King Taufa'ahau IV	40	25
557.	1 p. Four monarchs ..	1·25	70

SIZES: 60 × 40 mm., Nos. 549 and 551. 76 × 76 mm., Nos. 552 and 557. 57 × 56 mm., others.

117. Montreal Logo.

1976. First Participation in Olympic Games. Imperf. Self-adhesive.

(a). Type 117.

No.	Description		
558.	5 s. red, blk. & blue (postage)	15	10
559.	10 s. red, black and green	25	10
560.	25 s. red, black and brown	65	35
561.	35 s. red, black and mauve	75	40
562.	70 s. red, black and green	2·00	90

(b). Montreal logo optd. on Nos. 500/1, 504, 507.

No.	Description		
563. 111.	12 s. on 20 s. multicoloured (air) ..	30	15
564. –	14 s. on 16 s. mult. ..	30	15
565. –	16 s. multicoloured ..	35	15
566. 111.	38 s. on 40 s. mult. ..	1·00	45
567. –	75 s. multicoloured ..	2·25	95

118. Signatories of Declaration of Independence.

1976. Bicentenary of American Revolution. Imperf. Self-adhesive.

No.	Description		
568. 118.	9 s. multicoloured (postage)	40	15
569. –	10 s. multicoloured ..	40	15
570. –	15 s. multicoloured ..	70	35
571. –	25 s. multicoloured ..	1·25	60
572. –	75 s. multicoloured ..	3·75	1·75
573. –	12 s. multicoloured (air)	50	15
574. –	14 s. multicoloured ..	60	20
575. –	17 s. multicoloured ..	80	35
576. –	38 s. multicoloured ..	1·90	75
577. –	1 p. multicoloured ..	4·50	2·00

DESIGNS: Nos. 569/77 show the signatories to the Declaration of Independence.

119. Nathaniel Turner and John Thomas (Methodist Missionaries).

1976. 150th Anniv. of Christianity in Tonga. Imperf. Self-adhesive.

No.	Description		
578. 119.	5 s. mult. (postage) ..	20	15
579.	10 s. multicoloured ..	30	25
580.	20 s. multicoloured ..	50	40
581.	25 s. multicoloured ..	55	45
582.	85 s. multicoloured ..	2·25	1·90
583. –	9 s. multicoloured (air)	30	25
584. –	12 s. multicoloured ..	35	30
585. –	14 s. multicoloured ..	40	35
586. –	17 s. multicoloured ..	50	40
587. –	38 s. multicoloured ..	1·25	1·00

DESIGNS: Nos. 583/7 show Missionary Ship "Triton".

120. Emperor Wilhelm I and King George Tupou I.

1976. Centenary of Treaty of Friendship with Germany. Imperf. Self-adhesive.

No.	Description		
588. 120.	9 s. mult. (postage) ..	20	20
589.	15 s. multicoloured ..	30	30
590.	22 s. multicoloured ..	40	40
591.	50 s. multicoloured ..	90	90
592.	73 s. multicoloured ..	1·40	1·40
593. –	11 s. multicoloured (air)	25	25
594. –	17 s. multicoloured ..	40	40
595. –	18 s. multicoloured ..	40	40
596. –	31 s. multicoloured ..	60	60
597. –	39 s. multicoloured ..	70	70

DESIGNS—CIRCULAR: (52 mm. diameter). Nos. 593/7 show Treaty signing.

121. Queen Salote and Coronation Procession.

1977. Silver Jubilee. Imperf. Self-adhesive.

No.	Description		
598. 121.	11 s. mult. (postage) ..	1·50	30
599.	20 s. multicoloured ..	75	30
600.	30 s. multicoloured ..	1·00	30
601.	50 s. multicoloured ..	1·75	65
602.	75 s. multicoloured ..	2·25	85
603. –	15 s. multicoloured (air)	80	25
604. –	17 s. multicoloured ..	90	30
605. –	22 s. multicoloured ..	12·00	1·75
606. –	31 s. multicoloured ..	90	40
607. –	39 s. multicoloured ..	95	40

DESIGN—SQUARE: (59 × 59 mm.). Nos. 603/7 show Queen Elizabeth and King Taufa'ahau.

HAVE YOU READ THE NOTES AT THE BEGINNING OF THIS CATALOGUE?
These often provide answers to the enquiries we receive.

122. Tongan Coins.
(Illustration reduced. Actual size 53 × 48 mm.)

1977. 10th Anniv. of King's Coronation. Imperf. Self-adhesive.

No.	Description		
608. 122.	10 s. mult. (postage) ..	20	20
609.	15 s. multicoloured ..	25	25
610.	25 s. multicoloured ..	35	35
611.	50 s. multicoloured ..	75	75
612.	75 s. multicoloured ..	1·00	1·00
613. –	11 s. multicoloured (air)	25	20
614. –	17 s. multicoloured ..	30	30
615. –	18 s. multicoloured ..	30	30
616. –	39 s. multicoloured ..	45	45
617. –	1 p. multicoloured ..	1·50	1·50

DESIGN—OVAL: (64 × 46 mm.). Nos. 613/17 show 1967 Coronation Coin.

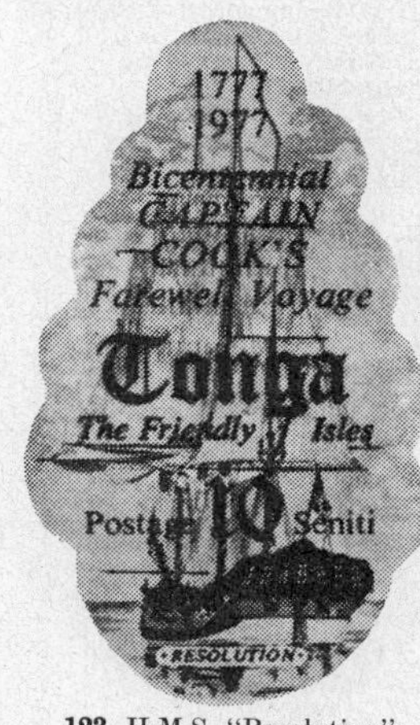

123. H.M.S. "Resolution".

1977. Bicentenary of Capt. Cook's Last Voyage. Imperf. Self-adhesive.

No.	Description		
618. 123.	10 s. mult. (postage) ..	1·40	60
619.	17 s. multicoloured ..	1·75	95
620.	25 s. multicoloured ..	3·00	1·75
621.	30 s. multicoloured ..	3·00	2·00
622.	40 s. multicoloured ..	3·75	2·50
623. –	15 s. multicoloured (air)	1·50	90
624. –	22 s. multicoloured ..	2·50	1·60
625. –	31 s. multicoloured ..	3·00	2·00
626. –	50 s. multicoloured ..	4·00	3·00
627. –	1 p. multicoloured ..	7·50	6·00

DESIGN: (52 × 46 mm.) Nos. 623/7 show Coin and extract from Cook's Journal.

124. Humpback Whale.
(Illustration reduced. Actual size 55 × 29 mm.)

1977. Whale Conservation. Imperf. Self-adhesive.

No.	Description		
628. 124.	15 s. black, grey and blue (postage)	1·00	40
629.	22 s. blk., grey and grn.	1·25	55
630.	31 s. blk., grey & orange	1·50	70
631.	38 s. blk., grey and lilac	2·00	95
632.	64 s. blk., grey and brn.	3·25	1·50
633. –	11 s. multicoloured (air)	1·00	35
634. –	17 s. multicoloured ..	1·25	50
635. –	18 s. multicoloured ..	1·25	50
636. –	39 s. multicoloured ..	2·00	1·00
637. –	50 s. multicoloured ..	2·75	1·40

DESIGN—HEXAGONAL: (66 × 51 mm.). Nos. 633/7 show Sei and Fin Whales.

1978. Various stamps surch.

No.	Description		
638. 115.	15 s. on 5 s. mult. (post.)	1·00	1·40
639. 119.	15 s. on 5 s. mult. ..	1·00	1·40
640. 117.	15 s. on 10 s. red, black and green	1·00	1·40
641. 119.	15 s. on 10 s. mult. ..	1·00	1·40
642. 121.	15 s. on 11 s. mult. ..	3·00	3·25
643. 114.	15 s. on 20 s. mult. ..	1·00	1·40
644. –	15 s. on 38 s. mult. (No. O 133)	1·00	1·40
645. –	17 s. on 9 s. mult. (No. 533) (air) ..	1·00	1·40
646. –	17 s. on 9 s. mult. (No. 583)	1·00	1·40
647. –	17 s. on 12 s. mult. (No. 534)	1·00	1·40
648. –	17 s. on 12 s. mult. (No. 573)	1·00	1·40
649. –	17 s. on 18 s. mult. (No. 595)	1·00	1·40

650. – 17 s. on 38 s. mult. (No. 527) .. .. .. 1·00 1·40
651. – 17 s. on 38 s. mult. (No. 556) .. .. .. 1·00 1·40
652. – 1 p. on 35 s. mult. (No. O 151) .. .. 24·00 24·00
653. – 1 p. on 38 s. mult. (No. 576) .. .. 6·50 8·00
654. – 1 p. on 75 s. mult. (No. 572) .. .. 6·50 8·00

The surcharges on Nos. 638/9 are formed by adding a "1" to the existing face value.

126. Flags of Canada and Tonga.

1978. 11th Commonwealth Games, Edmonton. Imperf. Self-adhesive.
655. 126. 10 s. blue, red and black (postage) 15 15
656. 15 s. multicoloured .. 25 25
657. 20 s. green, black & red 35 35
658. 25 s. red, blue and black 40 40
659. 45 s. black and red .. 90 90
660. – 17 s. black and red (air) 30 30
661. – 35 s. black, red and blue 60 60
662. – 38 s. black, red & green 75 75
663. – 40 s. black, red & green 80 80
664. – 65 s. black, red & brown 1·40 1·40
DESIGN—LEAF-SHAPED (39 × 40 mm.). Nos. 660/664, Maple Leaf.

127. King Taufa'ahau Tupou IV.

1978. 60th Birthday of King Taufa'ahau Tupou IV. Imperf. Self-adhesive.
665. 127. 2 s. black, deep blue and pale blue (postage) .. 10 10
666. 5 s. black, blue and pink 10 10
667. 10 s. blk., blue & mauve 20 20
668. 25 s. black, blue & grey 45 35
669. 75 s. black, blue & yell. 1·10 1·00
670. – 11 s. black, blue and yellow (air) 20 20
671. – 15 s. black, blue & brn. 30 25
672. – 17 s. black, blue & lilac 35 25
673. – 39 s. black, blue & green 60 55
674. – 1 p. black, blue & pink 1·75 1·40
DESIGNS—STAR-SHAPED (44 × 51 mm.). Nos. 670/674, Portrait of King.

128. Bananas.

1978. Coil Stamps. Imperf. Self-adhesive.
675. 128. 1 s. black and yellow .. 10 10
676. – 2 s. blue and yellow .. 10 10
677. – 3 s. brown and yellow .. 15 15
678. – 4 s. blue and yellow .. 15 15
679. – 5 s. red and yellow .. 15 15
680. – 6 s. pur., green & brown 20 20
681. – 7 s. blue, green & brown 30 30
682. – 8 s. red, green & brown 30 30
683. – 9 s. mve., green & brn. 30 30
684. – 10 j. green and brown .. 30 30
684a. – 13 s. mve., green & brn. 2·75 2·75
685. – 15 s. green and brown .. 50 50
686. – 20 s. brown and green .. 60 60
687. – 30 s. mve., brn. & grn. .. 70 70
688. – 50 s. blk., brn. and grn. 1·10 1·10
689. – 1 p. pur., brn. and grn. 1·90 1·90
689a. – 2 p. multicoloured .. 6·50 6·50
689b. – 3 p. multicoloured .. 8·50 8·50
DESIGNS—As Type 128. 2 s. to 5 s. Bananas, the number shown coinciding with the face value. 18 × 26 mm. 6 s. to 10 s. Coconuts. 17 × 30 mm. 13 s. to 1 p. Pineapples. 55 × 29 mm. 2 p., 3 p. Mixed fruit.

129. Humpback Whale.

1978. Endangered Wildlife. Multicoloured. Self-adhesive.
690. 15 s. Type 129 (postage) .. 70 30
691. 18 s. Insular Flying Fox .. 70 35
692. 25 s. Turtle 80 40
693. 28 s. Red Shining Parrot .. 90 50
694. 60 s. Type 129 .. .. 1·75 1·40
695. 17 s. Type 129 (air) .. 70 35
696. 22 s. As 18 s. 70 45
697. 31 s. As 25 s. 85 55
698. 39 s. As 28 s. .. .. 1·25 70
699. 45 s. As Type 129 .. .. 1·50 95

130. Metrication.

1979. Decade of Progress. Self-adhesive.
700. 130. 5 s. multicoloured (postage) 10 10
701. – 11 s. multicoloured .. 15 15
702. – 18 s. multicoloured .. 25 20
703. – 22 s. multicoloured .. 35 25
704. – 50 s. multicoloured .. 70 50
705. – 15 s. multicoloured (air) 20 20
706. – 17 s. multicloured .. 25 20
707. – 31 s. gold and blue .. 40 35
708. – 39 s. multicoloured .. 55 40
709. – 1 p. multicloured .. 1·40 1·25
DESIGNS:—VERT (58 × 55 mm.) 11 s., 17 s. Shipping routes. 22 s. New Churches. 50 s. 15 s. Air routes. 39 s. Government buildings. 1 p. Communications. TEAR-DROP, (35 × 52 mm.). 18 s. People building globe (U.S. Peace Corps). As Type 130. 31 s. Rotary International.

131. Various Envelopes bearing Self-adhesive Stamps.

1979. Death Centenary of Sir Rowland Hill and 10th Anniv of Tongan Self-adhesive Stamps. Self-adhesive.
710. 131. 5 s. multicoloured (post.) 10 10
711. 10 s. multicoloured .. 20 15
712. 25 s. multicoloured .. 55 35
713. 50 s. multicoloured .. 1·00 60
714. 1 p. multicoloured .. 2·00 1·25
715. – 15 s. multicoloured (air) 30 20
716. – 17 s. multicoloured .. 35 25
717. – 18 s. multicoloured .. 35 25
718. – 31 s. multicoloured .. 60 40
719. – 39 s. multicoloured .. 75 45
DESIGN—MULTI-ANGULAR (53 × 53 mm.). 15 s. to 39 s. Self-adhesive stamps.

132.

1979. Air. Coil stamps. Self-adhesive.
720. 132. 5 s. black and blue .. 15 15
721. 11 s. black and blue .. 25 25
722. 14 s. black and violet .. 25 25
723. 15 s. black and mauve 30 30
724. 17 s. black and mauve 30 30
725. 18 s. black and red .. 30 30
726. 22 s. black and red .. 35 35
726a. 29 s. black and red .. 3·50 3·75
727. 31 s. black and yellow .. 55 55
727a. 32 s. black and brown .. 4·00 4·50
728. 39 s. black and green .. 70 70
728a. 47 s. black and brown .. 5·00 5·50
729. 75 s. black and green .. 1·25 1·50
730. 1 p. black and green .. 1·75 2·00

133. Rain Forest, Island of Eua.

1979. Views as seen through the Lens of a Camera. Self-adhesive.
731. 133. 10 s. multicoloured (post.) 20 15
732. 18 s. multicoloured .. 25 25
733. 31 s. multicoloured .. 35 35
734. 50 s. multicoloured .. 60 45
735. 60 s. multicoloured .. 70 60
736. – 5 s. multicoloured (air) 10 10
737. – 15 s. multicoloured .. 25 20
738. – 17 s. multicoloured .. 25 25
739. – 39 s. multicoloured .. 50 40
740. – 75 s. multicoloured .. 80 75
DESIGN: 5 s. to 75 s. Isle of Kao.

134. King Tupou I, Admiral du Bouzet and Map of Tonga.

1979. 125th Anniv of France–Tonga Friendship Treaty. Self-adhesive.
741. 134. 7 s. multicoloured (post.) 10 12
742. 10 s. multicoloured .. 15 20
743. 14 s. multicoloured .. 20 25
744. 50 s. multicoloured .. 70 75
745. 75 s. multicoloured .. 1·00 1·10
746. – 15 s. multicoloured (air) 20 25
747. – 17 s. multicoloured .. 25 30
748. – 22 s. multicoloured .. 35 40
749. – 31 s. multicoloured .. 40 45
750. – 39 s. multicoloured .. 55 60
DESIGN: 15 s. to 39 s. King Tupou II, Napoleon III and "L'Aventure" (French warship).

1980. Olympic Games, Moscow. Nos. 710/19 surch. or optd. only (Nos. 753 and 755) **1980 OLYMPIC GAMES,** Olympic mascot and symbol.
751. 131. 13 s. on 5 s. multicoloured (postage) 30 30
752. – 20 s. on 10 s. multicoloured 40 40
753. – 25 s. multicoloured .. 45 45
754. – 33 s. on 50 s. multicoloured 55 55
755. – 1 p. multicoloured .. 2·00 2·00
756. – 9 s. on 15 s. multicoloured (air) 25 25
757. – 16 s. on 17 s. multicoloured 40 40
758. – 29 s. on 18 s. multicoloured 60 60
759. – 32 s. on 31 s. multicoloured 65 65
760. – 47 s. on 39 s. multicoloured 85 85

136. Scout at Camp-fire.
(Illustration reduced. Actual size 60 × 50 mm.)

1980. South Pacific Scout Jamboree, Tonga and 75th Anniv of Rotary International. Self-adhesive.
761. 136. 9 s. multicoloured (Postage) 30 15
762. 13 s. multicoloured .. 40 20
763. 15 s. multicoloured .. 40 20
764. 30 s. multicoloured .. 75 40
765. – 29 s. multicoloured (air) 75 45
766. – 32 s. multicoloured .. 80 45
767. – 47 s. multicoloured .. 1·10 70
768. – 1 p. multicoloured .. 2·00 1·25
DESIGN: 29 s. to 1 p. Scout activities and Rotary emblem.

1980. Various stamps surch.
769. 117. 9 s. on 35 s. red, black and mauve (postage) .. 30 30
770. 119. 13 s. on 20 s. multicoloured 45 45
771. 13 s. on 25 s. multicoloured 45 45
772. – 19 s. on 25 s. multicoloured (No. 571) 65 65
773. 114. 1 p. on 65 s. multicoloured 2·75 2·75
773a. – 5 p. on 25 s. multicoloured (No. O 213) .. .. 9·50 9·50
773b. – 5 p. on 2 p. multicoloured (No. O 214) .. .. 9·50 9·50
774. – 29 s. on 14 s. multicoloured (No. 585) (air) .. 80 80
775. – 29 s. on 39 s. multicoloured (No. 597) 80 80
776. – 32 s. on 12 s. multicoloured (No. 554) 95 95
777. – 32 s. on 14 s. multicoloured (No. 574) 95 95
778. – 47 s. on 12 s. multicoloured (No. 524) .. .. 1·40 1·40
779. – 47 s. on 12 s. multicoloured (No. 584) .. .. 1·40 1·40

138. Red Cross and Tongan Flags, with Map of Tonga.

1981. International Year for Disabled Persons. Self-adhesive.
780. 138. 2 p. multicoloured (postage) .. .. 1·50 1·00
781. 3 p. multicoloured .. 1·75 1·25
782. – 29 s. multicoloured (air) 30 20
783. – 32 s. multicoloured .. 35 25
784. – 47 s. multicoloured .. 45 30
DESIGN: Nos. 782/4, Red Cross Flag and Map depicting Tongatapu and Eua.

139. Prince Charles and King Taufa'ahau Tupou IV.

1981. Royal Wedding and Centenary of Treaty of Friendship between Tonga and Great Britain. Multicoloured. Self-adhesive.
785. 13 s. Type 139 .. .. 30 20
786. 47 s. Prince Charles and Lady Diana Spencer .. 45 30
787. 1 p. 50 Prince Charles and Lady Diana (different) 1·10 90
788. 3 p. Prince and Princess of Wales after wedding ceremony .. .. 2·00 1·40

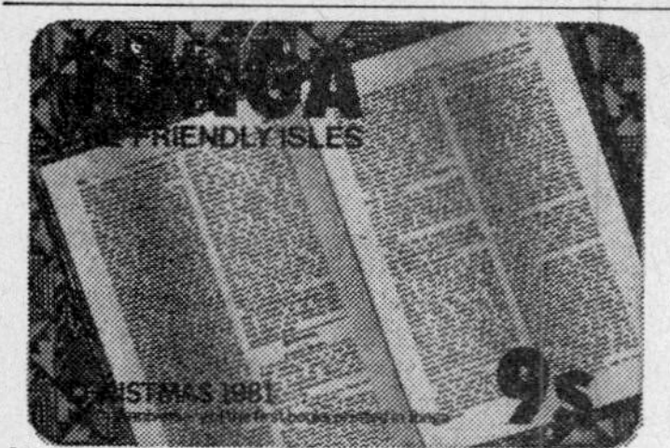

140. Report of Printing in Missionary Notices.

1981. Christmas. 150th Anniv of First Books Printed in Tonga. Multicoloured. Self-adhesive.

789. 9 s. Type **140** 25 15
790. 13 s. Missionary Notice report (different) .. 30 20
791. 32 s. Type in chase .. 75 40
792. 47 s. Bible class .. .. 1·25 70

141. Landing Scene.

1981. Bicentenary of Maurell's Discovery of Vava'u. Multicoloured. Self-adhesive.

793. 9 s. Type **141** 30 20
794. 13 s. Map of Vava'u .. 50 25
795. 47 s. "La Princesa" .. 2·00 1·25
796. 1 p. "La Princesa" (different) .. .. 4·50 3·00

142. Battle Scene.

1981. 175th Anniv of Capture of "Port au Prince" (ship). Each black and blue. Self-adhesive.

798. 29 s. Type **142** 45 25
799. 32 s. Battle scene (different) 50 30
800. 47 s. Map of the Ha'Apai Group 60 50
801. 47 s. Native canoes preparing to attack .. 60 50
802. 1 p. "Port au Prince" .. 1·25 75

143. Baden Powell at Brownsea Island, 1907.

1982. 75th Anniv of Boy Scout Movement and 125th Birth Anniv of Lord Baden-Powell (founder). Multicoloured. Self-adhesive.

803. 29 s. Type **143** 45 30
804. 32 s. Baden-Powell on his charger "Black Prince" 55 35
805. 47 s. Baden-Powell at Imperial Jamboree, 1924 75 45
806. 1 p. 50 Cover of first "Scouting for Boys" journal .. 1·90 1·25
807. 2 p. 50 Newsboy, 1900 and Mafeking Siege 3d. stamp 3·75 2·75

1982. No. 788 optd. **CYCLONE RELIEF T$1+50s POSTAGE & RELIEF.**

808. 1 p.+50 s. on 3 p. Prince and Princess of Wales after wedding ceremony 1·50 1·60

145. Ball Control.

1982. World Cup Football Championship, Spain. Multicoloured. Self-adhesive.

809. 32s. Type **145** 45 45
810. 47 s. Goalkeeping 60 60
811. 75 s. Heading .. .. 1·00 95
812. $1.50 Shooting .. .. 1·75 1·75

146. M.V. "Olovaha II".

1982. Inter-Island Transport. Multicoloured. Self-adhesive.

813. 9 s. Type **146** 10 10
814. 13 s. Type **146** 15 15
815. 47 s. SPIA "Twin Otter" 55 60
816. 1 p. As 47 s. .. .. 1·25 1·40

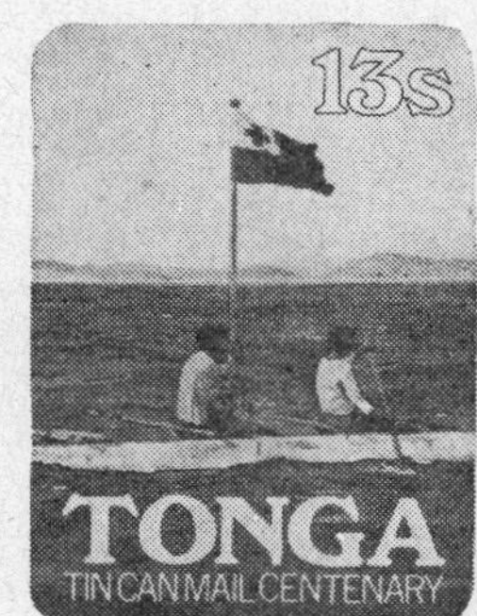

147. Mail Canoe.

1982. Centenary of Tin Can Mail. Self-adhesive.

817. **147.** 13 s. multicoloured .. 15 15
818. – 32 s. multicoloured .. 25 25
819. – 47 s. multicoloured .. 35 35
820. – 2 p. black and green .. 1·40 1·40

DESIGNS: 32 s. Mail canoe and ship. 47 s. Collecting Tin Can Mail. 2 p. Map of Niua Fo'ou.

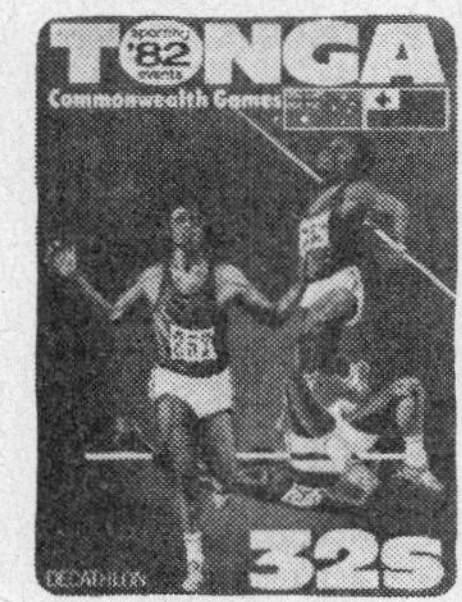

148. Decathlon.

1982. Commonwealth Games, Brisbane. Multicoloured. Self-adhesive.

823. 32 s. Type **148** 50 30
824. $1.50 Tongan Police band at opening ceremony (horiz.) .. .. .. 2·75 1·50

149. Pupils.

1982. Centenary of Tonga College. Multicoloured. Self-adhesive.

825. 5 s. Type **149** (Tongan inscription) .. 25 10
826. 5 s. Type **149** (Ringlish inscription) 25 10
827. 29 s. School crest and monument (Tongan incsr.) (29×22 mm.) .. 85 65
828. 29 s. As No. 827 but inscr. in English .. 85 65
829. 29 s. King George Tupou I (founder) and school (Tongan inscr.) (29×22 mm.) 85 65
830. 29 s. As No. 829 but inscr. at English 85 65

1982. Christmas. Nos. 817/9 optd. with **Christmas Greetings 1982.**

831. 13 s. Type **147** 15 15
832. 32 s. Mail boat and ship .. 35 35
833. 47 s. Collecting Tin Can Mail 40 50

151. H.M.S. "Resolution" and S.S. "Canberra".

1983. Sea and Air Transport. Multicoloured. Self-adhesive.

834. 29 s. Type **151** 75 75
835. 32 s. Type **151** 85 85
836. 47 s. Montgolfier's balloon and "Concorde" .. 1·50 1·50
837. 1 p. 50 As No. 836 .. .. 2·75 2·75

152. Globe and Inset of Tonga.

1983. Commonwealth Day. Multicoloured. Self-adhesive.

839. 29 s. Type **152** 35 30
840. 32 s. Tongan dancers .. 6·00 2·00
841. 47 s. Trawler 50 50
842. 1 p. 50 King Taufa'ahau Tupou IV and flag .. 1·75 1·75

153. SPIA "DH Twin Otter".

1983. Inauguration of Niuafo'ou Airport. Multicoloured. Self-adhesive.

843. 32 s. Type **153** 20 20
844. 47 s. Type **153** 25 25
845. 1 p. SPIA Boeing "707" 60 70
846. 1 p. 50 As No. 845 .. .. 80 1·25

154. "Intelsat IV" satellite.

1983. World Communications Year. Multicoloured. Self-adhesive.

847. 29 s. Type **154** 20 20
848. 32 s. "Intelsat IVA" satellite 25 25
849. 75 s. "Intelsat V" satellite 50 50
850. 2 p. Moon post cover (45×32 mm.) .. .. 1·10 1·40

155. Obverse and reverse of 1 p. Banknote.

1983. 10th Anniv of Bank of Tonga. Self-adhesive.

851. **155.** 1 p. multicoloured .. 60 65
852. 2 p. multicoloured .. 1·10 1·25

156. Early Printing Press.

1983. Printing in Tonga. Multicoloured. Self-adhesive.

853. 13 s. Type **156** 15 15
854. 32 s. Arrival of W. Woon .. 25 25
855. 1 p. Early Tongan print .. 50 60
856. 2 p. "The Tonga Chronicle" 90 1·25

157. Yacht off Coast.

1983. Christmas. Yachting off Vava'u. Multicoloured. Self-adhesive.

857. 29 s. Type **157** 25 25
858. 32 s. View of yacht from cave 25 25
859. 1 p. 50 Anchored yacht .. 80 1·00
860. 2 p. 50 Yacht off coast (different) .. .. 1·25 1·50

158. Abel Tasman and "Zeehan".

1984. Navigators and Explorers of the Pacific (1st series). Self-adhesive.

861. **158.** 32 s. green and black .. 80 80
862. – 47 s. violet and black 1·25 1·25
863. – 90 s. brown and black 2·00 2·00
864. – 1 p. 50 blue and black 3·00 3·00

DESIGNS: 47 s. Capt. Samuel Wallis and H.M.S. "Dolphin". 90 s. Capt. William Bligh and H.M.S. "Bounty". 1 p. 50, Capt. James Cook and H.M.S. "Resolution".

See also 896/9.

159. "Swainsonia casta". 160. Printer checking Newspaper.

1984. Marine Life. Multicoloured. Self-adhesive.

865. 1 s. Type **159** 15 15
866. 2 s. "Porites sp" 25 25
867. 3 s. "Holocentrus ruber" .. 30 30
868. 5 s. "Cypraea mappa viridis" 30 30
869. 6 s. "Dardanus megistos" (crab) 35 35
870. 9 s. "Stegostoma fasciatum" 35 35
871. 10 s. "Conus bullatus" .. 45 45
872. 13 s. "Pterois volitans" .. 45 45
873. 15 s. "Conus textile" .. 50 50
874. 20 s. "Dascyllus aruanus"
875. 29 s. "Conus aulicus" .. 60 60
876. 32 s. "Acanthurus 70 70
leucosternon" .. ..
877. 47 s. "Lambis truncata" .. 80 80
878. 1 p. "Millepora 1·10 1·10
dichotama" .. .. 2·50 2·50
879. 2 p. "Biggus latro" (crab)
880. 3 p. "Chicoreus palma- 4·00 4·00
rosea" .. .. 5·00 5·00
881. 5 p. "Thunnus albacares" 7·50 7·50

Nos. 878/81 are horizontal, 38×23 mm.

For these designs with normal perforations and gum see Nos. 999/1017 and 1087/95.

1984. 20th Anniv of "Tonga Chronicle" (newspaper). Self-adhesive.

882. **160.** 3 s. brown and blue .. 10 10
883. 32 s. brown and red .. 40 45

161. U.S.A. Flag and Running.

1984. Olympic Games, Los Angeles. Each in black, red and blue. Self-adhesive.

884. 29 s. Type **161** 25 25
885. 47 s. Javelin-throwing .. 30 30
886. 1 p. 50 Shot-putting .. 85 85
887. 3 p. Olympic torch .. 1·60 1·60

162. Sir George Airy and Dateline on World Map.

1984. Centenary of International Dateline. Multicoloured. Self-adhesive.

888. 47 s. Type **162** 75 75
889. 2 p. Sir Sandford Fleming and Map of Pacific time zones .. .. .. 3·00 3·25

163. Australia 1914 Kookaburra 6d. Stamp.

1984. "Ausipex" International Stamp Exhibition, Melbourne. Multicoloured. Self-adhesive.

890. 32 s. Type **163** 60 60
891. 1 p. 50 Tonga 1897 Parrot 2s. 6d. stamp .. .. 2·25 2·25

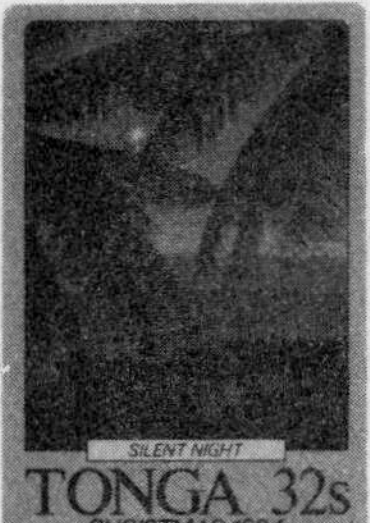

164. Beach at Sunset ("Silent Night").

1984. Christmas. Carols. Mult. Self-adhesive.

893. 32 s. Type **164** 40 45
894. 47 s. Hut and palm trees ("Away in a Manger") .. 60 65
895. 1 p. Sailing boats ("I Saw Three Ships") .. .. 1·25 1·40

1985. Navigators and Explorers of the Pacific (2nd series). As T **158**. Self-adhesive.

896. 32 s. black and blue .. 90 55
897. 47 s. black and green .. 1·25 75
898. 90 s. black and red .. 2·25 1·75
899. 1 p. 50 black and brown .. 3·25 2·50

DESIGNS: 32 s. Willem Schouten and "Eendracht". 47 s. Jacob Le Maire and "Hoorn". 90 s. Fletcher Christian and "Bounty". 1 p. 50 Francisco Maurelle and "La Princessa".

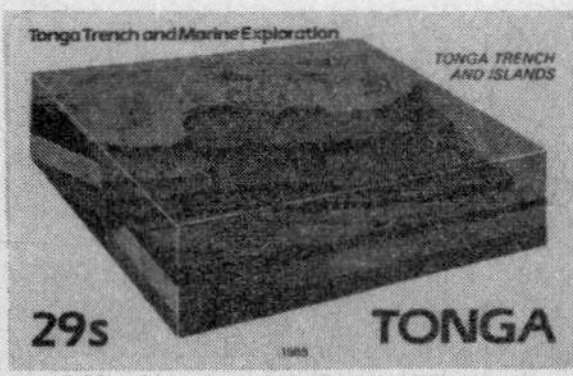

165. Section of Tonga Trench.

1985. Geological Survey of the Tonga Trench. Multicoloured. Self-adhesive.

900. 29 s. Type **165** .. .. 1·00 1·00
901. 32 s. Diagram of marine seismic survey .. .. 1·00 1·00
902. 47 s. Diagram of aerial oil survey (vert.) .. .. 1·25 1·25
903. 1 p. 50, Diagram of sea bed survey (vert.) .. .. 3·00 3·00

166. "Port au Prince" at Gravesend, 1805.

1985. 175th Anniv of Will Mariner's Departure for England. Multicoloured. Self-adhesive.

905. 29 s. Type **166** 30 35
906. 32 s. Capture of "Port au Prince", Tonga, 1806 .. 30 35
907. 47 s. Will Mariner on Tongan canoe, 1807 .. 45 50
908. 1 p. 50 Mariner boarding brig "Favourite", 1810 .. 1·40 1·50
909. 2 p. 50 "Cuffnells" in English Channel, 1811 .. 2·40 2·50

167. Quintal (Byron Russell) and Captain Bligh (Charles Laughton).

1985. 50th Anniv of Film "Mutiny on the Bounty". Multicoloured. Self-adhesive.

910. 47 s. Type **167** .. .. 1·75 1·75
911. 47 s. Captain Bligh and prisoners .. .. .. 1·75 1·75
912. 47 s. Fletcher Christian (Clark Gable) .. .. 1·75 1·75
913. 47 s. Mutineers threatening Bligh .. .. .. 1·75 1·75
914. 47 s. Bligh and Roger Byam (Franchot Tone) in boat .. .. .. 1·75 1·75

168. Lady Elizabeth Bowes-Lyon, 1910.

1985. Life and Times of Queen Elizabeth the Queen Mother and 75th Anniv of Girl Guide Movement. Self-adhesive.

915. **168.** 32 s. black, pink and brown 30 35
916. – 47 s. black, lilac and brown 45 50
917. – 1 p. 50 black, yellow and brown .. .. 1·40 1·50
918. – 2 p. 50 multicoloured 2·40 2·50

DESIGNS: 47 s. Duchess of York at Hadfield Girl Guides' Rally, 1931. 1 p. 50 Duchess of York in Girl Guide uniform. 2 p. 50 Queen Mother in 1985 (from photo by Norman Parkinson).

169. Mary and Joseph arriving at Inn.

1985. Christmas. Mult. Self-adhesive.

919. 32 s. Type **169** 25 30
920. 42 s. The shepherds .. 35 40
921. 1 p. 50 The Three Wise Men .. .. .. 1·25 1·40
922. 2 p. 50 The Holy Family .. 2·10 2·25

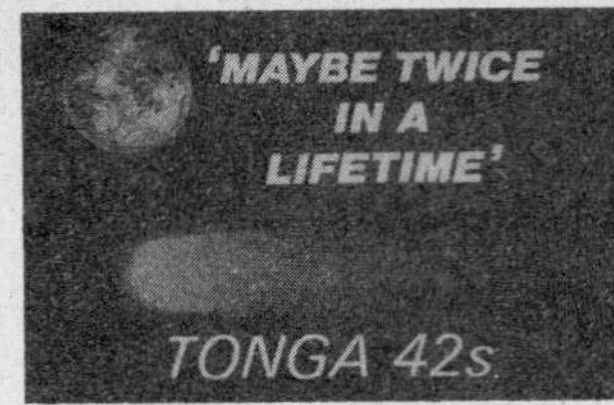

170. Comet and Slogan "Maybe Twice in a Lifetime".

1986. Appearance of Halley's Comet. Multicoloured.

923. 42 s. Type **170** 80 80
924. 42 s. Edmond Halley .. 80 80
925. 42 s. Solar System .. 80 80
926. 42 s. Telescope 80 80
927. 42 s. "Giotto" spacecraft .. 80 80
928. 57 s. Type **170** 90 90
929. 57 s. As No. 924 .. .. 90 90
930. 57 s. As No. 925 .. .. 90 90
931. 57 s. As No. 926 .. .. 90 90
932. 57 s. As No. 927 .. .. 90 90

Nos. 923/7 and 928/32 were each printed together, se-tenant, forming composite designs.

1986. Nos. 866/7, 869/70, 872, 874, 879 and 881 surch.

933. 4 s. on 2 s. "Porites sp." .. 10 10
934. 4 s. on 13 s. "Pterois volitans" 10 10
935. 42 s. on 3 s. "Holocentrus ruber" 30 35
936. 42 s. on 9 s. "Stegostoma fasciatum" 30 35
937. 57 s. on 6 s. "Dardanus megistos" 40 45
938. 57 s. on 20 s. "Dascyllus aruanus" 40 45
939. 2 p. 50 on 2 p. "Birgus latro" .. .. .. 2·10 2·25
940. 2 p. 50 on 5 p. "Thunnus albacares" .. .. 2·10 2·25

172. King Taufa 'ahau Tupou IV of Tonga.

1986. Royal Links with Great Britain and 60th Birthday of Queen Elizabeth II.

941. **172.** 57 s. multicoloured .. 65 65
942. – 57 s. multicoloured .. 65 65
943. – 2 p. 50 brown, black and blue .. .. 2·25 2·50

DESIGNS—HORIZ (as T **172**). No. 942, Queen Elizabeth II. Square (40 × 40 mm.). No. 943, Queen Elizabeth II and King Taufa'ahau Tupou IV, Tonga, 1970.

173. Peace Corps Nurse giving Injection.

1986. "Ameripex '86" International Stamps Exhibition, Chicago. 25th Anniv. of United States Peace Corps. Multicoloured.

944. 57 s. Type **173** 45 50
945. 1 p. 50 Peace Corps teacher and pupil .. .. 1·25 1·40

174. Hockey.

1986. Sporting Events. Multicoloured.

947. 42 s. Type **174** (World Hockey Cup for Men, London) 65 65
948. 57 s. Handball (13th Commonwealth Games, Edinburgh 75 75
949. 1 p. Boxing (13th Commonwealth Games, Edinburgh) .. .. 1·40 1·40
950. 2 p. 50 Football (World Cup Football Championship, Mexico) .. .. 3·50 3·50

175. 1886 1 d. King George I Definitive.

1986. Cent of First Tonga Stamps. Mult.

951 32 s. Type **175** 65 65
952 42 s. 1897 7½d. King George II inverted centre error 80 80
953 57 s. 1950 Queen Salote's 50th Birthday 1d. .. 1·00 1·00
954 2 p. 50 1986 Royal Links with Great Britain 2p. 50 3·00 3·00

176. Girls wearing Shell Jewellery.

1986. Christmas. Multicoloured.

956. 32 s. Type **176** 50 45
957. 42 s. Boy with wood carvings (vert.) 70 60
958. 57 s. Children performing traditional dance (vert.) 85 75
959. 2 p. Children in dugout canoe .. .. .. 2·75 3·00

1986. Scout Jamboree, Tongatapu. Nos. 957/8 optd. **BOY SCOUT JAMBOREE 5th–10th DEC '86.**

960. 42 s. Boy with wood carvings (vert.) .. .. 1·25 1·25
961. 57 s. Children performing traditional dance (vert.) 1·75 1·75

178. Dumont D'Urville and "L'Astrolabe".

1987. 150th Anniv. of Dumont D'Urville's Second Voyage. Multicoloured.

962. 32 s. Type **178** .. .. 1·10 1·10
963. 42 s. Tongan girls (from "Voyage au Pole et dans l'Oceanie") .. .. 1·40 1·40
964. 1 p. Contemporary chart .. 2·75 2·75
965. 2 p. 50 Wreck of "L'Astrolabe" .. .. 5·00 5·00

180. Two Paddlers in Canoe.

181. King Taufa'ahau Tupou IV.

1987. "Siv'a'alo" (Tonga–Fiji–Samoa) Canoe Race. Multicoloured.

967. 32 s. Type **180** 25 30
968. 42 s. Five paddlers 35 40
969. 57 s. Paddlers and canoe bow 45 50
970. 1 p. 50 Two paddlers (different) .. .. 1·10 1·25

1987. 20th Anniv. of Coronation of King Taufa'ahau Tupou IV. Self-adhesive.

972. **181.** 1 s. black and green .. 10 10
972d. 2 s. black and orange 10 10
973. 5 s. black and mauve 10 10
974. 10 s. black and lilac .. 10 10
975. 15 s. black and red .. 15 20
976. 32 s. black and blue .. 30 35

182. Arms and Tongan Citizens.

1987. 125th Anniv. of 1st Parliament.

977. **182.** 32 s. multicoloured .. 25 30
978. 42 s. multicoloured .. 35 40
979. 75 s. multicoloured .. 60 65
980. 2 p. multicoloured .. 1·60 1·75

183 Father Christmas Octopus and Rat with Sack of Presents

1987. Christmas. Cartoons. Multicoloured.

981 42 s. Type **183** 40 45
982 57 s. Delivering presents by outrigger canoe .. 60 65
983 1 p. Delivering presents by motorized tricycle .. 95 1·00
984 3 p. Drinking cocktails .. 2·75 3·00

184 King Taufa'ahau Tupou IV "Olovaha" (inter-island ferry), Oil Rig and Pole Vaulting
(Illustration reduced, actual size 59 × 43mm)

1988. 70th Birthday of King Taufa'ahau Tupou IV. Designs each show portrait. Mult.

985 32 s. Type **184** 30 35
986 42 s. Banknote, coins, Ha'amonga Trilithon and woodcarver .. 40 45
987 57 s. Rowing, communications satellite and Red Cross worker 60 65
988 2 p.50 Scout emblem, 1982 47 s. Scout stamp and Friendly Island Airways aircraft .. .. 2·40 2·50

See also Nos. 1082/5.

186 Athletics

1988. Olympic Games, Seoul. Multicoloured.

990 57 s. Type **186** 60 65
991 75 s. Yachting 70 75
992 2 p. Cycling .. .. 1·90 2·00
993 3 p. Tennis .. .. 2·75 3·00

187 Traditional Tongan Fale

1988. Music in Tonga. Multicoloured.

994 32 s. Type **187** 30 35
995 42 s. Church choir .. 40 45
996 57 s. Tonga Police Band outside Royal Palace .. 55 60
997 2 p.50 "The Jets" pop group .. .. .. 2·40 2·50

1988. Redrawn designs as Nos. 865/6, 868/9, 871/6 and 879/881 (some with altered values), and new values or designs, all with normal gum and perforations. Multicoloured.

999 1 s. Type **159** 10 10
1000 2 s. "Porites sp" .. 10 10
1001 4 s. "Pterois volitans" 10 10
1002 5 s. "Cypraea mappa viridis" 10 10
1003 6 s. "Dardanus megistos" (crab) 10 10
1004 7 s. Wandering albatross 10 10
1005 10 s. "Conus bullatus" .. 10 10
1006 15 s. "Conus textile" .. 15 20
1007 20 s. "Dascyllus aruanus" 20 25
1008 32 s. "Acanthurus leucosternon" 35 30
1009 35 s. Sea horse 35 30
1010 42 s. Lesser frigate bird .. 35 40
1011 50 s. "Conus aulicus" .. 40 45
1012 57 s. Brown booby .. 50 55
1013 1 p. "Chelonia mydas" (turtle) 90 95
1014 1 p. 50 Humpback whale 1·40 1·50
1015 2 p. "Birgus latro" (crab) 1·90 2·00
1016 3 p. "Chicoreus palma-rosae" .. .. 2·75 3·00
1017 5 p. "Thunnus albacares" 4·50 4·75
1017a 10 p. "Stegostoma fasciatum" .. .. 9·25 9·50

Nos. 1013/17, are horizontal, 41 × 22 mm, and No. 1017a vertical 26 × 41 mm.

For smaller designs, 19 × 22 mm, see Nos. 1087/95 .

188 Capt. Cook's H.M.S. "Resolution"

1988. Centenary of Tonga–U.S.A. Treaty of Friendship. Multicoloured.

1018 42 s. Type **188** 40 45
1019 57 s. "Santa Maria" .. 55 60
1020 2 p. Capt. Cook and Christopher Columbus 1·90 2·00

190 Girl in Hospital Bed

1988. Christmas. 125th Anniv of International Red Cross and 25th Anniv of Tongan Red Cross. Multicoloured.

1022 15 s. Type **190** (A) .. 15 20
1023 15 s. Type **190** (B) .. 15 20
1024 32 s. Red Cross nurse reading to young boy (A) 30 35
1025 32 s. Red Cross nurse reading to young boy (B) 30 35
1026 42 s. Red Cross nurse taking pulse (A) .. 40 45
1027 42 s. Red Cross nurse taking pulse (B) .. 40 45
1028 57 s. Red Cross nurse with sleeping child (A) .. 55 60
1029 57 s. Red Cross nurse with sleeping child (B) .. 55 60
1030 1 p. 50 Boy in wheelchair (A) .. .. .. 1·40 1·50
1031 1 p. 50 Boy in wheelchair (B) .. .. .. 1·40 1·50

Nos. 1022/3, 1024/5, 1026/7, 1028/9 and 1030/1 were printed together, se-tenant, in horizontal pairs throughout the sheets with the first stamp in each pair inscribed "INTERNATIONAL RED CROSS 125th ANNIVERSARY" (A) and the second "SILVER JUBILEE OF TONGAN RED CROSS" (B).

191 Map of Tofua Island and Breadfruit

1989. Bicent of Mutiny on the "Bounty". Multicoloured.

1032 32 s. Type **191** 60 60
1033 42 s. H.M.S. "Bounty" and chronometer .. 80 80
1034 57 s. Captain Bligh and "Bounty's" launch cast adrift .. .. .. 1·25 1·25

192 "Hypolimnas bolina"

1989. Butterflies. Multicoloured.

1036 42 s. Type **192** 70 70
1037 57 s. "Jamides bochus" .. 90 90
1038 1 p. 20, "Melanitis leda solandra" .. .. 1·50 1·50
1039 2 p. 50 "Danaus plexippus" .. .. 3·50 3·50

193 Football at Rugby School, 1870

1989. Inauguration of National Sports Stadium and South Pacific Mini Games, Tonga. Designs showing development of rugby, tennis and cricket. Multicoloured.

1040 32 s. Type **193** 30 35
1041 32 s. D. Gallaher (All Black's captain, 1905) and Springboks rugby match, 1906 .. .. 30 35
1042 32 s. King George V with Cambridge team, 1922 and W. Wakefield (England captain, 1926) 30 35
1043 32 s. E. Crawford (Ireland captain, 1926) and players on cigarette cards 30 35
1044 32 s. S. Mafi (Tonga captain, 1970's) and modern rugby match .. 30 35
1045 42 s. Royal tennis, 1659 .. 40 45
1046 42 s. Major Wingfield and lawn tennis, 1873 .. 40 45
1047 42 s. Oxford and Cambridge tennis teams, 1884 .. .. 40 45
1048 42 s. Bunny Ryan, 1910, and players on cigarette cards 40 45
1049 42 s. Boris Becker and modern tennis match .. 40 45
1050 57 s. Cricket match, 1743, and F. Pilch memorial 55 60
1051 57 s. W. G. Grace (19th-century cricketer) .. 55 60
1052 57 s. "Boys Own Paper" cricket article, 1909 .. 55 60
1053 57 s. Australian cricket team, 1909, and players on cigarette cards .. 55 60
1054 57 s. The Ashes urn, and modern cricket match 55 60

194 Short "S30" Flying Boat, 1939 (50th anniv of first flight)

1989. Aviation in Tonga. Multicoloured.

1055 42 s. Type **194** 80 80
1056 57 s. Vought "F4U Corsair", 1943 .. .. 1·25 1·25
1057 90 s. Boeing "737" at Fua'amotu Airport .. 1·75 1·75
1058 3 p. Montgolfier balloon, Wright biplane, "Concorde" and space shuttle (97 × 26 mm) .. 5·50 5·50

195 Aircraft landing

1989. Christmas. "Flying Home".

1059 **195** 32 s. grn, brn & orge 50 50
1060 – 42 s. grn, brn & lt grn 60 60
1061 – 57 s. green, brn & red 80 80
1062 – 3 p. green, brn & mve 3·75 3·75

DESIGNS: 42 s. Villagers waving to aircraft; 57 s. Outrigger canoe and aircraft; 3 p. Aircraft over headland.

197 1989 U.P.U. Congress Stamps

1989. "World Stamp Expo '89" International Stamp Exhibition, Washington.

1064 **197** 57 s. multicoloured .. 85 85

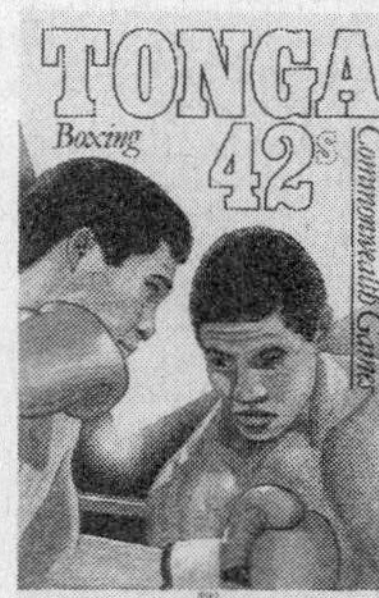

198 Boxing

1990. 14th Commonwealth Games, Auckland. Multicoloured.

1065 42 s. Type **198** 70 70
1066 57 s. Archery 85 85
1067 1 p. Bowls .. .. 1·40 1·40
1068 2 p. Swimming .. .. 2·50 2·50

MINIMUM PRICE

The minimum price quoted is 10p which represents a handling charge rather than a basis for valuing common stamps. For further notes about prices see introductory pages.

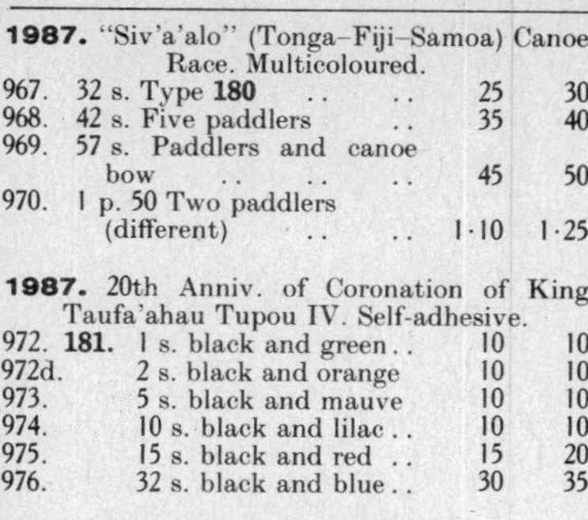

199 Wave Power Installation

1990. Alternative Sources of Electricity. Multicoloured.

1069 32 s. Type **199** 50 50
1070 57 s. Wind farm 85 85
1071 1 p. 20 Experimental solar cell vehicle 2·00 2·00

200 Penny Black

1990. 150th Anniv of the Penny Black.

1073 **200** 42 s. multicoloured 70 70
1074 – 42 s. multicoloured 70 70
1075 – 57 s. red and black 85 85
1076 – 1 p. 50 multicoloured 2·00 2·00
1077 – 2 p. 50 multicoloured 3·50 3·50

DESIGNS: 42 s. (1074) Great Britain 1840 Twopence Blue; 57 s. Tonga 1886 1d.; 1 p. 50, 1980 South Pacific Scout Jamboree and Rotary 75th anniv 2 p. official stamp; 2 p. 50, 1990 Alternative Sources of Electricity 57 s.

201 Departure of Canoe

1990. Polynesian Voyages of Discovery.

1078 **201** 32 s. green 55 55
1079 – 42 s. blue 80 80
1080 – 1 p. 20 brown 2·25 2·25
1081 – 3 p. violet 4·75 4·75

DESIGNS: 42 s. Navigating by night; 1 p. 20, Canoe and sea birds; 3 p. Landfall.

1990. Silver Jubilee of King Taufa'ahau Tupou IV. As Nos. 985/8, but inscr "Silver Jubilee of His Majesty King Taufa'ahau Tupou IV. 1965–1990" and with "TONGA" and values in silver.

1082 32 s. Type **184** 30 30
1083 42 s. Banknote, coins, Ha'amonga Trilithon and woodcarver 40 40
1084 57 s. Rowing, communications satellite and Red Cross worker 55 55
1085 2 p. 50 Scout emblem, 1982 47 s. Scout stamp and Friendly Island Airways aircraft 2·50 2·50

1990. As Nos. 1000, 1002, 1003 (value changed), 1005 and 1008 redrawn smaller, 19×22 mm. Multicoloured.

1087 2 s. "Porites sp." 10 10
1089 5 s. "Cypraea mappa viridis" 10 10
1092 10s. "Conus bullatus" 10 10
1093 15 s. "Dardanus megistos" (crab) 15 20
1095 32 s. "Acanthurus leucosternon" 30 35

202 Iguana searching for Food

1990. Endangered Species. Banded Iguana. Multicoloured.

1105 32 s. Type **202** 35 35
1106 42 s. Head of male 45 45
1107 57 s. Pair of iguanas during courtship 60 60
1108 1 p. 20 Iguana basking 1·40 1·40

203 Tourism

1990. 40th Anniv of United Nations Development Programme. Multicoloured.

1109 57 s. Type **203** 70 70
1110 57 s. Agriculture and Fisheries 70 70
1111 3 p. Education 3·25 3·25
1112 3 p. Healthcare 3·25 3·25

204 Boy

1990. Christmas. Rotary International Interact Project. Multicoloured.

1113 32 s. Type **204** 40 40
1114 42 s. Young boys 55 55
1115 2 p. Girls in western clothes 2·25 2·25
1116 3 p. Girls in traditional costumes 3·50 3·50

205 Safety at Work

1991. Accident Prevention. Multicoloured.

1117 32 s. Type **205** (English inscription) 30 35
1118 32 s. Safety at home (English inscription) 30 35
1119 32 s. As No. 1118 (Tongan inscription) 30 35
1120 32 s. As Type **205** (Tongan inscription) 30 35
1121 42 s. Safety in cars (English inscription) 40 45
1122 42 s. Safety on bikes (English inscription) 40 45
1123 42 s. As No. 1122 (Tongan inscription) 40 45
1124 42 s. As No. 1121 (Tongan inscription) 40 45
1125 57 s. Safety at sea (English inscription) 50 55
1126 57 s. Safety on the beach (English inscription) 50 55
1127 57 s. As No. 1126 (Tongan inscription) 50 55
1128 57 s. As No. 1125 (Tongan inscription) 50 55

207 Fishes in the Sea

1991. Heilala Week. Multicoloured.

1130 42 s. Type **207** 40 45
1131 57 s. Island and yacht 50 55
1132 2 p. Pile of fruit 1·90 2·00
1133 3 p. Turtle on beach 2·75 3·00

208 Tonga Temple

1991. Centenary of Church of Latter Day Saints in Tonga. Multicoloured.

1134 42 s. Type **208** 40 45
1135 57 s. Temple at night 50 55

209 Making T.V. Childcare Programme

1991. Telecommunications in Tonga. Mult.

1136 15 s. Type **209** 15 20
1137 15 s. T.V. satellite 15 20
1138 15 s. Mothers watching programme 15 20
1139 32 s. Man on telephone and woman with computer 30 35
1140 32 s. Telecommunications satellite 30 35
1141 32 s. Overseas customer on telephone 30 35
1142 42 s. Sinking ship 40 45
1143 42 s. Coastguard controller 40 45
1144 42 s. Maritime rescue 40 45
1145 57 s. Weather satellite above Southern Hemisphere 50 55
1146 57 s. Meteorologists collecting data 50 55
1147 57 s. T.V. weather map and storm 50 55

210 Women's Rowing Eight

1991. "Siu'a'alo" Rowing Festival. Mult.

1148 42 s. Type **210** 40 45
1149 57 s. Longboat 50 55
1150 1 p. Outrigger canoe 90 95
1151 2 p. Stern of fautasi (large canoe) 1·90 2·00
1152 2 p. Bow of fautasi 1·90 2·00

Nos. 1151/2 were printed together, se-tenant, forming a composite design

211 Turtles pulling Santa's Sledge

1991. Christmas. Multicoloured.

1153 32 s. Type **211** 30 35
1154 42 s. Santa Claus on roof of fala (Tongan house) 40 45
1155 57 s. Family opening presents 50 55
1156 3 p. 50 Family waving goodbye to Santa 3·25 3·50

212 "Pangai" (patrol boat)

1991. Royal Tongan Defence Force. Mult.

1157 42 s. Type **212** 40 45
1158 42 s. Marine in battle dress 40 45
1159 57 s. Tonga Royal Guards 50 55
1160 57 s. Raising the ensign on "Neiafu" 50 55
1161 2 p. "Savea" (patrol boat) (horiz) 1·90 2·00
1162 2 p. King Taufa'ahau Tupou IV inspecting parade (horiz) 1·90 2·00

1992. No. 1007 surch **1s**.

1163 1 s. on 20 s. "Dascyllus aruanus" 10 10

215 Japanese Attack on Pearl Harbor

1992 50th Anniv of Outbreak of Pacific War. Multicoloured.

1165 42 s. Type **215** 40 45
1166 42 s. Japanese invasion of the Philippines 40 45
1167 42 s. U.S. landings in the Gilbert Islands 40 45
1168 42 s. Landing on Iwo Jima 40 45
1169 42 s. Admiral Nimitz and Battle of Midway map 40 45
1170 42 s. General MacArthur and liberation of Philippines map 40 45
1171 42 s. Lt-Gen. Holland Smith and map of landings on Saipan and Tinian 40 45
1172 42 s. Major-Gen. Curtis Lemay and bombing of Japan map 40 45
1173 42 s. Japanese Mitsubishi A6M Zero 40 45
1174 42 s. Douglas SBD Dauntless 40 45
1175 42 s. Grumman FM-2 Wildcat 40 45
1176 42 s. Supermarine Seafire Mk.3 40 45

Nos. 1165/76 were printed together, se-tenant, forming a composite design.

INDEX

Countries can be quickly located by referring to the index at the end of this volume.

216 Boxing

1992. Olympic Games, Barcelona. Mult.

1177 42 s. Type **216** 40 45
1178 57 s. Diving 50 55
1179 1 p. 50 Tennis .. .. 1·40 1·50
1180 3 p. Cycling .. .. 2·75 3·00

AIRMAIL EXPRESS STAMPS

E 1 Owl in Flight
(Illustration reduced, actual size 57 × 42 mm)

1990.

E1 E 1 10 p. black, red and blue 9·25 9·50

OFFICIAL STAMPS

1893. Optd. **G.F.B.**

O 1. 5. 1d. blue .. .. .. 9·00 32·00
O 2. 6. 2d. blue .. .. .. 22·00 40·00
O 3. 5. 4d. blue .. .. .. 38·00 80·00
O 4. 6. 8d. blue .. .. .. 80·00 £140
O 5. 1s. blue .. .. .. 90·00 £160

1893. Nos. O 1/5 variously surch.

O 6. 5. ½d. on 1d. blue .. 13·00 38·00
O 7. 6. 2½d. on 2d. blue .. 18·00 32·00
O 8. 5. 5d on 4d. blue .. 18·00 32·00
O 9. 6. 7½d. on 8d. blue .. 18·00 50·00
O 10. 10d. on 1s. blue .. 22·00 55·00

1962. Air. Stamps of 1953 and 1961 optd. as Nos. 120/7 but with **OFFICIAL AIR MAIL** in addition.

O 11. 2d. blue .. .. .. 11·00 6·00
O 12. 5d. violet .. .. 12·00 6·50
O 13. 1s. brown .. .. 7·50 3·75
O 14. 5s. yellow and lilac .. 90·00 55·00
O 15. 10s. yellow and black .. 42·00 22·00
O 16. £1 yellow, red and blue .. 70·00 35·00

1963. Air. First Polynesian Gold Coinage Commemoration. As No. 138 but additionally inscr. "OFFICIAL". 1 koula coin. Diameter 3⅛ in. Imperf.

O 17. B. 15s. black on gold .. 3·50 4·50

1965. Air. Surch. as Nos. 151/61.

O 18. B. 30s. on 15s. (No. O 17) 3·00 3·50

1966. Air. Tupou College and Secondary Education Cent. No. 117 surch. **OFFICIAL AIRMAIL** and new value, with commem. inscr. as Nos. 168/73.

O 19. 10s. on 4d. green .. 45 35
O 20. 20s. on 4d. green .. 60 50

1967. Air. No. 112 surch. **OFFICIAL AIRMAIL ONE PA'ANGA.**

O 21. 1 p. on 5s. yellow & lilac 1·75 2·25

1967. Air. No. 114 surch. **OFFICIAL AIRMAIL** and new value.

O 22. 40s. on £1 yell., red & blue 50 50
O 23. 60s. on £1 yell., red & blue 70 70
O 24. 1 p. on £1 yell., red & blue 90 90
O 25. 2 p. on £1 yell., red & blue 1·50 1·50

1967. Air. Arrival of U.S. Peace Corps in Tonga. As No. 114, but imperf. and background colour changed, surch. as Nos. 216/27 but with **Official Airmail** in addition.

O 26. 30 s. on £1 multicoloured 20 25
O 27. 70 s. on £1 multicoloured 40 45
O 28. 1 p. 50, on £1 multicoloured 70 85

1968. 50th Birthday of King Taufa'ahua IV. No. 207 surch. **"HIS MAJESTY'S 50th BIRTHDAY OFFICIAL AIRMAIL"** and new value.

O 29. 40s. on 50s. red & blue .. 1·00 60
O 30. 60s. on 50s. red & blue .. 1·50 90
O 31. 1 p. on 50s. red & blue .. 2·25 1·50
O 32. 2 p. on 50s. red & blue .. 4·00 2·25

1968. Air. South Pacific Games Field and Track Trials, Port Moresby, New Guinea. As No. 114, but imperf., background colour changed, surch.

O 33. 20 s. on £1 multicoloured 15 15
O 34. 1 p. on £1 multicoloured 40 40

1969. Air. 3rd South Pacific Games, Port Moresby. As Nos. 290/4 surch. **OFFICIAL AIRMAIL.**

O 35. 70 s. red, green & turquoise 45 60
O 36. 80 s. red, orge. & turquoise 55 70

1969. Air. Oil Search. As No. 114, but imperf., background colour changed, and optd. **1969 OIL SEARCH** and new value.

O 37. 90 s. on £1 multicoloured 2·75 2·00
O 38. 1 p. 10 on £1 mult. .. 2·75 2·00

No. O 37 is additionally optd. **OFFICIAL AIRMAIL.**

1969. Air. Royal Visit. As No. 110, but imperf., colour changed, and surch. **Royal Visit MARCH 1970 OFFICIAL AIRMAIL** and new value.

O 39. 75 s. on 1s. red and yellow 3·00 1·50
O 40. 1 p. on 1s. red and yellow 3·50 2·00
O 41. 1 p. 25 on 1s. red & yellow 4·25 2·50

1970. Commonwealth Membership. As No. 112, but imperf and surch **Commonwealth Member, June, 1970** and **OFFICIAL AIRMAIL.**

O42 50 s. on 5 s. yellow & brn 60 50
O43 90 s. on 5 s. yellow & brn 80 70
O44 1p. 50 on 5 s. yell & brn 1·50 1·25

1970. Imperf. Self-adhesive. Colour of "TONGA" given for 6s to 10s.

O 45. 83. 1 s. yell., pur. & blk. 15 15
O 46. 2 s. yell., blue & black 20 20
O 47. 3 s. yell., brn. & black 25 25
O 48. 4 s. yell., green & black 25 25
O 49. 5 s. yell., red and black 30 30
O 50. 90. 6 s. blue 35 35
O 51. 7 s. mauve 40 40
O 52. 8 s. gold 45 45
O 53. 9 s. red 55 55
O 54. 10 s. silver 55 55

On the official issues Nos. O 45 to O 54, the value tablet is black (banana issue) or green (coconut issue). On the postage issues the colour is white.

See also Nos. O 82/91.

1970. Air. Cent. of British Red Cross. As No. 102 and 112, but imperf. in different colours and surch. **Centenary British Red Cross 1870-1970 OFFICIAL AIRMAIL** and value.

O 55. 30 s. on 1½d. green .. 1·00 1·00
O 56. 80 s. on 5s. yellow & brn. 3·00 3·00
O 57. 90 s. on 5s. yellow & brn. 3·00 3·00

1971. Air. 5th Death Anniv. of Queen Salote. As No. 113, but imperf. and colour changed surch. **OFFICIAL AIRMAIL 1965 IN MEMORIAM 1970** and value.

O 58. 20 s on 10s. orange .. 70 60
O 59. 30 s. on 10s. orange .. 90 80
O 60. 50 s. on 10s. orange .. 1·75 1·25
O 61. 2 p. on 10s. orange .. 6·50 5·00

1971. Air. Philatokyo '71 Stamp Exhib., Japan. Nos. O 55/7 optd. **PHILATOKYO '71** and Emblem.

O 62. 30 s. on 5d. green & yellow 40 40
O 63. 80 s. on 5d. green & yellow 1·00 1·00
O 64. 90 s. on 5d. green & yellow 1·25 1·25

1971. Air. As T **96** but inscr. "OFFICIAL AIRMAIL".

O 65. 14 s. multicoloured .. 55 55
O 65a. 17 s. multicoloured .. 65 65
O 66. 21 s. multicoloured .. 75 75
O 66a. 38 s. multicoloured .. 1·10 1·10

O **13.** Football.

1971. Air. 4th South Pacific Games, Tahiti. Imperf. Self-adhesive.

O 67. O 13. 50 s. multicoloured 40 55
O 68. 90 s. multicoloured 60 95
O 69. 1 p. 50 multicoloured 80 1·25

1971. Air. Investiture of Royal Tongan Medal of Merit. surch. **INVESTITURE 1971. OFFICIAL AIRMAIL.**

O 70. 89. 60 s. on 3 s. mult. 50 50
O 71. 80 s. on 25 s. mult. 70 70
O 72. 1 p. 10. on 7 s. mult. 80 80

O **15.** "U.N.I.C.E.F." and Emblem.

1971. Air 25th Anniv. of U.N.I.C.E.F. Imperf. Self-adhesive.

O 73. O 15. 70 s. multicoloured 90 90
O 74. 80 s. multicoloured 1·00 1·00
O 75. 90 s. multicoloured 1·10 1·10

1972. Air. Merchant Marine Routes. As T **100**, but inscr "OFFICIAL AIRMAIL". Imperf. Self-adhesive.

O76 20 s. multicoloured .. 50 40
O77 50 s. multicoloured .. 1·75 1·10
O78 1 p. 20 multicoloured .. 3·25 2·25

DESIGNS: Nos. O76/8, Map of South Pacific and "Aoniu".

1972. Air. 5th Anniv. of Coronation. Design similar to T **101**, but inscr. "OFFICIAL AIRMAIL".

O 79. 50 s. multicoloured .. 80 45
O 80. 70 s. multicoloured .. 1·10 60
O 81. 1 p. 50 multicoloured .. 2·40 1·00

DESIGN: (47 × 57 mm.). Nos. O 79/81, As Type **101**, but with different background.

1972. As Nos. 413/27, but inscr. "OFFICIAL POST".

(a) As. 413/17.

O 82. 83. 1 s. yellow, red & blk. 15 10
O 83. 2 s. yellow, green & blk. 20 15
O 84. 3 s. yellow, green & blk. 25 20
O 85. 4 s. yellow and black .. 25 20
O 86. 5 s. yellow and black .. 25 20

(b) As Nos. O 50/4, but colours changed. Multicoloured. Colour of "TONGA" given.

O 87. 90. 6 s. green 25 20
O 88. 7 s. green 30 25
O 89. 8 s. green 30 25
O 90. 9 s. green 30 25
O 91. 10 s. green 35 30

(c) As Nos. 423/7. Multicoloured. Colour of face-value given.

O 92. 102. 15 s. blue 55 45
O 93. 20 s. orange 70 60
O 94. 25 s. brown 80 70
O 95. 40 s. orange .. .. 1·75 1·50
O 96. 50 s. blue .. .. 2·00 1·75

1972. Air. Proclamation of Sovereignty over Minerva Reefs. As T **104**, but inscr. "OFFICIAL AIRMAIL".

O 97. 25 s. multicoloured .. 40 25
O 98. 75 s. multicoloured .. 1·25 70
O 99. 1 p. 50 multicoloured .. 2·50 1·25

1973. Air. Foundation of Bank of Tonga. No. 396 surch. **TONGA 1973 ESTABLISHMENT BANK OF TONGA OFFICIAL AIRMAIL,** star and value.

O 100. 100. 40 s. on 21 s. mult. .. 85 50
O 101. 85 s. on 21 s. mult. .. 1·75 90
O 102. 1 p. 25 on 21 s. mult. 2·00 1·10

1973. Silver Jubilee of Scouting in Tonga. Nos. O 76, O 74 and 319 surch. or optd.

O 103. – 30 s. on 20 s. mult. 15·00 3·50
O 104. O 15. 80 s. multicoloured 32·00 11·00
O 105. 89. 1 p. 40 on 50 s. mult. 48·00 24·00

OVERPRINT AND SURCHARGES: 30 s. **SILVER JUBILEE TONGAN SCOUTING 1948-1973,** scout badge and value. 80 s. **SILVER-JUBILEE 1948-1973** and scout badge. 1 p. 40 **OFFICIAL AIRMAIL 1948-1973 SILVER JUBILEE TONGAN SCOUTING** and value.

1973. Air. Bicentenary of Capt. Cook's Visit. Design similar to T **107**, but inscr. "OFFICIAL AIRMAIL".

O 106. 25 s. multicoloured .. 2·25 1·00
O 107. 80 s. multicoloured .. 6·00 2·75
O 108. 1 p. 30 multicoloured .. 7·50 4·00

DESIGN—HORIZ. (52 × 45 mm.). Nos. O 106/108, (bulk carrier) "James Cook".

1973. Air. Commonwealth Games, Christchurch. Nos. O67/9 optd **1974 COMMONWEALTH GAMES, CHRISTCHURCH.**

O 109. O 13 50 s. multicoloured 1·00 60
O 110. 90 s. multicoloured 1·75 1·00
O 111. 1 p. 50 multicoloured 2·50 1·75

O **19.** Dove of Peace.

1974. Air.

O 112. O 19. 7 s. grn., vio. & red 25 20
O 113. 9 s. grn., vio. & brn. 30 25
O 114. 12 s. grn., vio. & brn. 35 30
O 115. 14 s. grn., vio. & yell. 40 35
O 116. 17 s. multicoloured 50 45
O 117. 29 s. multicoloured 80 70
O 118. 38 s. multicoloured 1·00 90
O 119. 50 s. multicoloured 1·50 1·25
O 120. 75 s. multicoloured 2·00 1·75

1974. Centenary of U.P.U. As Nos. 488/97 but inscr. "OFFICIAL AIRMAIL".

O 121. 25 s. orange, grn. & blk. 60 35
O 122. 35 s. yell., red & blk. 75 45
O 123. 70 s. orge., bl. & blk. .. 1·75 1·00

DESIGNS—HORIZ. (43 × 40 mm.). Nos. O 121/3, Letters "UPU".

1974. Air. Tongan Girl Guides. As Nos. 498/507 inscr. "OFFICIAL AIRMAIL".

O 124. 45 s. multicoloured .. 4·00 1·75
O 125. 55 s. multicoloured .. 4·25 2·00
O 126. 1 p. multicoloured .. 7·50 3·75

DESIGNS—OVAL (36 × 52 mm.). Nos. O 124/6, Lady Baden-Powell.

1974. Air. Establishment of Royal Marine Institute. Nos. 446 and 451 surch. **Establishment Royal Marine Institute Official Airmail** and new value (Nos. O 127/8 also optd **Tonga Tonga**)

O 127. 30 s. on 15 s. mult. 2·00 80
O 128. 106. 35 s. on 16 s. mult. 2·25 1·00
O 129. 80 s. on 17 s. mult. 3·75 2·50

1975. Air. South Pacific Forum and Tourism. As T **113.** Imperf. Self-adhesive.

O 130. 50 s. multicoloured .. 1·10 80
O 131. 75 s. multicoloured .. 1·75 1·25
O 132. 1 p. 25 multicoloured .. 2·50 1·75

DESIGNS (49 × 43 mm.): 50 s. Jungle arch. 75 s., 1 p. 25 Sunset scene.

1975. Air. 5th South Pacific Games. As T **114.** Imperf. Self-adhesive.

O 133. 38 s. multicoloured .. 45 30
O 134. 75 s. multicoloured .. 80 60
O 135. 1 p. 20 multicoloured .. 1·40 1·25

DESIGN—OVAL (51 × 27 mm.). Nos. O 133/5, Runners on track.

O **21.** Tongan Monarchs.
(Illustration reduced. Actual size 69 × 39 mm.)

1975. Air. Centenary of Tongan Constitution. Imperf. Self-adhesive.

O 136. O 21. 17 s. multicoloured 30 25
O 137. 60 s. multicoloured 80 55
O 138. 90 s. multicoloured 1·25 75

1976. Air. First Participation in Olympic Games. As Nos. 558/67 but inscr. "OFFICIAL AIRMAIL".

O 139. 45 s. multicoloured .. 1·75 85
O 140. 55 s. multicoloured .. 2·00 1·00
O 141. 1 p. multicoloured .. 3·25 1·90

DESIGN—OVAL (36 × 53 mm.). Montreal logo.

1976. Air. Bicentenary of American revolution. As Nos. 568/77 but inscr. "OFFICIAL AIRMAIL".

O 142. 20 s. multicoloured .. 1·00 40
O 143. 50 s. multicoloured .. 2·25 1·00
O 144. 1 p. 15 multicoloured .. 4·75 2·50

1976. 150th Anniv. of Christianity in Tonga.

O 145. 65 s. multicoloured .. 1·75 1·40
O 146. 85 s. multicoloured .. 2·00 1·75
O 147. 1 p. 15 multicoloured .. 2·75 2·50

DESIGNS—HEXAGONAL (65 × 52 mm.). Lifuka Chapel.

1976. Air. Centenary of Treaty of Friendship with Germany.

O 148. 30 s. multicoloured .. 60 60
O 149. 60 s. multicoloured .. 1·40 1·40
O 150. 1 p. 25 multicoloured .. 2·75 2·75

DESIGN—RECTANGULAR (51 × 47 mm.). Text.

1977. Air. Silver Jubilee.

O 151. 35 s. multicoloured .. 3·00 50
O 152. 45 s. multicoloured .. 80 30
O 153. 1 p. multicoloured .. 1·10 50

DESIGN: 57 × 66 mm. Flags of Tonga and the U.K.

1977. Air. 10th Anniv. of King's Coronation.

O 154. 20 s. multicoloured .. 40 40
O 155. 40 s. multicoloured .. 80 80
O 156. 80 s. multicoloured .. 1·75 1·75

DESIGN—SQUARE: (50 × 50 mm.), 1967 Coronation Coin.

1977. Air. Bicent. of Capt. Cook's Last Voyage.

O 157. 20 s. multicoloured .. 2·50 1·60
O 158. 55 s. multicoloured .. 5·50 3·50
O 159. 85 s. multicoloured .. 8·00 5·50

DESIGN—RECTANGULAR: (52 × 46 mm.), Text.

1977. Air. Whale Conservation.

O 160. 45 s. multicoloured .. 2·25 1·25
O 161. 65 s. multicoloured .. 3·25 1·90
O 162. 85 s. multicoloured .. 3·75 2·25

DESIGN—HEXAGONAL: (66 × 51 mm.), Blue Whale.

1978. Air. Commonwealth Games, Edmonton.

O 163. 30 s. black, blue and red 45 45
O 164. 60 s. black, red and blue 1·00 1·00
O 165. 1 p. black, red and blue 1·60 1·60

DESIGN—"TEAR-DROP" (35 × 52 mm.). Games Emblem.

1978. 60th Birthday of King Taufa'ahau Tupou IV.

O 166. 26 s. black, red & yellow 35 30
O 167. 85 s. blk., brn. and yell. 1·10 1·00
O 168. 90 s. blk., violet & yell. 1·25 1·10

DESIGN—MEDAL-SHAPED (21 × 45 mm.). Portrait of King.

1978. Coil Stamps. As Nos. 675/89 but inscr. "OFFICIAL POST".

O 169. 1 s. purple and yellow .. 10 10
O 170. 2 s. brown and yellow .. 10 10
O 171. 3 s. red and yellow .. 10 10
O 172. 4 s. brown and yellow .. 10 10
O 173. 5 s. green and yellow .. 10 10
O 174. 6 s. brown and green .. 15 15
O 175. 7 s. black, green & brn. 20 20
O 176. 8 s. red, green & brown 20 20
O 177. 9 s. brown and green .. 25 25
O 178. 10 s. green and brown .. 25 25
O 179. 15 s. blk., brn. and grn. 35 35
O 180. 20 s. red, brown & green 40 40
O 181. 30 s. green and brown .. 50 50
O 182. 50 s. blue, brown & green 90 90
O 183. 1 p. violet, brn. & green 1·75 1·75

1978. Air. Endangered Wildlife. Multi.

O 184. 40 s. Type **129** .. 1·50 75
O 185. 50 s. Insular Flying Fox .. .. .. 1·50 85
O 186. 1 p. 10 Turtle .. .. 2·75 2·00

1979. Air. Decade of Progress, inscr. "OFFICIAL AIRMAIL".

O 187. G. 38 s. multicoloured .. 55 40
O 188. E. 74 s. multicoloured .. 1·00 75
O 189. A. 80 s. multicoloured .. 1·10 80

DESIGN—As Type 130, G. Tonga Red Cross.

1979. Air. Death Centenary of Sir Rowland Hill and 10th Anniv. of Tongan self-adhesive Stamps.

O 190. 45 s. multicoloured .. 90 60
O 191. 65 s. multicoloured .. 1·25 85
O 192. 80 s. multicoloured .. 1·60 1·10

DESIGN—HAND-SHAPED (45 × 53 mm.) 45 s. to 80 s. Removing self-adhesive stamp from backing paper.

O **22**. Blue-crowned Lory (with foliage).

1979. Air. Coil Stamps.

O 193. O **21**. 5 s. multicoloured 15 15
O 194. 11 s. multicoloured 25 25
O 195. 14 s. multicoloured 25 25
O 196. 15 s. multicoloured 30 30
O 197. 17 s. multicoloured 30 30
O 198. 18 s. multicoloured 30 30
O 199. 22 s. multicoloured 35 35
O 200. 31 s. multicoloured 55 55
O 201. 39 s. multicoloured 70 70
O 202. 75 s. multicoloured 1·25 1·50
O 203. 1 p. multicoloured .. 1·75 2·00

1979. Air. Views as seen through the lens of a camera.

O 204. 35 s. multicoloured .. 45 35
O 205. 45 s. multicoloured .. 55 40
O 206. 1 p. multicoloured .. 1·10 1·00

DESIGN: 35 s. to 1 p. Niuatoputapu and Tafahi.

1980. Air. 125th Anniv. of Tonga–France Friendship Treaty.

O 207. 40 s. multicoloured .. 55 60
O 208. 55 s. multicoloured .. 80 85
O 209. 1 p. 25 multicoloured .. 1·75 1·90

DESIGN: 40 s. to 1 p. 25, Basilica of Tonga.

1980. Air. Olympic Games, Moscow. Nos. O 190/2 surch.

O 210. 26 s. on 45 s. multicoloured 45 45
O 211. 40 s. on 65 s. multicoloured 75 75
O 212. 1 p. 10 on 1 p. mult. 2·25 2·25

O **23**. Blue-crowned Lory (without foliage).

1980. No. O 193 redrawn without foliage as Type O **23**.

O 213. O **23**. 5 s. multicoloured .. £100

1980. Air. South Pacific Scout Jamboree, Tonga and 75th Anniv. of Rotary International.

O 214. 25 s. multicoloured .. 70 40
O 215. 2 p. multicoloured .. 3·50 3·00

DESIGN: 25 s., 2 p. Scout camp and Rotary emblem.

1980. Air. No. O 145 surch.

O 216. 2 p. on 65 s. multicoloured 4·00 4·50

1983. Nos. 834/6 optd. **OFFICIAL**.

O 217. 29 s. Type **151** .. 2·75 2·75
O 218. 32 s. Type **151** .. 3·50 3·50
O 219. 47 s. Montgolfier's balloon and "Concorde" 5·00 5·00

1984. Nos. 865/79 and 881 optd. **OFFICIAL**.

O 220. 1 s. Type **159** 10 10
O 221. 2 s. "Porites sp" .. 15 15
O 222. 3 s. "Holocentrus ruber" 15 15
O 223. 5 s. "Cypraea mappa viridis" 15 15
O 224. 6 s. "Dardanus megistos" 15 15
O 225b. 9 s. "Stegostoma fasciatum" 30 30
O 226. 10 s. "Conus bullatus" 15 15
O 227. 13 s. "Pterois volitans" 20 20
O 228. 15 s. "Conus textile" .. 25 25
O 229. 20 s. "Dascyllus aruanus" 30 30
O 230. 29 s. "Conus aulicus" .. 35 35
O 231. 32 s. "Acanthurus leucosternon" .. 40 40
O 232. 47 s. "Lambis truncata" 55 55
O 233. 1 p. "Millepora dichotama" .. 1·25 1·25
O 234. 2 p. "Birgus latro" .. 2·00 2·00
O 235. 5 p. "Thunnus albacares" .. .. 4·75 4·75

1986. Nos. 933/9 optd. **OFFICIAL**.

O 236. 4 s. on 2 s. "Porites sp." 15 15
O 237. 4 s. on 13 s. "Pterois volitans" .. 15 15
O 238. 42 s. on 3 s. "Holocentrus ruber" .. 70 70
O 239. 42 s. on 9 s. "Stegostoma fasciatum" .. 70 70
O 240. 57 s. on 6 s. "Dardanus megistos" .. 85 85
O 241. 57 s. on 20 s. "Dascyllus aruanus" .. 85 85
O 242. 2 p. 50 on 2 p. "Birgus latro" .. .. 3·00 3·00

TRANSVAAL

Formerly South African Republic under Boer rule, annexed by Gt. Britain in 1877, restored to the Boers in 1881 and again annexed in 1900, and since 1919 a province of the Union of S. Africa.

12 pence = 1 shilling.
20 shillings = 1 pound.

1.

1869. Imperf. or roul.

61. 1. 1d. red .. .. .. 20·00 14·00
22. 1d. black .. .. .. 15·00 20·00
53. 3d. lilac .. .. .. 42·00 38·00
54a. 6d. blue .. .. .. 38·00 20·00
32. 1s. green .. .. .. 60·00 27·00

1874. Perf.

38a. 1. 1d. red .. .. .. 75·00 35·00
171. 1d. deep grey .. .. 1·75 75
172. 3d. black on red .. .. 9·50 2·25
173. 3d. red .. .. .. 5·00 1·00
173b. 3d. brown .. .. 19·00 2·25
39. 6d. blue .. .. .. £100 35·00
174. 1s. green .. .. .. 12·00 1·50

1877. Optd. V. R. TRANSVAAL. Imperf. or roul.

101. 1. 1d. red .. .. .. 20·00 20·00
102. 3d. lilac .. .. .. 70·00 32·00
103. 6d. blue .. .. .. 85·00 30·00
113. 6d. blue on red .. .. 65·00 42·00
104. 1s. green .. .. .. 80·00 40·00

1877. Optd. V. R. Transvaal. Imperf. or roul.

116 1 1d. red on blue .. .. 42·00 22·00
117 1d. red on orange .. 14·00 15·00
118 3d. lilac on brown .. 32·00 22·00
119d 3d. lilac on green .. 90·00 30·00
147 3d. lilac on blue .. 40·00 25·00
126 6d. blue on green .. 70·00 22·00
121 6d. blue on blue .. 48·00 22·00

9.

18.

1878. Perf.

156. 9. ½d. red .. .. .. 16·00 35·00
157a. 1d. brown .. .. .. 4·50 2·25
158. 3d. red .. .. .. 6·50 2·50
159. 4d. olive .. .. .. 9·00 4·25
160. 6d. black .. .. .. 4·50 3·25
161. 1s. green .. .. .. 90·00 30·00
162. 2s. blue .. .. .. £110 65·00

1879. Surch. **1 Penny.**

168. 9. 1d. on 6d. black .. 35·00 22·00

1882. Surch. **EEN PENNY.**

170. 9. 1d. on 4d. olive .. 4·75 3·50

1885.

175. 18. ½d. grey 30 80
176. 1d. red 30 10
177. 2d. purple 30 30
178. 2d. pale brown 40 10
179. 2½d. mauve .. .. .. 1·00 50
180. 3d. mauve .. .. .. 1·25 65
181. 4d. deep olive .. .. 2·00 65
182. 6d. blue .. .. .. 1·25 15
183. 1s. green .. .. .. 2·25 35
184. 2s. 6d. yellow .. .. 3·50 1·40
185. 5s. grey .. .. .. 4·25 1·75
186. 10s. brown .. .. 21·00 2·50
187. £5 green £3500 £170

1885. Surch. **HALVE PENNY** vert., reading up or down.

188 1 ½d. on 3d. red (No. 173) 1·25 2·00
192 18 ½d. on 3d. mauve .. 1·00 1·00
189 1 ½d. on 1s. green (No.174) 3·75 5·50

1885. Surch. with value in words and **Z.A.R.** both vert.

190 9 ½d. on 6d. black .. .. 7·50 11·00
191 2d. on 6d. black .. .. 1·50 1·50

1887. Surch. **2d.** and thick bar.

194. 18. 2d. on 3d. mauve .. 55 75

1893. Surch. **Halve Penny** and bars.

196 18 ½d. on 2d. pale brown .. 50 50

1893. Surch. in figures and words between bars. (A) in one line, (B) in two.

197. 18. 1d. on 6d. blue (A) .. 20 20
198. 2½d. on 1s. green (A) .. 40 50
199. 2½d. on 1s. green (B) .. 1·40 1·40

29. (Wagon with shafts)

30. (Wagon with pole)

1894.

200. 29. ½d. grey 15 10
201. 1d. red 15 10
202. 2d. pale brown 15 10
203. 6d. blue 75 40
204. 1s. green .. .. .. 3·50 4·00

1895.

205. 30. ½d. grey 15 10
206. 1d. red 15 10
207. 2d. pale brown 15 10
208. 3d. mauve 15 10
209. 4d. black 20 10
210. 6d. blue 90 55
211. 1s. green 60 30
212. 5s. grey 90 65
212a. 10s. brown .. .. .. 3·00 4·00
4·00 1·25

1895. Surch. **Halve Penny** and bar.

213. 30. ½d. on 1s. green 20 10

1895. Surch. **1d** and thick bar.

214. 18. 1d. on 2½d. mauve .. 20 10

33.

1895. Fiscal stamp optd. **POSTZEGEL.**

215. 33. 6d. red 50 65

34.

1895. Penny Postage Commem.

215b. 34. 1d. red 50 30

1896.

216. 30. ½d. green 15 10
217. 1d. red and green .. 15 10
218. 2d. brown and green .. 15 10
219. 2½d. blue and green .. 20 35
220. 3d. purple and green .. 20 35
221. 4d. olive and green .. 25 35
222. 6d. lilac and green .. 25 35
223. 1s. pale brown and green 35 10
224. 2s. 6d. violet and green 75 75

1900. Optd. **V.R.I.**

226. 30. ½d. green 15 15
227. 1d. red and green .. 15 15
228. 2d. brown and green .. 90 40
229. 2½d. blue and green .. 35 40
230. 3d. purple and green .. 35 40
231. 4d. olive and green .. 75 20
232. 6d. lilac and green .. 75 40
233. 1s. pale brown and green 75 70
234. 2s. 6d. violet and green .. 1·50 2·25
235. 5s. grey .. .. .. 2·50 3·75
236. 10s. brown .. .. .. 4·00 4·75
237. 18. £5 green £1800 £750

The majority of the £5 stamps, No. 237, on the market, are forgeries.

1901. Optd. **E.R.I.**

238. 30. ½d. green 15 15
239. 1d. red and green .. 15 10
240. 3d. purple and green .. 1·00 1·00
241. 4d. olive and green .. 1·00 1·25
242. 2s. 6d. violet and green .. 4·00 4·50

1901. Surch. **E.R.I. Half Penny.**

243. 30. ½d. on 2d. brown & green 15 15

38.

1902.

244 38 ½d. black and green .. 60 15
273 ½d. green 70 10
245 1d. black and red .. 55 10
274 1d. red 60 10
246 2d. black and purple .. 1·00 20
275 2d. purple .. .. 2·75 15
247 2½d. black and blue .. 1·75 45
276 2½d. blue .. .. .. 6·00 1·75
264 3d. black and green .. 2·00 15

265		4d. black and brown ..	2·00	30
266a		6d. black and orange ..	1·25	30
251	38	1s. black and green ..	6·00	2·75
267		1s. grey and brown ..	1·75	30
252		2s. black and brown ..	11·00	13·00
268		2s. grey and yellow ..	8·00	2·50
253		2s. 6d. mauve & black	8·00	5·50
270		5s. black & pur on yell	8·50	1·50
271		10s. black & pur on red	19·00	2·00
272		£1 green and violet ..	80·00	13·00
259		£5 brown and violet ..	£1200	£400

Nos. 267, 268 and all values of 2s. 6d. and above have the inscription "POSTAGE" on both sides. The rest are inscribed "POSTAGE" at left and "REVENUE" at right.

POSTAGE DUE STAMPS

D 1.

1907.

D 1.	D 1.	½d. black and green ..	1·50	1·25
D 2.		1d. black and red ..	2·00	70
D 3.		2d. brown	2·00	1·25
D 4.		3d. black and blue ..	2·50	2·00
D 5.		5d. black and violet ..	1·50	7·00
D 6.		6d. black and brown ..	3·75	8·00
D 7.		1s. red and black ..	6·50	5·00

TRAVANCORE

A state of S.E. India.
16 cash = 1 chuckram.
28 chuckrams = 1 rupee.

3. Conch or Chank Shell. **1.**

1888. Various frames.

9	3	4 cash pink	10	10
24	–	5 cash olive	30	10
34	–	5 cash brown	90	20
10	1	6 cash brown	30	10
11a	–	½ ch. purple	15	10
27	–	10 cash pink	30	10
13	–	¾ ch. black	50	10
39	–	¾ ch. mauve	30	10
14c	1	1 ch. blue	40	10
15		1¼ ch. purple	30	20
42		1½ ch. red	80	10
16a		2 ch. red	40	10
17	–	3 ch. violet	1·10	10
18a	1	4 ch. green	1·10	35
19	–	7 ch. purple	1·60	40
20	–	14 ch. orange	2·40	90

1906. Surch. in figures.

21	1	¼ on ½ ch. purple	10	10
22a	–	⅜ on ½ ch. purple	10	20

1921. Surch. in figures.

31	3	1 c. on 4 cash pink ..	10	15
57	–	1 c. on 5 cash brown ..	10	10
58	–	1 c. on 5 cash purple ..	30	15
50	1	1 c. on 1¼ ch. purple ..	10	15
59	–	2 c. on 10 cash pink ..	10	10
51	1	2 c. on 1¼ ch. purple ..	10	10
32		5 c. on 1 ch. blue ..	10	10

11. Sri Padmanabha Shrine.

13. Maharaja Sir Bala Rama Varma.

DESIGN — As Type 11: 10 cash, State chariot.

1931. Coronation.

47.	11.	6 cash black and green ..	30	35
48.	–	10 cash black and blue ..	30	30
49.	13.	3 ch. black and purple ..	40	45

16. Maharaja Sir Bala Rama Varma and Subramania Shrine.

1937. Temple Entry Proclamation.

60.	16.	6 cash red	30	30
61.	–	12 cash blue	60	15
62.	–	1½ ch. green	40	30
63.	–	3 ch. violet	1·25	50

DESIGNS: Portraits of the Maharaja and the temples of Sri Padmanabha (12 cash), Mahadeva (1½ ch.) and Kanyakumari (3 ch.)

17. Lake Ashtamudi.

18. Maharaja Sir Bala Rama Varma.

DESIGNS—As Type 18. 1½ ch., 3 ch. Bust of Maharaja. As Type 17: Sri Padmanabha Shrine (4 ch.). Bust of Maharaja and Cape Comorin (7 ch.) and Pachipari Irrigation Reservoir (14 ch.).

1939. 27th Birthday of Maharaja.

64.	17.	1 ch. green	90	10
65.	–	1½ ch. red	50	60
66.	18.	2 ch. orange	1·25	30
67.	–	3 ch. brown	1·40	10
68.	–	4 ch. red	90	40
69.	–	7 ch. blue	2·25	5·50
70.	–	14 ch. green	3·00	13·00

19. Maharaja and Aruvikara Falls.

1941. 29th Birthday of Maharaja.

71.	19.	6 cash violet	1·75	10
72.	–	¾ ch. brown	1·75	10

DESIGN: ¾ ch. Maharaja and Marthanda Varma Bridge, Alwaye.

1943. Stamps of 1939 and 1941 surch. in figures and capital letters.

73e	–	2 cash on 1½ ch. red (65) ..	20	10
74a	–	4 cash on ¾ ch. brown (72)	1·25	10
75a	19	8 cash on 6 cash red (as No. 71)	75	10

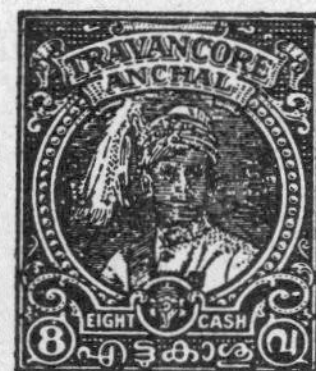

21. Maharaja Sir Bala Rama Varma.

1946. 34th Birthday of Maharaja.

76a.	21.	8 cash red	50	50

1946. No. O 103 optd. **SPECIAL.**

77.	19.	6 cash violet	4·25	1·50

OFFICIAL STAMPS

1911. Optd. **On S.S.**

O 1	3	4 cash pink	10	10
O 14	–	5 cash olive	30	10
O 29	–	5 cash brown	15	20
O 15	1	6 cash brown	15	10
O 54		½ ch. purple	15	10
O 18	–	10 cash pink	30	10
O 39	–	¾ ch. black	30	10
O 56	–	¾ ch. mauve	30	10
O 5	1	1 ch. blue	35	10
O 21		1¼ ch. purple	35	10
O 59	–	1½ ch. red	35	10
O 6		2 ch. red	30	10
O 8	–	3 ch. violet	30	10
O 10	1	4 ch. green	55	10
O 64	–	7 ch. purple	1·10	30
O 65	–	14 ch. orange	1·50	40

1932. Official stamps surch in figures.

O 74	–	6 c. on 5 cash olive ..	1·40	50
O 75	–	6 c. on 5 cash brown ..	15	15
O 83	–	12 c. on 10 cash pink ..	15	15
O 84	1	1 ch. 8 cash on 1¼ ch. red	35	25

1939. Optd. **SERVICE.**

O 85	1.	6 cash brown ..	70	10
O 94	–	¾ ch. mauve (No. 39)	5·50	15
O 96	17.	1 ch. green ..	35	10
O 97	–	1½ ch. red (No. 65)	85	10
O 95a	1.	1 ½ ch. red ..	2·75	1·00
O 98	17.	2 ch. orange ..	75	30
O 99	–	3 ch. brown (No. 67)	40	10
O 100	–	4 ch. red (No. 68)	75	35
O 101	–	7 ch. blue (No. 69)	2·25	35
O 102	–	14 ch. green (No. 70)	5·00	70

1942. Optd. **SERVICE.**

O 103.	19.	6 cash violet	30	10
O 104.	–	¾ ch. brown (No. 72) ..	75	10

1942. Nos. 73/5 optd. **SERVICE.**

O106a	–	2 cash on 1½ ch. red	35	10
O107a	–	4 cash on † ch. brown	40	10
O105	19	8 cash on 6 cash red	50	10

1947. Optd. **SERVICE.**

O 108.	21.	8 cash red	1·10	70

TRAVANCORE—COCHIN

In 1949 the states of Cochin and Travancore in S.E. India were united under the name of the United States of Travancore and Cochin.

12 pies = 1 anna; 16 annas = 1 rupee.

ONE ANNA
ഒരണ
(1.)

1949. Stamps of Travancore surch. as **T 1**

1e	19	2 p. on 6 cash violet ..	20	10
2c	21	4 p. on 8 cash red ..	40	10
3e	17	½ a. on 1 ch. green ..	35	15
4a	18	1 a. on 2 ch. orange ..	30	20
5c	11	2 a. on 4 ch. brown ..	90	35
6a	–	3 a. on 7 ch. blue (No. 69)	4·00	1·50
7b	–	6 a. on 14 ch. grn. (No. 70)	4·00	7·00

1949. No. 106 of Cochin optd. **U.S.T.C.**

8.	21.	1 a. orange	4·50	40·00

1950. No. 106 of Cochin optd. **T.-C.**

9.	21.	1 a. orange	5·50	35·00

1950. No. 9 surch with new value.

10.	21.	6 p. on 1 a. orange ..	1·60	10·00
11.		9 p. on 1 a. orange ..	1·40	10·00

5. Conch or Chank Shell. **6.** Palm Trees.

1950.

12.	5.	2 p. red	45	1·10
13.	6.	4 p. blue	70	3·00

OFFICIAL STAMPS

1949. Stamps of Travancore surch. as T **1.**

O 8	19.	2 p. on 6 cash (No. 71)	10	30
O 10	21.	4 p. on 8 cash (No. 76a)	15	10
O 11b	17.	½ a. on 1 ch. (No. 64)	10	10
O 12	18.	1 a. on 2 ch. (No. 66)	20	20
O 9a	–	2 a. on 4 ch. (No. 68)	40	35
O 14e	–	3 a. on 7 ch. (No. 69)	1·10	75
O 15	–	6 a. on 14 ch. (No. 70)	1·10	1·60

TRENGGANU

A state of the Federation of Malaya, incorporated in Malaysia in 1963.

100 cents = 1 dollar (Straits or Malayan).

1. Sultan Zain ul ab din. **2.**

1910.

1.	1.	1 c. green	50	1·00
2.		2 c. brown and purple ..	40	90
3.		3 c. red	1·75	1·50
4.		4 c. orange	3·00	5·00
5.		4 c. brown and green ..	2·00	3·75
5a.		4 c. red	60	1·75
6.		5 c. grey	1·25	2·00
7.		5 c. grey and brown ..	2·25	2·00
8.		8 c. blue	1·25	5·50
9a.		10 c. purple on yellow ..	3·00	1·75
10.		10 c. grn. and red on yell.	1·00	2·25
11.		20 c. mauve and purple	2·50	3·25
12.		25 c. green and purple ..	5·00	20·00
13.		30 c. purple and black ..	6·50	27·00
14.		50 c. black on green ..	4·50	5·50
15.		$1 black and red on blue	9·50	16·00
16.		$3 green and red on green	70·00	£140
17.	2.	$5 green and purple ..	90·00	£275
18.		$25 red and green ..	£700	

1917. Surch. **RED CROSS 2 c.**

19	1.	2 c. on 3 c. red	30	2·25
20		2 c. on 4 c. orange ..	70	9·50
21		2 c. on 4 c. brown & green	1·10	20·00
22		2 c. on 8 c. blue	50	20·00

4. Sultan Suleiman. **7.** Sultan Ismail.

1921. (a) T **4.**

48.	4.	1 c. black	50	45
26.		2 c. green	75	30
49.		3 c. green	65	75
50.		3 c. brown	10·00	4·75
27.		4 c. red	75	10
28.		5 c. grey and brown ..	2·00	2·50
51.		5 c. purple on yellow ..	1·25	55
52.		6 c. orange	2·25	30
53.		8 c. grey	10·00	90
29.		10 c. blue	2·00	15
54.		12 c. blue	3·50	3·25
30.		20 c. purple and orange ..	2·00	1·50
31.		25 c. green and purple ..	2·25	2·00
32.		30 c. purple and black ..	3·25	1·00
55.		35 c. red on yellow ..	3·50	8·00
33.		50 c. green and red ..	4·50	1·00
56.		$1 purple and blue on blue	9·00	3·50
57.		$3 green and red on green	30·00	65·00

(b) Larger type, as T **2**, but portrait of Sultan Suleiman.

25.		$5 green and red on yellow	65·00	£150
34.		$25 purple and blue ..	£450	£600
35.		$50 green and yellow ..	£1000	£1400
36.		$100 green and red ..	£3500	

1922. Optd. **MALAYA-BORNEO EXHIBITION.**

37.	4.	2 c. green	75	24·00
38.		4 c. red	3·50	24·00
39.		5 c. grey and brown ..	2·50	25·00
40.	1.	10 c. green & red on yellow	2·50	30·00
41.		20 c. mauve and purple ..	2·00	35·00
42.		25 c. green and purple ..	2·00	35·00
43.		30 c. purple and black ..	2·25	35·00
44.		50 c. black on green ..	2·50	35·00
45.		$1 black and red on blue	10·00	65·00
46.		$3 green and red on green	£110	£350
47.	2.	$5 green and purple ..	£190	£600

1941. Surch.

59.	4.	2 c. on 5 c. purple on yellow	6·00	4·50
60.		8 c. on 10 c. blue	7·00	4·50

1948. Silver Wedding. As T **10/11** of Aden.

61		10 c. violet	15	25
62		$5 red	20·00	30·00

1949. U.P.U. As T **20/23** of Antigua.

63.		10 c. purple	20	35
64.		15 c. blue	55	1·60
65.		25 c. orange	55	2·25
66.		50 c. black	90	2·50

1949.

67	7.	1 c. black	10	20
68		2 c. orange	10	20
69		3 c. green	20	80
70		4 c. brown	10	15
71		5 c. purple	30	50
72		6 c. grey	15	15
73		8 c. red	20	1·25
74		8 c. green	65	1·00
75		10 c. purple	15	10
76		12 c. red	65	1·75

77	7	15 c. blue	30	25
78		20 c. black and green ..	30	1·25
79		20 c. blue	80	25
80		25 c. purple and orange ..	30	55
81		30 c. red and purple ..	1·25	1·25
82		35 c. red and purple ..	70	1·00
83		40 c. red and purple ..	1·00	7·00
84		50 c. black and blue ..	40	60
85		$1 blue and purple ..	2·00	2·75
86		$2 green and red	9·50	13·00
87		$5 green and brown ..	38·00	38·00

1953. Coronation. As T 13 of Aden.

88	10 c. black and purple ..	30	30

1957. As Nos. 92/102 of Kedah but inset portrait of Sultan Ismail.

89	1 c. black	10	20
90	2 c. red	40	30
91	4 c. brown	10	10
92	5 c. red	10	10
93	8 c. green	3·25	60
94	10 c. brown	15	10
94a	10 c. purple	1·50	10
95	20 c. blue	20	30
96a	50 c. black and blue ..	30	60
97	$1 blue and purple ..	3·00	3·00
98	$2 green and red ..	5·00	6·00
99	$5 brown and green ..	7·00	8·00

8. "Vanda hookeriana".

1965. As Nos. 115/21 of Kedah, but inset portrait of Sultan Ismail Nasiruddin Shah, as in T 8.

100.	8.	1 c. multicoloured ..	10	30
101.	–	2 c. multicoloured ..	10	30
102.	–	5 c. multicoloured ..	10	10
103.	–	6 c. multicoloured ..	15	30
104.	–	10 c. multicoloured ..	20	10
105.	–	15 c. multicoloured ..	85	10
106.	–	20 c. multicoloured ..	1·25	30

The higher values used in Trengganu were Nos. 20/7 of Malaysia (National Issues).

9. Sultan of Trengganu.

1970. 25th Anniv. of Installation of H.R.H. Tuanku Ismail Nasiruddin Shah as Sultan of Trengganu.

107.	9.	10 c. multicoloured ..	25	50
108.		15 c. multicoloured ..	30	60
109.		50 c. multicoloured ..	65	1·60

10. "Papilio demoleus".

1971. Butterflies. As Nos. 124/30 of Kedah but with portrait of Sultan Ismail Nasiruddin Shah as in T 10.

110.	–	1 c. multicoloured ..	15	60
111.	–	2 c. multicoloured ..	30	60
112.	–	5 c. multicoloured ..	40	10
113.	10.	6 c. multicoloured ..	40	30
114.	–	10 c. multicoloured ..	40	10
115.	–	15 c. multicoloured ..	55	10
116.	–	20 c. multicoloured ..	75	40

The high values in use with this issue were Nos. 64/71 of Malaysia (National Issues).

11. "Durio zibethinus".

1979. Flowers. As Nos. 135/41 of Kedah, but with portrait of Sultan Ismail Nasiruddin Shah as in T 11.

118	1 c. "Rafflesia hasseltii" ..	10	30
119	2 c. "Pterocarpus indicus"	10	30
120	5 c. "Largerstroemia speciosa"	10	10
121	10 c. Type 11	10	10
122	15 c. "Hibiscus rosa-sinensis"	15	10
123	20 c. "Rhododendron scortechinii"	15	10
124	25 c. "Etlingera elatior" (inscr "Phaeomeria speciosa")	15	10

12. Sultan Mahmud.

1981. Installation of Sultan Mahmud.

125.	12.	10 c. black, blue and gold	15	40
126.		15 c. black, yell. and gold	20	30
127.		50 c. black, purple & gold	50	1·50

13. Rubber.

1986. As Nos. 152/8 of Kedah but with portrait of Sultan Mahmud and inscr. "TERENGGANU" as in T 13.

135.	1 c. Coffee	10	10
136.	2 c. Coconuts	10	10
137.	5 c. Cocoa	10	10
138.	10 c. Black pepper ..	10	10
139.	15 c. Type 13	10	10
140.	20 c. Oil palm	10	10
141.	30 c. Rice	10	15

POSTAGE DUE STAMPS

D 1.

1937.

D 1.	D 1.	1 c. red	6·50	50·00
D 2.		4 c. green	6·50	50·00
D 3.		8 c. yellow	48·00	£250
D 4.		10 c. brown	80·00	90·00

TRINIDAD

An island in the Br. W. Indies off the coast of Venezuela. Now uses stamps of Trinidad and Tobago.

12 pence = 1 shilling.
20 shillings = 1 pound.

2. Britannia. 4.

1851. Imperf.

2	2	(1d.) purple	4·75	55·00
3		(1d.) blue	4·25	35·00
5		(1d.) grey	26·00	45·00
8		(1d.) red	£120	50·00
25	4	4d. lilac	55·00	£275
28		6d. green	—	£425
29		1s. deep blue	60·00	£275

3.

1852. Imperf.

18.	3.	(1d.) blue	£4000	£650
19.		(1d.) grey	£4000	£450
20.		(1d.) red	11·00	£450

1859. Perf.

91	2	(1d.) red	9·00	50
75	4	4d. lilac	65·00	9·50
94		4d. grey	65·00	70
80		6d. green	38·00	3·00
63		1s. blue	£650	65·00
85		1s. purple	65·00	4·25
97		1s. yellow	65·00	2·50

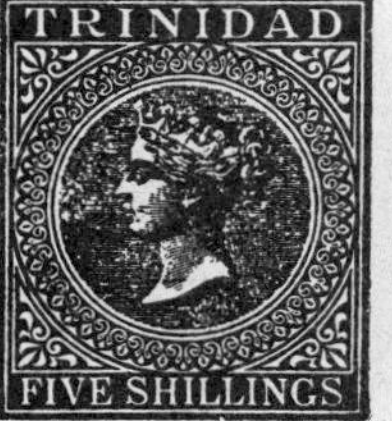

5. 10.

1869.

113.	5.	5s. red	20·00	40·00

1879. Surch. in words.

98.	2.	½d. lilac	7·00	4·75
101.		1d. red	15·00	30

1882. No. 95 surch. **1d.** with pen.

104.	4.	1d. on 6d. green	3·00	3·25

1883.

106.	10.	½d. green	30	15
107.		1d. red	1·75	10
108.		2½d. blue	4·00	15
110.		4d. grey	2·25	20
111.		6d. black	2·00	1·50
112.		1s. orange	2·00	1·50

11. Britannia. 12.

1896.

114	11	½d. purple and green ..	50	15
126		½d. green	35	55
115		1d. purple and red ..	2·50	10
127		1d. black on red ..	80	10
135		1d. red	80	10
117		2½d. purple and blue ..	2·00	15
128		2½d. pur. & blue on blue	4·50	25
137		2½d. blue	1·50	15
118		4d. purple and orange ..	3·75	6·50
129		4d. grn. & blue on buff	1·50	5·00
138		4d. grey & red on yell.	1·00	4·75
119		5d. purple and mauve ..	5·00	6·00
120		6d. purple and black ..	3·50	4·50
140	11	6d. purple and mauve ..	3·50	5·50
121		1s. green and brown ..	4·50	5·00
130		1s. blk. & blue on yell.	13·00	4·00
142		1s. pur. & blue on yell.	7·50	9·50
143		1s. black on green ..	1·00	1·25
122	12	5s. green and brown ..	28·00	55·00
131		5s. purple and mauve ..	25·00	42·00
123		10 s. green and blue ..	£100	£120
124		£1 green and red ..	85·00	£110

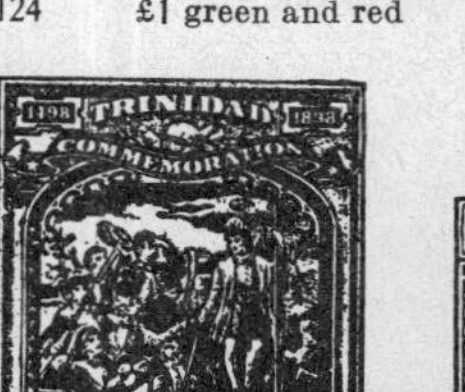

13. Landing of Columbus. 14.

1898. 4th Cent. of Discovery of Trinidad.

125.	13.	2d. brown and violet ..	1·50	50

1909. Figures in corners.

146.	14.	½d. green	80	10
147.	–	1d. red	35	10
148.	–	2½d. blue	4·50	1·25

On the 1d. figures are in lower corners only.

POSTAGE DUE STAMPS

D 1.

1885.

D 1	D 1	½d. black	22·00	35·00
D18		1d. black	30	80
D19		2d. black	30	75
D20		3d. black	30	1·25
D21		4d. black	1·50	7·00
D14		5d. black	6·50	8·50
D15		6d. black	6·00	9·50
D16		8d. black	12·00	14·00
D17		1s. black	12·00	23·00

For stamps in Type D 1 but with value in cents see under Trinidad and Tobago.

OFFICIAL STAMPS

1894. Optd. **O.S.**

O 1.	10.	½d. green	28·00	42·00
O 2.		1d. red	32·00	45·00
O 3.		2½d. blue	40·00	65·00
O 4.		4d. grey	40·00	70·00
O 5.		6d. black	40·00	70·00
O 6.		1s. orange	50·00	85·00
O 7.	5.	5s. red	£110	£190

1909. Optd. **OFFICIAL.**

O 8.	11.	½d. green	30	2·50
O 9.		1d. red	30	2·50

1910. Optd. **OFFICIAL.**

O 10.	14.	½d. green	1·00	1·75

TRINIDAD AND TOBAGO

Combined issues for Trinidad and Tobago, administratively, one colony. Part of the Br. Caribbean Federation from 1958 until 31 August, 1962, on becoming independent within the Br. Commonwealth.

1913. 12 pence = 1 shilling;
20 shillings = 1 pound.
1935. 100 cents = 1 West Indian dollar.

17. 18.

1913.

149 17 ½d. green 75 10
207 1d. red 20 20
208 1d. brown 20 30
209 2d. grey .. .. 1·00 1·25
151a 2½d. blue .. .. 1·50 30
211 3d. blue .. .. .. 1·75 1·75
152a 4d. black & red on yellow 50 3·00
153a 6d. purple and mauve .. 1·75 3·75
154 1s. black on green .. 75 2·50
155d 18 5s. purple and mauve .. 26·00 60·00
156 £1 green and red .. 90·00 £110

1915. Optd. cross over **21.10.15.**
174. **17.** 1d. red 40 40

1916. Optd. **19.10.16.** over cross.
175. **17.** 1d. red 10 30

1917. Optd **WAR TAX** in one line (No. 176) or two lines (others)
177 17 ½d. green 10 10
176 1d. red 15 70
180 1d. red 10 10

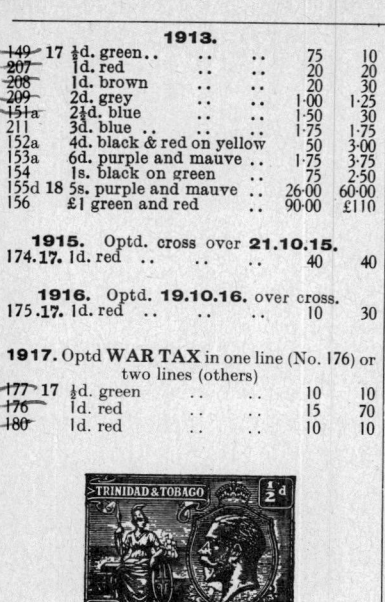

27.

1922.

218. **27.** ½d. green 10 10
219. 1d. brown 15 10
220a. 1½d. red 20 10
222. 2d. grey 20 30
223. 3d. blue 40 30
216. 4d. black & red on yellow 55 90
225. 6d. purple and mauve 2·00 12·00
226. 6d. green & red on green 80 30
227. 1s. black on green .. 90 90
228. 5s. purple and mauve .. 12·00 18·00
229. £1 green and red .. 85·00 £170

28. First Boca.

1935.

230a. **28.** 1 c. blue and green .. 10 10
231. – 2 c. blue and brown .. 30 10
232. – 3 c. black and red .. 20 10
233. – 6 c. brown and blue .. 1·00 30
234. – 8 c. green and orange .. 60 80
235. – 12 c. black and violet .. 1·00 45
236. – 24 c. black and green .. 35 40
237. – 48 c. green .. .. 4·00 11·00
238. – 72 c. green and red .. 16·00 18·00

DESIGNS: 2 c. Imperial College of Tropical Agriculture. 3 c. Mt. Irvine Bay, Tobago. 6 c. Discovery of Lake Asphalt. 8 c. Queen's Park, Savannah. 12 c. Town Hall, San Fernando. 24 c. Govt. House. 40 c. Memorial Park. 72 c. Blue Basin.

1935. Silver Jubilee. As T **13** of Antigua.
239. 2 c. blue and black .. 30 20
240. 3 c. blue and red 30 30
241. 6 c. brown and blue .. 80 1·75
242. 24 c. grey and purple .. 3·50 3·75

1937. Coronation. As T **2** of Aden.
243. 1 c. green 15 10
244. 2 c. brown 35 10
245. 8 c. orange 85 20

47. King George VI.

37. First Boca.

1938. Designs as 1935 issue but with portrait of King George VI as in T **37** and without "POSTAGE & REVENUE".
246. **37.** 1 c. blue and green .. 15 10
247. – 2 c. blue and brown .. 15 10
248. – 3 c. black and red .. 10·00 50
248a. – 3 c. green and purple .. 15 10
249. – 4 c. brown .. .. 23·00 1·00
249a. – 4 c. red 40 40
249b. – 5 c. mauve 15 10
250. – 6 c. brown and blue .. 20 15
251. – 8 c. olive and red .. 50 15
252a. – 12 c. black and purple .. 2·00 10
253. – 24 c. black and olive .. 35 10
254. – 60 c. green and red .. 7·00 40

NEW DESIGNS: 4 c. Memorial Park. 5 c. G.P.O. and Treasury. 60 c. as No. 238.

1940.
255. **47.** $1.20 green .. .. 3·75 25
256. $4.80 red .. .. 18·00 12·00

1946. Victory. As T **9** of Aden.
257. 3 c. brown 10 10
258. 6 c. blue 10 15

1948. Silver Wedding. As T **10/11** of Aden.
259. 3 c. brown 10 10
260. $4.80 red .. .. 14·00 13·00

1949. U.P.U. As T **20/23** of Antigua.
261 5 c. purple 30 10
262 6 c. blue 30 20
263 12 c. violet 30 30
264 24 c. green 30 20

1951. B.W.I. University College. As T **24/25** of Antigua, but inscr "TRINIDAD" only.
265. **22.** 3 c. green and brown .. 15 10
266. **23.** 12 c. black and violet .. 20 10

48. First Boca.

1953. Designs as 1938 and 1940 issues but with portrait of Queen Elizabeth in place of King George VI as in T **48** (1 c., 2 c., 12 c.) or facing left (others).
267. **48.** 1 c. blue and green .. 15 10
268. – 2 c. blue and brown .. 15 10
269. – 3 c. green and purple .. 15 10
270. – 4 c. red 20 10
271. – 5 c. mauve 30 10
272. – 6 c. brown and blue .. 30 10
273. – 8 c. olive and red .. 60 10
274. – 12 c. black and purple 30 10
275. – 24 c. black and olive .. 40 10
276. – 60 c. green and red .. 8·00 40
277. – $1.20 green 90 75
278a. – $4.80 red .. .. 5·50 7·50

1953. Coronation. As T **13** of Aden.
279. 3 c. black and green .. 10 10

1956. No. 268 surch. **ONE CENT.**
280. 1 c. on 2 c. blue & brown 20 40

1958. British Caribbean Federation. As T **28** of Antigua.
281. 5 c. green 20 10
282. 6 c. blue 25 15
283. 12 c. red 25 10

51. Cipriani Memorial.

53. Copper-rumped Hummingbird.

1960.
284. **51.** 1 c. stone and black .. 10 10
285. – 2 c. blue 10 10
286. – 5 c. blue 10 10
287. – 6 c. brown 10 10
288. – 8 c. green 10 10
289. – 10 c. lilac 10 10
290. – 12 c. red 10 10
291. – 15 c. orange (A) .. 90 45
291a. – 15 c. orange (B) .. 1·00 10
292. – 25 c. red and blue .. 35 10
293. – 35 c. green and black .. 1·00 10
294. – 50 c. yell., grey and blue 35 10
295. – 60 c. red, green and blue 45 20
296. **53.** $1.20 multicoloured .. 6·00 1·25
297. – $4.80 green and blue .. 4·50 4·50

DESIGNS—As Type **51**—HORIZ. 2c. Queen's Hall. 5 c. Whitehall. 6 c. Treasury Building. 8 c. Governor-General's House. 10 c. General Hospital, San Fernando. 12 c. Oil refinery. 15 c. (A) Crest, (B) Coat of Arms. 25 c. Scarlet Ibis. 35 c. Pitch Lake. 50 c. Mohammed Jinnah Mosque. VERT. 60 c. Anthurium lilies. As Type **53**: $4.80, Map of Trinidad and Tobago.

65. Scouts and Gold Wolf Badge.

1961. 2nd Caribbean Scout Jamboree. Design multicoloured. Background colours given.
298. **65.** 8 c. green 15 10
299. 25 c. blue 15 10

66. "Buccoo Reef" (painting by Carlisle Chang).

1962. Independence.
300. **66.** 5 c. turquoise 10 10
301. – 8 c. grey 10 10
302. – 25 c. violet 10 10
303. – 35 c. multicoloured .. 60 10
304. – 60 c. red, black and blue 80 40

DESIGNS: 8 c. Piarco Air Terminal. 25 c. Hilton Hotel, Port-of-Spain. 35 c. Greater Bird of Paradise and map. 60 c. Scarlet Ibis and map.

71. "Protein Foods".

1963. Freedom from Hunger.
305. **71.** 5 c. red 10 10
306. – 8 c. bistre 10 10
307. – 25 c. blue 20 10

72. Jubilee Emblem.

1964. Golden Jubilee of Trinidad and Tobago Girl Guides' Assn.
308. **72.** 6 c. yellow, blue and red 10 10
309. 25 c. yell., ultram. & blue 15 10
310. 35 c. yell., blue & green 15 10

73. I.C.Y. Emblem.

1965. Int. Co-operation Year.
311. **73.** 35 c. brown, grn. & yell. 25 10

74. Eleanor Roosevelt, Flag and U.N. Emblem.

1965. Eleanor Roosevelt Memorial Foundation.
312. **74.** 25 c. black, red & blue .. 10 10

75. Parliament Building.

1966. Royal Visit. Multicoloured.
313. 5 c. Type **75** 15 10
314. 8 c. Map, Royal Yacht "Britannia" and arms .. 1·00 70
315. 25 c. Map and flag .. .. 1·10 55
316. 35 c. Flag and panorama .. 1·25 70

1967. 5th Year of Independence. Nos. 288, 289, 291a and 295 optd. **FIFTH YEAR OF INDEPENDENCE 31st AUGUST 1967.**
318. 8 c. green 10 10
319. 10 c. lilac 10 10
320. 15 c. orange 10 10
321. 60 c. blue, green and red .. 25 10

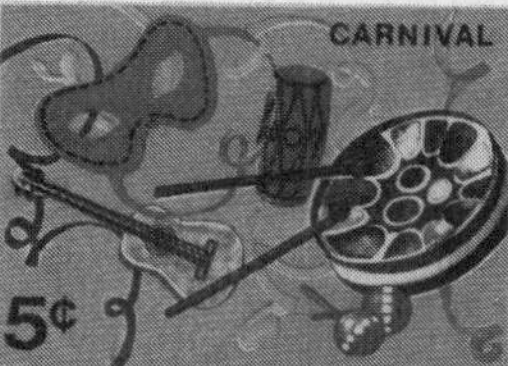

80. Musical Instruments.

1968. Trinidad Carnival. Multicoloured.
322. 5 c. Type **80** 10 10
323. 10 c. Calypso King .. 10 10
324. 15 c. Steel band 10 10
325. 25 c. Carnival procession 10 10
326. 35 c. Carnival King .. 10 10
327. 60 c. Carnival Queen .. 20 15
The 10, 35 and 60 c. are vert.

86. Doctor giving Eye-Test.

1968. 20th Anniv. of World Health Organization.
328. **86.** 5 c. red, brown and gold 10 10
329. 25 c. orange, brown & gold 15 10
330. 35 c. blue, black & gold 20 15

87. Peoples of the World and Emblem.

1968. Human Rights Year.
331. **87.** 5 c. red, black & yellow 10 10
332. 10 c. blue, black & yell. 10 10
333. 25 c. green, black & yell. 10 10

88. Cycling.

1968. Olympic Games, Mexico. **Mult.**
334. 5 c. Type **88** 10 10
335. 15 c. Weightlifting .. 10 10
336. 25 c. Relay-Racing .. 10 10
337. 35 c. Sprinting 15 10
338. $1.20 Maps of Mexico and Trinidad 45 30

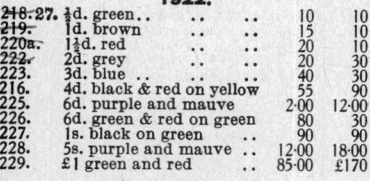

93. Cocoa Beans.

1969. Multicoloured.

No.	Description	Unused	Used
339.	1 c. Type **93**	10	10
340.	3 c. Sugar Refinery	10	10
341.	5 c. Rufous-vented Chachalaca.	40	10
342.	6 c. Oil Refinery	10	10
343.	8 c. Fertiliser Plant	10	10
344.	10 c. Green Hermit	40	10
345.	12 c. Citrus Fruit	15	30
346.	15 c. Arms of Trinidad and Tobago	10	10
347.	20 c. Flag and outline of Trinidad and Tobago	15	10
348.	25 c. As 20 c.	15	15
349.	30 c. Chaconia	25	10
350.	40 c. Scarlet Ibis	2·00	10
351.	50 c. Maracas Bay	25	40
352.	$1 Poui Tree	60	15
353.	$2.50 Fishing	80	2·50
354.	$5 Red House	1·50	3·00

Nos. 344/9 and 352 are vert.

108. Captain A. A. Cipriani (labour leader), and Entrance to Woodford Square.

1969. 50th Anniv. of Int. Labour Organization

No.	Description	Unused	Used
355. **108.**	6 c. black, gold and red	10	10
356. –	15 c. black, gold & blue	10	10

DESIGN: 15 c. Arms of Industrial Court and entrance to Woodford Square.

110. Cornucopia and Fruit.

1969. 1st Anniv. of C.A.R.I.F.T.A. Mult.

No.	Description	Unused	Used
357.	6 c. Type **110**	10	10
358.	10 c. Flags of Britain and member-nations	10	10
359.	30 c. Map showing C.A.R.I.F.T.A. countries	15	10
360.	40 c. Boeing "727" in flight	20	15

The 10 c. and 40 c. are horiz.

114. Space Module landing on Moon.

1969. 1st Man on the Moon. Multicoloured.

No.	Description	Unused	Used
361.	6 c. Type **114**	10	10
362.	40 c. Space module and astronauts on Moon's surface	15	10
363.	$1 Astronauts seen from inside space module	35	20

The 40 c. is vert.

117. Parliamentary Chamber, Flags and Emblems.

1969. 15th Commonwealth Parliamentary Assn. Conf., Port of Spain. Multicoloured.

No.	Description	Unused	Used
364.	10 c. Type **117**	10	10
365.	15 c. J. F. Kennedy College	10	10
366.	30 c. Parliamentary Maces	25	15
367.	40 c. Cannon and emblem	25	15

121. Congress Emblem. 124. "Man in the Moon".

1969. Int. Congress of the Junior Chamber of Commerce.

No.	Description	Unused	Used
368. **121.**	6 c. black, red and gold	10	10
369. –	30 c. gold, lake and blue	15	15
370. –	40 c. black, gold & blue	15	15

DESIGNS: (both incorporating the Congress emblem). HORIZ. 30 c. Islands at daybreak. VERT. 40 c. Palm trees and ruin.

1970. Carnival Winners. Multicoloured.

No.	Description	Unused	Used
371.	5 c. Type **124**	10	10
372.	6 c. "City beneath the sea"	10	10
373.	15 c. "Antelope" God Bamibara	15	10
374.	30 c. "Chanticleer Pheasant Queen of Malaya"	25	10
375.	40 c. Steel-band of the year	25	15

129. Statue of Gandhi.

1970. Gandhi Centenary Year (1969). Multicoloured.

No.	Description	Unused	Used
376.	10 c. Type **129**	20	10
377.	30 c. Head of Gandhi and flag of India (horiz.)	40	20

131. Symbols of Culture, Science, Arts and Technology.

1970. 25th Anniv. of U.N.

No.	Description	Unused	Used
378. **131.**	5 c. multicoloured	10	10
379. –	10 c. multicoloured	15	10
380. –	20 c. multicoloured	30	15
381. –	30 c. multicoloured	30	15

DESIGNS AND SIZES: 10 c. Children of different races, map and flag (34 × 25 mm.). 20 c. Noah's Ark, rainbow and dove (34 × 23 mm.). 30 c. New U.P.U. H.Q. Building (46 × 27½ mm.).

1970. Inaug. of National Commercial Bank. No. 341 optd. **NATIONAL COMMERCIAL BANK ESTABLISHED 1.7.70.**

No.	Description	Unused	Used
382.	5 c. multicoloured	10	10

134. "East Indian Immigrants" (J. Cazabon).

1970. 125th Anniv. of San Fernando. Paintings by Cazabon.

No.	Description	Unused	Used
383. **134.**	3 c. multicoloured	10	15
384. –	5 c. black, blue & ochre	10	10
385. –	40 c. black, blue & ochre	45	15

DESIGNS—HORIZ. 5 c. "San Fernando Town Hall". 40 c. "San Fernando Harbour, 1860" (J. Cazabon).

135. "The Adoration of the Shepherds" (detail, School of Seville).

1970. Christmas. Multicoloured.

No.	Description	Unused	Used
386.	3 c. Type **135**	10	10
387.	5 c. "Madonna and Child with Saints" (detail, Titian)	10	10
388.	30 c. "The Adoration of the Shepherds" (detail, Le Nain)	20	15
389.	40 c. "The Virgin and Child, St. John and an Angel" (Morando)	20	10
390.	$1 "The Adoration of the Kings" (detail, Veronese)	75	85

136. Red Brocket.

1971. Trinidad Wildlife. Multicoloured.

No.	Description	Unused	Used
392.	3 c. Type **136**	20	15
393.	5 c. Collared Peccary	25	15
394.	6 c. Paca	30	30
395.	30 c. Brazilian Agouti	1·50	3·00
396.	40 c. Ocelot	1·75	2·75

137. A. A. Cipriani. 138. "Virgin and Child with St. John" (detail Bartolommeo).

1971. 9th Anniv. of Independence. Mult.

No.	Description	Unused	Used
397.	5 c. Type **137**	10	10
398.	30 c. Chaconia medal	20	30

1971. Christmas.

No.	Description	Unused	Used
399. **138.**	3 c. multicoloured	10	10
400. –	5 c. multicoloured	10	10
401. –	10 c. multicoloured	15	10
402. –	15 c. multicoloured	20	15

DESIGNS: 5 c. Local Creche. 10 c. "Virgin and Child with Saints Jerome and Dominic" (detail, Lippi). 15 c. "Virgin and Child with St. Anne" (detail, Gerolamo dai Libri).

139. Satellite Earth Station, Matura.

1971. Satellite Earth Station. Mult.

No.	Description	Unused	Used
403.	10 c. Type **139**	10	10
404.	30 c. Dish antennae	20	20
405.	40 c. Satellite and the Earth	30	30

140. "Morpho peleides x achilleana".

1972. Butterflies. Multicoloured.

No.	Description	Unused	Used
407	3 c. Type **140**	40	10
408	5 c. "Eryphanis polyxena"	50	10
409	6 c. "Phoebis philea"	55	10
410	10 c. "Prepona laertes"	80	15
411	20 c. "Eurytides telesilaus"	1·25	1·40
412	30 c. "Eurema proterpia"	1·75	2·25

141. "Lady McLeod" (paddle-steamer) and McLeod Stamp.

1972. 125th Anniv. of 1st Trinidad Postage Stamp.

No.	Description	Unused	Used
413. **141.**	5 c. multicoloured	15	10
414. –	10 c. multicoloured	25	10
415. –	30 c. blue, brn. & blk.	70	45

DESIGNS: 10 c. Lady McLeod stamp and Map. 30 c. Lady McLeod and inscription.

142. Trinity Cross.

1972. 10th Anniv. of Independence. Mult.

No.	Description	Unused	Used
417.	5 c. Type **142**	10	10
418.	10 c. Chaconia Medal	10	10
419.	20 c. Humming-bird Medal	15	15
420.	30 c. Medal of Merit	15	20

See also Nos. 440/3.

143. Bronze Medal, 1964 Relay.

1972. Olympic Games, Munich. Multicoloured.

No.	Description	Unused	Used
422.	10 c. Type **143**	10	10
423.	20 c. Bronze, 1964 200 metres	30	10
424.	30 c. Silver, 1952 weight-lifting	40	15
425.	40 c. Silver, 1964 400 metres	40	20
426.	50 c. Silver, 1948 weight-lifting	40	50

144. "Adoration of the Kings" (detail, Dosso).

1972. Christmas. Multicoloured.

No.	Description	Unused	Used
428.	3 c. Type **144**	10	10
429.	5 c. "The Holy Family and a Shepherd" (Titian)	10	10
430.	30 c. As 5 c.	70	55

MINIMUM PRICE

The minimum price quoted is 10p which represents a handling charge rather than a basis for valuing common stamps. For further notes about prices see introductory pages.

145. E.C.L.A. Building, Chile.

1973. Anniversaries. Events described on stamps. Multicoloured.

435. 10 c. Type **145** 10 10
436. 20 c. Interpol emblem .. 45 20
437. 30 c. W.M.O. emblem .. 45 20
438. 40 c. University of the West Indies 45 20

1973. 11th Anniv. of Independence. Medals as T **142**. Multicoloured.

440. 10 c. Trinity Cross .. 10 10
441. 20 c. Medal of Merit .. 20 15
442. 30 c. Chaconia medal .. 20 20
443. 40 c. Humming-bird medal 30 30

146. G.P.O., Port of Spain.

1973. 2nd Commonwealth Conference of Postal Administrations, Trinidad. Mult.

445. 30 c. Type **146** 20 20
446. 40 c. Conference Hall, Chaguaramas (wrongly inscr. "Chagaramas" .. 30 30

147. "Madonna with Child" (Murillo).

1973. Christmas.

448. **147.** 5 c. multicoloured .. 10 10
449. $1 multicoloured .. 75 60

148. Berne H.Q. within U.P.U. Emblem.

1974. Centenary of Universal Postal Union. Multicoloured.

451. 40 c. Type **148** 35 25
452. 50 c. Map within emblem .. 35 50

149. "Humming Bird I" crossing Atlantic Ocean (1960).

1974. 1st Anniv. of World Voyage by H. and K. La Borde. Multicoloured.

454. 40 c. Type **149** 45 15
455. 50 c. "Humming Bird II" crossing globe 55 35

150. "Sex Equality".

1975. International Women's Year.

457. **150.** 15 c. multicoloured .. 15 10
458. 30 c. multicoloured .. 35 40

151. Common Vampire Bat, Microscope and Syringe.

1975. Isolation of Rabies Virus. Mult.

459. 25 c. Type **151** 40 30
460. 30 c. Dr. Pawan, instruments and book .. 50 35

152. Route-map and Tail of Boeing "707".

1975. 35th Anniv. of British West Indies Airways. Multicoloured.

461. 20 c. Type **152** 20 10
462. 30 c. "707" on ground .. 30 30
463. 40 c. "707" in flight .. 40 40

153. "From the Land of the Humming Bird".

1975. Carnival. 1974 Prizewinning Costumes. Multicoloured.

465. 30 c. Type **153** 10 10
466. $1 "The Little Carib" .. 40 50

154. Angostura Building, Port of Spain.

1976. 150th Anniv. of Angostura Bitters. Multicoloured.

468. 5 c. Type **154** 10 10
469. 35 c. Medal, New Orleans 1885/6 .. .. 20 25
470. 45 c. Medal, Sydney 1879 25 40
471. 50 c. Medal Brussels 1897 25 50

1976. West Indian Victory in World Cricket Cup. As T **126** of Barbados.

474. 35 c. Caribbean map .. 45 30
475. 45 c. Prudential Cup .. 55 40

155. "Columbus Sailing Through the Bocas" (Campins).

1976. Paintings, Hotels and Orchids. Mult.

479. 5 c. Type **155** 60 10
480. 6 c. Robinson Crusoe Hotel 10 30
482. 10 c. "San Fernando Hill" (J. Cazabon) 10 10
483. 12 c. "Paphinia cristata" 1·25 30
484. 15 c. Turtle Beach Hotel .. 40 40
485. 20 c. "East Indians in a Landscape" (J. Cazabon) 40 10
486. 25 c. Mt. Irvine Hotel .. 40 10
487. 30 c. "Caularthron bicornutum" .. .. 1·25 30
488. 35 c. "Los Gallos Point" (J. Cazabon) 70 10
489. 40 c. "Miltassia" .. 1·25 10
490. 45 c. "Corbeaux Town" (J. Cazabon) 80 10
491. 50 c. "Oncidium ampliatum" .. .. .. 1·50 20
492. 70 c. Beach facilities, Mt. Irvine Hotel 50 80
494. $2.50 "Oncidium papilio" 2·00 1·00
495. $5 Trinidad Holiday Inn 1·75 4·50

156. Hasely Crawford and Olympic Gold Medal.

1977. Hasely Crawford Commemoration.

501. **156.** 25 c. multicoloured .. 20 30

157. Lindbergh's Sikorsky "S-38", 1929.

1977. 50th Anniv. of Airmail Service. Mult.

503. 20 c. Type **157** 25 20
504. 35 c. Arrival of Charles and Anne Lindbergh .. 35 35
505. 45 c. Boeing "707", c. 1960 45 50
506. 50 c. Boeing "747", 1969 1·10 2·25

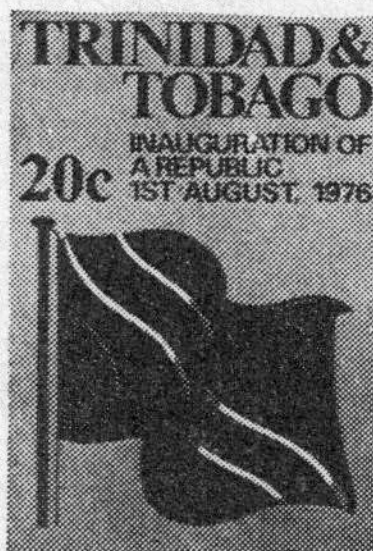

158. National Flag.

1977. Inauguration of Republic. Mult.

508. 20 c. Type **158** 15 10
509. 35 c. Coat-of-arms .. 25 25
510. 45 c. Government House .. 35 35

159. White Poinsettia.

1977. Christmas. Multicoloured.

512. 10 c. Type **159** 15 10
513. 35 c. Type **159** 25 10
514. 45 c. Red Poinsettia .. 35 25
515. 50 c. As 45 c. 45 60

160. Miss Janelle (Penny) Commissiong with Trophy.

1978. "Miss Universe 1977" Commemoration. Multicoloured.

517. 10 c. Type **160** 15 10
518. 35 c. Portrait 40 40
519. 45 c. In evening dress .. 55 65

161. Tayra.

1978. Wildlife. Multicoloured.

521. 15 c. Type **161** 20 10
522. 25 c. Ocelot 30 20
523. 40 c. Brazilian tree porcupine 50 30
524. 70 c. Tamandua .. .. 65 1·00

162. "Burst of Beauty".

1979. Carnival, 1978.

526. **162.** 5 c. multicoloured .. 10 10
527. – 10 c. multicoloured .. 10 10
528. – 35 c. multicoloured .. 10 10
529. – 45 c. multicoloured .. 10 10
530. – 50 c. brown, red & lilac 10 15
531. – $1 multicoloured .. 20 40

DESIGNS: 10 c. Rain worshipper. 35 c. "Zodiac". 45 c. Praying mantis. 50 c. "Eye of the Hurricane". $1, Steel orchestra.

163. Day Care.

1979. International Year of the Child. Multicoloured.

532. 5 c. Type **163** 10 10
533. 10 c. School feeding programme 10 10
534. 35 c. Dental care 25 15
535. 45 c. Nursery school .. 25 20
536. 50 c. Free bus transport .. 25 30
537. $1 Medical care 55 80

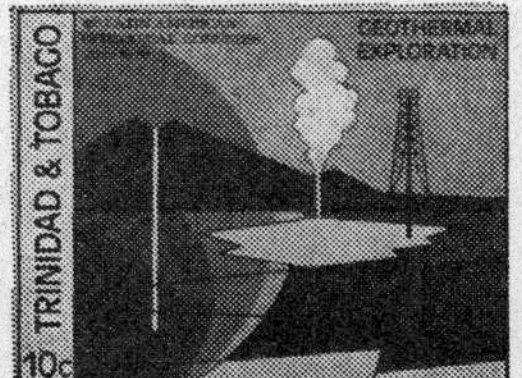

164. Geothermal Exploration.

1979. 4th Latin American Geological Congress. Multicoloured.
539. 10 c. Type **164** 15 10
540. 35 c. Hydrogeology .. 25 25
541. 45 c. Petroleum exploration 30 30
542. 70 c. Environmental preservation .. .. 40 1·00

165. 1879 1d. Stamp and Map of Tobago.

1979. Tobago Stamp Centenary.
544. **165.** 10 c. multicoloured .. 10 10
545. – 15 c. multicoloured .. 10 10
546. – 35 c. multicoloured .. 35 30
547. – 45 c. multicoloured .. 40 30
548. – 70 c. multicoloured .. 55 1·00
549. – $1 black, lilac & orange 75 1·50
DESIGNS: 15 c. 1879 3d. and 1880 ½d. surcharged on half of 6d. 35 c. 1879 6d. and 1886 ½d. surcharged on 6d. 45 c. 1879 1s. and 1886 ½d. surcharged on 2½d. 70 c. 1879 5s. and Great Britain 1856 1s. with "A14" (Scarborough, Tobago) postmark. $1, 1879 £1 and General Post Office, Scarborough, Tobago.

166. 1962 60 c. Independence Commemorative Stamp and Sir Rowland Hill.

1979. Death Centenary of Sir Rowland Hill. Multicoloured.
551. 25 c. Type **166** .. 30 15
552. 45 c. 1977 35 c. Inauguration of Republic commemorative 40 20
553. $1 1879 Trinidad ½d. surcharge and Tobago 1880 4d. .. .. 65 1·00

167. Poui Tree in Churchyard.

1980. Centenary of Princes Town. Mult.
555. 5 c. Type **167** 10 10
556. 10 c. Princes Town Court House 10 10
557. 50 c. Steam locomotive of the Royal Train, 1880 .. 60 90
558. $1.50 H.M.S. "Bacchante" (corvette) .. .. 1·00 1·60

1980. Population Census. Nos. 479/80 and 482 optd. **1844-1980 POPULATION CENSUS 12th MAY 1980.**
560. 5 c. Type **155** 10 20
561. 6 c. Robinson Crusoe Hotel, Tobago 10 30
562. 10 c. "Old View" (Cazabon) 15 20

169. Scarlet Ibis (male).

1980. Scarlet Ibis. Multicoloured.
563. 50 c. Type **169** .. 80 80
564. 50 c. Male and female .. 80 80
565. 50 c. Hen and nest .. 80 80
566. 50 c. Nest and eggs .. 80 80
567. 50 c. Chick in nest .. 80 80

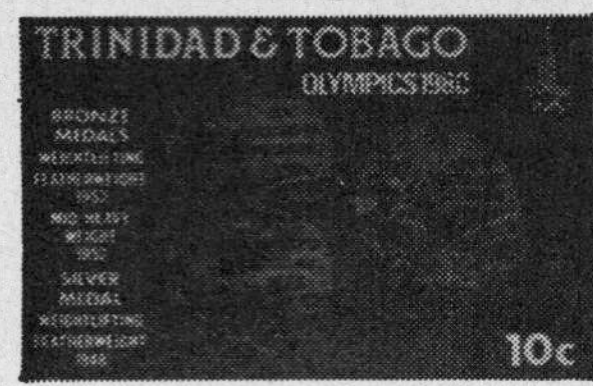

170. Silver and Bronze Medals for Weightlifting, 1948 and 1952.

1980. Olympic Games, Moscow. Multicoloured.
568. 10 c. Type **170** 10 10
569. 15 c. Hasely Crawford (100 metres sprint winner, 1976) and gold medal .. 10 10
570. 70 c. Silver medal for 400 metres and bronze medals for 4×400 metres relay, 1964 .. .. .. 30 45

171. Charcoal Production.

1980. 11th Commonwealth Forestry Conference. Multicoloured.
572. 10 c. Type **171** 10 10
573. 55 c. Logging 45 25
574. 70 c. Teak plantation .. 55 40
575. $2.50 Watershed management .. .. .. 1·40 1·50

172. Beryl McBurnie (dance and culture) and Audrey Jeffers (social worker).

1980. Decade for Women (1st issue). Mult.
577. $1 Type **172** .. 55 55
578. $1 Elizabeth Bourne (judiciary) and Isabella Teshier (government) 55 55
579. $1 Dr. Srella Abidh (public health) and Louise Horne (nutrition) 55 55
See also Nos. 680/2.

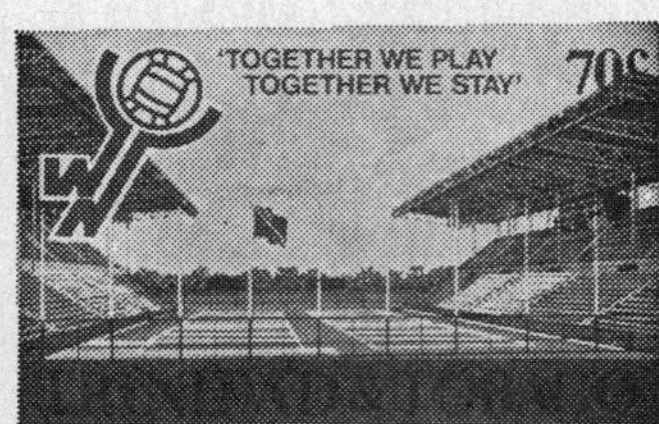

173. Netball Stadium.

1980. World Netball Tournament.
580. **173.** 70 c. multicoloured .. 30 45

174. I.Y.D.P. Emblem, Athlete and Disabled Person.

1981. International Year for Disabled Persons.
581. **174.** 10 c. green, black & red 15 10
582. – 70 c. orge., black & red 50 70
583. – $1.50 blue, blk. & red 90 1·40
584. – $2 flesh, black and red 1·25 1·75
DESIGNS: 70 c. Man with crutch. $1.50, Blind people. $2, I.Y.D.P. emblem.

175. "Our Land Must Live".

1981. Environmental Preservation. Mult.
585. 10 c. Type **175** 10 10
586. 55 c. "Our seas must live" 30 30
587. $3 "Our skies must live" 1·50 1·60

176. "Food or Famine".

1981. World Food Day. Multicoloured.
589. 10 c. Type **176** 10 10
590. 15 c. "Produce more" (threshing and milling rice) 10 10
591. 45 c. "Fish for food" (Bigeye) 30 20
592. 55 c. "Prevent hunger" .. 35 25
593. $1.50 "Fight malnutrition" 85 90
594. $2 "Fish for food" (Small-mouth Grunt) .. .. 1·10 1·25

177. "First Aid Skills".

1981. President's Award Scheme. Mult.
596. 10 c. Type **177** 20 10
597. 70 c. "Motor mechanics" 70 45
598. $1 "Expedition" .. 85 55
599. $2 Presenting an award .. 1·40 1·40

178. Pharmacist at Work.

1982. Commonwealth Pharmaceutical Conference. Multicoloured.
600. 10 c. Type **178** 10 10
601. $1 Gerritoute (plant) .. 1·25 1·25
602. $2 Rachette (plant) .. 2·00 2·25

179. "Production".

1982. 75th Anniv. of Boy Scout Movement. Multicoloured.
603. 15 c. Type **179** 45 10
604. 55 c. "Tolerance" .. 90 25
605. $5 "Discipline" .. .. 4·50 3·75

180. Charlotteville.

1982. 25th Anniv. of Tourist Board. Mult.
606. 55 c. Type **180** 35 25
607. $1 Boating 55 55
608. $3 Fort George .. .. 1·75 1·90

181. "Pa Pa Bois".

1982. Folklore. Local Spirits and Demons. Multicoloured.
609. 10 c. Type **181** 10 10
610. 15 c. "La Diablesse" .. 10 10
611. 65 c. "Lugarhoo", "Phantom" and "Soucouyant" 35 30
612. $5 "Bois de Soleil", "Davens" and "Mamma de l'Eau" .. .. 2·50 3·25

182. Cane Harvesting.

1982. Centenary of Canefarmers' Association. Multicoloured.
614. 30 c. Type **182** 15 15
615. 70 c. Farmers loading bullock cart 40 40
616. $1.50 Cane field in bloom 85 95

183. National Stadium.

1982. 20th Anniv. of Independence. Mult.
618. 10 c. Type **183** .. .. 10 1(
619. 35 c. Caroni water treatment plant 20 1
620. 50 c. Mount Hope maternity hospital .. 30 2
621. $2 National Insurance Board Mall, Tobago .. 80 1·2

184. Commonwealth Flags.

1983. Commonwealth Day. Multicoloured.
622. 10 c. Type **184** 10 1
623. 55 c. Satellite view of Trinidad and Tobago .. 25 2
624. $1 "Nodding Donkey" oil pump (vert.) .. 40
625. $2 Map of Trinidad and Tobago (vert.) .. .. 85 1·

185. BWIA "Tristar".

1983. 10th Anniv. of Caricom.
626. **185.** 35 c. multicoloured .. 80 60

186. V.D.U. Operator.

1983. World Communications Year. Mult.
627. 15 c. Type **186** 15 10
628. 55 c. Scarborough Post Office, Tobago 80 20
629. $1 Textel building .. 95 60
630. $3 Morne Blue E.C.M.S. station .. .. .. 2·40 1·90

187. Financial Complex.

1983. Conference of Commonwealth Finance Ministers.
631. **187.** $2 multicoloured .. 1·50 1·00

188. Kingfish.

1983. World Food Day. Multicoloured.
632. 10 c. Type **188** 20 10
633. 55 c. Flying Fish .. .. 1·00 40
634. 70 c. Queen Conch .. 1·25 1·00
635. $4 Red Shrimp .. .. 4·50 6·00

189. Bois pois. **190.** Castle Chess Pieces in Staunton and 17th-century Styles

1983. Flowers. Multicoloured.
686 5 c. Type **189** 15 10
687 10 c. Maraval lily .. 15 10
638 15 c. Star grass 20 20
639 20 c. Bois caco 10 10
640 25 c. Strangling fig .. 10 10
641 30 c. "Cassia moschata" .. 30 15
642 50 c. Chalice flower .. 15 15
643 65 c. Black stick 40 25
644 80 c. "Columnea scandens" 50 35
695 95 c. Cat's claws 40 40
696 $1 Bois l'agli 45 30
697 $1.50 "Eustoma exaltatum" 75 75
698 $2 Chaconia (39 × 29 mm) 95 95
649 $2.50 "Chrysothemis pulchella" (39 × 29 mm) 75 1·00
700 $5 "Centratherum punctatum" (39 × 29 mm) .. 1·50 1·50
701 $10 Savanna flower (39 × 29 mm) .. .. .. 2·75 3·00

Nos 636/8 and 640 exist with or without imprint date.

1984. 60th Anniv. of World Chess Federation. Multicoloured.
652. 50 c. Type **190** .. .. 1·50 35
653. 70 c. Staunton and 12th-century Bishops .. 1·75 75
654. $1.50 Staunton and 13th-century Queens .. .. 2·50 2·50
655. $2 Staunton and 19th-century Kings .. .. 3·00 3·50

191. Swimming. **192.** Slave Schooner and Shackles.

1984. Olympic Games, Los Angeles. Multicoloured.
656. 15 c. Type **191** 10 10
657. 55 c. Track and field events 30 20
658. $1.50 Sailing 70 80
659. $4 Cycling .. .. .. 2·00 2·50

1984. 150th Anniv. of Abolition of Slavery. Multicoloured.
661. 35 c. Type **192** .. 75 20
662. 55 c. Slave and "Slave Triangle" map .. .. 1·00 30
663. $1 "Capitalism and Slavery" (book by Dr. Eric Williams) .. 1·75 75
664. $2 Toussaint l'Ouverture (Haitian revolutionary) 2·25 1·90

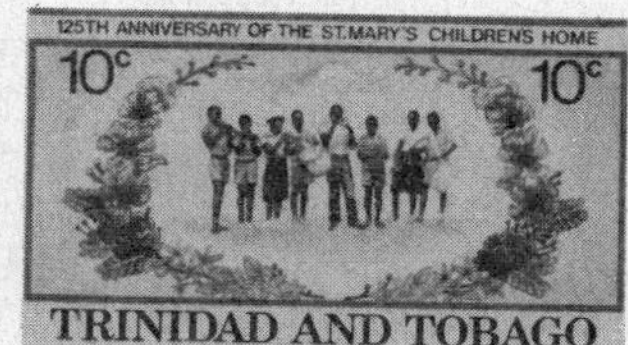

193. Children's Band.

1984. 125th Anniv. of St. Mary's Children's Home. Multicoloured.
666. 10 c. Type **193** 10 10
667. 70 c. St. Mary's Children's Home 40 40
668. $3 Group of children .. 2·00 2·25

194. Parang Band.

1984. Parang Festival. Multicoloured.
669. 10 c. Type **194** 10 10
670. 30 c. Music and poinsettia 20 15
671. $1 Bandola, bandolin and cuatro (musical instruments) 70 65
672. $3 Double bass, fiddle and guitar (musical instruments) .. .. .. 2·00 2·00

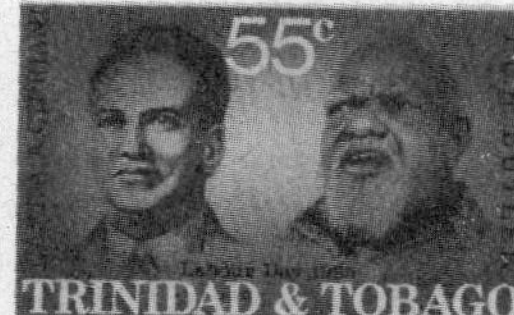

195. Capt. A. A. Cipriani and T. U. B. Butler

1985. Labour Day. Labour Leaders.
673. **195.** 55 c. black and red .. 45 45
674. – 55 c. black and yellow 45 45
675. – 55 c. black and green 45 45

Designs: No. 674, C. P. Alexander and Q. O'Connor. 675, A. Cola Rienzi and C. T. W. E. Worrell.

196. "Lady Nelson" (1928).

1985. Ships. Multicoloured.
676. 30 c. Type **196** 70 15
677. 95 c. "Lady Drake" (1928) 1·25 50
678. $1.50 "Federal Palm" (1961) .. .. .. 1·75 2·00
679. $2 "Federal Maple" (1961) 2·25 2·50

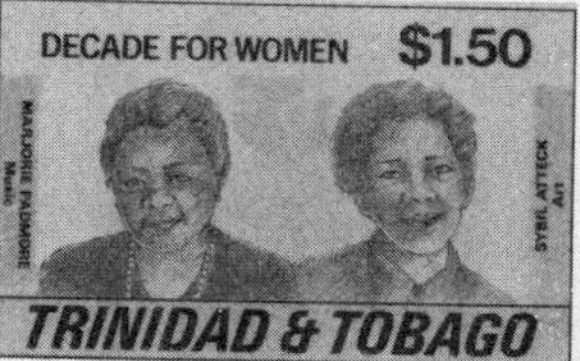

197. Marjorie Padmore (music) and Sybil Atteck (art).

1985. Decade for Women (2nd issue). Multicoloured.
680. $1.50 Type **197** .. .. 90 1·00
681. $1.50, May Cherrie (medical social worker) and Evelyn Tracey (social worker) .. .. .. 90 1·00
682. $1.50 Umilta McShine (education) and Jessica Smith-Phillips (public service) .. .. .. 90 1·00

198. Badge of Trinidad and Tobago Cadet Force (75th Anniv.)

1985. International Youth Year. Mult.
683. 10 c. Type **198** 15 10
684. 65 c. Guide badges (75th anniv of Girl Guide movement) 65 75
685. 95 c. Young people of Trinidad .. .. .. 90 1·00

199. Anne-Marie Javouhey (foundress).

1986. 150th Anniv. of Arrival of Sisters of St. Joseph de Cluny. Multicoloured.
702. 10 c. Type **199** 10 10
703. 65 c. St. Joseph's Convent, Port-of-Spain 35 50
704. 95 c. Children and statue of Anne-Marie Javouhey .. 45 75

200. Tank Locomotive "Arima".

1986. "Ameripex '86" International Stamp Exhibition, Chicago. Trinidad Railway Locomotives. Multicoloured.
705. 65 c. Type **200** .. 25 30
706. 95 c. Canadian-built loco motive No. "22" .. 35 40
707. $1.10 Tender engine .. 40 65
708. $1.50 Saddle tank 60 90

201. Scout Camp.

1986. 75th Anniv. of Trinidad and Tobago Boy Scouts. Multicoloured.
710. $1.70 Type **201** .. .. 1·00 1·25
711. $2 Scouts of 1911 and 1986 1·25 1·50

202. Queen and Duke of Edinburgh laying Wreath at War Memorial.

1986. 60th Birthday of Queen Elizabeth II. Multicoloured.
712. 10 c. Type **202** 10 10
713. 15 c. Queen with Trinidadian dignitaries aboard "Britannia" .. 20 10
714. 30 c. With President Ellis Clarke 30 15
715. $5 Receiving bouquet .. 2·50 3·00

203. Eric Williams at Graduation, 1935.

1986. 75th Birth Anniv. of Dr. Eric Williams. Multicoloured.
716. 10 c. Type **203** 15 10
717. 30 c. Premier Eric Williams (wearing red tie) .. 30 15
718. 30 c. As No. 717, but wearing black and orange tie 30 15
719. 95 c. Arms of University of West Indies and Dr. Williams as Pro-Chancellor (horiz.) 60 40
720. $5 Prime Minister Williams and Whitehall (horiz.) .. 2·00 2·00

204. "PEACE" Slogan and Outline Map of Trinidad and Tobago.

1986. International Peace Year. Mult.
722. 95 c. Type **204** .. 40 50
723. $3 Peace dove with olive branch .. .. .. 1·25 1·75

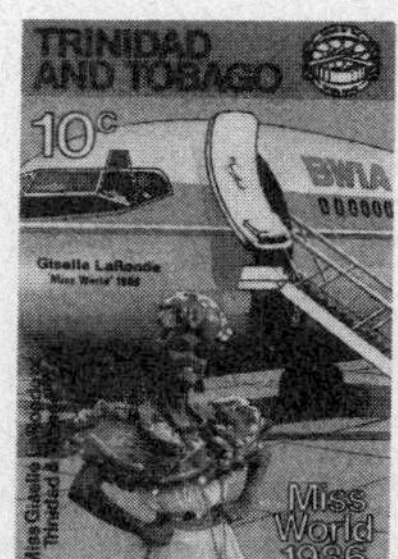

205. Miss Giselle La Ronde and "BWIA" Airliner.

1987. Miss World 1986. Multicoloured.

724.	10 c. Type **205**	20	10
725.	30 c. In swimsuit on beach	45	15
726.	95 c. Miss Giselle La Ronde	80	65
727.	$1.65 Wearing Miss World sash	1·25	1·50

206. Colonial Bank, Port of Spain.

1987. 150th Anniv. of Republic Bank. Mult.

728.	10 c. Type **206**	10	10
729.	65 c. Cocoa plantation	40	40
730.	95 c. Oil field	75	75
731.	$1.10 Belmont Tramway Company tramcar	1·00	1·00

207. Sergeant in Parade Order and Soldiers in Work Dress and Battle Dress.

1988. 25th Anniv. of Defence Force. Mult.

732.	10 c. Type **207**	20	10
733.	30 c. Women soldiers	60	20
734.	$1.10 Defence Force officers	1·25	1·00
735.	$1.50 Naval ratings and patrol boat	1·50	1·25

1988. West Indian Cricket. As T **186** of Barbados, each showing portrait, cricket equipment and early belt buckle. Mult.

736	30 c. George John	55	20
737	65 c. Learie Constantine	85	55
738	95 c. Sonny Ramadhin	1·00	85
739	$1.50 Gerry Gomez	1·75	1·75
740	$2.50 Jeffrey Stollmeyer	2·00	2·50

208 Uriah Butler (labour leader)

1988. 50th Anniv (1987) of Oilfield Workers Trade Union. Multicoloured.

741	10 c. Type **208**	10	10
742	30 c. Adrian Rienzi (O.W.T.U. president, 1937–42)	10	10
743	65 c. John Rojas (O.W.T.U. president, 1943–62)	15	20
744	$5 George Weekes (O.W.T.U. president, 1962–87)	1·25	1·40

209 Mary Werges and Santa Rosa Church

1988. Centenary of Borough of Arima. Mult.

745	20 c. Type **209**	10	10
746	30 c. Governor W. Robinson and Royal Charter	10	10
747	$1.10 Arrival of Governor Robinson	45	45
748	$1.50 Mayor J.F. Wallen and Centenary logo	65	65

1988. 300th Anniv of Lloyd's of London. As T **123** of Ascension. Multicoloured.

749	30 c. Queen Mother at Topping-out Ceremony of new building, 1984	15	10
750	$1.10 BWIA Tristar "500" airliner (horiz)	60	35
751	$1.55 Steel works, Trinidad (horiz)	75	45
752	$2 "Atlantic Empress" on fire off Tobago	90	55

210 Colonial Arms of Trinidad & Tobago and 1913 1d. Stamp

1989. Centenary of Union of Trinidad and Tobago. Multicoloured.

753	40 c. Type **210**	15	10
754	$1 Pre-1889 Tobago emblem and Tobago 1896 ½d. on 4d. stamp	50	30
755	$1.50 Pre-1889 Trinidad emblem and Trinidad 1883 4d. stamp	70	55
756	$2.25 Current Arms of Trinidad and Tobago and 1977 45 c. Republic commemorative	95	85

211 Common Piping Guan

1989. Rare Fauna of Trinidad and Tobago. Multicoloured.

757	$1 Type **211**	90	90
758	$1 "Phyllodytes auratus" (frog)	90	90
759	$1 "Cebus albifrons trinitatis" (monkey)	90	90
760	$1 Tamandua	90	90
761	$1 "Lutra longicaudis" (otter)	90	90

Nos. 757/61 were printed together, se-tenant, forming a composite background design.

212 Blind Welfare

1989. Anniversaries. Multicoloured.

762	10 c. Type **212** (75th anniv)	10	10
763	40 c. Port-of-Spain City Hall (75th anniv)	25	15
764	$1 Guides and Brownies (75th anniv)	75	40
765	$2.25 Red Cross members (50th anniv)	1·50	1·40

213 Tenor Pan

1989. Steel Pans (1st series). Multicoloured.

766	10 c. Type **213**	10	10
767	40 c. Guitar pans	15	15
768	$1 Cello pans	45	45
769	$2.25 Bass pans	85	85

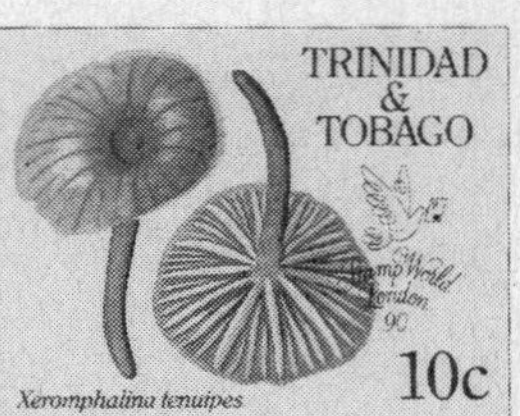

214 "Xeromphalina tenuipes"

1990. "Stamp World London 90" International Stamp Exhibition. Fungi. Mult.

770	10 c. Type **214**	10	10
771	40 c. "Dictyophora indusiata"	20	20
772	$1 "Leucocoprinus birnbaumii"	70	50
773	$2.25 "Crinipellis perniciosa"	1·50	1·75

215 Scarlet Ibis in Immature Plumage

1990. Scarlet Ibis. Multicoloured.

774	40 c. Type **215**	30	20
775	80 c. Pair in pre-nuptial display	55	50
776	$1 Male in breeding plumage	70	55
777	$2.25 Adult on nest with chick	1·60	1·75

216 Princess Alice and Administration Building

1990. 40th Anniv of University of West Indies. Multicolored.

778	40 c. Type **216**	20	15
779	80 c. Sir Hugh Wooding and Library	35	30
780	$1 Sir Allen Lewis and Faculty of Engineering	45	35
781	$2.25 Sir Shridath Ramphal and Faculty of Medical Sciences	1·00	1·25

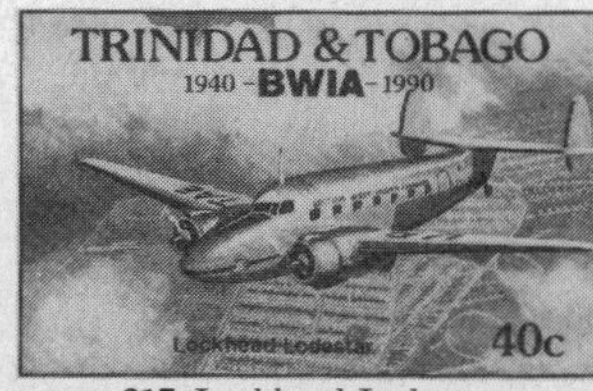

217 Lockheed Lodestar

1990. 50th Anniv of British West Indies Airways. Multicoloured.

782	40 c. Type **217**	20	15
783	80 c. Vickers Viking 1A	35	30
784	$1 Vickers Viscount 702	45	30
785	$2.25 Boeing 707	1·00	1·25

218 Yellow Oriole

1990. Birds. Multicoloured.

787	20 c. Type **218**	10	10
788	25 c. Green-rumped parrotlet	10	10
789	40 c. Fork-tailed flycatcher	10	15
790	50 c. Copper-rumped hummingbird	15	30
791	$1 Bananaquit	30	35
792	$2 Violaceous euphonia	55	60
793	$2.25 Channel-billed toucan	65	70
794	$2.50 Bay-headed tanager	70	75
795	$5 Green honeycreeper	1·40	1·50
796	$10 Cattle egret	2·75	3·00
797	$20 Golden olive woodpecker	5·50	5·75
798	$50 Peregrine falcon	14·00	14·50

219 "Lygodium volubile"

1991. Ferns. Multicoloured.

799	40 c. Type **219**	20	15
800	80 c. "Blechnum occidentale"	35	30
801	$1 "Gleichenia bifida"	45	35
802	$2.25 "Polypodium lycopodioides"	1·25	1·40

220 Trinidad and Tobago Regiment Anti-aircraft Battery

1991. 50th Anniv of Second World War. Multicoloured.

803	40 c. Type **220**	15	10
804	80 c. Fairey Barracuda attacking U-boat	30	30
805	$1 Avro Lancaster	40	35
806	$2.25 River class frigate escorting convoy	90	1·00

OFFICIAL STAMP

1913. Optd **OFFICIAL**.

O 14	**17** ½d. green	30	50

POSTAGE DUE STAMPS

1947. As Type **D 1** of Trinidad, but value in cents.

D26a	2 c. black	20	1·50
D27a	4 c. black	65	2·75
D28a	6 c. black	25	3·75
D29a	8 c. black	35	5·50
D30	10 c. black	85	2·75
D31a	12 c. black	40	6·00
D32	16 c. black	2·00	18·00
D33	24 c. black	3·75	7·50

D 2.

1969. Size 19 × 24 mm.

D 34. D 2. 2 c. green 15 1·75
D 35. 4 c. red 25 2·50
D 36. 6 c. brown 50 3·50
D 37. 8 c. violet 65 4·00
D 38. 10 c. red 65 4·00
D 39. 12 c. yellow 70 4·50
D 40. 16 c. green 15 1·50
D 41. 24 c. grey 20 1·75
D 42. 50 c. blue 35 2·25
D 43. 60 c. green 45 2·25

1976. Smaller design, 17 × 21 mm.

D 44. D 2. 2 c. green 10 65
D 45. 4 c. red 10 65
D 46. 6 c. brown 15 75
D 47. 8 c. lilac 15 75
D 48. 10 c. red 15 75
D 49. 12 c. orange 20 1·00

TRISTAN DA CUNHA

An island in the S. Atlantic Ocean west of So. Africa. Following a volcanic eruption the island was evacuated on 10 October 1961, but resettled in 1963.

1952. 12 pence = 1 shilling;
20 shillings = 1 pound.
1961. 100 cents = 1 rand.
1963. Reverted to sterling currency.

1952. Stamps of St. Helena optd. **TRISTAN DA CUNHA.**

1. 33. ½d. violet 15 85
2. 1d. black and green 30 1·25
3. 1½d. black and red 30 1·25
4. 2d. black and red 30 1·50
5. 3d. grey 40 1·25
6. 4d. blue 1·25 2·00
7. 6d. blue 3·00 2·50
8. 8d. green 2·50 3·00
9. 1s. brown 2·75 2·00
10. 2s. 6d. purple 19·00 14·00
11. 5s. brown 26·00 27·00
12. 10s. purple 48·00 55·00

1953. Coronation. As T **13** of Aden.

13. 3d. black and green 90 1·50

2. Tristan Crawfish.

DESIGNS—HORIZ. 1d. Carting flax. 2d. Big Beach Factory. 2½d. Yellow-nosed Albatross (sea birds). 4d. Tristan from S.W. 5d. Girls on donkeys. 6d. Inaccessible Is. from Tristan. 9d. Nightingale Is. 1s. St. Mary's Church. 2s. 6d. Southern elephant seal at Gough Is. 5s. Inaccessible Island Rail (bird). 10s. Spinning wheel. VERT. 1½d. Rockhopper Penguin. 3d. Island longboat.

1954.

14. 2. ½d. red and brown 10 10
15. – 1d. sepia and green 10 15
16. – 1½d. black and purple 2·50 30
17. – 2d. violet and orange 30 15
18. – 2½d. black and red 2·00 50
19. – 3d. blue and olive 80 20
20. – 4d. turquoise and blue 1·25 40
21. – 5d. green and black 1·25 40
22. – 6d. green and violet 1·25 45
23. – 9d. lilac and red 1·25 45
24. – 1 s. green and sepia 1·25 45
25. – 2s. 6d. sepia and blue 26·00 10·00
26. – 5s. black and red 48·00 16·00
27. – 10s. orange and purple 32·00 20·00

16. Starfish.

FISH: 1d. Concha Fish. 1½d. Klip Fish. 2d. Heron Fish. 2½d. Swordfish. 3d. Tristan Crawfish. 4d. Soldier Fish. 5d. "Five Finger" Fish. 6d. Mackerel. 9d. Stumpnose Fish. 1s. Blue Fish. 2s. 6d. Snoek. 5s. Shark. 10s. Black Right Whale.

1960. Value, fish and inscriptions in black.

28. 16. ½d. orange 15 30
29. – 1d. purple 15 15
30. – 1½d. turquoise 15 25
31. – 2d. green 20 20
32. – 2½d. sepia 25 20
33. – 3d. red 25 15
34. – 4d. olive 30 20
35. – 5d. yellow 45 30
36. – 6d. blue 50 25
37. – 9d. red 55 30
38. – 1s. brown 75 25
39. – 2s. 6d. blue 11·00 15·00
40. – 5s. green 28·00 22·00
41. – 10s. violet 48·00 40·00

1961. As 1960 issue but values in new currency. Value, fish and inscriptions black.

42. 16. ½ c. orange 10 15
43. – 1 c. purple (as 1d.) 15 15
44. – 1½ c. turquoise (as 1½d.) 35 20
45. – 2 c. sepia (as 2½d.) 40 20
46. – 2½ c. red (as 3d.) 50 20
47. – 3 c. olive (as 4d.) 65 20
48. – 4 c. yellow (as 5d.) 80 20
49. – 5 c. blue (as 6d.) 85 20
50. – 7½ c. red (as 9d.) 90 20
51. – 10 c. brown (as 1s.) 1·00 20
52. – 25 c. blue (as 2s. 6d.) 6·00 11·00
53. – 50 c. green (as 5s.) 28·00 22·00
54. – 1 r. violet (as 10s.) 48·00 42·00

1963. Tristan Resettlement. Nos. 176/88 of St. Helena optd. **TRISTAN DA CUNHA RESETTLEMENT 1963.**

55. 50. 1d. multicoloured 15 15
56. – 1½d. multicoloured 20 15
57. – 2d. red and grey 25 15
58. – 3d. multicoloured 30 20
59. – 4½d. multicoloured 50 30
60. – 6d. red, sepia and olive 75 15
61. – 7d. brown, black & violet 50 20
62. – 10d. purple and blue 50 15
63. – 1s. lemon, green & brown 50 15
64. – 1s. 6d. grey, black and blue 1·50 60
65. – 2s. 6d. red, yell. & turq. 1·00 45
66. – 5s. yellow, brown & green 5·00 1·25
67. – 10s. red, black and blue 6·50 1·25

1963. Freedom from Hunger. As T **28** of Aden.

68. 1s. 6d. red 90 30

1964. Cent of Red Cross. As T **33** of Antigua.

69. 3d. red and black 35 15
70. 1s. 6d. red and blue 65 20

31. South Atlantic Map.

1965.

71. 31. ½d. black and blue 15 15
72. – 1d. black and green 30 15
73. – 1½d. black and blue 30 15
74. – 2d. black and purple 30 15
75. – 3d. black & turquoise 30 15
75a. – 4d. black and orange 4·75 4·00
76. – 4½d. black and brown 30 15
77. – 6d. black and green 30 15
78. – 7d. black and red 30 15
79. – 10d. black and brown 30 15
80. – 1s. black and red 30 15
81. – 1s. 6d. black and olive 2·50 1·50
82. – 2s. 6d. black and brown 2·75 2·00
83. – 5s. black and violet 5·50 3·25
84. – 10s. blue and red 1·75 1·25
84a. – 10s. black and blue 17·00 10·00
84b. – £1 blue and brown 17·00 10·00

DESIGNS—HORIZ. 1d. Flagship of Tristan da Cunha. 1½d. "Heemstede". 2d. New England whaling ship. 3d. "Shenandoah". 4d. H.M.S. "Challenger". 4½d. H.M.S. "Galatea". 6d. H.M.S. "Cilicia". 7d. Royal Yacht "Britannia". 10d. H.M.S. "Leopard". 1s. M.V. "Tijsadane". 1s. 6d. M.V. "Tristania" 2s. 6d. M.V. "Boissevain". 5s. M.S. "Bornholm". 10s. (No. 84a) Research Vessel "R.S.A.". VERT. (No. 84), £1 Queen Elizabeth II (portrait as in T **31** but larger).

1965. Cent of I.T.U. As T **36** of Antigua.

85. 3d. red and grey 50 15
86. 6d. violet and orange 60 15

1965. I.C.Y. As T **37** of Antigua.

87. 1d. purple and turquoise 40 15
88. 6d. green and lavender 1·50 25

1966. Churchill Commem. As T **38** of Antigua.

89. 1d. blue 50 25
90. 3d. green 2·50 40
91. 6d. brown 3·50 45
92. 1s. 6d. violet 4·00 60

45. H.M.S. "Falmouth" at Tristan and Soldier of 1816.

1966. 150th Anniv. of Tristan Garrison.

93. 45. 3d. multicoloured 20 10
94. 6d. multicoloured 20 10
95. 1s. 6d. multicoloured 20 10
96. 2s. 6d. multicoloured 30 10

1966. World Cup Football Championship. As T **40** of Antigua.

97. 3d. multicoloured 25 10
98. 2s. 6d. multicoloured 65 20

1966. Inauguration of W.H.O. Headquarters, Geneva. As T **41** of Antigua.

99. 6d. black, green and blue 1·00 30
100. 5s. black, purple and ochre 1·25 70

1966. 20th Anniv of U.N.E.S.C.O. As T **54/6** of Antigua.

101. 10d. multicoloured 60 15
102. 1s. 6d. yell., violet & olive 65 15
103. 2s. 6d. black, pur. & orge. 80 20

46. Calshot Harbour.

1967. Opening of Calshot Harbour.

104. 46. 6d. multicoloured 10 10
105. 10d. multicoloured 10 10
106. 1s. 6d. multicoloured 10 10
107. 2s. 6d. multicoloured 15 15

1967. No. 76 surch. 4d and bars.

108. – 4d. on 4½d. black & brn. 10 10

48. Prince Alfred, First Duke of Edinburgh.

1967. Centenary of 1st Duke of Edinburgh's Visit to Tristan.

109. 48. 3d. multicoloured 10 10
110. 6d. multicoloured 10 10
111. 1s. 6d. multicoloured 10 10
112. 2s. 6d. multicoloured 15 10

49. Wandering Albatross.

1968. Birds. Multicoloured.

113. 4d. Type **49** 40 10
114. 1s. Wilkin's Finch 45 10
115. 1s. 6d. Tristan Thrush 50 15
116. 2s. 6d. Great Shearwater 90 20

53. Union Jack and Dependency Flag.

1968. 30th Anniv. of Tristan da Cunha as a Dependency of St. Helena.

117. 53. 6d. multicoloured 10 10
118. – 9d. sepia and blue 10 10
119. 53. 1s. 6d. multicoloured 10 10
120. – 2s. 6d. red and blue 15 10

DESIGN: 9d. and 2s. 6d. St. Helena and Tristan on chart.

55. Frigate.

1969. Clipper Ships.

121. 55. 4d. blue 40 10
122. – 1s. red 40 15
123. – 1s. 6d. green 45 20
124. – 2s. 6d. brown 50 25

DESIGNS: 1s. Full-rigged ship. 1s 6d. Barque. 2s 6d. Full-rigged clipper.

59. Sailing Ship off Tristan da Cunha.

1969. United Society for the Propagation of the Gospel. Multicoloured.

125. 4d. Type **59** 10 10
126. 9d. Islanders going to First Gospel Service 10 10
127. 1s. 6d. Landing of the First Minister 10 15
128. 2s. 6d. Procession outside St. Mary's Church 15 20

63. Globe and Red Cross Emblem.

1970. Centenary of British Red Cross.

129. 63. 4d. deep green, red and green 10 10
130. 9d. bistre, red and green 10 10
131. – 1s. 9d. drab, red and blue 20 15
132. – 2s. 6d. pur., red & blue 25 30

DESIGNS—VERT. Nos. 131/2 "Union Jack" and Red Cross Flag.

64. Crawfish and Longboat.

1970. Crawfish Industry. Multicoloured.

133. 4d. Type **64** 20 10
134. 10d. Packing and storing crawfish 25 10
135. 1s. 6d. Type **64** 35 25
136. 2s. 6d. As 10d. 40 30

1971. Decimal Currency. Nos. 72, etc. surch with new values.

137. 31. ½p. on 1d. black & green 15 15
138. – 1p. on 2d. black & purple 15 15
139. – 1½p. on 4d. blk. & orange 30 15
140. – 2½p. on 6d. blk. & green 30 15
141. – 3p. on 7d. black and red 30 15
142. – 4p. on 10d. blk. & brown 30 20
143. – 5p. on 1s. black and red 30 20
144. – 7½p. on 1s. 6d. blk. & olive 1·75 95
145. – 12½p. on 2s. 6d. blk. & brn. 2·00 2·50
146. – 15p. on 1½d. black & blue 3·50 3·00
147. – 25p. on 5s. black & violet 3·50 5·00
148. – 50p. on 10s. black and blue (No. 84a) .. 8·00 11·00

66. " Quest ".

1971. 50th Anniv. of Shackleton–Rowett Expedition.

149. 66. 1½p. multicoloured .. 90 30
150. – 4p. brown, green and light green .. .. 1·00 40
151. – 7½p. black, pur. & green 1·00 40
152. – 12½p. multicoloured .. 1·40 45

DESIGNS—HORIZ. 4p. Presentation of Scout Troop flag. 7½p. Cachet on pair of 6d. G.B. stamps. 12½p. Shackleton, postmarks, and longboat taking mail to the "Quest".

67. H.M.S. "Victory" at Trafalgar and Thomas Swain catching Nelson.

1971. Island Families. Multicoloured.

153. 1½p. Type **67** 25 30
154. 2½p. "Emily of Stonington" (P. W. Green) 35 40
155. 4p. "Italia" (Lavarello and Repetto) 40 50
156. 7½p. H.M.S. "Falmouth" (William Glass) 55 65
157. 12½p. American whaling ship (Rogers and Hagan) 65 80

68. Cow-Pudding.

1972. Multicoloured.

158. ½p. Type **68** 20 10
159. 1p. Peak Berry 40 10
160. 1½p. Sand Flower (horiz.) 40 15
161. 2½p. N.Z. Flax (horiz.) .. 40 15
162. 3p. Island Tree 40 15
163. 4p. Bog Fern 40 15
164. 5p. Dog Catcher 40 15
165. 7½p. Celery .. .. 2·00 30
166. 12½p. Pepper Tree .. 1·50 60
167. 25p. Foul Berry (horiz.) .. 1·75 1·50
168. 50p. Tussock .. .. 5·00 1·75
169. £1 Tussac (horiz.) .. 5·00 3·00

69. Launching.

1972. Tristan Longboats. Multicoloured.

170. 2½p. Type **69** 15 10
171. 4p. Under oars 20 10
172. 7½p. Coxswain. Arthur Repetto (vert.) 25 15
173. 12½p. Under Sail for Nightingale Island (vert.) 30 20

1972. Royal Silver Wedding. As T **52** of Ascension, but with Tristan Thrushes and Wandering Albatrosses in background.

174. 2½p. brown 35 40
175. 7½p. blue 15 40

71. Church Altar.

1973. Golden Jubilee of St. Mary's Church.

176. 71. 25 p. multicoloured .. 60 50

72. H.M.S. " Challenger's " Laboratory.

1973. Centenary of H.M.S. "Challenger's" Visit. Multicoloured.

177. 4p. Type **72** 30 25
178. 5p. H.M.S. "Challenger" off Tristan 30 25
179. 7½p. " Challenger's " pinnace off Nightingale Is. 30 30
180. 12½p. Survey route .. 40 40

73. Approaching English Port.

1973. 10th Anniv. of Return to Tristan da Cunha.

182. 73. 4p. brn., yellow & gold 25 25
183. – 5p multicoloured .. 25 25
184. – 7½p. multicoloured .. 35 35
185. – 12½p. multicoloured .. 45 45

DESIGNS: 5p. Survey party. 7½p. Embarking on " Bornholm ". 12½p. Approaching Tristan.

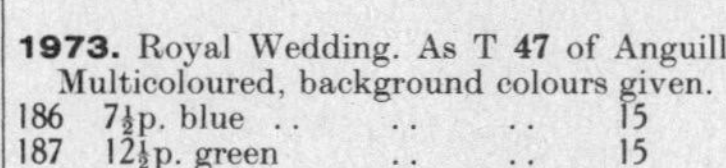

1973. Royal Wedding. As T **47** of Anguilla. Multicoloured, background colours given.

186 7½p. blue 15 10
187 12½p. green 15 10

74. Rockhopper Penguin and Egg.

1974. Penguins. Multicoloured.

188. 2½p. Type **74** .. .. 3·00 75
189. 5p. Rockhopper Penguins Colony Inaccessible Island .. .. 3·50 1·00
190. 7½p. Rockhopper Penguins fishing .. .. 4·00 1·25
191. 25p. Rockhopper Penguin and fledgling .. 4·50 1·50

76. Blenheim Palace.

1974. Birth Centenary of Sir Winston Churchill.

193. 76. 7½p. yellow and black .. 15 10
194. – 25p. black, brn. & grey 40 25

DESIGN: 25p. Churchill with Queen Elizabeth II.

77. " Plocamium fuscorubrum ".

1975. Sea Plants.

196. 77. 4p. red, lilac and black 15 10
197. – 5p. green, blue and turq. 15 15
198. – 10p. orge., brn. & pur. 20 15
199. – 20p. multicoloured .. 30 25

DESIGNS: 5p. " Ulva lactua ". 10p. " Epymeniai flabellata ". 20p. " Macrocystis pyrifera ".

78. Killer Whale.

1975. Whales. Multicoloured.

200. 2p. Type **78** 40 25
201. 3p. Rough-toothed dolphin 40 25
202. 5p. Black right whale .. 45 30
203. 20p. Fin whale .. .. 1·00 70

79. ½d. Stamp of 1952.

1976. Festival of Stamps.

204. 79. 5p. black, violet & lilac 15 20
205. – 9p. black, green & blue 15 25
206. – 25p. multicoloured .. 40 50

DESIGNS—VERT. 9p. 1953 Coronation stamp. HORIZ. 25p. Mail carrier " Tristania II ".

80. Island Cottage.

1976. Paintings by Roland Svensson (1st series). Multicoloured.

207. 3p. Type **80** 15 15
208. 5p. The potato patches (horiz.) 15 20
209. 10p. Edinburgh from the sea (horiz.) 20 25
210. 20p. Huts, Nightingale Is. 30 35

See also Nos. 234/7 and 272/5.

81. The Royal Standard.

1977. Silver Jubilee. Multicoloured.

212. 10p. Royal Yacht " Britannia " 25 30
213. 15p. Type **81** 15 20
214. 25p. Royal Family .. 25 25

82. H.M.S. " Eskimo ".

1977. Ship's Crests. Multicoloured.

215. 5p. Type **82** 20 15
216. 10p. H.M.S. " Naiad " .. 30 15
217. 15p. H.M.S. " Jaguar " .. 40 25
218. 20p. H.M.S. " London " .. 45 30

83. Great-winged Petrel.

1977. Birds. Multicoloured.

220. 1p. Type **83** 10 10
221. 2p. White-faced storm petrel 15 15
222. 3p. Hall's giant petrel .. 15 15
223. 4p. Soft-plumaged petrel .. 50 20
224. 5p. Wandering albatross .. 50 20
225. 10p. Kerguelen petrel .. 50 30
226. 15p. Swallow-tailed tern .. 50 55
227. 20p. Greater shearwater .. 85 55
228. 25p. Broad-billed prion .. 95 65
229. 50p. Great skua .. 1·50 1·00
230. £1 Common diving petrel 2·00 1·75
231. £2 Yellow-nosed albatross 4·25 3·25

The 3p. to £2 designs are vertical.

1978. Nos. 213/14 surch.

232. 4p. on 15p. Type **81** .. 2·25 6·50
233. 7½p. on 25p. Royal Family 2·25 6·50

1978. Paintings by Roland Svensson (2nd series). As T **80**. Multicoloured.

234. 5p. St. Mary's Church .. 15 15
235. 10p. Longboats .. 20 25
236. 15p. A Tristan home .. 25 30
237. 20p. The harbour, 1970 .. 30 40

85. King's Bull.

1978. 25th Anniv. of Coronation.

239. 85. 25p. brn., violet & silver 35 35
240. – 25p. multicoloured .. 35 35
241. – 25p. brn., violet & silver 35 35

DESIGNS: No. 240, Queen Elizabeth II. No. 241, Tristan crawfish.

86. Sodalite.

1978. Local Minerals.

242.	3p. Type **86**	25	10
243.	5p. Aragonite	30	15
244.	10p. Sulphur	45	25
245.	20p. Lava containing pyroxene crystal	65	35

87. Klipfish.

1978. Fishes.

246. **87.**	5p. blk., brown & green	10	10
247. –	10p. blk., brown & green	15	15
248. –	15p. multicoloured ..	20	20
249. –	20p. multicoloured ..	30	25

DESIGNS: 10p. " Fivefinger ". 15p. " Concha ". 20p. " Soldier ".

88. R.F.A. " Orangeleaf ".

1978. Royal Fleet Auxiliary Vessels. Multicoloured.

250.	5p. Type **88**	15	10
251.	10p. " R.F.A. Tarbatness "	20	10
252.	20p. " R.F.A. Tidereach "	35	25
253.	25p. " R.F.A. Reliant " ..	45	30

89. Southern Elephant-Seal.

1978. Wildlife Conservation. Multicoloured.

255.	5p. Type **89**	15	10
256.	10p. Afro-Australian fur seal	25	15
257.	15p. Tristan thrush ..	40	20
258.	20p. Nightingale finch ..	50	25

90. Tristan Longboat.

1978. Visit of H.M.S. " Queen Elizabeth 2 ". Multicoloured.

259.	5p. Type **90**	20	20
260.	10p. R.M.S. " Queen Mary "	25	30
261.	15p. R.M.S. " Queen Elizabeth "	30	35
262.	20p. R.M.S. " Queen Elizabeth 2 "	30	40

91. 1952 " TRISTAN DA CUNHA " overprint on St. Helena 10s. Definitive.

1979. Death Centenary of Sir Rowland Hill.

264. **91.**	5p. black, lilac & yellow	15	15
265. –	10p. black, red & green	20	20
266. –	25p. multicoloured ..	30	30

DESIGNS—HORIZ. 10p. 1954 5s. definitive. VERT.—25p. " TRISTAN DA CUNHA RESETTLEMENT 1963 " overprint on St. Helena 1d. definitive.

92. " The Padre's House ".

1979. International Year of the Child Children's Drawings. Multicoloured.

268.	5p. Type **92**	10	10
269.	10p. " Houses in the Village "	15	15
270.	15p. " St. Mary's Church "	15	15
271.	20p. " Rockhopper Penguins "	25	25

1980. Paintings by Roland Svensson (3rd series). As T **80**. Multicoloured.

272.	5p. " Stoltenhoff Island " (horiz.)	10	10
273.	10p. " Nightingale from the East " (horiz.) ..	15	20
274.	15p. " The Administrator's abode "	20	25
275.	20p. " Ridge where the goat jump off "	25	30

93. "Tristania II" (mail ship).

1980. " London 1980 " International Stamp Exhibition. Multicoloured.

277.	5p. Type **93**	15	15
278.	10p. Mail being unloaded at Calshot Harbour	15	15
279.	15p. Tractor transporting mail to Post Office ..	25	25
280.	20p. Ringing the " dong " to summon people to Post Office	30	30
281.	25p. Distributing mail ..	30	30

94. Queen Elizabeth the Queen Mother at Royal Opera House, 1976.

1980. 80th Birthday of The Queen Mother.

282. **94.**	14p. multicoloured ..	25	25

95. "Golden Hind".

1980. 400th Anniv. of Sir Francis Drake's Circumnavigation of the World. Multicoloured.

283.	5p. Type **95**	20	10
284.	10p. Drake's route ..	25	15
285.	20p. Sir Francis Drake ..	30	20
286.	25p. Queen Elizabeth I ..	40	25

96. " Humpty Dumpty ".

1980. Christmas. Scenes from Nursery Rhymes. Multicoloured.

287.	15p. Type **96**	20	25
288.	15p. " Mary had a little Lamb "	20	25
289.	15p. " Little Jack Horner "	20	25
290.	15p. " Hey Diddle Diddle "	20	25
291.	15p. " London Bridge " ..	20	25
292.	15p. " Old King Cole " ..	20	25
293.	15p. " Sing a Song of Sixpence "	20	25
294.	15p. " Tom, Tom the Piper's Son "	20	25
295.	15p. " The Owl and the Pussy Cat "	20	25

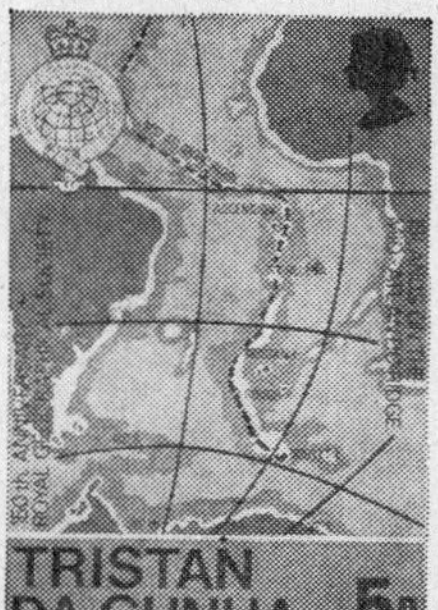

97. South Atlantic Ocean showing Islands on Mid-Atlantic Ridge.

1980. 150th Anniv. of Royal Geographical Society. Maps. Multicoloured.

296.	5p. Type **97**	15	15
297.	10p. Tristan da Cunha group	20	20
298.	15p. Tristan Island ..	30	30
299.	20p. Gough Island ..	35	40

98. Revd. Dodgson as Young Man.

1981. Centenary of Revd. Edwin Dodgson's Arrival on Tristan da Cunha. Multicoloured.

300.	10p. Type **98**	20	15
301.	20p. Dodgson and view of Tristan da Cunha (horiz.)	30	30
302.	30p. Dodgson with people of Tristan da Cunha ..	45	45

99. Detail from Captain Denham's Plan, 1853.

1981. Early Maps. Multicoloured.

304.	5p. Type **99**	15	10
305.	14p. From map by A. Dalrymple, 17 March 1781	25	20
306.	21p. From Captain Denham's plan, 1853 (different) ..	35	30

100. Wedding Bouquet from Tristan da Cunha.

1981. Royal Wedding. Multicoloured.

308.	5p. Type **100**	10	10
309.	20p. Investiture of Prince of Wales	25	25
310.	50p. Prince Charles and Lady Diana Spencer ..	65	65

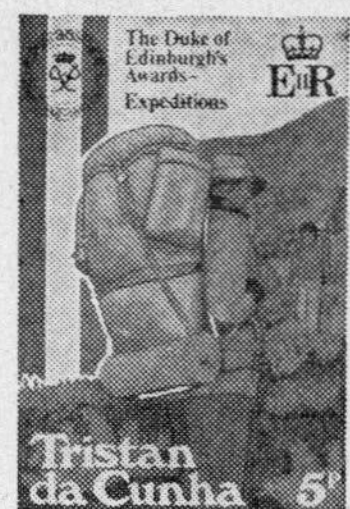

101. Explorer with Rucksack.

1981. 25th Anniv. of Duke of Edinburgh Award Scheme. Multicoloured.

311.	5p. Type **101**	10	10
312.	10p. Explorer at campsite	15	15
313.	20p. Explorer map reading	25	25
314.	25p. Duke of Edinburgh ..	30	30

102. Inaccessible Island Rail on Nest.

1981. Inaccessible Island Rail. Multicoloured.

315.	10p. Type **102**	30	30
316.	10p. Inaccessible Island Rail eggs	30	30
317.	10p. Rail chicks	30	30
318.	10p. Adult Rail	30	30

103. Six-gilled Shark.

1982. Sharks. Multicoloured.

319.	5p. Type **103**	20	10
320.	14p. Porbeagle Shark ..	35	20
321.	21p. Blue Shark	50	35
322.	35p. Hammerhead Shark	60	50

104. " Marcella ".

1982. Sailing Ships (1st series). Multicoloured.

323.	5p. Type **104**	30	35
324.	15p. " Eliza Adams " ..	35	50
325.	30p. " Corinthian " ..	60	80
326.	50 p. " Samuel and Thomas "	1·00	1·10

See also Nos. 341/44.

105. Lady Diana Spencer at Windsor, July 1981.

1982. 21st Birthday of Princess of Wales. Multicoloured.

327.	5p. Tristan da Cunha coat of arms	15	15
328.	15p. Type **105**	25	25
329.	30p. Prince and Princess of Wales in wedding portrait	45	45
330.	50p. Formal portrait ..	75	75

106. Lord Baden-Powell.

1982. 75th Anniv. of Boy Scout Movement. Multicoloured.

331. 5p. Type **106** 20 15
332. 20p. First Scout camp, Brownsea, 1907 .. 40 35
333. 50p. Local Scouts on parade (horiz.) 80 75

1982. Commonwealth Games, Brisbane, Nos. 224 and 228 optd. **1st PARTICIPATION COMMONWEALTH GAMES 1982.**

335. 5p. Wandering Albatross 10 10
336. 25p. Broad-billed Prion .. 35 30

108. Formation of Island.

1982. Volcanoes. Multicoloured.

337. 5p. Type **108** 15 15
338. 15p. Plan showing surface cinder cones and cross-section of volcano showing feeders .. 30 35
339. 25p. Eruption 45 50
340. 35p. 1961 Tristan eruption 65 70

1983. Sailing Ships (2nd series). As T **104.** Multicoloured.

341. 5p. "Islander" (vert.) .. 25 15
342. 20p. "Roscoe" 45 35
343. 35p. "Columbia" 60 55
344. 50p. "Emeline" (vert.) .. 80 80

109. Tractor pulling Trailer.

1983. Land Transport. Multicoloured.

345. 5 p. Type **109** 15 15
346. 15 p. Pack donkeys .. 25 25
347. 30 p. Bullock cart .. 50 50
348. 50 p. Landrover 75 75

110. Early Chart of South Atlantic.

1983. Island History. Multicoloured.

349. 1p. Type **110** 30 20
350. 3p. Tristao da Cunha's caravel 30 20
351. 4p. Notice left by Dutch on first landing, 1643 .. 30 20
352. 5p. 17th-century views of the island 30 20
353. 10p. British army landing party, 1815 .. .. 35 30
354. 15p. 19th-century view of the settlement 45 40
355. 18p. Governor Glass's house 45 40
356. 20p. The Revd. W. F. Taylor and Peter Green 50 50
357. 25p. "John and Elizabeth" (American whaling ship) 75 60
358. 50p. Letters Patent declaring Tristan da Cunha dependency of St. Helena 1·40 1·25
359. £1 Commissioning of H.M.S. "Atlantic Isle", 1944 .. 2·50 2·50
360. £2 Evacuation, 1961 .. 3·75 4·00

111. "Christ's Charge to St. Peter" (detail).

1983. 500th Birth Anniv. of Raphael.

361 **111** 10p. multicoloured .. 20 20
362 – 25p. multicoloured .. 35 35
363 – 40p. multicoloured .. 60 60

DESIGNS: 25p., 40p. Different details of "Christ's Charge to St. Peter".

112. 1938 6d. Stamp.

1984. 150th Anniv. of St. Helena as British Colony. Multicoloured.

365. 10p. Type **112** 15 15
366. 15p. 1938 1s. stamp .. 25 25
367. 25p. 1938 2s. stamp .. 35 35
368. 60p. 1938 10s. stamp .. 85 85

113. "Agrocybe praecox var. cutefracta".

1984. Fungi. Multicoloured.

369. 10p. Type **113** 40 40
370. 20p. "Laccaria tetraspora" 60 60
371. 30p. "Agrocybe cylindracea" (horiz.) 70 70
372. 50p. "Sacoscypha coccinea" (horiz.) .. .. 1·10 1·10

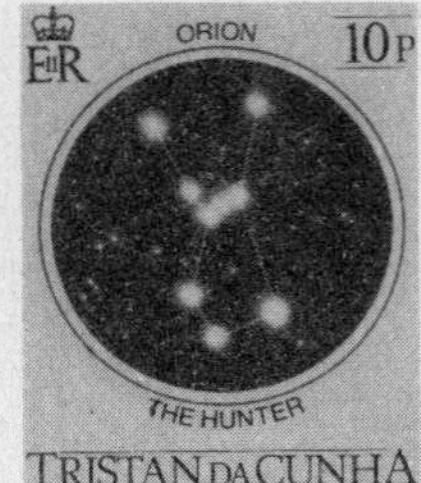

114. Constellation of "Orion".

1984. The Night Sky. Multicoloured.

373. 10p. Type **114** 45 40
374. 20p. "Scorpius" 65 50
375. 25p. "Canis Major" .. 75 60
376. 50p. "Crux" .. .. 1·10 1·00

115. Sheep-shearing.

1984. Tristan Woollens Industry. Mult.

377. 9p. Type **115** 20 20
378. 17p. Carding wool 30 30
379. 29p. Spinning 50 50
380. 45p. Knitting 75 75

116. "Christmas Dinner-table".

1984. Christmas. Children's Drawings. Multicoloured.

382. 10p. Type **116** 20 20
383. 20p. "Santa Claus in Ox Cart" 30 30
384. 30p. "Santa Claus in Longboat" 50 50
385. 50p. "The Nativity" .. 85 85

117. "H.M.S. 'Julia' Ashore, 1817" (Midshipman C. W. Browne).

1985. Shipwrecks (1st series).

386. **117.** 10p. bl. & light blue .. 50 50
387. – 25p. brown and green 1·00 1·00
388. – 35p. brown and yellow 1·25 1·25

DESIGNS—VERT. 25p. Bell from "Mabel Clark", St. Mary's Church. HORIZ. 35p. "Barque 'Glenhuntley' foundering, 1898" (John Hagan).

See also Nos. 411/14 and 426/8.

118. The Queen Mother at Ascot with Princess Margaret.

1985. Life and Times of Queen Elizabeth the Queen Mother. Multicoloured.

390. 10p. The Queen Mother and Prince Charles, 1954 20 30
391. 20p. Type **118** 40 55
392. 30p. Queen Elizabeth the Queen Mother 60 75
393. 50p. With Prince Henry at his christening .. .. 1·00 1·25

119. Jonathan Lambert and "Isles of Refreshment" Flag, 1811.

1985. Flags. Multicoloured.

395. 10p. Type **119** 50 50
396. 15p. 21st Light Dragoons guidon and cannon from Fort Malcolm (1816–17) (vert.) 70 70
397. 25p. White Ensign and H.M.S. "Falmouth" offshore, 1816 (vert.) .. 90 1·00
398. 60p. Union Jack and Tristan da Cunha (vert.) 2·00 2·25

120. Lifeboat heading for Barque "West Riding".

1985. Centenary of Loss of Island Lifeboat. Multicoloured.

399. 10p. Type **120** 35 55
400. 30p. Map of Tristan da Cunha .. .. 80 1·25
401. 50p. Memorial plaque to lifeboat crew .. .. 1·25 1·50

121. Halley's Comet, 1066, from Bayeux Tapestry.

1986. Appearance of Halley's Comet. Mult.

402. 10p. Type **121** 40 45
403. 20p. Path of Comet .. 65 70
404. 30p. Comet over Inaccessible Island .. .. 85 1·00
405. 50p. H.M.S. "Paramour" and map of South Atlantic .. .. .. 1·40 1·75

1986. 60th Birthday of Queen Elizabeth II. As T **110** of Ascension. Multicoloured.

406. 10p. With Prince Charles, 1950 .. .. .. 20 2
407. 15p. Queen at Trooping the Colour 30 3
408. 25p. In robes of Order of the Bath, Westminster Abbey, 1972 .. .. 50 5
409. 45p. In Canada, 1977 .. 90 9
410. 65p. At Crown Agents Head Office, London, 1983 .. .. .. 1·25 1·4

122. "S.V. 'Allanshaw' wrecked on East Beach, 1893" (drawing by John Hagan).

1986. Shipwrecks (2nd series).

411. 122. 9p. blue, deep blue and black 25 25
412. – 20p. green, yellow and black 45 45
413. – 40p. blue, violet and black 85 85

DESIGNS: 20p. Church font from wreck of "Edward Vittery", 1881. 40p. Ship's figurehead.

1986. Royal Wedding. As T **112** of Ascension. Multicoloured.

415 10p. Prince Andrew and Miss Sarah Ferguson .. 20 30
416 40p. Prince Andrew piloting helicopter, Digby, Canada, 1985 .. 80 1·10

123. Wandering Albatross.

1986. Flora and Fauna of Inaccessible Island. Multicoloured.

417 5p. Type **123** 20 30
418 10p. "Lagenophora nudicaulis" (daisy) 30 40
419 20p. "Cynthia virginiensis" (buttefly) 65 75
420 25p. Wilkin's finch .. 75 85
421 50p. White-chinned petrel 1·25 1·25

124. "Dimorphinoctua cunhaensis" (moth) and Edinburgh.

1987. Island Flightless Insects and Birds. Multicoloured.

422 10p. Type **124** 25 35
423 25p. "Tristanomyia frustilifera" (fly) and Crater Lake 55 65
424 35p. Inaccessible Island rail and Inaccessible Island 1·00 1·25
425 50p. Gough Island coot and Gough Island .. .. 1·50 1·50

125. Castaways from "Blenden Hall" attacking Sea Elephant, 1821.

1987. Shipwrecks (3rd series).

426. **125.** 11p. black and brown 30 30
427. – 17p. black and lilac .. 45 45
428. – 45p. black and green 1·00 1·00

DESIGNS—HORIZ. 17p. Barquentine "Henry A. Paull" stranded at Sandy Point, 1879. VERT. 45p. Gustav Stoltenhoff, 1871, and Stoltenhoff Island.

126. Rockhopper Penguin swimming.

1987. Rockhopper Penguins. Multicoloured.

430. 10p. Type **126** 35 30
431. 20p. Adult with egg .. 55 50
432. 30p. Adult with juvenile .. 75 70
433. 50p. Head of rockhopper penguin .. .. .. 1·25 1·10

127. Microscope and Published Report.

1987. 50th Anniv. of Norwegian Scientific Expedition. Multicoloured.

434. 10p. Type **127** 50 50
435. 20p. Scientists ringing yellow-nosed albatross .. 1·00 1·00
436. 30p. Expedition hut, Little Beach Point .. .. 1·40 1·40
437. 50p. S.S. "Thorshammer" (whale factory ship) .. 2·00 2·00

1988. Royal Ruby Wedding. Nos. 406/10 optd. **40TH WEDDING ANNIVERSARY.**

438. 10p. Princess Elizabeth with Prince Charles, 1950 20 25
439. 15p. Queen Elizabeth II at Trooping the Colour .. 30 35
440. 25p. In robes of Order of the Bath, Westminster Abbey, 1972 .. .. 50 55
441. 45p. In Canada, 1977 .. 90 95
442. 65p. At Crown Agents Head Office, London, 1983 .. .. .. 1·25 1·40

128. Nightingale Finch.

1988. Fauna of Nightingale Island. Mult.

443. 5p. Type **128** 20 15
444. 10p. Tristan thrush (immature) 30 25
445. 20p. Yellow-nosed albatross (chick) .. 50 45
446. 25p. Greater shearwater .. 60 55
447. 50p. Elephant seal .. 1·10 1·10

129. Painted Penguin Eggs.

1988. Tristan da Cunha Handicrafts. Mult.

448. 10p. Type **129** 25 25
449. 15p. Moccasins 35 35
450. 35p. Knitwear 75 75
451. 50p. Model longboat .. 1·10 1·10

130 Processing Blubber

1988. 19th-century Whaling. Multicoloured.

452 10p. Type **130** 25 25
453 20p. Harpoon guns .. 45 45
454 30p. Scrimshaw (carved whale bone) 65 65
455 50p. Whaling ships .. 1·10 1·10

1988. 300th Anniv of Lloyd's of London. As T **123** of Ascension.

457 10p. multicoloured .. 25 25
458 25p. multicoloured .. 55 55
459 35p. black and green .. 80 80
460 50p. black and red .. 1·25 1·25

DESIGNS: VERT—10p. New Lloyd's Building, 1988; 50p. "Kobenhavn" (barque). HORIZ— 25p. "Tristania II" (crawfish trawler); 35p. "St. Helena" (mail ship).

131 "Government House"

1988. Augustus Earle's Paintings, 1824. Mult.

461 1p. Type **131** 10 10
462 3p. "Squall off Tristan" .. 10 10
463 4p. "Rafting Blubber" .. 10 10
464 5p. "View near Little Beach" 10 15
465 10p. "Man killing Albatross" 20 25
466 15p. "View on The Summit" 30 35
467 20p. "Nightingale Island" .. 40 45
468 25p. "Earle on Tristan" .. 50 55
469 35p. "Solitude—Watching the Horizon" 70 75
470 50p. "Northeaster" .. 1·00 1·10
471 £1 "Tristan Village" .. 2·00 2·10
472 £2 "Governor Glass at Dinner" .. .. 4·00 4·25

132 Giant Petrel

1989. Fauna of Gough Island. Multicoloured.

473 5p. Type **132** 15 15
474 10p. Gough Island coot ("Gough Moorhen") .. 20 25
475 20p. Gough Island finch ("Gough Bunting") .. 40 45
476 25p. Sooty albatross .. 50 55
477 50p. Amsterdam fur seal 1·00 1·10

133 "Eriosorus cheilanthoides"

1989. Ferns. Multicoloured.

478 10p. Type **133** 35 35
479 25p. "Asplenium alvarezense" 75 75
480 35p. "Elaphoglossum hybridum" 85 85
481 50p. "Ophioglossum opacum" .. .. 1·40 1·40

134 Surgeon's Mortar

1989. Nautical Museum Exhibits. Mult.

482 10p. Type **134** 35 35
483 20p. Parts of darting-gun harpoon 60 60
484 30p. Ship's compass with binnacle-hood 80 80
485 60p. Rope-twisting device 1·60 1·60

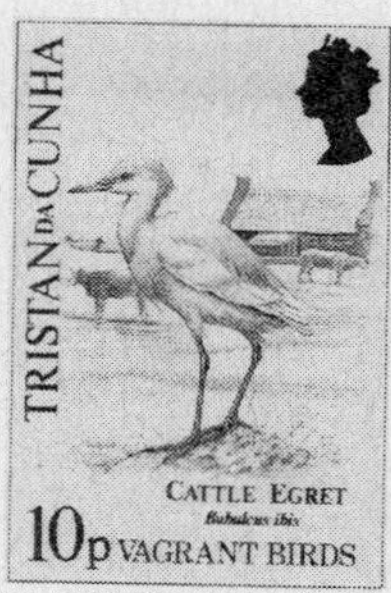

135 Cattle Egret

1989. Vagrant Birds. Multicoloured.

486 10p. Type **135** 45 35
487 25p. Spotted sandpiper .. 80 70
488 35p. Purple gallinule .. 1·00 90
489 50p. Barn swallow .. 1·40 1·40

136 "Peridroma saucia"

1990. Moths. Multicoloured.

490 10p. Type **136** 30 35
491 15p. "Ascalapha odorata" 40 45
492 35p. "Agrius cingulata" .. 80 90
493 60p. "Eumorpha labruscae" .. .. 1·50 1·60

137 Sea Urchin

1990. Echinoderms.

494 **137** 10p. multicoloured .. 40 30
495 – 20p. multicoloured .. 60 50
496 – 30p. multicoloured .. 85 75
497 – 60p. multicoloured .. 1·50 1·50

DESIGNS: 20p. to 60p. Different starfish.

1990. 90th Birthday of Queen Elizabeth the Queen Mother. As T **134** of Ascension.

498 25p. multicoloured .. 75 60
499 £1 brown and blue .. 2·50 2·40

DESIGNS—21 × 36 mm. 25p. Queen Mother at the London Coliseum. 29 × 37 mm. £1 Queen Elizabeth broadcasting to women of the Empire, 1939.

1990. Maiden Voyage of "St. Helena II". As T **137** of Ascension. Multicoloured.

500 10p. "Dunnottar Castle" (mail ship), 1942 .. 35 35
501 15p. "St. Helena I" at Tristan .. 50 50
502 35p. Launch of "St. Helena II" .. .. .. 1·00 1·00
503 60p. Duke of York launching "St. Helena II" .. 1·75 1·75

138 H.M.S. "Pyramus" (frigate), 1829

1990. Ships of the Royal Navy (1st series). Multicoloured.

505 10p. Type **138** 35 35
506 25p. H.M.S. "Penguin" (sloop), 1815 .. .. 80 80
507 35p. H.M.S. "Thalia" (screw corvette), 1886 .. 1·00 1·00
508 50p. H.M.S. "Sidon" (paddle frigate), 1858 .. 1·60 1·60

See also Nos. 509/12.

1991. Ships of the Royal Navy (2nd series). As T **138**. Multicoloured.

509 10 p. H.M.S. "Milford" (sloop), 1938 .. .. 35 35
510 25 p. H.M.S. "Dublin" (cruiser), 1923 .. .. 80 80
511 35 p. H.M.S. "Yarmouth" (cruiser), 1919 .. .. 1·00 1·00
512 50 p. H.M.S. "Carlisle" (cruiser), 1938 .. .. 1·60 1·60

140 Prince Alfred and H.M.S. "Galatea", 1867

1991. 70th Birthday of Prince Philip, Duke of Edinburgh.

514 **140** 10p. black, lt blue & bl 40 40
515 – 25p. black, lt grn & grn 80 80
516 – 30p. black, brn & yell 90 90
517 – 50p. multicoloured .. 1·40 1·40

DESIGNS: 25p. Prince Philip meeting local inhabitants, 1957; 30p. Prince Philip and Royal Yacht "Britannia", 1957; 50p. Prince Philip and Edinburgh settlement.

141 Pair of Gough Island Coots

1991. Endangered Species. Birds. Mult.

518 8p. Type **141** 30 30
519 10p. Gough Island finch 35 35
520 12p. Gough Island coot on nest 40 40
521 15p. Gough Island finch feeding chicks .. 50 50

1992. 500th Anniv of Discovery of America by Columbus and Re-enactment Voyages. As T **168** of St. Helena. Multicoloured.

522 10p. Map of re-enactment voyages and "Eye of the Wind" (cadet ship) .. 35 35
523 15p. Compass rose and "Soren Larsen" (cadet ship) 55 55
524 35p. Ships of Columbus .. 95 95
525 60p. Columbus and "Santa Maria" .. .. .. 1·50 1·50

1992. 40th Anniv of Queen Elizabeth II's Accession. As T **143** of Ascension. Mult.

526 10p. Tristan from the sea 35 35
527 20p. Longboat under sail 60 60
528 25p. Aerial view of Edinburgh 70 70
529 35p. Three portraits of Queen Elizabeth .. 90 90
530 65p. Queen Elizabeth II .. 1·75 1·75

142 "Caesioperca coatsii"

1992. Fishes. Multicoloured.

531 10p. Type **142** 35 35
532 15p. "Mendosoma lineatum" 55 55
533 35p. "Physiculus karrerae" 90 90
534 60p. "Decapterus longimanus" .. .. 1·50 1·50

POSTAGE DUE STAMPS

1957. As Type D **1** of Barbados.

D 1. 1d. red .. .. .. 1·75 5·00
D 2. 2d. yellow .. .. .. 2·25 4·50
D 3. 3d. green .. .. .. 3·50 5·50
D 4. 4d. blue .. .. .. 6·00 7·00
D 5. 5d. lake .. .. .. 5·00 16·00

D 2.

D 3. Outline Map of Tristan da Cunha.

1976.

D 11. D **2.** 1p. purple 10 30
D 12. 2p. green 10 35
D 13. 4p. violet 15 45
D 14. 5p. blue 15 50
D 15. 10p. brown 15 70

1986.

D 16. D **3.** 1p. brown and light brown 10 10
D 17. 2p. brown & orange 10 10
D 18. 5p. brown and red .. 10 15
D 19. 7p. black and violet 15 20
D 20. 10p. black and blue 20 25
D 21. 25p. black and green 50 55

TRUCIAL STATES

Seven Arab Shaikhdoms on the Persian Gulf and Gulf of Oman, in treaty relations with Great Britain. The following stamps were issued at the British Postal Agency at Dubai until it closed on 14 June 1963.

Individual issues were later made by Abu Dhabi, Ajman, Dubai, Fujeira, Ras al Khaima, Sharjah and Umm al Qiwain.

100 naye paise = 1 rupee.

1. Palms.

2. Dhow.

1961.

1. **1.** 5 n.p. green 30 10
2. 15 n.p. brown 30 10
3. 20 n.p. blue 40 10
4. 30 n.p. orange 40 10
5. 40 n.p. violet 40 10
6. 50 n.p. bistre 40 10
7. 75 n.p. grey 60 10
8. **2.** 1 r. green .. .. 3·00 40
9. 2 r. black .. .. 3·00 5·50
10. 5 r. red .. .. 4·50 10·00
11. 10 r. blue .. .. 12·00 19·00

TURKS ISLANDS

A group of islands in the Br. W. Indies, S.E. of the Bahamas, now grouped with the Caicos Islands and using the stamps of Turks and Caicos Islands. A dependency of Jamaica until August, 1962, when it became a Crown Colony.

12 pence = 1 shilling.

1.

1867.

55. **1.** 1d. brown .. .. .. 40·00 30·00
63. 1d. red .. .. .. 1·25 2·25
2. 6d. black .. .. .. 70·00 80·00
59. 6d. brown .. .. .. 2·00 2·75
3. 1s. blue .. .. .. 65·00 55·00
6. 1s. lilac £5000 £2000
60. 1s. brown .. .. .. 2·25 2·75
52. 1s. green £100 £100

1881. Surch. with large figures.

17 **1** ½ on 1d. red .. .. 50·00 55·00
7 ½ on 6d. black .. .. 55·00 70·00
9 ½ on 1s. blue .. .. 70·00 95·00
19 ½ on 1s. lilac .. .. 75·00 95·00
34 2½ on 1d. red £425
28 2½ on 6d. black £110 £140
29 2½ on 1s. lilac £550 £650
38 2½ on 1s. blue £450
47 4 on 1d. red £500 £450
42 4 on 6d. black £250 £300
45 4 on 1s. lilac £375

31.

34.

1881.

70. **31.** ½d. green 30 75
56. 2½d. brown .. .. .. 11·00 13·00
65. 2½d. blue .. .. .. 1·00 75
50. 4d. blue .. .. .. 75·00 60·00
57. 4d. grey .. .. .. 5·50 2·00
71. 4d. purple and blue .. 5·50 11·00
72. **34.** 5d. olive and red .. .. 2·25 10·00

1889. Surch. **One Penny.**

61. **31.** 1d. on 2½d. brown .. 4·50 9·50

1893. Surch ½d. and bar.

68 **31** ½d. on 4d. grey £100 £100

INDEX

Countries can be quickly located by referring to the index at the end of this volume.

TURKS AND CAICOS ISLANDS

(See TURKS ISLANDS.)

1900. 12 pence = 1 shilling.
20 shillings = 1 pound.
1969. 100 cents = 1 dollar.

35. Salt-raking. **36.**

1900.

110. **35.** ½d. green 40 15
102. 1d. red .. .. .. 2·75 75
103. 2d. brown .. .. 75 1·25
104a. 2½d. blue .. .. .. 90 1·00
112. 3d. purple on yellow .. 90 5·00
105. 4d. orange .. .. 3·50 7·00
106. 6d. mauve .. .. 1·25 5·50
107. 1s. brown .. .. 1·75 9·50
108. **36.** 2s. purple .. .. 38·00 55·00
109. 3s. red .. .. .. 48·00 70·00

37. Turk's-head Cactus.

38.

1909.

115. **37.** ¼d. mauve .. .. 30 1·00
116. ¼d. red 20 25
162. ¼d. black 15 50
117. **38.** ½d. green 20 25
118. 1d. red 20 30
119. 2d. grey .. .. 90 1·40
120. 2½d. blue .. .. .. 1·25 3·75
121. 3d. purple on yellow .. 1·75 2·00
122. 4d. red on yellow .. 3·00 7·00
123. 6d. purple .. .. 6·00 7·00
124. 1s. black on green .. 2·50 8·50
125. 2s. red on green .. 20·00 35·00
126. 3s. black on red .. 20·00 35·00

39.

1913.

129 **39** ½d. green .. .. 30 1·00
130 1d. red .. .. 75 1·10
131 2d. grey .. .. 1·10 1·25
132 2½d. blue .. .. 1·90 2·50
133d 3d. purple on yellow .. 1·50 4·00
134 4d. red on yellow .. 80 6·00
135 5d. green .. .. 3·50 8·50
136 6d. purple .. .. 2·25 3·25
137 1s. orange .. .. 1·50 4·00
138 2s. red on green .. 6·00 14·00
139 3s. black on red .. 15·00 25·00

1917. Optd. **WAR TAX** in one line.

143. **39.** 1d. red 10 50
144. 3d. purple on yellow .. 35 1·50

1918. Optd **WAR TAX** in two lines.

150 **39** 1d. red 10 60
153 3d. purple on yellow .. 10 80

44.

45.

1922. Inscr. "POSTAGE".

163. **44.** ½d. green 30 90
164. 1d. brown .. .. 40 2·75
165. 1½d. red .. .. 2·50 4·50
166. 2d. grey .. .. 40 2·00
167. 2½d. purple on yellow .. 30 60
168. 3d. blue .. .. .. 40 1·50
169. 4d. red on yellow .. 75 4·00
170. 5d. green .. .. 65 7·50
171. 6d. purple .. .. 60 2·75
172. 1s. orange .. .. 70 5·00
173. 2s. red on green .. 2·00 4·75
175. 3s. black on red .. 5·00 13·00

1928. Inscr. "POSTAGE & REVENUE".

No.	Type	Description	Unused	Used
176.	**45.**	½d. green	40	40
177.		1d. brown	40	70
178.		1½d. red	40	1·25
179.		2d. grey	35	30
180.		2½d. purple on yellow	35	1·00
181.		3d. blue	35	1·75
182.		6d. purple	40	2·75
183.		1s. orange	2·50	3·50
184.		2s. red on green	3·25	18·00
185.		5s. green on yellow	11·00	30·00
186.		10s. purple on blue	38·00	75·00

1935. Silver Jubilee. As T **13** of Antigua.

No.	Description	Unused	Used
187	½d. black and green	15	40
188	3d. brown and blue	1·50	1·75
189	5d. blue and green	1·50	2·25
190	1s. grey and purple	1·50	3·25

1937. Coronation. As T **2** of Aden.

No.	Description	Unused	Used
191	½d. green	10	10
192	2d. grey	40	15
193	3d. blue	60	20

46. Raking Salt.

47. Salt Industry.

1938.

No.	Type	Description	Unused	Used
194	**46**	¼d. black	10	10
195a		½d. green	15	50
196		1d. brown	15	10
197		1½d. red	30	15
198		2d. grey	40	30
199a		2½d. orange	1·00	55
200		3d. blue	20	20
201		6d. mauve	6·00	1·25
201a		6d. brown	15	15
202		1s. brown	2·25	5·50
202a		1s. olive	15	15
203a	**47**	2s. red	14·00	8·50
204a		5s. green	23·00	12·00
205		10s. violet	4·75	5·00

1946. Victory. As T **9** of Aden.

No.	Description	Unused	Used
206.	2d. grey	10	10
207.	3d. blue	15	10

1948. Silver Wedding. As T **10/11** of Aden.

No.	Description	Unused	Used
208.	1d. brown	15	10
209.	10s. violet	5·00	5·50

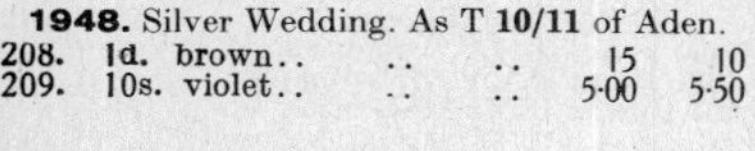

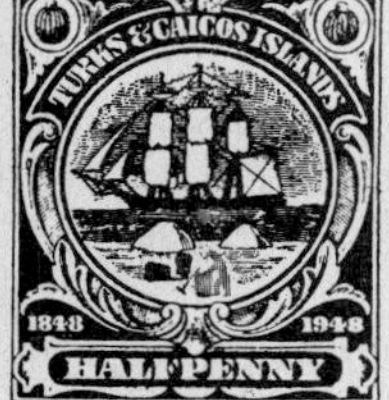

50. Badge of the Islands.

DESIGNS — HORIZ. 6d. Map of Turks and Caicos Is. 2s., 5s., 10s. Queen Victoria and King George VI.

51. Blue Ensign bearing Dependency Badge.

1948. Centenary of Dependency's Separation from the Bahamas.

No.	Type	Description	Unused	Used
210.	**50.**	½d. green	15	15
211.		2d. red	30	15
212.	**51.**	3d. blue	35	15
213.	–	6d. violet	30	20
214	–	2s. black and blue	35	35
215.	–	5s. black and green	80	60
216.		10s. black and brown	80	3·00

1949. U.P.U. As T **20/23** of Antigua.

No.	Description	Unused	Used
217.	2½d. orange	30	30
218.	3d. blue	40	40
219.	6d. brown	40	40
220.	1s. olive	40	30

65. Bulk Salt Loading.

66. Dependency's Badge.

1950.

No.	Type	Description	Unused	Used
221.	**65.**	½d. green	15	40
222.	–	1d. brown	15	65
223.	–	1½d. red	20	55
224.	–	2d. orange	15	40
225.	–	2½d. olive	20	50
226.	–	3d. blue	20	40
227.	–	4d. black and pink	1·50	70
228.	–	6d. black and blue	1·00	50
229.	–	1s. black and turquoise	55	40
230.	–	1s. 6d. black and red	2·00	3·25
231.	–	2s. green and blue	1·25	3·50
232.	–	5s. blue and black	6·00	3·75
233.	**66.**	10s. black and violet	13·00	13·00

DESIGNS—As Type **65**: 1d. Salt Cay. 1½d. Caicos mail. 2d. Grand Turk. 2½d. Diving for sponges. 3d. South Creek. 4d. Map. 6d. Grand Turk Light. 1s. Government House. 1s. 6d. Cockburn Harbour. 2s. Govt. Offices. 5s. Loading salt.

1953. Coronation. As T **13** of Aden.

No.	Description	Unused	Used
234.	2d. black and orange	15	80

1955. As 1950 but with portrait of Queen Elizabeth II.

No.	Description	Unused	Used
235.	5d. black and green	30	30
236.	8d. black and brown	70	20

DESIGNS—HORIZ. As Type **65**. 5d. M.V. "Kirksons". 8d. Greater Flamingoes in flight.

69. Queen Elizabeth II (after Annigoni).

70. Bonefish.

84. Brown Pelican.

1957.

No.	Type	Description	Unused	Used
237.	**69.**	1d. blue and red	15	20
238.	**70.**	1½d. grey and orange	15	30
239.	–	2d. brown and olive	15	15
240.	–	2½d. red and green	15	15
241.	–	3d. turquoise & purple	15	15
242.	–	4d. lake and black	20	15
243.	–	5d. green and brown	30	40
244.	–	6d. red and blue	75	20
245.	–	8d. red and black	2·25	10
246.	–	1s. blue and black	20	10
247.	–	1s. 6d. sepia and blue	1·25	50
248.	–	2s. blue and brown	3·00	2·25
249.	–	5s. black and red	75	2·00
250.	–	10s. black and purple	7·00	8·00
253.	**84.**	£1 sepia and red	30·00	16·00

DESIGNS—HORIZ. As Type **70**: 2d. Red grouper. 2½d. Spiny lobster. 3d. Albacore. 4d. Muttonfish snapper. 5d. Permit. 6d. Conch. 8d. Greater flamingoes. 1s. Spanish mackerel. 1s. 6d. Salt Cay. 1s. "Uakon" (Caicos sloop). 5s. Cable Office. As Type **84**: 10s. Dependency's badge.

83. Map of the Turks and Caicos Is.

1959. New Constitution.

No.	Type	Description	Unused	Used
251.	**83.**	6d. olive and orange	15	10
252.		8d. violet and orange	15	10

1963. Freedom from Hunger. As T **28** of Aden.

No.	Description	Unused	Used
254.	8d. red	20	10

1963. Cent of Red Cross. As T **33** of Antigua.

No.	Description	Unused	Used
255	2d. red and black	15	15
256	8d. red and blue	30	25

1964. 400th Birth Anniv of Shakespeare. As T **34** of Antigua.

No.	Description	Unused	Used
257.	8d. green	10	10

1965. Cent of I.T.U. As T **36** of Antigua.

No.	Description	Unused	Used
258.	1d. red and brown	10	10
259.	2s. green and blue	20	20

1965. I.C.Y. As T **37** of Antigua.

No.	Description	Unused	Used
260.	1d. purple and turquoise	10	10
261.	8d. green and lavender	20	10

1966. Churchill Commem. As T **38** of Antigua.

No.	Description	Unused	Used
262.	1d. blue	10	10
263.	2d. green	15	10
264.	8d. brown	15	10
265.	1s. 6d. violet	25	25

1966. Royal Visit. As T **39** of Antigua.

No.	Description	Unused	Used
266.	8d. black and blue	25	10
267.	1s. 6d. black and mauve	45	20

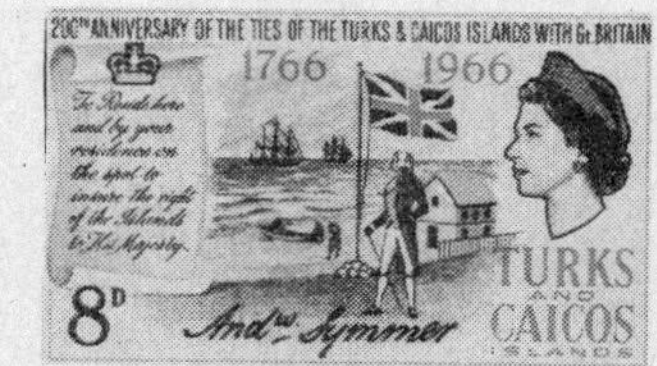

86. Andrew Symmer and Royal Warrant.

1966. Bicent. of "Ties with Britain".

No.	Type	Description	Unused	Used
268.	–	1d. blue and orange	10	10
269.	**86.**	8d. red, blue and yellow	10	10
270.	–	1s. 6d. multicoloured	15	10

DESIGNS: 1d. Andrew Symmer going ashore. 1s. 6d. Arms and Royal Cypher.

1966. 20th Anniv of U.N.E.S.C.O. As T **54/6** of Antigua.

No.	Description	Unused	Used
271.	1d. multicoloured	10	10
272.	8d. yellow, violet and olive	15	10
273.	1s. 6d. black, purple & orge.	20	40

88. Turk's Head Cactus.

DESIGNS—HORIZ. 1½d. Boat-building. 4d. Conch Industry. 1s. Fishing. 2s. Crawfish Industry. 3s. Maps of Turks and Caicos Islands and (inset) West Indies. 5s. Fishing Industry. 10s. Arms of Turks and Caicos Islands. VERT. 2d. Donkey Cart. 3d. Sisal Industry. 6d. Salt Industry. 8d. Skin-diving. 1s. 6d. Water-skiing. £1, Queen Elizabeth II.

1967.

No.	Type	Description	Unused	Used
274.	**88.**	1d. yellow, red and violet	10	10
275.	–	1½d. brown and yellow	10	10
276.	–	2d. grey and yellow	15	10
277.	–	3d. agate and green	20	10
278.	–	4d. mauve, blk. & turq.	30	10
279.	–	6d. brown and blue	30	10
280.	–	8d. yell., turq. & blue	20	10
281.	–	1s. purple and turquoise	20	10
282.	–	1s. 6d. yell., brn. & blue	50	20
283.	–	2s. multicoloured	60	85
284.	–	3s. mauve and blue	55	30
285.	–	5s. ochre, blue and light blue	1·25	1·75
286.	–	10s. multicoloured	1·75	2·25
287.	–	£1 blue, silver and red	3·25	4·75

102. Turks Islands 1d. Stamp of 1867.

1967. Stamp Cent.

No.	Type	Description	Unused	Used
288.	**102.**	1d. black and mauve	10	10
289.	–	6d. black and grey	10	10
290.	–	1s. black and blue	10	10

DESIGNS: 6d. Queen Elizabeth "Stamp" and Turks Islands 6d. Stamp of 1867. 1s. As Type **102** but shows the 1s. stamp of 1867 in place of the 1d.

104. Human Rights Emblem and Charter.

1968. Human Rights Year.

No.	Type	Description	Unused	Used
291.	**104.**	1d. multicoloured	10	10
292.		8d. multicoloured	10	10
293.		1s. 6d. multicoloured	10	10

105. Dr. Martin Luther King and "Freedom March".

1968. Martin Luther King. Commem.

No.	Type	Description	Unused	Used
294.	**105.**	2d. brown and blue	10	10
295.		8d. brown and lake	10	10
296.		1s. 6d. brn. and violet	10	10

1969. Decimal Currency. Nos. 274/87 surch., and new value in old design (¼ c.).

No.	Description	Unused	Used
297.	¼ c. mult. (as No. 286)	10	10
298.	1 c. on 1 d. yell., red & vio.	10	10
299.	2 c. on 2d. grey & yellow	10	10
300.	3 c. on 3d. agate and green	10	10
301.	4 c. on 4d. mve., blk. & turq.	10	10
302.	5 c. on 6d. brown and blue	10	10
303.	7 c. on 8d. yell., turq. & bl.	10	10
304.	8 c. on 1½d. brown & yell.	10	10
305.	10 c. on 1s. purple & turq.	20	10
306.	15 c. on 1s. 6d. yell., brn. & blue	25	10
307.	20 c. on 2s. multicoloured	30	25
308.	30 c. on 3s. mauve & blue	55	35
309.	50 c. on 5s. ochre, blue and light blue	1·00	45
310.	$1 on 10s. multicoloured	1·50	1·00
311a.	$2 on £1 blue, silver & red	1·50	3·00

107. "The Nativity with John the Baptist".

1969. Christmas. Scenes from 16th-cent. "Book of Hours". Multicoloured.

No.	Description	Unused	Used
312.	1 c. Type **107**	10	10
313.	3 c. "The Flight into Egypt"	10	10
314.	15 c. Type **107**	15	10
315.	30 c. As 3 c.	25	10

109. Coat of Arms.

1970. New Constitution.

316.	109.	7 c. multicoloured ..	20	10
317.		35 c. multicoloured ..	35	20

110. " Christ bearing the Cross ".

1970. Easter. Details from the "Small Engraved Passion".

318.	110.	5 c. grey and blue ..	10	10
319.	–	7 c. grey and red ..	10	10
320.	–	50 c. grey and brown ..	30	30

DESIGNS: 7 c. " Christ on the Cross" (Durer). 50 c. " The Lamentation for Christ " (Durer).

113. Dickens and Scene from " Oliver Twist ".

1970. Death Cent. of Charles Dickens.

321.	113.	1 c. blk. & brn. on yell.	10	10
322.	–	3 c. blk. & blue on flesh	10	10
323.	–	15 c. blk. & blue on flesh	15	10
324.	–	30 c. blk. & drab on blue	30	10

DESIGNS (showing Dickens and scene): 3 c. "A Christmas Carol". 15 c. "Pickwick Papers". 30 c. "The Old Curiosity Shop".

114. Ambulance – 1870.

1970. Cent. of British Red Cross. Mult.

325.		1 c. Type **114**	10	10
326.		5 c. Ambulance – 1970 ..	10	10
327.		15 c. Type **114**	20	10
328.		30 c. As 5 c.	30	10

115. Duke of Albemarle and Coat-of-Arms.

1970. Tercentenary of Issue of Letters Patent. Multicoloured.

329.		1 c. Type **115**	10	10
330.		8 c. Arms of Charles II and Elizabeth II ..	20	20
331.		10 c. Type **115**	20	15
332.		35 c. As 8 c.	40	65

116. Boat-building.

1971. Designs as Nos. 274/87, but values in decimal currency as T **116**.

333.	88.	1 c. yellow, red and violet	10	10
334.	–	2 c. slate and yellow (as No. 276)	10	10
335.	–	3 c. agate and green (as No. 277)	15	10
336.	–	4 c. mauve, black and turquoise (as No. 278)	40	10
337.	–	5 c. sepia and blue (as No. 279)	20	10
338.	–	7 c. yellow, turquoise & blue (as No. 280) ..	25	10
339.	116.	8 c. brown and yellow..	50	10
340.	–	10 c. purple and turq. (as No. 281).. ..	50	10
341.	–	15 c. yellow, brown and blue (as No. 282) ..	1·00	40
342.	–	20 c. mult. (as No. 283)	1·25	1·25
343.	–	30 c. purple and blue (as No. 284).. ..	1·75	80
344.	–	50 c. ochre, blue and light blue (as No. 285)	2·50	2·00
345.	–	$1 mult. (as No. 286) ..	2·75	3·00
346.	–	$2 blue, silver and red (as No. 287).. ..	4·00	7·50

117. Seahorse.

1971. Tourist Development. Multicoloured.

347.		1 c. Type **117**	10	10
348.		3 c. Queen Conch shell ..	10	10
349.		15 c. Oyster catcher ..	30	10
350.		30 c. Blue Marlin	30	15

Nos. 348/50 are horiz.

118. Pirate Sloop.

1971. Pirates. Multicoloured.

351.		2 c. Type **118**	10	10
352.		3 c. Pirate Treasure ..	10	10
353.		15 c. Marooned sailor ..	45	15
354.		30 c. Buccaneers	70	45

119. The Wilton Diptych (Left Wing).

1971 Christmas. Multicoloured.

355.		2 c. Type **119**	10	10
356.		2 c. The Wilton Diptych (Right Wing)	10	10
357.		8 c. Type **119**	10	10
358.		8 c. As No. 356	10	10
359.		15 c. Type **119**	20	10
360.		15 c. As No. 356	20	10

120. Cape Kennedy Launching Area.

1972. 10th Anniv. of Colonel Glenn's Splashdown. Multicoloured.

361.		5 c. Type **120**	10	10
362.		10 c. "Friendship 7" space capsule	10	10
363.		15 c. Map of Islands and splashdown	15	10
364.		20 c. N.A.S.A. Space Medal (vert.)	15	10

121. " Christ before Pilate " (Rembrandt).

1972. Easter.

365.	121.	2 c. black and lilac ..	10	10
366.	–	15 c. black and pink ..	15	10
367.	–	30 c. black and yellow..	25	15

DESIGNS—HORIZ. 15 c. " The Three Crosses " (Rembrandt). VERT. 30 c. " The Descent from the Cross " (Rembrandt).

122. Christopher Columbus.

1972. Discoverers and Explorers. Mult.

368.		½ c. Type **122**	10	10
369.		8 c. Sir Richard Grenville (horiz.)	30	10
370.		10 c. Capt. John Smith ..	35	10
371.		30 c. Juan Ponce de Leon (horiz.)	85	75

1972. Royal Silver Wedding. As T **52** of Ascension, but with Turk's-head Cactus and Spiny Lobster in backgroud.

372.		10 c. blue	10	10
373.		20 c. green	15	10

124. Treasure Hunting, c. 1700.

1973. Treasure.

374.	124.	3 c. multicoloured ..	10	10
375.	–	5 c. pur., silver & black	10	10
376.	–	10 c. pur., silver & black	20	10
377.	–	30 c. multicoloured ..	60	30

DESIGNS: 5 c. Silver Bank medallion (obverse). 10 c. Silver Bank medallion (reverse). 30 c. Treasure hunting, 1973.

125. Arms of Jamaica and Turks and Caicos Islands.

1973. Cent. of Annexation by Jamaica.

379.	125.	15 c. multicoloured ..	30	10
380.		35 c. multicoloured ..	60	20

126. Sooty Tern.

1973.

381	¼ c. Type **126**	10	15
382	1 c. Magnificent frigate-bird	20	30
383	2 c. Common noddy ..	30	30
384	3 c. Blue-grey gnatcatcher	85	40
385	4 c. Little blue heron ..	35	50
386	5 c. Catbird	30	20
387	7 c. Black whiskered vireo	2·25	20
388	8 c. Osprey	3·00	55
389	10 c. Greater flamingo ..	70	40
390	15 c. Brown pelican ..	1·25	50
459	20 c. Parula warbler ..	1·50	75
392	30 c. Northern mocking-bird	1·75	90
461	50 c. Ruby-throated hum-mingbird	1·50	2·00
462	$1 Bananaquit	2·25	2·75
463	$2 Cedar waxwing ..	3·75	4·50
464	$5 Painted bunting ..	3·50	4·00

127. Bermuda Sloop.

1973. Vessels. Multicoloured

396.		2 c. Type **127**	15	10
397.		5 c. H.M.S. " Blanche " ..	25	10
398.		8 c. U.S. privateer " Grand Turk " and P.O. Packet " Hinchinbrooke " ..	30	15
399.		10 c. H.M.S. " Endymion "	30	15
400.		15 c. R.M.S. " Medina " ..	35	70
401.		20 c. H.M.S. " Darling " ..	45	75

1973. Royal Wedding. As T **47** of Anguilla.

403.		12 c. blue	10	10
404.		18 c. blue	10	10

128. Duho (stool).

1974. Lucayan Remains. Multicoloured.

405.		6 c. Type **128**	10	10
406.		10 c. Broken wood bowl ..	15	10
407.		12 c. Greenstone axe ..	15	10
408.		18 c. Wood bowl	15	10
409.		35 c. Fragment of duho ..	20	20

129. G.P.O. Grand Turk.

1974. Centenary of U.P.U. Multicoloured.

426.		4 c. Type **129**	10	10
427.		12 c. Sloop and island map	20	10
428.		18 c. " UPU " and globe..	20	10
429.		55 c. Posthorn and emblem	35	35

130. Churchill and Roosevelt.

1974. Birth Centenary of Sir Winston Churchill. Multicoloured.
430. 12 c. Type **130** 15 15
431. 18 c. Churchill and vapour-trails 15 15

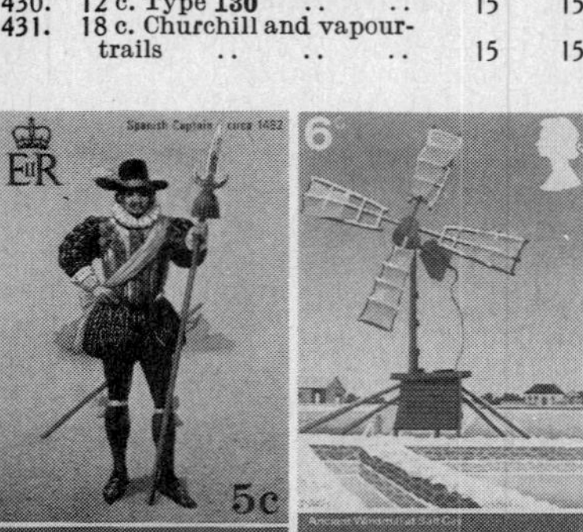

131. Spanish Captain, circa 1492. **132.** Ancient Windmill, Salt Cay.

1975. Military Uniforms. Multicoloured.
433. 5 c. Type **131** 10 10
434. 20 c. Officer, Royal Artillery 1783 .. .. 30 15
435. 25 c. Officer, 67th Foot, 1798 .. .. 35 15
436. 35 c. Private, 1st West India Regiment, 1833 .. .. 45 25

1975. Salt-raking Industry. Multicoloured.
438. 6 c. Type **132** 15 10
439. 10 c. Salt pans drying in sun (horiz.) 15 10
440. 20 c. Salt-raking (horiz.) 20 15
441. 25 c. Unprocessed salt heaps 20 20

133. Star Coral.

1975. Island Coral. Multicoloured.
442. 6 c. Type **133** 15 10
443. 10 c. Elkhorn coral 20 10
444. 20 c. Brain coral 35 15
445. 25 c. Staghorn coral 40 20

134. American Schooner.

1976. Bicent. of American Revolution Mult.
446. 6 c. Type **134** 30 10
447. 20 c. British ship of the line 70 15
448. 25 c. American privateer "Grand Turk" 70 20
449. 55 c. British ketch .. .. 1·25 60

135. 1s. 6d. Royal Visit Stamp of 1966.

1976. 10th Anniv. of Royal Visit. Mult.
466. 20 c. Type **135** 50 30
467. 25 c. 8d. Royal Visit stamp 60 30

HAVE YOU READ THE NOTES AT THE BEGINNING OF THIS CATALOGUE?
These often provide answers to the enquiries we receive.

136. " The Virgin and Child with Flowers " (C. Dolci).

1976. Christmas. Multicoloured.
468. 6 c. Type **136** 10 10
469. 10 c. " Virgin and Child " with St. John and an Angel ". (Studio of Botticelli) 10 10
470. 20 c. " Adoration of the Magi " (Master of Paraiso) 30 15
471. 25 c. " Adoration of the Magi " (French miniature) 30 20

137. Balcony Scene, Buckingham Palace.

1977. Silver Jubilee. Multicoloured.
472. 6 c. Queen presenting O.B.E. to E. T. Wood .. 10 10
473. 25 c. Queen with regalia .. 20 25
474. 55 c. Type **137** 40 55

138. Col. Glenn's " Mercury " Capsule.

1977. 20th Anniv. of U.S. Tracking Station. Multicoloured.
476. 1 c. Type **138** 10 10
477. 3 c. Moon buggy " Rover " (vert.) 10 10
478. 6 c. Tracking Station, Grand Turk 10 10
479. 20 c. Moon landing craft (vert.) 15 15
480. 25 c. Col. Glenn's rocket launch (vert.) 20 20
481. 50 c. " Telstar 1 " satellite 30 40

139. " Flight of the Holy Family " (Rubens).

1977. Christmas. 400th Birth Anniv. of Rubens. Multicoloured.
482. ¼ c. Type **139** 10 10
483. ½ c. " Adoration of the Magi " (1634) 10 10
484. 1 c. " Adoration of the Magi " (1624) 10 10
485. 6 c. " Virgin within Garland " 10 10
486. 20 c. " Madonna and Child Adored by Angels " .. 15 10
487. $2 " Adoration of the Magi " (1618) .. .. 1·25 1·25

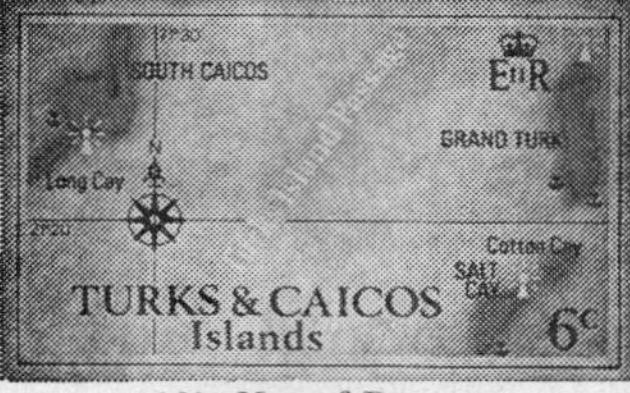

140. Map of Passage.

1978. Turks Island Passage. Multicoloured.
489. 6 c. Type **140** 10 10
490. 20 c. Caicos sloop passing Grand Turk Lighthouse 35 55
491. 25 c. Motor cruiser .. 40 65
492. 55 c. "Jamaica Planter" (freighter) .. .. 85 1·60

141. " Queen Victoria ". (Sir George Hayter).

142. Ampulla and Anointing Spoon.

1978. 25th Anniv. of Coronation. Mult.
(a) Monarchs in Coronation robes.
494. 6 c. Type **141** 10 10
495. 10 c. " King Edward VII " (Sir Samuel Fields) .. 10 10
496. 25 c. King George V. .. 20 15
497. $2 King George VI .. 1·00 1·00
(b) Coronation regalia. Self-adhesive.
499. 15 c. Type **142** 15 30
500. 25 c. St. Edward's Crown 15 30
501. $2 Queen Elizabeth II in Coronation robes .. 1·75 2·75
Nos. 499/501 come from booklets.

143. Wilbur Wright and " Flyer III ".

1978. 75th Anniv. of Powered Flight. Mult.
502. 1 c. Type **143** 10 10
503. 6 c. Wright brothers and Cessna " 337 " 10 10
504. 10 c. Orville Wright and " Electra " 10 10
505. 15 c. Wilbur Wright and " C-47 " 15 15
506. 35 c. Wilbur Wright and " Islander " 35 35
507. $2 Wilbur Wright and Wright biplane .. 1·25 1·50

144. Hurdling.

1978. 11th Commonwealth Games, Edmonton. Multicoloured.
509. 6 c. Type **144** 10 10
510. 20 c. Weightlifting 15 15
511. 55 c. Boxing 30 30
512. $2 Cycling .. .. 1·00 1·00

145. Indigo Hamlet.

1978. Fishes. Multicoloured.
514. 1 c. Type **145** 10 25
515. 2 c. Tobacco Fish .. 40 10
516. 3 c. Passing Jack 15 10
517. 4 c. Porkfish 40 20
518. 5 c. Spanish Grunt .. 20 20
519. 7 c. Yellowtail Snapper .. 50 15
520. 8 c. Foureye Butterflyfish 60 10
521. 10 c. Yellowfin Grouper .. 30 15
522. 15 c. Beau Gregory .. 50 30
523. 20 c. Queen Angelfish .. 30 30
524. 30 c. Hogfish .. .. 1·00 40
525. 50 c. Fairy Basslet .. 1·00 65
526. $1 Clown Wrasse .. .. 1·75 1·60
527. $2 Stoplight Parrotfish .. 3·25 2·50
528. $5 Queen Triggerfish .. 3·25 6·50
Some values exist both with or without imprint date at foot.

146. " Madonna of the Siskin ".

1978. Christmas Paintings by Durer. Mult.
529. 6 c. Type **146** 10 10
530. 20 c. " The Virgin and Child with St. Anne " .. 15 10
531. 35 c. " Paumgartner Nativity " (horiz.) 20 15
532. $2 " Praying Hands " .. 85 1·00

147. Osprey.

1979. Endangered Wildlife. Multicoloured.
534. 6 c. Type **147** 40 10
535. 20 c. Green Turtle 45 20
536. 25 c. Queen Conch .. 50 25
537. 55 c. Rough-toothed Dolphin 90 50
538. $1 Humpback Whale .. 1·50 1·25

148. " The Beloved " (painting by D. G. Rossetti).

1979. International Year of the Child. Multicoloured.
540. 6 c. Type **148** 10 10
541. 25 c. " Tahitian Girl " (P. Gauguin) 15 10
542. 55 c. " Calmady Children " (Sir Thomas Lawrence) 25 20
543. $1 " Mother and Daughter " (detail, P. Gauguin) .. 45 45

149. R.M.S.P. " Medina " and Handstamped Cover.

150. Cuneiform Script.

1979. Death Centenary of Sir Rowland Hill.

(a) As T **149**. Multicoloured.

545. 6 c. Type **149** 10 10
546. 20 c. Sir Rowland Hill and map of Caribbean .. 15 15
547. 45 c. R.M.S. "Orinoco" and cover bearing Penny Black Stamp .. 25 25
548. 75 c. R.M.S. "Shannon" and letter to Grand Turk 40 40
549. $1 R.M.S.P. "Trent" and map of Caribbean .. 55 55
550. $2 Turks Islands 1867 and Turks and Caicos Islands 1900 1d Stamps .. 90 90

(b) As T **150**. Self-adhesive (from booklets).

552. **150**. 5 c. black and green .. 10 10
553. – 5 c. black and green .. 10 10
554. – 5 c. black and green .. 10 10
555. – 15 c. black and blue .. 20 20
556. – 15 c. black and blue .. 20 20
557. – 15 c. black and blue .. 20 20
558. – 25 c. black and blue .. 30 30
559. – 25 c. black and blue .. 60 45
560. – 25 c. black and blue .. 30 30
561. – 40 c. black and red .. 45 45
562. – 40 c. black and red .. 45 45
563. – 40 c. black and red .. 45 45
564. – $1 black and yellow .. 1·10 1·25

DESIGNS—HORIZ. No. 553, Egyptian papyrus. No. 554, Chinese paper. No. 555, Greek runner. No. 556, Roman post horse. No. 557. Roman post ship. No. 558, Pigeon post. No. 559, Railway post No. 560, Packet paddle-steamer, No. 561. Balloon post. No. 562, First airmail. No. 563, Supersonic airmail. VERT. No. 564, Original stamp press.

152. "St. Nicholas", Prikra, Ukraine.

1979. Christmas. Religious Art. Multicoloured.

566. 1 c. Type **152** 10 10
567. 3 c. "Emperor Otto II with Symbols of Empire" (Master of the Registrum Gregorii) .. 10 10
568. 6 c. "Portrait of St. John" (Book of Lindisfarne).. 10 10
569. 15 c. "Adoration of the Majestas Domini" (prayer book of Otto II) 10 10
570. 20 c. "Christ attended by Angels" (Book of Kells) 15 15
571. 25 c. "St. John the Evangelist" (Gospels of St. Medard of Soissons), Charlemagne 20 15
572. 65 c. "Christ Pantocrator", Trocany, Ukraine .. 30 25
573. $1 "Portrait of St. John" (Canterbury Codex Aureus) 45 45

153. Pluto and Starfish.

1979. International Year of the Child. Walt Disney Cartoon Characters. At the Seaside. Multicoloured.

575. ¼ c. Type **153** .. 10 10
576. ½ c. Minnie Mouse in summer outfit .. 10 10
577. 1 c. Mickey Mouse underwater 10 10
578. 2 c. Goofy and turtle .. 10 10
579. 3 c. Donald Duck and dolphin 10 10
580. 4 c. Mickey Mouse fishing 10 10
581. 5 c. Goofy surfing .. 10 10
582. 25 c. Pluto and crab .. 45 20
583. $1 Daisy water-skiing .. 2·00 1·10

154. "Christina's World" (painting by Andrew Wyeth).

1979. Works of Art. Multicoloured.

585. 6 c. Type **154** 10 10
586. 10 c. Ivory Leopards, Benin (19th-cent.) .. 10 10
587. 20 c. "The Kiss" (painting by Gustav Klimt) (vert.) 15 15
588. 25 c. "Portrait of a Lady" (painting by R. van der Weyden) (vert.) .. 15 15
589. 80 c. Bull's head harp, Sumer c. 2600 B.C. (vert.) 30 30
590. $1 "The Wave" (painting by Hokusai) .. 45 45

155. Pied-billed Grebe.

1980. Birds. Multicoloured.

592. 20 c. Type **155** .. 60 15
593. 25 c. Ovenbirds at nest .. 65 20
594. 35 c. Hen Harrier.. .. 90 30
595. 55 c. Yellow-bellied Sapsucker .. .. 1·10 35
596. $1 Blue-winged Teal .. 1·40 80

156. Stamp, Magnifying Glass and Perforation Gauge.

1980. "London 1980" International Stamp Exhibition. Multicoloured.

598. **156**. 25 c. black and yellow.. 15 15
599. – 40 c. black and green .. 25 25

DESIGN: 40 c. Tweezers, stamp and perforation gauge.

157. Trumpet Triton.

1980. Shells. Multicoloured.

601. 14 c. Type **157** 20 20
602. 20 c. Measled Cowry .. 25 25
603. 30 c. True Tulip 35 35
604. 45 c. Lion's Paw 45 45
605. 55 c. Sunrise Tellin .. 55 55
606. 70 c. Crown Cone 70 70

158. Queen Elizabeth the Queen Mother.

1980. 80th Birthday of The Queen Mother.

607. **158**. 80 c. multicoloured .. 1·60 1·25

159. Doctor examining Child and Lions International Emblem.

1980. "Serving the Community". Mult.

609. 10 c. Type **159** 15 10
610. 15 c. Students receiving scholarships and Kiwanis International emblem .. 20 10
611. 45 c. Teacher with students and Soroptimist emblem 50 35
612. $1 Lobster trawler and Rotary International emblem .. .. .. 1·00 80

1980. Christmas. Scenes from Walt Disney's "Pinocchio". As T **153**. Multicoloured.

614. ¼ c. Scene from "Pinocchio" 10 10
615. ½ c. As puppet 10 10
616. 1 c. Pinocchio changed into a boy 10 10
617. 2 c. Captured by fox .. 10 10
618. 3 c. Pinocchio and puppeteer 10 10
619. 4 c. Pinocchio and bird's nest nose 10 10
620. 5 c. Pinocchio eating .. 10 10
621. 75 c. Pinocchio with ass ears 60 70
622. $1 Pinocchio underwater 80 95

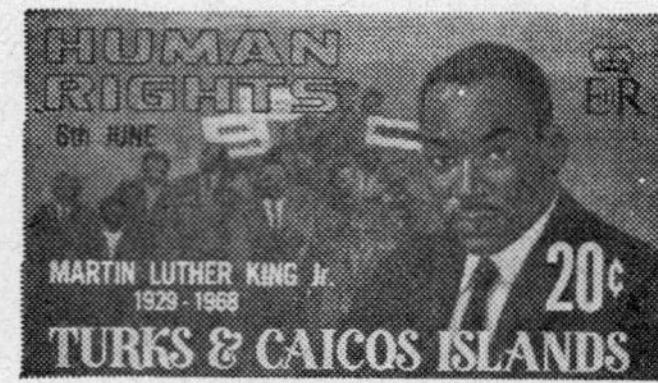

160. Martin Luther King Jr.

1980. Human Rights. Personalities. Mult.

624. 20 c. Type **160** 15 10
625. 30 c. John F. Kennedy .. 30 25
626. 45 c. Roberto Clemente (baseball player) .. 45 35
627. 70 c. Sir Frank Worrel (cricketer) 90 80
628. $1 Harriet Tubman .. 1·10 1·00

161. Yachts.

1980. South Caicos Regatta. Multicoloured.

630. 6 c. Type **161** 10 10
631. 15 c. Trophy and yachts .. 15 15
632. 35 c. Spectators watching speedboat race 25 20
633. $1 Caicos sloops 60 50

162. Night Queen Cactus.

1981. Flowering Cacti. Multicoloured.

635. 25 c. Type **162** 25 25
636. 35 c. Ripsaw Cactus .. 35 35
637. 55 c. Royal Strawberry Cactus 40 50
638. 80 c. Caicos Cactus .. 60 75

1981. 50th Anniv. of Walt Disney's Pluto (cartoon character). As T **153**. Multicoloured.

640. 10 c. Pluto listening to conch shell 10 10
641. 75 c. Pluto on raft and porpoise 75 75

1981. Easter. Walt Disney Cartoon Characters. As T **153**. Multicoloured.

643. 10 c. Donald Duck and Louie 20 20
644. 25 c. Goofy and Donald Duck 40 40
645. 60 c. Chip and Dale .. 85 85
646. 80 c. Scrooge McDuck and Huey .. .. .. 1·25 1·25

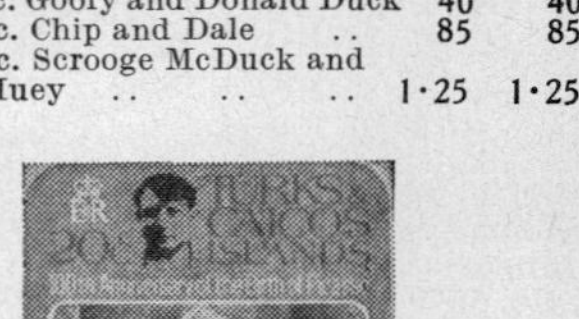

163. "Woman with Fan".

1981. Birth Centenary of Picasso. Mult.

648. 20 c. Type **163** 20 15
649. 45 c. "Woman with Pears" 35 30
650. 80 c. "The Accordionist" 60 50
651. $1 "The Aficionado" .. 80 80

164. Kensington Palace.

1981. Royal Wedding. Multicoloured.

653. 35 c. Prince Charles and Lady Diana Spencer .. 20 15
654. 65 c. Type **164** 35 30
655. 90 c. Prince Charles as Colonel of the Welsh Guards 45 45

165. Lady Diana Spencer.

1981. Royal Wedding. Booklet stamps. Multicoloured. Self-adhesive.

657. 20 c. Type **165** 25 30
658. $1 Prince Charles .. 50 1·00
659. $2 Prince Charles and Lady Diana Spencer .. 2·00 2·50

165. Marine Biology Observation.

1981. Diving. Multicoloured.

660. 15 c. Type **166** 20 15
661. 40 c. Underwater photography 50 35
662. 75 c. Wreck diving .. 90 70
663. $1 Diving with dolphins.. 1·25 1·00

1981. Christmas. As T **153** showing scenes from Walt Disney's cartoon film " Uncle Remus ".

665. ½ c. multicoloured .. 10 10
666. ½ c. multicoloured .. 10 10
667. 1 c. multicoloured .. 10 10
668. 2 c. multicoloured .. 10 10
669. 3 c. multicoloured .. 10 10
670. 4 c. multicoloured .. 10 10
671. 5 c. multicoloured .. 10 10
672. 75 c. multicoloured .. 60 60
673. $1 multicoloured .. 80 80

167. Map of Grand Turk, and Lighthouse.

1981. Tourism. Multicoloured.

675. 20 c. Type **167** .. 35 35
676. 20 c. Map of Salt Cay, and " industrial archaeology " 35 35
677. 20 c. Map of South Caicos, and " island flying " .. 35 35
678. 20 c. Map of East Caicos, and " beach combing " 35 35
679. 20 c. Map of Central Grand Caicos, and cave exploring 35 35
680. 20 c. Map of North Caicos, and camping and hiking 35 35
681. 20 c. Map of North Caicos, Parrot Cay, Dellis Cay, Fort George Cay, Pine Cay and Water Cay, and " environmental studies " 35 35
682. 20 c. Map of Providenciales, and scuba diving .. 35 35
683. 20 c. Map of West Caicos, and " cruising and bird sanctuary " 35 35
684. 20 c. Turks and Caicos Islands flag 35 35

168. "Junonia evarete"

1982. Butterflies. Multicoloured.

685 20 c. Type **168** 30 30
686 35 c. "Strymon maesites" 50 55
687 65 c. "Agraulis vanillae" .. 90 1·00
688 $1 "Eurema dina" .. 1·40 2·00

169. Flag Salute on Queen's Birthday.

1982. 75th Anniv. of Boy Scout Movement. Multicoloured.

690. 40 c. Type **169** 50 50
691. 50 c. Raft building .. 60 60
692. 75 c. Sea scout cricket match 1·10 1·40
693. $1 Nature study .. .. 1·50 1·60

1982. World Cup Football Championship, Spain.

695. **170.** 10 c. multicoloured .. 15 15
696. – 25 c. multicoloured .. 20 20
697. – 45 c. multicoloured .. 25 25
698. – $1 multicoloured .. 80 80

DESIGNS: 25 c. to $1. various footballers.

170. Footballer.

171. Washington crossing the Delaware and Phillis Wheatley (poetess).

1982. 250th Birth Anniv. of George Washington and Birth Centenary of Franklin D. Roosevelt.

700. 20 c. Type **171** 30 30
701. 35 c. George Washington and Benjamin Banneker (surveyor) 45 45
702. 65 c. Franklin D. Roosevelt meeting George Washington Carver (agricultural researcher) 80 80
703. 80 c. Roosevelt as stamp collector .. .. 1·00 1·00

172. " Second Thoughts ".

1982. Norman Rockwell (painter) Commemoration. Multicoloured.

705. 8 c. Type **172** 15 10
706. 15 c. " The Proper Gratuity " 20 20
707. 20 c. " Before the Shot " 25 25
708. 25 c. " The Three Umpires " 25 25

173. Princess of Wales.

1982. 21st Birthday of Princess of Wales. Multicoloured.

713. 8 c. Sandringham 35 55
714. 35 c. Prince and Princess of Wales .. .. .. 70 1·25
709. 55 c. As 8 c. 70 55
710. 70 c. As 35 c. 85 70
711. $1 Type **173** .. .. 1·25 1·25
715. $1.10 Type **173** .. .. 1·75 2·25

174. " Skymaster " over Caicos Cays.

1982. Aircraft. Multicoloured.

716. 8 c. Type **174** 15 15
717. 15 c. " Jetstar " over Grand Turk 20 25
718. 65 c. Helicopter over South Caicos 65 80
719. $1.10 Seaplane over Providenciales .. 1·10 1·25

1982. Christmas. Scenes from Walt Disney's Cartoon film " Mickey's Christmas Carol ". As T **153**. Multicoloured.

721. 1 c. Donald Duck, Mickey Mouse and Scrooge .. 10 10
722. 1 c. Goofy (Marley's ghost) and Scrooge 10 10
723. 2 c. Jiminy Cricket and Scrooge 10 10
724. 2 c. Huey, Dewy and Louie 10 10
725. 3 c. Daisy Duck and youthful Scrooge 10 10
726. 3 c. Giant and Scrooge .. 10 10
727. 4 c. Two bad wolves, a wise pig and a reformed Scrooge 10 10
728. 65 c. Donald Duck and Scrooge .. .. 1·00 65
729. $1.10 Mortie and Scrooge 1·60 1·10

175. West Caicos Trolley Tram.

1983. Trams and Locomotives. Mult.

731. 15 c. Type **175** 20 25
732. 55 c. West Caicos steam locomotive 65 70
733. 90 c. East Caicos sisal locomotive .. .. 90 1·00
734. $1.60 East Caicos steam locomotive .. .. 1·75 1·90

176. Policewoman on Traffic Duty.

1983. Commonwealth Day. Multicoloured.

736. 1 c. Type **176** 15 20
737. 8 c. Stylized sun and weather vane 15 20
738. 65 c. Yacht 85 90
739. $1 Cricket .. .. 1·50 1·60

177. " St. John and the Virgin Mary " (detail).

1983. Easter. Designs showing details from the " Mond Crucifixion " by Raphael. Multicoloured.

740. 35 c. Type **177** 20 25
741. 50 c. " Two Women " .. 30 35
742. 95 c. " Angel with two jars " 50 60
743. $1.10 " Angel with one jar " 60 80

178. Minke Whale.

1983. Whales. Multicoloured.

745. 50 c. Type **178** .. 1·00 1·00
746. 65 c. Black Right Whale .. 1·25 1·25
747. 70 c. Killer Whale .. 1·50 1·50
748. 95 c. Sperm Whale .. 1·75 1·75
749. $1.10 Cuvier's Beaked Whale .. .. 2·00 2·00
750. $2 Blue Whale .. .. 3·50 3·50
751. $2.20 Humpback Whale .. 3·75 3·75
752. $3 Long-finned Pilot Whale .. .. 4·75 4·75

179. First Hydrogen Balloon, 1783.

1983. Bicentenary of Manned Flight. Mult.

754. 25 c. Type **179** 25 25
755. 35 c. " Friendship 7 " .. 35 35
756. 70 c. First hot-air balloon, 1783 .. .. 70 70
757. 95 c. Space shuttle " Columbia " 90 90

180. Fiddler Pig.

1983. Christmas. Walt Disney Cartoon Characters. Multicoloured.

759. 1 c. Type **180** 10 10
760. 1 c. Fifer Pig 10 10
761. 2 c. Practical Pig 10 10
762. 2 c. Pluto 10 10
763. 3 c. Goofy 10 10
764. 3 c. Micky Mouse .. 10 10
765. 35 c. Gyro Gearloose .. 35 35
766. 50 c. Ludwig von Drake .. 50 50
767. $1.10 Huey, Dewey and Louie .. .. .. 1·00 1·00

181. Bermudan Sloop.

1983. Ships. Multicoloured.

769. 4 c. Arawak dug-out canoe 40 30
770. 5 c "Santa Maria" 50 30
771. 8 c. British and Spanish ships in battle 50 40
772. 10 c. Type **181** 40 40
773. 20 c. U.S. privateer "Grand Turk" 50 40
774. 25 c. H.M.S. "Boreas" .. 50 40
775. 30 c. H.M.S. "Endymion" attacking French ship, 1790s 75 50
776. 35 c. "Caesar" (barque) .. 60 50
777. 50 c. "Grapeshot" (American schooner) .. 60 60
778. 65 c. H.M.S. "Invincible" (battle cruiser) .. .. 1·00 1·00
779. 95 c. H.M.S. "Magicienne" 1·50 1·50
780. $1.10 H.M.S. "Durban", 1928 .. .. .. 2·25 2·25
781. $2 "Sentinel" (cable ship) 2·25 2·50
782. $3 H.M.S. "Minerva" .. 5·00 6·00
783. $5 Caicos sloop .. .. 7·50 8·00

182. Pres. Kennedy and Signing of Civil Rights Legislation.

1983. 20th Death Anniv. of J. F. Kennedy (U.S. President).

784. **182.** 20 c. multicoloured .. 20 15
785. $1 multicoloured .. 1·10 1·25

183. Clarabelle Cow Diving.

1984. Olympic Games, Los Angeles. Multicoloured.

A. Inscr. "**1984 LOS ANGELES**". B. Inscr. "**1984 OLYMPICS LOS ANGELES**" and Olympic Emblem.

		A		B	
786.	1 c. Type **183** ..	10	10	10	10
787.	1 c Donald Duck in 500m kayak race	10	10	10	10
788.	2 c. Huey, Dewey and Louie in 1000m kayak race	10	10	10	10
789.	2 c. Mickey Mouse in single kayak	10	10	10	10
790.	3 c. Donald Duck highboard diving	10	10	10	10
791.	3 c. Minnie Mouse in kayak slalom	10	10	10	10
792.	25 c. Mickey Mouse freestyle swimming	40	45	40	45
793.	Donald Duck playing water-polo	1·25	1·40	1·25	1·40
794.	$1 Uncle Scrooge & Donald Duck yachting ..	1·60	1·75	1·60	1·75

184. "Cadillac V–16", 1933.

1984. Classic Cars and 125th Anniv. of first Commercial Oil Well. Multicoloured.

796.	4 c. Type **184**	10	10
797.	8 c. Rolls-Royce "Phantom III", 1937 ..	15	15
798.	10 c. Saab "99", 1969 ..	15	15
799.	25 c. Maserati "Bora", 1973	40	40
800.	40 c. Datsun "260Z", 1970	65	65
801.	55 c. Porsche "917", 1971	80	80
802.	80 c. Lincoln "Continental" 1939	90	90
803.	$1 Triumph "TR3A", 1957	1·25	1·25

185. "Rest during the Flight to Egypt, with St. Francis".

1984. Easter 450th Death Anniv. of Correggio (painter). Multicoloured.

805.	15 c. Type **185**	20	15
806.	40 c. "St. Luke and St. Ambrose"	45	40
807.	60 c. "Diana and her Chariot"	65	65
808.	95 c. "The Deposition of Christ"	80	80

1984. Universal Postal Union Congress, Hamburg. Nos. 748/9 optd. **19TH UPU CONGRESS, HAMBURG, WEST GERMANY. 1874-1984.** Multicoloured.

810.	95 c. Sperm Whale ..	2·00	1·50
811.	$1.10 Goosebeak Whale ..	2·00	1·60

187. "The Adventure of the Second Stain".

1984. 125th Birth Anniv. of Sir Arthur Conan Doyle (author). Multicoloured.

813.	25 c. Type **187**	1·75	1·25
814.	45 c. "The Adventure of the Final Problem" ..	2·50	2·00
815.	70 c. "The Adventure of the Empty House" ..	4·00	3·25
816.	85 c. "The Adventure of the Greek Interpreter"	4·50	3·25

188. Clown-Fish.

1984. "Ausipex" International Stamp Exhibition, Melbourne. 175th Birth Anniv. of Charles Darwin. Multicoloured.

818.	5 c. Type **188**	40	30
819.	35 c. Monitor lizard ..	1·75	1·75
820.	50 c. Rainbow lory ..	2·50	2·50
821.	$1.10 Koalas	3·25	3·25

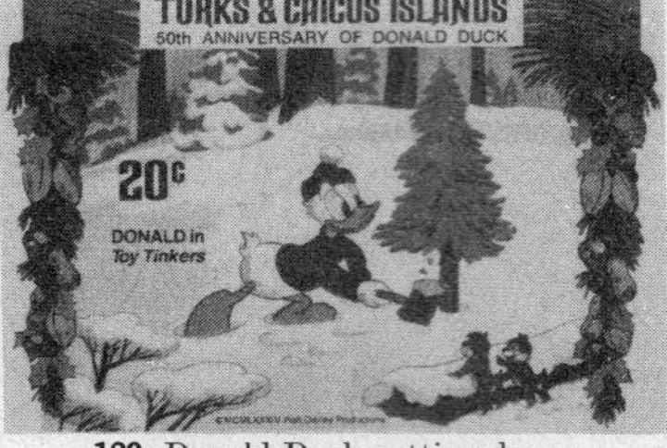

189. Donald Duck cutting down Christmas Tree.

1984. Christmas. Walt Disney Cartoon Characters. Designs showing scenes from "Toy Tinkers". Multicoloured.

823.	20 c. Type **189**	85	45
824.	35 c. Donald Duck and Chip n'Dale playing with train set	1·10	65
825.	50 c. Donald Duck and Chip n'Dale playing with catapult	1·60	85
826.	75 c. Donald Duck, Chip n'Dale and Christmas tree	2·25	1·40
827.	$1.10 Donald Duck, toy soldier and Chip n'Dale	2·50	1·90

190. Magnolia Warbler.

1985. Birth Bicentenary of John J. Audubon (ornithologist). Multicoloured.

829.	25 c. Type **190**	1·50	45
830.	45 c. Short-eared owl ..	2·25	80
831.	70 c. Mourning dove and eggs	2·50	1·50
832.	85 c. Caribbean martin ..	2·75	1·75

191. Leonardo da Vinci and Illustration of Glider Wing (15th century).

1985. 40th Anniv. of International Civil Aviation Organization. Pioneers. Mult.

834.	8 c. Type **191**	40	15
835.	25 c. Sir Alliott Verdon Roe and "C.102" jetliner (1949)	75	40
836.	65 c. Robert H. Goddard and first liquid fuel rocket (1926)	1·75	95
837.	$1 Igor Sikorsky and Sikorsky "VS300" helicopter (1939)	2·25	1·50

192. Benjamin Franklin and Marquis de Lafayette.

1985. Centenary of Statue of Liberty's Arrival in New York. Multicoloured.

839.	20 c. Type **192**	80	50
840.	30 c. Frederic Bartholdi (designer) and Gustave Eiffel (engineer) ..	90	60
841.	65 c. Sailing ship "Isere" arriving in New York with statue, 1885 ..	2·25	1·50
842.	$1.10 United States fund raisers Louis Agassiz, Charles Sumner, H. W. Longfellow and Joseph Pulitzer	2·50	1·75

193. Sir Edward Hawke and H.M.S. "Royal George".

1985. Salute to Royal Navy. Multicoloured.

844.	20 c. Type **193**	1·50	1·25
845.	30 c. Lord Nelson and H.M.S. "Victory" ..	2·00	1·75
846.	65 c. Admiral Sir George Cockburn and H.M.S. "Albion"	2·75	2·25
847.	95 c. Admiral Sir David Beatty and H.M.S. "Indefatigable" ..	3·75	3·00

194. Mark Twain riding on Halley's Comet.

1985. International Youth Year. Birth Annivs of Mark Twain (150th) and Jakob Grimm (Bicentenary). Multicoloured.

849	25 c. Type **194**	85	40
850	35 c. "Grand Turk" (Mississippi river steamer)	1·25	55
851	50 c. Hansel and Gretel and gingerbread house (vert)	1·50	75
852	95 c. Rumpelstiltskin (vert)	2·25	1·50

195. The Queen Mother outside Clarence House. **196.** King George II and Score of "Zadok the Priest" (1727).

1985. Life and Times of Queen Elizabeth the Queen Mother. Multicoloured.

854.	30 c. Type **195**	45	45
855.	50 c. Visiting Biggin Hill airfield (horiz.)	75	75
856.	$1.10 80th birthday portrait	1·90	1·90

1985. 300th Birth Anniv. of George Frederick Handel (composer). Multicoloured.

858.	4 c. Type **196** ..	65	40
859.	10 c. Queen Caroline and score of "Funeral Anthem" (1737)	1·00	50
860.	50 c. King George I and score of "Water Music" (1714)	2·75	1·50
861.	$1.10 Queen Anne and score of "Or la Tromba" from "Rinaldo" (1711) ..	4·75	3·75

1985. 300th Birth Anniv of Johann Sebastian Bach (composer). As T **206** of Antigua. Multicoloured.

863	15 c. Bassoon	1·00	40
864	40 c. Natural Horn ..	1·75	85
865	60 c. Viola d'amore ..	2·25	1·25
866	95 c. Clavichord	2·75	2·25

197. Harley-Davidson Dual Cylinder (1915) on Middle Caicos.

1985. Centenary of the Motor Cycle. Mult.

868.	8 c. Type **197**	40	30
869.	25 c. Triumph "Thunderbird" (1950) on Grand Turk	90	70
870.	55 c. BMW "K100RS" (1985) on North Caicos ..	1·75	1·50
871.	$1.20 Honda "1100 Shadow" (1985) on South Caicos	3·00	2·50

198. Pirates in Prison (Illustration reduced, actual size 50 × 37 mm.).

1985. 30th Anniv. of Disneyland, U.S.A. Designs showing scenes from "Pirates of the Caribbean" exhibition. Multicoloured.

873.	1 c. Type **198**	10	10
874.	1 c. The fate of Captain William Kidd	10	10
875.	2 c. Bartholomew Roberts	10	10
876.	2 c. Two buccaneers ..	10	10
877.	3 c. Privateers looting ..	10	10
878.	3 c. Auction of captives ..	10	10
879.	35 c. Singing pirates ..	1·25	55
880.	75 c. Edward Teach–"Blackbeard"	2·50	1·25
881.	$1.10 Sir Henry Morgan ..	2·75	1·60

MINIMUM PRICE

The minimum price quoted is 10p which represents a handling charge rather than a basis for valuing common stamps. For further notes about prices see introductory pages.

199. Brownies from China, Turks and Caicos and Papua New Guinea.

1985. 75th Anniv. of Girl Guide Movement and 35th Anniv. of Grand Turk Company. Multicoloured.

883. 10 c. Type **199** 75 30
884. 40 c. Brownies from Surinam, Turks and Caicos and Korea .. .. 1·75 1·25
885. 70 c. Guides from Australia, Turks and Caicos and Canada .. .. 2·50 2·00
886. 80 c. Guides from West Germany, Turks and Caicos and Israel .. 2·75 2·25

200. Iguana and Log.

1986. Turks and Caicos Ground Iguana. Multicoloured.

888. 8 c. Type **200** .. .. 1·00 70
889. 10 c. Iguana on beach .. 1·25 85
890. 20 c. Iguana at nest .. 1·75 1·75
891. 35 c. Iguana eating flowers 3·00 3·00

201. Duke and Duchess of York after Wedding.

1986. Royal Wedding. Multicoloured.

893. 35 c. Type **201** 65 55
894. 65 c. Miss Sarah Ferguson in wedding carriage .. 1·10 1·10
895. $1.10 Duke and Duchess of York on Palace balcony after wedding .. .. 1·75 2·00

202. "Prophecy of Birth of Christ to King Achaz".

1987. Christmas. Illuminated illustrations by Giorgio Clovio from "Farnese Book of Hours". Multicoloured.

897. 35 c. Type **202** .. .. 1·00 75
898. 50 c. "The Annunciation" 1·40 1·25
899. 65 c. "The Circumcision" 2·00 1·75
900. 95 c. "Adoration of the Kings" .. .. .. 3·00 3·50

203. H.M.S. "Victoria", 1889, and Victoria Cross.

1987. 150th Anniv. of Accession of Queen Victoria. Multicoloured.

902. 8 c. Type **203** 55 35
903. 35 c. "Victoria" (paddle-steamer) and gold sovereign.. .. .. 1·50 1·25
904. 55 c. Royal Yacht "Victoria and Albert I" and 1840 Penny Black stamp .. 1·75 1·75
905. 95 c. Royal Yacht "Victoria and Albert II" and Victoria Public Library 2·50 2·75

1987. Bicentenary of U.S. Consitution. As T **232** of Antigua. Multicoloured.

907. 10 c. State Seal, New Jersey 20 15
908. 35 c. 18th-century family going to church ("Freedom of Worship") (vert.) 55 55
909. 65 c. U.S. Supreme Court, Judicial Branch, Washington (vert.) .. 1·00 1·00
910. 80 c. John Adams (statesman) (vert.) .. .. 1·25 1·40

204 "Santa Maria"

1988. 500th Anniv (1992) of Discovery of America by Columbus (1st issue). Mult.

912 4 c. Type **204** 15 15
913 25 c. Columbus meeting Tainos Indians .. 65 50
914 70 c. "Santa Maria" anchored off Indian village .. .. .. 1·75 1·75
915 $1 Columbus in field of grain .. .. .. 2·25 2·25

See also Nos. 947/50, 1028/35 and 1072/9.

205 Arawak Artifact and Scouts in Cave, Middle Caicos

1988. World Scout Jamboree, Australia. Mult.

917 8 c. Type **205** 20 15
918 35 c. "Santa Maria", scouts and Hawks Nest Island (horiz) 55 55
919 65 c. Scouts diving to wreck of galleon .. 95 95
920 95 c. Visiting ruins of 19th-century sisal plantation (horiz) .. 1·40 1·40

1988. Royal Ruby Wedding. Nos. 772, 774 and 781 optd **40TH WEDDING ANNIVERSARY H.M. QUEEN ELIZABETH II H.R.H. THE DUKE OF EDINBURGH.**

922 10 c. Type **181** 30 30
923 25 c. H.M.S. "Boreas" .. 55 55
924 $2 "Sentinel" (cable ship) 3·25 3·25

207 Football

1988. Olympic Games, Seoul. Multicoloured.

925 8 c. Type **207** 15 15
926 30 c. Yachting 35 40
927 70 c. Cycling 85 90
928 $1 Athletics .. .. 1·25 1·40

208 Game-fishing Launch and Swordfish

1988. Billfish Tournament. Multicoloured.

930 8 c. Type **208** 20 15
931 10 c. Competitors with swordfish catch .. 30 15
932 70 c. Game-fishing launch 1·40 1·40
933 $1 Blue marlin .. .. 1·90 2·10

1988. Christmas. 500th Birth Anniv of Titian (artist). As T **238** of Antigua inscr "CHRISTMAS 1988" and with royal cypher at top right. Multicoloured.

935 15 c. "Madonna and Child with Saint Catherine" .. 30 30
936 25 c. "Madonna with a Rabbit" 40 40
937 35 c. "Virgin and Child with Saints" 50 50
938 40 c. "The Gypsy Madonna" 60 60
939 50 c. "The Holy Family and a Shepherd" .. 70 70
940 65 c. "Madonna and Child" .. 85 85
941 $3 "Madonna and Child with Saints" .. 3·75 3·75

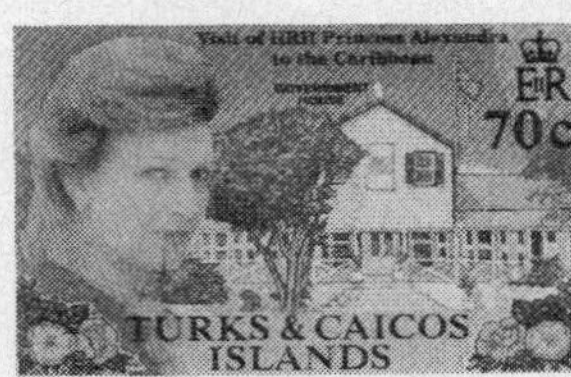

209 Princess Alexandra and Government House

1988. Visit of Princess Alexandra. Mult.

943 70 c. Type **209** .. .. 1·50 1·50
944 $1.40 Princess Alexandra and map of islands .. 2·50 2·50

210 Coat of Arms

1988.

946 **210** $10 multicoloured .. 10·50 11·00

1989. 500th Anniv (1992) of Discovery of America by Columbus (2nd issue). Pre-Columbian Carib Society. As T **247** of Antigua. Multicoloured.

947 10 c. Cutting tree bark for canoe (vert) 10 15
948 50 c. Body painting .. 60 65
949 65 c. Religious ceremony 75 80
950 $1 Canoeing (vert) .. 1·25 1·40

1989. "World Stamp Expo '89" International Stamp Exhibition, Washington. Bicentenary of the U.S. Presidency. As T **238** of Dominica. Multicoloured.

953 50 c. Andrew Jackson and "DeWitt Clinton" railway locomotive .. 60 65
954 50 c. Martin van Buren, Moses Walker and early baseball game 60 65
955 50 c. William H. Harrison and campaign parade .. 60 65
956 50 c. John Tyler, Davy Crockett and the Alamo, Texas 60 65
957 50 c. James K. Polk, California gold miner and first U.S. postage stamp 60 65
958 50 c. Zachary Taylor and Battle of Buena Vista, 1846 .. .. .. 60 65
959 50 c. Rutherford B. Hayes and end of Confederate Reconstruction .. 60 65
960 50 c. James A. Garfield and Battle of Shiloh .. 60 65
961 50 c. Chester A. Arthur and opening of Brooklyn Bridge, 1883 .. .. 60 65
962 50 c. Grover Cleveland, Columbian Exposition, Chicago, 1893, and commemorative stamp 60 65
963 50 c. Benjamin Harrison, Pan-American Union Building and map of Americas 60 65
964 50 c. William McKinley and Rough Rider Monument 60 65
965 50 c. Herbert Hoover, Sonya Heine (skater) and Ralph Metcalf (athlete) 60 65
966 50 c. Franklin D. Roosevelt with dog and in wheelchair 60 65
967 50 c. Statue of Washington by Frazer and New York World's Fair, 1939 .. 60 65
968 50 c. Harry S. Truman, Veterans Memorial Building, San Francisco, and U.N. emblem .. 60 65
969 50 c. Dwight D. Eisenhower and U.S. troops landing in Normandy, 1944 .. .. .. 60 65
970 50 c. John F. Kennedy and "Apollo 11" astronauts on Moon, 1969 .. .. 60 65

1989. Christmas. Paintings by Bellini. As T **259** of Antigua. Multicoloured.

971 15 c. "Madonna and Child" 25 25
972 25 c. "The Madonna of the Shrubs" 35 35
973 35 c. "The Virgin and Child" 45 45
974 40 c. "The Virgin and Child with a Greek Inscription" 55 55
975 50 c. "The Madonna of the Meadow" 65 65
976 65 c. "The Madonna of the Pear" 80 80
977 70 c. "The Virgin and Child" (different) .. 90 90
978 $1 "Madonna and Child" (different) .. .. 1·40 1·40

211 Lift-off of "Apollo 11"

1990. 20th Anniv of First Manned Landing on Moon. Multicoloured.

980	50 c. Type **211**	60	65
981	50 c. Lunar module "Eagle" on Moon	60	65
982	50 c. Aldrin gathering dust sample	60	65
983	50 c. Neil Armstrong with camera	60	65
984	50 c. "Eagle" re-united with command module "Columbia"	60	65

Nos. 980/4 were printed together, se-tenant, with Nos. 981/3 forming a composite design.

212 "Zephyranthes rosea"

1990. Island flowres. Multicoloured.

985	8 c. Type **212**	10	10
986	10 c. "Sophora tomentosa"	10	15
987	15 c. "Coccoloba uvifera"	15	20
988	20 c. "Encyclia gracilis"	25	30
989	25 c. "Tillandsia streptophylla"	30	35
990	30 c. "Maurandella antirrhiniflora"	35	40
991	35 c. "Tillandsia balbisiana"	40	45
992	50 c. "Encyclia rufa"	60	65
993	65 c. "Aechmea lingulata"	75	80
994	80 c. "Asclepias curassavica"	95	1·00
995	$1 "Caesalpinia bahamensis"	1·10	1·25
996	$1.10 "Capparis cynophallophora"	1·25	1·40
997	$1.25 "Stachytarpheta jamaicensis"	1·40	1·50
998	$2 "Cassia biflora"	2·25	2·40
1000	$10 "Opuntia bahamana"	11·50	12·00

213 Queen Parrotfish

1990. Fishes. Multicoloured.

1001	8 c. Type **213**	10	10
1002	10 c. Queen triggerfish	10	15
1003	25 c. Sergeant major	30	35
1004	40 c. Spotted goatfish	45	50
1005	50 c. Neon goby	60	65
1006	75 c. Nassau grouper	85	90
1007	80 c. Jawfish	95	1·00
1008	$1 Blue tang	1·10	1·25

214 Yellow-billed Cuckoo

1990. Birds (1st series). Multicoloured.

1010	10 c. Type **214**	10	15
1011	15 c. White-tailed tropic bird	15	20
1012	20 c. Kirtland's warbler	25	30
1013	30 c. Yellow-crowned night heron	35	40
1014	50 c. Black-billed whistling duck ("West Indian tree duck")	60	65
1015	80 c. Yellow-bellied sapsucker	95	1·00
1016	$1 American kestrel	1·10	1·25
1017	$1.40 Northern mocking-bird	1·60	1·75

See also Nos. 1050/7.

215. "Anartia jatrophae".

1990. Butterflies (1st series). Multicoloured.

1019	15 c. Type **215**	15	20
1020	25 c. "Phoebis sennae" (horiz)	30	35
1021	35 c. "Euptoieta hegesia" (horiz)	40	45
1022	40 c. "Hylephila phylaeus" (horiz)	45	50
1023	50 c. "Eurema chamberlaini" (horiz)	60	65
1024	60 c. "Brephidium exilis"	70	75
1025	90 c. "Papilio aristodemus" (horiz)	1·00	1·10
1026	$1 "Marpesia eleuchea"	1·10	1·25

See also Nos. 1081/8.

1990. 500th Anniv (1992) of Discovery of America by Columbus (3rd issue). New World Natural History–Fishes. As T **260** of Antigua. Multicoloured.

1028	10 c. Rock beauty	10	15
1029	15 c. Coney	15	20
1030	25 c. Red hind	30	35
1031	50 c. Banded butterflyfish	60	65
1032	60 c. French angelfish	70	75
1033	75 c. Blackbar soldierfish	85	90
1034	90 c. Stoplight parrotfish	1·00	1·10
1035	$1 French grunt	1·10	1·25

216 Penny "Rainbow Trial" in Blue

1990. 150th Anniv of the Penny Black.

1037	**216**	25 c. blue	30	35
1038	–	75 c. brown	85	90
1039	–	$1 blue	1·10	1·25

DESIGNS: 75 c. 1d. red-brown colour trial of December, 1840; $1 2d. blue of 1840.

217 Pillar Box No. 1, 1885

1990. "Stamp World London 90" Int. Stamp Exhibition. British Pillar Boxes.

1041	**217**	35 c. brown and grey	40	45
1042	–	50 c. blue and grey	60	65
1043	–	$1.25 blue and grey	1·40	1·50

DESIGNS: 50 c. Penfold box, 1866; $1.25, Air mail box, 1935.

1990. 90th Birthday of Queen Elizabeth the Queen Mother. As T **266** of Antigua.

1045	10 c. multicoloured	10	15
1046	25 c. multicoloured	30	35
1047	75 c. multicoloured	85	90
1048	$1.25 multicoloured	1·40	1·50

DESIGNS: 25, 75 c. $1.25 Recent photographs of the Queen Mother.

219 Stripe-headed Tanager

1990. Birds (2nd series). Multicoloured.

1050	8 c. Type **219**	10	10
1051	10 c. Black-whiskered vireo (horiz)	10	15
1052	25 c. Blue-grey gnatcatcher (horiz)	30	35
1053	40 c. Lesser scaup (horiz)	45	50
1054	50 c. White-cheeked pintail (horiz)	60	65
1055	75 c. Black-winged stilt (horiz)	85	90
1056	80 c. Common oyster-catcher	95	1·00
1057	$1 Tricoloured heron (horiz)	1·10	1·25

220 "Triumph of Christ over Sin and Death" (detail, Rubens)

1990. Christmas. 350th Death Anniv of Rubens. Multicoloured.

1059	10 c. Type **220**	10	15
1060	35 c. "St. Theresa Praying" (detail)	40	45
1061	45 c. "St. Theresa Praying" (different detail)	50	55
1062	50 c. "Triumph of Christ over Sin and Death" (different detail)	60	65
1063	65 c. "St. Theresa Praying" (different detail)	75	80
1064	75 c. "Triumph of Christ over Sin and Death" (different detail)	85	90
1065	$1.25 "St. Theresa Praying" (different detail)	1·40	1·50

221 Canoeing

1991. Olympic Games, Barcelona (1992). Mult.

1067	10 c. Type **221**	10	15
1068	25 c. 100 metre sprint	30	35
1069	75 c. Pole vaulting	85	90
1070	$1.25 Javelin	1·40	1·50

1991. 500th Anniv (1992) of Discovery of America by Columbus (4th issue). History of Exploration. As T **64** of Nevis. Mult.

1072	5 c. Henry Hudson in Hudson's Bay, 1611	10	10
1073	10 c. Roald Amundsen's airship "Norge", 1926	10	15
1074	15 c. Amundsen's "Gjoa" in the Northwest Passage, 1906	15	20
1075	50 c. Submarine U.S.S. "Nautilus" under North Pole, 1958	60	65
1076	75 c. Robert Scott's "Terra Nova", 1911	85	90
1077	$1 Byrd and Bennett's Fokker aircraft over North Pole, 1926	1·10	1·25
1078	$1.25 Lincoln Ellsworth's "Polar Star" on trans-Antarctic flight, 1935	1·40	1·50
1079	$1.50 Capt. James Cook in the Antarctic, 1772–75	1·75	1·90

222 "Anartia jatrophae"

1991. Butterflies (2nd series). Multicoloured.

1081	5 c. Type **222**	10	10
1082	25 c. "Historis osius"	30	35
1083	35 c. "Agraulis vanillae"	40	45
1084	45 c. "Junonia evarete"	50	55
1085	55 c. "Dryas julia"	65	70
1086	65 c. "Siproeta stelenes"	75	80
1087	70 c. "Appias drusilla"	80	85
1088	$1 "Ascia monuste"	1·10	1·25

223 Protohydrochoerus

1991. Extinct Species of Fauna. Mult.

1090	5 c. Type **223**	10	10
1091	10 c. Phororhacos	10	10
1092	15 c. Prothylacynus	15	20
1093	50 c. Borhyaena	60	65
1094	75 c. Smilodon	85	90
1095	$1 Thoatherium	1·10	1·25
1096	$1.25 Cuvieronius	1·40	1·50
1097	$1.50 Toxodon	1·75	1·90

1991. 65th Birthday of Queen Elizabeth II. As T **280** of Antigua. Multicoloured.

1099	25 c. Queen and Prince Philip at St. Paul's Cathedral, 1988	30	35
1100	35 c. Queen and Prince Philip	40	45
1101	65 c. Queen and Prince Philip at Garter Ceremony, 1988	75	80
1102	80 c. Queen at Windsor, May 1988	95	1·00

224 "Pluteus chrysophlebius"

1991. Fungi. Multicoloured.

1104	10 c. Type **224**	10	10
1105	15 c. "Leucopaxillus gracillimus"	15	20
1106	20 c. "Marasmius haematocephalus"	25	30
1107	35 c. "Collybia subpruinosa"	35	40
1108	50 c. "Marasmius atrorubens" (vert)	60	65
1109	65 c. "Leucocoprinus birnbaumii" (vert)	75	80
1110	$1.10 "Trogia cantharelloides" (vert)	1·25	1·40
1111	$1.25 "Boletellus cubensis" (vert)	1·40	1·50

1991. 10th Wedding Anniv of the Prince and Princess of Wales. As T **280** of Antigua. Multicoloured.

1113	10 c. Prince and Princess of Wales, 1987	10	10
1114	45 c. Separate photographs of Prince, Princess and sons	50	55

1115 50 c. Prince Henry in fire engine and Prince William applauding .. 60 65
1116 $1 Princess Diana in Derbyshire, 1990, and Prince Charles .. 1·10 1·25

1992. Death Centenary (1990) of Vincent van Gogh (artist). As T **195** of British Virgin Islands. Multicoloured.

1118 15 c. "Weaver with Spinning Wheel" .. 15 20
1119 25 c. "Head of a Young Peasant with Pipe" (vert) 30 35
1120 35 c. "Old Cemetery Tower at Nuenen" (vert) 40 45
1121 45 c. "Cottage at Nightfall" 50 55
1122 50 c. "Still Life with Open Bible" 60 65
1123 65 c. "Lane, Jardin du Luxembourg" .. 75 80
1124 80 c. "Pont du Carrousel and Louvre, Paris" .. 95 1·00
1125 $1 "Vase with Poppies, Cornflowers, Peonies and Chrysanthemums" (vert) .. .. .. 1·10 1·25

225 Series "8550" Steam Locomotive

1991. "Philanippon '91" International Stamp Exhibition, Tokyo. Japanese Steam Locomotives. Multicoloured.

1127 8 c. Type **225** 10 10
1128 10 c. Class "C 57" .. 10 10
1129 45 c. Series "4110" .. 50 55
1130 50 c. Class "C 55" .. 60 65
1131 65 c. Series "6250" .. 75 80
1132 80 c. Class "E 10" .. 95 1·00
1133 $1 Series "4500" .. 1·10 1·25
1134 $1.25 Class "C 11" .. 1·40 1·50

1991. Christmas. Religious Paintings by Gerard David. As T **211** of Lesotho. Mult.

1136 8 c. "Adoration of the Shepherds" (detail) .. 10 10
1137 15 c. "Virgin and Child Enthroned with Two Angels" 15 20
1138 35 c. "The Annunciation" (outer wings) 40 45
1139 45 c. "The Rest on the Flight to Egypt" .. 50 55
1140 50 c. "The Rest on the Flight to Egypt" (different) 60 65
1141 65 c. "Virgin and Child with Angels" 75 80
1142 80 c. "Adoration of the Shepherds" .. .. 95 1·00
1143 $1.25 "Perussis Altarpiece" (detail) .. 1·40 1·50

226 Garden overlooking Sea

1992. 40th Anniv of Queen Elizabeth II's Accession. Multicoloured.

1145 10 c. Type **226** 10 10
1146 20 c. Jetty 25 30
1147 25 c. Small bay 30 35
1148 35 c. Island road 40 45
1149 50 c. Grand Turk 60 65
1150 65 c. Beach 75 80
1151 80 c. Marina .. .. 95 1·00
1152 $1.10 Grand Turk (different) .. .. 1·25 1·40

TUVALU

Formerly known as the Ellice Islands and sharing a joint administration with the Gilbert group. On 1st January 1976 the two island-groups separated and the Ellice Is. were renamed Tuvalu.

100 cents = $1 Australian.

1. Tuvaluan and Gilbertese.

1976. Separation. Multicoloured.

1. 4 c. Type **1** 45 80
2. 10 c. Map of the Islands (vert.) 55 1·00
3. 35 c. Gilbert and Ellice canoes 75 1·50

1976. Nos. 173/87 of the Gilbert and Ellice Islands optd. **TUVALU.**

14. 1 c. Cutting toddy 30 20
20. 2 c. Lagoon fishing 80 40
21. 3 c. Cleaning pandanus leaves 90 30
22. 4 c. Casting nets .. .. 1·00 45
5. 5 c. Gilbertese canoe .. 80 60
15. 6 c. De-husking coconuts .. 90 40
6. 8 c. Weaving pandanus fronds 95 60
7. 10 c. Weaving a basket .. 1·50 80
16. 15 c. Tiger shark .. .. 1·00 65
23. 20 c. Beating a rolled pandanus leaf .. .. .. 1·00 1·00
24. 25 c. Loading copra .. 1·25 75
25. 35 c. Fishing at night .. 2·25 1·75
17. 50 c. Local handicrafts .. 1·75 80
18. $1 Weaving coconut screen 3·00 1·25
19. $2 Coat of Arms .. .. 3·00 1·25

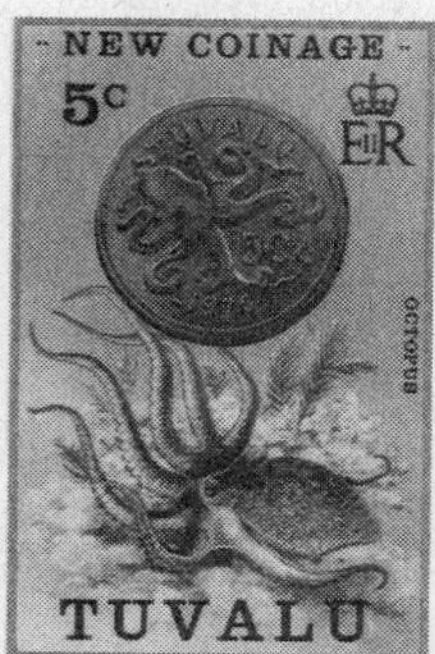

3. 50 c. Coin and Octopus.

1976. New Coinage. Multicoloured.

26. 5 c. Type **3** 25 15
27. 10 c. 10 c. coin and Red-eyed Crab 35 20
28. 15 c. 20 c. coin and Flying Fish 45 25
29. 35 c. $1 coin and Green Turtle 60 45

4. Niulakita and Seven-ridged Leathery Turtle.

1976. Multicoloured.

58 1 c. Type **4** 20 15
59 2 c. Nukulaelae and sleeping mat 20 25
60 4 c. Nui and talo (vegetable) 20 15
61 5 c. Nanumanga and grass skirt 25 15
62 6 c. Nukufetau and Coconut Crab 20 35
63 8 c. Funafuti and Banana tree 20 25
64 10 c. Map of Tuvalu .. 20 20
37 15 c. Niutao and Flying fish 1·00 20
38 20 c. Vaitupu and Naneapa (house) 70 20
66 25 c. Nanumea and fish-hook 1·25 20
67 30 c. Fatele (local dancing) 30 20
40 35 c. Te Ano (game) .. 60 20
68 40 c. Screw Pine .. 30 15
41 50 c. Canoe pole fishing .. 75 30
42 $1 Reef fishing by flare .. 80 40
43 $2 Living house .. 1·50 60
69 $5 M.V. "Nivanga" .. 8·00 5·00

5. Title Page of New Testament.

1976. Christmas. Mulicoloured.

45. 5 c. Type **5** 70 40
46. 20 c. Lotolelei Church, Nanumea 70 40
47. 25 c. Kelupi Church, Nui .. 70 40
48. 30 c. Mataloa o Tuvala Church, Vaitupu .. 80 40
49. 35 c. Dalataise o Keliso Church, Nanumanga .. 80 40

6. The Queen and Duke of Edinburgh after Coronation.

1977. Silver Jubilee. Multicoloured.

50. 15 c. Type **6** 75 30
51. 35 c. Prince Philip carried ashore at Vaitupu .. 1·00 40
52. 50 c. The Queen leaving Buckingham Palace .. 1·00 50

7. "Health".

1977. 30th Anniv. of South Pacific Commission. Multicoloured.

54. 5 c. Type **7** 20 20
55. 20 c. "Education" .. 25 20
56. 30 c. "Fruit-growing" .. 25 20
57. 35 c. Map of S.P.C. area .. 30 25

8. Scout Promise.

1977. 50th Anniv. of Scouting in the Central Pacific. Multicoloured.

73. 5 c. Type **8** 30 25
74. 20 c. Canoeing 30 25
75. 30 c. Scout shelter 40 30
76. 35 c. Lord Baden-Powell .. 40 30

9. Hurricane Beach (Expedition photo).

1977. Royal Society Expeditions.

77. **9.** 5 c. multicoloured .. 25 15
78. – 20 c. black and blue .. 40 20
79. – 30 c. black and blue .. 40 20
80. – 35 c. multicoloured .. 40 20

DESIGNS—VERT. 20 c. Boring apparatus on H.M.S. "Porpoise". 30 c. Dredging chart. HORIZ. 35 c. Charles Darwin and H.M.S. "Beagle".

10. Pacific Pigeon.

1978. Wild Birds. Multicoloured.

81. 8 c. Type **10** .. .. 1·00 35
82. 20 c. Eastern Reef Heron .. 1·25 50
83. 30 c. White Tern .. .. 1·75 60
84. 40 c. Lesser Frigate Bird .. 1·75 65

11. "Lawedua" (coaster).

1978. Ships. Multicoloured.

85. 8 c. Type **11** 15 15
86. 20 c. "Wallacia" (tug) .. 15 15
87. 30 c. "Cenpac Rounder" (freighter) 20 20
88. 40 c. "Pacific Explorer" (freighter) 25 20

1978. 25th Anniv. of Coronation. As Nos. 422/5 of Montserrat. Multicoloured.

89. 8 c. Canterbury Cathedral 10 10
90. 30 c. Salisbury Cathedral .. 10 10
91. 40 c. Wells Cathedral .. 15 10
92. $1 Hereford Cathedral .. 40 30

1978. Independence. Nos. 63/4, 37/8, 68/40 and 69 optd. **INDEPENDENCE 1ST OCTOBER 1978.**

94. 8 c. Funafuti and Banana tree 10 10
95. 10 c. Map of Tuvalu .. 10 10
96. 15 c. Niutao and Flying fish 10 10
97. 20 c. Vaitupu and Maneapa (house) 15 15
98. 30 c. Fatele (local dancing) 15 15
99. 35 c. Te Ano (game) .. 20 20
100. 40 c. Screw Pines .. 20 20

13. White Frangipani.

1978. Wild Flowers. Multicoloured.

101. 8 c. Type **13** 15 10
102. 20 c. Susana 15 10
103. 30 c. Tiale 20 15
104. 40 c. Inato 25 25

14. Squirrelfish.

1979. Fishes. Multicoloured.

105. 1 c. Type **14** 10 10
106. 2 c. Yellow-banded Goatfish 10 10
107. 4 c. Imperial Angelfish .. 10 10
108. 5 c. Rainbow Butterfly .. 15 10

109. 6 c. Blue Angelfish .. 15 10
110. 8 c. Blue-striped Snapper 15 10
111. 10 c. Orange Clownfish .. 25 10
112. 15 c. Chevroned Coralfish 25 10
113. 20 c. Fairy Cod 35 15
114. 25 c. Clown Triggerfish .. 35 20
115. 30 c. Long-nosed Butterfly 35 10
116. 35 c. Yellowfin Tuna .. 40 20
117. 40 c. Spotted Eagle Ray .. 40 10
117a. 45 c. Black-tipped Rock Cod .. .. .. 1·50 2·00
118. 50 c. Hammerhead Shark 50 20
119. 70 c. Lionfish (vert.) .. 65 30
120. $1 White-barred Triggerfish (vert.) 70 55
121. $2 Beaked Coralfish (vert.) 1·50 60
122. $5 Tiger Shark (vert.) .. 2·75 1·25

15. " Explorer of the Pacific ".

1979. Death Bicentenary of Capt. James Cook. Multicoloured.

123. 8 c. Type **15** 30 20
124. 30 c. Claiming a new island 40 25
125. 40 c. Observing the transit of Venus, 1769 .. .. 40 25
126. $1 Cook's death 50 35

16. Flying Boat and Nukulaelae Island.

1979. Internal Air Service. Multicoloured.

127. 8 c. Type **16** 15 15
128. 20 c. Flying boat and Vaitupu Island .. 20 20
129. 30 c. Flying boat and Nui Island 30 30
130. 40 c. Flying boat and Funafuti Island .. 35 35

17. Sir Rowland Hill, 1976 4 c. Separation of the Islands Commemorative and London's First Pillar Box, 1855.

1979. Death centenary of Sir Rowland Hill. Multicoloured.

131. 30 c. Type **17** 25 15
132. 40 c. Sir Rowland Hill, 1976 10 c. Separation commemorative and Penny Black 25 15
133. $1 Sir Rowland Hill, 1976 35 c. Separation commemorative and mail coach 50 30

18. Child's Face.

1979. International Year of the Child.

135. **18.** 8 c. multicoloured .. 10 10
136. – 20 c. multicoloured .. 15 10
137. – 30 c. multicoloured .. 15 15
138. – 40 c. multicoloured .. 20 25

DESIGNS: 20 c. to 40 c. Children's Faces.

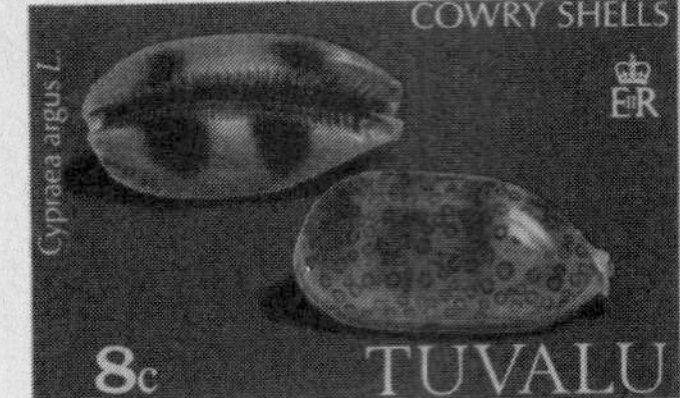

19. " Cypraea argus ".

1980. Cowrie Shells. Multicoloured.

139. 8 c. Type **19** 15 10
140. 20 c. " Cypraea scurra " .. 15 10
141. 30 c. " Cypraea carneola " 20 15
142. 40 c. " Cypraea aurantium " 30 20

20. Philatelic Bureau, Funafuti and 1976 8 c. Definitive.

1980. " London 1980 " International Stamp Exhibition. Multicoloured.

143. 10 c. Type **20** 15 15
144. 20 c. Nukulaelae postmark and 1976 2 c. definitive 25 20
145. 30 c. Fleet Post Office, U.S. Navy, airmail cover, 1943 25 25
146. $1 Map and arms of Tuvalu 50 45

21. Queen Elizabeth the Queen Mother at Royal Variety Performance, 1978.

1980. 80th Birthday of The Queen Mother.

148. **21.** 15 c. multicoloured .. 35 25

22. " Aethaloessa calidalis ".

1980. Moths. Multicoloured.

149. 8 c. Type **22** 10 10
150. 20 c. " Parotis suralis " .. 15 10
151. 30 c. " Dudua aprobola " 20 15
152. 40 c. " Decadarchis simulans " 20 15

23. Air Pacific. " Heron ".

1980. Aviation Commemorations. Mult.

153. 8 c. Type **23** 10 10
154. 20 c. Hawker Siddeley " 748 " 15 10
155. 30 c. " Sunderland " flying-boat 15 15
156. 40 c. Orville Wright and " Flyer " 20 15

COMMEMORATIONS: 8 c. 1st regular air service to Tuvalu, 1964. 20 c. Air service to Tuvalu. 30 c. War-time R.N.Z.A.F. flying-boat service to Funafuti, 1945. 40 c. Wright Brothers' 1st flight, 17 December, 1903.

1981. No. 118 surch. **45 CENTS.**

157. 45 c. on 50 c. Hammerhead Shark 25 40

25. "Hypolimnas bolina" (male).

1981. Butterflies. Multicoloured.

158. 8 c. Type **25** 15 10
159. 20 c. " Hypolimnas bolina elliciana " (female) .. 20 15
160. 30 c. " Hypolimnas bolina elliciana " (female) (different) 20 20
161. 40 c. " Junonia vallida " (male) 25 20

26. Brig " Elizabeth ", 1809.

1981. Ships (1st series). Multicoloured.

162. 10 c. Type **26** 20 20
163. 25 c. Brigantine "Rebecca", 1819 .. .. 25 30
164. 35 c. Whaling ship "Independence II", 1821 30 35
165. 40 c. H.M.S. "Basilisk", 1872 .. .. 35 40
166. 45 c. H.M.S. "Royalist", 1890 .. .. 40 50
167. 50 c. Barque "Olivebank", 1920 .. .. 40 50

See also Nos. 235/40, 377/80 and 442/5.

1981. Royal Wedding. Royal Yachts. As T **26/7** of Kiribati. Multicoloured.

168. 10 c. " Carolina " 10 15
169. 10 c. Princes Charles and Lady Diana Spencer .. 35 35
170. 45 c. " Victoria and Albert III " 20 20
171. 45 c. As No. 169 .. .. 30 30
172. $2 " Britannia " 50 50
173. $2 As No. 169 .. .. 1·75 1·75

27. U.P.U. Emblem.

1981. U.P.U. Membership.

177. **27.** 70 c. blue 30 30
178. $1 brown 50 60

28. Map of Funafuti, and Anchor.

1982. Amatuku Maritime School. Mult.

180. 10 c. Type **28** 10 10
181. 25 c. Motor launch .. 25 25
182. 35 c. School buildings and jetty 35 35
183. 45 c. School flag, and freighter 40 40

29. Caroline of Brandenburg-Ansbach, Princess of Wales, 1714.

1982. 21st Birthday of Princess of Wales. Multicoloured.

184. 10 c. Type **29** 10 10
185. 45 c. Coat of arms of Caroline of Brandenburg-Ansbach 20 15
186. $1.50 Diana, Princess of Wales 60 60

1982. Tonga Cyclone Relief. Nos. 170/1 optd. **TONGA CYCLONE RELIEF 1982 +20 c.**

187. 45 c.+20 c. " Victoria and Albert III " 30 50
188. 45 c.+20 c. Prince Charles and Lady Diana Spencer 50 75

1982. Birth of Prince William of Wales. Nos. 184/6 optd. **ROYAL BABY.**

189. 10 c. Type **29** 10 10
190. 45 c. Coat of arms of Caroline of Brandenburg-Ansbach 20 15
191. $1.50 Diana, Princess of Wales 60 60

31. Tuvalu and World Scout Badges.

1982. 75th Anniv. of Boy Scout Movement. Multicoloured.

192. 10 c. Type **31** 15 15
193. 25 c. Camp-fire 40 40
194. 35 c. Parade 45 45
195. 45 c. Boy Scout 55 55

32. Tuvalu Crest and Duke of Edinburgh's Standard.

1982. Royal Visit. Multicoloured.

196. 25 c. Type **32** 25 25
197. 45 c. Tuvalu flag and Queen's Royal Standard .. 40 40
198. 50 c. Portrait of Queen Elizabeth II 40 40

33. Fisherman's Hat and Equipment.

1983. Handicrafts. Multicoloured.

200. 1 c. Type **33** 30 10
201. 2 c. Cowrie shell handbags 30 10
202. 5 c. Wedding and baby food baskets 30 10
203. 10 c. Model canoe .. 30 10
203a. 15 c. Ladies' sun hats .. 1·25 80

204. 20 c. Palm climbing rope and platform with toddy pot 30 20
205. 25 c. Pandanus baskets .. 30 20
205a. 30 c. Basket tray and coconut stand .. .. 1·50 85
206. 35 c. Pandanus pillows and shell necklaces .. 30 30
207. 40 c. Round baskets and fans 30 35
208. 45 c. Reef sandals and fish trap 35 40
209. 50 c. Rat trap (vert.) .. 40 45
209a. 60 c. Fisherman's waterproof boxes (vert.) .. 2·25 90
210. $1 Pump drill and adze (vert.) 75 70
211. $2 Fisherman's hat and canoe bailers (vert.) .. 1·50 1·25
212. $5 Fishing rod, lures and scoop nets (vert.) .. 3·50 2·50

34. "Te Tautai" (trawler).

1983. Commonwealth Day. Multicoloured.
213. 20 c. Type **34** 15 15
214. 35 c. Traditional dancing, Motufoua School .. 25 25
215. 45 c. Satellite view of Pacific 30 30
216. 50 c. "Morning Star" (container ship) .. 40 40

35. "Pantala flavescens".

1983. Dragonflies. Multicoloured.
217. 10 c. Type **35** 20 10
218. 35 c. "Anax guttatus" .. 55 40
219. 40 c. "Tholymis tillarga" 60 45
220. 50 c. "Diplacodes bipunctata" 75 60

36. Brigade Members Racing.

1983. Centenary of Boy's Brigade. Mult.
221. 10 c. Type **36** 15 15
222. 35 c. B.B. members in outrigger canoe 40 45
223. $1 On parade .. .. 1·25 1·75

1983. No. 210 surch.
224. 60 c. on $1 Pump drill and adze 70 70

38. Montgolfier Balloon, 1783.

1983. Bicentenary of Manned Flight. Mult.
225. 25 c. Type **38** 30 30
226. 35 c. McKinnon (Grumman) "Turbogoose" (horiz.) 40 40
227. 45 c. Beechcraft "Super King Air 200" (horiz.) 50 50
228. 50 c. "Double Eagle II", balloon 60 60

39. Early Communications.

1983. World Communications Year. Mult.
230. 25 c. Type **39** 25 25
231. 35 c. Radio operator .. 30 30
232. 45 c. Modern teleprinter .. 35 35
233. 50 c. Funafuti transmitting station 40 40

1984. No. 208 surch.
234. 30 c. on 45 c. Reef sandals and fish trap 35 40

1984. Ships (2nd series). As T **26**. Mult.
235. 10 c. S.S. "Titus", 1897 .. 15 15
236. 20 c. S.S. "Malaita", 1905 20 20
237. 25 c. S.S. "Aymerie", 1906 20 20
238. 35 c. S.S. "Anshun", 1965 25 25
239. 45 c. M.V. "Beaverbank", 1970 .. .. .. 35 35
240. 50 c. M.V. "Benjamin Bowring", 1981 .. .. 35 35

41. Class "GS-4".

1984. Leaders of the World. Railway Locomotives (1st series). As T **41**. The first in each pair shows technical drawings and the second the locomotives at work.
241. 1 c. multicoloured 10 10
242. 1 c. multicoloured 10 10
243. 15 c. multicoloured .. 20 25
244. 15 c. multicoloured .. 20 25
245. 40 c. multicoloured .. 25 35
246. 40 c. multicoloured .. 25 35
247. 60 c. multicoloured .. 35 45
248. 60 c. multicoloured .. 35 45

DESIGNS: Nos. 241/2, Class "GS-4", U.S.A. (1941). 243/4, Class "AD 60", Australia (1952). 245/6, Class "C 38", Australia (1943). 247/8, "Lord of the Isles", Great Britain (1892).

See also Nos. 253/68, 273/80, 313/20 and 348/55.

42. "Ipomoea pes-caprae".

1984. Beach Flowers. Multicoloured.
249. 25 c. Type **42** 25 25
250. 45 c. "Ipomoea macrantha" 40 40
251. 50 c. "Triumfetta procumbens" 45 45
252. 60 c. "Portulaca quadrifida" 50 50

1984. Leaders of the World. Railway Locomotives (2nd series). As T **41**. The first design in each pair shows technical drawings and the second the locomotive at work.
253. 10 c. multicoloured. .. 15 15
254. 10 c. multicoloured .. 15 15
255. 15 c. multicoloured .. 15 20
256. 15 c. multicoloured .. 15 20
257. 20 c. multicoloured .. 20 30
258. 20 c. multicoloured .. 20 30
259. 25 c. multicoloured .. 20 30
260. 25 c. multicoloured .. 20 30
261. 40 c. multicoloured .. 20 30
262. 40 c. multicoloured .. 20 30
263. 50 c. multicoloured .. 20 40
264. 50 c. multicoloured .. 20 40
265. 60 c. multicoloured .. 25 45
266. 60 c. multicoloured .. 25 45
267. $1 multicoloured 30 55
268. $1 multicoloured 30 55

DESIGNS: Nos. 253/4, "Casey Jones" type locomotive, U.S.A. (1896). 255/6, "Triplex" type locomotive, U.S.A. (1914). 257/8, Class "370" Advanced Passenger Train, Great Britain (1981). 259/60, Class "4F" locomotive, Great Britain (1924). 261/2, Class "Tornado Rover" locomotive, Great Britain (1888). 263/4, "Broadlands" locomotive, Great Britain (1967). 265/6, Locomotive "Locomotion No. 1", Great Britain (1825). 267/8, Class "C57" locomotive, Japan (1937).

43. Exhibition Emblem.

1984. "Ausipex" International Stamp Exhibition, Melbourne. Multicoloured.
269. 60 c. Type **43** 30 40
270. 60 c. Arms of Tuvalu .. 30 40
271. 60 c. Tuvalu flag 30 40
272. 60 c. Royal Exhibition Building, Melbourne .. 30 40

1984. Leaders of the World. Railway Locomotives (3rd series). As T **41**. The first in each pair shows technical drawings and the second the locomotive at work.
273. 1 c. multicoloured 10 10
274. 1 c. multicoloured 10 10
275. 15 c. multicoloured .. 15 20
276. 15 c. multicoloured .. 15 20
277. 30 c. multicoloured .. 35 40
278. 30 c. multicoloured .. 35 40
279. $1 multicoloured .. .. 70 1·00
280. $1 multicoloured .. .. 70 1·00

DESIGNS: Nos. 273/4, Class "9700", Japan (1897). 275/6, Class "231" C/K, France. 277/8, Class "640", Italy (1907). 279/80, Class "4500", France (1906).

44. A. Shrewsbury.

1984. Leaders of the World. Cricketers. As T **44**. The first in each pair shows the cricketer in action and the second a head portrait.
281. 5 c. multicoloured 10 10
282. 5 c. multicoloured 10 10
283. 30 c. multicoloured .. 35 40
284. 30 c. multicoloured .. 35 40
285. 50 c. multicoloured .. 55 60
286. 50 c. multicoloured .. 55 60
287. 60 c. multicoloured .. 65 70
288. 60 c. multicoloured .. 65 70

DESIGNS: 281/2, A. Shrewsbury. 283/4 H. Verity. 285/6, E. H. Hendren. 287/8, J. Briggs.

45. Trees and Stars.

1984. Christmas. Children's Drawings. Multicoloured.
289. 15 c. Type **45** 10 10
290. 40 c. Fishing from outrigger canoes 20 20
291. 50 c. Three Wise Men bearing gifts 25 25
292. 60 c. The Holy Family .. 35 35

46. Morris Minor.

1984. Leaders of the World. Automobiles (1st series). As T **46**. The first in each pair shows technical drawings and the second paintings.
293. 1 c. blk, brown & yellow .. 10 10
294. 1 c. multicoloured 10 10
295. 15 c. black, pink and lilac 15 20
296. 15 c. multicoloured .. 15 20
297. 50 c. blk., brown & mauve 40 45
298. 50 c. multicoloured .. 40 45
299. $1 black, green and blue .. 60 80
300. $1 multicoloured 60 80

DESIGNS: Nos. 293/4, "Morris Minor". 295/6, Studebaker "Avanti". 297/8, Chevrolet "International Six". 299/300, Allard "J2".

See also Nos. 321/8, 356/71, 421/32 and 446/69.

47. Common Flicker.

1985. Leaders of the World. Birth Bicentenary of John J. Audubon (ornithologist). Multicoloured.
301. 1 c. Type **47** 10 10
302. 1 c. Say's phoebe 10 10
303. 25 c. Townsend's warbler 30 35
304. 25 c. Bohemian waxwing .. 30 35
305. 50 c. Prothonotary warbler 55 60
306. 50 c. Worm-eating warbler 55 60
307. 70 c. Broad-winged hawk 80 85
308. 70 c. Hen harrier 80 85

48. Black-naped Tern.

1985. Birds and their Eggs. Multicoloured.
309. 15 c. Type **48** 35 20
310. 40 c. White-capped noddy 75 50
311. 50 c. White-tailed tropicbird 85 60
312. 60 c. Sooty tern .. .. 1·00 70

1985. Leaders of the World. Railway Locomotives (4th series). As T **41**. The first in each pair shows technical drawings and the second the locomotive at work.
313. 5 c. multicoloured 10 10
314. 5 c. multicoloured 10 10
315. 10 c. multicoloured .. 10 10
316. 10 c. multicoloured .. 10 10
317. 30 c. multicoloured .. 30 35
318. 30 c. multicoloured .. 30 35
319. $1 multicoloured .. .. 75 1·00
320. $1 multicoloured .. .. 75 1·00

DESIGNS: Nos. 313/14, Class "Churchward 28XX", Great Britain (1905). 315/16, Class "KF", China (1935). 317/18, Class "99.77", East Germany (1952). 319/20, Pearson, Great Britain (1835).

1985. Leaders of the World. Automobiles (2nd series). As T **46**. The first in each pair shows technical drawings and the second paintings.
321. 1 c. black, green and deep green 10 10
322. 1 c. multicoloured 10 10
323. 20 c. black, pink and red .. 15 20
324. 20 c. multicoloured .. 15 20
325. 50 c. black, blue and violet 30 45
326. 50 c. multicoloured .. 30 45
327. 70 c. black, pink & brown 30 60
328. 70 c. multicoloured .. 30 60

DESIGNS: Nos. 321/2, Rickenbacker (1923). 323/4, Detroit-Electric two door Brougham (1914), 325/6, Packard "Clipper" (1941). 327/8, Audi "Quattro" (1982).

49. Curtiss "P-40N".

1985. World War II Aircraft. Multicoloured.
329. 15 c. Type **49** 60 20
330. 40 c. Consolidated "B-24 Liberator" .. .. 1·00 45
331. 50 c. Lockheed "PV-1 Ventura" .. .. 1·10 55
332. 60 c. Douglas "C-54 Skymaster" .. .. 1·10 65

50. Queen Elizabeth the Queen Mother.

1985. Leaders of the World. Life and Times of Queen Elizabeth the Queen Mother. Various portraits.
334. **50.** 5 c. multicoloured .. 10 10
335. – 5 c. multicoloured .. 10 10
336. – 30 c. multicoloured .. 15 20
337. – 30 c. multicoloured .. 15 20
338. – 60 c. multicoloured .. 25 35
339. – 60 c. multicoloured .. 25 35
340. – $1 multicoloured .. 40 55
341. – $1 multicoloured .. 40 55

Each value issued in pairs showing a floral pattern across the bottom of the portraits which stops short of the left-hand edge on the first stamp and of the right-hand edge on the second.

51. Guide playing Guitar.

1985. 75th Anniv. of Girl Guide Movement. Multicoloured.
343. 15 c. Type **51** 15 20
344. 40 c. Building camp-fire .. 40 45
345. 50 c. Patrol leader with Guide flag 50 55
346. 60 c. Guide saluting .. 60 65

1985. Leaders of the World. Railway Locomotives (5th series). As T **41**. The first in each pair shows technical drawings and the second the locomotive at work.
348. 10 c. multicoloured .. 10 15
349. 10 c. multicoloured .. 10 15
350. 40 c. multicoloured .. 40 45
351. 40 c. multicoloured .. 40 45
352. 65 c. multicoloured .. 70 75
353. 65 c. multicoloured .. 70 75
354. $1 multicoloured .. 1·10 1·25
355. $1 multicoloured .. 1·10 1·25

DESIGNS: Nos. 348/49, "Green Arrow", Great Britain (1936). 350/1, Class "SD-50" diesel locomotive, U.S.A. (1982). 352/3, "Flying Hamburger", Germany (1932). 354/5, Class "1070", Japan (1908).

1985. Leaders of the World. Automobiles (3rd series). As T **46**. The first in each pair shows technical drawings and the second paintings.
356. 5 c. black, grey and mauve 10 10
357. 5 c. multicoloured 10 10
358. 10 c. black, pink and red .. 10 15
359. 10 c. multicoloured .. 10 15
360. 15 c. black, brown and red 15 20
361. 15 c. multicoloured .. 15 20
362. 35 c. black, red and blue .. 30 40
363. 35 c. multicoloured .. 30 40
364. 40 c. black, lt. green & green 30 40
365. 40 c. multicoloured .. 30 40
366. 55 c. black, stone and green 35 40
367. 55 c. multicoloured .. 35 40
368. $1 black, dp. brown & brn. 55 70
369. $1 multicoloured 55 70
370. $1.50 black, pink and red 60 80
371. $1.50 multicoloured .. 60 80

DESIGNS: Nos. 356/7, Cord "L-29" (1929). 358/9, Horch "670 V-12" (1932). 360/1, Lanchester (1901). 362/3, Citroen "2 CV" (1950). 364/5, MGA (1957). 366/7, Ferrari "250 GTO" (1962). 368/9, Ford "V-8" (1932). 370/1, Aston Martin "Lagonda" (1977).

52. Stalk-eyed Ghost Crab.

1986. Crabs. Multicoloured.
372. 15 c. Type **52** 20 25
373. 40 c. Red and white painted crab 45 55
374. 50 c. Red-spotted crab .. 55 70
375. 60 c. Red hermit crab .. 70 90

1986. Ships (3rd series). Missionary Vessels. As T **26**. Multicoloured.
377. 15 c. "Messenger of Peace" 15 15
378. 40 c. "John Wesley" .. 35 40
379. 50 c. "Duff" 40 45
380. 60 c. "Triton" 50 55

1986. 60th Birthday of Queen Elizabeth II. As T **167** of British Virgin Islands. Mult.
381. 10 c. Queen wearing ceremonial cloak, New Zealand, 1977 .. .. 15 10
382. 90 c. Before visit to France, 1957 .. .. 55 75
383. $1.50 Queen in 1982 .. 70 1·00
384. $3 In Canberra, 1982 (vert.) 1·40 2·00

54. Peace Dove carrying Wreath and Rainbow.

1986. 25th Anniv. of United States Peace Corps.
386. **54.** 50 c. multicoloured .. 80 80

55. Island and Flags of Tuvalu and U.S.A.

1986. "Ameripex" International Stamp Exhibition, Chicago.
387. **55.** 60 c. multicoloured .. 85 85

56. South Korean Player.

1986. World Cup Football Championship, Mexico. Multicoloured.
388. 1 c. Type **56** 10 10
389. 5 c. French player .. 10 10
390. 10 c. West German captain with World Cup trophy, 1974 .. .. 10 10
391. 40 c. Italian player .. 50 40
392. 60 c. World Cup final, 1974 (59 × 39 mm.) 65 55
393. $1 Canadian team (59 × 39 mm.) .. .. 1·00 1·00
394. $2 Northern Irish team (59 × 39 mm.) .. .. 2·00 2·00
395. $3 English team (59 × 39 mm.) .. .. 3·00 3·00

1986. Royal Wedding (1st issue). As T **168** of British Virgin Islands. Multicoloured.
397. 60 c. Prince Andrew and Miss Sarah Ferguson .. 35 45
398. 60 c. Prince Andrew with prizewinning bull .. 35 45
399. $1 Prince Andrew at horse trials (horiz.) 60 75
400. $1 Miss Sarah Ferguson and Princess Diana (horiz.) 60 75

See also Nos. 433/6.

57. Mourning Gecko.

1986. Lizards. Multicoloured.
402. 15 c. Type **57** 55 55
403. 40 c. Oceanic stump-toed gecko .. .. .. 1·00 1·00
404. 50 c. Azure-tailed skink .. 1·25 1·25
405. 60 c. Moth skink .. .. 1·50 1·50

1986. "Stampex '86" Stamp Exhibition, Adelaide. No. 386 optd. **STAMPEX 86 ADELAIDE** and Kangaroo.
406. **54.** 50 c. multicoloured .. 40 45

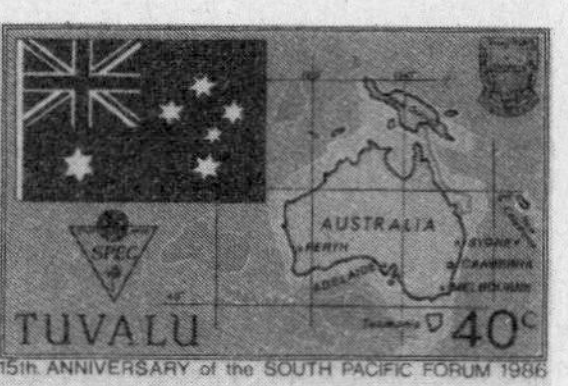

59. Map and Flag of Australia.

1986. 15th Anniv. of South Pacific Forum. Maps and national flags. Multicoloured.
407. 40 c. Type **59** 45 45
408. 40 c. Cook Islands 45 45
409. 40 c. Micronesia 45 45
410. 40 c. Fiji 45 45
411. 40 c. Kiribati 45 45
412. 40 c. Western Samoa .. 45 45
413. 40 c. Nauru 45 45
414. 40 c. Vanuatu 45 45
415. 40 c. New Zealand .. 45 45
416. 40 c. Tuvalu 45 45
417. 40 c. Tonga 45 45
418. 40 c. Solomon Islands .. 45 45
419. 40 c. Papua New Guinea .. 45 45
420. 40 c. Niue 45 45

1986. Automobiles (4th series). As T **46**. The first in each pair show technical drawings and the second paintings.
421. 15 c. multicoloured .. 15 15
422. 15 c. multicoloured .. 15 15
423. 40 c. multicoloured .. 35 40
424. 40 c. multicoloured .. 35 40
425. 50 c. multicoloured .. 45 50
426. 50 c. multicoloured .. 45 50
427. 60 c. multicoloured .. 55 60
428. 60 c. multicoloured .. 45 60
429. 90 c. multicoloured .. 65 75
430. 90 c. multicoloured .. 65 75
431. $1.50 multicoloured .. 75 1·10
432. $1.50 multicoloured .. 75 1·10

DESIGNS: Nos. 421/2, Copper "500" (1953). 423/4, Rover "2000" (1964). 425/6, Ruxton (1930). 427/8, Jowett "Jupiter" (1950). 429/30, Cobra "Daytona Coupe" (1964). 431/2, Packard Model F "Old Pacific" (1903).

1986. Royal Wedding (2nd issue). Nos. 397/400 optd. **Congratulations to T R H The Duke and Duchess of York**.
433. 60 c. Prince Andrew and Miss Sarah Ferguson .. 70 70
434. 60 c. Prince Andrew with prizewinning bull .. 70 70
435. $1 Prince Andrew at horse trials (horiz.) .. .. 1·00 1·00
436. $1 Miss Sarah Ferguson and Princess Diana (horiz.) .. .. .. 1·00 1·00

60. Sea Star.

1986. Coral Reef Life (1st series). Mult.
437. 15 c. Type **60** 45 45
438. 40 c. Pencil urchin .. 1·00 1·00
439. 50 c. Fragile coral .. .. 1·10 1·10
440. 60 c. Pink coral .. .. 1·25 1·25

See also Nos. 498/501 and 558/62.

1987. Ships (4th series). Missionary Steamers. As T **26**. Multicoloured.
442. 15 c. "Southern Cross IV" 50 50
443. 40 c. "John Williams VI" 1·00 1·00
444. 50 c. "John Williams IV" 1·25 1·25
445. 60 c. M.S. "Southern Cross" .. .. .. 1·40 1·40

1987. Automobiles (5th series). As T **46**. The first in each pair shows technical drawings and the second paintings.
446. 1 c. multicoloured 10 10
447. 1 c. multicoloured 10 10
448. 2 c. multicoloured 10 10
449. 2 c. multicoloured 10 10
450. 5 c. multicoloured 10 10
451. 5 c. multicoloured 10 10
452. 10 c. multicoloured .. 10 15
453. 10 c. multicoloured .. 10 15
454. 20 c. multicoloured .. 20 25
455. 20 c. multicoloured .. 20 25
456. 30 c. multicoloured .. 25 30
457. 30 c. multicoloured .. 25 30
458. 40 c. multicoloured .. 35 40
459. 40 c. multicoloured .. 35 40
460. 50 c. multicoloured .. 45 50
461. 50 c. multicoloured .. 45 50
462. 60 c. multicoloured .. 45 50
463. 60 c. multicoloured .. 45 50
464. 70 c. multicoloured .. 50 60
465. 70 c. multicoloured .. 50 60
466. 75 c. multicoloured .. 50 60
467. 75 c. multicoloured .. 50 60
468. $1 multicoloured .. 70 80
469. $1 multicoloured .. 70 80

DESIGNS: Nos. 446/7, Talbot-Lago (1938). 448/9, Du Pont "Model G" (1930). 450/1, Riley "RM" (1950). 452/3, Chevrolet "Baby Grand" (1915). 454/5, Shelby "Mustang GT 500 KR" (1968). 456/7, Ferrari "212 Export Barchetta" (1952). 458/9, Peerless "Model 48-Six" (1912). 460/1, Sunbeam "Alpine" (1954). 462/3, Matra-Ford "MS 80" (1969). 464/5, Squire $1\frac{1}{2}$ Litre (1934). 466/7, Talbot "105" (1931). 468/9, Plymouth "Model Q" (1928).

61. "Nephrolepis saligna".

1987. Ferns. Multicoloured.
471. 15 c. Type **61** 40 40
472. 40 c. "Asplenium nidus" .. 70 70
473. 50 c. "Microsorum scolopendria" 85 85
474. 60 c. "Pteris tripartita" .. 95 95

62. Floral Arrangement.

1987. Flowers and "Fous". Designs showing either floral arrangements or "fous" (women's headdresses). Multicoloured.
476. 15 c. Type **62** 15 15
477. 15 c. "Fou" 15 15
478. 40 c. "Fou" 35 40
479. 40 c. Floral arrangement .. 35 40
480. 50 c. Floral arrangement .. 45 50
481. 50 c. "Fou" 45 50
482. 60 c. "Fou" 55 60
483. 60 c. Floral arrangement .. 55 60

63. Queen Victoria, 1897 (photo by Downey).

1987. Royal Ruby Wedding and 150th Anniv of Queen Victoria's Accession.

No.	Type	Description	Unused	Used
484.	**63.**	40 c. brown, black and green	35	40
485.	–	60 c. purple, black and green	55	60
486.	–	80 c. brown, black and blue	70	75
487.	–	$1 brown, black and purple	90	95
488.	–	$2 multicoloured	1·75	1·90

DESIGNS: 60 c. Wedding of Princess Elizabeth and Duke of Edinburgh, 1947. 80 c. Queen, Duke of Edinburgh and Prince Charles, 1950. $1 Queen with Princess Anne, 1950. $2 Queen Elizabeth II, 1970.

64. Coconut Crab.

1987. Crustaceans. Multicoloured.

No.	Description	Unused	Used
490.	40 c. Type **64**	55	55
491.	50 c. Painted crayfish	70	70
492.	60 c. Ocean crayfish	80	80

65. Aborigine and Ayers Rock. (Illustration reduced. Actual size 60 × 40 mm.).

1987. World Scout Jamboree, Australia. Multicoloured.

No.	Description	Unused	Used
493.	40 c. Type **65**	40	40
494.	60 c. Capt. Cook and H.M.S. "Endeavour"	80	80
495.	$1 Scout saluting and Scout Park entrance	1·10	1·10
496.	$1.50 Koala and kangaroo	1·40	1·40

1988. Coral Reef Life (2nd series). As T **60**. Multicoloured.

No.	Description	Unused	Used
498.	15 c. Spanish dancer	50	50
499.	40 c. Hard corals	90	90
500.	50 c. Feather stars	1·00	1·00
501.	60 c. Staghorn corals	1·10	1·10

66. Red Junglefowl.

1988. Birds. Multicoloured.

No.	Description	Unused	Used
502.	5 c. Type **66**	10	10
503.	10 c. White tern	10	15
504.	15 c. Common noddy	15	20
505.	20 c. Phoenix petrel	20	25
506.	25 c. American golden plover	25	30
507.	30 c. Crested tern	30	35
508.	35 c. Sooty tern	30	35
509.	40 c. Bristle-thighed curlew	35	40
510.	45 c. Bar-tailed godwit	40	45
511.	50 c. Eastern Reef heron	45	50
512.	55 c. Great frigate bird	50	55
513.	60 c. Red-footed booby	55	60
514.	70 c. Rufous-necked sandpiper	65	70
515.	$1 Long-tailed koel	90	95
516.	$2 Red-tailed tropic bird	1·90	2·00
517.	$5 Banded rail	4·50	4·75

67 Jean-Henri Dunant (founder)

1988. 125th Anniv of International Red Cross.

No.	Type	Description	Unused	Used
518	**67**	15 c. red and brown	25	25
519	–	40 c. red and blue	60	60
520	–	50 c. red and green	75	75
521	–	60 c. red and purple	85	85

DESIGNS: 40 c. Junior Red Cross members on parade; 50 c. Red Cross worker with boy in wheelchair; 60 c. First aid training.

68 H.M.S. "Endeavour" (Illustration reduced, actual size 56 × 37 mm)

1988. Voyages of Captain Cook. Mult.

No.	Description	Unused	Used
523	20 c. Type **68**	55	55
524	40 c. Stern of H.M.S. "Endeavour"	80	80
525	50 c. Cook preparing to land at Tahiti (vert)	90	90
526	60 c. Maori chief (vert)	1·00	1·00
527	80 c. H.M.S. "Resolution" and Hawaiian canoe	1·25	1·25
528	$1 "Captain Cook" (after Nathaniel Dance) (vert)	1·50	1·50

69 "Ganoderma applanatum"

1988. Fungi (1st series). Multicoloured.

No.	Description	Unused	Used
530	40 c. Type **69**	75	65
531	50 c. "Pseudoepicoccum cocos" (brown leaf spot)	80	70
532	60 c. "Rigidoporus zonalis"	90	80
533	90 c. "Rigidoporus microporus"	1·40	1·10

See also Nos. 554/7.

70 Rifle-shooting (Illustration reduced, actual size 60 × 40 mm)

1988. Olympic Games, Seoul. Multicoloured.

No.	Description	Unused	Used
534	10 c. Type **70**	10	15
535	20 c. Judo	20	25
536	40 c. Canoeing	40	45
537	60 c. Swimming	55	60
538	80 c. Yachting	75	80
539	$1 Gymnastics	95	1·00

71 Queen Elizabeth II in Ceremonial Canoe

1988. 10th Anniv of Independence. Designs showing scenes from Royal Visit of 1982.

No.	Type	Description	Unused	Used
540	**71**	60 c. multicoloured	60	60
541		90 c. multicoloured	90	90
542		$1 multicoloured (horiz)	1·00	1·00
543		$1.20 multicoloured	1·25	1·25

72 Virgin Mary

1988. Christmas. Multicoloured.

No.	Description	Unused	Used
545	15 c. Type **72**	15	20
546	40 c. Christ Child	40	45
547	60 c. Joseph	55	60

73 Dancing Skirt and Dancer

1989. Traditional Dancing Skirts. Designs showing skirts and dancer silhouettes.

No.	Type	Description	Unused	Used
549	**73**	40 c. multicoloured	60	60
550	–	50 c. multicoloured	70	70
551	–	60 c. multicoloured	80	80
552	–	90 c. multicoloured	1·25	1·25

1989. Fungi (2nd series). As T **69**. Mult.

No.	Description	Unused	Used
554	40 c. "Trametes muelleri"	90	90
555	50 c. "Pestalotiopsis palmarum" (grey leaf spot)	1·10	1·10
556	60 c. "Trametes cingulata"	1·10	1·10
557	90 c. "Schizophyllum commune"	1·50	1·50

1989. Coral Reef Life (3rd series). As T **60**. Multicoloured.

No.	Description	Unused	Used
558	40 c. Pennant coralfish	75	75
559	50 c. Anemone fish	90	90
560	60 c. Batfish	1·00	1·00
561	90 c. Threadfin coralfish	1·50	1·50

75 Conch Shell

1989. Christmas. Multicoloured.

No.	Description	Unused	Used
564	40 c. Type **75**	55	55
565	50 c. Posy of flowers	70	70
566	60 c. Germinating coconut	75	75
567	90 c. Jewellery	1·25	1·25

76 "Cocus nucifera"

1990. Tropical Trees. Multicoloured.

No.	Description	Unused	Used
568	15 c. Type **76**	30	30
569	30 c. "Rhizophora samoensis"	50	50
570	40 c. "Messerschmidia argentea"	65	65
571	50 c. "Pandanus tectorius"	75	75
572	60 c. "Hernandia nymphae-ifolia"	85	85
573	90 c. "Pisonia grandis"	1·25	1·25

77 Penny Black with "Stamp World London 90" Emblem

1990. 150th Anniv of the Penny Black, and "Stamp World London 90" International Stamp Exhibition.

No.	Type	Description	Unused	Used
574	**77**	15 c. multicoloured	35	35
575		40 c. multicoloured	80	80
576		90 c. multicoloured	1·75	1·75

78 Japanese Camouflaged Freighter

1990. 50th Anniv of Second World War. Ships. Multicoloured.

No.	Description	Unused	Used
578	15 c. Type **78**	35	35
579	30 c. U.S.S. "Unimack" (seaplane tender)	60	60
580	40 c. "Amagari" (Japanese destroyer)	70	70
581	50 c. U.S.S. "Platte" (transport)	85	85
582	60 c. Japanese Shumushu Class escort	95	95
583	90 c. U.S.S. "Independence" (aircraft carrier)	1·50	1·50

79 "Erythrina fusca"

1990. Flowers. Multicoloured.

No.	Description	Unused	Used
584	15 c. Type **79**	25	25
585	30 c. "Capparis cordifolia"	45	45
586	40 c. "Portulaca pilosa"	55	55
587	50 c. "Cordia subcordata"	70	70
588	60 c. "Scaevola taccada"	80	80
589	90 c. "Suriana maritima"	1·25	1·25

80 Land Resources Survey

1990. 40th Anniv of United Nations Development Programme. Multicoloured.

590	40 c. Type **80**	55	55
591	60 c. Satellite earth station	75	75
592	$1.20 "Te Tautai" (trawler)	1·40	1·40

81 Mary and Joseph travelling to Bethlehem

1990. Christmas. Multicoloured.

593	15 c. Type **81**	25	25
594	40 c. The Nativity	55	55
595	60 c. Shepherds with flock	80	80
596	90 c. Wise Men bearing gifts	1·25	1·25

82 "Murex ramosus"

1991. Sea Shells. Multicoloured.

597	40 c. Type **82**	55	55
598	50 c. "Conus marmoreus"	65	65
599	60 c. "Trochus niloticus"	75	75
600	$1.50 "Cypraea mappa" ..	1·90	1·90

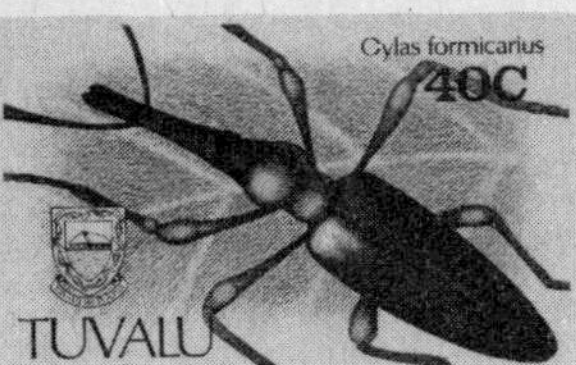

83 "Cylas formicarius" (beetle)

1991. Insects. Multicoloured.

601	40 c. Type **83**	60	60
602	50 c. "Heliothis armiger" (moth)	75	75
603	60 c. "Spodoptera litura" (moth)	90	90
604	$1.50 "Agrius convolvuli" (moth)	2·25	2·25

84 Green Turtle

1991. Endangered Marine Life. Multicoloured.

605	40 c. Type **84**	55	55
606	50 c. Humpback whale ..	65	65
607	60 c. Hawksbill turtle ..	75	75
608	$1.50 Sperm whale ..	2·00	2·00

85 Football

1991. 9th South Pacific Games. Multicoloured.

609	40 c. Type **85**	60	60
610	50 c. Volleyball	80	80
611	60 c. Lawn tennis ..	95	95
612	$1.50 Cricket	2·40	2·40

86 U.S.S. "Tennessee" (battleship)

1991. Second World War Ships. Mult.

613	40 c. Type **86**	60	60
614	50 c. "Haguro" (Japanese cruiser)	80	80
615	60 c. H.M.N.Z.S. "Achilles" (cruiser) ..	95	95
616	$1.50 U.S.S. "North Carolina" (battleship) ..	2·40	2·40

87 Traditional Dancers

1991. Christmas. Multicoloured.

617	40 c. Type **87**	60	60
618	50 c. Solo dancer	75	75
619	60 c. Dancers in green costumes	85	85
620	$1.50 Dancers in multi-coloured costumes ..	2·00	2·00

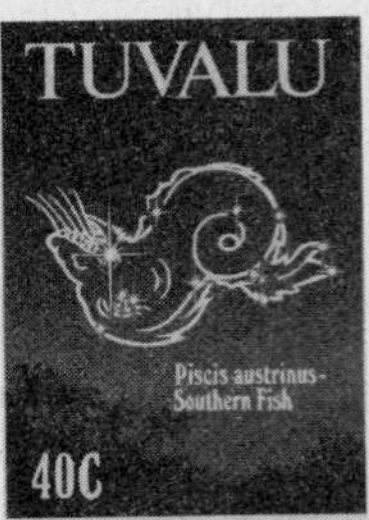

88 Southern Fish Constellation

1992. Pacific Star Constellations. Mult.

621	40 c. Type **88**	50	50
622	50 c. Scorpion	65	65
623	60 c. Archer	80	80
624	$1.50 Southern Cross ..	2·25	2·25

89 King George VI and Cargo Liner

1992. Centenary of British Occupation of Tuvalu. Multicoloured.

625	40 c. Type **89**	35	40
626	50 c. King George V and freighter with barges at wharf	45	50
627	60 c. King Edward VII and freighter	55	60
628	$1.50 Queen Victoria and warship	1·40	1·50

90 Columbus with King Ferdinand and Queen Isabella of Spain

1992. 500th Anniv of Discovery of America by Columbus.

629	90	40 c. blue and black ..	35	40
630	–	50 c. purple and black	45	50
631	–	60 c. green and black ..	55	60
632	–	$1.50 purple and black	1·40	1·50

DESIGNS: 50 c. Columbus and Polynesians; 60 c. Columbus and South American Indians; $1.50, Columbus and North American Indians.

OFFICIAL STAMPS

1981. Nos. 105/22 optd. **OFFICIAL.**

O 1.	14.	1 c. multicoloured ..	10	10
O 2.	–	2 c. multicoloured ..	10	10
O 3.	–	4 c. multicoloured ..	10	10
O 4.	–	5 c. multicoloured ..	10	10
O 5.	–	6 c. multicoloured ..	10	10
O 6.	–	8 c. multicoloured ..	10	10
O 7.	–	10 c. multicoloured ..	15	15
O 8.	–	15 c. multicoloured ..	20	20
O 9.	–	20 c. multicoloured ..	25	25
O 10.	–	25 c. multicoloured ..	30	30
O 11.	–	30 c. multicoloured ..	30	30
O 12.	–	35 c. multicoloured ..	35	35
O 13.	–	40 c. multicoloured ..	40	40
O 14.	–	45 c. multicoloured ..	45	45
O 15.	–	50 c. multicoloured ..	50	50
O 16.	–	70 c. multicoloured ..	75	75
O 17.	–	$1 multicoloured ..	1·10	1·10
O 18a.		$2 multicoloured ..	2·25	2·25
O 19.	–	$5 multicoloured ..	5·50	6·00

1983. Nos. 202/3a, 205/12, 224 and 234 optd. **OFFICIAL.**

O 20.	5 c. Wedding and baby food baskets	10	15
O 21.	10 c. Hand-carved model of canoe	10	15
O 22.	15 c. Ladies sun hats ..	15	20
O 23.	25 c. Pandanus baskets	25	30
O 24.	30 c. on 45 c. Reef sandals and fish trap ..	50	60
O 25.	30 c. Basket tray and coconut stand ..	30	40
O 26.	35 c. Pandanus pillows and shell necklaces ..	40	45
O 27.	40 c. Round baskets and fan	45	50
O 28.	45 c. Reef Sandals and fish trap ..	45	50
O 29.	50 c. Rat trap ..	50	60
O 30.	60 c. on $1 Pump drill and adze ..	75	85
O 31.	60 c. Fisherman's waterproof boxes	60	80
O 32.	$1 Pump drill and adze	1·00	1·00
O 33.	$2 Fisherman's hat and canoe bailers	1·75	2·00
O 34.	$5 Fishing rod, lures and scoop nets	4·25	4·75

1989. Nos. 502/17 optd **OFFICIAL**.

O 35	5 c. Type **66**	10	10
O 36	10 c. White tern ..	10	15
O 37	15 c. Common noddy	15	20
O 38	20 c. Phoenix petrel ..	20	25
O 39	25 c. American golden plover	25	30
O 40	30 c. Crested tern ..	30	35
O 41	35 c. Sooty tern ..	30	35
O 42	40 c. Bristle-thighed curlew	35	40
O 43	45 c. Bar-tailed godwit	40	45
O 44	50 c. Eastern reef heron	45	50
O 45	55 c. Great frigate bird	50	55
O 46	60 c. Red-footed booby	55	60
O 47	70 c. Rufous-necked sandpiper	65	70
O 48	$1 Long-tailed koel ..	90	95
O 49	$2 Red-tailed tropic bird	1·90	2·00
O 50	$5 Banded rail ..	4·50	4·75

POSTAGE DUE STAMPS

D 1. Tuvalu Crest.

1981.

D 1	D 1	1 c. black and purple	10	10
D 2		2 c. black and blue ..	10	10
D 3		5 c. black and brown	10	10
D 13		10 c. black and green	10	10
D 14		20 c. black and brown	15	20
D 15		30 c. black and orange	20	25
D 16		40 c. black and blue	30	35
D 17		50 c. black and green	40	45
D 18		$1 black and mauve ..	75	80

Some values exist with or without the imprint date at foot.

APPENDIX

The following stamps for individual islands of Tuvalu have either been issued in excess of postal needs, or have not been made available to the public in reasonable quantities at face value.

FUNAFUTI
1984.

Leaders of the World. Railway Locomotives (1st series). Two designs for each value, the first showing technical drawings and the second the locomotive at work. 15, 20, 30, 40, 50, 60 c., each ×2.

Leaders of the World. Automobiles (1st series). Two designs for each value, the first showing technical drawings and the second the car in action. 1, 10, 40 c., $1, each ×2.

Leaders of the World. Railway Locomotives (2nd series). Two designs for each value, the first showing technical drawings and the second the locomotive at work. 5, 15, 25, 35, 40, 55, 60 c. $1, each ×2.

1985

Leaders of the World. Automobiles (2nd series). Two designs for each value, the first showing technical drawings and the second the car in action. 1, 30, 55, 60 c., each ×2.
Leaders of the World. Railway Locomotives (3rd series). Two designs for each value, the first showing technical drawings and the second the locomotive at work. 5, 15, 35, 40, 50 c., $1, each ×2.
Leaders of the World. Life and Times of Queen Elizabeth the Queen Mother. Two designs for each value, showing different portraits. 5, 25, 80 c., $1.05, each ×2.

1986.

60th Birthday of Queen Elizabeth II. 10, 50 c., $1.50, $3.50.
Royal Wedding (1st issue). 60 c., $1, each ×2.
Royal Wedding (2nd issue). Previous Royal Wedding stamps optd. **Congratulations T.R.H. The Duke & Duchess of York.** 60 c., $1, each ×2
Railway Locomotives (4th series). Two designs for each value, the first showing technical drawings and the second the locomotive at work. 20, 40, 60 c., $1.50, each ×2.

1987.

Automobiles (3rd series). Two designs for each value, the first showing technical drawings and the second the car in action. 10, 20, 40, 60, 75, 80 c., $1, $1.50, each ×2.
Royal Ruby Wedding. 20, 50, 75 c., $1.20, $1.75.

1988.

Olympic Games, Seoul. 10, 20, 40, 50, 80, 90 c.

NANUMAGA

1984.

Leaders of the World. Automobiles (1st series). Two designs for each value, the first showing technical drawings and the second the car in action. 5, 10, 25, 30, 40 c., $1, each ×2.
Leaders of the World. British Monarchs. Two designs for each value, forming a composite picture. 10, 20, 30, 40, 50 c., $1, each ×2.
Leaders of the World. Automobiles (2nd series). Two designs for each value, the first showing technical drawings and the second the car in action. 5, 10, 50 c., $1, each ×2.

1985

Leaders of the World. Railway Locomotives. Two designs for each value, the first showing technical drawings and the second the locomotive at work. 10, 25, 50, 60 c., each ×2.
Leaders of the World. Flowers. 25, 30, 40, 50 c., each ×2.
Leaders of the World. Automobiles (3rd series). Two designs for each value, the first showing technical drawings and the second the car in action. 10, 25, 75 c., $1, each ×2.
Leaders of the World. Life and Times of Queen Elizabeth the Queen Mother. Two designs for each value, showing different portraits. 15, 55, 65, 90 c., each ×2.

1986.

60th Birthday of Queen Elizabeth II. 5 c., $1, $1.75, $2.50.
World Cup Football Championship, Mexico. 1, 2, 5, 10, 20, 35, 50, 60, 75 c., $1, $2, $4.
Royal Wedding (1st issue). 60 c., $1, each ×2.
Royal Wedding (2nd issue). Previous Royal Wedding stamps optd. as for Funafuti. 60 c., $1, each ×2.

1987.

Automobiles (4th series). Two designs for each value, the first showing technical drawings and the second the car in action. 5, 10, 15, 20, 25, 40, 60 c., $1, each ×2.
Royal Ruby Wedding. 15, 35, 60 c., $1.50, $1.75.

NANUMEA

1984.

Leaders of the World. Railway Locomotives (1st series). Two designs for each value, the first showing technical drawings and the second the locomotive at work. 15, 20, 30, 40, 50, 60 c., each ×2.
Leaders of the World. Famous Cricketers. Two designs for each value, the first showing a portrait and the second the cricketer in action. 1, 10, 40 c., $1, each ×2.

1985.

Leaders of the World. Automobiles (1st series). Two designs for each value, the first showing technical drawings and the second the car in action. 5, 40, 50, 60 c., each ×2.
Leaders of the World. Railway Locomotives (2nd series). Two designs for each value, the first showing technical drawings and the second the locomotive at work. 1, 35, 50, 60 c., each ×2.
Leaders of the World. Automobiles (2nd series). Two designs for each value, the first showing technical drawings and the second the car in action. 15, 20, 50, 60 c., each ×2
Leaders of the World. Cats. 5, 30, 50 c., $1, each ×2.
Leaders of the World. Life and Times of Queen Elizabeth the Queen Mother. Two designs for each value, showing different portraits. 5, 30, 75 c., $1.05, each ×2.

1986.

60th Birthday of Queen Elizabeth II. 10, 80 c., $1.75, $3.
World Cup Football Championship, Mexico. 1, 2, 5, 10, 25, 40, 50, 75, 90 c., $1, $2.50, $4.
Royal Wedding (1st issue). 60 c., $1, each ×2.
Royal Wedding (2nd issue). Previous Royal Wedding stamps optd. as for Funafuti. 60 c., $1, each ×2.
Automobiles (3rd series). Two designs for each value, the first showing technical drawings and the second the car in action. 10, 20, 35, 50, 75 c., $2, each ×2.

1987.

Royal Ruby Wedding. 40, 60, 80 c., $1, $2.

NIUTAO

1984.

Leaders of the World. Automobiles (1st series). Two designs for each value, the first showing technical drawings and the second the car in action. 15, 30, 40, 50 c., each ×2.

1984.

Leaders of the World. Railway Locomotives (1st series). Two designs for each value, the first showing technical drawings and the second the locomotive at work. 5, 10, 20, 40, 50 c., $1, each ×2.

1985.

Leaders of the World. Famous Cricketers. Two designs for each value, the first showing a portrait and the second the cricketer in action. 1, 15, 50 c., $1, each ×2.
Leaders of the World. Birth Bicent. of John J. Audubon (ornithologist). Birds. 5, 15, 25 c., $1, each ×2.
Leaders of the World. Automobiles (2nd series). Two designs for each value, the first showing technical drawings and the second the car in action. 20, 25, 40, 60 c., each ×2.
Leaders of the World. Railway Locomotives (2nd series). Two designs for each value, the first showing technical drawings and the second the locomotive at work. 10, 30, 45, 60, 75 c., $1.20, each ×2.
Leaders of the World. Life and Times of Queen Elizabeth the Queen Mother. Two designs for each value, showing different portraits. 15, 35, 70, 95 c., each ×2.

1986.

60th Birthday of Queen Elizabeth II. 5, 60 c., $1.50, $3.50.
Royal Wedding (1st issue). 60 c., $1, each ×2.
Royal Wedding (2nd issue). Previous Royal Wedding stamps optd. as for Funafuti. 60 c., $1, each ×2.

1987.

Royal Ruby Wedding. 60th Birthday of Queen Elizabeth II issue of 1986 optd. **40th WEDDING ANNIVERSARY OF H. M. QUEEN ELIZABETH II.** 5, 60 c., $1.50, $3.50.

NUI

1984.

Leaders of the World. Railway Locomotives (1st series). Two designs for each value, the first showing technical drawings and the second the locomotive at work. 15, 25, 30, 50 c., each ×2.
Leaders of the World. British Monarchs. Two designs for each value, forming a composite picture. 1, 5, 15, 40, 50 c., $1, each ×2.

1985.

Leaders of the World. Railway Locomotives (2nd series). Two designs for each value, the first showing technical drawings and the second the locomotive at work. 5, 15, 25 c., $1, each ×2.
Leaders of the World. Automobiles (1st series). Two designs for each value, the first showing technical drawings and the second the car in action. 25, 30, 40, 50 c., each ×2.
Leaders of the World. Famous Cricketers. Two designs for each value, the first showing a portrait and the second the cricketer in action. 1, 40, 60, 70 c., each ×2.
Leaders of the World. Life and Times of Queen Elizabeth the queen Mother. Two designs for each value, showing different portraits. 5, 50, 75, 85 c., each ×2.
Leaders of the World. Automobiles (2nd series). Two designs for each value, the first showing technical drawings and the second the car in action. 5, 15, 40, 60, 90 c., $1.10, each ×2.

1986.

60th Birthday of Queen Elizabeth II. 10, 80 c., $1.75, $3.
Royal Wedding (1st issue). 60 c., $1, each ×2.
Royal Wedding (2nd issue). Previous Royal Wedding stamps optd. as for Funafuti. 60 c., $1, each ×2.

1987.

Railway Locomotives (3rd series). Two designs for each value, the first showing technical drawings and the second the locomotive at work. 10, 25, 35, 40, 60, 75 c., $1, $1.25, each ×2.
Royal Ruby Wedding. 20, 50, 75 c., $1.20, $1.75.

1988.

Railway Locomotives (4th series). Two designs for each value, the first showing technical drawings and the second the locomotive at work. 5, 10, 20, 25, 40, 50, 60, 75 c., each ×2.

NUKUFETAU

1984.

Leaders of the World. Automobiles (1st series). Two designs for each value, the first showing technical drawings and the second the car in action. 10, 25, 30, 50, 60 c., each ×2.
Leaders of the World. British Monarchs. Two designs for each value, forming a composite picture. 1, 10, 30, 50, 60 c., $1, each ×2.

1985.

Leaders of the World. Famous Cricketers. Two designs for each value, the first showing a portrait and the second the cricketer in action. 1, 10, 55 c., $1, each ×2.
Leaders of the World. Railway Locomotives (1st series). Two designs for each value, the first showing technical drawings and the second the locomotive at work. 1, 10, 60, 70 c., each ×2.
Leaders of the World. Automobiles (2nd series). Two designs for each value the first showing technical drawings and the second the car in action. 5, 10, 15, 20, 50, 60, 75 c., $1.50, each ×2.
Leaders of the World. Life and Times of Queen Elizabeth the Queen Mother. Two designs for each value, showing different portraits. 10, 45, 65 c., $1, each ×2.

1986.

Leaders of the World. Railway Locomotives (2nd series). Two designs for each value, the first showing technical drawings and the second the locomotive at work. 20, 40, 60 c., $1.50, each ×2.
60th Birthday of Queen Elizabeth II. 5, 40 c., $2, $4.
Royal Wedding (1st issue). 60 c., $1, each ×2.
Royal Wedding (2nd issue). Previous Royal Wedding stamps optd. as for Funafuti. 60 c., $1, each ×2.

1987.

Railway Locomotives (3rd series). Two designs for each value, the first showing technical drawings and the second the locomotive at work. 5, 10, 15, 25, 30, 50, 60 c., $1, each ×2.
Royal Ruby Wedding. 60th Birthday of Queen Elizabeth II issue of 1986 optd. as for Niutao. 5, 40 c., $2, $4.

NUKULAELAE

1984.

Leaders of the World. Railway Locomotives (1st series). Two designs for each value, the first showing technical drawings and the second the locomotive at work. 5, 15, 40 c., $1 each ×2.
Leaders of the World. Famous Cricketers. Two designs for each value, the first showing a portrait and the second the cricketer in action. 5, 15, 30 c., $1, each ×2.
Leaders of the World. Railway Locomotives (2nd series). Two designs for each value, the first showing technical drawings and the second the locomotive at work. 5, 20, 40 c., $1, each ×2.

1985.

Leaders of the World. Automobiles (1st series). Two designs for each value, the first showing technical drawings and the second the car in action. 5, 35, 50, 70 c., each ×2.
Leaders of the World. Dogs. 5, 20, 50, 70 c., each ×2.
Leaders of the World. Railway Locomotives (3rd series). Two designs for each value, the first showing technical drawings and the second the locomotive at work. 10, 25, 50 c., $1, each ×2.
Leaders of the World. Automobiles (2nd series). Two designs for each value, the first showing technical drawings and the second the car in action. 10, 25, 35, 50, 75 c., $1, each ×2.
Leaders of the World. Life and Times of Queen Elizabeth the Queen Mother. Two designs for each value, showing different portraits. 5, 25, 85 c., $1, each ×2.

1986.

60th Birthday of Queen Elizabeth II. 10 c., $1, $1.50, $3.
Railway Locomotives (4th series). Two designs for each value, the first showing technical drawings and the second the locomotive at work. 10, 15, 25, 40, 50, 80 c., $1, $1.50, each ×2.
Royal Wedding (1st issue). 60 c., $1, each ×2.
Royal Wedding (2nd issue). Previous Royal Wedding stamps optd. as for Funafuti. 60 c., $1, each ×2.

1987.

Royal Ruby Wedding. 15, 35, 60 c., $1.50, $1.75.

VAITUPU

1984.

Leaders of the World. Automobile (1st series). Two designs for each value, the first showing technical drawings and the second the car in action. 15, 25, 30, 50 c., each ×2.
Leaders of the World. British Monarchs. Two designs for each value, forming a composite picture. 1, 5, 15, 40, 50 c., $1, each ×2.
Leaders of the World. Automobiles (2nd series). Two designs for each value, the first showing technical drawings and the second the car in action. 5, 15, 25, 30, 40, 50, 60 c., $1, each ×2.

1985.

Leaders of the World. Railway Locomotives (1st series). Two designs for each value, the first showing technical drawings and the second the locomotive at work. 10, 25, 50, 60 c., each ×2.
Leaders of the World. Butterflies. 5, 15, 50, 75 c., each ×2.
Leaders of the World. Automobiles (3rd series). Two designs for each value, the first showing technical drawings and the second the car in action. 15, 30, 40, 60 c., each ×2.
Leaders of the World. Life and Times of Queen Elizabeth the Queen Mother. Two designs for each value, showing different portraits. 15, 40, 65, 95 c., each ×2.

1986.

Leaders of the World. Railway Locomotives (2nd series). Two designs for each value, the first showing technical drawings and the second the locomotive at work. 5, 25, 80 c., $1, each ×2.
60th Birthday of Queen Elizabeth II. 5, 60 c., $2, $3.50.
Royal Wedding (1st issue). 60 c., $1, each ×2.
Royal Wedding (2nd issue). Previous Royal Wedding stamps optd. as for Funafuti. 60 c., $1, each ×2.

1987.

Railway Locomotives (3rd series). Two designs for each value, the first showing technical drawings and the second the locomotive at work. 10, 15, 25, 35, 45, 65, 85 c., $1, each ×2.
Royal Ruby Wedding. 60th Birthday of Queen Elizabeth II issue of 1986 optd. as for Niutao. 5, 60 c., $2, $3.50.

UGANDA

A Br. Protectorate in Central Africa until it attained independence within the British Commonwealth 1962. From 1903 to 1962 used the stamps we list under " Kenya, Uganda and Tanganyika ".

1895. 1,000 cowries = 2 rupees.
1896. 16 annas = 1 rupee.
1962. 100 cents = 1 shilling.

U G 20

2.

V.96.R 25 Uganda

3.

1895. Typewritten in black.

17 2	5 (c.) black	£1100	£850
18	10 (c.) black	£1100	£950
19	15 (c.) black	£800	£850
20	20 (c.) black	£900	£600
21	25 (c.) black	£750	£800
6	30 (c.) black	£1100	£1100
7	40 (c) black	£1800	£1100
8	50 (c.) black	£1000	£950
9	60 (c.) black	£1300	£1300

1895. Typewritten in violet.

35. 2.	5 (c.) violet	£350	£400
36.	10 (c.) violet	£325	£350
37.	15 (c.) violet	£375	£325
38.	20 (c.) violet	£300	£275
39.	25 (c.) violet	£450	£450
40.	30 (c.) violet	£550	£450
41.	40 (c.) violet	£450	£450
42.	50 (c.) violet	£450	£425
43.	100 (c.) violet	£2250	

1896. Typewritten in violet

44. 3.	5 (c.) violet	£300	£375
45.	10 (c.) violet	£300	£300
46.	15 (c.) violet	£300	£350
47.	20 (c.) violet	£250	£190
48.	25 (c.) violet	£325	
49.	30 (c.) violet	£350	£475
50.	40 (c.) violet	£350	£475
51.	50 (c.) violet	£350	£475
52.	60 (c.) violet	£1200	
53.	100 (c.) violet	£1200	£1200

U G A N D A
POSTAGE
V†R
1 ANNA
PROTECTORATE

4.

8.

1896.

55. 4.	1 a. black	7·50	8·50
56.	2 a. black	8·50	9·00
57.	3 a. black	9·50	11·00
58.	4 a. black	9·50	11·00
59.	8 a. black	15·00	18·00
60.	1 r. black	40·00	45·00
61.	5 r. black	£130	£170

1896. Optd. with large **L.**

70. 4.	1 a. black	90·00	80·00
71.	2 a. black	35·00	60·00
72.	3 a. black	90·00	£100
73.	4 a. black	50·00	85·00
74.	8 a. black	90·00	£110
75.	1 r. black	£180	£225
76.	5 r. black	£4500	£4500

1898.

84a. 8.	1 a. red	30	35
86.	2 a. brown	40	2·25
87a.	3 a. grey	3·50	7·00
88.	4 a. green	1·75	4·50
89.	8 a. green	2·75	14·00

Larger type with lions at either side of portrait.

90. –	1 r. blue	18·00	20·00
91. –	5 r. brown	48·00	55·00

1902. Stamps of British East Africa optd. UGANDA.

92. 11.	½ a. green	50	35
93.	2½ a. blue	50	1·40

11. Ripon falls and Speke Memorial.

1962. Centenary of Speke's Discovery of Source of Nile.

95. 11.	30 c. black and red	10	10
96.	50 c. black and violet	10	10
97.	1 s. 30 black and green	15	10
98.	2 s. 50 black and blue	40	55

12. Murchison Falls.

DESIGNS—As Type **12**: 10 c. Tobacco-growing. 15 c. Coffee-growing. 20 c. Ankole cattle. 30 c. Cotton. 50 c. Mountains of the moon. As Type **14**: 1 s. 30, Cathedrals and Mosque. 2 s. Copper mining. 10 s. Cement industry. 20 s. Parliamentary Buildings.

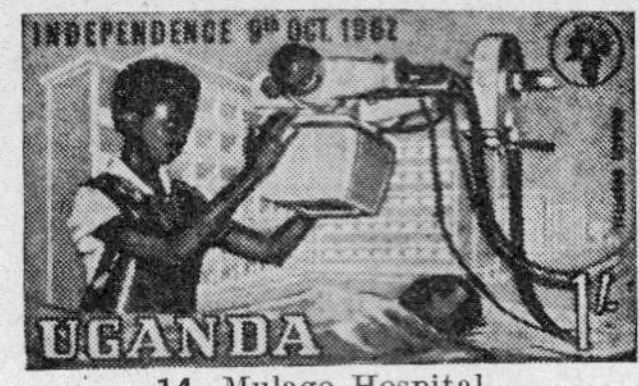

14. Mulago Hospital.

1962. Independence.

99. 12.	5 c. turquoise	10	10
100. –	10 c. brown	10	10
101. –	15 c. black, red & green	10	10
102. –	20 c. plum and buff	10	10
103. –	30 c. blue	10	10
104. –	50 c. black & turquoise	10	10
105. 14.	1 s. sepia, red & turq.	15	10
106. –	1 s. 30 orange & violet	20	10
107. –	2 s. black, red and blue	40	30
108. –	5 s. red and deep green	2·50	75
109. –	10 s. slate and brown	1·75	1·50
110. –	20 s. brown and blue	4·50	11·00

15. South African Crowned Crane.

16. Black Bee-eater.

18. Ruwenzori Turaco.

1965. Int. Trade Fair, Kampala.

111. 15.	30 c. multicoloured	10	10
112.	1 s. 30 multicoloured	20	10

1965. Birds.

113. 16.	5 c. multicoloured	10	10
114. –	10 c. brn., blk. & blue	10	10
115. –	15 c. yellow and brown	15	10
116. –	20 c. multicoloured	15	10
117. –	30 c. black and brown	1·25	10
118. –	40 c. multicoloured	80	30
119. –	50 c. blue and violet	25	10
120. –	65 c. red, blk. & grey	2·25	95
121. 18.	1 s. multicoloured	50	10
122. –	1 s. 30 brn., blk. & yell.	4·50	30
123. –	2 s. 50 multicoloured	4·25	65
124. –	5 s. multicoloured	7·00	2·00
125. –	10 s. multicoloured	9·50	6·50
126. –	20 s. multicoloured	21·00	24·00

DESIGNS: As Type **16**—HORIZ. 10 c. African jacana. 30 c. Sacred ibis. 65 c. Red-crowned bishop. VERT. 15 c. Orange weaver. 20 c. Narina trogon. 40 c. Blue-breasted kingfisher. 50 c. Whale-headed stork. As Type **18**—VERT. 1 s. 30, African fish eagle. 5 s. Lilac-breasted roller. HORIZ. 2 s. 50, Great blue turaco. 10 s, Black-collared lovebird. 20 s. South African crowned crane.

19. Carved Screen.

1967. 13th Commonwealth Parliamentary Assn. Conf. Multicoloured.

127.	30 c. Type **19**	10	10
128.	50 c. Arms of Uganda	10	10
129.	1 s. 30 Parliamentary Bldg.	10	10
130.	2 s. 50 Conference Chamber	15	70

20. "Cordia abyssinica".

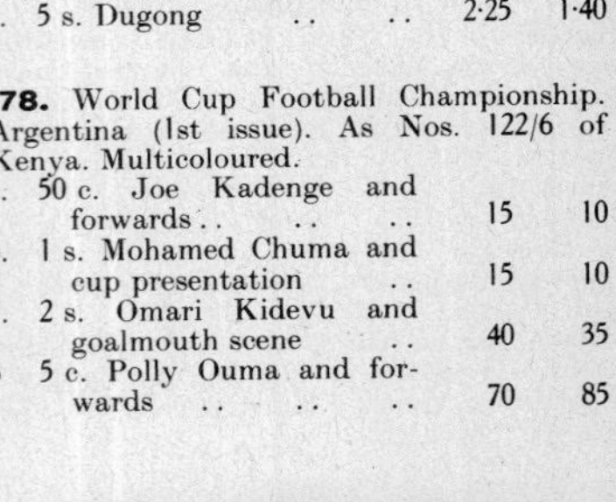

21. "Acacia drepanolobium".

1969. Flowers.

131 20.	5 c. brn., grn. & yell.	10	40
132 –	10 c. multicoloured	10	10
133 –	15 c. multicoloured	30	10
134 –	20 c. vio., olive & grn.	15	10
135 –	30 c. multicoloured	20	10
136 –	40 c. vio., grn. & grey	20	10
137 –	50 c. multicoloured	20	10
138 –	60 c. multicoloured	45	90
139 –	70 c. multicoloured	35	30
140 21.	1 s. multicoloured	20	10
141 –	1 s. 50 multicoloured	35	10
142 –	2 s. 50 multicoloured	70	60
143a –	5 s. multicoloured	1·25	10
144a –	10 s. multicoloured	3·75	10
145 –	20 s. multicoloured	11·00	15

DESIGNS—As Type **20**: 10 c. "Grewiasimilis". 15 c. "Cassia didymobotrya". 20 c. "Coleus barbatus". 30 c. "Ochna ovata". 40 c. "Ipomea spathulata". 50 c. "Spathodea nilotica". 60 c. "Oncoba spinosa". 70 c. "Carissa edulis". As Type **21**: 1 s. 50, "Clerodendrum myricoides". 2 s. 50, "Avanthus arboreus". 5 s. "Kigelia aethiopium". 10 s. "Erythrina abyssinica". 20 s. "Monodora myristica".

1975. Nos. 140a, 142a and 145a surch.

146.	2 s. on 1 s. multicoloured	2·00	1·50
147.	3 s. on 2 s. 50 multicoloured	20·00	35·00
148.	40 s. on 20 s. multicoloured	5·50	3·50

23. Millet.

24. Maize.

1975. Ugandan Crops.

149. 23.	10 c. blk., grn. & brn.	10	10
150. –	20 c. multicoloured	10	10
151. –	30 c. multicoloured	10	10
152. –	40 c. multicoloured	10	10
153. –	50 c. multicoloured	10	10
154. –	70 c. blk., grn. & turq.	15	15
155. –	80 c. multicoloured	15	15
156. 24.	1 s. multicoloured	15	15
157. –	2 s. multicoloured	30	30
158. –	3 s. multicoloured	50	45
159. –	5 s. multicoloured	90	75
160. –	10 s. multicoloured	1·50	1·25
161. –	20 s. grn., blk. & pur.	2·50	2·50
162. –	40 s. grn., bl. & orge.	5·00	4·75

DESIGNS: As Type **23**. 20 c. Sugar. 30 c. Tobacco. 40 c. Onions. 50 c. Tomatoes. 70 c. Tea. 80 c. Bananas. As Type **24**. 2 s. Pineapples. 3 s. Coffee. 5 s. Oranges. 10 s. Groundnuts. 20 s. Cotton. 40 s. Runner Beans.

Face value colours: 5 s. green. 10 s. brown. 20 s. mauve. 40 s. orange.

For these values with colours changed, see Nos. 220/3.

1976. Telecommunications Development. As Nos 56/60 of Kenya.

163.	50 c. Microwave tower	10	10
164.	1 s. Cordless switchboard	10	10
165.	2 s. Telephones	20	25
166.	3 s. Message Switching Centre	30	45

1976. Olympic Games, Montreal. As Nos. 61/5 of Kenya.

168.	50 c. Akii Bua, hurdler	15	10
169.	1 s. Filbert Bayi, runner	20	10
170.	2 s. Steve Muchoki, boxer	40	30
171.	3 s. East African flags	55	45

1976. Railway Transport. As Nos. 66/70 of Kenya.

173.	50 c. Tanzania-Zambia railway	20	10
174.	1 s. Nile Bridge, Uganda	35	10
175.	2 s. Nakuru Station, Kenya	75	45
176.	3 s. Class "A" loco, 1896	95	55

1977. Game Fish of East Africa. As Nos. 71/5 of Kenya. Multicoloured.

178.	50 c. Nile Perch	15	10
179.	1 s. Tilapia	20	10
180.	3 s. Sailfish	70	40
181.	5 s. Black Marlin	1·00	60

1977. Second World Black and African Festival of Arts and Culture. As Nos. 76/80 of Kenya. Multicoloured.

183.	50 c. Maasai Manyatta Village, Kenya	15	10
184.	1 s. "Heartbeat of Africa" (Ugandan dancers)	20	10
185.	2 s. Makonde sculpture, Tanzania	45	45
186.	3 s. "Early man and technology" (skinning hippopotamus)	60	80

1977. 25th Anniv. of Safari Rally. As Nos. 81/5 of Kenya. Multicoloured.

188.	50 c. Rally-car & villagers	15	10
189.	1 s. Starting-line	15	10
190.	2 s. Car fording river	35	35
191.	5 s. Car and elephants	90	1·00

1977. Centenary of Ugandan Church. As Nos. 86/90 of Kenya. Multicoloured.

193.	50 c. Canon Kivebulaya	10	10
194.	1 s. Modern Namirembe Cathedral	15	10
195.	2 s. Old Namirembe Cathedral	30	40
196.	5 s. Early congregation Kigezi	60	90

1977. As No. 155, surch.

198.	80 c. on 60 c. multicoloured	25	20

1977. Endangered Species. As Nos. 96/101 of Kenya. Multicoloured.

199.	50 c. Pancake Tortoise	30	10
200.	1 s. Nile Crocodile	45	10
201.	2 s. Hunter's Hartebeest	1·75	40
202.	3 s. Red Colobus monkey	2·00	75
203.	5 s. Dugong	2·25	1·40

1978. World Cup Football Championship. Argentina (1st issue). As Nos. 122/6 of Kenya. Multicoloured.

205.	50 c. Joe Kadenge and forwards	15	10
206.	1 s. Mohamed Chuma and cup presentation	15	10
207.	2 s. Omari Kidevu and goalmouth scene	40	35
208	5 c. Polly Ouma and forwards	70	85

26. Shot Putting.

1978. Commonwealth Games, Edmonton. Multicoloured.

210.	50 c. Type **26**	15	10
211.	1 s. Long jumping	15	10
212.	2 s. Running	30	30
213.	5 s. Boxing	55	70

1978. World Cup Football Championship, Argentina (2nd issue). As Nos. 205/8, but additionally inscr. " WORLD CUP 1978 ".

215.	50 c. Polly Ouma and forwards	15	10
216.	2 s. Omari Kidevu and goalmouth scene	15	10
217.	5 s. Joe Kadenge and forwards	1·00	90
218.	10 s. Mohamed Chuma and cup presentation	1·75	1·60

1978. As Nos. 159/62 but colours changed.

220.	5 s. mult. (face value in blue)	70	70
221.	10 s. mult. (face value in mauve)	1·00	1·25
222.	20 s. mult. (face value in brown)	1·50	2·00
223.	40 s. mult. (face value in red)	2·75	3·50

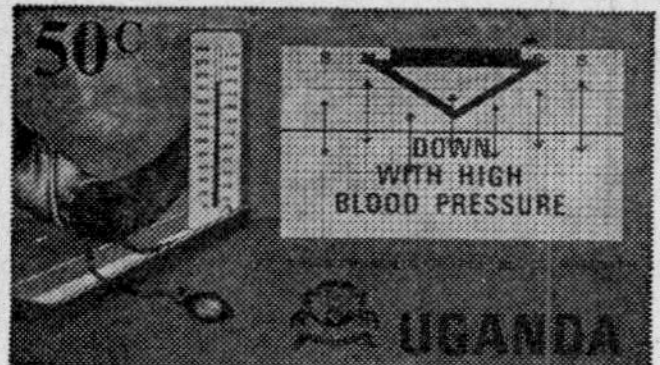

27. Measurements of High Blood Pressure.

1978. "Down with High Blood Pressure". Multicoloured.

224.	50 c. Type **27**	20	10
225.	1 s. Human heart	30	10
226.	2 s. Fundus of the eye ..	70	35
227.	5 s. Human kidneys ..	1·25	80

28. Off Loading Cattle.

1978. 75th Anniv. of First Powered Flight. Multicoloured.

229.	1 s. Type **28**	15	10
230.	1 s. 50, Passengers boarding "Islander" ..	20	15
231.	2 s. 70, Loading Coffee ..	40	35
232.	10 s. Wright "Flyer" and "Concorde"	1·50	1·25

29. Queen Elizabeth II leaving Owen Falls Dam.

1979. 25th Anniv. of Coronation. (1978) Multicoloured.

234.	1 s. Type **29**	15	10
235.	1 s. 50 Regalia	20	10
236.	2 s. 70 Coronation ceremony	45	20
237.	10 s. Royal family on balcony of Buckingham Palace	1·00	60

30. Dr. Joseph Kiwanuka (first Ugandan bishop).

1979. Centenary of Catholic Church in Uganda. Multicoloured.

239.	1 s. Type **30**	15	10
240.	1 s. 50 Lubaga Cathedral	15	10
241.	2 s. 70 Ugandan pilgrimage to Rome, Holy Year, 1975	20	25
242.	10 s. Friar Lourdel-Mapeera (early missionary) ..	60	80

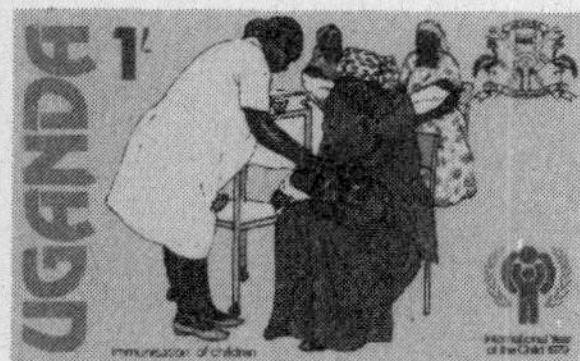

31. Immunisation of Children.

1979. International Year of the Child. Multicoloured.

244.	1 s. Type **31**	15	10
245.	1 s. 50 Handicapped children at play ..	20	20
246.	2 s. 70 Ugandan I.Y.C. emblem	35	35
247.	10 s. Children in class ..	80	90

1979. Liberation. Optd. **UGANDA LIBERATED 1979.** (a) Nos. 149/62.

249. **23.**	10 c. blk., grn. and brn.	10	10
250. –	20 c. multicoloured ..	10	10
251. –	30 c. multicoloured ..	10	10
252. –	40 c. multicoloured ..	10	10
253. –	50 c. multicoloured ..	10	10
254. –	70 c. blk., grn. and turq.	10	10
255. –	80 c. multicoloured ..	10	10
256. **24.**	1 s. multicoloured ..	15	15
257. –	2 s. multicoloured ..	20	25
258. –	3 s. multicoloured ..	35	40
259. –	5 s. multicoloured ..	55	60
260. –	10 s. multicoloured ..	1·10	1·25
261. –	20 s. grn., blk. and pur.	2·25	2·40
262. –	40 s. grn., black & orge.	4·50	4·75
	(b) Nos. 210/13.		
263.	50 c. Type **26** ..	10	10
264.	1 s. Long jumping ..	15	20
265.	2 s. Running	25	30
266.	5 s. Boxing	60	65
	(c) Nos. 207, 215, 217/18.		
267.	50 c. Polly Ouma and forwards	10	10
268.	2 s. Omari Kidevu and goalmouth scene	25	30
269.	5 s. Joe Kadenge and forwards	60	65
270.	10 s. Mohamed Chuma and cup presentation ..	1·25	1·40
	(d) Nos. 220/3.		
271.	5 s. multicoloured ..	55	60
272.	10 s. multicoloured ..	1·10	1·25
273.	20 s. multicoloured ..	2·25	2·40
274.	40 s. multicoloured ..	4·50	4·75
	(e) Nos. 229/32.		
275.	1 s. Type **28** ..	15	20
276.	1 s. 50 Passengers boarding "Islander" light aircraft	20	25
277.	2 s. 70 Loading coffee ..	40	45
278.	10 s. Wright "Flyer" and "Concorde" ..	1·25	1·40
	(f) Nos. 234/7.		
279.	1 s. Type **29**	15	20
280.	1 s. 50 Regalia ..	20	25
281.	2 s. 70 Coronation Ceremony	40	45
282.	10 s. Royal family on balcony of Buckingham Palace	1·75	1·90
	(g) Nos. 239/42.		
284.	1 s. Type **30**	15	20
285.	1 s. 50 Lubaga Cathedral	20	25
286.	2 s. 70 Ugandan pilgrimage to Rome, Holy Year, 1975	40	45
287.	10 s. Friar Lourdel-Mapeera (early missionary) ..	1·25	1·40
	(h) Nos. 244/8.		
289.	1 s. Type **31** ..	15	20
290.	1 s. 50 Handicapped children at play ..	20	25
291.	2 s. 70 Ugandan I.Y.C. emblem	40	45
292.	10 s. Children in class ..	1·25	1·40

35. Radio Wave Symbol.

1979. 50th Anniv. of International Consultative Radio Committee and International Telecommunications Union.

294. **35.**	1 s. multicoloured ..	15	10
295.	1 s. 50 multicoloured ..	20	10
296.	2 s. 70 multicoloured ..	35	35
297.	10 s. multicoloured ..	80	90

36. 20 s. Definitive Stamp of 1965 and Sir Rowland Hill.

1979. Death Centenary of Sir Rowland Hill. Multicoloured.

298.	1 s. Type **36**	15	10
299.	1 s. 50 1967 Commonwealth Parliamentary Association Conference 50 c. commemorative ..	25	10
300.	2 s. 70 1962 Independence 20 s. commemorative..	45	40
301.	10 s. Uganda Protectorate 1898 1 a.	1·00	1·50

37. Impala.

38. Lions with Cub.

1979. Wildlife. Multicoloured.

303.	10 c. Type **37**	10	10
304.	20 c. Large-spotted Genet	10	10
305.	30 c. Thomson's Gazelle ..	15	10
306.	50 c. Lesser Bushbaby ..	15	10
307.	80 c. Hunting Dog ..	20	10
308.	1 s. Type **38**	15	10
309.	1 s. 50 Gorilla	45	10
310.	2 s. Common Zebra ..	25	20
311.	2 s. 70 Leopard with cub ..	60	15
312.	3 s. 50 Black Rhinoceros ..	70	20
313.	5 s. Waterbuck	40	40
314.	10 s. African Buffalo ..	70	60
315.	20 s. Hippopotamus ..	80	1·25
316.	40 s. African Elephant ..	1·50	2·50

SIZES: As Type **37**, 10 c. to 80 c. As Type **38**, 1 s. to 40 s.

See also Nos. 433/9.

1980. "London 1980" International Stamp Exhibition. Nos. 298/301 optd. **LONDON 1980**

317. **36.**	1 s. multicoloured ..	15	10
318. –	1 s. 50 multicoloured ..	20	10
319. –	2 s. 70 multicoloured ..	35	25
320. –	10 s. multicoloured ..	80	80

40. Rotary Emblem.

1980. 75th Anniv. of Rotary International. Multicoloured.

322.	1 s. Type **40**	10	10
323.	20 s. Paul P. Harris (founder) with wheel-barrow containing "Rotary projects" (horiz.)	1·50	1·50

41. Football.

1980. Olympic Games, Moscow. Multicoloured.

325.	1 s. Type **41**	10	10
326.	2 s. Relay	10	10
327.	10 s. Hurdles	40	60
328.	20 s. Boxing	80	1·25

1981. Olympic Medal Winners. Nos. 325/8 optd.

330. **41.**	1 s. multicoloured ..	10	10
331. –	2 s. multicoloured ..	10	15
332. –	10 s. multicoloured ..	40	50
333. –	20 s. multicoloured ..	80	1·00

OVERPRINTS: 1 s. **FOOTBALL GOLD MEDALISTS C.S.S.R.** 2 s. **RELAY GOLD MEDALIST U.S.S.R.** 10 s. **HURDLES 110m GOLD MEDALIST THOMAS MUNKLET, D.D.R.** 20 s. **BOXING WELTERWEIGHT SILVER MEDALIST JOHN MUGABI, UGANDA.**

44. Heinrich von Stephan and U.P.U. Emblem.

1981. 150th Birth Anniv. of Heinrich von Stephan (founder of U.P.U.) Multicoloured.

336.	1 s. Type **44**	10	10
337.	2 s. U.P.U. Headquarters	15	15
338.	2 s. 70 Air mail, 1935 ..	20	20
339.	10 s. Mail transport by steam, 1927	80	80

45. Tower of London.

1981. Royal Wedding. Multicoloured.

	(a) Previously unissued stamps surch.		
341.	10 s. on 1 s. Prince Charles and Lady Diana Spencer	25	20
342.	50 s. on 5 s. Type **45**	40	30
343.	200 s. on 20 s. Prince Charles at Balmoral ..	1·50	1·25
	(b) Stamps reissued with new face values.		
345.	10 s. As No. 341 ..	15	15
346.	50 s. As Type **45** ..	20	20
347.	200 s. As No. 343 ..	50	50

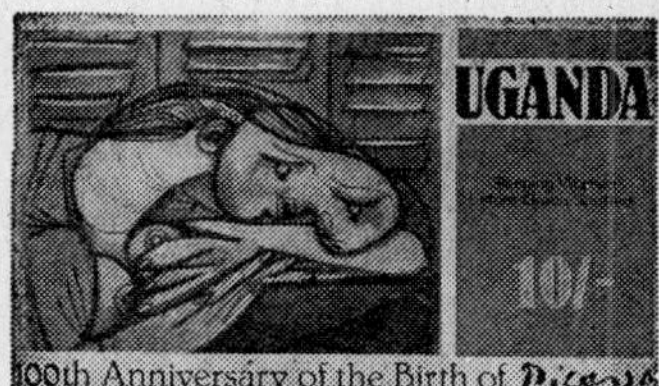

48. "Sleeping Woman before Green Shutters".

1981. Birth Centenary of Picasso. Mult.

349.	10 s. Type **48**	10	10
350.	20 s. "Bullfight" ..	20	20
351.	30 s. "Detail of a Nude asleep in a Landscape"	25	25
352.	200 s. "Interior with a Girl Drawing" ..	2·25	2·25

49. Deaf People using Sign Language.

1981. International Year for Disabled Persons. Multicoloured.

354.	1 s. Type **49** ..	10	10
355.	10 s. Disabled teacher in classroom ..	15	10
356.	50 s. Teacher and disabled children	70	50
357.	200 s. Blind person with guide dog	2·00	2·00

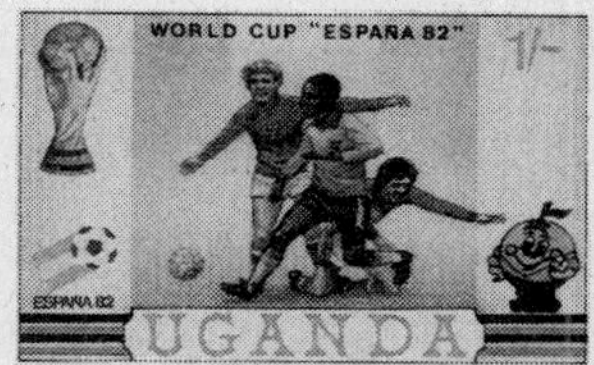

50. Footballers.

1981. World Cup Football Championships, Spain (1982).

359. **50.**	1 s. multicoloured ..	10	10
360. –	10 s. multicoloured ..	15	10
361. –	50 s. multicoloured ..	70	50
362. –	200 s. multicoloured ..	2·00	2·00

DESIGNS: Nos. 360/62, various football scenes.

51. Mpoma Satellite Earth Station.

1982. "Peaceful Use of Outer Space". Multicoloured.

364. 5 s. Type **51** 20 15
365. 10 s. "Pioneer II" (satellite) 30 25
366. 50 s. Space Shuttle .. 1·40 1·50
367. 100 s. "Voyager 2" (satellite) .. .. 2·50 2·75

52. Dr. Robert Koch.

1982. Centenary of Robert Koch's Discovery of Tubercle Bacillus. Multicoloured.

369. 1 s. Type **52** 30 10
370. 10 s. Microscope .. .. 1·00 40
371. 50 s. Ugandans receiving vaccinations .. .. 2·50 2·25
372. 100 s. Tubercle virus .. 3·75 3·25

1982. Princess of Wales. 21st Birthday. Nos. 345/7 optd. **21st BIRTHDAY HRH** Princess of Wales.

374. 10 s. Prince Charles and Lady Diana Spencer .. 20 15
375. 50 s. Type **45** 75 50
376. 200 s. Prince Charles at Balmoral .. .. 2·50 2·00

54. Yellow-billed Hornbill.

1982. Birds. Multicoloured.

378. 1 s. Type **54** 15 10
379. 20 s. Superb Starling .. 60 35
380. 50 s. Bateleur .. 1·25 1·50
381. 100 s. Saddle-bill stork .. 2·00 2·50

55. Scout Band.

1982. 75th Anniv. of Boy Scout Movement. Multicoloured.

383. 5 s. Type **55** 40 10
384. 20 s. Scout receiving Bata Shoe trophy 90 45
385. 50 s. Scouts with wheelchair patient .. .. 2·00 1·50
386. 100 s. First aid instruction 2·75 2·75

56. Swearing-in of Roosevelt.

1982. 250th Birth Anniv. of George Washington and Birth Centenary of Franklin D. Roosevelt. Multicoloured.

388. 50 s. Type **56** 30 30
389. 200 s. Swearing-in of Washington .. .. 1·25 1·25

57. Italy v West Germany.

1982. World Cup Football Championship Winners. Multicoloured.

392. 10 s. Type **57** 50 25
393. 200 s. Victorious Italian team .. .. .. 2·50 2·75

58. Dancers.

1983. Commonwealth Day. Cultural Art. Multicoloured.

395. 5 s. Type **58** 10 10
396. 20 s. Traditional currency 20 20
397. 50 s. Homestead 45 45
398. 100 s. Drums 85 85

59. "St. George and the Dragon" (Raphael).

1983. 500th Birth Anniv. of Raphael (painter). Multicoloured.

399. 5 s. Type **59** 10 10
400. 20 s. "St. George and the Dragon" (different) .. 30 30
401. 50 s. "Crossing the Red Sea" (detail) 70 70
402. 200 s. "The Expulsion of Heliodorus" (detail) .. 2·25 2·50

60. Map showing Namibia and U.N. Flag.

1983. Commemorations. Multicoloured.

404. 5 s. Type **60** 10 10
405. 200 s. 7th Non-aligned Summit Conference logo 1·25 1·75

61. Elephants in Grassland.

1983. Endangered Species (1st series). Mult.

406 5 s. Elephants in "Elephants' Graveyard" .. 60 20
407 10 s. Type **61** 90 35
408 30 s. Elephants at waterhole .. .. .. 2·00 1·50
409 70 s. Elephants having dust bath .. .. 3·25 2·75

See also Nos. 642 and 970/3.

1983. Centenary of Boy's Brigade. Nos. 383/6 optd **BOY'S BRIGADE CENTENARY 1883–1983**, or surch also.

411 5 s. Type **55** 10 10
412 20 s. Scout receiving Bata Shoe trophy 15 15
413 50 s. Scouts with wheelchair patient 25 30
414 400 s. on 100 s. First aid instruction .. .. 2·40 2·75

63. Mpoma Satellite Earth Station.

1983. World Communications Year. Mult.

416. 20 s. Type **63** 20 15
417. 50 s. Railroad computer and operator 55 55
418. 70 s. Cameraman filming lions 65 70
419. 100 s. Aircraft cockpit .. 85 1·00

1983. Nos. 303, 305/9 and 313 surch.

421 100 s. on 10 c. Type **37** .. 45 45
422 135 s. on 1 s. Type **38** .. 60 60
423 175 s. on 30 c. Thomson's gazelle 75 75
424 200 s. on 50 c. Lesser bush-baby 85 85
425 400 s. on 80 c. Hunting dog 1·60 1·60
426 700 s. on 5 s. Waterbuck .. 2·75 3·00
427 1000 s. on 1 s. 50 Gorilla .. 4·00 4·00

65. The Nativity.

1983. Christmas. Multicoloured.

428. 10 s. Type **65** 10 10
429. 50 s. Shepherds and Angels 25 30
430. 175 s. Flight into Egypt .. 80 1·00
431. 400 s. Angels blowing trumpets .. .. .. 1·90 2·25

1983. Nos. 308/12 and 315/16 but with face values in revalued currency.

433. 100 s. Type **38** 65 35
434. 135 s. Gorilla 75 50
435. 175 s. Common Zebra .. 95 70
436. 200 s. Leopard with cub .. 1·25 80
437. 400 s. Black Rhinoceros .. 2·00 2·00
438. 700 s. African Elephant .. 3·50 3·75
439. 1000 s. Hippopotamus .. 4·25 4·75

66. Ploughing with Oxen.

1984. World Food Day. Multicoloured.

440. 10 s. Type **66** 10 10
441. 300 s. Harvesting bananas 3·00 3·00

67. Ruth Kyalisiima, Sportsman of the Year 1983.

1984. Olympic Games, Los Angeles. Mult.

442. 5 s. Type **67** 10 10
443. 115 s. Javelin-throwing .. 40 45
444. 155 s. Wrestling 50 55
445. 175 s. Rowing 60 65

68. Entebbe Airport.

1984. 40th Anniv. of International Civil Aviation Organization. Multicoloured.

447. 5 s. Type **68** 15 10
448. 115 s. Loading cargo plane 1·50 1·50
449. 155 s. Uganda police helicopter .. .. .. 2·25 2·25
450. 175 s. East African Civil Flying School, Soroti .. 2·50 2·50

69. "Charaxes druceanus".

1984. Butterflies. Multicoloured.

452 5 s. Type **69** 25 10
453 115 s. "Papilio lormieri" .. 1·60 1·25
454 155 s. "Druryia antimachus" .. .. 2·00 1·50
455 175 s. "Salamis temora" .. 2·75 1·75

70. "Nothobranchius taeniopygus".

1985. Lake Fishes. Multicoloured.

457. 5 s. Type **70** 10 10
458. 10 s. "Bagrus dogmac" .. 15 10
459. 50 s. "Polypterus senegalus" 45 15
460. 100 s. "Clarias" 45 20
461. 135 s. "Mormyrus kannume" 50 35
462. 175 s. "Synodontis victoriae" 50 50
463. 205 s. "Haplochromis brownae" 60 60
464. 400 s. "Lates niloticus" .. 80 80
465. 700 s. "Protopterus aethiopicus" .. .. 1·00 1·00
466. 1000 s. "Barbus radcliffii" 1·25 1·25
467. 2500 s. "Malapterus electricus" .. .. 1·25 1·25

71. The Last Supper.

1985. Easter. Multicoloured.

468. 5 s. Type **71** 10 10
469. 115 s. Christ showing the nail marks to Thomas .. 70 40
470. 155 s. The raising of the Cross 80 50
471. 175 s. Pentecost 95 60

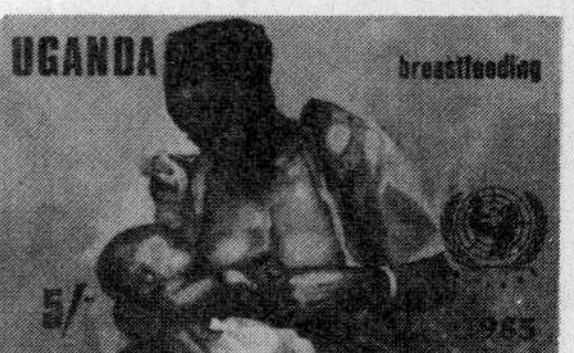

72. Breast Feeding.

1985. U.N.I.C.E.F. Child Survival Campaign. Multicoloured.

473. 5 s. Type **72** 10 10
474. 115 s. Growth monitoring 1·00 1·00
475. 155 s. Immunisation .. 1·40 1·40
476. 175 s. Oral re-hydration therapy .. .. 1·60 1·60

73. Queen Elizabeth the Queen Mother.

1985. Life and Times of Queen Elizabeth the Queen Mother and Decade for Women.
478 **73** 1000 s. multicoloured .. 2·00 2·10

74. Sedge Warbler.

1985. Birth Bicentenary of John J. Audubon (ornithologist) (1st issue). Multicoloured.
480. 115 s. Type **74** .. .. 1·00 1·00
481. 155 s. Cattle Egret .. .. 1·25 1·25
482. 175 s. Crested Lark .. 1·50 1·50
483. 500 s. Tufted Duck .. 2·00 2·00
See also Nos. 494/7.

1985. Olympic Gold Medal Winners, Los Angeles, Nos. 442/5 optd. or surch. also.
485. 5 s. Type **67** (optd. **GOLD MEDALIST BENITA BROWN-FITZGERALD USA**) 10 10
486. 115 s. Javelin-throwing (optd. **GOLD MEDALIST ARTO HAERKOENEN FINLAND**) 25 30
487. 155 s. Wrestling (optd. **GOLD MEDALIST ATSUJI MIYAHARA JAPAN**) 30 35
488. 1000 s. on 175 s. Rowing (surch. **GOLD MEDALIST WEST GERMANY**) .. .. 1·90 2·00

76. Women carrying National Women's Day Banner.

1985. Decade for Women. Multicoloured.
490. 5 s. Type **76** 10 10
491. 115 s. Girl Guides (horiz.) 1·25 1·25
492. 155 s. Mother Teresa (Nobel Peace Prize winner, 1979) .. .. 2·00 2·00
No. 491 also commemorates the 75th anniversary of Girl Guide movement.

1985. Birth Bicentenary of John J. Audubon (ornithologist) (2nd issue). As T **198** of Antigua. Multicoloured.
494 5 s. Rock ptarmigan .. 45 10
495 155 s. Sage grouse .. 1·50 1·25
496 175 s. Lesser yellowlegs .. 1·75 1·75
497 500s. Brown-headed cowbird .. .. 2·75 2·75

77. Man beneath Tree laden with Produce (F.A.O.).

1986. 40th Anniv. of U.N.O.
499. **77.** 10 s. multicoloured .. 10 10
500. – 180 s. multicoloured .. 60 30
501. – 200 s. blue, brn. & grn. 65 35
502. – 250 s. blue, blk. & red 70 40
503. – 2000 s. multicoloured .. 3·00 3·50
DESIGNS—HORIZ. 180 s. Soldier of U.N. Peace-Keeping Force. 250 s. Hands releasing peace dove. VERT. 200 s. U.N. emblem. 2000 s. Flags of U.N. and Uganda.

78. Goalkeeper catching Ball.

1986. World Cup Football Championship, Mexico. Multicoloured.
505. 10 s. Type **78** 10 10
506. 180 s. Player with ball .. 75 45
507. 250 s. Two players competing for ball .. 85 55
508. 2500 s. Player running with ball .. .. .. 4·00 4·50

1988. Liberation by National Resistance Army. Nos. 462 and 464/7 optd **NRA LIBERATION 1986**.
510 175 s. "Synodontis victoriae" 50 50
511 400 s. "Lates niloticus" .. 80 80
512 700 s. "Protopteris aethiopicus" .. 1·40 1·40
513 1000 s. "Barbus radcliffii" 1·75 2·00
514 2500 s. "Malapterus electricus" .. .. 3·25 3·50

1986. Appearance of Halley's Comet (1st issue). As T **123** of Anguilla. Multicoloured.
515. 50 s. Tycho Brahe and Arecibo Radio Telescope, Puerto Rico .. 20 10
516. 100 s. Recovery of astronaut John Glenn from sea, 1962 .. .. 35 15
517. 140 s. "The Star in the East" (painting by Giotto) 50 30
518. 2500 s. Death of Davy Crockett at the Alamo, 1835 .. .. .. 3·50 4·00
See also Nos. 544/7.

80. Niagara Falls.

1986. "Ameripex '86" International Stamp Exhibition, Chicago. American Landmarks. Multicoloured.
520. 50 s. Type **80** 15 10
521. 100 s. Jefferson Memorial, Washington D.C. .. 25 15
522. 250 s. Liberty Bell, Philadelphia 50 35
523. 1000 s. The Alamo, San Antonio, Texas .. .. 1·75 1·60
524. 2500 s. George Washington Bridge, New York-New Jersey .. .. .. 3·25 3·25

1986. 60th Birthday of Queen Elizabeth II. As T **125** of Anguilla.
526 100 s. black and yellow .. 25 15
527 140 s. multicoloured .. 30 20
528 2500 s. multicoloured .. 3·00 3·00
DESIGNS: 100 s. Princess Elizabeth at London Zoo. 140 s. Queen Elizabeth at race meeting, 1970. 2500 s. With Prince Philip at Sandringham, 1982.

81. "Gloria" (Colombia).

1986. Centenary of Statue of Liberty. Cadet sailing ships. Multicoloured.
530. 50 s. Type **81** 35 10
531. 100 s. "Mircea" (Rumania) 65 30
532. 140 s. "Sagres II" (Portugal) (horz.) .. 1·00 80
533. 2500 s "Gazela Primiero" (U.S.A.) (horiz.) .. 5·50 6·50

1986. Royal Wedding. As T **213** of Antigua. Multicoloured.
535. 50 s. Prince Andrew and Miss Sarah Ferguson (horiz.) 10 10
536. 140 s. Prince Andrew with Princess Anne at shooting match (horiz.) 20 20
537. 2500 s. Prince Andrew and Miss Sarah Ferguson at Ascot (horiz.) .. .. 2·75 3·00

1986. World Cup Football Championship Winners, Mexico. Nos. 505/8 optd. **WINNERS Argentina 3 W. Germany 2** or surch. also.
539. 50 s. on 10 s. Type **78** .. 10 10
540. 180 s. Player with ball .. 25 25
541. 250 s. Two players competing for ball .. 35 35
542. 2500 s. Player running with ball .. .. .. 2·75 3·25

1986. Appearance of Halley's Comet (2nd issue). Nos. 515/18 optd as T **218** of Antigua.
544. 50 s. Tycho Brahe and Arecibo Radio Telescope, Puerto Rico .. 20 15
545. 100 s. Recovery of astronaut John Glenn from sea, 1962 .. .. 35 20
546. 140 s. "The Star in the East" (painting by Giotto) 55 40
547. 2500 s. Death of Davy Crockett at the Alamo, 1835 .. .. .. 4·25 4·25

83. St. Kizito.

1986. Christian Martyrs of Uganda. Mult.
549. 50 s. Type **83** 10 10
550. 150 s. St. Kizito instructing converts 15 20
551. 200 s. Martyrdom of Bishop James Hannington, 1885 20 25
552. 1000 s. Burning of Bugandan Christians, 1886 .. .. .. 1·00 1·50

84. "Madonna of the Cherries" (Titian).

1986. Christmas. Religious Paintings. Mult.
554. 50 s. Type **84** 20 15
555. 150 s. "Madonna and Child" (Durer) (vert.) 50 30
556. 200 s. "Assumption of the Virgin" (Titian) (vert.) .. 60 35
557. 2500 s. "Praying Hands" (Durer) (vert.) .. .. 4·00 4·50

85. Red-billed Firefinch and Glory Lily.

1987. Flora and Fauna. Multicoloured.
559. 2 s. Type **85** 10 10
560. 5 s. African pygmy kingfisher and nandi flame .. 15 15
561. 10 s. Scarlet-chested sunbird and crown of thorns 20 25
562. 25 s. White rhinoceros and yellow-billed oxpecker .. 50 55
563. 35 s. Lion and elephant grass 70 75
564. 45 s. Cheetahs and doum palm 90 95
565. 50 s. Cordon bleu and desert rose .. .. 1·00 1·10
566. 100 s. Giant eland and acacia .. .. .. 2·00 2·10

86. Tremml's "Eagle" (longest man-powered flight), 1987.

1987. Milestones of Transportation. Mult.
568. 2 s. Type **86** 10 10
569. 3 s. Junkers "W-33L" "Bremen" (first east-west transatlantic flight), 1928 .. .. 10 10
570. 5 s. Lockheed "Winnie Mae" (Post's first solo round-the-world flight), 1933 .. .. .. 20 20
571. 10 s. "Voyager" (first nonstop round-the-world flight), 1986 .. .. 40 40
572. 15 s. Chanute biplane glider, 1896 .. .. 60 60
573. 25 s. Airship "Norge" and Polar Bear (first transpolar flight), 1926 .. 90 90
574. 35 s. Curtis biplane and U.S.S. "Pennsylvania" (first take-off and landing from ship), 1911 .. 1·25 1·25
575. 45 s. Shepard and "Freedom 7" spacecraft (first American in space), 1961 .. .. .. 1·40 1·40
576. 100 s. "Concorde" (first supersonic passenger flight), 1976 .. .. 3·50 3·50

87. Olympic Torch-bearer.

1987. Olympic Games, Seoul (1988) (1st issue). Multicoloured.
577. 5 s. Type **87** 10 10
578. 10 s. Swimming 20 25
579. 50 s. Cycling .. .. 1·00 1·10
580. 100 s. Gymnastics .. .. 2·00 2·10
See also Nos. 628/31.

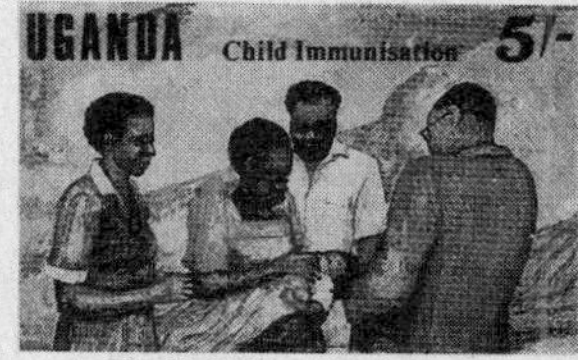

88. Child Immunization.

1987. 25th Anniv. of Independence. Mult.
582. 5 s. Type **88** 10 10
583. 10 s. Mulago Hospital, Kampala 20 25
584. 25 s. Independence Monument, Kampala City Park 50 55
585. 50 s. High Court, Kampala 1·00 1·10

89. Golden-backed Weaver.

1987. Birds of Uganda. Multicoloured.

587. 5 s. Type **89** 25 25
588. 10 s. Hoopoe 40 40
589. 15 s. Red-throated bee eater 50 50
590. 25 s. Lilac-breasted roller 75 75
591. 35 s. Pygmy goose .. 1·10 1·10
592. 45 s. Scarlet-chested sunbird .. .. .. 1·40 1·40
593. 50 s. Crowned crane .. 1·50 1·50
594. 100 s. Long-tailed fiscal shrike .. .. .. 2·50 2·50

90. Hippocrates (physician) and Surgeons performing Operation.

1987. Great Scientific Discoveries. Mult.

596. 5 s. Type **90** 30 30
597. 25 s. Einstein and deep space (Theory of Relativity) .. .. 1·25 1·25
598. 35 s. Isaac Newton and diagram from "Opticks" (Theory of Colour and Light) .. .. .. 1·50 1·50
599. 45 s. Karl Benz, and early Benz and modern Mercedes car .. .. 2·00 2·00

91. Scout with Stamp Album and Uganda Stamps.

1987. World Scout Jamboree, Australia. Multicoloured.

601. 5 s. Type **91** 10 10
602. 25 s. Scouts planting tree 50 55
603. 35 s. Canoeing, Lake Victoria 70 75
604. 45 s. Hiking 90 95

92. "The Annunciation".

1987. Christmas. Scenes from French diptych, c. 1250. Multicoloured.

606. 5 s. Type **92** 10 10
607. 10 s. "Nativity" 20 25
608. 50 s. "Flight into Egypt" 1·00 1·10
609. 100 s. "Adoration of the Magi" .. .. .. 2·00 2·10

93. Class "12" Light Shunter Locomotive.

1988. Locomotives of East Africa Railways. Multicoloured.

611 5 s. Type **93** 30 30
612 10 s. Class "92" diesel-electric 30 30
613 15 s. Locomotive No. 2506 35 35
614 25 s. Tank locomotive No. 126 .. .. .. 55 55
615 35 s. Class "31" locomotive 70 70
616 45 s. Class "31" locomotive (different) 85 85
617 50 s. Class "59" Double Garratt locomotive .. 95 95
618 100 s. Class "87" diesel-electric shunter .. 1·75 1·75

94. Columbite-tantalite.

1988. Minerals. Multicolured.

620. 1 s. Type **94** 10 10
621. 2 s. Galena 15 15
622. 5 s. Malachite 20 20
623. 10 s. Cassiterite 35 35
624. 35 s. Ferberite .. .. 1·00 1·00
625. 50 s. Emerald .. .. 1·40 1·40
626. 100 s. Monazite .. .. 2·25 2·25
627. 150 s. Microcline .. .. 3·25 3·25

95 Hurdling

1988. Olympic Games, Seoul (2nd issue). Mult.

628 5 s. Hurdling 10 10
629 25 s. High jumping .. 20 25
630 35 s. Javelin throwing .. 25 30
631 45 s. Long jumping .. 30 35

96 "Spathodea campanulata"

1988. Flowers. Multicoloured.

633 5 s. Type **96** 10 10
634 10 s. "Gloriosa simplex" .. 10 10
635 20 s. "Thevetica peruviana" (vert) 15 15
636 25 s. "Hibiscus schizopetalus" 20 25
637 35 s. "Aframomum sceptrum" 25 30
638 45 s. "Adenium obesum" 30 35
639 50 s. "Kigelia africana" (vert) 35 40
640 100 s. "Clappertonia ficifolia" 70 75

97 Elephants in Grassland (Type **61** redrawn)

1988. Endangered Species (2nd series).

642 **97** 10 s. multicoloured ..

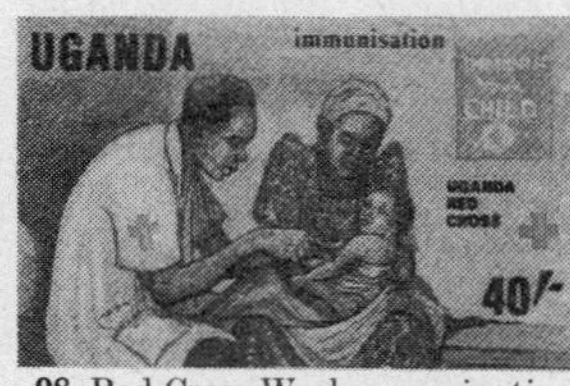

98 Red Cross Worker vaccinating Baby

1988. 125th Anniv of International Red Cross.

643 **98** 10 s. red, yellow & black 20 15
644 – 40 s. multicoloured .. 50 50
645 – 70 s. multicoloured .. 90 90
646 – 90 s. multicoloured .. 1·25 1·25

DESIGNS: 10 s. "AIDS" with test tube as "I"; 70 s. Distributing food to refugees; 90 s. Red Cross volunteers with accident victim.

1988. 500th Birth Anniv of Titian (artist). As T **238** of Antigua. Multicoloured.

648 10 s. "Portrait of a Lady" 10 10
649 20 s. "Portrait of a Man" 15 15
650 40 s. "Isabella d'Este" .. 25 30
651 50 s. "Vincenzo Mosti" .. 35 40
652 70 s. "Pope Paul III Farnese" 45 50
653 90 s. "Violante" 60 65
654 100 s. "Titian's Daughter Lavinia" 70 75
655 250 s. "Dr. Parma" .. 1·75 1·90

99 Giraffes, Kidepo Valley National Park

1988. National Parks of Uganda. Mult.

657 10 s. Type **99** 30 15
658 25 s. Zebras, Lake Mburo National Park 55 30
659 100 s. African buffalo, Murchison Falls National Park .. .. 1·50 1·50
660 250 s. Pelicans, Queen Elizabeth National Park 3·50 3·75

100 Doctor examining Child's Eyes

1988. 40th Anniv of W.H.O. Multicoloured.

662 10 s. Type **100** 10 10
663 25 s. Mental health therapist with patient .. 20 25
664 45 s. Surgeon performing operation 30 35
665 100 s. Dentist treating girl 70 75
666 200 s. Doctor examining child .. .. .. 1·40 1·50

1988. Christmas. "Santa's Helpers". As T **228** of Dominica showing Walt Disney cartoon characters. Multicoloured.

668 50 c. Father Christmas with list 50 50
669 50 c. Goofy carrying presents 50 50
670 50 c. Mickey Mouse on toy train 50 50
671 50 c. Reindeer at window 50 50
672 50 c. Donald Duck's nephew with building blocks 50 50
673 50 c. Donald Duck holding sack 50 50
674 50 c. Chip n'Dale on conveyor belt .. 50 50
675 50 c. Donald Duck's nephew operating conveyor belt .. 50 50

Nos. 668/75 were printed together, se-tenant, as a composite design.

1989. Olympic Gold Medal Winners, Seoul. Nos. 628/31 optd.

677 5 s. Type 95 (optd **110 M HURDLES R KINGDOM USA**) .. 10 10
678 25 s. High jumping (optd **HIGH JUMP G. AVDEENKO USSR**) 20 25
679 35 s. Javelin throwing (optd **JAVELIN T. KORJUS FINLAND**) 25 30
680 300 s. on 45 s. Long jumping (optd **LONG JUMP C. LEWIS USA**) .. .. 2·25 2·40

MORE DETAILED LISTS
are given in the Stanley Gibbons Catalogues referred to in the country headings.
For lists of current volumes see Introduction.

102 Goalkeeper with Ball

1989. World Cup Football Championship, Italy (1990) (1st issue). Multicoloured.

682 10 s. Type **102** 10 10
683 25 s. Player kicking ball (horiz) 10 10
684 75 s. Heading ball towards net (horiz) 10 15
685 200 s. Tackling 25 30

See also Nos. 849/52.

1989. Japanese Art. Paintings by Hokusai. As T **250** of Antigua. Multicoloured.

687 10 s. "Fuji and the Great Wave off Kanagawa" .. 10 10
688 15 s. "Fuji from Lake Suwa" 10 10
689 20 s. "Fuji from Kajikazawa" 10 10
690 60 s. "Fuji from Shichirigahama" .. 10 10
691 90 s. "Fuji from Ejiri in Sunshu" 10 15
692 120 s. "Fuji above Lightning" 15 20
693 200 s. "Fuji from Lower Meguro in Edo" .. 25 30
694 250 s. "Fuji from Edo" .. 30 35

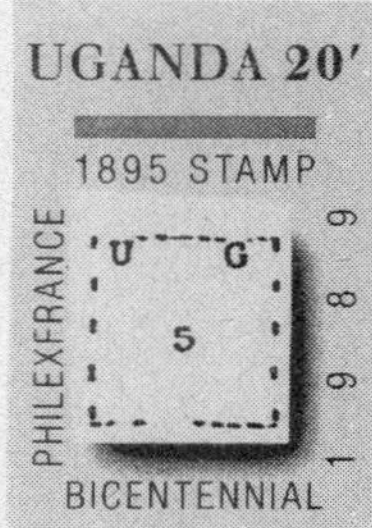

103 1895 5 Cowries Stamp

1989. "Philexfrance 89" International Stamp Exhibition, Paris.

696 **103** 20 s. black, red & brn 10 10
697 – 70 s. black, green & bl 10 10
698 – 100 s. black, vio & pink 10 15
699 – 250 s. blk, yell & lt yell 30 35

DESIGNS: 70 s. 1895 10 on 50 cowries stamp; 100 s. 1896 25 cowries stamp; 250 s. 1896 1 rupee stamp.

104 Scout advising on Immunization

1989. 2nd All African Scout Jamboree, Uganda, and 75th Anniv of Ugandan Scout Movement. Multicoloured.

701 10 s. Type **104** 10 10
702 70 s. Poultry keeping .. 10 10
703 90 s. Scout on crutches leading family to immunization centre .. 10 15
704 100 s. Scouts making bricks 10 15

105 "Suillus granulatus"

1989. Fungi. Multicoloured.

706	10 s. Type **105**	10	10
707	15 s. "Omphalotus olearius"	10	10
708	45 s. "Oudemansiella radicata"	10	10
709	50 s. "Clitocybe nebularis"	10	10
710	60 s. "Macrolepiota rhacodes"	10	10
711	75 s. "Lepista nuda"	10	15
712	150 s. "Suillus luteus"	20	25
713	200 s. "Agaricus campestris"	25	30

106 Saddle-bill Stork

1989. Wildlife at Waterhole. Multicoloured.

715	30 s. Type **106**	10	10
716	30 s. Eastern white pelican	10	10
717	30 s. Marabou stork	10	10
718	30 s. Egyptian vulture	10	10
719	30 s. Bateleur	10	10
720	30 s. African elephant	10	10
721	30 s. Giraffe	10	10
722	30 s. Goliath heron	10	10
723	30 s. Black rhinoceros	10	10
724	30 s. Common zebra and oribi	10	10
725	30 s. African fish eagle	10	10
726	30 s. Hippopotamus	10	10
727	30 s. Black-backed jackal and Eastern white pelican	10	10
728	30 s. African buffalo	10	10
729	30 s. Olive baboon	10	10
730	30 s. Bohar reedbuck	10	10
731	30 s. Lesser flamingo and serval	10	10
732	30 s. Shoebill stork	10	10
733	30 s. Crowned crane	10	10
734	30 s. Impala	10	10

Nos. 715/34 were printed together, se-tenant, forming a composite design showing wildlife at a waterhole.

107 Rocket on Launch Pad

1989. 20th Anniv of First Manned Landing on Moon. Multicoloured.

736	10 s. Type **107**	10	10
737	20 s. Lunar module "Eagle" on Moon	10	10
738	30 s. "Apollo 11" command module	10	10
739	50 s. "Eagle" landing on Moon	10	10
740	70 s. Astronaut Aldrin on Moon	10	10
741	250 s. Neil Armstrong alighting from "Eagle" (vert)	30	35
742	300 s. "Eagle" over Moon	35	40
743	350 s. Astronaut Aldrin on Moon (vert)	40	45

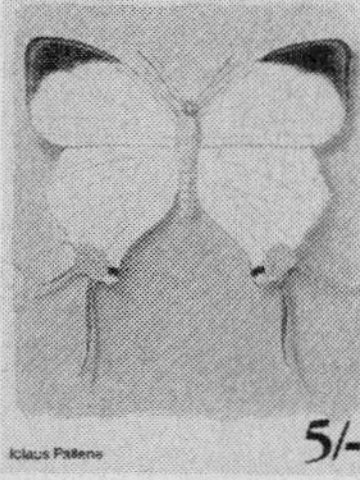

108 "Iolaus pallene"

1989. Butterflies. Multicoloured.

745	5 s. Type **108**	10	10
746	10 s. "Hewitsonia boisduvali"	10	10
747	20 s. "Euxanthe wakefieldi"	10	10
748	30 s. "Papilio echerioides"	10	10
749	40 s. "Acraea semivitrea"	10	10
750	50 s. "Colotis antevippe"	10	10
751	70 s. "Acraea perenna"	10	10
752	90 s. "Charaxes cynthia"	10	15
753	100 s. "Euphaedra neophron"	10	15
754	150 s. "Cymothoe beckeri"	20	25
755	200 s. "Vanessula milca"	35	30
756	400 s. "Mimacraea marshalli"	50	55
757	500 s. "Axiocerses amanga"	60	65
758	1000 s. "Precis hierta"	1·25	1·40
759	2000 s. As 1000 s.	2·40	2·75
759a	3000 s. "Euphaedra eusemoides"	3·75	4·00
759b	4000 s. "Acraea natalica"	4·75	5·00

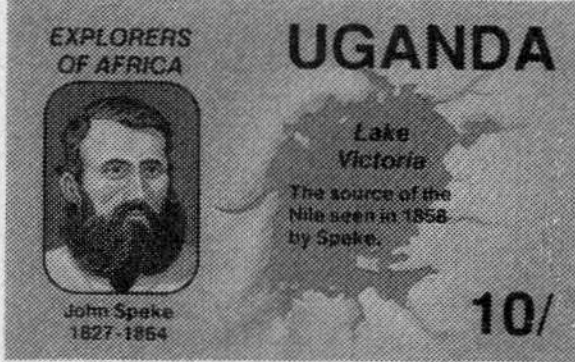

109 John Hanning Speke and Map of Lake Victoria

1989. Exploration of Africa. Multicoloured.

760	10 s. Type **109**	10	10
761	25 s. Sir Richard Burton and map of Lake Tanganyika	10	10
762	40 s. Richard Lander and Bakota bronze	10	10
763	90 s. Rene Caillie and mosque, Timbuktu	10	15
764	125 s. Sir Samuel Baker and Dorcas gazelle	15	20
765	150 s. Pharaoh Necho and ancient Phoenician merchant ship	20	25
766	250 s. Vasco da Gama and 15th-century caravel	30	35
767	300 s. Sir Henry Morton Stanley and "Lady Alice" (sectional boat)	35	40

110 Logo (25th anniv of African Development Bank)

1989. Anniversaries. Multicoloured.

769	10 s. Type **110**	10	10
770	20 s. Arrows and dish aerials (World Telecommunication Day)	10	10
771	75 s. Nehru and Gandhi (birth cent of Nehru)	10	15
772	90 s. Pan Am "Dixie Clipper" flying boat (50th anniv of first scheduled trans-Atlantic airmail flight)	10	15
773	100 s. George Stephenson and "Locomotion", 1825 (175th anniv of first practical steam locomotive)	10	15
774	150 s. "Concorde" cockpit (20th anniv of first test flight)	20	25
775	250 s. "Wapen von Hamburg" and "Leopoldus Primus" (galleons) (800th anniv of Port of Hamburg)	30	35
776	300 s. "Concorde" and cockpit interior (20th anniv of first test flight)	35	40

111 "Aerangis kotschyana"

1989. Orchids. Multicoloured.

778	10 s. Type **111**	10	10
779	15 s. "Angraecum infundibulare"	10	10
780	45 s. "Cyrtorchis chailluana"	10	10
781	50 s. "Aerangis rhodosticta"	10	10
782	100 s. "Eulophia speciosa"	10	15
783	200 s. "Calanthe sylvatica"	25	30
784	250 s. "Vanilla imperialis"	30	35
785	350 s. "Polystachya vulcanica"	40	45

1989. Christmas. Paintings by Fra Angelico. As T **259** of Antigua. Multicoloured.

787	10 s. "Madonna and Child"	10	10
788	20 s. "Adoration of the Magi"	10	10
789	40 s. "Virgin and Child enthroned with Saints"	10	10
790	75 s. "The Annunciation"	10	15
791	100 s. "Virgin and Child" (detail, "St. Peter Martyr" triptych)	10	15
792	150 s. "Virgin and Child enthroned with Saints" (different)	20	25
793	250 s. "Virgin and Child enthroned"	30	35
794	350 s. "Virgin and Child" (from Annalena altarpiece)	40	45

112 "Thevetia peruviana"

1990. "Expo '90" International Garden and Greenery Exhibition, Osaka (1st issue). Flowering Trees. Multicoloured.

796	10 s. Type **112**	10	10
797	20 s. "Acanthus eminens"	10	10
798	90 s. "Gnidia glauca"	10	15
799	150 s. "Oncoba spinosa"	20	25
800	175 s. "Hibiscus rosa-sinensis"	20	25
801	400 s. "Jacaranda mimosifolia"	45	50
802	500 s. "Erythrina abyssinica"	60	65
803	700 s. "Bauhinia purpurea"	90	95

See also Nos. 820/7.

1990. 50th Anniv of Second World War. As T **98** of Grenada Grenadines. Multicoloured.

805	5 s. Allied penetration of German West Wall, 1944	10	10
806	10 s. Flags of the Allies, VE Day, 1945	10	10
807	20 s. Capture of Okinawa, 1945	10	10
808	75 s. Appointment of Gen. De Gaulle to command all Free French forces, 1944	10	15
809	100 s. Invasion of Saipan, 1944	10	15
810	150 s. Airborne landing, Operation Market Garden, 1944	20	25
811	200 s. MacArthur's return to Philippines, 1944	25	30
812	300 s. Japanese attack on U.S. carrier, Coral Sea, 1942	35	40
813	350 s. First Battle of El Alamein, 1942	40	45
814	500 s. Naval Battle of Guadalcanal, 1942	60	65

1990. 90th Birthday of Queen Elizabeth the Queen Mother. As T **99** of Grenada Grenadines.

816	250 s. black, mauve & blue	30	35
817	250 s. black, mauve & blue	30	35
818	250 s. black, mauve & blue	30	35

DESIGNS: No. 816, Queen Elizabeth with corgi; 817, Queen Elizabeth wearing feathered hat; 818 Queen Elizabeth at wartime inspection.

1990. "EXPO 90" International Garden and Greenery Exhibition, Osaka (2nd issue). Nos. 778/85 optd **EXPO '90** and logo.

820	10 s. Type **111**	10	10
821	15 s. "Angraecum infundibulare"	10	10
822	45 s. "Cyrtorchis chailluana"	10	10
823	50 s. "Aerangis rhodosticta"	10	10
824	100 s. "Eulophia speciosa"	10	15
825	200 s. "Calanthe sylvatica"	25	30
826	250 s. "Vanilla imperialis"	30	35
827	350 s. "Polystachya vulcanica"	40	45

114 P.A.P.U. Emblem

1990. 10th Anniv of Pan-African Postal Union.

829 **114**	80 s. multicoloured	10	15

115 Unissued G. B. "V R" Penny Black

1990. 150th Anniv of the Penny Black.

831 **115**	25 s. multicoloured	10	10
832 –	50 s. red, black & green	10	10
833 –	100 s. multicoloured	10	15
834 –	150 s. multicoloured	20	25
835 –	200 s. multicoloured	25	30
836 –	300 s. multicoloured	35	40
837 –	500 s. multicoloured	60	65
838 –	600 s. multicoloured	70	75

DESIGNS: 50 s. Canada 1858–59 3d. Beaver; 100 s. Baden 1851 9 k. on green error; 150 s. Basel 1845 2½ r. Dove; 200 s. U.S.A. 1918 24 c. Inverted "Jenny" error; 300 s. Western Australia 1854 1d. Black Swan; 500 s. Uganda 1895 20 c. "narrow" typewritten stamp; 600 s. G. B. Twopenny blue.

116 African Jacana

1990. Wild Birds of Uganda. Multicoloured.

840	10 s. Type **116**	10	10
841	15 s. Ground hornbill	10	10
842	45 s. Kori bustard (vert)	10	10
843	50 s. Secretary bird	10	10
844	100 s. Egyptian geese	10	15
845	300 s. Goliath heron (vert)	35	40
846	500 s. Ostrich with chicks (vert)	60	65
847	650 s. Saddlebill stork (vert)	80	85

117 Roger Milla of Cameroon

1990. World Cup Football Championship, Italy (2nd issue). Multicoloured.

849 50 s. Type **117** 10 10
850 100 s. Ramzy of Egypt .. 10 15
851 250 s. David O'Leary of Ireland 30 35
852 600 s. Littbarsky of West Germany 70 75

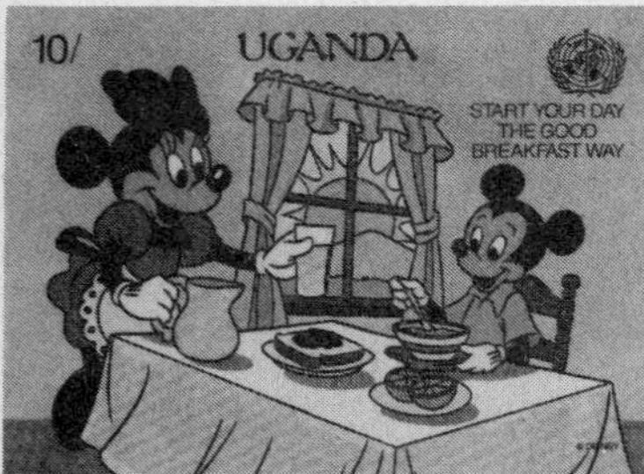

118 Mickey and Minnie Mouse at Breakfast

1990. Health and Safety Campaign. Designs showing Walt Disney cartoon characters. Multicoloured.

854 10 s. Type **118** 10 10
855 20 s. Donald Duck's nephews doing kerb drill 10 10
856 50 s. Donald and Mickey stopping Big Pete smoking 10 10
857 90 s. Mickey stopping Donald choking .. 10 15
858 100 s. Mickey and Goofy using seat belts .. 10 15
859 250 s. Mickey and Minnie dancing 30 35
860 500 s. Donald Duck's fitness class .. 60 65
861 600 s. Mickey's nephews showing lights at night 70 75

1990. Christmas. 350th Death Anniv of Rubens. As T **273** of Antigua, but inscr "CHRISTMAS 1990". Multicoloured.

863 10 s. "Baptism of Christ" (detail) (vert) 10 10
864 20 s. "St. Gregory the Great and other Saints" (detail) (vert) 10 10
865 100 s. "Saints Nereus, Domitilla and Achilleus" (detail) (vert) 10 15
866 150 s. "St. Gregory the Great and other Saints" (different detail) (vert) 20 25
867 300 s. "Saint Augustine" (detail) (vert) 35 40
868 400 s. "St. Gregory the Great and other Saints" (different detail) (vert) 50 55
869 500 s. "Baptism of Christ" (different detail) (vert) 60 65
870 600 s. "St. Gregory the Great and other Saints (different detail) (vert) 70 75

119 Census Emblem

1990. National Population and Housing Census.

872 **119** 20 s. multicoloured .. 10 10

120 Damselfly

1991. Fauna of Uganda's Wetlands. Mult.

874 70 s. Type **120** 10 10
875 70 s. Purple gallinule .. 10 10
876 70 s. Sitatunga 10 10
877 70 s. Purple heron .. 10 10
878 70 s. Bushpig 10 10
879 70 s. Vervet monkey .. 10 10
880 70 s. Long reed frog .. 10 10
881 70 s. Malachite kingfisher 10 10
882 70 s. Marsh mongoose .. 10 10
883 70 s. Painted reed frog .. 10 10
884 70 s. Jacana 10 10
885 70 s. Charaxes butterfly .. 10 10
886 70 s. Nile crocodile .. 10 10
887 70 s. Herald snake .. 10 10
888 70 s. Dragonfly 10 10
889 70 s. Lungfish 10 10

Nos. 874/89 were printed together, se-tenant, forming a composite design.

121 "Haplochromis limax"

1991. Fishes of Uganda. Multicoloured.

891 10 s. Type **121** 10 10
892 20 s. "Nothobranchius palmqvisti" 10 10
893 40 s. "Distichodus affinis" . 10 10
894 90 s. "Haplochromis sauvagei" 10 15
895 100 s. "Aphyosemion calliurum" 10 15
896 350 s. "Haplochromis johnstoni" 40 45
897 600 s. "Haplochromis dichrourus" 70 75
898 800 s. "Hemichromis bimaculatus" .. .. 95 1·00

1991. Olympic Games, Barcelona (1992). As T **268** of Antigua. Multicoloured.

900 20 s. Women's 100 metres hurdles 10 10
901 40 s. Long jump 10 10
902 125 s. Table tennis .. 15 20
903 250 s. Football 30 35
904 500 s. Men's 800 metres .. 60 65

122 Class "10" Steam Locomotive, Zimbabwe

1991. African Railway Locomotives. Mult.

906 10 s. Type **122** 10 10
907 20 s. Class "12" steam locomotive, Zimbabwe 10 10
908 80 s. Class "Tribal" steam locomotive, Tazara Railway 10 10
909 200 s. 4-6-0 type steam locomotive, Egypt .. 25 30
910 300 s. Mikado type steam locomotive, Sudan .. 35 40
911 400 s. Class "Mountain" Garrat steam locomotive, Uganda .. 50 55
912 500 s. Mallet type steam locomotive, Uganda .. 60 65
913 1000 s. 5 F 1 electric locomotive, South Africa 1·25 1·40

123 Lord Baden-Powell and Scout Emblem

1991. World Scout Jamboree, Mount Sorak, Korea.

915 **123** 20 s. multicoloured .. 10 10
916 – 80 s. multicoloured .. 10 15
917 – 100 s. multicoloured .. 10 15
918 – 150 s. black and green 20 25
919 – 300 s. multicoloured .. 35 40
920 – 400 s. multicoloured .. 50 55
921 – 500 s. multicoloured .. 60 65
922 – 1000 s. multicoloured 1·25 1·40

DESIGNS: 80 s. Scouts and Uganda 1982 100 s. anniversary stamp; 100 s. Scout encampment, New York World's Fair, 1939; 150 s. Cover and illustration from "Scouting for Boys"; 300 s. Cooking on campfire; 400 s. Aldrin and Armstrong on Moon; 500 s. Scout salutes; 1000 s. Statue to the Unkown Scout, Gillwell Park.

1991. "Philanippon '91" International Stamp Exhibition, Tokyo. As T **204** of Lesotho showing Walt Disney cartoon characters and Japanese traditions. Multicoloured.

924 10 s. Uncle Scrooge celebrating Ga-No-Iwai 10 10
925 20 s. Mickey Mouse removing shoes .. 10 10
926 70 s. Goofy leading carthorse 10 10
927 80 s. Daisy Duck and Minnie Mouse exchanging gifts .. 10 15
928 300 s. Minnie kneeling at doorway 35 40
929 400 s. Donald Duck and Mickey taking a hot volcanic sand bath .. 45 50
930 500 s. Clarabella Cow burning incense .. 60 65
931 1000 s. Mickey and Minnie writing New Year cards 1·25 1·40

1991. Death Cent (1990) of Vincent van Gogh (artist). As T **195** of British Virgin Islands. Multicoloured.

933 10 s. "Snowy Landscape with Arles" 10 10
934 20 s. "Peasant Woman binding Sheaves" (vert) 10 10
935 60 s. "The Drinkers" .. 10 10
936 80 s. "View of Auvers" .. 10 10
937 200 s. "Mourning Man" (vert) 25 30
938 400 s. "Still Life: Vase with Roses" 45 50
939 800 s. "The Raising of Lazarus" 90 95
940 1000 s. "The Good Samaritan" (vert) .. 1·25 1·50

1991. 65th Birthday of Queen Elizabeth II. As T **280** of Antigua. Multicoloured.

942 70 s. Queen and Prince Charles after polo match 10 10
943 90 s. Queen at Balmoral, 1976 .. .. .. 10 10
944 500 s. Queen with Princess Margaret, August 1980 60 65
945 600 s. Queen and Queen Mother leaving St. George's Chapel, Windsor 70 75

1991. 10th Wedding Anniv of Prince and Princess of Wales. As T **280** of Antigua. Multicoloured.

947 20 s. Prince and Princess of Wales in July 1986 .. 10 10
948 100 s. Separate photographs of Prince, Princess and sons .. 10 10
949 200 s. Prince Henry and Prince William .. 25 30
950 1000 s. Separate photographs of Prince and Princess in 1988 1·25 1·50

124 General Charles de Gaulle

1991. Birth Centenary (1990) of Charles de Gaulle (French statesman). Multicoloured.

952 20 s. Type **124** 10 10
953 70 s. Liberation of Paris, 1944 .. .. .. 10 10
954 90 s. De Gaulle with King George VI, 1940 .. 10 10
955 100 s. Reviewing free French troops, 1940 (horiz) 10 10
956 200 s. Broadcasting to France, 1940 (horiz) .. 25 30
957 500 s. De Gaulle in Normandy, 1944 (horiz) 60 65
958 600 s. De Gaulle at Albert Hall, 1940 (horiz) 70 75
959 1000 s. Inauguration as President, 1959 .. 1·25 1·40

125 "Volvariella bingensis"

1991. Fungi. Multicoloured.

961 20 s. Type **125** 10 10
962 70 s. "Agrocybe broadwayi" 10 10
963 90 s. "Camarophyllus olidus" 10 10
964 140 s. "Marasmius arborescens" 15 20
965 180 s. "Marasmiellus subcinereus" 20 25
966 200 s. "Agaricus campestris" 25 30
967 500 s. "Chlorophyllum molybdites" 60 65
968 1000 s. "Agaricus bingensis" .. .. 1·25 1·50

1991. Endangered Species (3rd series). As Nos. 406/9, but with changed face values, and additional horiz designs as T **61**. Mult.

970 100 s. Elephants in "Elephants' Graveyard" 10 10
971 140 s. Type **61** 15 20
972 200 s. Elephants at waterhole 25 30
973 600 s. Elephants having dust bath 70 75

POSTAGE DUE STAMPS

The Postage Due stamps of Kenya, Uganda and Tanganyika were used in Uganda until 2nd January, 1967.

D **1**.

D **3**. Lion.

1967.

D 7 D **1**. 5 c. red .. .. 15 1·50
D 8 10 c. green .. .. 15 1·50
D 9 20 c. blue .. .. 25 2·00
D 10 30 c. brown .. .. 35 2·50
D 11 40 c. purple .. .. 55 3·00
D 17 1 s. orange .. .. 2·50 8·00

These stamps exist in limited quantities overprinted **UGANDA LIBERATED 1979.**

1979. Liberation. As Nos. D12/17 optd. **LIBERATED 1979**

D 18.	D 1.	5 c. red	15	30
D 19.		10 c. green	15	30
D 20.		20 c. blue	20	30
D 21.		30 c. brown	20	40
D 22.		40 c. purple	25	40
D 23.		1 s. orange	25	40

1985. Animals.

D 24.	D 3.	5 s. black and turquoise ..	10	10
D 25.	–	10 s. black and lilac	10	10
D 26.	–	20 s. black and orange	10	10
D 27.	–	40 s. black and lilac	15	20
D 28.	–	50 s. black and blue	30	35
D 29.	–	100 s. black and mauve	60	65

DESIGNS: 10 s. African Buffalo. 20 s. Kob. 40 s. African Elephant. 50 s. Common Zebra. 100 s. Black Rhinoceros.

VANUATU

The New Hebrides became the Republic of Vanuatu on 30 July 1980.

1980. 100 centimes = 1 franc (Vanuatu).
1981. Vatus.

99. Island of Erromango and Kauri Pine.

1980. As Nos. 242/54 of New Hebrides but inscr. "VANUATU" and without royal and republican cyphers.

(a) Inscr. in English.

287E.	5 f. Type **99**	15	15
288E.	10 f. Territory map and copra making	15	15
289E.	15 f. Espiritu Santo and cattle	25	25
290E.	20 f. Efate and Vila P.O.	30	30
291E.	25 f. Malakula and head-dresses	35	35
292E.	30 f. Aoba, Maewo and pigs tusks	45	45
293E.	35 f. Pentecost and land diver	50	50
294E.	40 f. Tanna and John Frum cross ..	60	60
295E.	50 f. Shepherd Is. and outrigger canoe ..	65	70
296E.	70 f. Banks Is. and custom dancers ..	1·00	1·00
297E.	100 f. Ambrym and idols	1·25	80
298E.	200 f. Aneityum and baskets	1·40	1·40
299E.	500 f. Torres Is. and archer fisherman ..	2·50	3·00

(b) Inscr. in French.

287F.	Type **99**	35	15
288F.	10 f. Territory map and copra making	40	15
289F.	15 f. Espiritu Santo and cattle	45	25
290F.	20 f. Efate and Vila P.O.	50	30
291F.	25 f. Malakula and head-dresses	55	35
292F.	30 f. Aoba, Maewo and pigs tusks	55	45
293F.	35 f. Pentecost and land diver	60	50
294F.	40 f. Tanna and John Frum cross	90	60
295F.	50 f. Shepherd Is. and outrigger canoe ..	1·00	70
296F.	70 f. Banks Is. and custom dancers ..	1·40	1·00
297F.	100 f. Ambrym and idols	1·50	1·10
298F.	200 f. Aneityum and baskets	1·75	1·75
299F.	500 f. Torres Is. and archer fisherman ..	4·00	3·50

100. Rotary International.

1980. 75th Anniv. of Rotary International. Multicoloured.

(a) Inscr. in English.

300E.	10 f. Type **100**	10	10
301E.	40 f. Rotary emblem (vert.)	30	20

(b) Inscr. in French.

300F.	10 f. Type **100**	10	10
301F.	40 f. Rotary emblem (vert.)	30	20

101. Kiwanis Emblem and Globe.

1980. Kiwanis International (service club), New Zealand District Convention, Port Vila.

(a) Inscr. in English.

302E.	101.	10 f. gold, blue & brown	10	10
303E.	–	40 f. green and blue ..	30	20

(b) Inscr. in French.

302F.	101.	10 f. gold, blue & brn.	20	10
303F.	–	40 f. green and blue ..	50	25

DESIGN: 40 f. Kiwanis and Convention emblems.

102. " The Virgin and Child enthroned with Saints and Angels " (Umkreis Michael Pacher).

1980. Christmas. Details from Paintings. Multicoloured.

304.	10 f. Type **102**	10	10
305.	15 f. " The Virgin and Child with Saints, Angels and Donors " (Hans Memling)	10	10
306.	30 f. " The Rest on the Flight to Egypt " (Adriaen van der Werff)	20	20

103. Blue-faced Parrot Finch.

1981. Birds (1st series). Multicoloured.

307.	10 f. Type **103**	40	20
308.	20 f. Emerald Dove ..	60	40
309.	30 f. Golden Whistler ..	80	60
310.	40 f. Silver-shouldered Fruit Dove	90	75

See also Nos. 327/30.

104. Tribesman with Portrait of Prince Philip.

105. Prince Charles with his Dog, Harvey.

1981. 60th Birthday of Prince Philip, Duke of Edinburgh. Multicoloured.

311.	15 v. Type **104** ..	20	15
312.	25 v. Prince Philip in casual dress	30	20
313.	35 v. Queen and Prince Philip with Princess Anne and Master Peter Phillips	40	25
314.	45 v. Prince Philip in ceremonial dress ..	50	35

1981. Royal Wedding. Multicoloured.

315.	15 v. Wedding bouquet from Vanuatu	15	15
316.	45 v. Type **105**	25	25
317.	75 v. Prince Charles and Lady Diana Spencer ..	45	45

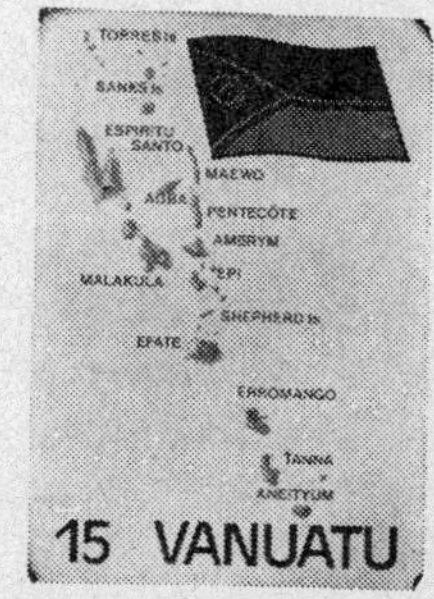

106. National Flag and Map of Vanuatu.

1981. 1st Anniv. of Independence.

318.	106.	15 v. multicoloured ..	20	15
319.	–	25 v. multicoloured ..	25	20
320.	–	45 v. yellow and brown	35	30
321.	–	75 v. multicoloured ..	60	70

DESIGNS – HORIZ. 25 v. Vanuatu emblem. 45 v. Vanuatu national anthem. VERT. 75 v. Vanuatu Coat of Arms.

107. Three Shepherds.

1981. Christmas. Children's Paintings. Mult.

322.	15 v. Type **107**	10	10
323.	25 v. Vanuatu girl with lamb (vert.) ..	15	15
324.	35 v. Angel as butterfly ..	15	20
325.	45 v. Boy carrying torch and gifts (vert.)	25	30

108. New Caledonian Myiagra Flycatchers.

1982. Birds (2nd series). Multicoloured.

327	15 v. Type **108** ..	45	20
328	20 v. Rainbow lorys ..	50	30
329	25 v. Buff-bellied fly-catchers	55	35
330	45 v. Collared grey fantails	80	65

109. " Flickingeria comata ".

1982. Orchids. Multicoloured.

331. 1 v. Type **109** 10 30
332. 2 v. "Calanthe triplicata" 10 30
333. 10 v. "Dendrobium sladei" 15 20
334. 15 v. "Dendrobium mohlianum" 20 20
335. 20 v. "Dendrobium macrophyllum" 25 30
336. 25 v. "Dendrobium purpureum" 30 35
337. 30 v. "Robiquetia mimus" 35 40
338. 35 v. "Dendrobium mooreanum" (horiz.) .. 40 50
339. 45 v. "Spathoglottis plicata" (horiz.) .. 55 70
340. 50 v. "Dendrobium seemannii" (horiz.) .. 60 80
341. 75 v. "Dendrobium conanthum" (horiz.) .. 95 1·50
342. 100 v. "Dendrobium macranthum" .. .. 1·25 1·50
343. 200 v. "Coelogyne lamellata" .. .. 2·25 2·50
344. 500 v. "Bulbophyllum longioscapum" .. .. 5·00 6·00

110. Scouts round Camp-fire.

1982. 75th Anniv. of Boy Scout Movement. Multicoloured.

345. 15 v. Type **110** 45 20
346. 20 v. First aid 50 25
347. 25 v. Constructing tower 55 40
348. 45 v. Constructing raft .. 80 70
349. 57 v. Scout saluting 1·25 1·25

111. Baby Jesus.

1982. Christmas, Nativity Scenes. Mult.

350. 15 v. Type **111** 30 25
351. 25 v. Mary and Joseph .. 45 35
352. 35 v. Shepherds (vert.) .. 55 60
353. 45 v. Kings bearing gifts (vert.) 70 90

112. "Euploea sylvester".

1983. Butterflies. Multicoloured.

355. 15 v. Type **112** 30 25
356. 15 v. "Hypolimnas octocula" 30 25
357. 20 v. "Papilio canopus hypsicles" 45 35
358. 20 v. "Polyura sacco" .. 45 35
359. 25 v. "Luthrodes cleotas" 50 40
360. 25 v. "Paranitica pumila" 50 40

113. President Afi George Sokomanu.

1983. Commonwealth Day. Multicoloured.

361. 15 v. Type **113** .. 15 10
362. 20 v. Fisherman and liner "Oriana" 20 15
363. 25 v. Herdsman and cattle 25 15
364. 75 v. World map showing position of Vanuatu with Commonwealth and Vanuatu flags 50 70

115. Montgolfier Balloon of De Rozier and D'Arlandes, 1783.

1983. Bicentenary of Manned Flight. Mult.

366. 15 v. Type **115** 15 15
367. 20 v. J. A. C. Charles balloon (first use of hydrogen, 1783) 25 25
368. 25 v. Blanchard and Jeffries crossing English Channel, 1785 .. .. .. 30 30
369. 35 v. Giffard's airship, 1852 (horiz.) 40 40
370. 40 v. "La France" (airship of Renard and Krebs, 1884) (horiz.) .. 45 45
371. 45 v. "Graf Zeppelin" (first aerial circumnavigation, 1929) (horiz.) 55 55

116. Mail at Bauefield Airport.

1983. World Communications Year. Mult.

372. 15 v. Type **116** 20 25
373. 20 v. Switchboard operator 30 35
374. 25 v. Telex operator .. 35 40
375. 45 v. Satellite Earth station 65 70

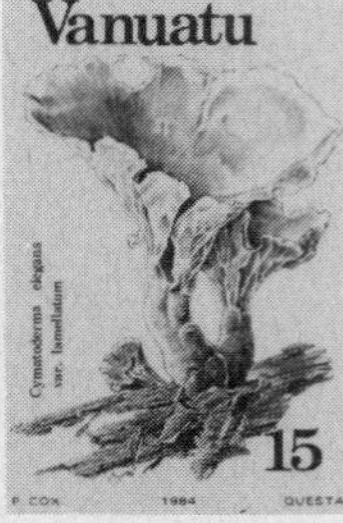

117. "Cymatoderma elegans var. lamellatum".

1984. Fungi. Multicoloured.

377. 15 v. Type **117** 40 25
378. 25 v. "Lignosus rhinoceros" 55 40
379. 35 v. "Stereum ostrea" (horiz.) 70 50
380. 45 v. "Ganoderma boninense .. .. .. 1·10 70

118. Port Vila.

1984. 250th Anniv. of "Lloyd's List" (newspaper). Multicoloured.

381. 15 v. Type **118** 20 25
382. 20 v. "Induna" (container ship) 30 35
383. 25 v. Air Vanuatu aircraft 35 40
384. 45 v. "Brahman Express" (container ship) 65 70

1984. Universal Postal Union Congress, Hamburg. As No. 371, but inscribed "UPU CONGRESS HAMBURG" and U.P.U. logo.

385. 45 v. multicoloured .. 65 70

119. Charolais.

1984. Cattle. Multicoloured.

386. 15 v. Type **119** 20 25
387. 25 v. Charolais-afrikander 35 40
388. 45 v. Friesian 65 70
389. 75 v. Charolais-brahman .. 1·10 1·25

120. "Makambo".

1984. "Ausipex" International Stamp Exhibition, Melbourne. Multicoloured.

390. 25 v. Type **120** 60 50
391. 45 v. "Rockton" .. .. 1·00 90
392. 100 v. "Waroonga" .. 1·90 2·50

121. Father Christmas in Children's Ward.

1984. Christmas. Multicoloured.

394. 25 v. Type **121** 40 40
395. 45 v. Nativity play .. 70 70
396. 75 v. Father Christmas distributing presents .. 1·25 1·25

1985. No. 331 surch.

397. 5 v. on 1 v. Type **109** .. 30 30

123. Ambrym Island Ceremonial Dance.

1985. Traditional Costumes. Multicoloured.

398. 20 v. Type **123** 30 35
399. 25 v. Pentecost Island marriage ceremony .. 35 40
400. 45 v. Women's grade ceremony, South West Malakula 65 70
401. 75 c. Ceremonial dance, South West Malakula .. 1·10 1·25

124. Peregrine Falcon Diving.

1985. Birth Bicentenary of John J. Audubon (ornithologist). Peregrine Falcon. Mult.

402. 20 v. Type **124** 60 35
403. 35 v. Peregrine Falcon in flight 75 50
404. 45 v. Peregrine Falcon perched on branch .. 90 80
405. 100 v. "Peregrine Falcon" (John J. Audubon) .. 1·60 1·75

125. The Queen Mother with the Queen on her 80th Birthday.

1985. Life and Times of Queen Elizabeth the Queen Mother. Multicoloured.

406 5 v. Duke and Duchess of York on Wedding Day, 1923 .. .. .. 10 1
407 20 v. Type **125** 35 3
408 35 v. At Ancona, Italy .. 55 5
409 55 v. With Prince Henry at his christening (from photo by Lord Snowdon) 85 8

126. "Mala" (patrol boat).

1985. 5th Anniv. of Independence and "Expo '85" World Fair, Japan. Multicoloured.

411. 35 v. Type **126** 45 5
412. 45 v. Japanese fishing fleet 65 7
413. 55 v. Vanuatu Mobile Force Band 75 8
414. 100 v. Prime Minister Fr. Walter H. Lini .. .. 1·40 1·5

127. "Youth Activities" (Alain Lagaliu).

1985. International Youth Year. Children's Paintings. Multicoloured.

416. 20 v. Type **127** 40 3
417. 30 v. "Village" (Peter Obed) 50 4
418. 50 v. "Beach and 'PEACE' Slogan" (Mary Estelle) 85 7
419. 100 v. "Youth Activities" (different) (Abel Merani) 1·50 1·5

128. Map of Vanuatu with National and U.N. Flags.

1985. 4th Anniv. of United Nation Membership.

420. **128.** 45 v. multicoloured .. 70 7

129. "Chromodoris elisabethina".

1985. Marine Life (1st series). Sea Slugs. Multicoloured.

421.	20 v. Type **129**	30	35
422.	35 v. "Halgerda aurantiomaculata" (horiz.) ..	45	50
423.	55 v. "Chromodoris kuniei" (horiz.)	75	80
424.	100 v. "Notodoris minor"	1·40	1·50

See also Nos. 442/5 and 519/22.

130. Scuba Diving.

1986. Tourism. Multicoloured.

425.	30 v. Type **30**	70	40
426.	35 v. Yasur volcano, Tanna	80	45
427.	55 v. Land diving, Pentecost Island	1·00	70
428.	100 v. Windsurfing	1·40	1·25

1986. 60th Birthday of Queen Elizabeth II. As T **110** of Ascension. Multicoloured.

429.	20 v. With Prince Charles and Princess Anne, 1951	25	30
430.	35 v. Prince William's christening, 1982	40	45
431.	45 v. In New Hebrides, 1974	55	60
432.	55 v. On board Royal Yacht "Britannia", Mexico, 1974	65	70
433.	100 v. At Crown Agents Head Office, London, 1983	1·10	1·25

131. Liner S.S. "President Coolidge" leaving San Francisco.

1986. "Ameripex '86" International Stamp Exhibition, Chicago. Sinking of S.S. "President Coolidge". Multicoloured.

434.	45 v. Type **131**	55	60
435.	55 v. S.S. "President Coolidge" as troopship, 1942	65	70
436.	135 v. Map of Espiritu Santo showing site of sinking, 1942	1·50	1·60

132. Halley's Comet and Vanuatu Statue.

1986. Appearance of Halley's Comet. Multicoloured.

438.	30 v. Type **132**	75	50
439.	45 v. Family watching Comet	95	80
440.	55 v. Comet passing Earth	1·10	1·25
441.	100 v. Edmond Halley	1·75	2·00

133. Daisy Coral.

1986. Marine Life (2nd series). Corals. Multicoloured.

442.	20 v. Type **133**	50	30
443.	45 v. Organ pipe coral	80	70
444.	55 v. Sea fan	90	90
445.	135 v. Soft coral	2·00	2·50

134. Children of Different Races.

1986. Christmas. International Peace Year. Multicoloured.

446.	30 v. Type **134**	75	50
447.	45 v. Church and boy praying	95	85
448.	55 v. U.N. discussion and Headquarters Building, New York	1·10	1·25
449.	135 v. People of different races at work	2·25	3·00

135. Datsun "240Z" (1969).

1987. Motor Vehicles. Multicoloured.

450.	20 v. Type **135**	30	30
451.	45 v. Ford "Model A" (1927)	60	60
452.	55 v. Unic lorry (1924–5)	70	70
453.	135 v. Citroen "DS19" (1975)	1·60	1·90

1987. Hurricane Relief Fund. No. 332, already surch., and Nos. 429/33, all surch. **Hurricane Relief Fund** and premium.

454.	20 v.+10 v. on 2 v. "Calanthe triplicata"	35	40
455.	20 v.+10 v. Queen Elizabeth II with Prince Charles and Princess Anne, 1951	35	40
456.	35 v.+15 v. Prince William's christening, 1982	60	65
457.	45 v.+20 v. Queen in New Hebrides, 1974	75	80
458.	55 v.+25 v. Queen on board Royal Yacht "Britannia", Mexico, 1974	95	1·00
459.	100 v.+50 v. Queen at Crown Agents Head Office, London, 1983	1·75	1·90

The surcharge on No. 454 also includes the word "Surcharge".

137. Young Coconut Plants.

1987. 25th Anniv. of I.R.H.O. Coconut Research Station. Multicoloured.

460.	35 v. Type **137**	40	45
461.	45 v. Coconut flower and fronds	55	60
462.	100 v. Coconuts	1·10	1·25
463.	135 v. Research station	1·60	1·75

The inscriptions on Nos. 462/3 are in French.

138. Spotted Hawkfish.

1987. Fishes. Multicoloured.

464	1 v. Type **138**	10	10
465	5 v. Moorish idol	10	10
466	10 v. Black-saddled puffer	10	15
467	15 v. Anemone fish	15	20
468	20 v. Striped surgeon	20	25
469	30 v. Six-barred wrasse	30	35
470	35 v. Purple queenfish	35	40
471	40 v. Long-jawed squirrelfish	40	45
472	45 v. Clown triggerfish	45	50
473	50 v. Scribed wrasse	50	55
474	55 v. Regal angelfish	55	60
475	65 v. Lionfish	65	70
476	100 v. Foresters hawkfish	1·00	1·10
477	300 v. Vermiculated triggerfish	3·00	3·25
478	500 v. Saddled butterfly fish	5·00	5·25

139. "Xylotrupes gideon" (beetle).

1987. Insects. Multicoloured.

479	45 v. Type **139**	55	60
480	55 v. "Phyllodes imperialis" (moth)	65	70
481	65 v. "Cyphogastra sp." (beetle)	75	80
482	100 v. "Othreis fullonia" (moth)	1·10	1·25

140. "Away in a Manger".

1987. Christmas. Christmas Carols. Mult.

483.	20 v. Type **140**	25	30
484.	45 v. "Once in Royal David's City"	55	60
485.	55 v. "While Shepherds watched their Flocks"	65	70
486.	65 v. "We Three Kings of Orient Are"	75	80

1987. Royal Ruby Wedding. Nos. 429/33 optd. **40TH WEDDING ANNIVERSARY.**

487.	20 v. Princess Elizabeth II with Prince Charles and Princess Anne, 1951	25	30
488.	35 v. Prince William's christening, 1982	40	45
489.	45 v. Queen Elizabeth II in New Hebrides, 1974	55	60
490.	55 v. On board Royal Yacht "Britannia", Mexico, 1974	65	70
491.	100 v. At Crown Agents Head Office, London, 1983	1·10	1·25

141. Dugong Cow and Calf.

1988. Dugong. Multicoloured.

492.	5 v. Type **141**	30	15
493.	10 v. Dugong underwater	45	15
494.	20 v. Two dugongs surfacing to breathe	70	50
495.	45 v. Four dugongs swimming	1·10	1·40

142 S.S. "Tambo"

1988. Bicentenary of Australian Settlement. Ships. Multicoloured.

496	20 v. Type **142**	20	25
497	45 v. S.S. "Induna"	50	55
498	55 v. S.S. "Morinda"	60	65
499	65 v. S.S. "Marsina"	70	75

143 Captain James Cook

144 Boxer in Training

1988. "Sydpex '88" National Stamp Exhibition, Sydney.

500	**143** 45 v. black and red	50	55

1988. Olympic Games, Seoul. Multicoloured.

502	20 v. Type **144**	20	25
503	45 v. Athletics	50	55
504	55 v. Signing Olympic agreement	60	65
505	65 v. Soccer	70	75

1988. 300th Anniv of Lloyd's of London. As T **123** of Ascension. Multicoloured.

507	20 v. Interior of new Lloyd's Building, 1988	25	25
508	55 v. "Shirrabank" (freighter) (horiz)	65	65
509	65 v. "Adela" (ferry) (horiz)	75	75
510	145 v. "General Slocum" (excursion steamer) on fire, New York, 1904	1·75	1·75

145 Agricultural Crops

1988. Food and Agriculture Organization. Multicoloured.

511	45 v. Type **145**	50	55
512	55 v. Fisherman with catch (vert)	60	65
513	65 v. Livestock on smallholding (vert)	70	75
514	120 v. Market women with produce	1·25	1·40

146 Virgin and Child ("Silent Night")

1988. Christmas. Carols. Multicoloured.

515	20 v. Type **146**	20	25
516	45 v. Angels ("Angels from the Realms of Glory")	50	55
517	65 v. Shepherd boy with lamb ("O Come all ye Faithful")	70	75
518	155 v. Baby ("In that Poor Stable how Charming Jesus Lies")	1·75	1·90

147 "Periclimenes brevicarpalis"

1989. Marine Life (3rd series). Shrimps. Mult.

519	20 v. Type **147**	20	25
520	45 v. "Lysmata grabhami"	50	55
521	65 v. "Rhynchocinetes sp"	70	75
522	150 v. "Stenopus hispidus"	1·75	1·90

148 Consolidated "Catalina" Flying Boat

1989. Economic and Social Commission for Asia and the Pacific. Aircraft.

523 **148** 20 v. black and blue .. 30 30
524 – 45 v. black and green 65 65
525 – 55 v. black and yellow 80 80
526 – 200 v. black and red .. 2·75 3·00

DESIGNS: 45 v. Douglas "DC-3"; 55 v. Embraer "EMB110 Bandeirante"; 200 v. Boeing "737-300".

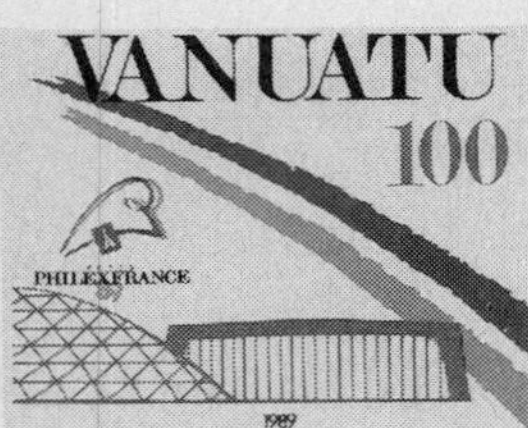

149 Porte de Versailles Hall No. 1

1989. "Philexfrance '89" International Stamp Exhibition, Paris. Multicoloured.

527 100 v. Type **149** .. .. 1·10 1·25
528 100 v. Eiffel Tower .. 1·10 1·25

Nos. 527/8 were printed together, se-tenant, forming a composite design.

1989. 20th Anniv of First Manned Landing on Moon. As T **126** of Ascension. Multicoloured.

530 45 v. Command module seen from lunar module 50 55
531 55 v. Crew of "Apollo 17" (30 × 30 mm) 60 65
532 65 v. "Apollo 17" emblem (30 × 30 mm) 70 75
533 120 v. Launch of "Apollo 17" .. .. .. 1·25 1·40

1989. "Melbourne Stampshow '89". No. 332 surch with Stampshow emblem.

535 100 v. on 2 v. "Calanthe triplicata" .. .. 2·00 2·00

151 New Hebrides 1978 "Concorde" 30 f. (French inscr) Stamp

1989. "World Stamp Expo '89", International Stamp Exhibition, Washington.

536 **151** 65 v. multicoloured .. 90 90

152 "Alocasia macrorrhiza"

1990. Flora. Multicoloured.

538 45 v. Type **152** 65 65
539 55 v. "Acacia spirorbis" .. 75 75
540 65 v. "Metrosideros collina" 85 85
541 145 v. "Hoya australis" .. 2·00 2·25

153 Kava (National plant)

1990. "Stamp World London 90" International Stamp Exhibition. Multicoloured.

542 45 v. Type **153** 75 75
543 65 v. Luganville Post Office .. .. .. 1·00 1·00
544 100 v. Mail plane and sailing packet .. .. 1·75 1·75
545 200 v. Penny Black and Vanuatu 1980 10 f. definitive .. .. .. 2·75 2·75

154 National Council of Women Logo

1990. 10th Anniv of Independence.

547 **154** 25 v. black and blue .. 40 40
548 – 50 v. multicoloured .. 75 75
549 – 55 v. purple, blk & buff 75 75
550 – 65 v. multicoloured .. 90 90
551 – 80 v. multicoloured .. 1·40 1·40

DESIGNS: 50 v. President Frederick Kalomuana Timakata; 55 v. Preamble to the Constitution; 65 v. Vanuaaku Pati party flag; 80 v. Reserve Bank of Vanuatu.

155 General De Gaulle at Bayeux, 1944

1990. Birth Centenary of General de Gaulle (French statesman). Multicoloured.

553 20 v. Type **155** 55 55
554 25 v. Generals De Lattre de Tassigny, De Gaulle, Devers and Patch in Alsace, 1945 .. .. 65 65
555 30 v. De Gaulle as President of the French Republic 75 75
556 45 v. De Gaulle at Biggin Hill, 1942 .. .. 90 90
557 55 v. Roosevelt, De Gaulle and Churchill, Casablanca, 1943 .. 1·00 1·00
558 65 v. General De Gaulle and Liberation of Paris, 1944 .. .. .. 1·00 1·00

156 Angel facing Right

1990. Christmas. Multicoloured.

559 25 v. Type **156** 45 45
560 50 v. Shepherds 75 75
561 65 v. Nativity 85 85
562 70 v. Three Kings 90 90
563 80 v. Angel facing left .. 1·00 1·00

Nos. 559/63 were printed together, se-tenant, forming a composite design.

157 "Parthenos sylvia"

1991. Butterflies. Multicoloured.

564 25 v. Type **157** 40 30
565 55 v. "Euploea leucostictus" 80 60
566 80 v. "Lampides boeticus" 1·10 1·25
567 150 v. "Danaus plexippus" 2·40 2·75

158 Dance Troupe from South West Malakula

1991. 2nd National Art Festival, Luganville. Multicoloured.

568 25 v. Type **158** 45 35
569 65 v. Women weavers and baskets .. .. 1·00 1·00
570 80 v. Woodcarver and carved animals, masks, dish and ceremonial figures .. .. .. 1·40 1·50
571 150 v. Musicians playing bamboo flute, youtatau and pan pipes .. .. 2·75 3·00

1991. Nos. 332/4 and 337 surch.

572 20 v. on 2 v. "Calanthe triplicata" 30 30
573 60 v. on 10 v. "Dendrobium sladei" 80 80
574 70 v. on 15 v. "Dendrobium mohlianum" .. 90 90
575 80 v. on 30 v. "Robiquetia mimus" .. .. 1·00 1·00

1991. 65th Birthday of Queen Elizabeth II and 70th Birthday of Prince Philip. As T **139** of Ascension. Multicoloured.

576 65 v. Queen Elizabeth II 1·00 1·00
577 70 v. Prince Philip .. 1·00 1·00

160 White-collared Kingfisher

1991. "Philanippon '91" International Stamp Exhibition, Tokyo. Birds. Multicoloured.

578 50 v. Type **160** 75 75
579 55 v. Palm lorikeet .. 80 80
580 80 v. Scarlet robin .. 1·25 1·25
581 100 v. Pacific swallow .. 1·40 1·40

161 Group of Islanders

1991. World AIDS Day. Multicoloured.

583 25 v. Type **161** 40 30
584 65 v. Caring for AIDS victim 85 85
585 80 v. AIDS shark .. 1·25 1·25
586 150 v. Children's playground .. .. 2·50 2·75

1992. 40th Anniv of Queen Elizabeth II's Accession. As T **143** of Ascension. Mult.

587 20 v. Reserve Bank of Vanuatu building, Port Vila 35 30
588 25 v. Port Vila 40 40
589 60 v. Mural, Parliament House 85 85
590 65 v. Three portraits of Queen Elizabeth .. 90 90
591 70 v. Queen Elizabeth II 1·25 1·40

162 Grumman F-4 "Wildcat"

1992. 50th Anniv of Outbreak of the Pacific War. Multicoloured.

592 50 v. Type **162** 50 55
593 55 v. Douglas SBD-3 "Dauntless" 55 60
594 65 v. Consolidated PBY-5A "Catalina" 65 70
595 80 v. U.S.S. "Hornet" (aircraft carrier) .. 80 85

VICTORIA

The S.E. state of the Australian Commonwealth, whose stamps it now uses.

12 pence = 1 shilling.
20 shillings = 1 pound.

1. Queen Victoria ("half length").

2. Queen on throne.

1850. Imperf.

28	1	1d. red to brown ..	£375	32·00
6		2d. lilac to grey ..	£1100	80·00
17		2d. brown	£500	95·00
31a		3d. blue	£350	30·00

1852. Imperf.

38	2	2d. brown to lilac ..	£110	22·00

3.

4.

1854. Imperf.

25	3	1s. blue	£650	22·00

1854. Imperf.

32a	4	6d. orange	£150	18·00
35		2s. green	£1000	£110

7. Queen on Throne.

8. Emblems in corners.

1856. Imperf.

40	7	1d. green	£120	90·00

1857. Imperf.

41	8	1d. green	95·00	13·00
45		2d. lilac	£160	10·00
43		4d. red	£160	7·50

1857. Rouletted.

62	8	1d. green	£300	14·00
70		2d. lilac	£150	5·50
49a	1	3d. blue	—	£140
71c	8	4d. red	£120	3·25
53a	4	6d. orange	—	35·00
54	3	1s. blue	—	80·00
56	4	2s. green on yellow ..	—	£350

1858. Rouletted.

73	7	6d. blue	£100	12·00

1859. Perf.

96	8	1d. green	65·00	4·50
99a		2d. lilac	£110	4·75
99		2d. grey	£100	4·75
78	1	3d. blue	—	£110
87		4d. red	£120	7·50
104	4	6d. black	£150	35·00
81a	3	1s. blue	£110	12·00
82	4	2s. green on yellow ..	£200	25·00
147		2s. blue on green ..	£140	3·75

9.

10.

1860. Perf.

00.	9.	3d. blue	£120	7·00
01.		3d. red	£100	25·00
02a.		4d. red	80·00	3·00
03.		6d. orange	£1600	£200
05.		6d. black	95·00	5·50

1861.

09.	10.	1d. green	55·00	4·50

11.

15.

1862.

113	11	6d. black	70·00	4·50

1863.

184c	15	1d. green	65·00	2·10
179		2d. lilac	50·00	3·25
190		4d. red	70·00	3·00
125		8d. orange	£300	50·00
194		8d. brown on red ..	75·00	5·00

16.

17.

18. 19.

1865.

150	16	3d. lilac	£160	20·00
187		3d. yellow	14·00	1·90
192	17	6d. blue	12·00	90
134		10d. grey	£450	£100
138		10d. brown on red ..	65·00	5·00
139b	18	1s. blue on blue ..	55·00	2·50
162	19	5s. blue on yellow ..	£1600	£300
198a		5s. blue and red ..	£130	12·00

1871. Surch. in figures and words.

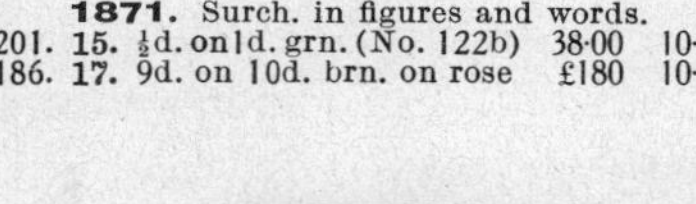

201.	15.	½d. on 1d. grn. (No. 122b)	38·00	10·00
186.	17.	9d. on 10d. brn. on rose	£180	10·00

24.

1870.

206a.	24.	2d. lilac	38·00	1·00

25.

26.

27.

29.

30.

1873.

208c	25	½d. red	3·75	50
215		½d. red on red ..	20·00	8·00
209c	26	1d. green	13·00	55
216		1d. green on yellow ..	50·00	11·00
217		1d. green on grey ..	£100	40·00
211	27	2d. mauve	10·00	35
218		2d. mauve on green ..	£120	10·00
219		2d. mauve on lilac ..	£1000	£400
220		2d. mauve on brown ..	£120	10·00
207b	29	9d. brown on red ..	55·00	7·50
302		9d. green	20·00	9·00
338		9d. red	8·00	1·75
214	30	1s. blue on blue ..	30·00	3·00

1876. Surch. in figures and words.

212.	29.	8d. on 9d. brown on red	£120	15·00

36.

33.

35.

1880. Frame differs in 4d.

232a	36.	1d. green	12·00	1·25
228	33.	2d. brown	12·00	30
229		2d. mauve	7·00	20
225a		4d. red	35·00	3·50
226	35.	2s. blue on green ..	£110	18·00

38.

39.

40.

41.

42.

43.

1884. Inscr. "STAMP DUTY".

243	38	½d. red	4·50	65
244	39	1d. green	5·25	30
245	40	2d. mauve	3·75	25
334	39	3d. yellow	5·25	55
247	41	4d. mauve	27·00	3·00
249a	39	6d. blue	24·00	2·10
239	42	8d. red on red ..	19·00	5·50
240	40	1s. blue on yellow ..	35·00	6·00
251	42	2s. green on green ..	25·00	3·00
341		2s. green on white ..	15·00	4·25
254b	43	2s. 6d. orange ..	75·00	10·00

1885. Optd. **STAMP DUTY.**

237.	16.	3d. yellow	60·00	22·00
238.	33.	4d. red	55·00	20·00
234.	30.	1s. blue on blue ..	95·00	20·00
236.	35.	2s. blue on green ..	80·00	18·00

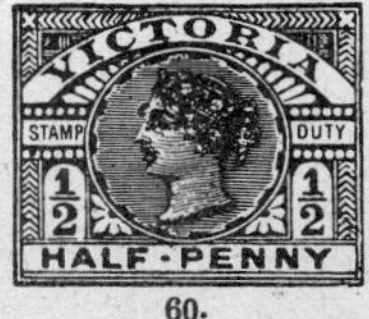

60.

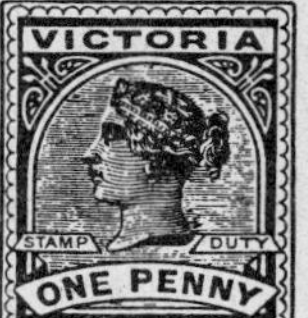

61.

62.

63.

64.

65.

66.

1886. Inscr. "STAMP DUTY".

283	60.	½d. lilac	15·00	3·00
304		½d. red	2·75	15
330		½d. green	4·75	40
285a	61.	1d. green	5·25	20
307	62.	2d. purple	2·10	10
335	63.	4d. red	4·75	95
288b	64.	6d. blue	6·50	50
289	65.	1s. brown	20·00	2·00
339		1s. red	10·00	1·40
290	66.	1s. 6d. blue	£120	65·00
340		1s. 6d. orange	14·00	4·75

68.

71.

69.

70.

1890. Inscr. "STAMP DUTY", except T **71.**

297	68.	1d. brown on red ..	3·50	1·25
298c		1d. brown	1·90	15
305a		1d. red	1·90	10
306	71.	1½d. green	4·00	1·50
327		1½d. red on yellow ..	3·00	1·75
300a	69.	2½d. red on yellow ..	5·50	70
333		2½d. blue	4·50	1·50
336	70.	5d. brown	5·50	95

73.

74.

1897. Charity

325.	73.	1d. (1s.) blue	18·00	18·00
326.	74.	2½d. (2s. 6d.) brown ..	80·00	60·00

76.

77.

1900. Charity.

346.	76.	1d. (1s.) brown ..	35·00	25·00
347.	77.	2d. (2s.) green	£100	80·00

1901.

349 **25** ½d. green .. .. 2·00 85
361 **68** 1d. olive .. .. 5·00 3·50
351 **16** 3d. orange .. .. 10·00 1·25
362 **39** 3d. green .. .. 21·00 5·00
352 **33** 4d. yellow .. .. 25·00 6·50
353 **17** 6d. green .. .. 9·00 5·00
354 **30** 1s. orange .. .. 30·00 15·00
348 **35** 2s. blue on red .. 35·00 10·00
355 **19** 5s. red and blue .. 45·00 18·00

1901. As previous types, but inscr. " POSTAGE " instead of " STAMP DUTY ".

399 **25** ½d. green .. .. 1·60 15
400 **36** 1d. red 80 10
366a **71** 1½d. red on yellow .. 2·10 55
367a **33** 2d. mauve .. .. 1·90 30
359a **69** 2½d. blue .. .. 2·75 20
403 **16** 3d. brown .. .. 4·00 55
369 **33** 4d. yellow .. .. 4·75 55
360a **70** 5d. brown .. .. 4·00 40
370 **71** 6d. green .. .. 7·50 80
407a **29** 9d. red .. .. 9·50 1·25
408 **30** 1s. orange .. .. 8·00 2·00
374 **35** 2s. blue on red .. 22·00 2·00
375a **19** 5s. red and blue .. 65·00 9·00

92.

1901. Frame differs for £2.

410 **92.** £1 red £275 £100
377 – £2 blue £550 £250

1912. Surch. ONE PENNY.

454. **33.** 1d. on 2d. mve. (No. 367a) 70 45

POSTAGE DUE STAMPS

D 1.

1890.

D 11. **D 1.** ½d. blue and red .. 2·25 1·90
D 12. 1d. blue and red .. 4·00 1·10
D 13. 2d. blue and red .. 6·00 90
D 4. 4d. blue and red .. 7·00 1·50
D 5. 5d. blue and red .. 6·00 2·00
D 6. 6d. blue and red .. 7·50 1·75
D 7. 10d. blue and red .. 70·00 35·00
D 8. 1s. blue and red .. 35·00 6·50
D 9. 2s. blue and red .. £110 45·00
D 10. 5s. blue and red .. £160 90·00

1895.

D59 **D 1** ½d. red and green .. 2·00 1·50
D43 1d. red and green .. 1·50 35
D17 2d. red and green .. 2·25 30
D32 4d. red and green .. 4·50 1·25
D49 5d. red and green .. 4·50 2·50
D20 6d. red and green .. 4·50 2·75
D21 10d. red and green .. 12·00 10·00
D22 1s. red and green .. 7·50 3·25
D23 2s. red and green .. 60·00 20·00
D24 5s. red and green .. £100 40·00

REGISTRATION STAMP

6.

1854. Imperf.

34 **6** 1s. red and blue .. .. £750 75·00

1857. Roul.

55 **6** 1s. red and blue £3500 £180

TOO LATE STAMP

1855. As Type **6** but inscr "TOO LATE". Imperf.

33 6d. lilac and green £600 £120

VICTORIA LAND

Stamps issued in connection with Capt. Scott's Antarctic Expedition.

12 pence = 1 shilling.

1911. Scott Expedition. Stamps of New Zealand optd. **VICTORIA LAND.**

A 2. **50.** ½d. green £500 £500
A 3. **52.** 1d. red .. .. 45·00 70·00

WADHWAN

A state of Kathiawar India. Now uses Indian stamps.

4 pice = 1 anna.

1.

1888.

5 **1** ½ pice black .. .. 4·00 4·50

WESTERN AUSTRALIA

The Western State of the Australian Commonwealth, whose stamps it now uses.

12 pence = 1 shilling.
20 shillings = 1 pound.

1. 2. 3.

1854. Imperf. or roul.

1. **1.** 1d. black £800 £180
25. 2d. orange .. .. 60·00 45·00
3. **2.** 4d. blue £225 £150
26. **1.** 4d. blue £180 £1200
28. 6d. green £1100 £400
4c. **3.** 1s. brown £325 £275

5. 7.

1857. Imperf. or roul.

15. **5.** 2d. brown on red .. £1700 £500
18. 6d. bronze .. £1800 £600

1861. Perf.

103 **1** 1d. red .. .. .. 12·00 60
76 1d. yellow .. .. 12·00 50
39 2d. blue .. .. .. 50·00 25·00
77 2d. yellow .. .. 16·00 50
104 2d. grey .. .. .. 26·00 1·00
56 4d. red .. .. .. 50·00 5·00
105 4d. brown .. .. 80·00 18·00
42 6d. brown .. .. £140 32·00
57 6d. violet .. .. 60·00 6·00
61 1s. green .. .. 80·00 12·00

1871.

141 **7** 3d. brown .. .. 4·50 50

1874. Surch ONE PENNY.

67 **1** 1d. on 2d. yellow .. .. £130 45·00

1884. Surch. in figures.

90. **1.** " ½ " on 1d. yellow .. 9·00 10·00
91a. **7.** 1d. on 3d. brown .. 26·00 7·50

12. 13.

14. 15.

1885.

94 **12** ½d. green .. .. 1·50 10
139a **13** 1d. red .. .. 2·75 10
96a **14** 2d. grey .. .. 8·00 25
113 2d. yellow .. .. 6·50 35
97 **15** 2½d. blue .. .. 5·50 35
98 4d. brown .. .. 6·00 35
99 5d. yellow .. .. 8·00 1·25
100 6d. violet .. .. 14·00 1·00
102 1s. green .. .. 17·00 2·00

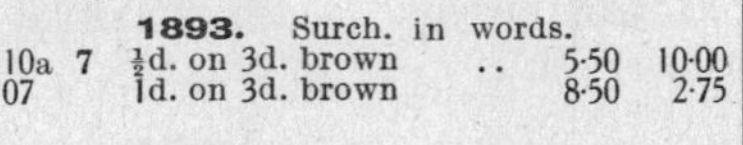

1893. Surch. in words.

110a **7** ½d. on 3d. brown .. 5·50 10·00
107 1d. on 3d. brown .. 8·50 2·75

23. 19.

24.

21. 28.

29. 30.

31. 32.

1901.

140 **23.** 2d. yellow .. .. 1·75 40
114 **19.** 2½d. blue .. .. 5·00 30
119 **24.** 4d. brown .. .. 5·50 90
143 **15.** 5d. olive .. .. 11·00 1·75
168 **19.** 6d. violet .. .. 9·50 3·25
121 **12.** 8d. green .. .. 20·00 2·50
145 **24.** 9d. orange .. .. 22·00 3·50
146 **19.** 10d. red .. .. 22·00 10·00
116 **21.** 1s. green .. .. 18·00 3·50
124b **28.** 2s. red on yellow .. 48·00 8·50
125 **29.** 2s. 6d. blue on red .. 40·00 8·00
126 **30.** 5s. green .. .. 80·00 18·00
127 **31.** 10s. mauve .. .. £180 48·00
128 **32.** £1 orange £300 £150

1906. Surch. **ONE PENNY.**

172. **23.** 1d. on 2d. yellow .. 80 30

ZAMBIA

Formerly Northern Rhodesia, attained independence on 24 October 1964, and changed its name to Zambia.

1964. 12 pence = 1 shilling;
20 shillings = 1 pound.
1968. 100 ngwee = 1 kwacha.

11. Pres. Kaunda and Victoria Falls.

1964. Independence.

91. **11.** 3d. sepia, green and blue .. 10 10
92. – 6d. violet and yellow .. 15 10
93. – 1s. 3d. multicoloured .. 20 15

DESIGNS—HORIZ. 6d. College of Further Education, Lusaka. VERT. 1s. 3d. Barotse Dancer.

14. Maize—Farmer and Silo. 22. Tobacco Worker.

1964.

94. **14.** ½d. red, black and green 10 20
95. – 1d. brown, black & blue 10 10
96. – 2d. red, brown & orange 10 10
97. – 3d. black and red .. 10 10
98. – 4d. black, brown & orge. 15 10
99. – 6d. orange, brown and turquoise 15 10
100. – 9d. red, black and blue .. 15 10
101. – 1s. black, bistre and blue 15 10
102. **22.** 1s. 3d. multicoloured .. 20 10
103. – 2s. multicoloured .. 25 10
104. – 2s. 6d. black and yellow 60 35
105. – 5s. black, yellow & green 1·25 45
106. – 10s. black and orange .. 3·25 3·25
107. – £1 multicoloured .. 3·25 4·25

DESIGNS—As Type **14:** VERT. 1d. Health—Radiographer. 2d. Chinyau Dancer. 3d. Cotton-picking. HORIZ. 4d. Angoni Bull. As Type **22:** HORIZ. 6d. Communications, Old and New. 9d. Zambezi Sawmills and Redwood Flower. 1s. Fishing at Mpulungu. 2s. 6d. Luangwa Game Reserve. 5 s. Education — Student. 10 s. Copper Mining. VERT. 2s. Tonga Basket-making. £1, Makishi Dancer.

28. I.T.U. Emblem and Symbols.

1965. Centenary of I.T.U.

108. **28.** 6d. violet and gold .. 15 10
109. 2s. 6d. grey and gold .. 70 90

29. I.C.Y. Emblem.

1965. Int. Co-operation Year.

110. **29.** 3d. turquoise and gold .. 10
111. 1s. 3d. blue and gold .. 35

30. State House, Lusaka.

1965. 1st Anniv. of Independence. Mult.
112. 3d. Type **30** 10 10
113. 6d. Fireworks, Independence Stadium 10 10
114. 1s. 3d. Clematopsis (vert.) 10 10
115. 2s. 6d. " Tithonia diversifolia " (vert.) 25 60

34. W.H.O. Building and U.N. Flag.

1966. Inauguration of W.H.O. Headquarters, Geneva.
116. 34. 3d. brown, gold and blue 15 10
117. 1s. 3d. violet, gold & blue 30 30

35. University Building.

1966. Opening of Zambia University.
118. 35. 3d. green and bronze .. 10 10
119. 1s. 3d. violet and bronze 10 10

36. National Assembly Building.

1967. Inaug. of National Assembly Building.
20. 36. 3d. black and gold .. 10 10
21. 6d. green and gold .. 10 10

37. Airport Scene.

1967. Opening of Luska Int. Airport.
22. 37. 6d. blue and bronze .. 10 10
23. 2s. 6d. brown & bronze 30 60

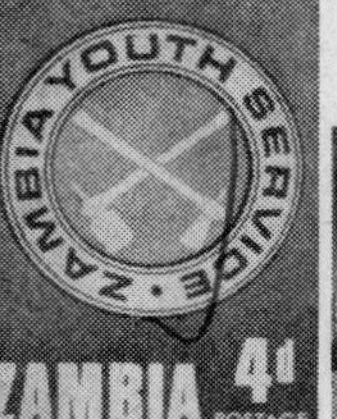

38. Youth Service Badge.

43. Lusaka Cathedral.

1967. National Development.
124. 38. 4d. black, red and gold 10 10
125. – 6d. black, gold and blue 10 10
126. – 9d. black, blue & silver 15 20
127. – 1s. multicoloured .. 30 10
128. – 1s. 6d. multicoloured .. 40 1·00

DESIGNS—HORIZ. 6d. " Co-operative Farming". 1s. 6d. Road link with Tanzania. VERT. 9d. "Communications". 1s. Coalfields.

1968. Decimal Currency.
129. 43. 1 n. multicoloured .. 10 10
130. – 2 n. multicoloured .. 10 10
131. – 3 n. multicoloured .. 10 10
132. – 5 n. brown and bronze 10 10
133. – 8 n. multicoloured .. 15 10
134. – 10 n. multicoloured .. 25 10
135. – 15 n. multicoloured .. 2·75 10
136. – 20 n. multicoloured .. 2·00 10
137. – 25 n. multicoloured .. 25 10
138. – 50 n. brown, orange and bronze 30 15
139. – 1 k. blue and bronze .. 3·25 20
140. – 2 k. black and bronze .. 2·25 1·25

DESIGNS—As T **43**: VERT. 2 n. Baobab tree. 5 n. National Museum, Livingstone. 8 n. Vimbuza dancer. 10 n. Tobacco picking. HORIZ. 3 n. Zambia Airways jetliner. LARGER (32 × 26 mm): 15 n. "Imbrasia zambesina" (moth). 1 k. Kafue Railway Bridge. 2 k. Eland. (26 × 22 mm): 20 n. South African crowned cranes. 25 n. Angoni warrior. 50 n. Chokwe dancer.

55. Ndola on Outline of Zambia.

1968. Trade Fair, Ndola.
141. 55. 15 n. green and gold .. 10 10

56. Human Rights Emblem and Heads.

1968. Human Rights Year.
142. 56. 3 n. blue, violet and gold 10 10

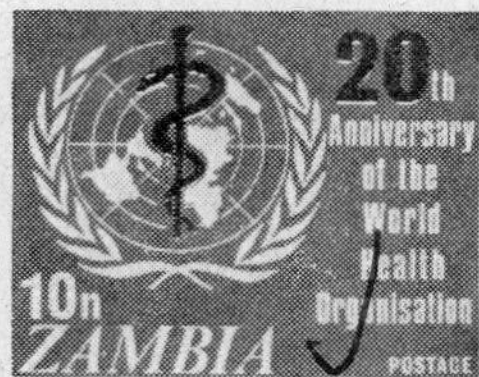

57. W.H.O. Emblem.

1968. 20th Anniv. of World Health Organization.
143. 57. 10 n. gold and violet .. 10 10

58. Group of Children.

1968. 22nd Anniv. of U.N.I.C.E.F.
144. 58. 25 n. black, gold & blue 15 70

59. Copper Miner.

1969. 50th Anniv. of Int. Labour Organization.
145. 59. 3 n. gold and violet .. 10 10
146. – 25 n. yellow, gold & brn. 60 70

DESIGN—HORIZ. 25 n. Poling a furnace.

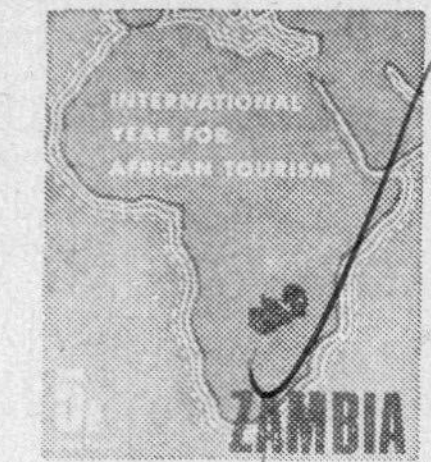

61. Zambia outlined on Map of Africa.

1969. Int. African Tourist Year. Mult.
147. 5 n. Type **61** 10 10
148. 10 n. Waterbuck 15 10
149. 15 n. Golden Perch .. 35 40
150. 25 n. Carmine Bee-Eater .. 1·00 1·00

Nos. 148/50 are horiz.

65. Satellite " Nimbus III " orbiting the Earth.

1970. World Meteorological Day.
151. 65. 15 n. multicoloured .. 15 40

66. Woman collecting Water from Well.

1970. Preventive Medicine.
152. 66. 3 n. multicoloured .. 10 10
153. – 15 n. multicoloured .. 15 15
154. – 25 n. blue, red and sepia 30 30

DESIGNS: 15 n. Child on scales. 25 n. Child being immunized.

67. " Masks " (mural by Gabriel Ellison).

1970. Conference of Non-Aligned Nations.
155. 67. 15 n. multicoloured .. 30 20

68. Ceremonial Axe.

1970. Traditional Crafts. Multicoloured.
156. 3 n. Type **68** 10 10
157. 5 n. Clay Smoking-Pipe Bowl 15 10
158. 15 n. Makishi Mask .. 35 40
159. 25 n. Kuomboka Ceremony 70 1·25

SIZES—HORIZ. 5 n. as T **68**. 25 n. 72 × 19 mm. VERT. 15 n. 30 × 47 mm.

69. Dag Hammarskjold and U.N. General Assembly.

1971. 10th Death Anniv. of Dag Hammarskjold. Multicoloured.
161. 4 n. Type **69** 10 10
162. 10 n. Tail of aircraft .. 10 10
163. 15 n. Dove of Peace .. 15 25
164. 25 n. Memorial tablet .. 35 1·50

70. Red-breasted Bream.

1971. Fish. Multicoloured.
165. 4 n. Type **70** 20 10
166. 10 n. Green-headed Bream 35 30
167. 15 n. Tiger fish .. .. 70 1·75

71. North African Crested Porcupine.

1972. Conservation Year (1st issue). Mult.
168. 4 n. Cheetah (horiz.) .. 20 25
169. 10 n. Lechwe (horiz.) .. 50 60
170. 15 n. Type **71** 80 85
171. 25 n. African elephant .. 2·00 2·25

Nos. 168/9 are size 58 × 21 mm.

1972. Conservation Year (2nd issue). As T **71**. Multicoloured.
172. 4 n. Soil conservation .. 20 20
173. 10 n. Forestry 40 45
174. 15 n. Water 60 70
175. 25 n. Maize .. .. 1·25 1·40

Nos. 174/5 are size 58 × 21 mm.

73. Zambian Flowers.

1972. Conservation Year (3rd issue). Mult.
177. 4 n. Type **73** 30 30
178. 10 n. "Papilio demodocus" (butterfly) 70 70
179. 15 n. "Apis mellifera" (bees) .. .. .. 1·25 1·25
180. 25 n. "Nomadacris septemfasciata" (locusts) .. 2·00 2·00

74. Mary and Joseph.

1972. Christmas. Multicoloured.

181.	4 n. Type **74**	10	10
182.	9 n. Mary, Joseph and Jesus	10	10
183.	15 n. Mary, Jesus and the shepherds	10	10
184.	25 n. The Three Wise Men	20	40

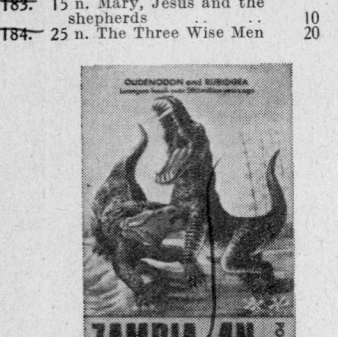

75. " Oudenodon " and " Rubidgea ".

1973. Zambian Prehistoric Animals. Mult.

185.	4 n. Type **75**	85	85
186.	9 n. Broken Hill Man ..	90	90
187.	10 n. " Zambiasaurus " ..	1·00	1·50
188.	15 n. " Luangwa drysdalli "	1·10	2·00
189.	25 n. " Glossopteris " ..	1·25	3·00

Nos. 186/9 are smaller (38 × 21 mm.) and show fossils.

76. " Dr. Livingstone I Presume ".

1973. Death Cent. of Livingstone. Mult.

190.	3 n. Type **76**	35	15
191.	4 n. Scripture Lesson ..	35	15
192.	9 n. Victoria Falls ..	70	40
193.	10 n. Scattering slavers ..	70	45
194.	15 n. Healing the sick ..	1·00	1·50
195.	25 n. Burial place of Livingstone's heart	1·40	2·25

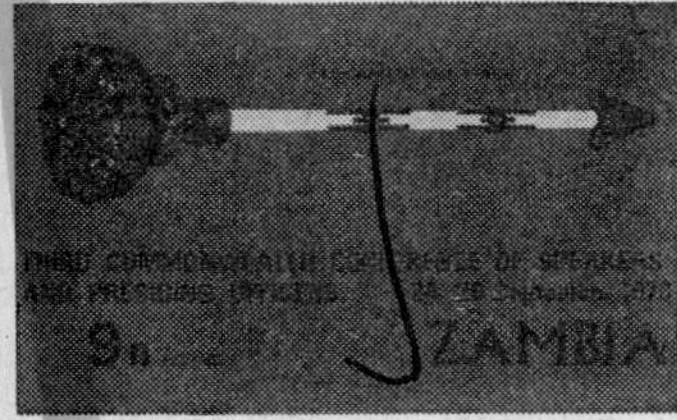

77. Parliamentary Mace.

1973. 3rd Commonwealth Conf., of Speakers and Presiding Officers, Lusaka.

196.	**77.**	9 n. multicoloured ..	80	65
197.		15 n. multicoloured ..	1·00	1·75
198.		25 n. multicoloured ..	1·50	2·50

78. Inoculation.

1973. 25th Anniv. of W.H.O. Multicoloured.

199.	4 n. Mother washing baby (vert.)	48·00	23·00
200.	9 n. Nurse weighing baby (vert.)	45	1·50
201.	10 n. Type **78** ..	50	2·00
202.	15 n. Child eating meal ..	90	3·50

79. U.N.I.P. Flag.

1974. 1st Anniv. of Second Republic. Mult.

203.	4 n. Type **79**	10·00	8·00
204.	9 n. Freedom House ..	40	1·50
205.	10 n. Army band	40	2·00
206.	15 n. "Celebrations" (dancers)	70	3·50
207.	25 n. Presidential chair ..	1·40	5·00

80. President Kaunda at Mulungushi.

1974. 50th Birthday of President Kaunda Multicoloured.

208.	4 n. Type **80**	1·00	1·00
209.	9 n. President's former residence	50	50
210.	15 n. President holding Independence flame ..	1·40	2·50

81. Nakambala Sugar Estate.

1974. 10th Anniv. of Independence. Mult.

211.	3 n. Type **81**	20	15
212.	4 n. Local market	20	15
213.	9 n. Kapiri glass factory ..	35	45
214.	10 n. Kafue hydro-electric scheme	40	50
215.	15 n. Kafue railway bridge	70	1·50
216.	25 n. Non-aligned Conference, Lusaka, 1970 ..	1·10	1·75

82. Mobile Post-van.

1974. Centenary of U.P.U. Multicoloured.

218.	4 n. Type **82**	20	15
219.	9 n. Aeroplane on tarmac	40	30
220.	10 n. Chipata Post Office ..	40	40
221.	15 n. Modern training centre	65	1·75

83. Dish Aerial.

1974. Opening of Mwembeshi Earth Station. Multicoloured.

222.	4 n. Type **83**	30	20
223.	9 n. View at dawn ..	65	50
224.	15 n. View at dusk ..	1·00	1·25
225.	25 n. Aerial view	1·50	2·25

84. Rhinoceros and Calf.

85. Independence Monument.

1975. Multicoloured.

226.	1 n. Type **84**	30	15
227.	2 n. Helmet Guinea fowl ..	30	15
228.	3 n. National Dancing Troupe	15	10
229.	4 n. African Fish Eagle ..	40	10
230.	5 n. Knife-edge Bridge ..	45	15
231.	8 n. Sitatunga (antelope) ..	45	15
232.	9 n. African Elephant, Kasaba Bay	75	15
233.	10 n. Temminck's Ground Pangolin	20	10
234.	15 n. Type **85**	30	10
235.	20 n. Harvesting groundnuts	65	65
236.	25 n. Tobacco-growing ..	70	30
237.	50 n. Flying Doctor service	90	1·40
238.	1 k. Lady Ross's Turaco ..	2·75	4·25
239.	2 k. Village scene	9·75	8·25

Nos. 234/239 are as Type **85**.

86. Map of Namibia.

1975. Namibia Day.

240.	**86.**	4 n. green and yellow	20	20
241.		9 n. blue and green ..	30	30
242.		15 n. orange & yellow	65	75
243.		25 n. red and orange ..	85	1·25

87. Erection of Sprinkler Irrigation.

1975. Silver Jubilee of Int. Commission on Irrigation and Drainage. Multicoloured.

244.	4 n. Type **87**	15	15
245.	9 n. Sprinkler irrigation ..	30	40
246.	15 n. Furrow irrigation ..	65	1·25

88. Mutondo.

1976. World Forestry Day. Multicoloured.

247.	3 n. Type **88**	25	10
248.	4 n. Mukunyu	25	10
249.	9 n. Mukusi	45	25
250.	10 n. Mopane	45	25
251.	15 n. Musuku	70	1·40
252.	25 n. Mukwa	85	1·75

MINIMUM PRICE

The minimum price quoted is 10p which represents a handling charge rather than a basis for valuing common stamps. For further notes about prices see introductory pages.

89. Passenger Train.

1976. Opening of Tanzania-Zambia Railway. Multicoloured.

253.	4 n. Type **89**	30	30
254.	9 n. Copper exports ..	55	55
255.	15 n. Machinery imports ..	90	95
256.	25 n. Goods train	1·40	1·75

90. Kayowe Dance.

1977. Second World Black and African Festival of Arts and Culture, Nigeria. Multicoloured.

258.	4 n. Type **90**	15	10
259.	9 n. Lilombola dance ..	25	25
260.	15 n. Initiation ceremony	45	50
261.	25 n. Munkhwele dance ..	75	1·25

91. Grimwood's Longclaw.

1977. Birds of Zambia. Multicoloured.

262.	4 n. Type **91**	40	10
263.	9 n. Shelly's Sunbird ..	70	60
264.	10 n. Black Cheeked Lovebird	70	60
265.	15 n. Locust Finch ..	1·40	2·00
266.	20 n. Black-Chinned Tinker bird	1·60	2·25
267.	25 n. Chaplin's Barbet ..	2·00	2·75

92. Girls with Building Blocks.

1977. Decade of Actions to Combat Racisn and Racial Discrimination. Mult.

268.	4 n. Type **92**	10	1
269.	9 n. Women dancing ..	15	2
270.	15 n. Girls with dove ..	25	6

93. Angels and Shepherds.

1977. Christmas. Multicoloured.

271.	4 n. Type **93**	10	1
272.	9 n. The Holy Family ..	10	1
273.	10 n. The Magi	10	1
274.	15 n. Jesus presented to Simeon	20	6

94. African Elephant and Road Check.

1978. Anti-poaching. Multicoloured.

75. 8 n. Type **94** 25 10
76. 18 n. Lechwe and canoe patrol 40 55
77. 28 n. Warthog 60 85
78. 32 n. Cheetah and game guard patrol .. .. 75 1·10

1979. Various stamps surch.

79. – 8 n. on 9 n. multicoloured (No. 232) 30 10
80. – 10 n. on 3 n. multicoloured (No. 228) 10 10
81. – 18 n. on 25 n. multicoloured (No. 236) 15 15
82. **85.** 28 n. on 15 n. multicoloured 20 25

96. Kayowe Dance.

979. Commonwealth Summit Conference, Lusaka. Multicoloured.

33. 18 n. Type **96** 15 25
34. 32 n. Kutambala dance .. 25 40
35. 42 n. Chitwansombo drummers 35 60
36. 58 n. Lilombola dance .. 50 80

97. " Kalulu and the Tug of War ".

979. International Year of the Child. **Mult.**

37. 18 n. Type **97** 40 30
38. 32 n. " Why the Zebra has no Horns " 55 55
39. 42 n. " How the Tortoise got his Shell " 60 85
90. 58 n. " Kalulu and the Lion " .. .. .. 80 1·00

98. Children of different races holding Anti-Apartheid Emblem.

979. International Anti-Apartheid Year. Multicoloured.

2. 18 n. Type **98** 15 25
3. 32 n. Children with toy car 25 40
4. 42 n. Young children with butterfly 35 60
5. 58 n. Children with microscope 50 80

99. Sir Rowland Hill and 2s. Definitive Stamp of 1964.

1979. Death Centenary of Sir Rowland Hill. Multicoloured.

296. 18 n. Type **99** 20 25
297. 32 n. Sir Rowland Hill and mailman 40 55
298. 42 n. Sir Rowland Hill and Northern Rhodesia 1963 ½d. definitive stamp .. 50 70
299. 58 n. Sir Rowland Hill and mail-carrying oxwaggon 65 1·10

1980. " London 1980 " International Stamp Exhibition. Nos. 296/299 optd. **LONDON 1980.**

301. **99.** 18 n. multicoloured .. 35 40
302. – 32 n. multicoloured .. 55 70
303. – 42 m. multicoloured .. 70 90
304. – 58 m. multicoloured .. 90 1·10

101. Rotary Anniv. Emblem.

1980. 75th Anniv. of Rotary International.

306. **101.** 8 n. multicoloured .. 10 10
307. 32 n. multicoloured .. 40 55
308. 42 n. multicoloured .. 45 80
309. 58 n. multicoloured .. 70 1·00

102. Running.

1980. Olympic Games, Moscow. Multicoloured.

311. 18 n. Type **102** 25 25
312. 32 n. Boxing 35 45
313. 42 n. Football 40 80
314. 58 n. Swimming .. .. 70 1·25

103. "Euphaedra zaddachi".

1980. Butterflies. Multicoloured.

316 18 n. Type **103** 15 15
317 32 n. "Aphnaeus questiauxi" 25 40
318 42 n. "Abantis zambesiaca" 40 80
319 58 n. "Spindasis modesta" 60 1·10

104. Zambia Coat of Arms.

1980. 26th Commonwealth Parliamentary Association Conference, Lusaka.

321. **104.** 18 n. multicoloured .. 15 25
322. 32 n. multicoloured .. 25 45
323. 42 n. multicoloured .. 30 65
324. 58 n. multicoloured .. 40 90

105. Nativity and St. Francis of Assisi (stained glass window, Ndola Church).

1980. 50th Anniv. of Catholic Church on the Copperbelt.

325. **105.** 8 n. multicoloured .. 10 10
326. 28 n. multicoloured .. 30 50
327. 32 n. multicoloured .. 30 50
328. 42 n. multicoloured .. 35 65

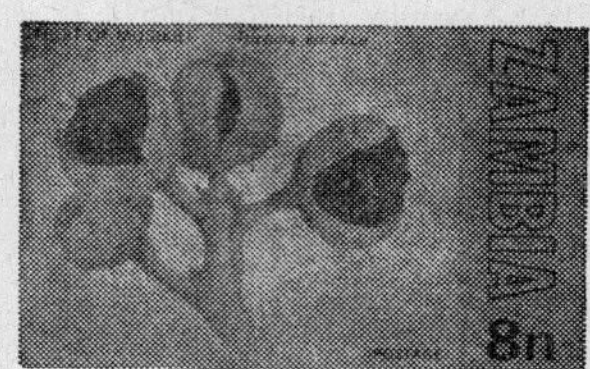

106. " Musikili ".

1981. World Forestry Day. Seedpods. **Mult.**

329. 8 n. Type **106** 10 10
330. 18 n. Mupapa 30 45
331. 28 n. Mulunguti 40 80
332. 32 n. Mulama .. .. 45 1·25

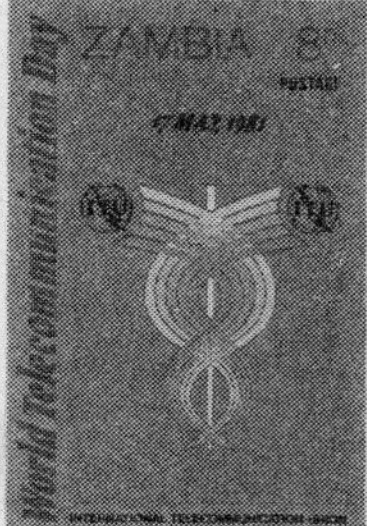

107. I.T.U. Emblems. **108.** Mask Maker.

1981. World Telecommunications and Health Day. Multicoloured.

333. 8 n. Type **107** 20 10
334. 18 n. W.H.O. emblems .. 45 35
335. 28 n. Type **107** 80 60
336. 32 n. As 18 n. 95 75

1981. Native Crafts. Multicoloured.

337. 1 n. Type **108.** 10 10
338. 2 n. Blacksmith 10 10
339. 5 n. Pottery making .. 10 10
340. 8 n. Straw-basket fishing 10 10
341. 10 n. Thatching 10 10
342. 12 n. Mushroom picking 1·25 65
343. 18 n. Millet grinding on stone 20 10
344. 28 n. Royal Barge paddler 40 10
345. 30 n. Makishi tight rope dancer 40 10
346. 35 n. Tonga Ila granary and house 45 10
347. 42 n. Cattle herding .. 45 40
348. 50 n. Traditional healer (38 × 26 mm.) 45 10
349. 75 n. Women carrying water (38 × 26 mm.) 45 50
350. 1 k. Pounding maize (38 × 26 mm.) 45 50
351. 2 k. Pipe smoking, Gwembe Valley Belle (38 × 26 mm.) 45 50

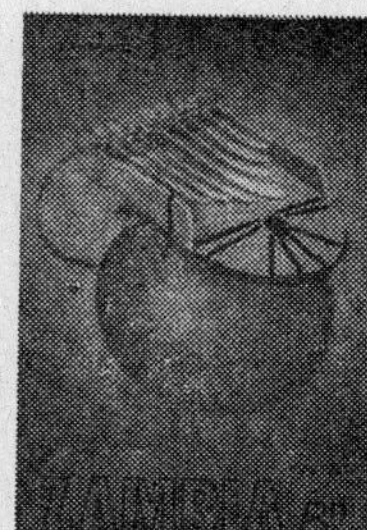

109. Kankobele.

1981. Traditional Musical Instruments. **Mult.**

356. 8 n. Type **109.** 25 10
357. 18 n. Inshingili 55 35
358. 28 n. Ilimba 80 80
359. 32 n. Bango .. .. 90 1·10

110. Banded Ironstone.

1982. Minerals (1st series). Multicoloured.

360. 8 n. Type **110.** 40 10
361. 18 n. Cobaltocalcite .. 1·00 70
362. 28 n. Amazonite .. .. 1·25 1·00
363. 32 n. Tourmaline .. 1·40 1·60
364. 42 n. Uranium ore .. 1·75 2·00

See also Nos. 370/4.

111. Zambian Scouts.

1982. 75th Anniv. of Boy Scout Movement. Multicoloured.

365. 8 n. Type **111.** 30 10
366. 18 n. Lord Baden-Powell and Victoria Falls .. 70 40
367. 28 n. Buffalo and Zambian Scout patrol pennant .. 70 50
368. 1 k. African Fish Eagle and Zambian Conservation badge .. .. 2·00 3·00

1982. Minerals (2nd series). As **T 110. Mult.**

370. 8 n. Bornite 60 10
371. 18 n. Chalcopyrite .. 1·50 75
372. 28 n. Malachite .. .. 2·00 2·00
373. 32 n. Azurite .. .. 2·00 2·00
374. 42 n. Vanadinite .. .. 2·50 3·00

112. Drilling Rig, 1926.

1983. Early Steam Engines. Multicoloured.

375. 8 n. Type **112** 40 10
376. 18 n. Fowler road locomotive, 1900 .. .. 60 60
377. 28 n. Borsig ploughing engine, 1925 .. .. 90 1·50
378. 32 n. Class "7" railway locomotive, 1900 .. 1·10 1·75

113. Cotton Picking.

1983. Commonwealth Day. Multicoloured.

379. 12 n. Type **113** 15 10
380. 18 n. Mining 30 30
381. 28 n. Ritual pot and traditional dances 30 50
382. 1 k. Violet-crested Turaco and Victoria Falls .. 2·25 3·50

114. " **Eulophia cucullata** ".

1983. Wild Flowers. Multicoloured.

383. 12 n. Type **114** .. 20 10
384. 28 n. " Kigelia africana " 35 40
385. 35 n. " Protea gaguedi " .. 45 70
386. 50 n. " Leonotis nepetifolia " 65 1·40

115. Giraffe.

1983. Wildlife of Zambia. Multicoloured.

388. 12 n. Type **115** 60 10
389. 28 n. Blue Wildebeest .. 80 60
390. 35 n. Lechwe 95 80
391. 1 k. Yellow Backed Duiker 2·00 3·00

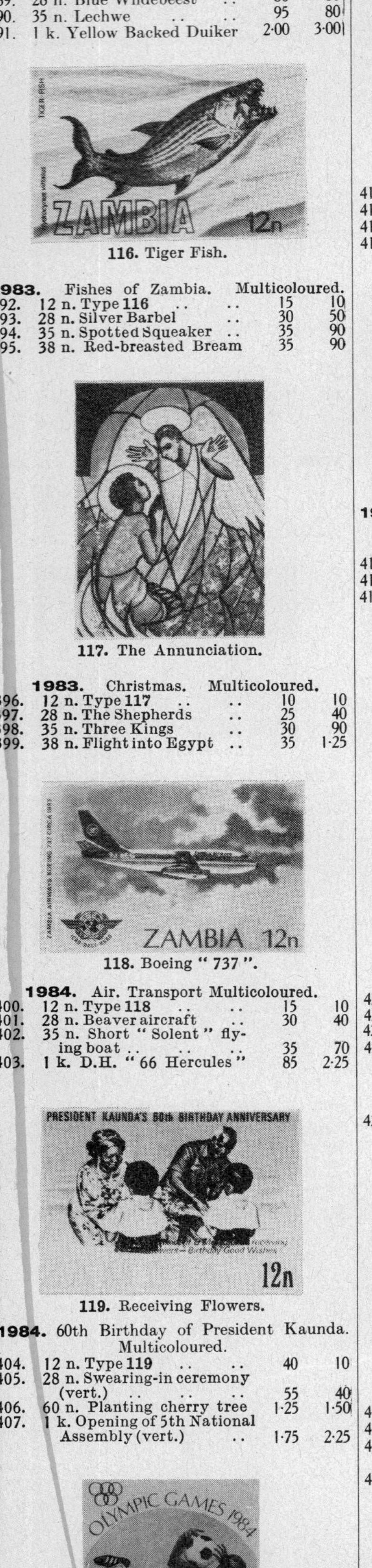

116. Tiger Fish.

1983. Fishes of Zambia. Multicoloured.

392. 12 n. Type **116** 15 10
393. 28 n. Silver Barbel .. 30 50
394. 35 n. Spotted Squeaker .. 35 90
395. 38 n. Red-breasted Bream 35 90

117. The Annunciation.

1983. Christmas. Multicoloured.

396. 12 n. Type **117** 10 10
397. 28 n. The Shepherds .. 25 40
398. 35 n. Three Kings .. 30 90
399. 38 n. Flight into Egypt .. 35 1·25

118. Boeing " 737 ".

1984. Air. Transport Multicoloured.

400. 12 n. Type **118** 15 10
401. 28 n. Beaver aircraft .. 30 40
402. 35 n. Short " Solent " flying boat 35 70
403. 1 k. D.H. " 66 Hercules " 85 2·25

119. Receiving Flowers.

1984. 60th Birthday of President Kaunda. Multicoloured.

404. 12 n. Type **119** 40 10
405. 28 n. Swearing-in ceremony (vert.) 55 40
406. 60 n. Planting cherry tree 1·25 1·50
407. 1 k. Opening of 5th National Assembly (vert.) .. 1·75 2·25

120. Football.

1984. Olympic Games, Los Angeles. Multicoloured.

408. 12 n. Type **120** 20 10
409. 28 n. Running 30 45
410. 35 n. Hurdling 40 60
411. 50 n. Boxing 50 80

121. Gaboon Viper.

1984. Reptiles. Multicoloured.

412. 12 n. Type **121** 15 10
413. 28 n. Chameleon 30 40
414. 35 n. Nile Crocodile .. 40 60
415. 1 k. Blue-headed Agama .. 85 2·25

122. Pres. Kaunda and Mulungushi Rock.

1984. 26th Anniv. of United National Independence Party and 20th Anniv. of Independence (1st issue). Multicoloured.

417. 12 n. Type **122** 30 10
418. 28 n. Freedom statue .. 45 45
419. 1 k. Pres. Kaunda and agricultural produce ("Lima Programme") .. .. 1·25 2·00

123. "Amanita flammeola".

1984. Fungi. Multicoloured.

420. 12 n. Type **123** 55 15
421. 28 n. "Amanita zambiana" 75 55
422. 32 n. "Temitomyces letestui" 1·00 85
423. 75 n. "Cantharellus minatescens" .. .. 1·75 2·00

1985. No. 237 surch.

424. 5 k. on 50 n. Flying-doctor service .. .. .. 1·00 1·60

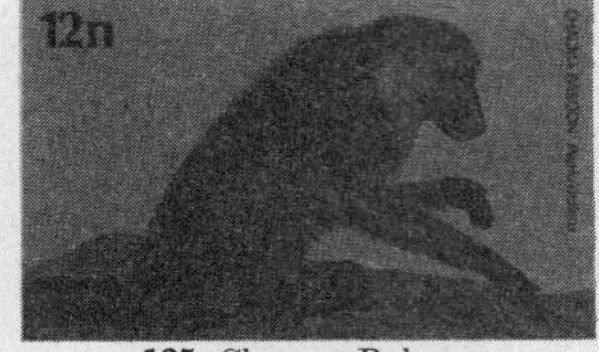

125. Chacma Baboon.

1985. Zambian Primates. Multicoloured.

425. 12 n. Type **125** 25 10
426. 20 n. Diademed monkey .. 40 20
427. 45 n. Diademed monkey (different) 70 70
428. 1 k. Savanna Monkey .. 1·00 1·10

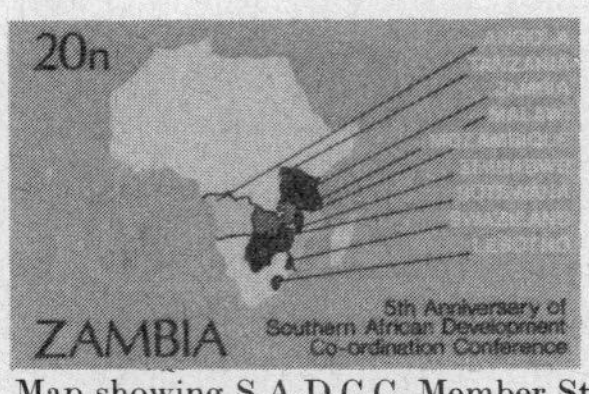

126. Map showing S.A.D.C.C. Member States.

1985. 5th Anniv. of Southern African Development Co-ordination Conference.

429. **126.** 20 n. multicoloured .. 40 15
430. – 45 n. black, blue and light blue .. .. 1·00 75
431. – 1 k. multicoloured .. 1·50 2·00

DESIGNS: 45 n. Mining. 1 k. Flags of member states and Mulungushi Hall.

127. The Queen Mother in 1980.

1985. Life and Times of Queen Elizabeth the Queen Mother.

432. **127.** 25 n. multicoloured .. 10 10
433. – 45 n. blue and gold .. 10 15
434. – 55 n. blue and gold .. 15 20
435. – 5 k. multicoloured .. 1·25 2·00

DESIGNS—VERT. 45 n. The Queen Mother at Clarence House, 1963. HORIZ. 55 n. With the Queen and Princess Margaret, 1980. 5 k. At Prince Henry's christening, 1984.

1985. Nos. 340 and 342 surch.

436 20 n. on 12 n. Mushroom picking .. .. .. 1·25 20
437 25 n. on 8 n. Straw-basket fishing 50 30

1985. 26th Anniv. of United National Independence Party (No. 438) and 20th Anniv. of Independence (2nd issue). As Nos. 417/19 but larger (55 × 34 mm.) On gold foil.

438. 5 k. As Type **122** .. .. 1·60 2·50
439. 5 k. Freedom Statue .. 1·60 2·50
440. 5 k. Pres. Kaunda and agricultural produce ("Lima Programme") .. 1·60 2·50

129. Postman and Lusaka Post Office, 1958.

1985. 10th Anniv. of Posts and Telecommunication Corporation. Multicoloured.

441. 20 n. Type **129** 25 10
442. 45 n. Postman and Livingstone Post Office, 1950. 45 20
443. 55 n. Postman and Kalomo Post Office, 1902 .. 55 40
444. 5 k. Africa Trans-Continental Telegraph Line under construction, 1900 .. .. .. 2·00 3·00

130. Boy in Maize Field.

1985. 40th Anniv. of United Nations Organization.

445. **130.** 20 n. multicoloured .. 30 10
441. – 45 n. black, bl. & brn. 40 20
447. – 1 k. multicoloured .. 70 90
448. – 2 k. multicoloured .. 1·25 1·60

DESIGNS: 45 n. Logo and "40". 1 k. President Kaunda addressing U.N. General Assembly, 1970. 2 k. Signing of U.N. Charter, San Francisco, 1945.

131. "Mylabris tricolor".

1986. Beetles. Multicoloured.

449. 35 n. Type **131** 10 10
450. 1 k. "Phasgonocnema melanianthe" 15 20
451. 1 k. 70 "Amaurodes passerinii" 25 40
452. 5 k. "Ranzania petersiana" 70 1·50

1986. 60th Birthday of Queen Elizabeth II. As T **110** of Ascension. Multicoloured.

453. 35 n. Princess Elizabeth at Flower Ball, Savoy Hotel, 1951 .. .. 10 10
454. 1 k. 25 With Prince Andrew, Lusaka Airport, 1979 .. .. 15 20
455. 1 k. 70 With President Kaunda 20 25
456. 1 k. 95 In Luxembourg, 1976 .. .. .. 25 30
457. 5 k. At Crown Agents Head Office, London, 1983. .. .. .. 60 80

1986. Royal Wedding. As T **112** of Ascension. Multicoloured.

458. 1 k. 70 Prince Andrew and Miss Sarah Ferguson .. 30 30
459. 5 k. Prince Andrew in Zambia, 1979 .. .. 80 1·25

132. Goalkeeper saving Goal.

1986. World Cup Football Championship Mexico. Multicoloured.

460. 35 n. Type **132** 50 1
461. 1 k. 25 Player kicking ball 1·25 1·0
462. 1 k. 70 Two players competing for ball .. .. 1·40 1·4
463. 5 k. Player scoring goal .. 3·00 3·5

133. Sculpture of Edmond Halley by Henry Pegram.

1986. Appearance of Halley's Comet.

464. **133.** 1 k. 25 multicoloured 55 3
465. – 1 k. 70 multicoloured 70 5
466. – 2 k. multicoloured .. 90 8
467. – 5 k. blue and black .. 2·50 2·7

DESIGNS: 1 k. 70, "Giotto" spacecraft approaching nucleus of Comet; 2 k. Studying Halley's Comet in 1682 and 1986; 5 k. Part of Halley's chart of southern sky.

134. Nativity.

1986. Christmas. Children's Paintings. Mult

468. 35 n. Type **134** 20 1
469. 1 k. 25 Visit of the Three Kings 75 5
470. 1 k. 60 Holy Family with shepherd and king .. 85 7
471. 5 k. Angel and christmas tree .. .. .. 2·50 3·

135. Train in Kasama Cutting.

1986. 10th Anniv. of Tanzania–Zambia Railway. Multicoloured.

472	35 n. Type **135**	20	10
473	1 k. 25 Train leaving Tunnel No. 21	35	40
474	1 k. 70 Train between Tunnels No. 6 and 7	40	60
475	5 k. Trains at Mpika Station	1·00	1·75

136. President Kaunda and Graduate.

1987. 20th Anniv. of University of Zambia. Multicoloured.

76.	35 n. Type **136**	20	10
77.	1 k. 25 University Badge (vert.)	50	40
78.	1 k. 60 University Statue	60	55
79.	5 k. President Kaunda laying foundation stone (vert.)	2·00	2·75

137. Arms of Kitwe. **138.** Chestnut-headed Crake.

1987. Arms of Zambian Towns. Mult.

80.	35 n. Type **137**	10	10
81.	1 k. 25 Ndola	15	20
82.	1 k. 70 Lusaka	20	25
83.	20 k. Livingstone	2·40	3·25

1987. Birds (1st series). Multicoloured.

34	5 n. Cloud-scraping cisticola	10	10
35	10 n. White-winged starling	10	10
36a	20 n. on 1 n. Yellow swamp warbler	20	10
37	25 n. Type **138**	20	10
38	30 n. Miombo pied barbet	10	10
39	35 n. Black and rufous swallow	30	20
90	40 n. Wattled crane	10	10
91	50 n. Slaty egret	10	10
92a	75 n. on 2 n. Olive-flanked robin	30	30
93	1 k. Bradfield's hornbill	30	15
94	1 k. 25 Boulton's puff-backed flycatcher ("Margaret's Batis")	30	30
95	1 k. 60 Anchiet's sunbird	35	35
96	1 k. 65 on 30 n. Miombo pied barbet	30	40
97	1 k. 70 Boehm's bee eater	45	45
98	1 k. 95 Perrin's bush shrike	45	45
99	2 k. Whale-headed stork ("Shoebill")	35	35
00	5 k. Taita falcon	75	55
01	10 k. on 50 n. Slaty egret	1·10	1·10
02	20 k. on 2 k. Whale-headed stork	2·10	2·50

Nos. 491, 493/5 and 497/502 are larger, size 4 × 39 mm.

No. 502 is surcharged "K20". For No. 499 urcharged "K20.00" see No. 594.

139. Look-out Tree, Livingstone.

1987. Tourism. Multicoloured.

03.	35 n. Type **139**	30	15
04.	1 k. 25 Rafting on Zambezi	60	40
05.	1 k. 70 Tourists photographing lions, Luangwa Valley	90	60
06.	10 k. White pelicans	4·00	4·00

1987. Various stamps surch. with new value.

(a) Nos. 432/5.

507.	**127.**	3 k. on 25 n. mult.	40	45
508.	–	6 k. on 45 n. blue and gold	85	90
509.	–	10 k. on 55 n. blue and gold	1·40	1·50
510.	–	20 k. on 5 k. mult.	2·75	3·00

(b) Nos. 453/7.

511.	3 k. on 35 n. Princess Elizabeth at Flower Ball, Savoy Hotel, 1951	40	45
512.	4 k. on 1 k. 25 With Prince Andrew, Lusaka Airport, 1979	55	60
513.	6 k. on 1 k. 70 With President Kaunda	85	90
514.	10 k. on 1 k. 95 In Luxembourg, 1976	1·40	1·50
515.	20 k. on 5 k. At Crown Agents Head Office, London, 1983	2·75	3·00

(c) Nos. 460/3.

516.	3 k. on 35 n. Type **132**	40	45
517.	6 k. on 1 k. 25 Player kicking ball	85	90
518.	10 k. on 1 k. 70 Two players competing for ball	1·40	1·50
519.	20 k. on 5 k. Player scoring goal	2·75	3·00

(d) Nos. 464/7.

520.	**133.**	3 k. on 1 k. 25 mult.	45	90
521.	–	6 k. on 1 k. 70 mult.	85	90
522.	–	10 k. on 2 k. mult.	1·40	1·50
523.	–	20 k. on 5 k. blue and black	2·75	3·00

141. De Havilland "Beaver".

1987. 20th Anniv. of Zambia Airways. Aircraft. Multicoloured.

524.	35 n. Type **141**	25	10
525.	1 k. 70 Douglas "DC-10"	75	35
526.	5 k. Douglas "DC-3 Dakota"	1·75	1·50
527.	10 k. Boeing "707"	2·75	3·00

142. Friesian/Holstein Cow.

1987. 40th Anniv. of F.A.O. Multicoloured.

528.	35 n. Type **142**	10	10
529.	1 k. 25 Simmental bull	20	25
530.	1 k. 70 Sussex bull	25	30
531.	20 k. Brahman bull	2·75	3·00

143. Mpoloto Ne Mikobango.

1987. People of Zambia. Multicoloured.

532.	35 n. Type **143**	10	10
533.	1 k. 25 Zintaka	20	25
534.	1 k. 70 Mufuluhi	25	30
535.	10 k. Ntebwe	1·40	1·50
536.	20 k. Kubangwa Aa Mbulunga	2·75	3·00

INDEX

Countries can be quickly located by referring to the index at the end of this volume.

144. Black Lechwe at Waterhole.

1987. Black Lechwe. Multicoloured.

537.	50 n. Type **144**	30	10
538.	2 k. Black lechwe resting by pool (horiz.)	75	40
539.	2 k. 50 Running through water (horiz.)	85	50
540.	10 k. Watching for danger	2·25	2·50

145 Cassava Roots

1988. International Fund for Agricultural Development. Multicoloured.

542	50 n. Type **145**	10	10
543	2 k. 50 Fishing	30	35
544	2 k. 85 Farmer and cattle	35	40
545	10 k. Picking coffee beans	1·25	1·40

146 Breast feeding

1988. U.N.I.C.E.F. Child Survival Campaign. Multicoloured.

546	50 n. Type **146**	10	10
547	2 k. Growth monitoring	25	30
548	2 k. 85 Immunization	35	40
549	10 k. Oral rehydration	1·25	2·00

147 Asbestos Cement

1988. Preferential Trade Area Fair. Mult.

550	50 n. Type **147**	10	10
551	2 k. 35 Textiles	25	30
552	2 k. 50 Tea	30	40
553	10 k. Poultry	1·25	2·25

148 Emergency Food Distribution

1988. 125th Anniv of International Red Cross. Multicoloured.

554	50 n. Type **148**	10	10
555	2 k. 50 Giving first aid	30	40
556	2 k. 85 Practising bandaging	35	50
557	10 k. Jean Henri Dunant (founder)	1·25	2·00

149 Aardvark

1988. Endangered Species of Zambia. Mult.

558	50 n. Type **149**	15	10
559	2 k. Temminck's ground pangolin	30	35
560	2 k. 85 Hunting dog	40	50
561	20 k. Black rhinoceros and calf	2·75	4·00

150 Boxing

1988. Olympic Games, Seoul. Multicoloured.

562	50 n. Type **150**	15	10
563	2 k. Athletics	30	35
564	2 k. 50 Hurdling	35	45
565	20 k. Football	2·75	4·00

151 Red Toad

1989. Frogs and Toads. Multicoloured.

567	50 n. Type **151**	15	10
568	2 k. 50 Puddle frog	40	40
569	2 k. 85 Marbled reed frog	45	55
570	10 k. Young reed frogs	1·40	2·25

152 Common Slit-faced Bat

1989. Bats. Multicoloured.

571	50 n. Type **152**	15	10
572	2 k. 50 Little free-tailed bat	45	55
573	2 k. 85 Hildebrandt's horseshoe bat	55	65
574	10 k. Peters' epauletted fruit bat	1·50	2·25

153 Pope John Paul II and Map of Zambia

1989. Visit of Pope John Paul II. Designs each with inset portrait. Multicoloured.

575	50 n. Type **153**	40	15
576	6 k. 85 Peace dove with olive branch	1·75	2·00
577	7 k. 85 Papal arms	2·00	2·25
578	10 k. Victoria Falls	2·50	3·00

1989. Various stamps surch with new value.

(a) On Nos. 339, 341/3, 345/6, 349 and 351.

579 1 k. 20 on 35 n. Tonga Ila granary and house .. 10 10
580 3 k. 75 on 5 n. Pottery making 15 15
581 8 k. 11 on 10 n. Thatching 30 30
582 9 k. on 30 n. Makishi tightrope dancer .. 30 30
583 10 k. on 75 n. Women carrying water (38 × 26 mm) 30 30
584 18 k. 50 on 2 k. Pipe-smoking, Gwembe Valley Belle (38 × 26 mm) 70 70
585 19 k. 50 on 12 n. Mushroom picking 70 70
586 20 k. 50 on 18 n. Millet grinding on stone .. 70 70

(b) On Nos. 484, 489, 493/5 and 497/500

587 70 n. on 35 n. Black and rufous swallow .. 10 10
588 3 k. on 5 n. Cloud-scraping cisticola 15 15
589 8 k. on 1 k. 25, Boulton's puff-back flycatcher ("Margaret's Batis") .. 30 30
590 9 k. 90 on 1 k. 70, Boehm's bee eater 40 40
591 10 k. 40 on 1 k. 60 Anchieta's sunbird .. 40 40
592 12 k. 50 on 1 k. Bradfield's hornbill 50 50
593 15 k. on 1 k. 95, Gorgeous bush shrike 60 60
594 20 k. on 2 k. Whale-headed stork ("Shoebill") .. 70 70
595 20 k. 35 on 5 k. Taita falcon 70 70

No. 594 shows the surcharge as "K20.00". The previously listed 20 k. on 2 k., No. 499, is surcharged "K20" only.

156 "Parinari curatellifolia"

1989. Edible Fruits. Multicoloured.

596 50 n. Type **156** 15 10
597 6 k. 50 "Uapaca kirkiana" 1·25 1·50
598 6 k. 85 Wild fig .. .. 1·25 1·75
599 10 k. Bottle palm .. 2·25 2·50

157 "Lamarckiana sp."

1989. Grasshoppers. Multicoloured.

600 70 n. Type **157** 15 10
601 10 k. 40 "Dictyopharus sp." .. .. .. 1·25 1·25
602 12 k. 50 "Cymatomena sp." 1·50 1·50
603 15 k. "Phymateus iris" .. 2·00 2·00

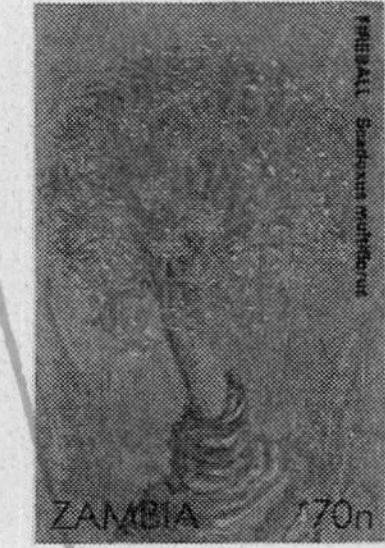

158 Fireball

1989. Christmas. Flowers. Multicoloured.

604 70 n. Type **158** 15 10
605 10 k. 40 Flame lily .. 1·00 1·00
606 12 k. 50, Foxglove lily .. 1·40 1·40
607 20 k. Vlei lily .. .. 2·40 2·40

159 Post Van, Postman on Bicycle and Main Post Office, Lusaka

1990. "Stamp World London 90" International Stamp Exhibition. Multicoloured.

608 1 k. 20 Type **159** 10 10
609 19 k. 50 Zambia 1980 18 n. butterflies stamp .. 1·25 1·25
610 20 k. 50, Rhodesia and Nyasaland 1962 9d. and Northern Rhodesia 1925 ½d. stamps .. .. 1·25 1·25
611 50 k. 1840 Penny Black and Maltese Cross cancellation .. .. .. 3·00 3·00

160 Footballer and Ball

1990. World Cup Football Championship, Italy.

612 **160** 1 k. 20 multicoloured 10 10
613 – 18 k. 50 multicoloured 1·00 1·00
614 – 19 k. 50 multicoloured 1·00 1·00
615 – 20 k. 50 multicoloured 1·00 1·00

DESIGNS: 18 k. 50 to 20 k. 50 Different football scenes.

161 Road Tanker

1990. 10th Anniv of Southern African Development Co-ordination Conference. Each showing map of Southern Africa. Multicoloured.

617 1 k. 20 Type **161** 10 10
618 19 k. 50 Telecommunications .. .. .. 1·00 1·00
619 20 k. 50 "Regional Co-operation" .. .. 1·00 1·00
620 50 k. Transporting coal by cable .. .. .. 3·00 3·00

162 Irrigation

1990. 26th Anniv of Independence. Mult.

621 1 k. 20 Type **162** 10 10
622 19 k. 50 Shoe factory .. 70 70
623 20 k. 50 Mwembeshi II satellite earth station .. 70 70
624 50 k. "Mother and Child" (statue) .. .. 1·75 2·00

1990. Birds (2nd series). As T **138**. Mult.

625 10 n. Livingstone's flycatcher 10 10
626 15 n. Bar-winged weaver 10 10
627 30 n. Purple-throated cuckoo shrike 10 10
628 50 n. Red-billed helmet shrike 10 10
629 50 n. As 10 n. 10 10
630 1 k. As 15 n. 10 10
631 1 k. 20 Western bronze-naped pigeon 10 10
632 2 k. As 30 n. 10 10
633 3 k. As 50 n. 10 10
634 5 k. As 1 k. 20 .. .. 10 10
635 15 k. Corncrake 25 30
636 20 k. Dickinson's grey kestrel 30 35
637 20 k. 50 As 20 k. 30 35
638 50 k. Denham's bustard .. 75 80

Nos. 635/8 are larger, size 23 × 39 mm.

163 The Bird and the Snake

1991. International Literacy Year. Folklore. Multicoloured.

639 1 k. 20 Type **163** 15 10
640 18 k. 50 Kalulu and the Leopard .. .. 1·00 1·00
641 19 k. 50 The Mouse and the Lion .. .. .. 1·00 1·00
642 20 k. 50 Kalulu and the Hippopotamus .. 1·00 1·00

164 Genet

1991. Small Carnivores. Multicoloured.

643 1 k. 20 Type **164** 15 10
644 18 k. 50 Civet .. .. 1·00 1·00
645 19 k. 50 Serval .. .. 1·00 1·00
646 20 k. 50 African wild cat .. 1·00 1·00

1991. Nos. 441/4 surch **K2**.

647 2 k. on 20 n. Type **129** .. 30 15
648 2 k. on 45 n. Postman and Livingstone Post Office, 1950 .. .. .. 30 15
649 2 k. on 55 n. Postman and Kalomo Post Office, 1902 30 15
650 2 k. on 5 k. African Trans-Continental Telegraph Line under construction, 1900 .. .. 30 15

166 Woman Cooking

1991. Soya Promotion Campaign. Mult.

651 1 k. Type **166** 10 10
652 2 k. Soya bean and field .. 10 10
653 5 k. Mother feeding child 15 15
654 20 k. Healthy and malnourished children .. 50 50
655 50 k. President Kaunda holding child 95 95

167 Chilubula Church near Kasama

1991. 500th Birth Anniv of St. Ignatius Loyola. Multicoloured.

656 1 k. Type **167** 10 10
657 2 k. Chikuni Church near Monze 10 10
658 20 k. Bishop Joseph du Pont 50 50
659 50 k. Saint Ignatius Loyola 95 95

168 "Adansonia digitata"

1991. Flowering Trees. Multicoloured.

660 1 k. Type **168** 10 10
661 2 k. "Dichrostachys cinerea" 10 1
662 10 k. "Sterospernum kunthianum" 25 25
663 30 k. "Azana garckeana" 70 70

1992. 40th Anniv of Queen Elizabeth II's Accession. As T **143** of Ascension. Mult.

664 4 k. Queen's House .. 10 1
665 32 k. Traditional village .. 50 55
666 35 k. Fishermen hauling nets 55 60
667 38 k. Three portraits of Queen Elizabeth .. 60 65
668 50 k. Queen Elizabeth II 75 80

169 "Disa hamatopetala"

1992. Orchids. Multicoloured.

669 1 k. Type **169** 10 1
670 2 k. "Eulophia paivaeana" 10 1
671 5 k. "Eulophia quartiniana" 10 1
672 20 k. "Aerangis verdickii" 30 3

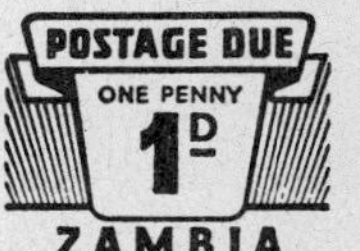
170 Kasinja Mask

1992. Tribal Masks. Multicoloured.

673 1 k. Type **170** 10 1
674 2 k. Chizaluke 10 1
675 10 k. Mwanapweu .. 15 2
676 30 k. Maliya 55 6

POSTAGE DUE STAMPS

D 3.

1964.

D 11. D **3.** 1d. orange 30 8
D 12. 2d. blue .. .. 35 1·1
D 13. 3d. lake .. .. 45 1·4
D 14. 4d. blue .. .. 45 1·7
D 15. 6d. purple .. .. 45 2·0
D 16. 1s. green .. .. 55 4·0

APPENDIX

The following stamps have either been issued in excess of postal needs, or have not been made available to the public in reasonable quantities at face value.

1984.

Olympic Games, Los Angeles. 90 n × 5, each embossed on gold foil.

1986.

Classic Cars 1 k. 50 × 25, each embossed on gold foil.

ZANZIBAR

A Br. Protectorate consisting of several islands off the coast of Tanganyika. E. Africa. Independent in 1963 and a republic within the Br. Commonwealth in 1964. The "United Republic of Tanganyika and Zanzibar" was proclaimed in July 1964, and the country was later renamed Tanzania. Separate issues for Zanzibar ceased on 1 Jan. 1968. and Tanzania stamps became valid for the whole country.

1895. 16 annas = 1 rupee.
1908. 100 cents = 1 rupee.
1936. 100 cents = 1 shilling.

1895. Stamps of India (Queen Victoria) optd. **Zanzibar.**

3.	**23.**	½ a. turquoise	3·00	2·50
4.		1 a. purple	3·25	3·00
5.		1½ a. brown	3·75	3·00
6.	–	2 a. blue	3·50	3·50
8.	–	2½ a. green	4·25	4·25
10.	–	3 a. orange	6·50	8·50
12.	–	4 a. green (No. 96) ..	8·00	9·50
13.	–	6 a. brown (No. 80) ..	9·00	10·00
15.	–	8 a. mauve	9·00	15·00
16.	–	12 a. purple on red ..	14·00	10·00
17.	–	1 r. grey	65·00	65·00
18.	**37.**	1 r. green and red ..	10·00	14·00
19.	**38.**	2 r. red and orange ..	28·00	42·00
20.		3 r. brown and green ..	30·00	42·00
21.		5 r. biue and violet ..	30·00	45·00

1895. Nos. 4/6 surch. **2½.**

23	**23**	2½ on 1 a. purple ..	£120	£100
22		2½ on 1½ a. brown ..	24·00	27·00
26	–	2½ on 2 a. blue ..	30·00	20·00

1896. Stamps of British East Africa (Queen Victoria) optd. **Zanzibar.**

41.	**11.**	½ a. green	21·00	15·00
42.		1 a. red	21·00	15·00
43.		2½ a. blue	75·00	40·00
44.		4½ a. yellow	30·00	42·00
45.		5 a. brown	35·00	18·00
46.		7½ a. mauve	24·00	32·00

13. Sultan Seyyid Hamed-bin-Thwain

19. Sultan Seyyid Hamoud-bin-Mahommed bin Said.

1896. The Rupee values are larger.

178	**13**	½ a. green and red ..	50	35
179		1 a. blue and red ..	60	45
180		2 a. brown and red ..	1·00	75
181		2½ a. blue and red ..	85	30
182		3 a. grey and red ..	2·25	60
183		4 a. green and red ..	1·50	1·00
184		4½ a. orange and red ..	2·50	70
166		5 a. brown and red ..	2·25	2·25
167		7½ a. mauve and red ..	2·25	2·25
187		8 a. olive and red ..	3·75	2·25
169	–	1 r. blue and red ..	9·00	9·00
171	–	2 r. green and red ..	13·00	9·50
172	–	3 r. purple and red ..	19·00	9·50
173	–	4 r. red	14·00	13·00
174	–	5 r. brown and red ..	18·00	15·00

1896. Surch. **2½.**

175.	**13.**	2½ on 4 a. green and red	48·00	28·00

1899. The Rupee values are larger.

188.	**19.**	½ a. green and red ..	55	25
189.		1 a. blue and red ..	1·25	20
190.		1 a. red	65	15
191.		2 a. brown and red ..	75	30
192.		2½ a. blue and red ..	1·00	50
193.		3 a. grey and red ..	1·25	1·40
194.		4 a. green and red ..	1·25	1·00
195.		4½ a. orange and red ..	3·50	2·25
196.		4½ a. black and red ..	4·75	4·75
197.		5 a. brown and red ..	1·50	1·25
198.		7½ a. mauve and red ..	2·25	3·25
199.		8 a. olive and red ..	2·25	3·50
200.	–	1 r. blue and red ..	15·00	12·00
201.	–	2 r. green and red ..	15·00	14·00
202.	–	3 r. purple and red ..	15·00	22·00
203.	–	4 r. red	24·00	35·00
204.	–	5 r. brown and red ..	35·00	42·00

1904. Surch. in words.

205.	**19.**	1 on 4½ a. orange and red	1·40	3·00
206.		1 on 4½ a. black and red ..	4·25	11·00
207.		2 on 4 a. green and red ..	11·00	16·00
208.		2½ on 7½ a. mauve and red	12·00	16·00
209.		2½ on 8 a. olive and red ..	13·00	26·00

23. Monogram of Sultan Seyyid Ali bin Hamoud bin Naherud.

1904. The Rupee values are larger.

210.	**23.**	½ a. green	65	15
211.		1 a. red	65	10
212.		2 a. brown	1·25	45
213.		2½ a. blue	1·60	35
214.		3 a. grey	1·50	1·25
215.		4 a. green	1·75	1·25
216.		4½ a. black	3·00	2·50
217.		5 a. brown	3·25	1·25
218.		7½ a. mauve	3·50	4·50
219.		8 a. olive	3·50	2·50
220.	–	1 r. blue and red ..	14·00	8·50
221.	–	2 r. green and red ..	12·00	24·00
222.	–	3 r. violet and red ..	32·00	55·00
223.	–	4 r. deep red and red ..	38·00	70·00
224.	–	5 r. brown and red ..	42·00	75·00

25.

27. Sultan Ali bin Hamoud.

26.

28. View of Port.

1908.

225.	**25.**	1 c. grey	25	25
226.		3 c. green	1·25	10
227.		6 c. red	3·00	10
228.		10 c. brown	1·50	1·75
229.		12 c. violet	3·75	55
230.	**26.**	15 c. blue	3·25	40
231.		25 c. brown	2·50	80
232.		50 c. green	3·25	3·50
233.		75 c. black	6·00	8·00
234.	**27.**	1 r. green	12·00	5·00
235.		2 r. violet	11·00	14·00
236.		3 r. brown	16·00	35·00
237.		4 r. red	27·00	60·00
238.		5 r. blue	32·00	48·00
239.	**28.**	10 r. green and brown ..	65·00	£110
240.		20 r. black and green ..	£160	£275
241.		30 r. black and brown	£250	£400
242.		40 r. black and orange ..	£400	
243.		50 r. black and mauve ..	£350	
244.		100 r. black and blue ..	£650	
245.		200 r. black and blue ..	£950	

29. Sultan Kalif bin Harub.

30. Sailing Canoe.

31. Dhow.

1913.

246	**29.**	1 c. grey	15	20
262		3 c. green	45	10
278		3 c. orange	15	10
279		4 c. green	50	60
280		6 c. red	30	50
281		6 c. purple on blue ..	35	10
264		8 c. purple on yellow ..	60	2·50
249		10 c. brown	80	75
265		10 c. green on yellow ..	60	35
283		12 c. violet	30	50
284		12 c. red	40	35
251		15 c. blue	1·00	30
286		20 c. blue	1·00	30
252		25 c. brown	80	45
288		50 c. green	1·25	2·00
254		75 c. black	1·50	1·75
290	**30.**	1 r. green	1·40	1·60
291		2 r. violet	2·50	4·50
292		3 r. brown	3·75	6·00
293		4 r. red	9·50	22·00
294		5 r. blue	12·00	42·00
295	**31.**	10 r. green and brown ..	40·00	95·00
260a		20 r. black and green ..	85·00	£160
260b		30 r. black and brown ..	£110	£200
260c		40 r. black and orange	£225	£350
260d		50 r. black and purple ..	£225	£350
260e		100 r. black and blue ..	£300	
260f		200 r. brown and black	£600	

32. Sultan Kalif bin Harub. **33.**

1926.

299.	**32.**	1 c. brown	15	10
300.		3 c. orange	15	15
301.		4 c. green	20	30
302.		6 c. violet	15	10
303.		8 c. grey	90	2·00
304.		10 c. olive	75	40
305.		12 c. red	1·50	10
306.		20 c. blue	40	30
307.		25 c. purple on yellow ..	3·00	2·50
308.		50 c. red	90	35
309.		75 c. brown	2·50	7·00

1936.

310.	**33.**	5 c. green	10	10
311.		10 c. black	10	10
312.		15 c. red	10	15
313.		20 c. orange	10	10
314.		25 c. purple on yellow ..	10	10
315.		30 c. blue	10	10
316.		40 c. brown	15	10
317.		50 c. red	15	10
318.	**30.**	1 s. green	45	10
319.		2 s. violet	55	30
320.		5 s. red	2·25	3·25
321.		7 s. 50 c. blue	7·00	8·00
322.	**31.**	10 s. green and brown ..	4·50	4·75

In Type **33** the letters of the word "CENTS" are without serifs. In Type **32** they have serifs.

36. Sultan Kalif bin Harub.

1936. Silver Jubilee of Sultan.

323.	**36.**	10 c. black and olive ..	70	30
324.		20 c. black and purple ..	70	30
325.		30 c. black and blue ..	1·50	35
326.		50 c. black and red ..	1·75	45

37. "Sham Alam" (Sultan's dhow).

1944. Bicentenary of Al Busaid Dynasty.

327.	**37.**	10 c. blue	15	40
328.		20 c. red	15	50
329.		50 c. green	15	30
330.		1 s. purple	15	45

1946. Victory. Optd. **VICTORY ISSUE 8th JUNE 1946.**

331.	**33.**	10 c. black	20	20
332.		30 c. blue	20	40

1945. Silver Wedding. As T **10/11** of Aden.

333	20 c. orange	25	40
334	10 s. brown	10·00	16·00

1949. U.P.U. As T **20/23** of Antigua.

335.	20 c. orange	30	35
336.	30 c. blue	90	50
337.	50 c. mauve	1·10	65
338.	1 s. green	1·10	1·25

39. Sultan Kalif bin Harub.

40. Seyyid Khalifa Schools, Beit-el-Ras.

1952.

339.	**39.**	5 c. black	10	10
340.		10 c. orange	10	10
341.		15 c. green	30	20
342.		20 c. red	20	20
343.		25 c. purple	35	10
344.		30 c. green	15	10
345.		35 c. blue	20	60
346.		40 c. brown	25	40
347.		50 c. violet	25	10
348.	**40.**	1 s. green and brown	25	10
349.		2 s. blue and purple ..	85	30
350.		5 s. black and red ..	1·50	1·50
351.		7 s.50 black & green ..	12·00	20·00
352.		10 s. red and black ..	6·00	3·25

41. Sultan Kalif bin Harub.

1954. 75th Birthday of Sultan.

353.	**41.**	15 c. green	10	10
354.		20 c. red	10	10
355.		30 c. blue	10	10
356.		50 c. purple	10	10
357.		1 s. 25 red	15	40

42. Cloves.

47. Dimbani Mosque.

43. Dhows.

1957.

358.	**42.**	5 c. orange and green	10	10
359.		10 c. green and red ..	10	10
360.	**43.**	15 c. green and sepia	10	30
361.	–	20 c. blue	10	10
362.	–	25 c. brown and black	10	10
363.	**43.**	30 c. red and black ..	15	10
364.	–	35 c. slate and green	15	15
365.	–	40 c. brown and black	15	10
366.	–	50 c. blue and myrtle	15	10
367.	**47.**	1 s. red and black ..	20	10
368.	**43.**	1 s. 25 c. slate and red	55	10
369.	**47.**	2 s. orange and green	60	30
370.	–	5 s. blue	3·00	1·75
371.	–	7 s. 50 c. green ..	3·00	4·00
372.	–	10 s. red	3·00	2·50

DESIGNS—As Type **47**—HORIZ. 20 c. Sultan's Barge. 25 c., 35 c., 50 c. Map of E. African coast. VERT. 40 c. Minaret Mosque. As Type **43**—VERT. 5 s., 7 s. 50 c., 10 s. Kibweni Palace.

49. Sultan Seyyid Sir Abdulla bin Khalifa.

1961. As 1957 issue but with portrait of Sultan Sir Abdulla as in T **49**.

373.	5 c. orange and green ..	10	10
374.	10 c. green and red ..	10	10
375.	15 c. green and sepia ..	20	40
376.	20 c. blue	15	10
377.	25 c. brown and black ..	15	10
378.	30 c. red and black ..	60	10
379.	35 c. slate and green ..	80	30
380.	40 c. brown and black ..	30	10
381.	50 c. blue and myrtle ..	30	10
382.	1 s. red and black ..	40	10
383.	1 s. 25 slate and red ..	80	35
384.	2 s. orange and green ..	40	40
385.	5 s. blue	90	1·00
386.	7 s. 50 green	2·25	9·00
387.	10 s. red	2·25	5·50
388.	20 s. sepia (Kibweni Palace)	12·00	21·00

50. "Protein Foods".

1963. Freedom from Hunger.

389.	**50.**	1 s. 30 sepia	55	30

51. Zanzibar Clove.

1963. Independence. Inscr. "UHURU 1963" Multicoloured.

390.	30 c. Type **51**	10	20
391.	50 c. "To Prosperity" (Zanzibar doorway) ..	10	25
392.	1 s. "Religious Tolerance" (mosque and churches)	10	1·25
393.	2 s. 50 "Towards the Light" (Mangapwani Cave)	15	2·25

No. 392 is horiz.

1964. Optd. **Jamhuri 1964** (a) Nos. 373/88.

414.	5 c. orange and green ..	10	10
415.	10 c. green and red ..	10	10
416.	15 c. green and sepia ..	10	10
417.	20 c. blue	10	10
418.	25 c. brown and black ..	10	10
419.	30 c. red and black ..	10	10
420.	35 c. slate and green ..	10	10
421.	40 c. brown and black ..	10	10
422.	50 c. blue and myrtle ..	10	10
423.	1 s. red and black ..	10	10
404.	1 s. 25 slate and red ..	20	20
425.	2 s. orange and green ..	25	10
426.	5 s. blue	50	35
427.	7 s. 50 green	65	1·00
428.	10 s. red	75	1·00
429.	20 s. sepia	1·50	1·75

(b) Nos. 390/3.

430.	30 c. multicoloured ..	10	10
431.	50 c. multicoloured ..	10	10
432.	1 s. 30 multicoloured ..	10	10
433.	2 s. 50 multicoloured ..	15	10

The opt. is in two lines on Nos. 421, 423, 425/429, 430, 431, 433.

NOTE. For the set inscribed "UNITED REPUBLIC OF TANGANYIKA & ZANZIBAR" see Nos. 124/7 of Tanzania.

58. Axe, Spear and Dagger.

1964. Multicoloured.

434.	5 c. Type **58**	10	10
435.	10 c. Bow and arrow breaking chains	10	10
436.	15 c. Type **58**	10	10
437.	20 c. As 10 c.	10	10
438.	25 c. Zanzibari with rifle ..	10	10
439.	30 c. Zanzibari breaking manacles	10	10
440.	40 c. As 25 c.	10	10
441.	50 c. As 30 c.	10	10
442.	1 s. Zanzibari, flag and sun	10	10
443.	1 s. 30 Hands breaking chains (horiz.) ..	15	10
444.	2 s. Hand waving flag (horiz.)	20	10
445.	5 s. Map of Zanzibar and Pemba on flag (horiz.) ..	55	20
446.	10 s. Flag on map ..	1·75	90
447.	20 s. National flag (horiz.)	2·25	7·00

68. Soldier and Maps.

1965. 1st Anniv. of Revolution.

448.	**68.**	20 c. lt. grn. & grn. ..	10	10
449.	–	30 c. brown & orange ..	10	10
450.	**68.**	1 s. 30 bl. & dp. bl. ..	10	10
451.	–	2 s. 50 violet and red ..	10	15

DESIGNS—VERT. 30 c., 2 s. 50, Building Construction.

70. Planting Rice.

1965. Agricultural Development.

452.	**70.**	20 c. sepia and blue ..	10	30
453.	–	30 c. sepia and mauve	10	30
454.	–	1 s. 30 sepia & orange	30	70
455.	**70.**	2 s. 50 sepia and green	50	2·00

DESIGN: 30 c. and 1 s. 30, Hands holding rice.

72. Freighter, Tractor, Factory, and Open Book and Torch.

1966. 2nd Anniv. of Revolution. Mult.

456.	20 c. Type **72**	10	10
457.	50 c. Soldier	10	10
458.	1 s. 30 Type **72** ..	10	10
459.	2 s. 50 Soldier	15	30

74. Tree-felling.

1966.

460.	**74.**	5 c. purple and olive	15	30
461.	–	10 c. purple and green	15	30
462.	–	15 c. purple and blue	15	30
463.	–	20 c. blue and orange	15	10
464.	–	25 c. purple & yellow	15	10
465.	–	30 c. purple & yellow	15	10
466.	–	40 c. brown and red ..	30	10
467.	–	50 c. green and yellow	30	10
468.	–	1 s. purple and blue ..	30	10
469.	–	1 s. 30 purple & turq.	30	40
470.	–	2 s. purple and green	30	15
471.	–	5 s. red and blue ..	80	3·50
472.	–	10 s. red and yellow ..	2·25	9·50
473.	**74.**	20 s. brown & mauve	4·25	17·00

DESIGNS—HORIZ. 10 c. 1 s. Clove cultivation. 15 c., 40 c. Chair-making. 20 c., 5 s. Lumumla College. 25 c., 1 s. 30, Agriculture. 30 c. 2 s. Agricultural workers. VERT. 50 c., 10 s. Zanzibar Street.

81. "Education".

1966. Introduction of Free Education.

474.	**81.**	50 c. black, bl. & orge.	10	20
475.		1 s. 30 black, blue & green	15	30
476.		2 s. 50 black, blue and pink	30	2·75

82. A.S.P. Flag.

1967. 10th Anniv. of Afro-Shirazi Party.

477.	**82.**	30 c. multicoloured ..	10	20
478.	–	50 c. multicoloured ..	10	20
479.	–	1 s. 30 multicoloured	10	40
480.	**82.**	2 s. 50 multicoloured	15	1·00

DESIGN—VERT. 50 c., 1 s. 30, Vice-President M. A. Karume of Tanzania, flag and crowd.

84. Voluntary Workers.

1967. Voluntary Workers Brigade.

481.	**84.**	1 s. 30 multicoloured	15	3
482.		2 s. 50 multicoloured	30	3·0

POSTAGE DUE STAMPS

Insufficiently prepaid.
Postage due.

1 cent.

D 1.

1930. Roul. or roul. × imperf.

D 1	D 1	1 c. black on orange	10·00	48·0
D 18		2 c. black on orange	4·50	16·0
D 3		3 c. black on orange	3·75	22·0
D 19		3 c. black on red ..	3·00	26·0
D 21		6 c. black on yellow	3·00	17·0
D 5		9 c. black on orange	2·25	12·0
D 6		12 c. black on orange	£4250	
D 7		12 c. black on green	£900	£47
D 22		12 c. black on blue ..	4·00	13·0
D 8		15 c. black on orange	2·50	12·0
D 9		18 c. black on orange	3·00	20·0
D 11		20 c. black on orange	3·75	17·0
D 12		21 c. black on orange	3·25	14·0
D 13		25 c. black on purple	£1700	£100
D 14		25 c. black on orange	£4000	
D 23		25 c. black on red ..	9·00	32·0
D 24		25 c. black on lilac ..	7·00	25·0
D 15		31 c. black on orange	8·00	35·0
D 16		50 c. black on orange	20·00	75·0
D 17		75 c. black on orange	65·00	£15

D 3.

1936.

D 25	D **3.**	5 c. violet	55	2·7
D 26		10 c. red	45	1·0
D 27		20 c. green	65	2·5
D 28a		30 c. brown ..	30	4·5
D 29a		40 c. blue	40	7·5
D 30a		1 s. grey	1·00	7·5

ZIL ELWANNYEN SESEL

Beginning in June 1980 stamps were issue for use in Zil Elwagne Sesel (Seychelles Oute Islands), including Aldabra, Coetivy, Farquha and the Amirante Islands.

100 cents = 1 rupee.

A. Inscr. "ZIL ELOIGNE SESEL".

1980. As Nos. 404/19 of Seychelles but insc "ZIL ELOIGNE SESEL".

1.	–	5 c. multicoloured ..	15	
2.	–	10 c. multicoloured ..	15	
3.	–	15 c. multicoloured ..	15	
4.	–	20 c. multicoloured ..	20	
5.	–	25 c. multicoloured ..	60	
6.	**103.**	40 c. multicoloured ..	30	
7.	–	50 c. multicoloured ..	30	
8.	–	75 c. multicoloured ..	35	
9.	–	1 r. multicoloured ..	75	4
10.	–	1 r. 10 multicoloured ..	40	4
11.	–	1 r. 25 multicoloured ..	90	4
12.	–	1 r. 50 multicoloured ..	45	3
13a.	–	5 r. multicoloured ..	65	
14a.	–	10 r. multicoloured ..	1·00	2·
15a.	–	15 r. multicoloured ..	1·75	2·
16.	–	20 r. multicoloured ..	2·00	3·

2. " Cinq Juin ".

1980. Travelling Post Office. Multicoloured.

17.	1 r. 50 Type **2**	30	15
18.	2 r. 10 Hand-stamping covers	40	20
19.	5 r. Map of Zil Eloigne Sesel	70	40

3. Yellowfin Tuna.

1980. Marine Life. Multicoloured.

20.	1 r. 50 Type **3**	20	15
21.	2 r. 10 Blue Marlin (fish) ..	35	20
22.	5 r. Sperm Whale	70	50

1981. Royal Wedding. As T **26/27** of Kiribati. Multicoloured.

23	40 c. " Royal Escape " ..	10	10
24	40 c. Prince Charles and Lady Diana Spencer ..	40	40
25	5 r. " Victoria and Albert "	40	40
31	5 r. As No. 24	75	1·00
27	10 r. " Britannia "	85	85
28	10 r. As No. 24	2·50	2·50

4. Wright's Skink.

1981. Wildlife. (1st series). Multicoloured.

32.	1 r. 40 Type **4**	15	15
33.	2 r. 25 Tree Frog	20	20
34.	5 r. Robber Crab	40	40

See also Nos. 45/7.

5. " Cinq Juin " (" Communications ").

1982. Island Development. Ships.

35. **5.**	1 r. 75 black and orange ..	50	20
36. –	1 r. 10 black and blue ..	60	30
37. –	5 r. black and red ..	70	50

Designs: 2 r. 10 "Junon" ("fisheries protection"). 5 r. "Diamond M. Dragon" (drilling ship).

B. Inscr. "ZIL ELWAGNE SESEL".

6. " Paulette ".

1982. Local Mail Vessels. Multicoloured.

38.	40 c. Type **6**	20	10
39.	1 r. 75 " Janette " ..	40	30
40.	2 r. 75 " Lady Esme "	50	40
41.	3 r. 50 " Cinq Juin " ..	60	50

7. Birds flying over Island.

1982. Aldabra, World Heritage Site. Mult.

42.	40 c. Type **7**	30	15
43.	2 r. 75 Map of the atoll ..	70	35
44.	7 r. Giant Tortoises ..	1·25	75

8. Red Land Crab.

1983. Wildlife (2nd series). Multicoloured.

45.	1 r. 75 Type **8**	25	25
46.	2 r. 75 Black Terrapin ..	35	35
47.	7 r. Madagascar Green Gecko	80	80

9. Map of Poivre Island and Ile du Sud.

1983. Island Maps. Multicoloured.

48.	40 c. Type **9**	10	10
49.	1 r. 50 Ile des Roches ..	25	25
50.	2 r. 75 Astove Island ..	40	40
51.	7 r. Coetivy Island	1·10	1·10

10. Aldabra Warbler.

1983. Birds. Multicoloured.

53.	5 c. Type **10**	10	10
54.	10 c. Zebra Dove	35	10
55.	15 c. Madagascar Nightjar	10	10
56.	20 c. Madagascar Cisticola	10	10
57.	25 c. Madagascar White-eye	50	10
58.	40 c. Mascarene Fody ..	10	10
59.	50 c. White-throated Rail ..	50	10
60.	75 c. Black Bulbul	15	20
61.	2 r. Western Reef Heron ..	1·25	55
62.	2 r. 10 Souimanga Sunbird	45	50
63.	2 r. 50 Madagascar Turtle Dove	55	60
64.	2 r. 75 Sacred Ibis	60	65
65.	3 r. 50 Black Coucal (vert.)	75	80
66.	7 r. Seychelles Kestrel (vert.)	1·50	1·60
67.	15 r. Comoro Blue Pigeon (vert.)	3·25	3·50
68.	20 r. Greater flamingo (vert.)	4·50	4·75

See also Nos. 165, etc. (1985).

11. Windsurfing.

1983. Tourism. Multicoloured.

69.	50 c. Type **11**	10	10
70.	2 r. Hotel	25	25
71.	3 r. View of beach	35	35
72.	10 r. Islands at sunset ..	1·40	1·75

1983. Nos. 23/8 surch.

73	30 c. on 40 c. "Royal Escape"	25	25
74	30 c. on 40 c. Prince Charles and Lady Diana Spencer	40	50
75	2 r. on 5 r. "Victoria and Albert II"	70	70
76	2 r. on 5 r. As No. 74 ..	1·00	1·40
77	3 r. on 10 r. "Britannia" ..	85	85
78	3 r. on 10 r. As No. 74 ..	1·40	1·75

12. Map of Aldabra and Commemorative Postmark.

1984. Re-opening of Aldabra Post Office. Multicoloured.

79.	50 c. Type **12**	15	20
80.	2 r. 75 White-throated rail	60	85
81.	3 r. Giant tortoise	60	95
82.	10 r. Red-footed booby ..	2·25	2·75

13. Fishing from Launch.

1984. Game Fishing. Multicoloured.

83.	50 c. Type **13**	15	15
84.	2 r. Hooked fish (vert.) ..	45	55
85.	3 r. Weighing catch (vert.)	60	75
86.	10 r. Fishing from boat (different)	2·00	2·50

14. Giant Hermit Crab.

1984. Crabs. Multicoloured.

87.	50 c. Type **14**	25	30
88.	2 r. Fiddler Crabs	65	85
89.	3 r. Sand Crab	80	1·25
90.	10 r. Spotted Pebble Crab ..	2·50	3·25

15. Constellation of "Orion".

1984. The Night Sky. Multicoloured.

91.	50 c. Type **15**	15	15
92.	2 r. "Cygnus"	50	55
93.	3 r. "Virgo"	75	80
94.	10 r. "Scorpio"	2·00	2·25

C. Inscr. "ZIL ELWANNYEN SESEL".

16. "Lenzites elegans".

1985. Fungi. Multicoloured.

95.	50 c. Type **16**	25	15
96.	2 r. "Xylaria telfairei" ..	70	50
97.	3 r. "Lentinus sajor-ceju" ..	90	70
98.	10 r. "Hexagonia tenuis" ..	2·75	2·50

1985. As Nos. 53/4, 57 and 61 but inscr. "Zil Elwannyen Sesel".

165	5 c. Type **10**	10	10
166	10 c. Zebra dove	10	10
103	25 c. Madagascar white eye	10	10
171	50 c. White-throated rail ..	10	10
226	2 r. Western reef heron ..	45	50

17. The Queen Mother attending Royal Opera House, Covent Garden.

1985. Life and Times of Queen Elizabeth the Queen Mother. Multicoloured.

115.	1 r. The Queen Mother, 1936 (from photo by Dorothy Wilding) ..	20	25
116.	2 r. With Princess Anne at Ascot, 1974	45	50
117.	3 r. Type **17**	65	70
118.	5 r. With Prince Henry at his christening (from photo by Lord Snowdon)	1·10	1·25

18. Giant Tortoise.

1985. Giant Tortoises of Aldabra (1st series). Multicoloured.

120.	50 c. Type **18**	40	20
121.	75 c. Giant tortoises at stream	45	30
122.	1 r. Giant tortoises on grassland	55	35
123.	2 r. Giant tortoise (side view)	90	70

For stamps as Nos. 120/3, but without circular inscription around W.W.F. emblem, see Nos. 153/6.

19. Phoenician Trading Ship (600 B.C.).

1985. Famous Visitors. Multicoloured.

125.	50 c. Type **19**	40	30
126.	2 r. Sir Hugh Scott and H.M.S. "Sealark", 1908	1·25	80
127.	10 r. Vasco da Gama and "Sao Gabriel", 1502 ..	3·50	2·75

1986. 60th Birthday of Queen Elizabeth II. As T **110** of Ascension. Multicoloured.

128.	75 c. Princess Elizabeth at Chester, 1951	20	25
129.	1 r. Queen and Duke of Edinburgh at Falklands Service, St. Paul's Cathedral, 1985 ..	20	25
130.	1 r. 50 At Order of St. Michael and St. George service, St. Paul's Cathedral, 1968 ..	35	40
131.	3 r. 75 In Mexico, 1975 ..	85	90
132.	5 r. At Crown Agents Head Office, London, 1983 ..	1·10	1·25

1986. Royal Wedding. As T **112** of Ascension. Multicoloured.

133.	3 r. Prince Andrew and Miss Sarah Ferguson on Buckingham Palace balcony	70	75
134.	7 r. Prince Andrew in naval uniform	1·60	1·75

20. "Acropora palifera" and "Tubastraea coccinea".

1986. Coral Formations. Multicoloured.

135.	2 r. Type **20**	60	60
136.	2 r. "Echinopora lamellosa" and "Favia pallida"	60	60
137.	2 r. "Sarcophyton sp." and "Porites lutea"	60	60
138.	2 r. "Goniopora sp." and "Goniastrea retiformis"	60	60
139.	2 r. "Tubipora musica" and "Fungia fungites"	60	60

Nos. 135/9 were printed together, se-tenant, forming a composite design.

21. "Hibiscus tiliaceus".

1986. Flora. Multicoloured.

140.	50 c. Type **21**	35	20
141.	2 r. "Crinum angustum"	1·40	80
142.	3 r. "Phaius tetragonus"	1·90	1·25
143.	10 r. "Rothmannia annae"	3·50	2·75

22. "Chaetodon unimaculatus".

1987. Coral Reef Fishes. Multicoloured.

144.	2 r. Type **22**	55	55
144.	2 r. "Ostorhincus fleurieu"	55	55
146.	2 r. "Platax orbicularis"	55	55
147.	2 r. "Abudefduf annulatus"	55	55
148.	2 r. "Chaetodon lineolatus"	55	55

Nos. 144/8 were printed together, se-tenant, forming a composite design.

23. Coconut.

1987. Trees. Multicoloured.

149.	1 r. Type **23**	45	45
150.	2 r. Mangrove	85	85
151.	3 r. Pandanus palm	1·25	1·25
152.	5 r. Indian almond	2·00	2·25

1987. Giant Tortoises of Aldabra (2nd series). Designs as Nos. 120/3 but without circular inscr. around W.W.F. emblem. Mult.

153.	50 c. As Type **18**	60	60
154.	75 c. Giant tortoises at pool	85	85
155.	1 r. Giant tortoises on grassland	1·25	1·25
156.	2 r. Giant tortoise (side view)	2·00	2·25

1987. Royal Ruby Wedding. Nos. 128/32 optd. **40TH WEDDING ANNIVERSARY.**

157.	75 c. Princess Elizabeth at Chester, 1951	20	20
158.	1 r. Queen and Duke of Edinburgh at Falklands Service, St. Paul's Cathedral, 1985	25	25
159.	1 r. 50 At Order of St. Michael and St. George service, St. Paul's Cathedral, 1968	40	40
160.	3 r. 75 In Mexico, 1975	90	90
161.	5 r. At Crown Agents Head Office, London, 1983	1·25	1·25

24. "Vallee de Mai" (Christine Harter).

1987. Tourism. Multicoloured.

162.	3 r. Type **24**	1·25	1·00
163.	3 r. Ferns	1·25	1·00
164.	3 r. Bamboo	1·25	1·00

Nos. 162/4 were printed together, se-tenant, forming the complete picture.

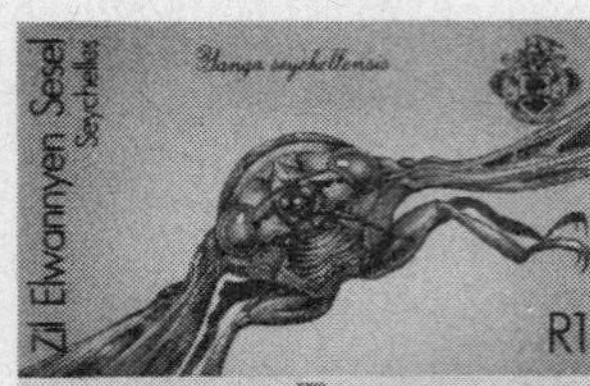

25 "Yanga seychellensis"

1988. Insects. Multicoloured.

180	1 r. Type **25**	40	30
181	2 r. "Belenois aldabraensis"	65	45
182	3 r. "Polyspilota seychelliana"	75	65
183	5 r. "Polposipus herculeanus"	1·25	1·10

1988. 300th Anniv of Lloyd's of London. As T **123** of Ascension. Multicoloured.

185	1 r. Modern Lloyd's Building, London	50	40
186	2 r. "Retriever" (cable ship) (horiz)	80	60
187	3 r. "Chantel" (fishing boat) (horiz)	1·25	90
188	5 r. Wreck of "Torrey Canyon" (tanker), Cornwall, 1967	1·75	1·40

27 "Father Christmas landing with Presents" (Jean-Claude Boniface)

1988. Christmas. Children's Paintings. Mult.

189	1 r. Type **27**	25	25
190	2 r. "Church" (Francois Barra) (vert)	45	45
191	3 r. "Father Christmas flying on Bird" (Wizy Ernesta) (vert)	65	65
192	5 r. "Father Christmas in Sleigh over Island" (Federic Lang)	1·10	1·10

1989. 20th Anniv of First Manned Landing on Moon. As T **126** of Ascension. Multicoloured.

193	1 r. Firing Room, Launch Control Centre	35	35
194	2 r. Crews of "Apollo–Soyuz" mission (30 × 30 mm)	60	60
195	3 r. "Apollo–Soyuz" emblem (30 × 30 mm)	80	80
196	5 r. "Apollo" and "Soyuz" docking in space	1·40	1·40

28 Dumb Cane

1989. Poisonous Plants (1st series). Mult.

198	1 r. Type **28**	40	40
199	2 r. Star of Bethlehem	70	70
200	3 r. Indian liquorice	95	95
201	5 r. Black nightshade	1·50	1·50

See also Nos. 214/17.

29 Tec-Tec Broth

1989. Creole Cooking. Multicoloured.

202	1 r. Type **29**	40	40
203	2 r. Pilaffa la Seychelloise	75	75
204	3 r. Mullet grilled in banana leaves	1·00	1·00
205	5 r. Daube	1·40	1·40

30 1980 Marine Life 5 r. Stamp

1990. "Stamp World London 90" International Stamp Exhibition. Designs showing stamps. Multicoloured.

207	1 r. Type **30**	30	30
208	2 r. 1980 5 r. definitive	55	55
209	3 r. 1983 2 r. 75 definitive	80	80
210	5 r. 1981 Wildlife 5 r.	1·40	1·40

1990. 90th Birthday of Queen Elizabeth the Queen Mother. As T **134** of Ascension.

212	2 r. multicoloured	60	60
213	10 r. black and brown	2·40	2·40

DESIGNS—21 × 36 mm. 2 r. Duchess of York with baby Princess Elizabeth, 1926. 29 × 37 mm. 10 r. King George VI and Queen Elizabeth visiting bombed district, London, 1940.

1990. Poisonous Plants (2nd series). As T **28**. Multicoloured.

214	1 r. Ordeal plant	40	40
215	2 r. Thorn apple	70	70
216	3 r. Strychnine tree	90	90
217	5 r. Bwa zasmen	1·40	1·40

1991. 65th Birthday of Queen Elizabeth II and 70th Birthday of Prince Philip. As T **139** of Ascension. Multicoloured.

234	4 r. Queen Elizabeth II	1·40	1·50
235	4 r. Prince Philip	1·40	1·50

31 "St. Abbs" (full-rigged ship), 1860

1991. Shipwrecks. Multicoloured.

236	1 r. 50 Type **31**	50	50
237	3 r. "Norden" (barque), 1862	95	95
238	3 r. 50 "Clan Mackay" (freighter), 1894	1·10	1·10
239	10 r. "Glenlyon" (freighter), 1905	2·75	2·75

1992. 40th Anniv of Queen Elizabeth II's Accession. As T **143** of Ascension. Mult.

240	1 r. Beach	30	30
241	1 r. 50 Aerial view of Desroches	50	50
242	3 r. Tree-covered coastline	90	90
243	3 r. 50 Three portraits of Queen Elizabeth II	1·00	1·00
244	5 r. Queen Elizabeth II	1·40	1·40

ZIMBABWE

Rhodesia became independent on 18 April 1980 and was renamed Zimbabwe.

100 cents = 1 dollar.

113. Morganite.

1980. As Nos. 555/69 of Rhodesia and new value inscr. "ZIMBABWE".

576. 1 c. Type **113** 20 10
577. 3 c. Amethyst 30 10
578. 4 c. Garnet 30 10
579. 5 c. Citrine 35 10
580. 7 c. Blue Topaz 35 10
581. 9 c. White Rhinoceros .. 15 10
582. 11 c. Lion 15 15
583. 13 c. Warthog 15 15
584. 15 c. Giraffe 15 20
585. 17 c. Common Zebra .. 15 20
586. 21 c. Odzani Falls .. 20 25
587. 25 c. Goba Falls 25 30
588. 30 c. Inyangombi Falls .. 30 50
588a. 40 c. Bundi Falls .. 3·50 3·25
589. $1 Bridal Veil Falls .. 1·10 2·00
590. $2 Victoria Falls .. 2·25 3·75

114. Rotary Anniv. Emblem.

1980. 75th Anniv. of Rotary International.

591. **114.** 4 c. multicoloured .. 10 10
592. 13 c. multicoloured .. 20 30
593. 21 c. multicoloured .. 35 55
594. 25 c. multicoloured .. 45 80

115. Olympic Rings.

1980. Olympic Games, Moscow.

596. **115.** 17 c. multicoloured .. 30 40

116. Gatooma Post Office, 1912.

1980. 75th Anniv. of Post Office Savings Bank.

597. **116.** 5 c. black and brown .. 10 10
598. – 7 c. black and orange 10 10
599. – 9 c. black and yellow .. 10 10
600. – 17 c. black and blue .. 25 25

DESIGNS: 7 c. Salisbury Post Office, 1912. 9 c. Umtali Post Office, 1901. 17 c. Bulawayo Post Office, 1895.

117. Stylised Blind Person.

1981. International Year for Disabled Persons. Multicoloured.

602. 5 c. Type **117** 10 10
603. 7 c. Deaf person 15 10
604. 11 c. Person with one leg .. 25 15
605. 17 c. Person with one arm 35 35

118. Msasa.

1981. National Tree Day. Multicoloured.

606. 5 c. Type **118** 10 10
607. 7 c. Mopane 15 15
608. 21 c. Flat-crowned Acacia 55 60
609. 30 c. Pod Mahogany .. 60 90

119. Painting from Gwamgwadza Cave, Mtoko Area.

1982. Rock Paintings. Multicoloured.

610. 9 c. Type **119** 65 20
611. 11 c. Epworth Mission, near Harare 65 20
612. 17 c. Diana's Vow near Harare 85 50
613. 21 c. Gwamgwadza Cave, Mtoko Area (different) .. 1·25 1·00
614. 25 c. Mucheka Cave, Msana Communal Land .. 1·50 1·75
615. 30 c. Chinzwini Shelter, Chiredzi Area .. .. 1·75 2·00

120. Scout Emblem.

1982. 75th Anniv. of Boy Scout Movement. Multicoloured.

616. 9 c. Type **120** 35 15
617. 11 c. Scouts around camp-fire 35 15
618. 21 c. Scouts map-reading 50 75
619. 30 c. Lord Baden-Powell 65 1·40

121. Dr. Robert Koch.

1982. Centenary of Dr. Robert Koch's Discovery of Tubercle Bacillus.

620. **121.** 11 c. orange, black and grey 75 25
621. – 30 c. multicoloured .. 1·75 2·00

DESIGN: 30 c. Man looking through microscope.

122. "Wing Woman" (Henry Mudzengerere).

1983. Commonwealth Day. Sculptures. Multicoloured.

622. 9 c. Type **122** 10 10
623. 11 c. "Telling Secrets" (Joseph Ndandarika) (horiz.) 15 10
624. 30 c. "Hornbill Man" (John Takawira) (horiz.) 35 45
625. $1 "The Chief" (Nicholas Mukomberanwa) .. 1·00 1·75

123. Traditional Ploughing Team (moving right)

1983. World Ploughing Contest. Mult.

626. 21 c. Type **123** 25 35
627. 21 c. Traditional ploughing team (moving left) .. 25 35
628. 30 c. Tractor ploughing .. 40 65
629. 30 c. Modern plough .. 40 65

The two designs of each value were issued in horizontal se-tenant pairs, forming composite designs throughout the sheets.

124. Postman on Cycle.

1983. World Communications Year. Mult.

630. 9 c. Type **124** 15 10
631. 11 c. Aircraft controller directing aircraft .. 20 10
632. 15 c. Switchboard operator 25 30
633. 17 c. Printing works .. 30 30
634. 21 c. Road transport (horiz.) 40 60
635. 30 c. Rail transport (horiz.) 60 90

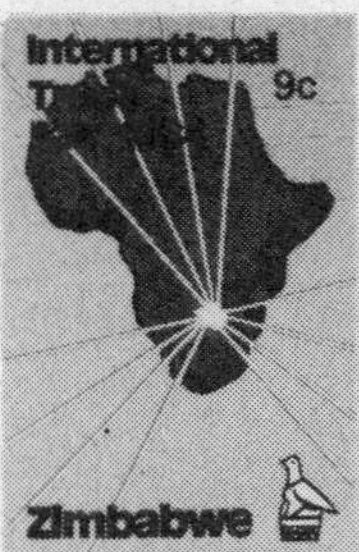

125. Map of Africa showing Zimbabwe.

1984. Zimbabwe International Trade Fair, 1984. Multicoloured.

636. 9 c. Type **125** 10 10
637. 11 c. Globe 15 10
638. 30 c. Zimbabwe flag and Trade Fair logo .. 45 35

126. Cycling.

1984. Olympic Games, Los Angeles. Children's Pictures. Multicoloured.

639. 11 c. Type **126** 30 15
640. 21 c. Swimming 40 40
641. 30 c. Running 55 65
642. 40 c. Hurdling 70 80

127. Liberation Heroes.

1984. Heroes' Day.

643 9 c. Type **127** 30 10
644 11 c. Symolic tower and flame (vert) 30 10
645 17 c. Bronze sculpture (vert) 50 20
646 30 c. Section of bronze mural 70 35

DESIGNS: 9 to 30 c. Various aspects of Heroes' Acre.

128. African Fish Eagle.

1984. Birds of Prey. Multicoloured.

647. 9 c. Type **128** 50 20
648. 11 c. Long crested eagle .. 50 20
649. 13 c. Bateleur 65 45
650. 17 c. Verreaux's eagle .. 80 45
651. 21 c. Martial eagle .. 90 1·25
652. 30 c. Bonelli's eagle .. 1·25 2·00

129. Class "9" Locomotive. No. 86.

1985. "Zimbabwe Steam Safaris". Railway Locomotives. Multicoloured.

653. 9 c. Type **129** 75 20
654. 11 c. Class "12" No. 190 .. 75 20
655. 17 c. Class "Garratt 15A" 1·25 85
656. 30 c. Class "Garratt 20A" "Gwaai" .. .. .. 2·00 2·25

130. "Intelsat V "Telecommunications Satellite.

1985. Earth Satellite Station, Mazowe. Multicoloured.

657. 26 c. Type **130** .. .. 1·50 50
658. 57 c. Earth Satellite Station, Mazowe (65 × 25 mm) .. .. 2·75 3·50

131. Tobacco.

1985. National Infrastructure. Multicoloured.

No.	Description		
659.	1 c. Type **131**	10	10
660.	3 c. Maize	10	10
661.	4 c. Cotton	10	10
662.	5 c. Tea	10	10
663.	10 c. Cattle	10	10
664.	11 c. Birchenough Bridge	20	10
665.	12 c. Ore stamp mill ..	50	10
666.	13 c. Gold pouring ..	50	15
667.	15 c. Dragline coal mining	50	15
668.	17 c. Uncut amethyst ..	50	20
669.	18 c. Electric locomotive ..	50	15
670.	20 c. Kariba Dam	50	15
671.	23 c. Elephants at water hole	50	15
672.	25 c. Sunset over Zambezi	40	20
673.	26 c. Baobab tree	40	20
674.	30 c. Ruins of Great Zimbabwe	45	20
675.	35 c. Traditional dancing	45	30
676.	45 c. Village women crushing maize	50	40
677.	57 c. Woodcarving ..	60	45
678.	$1 Playing Mbira (musical instrument)	1·00	65
679.	$2 Mule-drawn Scotch cart	1·75	2·00
680.	$5 Zimbabwe coat-of-arms	3·50	4·00

132. Chief Mutapa Gatsi Rusere and 17th century Seal.

1985. 50th Anniv. of National Archives. Multicoloured.

No.	Description		
681.	12 c. Type **132**	15	15
682.	18 c. Chief Lobengula, seal and 1888 Treaty ..	20	35
683.	26 c. Exhibition gallery ..	25	40
684.	35 c. National Archives building	30	60

133. Computer Operator.

1985. United Nations Decade for Women. Multicoloured.

No.	Description		
685.	10 c. Type **133**	45	10
686.	17 c. Nurse giving injection	75	45
687.	26 c. Woman student ..	1·40	1·75

134. Harare Conference Centre.

1986. Harare International Conference Centre. Multicoloured.

No.	Description		
688.	26 c. Type **134**	60	30
689.	35 c. Interior of conference hall	1·00	1·10

135. Grain Storage Silo.

1986. 6th Anniv. of Southern African Development Co-ordination Conference. Mult.

No.	Description		
690.	12 c. Type **135**	40	15
691.	18 c. Rhinoceros and hawk at sunset	1·50	1·00
692.	26 c. Map showing S.A.D.C.C. member states, and Boeing "737"	1·75	1·40
693.	35 c. Map and national flags of S.A.D.C.C. members	2·00	1·60

136. "Bunaeopsis jacksoni".

1986. Moths of Zimbabwe. Multicoloured.

No.	Description		
694	12 c. Type **136**	90	20
695	18 c. "Deilephila nerii" ..	1·40	60
696	26 c. "Bunaeopsis zaddachi"	1·75	1·00
697	35 c. "Heniocha apollonia"	2·10	2·40

137. Victoria Falls.

1986. 8th Non-Aligned Summit Conference. Multicoloured.

No.	Description		
698.	26 c. Type **137**	1·00	30
699.	$1 Ruins of Great Zimbabwe (62 × 24 mm.)	3·50	4·00

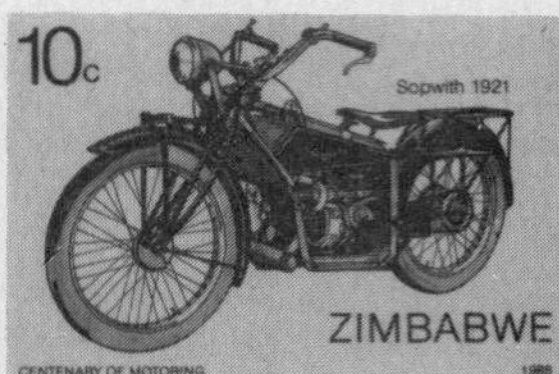

138. Sopwith Motorcycle (1921).

1986. Centenary of Motoring. Multicoloured.

No.	Description		
700.	10 c. Type **138**	55	10
701.	12 c. Gladiator motor car (1902)	55	30
702.	17 c. Douglas motorcycle (1920)	90	35
703.	26 c. Ford "Model A" (1930)	1·25	70
704.	35 c. Schacht motor car (1909)	1·40	1·60
705.	40 c. Benz three-wheeled car (1886)	1·40	1·60

139. Growth Monitoring.

1987. Child Survival Campaign. Mult.

No.	Description		
706.	12 c. Type **139**	90	1·00
707.	12 c. Breast-feeding ..	90	1·00
708.	12 c. Oral rehydration therapy	90	1·00
709.	12 c. Immunization ..	90	1·00

140. Barred Owlet.

1987. Owls. Multicoloured.

No.	Description		
710.	12 c. Type **140**	1·00	15
711.	18 c. Pearl-spotted owlet ..	1·50	70
712.	26 c. White-faced scops owl	2·00	1·10
713.	35 c. African scops owl ..	2·75	3·00

141. Brownie, Guide and Ranger saluting ("Commitment").

1987. 75th Anniv. of Girl Guides Association of Zimbabwe. Multicoloured.

No.	Description		
714.	15 c. Type **141**	30	15
715.	23 c. Guides preparing meal over campfire ("Adventure")	45	30
716.	35 c. Guide teaching villagers to read ("Service")	55	35
717.	$1 Handshake and globe ("International Friendship")	1·40	80

142. Common Grey Duiker.

1987. Duikers of Africa Survey. Mult.

No.	Description		
718.	15 c. Type **142**	30	15
719.	23 c. Zebra duiker	35	20
720.	25 c. Yellow-backed duiker	35	30
721.	30 c. Blue duiker	45	35
722.	35 c. Jentink's duiker ..	45	35
723.	38 c. Red duiker	55	40

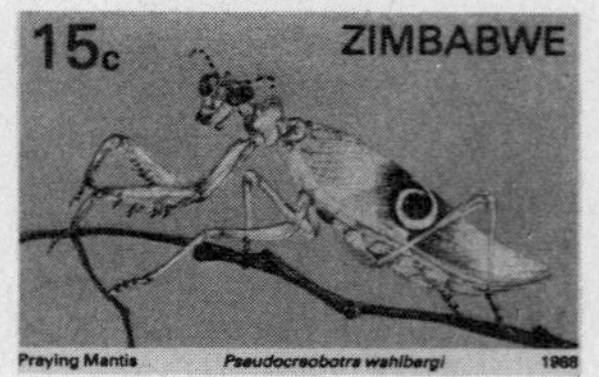

143. "Pseudocreobotra wahlberghi" (mantid).

1988. Insects. Multicoloured.

No.	Description		
724	15 c. Type **143**	30	15
725	23 c. "Dicranorrhia derbyana" (beetle) ..	40	20
726	35 c. "Dictyophorus spumans" (grasshopper)	50	25
727	45 c. "Chalcocoris rutilus" (bug)	75	35

144 "Cockerel" (Arthur Azevedo)

1988. 30th Anniv of National Gallery of Zimbabwe. Designs showing painting (38 c.) or sculptures (others). Multicoloured.

No.	Description		
728	15 c. Type **144**	15	10
729	23 c. "Man into Hippo" (Bernard Matemera) ..	25	20
730	30 c. "Spirit Python" (Henry Munyaradzi) ..	30	35
731	35 c. "Spirit Bird carrying People" (Thomas Mukarobgwa) (horiz) ..	30	25
732	38 c. "The Song of the Herd Boy" (George Nene) (horiz)	30	30
733	45 c. "War Victim" (Joseph Muzondo) (horiz)	35	40

145 "Aloe cameronii var. bondana"

1988. Aloes. Multicoloured.

No.	Description		
734	15 c. Type **145**	20	10
735	23 c. "Orbeopsis caudata"	35	20
736	25 c. "Euphorbia wildii" ..	35	20
737	30 c. "Euphorbia fortissima"	40	30
738	35 c. "Aloe aculeata" ..	40	35
739	38 c. "Huernia zebrina" ..	45	35

146 White-faced Whistling Duck

1988. Wild Ducks and Geese of Zimbabwe. Multicoloured.

No.	Description		
740	15 c. Type **146**	15	10
741	23 c. African pygmy goose	25	20
742	30 c. Hottentot teal ..	30	25
743	35 c. Comb duck ("Knob billed duck")	35	25
744	38 c. White-backed duck	35	25
745	45 c. Maccoa duck ..	45	30

147 O'Shaughnessy's Banded Gecko

1989. Geckos. Multicoloured.

No.	Description		
746	15 c. Type **147**	20	10
747	23 c. Tiger rock gecko ..	30	20
748	35 c. Tasman's gecko ..	45	30
749	45 c. Bibron's gecko ..	50	35

148 Spotted Leaved Arum-Lily

1989. Wild Flowers. Multicoloured.

No.	Description		
750	15 c. Type **148**	20	10
751	23 c. Grassland vlei-lily ..	25	20
752	30 c. Manica protea ..	30	30
753	35 c. Flame lily	30	30
754	38 c. Poppy hibiscus ..	40	35
755	45 c. Blue sesbania ..	45	40

149 Red-breasted Bream

1989. Fishes. Multicoloured.

No.	Description		
756	15 c. Type **149**	20	10
757	23 c. Chessa	30	20
758	30 c. Eastern bottle-nose	35	30
759	35 c. Vundu	35	30
760	38 c. Largemouth black bass	40	35
761	45 c. Tiger fish	50	40

150 Black Rhinoceros

1989. Endangered Species. Multicoloured.

No.	Description		
762	15 c. Type **150**	30	10
763	23 c. Cheetah	40	30
764	30 c. Wild dog	50	50
765	35 c. Pangolin	50	50
766	38 c. Brown hyena	55	60
767	45 c. Roan antelope	70	85

151 Tiger Fish

152 Headrest

153 Bicycles

1990. Multicoloured. (a) Wildlife. As T **151**.

No.	Description		
768	1 c. Type **151**	10	10
769	2 c. Helmet guineafowl	10	10
770	3 c. Scrub hare	10	10
771	4 c. Temminck's ground pangolin	10	10
772	5 c. Greater kudu	10	10
773	9 c. Black rhinoceros	10	10

(b) Cultural Artifacts. As T **152**.

No.	Description		
774	15 c. Type **152**	10	10
775	20 c. Hand axe and adze	10	10
776	23 c. Gourd and water pot	10	10
777	25 c. Snuff container	10	10
778	26 c. Winnowing tray and basket	10	10
779	30 c. Grinding stone	10	10

(c) Transport. As T **153**.

No.	Description		
780	33 c. Type **153**	10	10
781	35 c. Buses	10	10
782	38 c. Passenger train	10	15
783	45 c. Mail motorcycle and trailer	10	15
784	$1 Air Zimbabwe Boeing airliner	25	30
785	$2 Lorry	50	55

154 Pres. Mugabe and Joshua Nkomo at Signing of Unity Accord, 1987

1990. 10th Anniv of Independence. Mult.

No.	Description		
786	15 c. Type **154**	15	10
787	23 c. Conference Centre, Harare	20	15
788	30 c. Children in class	25	20
789	35 c. Intelsat aerial, Mazowe Earth Satellite Station	30	30
790	38 c. National Sports Stadium	30	40
791	45 c. Maize field	50	55

155 Runhare House, 1986

1990. Cent of the City of Harare. Mult.

No.	Description		
792	15 c. Type **155**	15	10
793	23 c. Market Hall, 1894	20	20
794	30 c. Charter House, 1959	25	25
795	35 c. Supreme Court, 1927	30	30
796	38 c. Standard Chartered Bank, 1911	30	30
797	45 c. The Town House, 1933	45	50

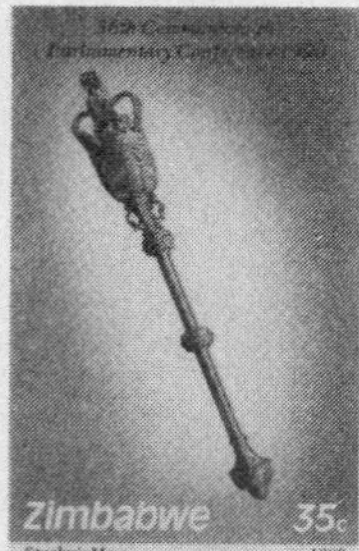

156 Speaker's Mace

1990. 36th Commonwealth Parliamentary Conference, Harare. Multicoloured.

No.	Description		
798	35 c. Type **156**	30	25
799	$1 Speaker's chair	70	75

157 Small-spotted Genet

1991. Small Mammals. Multicoloured.

No.	Description		
800	15 c. Type **157**	20	10
801	23 c. Red squirrel	20	15
802	35 c. Night-ape	35	35
803	45 c. Bat-eared fox	45	50

158 Hosho (rattles)

1991. Traditional Musical Instruments. Mult.

No.	Description		
804	15 c. Type **158**	15	10
805	23 c. Mbira (thumb piano)	15	10
806	30 c. Ngororombe (pan pipes)	15	10
807	35 c. Chipendani (mouth bow)	20	20
808	38 c. Marimba (xylophone)	20	20
809	45 c. Ngoma (drum)	20	20

159 Snot-apple

1991. Wild Fruits. Multicoloured.

No.	Description		
810	20 c. Type **159**	15	10
811	39 c. Marula	15	15
812	51 c. Mobola plum	20	20
813	60 c. Water berry	20	25
814	65 c. Northern dwaba berry	20	25
815	77 c. Mahobohobo	30	35

160 Bridal Veil Falls

1991. Commonwealth Heads of Government Meeting, Harare. Multicoloured.

No.	Description		
816	20 c. Type **160**	15	10
817	39 c. Meeting logo	15	10
818	51 c. Chinhoyi Caves	20	20
819	60 c. Kariba Dam	25	25
820	65 c. Victoria Falls	25	25
821	77 c. Balancing rocks	30	30

161 Lion

1992. Wildlife Conservation. Big Cats. Mult.

No.	Description		
822	20 c. Type **161**	10	10
823	39 c. Leopard	15	15
824	60 c. Cheetah	25	25
825	77 c. Serval	25	25

POSTAGE DUE STAMPS

D 4. Zimbabwe Bird (soapstone sculpture).

1980. As Nos. D 11/15 of Rhodesia but inscr. "ZIMBABWE".

No.	Type	Description		
D23	D 4	1 c. green	30	80
D24		2 c. blue	40	90
D25		5 c. violet	50	90
D26		6 c. yellow	70	1·60
D27		10 c. red	90	2·00

D 5.

1985.

No.	Type	Description		
D 8	5	1 c. orange	10	10
D 9		2 c. mauve	10	10
D30		6 c. green	10	10
D31		10 c. brown	10	10
D32		13 c. blue	10	10

1990. No. D27 surch **25**.

No.	Type	Description		
D33	D 4	25 c. on 10 c. red	6·00	6·00

ZULULAND

A territory of S.E. Africa, annexed by Great Britain in 1887, and incorporated in Natal in 1897.

12 pence = 1 shilling.
20 shillings = 1 pound.

1888. Stamps of Gt. Britain (Queen Victoria) optd. **ZULULAND.**

No.	Type	Description		
1.	**71.**	½d. red	2·00	2·50
2.	**57.**	1d. lilac	20·00	4·75
3.	**73.**	2d. green and red	11·00	16·00
4.	**74.**	2½d. purple on blue	14·00	17·00
5.	**75.**	3d. purple on yellow	22·00	20·00
6.	**73.**	4d. green and brown	25·00	35·00
7.	**78.**	5d. purple and blue	70·00	85·00
8.	**79.**	6d. purple on red	11·00	16·00
9.	**80.**	9d. purple and blue	65·00	65·00
10.	**82.**	1s. green	85·00	95·00
11.	–	5s. red (No. 181)	£500	£600

1888. Natal stamps optd. **ZULULAND.**

No.	Type	Description		
12c	**23**	½d. green	18·00	27·00
16	–	6d. lilac (No. 103)	45·00	45·00

3.

1894.

No.	Type	Description		
20.	**3.**	½d. mauve and green	1·50	3·50
21.		1d. mauve and red	5·00	70
22.		2½d. mauve and blue	12·00	6·00
23.		3d. mauve and brown	8·00	2·75
24.		6d. mauve and black	17·00	16·00
25.		1s. green	27·00	32·00
26.		2s. 6d. green and black	65·00	65·00
27.		4s. green and red	90·00	£110
28.		£1 purple on red	£450	£475
29.		£5 purple & black on red	£3250	£1200

ADDENDA AND CORRIGENDA

ASCENSION

145 Control Tower, Wideawake Airfield

1992. 50th Anniv of Wideawake Airfield. Multicoloured.

No.	Description	Unused	Used
578	15p. Type **145**	30	35
579	18p. Nose hangar . .	35	40
580	25p. Site preparation by U.S. Army engineers . .	50	55
581	70p. Laying fuel pipeline	1·40	1·50

AUSTRALIAN ANTARTIC TERRITORY

25 Adelie Penguin and Chick

1992. Antarctic Wildlife. Multicoloured.

No.	Description	Unused	Used
90	45 c. Type **25**	40	45
91	75 c. Elephant seal with pup	70	75
92	85 c. Northern giant petrel on nest with fledgeling . .	80	85
93	95 c. Weddell seal and pup	85	90
94	$1.20 Emperor penguins with chicks (vert) . .	1·10	1·25

BARBUDA

1992. Birth Centenary of Charles de Gaulle (French statesman). Nos. 1562/9 of Antigua optd **BARBUDA MAIL**.

No.	Description	Unused	Used
1334	10 c. Presidents De Gaulle and Kennedy, 1961 . .	10	10
1335	15 c. General De Gaulle with Pres. Roosevelt, 1945 (vert) . .	10	10
1336	45 c. Pres. De Gaulle with Chancellor Adenauer, 1962 (vert)	20	25
1337	60 c. De Gaulle at Arc de Triomphe, Liberation of Paris, 1944 (vert) . .	25	30
1338	$1 General De Gaulle crossing the Rhine, 1945	40	45
1339	$2 General De Gaulle in Algiers, 1944	85	90
1340	$4 Presidents De Gaulle and Eisenhower, 1960	1·75	1·90
1341	$5 De Gaulle returning from Germany, 1968 (vert)	2·10	2·25

CANADA

601 Ville-Marie in 17th Century

1992. "CANADA 92" International Youth Stamp Exhibition, Montreal. Multicoloured.

No.	Description	Unused	Used
1487	42 c. Type **601**	40	45
1488	42 c. Modern Montreal . .	40	45
1489	48 c. Compass rose, snow shoe and crow's nest of Cartier's ship "Grande Hermine"	50	55
1490	84 c. Atlantic map, Aztec "calendar stone" and navigational instrument	90	95

1992. Canadian Rivers (2nd series). As T **592** but horiz. Multicoloured.

No.	Description	Unused	Used
1492	42 c. Magaree River . .	40	45
1493	42 c. West (Eliot) River	40	45
1494	42 c. Ottawa River . .	40	45
1495	42 c. Niagara River . .	40	45
1496	42 c. South Saskatchewan River	40	45

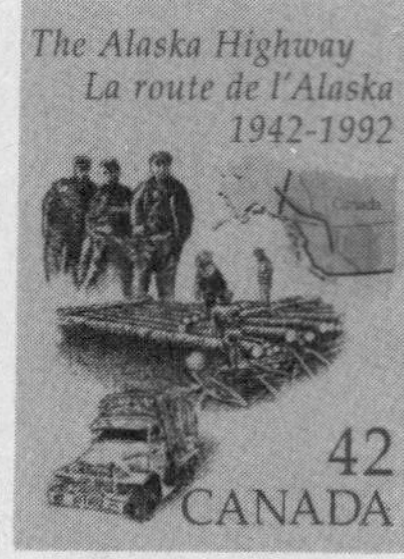

602 Road Bed Construction and Route Map

1992. 50th Anniv of Alaska Highway.

No.	Description	Unused	Used
1497	**602** 42 c. multicoloured . .	40	45

COCOS (KEELING) ISLANDS

61 "Lybia tessellata"

1992. Crustaceans. Multicoloured.

No.	Description	Unused	Used
252	5 c. Type **61**	10	10
254	20 c. "Trizopagurus strigatus"	20	25
256	40 c. "Thalamitoides quadridens"	40	45
257	45 c. "Calcinus elegans" (vert)	40	45
259	60 c. "Trapezia rufopunctata" (vert) . .	50	55
263	$3 "Trapezia cymodoce" (vert)	2·75	3·00

COOK ISLANDS

Add to Nos. 1261/8:

No.	Description	Unused	Used
1269	85 c. Red pencil sea urchin	55	60
1270	90 c. Red-spot rainbow fish	60	65
1271	$1 Black-lined maori wrasse	65	70
1272	$2 Longnose butterflyfish	1·25	1·40

251 Tiger

1992. Endangered Wildlife. Multicoloured.

No.	Description	Unused	Used
1279	$1.15 Type **251** . .	75	80
1280	$1.15 Indian elephant . .	75	80
1281	$1.15 Brown bear . .	75	80
1282	$1.15 Black rhinoceros . .	75	80
1283	$1.15 Chimpanzee . .	75	80
1284	$1.15 Argali	75	80

252 Columbus and Landing in New World (⅔-size illustration)

1992. 500th Anniv of Discovery of America by Columbus.

No.	Description	Unused	Used
1291	**252** $6 multicoloured . .	4·00	4·25

CYPRUS

276 Swimming

1992. Olympic Games, Barcelona. Mult.

No.	Description	Unused	Used
811	10 c. Type **276**	25	30
812	20 c. Long jump	50	55
813	30 c. Running	70	75
814	35 c. Discus	75	80

277 World Map and Emblem ("EXPO '92" Worlds Fair, Seville)

1992. Anniversaries and Events. Mult.

No.	Description	Unused	Used
815	20 c. Type **277**	50	55
816	25 c. European map and football (10th under-16 European Football Championship) . .	60	65
817	30 c. Symbols of learning (inauguration of University of Cyprus) . .	70	75

DOMINICA

255 "18th-Century Creole Dress" (detail) (Agostino Brunias)

1991. Creole Week. Multicoloured.

No.	Description	Unused	Used
1499	45 c. Type **255** . .	20	25
1500	60 c. Jing Ping band . .	25	30
1501	$1 Creole dancers . .	40	45

256 Island Beach

1991. Year of Environment and Shelter. Mult.

No.	Description	Unused	Used
1503	15 c. Type **256**	10	10
1504	60 c. Imperial amazon . .	25	30

1991. Christmas. Religious Paintings by Jan van Eyck. As T **291** of Antigua. Mult.

No.	Description	Unused	Used
1506	10 c. "Virgin Enthroned with Child" (detail) . .	10	10
1507	20 c. "Madonna at the Fountain"	10	10
1508	35 c. "Virgin in a Church"	15	20
1509	45 c. "Madonna with Canon van der Paele"	20	25
1510	60 c. "Madonna with Canon van der Paele" (detail)	25	30
1511	$1 "Madonna in an Interior"	40	45
1512	$3 "The Annunciation" . .	1·25	1·40
1513	$5 "The Annunciation" (different)	2·10	2·25

1992. 40th Anniv of Queen Elizabeth II's Accession. As T **292** of Antigua. Mult.

No.	Description	Unused	Used
1515	10 c. Coastline	10	10
1516	15 c. Mountains overlooking small village . .	10	10
1517	$1 River estuary . .	40	45
1518	$5 Waterfall	2·10	2·25

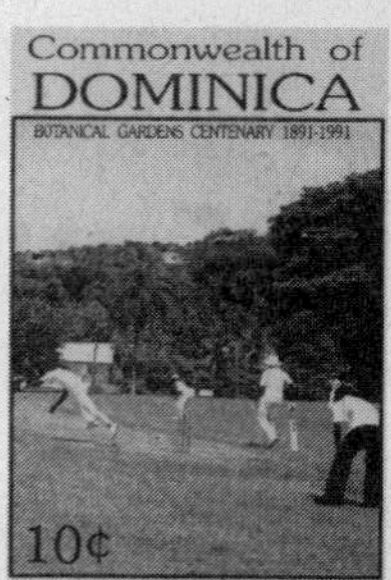

257 Cricket Match

1992. Centenary (1991) of Botanical Gardens. Multicoloured.

No.	Description	Unused	Used
1520	10 c. Type **257**	10	10
1521	$4 Cricket match (different)	1·75	1·90

GRENADINES OF ST. VINCENT

1991. 750th Anniv of Hanover. As T **285** of Antigua. Multicoloured.

No.	Description	Unused	Used
807	$2 Georg Laves (architect) and Hoftheatre . .	85	90

1991. 40th Anniv of Queen Elizabeth II's Accession. As T **292** of Antigua. Mult.

No.	Description	Unused	Used
809	15 c. View across bay . .	10	10
810	45 c. Schooner at anchor, Mayreau	20	25
811	$2 Hotel on hillside . .	85	90
812	$4 Tourist craft at anchor	1·75	1·90

INDIA

1183 Goat Seal from Harappa Culture, 2500 to 1500 B.C.

1992. 5th International Goat Conference, New Delhi.

1495 **1183** 6 r. blue and brown 25 30

1184 Early 19th-Century Letter with Mail Pouch and National Archives Building, New Delhi

1992. Centenary (1991) of National Archives.

1496 **1184** 6 r. multicoloured .. 25 30

LESOTHO

214 Minnie Mouse as Spanish Lady, 1540–1660

1992. "Granada '92" International Stamp Exhibition, Spain, and "World Columbian Stamp Expo '92" Exhibition, Chicago. Designs showing Walt Disney cartoon characters in traditional Spanish and American costumes. Multicoloured.

1089	20 s. Type **214**	10	10
1090	30 s. Donald Duck as Red Indian making arrow-heads	10	10
1091	40 s. Goofy as Red Indian playing lacrosse ..	15	20
1092	50 s. Mickey Mouse as Don Juan at Lepanto, 1571	20	25
1093	70 s. Donald in Galician costume, 1880	30	35
1094	1 m. Mickey the Indian and Donald the Settler planting corn	40	45
1095	2 m. Daisy Duck in Aragonese costume, 1880	80	85
1096	3 m. Minnie doing Red Indian bead work ..	1·25	1·50

NOTE. The first supplement containing new issues not in this catalogue or the Addenda appeared in the October 1992 number of *Gibbons Stamp Monthly.*

INDEX

CATALOGUES

THEMATIC CATALOGUES

The popularity of collecting stamps by theme has increased significantly in recent years. 'Collect Birds on Stamps', the first Stanley Gibbons thematic catalogue was launched in 1983 and proved an instant success. Further titles are in preparation.

2864 Collect Birds on Stamps
2852 Collect Mammals on Stamps
2888 Collect Railways on Stamps
2889 Collect Ships on Stamps
2890 Collect Fungi on stamps
2895 Collect Butterflies and Other Insects on stamps
2866 Collect Chess on Stamps

THE STANLEY GIBBONS STAMP CATALOGUE PARTS 2-22

2831 Part 2 Austria & Hungary
2832 Part 3 Balkans
2833 Part 4 Benelux
2834 Part 5 Czechoslovakia & Poland
2836 Part 7 Germany
2837 Part 8 Italy & Switzerland
2837 Part 9 Portugal & Spain
2839 Part 10 Russia
2840 Part 11 Scandinavia
2841 Part 13 Africa since Independence A-E
2842 Part 13 Africa since Independence F-M
2843 Part 14 Africa since Independence N-Z
2844 Part 15 Central America
2845 Part 16 Central Asia
2846 Part 17 China
2847 Part 18 Japan & Korea
2848 Part 19 Middle East
2849 Part 20 South America
2850 Part 21 South-East Asia
2851 Part 22 United States

STANLEY GIBBONS CONCISE CATALOGUES

The listings are based on those in the British Commonwealth Catalogue but enhanced by a host of additional information including watermark varieties, errors, first day covers, booklets, 'specimens' and much else—all combined into a single, inexpensive volume covering the most popular collecting areas. Without doubt the perfect catalogue for the more ambitious collector.

2887 Great Britain Concise
2892 Australia Concise
2893 New Zealand Concise

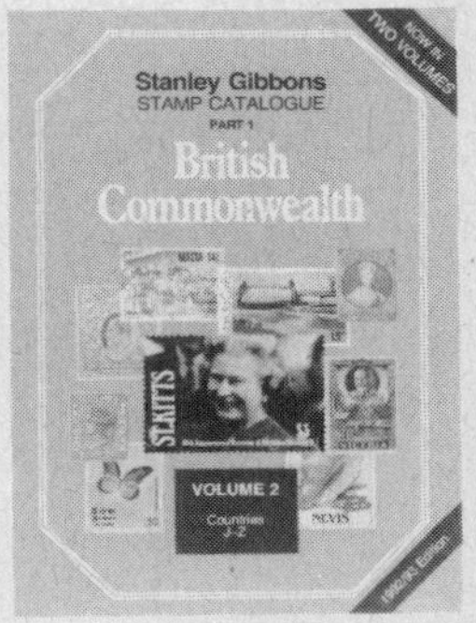

THE STANLEY GIBBONS BRITISH COMMONWEALTH CATALOGUE

Recognised worldwide as the standard guide to British and Commonwealth stamp values, this fine casebound catalogue is now published in two volumes and appears annually during summer.

Each edition is extensively revised and incorporates all the latest issues, much new information on earlier stamps and, of course, current market prices.

No Commonwealth collector can afford to be without the very latest edition of this indispensable catalogue.

2811 Part 1 British Commonwealth Catalogue
Vol 1 Countries A-I
2812 Part 1 British Commonwealth Catalogue
Vol 2 Countries J-Z

GUIDES & HANDBOOKS

STANLEY GIBBONS STAMP COLLECTING SERIES

Well illustrated handbooks packed with essential information for all collectors.

2760 Stamp Collecting: How to Start. Written especially for the beginner, this handbook gives an outline of the basic essentials of the hobby.

2671 Stamp Collecting: How to Identify Stamps. An indispensable companion to any collection. Packed full with information on both normal and unfamiliar scripts.

2762 Stamp Collecting: Collecting by Theme. Sound, practical advice on how to form and develop a thematic collection - including an A—Z to collecting subjects.

2763 Stamp Collecting: How to Arrange and Write-up a Stamp Collection. How to present a collection in the best possible way.

2766 The Stanley Gibbons Guide to Stamp Collecting. This book - a philatelic classic - tells, the story of the past, stamp designing and printing . . . in fact everything you need to know about this fascinating hobby. Hard Bound.

2740 Stamp Collection: Philatelic Terms Illustrated new edition by James Mackay. A real dictionary of stamp collecting, fully illustrated in colour and black and white - should be on every collector's bookshelf!

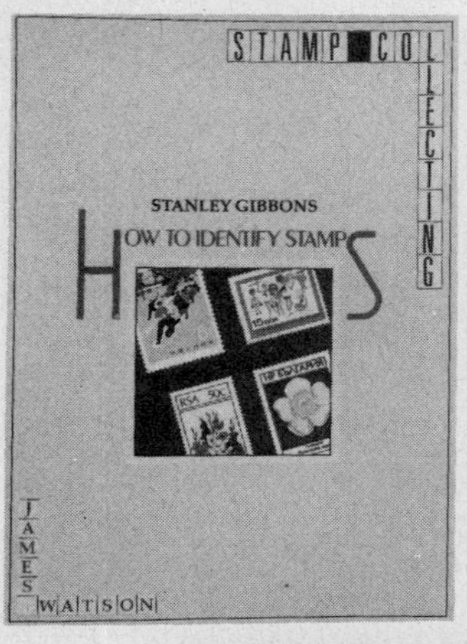

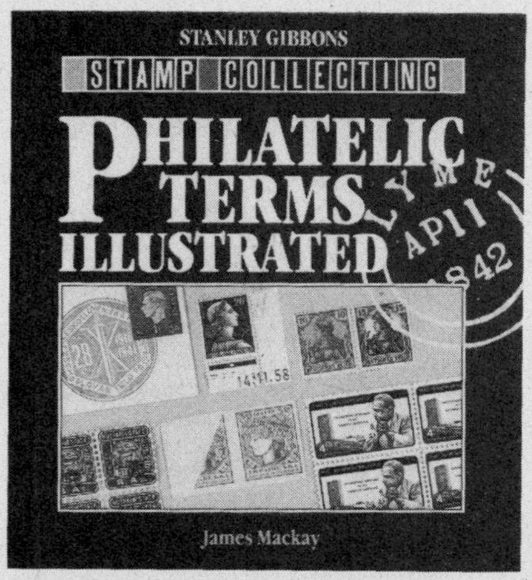

HANDBOOKS

2722 Enjoy Stamp Collecting by James Negus. A useful little booklet designed to give the junior collector a basic grounding in Stamp Collecting - great stocking filler at Christmas time!

2765 The Superbook of Stamp Collecting. An attractive, informative introduction. Includes a glossary of philatelic terms. An excellent gift for a young collector.

2767 Focus on Stamps gives a fine introduction to the hobby. Attractively designed and illustrated and packed full of helpful hints for the beginner. 76 pages, hundreds of colour pictures.

2776 The New Observer's Book of Stamp Collecting by Anthony New. Experienced collectors as well as beginners will benefit from the advice contained in this informative little book. Pocket sized with a great many colour illustrations. Highly recommended.

ALBUMS

G.B. STAMP ALBUMS

The Windsor Album (now in three volumes). Four printed loose-leaf albums for the postage, postage due and official stamps of Great Britain from 1840 to date, with a section for pre-independence Channel Islands and Isle of Man issues. The leaves, 11¼ x 9¾ in., are of a quality cartridge with space for stamps on one side, the opposite side showing a detailed illustrated catalogue. Kept up-to-date by means of supplements which are issued annually.

5240/5242/5428 Popular Edition
In handsome spring-back binders—a choice of red or green. Boxed. Volume One 1840-1970; Volume Two 1971-1981; Volume Three 1982-1990; Volume Four, 1991 onward.

5244/5246/5483 Windsor Sovereign
Bound in tan leather finish PVC with raised spine, gold blocked, this 22-ring deluxe album is the perfect setting for your GB collection. PVC covered slip case.

5250/5252 G.B. 'One-Country' Album (in two volumes)
Ideal for a straightforward collection and complete from 1840. Four-ring binder in padded leather finish PVC, with fully illustrated white cartridge leaves, 10⅞ x 8¾ in. Volume Two updated with supplements annually. Boxed. A strong seller!

ONE-COUNTRY STAMP ALBUMS

Elegant padded PVC ring-binders. The loose-leaves are of pure white cartridge, 10⅞ x 8¾ in., and fully illustrated. Supplements which are issued annually keep the albums up-to-date. Boxed. For collectors who wish to specialise easily!

5526 Guernsey
Complete 1941-date, 22-ring binder.

5527 Jersey
Complete 1941-date, 22-ring binder.

5256 Isle of Man
Is designed to house the 1958-1971 Regionals and the issues of the Independent Postal Administration since 1973; 22-ring binder.

5258 Australia
Provides spaces for all issues of Australia since 1913 up to 1990; four-ring binder. Annual supplements available.

5260 Canada
Has spaces for a straightforward collection of Canada since 1851 up to 1990; four-ring binder. Annual supplements available.

5262 New Zealand
Is designed to house the fascinating issues of this country from 1855 up to 1990; four-ring binder. Annual supplements available.

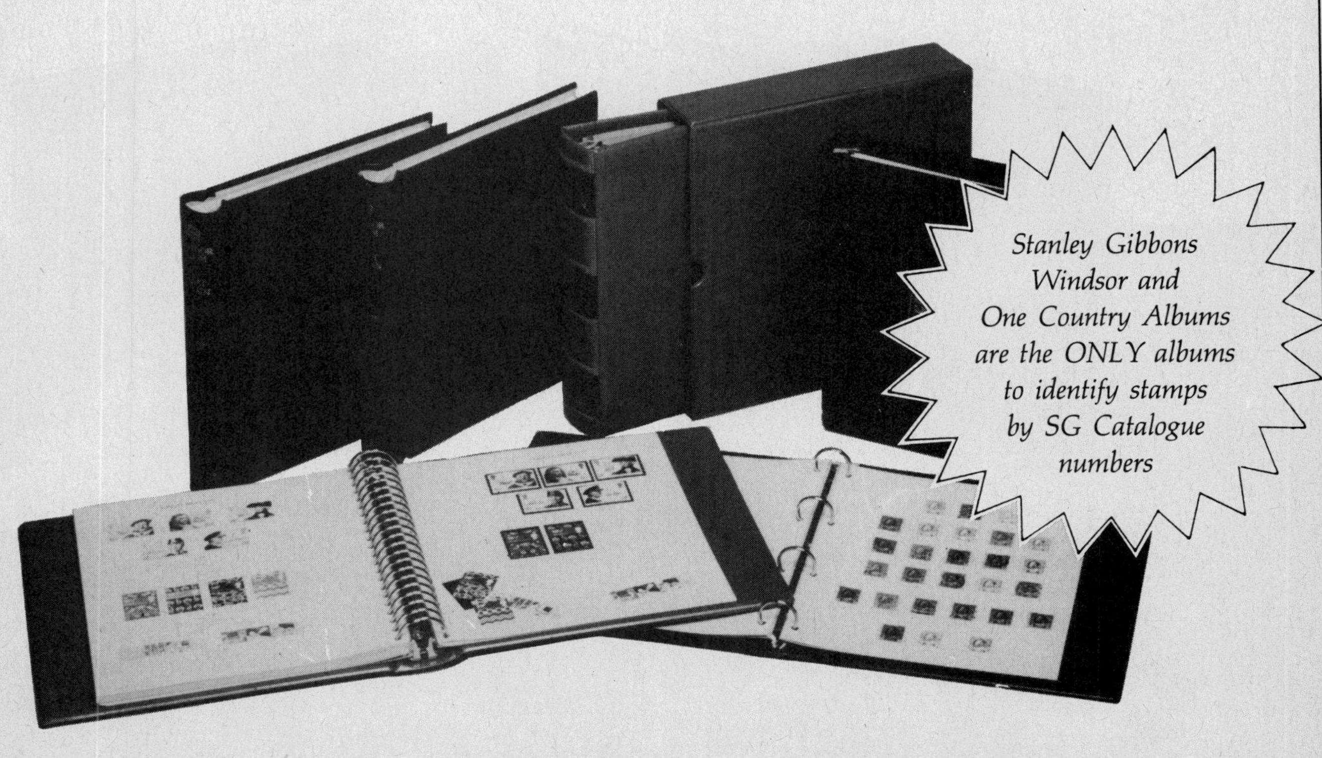
*Stanley Gibbons
Windsor and
One Country Albums
are the ONLY albums
to identify stamps
by SG Catalogue
numbers*

ALBUMS

SPRING-BACK STAMP ALBUMS

Research has shown that many collectors prefer a blank spined album and, ever mindful of the need to supply what the collector needs, all our springback albums are now untitled on the spine.

For collectors who prefer to have their albums titled in the traditional way, a free sheet of self-adhesive titles is included with every springback album and binder. This includes gold-blocked title panels in the familiar designs, a selection of country titles and a run of volume numbers which will enable you to identify albums on the shelf much more clearly than has been possible hitherto.

0331 Tower
A choice of red, green or black gold-blocked binder and with 100 feint grey quadrille-ruled leaves of white cartridge, $11 \times 9\frac{3}{4}$ in. Boxed.

0384 Senator Medium
Is complete with fifty white leaves finely printed in feint grey quadrille, $10\frac{1}{4} \times 8\frac{3}{4}$ in., and there's a choice of a red, green or black binder, gold-blocked.

0386 Senator Standard
Is bound in a choice of three colours: red, green or black—and is complete with 100 white leaves, finely printed in feint grey quadrille, size $11\frac{1}{8} \times 9\frac{7}{8}$ in. Boxed. One of our best selling albums!

3810 Simplex Medium
Has fifty leaves of high quality special cream paper, feint quadrille-ruled within a decorative border in light green, size $10\frac{1}{4} \times 8\frac{3}{4}$ in. Binder choice of black, green or red, gold-blocked on the spine.

3812 Simplex Standard
The $11\frac{1}{8}$ and $9\frac{7}{8}$ in. binder is available in a choice of either black, green or red and comes with 100, high-quality cream leaves. These have a subtle decorative border and are quadrille ruled.

Transparent interleaving in packets of 100 sheets is available for all our spring-back albums.

ALBUMS

THE UNIVERSAL SYSTEM

The 'Universal' Multi-Ring system offers today's collector everything he needs—flexibility combined with quality. Stamps, covers and stamp booklets can be mounted with a selection of leaves—thirteen different formats—giving your collection a united attractive presentation, either in the same 22-ring binder or series of binders. **Universal Binders** are available in red, blue or brown grained PVC, gold-blocked on the spine and presented in a smart box.

TRADITIONAL STAMP PAGES

There are three types of traditional album page, in a new larger size—11 × 9½ in.; white leaves faced with transparent glassine interleaving, white leaves unfaced, and black leaves faced.

BOOKLET PAGES

Both current British Post Office folding booklets and the older-style stitched booklets can be displayed. Folded booklets, including the latest 'window' style, can be seen on both sides, without handling, and booklets from many other countries can be taken too. Leaves, size 11 × 8¾ in., are available in packs of three.

PRESENTATION PACK PAGES

British Post Office Presentation Packs, Year Packs and Souvenir Books can be safely housed and securely mounted and protected in these pages—even the larger size packs issued since February 1982.

COVER POCKETS

No need for photo-corners or separate albums any-more—first day and other covers can be mounted with the main issue! There are two Universal cover pocket types—single and double crystal clear pockets 11 × 9½ in. Both open at the top, ensuring that covers do not slip out against the album ring; both take the Post Office First Day Cover size—single pockets take covers up to 8½ × 10½ in.

Now you've the display medium you need—but can spend most of your money on stamps!!

ACCESSORIES

From Stamp Hinges to Ultra Violet Lamps; from Tweezer and Magnifiers to Colour Keys and Watermark Detectors - Stanley Gibbons accessories are the answer to every collector's requirements.

The range has been completely revised with an improved selection of tweezers and the addition of a drying book and photo mounts for cover and postcard collectors.

A new range of magnifiers has been introduced which allows a wider variety of choice with each item having been carefully selected for its quality and value for money.

Current details of our superb range are available direct from Stanley Gibbons or your favourite supplier.

Stanley Gibbons Publications Ltd.,
5 Parkside, Christchurch Road,
Ringwood, Hampshire BH24 3SH

Telephone 0425 472363